Caravan Eu

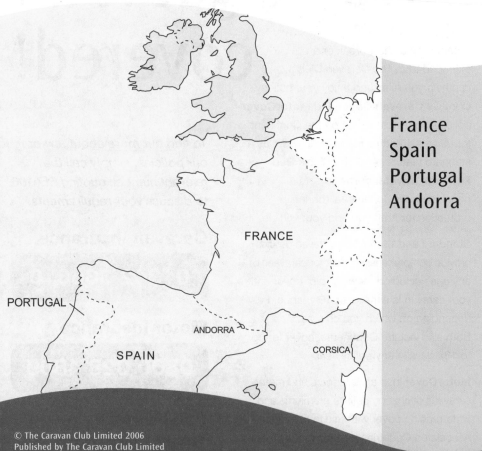

France
Spain
Portugal
Andorra

FRANCE

PORTUGAL

ANDORRA

SPAIN

CORSICA

© The Caravan Club Limited 2006
Published by The Caravan Club Limited
East Grinstead House, East Grinstead,
West Sussex RH19 1UA

Telephone Numbers:
General Enquiries: 01342 326944
Travel Service Reservations: 01342 316101
Brochure Requests: 01342 327410
General Fax: 01342 410258
Website: www.caravanclub.co.uk
Email: enquiries@caravanclub.co.uk

Editor: Bernice Hoare
Email: bernice.hoare@caravanclub.co.uk

Book trade sales and distribution: Kuperard,
Tel: 020 8446 2440, www.kuperard.co.uk

Maps and distance charts generated from Collins Bartholomew
Digital Database.

Maps © Collins Bartholomew Ltd 2005, reproduced by
permission of HarperCollins Publishers

ISBN 1-85733-402-7

Front cover photo: Dinard beach, Brittany, kindly supplied by
Brittany Tourist Board. Photographer: Jean-Patrick Gratien.

Touring abroad?
We've got it all covered!

Whether it's a short break or an extended tour, The Caravan Club can help you relax and enjoy your holiday. Our **5Cs Caravan Cover** and **MotorCover** policies both include use on the Continent for up to six months in any policy year as a standard feature. And The Club's **Red Pennant Travel Insurance** sets a benchmark for Continental touring protection for both you and your vehicle.

Standard and Super 5Cs caravan policies provide comprehensive cover for caravans of any age, including 'new-for-old' cover until your caravan is either 3 or 10 years old, depending on which you choose. Both also include Continental cover for up to 182 days in any policy year.

MotorCover insurance for cars and motor caravans offers competitive premiums and wide-ranging cover with use in EU and Associated Countries for trips of up to six months duration as a standard feature.

Red Pennant serves a variety of needs including single trip and annual multi-trip policies. Whether you take motoring holidays, package flights or a combination of both, we can provide an insurance solution at a competitive price.

To find out more about any of our policies, simply call the relevant number, quoting CE0106, to discuss your requirements.

Caravan Insurance

01342 336610

Motor Insurance

0800 028 4809

Red Pennant Travel Insurance

01342 336633

THE CARAVAN CLUB

QUICK QUOTATIONS INSTANT COVER INSURANCE SERVICES

CONTENTS - CARAVAN EUROPE 1

CONTENTS - CARAVAN EUROPE 1

See also alphabetical index at the back of the guide

THE CARAVAN CLUB

Dear Caravanner

Welcome to **Caravan Europe 2006**.

Whether you are new to Continental caravanning or a veteran of many Channel crossings; whether you are away for a long weekend or venturing long distance on that trip of a lifetime, you'll find **Caravan Europe** a key item of equipment during your travels.

You'll find details of thousands of wonderful campsites, as well as advice, guidance and helpful hints on all aspects of motoring abroad, be it with a touring caravan, a motor caravan or trailer tent. Take the time to browse through the introductory chapters as you plan your holiday – the information they contain will help ensure an enjoyable and carefree trip. And remember, **Caravan Europe** is compiled with the help of reports about campsites which caravanners and users of the guide have themselves visited.

As the Club's centenary in 2007 draws near and as **Caravan Europe** approaches its 50th edition in 2008, we are confident that this guide represents an outstanding blend of knowledge, advice and experience which will help make your holiday one that stays in the memory for a long time to come. Have a great time!

Yours sincerely

Trevor A Watson
Director General

It's worth reflecting that access holiday sites is through

Members save up to £7 per night on pitch fees at Club Sites

The Caravan Club offers an unrivalled choice of superb sites in glorious locations, all beautifully maintained and sensitively landscaped. Most Club Sites are graded 4 or 5 stars by Quality in Tourism and resident wardens ensure each visit meets or exceeds expectations. Join today and you can save the cost of your subscription fee in just 5 nights with member discounts on Site fees.

Plymouth Sound

Join the No.1 Club! Call us free on 0800 328 6635

to the largest choice of superb
The Caravan Club

The largest network of superb sites, most for members only

You'll be spoilt for choice, whether you want peace and quiet or a family friendly holiday near the seaside. Members save up to £7 per night on pitch fees at Club Sites.

Certificated Locations are exclusive to members providing beautiful small 5-van sites in idyllic locations.

More Help & Advice

New to caravanning or truly experienced, we're here to help members every step of the way.

Our invaluable FREE Technical Helpline provides you with a wealth of knowledge and advice on every aspect of caravanning.

So much more for members

Every month you'll receive a FREE Club Magazine packed with news, views and reviews – we think worth the cost of membership alone!

You'll enjoy access to a vast number of benefits and value-for-money services, such as insurance, breakdown assistance and travelling abroad, which could save your subscription many times over.

Morvich

There are around 200 Club Sites, shown here as red dots. There are also over 2,600 Certificated Locations, rural sites for no more than five 'vans, and exclusively for members. With our overseas Sites, members have access to over 3,000 Sites.

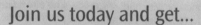

Join us today and get...

- Access to some 200 Club Sites, many for members only
- Exclusive access to advance booking service by phone or online
- Exclusive access to over 2,600 Certificated Locations
- Free Club Magazine – we think worth the subscription alone

- Access to the UK's No.1 Caravan Insurance Scheme
- Explore Britain & Ireland voucher booklet with over 500 discounts on attractions across the country
- Access to European Travel Service
- FREE expert information & advice
- Plus Sites Directory, Site Collection, map and much, much more.

THE CARAVAN CLUB

INTRODUCTION

The information contained in this guide is presented in the following major categories:

HANDBOOK

General information about touring in Europe, including legal requirements, advice and regulations, appears in the Handbook chapters at the front of the guide under the following section headings:

PLANNING AND TRAVELLING

DURING YOUR STAY

These two sections are divided into chapters in alphabetical order, not necessarily the order of priority. Where additional information is provided in another chapter, cross-references are provided.

COUNTRY INTRODUCTIONS

Following on from the Handbook chapters are the individual Country Introduction chapters containing information, regulations and advice specific to each country featured in the guide. These Country Introductions should be read carefully in conjunction with the Handbook chapters of the guide before you set off on holiday. Cross-references to other chapters are provided where appropriate.

CAMPSITE ENTRIES

After each Country Introduction there is an alphabetical list of place names in that country, together with campsites in and around those places, listed clockwise from the north. The scale used for our Sites Location Maps means that it is not possible to pinpoint on them every town or village where there is a campsite listed. Where we cannot show an individual town or village on a Sites Location Map, we will list it under another town which then acts as a central point for campsites within that particular area. With rare exceptions, such as Paris or Berlin, sites are listed under towns up to a maximum of 15 kilometres away. The place names used as a central point are usually, but not always, the largest towns in each region; some may be only small villages.

A cross-reference system is incorporated within the campsite listings. Simply look for the name of the town or village where you wish to stay. If a campsite is not listed under the name of the town itself, then a cross-reference should indicate an alternative village or town name under which it may be found in the guide.

To maintain consistency throughout the site entries listed in the guide, no accent marks are inserted and local versions of town or city names are used, eg:

Bruxelles instead of **Brussels**

Den Haag instead of **The Hague**

Firenze instead of **Florence**

Lisboa instead of **Lisbon**

Praha instead of **Prague**

Except in the case of those campsites marked ABS at the end of their site entries, the Caravan Club has no contractual arrangements with any of the sites featured in this guide. Furthermore, even in the case of sites with which the Club is contracted, it has no direct control over day-to-day operations or administration. Only those sites marked ABS have been inspected by Caravan Club staff.

It is assumed by the Caravan Club Ltd, but not checked (except in the case of sites marked ABS), that all campsites fall under some form of local licensing, which may or may not take account of matters of safety and hygiene. Caravanners will be aware of the varying standards between countries and are responsible for checking such matters to their own satisfaction.

SITES LOCATION MAPS

For all countries, each town and village listed has a map reference number, which relates to a Sites Location Map at the end of that country's site entries. Place names are shown on the maps in two colours; red where there is a site open all year (or for approximately eleven months of the year), or black where only seasonal sites have been reported. **Please note: these maps are for site location purposes only; a detailed road map or atlas is essential for planning your route and touring.**

SITE REPORT FORMS

Virtually all the site reports in these guides are submitted by caravanners, whether or not members of the Caravan Club. Sites which are not reported on for four years may be deleted from the guides. We rely, therefore, on holidaymakers to tell us about old favourites re-visited, as well as new discoveries.

Please help the Caravan Club to update its campsite information by reporting on the sites you visit. You will find a small number of site report forms towards the back of the guide and we hope that you will complete and return them to us. An abbreviated site report form is also provided if you are reporting no changes, or only very insignificant changes, to a site entry. Additional loose forms are available on request, including a larger A4 version, and forms may also be downloaded from our website, www.caravanclub.co.uk

For an explanation of abbreviations used, refer to the *Abbreviations* chapter in the section *HOW TO USE THE GUIDE*, or use the tear-out bookmark at the front of the guide which shows the most common abbreviations used.

Please send in reports as soon as possible. Information contained in reports received by **September** will be used, wherever possible, in the compilation of next year's edition of Caravan Europe. Reports received after this date are still welcome and will be retained for entry in subsequent editions. The Editor regrets that she is unable to respond individually to site reports submitted or to process information contained in a batch of receipts.

Tips for Completing Site Report Forms

The following are a few tips for completing site report forms:

- Try to fill in a form while at the campsite or shortly after your stay. Once back at home it can be difficult to remember details of individual sites, especially if you visited several during your trip.

- When giving directions to a site, remember to include the direction of travel, eg 'from north on N137, turn left onto D975 signposted Combourg' or 'on N83 from Poligny turn right at petrol station in village'. Where possible give road numbers, together with junction numbers where you exit from motorways or main roads, and/or kilometre post numbers. It is also helpful to mention useful landmarks

such as bridges, roundabouts, traffic lights or prominent buildings, and whether the site is signposted.

- When noting the compass direction of a site **this must be in the direction FROM THE TOWN the site is listed under, TO THE SITE and not the compass direction from the site to the town.** Distances are measured in a straight line and may differ from the actual distance by road.

- If you are amending only a few details about a site there is no need to tick all the boxes on the longer version form. You may prefer to use the abbreviated version but, in any event, do please remember to give the site name and the town or village it is listed under.

- If possible, give precise opening and closing dates, eg 15 March to 30 September. This information is particularly important for early and late season travellers.

The Editor of Caravan Europe very much appreciates the time and trouble taken by caravanners in submitting reports on campsites you have visited; without your valuable contributions it would be impossible to update the guide.

Every effort is made to ensure that information contained in this publication is accurate and that details given in good faith by caravanners on site report forms are accurately reproduced or summarised. The Caravan Club Ltd has not checked these details by inspection or other investigation and cannot accept responsibility for the accuracy of these reports as provided by caravanners, or for errors, omissions or their effects. In addition The Caravan Club Ltd cannot be held accountable for the quality, safety or operation of the sites concerned, or for the fact that conditions, facilities, management or prices may have changed since the last recorded visit. Any recommendations, additional comments or opinions have been contributed by caravanners and are not necessarily those of the Caravan Club.

The inclusion of advertisements or other inserted material does not imply any form of approval or recognition, nor can The Caravan Club Ltd undertake any responsibility for checking their accuracy.

Acknowledgements

The Caravan Club's thanks go to the AIT/FIA Joint Committee (OTA), the Alliance Internationale de Tourisme (AIT), the Fédération International de Camping et de Caravaning (FICC) and to the national clubs and tourist offices of those countries who have assisted with this publication.

ABBREVIATIONS

In general, abbreviations are the straightforward shortening of words and, in most cases, the meaning will be obvious. Abbreviations used within site entries are as follows:

EXPLANATION OF A SITE ENTRY

NANTES

The town named will be the nearest town marked on the relevant Sites Location Map at the end of each country's site entry listings. Look for the town or village where you wish to stay. If appropriate you will be referred to another central point in the area under which this town/village is listed.

3G4 or A3

Sites Location Map reference.

(3km SW)

Site is 3km south west **from the centre** of the town the site is listed under, taking a direct line on a map. All distances are in kilometres and metres. If no distance is listed, the site is close to the town centre.

urban

Site is located within a city or town, or the outskirts.

rural

Site is located within a village or country location.

coastal

Site is within one kilometre of the coast.

name & address

Site and/or reservation address for accommodation. Full details are provided even if the site does not accept advance bookings.

[(048) 2981234; fax (048) 2983456]

Telephone number and code, plus fax number where known. Where codes start with a 0 this is usually (but not always) omitted when telephoning from another country. The fax number is followed by the site's email and/or website address, if known.

directions

Instructions provided by members on a previous visit and checked where possible (see *Other Abbreviations*).

fees

Charges per night in high season for car, caravan + 2 adults as at year of last report; **dep** – deposit required (may be non-refundable). **You are advised to check fees when booking, or at least before siting, as those shown can be used only as a guide. Rates shown do not necessarily include electricity or showers unless indicated, or local taxes.**

(CChq acc)

The site accepts camping cheques – see the chapter *Continental Campsites* for details.

SITE DESCRIPTION ABBREVIATIONS

Each entry assumes the following unless stated otherwise:

Level ground, open grass pitches, drinking water on site, clean wc unless otherwise stated; own sanitation required if wc not listed; site is good and suitable for any length of stay within the dates specified.

size

sm – max 50 pitches
med – 51 to 50 pitches
lge – 150 to 500 pitches
v lge – 500+ pitches

levels

sl – sloping site
pt sl – sloping in parts
terr – terraced site

shade

shd – plenty of shade
pt shd – part shaded
unshd – no shade

pitches

hdg pitch – hedged pitches
mkd pitch – marked or numbered pitches
hdstg – hard standing or gravel

SITE FACILITY ABBREVIATIONS

ABS
Advance Booking Service (pitch reservation can be made through the Caravan Club's Travel Service)

adv bkg
Advance bookings are accepted;
adv bkg rec – advance bookings recommended
bkg fee – booking fee may be required

baby facs
Nursing room/bathroom for babies

beach
Beach for swimming nearby;
1km – distance to beach;
sand beach – sandy beach
shgl beach – shingle beach

bus/metro/tram
Public transport within an easy walk of the site

CCI or CCS
Camping Card International or Camping Card Scandinavia accepted

chem disp
Dedicated chemical toilet disposal facilities;
(wc) – no dedicated point; disposal via wc only

CL- type
Very small, privately-owned, informal and usually basic, farm or country site similar to those in the Caravan Club's network of Certificated Locations

dogs
Dogs allowed on site with appropriate certification (a daily fee may be quoted)

el pts
Mains electric hook-ups available for a fee;
inc – cost included in site fee quoted
10A – amperage provided
conn fee – one-off charge for connection to metered electricity supply
rev pol – reversed polarity may be present (see *Electricity and Gas* in the section **DURING YOUR STAY**)

Eng spkn
English spoken by campsite staff

entmnt
Entertainment facilities or organised entertainment; **child entmnt** – children's club/entertainment

fam bthrm
Bathroom for use of families with small children

gas
Supplies of bottled gas available on site or nearby

ice
Ice delivery or ice machine and/or freezer/fridge available

internet
Internet point for use by visitors to site

lndtte
Washing and drying machines, sometimes other equipment available;
lndry rm – laundry room with only basic clothes washing facilities

Mairie
Town hall (France); will usually make municipal site reservations

mv service pnt
Special waste discharge point for motor caravans; fresh water tap and rinse facilities should also be available

NH
Suitable as a night halt

noisy
Noisy site with reasons given;
quiet – peaceful, tranquil site

open 1 Apr-15 Oct
Where no specific date is given, opening dates are assumed to be inclusive, ie Apr-Oct – beginning April to the end of October
(NB: opening dates may vary from those advertised; check in advance before making a long journey, particularly when travelling out of the main holiday season.)

phone
Public payphone on or adjacent to site

playgrnd
Children's playground

pool
Swimming pool (may be open high season only);
htd – heated pool
covrd – indoor pool or with retractable cover

poss cr
During high season site may be crowded or overcrowded

red 10 days
Reduction for stays longer than specified number of days

red CCI/CCS
Reduction in fees on production of a Camping Card International or Camping Card Scandinavia

rest
Restaurant;
bar – bar
BBQ – barbecues allowed
cooking facs – communal kitchen area
snacks – snack bar, cafeteria or takeaway

serviced pitch
Electric hook-ups and mains water inlet and grey water waste outlet to pitch;
all – to all pitches
50% – percentage of pitches

sh stay
Suitable for a short stay of less than a week

shop(s)
Shop on site;
adj – shops next to site
500m – nearest shops
supmkt – supermarket
hypmkt – hypermarket
tradsmn – tradesmen call at the site, eg baker

shwrs
Hot showers available for a fee;
inc – cost included in site fee quoted

ssn
Season;
high ssn – peak holiday season
low ssn – out of peak season

50% statics
Percentage of static caravans/mobile homes/chalets/fixed tents/cabins or long term seasonal pitches on site, including those run by tour operators

sw
Swimming nearby;
1km – nearest swimming
lake – in lake
rv – in river

TV rm
TV room;
cab/sat – cable or satellite connections to pitches

wc
Clean flushing toilets on site;
(cont) – Continental type with floor-level hole
htd – sanitary block centrally heated in winter/low season
own san – use of own sanitation facilities recommended

OTHER ABBREVIATIONS

AIT	Alliance Internationale de Tourisme
a'bahn	Autobahn
a'pista	Autopista
a'route	Autoroute
a'strada	Autostrada
adj	Adjacent, nearby
alt	Alternative
app	Approach, on approaching
arr	Arrival, arriving
avail	Available
bdge	Bridge
bef	Before
bet	Between
C	Century, eg 16thC
c'van	Caravan
cc acc	Credit cards accepted (check with site for specific details)
cent	Centre or central
clsd	Closed

conn	Connection		opp	Opposite
cont	Continue or Continental (wc)		o'fits	Outfits
conv	Convenient		o'skts	Outskirts
covrd	Covered		poss	Possible, possibly
dep	Deposit		R	Right
diff	Difficult, with difficulty		rd	Road or street
dir	Direction		rec	Recommend/ed
dist	Distance		recep	Reception
dual c'way	Dual carriageway		red	Reduced, reduction (for)
E	East		req	Required
ent	Entrance/entry to		rlwy	Railway line
ess	Essential		rm	Room
excel	Excellent		rndabt	Roundabout
facs	Facilities		rte	Route
FIA	Fédération Internationale de l'Automobile		rv/rvside	River/riverside
			S	South
FICC	Fédération Internationale de Camping & de Caravaning		san facs	Sanitary facilities, wc, showers, etc
FKK/FNF	Naturist federation, ie naturist site		sep	Separate
			sp	Sign post, signposted
foll	Follow		sq	Square
fr	From		ssn	Season
g'ge	Garage		stn	Station
gd	Good		strt	Straight, straight ahead
hr(s)	Hour(s)		thro	Through
immac	Immaculate		traff lts	Traffic lights
immed	Immediately		twd	Toward(s)
inc	Included/inclusive		unrel	Unreliable
indus est	Industrial estate		vg	Very good
INF	Naturist federation, ie naturist site		vill	Village
			W	West
int'l	International		w/e	Weekend
junc	Junction		x-ing	Crossing
km	Kilometre		x-rds	Cross roads
L	Left			
ltd	Limited			
mkd	Marked			
mkt	Market			
m'van	Motor caravan			
m'way	Motorway			
N	North			
narr	Narrow			
nr, nrby	Near, nearly, nearby			

SYMBOLS USED

◆ Unspecified facilities for disabled guests – check before arrival

† Open all year

* Last year site report received (see Campsite Entries in Introduction)

CARAVANNING ABROAD – ADVICE FOR FIRST-TIMERS

You're seasoned caravanners around Britain and you've probably been caravanning for a few years. Now the time has come to make that trip you've been dreaming of, but understandably you feel a little apprehensive at the thought of taking your caravan or motor caravan across the Channel for the first time.

The advice in this section is a summary of the comprehensive information contained in the Handbook pages of this guide, and is designed to give you the confidence to take that first trip, and make it one of many enjoyable and rewarding holidays. Laws, customs, regulations and advice differ from country to country and you are strongly advised to study all the chapters in this Handbook section carefully, in conjunction with the relevant Country Introductions for the countries you are planning to visit.

BEFORE YOU TRAVEL

Choosing Your Campsite

The golden rule is not to be too ambitious. The south of France or southern Spain are exciting destinations but on your first visit you will probably not want to travel too far from your port of arrival and there are many good quality sites near the main French Channel ports. If France does not appeal, think about Belgium or the Netherlands where English is especially widely spoken.

If you use a daytime ferry crossing it may be a good idea to spend your first night at a campsite relatively near the port of arrival in order to give yourself a little time to get used to driving on the right. You will then be fresh for an early start the next morning when traffic is relatively light.

Decide whether you want a site near the seaside or in the country, quiet or lively, with facilities for children or near specific interests, such as vineyards, chateaux, sports facilities, etc. During the peak holiday season the volume of traffic and tourists might be daunting, but remember that in low season not all site facilities will be open. Advance booking is recommended if you do travel during the peak school holiday period in July and August, or over Easter, and this is particularly true if you are visiting a popular tourist resort.

The chapter in this guide entitled *Continental Campsites* tells you what to expect and has suitably-worded letters in five languages to help you make your own campsite bookings. For peace of mind you may prefer to use the Caravan Club's Advance Booking Service which offers Club members a booking service to over 200 Continental campsites throughout Europe. This service gives freedom and flexibility of travel while eliminating any language problems, expensive international deposit payments or waiting for replies by letter or email. Furthermore, you will have the reassurance of a confirmed pitch reservation and pitch fees paid in advance.

All the sites in the Club's Advance Booking Service are listed in this guide and are marked 'ABS' in their site entries. The Caravan Club cannot make advance reservations for any other campsites.

The Travel Service in Europe brochure gives full details of the ABS and of those sites to which it applies, as well as information on special offers with ferry operators, the Club's range of 'package' inclusive holidays for caravanners and Red Pennant Motoring & Personal Holiday Insurance. Telephone 01342 327410 to request a copy or see www.caravanclub.co.uk

Choosing Your Ferry Crossing

There is a wide choice of ferry operators and routes to the Continent and the use of long or short ferry crossings, or the Channel Tunnel, is a matter of personal preference and convenience. The Channel Tunnel and crossings from Dover to Calais are the quickest, but if you have a long drive from home to your departure port, you may prefer the chance to relax for a few hours and enjoy a meal on an overnight crossing, which means you arrive fresh at the other end.

Make sure you know the overall height of your vehicle(s); vehicle decks on some ferries have areas where height is restricted, and this should be checked when making your booking. The chapter *Ferries and the Channel Tunnel* contains a list of ferry routes and additional information.

The Club's website, www.caravanclub.co.uk, has a direct link through to a number of the most popular ferry operators' reservations systems and Club members can make their own reservations while still taking advantage of the Club's negotiated offers and the ferry companies' own early booking offers.

Insurance

All UK motor vehicle policies give you the legal minimum of insurance for EU countries, but it is important to check whether your comprehensive cover becomes third-party only when you leave the UK.

As far as travel insurance is concerned, the Caravan Club's Red Pennant Motoring & Personal Holiday Insurance gives you maximum protection from a variety of mishaps which might otherwise ruin your holiday. Even if you lose the use of your car, caravan or motor caravan, Red Pennant guarantees that your holiday can continue if you wish, helping to get you back on the road as quickly as possible. This is backed by the Club's own helpline with multi-lingual staff available 24 hours a day, 365 days a year.

If you are going to leave your home unoccupied for any length of time, check your house and contents insurance policies regarding any limitations or regulations.

You will find further details, information and advice in the chapter *Insurance*.

Documents

All members of your party should have a valid passport, including children under 16 who are not already included on a parent's passport. The chapter *Documents* sets out the requirements and explains how to apply for a passport.

A photocard driving licence or the pink/green EU version of the UK driving licence is universally acceptable. However, holders of an old-style green UK licence or a Northern Irish licence issued prior to 1991 are recommended to update it to a photocard licence, or obtain an International Driving Permit (IDP) to accompany their old-style UK licence in order to avoid any local difficulties.

In some countries passports must be carried at all times as a form of photographic identification.

You should also carry your Vehicle Registration Certificate (V5C), insurance certificate and MOT roadworthiness certificate, if applicable, together with a copy of your CRIS document in respect of your caravan.

*See the chapter **Documents** in the section **PLANNING AND TRAVELLING** for full details.*

Vehicles and Equipment

Ensure your car and caravan are properly serviced and ready for the journey, paying particular attention to tyres and tyre pressures. Ensure caravan tyres are suited to the maximum weight of the caravan and the maximum permitted speed when travelling abroad – see the chapter *Motoring – Advice and Equipment* and the Technical Information chapter of the Caravan Club's UK Sites Directory and Handbook.

Take a well-equipped spares and tool kit. Spare bulbs, a warning triangle (two are required in some countries), a fire extinguisher and a first-aid kit are legal requirements in many European countries. In Austria, Italy, Portugal and Spain a reflectorised jacket is now required to be worn by drivers who leave their vehicle when it is stopped on the carriageway, but it is sensible to do so in any country, and a second jacket is a common-sense requirement for any passenger who also gets out of your vehicle to assist. A spare tyre for car and caravan and nearside and offside extending mirrors are essential.

Adjust your headlights to deflect to the right instead of the left by the use of headlamp converters or beam deflectors, available from motor accessory shops or your car dealer. Even when not planning to drive at night, you will need to switch your headlights on in tunnels or if visibility is poor. Some countries require dipped headlights to be used during daylight hours. Bulbs are more likely to fail with constant use and you are recommended to carry spares.

Money

It is a good idea to carry a small amount of foreign currency, including loose change, for countries you are travelling through in case of emergencies, or when shopping. In addition you may take travellers' cheques or use your credit or debit card on arrival at your destination to obtain cash from cash dispensers, which are often found in supermarkets as well as outside banks. The rate of exchange is often as good as anywhere else; look for the same symbol on the machine as on your debit or credit card.

Credit cards issued by British banks may not be universally accepted and it is wise to check before incurring expenditure. The French system of 'chip and PIN' cards, which has been in use for a number of years, has had to be modified to make it compatible with that used in the rest of Europe and, until the system is modified across the whole country (scheduled for 2006), you may still be required to sign a receipt as before. In some countries you may be asked to produce your passport for photographic identification purposes when paying by credit card. See the chapter *Money* and Country Introductions for further information.

ON THE JOURNEY

Ferries

Report to the check-in desk at the port/Eurotunnel terminal allowing plenty of time, say an hour, before the scheduled boarding time. As you approach the boarding area after passport control and Customs, staff will direct you to the waiting area or the boarding lane for your departure. As you are driving a 'high vehicle' you may be required to board first, or last. While waiting to board stay with your vehicle(s) so that you can board immediately when instructed to do so. Virtually all ferries operate a 'drive on – drive off' system and you will not normally be required to perform any complicated manoeuvres, nor to reverse.

Whilst waiting, turn off the 12v electric supply to your fridge to prevent your battery going flat. Most fridges will stay adequately cool for several hours, as long as they are not opened. If necessary, place an ice pack or two (as used in cool boxes) in the fridge.

You may be required to show that your gas supply has been turned off correctly. Neither the ferry companies nor Eurotunnel permit you to carry spare petrol cans, empty or full, and Eurotunnel will not accept vehicles powered by LPG or dual-fuel vehicles. However Eurotunnel will accept vehicles fitted with LPG tanks for the purposes of heating, lighting, cooking or refrigeration, subject to certain conditions.

If your vehicle has been converted and is powered by LPG, some ferry companies require a certificate showing that the conversion has been carried out to the manufacturer's specification.

You will be instructed when to drive onto the ferry and, once on board, will be directed to the appropriate position. Treat ferry access ramps with caution, as they may be steep and/or uneven. Drive slowly as there may be a risk of grounding of any low point on the tow bar or caravan hitch. If your ground clearance is low, consider whether removing your stabiliser and/or jockey wheel would help.

Once boarded apply your car and caravan brakes. Vehicles are often parked close together and many passengers leaving their vehicles will be carrying bags for the crossing. It may, therefore, be wise to remove extended rear view mirrors as they may get knocked out of adjustment or damaged.

Make sure your car and caravan are secure and that, wherever possible, belongings are out of sight. Ensure that items on roof racks or cycle carriers are difficult to remove – a long cable lock may be helpful. In view of recent problems with stowaways on cross-Channel ferries and trains, check that your outfit is free of unexpected guests at the last practical opportunity before boarding.

Note the deck and staircase numbers for when you return; there is nothing more embarrassing than to discover, when you eventually find them, that your vehicles are blocking other motorists in! You will not usually be permitted access to your vehicle(s) during the crossing so take everything you require with you, including passports, tickets and boarding cards. On those ferry routes on which it is possible to carry pets, they are usually required to remain in their owners' vehicles or in kennels on the car deck. On longer ferry crossings you should make arrangements at the on-board

Information Desk for permission to visit your pet at suitable intervals in order to check its well-being.

See also *Pet Travel Scheme* under *Documents* in the section **PLANNING AND TRAVELLING**.

If you have booked cabins or seats go to the Information Desk immediately after boarding to claim them. Many ferries have a selection of restaurants and cafés, a children's play area, even a cinema, disco or casino as well as a shop, to while away the time during the crossing. If you wish to use the main restaurant it may be advisable to make an early reservation.

Listen carefully to on-board announcements, one of which will be important safety information at the time of departure. A further announcement will be made when it is time to return to your vehicle(s). Allow plenty of time to get down to the car deck and find your vehicle. Don't start your engine until vehicles immediately in front of you start to move. Once off the ferry you may want to pull over into a parking area to allow the queue of traffic leaving the ferry to clear.

Eurotunnel

On arrival at the Eurotunnel terminal, approach one of the toll booths displaying a car/caravan or motor caravan sign and produce your ticket. Having checked in you may, if you wish, visit the terminal to make any last minute purchases etc, and then follow signs to passport control and Customs. Your gas valves will be closed and sealed as a safety precaution and you will be asked to open the roof vents. You will then join the waiting area allocated for your departure and will be directed onto the single-deck wagons of the train and told to park in gear with your brake on. You then stay in or around your car/motor caravan for the 35-minute journey but will not be allowed to use your caravan until arrival. Useful information and music are supplied via the on-board radio station. On arrival, close the roof vent and release the caravan brake and, when directed by the crew, drive off – remembering to drive on the right!

Motoring on the Continent

The chapter *Motoring – Advice and Equipment* and the Country Introductions cover all aspects of motoring on the Continent, but the following additional points may be helpful for nervous 'first-timers'.

Most roads are not as busy as those in the UK, but avoid rush hours in larger towns. There are fewer lorries on the roads at weekends and in France in particular, roads are quieter between noon and 2pm, and good progress can often be made.

You are most likely to forget to drive on the right when pulling away from a parked position. It may be helpful to make yourself a sign and attach it to the dashboard, reminding yourself to drive on the right. This can be removed before driving and replaced each time you stop. Alternatively, make a member of your party responsible for reminding the driver every time you start the car. Pay particular attention when turning left or when leaving a rest area, service station or campsite, and after passing through a one-way system.

Make sure the road ahead is clear before overtaking. Stay well behind the vehicle in front and, if possible, have someone with good judgement in the left-hand seat to give you the 'all clear'.

In your eagerness to reach your destination, don't attempt vast distances in a single stint. Share the driving, if possible, and plan to break your journey overnight at a suitable site. There are thousands of sites listed in this guide and many are well-situated near motorways and main roads.

Remember speed limit signs are in kilometres per hour, not miles per hour.

You will be charged tolls to use many European motorways. Credit cards are widely accepted in payment, but not always. The Country Introductions provide full details. Motorways provide convenient service stations and areas for a rest and a picnic en-route but, for your own safety, find a proper campsite for an overnight stop.

Beware STOP signs. You will encounter more of them than you find in the UK. Coming to a complete halt is compulsory in most European countries and failure to do so may result in a hefty fine.

The maximum legal level of alcohol in the blood in most European countries is much lower than that permitted in the UK. It is better not to drink at all when driving, as offenders are heavily fined.

DURING YOUR STAY

Arriving at the Campsite

Go to the site reception and fill in any registration forms required. You may need to leave your Camping Card International/ Camping Card Scandinavia or passport. In some countries where you must carry your passport at all times as a form of photographic identity, a CCI is essential.

If you have not booked in advance it is perfectly acceptable to ask to have a look around the site before deciding whether to stay or accept a particular pitch.

Pitches are usually available when the site re-opens after the lunch break and not normally before this time. Aim to arrive before 7pm or you may find site reception closed; if this is the case you will probably find a member of staff on duty in the bar. It is essential to arrive before 10pm as the gates on most sites are closed for the night at this time. If you are delayed, remember to let the site know so that they will keep your pitch. When leaving, you will need to vacate your pitch by midday at the latest. Check with site staff.

Many sites offer various sporting activities, such as tennis, fishing, watersports, horseriding and bicycle hire, as well as entertainment programmes for children and/or adults in high season. Many also have a snack bar, restaurant or bar. Restrictions may apply on the use of barbecues because of the risk of fire; always check with site staff before lighting up.

Dogs are welcome on many campsites but some will not allow them at all, or during the high season, or will require them to be on a lead at all times. Check in advance. In popular tourist areas local regulations may ban dogs from beaches during the summer months.

If you have any complaints, take them up with site staff/owners there and then. It is pointless complaining after the event, when something could have been done to improve matters at the time.

Electricity and Gas

Calor Gas is not available on the Continent. Campingaz is widely available but, unless your caravan is new and already fitted with with a special bulkhead-mounted regulator, you will need an adaptor to connect to a Calor-type butane regulator. Alternatively carry sufficient for your stay, subject to the cross-Channel operator's regulations which may restrict you to three, two or even only one gas cylinder. Check when making your booking. See the chapter *Electricity and Gas* for further information.

Voltage on most sites is usually 220v or 230v nominal but may be lower. Most UK mains appliances are rated at 220v to 240v and usually work satisfactorily. You will need your mains lead that you use in the UK as many sites have the European standard EN60309-2 connectors, (formerly CEE17) which your UK 3-pin connector will fit. On some sites you may need a Continental 2-pin adaptor available from UK caravan accessory shops.

Caravanners may encounter the problem known as reverse polarity. This is where the site supply's 'live' line connects to the caravan's 'neutral' and vice versa and is due to different standards of plug and socket wiring that exist in other countries. The Club, therefore, recommends checking the polarity immediately on connection, using a polarity tester, obtainable from a caravan accessory shop before you leave home.

The caravan mains electrical installation should not be used while a reversed polarity situation exists. Ask the site manager if you can use an alternative socket or bollard, as the problem may be restricted to that particular socket only. Frequent travellers to the Continent who are electrically competent often make themselves up an adaptor, clearly marked reversed polarity with the live and neutral wires reversed. This can be tried in place of the standard connector, to see if the electricity supply then reverts to 'normal'.

See the chapter *Electricity and Gas* and Country Introductions for further information.

Food and Water

There is a limit to the amount of food which may be imported into other countries, although Customs will rarely be interested unless their attention is drawn to it.

Caravanners should be reasonable in the amount of foodstuffs they take with them. Experience of foreign cuisine is part of the enjoyment of a Continental holiday and there is little point in taking large supplies of food other than basics or children's special favourites.

In remoter parts of some countries the choice of items in food shops may be limited, compared to most British supermarkets, and you may find local markets to be a good source of fresh fruit, vegetables, cheese, fish and meat. When shopping it may be helpful to take your own supply of plastic carrier bags and a cool box in hot weather.

On the Continent generally it is sometimes difficult to obtain supplies of fresh milk, bread and cereals at campsite shops, particularly outside the summer season. It may be useful to pack a supply of basic items such as tea, coffee, fruit squash, cereals and powdered or long-life milk.

In the countries covered by this guide drinking water is clean and safe, but you may find the taste different from your own local mains supply. Bottled water is cheap and widely available.

Insect Control

Mosquitoes and flies can be a serious nuisance as well as being dangerous to health. Although an effective insect repellent is essential as the simplest form of protection, insect screens on windows, door and roof vents will provide complete protection. Most modern caravans have fly screens installed as part of the window roller-blind system. Older caravans may be equipped using DIY kits available from most caravan accessory shops or DIY stores. If you have difficulty in finding such a kit, the Caravan Club's Technical Office will provide Club members with a list of suppliers on request.

There are numerous sprays on the market to kill flies, ants and mosquitoes and insect repellent coils left burning at night are also an effective preventative device, as are anti-insect tablets which slot into a special electric heating element. These are available from High Street chemists and caravan accessory outlets.

Safety

Everyone wants you to relax and enjoy your holiday. The Caravan Club tries to help you achieve that aim and, in common with other responsible organisations, takes steps to ensure your well-being on site. Safety is largely your own responsibility – taking sensible precautions and being aware of possible hazards won't spoil your holiday, but a careless attitude might.

A comprehensive chapter entitled *Safety and Security*, together with specific information relevant to particular countries in the appropriate Country Introductions, covers all aspects of your own and your family's personal safety while on holiday. You are strongly advised to read these sections carefully and follow the advice contained in them.

Medical Matters

Before you leave home obtain a booklet T6 from your local post office and complete the application form for a European Health Insurance Card (EHIC) which entitles you to reciprocal emergency health care in the EU and some other countries. The EHIC is issued on an individual rather than a family basis and it replaces the Form E111 which is no longer valid.

Check with your GP the generic name of any prescription medicines you are taking. If you need more or lose your supply, the generic name will help a doctor or pharmacist to identify them. Keep receipts for any medication or treatment purchased abroad, plus the labels from the medicines, as these will be required if you make a claim on your travel insurance on returning home.

If you are unfortunate enough to have an accident, take some photographs to back up the written description on your claim form.

For further advice and information see the chapter *Medical Matters*.

Other Information

All major European countries maintain tourist offices in or near London who will supply information on their respective countries. Addresses and contact details are given in each Country Introduction.

The AA Information Centre provides traffic information on UK roads including routes to ferry ports on 09003 401100 (calls charged at 60p per minute) or dial 401100 only from a mobile telephone. Both the AA and RAC have useful websites with access for non-members: www.theaa.com and www.rac.co.uk

CHECKLIST

It is assumed that users of this guide have some experience of caravanning and are well aware of the domestic and personal items necessary for trips away in their caravans, and of the checks to be made to vehicles before setting off. The Caravan Club's Technical Office will supply a copy of a leaflet 'Things to Take' on request to Club members, or see www.caravanclub.co.uk

The following is intended merely as an 'aide memoire' and covers some of those items which may be necessary:

Car

Extending mirrors
Fire extinguisher
First aid kit
Fuses
Headlight converters/deflectors
Jack and wheelbrace
Mobile phone charger
Nationality stickers – GB or IRL (car and caravan)
Puncture kit
Radiator hose
Reflectorised safety jacket(s)
Snow chains (if winter caravanning)
Spare bulbs
Spare key
Spare parts, eg fan belt
Spare wheel/tyre
Stabiliser
Tool kit
Tow ball cover
Tow rope
Warning triangle (2 for Spain)

Caravan

Awning and groundsheet
Bucket
Chemical toilet and fluid/sachets
Corner steady tool and pads
Coupling lock
Electrical extension lead and adaptor(s)
Extra long motor caravan water hose pipe
Fire extinguisher
Gas cylinders
Gas regulator (Campingaz)
Gas adaptor and hoses (where regulator is fitted to the caravan)
Hitch and/or wheel lock
Insect screens
Levelling blocks
Mains polarity tester
Nose weight gauge
Peg mallet
Spare bulbs, fuses and lengths of wire
Spare key
Spare 7-pin plug
Spare water pump
Spare wheel/tyre
Spirit level
Step and doormat
Submersible water pump
Water containers - waste/fresh
Water hoses – waste/fresh
Wheel clamp

Documents and Papers

Address book, contact telephone numbers
Camping Card International/Camping Card Scandinavia
Car/caravan/motor caravan insurance certificates
Cheque book, bank card
Campsite booking confirmation(s)
Caravan Club membership card
Caravan Europe guide book
Copy of your CRIS document
Credit/debit cards, contact numbers in the event of loss
Currency and travellers' cheques
Driving licence (photocard or green/pink EU version)
European Health Insurance Card
European Accident Statement
Ferry ticket and timetable
Green card (some countries)
International Driving Permit (if applicable)
Letter of authorisation from vehicle owner (if applicable)
Maps and guides
MOT roadworthiness certificate (if applicable)
NHS medical card
Passport and visas (if applicable)
Pet's passport and addresses of vets abroad
Phrase books
Telephone card
Travel insurance documents (Red Pennant)
Vehicle registration certificate V5C

CONTINENTAL CAMPSITES

INTRODUCTION

Finding a campsite on the Continent is not usually difficult. Many excellent sites belong to local municipalities; others are run by families or private companies, or by camping, touring or automobile clubs. Although these private sites are usually open to non-members who hold a Camping Card International, some are reserved for their own members.

Compared with Caravan Club sites in the UK, pitches may be small and 80 square metres is not uncommon, particularly in Spain, Italy, Germany, Portugal and Switzerland. This may present problems for large outfits and/or with the erection of awnings. Elsewhere, for example in the south of France in summer, it may be difficult to erect an awning because of hard ground conditions.

Generally the approaches and entrances to campsites are well signposted, but often only with a tent or caravan symbol or with the word 'Camping', rather than the full site name.

There are usually sinks for washing-up and laundry and many sites provide washing machines and dryers. Most have a shop in high season, even if only for basic groceries, but many stock a wide variety of items. Often they have a restaurant or snack bar and sometimes a swimming pool, leisure facilities, TV and games room. Occasionally there may be a car wash, petrol pumps, hairdresser, sauna, solarium, internet access point, bureau de change or a tourist information office.

In the high season all campsite facilities are usually open and some sites offer organised entertainment for children and adults as well as local excursions. However, bear in mind that in the months of July and August, toilets, washing facilities and pitch areas will be under the greatest pressure.

BOOKING A CAMPSITE

It is now normal practice to pre-book pitches on campsites during the high season months of July and August. Some sites impose a minimum length of stay during this time in order to guarantee their business. Usually there are one or two unreserved pitches available for overnight tourers.

Although pre-booking sites en route to holiday destinations is not essential, you should plan to arrive for the night no later than 4pm (even earlier at popular resorts), in order to secure a good pitch, since after that time sites fill up rapidly. If you are planning a long stay it is advisable to contact campsites early in the year (January is not too early). Where known, sites' fax numbers and internet and email addresses are given in site entries and often it is possible to book directly via a campsite's website. Otherwise write, enclosing an International Reply Coupon, obtainable from main post offices and valid virtually all over the world, or letters may be ignored. Not all campsites accept advance bookings.

To assist you, suitably-worded letters in English, German, French, Spanish and Italian are provided at the end of this chapter. A suitably-worded response is also provided, in the same five languages, which should encourage the site operator to reply. In any event it is worth remembering that rarely will a site reserve a special place for you. The acceptance of a reservation merely means you will be guaranteed a space to park; the best pitches are allocated first.

Campsites that accept advance bookings may also require a deposit and this should be sent by credit card, by bank draft or by means of the post office's international registered service. A word of warning: **some campsites regard the deposit as a booking fee and will not deduct this amount from your final bill.**

CARAVAN CLUB ADVANCE BOOKING SERVICE

The Caravan Club's Travel Service offers Club members a campsite advance booking service (to which terms and conditions apply) to over 200 Continental campsites throughout Europe. This service gives freedom and flexibility of travel but with the reassurance of a confirmed pitch reservation and pitch fees paid in advance. Full details of this service, plus information on special offers with ferry operators, the Club's range of 'package'

Inclusive Holidays for caravanners and details of Red Pennant Motoring & Personal Holiday Insurance appear in the Travel Service in Europe brochure – telephone 01342 327410 to request a copy, or see www.caravanclub.co.uk

Booking an ABS site through the Caravan Club gives you a price guarantee – whatever happens to exchange rates, there will be no surcharges.

All the sites in the Club's Advance Booking Service are listed in this guide and are marked 'ABS' in their site entries. **The Caravan Club cannot make advance reservations for any other campsites listed in this guide.**

CAMPING CHEQUES

The Caravan Club operates a low season scheme in association with *Camping Cheques* offering Club members flexible touring holidays. The scheme covers approximately 600 sites in 18 European countries.

Camping cheques are supplied as part of a package which includes return ferry fare and a minimum of seven camping cheques. Each camping cheque is valid for one night's low season stay for two people, plus car and caravan/motor caravan/trailer tent and electricity. Full details are contained in the Club's Travel Service in Europe brochure.

Those sites which feature in the camping cheques scheme and which are listed in this guide and are marked 'CChq' in their site entries.

CARAVAN STORAGE ABROAD

The advantages of storing your caravan on a campsite on the Continent are immediately apparent, not least being the avoidance of the long tow to your destination, together with a saving in ferry and petrol costs. A number of campsites advertise a long-term storage facility or you may negotiate with a site that you have found which appeals to you.

However, there are pitfalls and understandably insurers in the UK are reluctant to insure a caravan which will be out of the country most of the time. There is also the question of invalidity of the manufacturer's warranty for caravans less than three years old if the supplying dealer does not carry out annual servicing.

*See also **Insurance** in the section **PLANNING AND TRAVELLING**.*

ELECTRICITY SUPPLY

For your own safety you are strongly advised to read the chapter *Electricity and Gas* under *PLANNING AND TRAVELLING*.

Many campsites now include electricity and/or shower facilities in the 'per night' price and where possible this has been included in site entries. However, where these are not included, a generous allowance should be made in your budget. It is not unknown for sites to charge up to the equivalent of £4 per night or more for electric hook-ups and up to £2 per shower. In winter sports areas, charges for electricity are generally higher in winter.

The system for charging for electricity varies from country to country and you may pay a flat daily rate or, notably in Germany and Austria, a connection charge plus a metered charge for electricity consumed. The Country Introductions contain specific information on electricity supply.

FACILITIES AND SITE DESCRIPTION

Information is given about the characteristics of the campsite and availability of facilities on site or within a reasonable distance, as reported to the Editor of this guide. Comments (in inverted commas) are those of caravanners visiting the site and it must be understood that people's tastes, opinions, priorities and expectations differ. Please also bear in mind that campsites change hands, opening dates change and standards may rise or fall, depending on the season.

Facilities Out Of Season

During the low season (this can be any time except July and early August) campsites may operate with limited facilities and shops, swimming pools, bars and restaurants may be closed. A municipal site warden may visit only to collect fees which are often negotiable during the low season.

Sanitary Facilities

Facilities normally include toilet and shower blocks with wash basins and razor sockets but toilets are not always fitted with seats, for ease of cleaning. The abbreviation 'wc' indicates the normal, pedestal type of toilet found in the UK. Some sites have footplate 'squatter' toilets and, where this is known, this is indicated by the abbreviation 'cont'.

It is recommended that you take your own universal flat plug (to fit all basin sizes) and toilet paper. During the low season it is not uncommon for only a few toilet and shower cubicles to be in use on a 'unisex' basis and they may not be cleaned as frequently as they are during the site's busy season. Hot water, other than for showers, may not be generally available.

While many campsites have in recent years upgraded their sanitary facilities in line with visitors' expectations, you may find that some are still unheated and may not offer items such as pegs to hang clothes/towels on, or shelves for soap and shampoo. Rarely, there may be no shower curtains or shower cubicle doors and hence little or no privacy.

Waste Disposal

Site entries in this guide indicate (when known) where a campsite has a chemical disposal facility and/or motor caravan service point, which is assumed to include a waste (grey) water dump station and toilet cassette-emptying point.

Continental caravanners in general tend to prefer to use a site's toilet and shower facilities, together with its dishwashing and vegetable preparation areas, more than their British counterparts, who prefer to use their own. Caravanners used to the level of facilities for the disposal of waste water on Caravan Club sites will find, more often than not, that facilities on Continental campsites do not match them.

Chemical disposal points are frequently difficult to locate and may be fixed at a high level requiring some strenuous lifting of cassettes in order to empty them. Alternatively, disposal may simply be down a toilet – continental or otherwise, but check at reception before doing so. Wastemaster-style emptying points are not common and you may be expected to empty your Wastemaster down the drain under a drinking water tap. On some occasions, this is also the only place to rinse a toilet cassette! You may like to carry a bottle of disinfectant spray to use on water taps if necessary.

At some campsites, notably in Switzerland and Germany, you may have to purchase special plastic bags for the disposal of rubbish, or pay a daily 'rubbish charge'. You may also find that you are expected to use recycling bins placed around the campsite.

LUNCH BREAKS

Some campsites close for a lengthy lunch break, sometimes as long as three hours, and occasionally there is no access for vehicles during this period. In addition, use of vehicles within the site may be restricted during certain hours to ensure a period of quiet. You are advised to check individual campsite regulations on arrival.

MOTOR CARAVANNERS

Increasingly towns and villages across Europe are providing dedicated overnight or short stay areas specifically for motor caravanners, many with good security, electricity, water and waste facilities. These are known as 'Aires de Service' or 'Stellplatz'. Likewise, to cater for this growing market, many campsites in popular tourist areas have separate overnight areas of hardstanding with appropriate facilities often just outside the main campsite area. Fees are generally very reasonable.

A number of organisations, for example ADAC (Germany), the Fédération Française de Camping et de Caravaning and Bel-air Camping-Caravaning (France) publish guides listing thousands of these sites in several countries.

Where known, information on the general availability of public transport within easy reach of a campsite, as supplied by caravanners, is given in the site entries in this guide.

MUNICIPAL CAMPSITES

For value for money, municipal sites are usually hard to beat and in France in particular, where they are found in many towns and villages, they have on the whole improved in recent years. Bookings for a municipal site can usually be made through the local town hall (Mairie) during office hours.

Outside the high season you may find significant numbers of workmen, market traders and itinerants resident on municipal sites – sometimes in a separate, designated area. Where their presence is not welcome some sites refuse entry to caravans with twin-axles ('deux essieux' in French) or restrict entry by caravan height, weight or length. It is advisable to check if any restrictions apply if booking in advance. Recent visitors report that bona fide caravanners with twin-axle or over-height/weight/length caravans may be allowed entry but this is negotiable with site staff at the time of arrival.

When approaching a town you may find that municipal sites in particular are not always named. Signposts may simply state 'Camping' or show a tent symbol.

NATURIST CAMPSITES

Several naturist sites are included in the guide, mainly in France, Spain, Germany and Croatia, and they are shown with the word 'naturist' after their site name. Many naturist sites and holiday centres welcome visitors who are not practising naturists, nudity being a requirement only in the swimming pool area. Many also have separate beach areas for naturists. However, visitors to these sites aged 16 and over usually require an INF card or Naturist Licence and this is covered by membership of British Naturism (tel 01604 620361 or www.british-naturism.org.uk). Alternatively, holiday membership is available on arrival at any recognised naturist site (a passport-size photograph is required). When looking for a site you will find that recognised naturist campsites generally display the initials FNF, INF or FKK on their signs.

OPENING DATES

Opening dates (where known) are given for campsites in this guide, many of which are open all year. However, sometimes sites may close without notice, for example, for refurbishment work or because of a change of ownership or simply because of a lack of visitors. When a site is officially closed, owners who live on site may sometimes accept visitors for an overnight or short stay if, for example, they are working on site.

It is always best to contact campsites in advance as owners, particularly in Spain and the south of France, have a tendency to shut campsites when business is slack. Otherwise you may arrive to find the gates of an 'all year' campsite very firmly closed. Municipal campsites' published opening dates cannot always be relied on at the start and end of the season. It is advisable to phone ahead or arrive early enough to be able to find an alternative site if your first choice is closed.

PETS ON CAMPSITES

See also Pet Travel Scheme under Documents in the section PLANNING AND TRAVELLING.

In general, dogs are welcome on many Continental campsites provided they conform to necessary legislation and vaccination requirements, and provided they are kept under control. There is usually a daily charge. Owners must conform to site regulations concerning dog-walking areas and fouling and may find restricted areas within a site where dogs are not permitted. There may also be limits on the number of dogs or type or breed of dog accepted. In popular tourist areas local regulations may ban dogs from beaches during the summer months.

Some sites will not allow dogs at all, or will require them to be on a lead at all times, or will not allow them during the peak holiday season. This is useful information for those who object to dogs on site.

A Club member has advised us that, on occasion, site owners and/or farmers on whose land a site is situated use poison to control rodents. Warning notices are not always posted and you are strongly advised to check if staying on a rural site and accompanied by a dog.

In the event that your pet is taken ill abroad, a campsite, if it accepts pets, will usually have information about local vets. Failing that, most countries have a telephone directory similar to the Yellow Pages, for example look on www.pagesjaunes.fr for France or www.paginas-amarillas.es for Spain.

Most European countries require pets to wear a collar at all times identifying their owners. If your pet goes missing, report the matter to the local police and the local branch of that country's animal welfare organisation.

PRICES

Campsite prices per night (for a car, caravan and two adults) are shown in local currency. In the newest EU Member States included in this guide – Czech Republic, Hungary, Poland, Slovakia and Slovenia – together with Croatia, euros are usually accepted for payment of campsite fees and other goods and services instead of local currency.

Payment of campsite fees should be made at least two hours before departure. It is worth remembering that if you stay on site after midday you may be charged for an extra day. Many campsites shown in this guide as accepting credit card payments may not do so for an overnight or short stay because of high commission charges. Alternatively, a site will impose a minimum limit, or will accept credit cards only in the peak season. It is always advisable to check the form of payment required when you check in.

It is common for campsites to impose extra charges for the use of swimming pools and other leisure facilities, for showers and laundry facilities, for the erection of awnings and for the disposal of rubbish.

REGISTERING ON ARRIVAL

It is usual to have to register in accordance with local police requirements, and to produce an identity document which the campsite office may retain during your stay. Most sites now accept the Camping Card International (or Camping Card Scandinavia in Denmark, Finland, Norway or Sweden) instead of a passport and, where known, these sites are marked CCI or CCS in the guide. If you do deposit your passport, make sure you have sufficient money for your stay if you are relying on travellers' cheques, as a passport must be produced when cashing them. Your identity document will then be returned to you when you settle your bill on departure. Cash may be required on arrival as a deposit on a barrier 'swipe' card. The amount will vary from site to site; in France €25 or €30 is usual.

TELEPHONE NUMBERS

These are given for most campsites listed in the guide, together with fax numbers and website or email addresses where known. The telephone numbers assume you are in the country concerned and the initial zero should be dialled, where applicable. If you are telephoning from outside the country the initial zero is usually (but not always) omitted. For more details see individual Country Introductions or the chapter *Keeping in Touch*.

GENERAL ADVICE

- Most campsites close from 10pm until 7am or 8am. However, late night arrival areas are sometimes provided for late travellers.

Motor caravanners, in particular, should check the gate/barrier closing time before going out for the evening in their vehicle.

- If possible inspect the site and facilities before booking in. If your pitch is allocated at check-in, ask to see it first, checking conditions and access, as marked or hedged pitches can sometimes be difficult for large outfits. Riverside pitches can be delightful but keep an eye on water levels; in periods of heavy rain these may rise rapidly and the ground become boggy.

- It is usual for campsites to make a charge for children. In some countries it is quite common for site owners to charge the full adult daily rate for children from as young as three years. This is particularly so in France.

- Local authorities in some countries impose a tourist tax on all people staying in hotels and on campsites. This averages around the equivalent of 50 pence per night per person and may not be included in the prices shown in this guide's campsite entries. Check on arrival. Similarly, VAT may be payable on top of your campsite fees and this may not be included in prices listed in this guide.

- Speed limits on site are usually restricted to 10 km/h (6 mph). You may be asked to park your car in a parking area away from your caravan. At some sites if you return after 10pm you may have to park your car by an entrance barrier or overnight parking area and walk to your caravan.

- French regulations ban the wearing of boxer shorts-style swimming trunks in pools. This rule may be strictly enforced by inspectors who have the power to close a site's swimming pool. As a result site owners may insist on the wearing of conventional (brief-style) swimming trunks.

COMPLAINTS

If you have a complaint, take it up with site staff or owners at the time, so that it can be dealt with promptly. It is pointless complaining after the event, when action could have been taken at the time to improve matters. In France, if your complaint cannot be settled directly with the campsite, and if you are sure you are within your rights, you may take the matter up with the Préfecture of the 'département' in question.

The Caravan Club has no control or influence over campsite operations or administration and, apart from a small number of sites with which it is contracted (marked ABS in site entries) and on which it has made a booking for you, cannot intervene in any dispute a visitor may have with a particular site.

SPECIMEN SITE BOOKING LETTERS

See the following pages and ***Booking a Campsite*** earlier in this section. The website www.babelfish.altavista.com allows simple translations into a number of languages and you may find it useful when communicating with campsites.

SITE BOOKING LETTER – ENGLISH

Date: Address (block caps) ....

....

....

Tel No: (0044) ....

Fax No: (0044) ....

Email ....

Dear Sir/Madam

I wish to make a reservation as follows:

Arriving (date and month) .... **Departing** (date and month) .... (...... nights)

Adults   ....   **Children (+ ages)** ....

Car ☐   **Caravan** ☐   **Motor Caravan** ☐   **Trailertent** ☐

Electrical Hook-up ☐   **Awning** ☐   **Extra tent** ☐

I look forward to an early reply and enclose an International Reply Coupon and addressed envelope. When replying please advise all charges and deposit required. I look forward to meeting you and visiting your site.

Yours faithfully

[Name in block capitals after signature]

Caravan Club Membership No ....

✂ --

REPLY

Date: Address ....

....

....

Dear Mr/Mrs/Ms ....

Thank you for your reservation from .... to .... (.......... nights).

- **YES, OK** – I am pleased to confirm your reservation (with/without electrical hook-up) and look forward to welcoming you.
- **NO, SORRY** – I regret that the site is fully booked for the dates you request.

Yours faithfully

....

SITE BOOKING LETTER – FRENCH

Date: Adresse (lettres majuscules) ....

....

....

Tél :   (0044) ....

Fax :   (0044) ....

Email...

Monsieur/Madame

J'aimerais désire effectuer la réservation suivante :

Arrivée (jour et mois) .... **Départ** (jour et mois) .... (.......... nuits)

Adultes ....   **Enfants (+ âges)** ....

Voiture ☐   **Caravane** ☐   **Camping car** ☐   **Tente-remorque**   ☐

Branchement électrique ☐   **Auvent** ☐   **Tente supplémentaire** ☐

Ci-joint un coupon-réponse international et une enveloppe avec mon adresse. En vous remerciant par avance pour votre réponse je vous demanderais de bien vouloir me communiquer vos tarifs complets ainsi que le montant des arrhes à verser.

En attendant le plaisir de faire votre connaissance et de séjourner sur votre terrain, je vous prie de croire, Monsieur/Madame, à l'assurance de mes sentiments les meilleurs.

(Nom en lettres majuscules après la signature)

No. d'adhérent du Caravan Club ....

✂---

REPONSE

Date: Adresse ....

....

....

Monsieur/Madame/Mademoiselle ....

J'accuse réception de votre bulletin de réservation pour la période

du .... au .... (..........nuits).

- **OUI** – Je confirme votre réservation (avec/sans branchement électrique) en attendant le plaisir de faire votre connaissance.

- **NON** – Je suis au regret de vous informer que le terrain est complet pendant la période de votre choix.

Veuillez croire, Monsieur/Madame/Mademoiselle, à l'assurance de mes sentiments les meilleurs.

....

SITE BOOKING LETTER – GERMAN

Datum: Anschrift (in Großbuchstaben) ....

....

....

Telefonnummer.: (0044) ....

Faxnummer: (0044) ....

Email ....

Sehr geehrter Herr/sehr geehrte Dame

Ich möchte wie folgt reservieren:

Ankunft (Tag und Monat) .... **Abreise** (Tag und Monat) .... (...... Nächte)

Erwachsene .... **Kinder (in Alter von)** ....

Auto ☐   **Caravan** ☐   **Wohnmobil** ☐   **Klappwohnwagen** ☐

Elektr. Anschluß ☐   **Vordach** ☐   **Extra Zelt** ☐

Ich sehe einer baldigen Antwort entgegen und lege einen internationalen Antwortschein und addressierten Umschlag bei. Bitte führen Sie in Ihrem Antwortschreiben sämtliche erforderlichen Gebühren und Anzahlungen an. Ich freue mich auf den Aufenthalt auf Ihrem Campingplatz und hoffe, Sie dort zu treffen.

Mit freundlichen Grüßen

(Unterschrift und Name in Großbuchstaben)

Caravan Club Mitgliednummer ....

✂ --

ANTWORT

Datum: Anschrift: ....

....

....

....

Herrn/Frau/Fräulein ....

Vielen Dank für Ihre Reservierung von .... bis .... (......... Übernachtungen).

- **JA, OK** – Ich kann Ihre Reservierung (mit/ohne elektr. Anschluß) bestätigen und freue mich, Sie hier zu begrüßen.

- **NEIN, LEIDER** – Ich bedaure, daß der Campingplatz für die von Ihnen gewünschte Zeit voll belegt ist.

Mit freundlichen Grüßen

....

Fecha: Dirección (letra de imprenta) ....

....

....

N° de tel: (0044) ....

N° de fax: (0044) ....

Email ....

Estimado Sr/Estimada Sra/Srta

Deseo realizar la siguiente reserva:

Llegada (fecha y mes) .... **Salida** (fecha y mes) .... (......... noches)

Adultos ....   **Niños** (+edades) ....

Coche ☐   **Caravana** ☐   **Caravana de motor** ☐   **Tienda con remolque** ☐

Enganche eléctrico ☐   **Toldo** ☐   **Tienda adicional** ☐

Espero con interés recibir su confirmación y tengo el gusto de adjuntar un cupón de respuesta internacional y un sobre con mi dirección. Cuando responda tenga la amabilidad de indicar todos los recargos y depósitos necesarios. Espero con ilusión conocerle y visitar su cámping.

Atentamente:

[Nombre en letra de imprenta después de la firma]

No. de socio del Caravan Club ....

✂---

Fecha: Dirección ....

....

....

Estimado Sr/Estimada Sra/Srta

Agradecemos su reserva del .... al .... (......... noches).

- **SI** – Tenemos el gusto de confirmar su reserva (con/sin enganche eléctrico) y esperamos con ilusión darle la bienvenida.
- **LO SENTIMOS** – Desafortunadamente le cámping está lleno durante las fechas que ha solicitado.

Atentamente:

....

SITE BOOKING LETTER - ITALIAN

Data: Indirizzo (stampatello) ....

....

....

N° Tel: (0044) ....

N° Fax: (0044) ....

Email ....

Egregio Signore/Signora

Desidero fare una prenotazione come segue:

Arrivo (giorno e mese) .... **Partenza** (giorno e mese) .... (....... notti)

Adulti .... **Bambini** (+ età) ....

Automobile ☐   **Roulotte/Caravan** ☐   **Camper** ☐   **Tenda a rimorchio** ☐

Allacciamento elettrico ☐   **Tendone** ☐   **Tenda addizionale** ☐

Attendo un sollecito riscontro ed allego un Coupon di Risposta Internazionale con busta indirizzata. Quando risponde, la prego di farmi sapere tutte le tariffe ed il deposito richiesti. Attendendo di incontrarla e di visitare il suo campeggio, la prego di gradire i miei distinti saluti.

[Nome in stampatello dopo la firma]

No. d'associazione al Caravan Club

✂--

RISPOSTA

Data: Indirizzo ....

....

....

Egregio Signore/Signora ....

La ringrazio per il modulo di prenotazione da .... a .... (...... notti).

- **SI, OK** – Sono lieto di confermare la sua prenotazione (con/senza allacciamento elettrico) e attendo di incontrarla.

- **NO, MI DISPIACE** – Mi dispiace ma il campeggio è completamente prenotato per le date da lei richieste.

Distinti saluti.

....

CUSTOMS REGULATIONS

TRAVELLING WITHIN THE EUROPEAN UNION

No tax or duty is payable on entry to the UK on goods you have bought tax-paid in other European Union countries which are for your own use, and which have been transported by you. VAT and duty are included in the price of goods purchased and travellers can no longer buy duty-free or tax-free goods on journeys within the EU, namely Austria, Belgium, Cyprus, the Czech Republic, Denmark, Estonia, Finland, France, Germany, Greece, Hungary, Republic of Ireland, Italy, Latvia, Lithuania, Luxembourg, Malta, the Netherlands, Poland, Portugal, Slovakia, Slovenia, Spain (not the Canary Islands), Sweden and the UK (not the Channel Islands). Gibraltar is part of the EU but Customs allowances for outside the EU apply.

The following are guidance levels for the import of alcohol and tobacco based on European law, but Customs do not enforce any absolute limits. No one under 17 years is entitled to the tobacco or alcohol allowances.

3,200 cigarettes

400 cigarillos

200 cigars

3kg tobacco

10 litres of spirits

20 litres of fortified wine (such as port or sherry)

90 litres of wine

110 litres of beer

However, for an interim period the UK is maintaining limits on the amount of cigarettes and some tobacco products that travellers are able to import into the UK for their own use from eight of the new EU member states, without paying UK duty, namely the Czech Republic, Estonia, Hungary, Latvia, Lithuania, Poland, Slovakia and Slovenia. The limits are 200 cigarettes from all these countries, together with 50 cigars or 100 cigarillos or 250 gm of tobacco from the Czech Republic and 200 cigarettes or 250 gm of tobacco from Estonia.

If you are suspected of having more than these amounts you may be stopped and questioned by a Customs officer. If you are unable or refuse to provide a satisfactory response, the officer may well conclude that the goods are for a commercial purpose or for payment or re-sale (including to family members) and you risk having them seized, together with any vehicle used to transport them, and they may not be returned.

When entering the UK from another member state of the EU without having travelled to or through a non-EU country, you should use the blue channel or exit reserved for EU travellers, provided your purchases are within the limits for imports from that country and you are not importing any restricted or prohibited goods, details of which are given later in this chapter. See individual Country Introductions for further information.

TRAVELLING OUTSIDE THE EUROPEAN UNION

Duty-free goods may be purchased if travelling from the UK direct to a country outside the EU. The allowances for goods you may take into a non-EU country are shown in the relevant Country Introductions.

Duty-free allowances for travellers returning to the UK from a non-EU country are as follows. No one under 17 years is entitled to the tobacco or alcohol allowances.

200 cigarettes, or 100 cigarillos, or 50 cigars, or 250 gms tobacco

1 litre of spirits, or 2 litres of fortified wine, sparkling wine or other liqueurs

2 litres of still table wine

60 cc of perfume, 250 cc of toilet water

£145 worth of all other goods including gifts and souvenirs

When entering the UK from a non-EU country, or having travelled to or through a non-EU country, you should go through the red Customs channel or use the telephone at the Red Point if you have exceeded your Customs allowances, or if you are carrying any prohibited, restricted or commercial goods.

Use the green channel if you have 'nothing to declare'.

All dutiable items must be declared to Customs on entering the UK; failure to do so may mean that you forfeit them and your vehicle(s). Customs officers are legally entitled to examine your baggage and your vehicles and you are responsible for packing and unpacking. Whichever channel you use, you may be stopped by a Customs officer and searched. If you are caught with goods that are prohibited or restricted, or goods in excess of your Customs allowances, you risk heavy fines and possibly a prison sentence.

For further information contact HM Revenue & Customs National Advice Service on 0845 010 9000 (+44 208 929 0152 from outside the UK) or see www.hmrc.gov.uk

BOATS

Virtually all boats of any size taken abroad by road, except for very small craft, must carry registration documents when leaving UK waters. Contact the the Maritime and Coastguard Agency on 0870 6006505 or www.mcga.gov.uk for details. The Royal Yachting Association recommends that all boats have marine insurance and can provide details of the rules and regulations for taking a boat to countries bordering the Atlantic Ocean, and the Baltic, Mediterranean and Black Seas – tel 0845 345 0400, www.rya.org.uk. Some countries require owners of certain types of vessels to have an International Certificate of Competence and information is contained in RYA publications.

If planning to take a boat abroad check with the appropriate tourist office before departure, as rules and regulations for boat use vary from country to country. Third party insurance is compulsory in most European countries and is advisable elsewhere.

CURRENCY

There is no limit to the amount of sterling notes you may take out of the country. Some countries apply limits to the import and export of their own currencies and details are in the relevant Country Introductions.

FOOD

Passengers from within the EU may bring into the UK personal imports of food without restriction. Andorra, the Canary Islands, the Channel Islands, the Isle of Man, Norway and San Marino are treated as part of the EU for these purposes. However, there are strict controls on bringing meat, food and plants into the UK from outside the EU, including Liechtenstein and Switzerland, as these items can carry animal or plant pests and diseases which may damage our environment or public health. HM Revenue & Customs publish a leaflet broadly setting out the rules, entitled 'If in Doubt, Leave it Out!' obtainable from their website, www.hmrc.gov.uk or telephone the National Advice Service on 0845 010 9000. Information can also be obtained from The Food Standards Agency on 020 7276 8000, www.food.gov.uk/import or from DEFRA (Department for Environment, Food and Rural Affairs) on 08459 335577, www.defra.gov.uk

MEDICINES

If you intend to take medicines with you when you go abroad you should obtain a copy of HMRC Notice 4, 'Taking Medicines With You When You Go Abroad,' from HM Revenue & Customs National Advice Service on 0845 010 9000 or from www.hmrc.gov.uk. Alternatively contact the Drugs Enforcement Policy Team, HM Revenue & Customs, New King's Beam House, 22 Upper Ground, London SE1 9PJ, tel 020 7865 5767, fax 020 7865 5910.

There is no limit to the amount of medicines you buy without prescription, but medicines prescribed by your doctor may contain controlled drugs (ie subject to control under the Misuse of Drugs legislation) and you should check the allowances for these – in good time – in case you need to obtain a licence from the Home Office. In general, the permitted allowance for each drug is calculated on an average 15 day dose.

MOTOR VEHICLES AND CARAVANS

Travellers between member states of the EU are entitled to import temporarily a motor vehicle, caravan or trailer into other member states without any Customs formalities.

Motor vehicles and caravans may be temporarily imported into non-EU countries generally up to a maximum of six months in any twelve month period, provided they are not hired, sold or otherwise disposed of in that country. Temporarily imported vehicles should not be left behind after the importer has left, should not be used by residents of the country visited and should not be left longer than the permitted period.

Anyone intending to stay longer than six months, take up employment or residence, or intending to dispose of a vehicle should seek advice well in advance of their departure, for example from one of the motoring organisations. Anyone temporarily importing a vehicle which does not belong to them – either hired or borrowed – should carry a letter of authority from the vehicle owner.

See the chapter Documents in the section PLANNING AND TRAVELLING for further details.

Use Of Caravan By Persons Other Than The Owner

Many caravan owners reduce the cost of a holiday by sharing their caravan with friends or relatives. Either the caravan is left on the Continent on a campsite or it is handed over at the port. In making these arrangements it is important to consider the following:

- The total time the vehicle spends in the country must not exceed the permitted period for temporary importation.

- The owner of the caravan must provide the other person with a letter of authority. It is forbidden to accept a hire fee or reward.

- The number plate on the caravan must match the number plate on the tow car used.

- Each driver's motor insurer must be informed if a caravan is being towed and any additional premium must be paid. Both drivers' Green Cards (if applicable) must be annotated in the recognised way to show that a caravan is being towed.

- If using The Caravan Club's Red Pennant Motoring & Personal Holiday Insurance, both drivers must be members of the Caravan Club and both must pay the usual fee.

PERSONAL POSSESSIONS

Generally speaking, visitors to countries within the EU are free to carry reasonable quantities of any personal articles, including valuable items such as jewellery, cameras, etc required for the duration of their stay. It is sensible to carry sales receipts for new items, particularly of a foreign manufacture, in case you need to prove that tax has already been paid.

Visitors to non-EU countries may temporarily import personal items on condition that the articles are the personal property of the visitor and that they are not left behind when the importer leaves the country. If you are carrying a large number of personal possessions, it may be an idea to draw up an inventory to present to Customs officers if requested.

PROHIBITED AND RESTRICTED GOODS

Just because something is on sale in another country does not mean it can be freely brought back to the UK. The importation of some goods is restricted or banned in the UK, mainly to protect health and the environment. These include:

- Endangered species, including birds and plants, whether alive or dead (eg stuffed), and goods made from them such as spotted cat furs, ivory, reptile leather, hides, tortoiseshell, teeth, feathers, and coral.

- Certain plants and their produce, including trees, shrubs, potatoes, certain fruit, bulbs and seeds.

- Controlled, unlicensed or dangerous drugs eg opium, cannabis, LSD, morphine etc.

- Counterfeit or pirated goods such as fake watches, CDs and sports shirts; goods bearing a false indication of their place of manufacture or in breach of UK copyright.

- Offensive weapons such as flick knives, knuckledusters, push daggers or knives disguised as everyday objects.

- Indecent and obscene material depicting extreme violence or featuring children, such as DVDs, magazines, videos, books and software.

This list is by no means exhaustive; if in doubt contact HM Revenue & Customs National Advice Service for more information or, when returning to the UK, go through the red Customs channel and ask a Customs officer. It is your responsibility to make sure that you are not breaking the law. Never attempt to mislead or hide anything from Customs officers; penalties are severe.

DOCUMENTS

CAMPING CARD INTERNATIONAL (CCI)

The Camping Card International (CCI) is available to members of the Caravan Club and other clubs affiliated to the international organisations, the AIT, FIA and FICC. It is regarded as a camper's identity document and may be deposited with a campsite manager in place of a passport. A CCI is, therefore, essential in those countries where a passport must be carried at all times, and is recommended elsewhere. However, it is not a legal document and campsite managers are within their rights to demand other means of identification. Many campsites throughout Europe give a reduction to cardholders.

The CCI is provided automatically, free of charge, to Caravan Club members taking out the Club's Red Pennant Motoring & Personal Holiday Insurance. It provides comprehensive third party personal liability cover worldwide for the Club member and his passengers (maximum eleven people travelling together) and is valid for one year from the month of issue. Third party cover has been extended to include damages incurred while CCI holders are staying in rented accommodation or hotels as well as campsites. Details of the terms and conditions and level of indemnity are provided with the card.

The CCI is no longer accepted at a number of campsites in Sweden.

See individual Country Introductions for more information.

DRIVING LICENCE & INTERNATIONAL DRIVING PERMIT (IDP)

Driving Licence

A full, valid driving licence should be carried at all times when travelling abroad as, unlike in the UK where there is a discretionary period, it must be produced on demand. Failure to do so may result in an immediate fine, eg in France. If your driving licence is due to expire while you are away it can normally be renewed up to three months before the expiry date. If you need to renew your licence more than three months ahead of the expiry date write to the DVLA and they will try to help.

All European Union countries, including those which joined in 2004, should recognise the pink EU-format driving licence introduced in the UK in 1990, subject to the minimum age requirements of the country concerned (18 years in all countries covered by this guide for a vehicle with a maximum weight of 3,500 kg and carrying not more than 8 people). However, there are exceptions, eg Slovenia, and the Country Introduction chapter contains details.

Holders of the old-style green UK paper licences or licences issued in Northern Ireland prior to 1991, which are not to EU format, are strongly recommended to update them to a photocard licence before travelling in order to avoid any local difficulties with the authorities, or to obtain an International Driving Permit. A photocard driving licence is also useful as a means of photographic identification in other situations, eg using a credit card in Spain and Scandinavia when the display of identification is usually required. These old-style paper licences will still be valid within the UK until they expire, provided all details are correct.

The DVLA no longer issues paper licences and if you need to renew your licence or need a new one for any purpose you must apply to the DVLA Swansea (DVLNI Coleraine for residents of Northern Ireland) for a photocard licence. Application forms are available from most post offices or directly from the DVLA on 0870 240 0009. When applying, allow enough time for your application to be processed and do not apply if you plan to hire a car in the UK or abroad in the near future. Do not send your passport as your identity document if you are likely to need it soon.

Your photocard application form must be accompanied by an identity document, eg passport. Selected post offices offer a premium checking service for photocard applications for a fee of £4.00, in addition to the driving licence fee. The use of this service, means that your identity document and application form will be checked by post office staff for accuracy and completeness and your identity document will be returned to you immediately. Your application will then be forwarded to the DVLA. For more information about the post office checking service telephone 08457 223344 or visit the website www.dvla.gov.uk

If you have any questions regarding photocard driving licences, call DVLA customer enquiries on 0870 240 0009 between 8am and 8.30pm Monday to Friday, 8am to 5.30pm Saturday, fax 01792 783071, email drivers.dvla@gtnet.gov.uk or visit the website www.dvla.gov.uk

International Driving Permit (IDP)

If you hold a British photocard driving licence, no other form of photographic identification is required to drive in any of the countries covered by this guide. If you plan to travel further afield then an IDP may still be required and you should check with one of the motoring organisations which issues them, namely the AA, Green Flag, the RAC or the RSAC, whether or not you are a member. An IDP costs £5.50 and is valid for a period of 12 months from the date of issue but may be post-dated up to three months in advance. To apply for an IDP you will need to be resident in Great Britain, have passed a driving test and be over 18 years of age. When abroad you should always carry your national driving licence with you as well as your IDP.

EUROPEAN HEALTH INSURANCE CARD – EMERGENCY MEDICAL BENEFITS

For information on how to apply for a European Health Insurance Card (EHIC) and the medical care it entitles you to, see the chapter *Medical Matters* in the section *DURING YOUR STAY*.

MOT CERTIFICATE

It is strongly recommended that you carry your vehicle's MOT certificate of roadworthiness (if applicable) when travelling on the Continent as it may be required by the local police if an accident occurs, or in the event of random vehicle checks. If your MOT certificate is due to expire while you are away you should have the vehicle tested before you leave.

PASSPORT

The following information applies only to British citizens and subjects holding, or entitled to hold, a passport bearing the inscription 'United Kingdom of Great Britain and Northern Ireland'. British subjects, British overseas citizens and British dependent territories citizens may need visas that are not required by British citizens. Check with the authorities of the country you are due to visit at their UK Consulate or Embassy. Citizens of other countries should apply to their Embassy, Consulate or High Commission for information.

Each person must hold or be named on a valid passport. Children, including babies, who are not already included on a valid passport need to hold their own passport if they are to travel abroad. It is not now possible to add or include children on a parent's British passport. A standard British passport is valid for ten years, but if issued to children under 16 years of age it is valid for five years.

Children who are already included on an existing passport (one issued before October 1998) may continue to travel with the passport holder until either the child reaches the age of 16, or the passport on which the child is included expires or needs to be amended, whichever comes first. Children aged 16 and over (aged 15 if entering the Czech Republic) must hold their own passport. Rules about children's passports also differ for travel to the United States; telephone the United Kingdom Passport Service (UKPS) Adviceline on 0870 5210410 (24 hours, 7 days a week) for more information or see www.ukpa.gov.uk

Full information and application forms are available from main post offices or from www.ukpa.gov.uk where you can complete an on-line application. Allow at least three weeks for an application for a first-time or renewal passport (four weeks if pre-applying on-line) and at least one week for the replacement of a lost, stolen or damaged passport. So apply early, well before your holiday and do not book a holiday at short notice without first checking that you have a valid passport.

There is the option of a guaranteed same-day premium service for passport renewals, amendments or extensions only, or a one-week fast track service for new passport applications and for the replacement of lost, stolen or damaged passports. Except in an emergency you will not be able to obtain a first passport or a replacement for a lost, stolen or damaged passport in less than a week. Additional fees are payable for the premium and fast track services which are available to personal callers at UKPS counters, but you will need an appointment – telephone the UKPS Adviceline.

There are UKPS regional offices in Belfast, Durham, Glasgow, Liverpool, London, Newport and Peterborough. All regional UKPS offices are open for urgent, personal (appointment-only) applications from Monday to Friday (and on Saturday in London).

The UKPS has arranged for main post offices and other selected High Street partners to accept passport applications on their behalf by means of a 'check and send' service. For a £7 handling charge staff will check the forms and supporting documents for completeness and forward the application securely to the designated regional UKPS office. The passport is then sent directly to the applicant from the issuing office. Priority is given to applications made using this service.

Although the United Kingdom is part of the European Union, you must still carry a full, valid passport with you every time you travel within Europe, including on day trips and via Eurostar. Many countries no longer routinely check passports at frontiers, but visitors must still be able to produce a valid form of identity and nationality at all times and, in the case of British travellers, this is a standard 10-year passport. While abroad, it will help gain access to assistance from British Consular services and to banking services and in addition immigration authorities may check your passport on return to the UK.

Many countries require you to carry your passport at all times. It is advisable to keep a separate record of your passport details and leave a photocopy of the personal details page with a relative or friend at home. Enter next-of-kin details in the back of your passport. In order to avoid any possible local difficulties with immigration authorities, it is advisable to ensure you have at least three months' validity left on your passport to visit countries in the EU, and six months' validity elsewhere. You may renew your passport up to nine months before expiry, without losing the validity of the current one.

Single parents or other adults travelling alone with children should be aware that some countries require documentary evidence of parental responsibility before allowing lone parents to enter the country or, in some cases, before permitting the children to leave the country. For further information on exactly what will be required at immigration, contact the Embassy or Consulate of the countries you intend to visit before you travel.

PET TRAVEL SCHEME (PETS)

Think carefully before taking your pet abroad. Dogs used to the UK's temperate climate may find it difficult to cope with prolonged periods of hot weather. In addition, there are diseases transmitted by ticks, mosquitoes or sandflies, particularly in southern Europe, to which dogs from the UK have no natural resistance. Consult your vet about preventative treatment well in advance of your planned holiday. You need to be sure that your dog is healthy enough to travel and, if in any doubt, it may be in its best interests to leave it at home.

Adequate travel insurance for your pet is essential in the event of an accident abroad requiring extensive veterinary treatment, emergency repatriation or long-term care if treatment lasts longer than your holiday. Travel insurance should include liability cover in the event that your pet injures another animal, person or property while abroad.

The Pets Travel Scheme (PETS) allows pet dogs, cats and a number of other animals from certain qualifying European countries to enter the UK without quarantine, providing they have an EU pet passport, and it also allows pets to travel from the UK to another qualifying EU country. All of the countries covered by this guide (including Gibraltar and Liechtenstein) are qualifying countries. However, the procedures to be followed to obtain the passport are lengthy and the regulations of necessity strict. If you are proposing to take your pet abroad you should check the latest available information from your vet or the PETS Helpline 0870 241 1710 between 8am and 5pm Monday to Friday. You may also contact the Helpline by email on pets.helpline@defra.gsi.gov.uk or fax 020 7904 6206. More information is also available from the website for the Department for Environment, Food and Rural Affairs (DEFRA), www.defra.gov.uk

The scheme operates on certain sea, air and rail routes to England, including ferry routes from Boulogne, Caen, Calais, Cherbourg, Dieppe, Dunkerque, Ijmuiden (Amsterdam), Le Havre, Hook of Holland, Roscoff,

Rotterdam, St Malo, Santander and Zeebrugge. It also operates on Eurotunnel services from Calais to Folkestone, but only guide dogs are permitted to travel on Eurostar trains. Some routes may only operate at certain times of the year; routes may change and new ones may be added – check with the PETS Helpline for the latest information.

Pets normally resident in the Channel Islands, Isle of Man and the Republic of Ireland can also enter the UK under PETS from qualifying countries if they comply with the rules. Pets resident anywhere in the British Isles (including the Republic of Ireland) will continue to be able to travel freely within the British Isles and will not be subject to PETS rules. Owners of pets entering the Channel Islands or the Republic of Ireland from outside the British Isles should contact the appropriate authorities in those countries for advice on approved routes and other requirements.

It is against the law in the UK to possess certain types of dogs (unless an exemption certificate is held) and the introduction of PETS does not affect this ban.

Broadly speaking, dogs are welcome on many European campsites provided they conform to necessary legislation and vaccination requirements. It is essential that you plan ahead and that you meet all the required conditions for the countries you intend to visit. In addition, you should check with individual campsites before embarking on your journey as they may impose restrictions on the number, breed and size of dogs they accept. Be prepared to present documentary evidence of vaccinations on arrival at a campsite. Some campsites will not allow dogs at all, or will require them to be on a lead at all times, or will not allow them during the peak holiday season.

Some countries have laws about certain breeds of dogs and about transporting dogs in cars and, where known, this is covered in the relevant Country Introductions. Information and advice on the welfare of animals before and during a journey is also available on the DEFRA website.

For a list of vets near Continental ports, look in the local equivalent of the Yellow Pages telephone directory, eg www.pagesjaunes.fr for France or www.paginas-amarillas.es for Spain.

VEHICLE EXCISE LICENCE

While driving abroad it is necessary to display a current UK vehicle excise licence (tax disc). If your vehicle tax disc is due to expire while you are abroad you may apply to re-license the vehicle at a post office, or by post, or in person at a DVLA local office up to two months in advance. If you give a despatch address abroad the licence can be sent to you there.

VEHICLE REGISTRATION CERTIFICATE

Your Vehicle Registration Certificate, V5C should always be carried when travelling abroad. If you do not have one you should apply to a DVLA local office on form V62. If you need to travel abroad during this time you will need to apply for a Temporary Registration Certificate if you are not already recorded as the vehicle keeper. There is a fee for this service. Telephone DVLA Customer Enquiries on 0870 2400009 for more information.

Caravan - Proof of Ownership

Britain and Ireland are the only European countries where caravans are not formally registered in the same way as cars. This may not be fully understood by police and other authorities on the Continent. You are strongly advised, therefore, to carry a copy of your Caravan Registration Identification Scheme (CRIS) document.

Hired or Borrowed Vehicles

If using a borrowed vehicle you must obtain a letter of authority to use the vehicle from the registered owner. You should also carry the Vehicle Registration Certificate (V5C).

In the case of hired or leased vehicles, when the user does not normally possess the V5C, ask the company which owns the vehicle to supply a Vehicle On Hire Certificate, form VE103B, or telephone the AA's Information Line on 08705 500600 to request an application form for a Certificate. Alternatively, you can download a form from the RAC's website, www.rac.co.uk, or call their Travel Sales on 0800 550055.

VISAS

British citizens holding a full UK passport do not require a visa for entry into any of the countries covered by this guide. EU countries normally require a permit for stays of more than three months. Permits can be obtained during your stay on application to the local police or civic authorities.

FERRIES AND THE CHANNEL TUNNEL

The Caravan Club is an agent for most major ferry companies operating services to the Continent, Scandinavia and Ireland, and each year provides thousands of Club members with a speedy and efficient booking service, using modern computerised reservations systems. The Club's Travel Service in Europe brochure (available in November) features a range of special offers with ferry operators (some of them exclusive to the Caravan Club), together with full information on the Club's Continental campsite Advance Booking Service, its range of 'package' Inclusive Holidays, and Red Pennant Motoring & Personal Holiday Insurance. Telephone 01342 327410 to obtain a brochure or see our website, www.caravanclub.co.uk

In addition, during the course of the year, new special ferry offers and promotions are negotiated and details of these are featured regularly on the Travel Service News page of The Caravan Club Magazine and on the Club's website, www.caravanclub.co.uk

The Club's website has a direct link through to a number of the most popular ferry operators' reservations systems and Club members can make their own reservations and still take advantage of the Club's negotiated offers and the ferry companies' own early booking offers. The requisite deposit is taken by credit card and the balance collected ten weeks prior to departure date.

When planning a holiday abroad with your caravan, bear in mind the following points:

- If travelling in July or August, or over peak weekends during school holidays, such as Easter and half-term, it is advisable to make a reservation as early as possible, particularly if you need cabin accommodation.

- Space for caravans on ferries is usually limited and in some cases is restricted to less than half a dozen caravans on certain sailings. Off-peak crossings, which may offer savings for caravanners, are usually filled very quickly.

- When booking any ferry crossing, account must be taken of boats, bicycles, skylights and roof boxes, if applicable, in the overall height/length of the car and caravan outfit or motor caravan, as ferry operators usually require total dimensions to be declared. It is important, therefore, to report length and height of outfits accurately when making ferry bookings, as vehicles which have been under-declared may be turned away at boarding.

- Individual ferry companies may impose vehicle length or height restrictions according to the type of vessel in operation, ie catamarans, fast-craft or conventional ferries. On some routes more than one kind of vessel may be operating. Always check when making your booking.

- Advise your booking agent at the time of making your ferry reservation of any disabled passengers, or any who have special needs. Ferry companies can then make the appropriate arrangements for anyone requiring assistance at ports or on board ships.

- For residents of both Northern Ireland and the Republic of Ireland travelling to the Continent via the British mainland, Brittany Ferries, Irish Ferries and P & O Irish Sea offer special 'Landbridge' or 'Ferrylink' through-fares for combined crossings on the Irish Sea and the English Channel or North Sea, although the Club's own individually booked offers are often better value.

- The table on the following page shows current ferry routes from the UK to the Continent and Ireland. Some ferry routes may not be operational all year and during peak holiday periods the transportation of caravans or motor caravans may be restricted or not permitted. Current information on ferry timetables and tariffs can be obtained from the Caravan Club's Travel Service or from a travel agent, or from the appropriate ferry operators' websites.

- Reservations may be made by telephoning the Caravan Club's Travel Service on 01342 316101 or on www.caravanclub.co.uk

Route	Operator	Approximate Duration	Frequency
BELGIUM			
Hull – Zeebrugge	P & O Ferries	12½ hrs	Daily
Ramsgate – Ostend†	Transeuropa Ferries	4 hrs	4 Daily
Rosyth – Zeebrugge	Superfast Ferries	17½	Daily
DENMARK			
Harwich – Esbjerg	DFDS Seaways	17 hrs	4 weekly
FRANCE			
Dover – Boulogne*†	SpeedFerries	50 mins	5 daily
Dover – Calais	P & O Ferries	1¼ hrs	25 daily
Dover – Calais	SeaFrance	1¼-1½ hrs	15 daily
Dover – Dunkirk	Norfolkline	2 hrs	10 daily
Folkestone – Calais	Eurotunnel	35 mins	3 per hour
Newhaven–Dieppe	Transmanche Ferries	4 hrs	3 daily
Plymouth – Roscoff	Brittany Ferries	4¾ / 6 hrs	3 daily
Poole – Cherbourg	Brittany Ferries	2¼ hrs / 6¾ hrs	3 daily
Poole – St Malo (via Channel Islands)	Condor Ferries	4½ hrs	Daily
Portsmouth – Caen	Brittany Ferries	5¾ / 7 hrs	4 daily
Portsmouth – Cherbourg	Brittany Ferries	3 / 4¾ hrs	3 daily
Portsmouth – St Malo	Brittany Ferries	10¾ hrs	Daily
Weymouth – St Malo (via Channel Islands)	Condor Ferries	5¼ / 7¾ hrs	Daily
GERMANY			
Harwich – Cuxhaven**	DFDS Seaways	18½ hrs	4 weekly
IRELAND – NORTHERN			
Cairnryan – Larne	P & O Irish Sea	1 / 1¾ hrs	9 daily
Fleetwood – Larne	Stena Line	8 hrs	3 daily
Stranraer – Belfast	Stena Line	1¾ / 3½ hrs	8 daily
Troon – Larne	P & O Irish Sea	1 hr 50 mins	2 daily
IRELAND – REPUBLIC			
Cork – Roscoff	Brittany Ferries	11 hrs	Weekly
Fishguard – Rosslare	Stena Line	1¾ / 3½ hrs	5 daily
Holyhead – Dublin	Irish Ferries	1¾ hr / 3¼ hrs	5 daily
Holyhead – Dublin	Stena Line	3¼ hrs	2 daily
Holyhead – Dun Loaghaire	Stena Line	1 hr 40 mins	3 daily
Liverpool – Dublin	P & O Irish Sea	7½ hrs	2 daily
Pembroke – Rosslare	Irish Ferries	3¾ hrs	2 daily
Rosslare – Cherbourg	Irish Ferries	18½ hrs	4 weekly
Rosslare – Roscoff	Irish Ferries	17 hrs	2 weekly
Swansea – Cork†	Swansea Cork Ferries	10 hrs	6 weekly
NETHERLANDS			
Harwich – Hook of Holland	Stena Line	3¾ / 6½ hrs	4 daily
Hull – Rotterdam	P & O Ferries	10 hrs	Daily
Newcastle – Amsterdam (Ijmuiden)	DFDS Seaways	15 hrs	Daily
NORWAY			
Newcastle – Bergen	Fjord Line	25 hrs	3 weekly
Newcastle – Haugesund	Fjord Line	21 hrs	3 weekly
Newcastle – Kristiansand	DFDS Seaways	17¾ hrs	2 weekly
Newcastle – Stavanger	Fjord Line	18½ hrs	3 weekly
SPAIN			
Plymouth – Santander	Brittany Ferries	18 hrs	2 weekly
Portsmouth – Bilbao	P & O Ferries	29 / 35 hrs	3 weekly
SWEDEN			
Newcastle – Gothenberg**	DFDS Seaways	26 hrs	2 weekly

*   Cars and small motor caravans only.
** NB For technical reasons it is sometimes necessary to reverse outfits off ferries on these routes.
† Not bookable through the Club's Travel Service.

CHANNEL TUNNEL

Eurotunnel accepts cars, caravans and motor caravans (except those running on LPG and dual-fuel vehicles) on their service between Folkestone and Calais. Whilst they do accept traffic on a 'turn up and go' basis, they now offer a full reservation service for all departures with exact timings confirmed on booking.

All the above information was current at the time this guide was compiled in the autumn of 2005 and may be subject to change during 2006.

GAS – SAFETY PRECAUTIONS AND REGULATIONS ON FERRIES AND IN THE CHANNEL TUNNEL

- Gas cylinders should be of a type specifically recommended by the Department of Trade & Industry.

- UK-based cross-Channel ferry companies usually allow up to three gas cylinders per caravan, including the cylinder currently in use. However some restrict this even further, eg Brittany Ferries, Fjord Line, SeaFrance and Stena Line allow a maximum of two cylinders, providing they are securely fitted into your caravan. It is advisable to check with the ferry company before setting out.

- Cylinder valves should be fully closed and covered with a cap, if provided, and should remain closed during the crossing. Ensure gas cookers and fridges are properly turned off. Cylinders should be fixed securely in or on the caravan in the manner intended and in the position designated by the caravan manufacturers.

- Ships' crew may wish to inspect each cylinder for leakage before shipment and to reject leaking cylinders. If cylinders are likely to be inaccessible within an unaccompanied vehicle, arrangement should be made for the shipper to observe this precaution.

- Eurotunnel will allow vehicles fitted with LPG tanks for the purpose of heating, lighting, cooking or refrigeration to use their services but regulations stipulate that a total of no more than 73 litres or 47 kg of gas can be carried through the Channel Tunnel. Eurotunnel security staff carry out safety inspections on all vehicles carrying LPG. The caravan door will be sealed by a sticker. **Vehicles powered with LPG or equipped with a dual-fuel system cannot be carried through the Channel Tunnel.**

- Most ferry companies are willing to accept LPG-powered vehicles provided they are advised at the time of booking. During the crossing the tank must be no more than 75% full and it must be turned off. In the case of vehicles converted to use LPG, some ferry companies also require a certificate showing that the conversion has been carried out to the manufacturer's specification.

- The carriage of spare petrol cans, whether full or empty, is not permitted on ferries or through the Channel Tunnel.

PETS ON FERRIES AND EUROTUNNEL

Following the success of the Pets Travel Scheme, the number of ferry routes on which it is possible to carry pets has been extended and it is now possible to take your pet not only on cross-Channel sailings from Dover to Calais, but also direct to Spain on the Plymouth-Santander route and to Holland on Stena Line's route from Harwich to the Hook of Holland. At the time this guide was compiled the cost of return travel for a pet to France, Holland or Spain was £10 to £35. Advance booking is essential as restrictions apply to the number of animals allowed on any one departure. Make sure you understand the carrier's terms and conditions for transporting pets.

On arrival at the port ensure that ferry staff know that your vehicle contains an animal. Pets are normally required to remain in their owners' vehicle or in kennels on the car deck and, for safety reasons, access to the vehicle decks while the ferry is at sea may be restricted. On longer ferry crossings you should make arrangements at the on-board Information Desk for permission to visit your pet at suitable intervals in order to check its well-being.

See also Pet Travel Scheme under Documents in the section PLANNING AND TRAVELLING.

CARAVAN CLUB SITES NEAR PORTS

Once you have chosen your ferry crossing and worked out your route to the port of departure you may like to consider an overnight stop at one of the following Club sites, especially if your journey to or from home involves a long drive. Advance booking is recommended either by telephone, by post or via the Club's website, particularly if you are planning to stay during July and August or over Bank Holidays. Full details can be found in your Sites Directory & Handbook 2005/06.

Port	Nearest Site and Town	Tel No.
Cairnryan, Stranraer	New England Bay, Drummore	01776 860275
Dover, Folkestone,	Black Horse Farm, Folkestone	01303 892665
Channel Tunnel	Daleacres, Hythe	01303 267679
Fishguard, Pembroke	Freshwater East, Pembroke	01646 672341
Harwich	Colchester Camping, Colchester	01206 545551
Holyhead	Penrhos, Brynteg	01248 852617
Hull	Beechwood Grange, York	01904 424637
	Rowntree Park, York	01904 658997
Newcastle upon Tyne	Old Hartley, Whitley Bay	0191 237 0256
Newhaven	Sheepcote Valley, Brighton	01273 626546
Plymouth	Plymouth Sound, Plymouth	01752 862325
Poole	Hunter's Moon, Wareham	01929 556605
Portsmouth	Rookesbury Park, Fareham	01329 834085
Rosslare	River Valley, Wicklow	00353 (404) 41647
Swansea	Gowerton, Gowerton	01792 873050
Weymouth	Crossways, Weymouth	01305 852032

When seasonal Club sites near the ports are closed, the following, which are open all year or most of the year (but may not be 'on the doorstep' of the ports in question) may be useful overnight stops for early and late season travellers using cross-Channel, Irish Sea or North Sea ports. All 'open all year' sites offer a limited supply of hard standing pitches.

Port	Nearest Site and Town	Tel No.
Dover, Folkestone,	Black Horse Farm, Folkestone	01303 892665
Channel Tunnel	Abbey Wood, London	020 8311 7708
	Alderstead Heath, Redhill	01737 644629
	Amberley Fields, Crawley	01293 524834
	Crystal Palace, London	020 8778 7155
Fishguard, Pembroke, Swansea	Pembrey Country Park, Llanelli	01554 834369
Hull	Rowntree Park, York	01904 658997
Newhaven	Sheepcote Valley, Brighton	01273 626546
Portsmouth	Abbey Wood, London	020 8311 7708
	Alderstead Heath, Redhill	01737 644629
	Amberley Fields, Crawley	01293 524834
	Crystal Palace, London	020 8778 7155

NB Amberley Fields, Daleacres, Hunter's Moon, Old Hartley and Rookesbury Park are open to Caravan Club members only. Non-members are welcome at all the other Caravan Club sites listed above.

Full details of all these sites can be found in the Caravan Club's Sites Directory & Handbook 2005/06.

INSURANCE

CAR, MOTOR CARAVAN AND CARAVAN INSURANCE

Insurance cover for motor car, motor caravan and caravan while travelling abroad is of the utmost importance. Travel insurance, such as the Caravan Club's Red Pennant Motoring & Personal Holiday Insurance (available to members only), not only minimises duplicate cover offered by normal motor and caravan insurance, but also covers contingencies which are not included, eg despatch of spare parts, medical and hospital fees, hire vehicles, hotel bills, vehicle recovery etc.

See Holiday Insurance later in this section.

In order to be covered for a period abroad the following action is necessary:

- **Caravan** – Inform your caravan insurer/broker of the dates of your holiday and pay any additional premium required. The Caravan Club's 5Cs Insurance gives free cover up to 182 days.

- **Motor Car or Motor Caravan** – If your journey is outside the EU or Associated Countries inform your motor insurer/broker of the dates of your holiday, together with details of all the countries you will be visiting, and pay any additional premium. Also inform them if you are towing a caravan and ask them to include it on your Green Card if you need to carry one.

The Caravan Club's MotorCover Motor Insurance scheme extends to provide full policy cover for European Union or Associated Countries free of charge, provided the total period of foreign travel in any one annual period of insurance does not exceed 180 days. It may be possible to extend this period, although a charge will be made. The cover provided is the same as a Club member enjoys in the United Kingdom, rather than the minimum legal liability cover required by law in the country visited.

Should you be delayed beyond the limits of your insurance you **must**, without fail, instruct your insurer/broker to maintain cover.

Green Card

All countries oblige visiting motorists to have motor insurance cover for their legal liability to third parties. An International Motor Insurance Certificate, commonly known as a Green Card, is evidence of compliance with this requirement. However, motorists visiting European Union and Associated Countries (listed on the next page) do not need an actual Green Card, as a UK Certificate of Motor Insurance is now accepted by law in all the listed countries, as evidence that the obligatory motor insurance cover is in force.

Travellers outside the European Union and Associated Countries will need to obtain a Green Card document, for which insurers usually make a charge. In the instance of a Green Card being issued, your motor insurers should be asked to include reference on it to your caravan. If visiting motorists do not have evidence of the obligatory insurance cover, you may have to pay for temporary insurance when you arrive at a country's border.

Whether or not a Green Card is required, it is still normally necessary for you to notify your insurer/broker of your intention to travel outside the UK and obtain confirmation that your policy has been extended to include use of the insured vehicle abroad. Because of the cost of claims that can arise on the Continent, your insurers may not automatically provide full policy cover when abroad. You should ensure that your vehicle and caravan policies provide adequate cover for your purposes, rather than the limited cover that the country you are visiting obliges you to have.

European Accident Statement

You should also request a European Accident Statement to record details of any accident that you may be involved in with your motor vehicle. Travelling with your vehicle registration certificate, MOT certificate (if applicable), vehicle insurance certificate, copy of your CRIS document, European Accident Statement and valid pink EU-format or photocard UK driving licence should be sufficient should you be stopped by a routine police check or following an accident. These documents should not be left in the vehicle when it is unattended.

European Union and Associated Countries

European Union: Austria, Belgium, Cyprus, Czech Republic, Denmark, Estonia, Finland, France, Germany, Greece, Hungary, Ireland, Italy, Latvia, Lithuania, Luxembourg, Malta, Netherlands, Poland, Portugal, Slovakia, Slovenia, Spain, Sweden and the United Kingdom.

Associated Countries (ie non-EU signatories to the motor insurance 'Multilateral Guarantee Agreement): Croatia, Iceland, Norway, Switzerland and Liechtenstein.

In spite of the foregoing, you may wish to obtain an actual Green Card if visiting Greece, Hungary or Slovakia so as to avoid local difficulties which can sometimes arise in these countries. If you do not take a Green Card you should carry your vehicle insurance certificate. **Visitors to countries outside the European Union and Associated Countries, and in particular eastern European countries, should check that their motor insurer will provide the necessary extension of cover.**

Bail Cover for Spain

Although motor insurers have progressed to remove the need to provide this cover, as a precautionary measure bail cover will continue to be provided with the Caravan Club's Red Pennant Motoring & Personal Holiday Insurance and is also available if you arrange your motor insurance through the Club's MotorCover Motor Insurance scheme.

Caravans Stored Abroad

Caravan insurers will not normally insure caravans left on campsites or in storage abroad. In these circumstances specialist policies are available from Bakers of Cheltenham; tel 01242 528844, www.bakersofcheltenham.co.uk, email bakers@towergate.co.uk or Drew Insurance; tel 0845 4565758, www.drewinsurance.co.uk, email mail@kdib.co.uk

Legal Costs Abroad

A person who is taken to court following a road traffic accident in a European country runs the risk of having to pay legal costs personally, even if (s)he is cleared of any blame.

Motor insurance policies in the UK normally include cover for legal costs and expenses incurred with the insurer's consent and arising from any incident that is covered under the terms and conditions of the policy. The Caravan Club's MotorCover Motor Insurance scheme incorporates such cover and, in addition, offers an optional legal expenses insurance to help you recover any other losses that are not covered by your motor insurance policy. Similar cover is also offered as an addition to the Club's 5Cs Caravan Insurance scheme.

HOLIDAY TRAVEL INSURANCE

Having insured your vehicles, there are other risks to consider and it is essential to take out adequate travel insurance. The Caravan Club's Red Pennant Motoring & Personal Holiday Insurance is designed to provide as full a cover as possible, in keeping with a reasonable fee. The Club's scheme is tailor-made for the caravanner and motor caravanner and includes cover against the following:

- Recovery of vehicles and passengers
- Towing charges
- Emergency labour costs
- Chauffeured recovery
- Storage fees
- Spare parts location and despatch
- Continuation of holiday travel, ie car hire etc
- Continuation of holiday accommodation, ie hotels etc
- Emergency medical and hospital expenses
- Legal expenses
- Emergency cash transfers
- Loss of deposits/cancellation cover
- Personal accident benefits
- Personal effects and baggage insurance
- Loss of cash or documents
- Cost of telephone calls

If you are proposing to participate in dangerous sports activities, such as skiing, hang-gliding or mountaineering, check that your personal holiday insurance includes cover for such sports, and that it incorporates mountain rescue and helicopter rescue costs.

Look carefully at the exemptions to your insurance policy, including exemptions relating to pre-existing medical conditions and the use of alcohol. Be sure that you declare any pre-existing medical conditions to your insurer.

For Club members increased cover may be obtained by taking out **Plus** cover. The Club also offers a range of annual multi-trip and long stay holiday insurance schemes for Continental and worldwide travel. For more details and policy limits refer to the Travel

Service in Europe brochure from the Caravan Club.

Holiday Insurance for Pets

Adequate travel insurance for your pet is a wise precaution in case an incident or illness abroad requires extensive veterinary treatment, emergency repatriation or long-term care if necessary treatment lasts longer than your holiday. Your vet should be able to supply information on appropriate insurance policies.

Think very carefully before taking your pet abroad. In the event of an accident involving your vehicle(s) or of someone in your party falling ill and needing urgent repatriation, you may face the need for emergency accommodation for your pet, or have difficulty in finding a responsible third party to get your pet back home.

The Club's Red Pennant Motoring & Personal Holiday Insurance covers extra expenses in respect of your pet that may arise as part of a claim for an incident normally covered under the Red Pennant policy. It does not, however, cover costs arising from an injury to, or the illness of your pet, or provide any legal liability cover to you as a pet owner. If you already have such cover in the UK for your pet, you may be able to get it extended to provide cover whilst abroad.

HOME INSURANCE

Most home insurers require advance notification if you are leaving your home empty for 30 days or more. They often require that all water is drained off, mains services (except electricity) are turned off and that somebody visits the home once a week. Check your policy documents or speak to your insurer/broker.

MARINE INSURANCE

Car Ferries

Vehicles accompanied by the owner are normally conveyed in accordance with the terms of the carrying companies' published bye-laws or conditions, and if damage is sustained during loading, unloading or shipment, this must be reported at the time to the carrier's representative. Any claim arising from such damage must be notified in writing to the carrier concerned within three days of the incident. It is unwise to rely on being able to claim from the carrier in respect of damage etc, and transit insurance is advised.

The majority of motor policies cover vehicles during short sea crossings up to 65 hours normal duration – check with your insurer. The Caravan Club's 5Cs policy automatically covers you for crossings of any length within the area covered by Red Pennant Motoring & Personal Holiday Insurance.

Boats

The Royal Yachting Association recommends that all boats have marine insurance. Third party insurance is compulsory for some of the countries covered by this guide, together with a translation of the insurance certificate into the appropriate language(s). Check with your insurer/broker before taking your boat abroad.

MEDICAL INSURANCE

See the chapter Medical Matters in the section DURING YOUR STAY.

PERSONAL EFFECTS INSURANCE

The majority of travellers are able to cover their valuables such as jewellery, watches, cameras, bikes and, in some instances, small craft under the All Risks section of their Householders' Comprehensive Policy.

The chapters *Safety and Security* under *DURING YOUR STAY* and *Money* in *PLANNING AND TRAVELLING* contain important advice and information on personal security.

VEHICLES LEFT BEHIND ABROAD

If you are involved in an accident or breakdown while on the Continent which requires you to leave a vehicle behind when returning home, you must ensure that your normal insurance cover is maintained to cover the period that the vehicle remains on the Continent, and that you are covered for the journey back to your home address.

You should remove all items of baggage and personal effects from your vehicle before leaving it unattended. If this is not possible you should check with your insurer/broker to establish whether extended cover can be provided. In all circumstances, you must remove any valuables and items which might attract Customs duty, including wines, beer and spirits.

INTERNATIONAL HOLIDAYS 2006

INTERNATIONAL HOLIDAYS, IMPORTANT DATES & UK BANK HOLIDAYS

January	1	Sunday	New Year's Day
	2	Monday	Bank Holiday UK
	6	Friday	Epiphany
	29-31	Sunday-Tuesday	Chinese New Year*
	31	Tuesday	Al Hijra – Islamic New Year*
March	1	Wednesday	St David's Day, Ash Wednesday
	17	Friday	St Patrick's Day
	26	Sunday	British Summer Time begins
April	9	Sunday	Palm Sunday (start of Holy Week)
	14	Friday	Good Friday; Bank Holiday UK
	16	Sunday	Easter Day
	17	Monday	Easter Monday; Bank Holiday UK
	23	Sunday	St George's Day, Christian Orthodox Easter Day
May	1	Monday	May Day Bank Holiday UK
	25	Thursday	Ascension Day
	29	Monday	Spring Bank Holiday UK
June	4	Sunday	Whit Sunday (Pentecost)
	15	Thursday	Corpus Christi
August	15	Tuesday	Assumption
	28	Monday	Bank Holiday UK
September	23	Saturday	Jewish New Year (Rosh Hashanah)
	24	Sunday	First Day of Ramadan*
October	2	Monday	Jewish Day of Atonement (Yom Kippur)
	24	Tuesday	Ramadan ends*
	29	Sunday	British Summer Time ends
	31	Tuesday	Halloween
November	1	Wednesday	All Saints' Day
	12	Sunday	Remembrance Day
	30	Thursday	St Andrew's Day
December	8	Friday	Immaculate Conception
	25	Monday	Christmas Day
	26	Tuesday	St Stephen's Day; Boxing Day UK

* Subject to the lunar calendar

Notes:
1)   When a holiday falls on a Sunday it will not necessarily be observed the following day.
2)   Public holidays in individual countries are listed in the relevant Country Introduction sections.

MONEY

Take your holiday money in a mixture of cash, travellers' cheques and credit and/or debit cards. Do not rely exclusively on only one method of payment.

LOCAL CURRENCY

It is a good idea to carry a small amount of foreign currency, including loose change, for countries you are travelling through, in case of emergencies or when shopping or using parking meters. French supermarket trolleys, for example, usually require a euro coin to be inserted in the trolley-release mechanism, refundable when the trolley is returned.

Take sufficient cash for your immediate needs on arrival. Even if you intend to use credit and debit cards for most of your holiday spending, it makes sense to take some cash to tide you over until you are unable to find a cash machine (ATM).

Minimum commission rates vary but expect to pay 1% or 2% commission when buying or selling foreign currency, with a minimum charge of £3. Most banks and exchange offices stock the more common currencies, but it is wise to order in advance in case demand is heavy at the time you intend to travel, or if you require an unusual currency. It can pay to shop around and compare commission and exchange rates together with minimum charges.

Many suppliers now offer commission-free transactions, whereas some will charge a flat fee which makes it more economic to change large amounts of cash, and some offer a 'buy back' service. Currency can be ordered by telephone or online for delivery to your home or office address on payment of a handling charge. For example, the Post Office allows you to order currency by telephone (08458 500900) or online for collection at any post office the next day, www.postoffice.co.uk. There are a number of other online suppliers, eg www.travelex.co.uk, and most of the High Street banks offer their customers currency and travellers' cheque purchase online.

Your credit/debit card issuer may charge a cash advance fee, in addition to the commission and/or handling charge, in respect of the purchase of travel money, whether by telephone, over the internet or over the counter. Maestro/Switch cards do not incur a cash advance fee.

Although there is no restriction on the amount of sterling you are permitted to carry, in some countries regulations control the amount of currency that may be imported or exported by foreign visitors and you will find details, where applicable, in the relevant Country Introductions. Your bank will also be able to supply up-to-date information and advice.

Visitors have reported that banks and money exchanges in eastern Europe may not be willing to accept Scottish and Northern Irish bank notes and may be reluctant to change any sterling which has been written on, is creased or worn or is not in virtually mint condition.

Exchange rates (as at October 2005) are given in the Country Introductions in this guide. A list of the most frequently used currency conversions may be found on Ceefax BBC2, or from your bank or in national newspapers. Alternatively, www.oanda.com updates currency rates around the world daily and allows you to print a handy currency converter to take with you on your trip.

TRAVELLERS' CHEQUES

Travellers' cheques can be cashed or used as payment for goods or services in almost all countries, and are the safest way of carrying large sums of money. They can be replaced quickly – usually within 24 hours – in the event of loss or theft. Travellers' cheques may be accepted where credit cards are not and are useful if you are travelling off the beaten track or in far-flung locations, but bear in mind that small bank branches may not offer foreign exchange services. Commission is payable when you buy the cheques and/or when you cash them in.

In addition to using the euro in all twelve participating euro zone countries without the need for costly currency conversions, it is now possible to buy euro travellers' cheques for use within the euro zone. Many banks offer fee-free encashment of euro travellers' cheques and you should check with the issuer or sales agent and also check with individual bank branches before cashing them. Some recent visitors to Spain, Portugal and Italy have reported high commission charges when cashing foreign currency and/or euro travellers' cheques, together with a high minimum charge. For American Express travellers' cheque holders there is a list of European banks providing fee-free encashment on the Amex website, www.americanexpress.co.uk. Information on where to cash MasterCard and Visa travellers' cheques, and the fees charged, can be found on www.cashmycheques.com

US dollar travellers' cheques or, more recently, euro travellers' cheques are frequently used for payment in countries which have a 'soft' currency, ie one which cannot be traded on the international markets. Your bank will advise you.

CREDIT AND DEBIT CARDS

Credit cards and debit cards are a convenient, safe and often cheaper way of spending abroad and increasingly travellers use them for the bulk of their holiday purchases. In addition to using a card to pay for goods and services wherever your card logo is displayed, you can obtain cash advances at most banks, and money can be obtained from cash machines with the same PIN as you use in the UK. MasterCard and Visa list the location of their cash dispensers in countries throughout the world on www.mastercard.com and http://visa.via.infonow.net/locator/eur

Credit and debit cards with the Visa, MasterCard or Maestro symbol may be used to buy goods and services, and to withdraw cash. Check the logo before using your card, especially at cash machines, where your card may not reappear once inserted.

For credit card use abroad most banks impose a foreign currency conversion charge (up to 2.75% per transaction) which is usually the same for both credit and debit cards. If you use your credit card to withdraw cash there will be a further commission charge of up to 2% and you may also be charged higher interest rates. Liverpool Victoria which issues the Caravan Club's credit card, marketed by Frizzell, makes no charge on purchases in EU countries but charges 2.75% in all other countries. Cash withdrawals abroad are currently subject to a 1.5% handling charge – minimum £1.50.

Most card issuers charge interest on cash withdrawals from the date of withdrawal, rather than the payment due date, even if the bill is paid off in full. The exchange rate applied will be that in effect when the transaction is processed in the UK and is frequently advantageous compared to across-the-counter rates of exchange. Check with your bank for details.

When paying with a credit or debit card retailers may offer you the choice of currency for payment, ie a euro amount will be converted into sterling and then charged to your credit card account. You will be asked to sign an agreement to accept the conversion rate used and final amount charged and, having done so, there is no opportunity to change your mind or obtain a refund. The exchange rate used is unlikely to be as favourable as that used by your credit/debit card issuer.

Check the expiry date of your cards before you leave and memorise the PIN for each card, as you will need it for making purchases in some countries, as well as for making withdrawals from cash machines. If you have several cards, take at least two in case you come across gaps in acceptance of certain cards, eg shops which accept only MasterCard. If you are planning an extended journey, it is possible to arrange for your credit or charge card account to be cleared each month by variable direct debit, ensuring that bills are paid on time and no interest is charged.

British credit and debit card issuers now supply their customers with 'chip and PIN' cards; cards with a magnetic strip only having been phased out. However, British credit cards may not be universally accepted and it is wise to check before incurring expenditure. 'Chip and PIN' cards have been used in France for a number of years. However, the French system has had to be modified to make it compatible with the rest of Europe and, until its system is modified accross the whole country (sheduled for 2006) you may still be required to sign a receipt as before.

It is advisable to contact your credit card issuer before you leave home to warn them that you are travelling abroad. In the battle against credit card fraud card issuers are frequently likely to query transactions which they regard as unusual or suspicious. This may result in a retailer at the point of sale having to telephone for authorisation and/or confirmation of a customer's details. Difficulties can occur if there is a language barrier or if the retailer is unwilling to bother with further checks and your card may be declined or, worse still, temporarily stopped. In this instance you should insist that the retailer contacts the local authorisation centre but, in any event, it may also be helpful to carry your card issuer's helpline number with you.

EMERGENCY CASH

If an emergency or robbery means that you need cash in a hurry, then friends or relatives at home can use the Post Office's secure, instant money transfer service. This MoneyGram service, which does not necessarily require the sender to use a bank account or credit card, enables the transfer of money to over 70,000 locations around the world. Transfers take approximately ten minutes; charges are levied on a sliding scale.

Western Union operates a similar secure, worldwide service and has offices throughout the world located in banks, post offices, travel agents, stations and shops. Their telephone lines are open 24 hours, telephone 0800 833833 (00353 669792719 if calling from outside the UK), www.westernunion.co.uk

As a last resort, go to the nearest embassy or consulate for help. The Foreign & Commonwealth Office in London can arrange for a relative or friend to deposit funds which will be authorised for payment by embassy staff.

See individual Country Introductions for embassy and consulate addresses.

Most travel insurance policies will cover you for only a limited amount of lost or stolen cash (usually between £250 and £500) and you will probably have to wait until you return home for reimbursement.

THE EURO

The euro is now the only legal tender in the following countries covered by this guide: Austria, Belgium, Finland, France, Germany, Greece, Italy, Luxembourg, the Netherlands, Portugal and Spain. In addition the Republic of Ireland, the states of Andorra, Monte Carlo, San Marino and the Vatican City have also adopted the euro.

Denmark, Sweden and the UK, although member states of the EU, do not currently participate in the euro and their currencies are unaffected. It is anticipated that the ten new member states which joined the EU in 2004 will all eventually join the single currency in 2007. In the meantime, you will usually find euros readily accepted in these countries in payment for goods and services.

Apart from Luxembourg, each country produces its own euro notes and coins. There are seven euro banknotes in denominations of 5, 10, 20, 50, 100, 200 and 500 euros incorporating illustrations representing the seven ages of Europe's cultural history, and eight coins ranging from one cent to two euros. Banknotes are identical in each country and each coin has an identical face. However the reverse side of coins differs from country to country. Each version is valid in all the countries of the euro zone.

HOLIDAY MONEY SECURITY

- Treat your cards and travellers' cheques as carefully as you would cash. Use a money belt, if possible, to conceal cards and valuables and do not keep all your methods of payment in the same place. Split money and travellers' cheques between members of your party.

- If you keep a wallet in your pocket, place a rubber band around it, as it is then more difficult for a pickpocket to slide the wallet out without your noticing.

- To avoid credit card 'cloning' never let your credit card out of your sight – in restaurants follow the waiter to the till or insist that the card machine is brought to your table. This is particularly important as you may frequently find that your signature on a transaction slip is not checked against the signature on your card. If you do allow your card to be taken and it is gone for more than a minute, become suspicious.

- Always check that your credit card vouchers are properly filled in and in the correct currency. If a manual card machine is used, take the black carbon sheets and destroy them, but always keep a copy of the voucher. It has been known for unscrupulous retailers to add a nought after a customer has signed a voucher.

- If you suspect your card has been fraudulently used, or if your cards are lost or stolen, or if a cash machine retains your card, call the issuing bank immediately. All the major credit card companies operate a 24-hour emergency helpline. If you are unlucky enough to become a victim of cash machine fraud, your bank will refund the money stolen, provided you have not been negligent or careless.

- Keep your card's magnetic strip away from other cards and objects, especially if they are also magnetic. If the card is damaged in any way, electronic terminals may not accept your transaction.

- Keep your travellers' cheques and sales advice slip separate so that you have a record of the numbers in case of loss. Keep a record of where and when you cash your travellers' cheques and the numbers. If they are lost or stolen, contact the appropriate refund service immediately.

- Join a credit card protection plan (the Caravan Club offers one for its members) so that in the event of loss or theft, one telephone call will cancel all your cards and arrange replacements.

- Take care when using cash machines. If the machine is obstructed or poorly lit, avoid it. If someone near the machine is behaving suspiciously or makes you feel uneasy, find another one. If there is something unusual about the cash machine do not use it and report the matter to the bank or owner of the premises. Do not accept help from strangers and do not allow yourself to be distracted.

- Be aware of your surroundings and if someone is watching you closely do not proceed with the transaction. Shield the screen and keyboard so that anyone waiting to use the machine cannot see you enter your PIN or transaction amount. Put your cash, card and receipt away immediately. Count your cash later and always keep your receipt to compare with your monthly statement.

- If you bank over the internet and are using a computer in a public place such as a library or cybercafé, do not leave the PC unattended and ensure that no-one is watching what you type. Always log off from internet banking upon completion of your session. This will prevent the viewing of previous pages of your online session via the computer.

- If you arrive at a cash machine by car, do not leave the engine running or the car unlocked while you use the machine.

*See also **Security and Safety** in the section **DURING YOUR STAY**.*

PLANNING AND TRAVELLING
MOTORING - ADVICE AND EQUIPMENT

PREPARING FOR YOUR JOURNEY

Caravanning is first and foremost a relaxation and to arrive at your holiday destination on edge – or worse still, not at all because of an accident on the road – is not a good way to start a holiday. Adequate and careful preparation of your vehicles should be your first priority to ensure a safe and trouble-free journey.

Make sure your car and caravan are properly serviced before you depart and take a well-equipped spares kit and a spare wheel and tyre for your caravan; the lack of this is probably the main single cause of ruined holidays.

Re-read the Technical Information section of your UK Sites Directory & Handbook as it contains a wealth of information which is relevant to caravanning anywhere in the world.

The Caravan Club offers a free advice service to Club members, whether newcomers to caravanning or old hands, on technical and general caravanning matters and publishes information sheets on a wide range of topics, all of which members can download from the Club's website. Alternatively, write to the Club's Technical Department or telephone for more details. For advice on issues specific to countries other than Great Britain, Club members should contact the Travel Service Information Officer.

DRIVING ON THE CONTINENT

Probably the main disincentive to travel abroad, particularly for caravanners, is the need to drive on the right-hand side of the road. However, for most people this proves to be no problem at all after the first hour or so. There are a few basic, but important, points to remember:

- Buy a good road map or atlas and plan ahead to use roads suitable for towing. See *Route Planning* later in this chapter.

- In your eagerness to reach your destination, don't attempt vast distances in a single stint. Share the driving, if possible, and plan to break your journey overnight at a suitable site. There are thousands of sites listed in this guide and many are well situated near motorways and main roads.

- Adjust your mirrors for maximum rear-view observation. An offside (UK nearside) mirror is essential.

- Make sure the road ahead is clear before overtaking. Stay well behind the vehicle in front and, if possible, have someone with good judgement in the left-hand seat to give you the 'all clear'.

- If traffic builds up behind you, pull over safely and let it pass.

- Pay particular attention when turning left, when leaving a rest area/service station/campsite, or after passing through a one-way system to ensure that you continue to drive on the right-hand side of the road.

- Adjust your headlights to deflect to the right instead of the left by the use of headlamp converters or beam deflectors. Some beam deflectors cannot be used on quartz halogen lamps.

- While travelling, particularly in the height of the summer, it is wise to stop approximately every two hours (at the most) to stretch the legs and take a break.

- In case of breakdown or accident, use hazard warning lights and warning triangle(s).

- The AA Information Centre provides information on UK roads including routes to ferry ports on 09003 401100 or 401100 from a mobile phone (calls charged at 60p per minute). Both the AA and RAC have useful websites with access for non-members: www.theaa.com and www.rac.co.uk

Another disincentive for caravanners to travel abroad is the worry about roads and gradients in mountainous countries. Britain has worse gradients on many of its main roads than almost any other European country and traffic density is far higher in the UK. The chapter *Mountain Passes and Tunnels* under *PLANNING AND TRAVELLING* gives detailed advice on using mountain passes.

Another worry involves vehicle breakdown and language difficulties. The Caravan Club's comprehensive and competitively priced Red Pennant Motoring & Personal Holiday Insurance is geared to handle all these contingencies with multi-lingual staff available at the Club's headquarters 24 hours a day throughout the year.

Some Final Checks

Experienced caravanners will be familiar with the checks necessary before setting off, and the following list is a reminder:

- All car and caravan lights are working and a set of spare bulbs is packed.

- The coupling is correctly seated on the towball and the breakaway cable is attached.

- All windows, vents, hatches and doors are shut.

- Drain all on-board water systems.

- Car wing mirrors are adjusted for maximum visibility.

- Corner steadies are fully wound up and the brace is handy for your arrival on site.

- Any fires or flames are extinguished and the gas cylinder tap is turned off. Fire extinguishers are fully charged and close at hand.

- The over-run brake is working correctly.

- The jockey wheel is raised and secured, the handbrake is released.

DRIVING OFFENCES

You are obliged to comply with the traffic rules and regulations of the countries you visit. Authorities in a number of countries in Europe (Belgium, Denmark, Hungary, Ireland, Norway, Spain, Sweden, the Netherlands and the United Kingdom) have commissioned an agency, Euro Parking Collection, to recover outstanding fines on their behalf. Their surveillance equipment is installed in, as yet, a limited number of sites. If you, as the registered keeper of your vehicle, commit a traffic offence, for example, a parking infringement, failure to pay a road toll, failure to stop at a red light, or use of a bus lane, then EPC will trace the vehicle with the assistance of the DVLA and you can expect to receive a notice setting out the fine payable, followed by reminders, and possibly a visit from the bailiffs if you don't pay up!

Some foreign police officers can look rather intimidating to British citizens used to unarmed police. Needless to say, they expect you to be polite and show respect and, in return, they are generally helpful and may well be lenient to a visiting motorist. Never consider offering a bribe!

The authorities in many countries are hard on parking and speeding offenders. Visiting motorists should not be influenced by the speed at which locals drive; they often know where the speed traps are and can slow down in time to avoid being caught! In Scandinavia, for example, fines for speeding are spectacularly high and speed traps so frequent that it is not worth taking the risk of driving over the speed limit. In general, it is no use protesting if caught, as those who refuse to pay may have their vehicle impounded.

The maximum legal level of alcohol in the blood in many Continental countries is lower than that in the UK, and many police forces are authorised to carry out random breath tests. It is wise to adopt the 'no drink when driving' rule at all times; offenders are heavily fined all over Europe and penalties can include confiscation of driving licence, vehicle(s) and even imprisonment.

Be particularly careful if you have penalty points on your UK driving licence. If you commit an offence on the Continent which attracts penalty points, local police may well do checks on your licence to establish whether the addition of those points would render you liable to disqualification. You will then have to find other means to get yourself and your vehicle(s) home.

On-the-Spot Fines

Many countries allow their police officers to issue fines which must be paid on-the-spot, up to certain limits. These may be a deposit for a larger fine which will be issued to your home address. In most countries credit cards are not accepted in payment of on-the-spot fines and you may find yourself accompanied to the nearest cash machine. Always obtain a receipt for money handed over.

FUEL

During ferry crossings make sure your petrol tank is not over-full. Don't be tempted to carry spare petrol in cans; the ferry companies and Eurotunnel forbid this practice and even the carriage of empty cans is prohibited.

Grades of petrol sold on the Continent are comparable to those sold in the UK with the same familiar brands on sale; 3 Star is frequently known as 'Essence' and 4 Star as 'Super'. Diesel is sometimes called 'Gasoil' and is available in all the countries covered by this guide. The fuel prices given in the table at the end of this chapter were correct according to the latest information available in October 2005. Fuel prices and availability can be checked on BBC2 Ceefax and on the AA's website: www.theaa.com

Automotive Liquified Petroleum Gas

The increasing popularity of LPG and use of dual-fuelled vehicles means that the availability of automotive LPG on the Continent has become an important issue for some drivers, and the Country Introductions in this guide provide more information. There is a European guide published by EURO Geografiche Mencattini in Italy, listing approximately 11,000 LPG refuelling stations in 25 European countries. Contact EGM, Via Po, 52100 Arezzo, Italy, tel. 0039 0575 900010, fax 0039 0575 911161, www.egm.it, email eurogeo@egm.it

There are different tank-filling openings in use in different countries. Pending the adoption of a common European filling system, the Liquid Petroleum Gas Association and the major fuel suppliers recommend the use of either of the two types of Dutch bayonet fitting. The LPGA also recommends that vehicle-filling connections that require the use of adaptors, for filling with the Dutch bayonet filling guns, should not be used. However, the Club recognises that in some circumstances it may be necessary to use an adaptor on the Continent and these are available from Autogas 2000 on 01845 523213, www.autogas.co.uk

Lead Replacement Petrol

Leaded petrol has been withdrawn from sale in most countries in Europe and, in general, will only be available to specialist interest groups such as classic car clubs. It is likely to be expensive and difficult to find. In those countries, such as Germany, Austria, Belgium, the Netherlands and Scandinavia, where Lead Replacement Petrol has been on the market for some time, it is being phased out from bulk sales through petrol pumps because of falling levels of demand. The only alternative,

therefore, will be a bottled additive sold at service stations.

If you plan to do a lot of long-distance towing, or if you have a high performance engine, it is advisable to confirm with the manufacturers of LRP or fuel additives that these substances will provide a sufficient degree of protection for your engine under the additional load imposed by towing. Alternatively, it may be necessary to modify your engine.

Generally LRP is sold from the same pumps previously used for leaded petrol, ie red or black pumps, and may be labelled 'Super Plus', 'Super 98' or 'Super MLV', but it is advisable to check before filling up if this is not clear from information at the pump. If your car is designed to run on unleaded petrol and is fitted with a catalytic converter **never use leaded fuel** as it will poison the catalyst.

If your car is designed to run on unleaded petrol but is not fitted with a catalyst and you accidentally fill it with leaded petrol, make sure the next fill is with the correct petrol and there should be no damage done. If you are unable to find a petrol station selling LRP and/or additives, the occasional tankful of unleaded fuel is unlikely to cause any long term damage to your engine, although engine performance may be temporarily impaired in some instances.

Where specifically known, further information is given in the Country Introductions.

Unleaded Petrol and Diesel

In all European countries unleaded petrol and diesel are widely available. In less populated regions it is a sensible precaution to travel with a full petrol tank and to keep it topped up.

*See the **Fuel Price Guide Table** at the end of this chapter.*

MOTOR CARAVANS TOWING CARS

A motor caravan towing a small car is illegal in most European countries, although such units are sometimes encountered. Motor caravanners wishing to tow a small car abroad should transport it on a braked trailer so that all four of the car's wheels are off the road.

MOTORWAY TOLLS

For British drivers who may never, or rarely, have encountered a toll booth, there are a couple of points to bear in mind. First of all, you will be on the 'wrong' side of the car for the collection of toll tickets at the start of the motorway section and payment of tolls at the end. If you are travelling without a front seat passenger, this can mean a big stretch or a walk round to the other side of the car. Most toll booths are solidly built and you should be careful of any high concrete kerbs when pulling up to them.

On entering a stretch of motorway you will usually have to stop at a barrier and take a ticket from a machine to allow the barrier to rise. Avoid the lanes dedicated to vehicles displaying electronic season tickets. You may encounter toll booths without automatic barriers where it is still necessary to take a ticket and, if you pass through without doing so, you may be fined. On some stretches of motorway there are no ticket machines as you enter and you simply pay a fixed sum when you exit.

Your toll ticket will indicate the time you entered the motorway. Be warned that in some countries electronic tills at exit booths calculate the distance a vehicle has travelled and the journey time. The police are automatically informed if speeding has taken place and fines are imposed. If you lose your ticket you will have to pay the maximum toll for that particular stretch of road.

Payment can be made by credit cards in most, but not all countries covered by this guide and the Country Introductions contain specific information.

PARKING

Make sure you check local parking regulations, as heavy fines may be imposed and unattended vehicles towed away. Look out for road markings and for short-term parking zones. Big cities often have special parking regulations and it is best to ask about them on arrival. Ensure you are in possession of parking discs in towns where they are required. As a general rule, park on the right-hand side of the road in the direction of traffic flow, avoiding cycle and bus lanes and tram tracks. Vehicles should not cause an obstruction and should be adequately lit when parked at night.

In parts of eastern Europe car theft may be a problem and you are advised to park only in officially designated car parks whenever possible.

Parking Facilities for the Disabled

The standardised European Blue (formerly Orange) Badge Scheme means that local police and parking officials recognise the fact that a foreign disability badge holder enjoys the same concessions as local disabled people.

Most EU countries operate a system of parking concessions for the disabled and make reciprocal arrangements for foreign visitors displaying the badge issued under their own national scheme. Under these arrangements, Blue Badge holders are entitled to take advantage of concessions provided in the participating country as if they were residents. However, if you are in any doubt about your rights, do not park.

Further information is contained in the Country Introductions in this guide and full details can be found in the explanatory leaflet 'European Parking Card for People with Disabilities' obtainable from the Department for Transport's publications centre on 0870 1226236 (national call rate), or write to the Department for Transport (Free Literature), PO Box 236, Wetherby LS23 7NB. You may also download it from www.dft.gov.uk

PRIORITY AND ROUNDABOUTS

See *European Road Signs* at the end of this chapter and *Country Introductions*.

When driving on the Continent it is essential to be aware of other vehicles which may have priority over you, joining the road you are already using, from the right. Road signs indicate priority or loss of priority and motorists must be sure that they understand the signs.

Care should be taken at intersections and you should never rely on being given right of way, even if you have priority, especially in small towns and villages where local, often slow-moving, traffic will take right of way. Always give way to public service and military vehicles and to buses, trams and coaches.

Generally, priority at roundabouts is given to vehicles entering the roundabout unless signposted to the contrary, for example in France (see Country Introduction). This is a reversal of the UK rule and care is needed when travelling anti-clockwise round a roundabout. Keep to the outside lane, if possible, to make your exit easier.

ROAD SIGNS AND MARKINGS

See **European Road Signs** at the end of this chapter and **Country Introductions**.

You will often encounter STOP signs in situations which, in the UK, would probably be covered by a Give Way sign. Be particularly careful; coming to a complete halt is usually compulsory, even if local drivers seem unconcerned by it, and failure to do so may result in a fine. Be particularly careful in areas where maintenance of roads may be irregular and white lines have worn away.

A solid single or double white line in the middle of the carriageway always means no overtaking.

Direction signs in general may be confusing, giving only the name of a town on the way to a larger city, or simply the road number and no place name. They may be smaller than you expect and not particularly easy to spot. The colours of signs indicating different categories of road may differ from those used in the UK. For example, motorway signs may be green (not blue) and non-motorway signs may be blue, rather than green as they are in the UK. This can be particularly confusing, for example when crossing from France where motorway signs are blue, into Switzerland or Italy where they are green.

Across the EU you will find that major routes have not only an individual road number, such as A6, but also a number beginning with an 'E' on a green and white sign. Routes running from east to west have even 'E' numbers, whereas routes running from north to south have odd numbers. This can be helpful when planning long-distance routes across international frontiers.

Pedestrian Crossings

Stopping to allow pedestrians to cross the road at zebra crossings is not nearly as common a practice as it is in the UK. Pedestrians often do not expect to cross until the road is clear and may be surprised if you stop to allow them to do so. Check your mirrors carefully when braking as other drivers behind you, not expecting to stop, may be taken by surprise. The result may be a rear-end shunt or, worse still, vehicles overtaking you at the crossing and putting pedestrians at risk.

SPEED LIMITS

Remember speed limit signs are in kilometres per hour, not miles per hour. General speed limits in each country are given in the table at the end of this chapter. Refer to individual Country Introductions for details of any variations.

Radar-detection devices, whether in use or not, are illegal in many countries, and generally, it is understood, elsewhere on the Continent, and should not be carried in your vehicle.

Speed cameras are becoming more widespread throughout Europe but you should not expect them to be highly visible, as they are in the UK. In many instances, for example on the German motorway network, they may be hidden or deliberately inconspicuous. The use of unmarked police cars is commonplace.

TRAFFIC LIGHTS

Traffic lights may not be placed as conspicuously as they are in the UK and you may find that they are smaller, differently shaped or suspended across the road, with a smaller set on a post at the roadside. You may find that lights change directly from red to green, bypassing amber completely. Flashing amber lights generally indicate that you may proceed with caution but must give way to pedestrians and other vehicles. A green filter light should be treated with caution as you may still have to give way to pedestrians who have a green light to cross.

You may find that drivers are not particularly well-disciplined about stopping as they approach a light as it turns red and if they are behind you in this situation, they will expect you to accelerate through it rather than brake hard to obey the light. Therefore be cautious when approaching a green light, especially if you are in a relatively fast-moving stream of traffic. Similarly, be careful when pulling away from a green light and check left and right just in case a driver on the road crossing yours jumped a red light.

EQUIPMENT

BICYCLES AND MOTORBIKES TRANSPORTATION REGULATIONS

Regulations vary from country to country and, where known, these are set out in the relevant Country Introductions. As a general rule, however, separate registration and insurance documents are required for a motorbike or scooter and such vehicles must be carried on an approved carrier in such a way that they do not obscure rear windows, lights, reflectors or number plates. Vehicles should not be overloaded, ie exceed the maximum loaded weight recommended by the manufacturer.

CAR TELEPHONES

In the countries covered by this guide it is illegal to use a hand-held car phone or mobile phone while driving; hands-free equipment should be fitted in your vehicle.

See individual Country Introductions for further information.

FIRST AID KIT

A first aid kit, in a strong dust-proof box, should be carried in case of emergency. This is a legal requirement in several countries.

See Essential Equipment Table at the end of this chapter and the chapter Medical Matters.

FIRE EXTINGUISHER

As a recommended safety precaution, an approved fire extinguisher should be carried in all vehicles. It is a legal requirement in several countries.

See Essential Equipment Table at the end of this chapter.

GLASSES

It is a legal requirement in some countries, eg Spain, for residents to carry a spare pair of glasses if they are needed for driving and it is recommended that visitors also comply. Elsewhere, if you do not have a spare pair, you may find it helpful to carry a copy of your prescription.

LIGHTS

When driving on the Continent headlights must be adapted, using a conversion kit available from motor accessory shops, in order to ensure that the dipped beam is deflected and does not dazzle oncoming traffic. Even if you do not intend to drive at night, it is important to adapt your headlights as you may need to use them in heavy rain or fog and in tunnels. Remember to remove the beam converters on returning to the UK. It is no longer necessary to tint headlamps yellow when visiting France.

If you car is fitted with high-intensity discharge or xenon headlamps beam converters will not work. Check with your dealer or in your vehicle manual as you should be able to switch the beam over for Continental driving.

Remember also to adjust headlights according to the load being carried and to compensate for the weight of the caravan on the back of the car.

Dipped headlights should be used in poor weather conditions such as fog, snowfall or heavy rain and in a tunnel even if it is well lit and you may find police waiting at the end of a tunnel to check vehicles. In some countries dipped headlights are compulsory at all times, in others they must be used in built-up areas or on motorways.

Take a full set of spare light bulbs. This is a legal requirement in several countries.

See Essential Equipment Table at the end of this chapter.

On the Continent headlight flashing is used as a warning of approach or as an overtaking signal at night, and not, as in the UK, an indication that you are giving way, so use with great care in case it is misunderstood. When another driver flashes you, make sure of his intention before moving.

Hazard Warning Lights

Generally hazard warning lights should not be used in place of a warning triangle, but they may be used in addition to it.

NATIONALITY PLATE

A nationality plate of an authorised design must be fixed to the rear of the car and caravan on a vertical or near-vertical surface. Checks are made and a fine may be imposed for failure to display a correct nationality plate. These are provided free to members taking out the Caravan Club's Red Pennant Motoring & Personal Holiday Insurance.

Regulations allow the optional display of the GB Euro-Symbol – a circle of stars on a blue background, with the EU Member State's national identification letter(s) below – on UK car registration number plates and, for cars with such plates, the display of a conventional nationality sticker or plate is unnecessary when driving within the EU. However, it is still required when driving outside the EU (except in Switzerland) even when number plates incorporate the GB Euro-Symbol, and it is still required for all vehicles without Euro-Symbol plates. Registration plates displaying the GB Euro-Symbol must comply with the appropriate British Standard.

REAR VIEW/WING MIRRORS

In order to comply with local regulations and avoid the attention of local police forces ensure that your vehicle has two external mirrors which allow you to view both sides of your caravan or trailer – over their entire length – from behind the steering wheel. Some countries stipulate that rear view mirrors should extend beyond the width of the caravan but should be removed or folded in when travelling solo, and this is common-sense advice for all countries.

REFLECTORISED WAISTCOAT/JACKET

Legislation has been introduced in some countries in Europe (see individual Country Introductions) requiring drivers to wear a reflectorised jacket or waistcoat if leaving a vehicle which is immobilised on the carriageway outside a built-up area (day or night). This is a common-sense requirement which will probably be extended to other countries and which should be followed wherever you drive. A second jacket is also recommended for a passenger who may need to assist in an emergency repair. The jackets are widely available from motor accessory shops and should conform to at least European Standard EN471, Class 2.

ROUTE PLANNING

Detailed, large-scale maps of the country you are visiting are essential. Navigating your way around other countries can be confusing, especially for the novice, and the more care you take planning your route, the more enjoyable will be the journey to your holiday destination. Before setting out, study maps and distance charts. Main roads in Europe with major roadworks may be checked on BBC2 Ceefax, travel information pages.

There are a number of websites offering a routes service and/or traffic information, such as www.theaa.com, www.viamichelin.com and www.mappy.com which, amongst other things, provides city centre maps for major towns across Europe. If you propose travelling across mountain passes check whether the suggested route supplied by the website takes account of passes or tunnels where caravans are not permitted or recommended.

See the chapter Mountain Passes and Tunnels.

SEAT BELTS

The wearing of seat belts is compulsory in all the countries featured in this guide. On-the-spot fines will be incurred for failure to wear them and compensation for injury may be reduced by 50% if seat belts are not worn. Many countries prohibit children under a certain age/height from sitting in the front of a car without seat belts or a special child restraint.

Never fit a rearward-facing child seat or restraint in a seat with a frontal airbag.

See Essential Equipment Table at the end of this chapter and Country Introductions.

SNOW CHAINS

Snow chains may be necessary on some roads in winter. They are compulsory in some countries during the winter where indicated by the appropriate road sign, when they must be fitted on at least two drive-wheels. Polar Automotive Ltd sells and hires out snow chains, tel 01892 519933, fax 01892 528142 (20% discount for Caravan Club members), www.snowchains.com

SPARES

Caravan Spares

On the Continent it is generally much more difficult to obtain spares for caravans than for cars and it will usually be necessary to obtain spares from the UK manufacturer or dealer.

Spares Kits

Some motor manufacturers can supply spares kits for a selected range of models; contact your dealer for details. The choice of spares will depend on the vehicle, how long you are likely to be away and your own level of competence in car maintenance, but the following is a list of basic items which should cover the most common causes of breakdown:

    Radiator top hose
    Fan belt
    Fuses and bulbs
    Windscreen wiper blade
    Length of 12v electrical cable
    Tools, torch and WD40 or equivalent water repellent spray

When ordering spare parts for despatch abroad you must be able to identify them clearly and a workshop manual is useful for this purpose.

SPARE WHEEL

Your local caravan dealer should be able to supply an appropriate spare wheel. If you have any difficulty in obtaining one, the Caravan Club's Technical Department will provide members with a list of suppliers' addresses on request.

Tyre legislation across Europe is more or less fully harmonised and, while the Club has no specific knowledge of laws on the Continent regarding the use of space-saver spare wheels, there should be no problems in using such a wheel provided its use is strictly in accordance with the manufacturer's instructions.

TOWING BRACKET

The vast majority of cars registered after 1 August 1998 are legally required to have a European Type approved towing bracket (complying with European Directive 94/20) carrying a plate giving its approval number and various technical details, including the maximum noseweight. The approval process includes strength testing to a higher value than provided in the previous British Standard, and confirmation of fitting to all the car manufacturer's approved mounting points. Your car dealer or specialist towing bracket fitter will be able to give further advice. Checks may be made by foreign police. (This requirement does not currently apply to motor caravans.)

TYRES

Safe driving and handling when towing a caravan or trailer are very important and one major factor which is frequently overlooked is tyre condition. Your caravan tyres must be suitable for the highest speed at which you can legally tow (up to 81 mph in France), not for any lower speed at which you may choose to travel. Some older British caravans (usually over six years old) may not meet this requirement and, if you are subject to a police check, this could result in an on-the-spot fine for each tyre, including the spare. Check your tyre specification before you leave and, if necessary, upgrade your tyres. The Caravan Club's technical advice leaflet 'Tyres and Wheels', available to members on the Club's website or by post, explains how to check if your tyres are suitable.

Most countries require a minimum tread depth of 1.6 mm over the central part of the whole tyre, but motoring organisations recommend at least 3 mm across the whole tyre. If you plan an extended trip and your tyres are likely to be more worn than this before you return home, replace them before you leave.

Winter tyres should be used in those countries with a severe winter climate to provide extra grip on snow and ice. If you intend to make an extended winter trip to Alpine or Scandinavian areas or to travel regularly to them, it would be advisable to buy a set of winter tyres. Your local tyre dealer will be able to advise. For information on regulations concerning winter tyres and/or spiked or studded tyres, see the appropriate Country Introductions.

Sizes

It is worth noting that some sizes of radial tyre to fit the 13" wheels normally used on UK caravans are virtually impossible to obtain abroad, eg 175R13C.

Tyre Pressures

Tyre pressure should be checked and adjusted when the tyres are cold; checking warm tyres will result in a higher pressure reading. The correct pressures will be found in your car handbook, but unless it states otherwise it is wise to add an extra four to six pounds per square inch to the rear tyres of a car when towing to improve handling and to carry the extra load on the hitch.

Make sure you know what pressure your caravan tyres should be. Some require a pressure much higher than that normally used for cars. Check your caravan handbook for details.

After a Puncture

The Club does not recommend the general use of liquid sealants for puncture repair. Such products should not be considered to achieve a permanent repair, and may indeed render the tyre irreparable. If sealant is used to allow the vehicle to be removed from a position of danger, eg motorway hard shoulder, the damaged tyre should be removed from the vehicle as soon as is practical. Following a caravan tyre puncture, especially on a single-axle caravan, it is advisable to have the opposite side (non-punctured) tyre removed from its wheel and checked inside and out for signs of damage resulting from overloading during the deflation of the punctured tyre.

Failure to take this precaution may result in an increased risk of a second tyre deflation within a very short space of time.

WARNING TRIANGLES

In almost all European countries it is a legal requirement to use a warning triangle in the event of a breakdown or accident; some countries require two. It is strongly recommended that approved red warning triangles be carried as a matter of course.

See Essential Equipment Table at the end of this chapter.

A warning triangle should be placed on the road approximately 30 metres (100 metres on motorways) behind the broken down vehicle on the same side of the road. Always assemble the triangle before leaving your vehicle and walk with it so that the red, reflective surface is facing oncoming traffic. If a breakdown occurs round a blind corner, place the triangle in advance of the corner. Hazard warning lights may be used in conjunction with the triangle but they do not replace it.

Technical information compiled with the assistance of the Automobile Association..

FUEL PRICE GUIDE

Country	UNLEADED			DIESEL
	Price and Octane Rating Available		Translation of Unleaded	
Austria	75.0	95, 98	Bleifrei	69.8
Belgium	95.2	95, 98	Sans plomb or loodvrije	78.4
Croatia	68.6	95, 98	Eurosuper or bez olova	59.7
Czech Republic	71.8	95, 98	Natural or bez olova	71.8
Denmark	92.2	92, 95, 98	Blyfri	80.1
Finland	89.6	95, 98	Lyijyton polttoaine	70.2
France	85.2	95, 98	Essence sans plomb	73.9
Germany	90.0	91, 95, 98	Bleifrei	77.5
Gibraltar	67.0	95		62.0
Greece	65.8	95, 100	Amoliwdi wensina	64.9
Hungary	84.0	95, 98	Olommentes uzemanyag	79.8
Italy	87.3	95, 98	Sensa piombo	79.5
Luxembourg	76.5	95, 98	Sans plomb	63.8
Netherlands	100.8	95, 98	Loodvrije	77.1
Norway	95.0	95, 98	Blyfri	88.9
Poland	79.7	95, 98	Bezolowiu	72.2
Portugal	85.9	95, 98	Sem chumbo	69.3
Slovakia	69.1	95, 98	Natural or olovnatych prisad	73.3
Slovenia	67.8	95, 98	Brez svinca	66.2
Spain	72.3	95, 98	Sin plomo	66.5
Sweden	89.5	95, 96, 98	Blyfri normal, premium	82.1
Switzerland	72.1	95, 98	Bleifrei or sans plomb or sensa piomba	77.0

Fuel prices courtesy of the Automobile Association

Prices shown are in pence per litre and use currency exchange rates at the time this guide was compiled. They should be used for guideline comparison purposes only. Differences in prices actually paid may be due to currency fluctuations as well as regional variations.

In many countries leaded petrol has been withdrawn but Lead Replacement Petrol contains the necessary additive. Alternatively a lead substitute additive can be bought at petrol stations and added to the fuel tanks of cars which do not run on unleaded petrol. It is understood that it is the same additive as used in the UK and that 10ml will treat 10 litres of petrol.

SPEED LIMITS

Kilometres per hour (see Conversion Table below for equivalent miles per hour)

Country	Built-Up Areas	Open Road		Motorways		
		Solo	Towing	Solo	Towing	Minimum Speed
Andorra	40	70	70	n/a	n/a	n/a
Austria*	50	100	80	130	100	60
Belgium*	30-50	90	90	120	120	70
Croatia*	40-50	90-100	80	110-130	80	-
Czech Republic*	50	90	80	130	80	80
Denmark*	50	80-90	70	110-130	80	40
Finland*	50	80-100	80	100-120	80	-
France* Normal	50	90	90	110-130	110-130	80
France* Bad Weather	50	80	80	110	110	-
Germany*	50	100	80	130**	80	60
Greece	50	90-110	80	120	80	-
Hungary	50	90-110	70	130	80	-
Italy*	50-70	90-110	70	130-150	80	-
Luxembourg*	50	90	75	120	90	-
Netherlands*	50	80-100	80	120	80	60
Norway	50	80	80	90	80	-
Poland*	50-60	90-110	70-80	130	80	40
Portugal*	50	90-100	70	120	100	40
Slovakia*	60	90	80	130	80	50
Slovenia*	50	90-100	80	130	80	-
Spain	50	90-100	70-80	120	80	60
Sweden*	50	70-90	70-80	110	80	-
Switzerland*	50	80	60	100-120	80	60

Converting Kilometres to Miles

km/h	20	30	40	50	60	70	80	90	100	110	120	130
mph	13	18	25	31	37	44	50	56	62	68	74	81

NOTES: 1) * See Country Introductions for further details, including special speed limits, eg for motor caravans ± 3,500 kg, where applicable.

2) ** No upper limit on some sections.

3) In some countries speed limits in residential areas may be as low as 20 or 30 km/h

ESSENTIAL EQUIPMENT

See also the information contained in this chapter and in the relevant Country Introductions

Country	Warning Triangle	Spare Bulbs	Child Seat Belts or Restraints	First Aid Kit	Additional Equipment to be Carried/Used
Andorra	Yes	Yes	Under 10 yrs in rear seats only	Rec	Dipped headlights in poor daytime visibility.
Austria	Yes	Rec	Under 12 yrs or less than 1.5m tall, front and rear seats.	Yes	Dipped headlights at all times. Reflectorised waistcoat.*
Belgium	Yes	Rec	Under 12 yrs, front and rear seats.	Rec	Dipped headlights in poor daytime visibility.
Croatia	Yes (2 for vehicles with trailer)	Yes	Under 12 yrs in rear seats only.	Yes	Dipped headlights at all times. All cars must have a towbar or carry a towrope.
Czech Rep	Yes	Yes	Under 12 yrs or under 18 yrs and less than 1.5m tall, front seats	Yes	Dipped headlights during day end October to end March. Wearers of glasses to carry a spare pair.*
Denmark	Yes	Rec	Under 3 yrs, front and rear seats. Over 3 yrs seat belts + booster cushion.	Rec	Dipped headlights at all times. Indicators compulsory on motorways when overtaking or changing lanes; hazard warning lights to be used when queues or dangers ahead.
Finland	Yes	Rec	Under 3 yrs in rear. Under 12 yrs and/or less than 1.5m tall	Rec	Dipped headlights at all times. Winter tyres December to February.
France	Yes (2 rec)	Yes	Under 10 yrs.	Rec	Dipped headlights at all times outside built-up areas.
Germany	Yes	Rec	Under 12 yrs and/or less than 1.5m tall, front and rear seats.	Yes	Dipped headlights in poor daytime visibility and in tunnels. Vehicles over 2,800 kg to carry portable yellow flashing light.
Greece	Yes	Rec	Under 12 yrs must travel in rear seats.	Yes	Fire extinguisher. Dipped headlights in towns at night and in poor daytime visibility.
Hungary	Yes	Rec	Under 12 yrs and/or less than 1.5m tall in front or rear seats.	Yes	Dipped headlights in daytime outside built-up areas and in built-up areas at night.
Italy	Yes	Rec	Under 4 yrs front and rear seats; under 12 yrs in front seats.	Rec	Dipped headlights outside built-up areas, on motorways, major roads and in tunnels at all times. Reflectorised waistcoat.*
Luxembourg	Yes	Rec	Under 12 yrs and/or less than 1.5m tall in front and rear seats; under 3 yrs in rear seat.	Rec	Dipped headlights at night in built-up areas and in daytime in bad weather.
Netherlands	Yes	Rec	Under 12 yrs and/or less than 1.5m tall in front and rear seats.	Rec	Dipped headlights at night and in bad weather.
Norway	Yes	Yes	Under 4 yrs.	Rec	Dipped headlights at all times.
Poland	Yes	Rec	Under 12 yrs and/or less than 1.5m tall in front and rear seats.	Yes	Dipped headlights during day October to March and in poor daytime visibility.
Portugal	Yes	Rec	Under 12 yrs in rear seats only.	Rec	Dipped headlights in poor daytime visibility, in tunnels and on main road linking Aveiro-Vilar Formoso at Spanish frontier (IP5). Reflectorised waistcoat.*
Slovakia	Yes	Yes	Under 12 yrs and/or less than 1.5m tall in rear seats only.	Yes	Dipped headlights at all times between 15 Oct and 15 March.
Slovenia	Yes (2 for vehicle with trailer)	Yes	Under 12 yrs in rear seats only. All children in safety seat suitable for their size.	Yes	Dipped headlights at all times. Hazard warning lights when reversing. Winter tyres between 15 Nov and 15 March or carry snow chains.
Spain	Yes (2 Rec)	Yes	Under 12 yrs and less than 1.5m tall.	Rec	Dipped headlights in tunnels and on 'special' roads.* Wearers of glasses rec to carry a spare pair. Reflectorised waistcoat.*
Sweden	Yes	Rec	Under 7 yrs.	Rec	Dipped headlights at all times.
Switzerland (inc Liechtenstein)	Yes	Rec	Under 13 yrs.	Yes	Dipped headlights at all times. Dipped headlights in tunnels.

NOTES:
1) All countries: seat belts (if fitted) must be worn by all passengers.
2) Rec: not compulsory but strongly recommended.
3) Never fit a rearward-facing child restraint seat in a seat with a frontal airbag.
4) Headlamp converters, spare bulbs, fire extinguisher, first aid kit and reflectorised waistcoat are recommended for all countries.
5) 1.5m = 5 feet.
* See Country Introduction for further information

Easy does it!

The Club's programme of Inclusive Holidays for 2005 features many of our members' favourites including walking and gastronomic holidays in France, together with a few new additions to tempt you. The Grand Tour in 2005 will incorporate time in both Rome and Florence allowing plenty of time to soak up the culture as well as the sun, whilst we shall also be repeating our tour of Norway and escorted tours to the Italian Lakes and Andalucia.

Our Inclusive Holidays can be booked in conjunction with any ferry crossing, other en route sites and Red Pennant travel insurance, if required.

Find out more in our 'Travel Service in Europe' brochure

For your copy phone us on **01342 327410**

or visit our web site **www.caravanclub.co.uk**

THE CARAVAN CLUB

Travel Service in Europe 2005/2006

Keep this safe for next year too. Separate Price Supplement enclosed

- Guide to campsites, opening dates, descriptions, locations and facilities
- Red Pennant travel insurance and travel choices
- Inclusive Holiday selection, Camping Cheques

NEW FOR 2005

- 19 new European campsites including sites in Croatia and Belgium
- Mobile homes and boat hire
- Les Castels Privilege Card

SELECTION OF EUROPEAN ROAD SIGNS

The signs below represent a selection of standard and non-standard road signs relevant to the countries shown.

AUSTRIA

Speed Restrictions

Diversions

Buses only

Federal road with priority

Federal road without priority

Street lights not on all night

Tram turns at yellow or red

BELGIUM

You may pass right or left

Residential zone

End of residential zone

No parking from the 1st-15th of the month

No parking from the 16th-end of the month

Cyclists have priority over turning traffic

Cyclists have priority at junction

Limited duration parking zone

Parking reserved for campervans

Use of Cruise Control prohibited

DENMARK

Traffic merges

Minimum speed limit

Recommended speed limit

Compulsory slow lane

1 hour parking zone

Place of interest

Maximum width

FINLAND

Reindeer

Detour

Restriction applies 8-17 hrs (Mon-Fri)

Restriction applies 8-13 hrs (Sat)

Restriction applies 8-14 hrs (Sun)

FRANCE

Priority road

End of priority road

Traffic on the roundabout has priority

Give way

Continuation of restriction

Alternative holiday routes

Information centre for holiday route

GERMANY

Autobahn number

Federal highway number

European road number

Advance direction sign at approach to motorway

One-way street

Recommended speed limit

They may also be seen in other countries in which case they have a similar definition.

GERMANY

Keep distance shown

Alternative route

Bus or tram stop

Turn right at red light

ITALY

Restricted parking

No fires

Snow chains required

NETHERLANDS

Residential zone

Parking for permit holders only

Disc parking zone

Park and ride

Maximum speed limit

Built-up area

Cycle track

No entry for motorcycles

Compulsory route for hazardous goods

PORTUGAL

End of parking restriction

NORWAY

Passing place (on narrow roads)

Ski runs

Bus lane

Lane ends

Entering traffic has priority

Lanes merge

Tunnel

SPAIN

Use dipped headlights

Autovia

Via rapida

Turning permitted

Limited parking zone

Viewpoint

Water

SWITZERLAND

Postal vehicles have priority

Motorway

Single carriageway motorway

Parking disc compulsory

Slow lane

Emergency lane

Emergency stopping area

Tunnel-lights compulsory

Level crossing

SWEDEN

Elk

Additional stop sign

Slow lane

Tunnel

Reproduced by kind permission of The Automobile Association

EUROPEAN DISTANCES

Distances are shown in kilometres and are calculated
from town/city centres along the most practicable roads,
although not necessarily taking the shortest route.

1 km = 0.62 miles

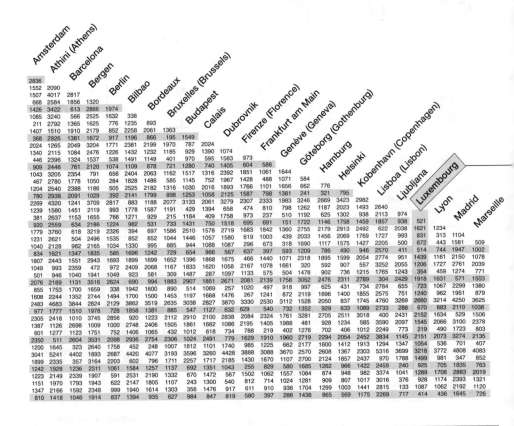

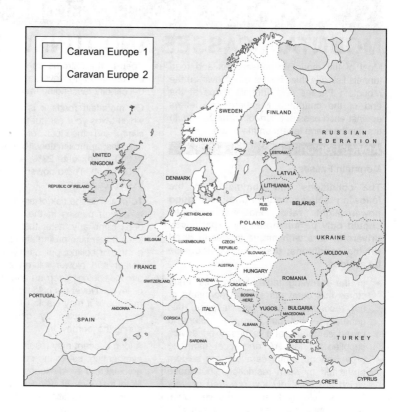

Caravan Europe 1
Caravan Europe 2

Luxembourg - Warszawa (Warsaw) = 1289 km

	Marseille	Milano (Milan)	München (Munich)	Napoli (Naples)	Oslo	Paris	Porto	Praha (Prague)	Roma (Rome)	Rovaniemi	Salzburg	Sevilla (Seville)	Stockholm	Strasbourg	Thessalonika	Toulouse	Tromso	Valencia	Venzia (Venice)	Warszawa (Warsaw)	Wien (Vienna)	Zagreb
Milano (Milan)	509																					
München (Munich)	1002	497																				
Napoli (Naples)	1078	763	1104																			
Oslo	2039	1707	1525	2634																		
Paris	771	847	834	1600	1483																	
Porto	1503	1979	2344	2548	3057	1572																
Praha (Prague)	1380	868	379	1487	1313	1026	2592															
Roma (Rome)	879	564	905	217	2435	1402	2350	1288														
Rovaniemi	3625	3159	2684	3817	1560	2941	4581	2505	3604													
Salzburg	1038	544	139	1096	1668	990	2508	372	897	2821												
Sevilla (Seville)	1506	1982	2348	2551	3286	1801	626	2700	2352	4733	2510											
Stockholm	2378	2033	1553	2662	538	1823	3398	1341	2463	1170	1697	3627										
Strasbourg	803	488	359	1255	1293	490	2056	595	1056	2742	516	2124	1619									
Thessalonika	2135	1642	1577	2116	3035	2426	3655	1688	1903	4197	1446	3631	3082	1952								
Toulouse	407	883	1249	1452	2182	696	1102	1601	1253	3748	1411	1228	2520	1026	2508							
Tromso	4083	3717	3242	4375	1720	3499	5139	3063	4162	597	3385	5291	1719	3300	4755	4306						
Valencia	852	1328	1694	1897	2705	1387	925	2046	1698	4189	1857	663	3044	1471	2949	637	4767					
Venzia (Venice)	763	269	472	722	2001	1110	2234	808	523	3178	433	2237	2029	740	1392	1137	3736	1582				
Warszawa (Warsaw)	2019	1516	994	1969	1400	1606	3181	612	1770	1189	3340	1456	852	1234	1702	2240	3274	2685	1264			
Wien (Vienna)	1321	827	398	1279	1597	1231	2797	284	1080	2797	291	2794	1625	760	1376	1694	3355	2140	575	686		
Zagreb	1120	626	556	1078	2020	1407	2590	661	879	3184	428	2593	2048	933	1013	1493	3742	1939	374	993	374	
Zürich	726	280	312	1047	1455	586	2044	680	848	2933	437	2047	1782	230	1930	947	3491	1392	532	1319	730	806

67

MOUNTAIN PASSES AND TUNNELS

Most of the mountain passes, rail and road tunnels listed in this chapter are shown on the Mountain Passes and Tunnels maps at the end of the chapter. Numbers and letters against each pass and tunnel correspond with the numbers and letters on the maps.

ADVICE FOR DRIVERS

Mountain Passes

The conditions and comments in the following table assume an outfit with good power/weight ratio. Mountain passes should only be attempted by experienced drivers in cars with ample power in good driving conditions; they should otherwise be avoided.

- In the following table, where the entry states that caravans are not permitted or not recommended to use a pass, this generally – but not always – refers to towed caravans, and is based on advice supplied by the AA and local motoring organisations. Motor caravans are seldom prohibited by such restrictions, but those which are relatively low powered or very large should find an alternative route. Always obey roads signs at the foot of a pass, especially those referring to heavy vehicles, which may apply to some large motor caravans.

- Do not attempt to cross passes at night or in bad weather. Before crossing, seek local advice if touring during doubtful periods of the year. Warning notices are usually posted at the foot of a pass if it is closed, or if chains or snow tyres must be used.

- Caravanners are naturally more sensitive than other motorists to gradients and traffic and road conditions on mountain passes. Take particular care when negotiating blind hairpins. The maximum gradient is usually on the inside of bends but exercise caution if it is necessary to pull out. Always engage a lower gear before taking a hairpin bend and give priority to vehicles ascending. Give priority to postal service vehicles – signposts usually show their routes. Do not go down hills in neutral gear.

- Keep to the extreme right of the road and be prepared to reverse to give way to descending/ascending traffic.

- On mountain roads it is not the gradient which taxes your car but the duration of the climb and the loss of power at high altitudes; approximately 10% at 915 metres (3,000 feet), and 23% at 2,133 metres (7,000 feet). Turbo power restores much of the lost capacity.

- To minimise the risk of engine-overheating, take high passes in the cool of the day, don't climb any faster than necessary and keep the engine pulling steadily. To prevent a radiator boiling, pull off the road, turn the heater and blower full on and switch off airconditioning. Keep an eye on water and oil levels. Never put cold water into a boiling radiator or it may crack. Check the radiator is not obstructed by debris sucked up during the journey.

- A long descent may result in vehicle brakes overheating; select the correct gear for the gradient and avoid excessive use of brakes. Note that even if using engine braking to control the outfit's speed, the caravan brakes may activate due to the action of the overrun mechanism, causing them to overheat. Use lay-bys and lookout points to stop and allow brakes to cool down.

- Snow prevents road repairs being carried out during winter months resulting in increased road works during the summer which may cause delays for drivers. During certain hours, one-way traffic only may be permitted on certain routes. Information will be posted at each end of the road.

- Precipitous road sides are rarely totally unguarded; on older roads stone pillars are placed at close intervals. However, those without a good head for heights should consider alternative routes.

- In mountainous areas always remember to leave the blade valve of your portable toilet open a fraction whilst travelling. This avoids pressure build-up in the holding tank. Similarly, a slightly open tap will avoid pressure build up in water pipes and fittings.

Tunnels

British drivers do not often encounter road tunnels but they are a common feature on the Continent, for example, along stretches of Italian coastline and lakes, and through mountain ranges. Tolls are usually charged for use of major tunnels and you will find details of these later in this chapter.

Ensure you have sufficient fuel in your tank. Emergency situations often involve vehicles stranded because of a lack of fuel.

In bright sunshine when approaching a tunnel, slow down to allow your eyes to adjust and look out for poorly-lit vehicles in front of you and for cyclists. Take off sunglasses before entering a tunnel and take care again when emerging into sunshine at the other end.

Signposts usually indicate a tunnel ahead and its length. Once inside the tunnel, maintain a safe distance from the vehicle in front in case the driver brakes sharply.

Dipped headlights are usually required by law even in well-lit tunnels. Switch them on before entering a tunnel. Some tunnels may be poorly lit or unlit.

Snow chains, if used, must be removed before entering a tunnel and there are lay-bys for this purpose.

Minimum and maximum speed limits usually apply. 'No overtaking' signs must be strictly observed. Never cross central single or double line(s). If overtaking is permitted in twin-tube tunnels only, bear in mind that it is very easy to underestimate distances and speed when driving in a tunnel.

In order to minimise the effects of exhaust fumes close all car windows and set the ventilator to circulate the air, or operate the air conditioning system coupled with the recycled air option.

Watch out for puddles caused by dripping or infiltrating water.

If there is a traffic jam, switch your hazard warning lights on and stop a safe distance from the vehicle in front. Sound the horn only in a real emergency. Never change driving direction unless instructed to do so by security staff.

If you break down, try to reach the next lay-by and call for help from the nearest emergency phone. Modern tunnels have video surveillance systems to ensure prompt assistance in an emergency. If you cannot reach a lay-by, place your warning triangle at least 100 metres behind your vehicle. Passengers should leave the vehicle through doors on the right-hand side only.

MOUNTAIN PASS INFORMATION

- The dates of opening and closing given in the following table are approximate and inclusive. Before attempting late afternoon or early morning journeys across borders, check their opening times. A number of border crossings close at night.

- Gradient figures take the mean figure on hairpin bends and may be steeper at the inside of curves, particularly on older roads. Gradients listed are the maximum at any point on the pass.

- Gravel surfaces (such as dirt and stone chips) vary considerably; they are dusty when dry and slippery when wet. Where known to exist, this type of surface has been noted.

- In fine weather wheel chains or snow tyres will only be required on very high passes, or for short periods in early or late summer. In wintry conditions you will probably need to use them at altitudes exceeding 600 metres (approx 2,000 feet).

Abbreviations

MHV	Maximum height of vehicle
MLV	Maximum length of vehicle
MWV	Maximum width of vehicle
MWR	Minimum width of road
OC	Occasionally closed between dates stated
UC	Usually closed between dates stated
UO	Usually open between dates stated, although a fall of snow may obstruct the road for 24-48 hours. Wheel chains or snow tyres may be necessary.

MOUNTAIN PASSES AND TUNNELS REPORT FORM

The Caravan Club welcomes up-to-date information on mountain passes and tunnels from caravanners who use them during the course of their holidays. Report forms are included at the end of this chapter. Please complete and return as soon as possible after your journey.

CONVERTING GRADIENTS

20%	=	1 in 5	11%	=	1 in 9
16%	=	1 in 6	10%	=	1 in 10
14%	=	1 in 7	8%	=	1 in 12
12%	=	1 in 8	6%	=	1 in 16

MOUNTAIN PASSES

	PASS HEIGHT IN METRES (FEET)	FROM TO	MAX GRADIENT	CONDITIONS AND COMMENTS
①	Achenpass (Austria – Germany) 941 (3087)	Achental *Glashutte*	14%	UO. Well-engineered road. Gradient not too severe.
②	Albula (Switzerland) 2312 (7585)	Tiefencastel *La Punt*	10%	UC Nov-early Jun. MWR 3.5m (11'6") MWV 2.25m (7'6") Inferior alternative to the Julier; tar and gravel; fine scenery. **Not rec for caravans.** Alternative rail tunnel. See *Rail Tunnels* in this section.
③	Allos (France) 2250 (7382)	Colmars *Barcelonette*	10%	UC early Nov-early Jun. MWR 4m (13'1") Very winding, narrow, mostly unguarded but not difficult otherwise; passing bays on southern slope; poor surface, MWV 1.8m (5'11"). **Not rec for caravans.**
④	Aprica (Italy) 1176 (3858)	Tresenda *Edolo*	9%	UO. MWR 4m (13'1") Fine scenery; good surface; well-graded. Narrow in places; watch for protruding rock when meeting oncoming traffic. Easier E - W.
⑤	Aravis (France) 1498 (4915)	La Clusaz *Flumet*	9%	OC Dec-Mar. MWR 4m (13'1"). Fine scenery; fairly easy road. Poor surface in parts on Chamonix side. Some single-line traffic.
⑥	Arlberg (Austria) 1802 (5912)	Bludenz *Landeck*	13%	OC Dec-Apr. MWR 6m (19'8"). Good modern road with several pull-in places. Steeper fr W easing towards summit; heavy traffic. **Pass road closed to caravans/trailers.** Parallel road tunnel available (poss long queues). See *Road Tunnels* in this section.
(-)	Aubisque (France) 1710 (5610)	Eaux Bonnes *Argelés-Gazost*	10%	UC mid Oct-Jun. MWR 3.5m (11'6") Very winding; continuous but easy ascent; descent incl Col de Soulor 1450m (4757 feet); 8km (5miles) of very narrow, rough, unguarded road with steep drop. **Not rec for caravans.**
⑦	Ballon d'Alsace (France) 1178 (3865)	Giromagny *St Maurice-sur-Moselle*	11%	OC Dec-Mar. MWR 4m (13'1") Fairly straightforward ascent/descent; narrow in places; numerous bends.
⑧	Bayard (France) 1248 (4094)	Chauffayer *Gap*	14%	UO. MWR 6m (19'8") Part of the Route Napoleon. Fairly easy, steepest on the S side with several hairpin bends. Negotiable by caravans from N-to-S via N75 and Col de la Croix Haute, avoiding Gap.
⑨	Bernina (Switzerland) 2330 (7644)	Pontresina *Poschiavo*	12.5%	OC Dec-Mar. MWR 5m (16'5") MWV 2.25m (7'6") Fine scenery. Good with care on open narrow sections towards summit on S-side.
(-)	Bonaigua (Spain) 2072 (6797)	Viella (Vielha) *Esterri d'Aneu*	8.5%	UC Nov-Apr. MWR 4.3m (14'1") Twisting, narrow road with many hairpins and some precipitous drops. **Not rec for caravans.** Alternative route to Lerida (Lleida) through Viella (Vielha) Tunnel is open in winter.

	PASS HEIGHT IN METRES (FEET)	FROM TO	MAX GRADIENT	CONDITIONS AND COMMENTS
⑩	**Bracco** (Italy) 613 (2011)	Riva Trigoso *Borghetto di Vara*	14%	UO. MWR 5m (16'5") A two-lane road more severe than height suggests due to hairpins and volume of traffic; passing difficult. Rec cross early to avoid traffic. Alternative toll m'way available.
⑪	**Brenner (Europabrucke)** (Austria – Italy) 1374 (4508)	Innsbruck *Vipiteno/Sterzing*	14%	UO. MWR 6m (19'8") Parallel toll m'way A13/E45 (6%) suitable for caravans. Heavy traffic may delay at Customs. Pass road closed to vehicles towing trailers.
⑫	**Brouis** (France) 1279 (4196)	Nice *Col de Tende*	12.5%	UO. MWR 6m (19'8") Good surface but many hairpins. Steep gradients on approaches. Height of tunnel at Col de Tende is 3.8m (12'4") **Not rec for caravans.**
⑬	**Brünig** (Switzerland) 1007 (3340)	Brienzwiler Station *Giswil*	8.5%	UO. MWR 6m (19'8") MWV 2.5m (8'2") An easy but winding road; heavy traffic at weekends; frequent lay-bys.
⑭	**Bussang** (France) 721 (2365)	Thann *St Maurice-sur-Moselle*	7%	UO. MWR 4m (13'1") A very easy road over the Vosges; beautiful scenery.
⑮	**Cabre** (France) 1180 (3871)	Luc-en-Diois *Aspres-sur-Buëch*	9%	UO. MWR 5.5m (18') An easy pleasant road, winding at Col de Cabre.
⑯	**Campolongo** (Italy) 1875 (6152)	Corvara in Badia *Arabba*	12.5%	OC Dec-Mar. MWR 5m (16'5") A winding but easy ascent; long level stretch on summit followed by easy descent; good surface. Fine scenery.
❶⑦	**Cayolle** (France) 2326 (7631)	Barcelonnette *Guillaumes*	10%	UC early Nov-early Jun. MWR 4m (13'1") Narrow, winding road with hairpin bends; poor surface, broken edges with steep drops. Long stretches of single-track road with passing places. **Caravans prohibited.**
(-)	**Chavade** (France) 1266 (4140)	Pradelles *Aubenas*	12%	UO. Straightforward for caravans; long drag from S, steepest, slowest section is climb from SE which passes through narrow valley. Poss heavy traffic, difficult in hot weather, very scenic, open all year. MWR not known.
⑱	**Costalunga (Karer)** (Italy) 1753 (5751)	Cardano *Pozza*	16%	OC Dec-Apr. MWR 5m (16'5") A good well-engineered road but mostly winding with many blind hairpins. Caravans prohibited.
❶⑨	**Croix** (Switzerland) 1778 (5833)	Villars-sur-Ollon *Les Diablerets*	13%	UC Nov-May. MWR 3.5m (11'6") A narrow and winding route but extremely picturesque. Not rec for caravans.

	PASS HEIGHT IN METRES (FEET)	FROM *TO*	MAX GRADIENT	CONDITIONS AND COMMENTS
20	**Croix-Haute** (France) 1179 (3868)	Monestier-de-Clermont *Aspres-sur-Buëch*	7%	UO on N75. MWR 5.5m (18') Well-engineered; several hairpin bends on N side.
(-)	**Envalira** (Andorra) 2407 (7897)	Pas de la Casa *Andorra*	12.5%	OC Nov-Apr. MWR 6m (19'8") Good road with wide bends on ascent and descent; fine views. MHV 3.5m (11'6") on N approach near l'Hospitalet. Early start rec in summer to avoid border delays. Envalira Tunnel (toll) reduces congestion. See *Road Tunnels* in this section.
(-)	**Escudo** (Spain) 1011 (3317)	Santander *Burgos*	14%	UO. MWR probably 5m (16'5") Asphalt surface but many bends and steep gradients. Not rec in winter. N611/N627 easier route.
21	**Falzárego** (Italy) 2117 (6945)	Cortina d'Ampezzo *Andraz*	8.5%	OC Dec-Apr. MWR 5m (16'5") Well-engineered bitumen surface; many hairpin bends on both sides.
22	**Faucille** (France) 1323 (4341)	Gex *Morez*	10%	UO. MWR 5m (16'5") Fairly wide, winding road across the Jura mountains; negotiable by caravans but probably better to follow route via La Cure-St Cergue-Nyon.
23	**Fern** (Austria) 1209 (3967)	Nassereith *Lermoos*	10%	UO. MWR 6m (19'8") Obstructed intermittently during winter. An easy pass but slippery when wet; heavy traffic at summer weekends. Connects with Holzleiten Sattel Pass at S end for travel to/from Innsbruck – see below.
24	**Flexen** (Austria) 1784 (5853)	Lech *Rauzalpe (nr Arlberg Pass)*	10%	UO. MWR 5.5m (18') The magnificent 'Flexenstrasse', a well-engineered mountain road with tunnels and galleries. The road from Lech to Warth, N of the pass, is usually closed Nov-Apr due to danger of avalanche. Not rec for caravans.
25	**Flüela** (Switzerland) 2383 (7818)	Davos-Dorf *Susch*	12.5%	OC Nov-May. MWR 5m (16'5") MWV 2.3m (7'6") Easy ascent from Davos; some acute hairpin bends on the E side; bitumen surface.
26	**Forclaz** (Switzerland – France) 1527 (5010)	Martigny *Argentière*	8.5%	UO Forclaz; OC Montets Dec-early Apr. MWR 5m (16'5") MWV 2.5m (8'2") Good road over the pass and to the border; long, hard climb out of Martigny; narrow and rough over Col des Montets.
27	**Foscagno** (Italy) 2291 (7516)	Bormio *Livigno*	12.5%	OC Nov-May. MWR 3.3m (10'10") Narrow and winding through lonely mountains, generally poor surface. Long winding ascent with many blind bends; not always well-guarded. The descent includes winding rise and fall over the Passo d'Eira 2200m (7,218). Not rec for caravans.

	PASS HEIGHT IN METRES (FEET)	FROM *TO*	MAX GRADIENT	CONDITIONS AND COMMENTS
28	**Fugazze** (Italy) 1159 (3802)	Roverto *Valli del Pasubio*	14%	UO. MWR 3.5m (11'6") Very winding with some narrow sections, particularly on N side. The many blind bends and several hairpin bends call for extra care. Not rec for caravans.
29	**Furka** (Switzerland) 2431 (7976)	Gletsch *Realp*	11%	UC Oct-Jun. MWR 4m (13'1") MWV 2.25m (7'6") Well-graded road with narrow sections and several hairpin bends on both ascent and descent. Fine views of the Rhone Glacier. Beware of coaches and traffic build-up. Not rec for caravans. Alternative rail tunnel available. See *Rail Tunnels* in this section.
30	**Galibier** (France) 2645 (8678)	Lauteret Pass *St Michel-de-Maurienne*	12.5%	UC Oct-Jun. MWR 3m (9'10") Mainly wide, well-surfaced but unguarded and narrow over summit. Rise over the Col du Telegraphe then 11 more hairpin bends. Ten hairpin bends on descent then 5km (3.1 miles) narrow and rough. Limited parking at summit. Not rec for caravans. (The tunnel under the Galibier summit is closed).
31	**Gardena (Grödner-Joch)** (Italy) 2121 (6959)	Val Gardena *Corvara in Badia*	12.5%	OC Dec-Jun. MWR 5m (16'5") A well-engineered road, very winding on descent. Fine views. Caravans prohibited.
32	**Gavia** (Italy) 2621 (8599)	Bormio *Ponte di Legno*	20%	UC Oct-Jul. MWR 3m (9'10") MWV 1.8m (5'11") Steep and narrow with frequent passing bays; many hairpin bends and gravel surface; not for the faint-hearted; extra care necessary. Not rec for caravans. Long winding ascent on Bormio side.
33	**Gerlos** (Austria) 1628 (5341)	Zell-am-Ziller *Wald*	9%	UO. MWR 4m (13'1") Hairpin ascent out of Zell to modern toll road; the old, steep, narrow and winding route with passing bays and 14% gradient is not rec but is negotiable with care; toll: motor caravan or solo car €7.00. Views of Krimml waterfalls. Caravans prohibited.
34	**Gorges du Verdon** (France) 1032 (3386)	Castellane *Moustiers-Ste Marie*	9%	UO. MWR probably 5m (16'5") Col d'Ayen and Col d'Olivier. Moderate gradients but slow, narrow and winding. Poss heavy traffic.
35	**Grand St Bernard** (Switzerland – Italy) 2473 (8114)	Martigny *Aosta*	11%	UC Oct-Jun. MWR 4m (13'1") MWV 2.5m (8' 2") Modern road to entrance of road tunnel (UO), then narrow but bitumen surface over summit to border; also good in Italy. Suitable for caravans using tunnel. Pass road closed to vehicles towing trailers. See *Road Tunnels* in this section.
36	**Grimsel** (Switzerland) 2164 (7100)	Innertkirchen *Gletsch*	10%	UC mid Oct-late June. MWR 5m (16'5") MWV 2.25m (7'6") A fairly easy, modern road with heavy traffic at weekends. A long winding ascent, finally hairpin bends; then a terraced descent with six hairpins into the Rhone Valley. Good surface; fine scenery.

	PASS HEIGHT IN METRES (FEET)	FROM TO	MAX GRADIENT	CONDITIONS AND COMMENTS
37	**Grossglockner** (Austria) 2503 (8212)	Bruck-an-der-Grossglocknerstrasse / Heiligenblut	12.5%	UC late Oct-early May. MWR 5.5m (18') Well-engineered but many hairpins; heavy traffic; moderate but very long ascent. Magnificent scenery. Negotiable preferably S to N by caravans. Avoid side road to highest point at Edelweissespitze if towing, as road is very steep and narrow. Toll: car + caravan or motor caravan €26 high season. Road closed from 2200-0500 hrs (summer). Alternative Felbertauern road tunnel between Lienz and Mittersil (toll). See *Road Tunnels* in this section.
(-)	**Guadarrama** (Spain) 1511 (4957)	Guadarrama / San Rafael	14%	UO. MWR 6m (19'8") This pass to NW of Madrid may be avoided by using A6 motorway from Villalba to San Rafael or Villacastin (toll).
38	**Hahntennjoch** (Austria) 1894 (6250)	Pfafflar / Imst	15%	UC Nov-May. A minor pass; caravans prohibited.
39	**Hochtannberg** (Austria) 1679 (5509)	Schröcken / Warth (nr Lech)	14%	OC Jan-Mar. MWR 4m (13'1") A reconstructed modern road. W to E long ascent with many hairpins. Easier E to W. Not rec for caravans or trailers.
40	**Holzleiten Sattel** (Austria) 1126 (3694)	Nassereith / Obsteig	12.5%	(12.5%), UO. MWR 5m (16'5") Road surface good on W side; poor on E. Light traffic; gradients no problem but not rec for caravans or trailers.
(-)	**Ibañeta (Roncevalles)** (France – Spain) 1057 (3468)	St Jean-Pied-de-Port / Pamplona	10%	UO. MWR 4m (13'1") Slow and winding, scenic route.
41	**Iseran** (France) 2770 (9088)	Bourg-St Maurice / Lanslebourg	11%	UC mid Oct-late Jun. MWR 4m (13'1") Second highest pass in the Alps. Well-graded with reasonable bends, average surface. Several unlit tunnels on N approach. Not rec for caravans.
42	**Izoard** (France) 2360 (7743)	Guillestre / Briançon	12.5%	UC late Oct-mid Jun. MWR 5m (16'5") Fine scenery. Winding, sometimes narrow with many hairpin bends; care required at several unlit tunnels near Guillestre. Not rec for caravans.
43	**Jaun** (Switzerland) 1509 (4951)	Broc / Reidenbach	10%	UO. MWR 4m (13'1") MWV 2.25m (7'6") A modern but generally narrow road; some poor sections on ascent and several hairpin bends on descent.
44	**Julier** (Switzerland) 2284 (7493)	Tiefencastel / Silvaplana	13%	UO. MWR 4m (13'1") MWV 2.5m (8'2") Well-engineered road approached from Chur via Sils. Fine scenery. Negotiable by caravans, preferably from N to S. Alternative rail tunnel from Thusis to Samedan. See *Rail Tunnels* in this section.

	PASS HEIGHT IN METRES (FEET)	FROM TO	MAX GRADIENT	CONDITIONS AND COMMENTS
45	**Katschberg** (Austria) 1641 (5384)	Spittal *St Michael*	20%	UO. MWR 6m (19'8") Good wide road with no hairpins but steep gradients particularly from S. Suitable only light caravans. Parallel Tauern/Katschberg toll motorway and road tunnels. See *Road Tunnels* in this section.
46	**Klausen** (Switzerland) 1948 (6391)	Altdorf *Linthal*	10%	UC late Oct-early Jun. MWR 5m (16'5") MWV 2.25m (7' 6") Narrow and winding in places, but generally easy in spite of a number of sharp bends; no through route for caravans as they are prohibited from using the road between Unterschächen and Linthal.
47	**Larche (della Maddalena)** (France – Italy) 1994 (6542)	La Condamine-Châtelard *Vinadio*	8.5%	OC Dec-Mar. MWR 3.5m (11'6") An easy, well-graded road; long, steady ascent on French side, many hairpins on Italian side. Fine scenery; ample parking at summit.
48	**Lautaret** (France) 2058 (6752)	Le Bourg-d'Oisans *Briançon*	12.5%	OC Dec-Mar. MWR 4m (13'1") Modern, evenly graded but winding, and unguarded in places; very fine scenery; suitable for caravans but with care through narrow tunnels.
49	**Leques** (France) 1146 (3760)	Barreme *Castellane*	8%	UO. MWR 4m (13'1") On Route Napoleon (N85). Light traffic; excellent surface; narrow in places on N ascent. S ascent has many hairpins.
50	**Loibl (Ljubelj)** (Austria – Slovenia) 1067 (3500)	Unterloibl *Kranj*	20%	UO. MWR 6m (19'8") Steep rise and fall over Little Loibl pass to 1.6km (1 mile) tunnel under summit. Caravans prohibited. The old road over the summit is closed to through-traffic.
51	**Lukmanier (Lucomagno)** (Switzerland) 1916 (6286)	Olivone *Disentis*	9%	UC early Nov-late May. MWR 5m (16'5") MWV 2.25m (7'6") Rebuilt, modern road.
52	**Maloja** (Switzerland) 1815 (5955)	Silvaplana *Chiavenna*	9%	UO. MWR 4m (13'1") MWV 2.5m (8'2") Escarpment facing S; fairly easy, but many hairpin bends on descent; negotiable by caravans but possibly difficult on ascent.
53	**Mauria** (Italy) 1298 (4258)	Lozzo di Cadore *Ampezzo*	7%	UO. MWR 5m (16'5") A well-designed road with easy, winding ascent and descent.
54	**Mendola** (Italy) 1363 (4472)	Appiano/Eppan *Sarnonico*	12.5%	UO. MWR 5m (16'5") A fairly straightforward but winding road, well-guarded.
55	**Mont Cenis** (France – Italy) 2083 (6834)	Lanslebourg *Susa*	12.5%	UC Nov-May. MWR 5m (16'5") Approach by industrial valley. An easy highway with mostly good surface; spectacular scenery; many stopping places. Alternative Fréjus road tunnel available. See *Road Tunnels* in this section.

	PASS HEIGHT IN METRES (FEET)	FROM TO	MAX GRADIENT	CONDITIONS AND COMMENTS
56	Monte Croce di Comélico (Kreuzberg) (Italy) 1636 (5368)	San Candido Santo Stefano di Cadore	8.5%	UO. MWR 5m (16'5") A winding road with moderate gradients, beautiful scenery.
57	Montgenèvre (France – Italy) 1850 (6070)	Briançon Cesana Torinese	9%	UO. MWR 5m (16'5") An easy, modern road with some tight hairpin bends. Much used by lorries; may be necessary to travel at their speed and give way to oncoming large vehicles on hairpins.
58	Monte Giovo (Jaufen) (Italy) 2094 (6870)	Merano Vipiteno/Sterzing	12.5%	UC Nov-May. MWR 4m (13'1") Many well-engineered hairpin bends; good scenery. Caravans prohibited.
	Montets (See Forclaz)			
59	Morgins (France – Switzerland) 1369 (4491)	Abondance Monthey	14%	UO. MWR 4m (13'1") A lesser used route through pleasant, forested countryside crossing French/Swiss border. Not rec for caravans.
60	Mosses (Switzerland) 1445 (4740)	Aigle Château d'Oex	8.5%	UO. MWR 4m (13'1") MWV 2.25m (7'6") A modern road. Aigle side steeper and narrow in places.
61	Nassfeld (Pramollo) (Austria – Italy) 1530 (5020)	Tröpolach Pontebba	20%	OC Late Nov-Mar. MWR 4m (13'1") The winding descent into Italy has been improved but not rec for caravans.
(-)	Navacerrada (Spain) 1860 (6102)	Madrid Segovia	17%	OC Nov-Mar. Sharp hairpins. Possible but not rec for caravans.
62	Nufenen (Novena) (Switzerland) 2478 (8130)	Ulrichen Airolo	10%	UC Mid Oct-mid Jun. MWR 4m (13'1") MWV 2.25m (7'6") The approach roads are narrow, with tight bends, but the road over the pass is good; negotiable with care. Long drag from Ulrichen.
63	Oberalp (Switzerland) 2044 (6706)	Andermatt Disentis	10%	UC Nov-late May. MWR 5m (16'5") MWV 2.5m (8'2") A much improved and widened road with modern surface; many hairpin bends, but long level stretch on summit. Alternative rail tunnel during the winter. See Rail Tunnels in this section. Caravans not permitted.
64	Ofen (Fuorn) (Switzerland) 2149 (7051)	Zernez Santa Maria-im-Münstertal	12.5%	UO. MWR 4m (13'1") MWV 2.25m (7'6") Good road through Swiss National Park.

	PASS HEIGHT IN METRES (FEET)	FROM TO	MAX GRADIENT	CONDITIONS AND COMMENTS
65	Petit St Bernard (France – Italy) 2188 (7178)	Bourg-St Maurice *Pré-St Didier*	8.5%	UC mid Oct-Jun. MWR 5m (16'5") Outstanding scenery, but poor surface and unguarded broken edges near summit. Easiest from France; sharp hairpins on climb from Italy. Closed to vehicles towing another vehicle.
(-)	Peyresourde (France) 1563 (5128)	Arreau *Bagnères-de-Luchon*	10%	UO. MWR 4m (13'1") Somewhat narrow with several hairpin bends, though not difficult. Not rec for caravans.
(-)	Picos de Europa or Puerto de San Glorio (Spain) 1609 (5279)	Unquera *Riaño*	12%	UO. MWR probably 4m (13'1") N621 mostly narrow and winding with some hairpin bends, especially over Puerto de San Glorio.
66	Pillon (Switzerland) 1546 (5072)	Le Sépey *Gsteig*	9%	OC Jan-Feb. MWR 4m (13'1") MWV 2.25m (7'6") A comparatively easy, modern road.
67	Plöcken (Monte Croce-Carnico) (Austria – Italy) 1362 (4468)	Kötschach *Paluzza*	14%	OC Dec-Apr. MWR 5m (16'5") A modern road with long, reconstructed sections; OC to caravans due to heavy traffic on summer weekends; delay likely at the border. Long, slow, twisty pull from S, easier from N.
68	Pordoi (Italy) 2239 (7346)	Arabba *Canazei*	10%	OC Dec-Apr. MWR 5m (16'5") An excellent modern road with numerous hairpin bends; fine scenery. Long drag when combined with Falzarego pass.
(-)	Port (France) 1249 (4098)	Tarascon-sur-Ariège *Massat*	10%	OC Nov-Mar. MWR 4m (13'1") A fairly easy, scenic road, but narrow on some bends.
(-)	Portet d'Aspet (France) 1069 (3507)	Audressein *Fronsac*	14%	UO. MWR 3.5m (11'6") Approached from W by the easy Col des Ares and Col de Buret; well-engineered but narrow road; care needed on hairpin bends. Not rec for caravans.
69	Pötschen (Austria) 982 (3222)	Bad Ischl *Bad Aussee*	9%	UO. MWR 7m (23') A modern road. Good scenery.
(-)	Pourtalet (France – Spain) 1792 (5879)	Eaux-Chaudes *Biescas*	10%	UC late Oct-early Jun. MWR 3.5m (11'6") A fairly easy, unguarded road, but narrow in places. Easier from Spain, steeper in France. Not rec for caravans.
(-)	Puymorens (France) 1915 (6283)	Ax-les-Thermes *Bourg-Madame*	10%	OC Nov-Apr. MWR 5.5m (18') MHV 3.5m (11'6") A generally easy, modern tarmac road, but narrow, winding and with poor surface in places; not suitable for night-driving. Parallel toll road tunnel available. See *Road Tunnels* in this section.

	PASS HEIGHT IN METRES (FEET)	FROM TO	MAX GRADIENT	CONDITIONS AND COMMENTS
(-)	Quillane (France) 1714 (5623)	Quillan Mont-Louis	8.5%	OC Nov-Mar. MWR 5m (16'5") An easy, straightforward ascent and descent.
70	Radstädter-Tauern (Austria) 1738 (5702)	Radstadt Mauterndorf	16%	OC Jan-Mar. MWR 5m (16'5") N ascent steep but not difficult otherwise; but negotiable by light caravans using parallel toll m'way through tunnel. See *Road Tunnels* in this section.
71	Résia (Reschen) (Italy – Austria) 1504 (4934)	Spondigna Pfunds	10%	UO. MWR 6m (19'8") A good, straightforward alternative to the Brenner Pass. Fine views but no stopping places.
72	Restefond (La Bonette) (France) 2802 (9193)	Barcelonnette St Etienne-de-Tinée	16%	UC Oct-Jun. MWR 3m (9'10") The highest pass in the Alps. Rebuilt, resurfaced road with rest area at summit. Winding with hairpin bends. **Not rec for caravans.**
73	Rolle (Italy) 1970 (6463)	Predazzo Mezzano	9%	OC Dec-Mar. MWR 5m (16'5") A well-engineered road with many hairpin bends on both sides; very beautiful scenery; good surface.
	Rombo (See Timmelsjoch)			
(-)	Routes des Crêtes (France) 1283 (4210)	St Dié Cernay	12.5%	UC Nov-Apr. MWR 4m (13'1") A renowned scenic route crossing seven ridges, with the highest point at Hotel du Grand Ballon. **Not rec for caravans.**
74	St Gotthard (San Gottardo) (Switzerland) 2108 (6916)	Göschenen Airolo	10%	UC mid Oct-early Jun. MWR 6m (19'8") MWV 2.5m (8'2") MHV 3.6m (11'9") Modern, fairly easy two- to three-lane road. Heavy traffic. Alternative road tunnel. See *Road Tunnels* in this section.
(-)	Ste Marie (France) 772 (2543)	Wisembach Ste Marie-aux-Mines	13%	UO on N59. MWR 6m (19'5") Slow, winding road with rough surface in places. Negotiable by caravans but not rec. Alternative road tunnel closed April 2004 for up to 3 years.
75	San Bernardino (Switzerland) 2066 (6778)	Mesocco Hinterrhein	10%	UC Oct-late Jun. MWR 4m (13'1") MWV 2.25m (7'6") Easy modern roads on N and S approaches to tunnel, narrow and winding over summit via tunnel suitable for caravans. See *Road Tunnels* in this section.
76	Schlucht (France) 1139 (3737)	Gérardmer Munster	7%	UO. MWR 5m (16'5") An extremely picturesque route crossing the Vosges mountains, with easy, wide bends on the descent. Good surface.
77	Seeberg (Jezersko) (Austria – Slovenia) 1218 (3996)	Eisenkappel Kranj	12.5%	UO. MWR 5m (16'5") An alternative to the steeper Loibl and Wurzen passes; moderate climb with winding, hairpin ascent and descent. **Not rec for caravans.**

	PASS HEIGHT IN METRES (FEET)	FROM TO	MAX GRADIENT	CONDITIONS AND COMMENTS
78	**Sella** (Italy) 2240 (7349)	Plan *Canazei*	11%	OC Dec-Jan. MWR 5m (16'5") A well-engineered, winding road; exceptional views of Dolomites; **not rec for caravans.**
(-)	**Semmering** (Austria) 985 (3232)	Mürzzuschlag-im- Mürztal *Gloggnitz*	6%	UO MWR 6m (19'8") A fine, well-engineered highway; good views; several hairpins.
79	**Sestriere** (Italy) 2033 (6670)	Cesana Torinese *Pinarolo*	10%	UO MWR 6m (19'8") Mostly bitumen surface. Fairly easy; fine scenery.
80	**Silvretta (Bielerhöhe)** (Austria) 2032 (6666)	Partenen *Galtur*	11%	UC late Oct-early Jun. MWR 5m (16'5") Mostly reconstructed; 32 easy hairpin bends on W ascent; E side more straightforward. Toll €10.90 for car, €13.44/€16.71 for motor caravan up to/over 3,500 kg; caravans prohibited.
81	**Simplon** (Switzerland – Italy) 2005 (6578)	Brig *Domodóssola*	11%	OC Nov-Apr. MWR 7m (23') MWV 2.5m (8'2") An easy, reconstructed, modern road, 21km (13 miles) long, continuous ascent to summit; good views. Surface better on Swiss side. Alternative rail tunnel fr Kandersteg in operation from Easter to September.
(-)	**Somosierra** (Spain) 1444 (4738)	Madrid *Burgos*	10%	OC Mar-Dec. MWR 7m (23') May be blocked following snowfalls. Snow-plough swept during winter months but wheel chains compulsory after snowfalls. Well-surfaced dual carriageway, tunnel at summit.
(-)	**Somport** (France – Spain) 1632 (5354)	Bedous *Jaca*	10%	UO. MWR 3.5m (11'6") A favoured, old-established route; generally easy but narrow with many unguarded bends on French side; excellent road on Spanish side. Fairly well-surfaced. Use of road tunnel advised – see *Road Tunnels* in this section.
82	**Splügen** (Switzerland – Italy) 2113 (6932)	Splügen *Chiavenna*	13%	UC Nov-Jun. MWR 3.5m (11'6") MHV 2.8m (9'2") MWV 2.25m (7'6") Mostly narrow and winding, with extremely tight hairpin bends, not well guarded; care also required at many tunnels/galleries. **Not rec for caravans.**
83	**Stelvio** (Italy) 2757 (9045)	Bormio *Spondigna*	12.5%	UC Oct-late Jun. MWR 4m (13'1") MLV 10m (32') Third highest pass in Alps; 40-50 acute hairpin bends either side, all well-engineered; good surface, traffic often heavy. Hairpin bends too acute for long vehicles. **Not rec for caravans.**
84	**Susten** (Switzerland) 2224 (7297)	Innertkirchen *Wassen*	9%	UC Nov-Jun. MWR 6m (19'8") MWV 2.5m (8'2") Very scenic and well-guarded road; easy gradients and turns; heavy traffic at weekends. Negotiable by caravans with care, but not for the faint-hearted.
85	**Tenda (Tende)** (Italy – France) 1321 (4334)	Borgo S Dalmazzo *La Giandola*	9%	UO. MWR 6m (19'8") Well-guarded, modern road with several hairpin bends; road tunnel (height 3.8m) at summit narrow with poor road surface. Less steep on Italian side. **Caravans prohibited during winter.**

	PASS HEIGHT IN METRES (FEET)	FROM TO	MAX GRADIENT	CONDITIONS AND COMMENTS
86	**Thurn** (Austria) 1274 (4180)	Kitzbühel *Mittersill*	8.5%	UO. MWR 5m (16'5") MWV 2.5m (8'2") A good road with narrow stretches; N approach rebuilt. Several good parking areas.
87	**Timmelsjoch (Rombo)** (Austria – Italy) 2509 (8232)	Obergurgl *Moso*	14%	UC mid Oct-Jun. MWR 3.5m (11'6") Border closed at night 8pm to 7am. The pass is open to private cars **without trailers only**, as some tunnels on Italian side too narrow for larger vehicles; toll road. Easiest N to S.
88	**Tonale** (Italy) 1883 (6178)	Edolo *Dimaro*	10%	UO. MWR 5m (16'5") A relatively easy road; steepest on W; long drag. Fine views.
(-)	**Toses (Tosas)** (Spain) 1800 (5906)	Puigcerda *Ribes de Freser*	10%	UO MWR 5m (16'5") A fairly straightforward, but continuously winding, two-lane road with many sharp bends; some unguarded edges.
(-)	**Tourmalet** (France) 2114 (6936)	Luz-St Sauveur *Ste Marie-de-Campan*	12.5%	UC Oct-mid Jun. MWR 4m (13'1") The highest French Pyrenean route; approaches good, though winding and exacting over summit; sufficiently guarded. **Not rec for caravans.**
89	**Tre Croci** (Italy) 1809 (5935)	Cortina d'Ampezzo *Auronzo di Cadore*	11%	OC Dec-Mar. MWR 6m (19'8") An easy pass; fine scenery.
90	**Turracher Höhe** (Austria) 1763 (5784)	Predlitz *Ebene-Reichenau*	23%	UO. MWR 4m (13'1") Formerly one of the steepest mountain roads in Austria; now improved. Steep, fairly straightforward ascent followed by a very steep descent; good surface and mainly two-lane; fine scenery. **Not rec for caravans.**
91	**Umbrail** (Switzerland – Italy) 2501 (8205)	Santa Maria-im-Münstertal *Bormio*	9%	UC Nov-early Jun. MWR 4.3m (14'1") MWV 2.25m (7'6") Highest Swiss pass; mostly tarmac with some gravel surface. Narrow with 34 hairpin bends. **Not rec for caravans.**
92	**Vars** (France) 2109 (6919)	St Paul-sur-Ubaye *Guillestre*	9%	OC Dec-Mar. MWR 5m (16'5") Easy winding ascent and descent with 14 hairpin bends; good surface.
93	**Wurzen (Koren)** (Austria – Slovenia) 1073 (3520)	Riegersdorf *Kranjska Gora*	20%	UO. MWR 4m (13'1") Steep two-lane road, otherwise not particularly difficult; better on Austrian side; heavy traffic summer weekends; delays likely at the border. **Caravans prohibited.**
94	**Zirler Berg** (Austria) 1009 (3310)	Seefeld *Zirl*	16.5%	UO. MWR 7m (23') S-facing escarpment, part of route from Garmisch to Innsbruck; good, modern road. Heavy tourist traffic and long steep descent with one hairpin bend into Inn Valley. Steepest section from hairpin bend down to Zirl. **Caravans not permitted northbound and not rec southbound.**

Technical information by courtesy of the Automobile Association

MAJOR RAIL TUNNELS

	Tunnel	Route	Journey Time	General Information/ Comments	Contact
Ⓐ	**Albula** (Switzerland) 5.9km (3.5 miles)	**Chur-St Moritz** Thusis-Samedan	90 mins	MHV 2.8m Up to 9 shuttle services per day all year; advance booking compulsory. Car + caravan (up to 10m), 2 adults CHF 338 (weekends)	Thusis (081) 6511113 Samedan (081) 2885511 www.rhb.ch
Ⓑ	**Furka** (Switzerland) 15.4km (9.5 miles)	**Andermatt-Brig** Realp-Oberwald	15 mins	Hourly all year from 6am to 9pm weekdays; half-hourly weekends. Car, caravan, 2 adults CHF 50 (summer)	Realp (041) 8871446 Oberwald (027) 9731141 www.fo-bahn.ch
Ⓒ	**Oberalp** (Switzerland) 28km (17.3 miles)	**Andermatt-Disentis** Andermatt-Sedrun	60 mins	MHV 2.5m 2-6 trains daily (Christmas-Easter only).. Advance booking compulsory. Car, caravan, 2 adults CHF 151	Andermatt (041) 8887511 Sedrun (081) 9204711 www.fo-bahn.ch
Ⓓ	**Lotschberg** (Switzerland) 14km (8.7 miles)	**Bern-Brig** Kandersteg-Goppenstein	15 mins	MHV 2.9m Frequent all year half-hourly service, advance booking unnecessary; extension to Hohtenn operates when Goppenstein-Gampel road is closed. Car, caravan, 2 adults CHF 50	Kandersteg (0900) 553333 www.bls.ch
Ⓔ	**Simplon** (Switzerland – Italy)	**Brig-Domodossola** Brig-Iselle	20 mins	10 trains daily, all year. Car, caravan CHF 38 Motor caravan (up to 3,500 kg) SFr 19	(0900) 300300 www.cff.ch
	Lotschberg/Simplon (Switzerland – Italy)	**Bern-Domodossola** Kandersteg-Goppenstein	75 mins	Limited service 1 to 3 days a week (1 to 10 times a day) for vehicles max height 2.5m, motor caravans up to 3,500 kg	(0900) 553333 www.bls.ch
Ⓕ	**Vereina** (Switzerland) 19.6km (11.7 miles)	**Klosters-Susch** Selfranga-Sagliains	17 mins	MLV 12m Half-hourly daytime service all year. Car, caravan, 2 adults CHF 54 (summer). Motor caravan up to 2,800 kg CHF 30 (summer), over 2,800 kg CHF 40. Restricted capacity for vehicles over 3.3m high during winter w/ends and public holidays. Steep approach to Klosters.	(081) 2883737 (recorded) www.rhb.ch

NOTES:

1)   All fares are one-way; for return fares double the single fare.
2)   Detailed timetable and tariff lists are available from the appropriate tourist offices.

MAJOR ROAD TUNNELS

	Tunnel	Route and Height above Sea Level	General Information and Comments	Toll	
G	**Arlberg** (Austria) 14km (8.75 miles)	**Langen-St Anton** 1,220m (4,000')	Parallel and to S of Arlberg Pass which is closed to caravans/trailers. Credit cards accepted.	Car + caravan/trailer, motor caravan up to 3,500 kg	€8.50*
				Vehicle over 3,500 kg	€13.30*
-	**Bielsa** (France – Spain) 3.2km (2 miles)	**Bielsa-Aragnouet** 1,830m (6,000')	Open 24 hours but possibly closed Oct-Easter; good road surface, steep on French side with many bends; steep gradients near summit; N to S winding ascent. No tolls.		
H	**Bosruck** (Austria) 5.5km (3.4 miles)	**Spital am Pyhrn-Selzthal** 742m (2,434')	To E of Pyhrn pass; with Gleinalm Tunnel (see below) forms part of A9 a'bahn between Linz & Graz. Max speed 80 km/h (50 mph). Use dipped headlights, no overtaking. Occasional emergency lay-bys with telephones.	Car, car + caravan, motor caravan up to 3,500 kg	€4.50*
				Motor caravan over 3,500 kg	€6.60*
-	**Cadi** (Spain) 5km (3 miles)	**Bellver de Cerdanya-Baga** 1,220m (4,000')	W of Toses (Tosas) pass; link from Seo de Urgel to Andorra; excellent approach roads; heavy traffic at weekends.	Car, car + single axle caravan/trailer, motor caravan	€8.84
				Car + twin axle caravan/trailer	€16.79
-	**Envalira** (France – Spain) 2.8km (1.75 miles)	**Pas de la Casa-El Grau Roig** 2,000m (6,562')	Tunnel width 8.25m.	Car	€4.70
				Car + caravan	€10.70
I	**Felbertauern** (Austria) 5.3km (3.25 miles)	**Mittersill-Matrei** 1,525m (5,000')	MWR 7m (23'), tunnel height 4.5m (14'9"). W of and parallel to Grossglockner pass; downwards gradient of 9% S to N with sharp bend before N exit. Wheel chains may be needed on approach Nov-Apr.	Car, car + caravan, motor caravan	€10.00
J	**Frejus** (France – Italy) 12.8km (8 miles)	**Modane-Bardonecchia** 1,220m (4,000')	MWR 9m (29'6"), tunnel height 4.5m (14'9") Min/max speed 60/70 km/h (37/44 mph) Return tickets valid until midnight on 7th day after day of issue. Season tickets are available. Approach via A43 and N6; heavy use by freight vehicles. Good surface on approach roads.	Vehicle & vehicle combination with front axle height less than 1.3m & total height less than 2m	€30.50
				Vehicle & vehicle combination not in above catetory, with total height less than 3m	€40.40
K	**Gleinalm** (Austria) 8.3km (5 miles)	**St Michael-Fiesach (nr Graz)** 817m (2,680')	Part of A9 Pyhrn a'bahn.	Car, car + caravan, motor caravan up to 3,500 kg	€7.50*
				Motor caravan over 3,500 kg	€9.50*

	Tunnel	Route and Height above Sea Level	General Information and Comments	Toll	
L	**Grand St Bernard** (Switzerland – Italy) 5.9km (3.6 miles)	**Bourg St Pierre-St Rhemy** 1,925m (7,570')	MHV 4m (13'1"), MWV 2.5m (8'2.5"). MLV 18m (60'). Min/max speed 40/80 km/h (24/50 mph). Passport check, Customs & toll offices at entrance; breakdown bays at each end with telephones; return tickets valid one month. Although approaches are covered, wheel chains may be needed in winter. Season tickets are available Tel: (027) 7871206 for information (Switzerland) or 0165 780904 (Italy) www.sitrasb.it	Car (height from front axle up to 1.3m), total height up to 2m	CHF 29* or €22.40
				Car + caravan/trailer, motor caravan vehicle with 2 axles (height from front axle over 1.3m), total height between 2m and 3m	CHF 45* or €34.80
				Slightly higher charges apply from the Italian side due to the addition of VAT.	
M	**Karawanken** (Austria – Slovenia) 8km (5 miles)	**Rosenbach-Jesenice** 610m (2,000')		Car + caravan/trailer, motor caravan up to 3,500 kg	€6.50*
				Vehicle over 3,500 kg	€10.50*
N	**Mont Blanc** (France – Italy) 11.6km (7 miles)	**Chamonix-Entreves** 1,220m (4,000')	MHV 4.3m (14'1"), MWV 2.8m (9'2"). Max speed in tunnel 70 km/h (44 mph) – lower limits when exiting; min speed 50 km/h. Leave 150m between vehicles; ensure enough fuel for 30km. Return tickets valid until midnight on 7th day after issue. Season tickets are available. www.tunnelmb.com	Vehicle & vehicle combination with front axle height up to 1.3m & total height up to 2m	€30.50
				Vehicle & vehicle combination not in above catetory, with total height less than 3m	€40.40
O	**Munt La Schera** (Switzerland – Italy) 3.5km (2 miles)	**Zernez-Livigno**	MHV 3.6m (11'9"), MWV 2.5m (8'2"). Open 8am to 8pm; single lane traffic controlled by traffic lights; roads from Livogno S to the Bernina Pass and Bormio closed Dec-Apr. Tel: (081) 8561888	Car	CHF 15
				Car + caravan	CHF 15
				Motor caravan	CHF 20
-	**Puymorens** (France – Spain)	**Ax-les-Thermes-Puigcerda** 1,915m (6,000')	MHV 3.5m (11'6"). Part of Puymorens pass.	Vehicle with height up to 2m & total weight up to 3,500 kg, with/without caravan	€5.40
				Vehicle with height 2m to 3m & total weight up to 3,500 kg	€10.90
				Vehicle with 2 axles & height over 3m, or with total weight over 3,500 kg	€16.50
				Vehicle & vehicle combination with 3 or more axles with height over 3m, or with total weight over 3,500 kg	€27.40

Tunnel	Route and Height above Sea Level	General Information and Comments	Toll
- Somport (France – Spain) 8.6km (5.3 miles)	Urdos-Canfranc 1,190m (3,904')	Tunnel height 4.55m (14'9"), width 10.5m (34'). Max speed 90 km/h (56 mph); leave 100m between vehicles.	Only for vehicles up to 3,500 kg. No tolls.
P St Gotthard (Switzerland) 16.3km (10 miles)	Göschenen-Airolo 1,159m (3,800')	Tunnel height 4.5m (14'9"), single carriageway 7.5m (25') wide. Max speed 80 km/h (50 mph). No tolls, but tunnel is part of Swiss motorway network and a motorway vignette must be displayed. Tunnel closed 8pm to 5am Monday to Friday for periods during June and September. Heavy traffic and delays high season. www.gotthard-strassentunnel.ch; www.astra.admin.ch	
- Ste Marie-aux-Mines (France) 13km (8 miles)	St Die-Selestat	Maurice Lemaire tunnel on N59/N159 bypassing the heavily trafficked Col de Ste Marie. This tunnel closed in April 2004 for up to three years.	
Q San Bernardino (Switzerland) 6.6km (4 miles)	Hinterrhein-San Bernadino 1,644m (5,396')	Tunnel height 4.8m (15'9"), width 7m (23'). No stopping or overtaking; keep 100m between vehicles; breakdown bays with telephones. Max speed 80 km/h (50 mp/h) No tolls, but tunnel is part of Swiss motorway network and a Swiss motorway vignette must be displayed.	
R Tauern and Katschberg (Austria) 6.4km (4 miles) & 5.4km (3.5 miles)	Salzburg-Villach 1,340m (4,396') & 1,110m (3,642')	The two major tunnels on the A10. Both tunnels height 4.5m (14'9"), width 7.5m (25').	Car, car + motor caravan up to 3,500 kg €9.50* Motor caravan over 3,500 kg €13.60*
- Vielha (Viella) 5km (3.1 miles)	Vielha (Viella)-Pont de Suert 1,635m (5,390')	Single carriageway; gentle gradients on both sides. Some rough sections with pot holes on the approaches and in the tunnel.	No tolls.

Technical information compiled with the assistance of the Automobile Association

* Plus the cost of a motorway vignette – see the relevant Country Introduction.

NOTES:
1) Dipped headlights should be used (unless stated otherwise) when travelling through road tunnels, even when the road appears to be well lit. In some countries police make spot checks and impose on-the-spot fines.

2) During the winter wheel chains may be required on the approaches to some tunnels. These must not be used in tunnels and lay-bys are available for the removal and refitting of wheel chains.

3) Toll charges shown in the table above are the 2005 rates and should be used as a guide only.

We can help smooth your crossing

We can't guarantee the weather, but do you know that The Caravan Club operates a comprehensive Travel Service that can save you time and money too?

We can make planning your trip to the Continent much easier – book your ferry crossing, often having negotiated special deals on your behalf, and reserve you a place at one of around 200 recommended campsites throughout Europe. These services are also now available via The Club's web site **www.caravanclub.co.uk**

And that's not all. For your total peace of mind, Red Pennant - our comprehensive European travel insurance is specially designed for caravanners with annual options at competitive prices.

If you prefer completely hassle-free holidays, why not take a look at our superb range of Inclusive Holidays, some of which offer special interest activities including food and wine tasting, and walking and painting.

Find out more in our 'Travel Service in Europe' brochure

For your copy phone us on **01342 327410**

or visit our web site www.caravanclub.co.uk

THE CARAVAN CLUB
Travel Service in Europe 2005/2006
Keep this safe for next year too. Separate Price Supplement enclosed

- Guide to campsites, opening dates, descriptions, locations and facilities
- Red Pennant travel insurance and travel choices
- Inclusive Holiday selection, Camping Cheques
NEW FOR 2005
- 19 new European campsites including sites in Croatia and Belgium
- Mobile homes and boat hire
- Les Castels Privilege Card

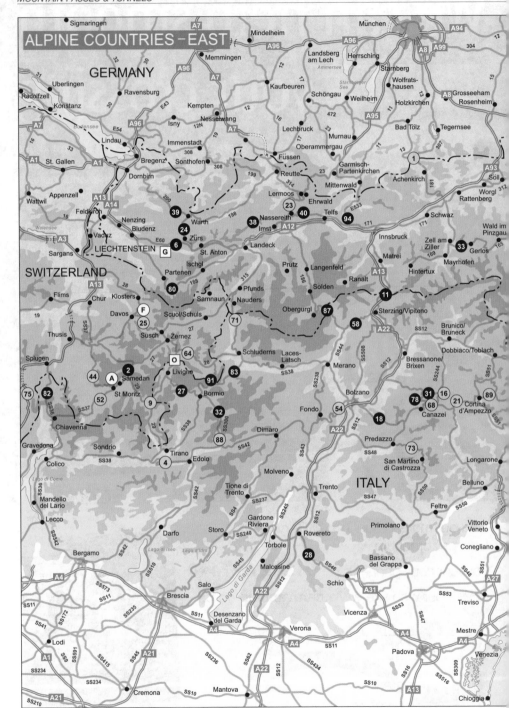

Motorway		
Motorway (Proposed)		
Motorway Road Tunnel		
Major/Main Roads		
(1)	Mountain Passes Suitable for Caravans	
(2)	Mountain Passes Unsuitable for Caravans	
(A)	Major Rail Tunnels	
(G)	Major Road Tunnels	

2000m - +3000m
1000m - 2000m
100m - 1000m
0 - 100m

0   10   20   30   40   50km

These maps should be used in conjunction with the information
in the Mountain Passes and Tunnels tables in this chapter.

MOUNTAIN PASSES AND TUNNELS

PASSES/TUNNEL REPORT FORM

Name of Pass/Tunnel ....

To/From ....

Date Travelled ....

Comments (eg gradients, traffic, road surface, width of road, hairpins, scenery)

....

....

....

....

ARE YOU A: Caravanner	Motor Caravanner	Trailer-tenter?

===

PASSES/TUNNEL REPORT FORM

Name of Pass/Tunnel ....

To/From ....

Date Travelled ....

Comments (eg gradients, traffic, road surface, width of road, hairpins, scenery)

....

....

....

....

ARE YOU A: Caravanner	Motor Caravanner	Trailer-tenter?

CONVERSION TABLES

LENGTH AND DISTANCE

Centimetres/Metres	Inches/Feet/Yards	Inches/Feet/Yards	Centimetres/Metres
1 cm	0.4 in	1 in	2.5 cm
5 cm	2 in	6 in	15 cm
10 cm	4 in	1 ft	30 cm
25 cm	10 in	3 ft/1 yd	90 cm
1 m	3 ft 3 in	10 yds	9 m
100 m	110 yds	100 yds	91 m
Kilometres	**Miles**	**Miles**	**Kilometres**
1	0.6	1	1.6
5	3.1	5	8.1
10	6.2	10	16.1
25	15.5	25	40.2
50	31.1	50	80.5
100	62.2	100	160.9

WEIGHT

Grams/Kilograms	Ounces/Pounds	Ounces/Pounds	GramsKilograms
10 gm	0.3 oz	1 oz	28 gm
100 gm	3.5 oz	8 oz	226 gm
1 kg	2 lb 3 oz	1 lb	453 gm
10 kg	22 lb	10 lb	4.54 kg
25 kg	55 lb	50 lb	22.65 kg

CAPACITY

Millilitres/Litres	Fluid Ounces/Pints/Gallon	Fluid Ounces/Pints/Gallon	Millilitres/Litres
10 ml	0.3 fl oz	1 fl oz	28 ml
100 ml	3.5 fl oz	20 fl oz/1 pint	560 ml
1 litre	1.8 pints	1 gallon	4.5 litres
10 litres	2.2 gallons	5 gallons	22.7 litres
50 litres	11 gallons	10 gallons	45.5 litres

AREA

Hectares	Acres	Acres	Hectares
1	2.5	1	0.4
5	12.4	5	2
10	24.7	10	4
50	123.5	50	20.2
100	247.1	100	40.5

MAP SCALES

Scale	Equivalent Distance	
1:15 000	1 cm = 0.15 km	1 in = ¼ mile
1:50 000	1 cm = 0.5 km	1 in = ¾ mile
1:100 000	1 cm = 1 km	1 in = 1¾ miles
1:200 000	1 cm = 2 km	1 in = 3¼ miles
1:400 000	1 cm = 4 km	1 in = 6¼ miles
1:500 000	1 cm = 5 km	1 in = 8 miles
1:750 000	1 cm = 7.5 km	1 in = 12 miles
1:1 000 000	1 cm = 10 km	1 in = 16 miles
1:1 250 000	1 cm = 12.5 km	1 in = 20 miles
1:2 000 000	1 cm = 20 km	1 in = 32 miles

TYRE PRESSURES

Bar	PSI (lb/sq.in)	Bar	PSI (lb/sq.in)
1.0	15	2.0	29
1.5	22	2.5	36

ELECTRICITY AND GAS

ELECTRICITY – GENERAL ADVICE

Electricity on Continental campsites is usually 220 volts nominal, but in practice may be considerably less. A common voltage of 230 volts has begun to be introduced throughout Europe. Most appliances sold in the UK are rated at 220-240 volts and usually work satisfactorily. Some high-powered equipment, such as microwave ovens, may not function well – consult the manufacturer's literature for further information.

The Country Introductions in this guide contain information on amperage supplied in individual countries (where known). Frequently you will be offered a choice of amperage and the following table gives an approximate idea of which appliances can be used (erring on the side of caution) – you can work it out more accurately by noting the wattage of each appliance in your caravan. The kettle given is the caravan type, not a household kettle which usually has at least a 2000 watt element. Note that each caravan circuit also has a maximum amp rating which should not be exceeded.

ELECTRICAL CONNECTIONS – EN60309-2 (CEE17)

Whilst there is a European Standard for connectors, EN60309-2, (formerly CEE17) this is not retrospective so you may find some Continental campsites where your UK 3-pin connector, which **is** to European Standard, will not fit. Accurate information is not easy to come by, but in Austria, Belgium, Denmark, Germany, Luxembourg, and the Netherlands most sites are fitted with CEE17 hook-ups, but not necessarily to all pitches. Spain, France, Italy, Switzerland are gradually changing over, but older style hook-ups may still be encountered. In other countries in Scandinavia and eastern Europe there may be few, if any CEE connections. See Country Introductions for more information.

Different connectors may be found within one campsite, as well as within one country. If you find your CEE17 connector does not fit, apply to the campsite warden to hire an adaptor.

Even with European Standard connections, poor electrical supplies are possible; the existence of the EN60309-2 (CEE17) standard should not be taken as an automatic sign of a modern system.

AMPS	WATTAGE (APPROX)	FRIDGE	BATTERY CHARGER	AIR CONDITIONING	COLOUR TV	WATER HEATER	KETTLE (750W)	HEATER (1KW)
2	400	✓	✓					
4	800	✓	✓		✓	✓		
6	1200	✓	✓	*	✓	✓	✓	
8	1600	✓	✓	✓**	✓	✓	✓	✓**
10	2000	✓	✓	✓**	✓	✓	✓	✓**
16	3000	✓	✓	✓	✓	✓	✓	✓**

*   Possible, depending on wattage of appliance in question
**   Not to be used at the same time as other high-wattage equipment

(MAINS CONTINENTAL)

Site Hook-up Adaptor

ADAPTATEUR DE PRISE AU SITE (SECTEUR)   CAMPINGPLATZ-ANSCHLUSS (NETZ)

MAINS ADAPTOR
Adaptateur secteur
Netzanschlußstecker

EXTENSION LEAD TO CARAVAN
Câble de rallonge à la caravane
Verläangerumgskabel zum wohnwagen

SITE OUTLET
Prise du site
Campingplatz-Steckdose

16 amp 230 volt AC

Other Connections

French – a 2-pin plus earth socket. Adaptors available from UK caravan accessory shops.

German – the 2-pin plus 2 earth strips, found in Norway and Sweden and possibly still Germany.

If the campsite does not have a modern EN60309-2 (CEE17) supply, ask to see the electrical protection for the socket outlet. If there is a device marked with $I_{\Delta n}$ = 30mA, then the risk is minimised.

HOOKING UP TO THE MAINS

Connection

Should always be in the following order:

- Check your caravan isolating switch is at 'off'.

- Uncoil the connecting cable from the drum. **A coiled cable with current flowing through it may overheat.** Take your cable and insert the connector (female end) into the caravan inlet.

- Insert the plug (male end) into the site outlet socket.

- Switch caravan isolating switch 'on'.

- Preferably insert a polarity tester into one of the 13-amp sockets in the caravan to check all connections are correctly wired. **Never leave it in the socket.** Some caravans have these devices built in as standard.

It is recommended that the supply is not used if the polarity is incorrect *(see Reversed Polarity opposite)*.

WARNING

In case of doubt or, if after carrying out the above procedures the supply does not become available, or if the supply fails, consult the campsite operator or his agent or a qualified electrician.

From time to time, you may come across mains supplies which differ in various ways from the common standards which prevail on most sites. The test equipment built into your caravan or readily available for everyday use may not be able to confirm that such systems are satisfactory and safe to use. While it is likely that such systems will operate your electrical equipment adequately in most circumstances, it is feasible that the protective measures in your equipment may not work effectively in the event of a fault. To ensure safety, the Club recommends that unless the system can be confirmed as safe, it should not be used.

Disconnection

- Switch your caravan isolating switch 'off'.

- At the site supply socket withdraw the plug.

- Disconnect the cable from the caravan.

REVERSED POLARITY

Even when the site connector is to European Standard, UK caravanners are still likely to encounter the problem known as reversed polarity. This is where the site supply's 'live' line connects to the caravan's 'neutral' and vice versa. The Club strongly recommends checking the polarity immediately on connection, using a polarity tester. One tester available from most caravan accessory shops is made by W4 (see illustration above).

The caravan mains electrical installation **should not be used** while reversed polarity exists. Try using another nearby socket instead, which may cure the problem. Frequent travellers to the Continent who are electrically competent often make up an adaptor themselves, clearly marked reversed polarity, with the live and neutral wires reversed. (The 'German' plug can simply be turned upside down, so no further adaptor is required.) If these steps do not rectify the reversed polarity, the site supply may be quite different from that used in the UK and we recommend, for your own safety, that you disconnect from the mains and **do not use this facility.**

Using a reversed polarity socket will probably not affect how an electrical appliance works BUT your protection in the event of a fault is greatly reduced. For example, a lamp socket may still be live as you touch it while replacing a blown bulb, even if the light switch is turned off.

Even when polarity is correct, it is also a wise precaution to check that a proper earth connection exists. This can be done with a proprietary tester. If there is any doubt about the integrity of the earth system, DO NOT USE THE SUPPLY.

Kew Technik produces a UK/Europe mains electricity testing kit which includes adaptors/conversion leads for Continental site sockets; telephone their Helpline on 01256 864100 (office hours), email sales@kewt.co.uk

SHAVER SOCKETS

Most campsites provide shaver sockets on which the voltage is generally marked as either 220V or 110V. Using an incorrect voltage may cause the shaver to become hot or to fail. The 2-pin adaptor obtainable in the UK is sometimes too wide for Continental sockets. It is advisable to buy 2-pin adaptors on the Continent, where they are readily available. Many shavers will operate on a range of voltages and these are most suitable when travelling abroad.

GAS – GENERAL ADVICE

As a guide, plan to allow 0.45 kg of gas a day for normal summer usage. This should be quite sufficient, unless you use gas for your refrigerator.

With the exception of Campingaz, LPG cylinders normally available in the UK cannot be exchanged abroad. If possible take sufficient gas with you for the holiday and bring back the empty cylinder. If an additional cylinder is required for a holiday, and it is returned within one year of hire date, then 70% of the the hire charge will be refunded.

It is preferable to purchase a Campingaz regulator to use with Campingaz cylinders while you are abroad, especially if you are taking a long holiday. It is also wise to hold a spare Calor gas container in reserve in case you experience difficulty in renewing Campingaz supplies locally. With 130,000 stockists in 100 countries, however, these occasions should be rare, but prices may vary considerably from country to country. Alternatively, adaptors are available from Campingaz/Calor stockists to enable use of the normal Calor 4.5 kg regulator with a Campingaz cylinder.

Cylinder gas under other brand names is widely distributed and is obtainable in most European countries. During winter touring it is advisable to use propane gas and it may be necessary to purchase a cylinder of gas, plus the appropriate regulator or adaptor hose, in the country being visited. It is also advisable to compare prices carefully between the different brands and to check that cylinders fit into your gas cylinder locker. See individual Country Introductions for further information.

When using other brands of gas a loan deposit is required, and when buying a cylinder for the first time you should also purchase the appropriate regulator or adaptor hose, as European pressures vary considerably. As in the UK, some operate at 28m.bar for butane and 37m.bar for propane; others 30 or 50m.bar for both products, and in some parts of France and Belgium at even higher pressures.

The use of 30m.bar is being standardised for both types of gas. On the latest model caravans (2004 and later) a 30.m bar regulator suited to both propane and butane use is fitted. This is connected to the cylinder by an adaptor hose, and different hoses may be needed for different brands of gas. Availability of hoses and adaptors on the Continent is variable at present, and owners of new caravans may find it prudent to buy a Campingaz adaptor in the UK, to ensure at least that this commonly available make of gas can be used. Hoses and adaptors for other brands of gas used on the Continent are not currently available in the UK.

WARNING

Refilling your own UK standard cylinder is prohibited by law in most countries, unless it is carried out at certain designated filling plants. Since these plants are few and far between, are generally highly mechanised and geared for cylinders of a particular size and shape, the process is usually impracticable. Nevertheless, it is realised that many local dealers and site operators will fill your cylinders regardless of the prohibition.

The Caravan Club does not recommend this practice; there is real danger if cylinders are incorrectly filled.

- Cylinders must **never** be over-filled under any circumstances.

- Butane cylinders should only be filled with butane and **not propane,** which is a commonly used gas in Europe.

For information about the carriage of gas cylinders on ferries and in the Channel Tunnel, including safety precautions and regulations see the chapter Ferries and Channel Tunnel in the section PLANNING AND TRAVELLING.

The Editor of Caravan Europe would welcome information from members on the availability (or otherwise) of gas cylinders, especially in eastern Europe and Scandinavia.

KEEPING IN TOUCH

EMAILS AND TEXT MESSAGES

There are internet cafés or cybercafés all over the world where you can log onto the internet and collect and send emails. This is a quick and easy way to keep in touch with family, friends and business at home. You will be charged for the time you are logged on. Some campsites now have computer rooms or facilities for their guests to access the internet.

Advances in wireless technology mean that it is now possible to use hand-held devices equipped with a keyboard which enable the sending and receiving of emails and website browsing. They also function as an organiser, address book and, of course, telephone!

Using a mobile phone to send text messages is a cost-effective way of keeping in touch. A number of websites offer a free SMS text message service to mobile phones, eg www.cbfsms.com. No pre-registering is required.

INTERNATIONAL DIRECT DIAL CALLS

The international access code for the UK is 0044 (for calls from Poland dial 0, wait for the second tone and then dial 044). To make an IDD call, first dial the international access code from the country you are in, then the national country code to the country you are calling, followed by the local number you wish to reach, eg from the UK to France, dial 00, then 33 for France, then the local ten-digit number omitting the first 0. International access codes are given in the Country Introductions in this guide.

Most, but not all, countries include an initial 0 in the area code when telephone numbers are quoted. With the exception of Italy where the 0 must be dialled, this initial 0 should not be dialled when calling from outside the country in question. Area codes in Spain do not have an initial 0 but have an initial number 9 which should always be dialled.

Ring tones vary from country to country and the UK's double ring is not necessarily used in other countries. For example when dialling a number in France you will hear long, equal on and off tones, slower than the UK's engaged tone, and in Germany and Spain you will hear short, single tones separated by longer pauses.

International calls can be made from call boxes in countries covered by this guide using coins or phonecards, and often instructions are given in English. When telephoning allow for time differences between countries.

INTERNATIONAL TELEPHONE CARDS

Global calling cards offer rates for international calls which are normally cheaper than credit card or local phonecards. Payment methods vary, but are usually by monthly direct debit from your credit card or bank account. Also widely available are pre-paid international phonecards which are available locally from post offices, newsagents, kiosks or shops, and rechargeable cards which require a credit card top-up when your credit reduces to a certain level.

RADIO AND TELEVISION

Radio Broadcasts

The BBC World Service broadcasts 24 hours a day from a worldwide network of short wave transmitters, via satellite and via the internet. World Service programmes are also accessible 24 hours a day on the internet at www.bbc.co.uk/worldservice. All programmes are announced in Greenwich Mean Time (GMT). Local time differences are shown in individual Country Introductions. BBC UK edition news can be seen on http://news.bbc.co.uk

Car radios are normally unable to receive short wave and some portable radios do not have this facility. Reception on short wave may be variable and the best frequency to tune into may not be the same each day. Outdoor reception is usually better than indoors so use your radio by a window or acquire an outside aerial. Use higher frequencies (lower metre bands) during daylight hours and lower frequencies (higher metre bands) after dark.

Digitally-tuned radios with long, medium and short wave bands together with FM, make it easier to pinpoint your choice of British or foreign radio stations precisely and store them in a memory.

The following are the main frequencies used by the World Service on short wave at various times of the day. Try all the frequencies and see which gives the best reception at particular times.

Frequencies	kHz
West and South-West Europe	198, 648, 1296, 6195, 9410, 12095
East and South-East Europe	6195, 9410, 12095, 15565, 17640

Listeners in Belgium, the Netherlands, Luxembourg, north-west Germany, northern France and western Denmark may listen to BBC Radio 5 Live on either 693 or 909 kHz medium wave or BBC Radio 4 on 198 kHz long wave.

In addition, many local radio stations broadcast BBC World Service programmes in English on FM frequencies. The BBC publishes a free twice-yearly guide to World Service English-language programme schedules and key frequencies worldwide. For a copy write to BBC World Service Audience Relations, PO Box 76, London WC2B 4PH or email worldservice@bbc.co.uk. You can also find programme details at www.bbc.co.uk/worldservice and you can subscribe to a free weekly email subscription service for World Service programmes.

BBC News Online is available on WAP-compatible mobile phones, palmtop computers and other wireless handheld devices – see www.bbc.co.uk/worldservice for set-up information. Mobile network providers such as O2, T-Mobile and Orange have links to the BBC from their own portals; look in their News sections or do a search for BBC News.

Television Equipment

UK specification televisions are designed to receive only UK transmissions using the PAL 1 system, so if you wish to receive Continental programmes in sound and vision you will need a multi-standard television set. UK-only specification televisions receive vision only.

The most widely used system in western Europe is PAL B/G. France, Luxembourg and Monaco use a different system called SECAM L. Eastern Europe uses SECAM D/K. Most specialist suppliers will stock multi-standard television sets that accommodate all these variations, but if you experience difficulties the Caravan Club's Technical Office will provide a list of suppliers to Club members on request.

Satellite Television

Satellite dishes are becoming an increasingly common sight on caravans both at home and abroad. A satellite dish mounted on the roof or clamped to a pole fixed to the hitch or draw bar, or one mounted on a foldable, free-standing tripod, will provide good reception and minimal interference. Remember, however, that mountains or tall trees in the immediate vicinity of your dish may interfere with signals. As dishes become smaller and easier to use, numerous methods of fixing them have become available and a specialist dealer will be able to advise you. You will also need an aerial, a receiver, preferably with a Scart socket and remote control, a decoder or 'digibox' if you wish to watch subscription channels and, ideally, a satellite-finding meter. A number of portable systems are available which are suitable for the caravan market; contact a caravan accessory dealer or specialist electrical retailer.

There are hundreds of TV stations accessible both in the UK and in Europe, together with dozens of English-language radio stations including BBC broadcasts. In order to watch subscription channels you will need a Sky viewing card and it is contrary to Sky's terms and conditions to remove this from your subscription address. In order to take a digibox on holiday, therefore, you will need to purchase one outright. However, Sky have recently launched a non-subscription satellite service for a one-off charge covering a digibox, dish, viewing card and installation – further details from Sky or on www.satelliteforcaravans.co.uk. The viewing card can be used in any digibox.

Recent changes to the BBC's and ITV's satellite operations mean that their signals, while not as widespread throughout Europe as they used to be, are now 'free-to-air' throughout most of France, Belgium and the Netherlands, together with those parts of Germany, Switzerland and Spain bordering them. You should need only a 60 cm dish to access these 'free-to-air' channels. These changes also mean, however, that it is no longer possible to watch the BBC or ITV1 in the south of Spain, Portugal or Italy.

See the website www.satelliteforcaravans.co.uk for the latest changes and developments.

USING MOBILE PHONES ABROAD

Mobile phones have an international calling option called 'roaming' which will automatically search for a local network when you switch your phone on wherever you are in Europe. You should contact your service provider to obtain advice on the charges involved as these are partly set by the foreign networks you use and fluctuate with exchange rates.

There are no further formalities and the phone will work in exactly the same way as in the UK. When calling UK landline or mobile phone numbers, prefix the number with +44 and drop the initial 0 of the area code. Format telephone numbers in your phone's memory in this way, and you will get through to those numbers when dialling from the memory, whether you are in the UK or abroad.

If you are making calls within the country you are visiting, just dial the standard dialling code but not the international code – rather like using your phone in the UK. To make a call to a country other than the UK, simply replace the +44 country code with the applicable country code, eg +33 for France.

Users should note that if you receive an incoming call while abroad, the international leg of the call will be charged to your mobile phone account because the caller has no way of knowing that (s)he is making an international call. It is possible to bar or divert incoming calls when abroad and your service provider will supply a full list of options.

Because mobile phones will only work if within range of a base station reception in some rural areas may be patchy, but coverage is usually excellent in main towns and near main roads and motorways. Approximate coverage maps can be obtained from many dealers.

Mobile service providers offer cheaper calls abroad by means of 'bolt-ons', on payment of a monthly fee and this may be an option if you travel frequently abroad or intend to be away for a long time. Alternatively, it is possible to buy a different SIM card which will enable your mobile phone to operate on a foreign mobile network more cheaply. You simply replace the SIM card in your phone with the new card when you go abroad, remembering to leave a message on the old card telling callers that you have temporarily changed number. This service is offered by www.SIM4travel.co.uk and www.0044.co.uk, or you may find it simpler to buy a SIM card abroad abroad. Before doing this, check with your UK service provider whether it has locked your phone against the use of a different SIM card and what, if anything, it will charge to unlock it. The website www.0044.co.uk has instructions on how to unlock your phone.

Increasingly legislation in Europe forbids the use of mobile or car phones while driving except when using hands-free equipment. **If you are involved in an accident while driving and, at the same time, using a hand-held mobile phone, your insurance company may refuse to honour the claim.**

Make a note of your mobile phone's serial number, your own telephone number and the number of your provider's customer services and keep them in a safe place separate from your mobile phone. Remember to pack your charger and travel adaptor. Charging packs are available from major mobile phone retailers which provide a power source to recharge your phone if you do not have access to a mains supply. Whichever network you use, check that you have the instructions for use abroad.

MEDICAL MATTERS

Travel abroad is now so common that it is easy to forget the health risks which may be involved and the fact that very few countries offer such easy access to medical facilities as Britain. Obtaining medical treatment abroad can seem complicated to UK residents used to the NHS. In most countries around the world you will have to pay, often large amounts, for relatively minor treatment.

This chapter offers advice and information on what to do before you travel, how to avoid the need for health care when away from home, and what to do when you return. Specific advice on obtaining emergency medical treatment in the countries covered by this guide is contained in the relevant Country Introductions.

BEFORE YOU TRAVEL

If you have any pre-existing medical conditions it is wise to check with your GP that you are fit to travel. If your medical condition is complex then ask your doctor for a written summary of your medical problems and a list of medications currently used, together with other treatment details, and have it translated into the language of the country you are visiting. This is particularly important for travellers whose medical conditions require them to use controlled drugs or hypodermic syringes, in order to avoid any local difficulties with Customs. The Caravan Club does not offer a translation service.

See Customs Regulations in the section PLANNING AND TRAVELLING.

Check the health requirements for your destination; these may depend not only on the countries you are visiting, but which parts, at what time of the year and for how long. If you are travelling to an unusual destination or heading well off the beaten track, or if you simply want to be sure of receiving the most up-to-date advice, the Medical Advisory Service for Travellers Abroad (MASTA) operates a Health Line which will provide a written personal Health Brief designed to meet your specific travel needs, together with information on recommended health products. To obtain a Health Brief ring 0906 5501402

(£1 per minute) or use MASTA's on-line Health Brief generator on www.masta.org. There is a small charge for a Health Brief which can cover up to ten countries to be visited. Information is also available on BBC2 Ceefax travel pages.

Always check that you have enough of your regular medications to last the duration of your holiday, and carry a card giving your blood group and details of any allergies or dietary restrictions. A translation of these may be useful when visiting restaurants. If you need prescribed medicines while abroad, check on their availability at your destination since your doctor can normally prescribe only a limited quantity under the NHS. Ask your doctor for the generic name of any drugs you use, as brand names may be different.

If you don't already know it, find out your blood group. In an emergency this may well ensure prompt treatment. If you have any doubts about your teeth or plan to be away a long time, have a dental check-up. It may be difficult and expensive to obtain dental treatment abroad. An emergency dental kit is available from main branches of Boots which will allow you temporarily to restore a crown, bridge or filling, or to dress a broken tooth until you can get to a dentist. For further information see www.dentanurse.com or telephone 01981 500135.

EUROPEAN HEALTH INSURANCE CARD (EHIC)

UK residents who are temporarily visiting another EU member state, as well as Iceland, Liechtenstein, Norway or Switzerland, are entitled to receive any necessary state- provided treatment during their stay, on the same terms as an 'insured' resident of the country being visited. This includes on-going medical care for pre-existing conditions, ie medication, blood tests and injections, as well as treatment in the event of an emergency.

Before leaving home you will need to obtain a European Health Insurance Card (EHIC). This has replaced the E111 which is no longer valid. Post offices hold application forms for the EHIC but the cards are issued by a central processing agency. You can also apply by telephoning 0845 6062030 or online on www.dh.gov.uk. An EHIC is required by each individual family member, so allow enough time before your departure to obtain them. The EHIC is free of charge and is valid for three to five years. It has been issued automatically to those who applied in 2005 for the new E111 form and ticked the box to receive an EHIC card.

The card is plastic and shows name and date of birth and a personal identification number. It holds no electronic or clinical data.

Private treatment is generally not covered and state-provided treatment may not cover everything that you would expect to receive free of charge from the NHS. If charges are made, these cannot be refunded by the British authorities and **it is strongly recommended that you arrange additional travel insurance before leaving home – see below.**

An EHIC issued in the UK is valid provided the holder remains ordinarily resident in the UK and eligible for NHS services. Restrictions may apply to nationals of other countries resident in the UK. For full details see the Department of Health's website, www.dh.gov.uk or call its Customer Service Centre on 020 7210 4850.

Health care entitlement under the EHIC does not cover visits abroad specifically to obtain medical treatment, such as a hip replacement, or any other medical treatment, operations or consultations.

HOLIDAY TRAVEL INSURANCE

Despite the fact that you have an EHIC you may incur thousands of pounds of medical costs if you fall ill or have an accident, even in countries with which Britain has reciprocal health care arrangements. Separate travel insurance adequate for your destination is essential, such as the Caravan Club's Red Pennant Motoring & Personal Holiday Insurance, available to Club members. The cost of bringing a person back to the UK, in the event of illness or death, is **never** covered, even under reciprocal arrangements.

To summarise: make sure you have all the documents you need before travelling (even for a day trip) and before you need to seek treatment, ie your passport, EHIC, proof of UK residence such as a driver's licence or NHS card, and adequate travel insurance.

FIRST AID

A first aid kit containing at least the basic requirements is an essential item and in some countries it is compulsory (see the *Essential Equipment Table* in the chapter *Motoring – Advice and Equipment*). Ready-made kits are available from most large chemists or direct from the British Red Cross, and should contain items such sterile pads, assorted dressings and plasters, crepe/elastic bandages, hypo-allergenic tape, antiseptic wipes or cream, painkillers, gauze, cotton wool, scissors, finger stall, eye bath and tweezers. Add to that travel sickness remedies, a triangular bandage, a pair of light rubber gloves and a pocket mask in case you ever find yourself in a situation where you need to give mouth-to-mouth resuscitation. Above all, carry something for the treatment of upset stomachs, which spoil more holidays than anything else.

First Aid Manual And Training

It is always wise to carry a good first aid manual containing useful advice and diagrams. The British Red Cross publishes a comprehensive First Aid Manual in conjunction with St John Ambulance and St Andrew's Ambulance Association which is available from bookshops. First aid essentials are also covered in a number of readily-available compact guide books. RTFB Publishing produces a useful quick reference health guide for travellers, entitled What Should I Do? priced £3.50, plus health phrase books in French and Spanish for £1.99 each. Telephone 023 8022 9041 or see www.whatshoulddo.com for further details and orders.

Even if you have no formal first aid training, it is still possible to help accident victims and even save lives by following basic first aid procedures, but there is no substitute for taking a first aid course. Your local telephone directory will give you the contact number for the nearest branch of the British Red Cross, St John Ambulance or St Andrew's Ambulance Association, all of which hold courses throughout the country.

VACCINATIONS

It is advisable to ensure your tetanus and polio inoculations are up-to-date before going on holiday, ie booster shots within the last ten years.

Other vaccinations are not normally necessary in Europe but walkers planning long trips in grassy/wooded areas in some parts of central and eastern Europe, including Scandinavia, should seek medical advice well ahead of their planned departure date about immunisation against tick-borne encephalitis, a viral disease transmitted by the bite of an infected tick. This is a very local risk confined to spring and summer when ticks are active in the scrubland around forested areas and on the vegetation along forest paths or animal trails.

The Department of Health advises long stay visitors to some eastern European countries to consider vaccination against hepatitis A. See the relevant Country Introductions.

DURING YOUR STAY

When applying for medical treatment in a non-EU country, you may be asked for your NHS Medical Card. You are advised to take this with you if visiting a non-EU country. Residents of the Republic of Ireland should apply to their Regional Health Executive. Residents of the Isle of Man and Channel Islands, which are not members of the EU, should check with their own health authorities about reciprocal arrangements with some other countries, details of which are available locally.

If you require treatment in an EU country but do not have an EHIC or are experiencing difficulties in getting your EHIC accepted, you may telephone the Department for Work & Pensions, Medical Benefits Section in Newcastle-upon-Tyne for assistance (tel 0191 218 7547). The office is open between 8am and 8pm Monday to Friday. The department will fax documents if necessary.

CLAIMING REFUNDS

If you are entitled to a refund from the authorities of the country in which you received treatment, you may do this in that country either in person or by post. You must submit the original bills, prescriptions and receipts (keep photocopies for your records). The booklet T6 contains details of how to claim refunds or visit the Department of Health's website, www.dh.gov.uk/travel advice

If you leave a claim until your return home you should apply to the Department for Work & Pensions in Newcastle-upon-Tyne for a form POD1679. The DWP will liaise with overseas authorities on your behalf to obtain a refund, which may take some time.

ACCIDENTS AND EMERGENCIES

If you are unfortunate enough to be involved in, or witness a road accident, or become involved in an emergency situation, firstly summon help early by any means available, giving the exact location of the accident or emergency and the number of casualties. Notify the police; most police officers have first aid training. The local numbers to contact police, fire service or ambulance are listed in each individual Country Introduction.

If you witnessed an accident the police may question you about it. Tell them exactly what you saw (the facts only) and do not venture opinions of any kind or seek to apportion blame. Give your name and address to all parties involved.

Before leaving the scene, make a brief note and a rough sketch to indicate details of the time you arrived and left, the position of the vehicles and the injured, the surface of the road, camber, potholes, etc, the weather at the time of the accident, skid marks and their approximate length – in fact anything you feel might be relevant – then date it and sign it. You may never be called on to use these notes, but if you are, you have a written record made at the time and of great value. Trying to recall details of the event several weeks, even months later can be difficult.

INSECT BITES

Most of the temperate parts of Europe have their fair share of nuisance insects, particularly near lakes, and it is wise to carry insect repellant devices as mosquitoes and midges may be a problem. A number of products are available including impregnated wrist and ankle bands and insect repellant sprays and coils. Check with your chemist for suitable products. Covering exposed skin with long trousers and long-sleeved shirts is recommended after dark.

POLLUTION

Pollution of sea water at some Continental coastal resorts, including the Mediterranean, may still present a health hazard, although within the EU the general situation is improving. In many popular resorts where the water quality may present risks, eg in rivers and lakes as well as at the coast, signs are erected which forbid bathing:

French: *Défense de se baigner* or *Il est défendu de se baigner*

Italian: *Vietato bagnarsi* or *Evietato bagnarsi*

Spanish: *Prohibido bañarse* or *Se prohibe bañarse*

RABIES

Rabies is a serious hazard in many countries, including parts of Europe, and is usually fatal unless treatment is given immediately, before symptoms develop. However, it is extremely rare in domestic animals in the EU and the chances of being bitten or scratched by a rabid animal during the course of a European holiday are remote.

However, you should be aware that you can contract rabies if you are bitten, scratched or even licked by an infected dog, cat, fox, bat or other animal. **Do not approach or touch animals, particularly if they are behaving oddly, and instruct children not to do so.** Rabies-infected wild animals often appear to be tame.

If you are bitten or scratched by an animal while abroad, the Department of Health recommends that you should wash the wound and seek medical attention immediately. Assuming the animal is not wild or stray, attempt to obtain its owner's details and find out if it has had a recent rabies vaccination. Inform the local police of the incident and tell your GP as soon as you return home.

The UK is still rabies free; **DO NOT** bring any animals into the UK without first complying with the legal requirements. To do so could endanger lives.

SUN PROTECTION

For many people, getting a good suntan is an essential part of a holiday, but too much sun can also cause sunburn which may ruin a holiday. Never underestimate how ill careless exposure to the sun may make you. UVA and UVB ultraviolet radiation are the main cause of long term damage to the skin in the form of premature skin ageing and skin cancer. It is important to protect yourself and your family

from their effects. Use a good quality sun cream with balanced UVA/UVB protection suitable for your skin type, and re-apply frequently, especially if you are perspiring heavily or swimming. Use a product's sun protection factor (SPF) as a guide; broadly speaking, the higher the SPF the greater the protection. Avoid sitting in the sun during the hottest part of the day between 11am and 3pm.

Children need extra protection as they tend to stay out in the sun longer and are unaware of the dangers of over-exposure. Use a total sun block cream and apply liberally half an hour before going out in the sun to allow time for it to develop. Children burn easily and most skin damage is caused in childhood. Keep babies out of the sun at all times.

If you are not used to the heat it is very easy to fall victim to heat exhaustion or heat stroke. When first in a warm country it is very important that the whole family drinks more fluid than at home. If you feel thirsty, or your urine is very dark yellow, then you are becoming dehydrated and need to increase your fluid intake. The symptoms of sunstroke include headache, tiredness, weakness and thirst, leading to confusion, disorientation and, in very extreme cases, coma and even death. Avoid strenuous exercise, drink plenty of water or soft drinks – alcohol, tea and coffee only increase dehydration.

Precautions

- Wear a broad-brimmed sun hat and light, loose-fitting clothing made of tightly woven fabrics. Swimming in shallow water does not protect from the sun as water and sand reflect rays onto your skin. Cover up with a cotton T-shirt when swimming. Wear good quality sunglasses which filter UV rays.

- If possible store sun cream or lotion in a cool place or at least in the shade. Exposure to heat may damage it and it is probably not a good idea to use last year's leftover cream.

- Anyone showing signs of serious over-exposure to the sun should be placed indoors or in the shade, encouraged to sip water and kept cool by fanning or sponging down with cool water. Call a doctor if the patient becomes unconscious.

WATER AND FOOD

Water from mains supplies throughout Europe is generally good but the level of chemical treatment may make it unpalatable and you may prefer to use bottled water. In doubtful cases, where water is cloudy or not clear of all particles, water should be boiled, or water sterilisation tablets used. These are obtainable from most UK chemists and may be used for washing vegetables and fresh fruit. Always boil or sterilise water if it does not come from the mains, or preferably use bottled water in sealed containers.

Food poisoning is a potential risk anywhere in the world, but in extremely hot conditions a common-sense approach is called for. It is wise to protect food being left for any length of time with a fly net and to avoid food that has been kept warm for prolonged periods or left unrefrigerated for more than two to four hours. If the source is uncertain, do not eat unpasteurised dairy products, ice-cream, under-cooked meat, fish or shellfish, salads, raw vegetables or dishes containing mayonnaise.

RETURNING HOME

If you become ill on your return do not forget to tell your doctor that you have been abroad and which countries you have visited. Even if you have received medical treatment in another country, always consult your doctor if you have been bitten or scratched by an animal while on holiday.

If you were given any medicines in another country, it may not be legal to bring them back into the UK. If in doubt, declare them at Customs when you return.

If you develop an upset stomach while away or shortly afterwards, and your work involves handling food, tell your employer immediately.

Claim on your travel insurance as soon as possible for the cost of any medical treatment. Holders of an EHIC should put in a claim for a refund as soon as possible – see *Claiming Refunds* earlier in this chapter.

SAFETY AND SECURITY

Everyone wants to relax and enjoy their holiday. Britain has strong and effective safety legislation and a tradition of closely following the law, which is sometimes not the case in other countries. The Caravan Club has always given safety a high priority at its UK sites and will continue to do so. However, visitors to Europe often find that sites do not always come up to Club standards on electrical safety, hygiene and fire precautions.

Safety is largely your own responsibility; taking sensible precautions and being aware of possible hazards won't spoil your holiday, but a careless attitude might. Take a few minutes when you arrive on site to ensure that everyone, from the youngest upwards, understands where everything is, how things work and where care is needed to avoid an accident. The following advice will help you and your family have a safe and trouble-free holiday.

OVERNIGHT STOPS

The Caravan Club strongly recommends that overnight stops should always be at campsites and not at motorway service areas, ferry terminal car parks or isolated 'aires de service' or 'aires de repos' on motorways where robberies, muggings and encounters with asylum-seekers are occasionally reported. If you ignore this advice and decide to use these areas for a rest during the day or overnight, then you are advised to take appropriate precautions, for example, shutting all windows, securing locks and making a thorough external check of your vehicle(s) before departing.

Having said that, there is a wide network of 'Stellplatz' and 'Aires de Services' in cities, towns and villages across Europe, many specifically for motor caravanners, and many with good security and overnight facilities. It is rare that you will be the only vehicle staying on such areas, but take sensible precautions and avoid any that are isolated.

AROUND THE CAMPSITE

- Once you've settled in, take a walk around the site to familiarise yourself with its layout and ensure that your children are familiar with it and know where their caravan is. Even if you have visited the site before, layout and facilities may have changed. Make sure that children are aware of any places where they should not go.

- Locate the nearest fire-fighting equipment and the nearest telephone box and emergency numbers.

- Natural disasters are rare, but always think what could happen. A combination of heavy rain and a riverside pitch could lead to flash flooding, for instance, so make yourself aware of site evacuation procedures.

- Be aware of sources of electricity and cabling on and around your pitch. Advice about electrical hook-ups is given in detail in this guide in the chapter *Electricity and Gas* in the section DURING YOUR STAY and it is recommended that you read it carefully.

- If staying at a farm site, remember that the animals are not pets. Do not approach any animal without the farmer's permission and keep children supervised. Make sure they wash their hands after touching any farm animal.

- A Club member has advised us that, on occasion, site owners and/or farmers on whose land a site is situated, use poison to control rodents. Warning notices are not always posted and you are strongly advised to check if staying on a rural site and accompanied by your dog.

- Common sense should tell you that you need to be careful if the site is close to a main road or alongside a river. Remind your children about the Green Cross Code and encourage them to use it. Adults and children alike need to remember that traffic is on the 'wrong' side of the road.

- Incidents of theft from visitors to campsites are rare but when leaving your caravan unattended make sure you lock all doors and shut windows. Conceal valuables from sight and lock bicycles to a tree or to your caravan.

CHILDREN AT PLAY

- Watch out for children as you drive around the site and observe the speed limit (walking pace).

- Children riding bikes should be made aware that there may be patches of sand or gravel around the site and these should be negotiated at a sensible speed. Bikes should not be ridden between or around tents or caravans.

- Children's play areas are generally unsupervised. Check which installations are suitable for your children's ages and abilities and agree with them which ones they may use. Read and respect the displayed rules. Remember it is your responsibility to know where your children are at all times.

- Be aware of any campsite rules concerning ball games or use of play equipment, such as roller blades and skateboards. Check the condition of bicycles which you intend to hire.

- When your children attend organised activities, arrange when and where to meet afterwards.

FIRE

Caravans are perfectly safe provided you follow a few basic safety rules. Any fire that starts will spread quickly if not properly dealt with. Follow these rules at all times:

- Never use portable paraffin or gas heaters inside your caravan. Gas heaters should only be fitted when air is taken from outside the caravan.

- Never search for a gas leak with naked light. If gas is smelt, turn off the cylinder immediately, extinguish all naked flames and seek professional help.

- Never change your gas cylinder regulator inside the caravan.

- Never place clothing, tea towels or any other items over your cooker or heater to dry.

- Never leave children alone inside a caravan.

- Never leave matches where children can reach them.

- Never leave a chip pan or saucepan unattended.

- Keep heaters and cookers clean and correctly adjusted.

- Know where the fire points and telephones are on site and know the site fire drill.

- Establish a family fire drill.

- Where regulations permit the use of barbecues, take the following precautions to prevent fire:

Never locate a barbecue near trees, hedges or accommodation.

Have a bucket of water to hand in case of sparks.

Only use recommended fire-lighting materials.

Do not leave a barbecue unattended when lit and dispose of hot ash safely.

Make adequate arrangements for your children and do not let them play near a lit barbecue.

Procedures if a Fire Starts:

- Get everyone out of the caravan.

- Raise the alarm.

- Call the fire brigade.

- Turn off the gas cylinder valve.

- Attack the fire with suitable extinguishers.

- Apply first aid.

SWIMMING POOLS

Make the first visit to the pool area a 'family exploration' not only to find out what is available, but also to identify features and check information which could be vital to your family's safety. Even if you have visited the site before, the layout may have changed, so check the following:

- Pool layout – identify shallow and deep ends and note the position of safety equipment. Check that poolside depth markings are accurate and whether there are any sudden changes of depth in the pool. The bottom of the pool should be clearly visible. Ensure when diving into a pool that it is deep enough for you to do so safely.

- Are there restrictions about diving and jumping into the pool? Are some surfaces slippery when wet?

- Check opening and closing times. For pools with a supervisor or lifeguard, note any times or dates when the pool is not supervised, eg lunch break, low season. Read safety notices and rules posted around the pool. Check the location of any rescue equipment.

- Establish your own rules about parental supervision. Age and swimming ability are important considerations and at least one responsible adult who can swim should accompany and supervise children at the pool. Remember that a shallow paddling pool can present a danger to young children. Even if a lifeguard is present, you are responsible for your children and must watch them closely.

- Do not swim just after a meal, nor after drinking alcohol.

Water Slides

- Take some time to watch other people using the slides so that you can see the speed and direction when entering the water. Find out the depth of water in the landing area. Ensure that your children understand the need to keep clear of the landing area.

- Consider and agree with your children which slides they may use. Age or height restrictions may apply.

- Check the supervision arrangements and hours of use; they may be different from the main pool times.

- Check and follow any specific instructions on the proper use of each slide. The safest riding position is usually feet first, sitting down. Never allow your children to stand or climb on the slide.

- Do not wear jewellery when using slides.

BEACHES, LAKES AND RIVERS

- Check any warning signs or flags before you swim and ensure that you know what they mean. Check the depth of water before diving and avoid diving or jumping into murky water, as submerged swimmers or objects may not be visible.

- Familiarise yourself with the location of safety apparatus and/or lifeguards.

- Children can drown in a very short time and in relatively small amounts of water. Supervise them at all times when they are in the water and ensure that they know where to find you on the beach.

- Use only the designated areas for swimming, windsurfing, jetskiing etc. Use life jackets where appropriate. Swim only in supervised areas whenever possible.

- Familiarise yourself with tides, undertows, currents and wind strength and direction before you or your children swim in the sea. This applies in particular when using inflatables, windsurfers, body boards or sailing boats. Sudden changes of wave and weather conditions combined with fast tides and currents are particularly dangerous.

- Establish whether there are submerged rocks or a steeply shelving shore which can take non-swimmers or weak swimmers by surprise. Be alert to the activities of windsurfers or jetskiers who may not be aware of the presence of swimmers.

ON THE ROAD

- Do not leave valuable items on car seats or near windows in caravans, even if they are locked. Ensure that items on roof racks or cycle carriers are difficult to remove – a long cable lock may be helpful.

- In view of recent problems with stowaways on cross-Channel ferries and trains, check that your outfit is free from unexpected guests at the last practical opportunity before boarding.

- Beware of a 'snatch' through open car windows at traffic lights, filling stations, in traffic jams or at 'fake' traffic accidents. When driving through towns and cities keep your doors locked. Keep handbags, valuables and documents out of sight at all times.

- If flagged down by another motorist for whatever reason, take care that your own car is locked and windows closed while you check outside, even if someone is left inside. Be particularly careful on long, empty stretches of motorway and if you stop for fuel. Even if the people flagging you down appear to be officials (eg wearing yellow reflective jackets or dark, 'uniform-type' clothing) show presence of mind and lock yourselves in immediately. They may appear to be friendly and helpful, but may be opportunistic thieves prepared to resort to violence. Have a mobile phone to hand and, if necessary, be seen to use it. Keep a pair of binoculars handy for reading registration numbers too.

- Road accidents are a significant risk in some countries where traffic laws may be inadequately enforced and roads may be poorly maintained, road signs and lighting inadequate and driving standards poor. The traffic mix may be more complex with animal-drawn vehicles, pedestrians, bicycles, cars, lorries, and perhaps loose animals, all sharing the same space. In addition you will be driving on the 'wrong' side of the road and should, therefore, be especially vigilant at all times. Avoid driving at night on unlit roads.

- Pursuing an insurance claim abroad can be difficult and it is essential, if you are involved in an accident, to take all the other driver's details and complete a European Accident Statement supplied by your motor vehicle insurer.

- It's a good idea to keep a fully-charged mobile phone with you in your car with the number of your breakdown organisation saved into it.

PERSONAL SECURITY

There is always the risk of being the victim of petty crime whichever country you are in and, as a foreigner, you may be more vulnerable. But the number of incidents is very small and the fear of crime should not deter you from caravanning abroad.

The Foreign & Commonwealth Office's Consular Division produces a range of material to advise and inform British citizens travelling abroad about issues affecting their safety, including political unrest, lawlessness, violence, natural disasters, epidemics, anti-British demonstrations and aircraft safety. Contact the FCO Travel Advice Unit on 0870 606 0290, fax 020 7008 0155, email consular.fco@gtnet.gov.uk or see BBC2 Ceefax. The full range of notices is also available on the FCO's website, www.fco.gov.uk/travel

Specific advice on personal security relating to countries covered by this guide is given in the relevant Country Introductions, but the following are a few general precautions to ensure that you have a safe and problem-free holiday:

- Leave valuables and jewellery at home. If you do take them, fit a small safe in your caravan and keep them in the safe or locked in the boot of you car. Do not leave money or documents, such as passports, in a car glovebox, or leave handbags and valuables on view. Do not leave bags in full view when sitting outside at cafés or restaurants. Do not leave valuables unattended on the beach.

- When walking be security conscious. Avoid unlit streets at night, walk well away from the kerb and carry handbags or shoulder bags on the side away from the kerb. The less of a tourist you appear, the less of a target you are. Never read a map openly in the street or carry a camera over your shoulder.

- Carry only the minimum amount of cash. Distribute cash, travellers' cheques, credit cards and passports amongst your party; do not rely on one person to carry everything. Never carry a wallet in your back pocket. A tuck-away canvas wallet, moneybelt or 'bumbag' can be useful and waterproof versions are available. It is normally advisable not to resist violent theft.

- Keep a separate note of bank account and credit card numbers and serial numbers of travellers' cheques. Join the Caravan Club's Credit Card Protection Plan (Club members only) or other card protection scheme so that, in the event of theft, one phone call will cancel all cards and arrange replacements.

- Keep a separate note of your holiday insurance reference number and emergency telephone number.

- Keep a separate record of your passport details, preferably in the form of a certified copy of the details pages. Fill in the next-of-kin details in your passport. A photocopy of your birth certificate may also be useful.

- Many large cities have a drug problem with some addicts pickpocketing to fund their habit. Pickpockets often operate in groups, including groups of children. Stay alert, especially in crowds, on trains and stations, near banks and foreign exchange offices, and when visiting well-known historical and tourist sites.

- Beware of bogus plain-clothes policemen who may ask to see your foreign currency and passport. If approached, decline to show your money or to hand over your passport but ask for credentials and offer instead to go with them to the nearest police station.

- Do not use street money-changers; in some countries it is illegal.

- Laws vary from country to country and so does the treatment of offenders; find out something about local laws and customs and respect them.

- Do respect Customs regulations. Smuggling is a serious offence and can carry heavy penalties. Do not carry parcels or luggage through Customs for other people and do not cross borders with people you do not know, such as hitchhikers. If you are in someone else's vehicle do not cross the border in it – get out and walk across; you do not know what might be in the vehicle. Do not drive vehicles across borders for other people.

- Hobbies such as birdwatching and train, plane and ship-spotting, and the use of cameras or binoculars may be misunderstood (particularly near military installations) and you may risk arrest. If in doubt, don't.

- In the event of a natural disaster or if trouble flares up, contact family and friends to let them know that you are safe, even if you are nowhere near the problem area. Family and friends may not know exactly where you are and may worry if they think you are in danger.

BRITISH CONSULAR SERVICES ABROAD

Consular staff offer practical advice, assistance and support to British travellers abroad. They can, for example, issue emergency passports, contact relatives and friends in the event of an accident or death,

advance emergency loans and, in certain circumstances, make representations on your behalf to local authorities. But there are limits to their powers and a British Consul cannot, for example, give legal advice, intervene in court proceedings, put up bail, pay for legal or medical bills, or for funerals or the repatriation of bodies, or undertake work more properly done by banks, motoring organisations or travel insurers.

Most British Consulates operate an answerphone service outside office hours giving opening hours and arrangements for handling emergencies. If you require Consular help outside office hours you may be charged a fee for calling out a Consular Officer. In countries outside the European Union where there are no British Consulates, you can get help from the Embassies and Consulates of other EU member states.

If you have anything stolen, eg money or passport, report it first to the local police and insist on a statement about the loss. Since 11 September 2001 the situation regarding lost or stolen British passports has changed. It is no longer possible to obtain a local police report and travel home using that in place of a passport. It is now necessary to obtain a replacement passport from a British Consul.

In the event of a fatal accident or death from whatever cause, get in touch with the nearest Consulate at once.

If you commit an offence you must expect to face the consequences. If you are charged with a serious offence, insist on the British Consulate being informed. You will be contacted as soon as possible by a Consular Officer who can advise on local procedures, provide access to lawyers and insist that you are treated as well as nationals of the country which is holding you. However, (s)he cannot get you released as a matter of course.

BRITISH AND IRISH EMBASSY AND CONSULAR ADDRESSES

These can be found in the relevant Country Introductions.

ANDORRA

Andorra is a tiny, isolated, mountainous, landlocked principality on the southern slopes of the Pyrenees and is administered jointly by France and Spain. In recent years it has achieved considerable prosperity, largely due to its tourist industry and tax-free status. It boasts dramatic scenery and some of the best skiing, hiking and birdwatching in the region. Andorra merits more than merely a one-night shopping stop en route to France or Spain.

ESSENTIAL FACTS

Capital: Andorra-la-Vella (population 20,400)
Area: 468 sq km
Bordered by: France, Spain
Terrain: Rugged mountains dissected by narrow valleys
Climate: Temperate with cold, snowy winters and warm, dry summers; snow on the highest peaks often until July
Highest Point: Coma Pedrosa 2,946 m
Population: 70,500
Languages: Catalan (official), French, Spanish
Religion: Predominantly Roman Catholic
Government: Parliamentary democracy
Local Time: GMT/BST + 1, ie 1 hour ahead of the UK all year
Currency: Euro divided into 100 cents; £1 = €1.47, €1 = 67 pence*

TOURIST INFORMATION

ANDORRAN DELEGATION
63 WESTOVER ROAD
LONDON SW18 2RF
Tel: 020 8874 4806 (office hours)
Fax: 020 8874 4806
www.andorraonline.ad or www.andorra.ad
Postal or telephone enquiries only

OPENING HOURS

Banks – Mon-Fri 9am-1pm & 3pm-5pm; Sat 9am-12 noon.

Post Offices – Mon-Fri 8.30am-2.30pm; Sat 9am-12 noon; extended opening hours in July and August at the main French post office in Andorra-la-Vella.

Shops – Mon-Sat 9am-8pm/9pm; Sun 9am-7pm; small shops may close between 1pm and 4pm.

PUBLIC HOLIDAYS 2006

Jan 1, 6; Mar 14 (Constitution Day); Apr 13, 14, 17; May 1, 25; Jun 5, 24 (St John's Day); Aug 15; Sep 8 (National Day); Nov 1, 4 (St Charles's Day); Dec 8, 25, 26, 31. Individual parishes celebrate other holidays and festivals in the summer months.

TELEPHONING

From the UK dial 00376 for Andorra plus the 6-digit number. To call the UK from Andorra dial 0044, omitting the initial zero of the area code.

Mobile phones – roaming agreements with all major GSM networks; use of hand-held phones prohibited when driving.

Emergency numbers – Police 110; Fire brigade 118; Ambulance 118. From a mobile phone dial 112 for any service.

Exchange rates as at October 2005

COUNTRY INTRODUCTION

The following introduction to Andorra should be read in conjunction with the important information contained in the Handbook chapters at the front of this guide.

CAMPING AND CARAVANNING

In general French and Spanish regulations in respect of camping, caravanning and motoring apply to Andorra. Casual/wild camping is not permitted.

COUNTRY INFORMATION

Electricity and Gas

See Electricity and Gas in the section DURING YOUR STAY.

The power supply is 220/230 volts. All types of Campingaz are available.

Medical Services

European Health Insurance Cards are not accepted as there are no reciprocal emergency health care arrangements with Britain, and you will be required to pay the full cost of medical treatment. You are strongly recommended to obtain comprehensive travel and medical insurance before travelling, such as the Caravan Club's Red Pennant Motoring & Personal Holiday Insurance.

See Medical Matters in the section DURING YOUR STAY.

Safety and Security

See Safety and Security in the section DURING YOUR STAY.

Street crime is almost unknown but the usual precautions of taking care of passports and money should be followed.

Your visit to Andorra is likely to be trouble-free but Andorra shares with the rest of Europe a threat from international terrorism, which could be indiscrimate and against civilian targets.

British/Irish Embassy/Consulate-General

There is no British Embassy or Consultate-General's office, or Irish Embassy in Andorra. See under Spain. There is a British Honorary Consul:

AVINGUDA SANT ANTONI 23
CAL SASTRE VELL 1R
AD-400 La Massana
Tel: 839840
britconsul@andorra.ad

CUSTOMS REGULATIONS

Andorra has two 24-hour border posts, one on the French side at Pas de la Casa, and the other on the Spanish side at La Farga de Moles. There are no Customs formalities on entering Andorra and no restrictions on imports.

Andorra is well-known for its duty-free shopping opportunities, but visitors must be aware that strict limits, as follow, apply to goods which may be taken into France or Spain on leaving Andorra and it is understood that Customs checks may be made.

1.5 litres of spirits

5 litres of table wine

300 cigarettes or 150 cigarillos or 75 cigars or 400 gm of tobacco

75 gm of perfume and 375 ml of eau de toilette

Other items up to the value of €525

Alcohol and tobacco allowances apply only to persons aged 17 or over.

DOCUMENTS

You are required to carry your passport at all times.

A Green Card is necessary when driving in Andorra.

See Documents and Insurance in the section PLANNING AND TRAVELLING.

MOTORING

Alcohol

The maximum permitted level of alcohol in the blood is 0.05%, ie lower than in the UK. Penalties for exceeding this limit are severe.

Fuel

See Fuel under Motoring in the section PLANNING AND TRAVELLING.

Diesel is available but there are no LPG suppliers. Credit cards are accepted at most filling stations.

Roads

Main roads are prefixed 'N' and side roads are prefixed 'V'. There are no motorways in Andorra.

The pass from the French border at l'Hospitalet and Port d'Envalira is well engineered with a maximum gradient of 12.5% (1 in 8), but the gradient is very extensive. It is the highest pass in the Pyrenees, reaching 2,407 metres (7,897 feet). Except for short periods following heavy snowfalls, it is open all year. The 2.8 km Envalira Tunnel connects Pas de la Casa and El Grau Roig and avoids the highest part of the pass.

The main road to Barcelona from Andorra is the C14/C1412/N141b via Ponts and Calaf. It is continually being improved and has a good surface throughout. This road avoids any high passes.

The N260 along the south side of Andorra via Bourg Madame, Puigcerda and La Seo de Urgel has been re-made and has a good surface.

The N152/C26/C66 from Andorra to Gerona via the Toses Pass, Ripoli and Olot is an extremely scenic route but the Toses Pass can be difficult in winter. The road surface is excellent and the maximum gradient is 10% (1 in 10) up to a height of 1,800 metres (5,906 feet).

See Mountain Passes and Tunnels in the section PLANNING AND TRAVELLING.

It is advisable to stick to main roads when towing and not to attempt the many unsurfaced roads.

Speed Limits

All vehicles are restricted to 70 km/h (44 mph) on the open road and to 40 km/h (25 mph) in built-up areas.

Traffic Jams

There is heavy traffic in Andorra-la-Vella most days in the year.

During the peak summer holiday period you are likely to encounter queues of traffic on the Envalira pass from France into Andorra. Traffic is at its worst in the morning from France and in the afternoon and evening from Andorra. The Envalira Tunnel has reduced congestion and travel time on this busy route. However, in the peak summer season an early start is recommended from both the French and Andorran sides to avoid possible traffic congestion.

Traffic Regulations

French traffic regulations are in force *(see France Country Introduction)*. Warning triangles and spare bulbs are required for France and Spain. It is also recommended that a first aid kit be carried.

Police are empowered to impose on-the-spot fines for violations of traffic regulations.

MOTORWAYS

There are no motorways in Andorra.

TOURING

- Andorra is a shopper's paradise and claims to have more than 4,000 shops. It is a 'free' territory and there are no Customs formalities to worry about on entry but checks will be made on returning to the European Union *(see Customs Regulations in this section)*. Some of the cheapest buys are spirits, sports goods, electrical and camera equipment, jewellery and clothing.

- There are tourist offices situated in all the main towns. In Andorra-la-Vella the tourist office is on Placa de la Rotonda, tel 827 117. Tourist information can also be obtained from the Andorra Chamber of Commerce on Carrer Doctor Vilanova, tel: 820 214, email: sindicatdiniciativa@andorra.ad

- BBC World Service radio may be heard in English on local frequencies 89.0 and 89.5 FM.

ANDORRA

SITES IN ANDORRA

†ANDORRA LA VELLA *8G3* (7km NE Urban) Camping Internacional, Ctra de Vila s/n, Encamp [tel/fax 831 609; info@campinginternacional.com; www.campinginternacional.com] On rd thro Encamp turn at traff lts & motor museum. Med, mkd pitch, pl sl, pt shd; wc; chem disp; mv service pnt; shwrs inc; el pts (6A) €3.50; lndtte; shop; supmkt 100m; tradsmn; snacks; bar; htd pool; TV rm; 40% statics; phone; bus; adv bkg; poss v cr; Eng spkn; quiet; CCI. "Sm pitches; gd rests nr; friendly, family-run." €17.00   2004*

We're having a great holiday - must fill in some site report forms and send them to The Club as soon as possible.

†ANDORRA LA VELLA *8G3* (600m S Urban) Camping Valira, Ave de Salou, Andorra-la-Vella [tel/fax 822 384] Site on E site of main rd S fr Andorra-la-Vella; behind sports stadium; clearly sp. Lge, hdstg, terr, pt shd; htd wc; chem disp; mv service pnt; shwrs inc; el pts (6A) inc (no earth); gas; lndtte; ice; shop; rest; snacks; bar; playgrnd; covrd pool; Eng spkn; adv bkg; quiet; CCI. "Conv NH for shopping; excel facs; vg rest; be aware of sudden storms blowing up." ♦ €24.00   2005*

†ANDORRA LA VELLA *8G3* (3km SW) Camping Huguet, Ctra de Fontaneda, St Julia de Loria [tel 843 718; fax 843 803] Site at S end of St Julia. NE fr Spain site 2km fr frontier. After petrol stn & Mamot supmkt turn L over sm rv bdge. Sp & visible fr main rd. Sm, pt shd; wc; chem disp; shwrs inc; el pts (6A) inc (no earth); lndtte; shop high ssn; supmkt 100m; rest, snacks, bar 1km; playgrnd; rv fishing; Eng spkn; adv bkg; quiet; CCI. "Excel facs; take care with el pts; poor value for money high ssn." €23.50   2005*

†CANILLO *8G3* (Urban) Camping Pla, Ctra General s/n, Canillo [tel 851 333; fax 851 280; campingpla@cyberandorra.com; www.camping pla.cyberandorra.com] App Canillo fr S, pass petrol stn on R; take 1st exit at rndabt, over bdge & turn L to site. Med, mkd pitch, pt shd; htd wc; chem disp; baby facs; shwrs inc; el pts (5-10A) €2.50; gas; lndtte; rest, snacks in town; bar; playgrnd; htd, covrd pool & sports facs in town; skilift 100m; 75% statics; dogs; bus adj; Eng spkn; adv bkg. "Excel location for skiing." €14.50   2005*

CANILLO *8G3* (300m SW Rural) Camping Bona Estada, Ctra General, Canillo [tel 852 582] On lower side main rd, ent beside filling stn, over bdge. Sm, pt shd; wc; shwrs; el pts inc; shop 500m; rest, snacks, bar, BBQ; pool, sports facs in Canillo; rv sw; dogs; Eng spkn; CCI. "Fair NH." 15 Jun-30 Sep.   2003*

†MASSANA, LA *8G3* (2km N Rural) Camping Borda d'Ansalonga, Ctra del Serrat, Ordino [tel 850 374; fax 735 400; campingansalonga@andorra.ad; www.campingansalonga.ad] Fr Andorra-la-Vella foll sp La Massana & Ordino. Turn L twd El Serrat, site on R, well sp. Lge, pt shd; htd wc; chem disp; baby facs; shwrs inc; el pts (10A) €4.50; gas; lndtte; shop; tradsmn; rest; bar; BBQ; playgrnd; pool; games rm; winter statics for skiers; dogs; phone; Eng spkn; quiet; CCI. "Statics moved to storage area in summer; excel tourist info; quieter than sites on main thro rte." €17.50   2004*

This site entry hasn't been updated for a while; we'd better fill in a site report form and send it to The Club.

†MASSANA, LA *8G3* (2km NW Rural) Camping Xixerella, Crta de Pal, Erts [tel 836 613; fax 839 113] Fr Andorra la Vella take rd for La Massana; fr there foll sps for Xixerella & vill of Pal. Site on L. Med, terr, pt shd; htd wc; chem disp; htd shwrs; el pts (3-6A) inc; lndtte; shop; rest; bar; playgrnd; pool; crazy golf; entmnt; phone; Eng spkn; adv bkg; quiet; cc acc; CCI. "Lovely site; clean, modern facs; gd mountain walks; gd sh stay." ♦ €17.20   2004*

FRANCE

France is the largest country in Western Europe and undoubtedly the most diverse. In terms of landscape, art, architecture, culture and history it is unsurpassed, reflecting the influence of centuries of civilisation and balancing the traditional and modern in a lifestyle that others can only envy. Not surprisingly, it is the favourite destination for British caravanners.

ESSENTIAL FACTS

Capital: Paris (population 13 million)
Area: 551,030 sq km
Bordered by: Andorra, Belgium, Germany, Italy, Luxembourg, Monaco, Spain, Switzerland
Terrain: Mostly flat plains or gently rolling hills in north and west; mountain ranges in south and east
Climate: Temperate climate with regional variations; generally warm summers and cool winters; harsh winters in mountainous areas; hot summers in central and Mediterranean areas
Coastline: 3,427 km
Highest Point: Mont Blanc 4,807 m
Population: 60.7 million
Language: French
Religion: 83% Roman Catholic
Government: Republic
Local Time: GMT/BST + 1, ie 1 hour ahead of the UK all year
Currency: Euro divided into 100 cents; £1 = €1.47, €1 = 67 pence*

TOURIST INFORMATION

FRENCH GOVERNMENT TOURIST OFFICE
MAISON DE LA FRANCE
178 PICCADILLY
LONDON W1J 9AL
Tel: 09068 244123
Mon-Fri 10am-6pm, Sat 10am-5pm
Personal visits/written requests preferred
www.franceguide.com
info.uk@franceguide.com

OPENING HOURS

Banks – Tues-Sat 9am-1pm & 3pm-5pm; in Paris Mon-Fri 10am-5pm; in busy centres some banks open on Saturday & close on Monday. Early closing the day before a public holiday.

Museums – Daily 10am-5pm; closed Monday or Tuesday, check locally.

Post Offices – Mon-Fri 8am-7pm; Sat 8am-12 noon

Shops – Mon-Sat 9am/10am-7pm (supermarkets to 9pm/10pm); food shops generally close all or half-day on Monday; in small towns shops close for lunch noon – 2 pm.

PUBLIC HOLIDAYS 2006

Jan 1; Apr 17; May 1, 8, (VE Day), 25, Jul 14 (Bastille Day); Aug 15; Nov 1, 11 (Armistice Day); Dec 25. School summer holidays extend over July and August.

TELEPHONING AND THE INTERNET

From the UK dial 0033 for France and omit the initial 0 of the 10-digit number. To call the UK from France dial 0044, omitting the initial zero of the area code. Mobile phone numbers start 06. The international dialling code for Monaco is 00377.

Mobile phones – roaming agreements with all major GSM networks; the use of mobile phones is prohibited while driving and at petrol stations.

Public phones – operated with telephone cards.

Internet – cyber cafés in most towns; public terminals in post offices (pre-paid card) and France Telecom kiosks in major cities. Charges from €3-9 per hour.

Emergency numbers – Police 17; Fire brigade 18; Ambulance 15. Or dial 112 and request the service you require; from a mobile phone dial 112 for any service.

Exchange rates as at October 2005

The following introduction to France should be read in conjunction with the important information contained in the Handbook chapters at the front of this guide.

CAMPING AND CARAVANNING

There are approximately 9,000 campsites throughout France classified from 1 to 4 stars, together with almost 2,000 small farm sites. All classified sites must display their classification, current charges, capacity and site regulations at the site entrance. Some sites have an inclusive price per pitch, whereas others charge per person + vehicle(s) + pitch. It is worth remembering that if you stay on site after midday you may be charged for an extra day. Seasonal dates and child ages vary from site to site and it is quite common for site owners to charge the full adult daily rate for children from seven years and sometimes from as young as three years.

Visitors are usually required to pay a tourism tax (taxe de séjour) which is imposed by the local authority and varies from 15 cents to €1.07 per person per day, according to the quality and standard of accommodation. Where the tourism tax is not at a flat rate, children under 4 years of age are exempt and children under 10 are charged half the rate. This tax is collected by campsite owners and will be included in your bill.

Casual/wild camping is prohibited in many state forests, national parks and nature reserves. It is also prohibited in all public or private forests in the départements of Landes and Gironde, along the Mediterranean coast including the Camargue, parts of the Atlantic and Brittany coasts, Versailles and Paris, and along areas of coast that are covered by spring tides.

There is a wide network of 'aires de services' in cities, towns and villages across France, many specifically for motor caravanners, and many with good security and overnight facilities. It is rare that yours will be the only motor caravan ('camping-car' in French) staying on such areas, but take sensible precautions and avoid any that are isolated. *See Safety and Security later in this chapter and in the section DURING YOUR STAY.* The Fédération Française de Camping et de Caravaning (FFCC) publishes a 'Guide Officiel Aires de Services Camping-Car', listing 'aires' and stopping places specifically set aside for motor caravans in France and a number of other countries.

Motor caravanners are also welcome to free overnight parking at approximately 720 vineyards and farms throughout France through an organisation called France Passion. Your motor caravan must be completely self-contained and you must have your own sanitation. In addition you must arrive and depart in daylight hours. Membership runs from Easter to Easter and is open to motor caravanners only. Write for an application form to France Passion, BP 57, 84202 Carpentras or email: info@france-passion.com, www.france-passion.com

A Camping Card International is recommended and accepted by most sites. It is essential at sites in areas of natural beauty.

The Camping Club de France owns a number of sites in France and has partnership agreements with hundreds of others. Members of the CC de F pay reduced rates at these sites. Caravanners wishing to join the CC de F pay an annual fee of €41 per family (charges in 2005). Contact the CC de F at 5 bis Rue Maurice Rouvier, 75014 Paris, tel (0)1 58 14 01 23, fax (0)1 45 40 01 07 or www.campingclub.asso.fr. In addition there are sites managed by, or working in association with, the Fédération Française de Camping & de Caravaning (FFCC) which give a 10% discount to holders of a CCI; these are marked 'FFCC' in the site entry listings.

Municipal campsites are found in most towns and many villages in France. These may usually be booked in advance through the local town hall (Mairie) during normal office hours. Municipal campsites' published opening dates cannot always be relied on at the start and end of the season and it is advisable to phone ahead or arrive early enough to be able to find an alternative site if your first choice is closed.

In order to deter itinerants and market traders, some municipal sites are restricting entrance by van height or length and some refuse to accept vans with twin-axles ('deux essieux' in French). It is advisable to check for restrictions when booking in advance. Recent visitors report that bona fide caravanners with twin-axle caravans may be allowed entry, but this is negotiable with the warden at the time of arrival. When approaching a town you may find that municipal sites are not always named. Signposts may simply state 'Camping' or show a tent or caravan symbol.

July and August are the busiest holiday months and campsites in popular tourist areas, such as the Atlantic Coast, Brittany or the south of France, may be crowded. To be certain of a pitch, book early or ask for copies of the Caravan Club's Travel Service in Europe brochure which gives full details of our Advance Booking Service network of approximately 140 French sites. Campsites included in the Travel Service network are marked ABS in their site entries in this guide. **The Caravan Club cannot make advance reservations for any other campsites listed in this guide.**

Many French campsites now ban the wearing of boxer-style shorts in swimming pools on hygiene grounds. Visitors are advised to ensure that everyone in their party wears a proper, brief-style swimming costume. Many sites also require swimmers to wear swimming caps.

During the low season it is not uncommon for only a few toilet and shower cubicles to be in use on a 'unisex' basis and they may not be cleaned as frequently as they are during the site's busy season. Hot water, other than for showers, may not be generally available.

Following flooding in recent years some authorities in southern France have introduced more severe regulations concerning sites which are potentially vulnerable to floods. It is understood many sites have been advised to limit their opening dates to mid-April/early May until end August/mid-September. **Low season visitors are recommended to telephone ahead to sites they plan to visit, particularly in the south of France, to check if they are open on the dates required.**

Recently certain areas of southern France have experienced severe water shortages, with a consequent increased fire risk. This may result in some local authorities imposing restrictions on the use of barbecues at short notice. When they are used, you should be vigilant in ensuring that they do not pose a fire risk.

The French Government Tourist Office publishes information about holiday centres approved by the French Federation of Naturism, including many which are particularly keen to welcome foreign guests. Visitors aged 15 and over are recommended to have a Naturist Licence, although this is no longer compulsory at many naturist centres. A licence can be obtained in advance from British Naturism (tel 01604 620361, fax 01604 230176, www.british-naturism.org.uk) or on arrival at any recognised naturist campsite. For further details contact the FFN at 5 Rue Regnault, 93500 Pantin, fax (0)1 48 45 59 05, email fedenat@ffn-naturisme.org, www.ffn-naturisme.com or see www.naturisme.fr for details of naturist centres throughout the country.

All place names used in the Site Entry listings which follow can be found in Michelin's Touring & Motoring Atlas for France, scale 1:200,000 (1 cm = 2 km).

Affiliated National Club

FEDERATION FRANCAISE DE CAMPING ET DE CARAVANING
78 RUE DE RIVOLI
F-75004 PARIS
Tel: 01 42 72 84 08, Fax: 01 42 72 70 21
www.ffcc.fr
ffcc@wanadoo.fr

COUNTRY INFORMATION

Cycling

A number of French towns are actively promoting the use of bicycles. Initiatives include increasing the number of cycle paths, providing parking space for bicycles, constructing shelters and cycle hire points in car parks. You may hire bicycles at many local tourist offices and from some railway stations.

The wearing of cycle safety helmets is not yet officially compulsory, but is highly recommended.

Transportation of Bicycles

Transportation on a support fixed to the rear of a vehicle is permitted provided the rear lights and number plate are not obscured.

Electricity and Gas

The power supply in France is 230 volts and the current on campsites is usually between 6 and 20 amps. Plugs have two round pins. Most campsites now have CEE connections. Visitors from the UK should be aware of the problem of reversed polarity which may be found on sites in France. If embarking on a tour of several campsites it may be useful to take two differently wired electric cables and adaptors, one wired normally and one wired for reversed polarity.

See Electricity and Gas in the section DURING YOUR STAY.

The full range of Campingaz cylinders is widely available from large supermarkets and hypermarkets. Other popular brands of gas which visitors have found to be economical and easy to use are Primagaz, Butagaz and Totalgaz. A loan deposit is required, and caravanners who are purchasing a cylinder for the first time should also purchase the

FRANCE

appropriate regulator or adaptor hose, as cylinder connections vary considerably. It is advisable to compare prices carefully between the different brands and to check that cylinders fit into your gas cylinder locker.

Entry Formalities

British and Irish passport holders may stay in France for up to three months. Visitors remaining more than three months must obtain a sojourn permit (carte de séjour) from the police station or town hall (Mairie) of their French place of residence.

On arrival at a hotel visitors are usually asked to complete a form for identification purposes. At campsites visitors presenting a Camping Card International do not have to complete such a form.

Regulations for Pets

See **Pet Travel Scheme** under **Documents** in the section **PLANNING AND TRAVELLING**.

Pitbulls, or dogs that look like pitbulls, boerbulls and dogs related to the Tosa breed, and other potentially dangerous dogs are not permitted to enter France. Other breeds, such as Rottweilers, American and Staffordshire bull terriers, must be accompanied by a document certifying their date of birth and pedigree. These dogs must be on a lead and muzzled at all times, including in your car. Visitors may not import more than three animals.

In popular tourist areas local regulations may ban dogs from beaches during the summer months.

Medical Services

British nationals requiring emergency treatment can take advantage of the French health services on production of a European Health Insurance Card which will cover you for up to 70% of the cost of emergency health care at state hospitals or visits to medical practitioners. For the address of a doctor 'conventionné', ie working within the French health system, ask at a pharmacy. Pharmacies are able to dispense first aid treatment but will charge a fee. You will be charged for a consultation with a doctor or dentist and should obtain a signed statement of treatment ('feuille de soins') in order to claim a refund. Prescriptions are dispensed at pharmacies; the prescription will be returned to you and you should attach this, together with the stickers (vignettes) attached to the packaging of any medication or drugs, to the 'feuille de soins' in order to obtain a refund. Applications for refund

should be sent to a local sickness insurance office (Caisse Primaire d'Assurance-Maladie) and you will receive payment at your home address within about two months.

For treatment at an approved hospital you can claim a refund of 75% of the costs. There is also a fixed daily charge which is not refundable. You must pay in full for outpatient treatment and then claim a refund from a CPAM office.

All visitors should take out comprehensive travel insurance to cover all eventualities, such as the Caravan Club's Red Pennant Motoring & Personal Holiday Insurance. For sports activities such as skiing and mountaineering, travel insurance must include provision for mountain rescue services and helicopter costs. Visitors to the Savoie and Haute-Savoie areas should be aware that an accident or illness may result in a transfer to Switzerland for hospital treatment. There is now a reciprocal health care agreement for British citizens in Switzerland, but you will be required to pay the full costs of treatment and afterwards apply for a refund.

RTFB Publishing produces a useful quick reference health guide for travellers priced £4.99, plus health phrase books in French and Spanish, price £1.99 each. Telephone 023 8022 9041 or see www.whatshouldido.com for further details and orders.

Rabies cases occasionally occur in France, and you should therefore avoid contact with cats and dogs.

See **Medical Matters** in the section **DURING YOUR STAY**.

Safety and Security

See **Safety and Security** in the section **DURING YOUR STAY**.

Roads in France are of an excellent standard but speed limits are higher than in the UK and the accident rate is greater. Drivers undertaking long journeys in or through France should plan carefully and take sufficient breaks; a minimum of 15 minutes every two hours is recommended.

Cars with foreign number plates may be targeted by thieves. Always lock car doors, particularly when driving in populated areas of the south of France, especially in the Marseille to Menton area. It is a common occurrence for bags to be snatched from the front passenger seat, usually by individuals on motorbikes, often when the vehicle is stationary at traffic lights. Conceal bags and purses when driving and never leave valuables in a vehicle, even for a short period of time or when you are nearby.

Pedestrians should beware of bagsnatchers operating on foot and from motorbikes. Do not leave bags in full view when sitting outside at cafés or restaurants. Do not leave valuables unattended on the beach.

Thieves and pickpockets operate on the Paris metro and RER, especially RER line B, and you should be especially vigilant.

Incidents have been reported of cars being stolen or passengers being robbed after drivers have been tricked into stopping by thieves, who either obstruct the road or distract them – for example by flashing headlights as a bogus warning, flagging down drivers for a lift or indicating that your vehicle has a flat tyre. Keep your vehicle doors locked, if flagged down by another motorist in this way, while you investigate the alleged problem and be extremely wary. Ensure that car keys are not left in the ignition if you leave your vehicle.

There has also been an increase in the number of thefts of alcohol and cigarettes in the Calais area from British-registered cars, some of which have included attacks on tourists loading shopping into their vehicles. Valuables, including tobacco and alcohol, should not be left unattended in parked cars and should be kept out of sight at all times.

Visitors to Commonwealth War Grave cemeteries in northern France, many of which are in isolated areas, are advised not to leave handbags or other valuables in parked cars, as they can be a target for thieves.

The Caravan Club strongly recommends that overnight stops should always be at campsites and not at motorway service areas, ferry terminal car parks or 'aires de service' or 'aires de repos' where robberies, muggings and encounters with asylum-seekers are occasionally reported. This advice applies to **all** motorways, but particularly to isolated rest areas (those without petrol stations or caféterias), on the A10 between Paris and Bordeaux. There have been several cases of burglary during the night whilst travellers are asleep inside their caravans, the victims first being rendered unconscious by the thieves using gas. If you ignore this advice and decide to use these areas for a rest during the day or overnight, then you are advised to take appropriate precautions, for example, avoiding parking in isolated or dark areas, shutting all windows, securing locks and making a thorough external check of your vehicle(s) before departing. Consider fitting an alarm to your caravan.

Fires can be a regular occurrence in forested areas along the Mediterranean coast and in Corsica during summer months. They are generally extinguished quickly and efficiently but short-term evacuations are sometimes necessary. Visits to forested areas will generally be trouble-free, but if you plan to stay in a forested area you should familiarise yourself with local emergency procedures in the event of fire.

France shares with the rest of Europe a threat from international terrorism. Attacks could be indiscriminate and against civilian targets, including tourist attractions. The French authorities have raised their level of security, particularly at airports and on public transport, following the bombings in Madrid in March 2004. You should be vigilant in public places and in areas frequented by tourists.

On Corsica the Corsican nationalist group, FLNC, has been responsible for a continuing series of sporadic bomb attacks on public buildings. While there is no specific threat to British tourists, visitors should take care, particularly in town centres and near public buildings, and be wary of unattended packages.

In Corsica you are advised to avoid leaving your vehicle(s) unattended by the roadside, especially on coastal/beach roads, as thefts are frequent.

British Embassy

35 RUE DU FAUBOURG ST HONORE
F-75383 PARIS CEDEX 08
Tel: 01 44 51 31 00,
www.amb-grandebretagne.fr
webmaster@amb-grandebretagne.fr

British Consulates-General

353 BOULEVARD DU PRESIDENT WILSON
F-33073 BORDEAUX CEDEX
Tel: 05 57 22 21 10
postmaster.bordeaux@fco.gov.uk

11 SQUARE DUTILLEUL, F-59800 LILLE
Tel: 03 20 12 82 72
postmaster.lille@fco.gov.uk

24 RUE CHILDEBERT, F-69002 LYON
Tel: 04 72 77 81 70
postmaster.lyon@fco.gov.uk

FRANCE

24 AVENUE DE PRADO, F-13006 MARSEILLES
Tel: 04 91 15 72 10
Marseille.Consular.marseille@fco.gov.uk

There are also Honorary Consulates in Amiens, Boulogne-sur-Mer, Calais, Cherbourg, Clermont-Ferrand, Dunkerque, Le Havre, Lorient, Monaco, Montpellier, Nantes, Nice, St Malo, Toulouse and Tours.

Irish Embassy

4 RUE RUDE, F-75116 PARIS
Tel: 01 44 17 67 00 Fax: 01 44 17 67 36
paris@iveagh.irlgov.ie

There are also Irish Consulates-General in Antibes and Lyon, and an Honorary Consulate in Cherbourg.

CUSTOMS REGULATIONS

Caravans and Motor Caravans

A caravan, motor caravan or trailer imported into France from an EU country may remain indefinitely. The importer must be in possession of the purchase invoice showing that tax (VAT) has been paid in the country of origin. The temporary importation of a caravan by persons other than the owner is subject to written authorisation from the owner.

Maximum permitted vehicle dimensions are height 4 metres, width 2.55 metres, length 12 metres excluding the towbar, and total combined length of car + caravan 18.75 metres.

There are no Customs controls at the borders with EU countries, but border police may carry out identity checks. Some border crossings in the Alps to Italy and in the Pyrénées to Spain close in winter. Border crossing posts with Germany are open continuously, except for those on ferries crossing the Rhine. Customs offices on main tourist traffic routes to Switzerland are permanently open.

Alcohol and Tobacco

There are no limits on the importation of goods into France which have been purchased in an EU country, provided that these goods are for the importer's personal use. However, the Customs authorities have fixed indicative limits on alcohol and tobacco as follows:

10 litres of spirits
20 litres of fortified wine
90 litres of wine
110 litres of beer
800 cigarettes
400 cigarillos or 200 cigars or 1 kg of tobacco

Duty-Free Imports

Duty-free shopping is permitted in Andorra but there are strict limits on the amount of goods which can be imported into France from Andorra, and Customs checks are frequently made. Each person is permitted to import the following items from Andorra free of duty or tax:

1.5 litres of spirits
5 litres of table wine
300 cigarettes or 150 cigarillos or 75 cigars or 400 gm of tobacco
75 gm of perfume and 375 ml of eau de toilette
Other items up to the value of €525
Alcohol and tobacco allowances only apply to persons aged 17 or over.

Currency

Unlimited foreign currency may be imported or exported but amounts exceeding the equivalent of €7,600 in foreign currency should be declared on entry and departure.

See also Customs Regulations in the section PLANNING AND TRAVELLING.

DOCUMENTS

Driving Licence

The French police can ask any motorist for his/her driving licence. Failure to produce this immediately will incur a fine, followed by a further, much heavier fine if it is not presented at a police station within five days.

You should also carry your original vehicle registration document, insurance certificate and MOT certificate (if applicable), together with a letter of authority from the owner of the vehicle if it is not registered in your name. A copy of your CRIS document is also advisable.

Passport

Everyone, whether French or foreign, must carry identity papers, ie a passport, at all times as the police are empowered to check a person's identity at any time.

See Documents in the section PLANNING AND TRAVELLING.

MONEY

See Money in the section PLANNING AND TRAVELLING.

- Travellers' cheques are accepted as a means of payment in most establishments. Handling charges for exchanging travellers' cheques and bank notes may vary considerably and it is recommended that you check the handling charge and rate of commission before the transaction goes through. If using euro travellers' cheques, it is understood that some French banks will not accept them from non-account holders, but that branches of Banque de France will generally cash them. Similarly, some, but not all, post offices will cash euro travellers' cheques. You should not have problems using euro travellers' cheques in payment for goods and services.

- Major credit cards are widely accepted, including for the payment of motorway tolls and for withdrawals from cash dispensers with a PIN number. Visa cards are displayed as 'Carte Bleue'. Automatic petrol pumps do not generally accept credit cards issued outside France.

- 'Chip and PIN' cards have been in use in France for a number of years. However, the French system has had to be modified to make it compatible with that used in the rest of Europe and, until the system is modified across the whole country (scheduled for 2006), you may still be required to sign a receipt as before.

- Cardholders are recommended to carry their credit card issuer/bank's 24-hour UK contact number in case of loss or theft.

MOTORING

Alcohol

The maximum legal level of alcohol in the blood is less than in the UK, at 0.05%. It is advisable to adopt the 'no drink and drive' rule at all times; penalties are severe. The police carry out random breath tests.

Breakdown Service

It is prohibited to tow a motor vehicle except in the case of a breakdown or an accident and only if the distance to be travelled is short. This practice is totally prohibited on motorways where the assistance of a recovery vehicle must be sought.

Breakdown and accident assistance on motorways and motorway service and rest areas must be obtained by contacting the police. They can be called from one of the orange emergency telephones placed approximately every 2 km or, if in a service area, by asking service station staff to contact the police for you. The police will arrange breakdown and towing assistance. No garage's vehicles will enter the motorway without police authority and the police only respond to calls made from the motorway area.

Charges for motorway assistance are fixed by the government. The tariff (2005) for breakdown service is €87 on a motorway or express road equipped with emergency telephones. This covers the cost of up to 30 minutes repairing your vehicle (up to 3,500 kg) on-the-spot. The cost of towing it up to 5 km beyond the next motorway exit is €87 for vehicles up to 1,800 kg and €109 for vehicles up to 3,500 kg. Higher fees are charged for breakdown assistance between 6pm and 8am and at weekends and public holidays. Charges are subject to change.

In the event of an accident off the motorway where people are injured or emergency assistance is required, dial 17 from any phone. A European Accident Statement form should be completed and signed by all persons involved in an accident.

Essential Equipment

See Essential Equipment and Essential Equipment Table under Motoring in the section PLANNING AND TRAVELLING.

Lights

Headlights must be adjusted for driving on the right. A trial took place in 2005 whereby drivers were required to use dipped headlights at all times (day and night) outside built-up areas. At the time this guide was compiled it was not known whether this would become a permanent requirement in law.

In built-up areas dipped headlights must be used in poor visibility, ie in fog or rain, and in tunnels. Bulbs are more likely to fail with constant use and you are required to carry spares at all times. Drivers able to replace a faulty bulb when requested to do so by the police may not avoid a fine, but may avoid the expense of calling out a garage.

If a driver flashes his headlights in France, he is generally indicating that he has priority and you should give way, contrary to standard practice in the UK. Between sunset and sunrise, warning must be given by flashing your headlights, rather than using your horn, except in cases of immediate danger.

Seat Belts

Seat belts must be worn by the driver and all passengers. Children under 10 years of age must sit in the back of the vehicle and use an approved child seat or restraint adapted to their size. It is the driver's responsibility to ensure that all passengers aged under 18 are wearing a seat belt or suitable restraint.

Tyres

Studded tyres may be used from early November to the end of March on vehicles weighing less than 3,500 kg; this period may be extended in periods of bad weather. Speed is restricted to 90 km/h (56 mph).

Snow chains must be fitted to vehicles using snow-covered roads in compliance with road signs. Chains may be hired from most tyre specialist garages or bought from hypermarkets, especially in mountainous areas. Polar Automotive Ltd sell and hire out snow chains, tel 01892 519933, fax 01892 528142 (20% discount for Caravan Club members), www.snowchains.com

Warning Triangles

Temporarily imported vehicles must be equipped with either hazard warning lights or a warning triangle (compulsory for cars towing a caravan or trailer, and for vehicles over 3,500 kg.) Warning triangles are recommended, as breakdown may affect a vehicle's electrics. The French Government Tourist Office recommends carrying two triangles.

A warning triangle must be placed on the carriageway 30 metres from the obstacle so that it may be seen at a distance of 100 metres in clear weather by drivers approaching along the same lane of traffic.

Fuel

Unleaded petrol pumps are marked *Essence sans Plomb*. Diesel pumps are marked *Gas Oil* or *Gazole*. Lead replacement petrol is sold under the name of *Supercarburant* or *Super ARS*.

Many petrol stations sell LPG (also called Gepel or GPL), especially on motorways. Maps showing their company's outlets are issued free by most LPG suppliers, eg Shell, Elf etc. A list of their locations is also available on-line on http://stations.gpl.online.fr

Filling stations often close on Sundays and those at supermarkets, where petrol is generally cheaper, may close for lunch. At supermarkets it is advisable to check the height and width clearance before towing past the pumps, or alternatively fill up when travelling solo.

Credit cards are generally accepted at filling stations. Some automatic pumps are operated by credit cards but these generally do not accept credit cards issued outside France. A sign on the petrol pump usually indicates this.

See also Fuel under Motoring in the section PLANNING AND TRAVELLING.

Motor Caravans

French legislation prohibits motor caravans from towing a car. Motor caravanners wishing to tow a car should put it on a trailer so that all four wheels are off the ground.

Overtaking and Passing

Overtaking where there is a solid single or double centre line is heavily penalised.

On steep gradients, vehicles travelling downhill must give way to vehicles travelling uphill. If one vehicle must reverse, it is the vehicle without a trailer (as opposed to a combination of vehicles) or the lighter weight vehicle which must do so. If both vehicles are of the same category, the vehicle travelling downhill must reverse, unless it is clearly easier for the vehicle travelling uphill, eg if there is a convenient passing place nearby.

Outside built-up areas, outfits totalling more than 3,500 kg or more than 7 metres in length are required by law to leave at least 50 metres between themselves and the vehicle in front. They are only permitted to use the two right-hand lanes on roads with three or more lanes and, where overtaking is difficult, should slow down or stop to allow other smaller vehicles to pass.

Parking

As a general rule, all prohibitions are indicated by road signs or by yellow markings on the kerb. Stopping or parking on the left-hand side of the road is prohibited except in one-way streets. Parking meters and 'pay and display' machines are commonplace and in Paris some machines take credit cards.

If you need to stop on the open road ensure that your vehicle(s) are driven off the road.

In Paris, two red routes have been created, on which stopping and parking are absolutely prohibited. The east-west route includes the left banks of the River Seine and the Quai de la Mégisserie; the north-south route includes the Avenue du Général Leclerc, part of the Boulevard St-Michel, the Rue de Rivoli, the Boulevards Sebastopol, Strasbourg, Barbes and Ornano, Rue Lafayette and Avenue Jean Jaures.

Caravans and motor caravans are prohibited from parking in the area from the Champs Elysées to the Place de la Concorde, in the Champs de Mars (Eiffel Tower) area, in the Bois de Boulogne (outside the campsite), in the Bois de Vincennes and, in general, near historic monuments. Elsewhere, caravanners must observe parking restrictions indicated by signs.

It is not permitted to park motor caravans in Nice or Cannes. Overnight parking of caravans or motor caravans is not permitted in Monaco. Caravans in transit are permitted but they must not be parked.

In Paris it is prohibited to leave a parked vehicle in the same place for more than 24 consecutive hours. This provision also applies to the departments of Haut-de-Seine, Seine-St Denis and Val-de-Marne, which surround Paris.

Blue zones, ie places where parking is controlled by parking discs, are indicated by road signs and blue markings on the carriageway. Parking is limited to 1½ hours between 9am and 7pm. Parking discs are not compulsory on Sundays and public holidays. Discs may be obtained from police stations, tourist offices and some shops.

Illegally parked vehicles, even if registered abroad, may be towed away, impounded or immobilised by wheel clamps.

It is forbidden to spend the night in a caravan at the roadside.

Be warned that parking by touch is common on crowded streets. Drivers park very close to other cars but leave their handbrake off. A driver wanting to leave the parking space shunts against the cars in front and behind to get them out of the way.

Parking for the Disabled

Although there is a national system of parking concessions, local variations may apply; check locally. On roads and in car parks, parking places reserved for disabled people are marked with a wheelchair symbol.

Public car parks do not generally offer concessions, but you may park beyond the time limit on roads where parking is free but restricted by time. Except in Paris, where vehicles displaying a disabled person's parking card may be parked on roads free of charge, you must pay to park on roads where payment is required. Do not park on roads where waiting is prohibited, or in pedestrian zones.

See also Parking Facilities for the Disabled under Motoring in the section PLANNING AND TRAVELLING.

Priority

See European Road Signs under Motoring in the section PLANNING AND TRAVELLING.

In France, although the old rule of 'priority from the right' no longer applies on major junctions and roundabouts, it is still advisable to be watchful, particularly in some towns where the yellow lozenge signs still exist. Outside built-up areas, all main roads of any importance have right of way, indicated by:

- A red-bordered triangle showing a black arrow with horizontal bar on a white background.
- A yellow diamond within a white diamond.

On entering towns, the same sign will often have a line through it, warning that vehicles may pull out from a side road on the right and will have priority.

Roundabouts

At roundabouts, drivers must give way to traffic already on the roundabout. This is indicated by a red-bordered triangular sign showing a roundabout symbol with the words 'Vous n'avez pas la priorité' or 'Cédez le passage' underneath. However, in a few areas the old ruling of priority given to traffic entering the roundabout still applies and where the sign is not present you should approach with care.

See Priority and Roundabouts under Motoring in the section PLANNING AND TRAVELLING.

Roads

France has a very extensive network of good quality roads falling into three categories: autoroutes (A) ie motorways, national (N) roads and departmental (D) roads. There are over 8,000 kilometres of motorways, on most of which tolls are levied. British motorists will find French roads relatively uncongested. Lorries are not allowed on the road for a 24-hour period from 11pm on Saturdays and the eve of public holidays.

Visitors to Corsica are warned that most road accidents occur during the tourist season. Many roads in Corsica are mountainous and narrow, with numerous bends. Drivers should be extra vigilant and beware of wandering animals.

For information on traffic problem areas, see *Traffic Jams* later in this section.

Road Signs and Markings

Directional signposting on major roads is generally good. Signs may be placed on walls pointing across the road they indicate and this

FRANCE

may be confusing at first until you get the feel for them. The words 'tout droit' have nothing to do with turning right – they mean 'go straight ahead' or 'straight on'. Road signs on approach to roundabouts usually do not show road numbers – these are shown at each exit off the roundabout – so make sure you know the names of places along your proposed route, and not just the road numbers.

Lines on the carriageway are generally white. A yellow zigzag line indicates a bus stop, blue markings indicate that parking is restricted and yellow lines on the edge of the roadway indicate that stopping and/or parking is prohibited. A solid single or double white line in the centre of the road indicates that overtaking is not permitted.

STOP signs mean stop. Creeping slowly in a low gear will not do, even if local drivers do so. You must come to a complete halt otherwise you may be liable to a fine.

Whilst road signs conform to international standards, some commonly used signs you may see include:

Attention – *Caution*
Bouchon – *Traffic jam*
Chausée deformée – *Uneven road*
Chemin sans issue – *No through road*
Créneau de dépassement – *2-lane passing zone, dual carriageway*
Déviation – *Diversion*
Fin d'interdiction de stationner – *End of prohibited parking*
Gravillons – *Loose chippings*
Itineraire bis – *Alternative route*
Nids de poules – *Potholes*
Péage – *Toll*
Poids lourds – *Lorries*
Ralentissez – *Slow down*
Rappel – *Continued restriction (eg, no overtaking or speed limit)*
Rétrécissement – *Narrow lane*
Route barrée – *Road closed*
Sens interdit – *No entry*
Sens unique – *One-way street*
Sortie d'usine – *Factory exit*
Stationnement interdit – *No parking*
Tout droit – *Straight on*
Toutes directions – *All directions*
Travaux – *Road works*
Virages – *Bends*

Traffic Lights

- There is no amber light after the red light in the traffic light sequence.

- Flashing amber light indicates caution, slow down, proceed but give way to vehicles coming from the right.

- Flashing red light indicates no entry; it is also used to mark level crossings, obstacles, etc.

- A yellow arrow at the same time as a red light indicates that drivers may turn in the direction of the arrow, provided they give way to vehicles travelling in the flow of traffic which they are entering, and to pedestrians.

- Watch out for traffic lights which may be mounted high above the road and hard to spot.

Speed Limits

See Speed Limits Table under Motoring in the section PLANNING AND TRAVELLING.

Motorists should be aware that radar detectors are illegal in France, whether in use or not. If caught, drivers are liable to both a fine and confiscation of the device, and possibly confiscation of your vehicle if unable to pay the fine. Such devices should be removed from your vehicle before travelling to France.

The use of mobile speed cameras has increased recently; these may be in inconspicuously parked camera vans or on motor bikes, or they may be hand-held. Oncoming drivers may flash warnings, but headlight-flashing for this purpose is actually illegal, so do not be tempted to do it yourself.

Inside Built-up Areas

The general speed limit is 50 km/h (31 mph) which may be raised to 70 km/h (44 mph) on important through-roads or as indicated by the appropriate sign. The beginning of a built-up area is marked by a road sign giving the name of the town or village in black letters on a light background with a red border. The end of the built-up area is indicated by the same sign with a red diagonal line through it. Signs showing the name of a locality in white letters on a blue background do not indicate a built-up area for the purpose of this regulation.

Therefore, when you enter a town or village, even if there is no actual speed limit warning sign, the town sign itself indicates that you are entering a 50 km/h (31 mph) zone. The end of the 50 km/h zone is indicated by the place name sign crossed out, as described above. The word 'rappel' under a speed limit sign is a reminder of that limit.

The speed limit on stretches of motorway in built-up areas is 110 km/h (68 mph), except the Paris ring road where the limit is 80 km/h (50 mph).

Outside Built-up Areas

General speed limits are as follows:

- On normal roads 90 km/h (56 mph)

- On dual-carriageways with two lanes in each direction, and toll-free motorways 110 km/h (68 mph)

- On toll motorways 130 km/h (81 mph)

These limits also apply to private cars towing a trailer or caravan, provided the total weight does not exceed 3,500 kg. Vehicles over 3,500 kg are classed as goods vehicles and the speed limit on motorways is 110 km/h (68 mph) while on dual carriageways it is 80-100 km/h (50-62 mph) and on other roads 80 km/h (50 mph).

In case of rain or adverse weather conditions, the speed limits are lowered as follows:

- On motorways 110 km/h (68 mph)

- On urban motorways and dual carriageways 100 km/h (62 mph)

- On other roads 80 km/h (50 mph)

A speed limit of 50 km/h (31 mph) applies on motorways in foggy conditions when visibility is less than 50 metres.

Minimum Speed

There is a minimum speed of 80 km/h (50 mph) in daylight on motorways for vehicles travelling in the left (outside) lane if visibility is good and weather conditions normal.

Recently-Qualified Drivers

The minimum age to drive in France is 18 years. Driving on a provisional licence is not allowed. In addition to complying with all speed limits, during the first two years after passing their test, drivers must not exceed 80 km/h (50 mph) on roads, 100 km/h (62 mph) on dual carriageways or 110 km/h (68 mph) on motorways.

Rumble Strips and Sleeping Policemen

These means of slowing vehicles are becoming more prevalent, particularly, it is reported, in the Massif Central. They are much more offensive than the British versions and should be shown the greatest respect. The advance warning sign says *Ralentissez* (slow down).

Tunnel Speed

In long road tunnels there are lower maximum speed limits; in addition, minimum speeds are enforced.

Traffic Jams

The busiest motorways in France are the A6 and the A7 (the Autoroute du Soleil) from Paris via Lyon to the south. Travelling from the north, bottlenecks are often encountered at Auxerre, Chalon-sur-Saône, Lyon, Valence and Orange. An alternative route to the south is the A20, which is largely toll-free, or the toll-free A75 via Clermont-Ferrand.

During periods of severe congestion on the A6, A7 and A10 Paris-Bordeaux motorways, traffic police close off junctions and divert holiday traffic onto alternative routes or 'Itinéraires Bis' which run parallel to main roads. Yellow and black signs indicate these routes. For a summer traffic calendar, indicating when certain areas are most prone to traffic jams, together with regional telephone numbers to call for traffic and travel information, see www.bison-fute. equipement.gouv.fr (in French only).

A number of Bison Futé information centres located on main national roads are open during the peak summer holiday traffic period, either daily or at weekends, and on public holidays. These centres offer free up-to-date information about the current traffic situation and possible alternative routes. In addition, travel information may be obtained from orange emergency call boxes located every 4 km on main roads and every 2 km on motorways. Calls are free.

In general, Friday afternoons and Saturday mornings are busiest on roads leading to the south, and on Saturday and Sunday afternoons roads leading north may well be congested.

It is still generally true that many French people drop everything for lunch and, therefore, between noon and 2pm roads are quieter and good progress can often be made.

During the first and last few days of August roads are particularly busy because of the start and end of French school holidays. Avoid driving on these days if possible.

For traffic reports tune into Autoroute-Info on 107.7 FM for updates on traffic and weather, roadworks and safety, as well as information on tourist attractions. Information on traffic conditions on autoroutes may be obtained on www.autoroutes.fr (in English), www.cofiroute.fr or www.bison-fute.equipement.gouv.fr

FRANCE

Violation of Traffic Regulations

Heavy fines and penalties are in force for motoring offences. The police in some areas are authorised to impose and collect fines on-the-spot up to €375. Violations include minor infringements such as an excess at a parking meter, not wearing a seat belt or not respecting a stop sign, with maximum fines of up to €750. More serious infringements such as dangerous overtaking, crossing a continuous central white line and driving at very high speeds, can result in confiscation of your driving licence.

Police are particularly strict about speeding and many automatic speed controls and speed cameras have been introduced and more are planned. Motorists caught doing more than 40 km/h (25 mph) over the speed limit face immediate confiscation of their driving licence. No distinction is made between French and foreign drivers. British motorists without a co-driver could be left stranded and face heavy costs to get their vehicle(s) home, which would not be covered by insurance.

A new category of offence has been created for drivers who deliberately put the lives of others in danger, with a maximum fine of €15,000. Failure to pay may result in your car being impounded. Your driving licences may also be suspended for up to five years.

Computerised tills at motorway tollbooths tell the cashier not only how much a driver needs to pay, but also whether he has been speeding. By calculating the distance a vehicle has travelled and the journey time, the computer will indicate by means of a red light whether the speed limit has been exceeded, prompting the cashier to call the police. The maximum fine is €375 which must be paid immediately.

By pleading guilty and paying fines on-the-spot or within 24 hours, motorists can avoid court action and even reduce the fine. These fines must be paid in euros, though in some cases travellers' cheques may be accepted. Cheques and credit cards are not accepted. A receipt should be requested showing the full amount paid.

In some cases instead of, or in addition to, a fine or prison sentence, a vehicle may be confiscated. Although this measure is not often taken, the main offences for which it may be applied are hit and run, refusal to stop when requested, or driving under the influence of alcohol. In such a case, the vehicle becomes the property of the French Government.

A driver involved in an accident, or who has committed a traffic offence such as speeding or not wearing a seatbelt, must take a saliva drugs test.

The authorities are concerned at the serious overloading of many British-registered vehicles touring in France. Drivers of overloaded vehicles may be prosecuted and held responsible for any accident in which they are involved.

MOTORWAYS

France has over 8,000 kilometres of excellent motorways and more are under construction or being planned. Tolls are payable on most routes according to distance travelled and category of vehicle(s) and, because motorways are privately financed, prices per kilometre vary. On sections around cities and large towns no tolls are levied. Credit cards are accepted throughout the motorway network. On some sections toll collection is by automatic machine accepting cash payments. If change is required use the separate marked lane. The website www.autoroutes.fr allows you to calculate the tolls payable and to plan a route.

Emergency telephones connected to the police are located every 2 km.

Motorway Service Areas

Stopping is allowed for a few hours at the service areas of motorways, called 'aires', and some have sections specially laid out for caravans. All have toilet facilities and water supply but at 'aires' with only basic facilities, water may not be suitable for drinking indicated by a sign 'eau non potable'. In addition 'aires de repos' have picnic and play areas, whereas 'aires de service' resemble our motorway service areas with fuel, shop, restaurant and parking for all types of vehicle. It should be noted that toll (péage) tickets are only valid for 24 or 48 hours depending on the particular autoroute concerned – check your ticket for details.

Michelin's Motorway Atlas of France gives the location of 'aires' throughout the country. **'Aires' are not campsites and, for reasons of security, the Caravan Club recommends that those seeking an overnight stop should leave the motorway system and find a suitable campsite.**

See Safety and Security earlier in this chapter.

Motorway Tolls

Class 1 – Vehicle up to 2 m in height (measured from the ground) with or without caravan/trailer up to 2 m (excluding roof rack/antennae etc), and with total weight up to 3,500 kg.

Class 2 – Vehicle with height between 2 m and 3 m and total weight up to 3,500 kg; vehicles in

Class 1 towing a caravan or trailer with height between 2 m and 3 m.

Class 3 – Vehicle with 2 axles and height over 3 m, or with total weight over 3,500 kg.

Class 4 – Vehicle or combination of vehicles with 3 axles or more, with height over 3 m, or with total weight over 3,500 kg.

Road	Total Journey	Class 1	Class 2	Class 3	Class 4
A1	Paris to Lille* (Autoroute du Nord)	10.10	14.90	21.50	29.40
A2	Combles (Junc A1) to Belgian border	4.30	6.50	9.20	12.20
A4	Paris to Reims (Autoroute de l'Est)	8.70	13.10	19.30	25.10
	Paris to Metz	20.30	30.50	45.10	59.40
	Metz to Strasbourg	10.30	15.50	21.70	29.10
	Paris to Strasbourg	30.90	46.60	67.80	89.90
A5	Melun to Langres	13.50	17.70	32.20	44.50
A6	Paris to Lyon (Autoroute du Soleil)	28.20	36.90	66.10	91.30
	Paris to Beaune	17.00	19.50	39.70	54.20
A7	Lyon to Marseille (Autoroute du Soleil)	17.70	27.50	36.50	49.50
A8	Aix-en-Provence to Menton (Italian Border)	17.40	26.30	36.00	49.70
A9	Orange (A7) to Le Perthus (Spanish Border)	19.50	30.30	41.80	55.00
A10	Paris to Poitiers (Autoroute Aquitaine)	29.50	46.50	64.20	87.90
	Poitiers to Bordeaux	17.00	26.20	36.20	48.70
A11	Paris to Le Mans West (Autoroute L'Océane)	16.50	28.80	34.50	48.60
	Le Mans to Nantes	7.00	16.60	25.80	33.10
A13	Paris to Caen (Autoroute de Normandie)	11.90	18.00	24.00	34.60
A16	Paris to Boulogne	16.30	24.40	34.90	51.00
A20	Gignac to Montauban Nord	10.00	15.50	21.00	30.30
A26/A1	Paris to Calais (A26/A1)	18.20	27.20	37.90	50.80
	Calais to Reims	16.60	25.20	35.40	47.90
	Reims to Troyes (A5)	7.90	11.70	19.20	24.50
A29	Le Havre (A13) to St Saëns (A28)	6.10	9.20	12.00	16.80
A31	Beaune to Metz (Luxembourg Border)	12.60	16.50	29.50	40.80
A36	Beaune to Mulhouse (German Border)	13.20	17.30	31.90	44.00
A39	Dijon to Bourg-en-Bresse	7.50	9.90	17.80	24.60
A40	Macon to Genève (Swiss Border)	13.40	19.60	32.50	43.80
A41	Grenoble to Scientrier (A40)	12.50	18.40	24.50	34.00
A42	Lyon to Pont d'Ain (A40)	3.30	4.30	8.00	11.00
A43	Lyon to Chambéry	9.40	15.10	20.00	26.30
	Chambéry to St Michel-de-Maurienne	10.10	15.30	28.10	37.90
A48	Bourgoin (A43) to Grenoble	4.50	7.20	9.30	12.20
A49	Grenoble to Valence	5.30	8.10	10.90	14.80
A50	Aix-en-Provence to Toulon	6.40	9.70	13.40	18.40
A51	Aix-en-Provence to Sisteron	9.30	14.20	19.50	26.80
A52	Chateauneuf-le-Rouge (A8) to Aubagne	3.10	4.70	6.50	9.00
A54	Arles to Nîmes	1.30	2.00	2.90	3.70
A57	Toulon to Le Cannet-des-Maures (A8)	1.90	2.90	4.00	5.50

FRANCE

Road	Total Journey	Class 1	Class 2	Class 3	Class 4
A61	Toulouse to Narbonne Sud	10.60	17.30	22.90	30.10
A62	Bordeaux to Toulouse	15.80	24.50	33.30	44.60
A63	Bordeaux to Spanish Border	6.20	9.60	11.50	16.00
A64	Bayonne to St Gaudens	12.10	18.60	25.50	34.30
A66	Toulouse to Pamiers	4.30	6.80	9.00	12.20
A68	Toulouse to Montrastruc	1.20	1.90	2.70	3.70
A71	Orléans to Clermont Ferrand	20.00	27.00	46.20	63.30
A72	Clermont Ferrand to St Etienne	9.20	14.30	20.30	26.50
A77	Dordives (A6) to Nevers	4.10	5.40	10.10	13.90
A81	Le Mans to Laval	8.30	12.00	18.20	23.60
A83	Nantes to Niort	9.80	15.00	21.20	28.00
A85	Angers to Tours	5.30	7.40	10.80	13.90
A89	Bordeaux (Arveyres) to Mussidan	8.00	12.40	16.60	24.40
	Tulle (St Germain) to Le Sancy	8.20	12.60	17.40	24.60

Toll charges in Euros

* Different charge bands apply at different times and on Sundays and public holidays

The toll table provides a guide to motorway tolls between main towns. These were in effect in autumn 2005 and are subject to change during 2006. A more detailed list of toll charges is available to Caravan Club members from the Club's Travel Service Information Officer. There are numerous stretches of motorway, particularly around large cities, where no tolls are levied.

Payments may be made in cash, by credit card, or by euro travellers' cheques. Avoid 'télépéage' toll booths which are for residents with pre-paid window stickers.

Motorists driving Class 2 vehicles adapted for the transport of disabled persons pay the toll specified for Class 1 vehicles. Holding a disabled person's Blue Badge does not automatically entitle foreign motorists to pay Class 1 charges, and the decision whether to downgrade from Class 2 to 1 will be made by the person at the toll booth, based on experience of similar vehicles registered in France.

Toll Bridges

Tolls are charged across the Pont de Tancerville on the River Seine estuary near Le Havre (A15) and the Pont de Normandie near Honfleur. Current charges are €2.90 and €5.80 respectively for car/caravan outfits and motor caravans

The Pont de l'Ile d'Oléron and Pont de la Seudre (linking La Tremblade with Marennes) south-west of Rochefort are toll-free, but a return charge is made on the Pont de l'Ile de Ré from La Rochelle to the Ile de Ré of €9-16.50 for a car or a motor caravan and €15-27 for a car plus caravan, depending on the time of year.

The 2.5 km long Millau Viaduct opened in December 2004 on the A75 autoroute. The maximum charge for a car and caravan is €9.70 and for a motor caravan €17.90.

Touring

- France is divided administratively into 'régions', each of which consists of several 'départements'. There are 95 départements in total including Corsica, and these are approximately equivalent to our counties, although with more autonomy.

- The capital, Paris, hub of the region known as the Ile de France, remains the political, economic, artistic, cultural and tourist centre of France. A Paris city passport is valid for a year and costs €5. It offers discounts at many well-known attractions, as well as special offers on shopping, excursions and other services. You can buy it online from www.parisinfo.com or from tourist and information offices in Paris.

- Much of France remains undiscovered because visitors lack the time, inclination or courage to deviate from the proscribed checklist of what-to-see. Often it's just a question of taking N and D roads instead of autoroutes; many of the country's most appealing treasures – whether man-made or natural features – are sometimes only a step away from familiar sites. Ask at local tourist information offices and Syndicats d'Initiative for leaflets about routes connecting points of interest and discover some of those 'off the beaten track' places. 'Bison futé' or 'bis' routes tend to follow more scenic roads; see www.bison-fute.equipement.gouv.fr

- Under 18's are admitted free and visitors over 60 years old are entitled to reduced price entrance to national museums. National museums, including the Louvre, are closed on Tuesday with the exception of Versailles, the Trianon Palace and the Musée d'Orsay which are closed on Monday. Entrance to national museums, including the Louvre, is free on the first Sunday of the month, except during the summer. Municipal museums are closed on Monday and most museums close on Easter Sunday/Monday and on public holidays.

- Ferry services operate for cars and passengers between Poole and Portsmouth and St Malo via Jersey and Guernsey. Caravans and motor caravans are permitted to enter Jersey between March and October, subject to certain conditions, including pre-booking direct with a registered campsite. For further information and a list of campsites on Jersey where caravans are permitted, please see www.jersey.com or contact the Club's Travel Service Information Officer.

- There are three campsites on Guernsey but, for the moment, caravans are not permitted to enter the island. However, motor caravans may be accepted providing permission is first obtained from the Island Development Committee.

  For further details contact the Club's Travel Service Information Officer.

- Car ferry services operate all year across the Gironde estuary between Royan and Le Verdon (approximately €50 for car, caravan and 2 adults), and between Blaye and Lamarque north of Bordeaux.

- Ferry services operate from Marseille, Nice and Toulon to Corsica. For information contact:

  SOUTHERN FERRIES
  30 CHURTON STREET
  LONDON SW1V 2LP
  Tel: 020 7976 6340
  www.sncm.fr

- Sunday lunch is an important occasion for French families; if you have found a restaurant that appeals to you it is advisable to book in advance. Many restaurants are not open on Sunday evening. Restaurants must display priced menus outside and most offer a set menu 'plat du jour' or 'table d'hôte' which represents good value. A service charge of 15% is included in restaurant bills but if you have received good service a tip may be left.

- Pasteurised milk is available everywhere; ask for 'lait frais pasteurisé'. When water is not drinkable there is usually a notice EAU NON-POTABLE.

- The website www.tourisme.fr contains useful information about regional and local tourist offices.

- Information on shopping in Calais, including tips on where best to buy wine, beer, cigarettes etc and DIY supplies, plus opening hours and price comparisons, can be found on www.day-tripper.net

- Senior citizens aged 60 and over are entitled to a 25% discount when using French railways. Show your passport as proof of age.

FRANCE

FRANCE / ANDORRA

Distances are shown in kilometres and are calculated from town/city centres
along the most practicable roads, although not necessarily taking the shortest route.

1km = 0.62 miles

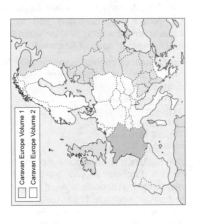

La Rochelle to Toulouse = 424km

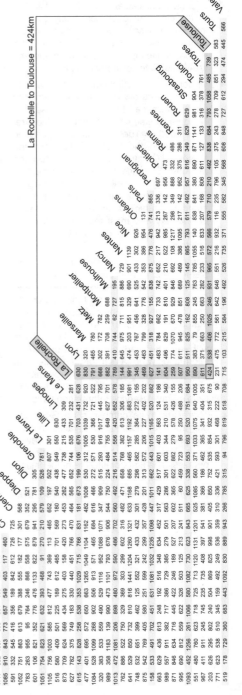

REGIONS AND DEPARTMENTS OF FRANCE

ALSACE
67 Bas-Rhin
68 Haut-Rhin

AQUITAINE
24 Dordogne
33 Gironde
40 Landes
47 Lot-et-Garonne
64 Pyrénées-Atlantiques

AUVERGNE
03 Allier
15 Cantal
43 Haute-Loire
63 Puy-de-Dôme

BOURGOGNE
21 Côte-d'Or
58 Nièvre
71 Saône-et-Loire
89 Yonne

BRETAGNE
22 Côtes-d'Armor
29 Finistère
35 Ille-et-Vilaine
56 Morbihan

CENTRE
18 Cher
28 Eure-et-Loir
36 Indre
37 Indre-et-Loire
41 Loir-et-Cher
45 Loiret

CHAMPAGNE-ARDENNE
08 Ardennes
10 Aube
51 Marne
52 Haute-Marne

CORSE
02A Corse-du-Sud
02B Haute-Corse

FRANCHE-COMTE
25 Doubs
39 Jura
70 Haute-Saône
90 Territoire-de-Belfort

LANGUEDOC-ROUSSILLON
11 Aude
30 Gard
34 Hérault
48 Lozère
66 Pyrénées-Orientales

LIMOUSIN
19 Corrèze
23 Creuse
87 Haute-Vienne

LORRAINE
54 Meurthe-et-Moselle
55 Meuse
57 Moselle
88 Vosges

MIDI-PYRENEES
09 Ariège
12 Aveyron
31 Haute-Garonne
32 Gers
46 Lot
65 Hautes-Pyrénées
81 Tarn
82 Tarn-et-Garonne

NORD/PAS-DE-CALAIS
59 Nord
62 Pas-de-Calais

NORMANDIE
14 Calvados
27 Eure
50 Manche
61 Orne
76 Seine-Maritime

PARIS-ILE DE FRANCE
75 Paris
77 Seine-et-Marne
78 Yvelines
91 Essonne
92 Haut-de-Seine
93 Seine-St-Denis
94 Val-de-Marne
95 Val-d'Oise

PAYS DE LA LOIRE
44 Loire-Atlantique
49 Maine-et-Loire
53 Mayenne
72 Sarthe
85 Vendée

PICARDIE
02 Aisne
60 Oise
80 Somme

POITOU-CHARENTES
16 Charente
17 Charente-Maritime
79 Deux-Sèvres
86 Vienne

PROVENCE-COTE D'AZUR
04 Alpes-de-Haute-Provence
05 Hautes-Alpes
06 Alpes-Maritimes
13 Bouches-du-Rhône
83 Var
84 Vaucluse

RHONE-ALPS
01 Ain
07 Ardèche
26 Drôme
38 Isère
42 Loire
69 Rhône
73 Savoie
74 Haute-Savoie

The first two digits of a French postcode correspond
to the number of the department in which that town or village is situated

Source : French Government Tourist Office

ABBEVILLE *3B3* (14km SE Rural) **Camp Municipal La Peupleraie, 80510 Long** [03 22 31 84 27 or 03 22 31 80 21; fax 03 22 31 82 39; bacquet. lionel@free.fr; www.long.fr] Exit A16 at junc 21 for N1 N then turn L at Ailly-le-Clocher onto D32 for Long & foll sp. Med, mkd pitch, pt shd; wc (some cont); chem disp; shwrs inc; el pts (6A) inc (long lead req); lndry rm; tradsmn; shop, rest, snacks, bar in vill; BBQ; playgrnd; fishing adj; 90% seasonal statics; dogs; phone adj; poss cr; adv bkg; cc not acc; CCI. "V attractive area beside Somme; many places of interest to visit; gd walking/cycling by rv; vg site; site busy 1st week Sep - flea mkt in town; office open 0800-1100 but warden lives on site." 15 May-31 Oct. € 10.00   2005*

ABBEVILLE *3B3* (14km SE) **Camping Le Grand Pre, 80510 Long** [03 23 68 02 22] At S end of Abbeville take D901 to Pont-Remy & Liercourt, D3 to Catelet; turn N in Catelet across rlwy to vill of Long; site on L bef Somme bdge in 500m. Med, pt shd; wc; chem disp; shwrs; el pts (6A) inc (poss rev pol); shops 1km; tradsmn/baker; 70% statics; dogs; poss cr; adv bkg; quiet; CCI. "Fishing & sp walks; welcoming owners live on site; park on rd when wet." € 11.30   2005*

ABBEVILLE *3B3* (5km S Urban) **Camp Municipal Le Marais Communal, Rue Marais de Tulsac, 80132 Mareuil-Caubert** [03 22 31 62 37 or 03 22 24 11 46; fax 03 22 31 34 28; mairie-mareuil@wanadoo.fr] Leave A28 at junc 3 sp Moyenneville. At T-junc turn L onto D928; foll camping sp. In 1.7km turn sharp R, then L thro houses to site by stadium. Med, mkd pitch, pt shd; wc; chem disp; shwrs; el pts (6A) €2.50 (poss rev pol); shop & 5km; rest 5km' 25% statics; quiet; CCI. "No twin-axles or van over 8m; friendly, clean site; barrier open 0800-2200; gd NH." 1 Apr-30 Sep. € 10.00   2005*

ABBEVILLE *3B3* (9km SW Rural) **Camping Le Val de Trie, Bouillancourt-sous-Miannay, 80870 Moyenneville** [03 22 31 48 88; fax 03 22 31 35 33; raphael@camping-levaldetrie.fr; www.camping-levaldetrie.fr] Fr A28 exit junc 2 onto D925 sp Cambron. In 5km at Miannay turn S onto D86 sp Bouillancourt. Site thro vill on L. Site sp fr A28. Med, hdg/mkd pitch, hdstg, pt sl, pt shd; htd wc; chem disp; serviced pitches; baby facs; shwrs inc; el pts (6A) €3.40; gas; lndtte; ice; shop; tradsmn; snacks; bar; BBQ; playgrnd; htd pool; paddling pool; sand beach 15km; lake fishing; cycle hire; games rm; entmnt; child entmnt; TV rm; 1% statics; dogs €1.30; phone; Eng spkn; adv bkg; quiet; cc acc; red long stay/low ssn; CCI. "Poss boggy after heavy rain; conv Calais; v helpful owner; interesting area; v pleasant site." ♦ 1 Apr-31 Oct. € 18.70 (CChq acc)   2005*

See advertisement opposite

ABILLY see Descartes *4H2*

ABRETS, LES *9B3* (2km E Rural) **Camping Le Coin Tranquille, Le Verroud, 38490 Les Abrets** [04 76 32 13 48; fax 04 76 37 40 67; contact@coin-tranquille.com; www.coin-tranquille.com] Fr N exit A43 at junc 10 Les Abrets & foll D592 to town cent. At rndbt at monument take N6 twd Chambery/Campings. Foll sp Le Coin Tranquille. Cross level x-ing, site at end of rd. Fr S on A48 exit junc 10 at Voiron onto N75 to Les Abrets. Turn R at rndabt twd Le Pont-de-Beauvoisin, then as above. Lge, hdg/mkd pitch, pt shd; wc (some cont); chem disp; mv service pnt; baby facs; shwrs inc; el pts (6A) inc (poss rev pol & long lead poss req); gas; lndtte; ice; shop; tradsmn; rest; snacks; bar; BBQ; playgrnd; pool + paddling pool in ssn; cycle hire; archery; horseriding & fishing 7km; golf 15km; games area; entmnt; TV rm; dogs €1; Eng spkn; adv bkg ess high ssn; noisy high ssn; red low ssn; cc acc; CCI. "Lovely walks; lge indiv, narr pitches; poss flooding in wet weather; clean san facs; gd, well-organised site but a dist to travel to many places of interest; local tourist info avail fr recep; gd rest; v helpful & friendly staff; well-maintained facs; although a busy/noisy site, some quiet pitches are avail - request bkg; excel activities for children." ♦ 1 Apr-1 Nov. € 29.50 (CChq acc) ABS - M05   2005*

ABRETS, LES *9B3* (3km S Rural) **Camp Municipal Le Calatrin, 38850 Paladru** [04 76 32 37 48; fax 04 76 32 42 02; calatrin@aol.com] S on N75 turn R onto D50 to Paladru; site 1km beyond vill on L on brow of hill. Med, mkd pitch, some terr, mainly sl, pt shd; wc (some cont); chem disp; shwrs inc; el pts (5A) €2 (long lead poss req); gas; lndtte; ice; shops 500m; BBQ; playgrnd; lake sw & shgl beach adj; fishing; watersports; TV; 50% statics; dogs; adv bkg; quiet; CCI. "V helpful staff." 1 Apr-30 Sep. € 13.00   2004*

ABRETS, LES *9B3* (8km S Rural) **Camping International Le Lac, Lac de Paladru, 38620 Montferrat** [04 76 32 31 67; fax 04 76 32 38 15] N75 5km S of Les Abrets turn R onto D50 dir Paladru. Turn L sp Veronniere/Charavines, site on R on lakeside. Lge, mkd pitch, pt shd; wc; chem disp; shwrs inc; el pts (6A) inc; lndtte; tradsmn; rest; snacks; bar; BBQ; playgrnd; lake sw & shgl beach; fishing; sailing; 25% statics; dogs; phone; Eng spkn; adv bkg; quiet; cc acc; CCI. "Lovely lake with gently shelving beach; poss supervised sw; gd touring base." ♦ 14 Apr-30 Sep. € 12.50   2002*

ABRETS, LES *9B3* (11km SW) **Camp Municipal du Bord du Lac, 38850 Bilieu** [04 76 06 67 00 or 04 76 06 62 41 (Mairie); fax 04 76 06 67 15; mairie.bilieu@pays-voironnais.com] S on N75 fr Les Abrets. Turn R onto D50. Just bef Paladru, turn L to Charavines. site on R on ent Bilieu, by lakeside. Med, mkd pitch, pt sl, terr, pt shd; htd wc; chem disp; shwrs inc; el pts (5A) €2; lndtte; tradsmn; playgrnd; 70% statics; dogs; poss cr; quiet; CCI. "No sw in lake fr site, only boat launch; pitch access poss diff; gd NH/sh stay." 15 Apr-30 Sep. € 7.65   2003*

FRANCE

ABZAC see Coutras *7C2*

ACCOUS *8G2* (Rural) **Camping Despourrins, Route du Somport, 64490 Accous** [05 59 34 71 16] On N134 rte to & fr Spain via Somport Pass. Site sp on main rd. Sm, pt shd; wc (some cont); shwrs inc; el pts (6A) €2.30; lndry rm; shop 500m; quiet but some rd noise. "Clean, tidy NH conv Col de Somport; gd NH." 1 Mar-31 Oct. € 7.80   2004*

†**ACY EN MULTIEN** *3D3* (700m SE Rural) **Caravaning L'Ancien Moulin, 60620 Acy-en-Multien** [tel/fax 03 44 87 21 28; secretariat@ campingclub.asso.fr; www.campingclub.asso.fr] Leave A4 at junc 19 & turn L onto D401 to Lizy-sur-Ourcq. Cross rv & turn R then L onto D147 dir May-en-Multien. 1km then L onto D14 dir May. Cross D405 onto D420 (becomes D332) dir Rosoy-en-Multien & site is on L 2km after Rosoy, 500m bef Acy-en-Multien. Med, mkd pitch, pt shd; htd wc; chem disp; shwrs inc; el pts (6A) inc; lndtte; shops, rest, snacks, bar, playgrnd 1km; fishing; volleyball; ping-pong; TV rm; 90% statics; dogs; Eng spkn; adv bkg; quiet; CCI 5%. "V helpful, friendly staff; 30km fr Disneyland Paris & nr 2 other theme parks; pitches by mill pool; poss aircraft noise; vg sh stay." ♦ € 18.60   2003*

ADRETS DE L'ESTEREL, LES see Napoule, La *10F4*

AGAY *10F4* (700m E Coastal) **Camping Agay Soleil, Route de Cannes, 83700 Agay** [04 94 82 00 79; fax 04 94 82 88 70; camping-agay-soleil@wanadoo.fr] E fr St Raphael on N98 site on R after passing Agay dir Cannes. Med, mkd pitch, hdstg, pt sl, terr, pt shd; wc; chem disp; mv service pnt; baby facs; shwrs inc; el pts (6A) €3.70; gas; lndtte; shop & 500m; rest, snacks, bar high ssn; playgrnd adj; sand beach adj; watersports; games area; some statics; no dogs high ssn; phone adj; train & bus 500m; poss cr; Eng spkn; adv bkg ess Easter to Aug; CCI. "Superb location on sea front; excel modern facs; many pitches too sm for awning; extra charge beach pitches; coach tours bookable; excel. " ♦ 15 Mar-5 Nov. € 25.00 (3 persons)   2005*

AGAY *10F4* (1.5km S Coastal) **Royal Camping, Plage de Camp-Long, 83530 Agay** [tel/fax 04 94 82 00 20] On N98 twd St Raphael. Turn at sp Tiki Plage & site. Stop in ent rd at recep bef ent site. Sm, mkd pitch, hdstg, pt shd; wc; chem disp; shwrs inc; el pts (6A) inc; gas; lndtte; ice; shops; tradsmn; rest, snacks, bar 300m; sand beach adj; dogs; phone; bus 200m; poss cr; Eng spkn; adv bkg €63 dep & €17 bkg fee; quiet but some rd/rlwy noise; CCI. "Gd walks; some pitches adj to beach in sep area; vg." ♦ ltd. 15 Mar-31 Oct. € 30.50   2005*

AGAY *10F4* (600m NW Coastal) **Camping des Rives de l'Agay, Ave de Gratadis, 83530 Agay** [04 94 82 02 74; fax 04 94 82 74 14; reception@lesrivesdelagay.fr; www.lesrivesdelagay.fr]
Fr Agay take D100 dir Valescure, site in 400m on L. NB Dangerous bend & steep ent. Med, hdg/mkd pitch, shd; htd wc; chem disp; baby facs; shwrs inc; el pts (6A) inc; gas; lndtte; ice; shop & 1km; rest; snacks; bar; htd pool (Mar-Nov); sand beach 500m; dogs €2; poss cr; Eng spkn; adv bkg; poss noisy; CCI. "San facs & pool v clean; gd pool with shade; easy walk to Agay; excel site." ♦
1 Mar-2 Nov. € 31.00 (3 persons)   2005*

We're having a great holiday - must fill in some site report forms and send them to The Club as soon as possible.

AGAY *10F4* (8km NW Rural) **LES CASTELS Esterel Caravaning, Ave des Golfs, 83530 Agay** [04 94 82 03 28; fax 04 94 82 87 37; contact@esterel-caravaning.fr; www.esterel-caravaning.fr or www.les-castels.com] Fr A8 foll sps for St Raphaël & immed foll sp 'Agay (par l'interieur)/Valescure' into Ave des Golfs, approx 6km long. Pass golf courses & at end of rd turn L at rndabt twds Agay. Site 800m on L. Lge, mkd pitch, terr, pt shd; htd wc (some cont); chem disp; mv service pnt; shwrs inc; baby facs; indiv san facs to some pitches (extra charge); el pts (5A) inc (poss rev pol); gas; lndtte; lndry rm; ice; shop; tradsmn; rest; snacks; bar; no BBQ; playgrnd; htd pools; waterslide; sand beach 3km; lake sw 20km; tennis; mini-golf; squash; cycle hire; archery; games rm; fitness rm; entmnt; underground disco; TV rm; internet; 50% statics; dogs €2; poss v cr; Eng spkn; adv bkg; red low ssn/long stay; cc acc; CCI. "Superb site; conv Gorges du Verdon, Massif de l'Esterel, Monaco, Cannes & St Tropez; gd for families - excel leisure activities; ltd lge pitches avail; excel rest; mkt Wed." ♦
1 Apr-30 Sep. € 42.00 ABS - C21   2005*

See advertisement

AGDE *10F1* (4.5km SE Coastal) **Camp Municipal La Clape, 2 Rue du Gouverneur, 34300 Agde** [04 67 26 41 32 or 04 67 94 41 83; fax 04 67 26 45 25; clape@capdagde.com; www.capdagde.com] Foll sp Cap d'Agde, keep L at 1st gantry, L at 2nd gantry foll camping sp. Turn R at rndabt. Camp ent by lge free car pk. Lge, pt shd, mkd pitch; wc; shwrs; el pts (4-6A) €2.90; lndtte; ice; shop; rest; snacks; sand beach adj; pool adj; entmnt; games area; poss cr; quiet; red low ssn; cc acc; CCI. "Ltd facs & lack of maintenance early in ssn; poor management." 1 Apr-30 Sep. € 20.30
                                                    2002*

AGDE *10F1* (1km S Rural) **Domaine des Champs Blancs, Route de Rochelongue, 34300 Agde** [04 67 94 23 42; fax 04 67 21 36 75; champs-blancs@wanadoo.fr; www.champs-blancs.fr]
Exit fr A9 & foll sps to Agde (not Cap d'Agde). Thro cent of Agde foll sps to campsite & Rochelongue. Site on R after bdge over dual c'way. V lge, hdg pitch, shd; wc; chem disp; mv service pnt; individ san facs on pitches (extra charge); shwrs inc; el pts €3 (poss rev pol); gas; lndtte; ice; shop, rest, snacks, bar adj; playgrnd; 2 htd pools; waterslide; sand beach adj; tennis; games area; golf 2km; 10% statics; dogs €2; adv bkg; quiet; CCI. "Friendly site; excel san facs; hot shwrs but all other taps cold; vg." ♦ 9 Apr-30 Sep. € 38.00 (CChq acc)
                                                    2005*

AGDE *10F1* (4km S Coastal) **Camping de la Tamarissiere, 4 Rue du Commandant Malet, 34300 Agde** [04 67 94 79 46; fax 04 67 94 78 23; contact@camping-tamarissiere.com; www.camping-tamarissiere.com] At Agde bdge take D32E on R bank of Rv Herault to La Tamarissiere; sp. V lge, mkd pitch, pt sl, shd; wc; shwrs; el pts (6A) €3.50; lndtte; ice; shop; rest; snacks; bar; playgrnd; sand beach adj; games area; cycle hire; entmnt; harbour nr for boat owners; mkt every morning at site ent; 5% statics; dogs €2.60; adv bkg; quiet; cc acc; red long stay; CCI. "Sandy site under pines; ferry across rv; gate shut 2200-0700; vg facs." ♦ 15 Apr-15 Sep. € 19.00   2005*

AGDE *10F1* (2km SW) **Camping International Neptune, Route du Grau, 34300 Agde** [04 67 94 23 94; fax 04 67 94 48 77; info@campingleneptune.com; www.campingleneptune.com]
Fr A9 exit junc 34 onto N312, then E on N112. Foll sp Grau d'Agde after x-ing bdge. Site on D32E on E bank of Rv Herault on 1-way system. Lge, hdg/mkd pitch, pt shd; wc; chem disp; baby facs; fam bthrm; shwrs inc; el pts (6-10A) inc; gas; lndtte; shop & bar in ssn; hypmkt 4km; rest 2km; BBQ; playgrnd; htd pool; paddling pool; sand beach 2km; tennis; games area; entmnt; TV; 10% statics; dogs €3 (no Pitbulls or Rottweillers); phone; bus 2km; poss cr; Eng spkn; adv bkg rec; quiet; cc acc; red low ssn; CCI. "Peaceful, pleasant site; liable to flood after heavy rain; helpful owners; modern facs; easy cycle to vill; rv cruises avail." 1 Apr-30 Sep. € 27.50 (CChq acc)
                                                    2005*

AGDE *10F1* (3km SW Coastal) **Camping Les Romarins, Le Grau d'Agde, 34300 Agde** [04 67 94 18 59; fax 04 67 26 58 80; contact@romarins.com] Fr Agde take rd to Grau d'Agde, site at ent to Grau d'Agde adj Rv Herault. Med, mkd pitch, pt hdg pitch, shd; wc; shwrs inc; el pts (6A) inc; lndtte; shop 500m; rest; snacks; bar; playgrnd; pool; sand beach 1km; cycle hire; 10% statics; dogs €2.20; poss cr; Eng spkn; adv bkg; quiet; CCI. "Pleasant town with many bars, rests; shops; helpful owner." ♦ ltd. 1 May-15 Sep. € 23.20   2004*

†AGEN *8E3* (12km SE Rural) **Camping au Lie,** 47220 Caudecoste [05 53 87 42 93 or 01473 832388 (UK); td.smith@tiscali.fr; www. aulie.co.uk] Fr N113 dir Toulouse, turn off sp Layrac approx 8km SE of Agen. Do not use bdges across Rv Garonne at St Nicholas-de-la-Balerme (shut) or Sauveterre-St Denis (width restrict). Fr A62 exit junc 7 & turn R at 1st rndabt sp Layrac. Drive thro vill & turn L at 2nd traff lts (sharp turn) sp Caudecoste, cross bdge over Rv Gers & Caudecosts sp 1st R (silver horse at junc). In Caudecoste take D290 sp Miradoux, cross m'way in approx 1km, on L is farmhouse with pond, turn L just after this onto sm rd with grass growing in middle. At T-junc turn R, site on R. Sm, pt shd, wc; chem disp; shwrs inc; el pts (6A) inc; shops, rest, bar in vill; pool; c'van storage avail; quiet. "Hot water, lndry facs & use of bikes inc; peaceful countryside; delightful vill; welcoming British owners; excel meals avail at farm house, inc coeliac & vegetarian; excel." ♦ ltd. € 18.00   2005*

AGEN *8E3* (8km NW) **Camping Le Moulin de Mellet,** 47490 St Hilaire-de-Lusignan [05 53 87 50 89; fax 05 53 47 13 41; moulin. mellet@wanadoo.fr; www.camping-moulin-mellet. com] NW fr Agen on N113 twd Bordeaux for 5km. At traff lts just bef Colayrac-St Cirq take D107 N twd Prayssas for 3km. Site on R. Sm, pt shd; wc; chem disp; baby facs; shwrs inc; el pts (10-16A) €2.40; gas; lndry rm; ice; shop 3km; tradsmn high ssn; rest; snacks; BBQ; snacks; playgrnd; pools; dogs €1; adv bkg; quiet; Eng spkn; CCI. "Excel; v helpful & friendly Dutch owners; RVs & twin-axles phone ahead; delightful site; lge pool; small children's farm." ♦ 1 Apr-15 Oct. € 13.60   2005*

AGON COUTAINVILLE *1D4* (NE Urban/Coastal) **Camp Municipal Le Martinet, Blvd Lebel Jehenne,** 50230 Agon-Coutainville [02 33 47 05 20 or 02 33 47 07 56; fax 02 33 47 90 85; martinet marais@wanadoo.fr] Fr Coutances take D44 to Agon-Coutainville; site sp nr Hippodrome. Med, pt shd; wc; shwrs inc; el pts (5A) €2.20; lndry rm; shop 250m; playgrnd; sand beach 1km; 85% statics; dogs €1.30; bus; poss cr; CCI. "V pleasant site; touring pitches ltd." ♦ 1 Apr-30 Oct. € 11.20   2004*

AGON COUTAINVILLE *1D4* (600m NE Urban) **Camp Municipal Le Marais, Blvd Lebel Jehenne,** 50230 Agon-Coutainville [02 33 47 05 20; fax 02 33 47 90 85; martinetmarais@wanadoo.fr] Fr Coutances take D44 to Agon-Coutainville. Site sp adj Hippodrome. Lge, unshd; wc; chem disp; el pts (5A) inc; lndtte; shops adj; tradsmn; playgrnd; sand beach 600m; sailing; fishing; dogs €2.20; adv bkg; quiet. ♦ 1 Jul-1 Sep. € 12.85   2003*

AGON COUTAINVILLE *1D4* (6km SE) **Camp Municipal Les Gravelets, 50590 Montmartin-sur-Mer** [tel/fax 02 33 47 70 20; campgrav@chez. com] Fr Coutances take D971 twd Granville. Turn W at Hyenville to Montmartin-sur-Mer, site sp in vill. Med, terr, pt shd; wc; shwrs inc; el pts (6A) €1.90; lndry rm; shop 300m; tradsmn; playgrnd; sand beach, fishing & sailing 2km; tennis adj; dogs €0.70; adv bkg; quiet; CCI. ♦ 1 Apr-30 Oct. € 7.00   2003*

This site entry hasn't been updated for a while; we'd better fill in a site report form and send it to The Club.

AGUESSAC see Millau *10E1*

AIGLE, L' *4E2* (5km NW Rural) **Camp Municipal des Sts-Peres, 61550 St Evroult-Notre-Dame-du-Bois** [02 33 34 81 97 or 02 33 34 93 12 (Mairie)] Fr L'Aigle on D13, on ent vill site on L by lake. Sm, terr, pt shd; wc; chem disp (wc); shwrs; el pts (10A) €2.50; shop, rest, snacks, bar 500m; playgrnd; lake sw adj; watersports; fishing; mini-golf; dogs; no adv bkg; poss noisy; CCI. "Pleasant lakeside vill." ♦ 1 Apr-30 Sep. € 6.00   2005*

AIGREFEUILLE D'AUNIS *7A1* (2km N Rural) **Camp Municipal de la Garenne, 17220 St Christophe** [05 46 35 51 79 or 05 46 35 16 15; fax 05 46 35 64 29; saintchristophe@wanadoo17. com] Fr Aigrefeuille d'Aunis take the D112 2.5km N to the vill of St Christophe, site sp. Sm, hdg, mkd pitch, pt shd; wc; chem disp; mv service pnt; shwrs inc; el pts (4A) €2.40; ice; lndry rm; shop 250m; playgrnd; sand beach 20km; tennis; horseriding; lake fishing 3km; dogs €1; quiet; CCI. "V clean site in sm vill; unreliable opening dates, phone ahead low ssn." ♦ 1 May-15 Sep. € 8.20   2003*

AIGREFEUILLE D'AUNIS *7A1* (W) **Camping La Taillee, 3 Rue du Bois Gaillard, 17290 Aigrefeuille-d'Aunis** [tel/fax 05 46 35 50 88; vacances@ lataillee.com; www.lataillee.com] Take D939 outside La Rochelle, exit sp Aigrefeuille & fork R immed to 1st major R turn sp 'Equipement'. Take 1st L at mini-rndabt to site on L in 100m. Take care over hump. Med, pt shd; wc; chem disp; baby facs; shwrs inc; el pts (6A) €3.10; ice; shops 500m; bar; BBQ; playgrnd; pool adj; games rm; mini-golf; lake 900m; dogs €2.10; quiet; CCI. "Extremely pleasant, clean site; excel pool adj; vg security; phone ahead low ssn to check open." ♦ 4 May-30 Sep. € 13.00   2004*

AIGUES MORTES *10F2*. **See also sites listed under La Grande Motte and Le Grau du Roi.**

AIGUES MORTES *10F2* (5km N) **Camping Fleur de Camargue, 30220 St Laurent-d'Aigouze** [04 66 88 15 42; fax 04 66 88 10 21; sarlaccv@aol.com; www.fleur-de-camargue.com]
N fr Aigues-Mortes at junc with D58 over high-level bdge on D46, site 3km on L on D46. Med, mkd pitch, pt shd; wc; chem disp; mv service pnt; shwrs inc; el pts (10A) inc; gas; lndtte; ice; shops 2km; tradsmn; rest; snacks; bar; playgrnd; pool; paddling pool; sand beach 11km; rv & fishing 3km; entmnt; TV rm; 20% statics; dogs €4; phone; bus; adv bkg; quiet; cc acc; CCI. "V pleasant owners; relaxing, quiet site; v clean facs; no stand pipes - water only in facs blocks; lge pitches." ♦ 3 Apr-9 Oct. € 23.60 (CChq acc)   2005*

AIGUES MORTES *10F2* (2km E Rural) **Camping a la Ferme (Loup), Le Mas de Plaisance, 30220 Aigues-Mortes** [04 66 53 92 84 or 06 22 20 92 37]
Site sp in Aigues-Mortes or foll D58 dir Stes-Maries-de-la-Mer, then R along farm road (v narr & potholed) at end of rv bdge. Sm, pt shd; wc; chem disp; mv service pnt; shwrs inc; el pts inc; lndry rm; BBQ; quiet; CCI. "Excel CL-type site; superb san facs; v helpful owners; set in marshes - gd birdwatching; rec not to use water at m'van service point as off irrigation system - other water points avail." 1 Apr-30 Sep. € 17.00   2005*

AIGUES MORTES *10F2* (3.5km W Rural) **Camping La Petite Camargue, 30220 Aigues-Mortes** [04 66 53 98 98; fax 04 66 53 98 80; info@yellohvillage-petite-camargue.com; www.yelloh village-petite-camargue.com & www.homair-vacances.fr] Heading S on N979 take D62 bef Aigues-Mortes & go over canal bdge twd Montpellier; site on R in 1.5km; sp. V lge, mkd pitch, pt shd; wc; mv service pnt; chem disp (wc); some serviced pitch; baby facs; shwrs inc; el pts (6A) inc; gas; lndtte; ice; shop; rest; snacks; bar; BBQ (gas/charcoal only); playgrnd; pool; sand beach 3km; tennis; games rm; horseriding; archery; cycle hire; entmnt; many statics; dogs €3; bus to beach high ssn; Eng spkn; adv bkg; red low ssn; cc acc; CCI. "Returnable dep req for ent token; lively, busy, youth-orientated commercial site with lots of sports facs; some sm pitches; conv Nimes, Pont du Gard, Camargue, Cevennes; mkt Wed & Sun; take care overhead trees." ♦ 29 Apr-16 Sep. € 42.00
ABS - C04   2005*

AIGUEZE see Pont St Esprit *9D2*

AIGUILLON SUR MER, L' *7A1* (Coastal) **Camp Municipal de la Baie, Blvd du Communal, 85460 L'Aiguillon-sur-Mer** [02 51 56 40 70; fax 02 51 97 11 57] On D46 fr La Tranche, cross bdge into Aiguillon-sur-Mer. Foll main rd to R; after it turns L site on R in 100m. Lge, pt shd; wc; shwrs inc; el pts (6A); lndtte; playgrnd; pool 500m; waterslide; sand beach 600m; TV; poss cr; adv bkg; quiet; red long stay/low ssn. "Gd beaches in area."
1 Apr-30 Sep.   2003*

AIGUILLON SUR MER, L' *7A1* (1km W Coastal) **Camp Municipal La Cote de Lumiere, Place du Dr Pacaud, 85460 La Faute-sur-Mer** [02 51 97 06 16; fax 02 51 27 12 21] On D46 E of La Tranche, thro town. Site bef bdge over rv. Lge, shd; wc (some cont); shwrs inc; el pts (6A) €3; lndtte; shop; snacks; playgrnd; sand beach 300m; dogs; quiet; cc acc; CCI. "Naturist beach adj; bird sanctuary, oyster/mussel beds adj; poss prob with insects." ♦
1 Apr-15 Oct. € 13.50 (3 persons)   2004*

AIGUILLON SUR MER, L' *7A1* (1km W Coastal) **Camping Le Bel Air, 85460 L'Aiguillon-sur-Mer** [02 51 56 44 05 or 02 54 77 33 08 (LS); fax 02 51 97 15 58; camping.belair@wanadoo.fr; www.campingbelair.com or www.homair-vacances.fr]
Fr La Roche-sur-Yon take D747 to La Tranche-sur-Mer via coast rd D46 to La Faute-sur-Mer. Cross bdge to L'Aiguillon-sur-Mer. Site 1km W of town on D44. Sp fr all dir. Lge, pt shd; wc; baby facs; shwrs; el pts (3A) €4; lndtte; ice; shop; rest; snacks; bar; BBQ; playgrnd; pool; waterslide; sand beach 800m; entmnt; child entmnt; mini-golf; cycle hire; pony trekking; archery; some statics; dogs €2; adv bkg.
3 Apr-18 Sep. € 18.00   2003*

AIGURANDE *7A4* (14km SW) **Camp Municipal Font Bonne, Crozant, 23160 St Sebastien** [06 85 96 53 79; fax 05 55 89 83 80] Fr N20 take D36 to Eguzon R on D973 after 11km L on D30 to Crozant. Site sp in vill. Sm, mkd pitch, pt sl, pt shd; wc (cont); shwrs inc; el pts €1.85; lndry rm; shops, rest, snacks, bar 500m; BBQ; playgrnd; lake sw 7km; dogs €0.50; adv bkg; quiet; cc not acc. "Attractive vill on Lake Chambon; rvside walk."
1 May-30 Sep. € 6.10   2004*

AILLY SUR NOYE *3C3* (1km S Rural) **Camp Municipal du Val de Noye, 80250 Ailly-sur-Noye** [03 22 41 02 11] Fr Amiens take D7 S thro St Fuscien to Ailly-sur-Noye, then D193 SW for 1km to Berny-sur-Noye & lakeside. Or fr N1 turn E onto D920 to Ailly-sur-Noye. Med, mkd pitch, shd; wc; own san rec; chem disp; mv service pnt; shwrs inc; el pts (3A) €2.20; tradsmn; shops 1km; playgrnd; lake sw, fishing, boating adj; 20% statics; dogs; 15% red 3+ days & 5% red low ssn; CCI. "Pleasant NH; fishing fr site free; leisure park adj; some rlwy noise; ltd facs low ssn." 1 Apr-31 Oct. € 7.00   2004*

†**AIME** *9B3* (5km NE Rural) **Camping de Montchavin, 73210 Bellentre** [04 79 07 83 23; fax 04 79 07 80 18; montchavin@wanadoo.fr]
On N90 fr Moutiers to Bourg-St Maurice (ignore site sps on N90); at 20km turn R onto D87E sp Landry & Montchavin-les-Coches; in 14km turn R D220 in 500m turn L D225; site in 7km on L at Montchavin. Med, mkd pitch, terr, pt shd; htd wc; mv service pnt; shwrs inc; el pts (4-10A) €3.50-€7.10; gas; lndtte; ice; shops 500m; 60% statics; adv bkg (ess Jul/Aug & winter); quiet; cc not acc. "Site at 1200m; steep hill to shops; walking in summer, skiing in winter; magnificent setting, great views; cent for mountain activities; site clsd Oct." € 11.75   2005*

FRANCE

AINHOA *8F1* (2.5km SW) **Camping Xokoan,** Quartier Dancharia, 64250 Ainhoa [05 59 29 90 26; fax 05 59 29 73 82] Fr St Jean-de-Luz take D918 to St Pee-sur-Nivelle. Shortly after St Pee take D3 sp Dancharia then turn L at Spanish border post. Site is 25m on R. Long ent is narr & tortuous, poss diff for long o'fits. Sm, pt sl, pt shd; wc; shwrs inc; el pts (6A) inc; lndtte; shop nr; rest; snacks; bar; playgrnd; adv bkg; quiet; CCI. "Conv for Spain & Pyrenees; gd walks, lovely scenery; site set in grounds of sm hotel." 1 Mar-30 Nov. € 14.00   2004*

AINHOA *8F1* (NW) **Aire Naturelle Harazpy,** 64250 Ainhoa [tel/fax 05 59 29 89 38] Take D918 E fr St Jean-de-Luz sp Espelette: in approx 29km turn R on D20 sp Ainhoa. App church in Ainhoa turn R thro open car park to rd at rear. Sh distance to site (sp). Sm, mkd pitch, terr, pt sl, pt shd; wc; mv service pnt; shwrs; el pts (10A) inc; lndtte; sm shop; tradsmn; lake sw 10km; dogs; phone; adv bkg; quiet; cc not acc; CCI. "Conv Spanish border; helpful warden; excel walking area. " ♦ 15 Jun-30 Sep. € 13.50   2004*

AIRE SUR LA LYS *3A3* (2km NE Urban) **Camp Municipal de la Lys,** Rue de Fort Gassion, 62120 Aire-sur-la-Lys [03 21 95 40 40; fax 03 21 95 40 41] Fr town cent, find main sq & exit to R of town hall. Thro traff lts turn R into narr lane just bef rv bdge dir of Hazelbrouck. Site poorly sp. Sm, hdg/mkd pitch, hdstg, unshd; wc; chem disp (wc only); shwrs inc; some el pts inc; quiet. "Ltd touring pitches; ltd but clean san facs; not suitable lge o'fits; emergency NH only." € 5.00   2004*

AIRE SUR L'ADOUR *8E2* (Urban) **Camping Les Ombrages** de l'Adour, 40800 Aire-sur-l'Adour [tel/fax 05 58 71 64 70 or 05 58 71 75 10; hetapsarl@yahoo.fr; www.camping-adour-landes. com] Turn E on S side of bdge over Rv Adour in town. Site close to bdge & sp, past La Arena off rd to Bourdeaux. Med, pt shd; wc; chem disp; mv service pnt; shwrs inc; el pts (10A) €2.80; ice; lndtte; shop; snacks; playgrnd; pool 500m; sports area; canoing, fishing, tennis 500m; dogs €1.60; poss cr; red low ssn. "Vg; boil water or use bottled; v clean facs; mkt Tues." 20 Apr-30 Sep. € 13.90   2005*

†**AIRE SUR L'ADOUR** *8E2* (9km E Rural) **Camping Le Lahount,** 32400 Lelin-Lapujolle [tel/fax 05 62 69 64 09 or 06 81 52 39 15; camping.de. lahount@wanadoo.fr] SE fr Aire-sur-l'Adour on D935, turn L in St Germe dir Lelin-Lapujolle. In 1.5km turn L, site on R, sp. Med, mkd pitch, terr, pt shd; wc; mv service pnt; baby facs; shwrs inc; el pts (10A) €2.50; lndtte; ice; shop; rest; snacks; bar; playgrnd; pool; lake fishing; games area; cycle hire; entmnt; 60% statics; dogs; phone; adv bkg; cc acc; CCI. "Gd sh stay/NH." € 11.00   2002*

AIRES, LES see Lamalou les Bains *10F1*

AIRVAULT *4H1* (1km N Rural) **Camping La Courte Vallee,** 79600 Airvault [05 49 64 70 65 or 05 49 63 45 06 (LS); fax 05 49 94 17 78; camping@ caravanningfrance.com; www.caravanningfrance. com] Fr N, S or W leave D938 sp Parthenay to Thuars rd at La Maucarriere twd Airvault & foll lge sp to site. Site on D121 twd Availles-Thouarsis N of town. NB If app fr NE or E c'vans not permitted down main street of Airvault & should watch carefully for sp R at the Gendarmerie. Well sp fr all dirs. Med, hdg/mkd pitch, some hdstg, pt sl, pt shd; wc; chem disp; mv service pnt; shwrs inc; el pts (8A) inc; gas; lndtte; tradsmn; rest/bar in town; snacks; BBQ; playgrnd; pool; internet; fishing; cycling; walking; c'van storage; internet; 8% statics; dogs €2; recep 0830-2030; adv bkg; quiet; red long stay; cc not acc; CCI. "Popular, peaceful, well-maintained site; v clean facs; excel wc block; extremely helpful, pleasant British owners; conv Loire, Futuroscope; wine-tasting visits; mkt Sat; walking dist to town." ♦ 8 Apr-30 Sep. € 28.75 ABS - L14   2005*

†**AIX EN PROVENCE** *10F3* (9km E Rural) **Camping Ste Victoire,** La Paradou, 13100 Beaurecueil [04 42 66 91 31; fax 04 42 66 96 43; campingvictoire@aol.com] Exit A8/E80 junc 32 onto N7 dir Aix, then R onto D58 & foll sp for 3km. Sm, hdg/mkd pitch, shd; htd wc (some cont); chem disp; mv service pnt; shwrs inc; el pts (4-6A) €2.20-3.10 (some rev pol & poss no neutral); lndtte; ice; shop 3km; tradsmn; playgrnd; pool 9km; rv 1km; archery; cycle hire; TV; dogs €1.10; phone; bus; site clsd mid-Dec to mid-Jan; adv bkg; quiet; 10% red long stay; no cc acc; CCI. "Site in attractive hilly, wooded country; gd walking & climbing; v friendly, helpful staff; lovely views some pitches; ltd, basic facs low ssn; lovely site." ♦ € 11.30   2005*

AIX EN PROVENCE *10F3* (1km SE Urban) **Camping L'Arc-en-Ciel, 13100 Aix-en-Provence** [04 42 26 14 28] Exit a'route A8/E80 at junc 31 onto N7 dir SE; pass under a'route & site ent immed on R; sp. Take care at ent. NB Access easier if go past site for 1km to rndabt, turn round & app fr S. Sm, hdg/mkd pitch, terr, shd; htd wc; chem disp; shwrs inc; el pts (6A) €3 (poss rev pol); gas; lndtte; shops 500m; rest, snacks, bar 100m; BBQ; playgrnd; lge pool; fishing; canoeing; games area; golf 1km; TV; dogs; phone; bus; Eng library; poss cr; Eng spkn; adv bkg; m'way noise not too intrusive; cc not acc; CCI. "Delightful, clean site; vg, friendly, helpful staff; well supervised; pitches poss sm; baker & grocer within 100m; excel pool; gd dog walk adj; conv bus to town cent, & to Marseille; highly rec." 1 Apr-30 Sep. € 17.20   2005*

FRANCE

†AIX EN PROVENCE *10F3* (3km SE Urban) **Airotel Chantecler, Val-St Andre, 13100 Aix-en-Provence** [04 42 26 12 98; fax 04 42 27 33 53; chantecler@wanadoo.fr; www.airotel-chantecler.com] Fr town inner ring rd foll sps Nice-Toulon, after 1km pass sp for a'routes on R look for sp Chantecler to L of dual c'way. Foll camp sp past blocks of flats. Well sp in Val-St Andre. If on A8 exit at junc 31 sp Val-St Andre; site sp. Lge, hdg pitch, hdstg, sl, pt terr, pt shd; htd wc; chem disp; mv service pnt; shwrs inc; el pts (6A) €3.60; gas; lndtte; ice; shop; tradsmn; rest in ssn; snacks; bar; BBQ; playgrnd; pool; entmnt; TV; dogs; bus; poss cr; adv bkg; some rd noise; cc acc; red long stay; CCI. "Lovely 'rural' site in urban area; facs ltd low ssn; some site rds steep - gd power/weight ratio rec; access poss diff some pitches; rec request low level pitch; frequent bus to Aix; bus to Marseilles fr Aix; gd site, well-maintained; excel san facs at top of site; vg touring base; excel." ♦ € 18.00   2005*

AIX LES BAINS *9B3* (3km N) **Camp Municipal Roger Milesey, 73100 Gresy-sur-Aix** [04 79 88 28 21 or 04 79 34 80 50 (Mairie)] Site on N201 bet Aix-les-Bains & Albens-Annecy in vill of Gresy; exit A41 at Aix N; turn L at supmkt flag sp to N201; turn R & site on L in approx 1km. Sm, pt shd; wc (some cont); chem disp; 70% seviced pitches; shwrs; el pts (10A) €2.30; gas 1km; ice; lndtte, shop & rest in vill; lake sw 3km; tennis adj; dogs €1.20; quiet; adv bkg; CCI. "Higher charges for 1 night only; vg." ♦ 1 Jun-30 Sep. € 9.60   2005*

AIX LES BAINS *9B3* (7km SW) **Camping International de l'Ile aux Cygnes, La Croix Verte, 501 Blvd Ernest Coudurier, 73370 Le Bourget-du-Lac** [04 79 25 01 76; fax 04 79 25 32 94; camping@bourgetdulac.com; www.bourgetdulac.com] Fr N foll Bourget-du-Lac & Lac sp soon after Tunnel Le Chat. Fr Chambery take N504 dir Aix-les-Bains; foll sp to Le Bourget-du-Lac & Le Lac, bear R at Camping/Plage sp to site at end of rd. Lge, shd; wc (cont); baby facs; shwrs inc; el pts (6A) €3.35; gas; lndtte; ice; shop; tradsmn; rest; snacks; bar; playgrnd; lake beach & sw; waterslide; boating; watersports; entmnt; TV; some statics; dogs €1.30; phone; bus; adv bkg; quiet; red low ssn; CCI. "On beautiful lake; mountain scenery; old facs, need modernising; ground stoney." ♦ 1 May-30 Sep. € 16.70   2005*

AIX LES BAINS *9B3* (3km W) **Camping International du Sierroz, Blvd Robert Barrier, Route du Lac, 73100 Aix-les-Bains** [tel/fax 04 79 61 21 43; campingsierroz@aixlesbains.com] Fr Annecy on N201, thro Aix-les-Bains, turn R at site sp. Keep to lakeside rd, site on R. Lge, hdg/mkd pitch, pt sl, shd; htd wc; chem disp; mv service pnt; baby facs; shwrs inc; el pts (3-6A) inc; gas; lndtte; ice; shop; tradsmn; rest; snacks; bar; playgrnd; pool 1km; games area; golf 4km; TV; 5% statics; dogs €1.55; poss cr; no adv bkg; quiet; pleasant location; vg san facs." ♦ 15 Mar-15 Nov. € 18.50   2003*

AIX LES BAINS *9B3* (2.5km NW Urban) **Camping Alp'Aix, 20 Blvd du Port aux Filles, 73100 Aix-les-Bains** [04 79 88 97 65; camping.alp.aix@wanadoo.fr] Fr N or S on N201 turn at rndabt sp 'Lac/Ports/Campings'. Nr Petit Port turn off Blvd Barrier into Bldv du Port au Filles, site on L in 200m. Med, hdg/mkd pitch, shd; htd wc; chem disp; shwrs inc; el pts (6-10A) €2; gas; lndtte; ice; sm shop; tradsmn; rest, bar 500m; BBQ; playgrnd; 2 pools; lake sw 200m; watersports nr; TV; some statics; dogs €1.10; bus 50m; poss cr; adv bkg rec high ssn; quiet; noise fr lake bandstand; red long stay. "Ltd san facs; excel, well-run site; conv lakes & ports, lake prom; ask at recep for free bus pass to Aix." ♦ ltd. 15 Apr-30 Sep. € 11.80   2005*

AIXE SUR VIENNE *7B3* (Urban) **Camp Municipal Les Greves, Ave des Greves, 87700 Aixe-sur-Vienne** [tel/fax 05 55 70 12 98 or 05 55 70 77 00 (Mairie); camping@mairie-aixesurvienne.fr] 13km SW fr Limoges, on N21 twds Perigueux, cross bdge over Rv Vienne & in about 600m turn to R (site sp) by rv. Steep down hill app & U-turn into site - take care gate posts! Med, shd; wc (cont); chem disp; mv service pnt; shwrs inc; el pts (10A) €2.30; lndtte; shops adj; tradsmn; rest, snacks, bar 500m; playgrnd; pool adj; rv sw; fishing; quiet; poss cr; adv bkg; dogs; "Conv touring Limoges area & Vienne valley; several chateaux easy reach; on banks of rv with public path outside hedge; excel rv bank pitches; v clean site & san facs; gd disabled facs; no twin-axles." ♦ 1 Jun-30 Sep. € 10.00   2005*

AIZELLES *3C4* (Rural) **Camping Gites/Aire Naturelle (Bartholome), Rue du Moulin, 02820 Aizelles** [03 23 22 41 18] Fr Laon take N44 dir Reims; in 13km turn L on D88 to Aizelles; site sp in vill 'Camping a la Ferme'. Fr Reims on N44 turn R to Aizelles on D889 past Corbeny. Turn onto Rue du Moulin & site on R in 250m. Camping sp at church says 100m but allow 300m to see ent. Sm, pt sl, pt shd; wc; chem disp; shwrs €1; el pts (4-6A) €3.50; shop 2km; tradsmn; playgrnd; 75% statics; poss cr; some Eng spkn; quiet but poss noisy w/e; cc not acc; CCI. "Clean, tidy, beautifully kept CL-type farm site; friendly helpful owner; lovely quiet vill nrby; gates clsd 2200-0700; facs ltd but adequate; conv for ferry; excel." 15 Apr-30 Sep. € 14.10   2005*

AIZENAY *2H4* (1.5km SE) **Camp Municipal La Foret, Route de la Roche, 85190 Aizenay** [02 51 34 78 12; fax 02 51 94 60 46] Exit Aizenay on D948 twd La Roche-sur-Yon. Site 1.5km on L. Med, mkd pitch, pt shd; wc; chem disp; mv service pnt; shwrs inc; el pts (6A); gas; lndtte; ice; shop 1km; rest 1.5km; snacks; bar; BBQ; playgrnd; htd pool; lake beach & sw 1km; tennis; 10% statics; dogs; phone; adv bkg (dep req); quiet; cc acc; red low ssn/CCI. ♦ ltd. 15 May-30 Sep.   2003*

AIZENAY *2H4* (6km NW Rural) **Camping La Residence du Lac, Chemin du Village Vacances, 85190 Mache** [tel/fax 02 51 55 20 30; laresidence dulac@libertysurf.fr; www.residence-du-lac.com] Fr Aizenay take D948 twds Challans. Take D40 to Mache, pass church & sw pool, site sp. Med, hdg pitch, hdstg, pt sl, pt shd; wc; chem disp; mv service pnt; baby facs; shwrs inc; el pts (16A) €3; gas; lndtte; ice; shop; snacks; bar; playgrnd; htd pool; sand beach 20km; lake sw adj; tennis 200m; fishing; watersports; games area; entmnt; 97% statics; dogs; Eng spkn; adv bkg; quiet; CCI. "Space for only 2-4 touring c'vans on rough ground." ♦ 15 Jun-15 Sep. € 16.00   2005*

AIZENAY *2H4* (6km NW Rural) **Camping Val de Vie Sarl, Rue du Stade, 85190 Mache** [tel/fax 02 51 60 21 02; campingvaldevie@aol.com] Fr Aizenay on D948 dir Challans. After 5km turn L onto D40 to Mache. Fr vill cent cont twd Apremont. Sm, blue site sp 100m on L. Med, hdg/mkd pitch, pt sl, pt shd; wc; chem disp; 10% serviced pitch; baby facs; fam bthrm; shwrs inc; el pts (4-10A) €2.90-3.50; lndtte; ice; shops 200m; BBQ; playgrnd; pool; beach 20km; tennis adj; lake 300m; fishing; boat hire; cycle hire; 10% statics; dogs €2; phone in vill; Eng spkn; adv bkg (dep); quiet; red low ssn; CCI. "Lovely clean site & facs; friendly British owners; peaceful, pleasant rural location in pretty vill; gd touring cent; gd cycling; steel pegs useful." ♦ 1 May-30 Sep. € 17.00   2005*

ALBAN *8E4* (Rural) **Camp Municipal La Franqueze, 81250 Alban** [05 63 55 91 87 or 05 63 55 82 09 (Mairie); fax 05 63 55 01 97; mairie.alban@wanadoo.fr] W of Albi on D999 turn L at ent to Alban. Site 300m on R, sp. Sm, hdg pitch, pt sl, pt shd; wc; shwrs; el pts (6A) €1.80; ice; lndtte; playgrnd; rv fishing; adv bkg; quiet; CCI. "In beautiful country conv Tarn Valley; friendly warden; excel long stay." 1 Jun-30 Sep. € 6.30   2005*

ALBAS see Castelfranc *7D3*

ALBERT *3B3* (500m N Urban) **Camp Municipal du Velodrome, Rue Henry Dunant, 80300 Albert** [03 22 75 22 53] Fr town cent take Rue Godin E adjacent to Basilica & foll sp for site. Easiest access fr Bapaume (N) towards Albert; turn R at camping sp on edge of town. Med, mkd pitch, unshd; wc; chem disp; mv service pnt; shwrs €1.65; el pts (4-10A) €3-3.25 (rev pol); shop 1km; 40% statics; poss cr in high ssn; adv bkg; CCI. "Clean, well-run site with excel facs; ideal for WWI battlefields; fishing adj; warden 1000-1200 & 1700-1900 low ssn, if absent lift barrier & site self." ♦ 1 Apr-30 Sep. € 7.20
                    2005*

ALBERT *3B3* (10km N Rural) **Camping Les Galets, Route de Beaumont, 80560 Auchonvillers** [03 22 76 28 79; jlrenshaw@hotmail.com] Fr Albert take D929 dir Bapaume. At Pozieres turn L to Thiepval on D73. Cont to Hamel & Auchonvillers. At x-rds in Auchonvillers turn R & foll rd D163 to Beaumont, site on R after 1km. Sm, pt sl, pt shd; 2 wc in barn, 2 shwrs; ltd el pts (5A) €1.50; shop 3km; rest; Eng spkn; v quiet; CCI. "CL-type site in field of British-owned B&B; conv battlefields; vg." Easter-15 Oct. € 10.00   2004*

ALBERT *3B3* (5km NE Rural) **International Camping Bellevue, 25 Rue d'Albert, 80300 Authuille** [03 22 74 59 29; fax 03 22 74 05 14] Take D929 Albert to Bapaume rd; in 3km turn L at La Boiselle, foll sp to Aveluy cont to Authuille. Site on R in vill cent. Med, hdg pitch, pt sl, pt shd; wc; chem disp; shwrs; el pts (5A) inc (rev pol); ice; rest; shop 7km; tradsmn; playgrnd; rv fishing 500m; 80% statics; adv bkg; quiet; poss noisy at w/e; CCI. "Useful touring Somme WW1 battlefield; walking dist of Thiepval Ridge; basic, v dated san facs poss unclean low ssn; NH only." 1 Mar-31 Oct. € 13.50
                    2004*

ALBERT *3B3* (10km SE Rural) **Camp Municipal Les Charnilles, 80340 Cappy** [03 22 76 14 50; fax 03 22 76 62 74] Fr Albert S on D329 to Bray-sur-Somme; turn L in Bray onto D1; 100m after vill sp Cappy, turn R (opp D197 to Lille). Site in 500m at end of lane. Med, hdg/mkd pitch, hdstg, pt shd; htd wc; chem disp; shwrs; el pts (6A) inc; lndry rm; shops 1km; tradsmn; quiet; cc not acc; CCI. "Clean, well-laid out site; owner friendly & helpful; conv A1 a'route; pretty vill on Rv Somme; ltd touring pitches." 15 Mar-31 Oct. € 10.00   2004*

ALBERT *3B3* (10km SW Rural) **Camping Les Puits Tournants, 6 Rue du Marais, 80800 Sailley-le-Sec** [tel/fax 03 22 76 65 56; camping. puitstournant@wanadoo.fr; www.camping-les-puits-tournants.com] Fr Bapaume on D929 dir Amiens, at Albert take D42 S to Sailley-Laurette then turn R onto D223 to Sailly-le-Sec & foll sp. Or fr A1 junc twd Albert onto N29. At Lamotte-Warfusee R onto D42 to Sailley-Laurette, turn L to Sailley-le-Sec. Med, some hdg pitch, some hdstg; pt shd; htd wc; chem disp; mv service pnt; shwrs inc; el pts (4A) €2.50; gas; lndtte; ice; shop; tradsmn; BBQ; playgrnd; pool; lake & rv sw; fishing; sports area; canoe & cycle hire; tennis 2km; horseriding 5km; TV rm; 60% statics; dogs; adv bkg; quiet. "Excel site." ♦ 1 Apr-31 Oct. € 16.00 (3 persons) (CChq acc)   2005*

ALBERTVILLE *9B3* (Urban) **Camp Municipal des Adoubes, Pont des Adoubes, Ave de Camping, 73200 Albertville** [04 79 32 06 62 or 04 79 32 04 02; fax 04 79 32 87 09; sylvaine.bouchet@albertville. com; www.albertville.com] 200m fr town cent; over bdge on banks of Rv Arly. Med, unshd; wc (cont); own san; chem disp (wc); shwrs inc; el pts (3A) inc; ice; gas; lndtte; shop 200m; tradsmn; rest, bar 200m; playgrnd; pool 1km; entmnt; dogs €0.80; poss cr; Eng spkn; adv bkg; some rd noise; 20% red CCI. "Fair NH; v helpful warden." 28 Apr-23 Sep. € 13.30   2004*

ALBERTVILLE *9B3* (3km NE Rural) **Camping Les Marmottes, 73200 Venthon** [04 79 32 57 40] Fr Albertville take N90 SE, exit junc 32 for Tours-en-Savoie on D990. Drive thro vill, site on R outside vill limits sign. Med, pt sl, pt shd; htd wc (some cont); chem disp; mv service pnt; shwrs inc; el pts (3-10A) inc; lndry rm; shops 3km; poss cr; adv bkg; no cc acc; quiet. "Gd views of Alps in all dirs; vg long/sh stay." Easter-15 Sep. € 13.40   2005*

ALBERTVILLE *9B3* (2km SE Urban) **Camping La Maladiere, 2263 Route de Tours, 73200 Albertville** [tel/fax 04 79 37 80 44]   SE fr cent Albertville take N90 twds Moutiers. After approx 4km turn off sp La Bathie & Tours-en-Savoie. Turn L under D90 & left onto D990 thro Tours-en-Savoie. Site 300m after exit sp on R. Sm, pt shd; wc; shwrs inc; el pts (10A) €4,30; ice; playgrnd; 50% statics; poss cr; adv bkg; quiet. "Gd NH." ♦ 15 Feb-15 Nov. € 7.00   2002*

ALBI *8E4* (1.5km E Urban) **Camping Caussels, Chemin du Camping, 81000 Albi** [tel/fax 05 63 60 37 06] Fr Albi head twd Millau on D999 sp Lacaune/St Juery & Camping for about 1.5km; at hypmkt immed turn L into rd to site. Fr W round ring rd to D999 sp Millau foll picture camping/piscine sp. Med, mkd pitch, pt terr, shd; wc (some cont); chem disp; shwrs inc; el pts (4-10A) €2.50-4.50; lndtte; ice; supmkt adj; snacks; BBQ; playgrnd; pool adj (caps ess); 5% statics; poss cr; Eng spkn; adv bkg; quiet; red CCI. "Fair NH; helpful staff; c clean; pitches unlevel - soft in wet - & some poss diff lge o'fits due trees." 1 Apr-15 Oct. € 11.00   2004*

ALBIAS see Montauban *8E3*

ALBINE *8F4* (Rural) **Camping de l'Estap, 81240 Albine** [05 63 98 34 74; fred@infonie.fr] Fr Mazamet on N112 dir Beziers exit on R (D88) sp Albine. Site in 2km. Sm, hdg/mkd pitch, hdstg, terr, pt shd; wc; chem disp; shwrs inc; el pts (6A) €2.70; lndtte; tradsmn; snacks; bar; pools; sports area; fishing; poss cr; Eng spkn; adv bkg dep req; quiet; CCI. "Excel base for Haute Languedoc; superb views; v friendly, helpful owner; excel long/sh stays." 1 Apr-15 Sep. € 10.50   2004*

ALBON see St Rambert d'Albon *9C2*

ALBOUSSIERE *9C2* **Camp Municipal, 07440 Alboussiere** [04 75 58 20 91 or 04 75 58 30 64] App fr Valence on D533 (Valence-Lamastre) turn L on ent vill of Alboussiere onto D219 sp Vernoux. (Do not take D14 which is 1st Vernoux turn). Site sp. Med, pt shd; wc; shwrs inc; el pts (15-20A) €2.30-€3.05; ice; lndry rm; shops 1.2km; playgrnd; tennis; rv fishing; lake sw adj; adv bkg; quiet. 15 Jun-15 Sep. € 6.55   2002*

ALENCON *4E1* (1km SW Rural) **Camp Municipal de Guerame, 65 Rue de Guerame, 61000 Alencon** [tel/fax 02 33 26 34 95] Located nr town cent. Fr N on N138 take N12 W (Carrefour sp). In 5km take D1 L sp Conde-sur-Sarthe. At rndabt turn L sp Alencon then R immed after Carrefour supmkt, foll site sp. Med, hdg pitches, hdstg, pt shd; htd wc (some cont); chem disp; mv service pnt; baby facs; shwrs inc; baby facs; el pts (5A) €2.85 (long cable for some pitches); lndtte; ice; shop, snacks, bar adj; BBQ; playgrnd; pool complex 700m; tennis; boating; rv fishing; canoeing; cycle hire; horseriding; entmnt; TV rm; dogs €1.65; poss cr; Eng spkn; adv bkg; quiet but w disco noise; no cc acc; CCI. "Sm pitches, some poss flooded in heavy rain; helpful warden; gd, clean san facs; o'night area for m'vans at site ent; security code-operated barrier; barrier/recep clsd 1800 low ssn; gd rvside walk; arboretum nrby; low ssn phone ahead to check site open." ♦ 1 Apr-31 Oct. € 9.30   2005*

See advertisement

FRANCE

ALES *10E1* (13km SE) **Camping Les Vistes,** 30360 St Jean-de-Ceyrargues [04 66 83 29 56 or 04 66 83 28 09; info@lesvisites.com; www.lesvistes.com] Fr Ales take D981 sp Uzes. After 12km take D7 S sp Brignon. At St Jean-de-Ceyrargues foll sp. Site S of vill on D7. Med, hdg/mkd pitch, pt sl, pt shd; wc; chem disp; baby facs; fam bthrm; shwrs inc; el pts (4A) €2.30; lndtte; shops, rest, bar 2km; tradsmn high ssn; playgrnd; pool; TV rm; Eng spkn; quiet; CCI. "Excel views; excel pools; conv for Pont du Gard, Uzes; diff access some pitches; excel all stays." ♦ 1 Apr-30 Sep. € 15.00   2005*

ALES *10E1* (6km S Rural) **Camping Mas Cauvy,** 30380 St Christol-les-Ales [04 66 60 78 24; http://fermemascauvy.free.fr] Fr Ales on N110 S sp Montpellier. At S end of Christol-les-Arles take 2nd rd on L after the stone needle. Foll sp to site. Site in 1.5km. Sm, pt terr, pt shd; wc; chem disp (wc); shwrs inc; el pts (6A) €2.50; gas 1.5km; lndtte; ice; shop 1.5km; tradsmn; BBQ; playgrnd; pool; tennis 3km; bus (1km); dogs €2; poss cr; adv bkg (dep req); quiet. "V attractive, friendly CL-type site with lovely views; book early for shd pitch; 10% red on local attractions; excel long/sh stay." 1 Apr-30 Sep. € 10.50   2005*

ALES *10E1* (5km NW Rural) **Camping La Croix Clementine,** Route de Mende, 30480 Cendras [04 66 86 52 69; fax 04 66 86 54 84; clementine@clementine.fr; www.clementine.fr] Fr Ales cent foll sp Toutes Directions to N106 sp Grand Colombe/Mende. Rv on R. At right lts (g'ge on corner) turn L sp Grande Colombe. 5km after Cendras turn L on D32, site on L 1.5km. Site sp fr Ales cent. Lge, pt sl, terr, pt shd; wc (some cont); shwrs inc; el pts (10A) inc; lndtte; shop; rest; snacks; playgrnd; 3 pools; rv sw 3km; tennis; games area; cycle hire; mini-golf; games rm; TV rm; entmnt; statics; poss cr; Eng spkn; adv bkg rec high ssn (dep req); ltd facs low ssn; quiet. "Excel family-run site; friendly, helpful staff; gd value winter storage avail." ♦ 1 Apr-15 Sep. € 21.00   2003*

†**ALET LES BAINS** *8G4* (Rural) **Camping Val d'Aleth,** Chemin de la Paoulette, 11580 Alet-les-Bains [04 68 69 90 40; fax 04 68 69 94 60; info@valdaleth.com; www.valdaleth.com] Fr Limoux S on D118 twd Quillan; in approx 8km ignore 1st L turn over Aude bdge into vill but take alt rte for heavy vehicles. Immed after x-ing rv, turn L in front of casino & ent town fr S; site sp on L. Sm, shd, hdg/mkd pitch, hdstg, pt sl; wc (some cont); chem disp (wc); shwrs inc; el pts (4-10A) €2.50-4; gas; lndtte; ice; shop adj; BBQ (gas only); playgrnd; pool 1km; rv/beach adj; cycle hire; dogs €1.20; phone; poss cr; adv bkg (dep req); some rd & train noise, church bells; cc not acc; 10% red low ssn 3+ days; cc not acc; CCI. "Rvside site in attractive vill with excel rests; awnings extra; British owners; v clean san facs but poss stretched high ssn; shwrs under cover but outside; sm pitches (lge o'fits will need to book); church bells; conv Carcassonne & wine cellars of Limoux." € 11.00   2005*

ALEX see Annecy *9B3*

ALLANCHE *7C4* (2km SE Rural) **Camp Municipal du Camp Vallat,** 15160 Allanche [04 71 20 45 87; fax 04 71 20 49 26] Fr Clermont-Ferrand on A75 take exit Massiac, site on N side of D679. Med, pt sl, pt shd; wc; chem disp; mv service pnt 1km; shwrs; el pts (6A) €1.85; lndtte; shops 2km; rest; snacks; bar; playgrnd; rv 5km; v quiet; CCI. "Steep steps to san facs; attractive rural surroundings; mkt Tues." ♦ 15 Jun-15 Sep. € 4.10   2005*

ALLAS LES MINES see Sarlat la Caneda *7C3*

ALLEGRE *9C1* (N Rural) **Camp Municipal La Pinede,** Le Chier, 43270 Allegre [04 71 00 76 79 or 04 71 00 71 21 (Mairie); mairie.allegre@wanadoo.fr] N on D13 fr Allegre site visible on N edge of Allegre. Sm, pt shd; wc (some cont); shwrs; el pts (3-6A) €1.40-€2.30; gas; shop in vill; dogs €1; poss cr; quiet; adv bkg. 1 Jun-30 Sep. € 7.30   2002*

ALLEGRE *9C1* (2km NE Rural) **LES CASTELS** Le Chateau de Boisson, 30500 Allegre-les-Fumades [04 66 24 85 61 or 04 66 24 82 21; fax 04 66 24 80 14; reception@chateaudeboisson.com; www.chateau-boisson.com or www.les-castels.com] Fr Ales NE on D904, turn R after Les Mages onto D132, then L onto D16 for Boisson. Fr A7 take exit 19 Pont l'Esprit, turn S on N86 to Bagnols-sur-Ceze & then D6 W. Before Vallerargues turn R onto D979 Lussan, then D37 & D16 to Boisson. Lge, hdg/mkd pitch, pt sl, shd; wc; chem disp; shwrs inc; el pts (5-6A) inc; gas; lndtte; shop; tradsmn; rest; snacks; bar; no BBQ; playgrnd; 2 pools (1 htd & covrd); tennis; mini-golf; cycle hire; entmnt; 80% statics; no dogs Jul/Aug; phone; poss cr; Eng spkn; adv bkg (dep req + bkg fee); quiet; 15% red 15+ days, red low ssn; cc acc. "Vg, well-run site; peaceful." ♦ 10 Apr-30 Sep. € 31.00   2005*

See advertisement

ALLEGRE *9C1* (2km S) **Camping Le Domaine des Fumades,** 30500 Allegre [04 66 24 80 78; fax 04 66 24 82 42; domaine.des.frumades@wanadoo.fr; www.domaine-des-fumades.com] Take Bollene exit fr A7 m'way, foll sps to Bagnols-sur-Ceze, take D6 twd Ales; 10km bef Ales turn R sp Les Fumades on D7 to site in 5km; easy to find fr Ales ring rd. Med, pt shd; wc; chem disp; baby facs; shwrs inc; el pts (4A) inc; gas; lndtte; shop; rest; bar; playgrnd; pool & paddling pool; tennis; golf & watersports nr; dogs €1.90; adv bkg. "V pleasant location; friendly staff; beautiful site; well-run." ♦ 11 May-8 Sep. € 26.50   2002*

ALLEMANS DU DROPT see Miramont de Guyenne *7D2*

ALLEMONT see Bourg d'Oisans, Le *9C3*

ALLES SUR DORDOGNE see Bugue, Le *7C3*

ALLEVARD *9B3* (11km S Rural) **Camp Municipal Neige & Nature, Chemin de Montarmand, 38580 La Ferriere-d'Allevard** [tel/fax 04 76 45 19 84; contact@neige.nature.fr; www.neige-nature.fr] Fr Allevard take D525A S to La Ferriere; foll sp Collet & Le Pleynet. Sm, hdg/mkd pitch, pt sl, terr, pt shd; htd wc; chem disp; baby facs; shwrs; el pts (10A) €3.40; gas 200m; lndtte; ice; shop 200m; snacks; bar; playgrnd; games area; TV; entmnt; rv & lake fishing; Eng spkn; adv bkg (dep req); quiet; red long stay. "Outstanding site in wonderful scenery; many mkd walks, some strenuous." ♦ ltd. 15 May-15 Sep. € 13.50   2005*

ALLONNES see Saumur *4G1*

ALTKIRCH *6F3* (1km SE Rural) **Camping Les Acacias, Chemin de Hirtzbach, 68130 Altkirch** [03 89 40 69 40] Sp on D419 on app to town fr W. Sp in town. Sm, mkd pitch, shd; htd wc (some cont); chem disp; baby facs; shwrs inc; el pts (10A) €3; shop in ssn & 1km; rest; snacks; bar; playgrnd; pool 1km; dogs €0.80; Eng spkn; adv bkg rec high ssn; quiet; CCI. "Gd, clean facs; office clsd until 1700 in afternoon - site yourself & pay later; gd NH." 15 Apr-15 Oct. € 8.50   2005*

ALTKIRCH *6F3* (12.5km SW Rural) **Camp Municipal des Lupins, Rue de l'Ancienne Gare, 68500 Seppois-le-Bas** [tel/fax 03 89 25 65 37; leslupins@wanadoo.fr] SW fr Altkirch on D432, after 3km turn R to Hirtzbach on D17 foll sp to Seppois-le-Bas. Site sp in vill. Med, mkd pitch, pt shd; htd wc; chem disp; shwrs inc; baby facs; el pts (6A) €3.20; ice; lndtte; shop 500m; supmkt nrby; tradsmn; rest; snacks; bar 100m; BBQ; playgrnd; pool; paddling pool; games area; TV; walking; fishing; golf 5km; 60% statics; dogs; phone; adv bkg; quiet midwk; noisy w/e; cc acc; 10% red CCI. "Excel mod facs; Belfort worth visit; stork sanctuary adj; 1 hour Germany; 30 mins Switzerland; lge groups w/e." ♦ 1 Apr-31 Oct. € 11.10   2005*

ALVIGNAC see Rocamadour *7D3*

ALZONNE *8F4* (3km N Rural) **Camping a la Ferme, Domaine de Contresty, 800013 Raissac-sur-Lampy** [04 68 76 04 29; jh_cante@club.fr; www.aude-tourisme.com] Take N113 W fr Carcassonne; after 12km in Alzonne take 2nd R after traff lts, sp Camping a la Ferme. In 2km turn L sp Contresty. Sm, pt shd; wc; chem disp (wc); shwrs inc; el pts (6A) €3; lndtte; ice; tradsmn; BBQ; playgrnd; pool; no dogs; bus 2km; adv bkg; v quiet. "CL-type site on hilltop; views of Pyrenees; excel for Carcassonne (18km); Cathar castles; gd birdwatching; helpful, friendly owner." ♦ 1 Apr-30 Oct. € 17.00   2005*

AMBAZAC *7B3* (1.8km NE Rural) **Camp Municipal de Jonas, 87240 Ambazac** [05 55 56 60 25] Fr A20 foll sp to Ambazac; site on D914. Med, terr, pt shd (mainly cont); shwrs inc; el pts (10A) €2.05; ice; shop & 2km; playgrnd; lake sw, fishing, watersports & shgl beach adj; quiet but some noise at night. "Friendly staff; excel waterside site; san facs need upgrade but clean." 1 Jun-15 Sep. € 6.90   2004*

AMBERT *9B1* (1km S Urban) **Camping Les Trois Chenes, Rue de la Chaise-Dieu, 63600 Ambert** [04 73 82 34 68 or 04 73 82 23 95 (LS); fax 04 73 82 44 00; tourisme@ville-ambert.fr] On main rd D906 S twd Le Puy bet Leisure Park & Aquacentre. Med, hdg/mkd pitch, pt shd, serviced pitch; wc (some cont); chem disp; el pts (10A) €2.90; gas 400m; lndtte; ice; supermkt adj; tradsmn; rest nrby; playgrnd; htd pool adj; waterslide; dogs €1; poss cr; adv bkg (dep €22.90); quiet but some traff noise; cc not acc; CCI. "Clean san facs; vg; steam train adj, steam museum & working paper mill nr; pretty rvside walk to town; rec arrive bef noon in peak." ♦ 8 May-29 Sep. € 11.10   2005*

AMBERT *9B1* (9km S) **Camping de la Graviere, 63940 Marsac-en-Livradois** [04 73 95 60 08 or 04 73 95 61 62 (Mairie); fax 04 73 95 66 87] Ent vill fr Ambert foll sp to camp, turn L off N106. Med, pt shd; wc; shwrs inc; el pts (5A) inc (long lead poss req); ice; lndry rm (no hot water); shop 500m; tennis; playgrnd; fishing adj; quiet. "Warden calls; unreliable opening dates, phone ahead." 15 May-15 Oct. € 8.10   2004*

AMBERT *9B1* (10km W Rural/Urban) **Camp Municipal Saviloisirs (formerly Village Camping)**, 63890 St Amant-Roche-Savine [tel/fax 04 73 95 73 60 or 04 73 95 70 22 (Mairie)] W fr Ambert on D996 to St Amant, turn R onto D37 into vill. In vill cent turn R & foll site sp. Bear L at lge building facing, site on L. Sm, hdg/mkd pitch, pt shd; wc; chem disp; shwrs inc; el pts (16A) inc (rev pol); ice; lndtte; rest 300m; shops adj; playgrnd; rv 1km; lake 1km; fishing 1km; cycle hire; horseriding; archery; entmnt; TV; dogs; quiet; CCI. "Tranquil vill site in beautiful area; spotless; mod facs; pleasant staff; easy walk to town; woodland walks." 1 May-30 Sep. € 8.80   2005*

Some of these sites have changed their opening dates - we'd better fill in some site report forms and let the editor of the guide know.

AMBLETEUSE see Wimereux *3A2*

AMBOISE *4G2* (Urban) **Camp Municipal L'Ile d'Or**, 37400 Amboise [02 47 57 23 37; fax 02 47 23 19 80; sports.loisirs@ville-amboise.fr] Site on island in middle of Rv Loire; access fr bdge spanning rv; fr Paris-Tours-Poitiers a'route exit at Tours Centre. Take D751 dir Blois. In Amboise get in L lane to cross bdge to site. Lge, mkd pitch, pt shd; wc; chem disp; mv service pnt; shwrs inc; el pts (6A) €1.90 (poss rev pol); lndtte; ice; shop & 1km; rest; snacks; bar; playgrnd; pool & waterslide 2km (high ssn); tennis; fishing; entmnt; TV; dogs €1; phone; poss cr; Eng spkn; rd noise; cc acc; CCI. "Twin-axle vans not acc; conv Amboise Chateau & Loire Valley; lge wooded island; bureau open 0800-1330 & 1400-2100 high ssn; clean facs but clsd afternoons low ssn; easy walk to town; midsummer week music festival in adj park (v noisy) so check festival date; poss poor security; €20 dep req for barrier pass." ♦ Easter-30 Sep. € 9.90   2005*

AMBOISE *4G2* (4km N Rural) **Camp Municipal des Patis**, 37530 Nazelles-Negron [02 47 57 71 07 or 02 47 23 71 71] Fr Amboise, take N152 twd Tours & turn R (N) onto D5 to Nazelles-Negron. Foll sp to vill. Site N of bdge over Rv Cisse on R. Med, mkd pitch, shd; wc (some cont); chem disp; shwrs inc; el pts (6A) €2.13 (long lead poss req); lndry rm; shops 100m; playgrnd; dogs €0.82; quiet; CCI. "Clean, well-kept site; boggy in wet weather; gd facs; security gate operated by part-time warden; low ssn open only 0900-1000 & 1800-1900 - unsuitable for m'vans; key issued for lower barrier; no lge vans or twin-axles, v ltd off-site parking for car+van; vg long/sh stay/NH." 1 May-30 Sep. € 10.00   2005*

†**AMBOISE** *4G2* (6km NE Rural) **Camping Le Jardin Botanique, 9 bis, Rue de la Riviere**, 37530 Limeray [02 47 30 13 50; fax 02 47 30 17 32; info@camping-jardinbotanique.com; www.camping-jardinbotanique.com] Fr Amboise on N152 on N side of Rv Loire dir Blois, site sp in Limeray. Med, hdg/mkd pitch, hdstg, pt shd; htd wc (some cont); chem disp; mv service pnt; baby facs; fam bthrm; shwrs inc; el pts (10A); gas; lndtte; shop 2km; tradsmn; rest; snacks; bar; BBQ; playgrnd; pool; sand beach 15km; tennis; games area; cycle hire; TV; 15% statics; dogs €1.50; Eng spkn; adv bkg; red long stay/CCI. "Gd touring base Loire chateaux & vineyards; 500m fr rv; gd cycle rtes; v friendly." ♦ € 13.50   2005*

See advertisement above

AMBOISE *4G2* (3km E Rural) **Camp Municipal Le Verdeau**, 37530 Charge [02 47 57 04 22 or 02 47 57 04 01 (Mairie); fax 02 47 57 41 52] Fr Amboise take D751 twd Blois, site sp on L. Med, pt shd; wc; chem disp; shwrs inc; el pts (5A); lndtte; tradsmn; playgrnd; rv fishing & boating; tennis; dogs; no twin-axle c'vans; adv bkg rec high ssn; quiet; CCI. "Gd cent for Loire Valley; site barrier clsd 1100-1600." ♦ 1 Jul-31 Aug.   2004*

AMBON PLAGES see Muzillac *2G3*

AMBRIERES LES VALLEES see Mayenne *4E1*

FRANCE

AMIENS *3C3* (8km N Rural) **Camping du Chateau,** 80260 Bertangles [03 22 93 37 73; fax 03 22 93 68 36; camping.bertangles@wanadoo.fr] Foll N25 N of Amiens; after 8km turn W on D97 to Bertangles. Well sp in vill. Sm, hdg pitch, pt sl, pt shd; wc; chem disp; shwrs inc; el pts (5A) €2.40 (poss rev pol); ice; tradsmn; tabac/bar in vill 6km; bus; poss cr; quiet but slight rd noise; red 8+ days; no cc acc; CCI. "Amiens v attractive city with marvellous cathedral; early arr rec; spotless san facs; vg warden; conducted tours of chateau high ssn; gd walks; gates open 0800-2200; excel." ♦ ltd. 21 Apr-11 Sep. € 11.50   2005*

AMIENS *3C3* (8km NW Rural) **Camping Parc des Cygnes, 111 Rue de Montieres, 80080 Amiens-Longpre** [tel/fax 03 22 43 29 28; camping. amiens@wanadoo.fr; www.parcdescygnes.com] Exit A16 junc 20 or fr ring rd Rocade Nord exit junc 40. Foll sp Amiens, Longpre D412 & site. Med, mkd pitch, pt shd; htd wc; chem disp; baby facs; shwrs; el pts (6A) inc; gas; lndtte; shop; snacks; bar; BBQ; playgrnd; fishing; cycle hire; games rm; internet; TV; dogs €1.60; bus; adv bkg; quiet; cc acc. "V pleasant site; helpful staff; gd canal-side cycling to city; office open 0830-2000 high ssn - ring bell by recep if clsd; Amiens cathedral worth visit & floating gardens." ♦ 1 Apr-15 Oct. € 22.20 ABS - P11   2005*

See advertisement above

AMPILLY LE SEC see Chatillon sur Seine *6F1*

ANCENIS *2G4* (12km E) **Camping de l'Ile Batailleuse, St Florent-le-Vieil, 44370 Varades** [02 40 83 45 01] On Ancenis-Angers rd N23 turn S in Varades onto D752 to St Florent-le-Vieil. After x-ing 1st bdge over Loire site on L on island immed bef 2nd bdge. Med, pt shd; wc; chem disp; shwrs inc; el pts (10A) €2; shops 1km; rest 20m; playgrnd; pool 1km; tennis 1km; cycle hire; games area; dogs €1; poss cr; Eng spkn; quiet but poss road noise; CCI. "Basic, clean site; main shwr facs up stone staircase; facs for disabled on grnd floor; panoramic views of Loire in town; gd cycle rtes along Loire." ♦ 28 Apr-9 Oct. € 11.00   2005*

ANCENIS *2G4* (5km SW Rural) **Camping La Peche (formerly Camp Municipal de Beauregret),** 49530 Drain [02 40 98 20 30; fax 02 40 98 23 29] Fr Ancenis take D763 S for 2km, turn R onto D751 & cont for 3km. Site on R bef vill of Drain on L. Sm, hdg pitch, pt shd; wc; own san rec; chem disp; mv service pnt; shwrs inc; el pts (6-10A) €1.80-2.20 (poss rev pol); ice; lndtte; shop nr; BBQ; playgrnd; lake nrby; games area; entmnt; TV rm; phone; adv bkg; quiet. "Secluded site; gd fishing; san facs up steel steps, poss poor low ssn; poss not suitable lge o'fits." ♦ 1 May-30 Sep. € 6.50   2005*

Will you fill in the site report forms at the back of the guide, or shall I?

ANCENIS *2G4* (1km W Rural) **Camping de l'Ile Mouchet, La Davrays, 44150 Ancenis** [02 40 83 08 43 or 06 83 52 73 44; fax 02 40 83 16 19; efberthelot@wanadoo.fr; www. camping-estivance.com] Fr S turn L immed after x-ing Rv Loire & foll sp; site on banks of Loire. Med, mkd pitch, pt shd; wc; chem disp; mv service pnt; shwrs inc; el pts (6-10A) €2.30; lndtte; gas; shops adj; rest, snacks, bar high ssn; playgrnd; pool; rv sw nr; tennis 50m; games rm; TV; 12% statics; dogs; Eng spkn; adv bkg; quiet; cc acc; red low ssn/CCI. "Warden calls am & pm; rvside walk; ltd facs low ssn; excel." ♦ 1 Apr-7 Oct. € 11.50   2005*

ANDELOT BLANCHEVILLE *6F1* (1km W Rural) **Camping du Moulin, Rue du Moulin, 52700 Andelot-Blancheville** [03 25 01 60 50 or 03 25 01 33 31 (Mairie); fax 03 25 03 77 54] Fr N on N74 site sp on ent Andelot-Blancheville. Foll sp & turn L onto D147. Site on R in 1km. Med, hdg/mkd pitch, pt shd; wc; chem disp; shwrs inc; el pts (9A) inc; lndry rm; tradsmn; playgrnd; TV rm; dogs; Eng spkn; quiet; CCI. "Gd NH on journey S; beside rv." 1 Jun-15 Sep. € 10.20   2004*

ANDELYS, LES *3D2* (1km S Urban) **Camping L'Ile des Trois Rois**, 27700 Les Andelys [02 32 54 23 79; fax 02 32 51 14 54; campingtroisrois@aol.com; www.camping-troisrois.com] Fr Louviers after x-ing bdge over Seine, R at junc of D135 & D313 S of Les Andelys. Site on R in 100m. Lge, unshd; htd wc (cont); chem disp; mv service pnt; shwrs inc; el pts (6A) €3; lndtte; shop; tradsmn; rest; snacks; bar; BBQ; playgrnd; pool; fishing; bowling alley; 25% statics sep; dogs €1.50; phone; poss cr; Eng spkn; quiet; CCI. "Excel position on Rv Seine; ruins of Chateaux Gaillard opp; conv for Rouen, Evreux, Giverny; well cared for & san facs clean; dep for barrier key; excel." ♦ 1 Apr-31 Oct. € 13.00
2005*

†**ANDERNOS LES BAINS** *7D1* (3km NE Rural) **Camping Les Arbusiers (formerly Municipal)**, Ave de Bordeaux, 33510 Andernos-les-Bains [05 56 82 12 46] 7km E of Ares fr Bordeaux on D106, take D215 sp Andernos. Site on L in 2km, ent rd to airport. Lge, hdg/mkd pitch, pt shd; wc; chem disp; shwrs inc; el pts (6A) inc (poss rev pol); lndry rm; shop 2km; snacks; bar; BBQ; pool; sand beach 3km; 50% statics; dogs; Eng spkn; quiet; cc acc. "Friendly staff; fair long/sh stay." € 12.30   2003*

ANDERNOS LES BAINS *7D1* (3km NE) **Camping Pleine Foret**, Ave de Bordeaux, 33510 Andernos-les-Bains [05 56 82 17 18; fax 05 56 26 01 65; pleine.foret@wanadoo.fr; www.campingpleine foret.com] Take D106 fr Bordeaux, & app Andernos on D215 site on R opp sm airfield. Lge, shd; wc; shwrs; el pts (6A) €3; lndtte; playgrnd; pool; beach 2.5km; sailing 2.5km; entmnt; mostly statics; dogs; poss cr; quiet. "Tourers put on edge of site, app rds narr within site, care needed; recep clsd 1230-1500." 1 Apr-30 Sep. € 20.00   2005*

ANDERNOS LES BAINS *7D1* (2.5km SE Coastal) **Camping Fontaine Vieille**, 4 Blvd du Colonel Wurtz, 33510 Andernos-les-Bains [05 56 82 01 67; fax 05 56 82 09 81; FONTAINE-VIEILLE-SA@ wanadoo.fr; www.fontainevieille.com] Take D106 fr Bordeaux then D215 on L after 40km sp Andernos. Well sp. Site situated 600m off D3. V lge, hdg/mkd pitch, pt shd; wc (some cont); chem disp; mv service pnt; baby facs; shwrs inc; el pts (5A) inc; gas; lndtte; shop & 3km; rest; snacks; bar; pool/waterpark; sand beach adj; watersports inc windsurfing; games area; tennis; entmnt; TV; dogs €3; adv bkg rec high ssn; quiet; cc acc; red long stay/low ssn. "Organised bus trips & sports; some pitches sea view (extra charge); excel for families." ♦ 1 Apr-30 Sep. € 24.50   2005*

See advertisement above

ANDERNOS LES BAINS *7D1* (5km SE Coastal) **Camping Le Coq Hardi**, Cassy, 33138 Lanton [05 56 82 01 80; fax 05 56 82 16 11] At Facture on N250 fr Bordeaux turn R on D3 twd Andernos. Site on L sp at Cassy. Lge, pt shd; wc (cont); chem disp; mv service pnt; shwrs inc; el pts (6A) €3.50 (poss rev pol); gas; ice; shop high ssn; snacks; playgrnd; htd pool; paddling pool; sand beach adj; indoor sports hall; entmnt; 15% statics; dogs; phone; bus adj; adv bkg (fee €16); quiet low ssn; CCI. "Gd rests, shops nrby; pleasant view; peaceful low ssn; v helpful owners; gd pitches; vg long stay." 15 May-15 Sep. € 17.40   2003*

†**ANDERNOS LES BAINS** *7D1* (5km SE Coastal) **Camping Le Roumingue**, 60 Ave de la Liberation, 33138 Lanton [05 56 82 97 48; fax 05 56 82 96 09; info@roumingue.com; www.roumingue.com] Approx 7km SE of Andernos-les-Bains on D3 bet Cassy & Lanton. Lge, hdg/mkd pitch, pt shd; wc (some cont); mv service pnt; chem disp; serviced pitches; shwrs inc; el pts (6A) €4.35; gas; ice; lndtte; shop; tradsmn; rest; snacks; bar; playgrnd; pool; guarded private sand beach adj; lake sw; tennis; fishing; windsurfing; games/sports area; entmnt; TV; 50% statics; dogs €2.30; poss cr; Eng spkn; adv bkg (dep req); cc acc; red low ssn/long stay; CCI. "Family site; lge entmnt complex; many facs/activities; access rds & pitches liable to flooding low ssn; v ltd facs low ssn." ♦ € 22.00   2003*

FRANCE

ANDERNOS LES BAINS *7D1* (6km W Coastal) **Airotel Les Viviers, Route de Cap-Ferret, Claouey, 33950 Lege-Cap-Ferret [05 56 60 70 04; fax 05 57 70 37 77; lesviviers@wanadoo.fr; www.airotel-les-viviers.com]** Exit A10/A630 W for airport & Bordeaux-Merignac. Take D106 (sp Cap-Ferret), on exit vill of Claouey (on W side of Bassin d'Arcachon). Camp sp as being 1km away but ent on L after LH bend. V lge, hdg/mkd pitch, pt shd; htd wc; mv service pnt; chem disp; baby facs; sauna; shwrs inc; el pts (10A) €6; gas; lndtte; supmkt; rest; snacks; bar; BBQ (gas/elec); playgrnd; htd, covrd pool; paddling pool; waterslide; sea water lagoon adj with private sand beach adj; fishing; sailing; windsurfing; tennis; cycle hire; mini-golf; games area; games rm; cinema; entmnt; child entmnt; TV rm; 27% statics; dogs €4; bus; Eng spkn; adv bkg ess (bkg fee); quiet; cc acc; red long stay/low ssn/CCI. "Sand pitches; v clean san facs; free night bus along peninsular; vg." ♦ 8 Apr-1 Oct. € 37.00
2005*

See advertisement above

ANDERNOS LES BAINS *7D1* (6km W Coastal) Camp Municipal Les Embruns, Claouey, 33950 Lege-Cap-Ferret [05 56 60 70 76 or 05 56 03 84 00 (Mairie); fax 05 56 60 32 32] Foll D106 Bordeaux to Cap-Ferret. On ent Claouey turn R at 1st set of traff lts. Site sp. V lge, pt sl, shd; wc; chem disp; shwrs inc; el pts inc; lndtte; ice; shops adj; playgrnd; sand beach 700m; entmnt; statics; quiet. "Well laid out & organised; disco outside." ♦ 1 Feb-15 Dec. € 11.60
2003*

ANDERNOS LES BAINS *7D1* (6km W Coastal) **Camping Bremontier, Crohot, 33950 Lege-Cap-Ferret [tel/fax 05 56 60 03 99]** Fr Andernos NW on D3 to Ares. Take Cap Ferret rd D106. 1km after Lege turn R on D106E sp Le Crohot. Site at end of rd in 5km. Fr Bordeaux stay on D106 thro Ares & Lege & on D106E. Site at end of rd in 6km. Med, shd; wc; shwrs inc; el pts (5A) €3.10; gas; shop; sand beach 500m; dogs; quiet. 1 May-15 Sep. € 15.00
2003*

ANDERNOS LES BAINS *7D1* (5km NW Coastal) Camp Municipal Les Goelands, Ave de la Liberation, 33740 Ares [05 56 82 55 64; fax 05 56 82 07 51; camping-les.goelands@ wanadoo.fr; www.goelands.com] Fr Bordeaux m'way by-pass take D106 for Cap-Ferret. At Ares take D3 SE twd Andernos. Site on R 200m after end of Ares town sp. Site sp. Lge, mkd pitch, shd; wc; chem disp; shwrs inc; el pts (6A) €3.25; gas; lndtte; ice; shop; rest; snacks; bar; sand beach 300m; seawater lake 200m; dogs; poss cr; adv bkg; quiet; red low ssn; CCI. "Many gd beaches." ♦ 1 Apr-31 Oct. € 15.50   2002*

ANDERNOS LES BAINS *7D1* (5km NW Coastal) Camping La Cigale, Route de Lege, 33740 Ares [05 56 60 22 59; fax 05 57 70 41 66; campinglacigaleares@wanadoo.fr] Fr Andernos proceed NW on D3 to Ares. Take Cap-Ferret rd D106. Site on L in 1km. Med, shd; wc; shwrs inc; el pts (6A) inc; gas; lndtte; shop; rest; snacks; bar; BBQ; playgrnd; pool; beach 900m; games area; entmnt; TV; some statics; poss cr; adv bkg rec high ssn; quiet. ♦ 11 Apr-10 Oct. € 26.30   2003*

ANDERNOS LES BAINS *7D1* (5km NW Coastal) Camping Pasteur Vacances, 1 Rue Pasteur, 33740 Ares [05 56 60 33 33; fax 05 56 60 05 05; pasteur.vacances@wanadoo.fr] Take D106 Bordeaux-Ares. At rndabt in Ares cent take D3 twd Andernos. Turn R at camp sp, site on L. Sm, pt shd; wc; mv service pnt; shwrs inc; el pts (10A) inc; lndtte; snacks; shop adj; playgrnd; pool; beach adj & lake sw; dogs €2; poss cr; quiet; adv bkg; Eng spkn. "Friendly owners; cycle path round Arcachon Basin; gd long/sh stay." ♦ 1 Apr-30 Sep. € 19.50   2002*

†**ANDERNOS LES BAINS** *7D1* (7.5km NW Rural) Camping La Prairie, 93 Ave du Medoc, 33950 Lege-Cap-Ferret [tel/fax 05 56 60 09 75; camping-la-prairie@wanadoo.fr] Site 1km N of Lege-Cap-Ferret on D3 dir Porge. Med, pt shd; htd wc; chem disp; shwrs inc; el pts (10A) €2.85; lndtte; shop; snacks; BBQ; playgrnd; sand beach 5km; games area; games rm; entmnt; some statics; dogs €1.40; adv bkg; quiet; CCI. "Gd site." € 10.20
                    2005*

ANDERNOS LES BAINS *7D1* (8km NW Rural) Camping Mer et Foret, 101 Ave du Medoc, 33950 Lege-Cap-Ferret [05 56 60 18 36 or 05 56 60 16 99; fax 05 56 60 39 47] Fr Bordeaux take D106 W dir Ares. Fr cent Ares take D3 N sp Lege-Cap-Ferret. Site on L in 5km adj 'Camping Prairie'. Med, mkd pitch, pt shd; wc; chem disp; mv service pnt; shwrs €0.75; el pts (3-6A) €1.25-2.50; shop 2km; tradsmn; sand beach 6km; dogs; phone; quiet; CCI. "Gd for Arcachon Basin; clean & cheap for area; vg long stay." ♦ ltd. 1 Apr-30 Sep. € 8.50   2005*

ANDOUILLE see Laval *2F4*

ANDRYES see Clamecy *4G4*

ANDUZE *10E1* (5km E) Camping du Domaine de Gaujac, 30140 Boisset-et-Gaujac [04 66 61 80 65; fax 04 66 60 53 90; gravieres@clubinternet.fr; www.homair-vacances.fr or www.domaine-de-gaujac.com] Foll sp fr Ales take N110 S & turn R at D910 dir Anduze. At Bagard (3km bef Anduze) turn L at mini rndabt onto D264 dir Boisset & Gaujac. At next rndbt turn R, then immed L. Foll vill & camping sp. Lge, pt terr, shd; htd wc (some cont); chem disp; mv service pnt; some serviced pitches; shwrs inc; baby facs; el pts (4-6A) €3-3.50; gas; lndtte; ice; shop; rest; snacks; bar; BBQ; playgrnd; 2 htd pools; rv sw adj; fishing; tennis; cycle hire; games area; games rm; entmnt; internet; TV; 30% statics; dogs €2.50; Eng spkn; adv bkg rec high ssn; quiet; red low ssn. "V tranquil; helpful, friendly family owners; new htd san block 2004; Trabuc caves, Tarn gorges nrby. ♦ 1 Apr-30 Sep. € 18.50 (CChq acc)   2004*

ANDUZE *10E1* (2.5km SE) Camping Le Malhiver, Route de Nimes, 30140 Anduze [tel/fax 04 66 61 76 04] S fr Ales on N110; W on D910 to Anduze. In Anduze take D907 SE twds Nimes. Site on L, 200m after rlwy bdge. Med, mkd pitch, pt shd; wc; chem disp; serviced pitches; shwrs inc; el pts (6A) inc; gas; lndtte; shop 2km; tradsmn; rest; playgrnd; pool; rv adj; 10% statics; phone; adv bkg ess; quiet but some rd noise; CCI. "Delightful, well-kept site in superb location; vg facs but v ltd low ssn; gd base for Cevennes area." ♦ 1 May-15 Sep. € 23.00   2003*

ANDUZE *10E1* (10km W) Camping La Pommeraie, 30140 Thoiras [04 66 85 20 52; fax 04 66 85 20 53; info@la-pommeraie.fr] Fr Ales take N110, & D910 to Anduze, over bdge, R onto D907. In 6km L under rlwy onto D57, site on L 2.5km bef Lasalle. Med, shd; wc; baby facs; shwrs; el pts (6A) €4.50; gas; lndtte; shop; rest; snacks; bar; cooking facs; playgrnd; 2 pools; rv sw & beach adj; tennis; games area; entmnt; TV rm; some statics; dogs €3; adv bkg; quiet; red low ssn. Easter-30 Sep. € 16.50   2003*

ANDUZE *10E1* (1.4km NW) Camping Castel Rose, 30140 Anduze [04 66 61 80 15; castel.rose@ wanadoo.fr] Fr Ales S on N110 W on N910A to Anduze. Foll sp Camping L'Arche. Lge, shd; wc; shwrs inc; el pts (6-10A) €3-3.50; gas; lndtte; shop; rest; snacks; bar; pool; rv sw; fishing; boating; entmnt; TV; dogs €2; poss cr; adv bkg rec high ssn. "Gd cent touring Cevennes; attractive countryside." 16 Apr-18 Sep. € 16.00   2005*

ANDUZE *10E1* (1.5km NW Rural) Camping Les Fauvettes, 30140 Anduze [tel/fax 04 66 61 72 23] Site sp fr D907 to St Jean-du-Gard. Med, pt sl, terr, pt shd; wc; shwrs inc; el pts (6A) €2.60; gas; ice; shop; snacks; playgrnd; pool; waterslide; fishing; entmnt; TV; dogs €1.52; adv bkg; quiet. 1 May-20 Sep. € 15.25   2002*

ANDUZE *10E1* (2km NW Rural) **Camping L'Arche, Quartier de Labahou, 30140 Anduze** [04 66 61 74 08; fax 04 66 61 88 94; camping. arche@wanadoo.fr] Fr Ales S on N110/D910A to Anduze. On D907; sp on R. Access poss dff lge o'fits/m'vans. Lge, mkd pitch, shd; htd wc; chem disp; mv service pnt; baby facs; shwrs inc; el pts (6-10A) €1.70; gas; lndtte; shop; tradsmn; rest; snacks; bar; BBQ; playgrnd; rv sw; entmnt; TV; dogs €2.70; Eng spkn; adv bkg; quiet; red long stay; CCI. "Well-run site; gd san facs; beautiful area; bamboo gardens worth visit; 24hr security patrols." ♦ 21 Mar-30 Sep. € 22.90   2005*

ANDUZE *10E1* (4km NW Rural) **Camping-Caravaning Cevennes Provence, Corbes-Thoiras, 30140 Anduze** [04 66 61 73 10; fax 04 66 61 60 74; marais@camping-cevennes-provence.fr; www. camping-cevennes-provence.fr] Fr Anduze D907 & D284 along rvside after bdge, site sp. Lge, mkd pitch, terr, shd; wc (some cont); chem disp; serviced pitches; mv service pnt; baby facs; shwrs inc; el pts (10A) €3.70; gas; lndtte; ice; shop, rest, snacks, bar; playgrnd; shgl beach & rv sw adj; games area; games rm; TV; some statics; dogs €1.90; Eng spkn; adv bkg; quiet; red low ssn; CCI. "Ideal base for area; helpful recep; gd walking; vg." ♦ 20 Mar-1 Nov. € 17.50   2004*

ANET *3D2* (500m N Urban) **Camp Municipal, Rue des Cordeliers, 28260 Anet** [02 37 41 42 67 or 02 37 62 55 25 (Mairie); fax 02 37 62 20 99] Take D928 NE fr Dreux; in Anet thro town & turn R at chateau; turn L on rd to Ezy & Ivry (camp sp on corner), site in 150m N of rv. Lge, pt shd; wc; chem disp (wc); 75% serviced pitches; shwrs €1; el pts (5A) inc; lndry rm; supmkt 1km; playgrnd; tennis; rv adj; lake sw & fishing 2km; 95% statics (sep area); dogs; poss cr at w/e; Eng spkn; cc not acc; CCI. "Rvside pitches; ground v soft in wet; nice walks in forest; lovely walk to town; level walk to town; easy drive to Paris; peaceful site; helpful warden; v clean facs." 1 Apr-31 Oct. € 7.30   2005*

ANET *3D2* (1km N Urban) **Camp Municipal Les Trillots, Chemin des Trillots, 27530 Ezy-sur-Eure** [02 37 64 73 21 or 02 37 64 73 48 (Mairie)] N fr Dreux on D928/D143. Site on N site of Rv Eure. Med, unshd; htd wc; shwrs inc; el pts (4-8A) €1.78-2.68; lndtte; supmkt nr; rest, snacks, bar 1km; BBQ; 90% statics; dogs; quiet, "Pleasant rvside walk." 1 May-15 Nov. € 3.50   2005*

ANGERS *4G1* (10km SE Rural) **Escapades Terre Oceane Camping Caroline, Route de la Bohalle, 49800 Brain-sur-l'Authion** [02 41 80 42 18 or 05 46 55 10 01; fax 05 46 55 10 00; info@ campingterreoceane.com; www.campingterre oceane.com] Turn off N147 onto D113, site sp E of Angers at ent to vill. Med, mkd pitch, pt shd; wc; chem disp; shwrs inc; el pts (10A) €3; lndtte; ice; shop 300m; snacks; BBQ; playgrnd; htd pool; paddling pool; tennis; fishing nrby; entmnt; child entmnt; TV rm; statics; dogs; adv bkg; some rd & rlwy noise (& owls, woodpeckers); cc acc. "Gd touring base." ♦ 17 Jun-16 Sep. € 12.00   2005*

ANGERS *4G1* (5km S Urban) **Camp Municipal de l'Ile du Chateau, 49130 Les Ponts-de-Ce [tel/fax 02 41 44 62 05; ile-du-chateau@wanadoo.fr; www.camping-ileduchateau.com]** Fr Angers take N160 (sp Cholet) to Les Ponts-de-Ce. Turn R at traff lts in town opp Hotel de Ville, & site in 500m. Med, hdg pitch, pt shd; wc; chem disp; child/baby facs; shwrs inc; el pts (6A) €2.70; lndtte; ice; shops 1km; tradsmn; snacks; bar; BBQ; playgrnd; pool, waterslide adj; sand beach 500m; tennis; mini-golf; golf 5km; TV; dogs €1.50; phone; poss cr; Eng spkn; quiet; red low ssn; cc acc; CCI. "Access to site warden-controlled, off ssn recep opening times vary; excel pool adj; gd touring base for chateaux, vineyards; gd long/sh stay." ♦ 1 Apr-30 Sep. € 11.70   2005*

ANGERS *4G1* (6km SW) **Camp Municipal Le Chateau, 25 Rue Chevriere, 49080 Bouchemaine** [02 41 77 11 04 or 02 41 22 20 00 (Mairie); adm. generale@ville-bouchemaine.fr] Fr Angers take N160 S, at intersection with D112 W sp Bouchemaine. Cross Rv Maine via suspension bdge. At rndabt on W bank turn L, site on L in 100m adj rv. Fr Chateau-Gontier take N162, then D106, then D102E. Bouchemaine well sp. Med, pt shd; wc; chem disp; shwrs inc; el pts (16A) €2.50 (poss rev pol); lndtte; ice; shops 1km; rest 500m; pool 500m; games area; dogs €1.05; phone; bus; poss cr; adv bkg quiet; CCI. "Recep clsd 1200-1500; san facs & chem disp upstairs, so diff for disabled; site a bit tired end of ssn; friendly, helpful warden." 1 Jun-31 Aug. € 10.00   2005*

ANGERS *4G1* (5km W Urban) **Camping du Lac de Maine, Ave du Lac de Maine, 49000 Angers** [02 41 73 05 03; fax 02 41 73 02 20; camping@ lacdemaine.fr; www.lacdemaine.fr] W fr Angers on N23, exit at 'Quartier du Lac de Maine then foll sp to site & Bouchemaine. After 4 rndabts site on L; sp W of Rv Maine. Fr S on N160 or A87, turn onto D4 at Les Ponts-de-Ce. In 6km, cross Rv Maine to Bouchemaine & turn R to Pruniers dir Angers. Site on R at Pruniers town exit sp. Lge, hdg/mkd pitch, pt shd; htd wc; chem disp; mv service pnt; serviced pitches; baby facs; shwrs inc; el pts (10A) €3.20 (rev pol); gas; lndtte; shop 1.5km; tradsmn; hypmkt 2km; rest, snacks & bar in ssn; BBQ; playgrnd; htd pool; paddling pool; sand beach 800m; fishing; boating; windsurfing 500m; tennis 800m; cycle hire; internet; TV; 10% statics; dogs €2; bus; phone; Eng spkn; adv bkg (dep req); quiet but some rd noise; cc acc; red low ssn/long stay; 10% red CCI. "Vg site; conv Loire chateaux; excel facs; extremely helpful young managers; conv bus to Angers cent." ♦ 25 Mar-10 Oct. € 16.00 (CChq acc)   2005*

See advertisement on next page

FRANCE

†ANGERVILLE *4E3* (10km SE Rural) **Parc Loisirs de la Chesnaie, 45480 Autruy-sur-Juine** [02 38 39 57 07; fax 02 38 39 50 87] S on N20, exit for Angerville & in vill turn R onto D6/D22 twd Andonville (sp Pithiviers). Immed on leaving Andonville turn sharp L sp Fromonvilliers, site sp at next R turn, site at end of rd past Camp La Joulliere. Fr S A10 exit junc 13 ont N20 N & take exit for Angerille then foll as above. Lge, mkd pitch, pt shd; wc; shwrs inc; el pts (6A) €2.50; lndtte; shop; pool; 98% statics; dogs; phone; quiet; adv bkg; CCI. "Only 5 touring pitches; ess to phone ahead; useful winter NH nr Orleans (unhtd facs)." € 13.00   2004*

> As we're travelling out of season, we'd better phone ahead to check that the site is actually open.

ANGLES DU TARN see Brassac *8F4*

ANGLURE *4E4* (500m) **Camp Municipal, Route de Bagneux, 51260 Anglure** [03 26 42 71 35 (Mairie)] S fr Sezanne on D373, turn R in cent of Anglure, sp. Sm, pt shd; wc; el pts (3-5A); shops 500m; rv adj; quiet; many statics. "NH only." 15 Apr-Sep.   2002*

ANGOULEME *7B2* (15km N Rural) **Camp Municipal Les Platanes, 16330 Montignac-Charente** [05 45 39 89 16 or 05 45 39 70 09 (Mairie); fax 05 45 22 26 71] Fr N, on N10, turn W on D11 then N on D737 thro vill onto D15. Narr rds on app, site on R by Rv Charente. Med, pt shd; wc (cont); chem disp; shwrs inc; el pts (4-12A) €2.20-€4 (rev pol); gas 2km; lndry rm; ice; shop 800m; rest, snacks in vill; bar; rv sw & fishing adj; canoeing; direct access to rv; dogs; poss cr; quiet; 25% red 16 days; cc not acc; CCI. "Pleasant vill, grassy site; excel clean facs; friendly staff; many trees; no twin-axle vans; ltd access times for m'vans - height barrier; gd long/sh stay." ♦ 1 Jun-31 Aug. € 10.35   2005*

ANGOULEME *7B2* (10km NW Rural) **Camping Marco de Bignac (formerly Les Sablons), Chemin de la Résistance, 16170 Bignac** [05 45 21 78 41; fax 05 45 21 52 37; marcodebignac@wanadoo.fr; www.camping-marco-bignac.com] Fr N10 approx 14km N Angouleme take exit La Touche & foll D11 W thro Vars; at Basse turn R onto D117 & foll sp in Bignac. Med, mkd pitch, pt shd; htd wc; chem disp; mv service pnt; shwrs inc; child/baby facs; el pts (3-6A) €2.50-4; gas; ice; shops 3km; tradsmn; rest; snacks; bar high ssn; playgrnd; htd pool high ssn; tennis; mini-golf; lake adj, fishing & watersports; children's zoo; fishing; tennis; pedalos; badminton; few statics; dogs; phone; poss cr; adv bkg (dep req + bkg fee); quiet; red long stay/low ssn; cc acc; 5% red CCI. "Attractive, peaceful, shady lakeside site; gd rest; v helpful & welcoming British owners; library of Eng books; clean san facs; no lndtte but owner takes washing in high ssn; conv Charente region; highly rec - worth long drive; excel long stay." ♦ 15 May-15 Sep. € 19.00   2005*

ANGOULINS SUR MER see Rochelle, La *7A1*

ANNECY *9B3* (8km SE Rural) **Camping de la Ferme de Ferrieres, 74290 Alex** [04 50 02 87 09; fax 04 50 02 80 54] Take D909 on E side of lake out of Annecy twds Thones; look out for sp on L after turn off to Chateau de Menthon. Med, pt sl, terr, pt shd; wc (cont); chem disp; baby facs; shwrs inc; el pts (5A) inc; lndtte; shop & 2km; tradsmn; snacks; playgrnd; lake sw 6km; poss cr; quiet; phone; adv bkg; CCI. "Spectacular views; friendly owner; away fr the crowds; v clean; mostly tents; fair sh stay; pitches v muddy when wet." ♦ ltd. 1 Jun-30 Sep. € 11.30   2002*

ANNECY *9B3* (8km SE) **Camping Le Clos Don Jean, 74290 Menthon-St-Bernard [tel/fax 04 50 60 18 66; jacob@nwc.fr]** Fr N site clearly sp fr vill of Menthon. L uphill 400m. Med, mkd pitch, pt sl, pt shd; wc (some cont); chem disp; shwrs inc; el pts (3-10A) €2-2.45; gas; lndtte; shop; playgrnd; lake sw 900m; dogs €0.60; poss cr; Eng spkn; quiet; CCI; "Excel site; san facs spotless; fine views of chateau & lake; orchard setting; vg long stay." ♦ ltd. 1 Jun-15 Sep. € 15.00   2004*

ANNECY *9B3* (8km SE) **Camping Le Fier, 74290 Alex** [04 50 02 89 11 or 04 50 02 14 54 (LS)] Take D909 out of Annecy twd Thones. After 12km site on R past turn to Alex; clearly sp. Lge, pt shd; wc; shwrs; el pts (3A); ice; shops 1km; playgrnd; lake sw 6km; some rd noise. "Gd; picturesque situation, away fr crowds." 28 Jun-1 Sep. € 7.01   2002*

ANNECY *9B3* (9km SE Urban) **Camp Municipal Les Champs Fleuris, Les Perris, 74410 Duingt** [04 50 68 57 31 or 04 50 68 67 07 (Mairie); fax 04 50 77 03 17; camping@duingt.fr; http://camping.duingt.fr] Fr Annecy take N508 sp Albertville. Site on R bef Duingt vill. Look out for sm sp. Med, mkd pitch, terr, pt shd; htd wc; chem disp; mv service pnt; shwrs inc; el pts (3-10A) €2-4; gas 1km; lndtte; ice; shops 1km; tradsmn; rest, snacks, bar 500m; BBQ; playgrnd; lake sw adj; 3% statics; dogs €1.50; phone; bus 200m; poss cr; Eng spkn; adv bkg; quiet; CCI. "V helpful staff; gd for walking, touring, cycling (cycle rte to Annecy); vg all stays." ♦ 15 May-4 Sep. € 12.90   2004*

ANNECY *9B3* (10km SE Rural) **Camping Le Familial, Route des Champs Fleuris, 74410 Duingt** [tel/fax 04 50 68 69 91; camping.lefamilial@laposte.net; www.annecy-camping-familial.com] Fr Annecy on N508 twd Albertville. 5km after St Jorioz turn R at site sp Entrevernes onto D8, foll sp past Camping Champs Fleuris. Sm, mkd pitch, some hdstg, pt sl, pt shd; wc; shwrs inc; el pts (5-6A) €2.70-2.90; lndtte; tradsmn; playgrnd; lake & shgl beach 500m; TV rm; dogs €1.40; some Eng spkn; adv bkg rec Jul/Aug (dep req); quiet but rd noise; CCI. "Gd site; poss ltd facs high ssn; scenic area, gd views; friendly owner; gd atmosphere; communal meals & fondu evenings." ♦ ltd. 1 Apr-15 Oct. € 11.30   2005*

ANNECY *9B3* (10km SE Rural) **Camping Le Solitaire du Lac, Route de Sales, 74410 St Jorioz** [tel/fax 04 50 68 59 30 or 06 88 58 94 24; campinglessolitaire@wanadoo.fr] Exit Annecy on N508 twd Albertville. Site sp on N o'skts of St Jorioz. Med, hdg/mkd pitch, pt shd; wc (some cont); chem disp; mv service pnt; shwrs inc; el pts (6A) €3.50; gas; lndtte; ice; supmkts 2km; tradsmn; rest; snacks; bar & 2km; BBQ; playgrnd; lake sw; boat-launching; games areas; cycle track; 10% statics; dogs €1.52; poss cr; Eng spkn; adv bkg (dep req); v quiet; red low ssn/long stay; cc acc; CCI. "Conv touring Haute Savoie; highly rec, gd value, clean, efficient site; sh walk to public beach on lake & water bus to Annecy; cycle path nr site; lge pitches; poss muddy after heavy rain." 15 Apr-20 Sep. € 16.50 (3 persons)   2005*

ANNECY *9B3* (12km SE Rural) **Camping Le Lac, Angon, 74290 Talloires** [04 50 60 73 16; fax 04 50 60 77 42; camping@lelaccamping.com] Take D909 fr Annecy to Talloires. Site on R off D909A S of Talloires on lakeside. Use most S of 2 ent with long o'fit. Med, mkd pitch, pt sl, pt shd; wc; chem disp (wc); shwrs inc; el pts (4A) €2.50; lndry rm; ice; shops, rest, bar 1km; BBQ; playgrnd; lake sw adj; boat-launching facs; 10% statics; dogs €1.10; poss cr; some rd noise; cc acc; CCI. "Magnificent views, quiet & tranquil in low ssn; beware grounding at ent; basic facs." 1 Jun-30 Sep. € 15.50   2003*

ANNECY *9B3* (14km SE Rural) **Aire Naturelle Le Combarut (Cottard), 74410 St Eustache** [04 50 32 00 20] Take N508 S fr Annecy to Sevrier, turn R onto D912, site on farm just bef St Eustache. Sm, shd; wc (cont); shwrs; el pts €1.50; quiet. "Basic facs but spotless; gd mountain views; tortuous access on winding rds, but not diff with care." 1 Jun-30 Sep. € 8.40   2002*

ANNECY *9B3* (1.5km S) **Camp Municipal Le Belvedere, 8 Route du Semmoz, 74000 Annecy** [04 50 45 48 30; camping@ville-annecy.fr] Fr A41 take N508 at junc 16 & foll sp to Albertville & hospital thro Annecy, turn L at lights & up hill. Where main rd bends sharp L downhill bear R leaving hospital on your L. Take next R uphill, Rte du Semnoz (D41); bear R then L & site on R in 250m. Lge, mkd pitch, pt sl, terr, pt shd; htd wc; chem disp; shwrs inc; el pts (10A) inc (poss rev pol); gas; lndtte; ice; shop; rest; snacks; playgrnd; cycle hire; sailing; fishing; forest walks; excursions; TV; dogs; phone; Eng spkn; adv bkg; poss noisy; cc acc; CCI. "Staff helpful; neat, tidy site; lit at night; beautiful setting; steep footpath to town but easy walking dist; 50% tents; simple but gd food in rest." ♦ 2 Apr-10 Oct. € 20.30   2005*

ANNECY *9B3* (5km S Urban) **Camping au Coeur du Lac, Les Choseaux, 74320 Sevrier** [04 50 52 46 45; fax 04 50 19 01 45; info@aucoeurdulac.com] S fr Annecy on N508 sp Albertville. Pass thro Sevrier cent. Site on L at lakeside 1km S of Sevrier. 300m after MacDonald's. Med, mkd pitch, terr, pt sl, pt shd, some hdstg; wc (some cont); chem disp; mv service pnt; shwrs inc; el pts (4-13A) €2.80-7, long cable rec; lndtte; shop; supmkt with petrol 2km; snacks; playgrnd; lake sw; yachting; grass & shgl beach; cycle/boat hire; entmnt; dogs low ssn only; bus nrby; info office 1km N; poss cr; some Eng spkn; adv bkg ess high ssn; quiet but some rd noise; red low ssn; cc acc; CCI. "Excel, esp low ssn; gd views fr upper terr overlooking Lac Annecy; tight for lge o'fits as sm, sl pitches; gd san facs; excel." ♦ 4 Apr-30 Sep. € 16.00   2005*

FRANCE

Village Camping EUROPA
Lac d'Annecy

Charming site, 400 meters from the Lake of
Annecy. 1 heated swimming pool, 1 water complex
(with 5 water slides, waterfalls, children's games,
Jacuzzi, lagoon). Restaurant with specialities of
the Savoy region – Quality installations
– Special offer for groups – Chalets and mobile
homes to let – Situated next to a cycling track.

1444, route d'Albertville - F - 74410 ST-JORIOZ
Tel: 33 (0)4 50 68 51 01 - Fax: 33 (0)4 50 68 55 20
www.camping-europa.com • info@camping-europa.com

ANNECY *9B3* (6km S) **Camping Le Panoramic,**
Allevard, 74320 Sevrier [tel/fax 04 50 52 43 09]
S fr Annecy to Sevrier on N508 turn R at rndabt
(Champion supmkt) in Sevrier on D912, cont for 3km
to bdge & site 1st L after bdge, easy access up
hillside. Lge, mkd pitch, pt sl, terr, pt shd; wc; chem
disp; shwrs inc; el pts (3A) inc (some rev pol); lndtte;
ice; shop; supmkt 2km; tradsmn; rest; snacks; bar;
playgrnd; pool; beach 2km; lake sw; TV; dogs €1.60;
poss cr; Eng spkn; adv bkg; quiet; cc acc; CCI. "Rec
for families; lovely views of lake & mountains;
blocks/wedges ess for sl pitches; fantastic pool; vg
long stay." ♦ ltd. 1 May-30 Sep. € 20.80   2003*

ANNECY *9B3* (6.5km S Urban) **Camping de**
l'Aloua, 492 Route de Piron, 74320 Sevrier
[tel/fax 04 50 52 60 06 or 04 50 52 64 54 (LS);
camping.aloua@hotmail.com]
Foll sp for Albertville N508 S fr Annecy. Site on E side,
approx 1.4km S of Sevrier vill. Turn L at Champion
supmkt rndabt & foll sp twd lake. Lge, pt hdg/mkd
pitch, shd; wc (some cont); chem disp; mv service pnt;
shwrs inc; el pts (6A) €3; gas 400m; lndtte; ice; shop;
supmkt 400m; tradsmn; rest; snacks; bar; playgrnd;
shgl beach 300m; lake sw, fishing, boating &
watersports adj; archery; entmnts; TV; phone; poss cr;
quiet; Eng spkn; adv bkg (€45.80 dep + bkg fee); CCI.
"Gd base for lake (no dir access to lake fr site); cycle
track around lake; night security; poss noisy at night
with youths & some rd noise; basic san facs; pleasant
owners; gd takeaway." ♦ ltd. 20 Jun-10 Sep. € 14.60
                                                    2005*

ANNECY *9B3* (6.5km S Urban) **Camping FFCC**
Les Rives du Lac (formerly Parc Claude Gelain
(ACCCF), 331 Chemin du Communaux, Les
Mongets, 74320 Sevrier [tel/fax 04 50 52 40 14;
lesrivesdulac@ffcc.fr; www.ffcc.fr] Take N508 S
fr Annecy sp Albertville, thro Sevrier sp FFCC. Turn
L 100m past (S) Lidl supmkt, cross cycle path & turn
R & foll sp FFCC keeping parallel with cycle path.
Site on L in 400m, S of Sevrier. Med, mkd pitch, pt
shd; wc; chem disp; mv service pnt; baby facs;
shwrs inc; el pts (6A) €3; lndtte; shops 500m;
playgrnd; shgl beach; lake sw; sailing; fishing;
walking; entmnt; 10% statics; bus nr; poss cr; adv
bkg; quiet; red CC members (not Jul/Aug); CCI.
"V helpful wardens; generous pitches; beautiful
situation; water bus to Annecy nr; gd touring base."
10 Apr-15 Oct. € 18.90   2005*

ANNECY *9B3* (9km S Urban) **Camping International**
du Lac d'Annecy, 1184 Route d'Albertville, 74410
St Jorioz. [tel/fax 04 50 68 67 93; www.camp
annecy.com] Fr Annecy take N508 sp Albertville.
Site on R just after St Jorioz. Med, mkd pitch, some
hdstg, pt shd; wc; chem disp; mv service pnt; shwrs
inc; el pts (6A) inc; gas; ice; BBQ; lndtte; shop 2km;
tradsmn; snacks; bar; playgrnd; pool; lake sw; cycle
hire; games area; TV rm; 30% statics; dogs €2;
poss cr; rd noise; phone; Eng spkn; CCI. "Friendly
owner, vg long/sh stay, excel for touring lake area;
gd rest nrby." 1 Jun-15 Sep. € 21.00   2004*

ANNECY *9B3* (9km S Rural) **Village Camping**
Europa, 1444 Route d'Albertville, 74410 St Jorioz
[04 50 68 51 01; fax 04 50 68 55 20; info@
camping-europa.com; www.camping-europa.
com] Fr Annecy take N508 sp Albertville. Site on R
800m S of St Jorioz dir Albertville. Look for lge
yellow sp on o'skirts of St Jorioz. Lge, hdg/mkd
pitch, pt shd, wc; chem disp; mv service pnt; some
serviced pitches; baby facs; shwrs inc; el pts (6A)
inc; gas; lndtte; ice; shop adj; tradsmn; rest; snacks;
bar; BBQ (gas); playgrnd; htd pool; waterslides;
jacuzzi; sand beach (lake) 500m; windsurfing; boat
hire; fishing; cycle hire; cycle track adj; child entmnt;
TV rm; internet; dogs €2; Eng spkn; adv bkg; quiet
but main rd adj; cc acc; red long stay/low ssn; CCI.
"Friendly staff; vg rest; beautiful area, conv
Chamonix & Mont Blanc; gd tourist base; excel." ♦
6 May-13 Sep. € 27.00   2005*

See advertisement above

ANNECY *9B3* (7km SW) **Aire Naturelle La Vidome**
(Lyonnaz), 74600 Montagny-les-Lanches [tel/fax
04 50 46 61 31; j.lyonnaz@wanadoo.fr]
Exit Annecy on N201 sp Aix-les-Bains/Chambery;
after 6km at Le Treige turn R sp Montagny-les-
Lanches. In 1km turn R in Avulliens; site on R in
100m. Sm, pt sl, pt shd; wc; chem disp; shwrs; el pts
(3-10A) €1.50-3.50; lndtte; meals avail; hypermkt
3km; playgrnd; pool 3km; beach & mini-golf 10km;
fishing 1km; horseriding 1km; quiet but some rd
noise; adv bkg; gd views; CCI. "Excel site; friendly
owners; excel san facs; access poss tight for lge
o'fits." 1 May-30 Sep. € 9.10   2004*

Camping Le Rossignol ★★★ *Ideally situated between Cannes and Nice, at 1200 m from the beaches and Marineland; in green, quiet and nice settings, the campsite Le Rossignol offers you marked pitches and chalets to let.*

2074, av.Jean Michard Pelissier 06600 Antibes
Tél : 00 33 4 93 33 56 98
Fax : 00 33 4 92 91 98 99
www.campinglerossignol.com
E-mail : campinglerossignol@wanadoo.fr

ANNECY *9B3* (9km SW) **Aire Naturelle Le Pre Ombrage (Metral)**, 74600 Montagny-les-Lanches [04 50 46 71 31] Exit Annecy on N201 sp Aix-les-Bains/Chambery, after 8km at Le Treige turn R sp Montagny-les-Lanches; site sp in vill. Sm, pt sl, pt shd; wc; chem disp; shwrs inc; el pts; shops 3km; lake sw 12km; pool 3km; playgrnd; adv bkg; quiet; CCI. "Friendly family-run farm in orchard; excel view; produce avail; gd sh stay." 15 Jun-30 Sep.   2002*

ANNECY *9B3* (12km SW Rural) **Aire Naturelle Jouvenod (Mercier)**, 460 Route de Jouvenod, 74540 Alby-sur-Cheran [04 50 68 15 75] Take the A41 SW fr Annecy, turn off at junc 15 twds Alby-sur-Cheran. Foll sp in vill. Sm, pt sl, pt shd; wc; chem disp; mv service pnt; shwrs inc; el pts (10A) €2; shop 3km; playgrnd; beach & boating 13km; lake sw & fishing 8km; tennis; 10% statics; dogs; phone; Eng spkn; cc not acc. "Farm site; 20 pitches; gd views & hill/woodland walks; Alby pretty medieval town." 15 Jun-15 Sep. € 7.50   2004*

ANNECY *9B3* (8km NW Rural) **Camping La Caille**, 18 Chemin de la Caille, 74330 La Balme-de-Sillingy [04 50 68 85 21; fax 04 50 68 74 56; contact@aubergedelacaille.com] Fr Annecy take N508 dir Bellgarde-sur-Valserine. On leaving rndabt at end of La Balme-de-Sillingy, foll sp. Site on R in 1km. Sm, hdg/mkd pitch, pt sl, shd; wc; chem disp; el pts (4-6A) inc; ice; lndtte; shop 750m; tradsmn; rest; snacks; bar; playgrnd; pool; 25% statics; dogs €3; adv bkg; quiet; CCI. "Gd sh stay." ♦ 1 May-30 Sep. € 19.20   2004*

ANNECY *9B3* (10km NW Rural) **Aire Naturelle (Langin)**, 74330 Choisy [04 50 77 41 65; fax 04 50 77 45 01; 352@wanadoo.fr] On D3 bet N201 & N508; on N201 at vill of Allonzier-la-Caille turn off & foll sps to site; or fr rndabt in La Balme-de-Sillingy on N508 foll sp to Choisy. Sm, pt sl, pt shd; wc; chem disp; mv service pnt; shwrs inc; el pts (6A); lndtte; ice; sm shop; rest 7km; snacks; BBQ; playgrnd; pool; dogs €1.60; Eng spkn; adv bkg; quiet; CCI. "Beautiful mountain scenery; v friendly owners; pool gd for children; peaceful; blocks req for some pitches; gd family site; excel long stay." 14 Apr-30 Sep. € 21.50   2003*

ANNET SUR MARNE see Meaux *3D3*

ANNEYRON see St Rambert d'Albon *9C2*

ANNONAY *9C2* (Urban) **Camp Municipal de Vaure**, 07100 Annonay [04 75 32 47 49 or 04 75 33 46 54; fax 04 75 32 28 22; www.mairie-annonay.fr] Sp fr o'skts of town & foll sp St Etienne. Fr St Etienne & NW turn L at 1st rndabt & pass Intermarche, foll camping/piscine sp to site. Sm, pt shd; wc (some cont); shwrs inc; el pts (6A) inc; lndtte; snacks; bar; supmkt adj; htd, covrd pool; games area; few statics; cr; quiet. "Helpful staff; poss itinerants; barrier key dep." 1 Apr-31 Oct. € 9.20   2004*

ANOULD see Corcieux *6F3*

ANSE see Villefranche sur Saone *9B2*

ANTIBES *10E4* (2km N Rural) **Camping Caravaning Le Rossignol, Ave Jean Michard-Pelissier, Juan-les-Pins**, 06600 Antibes [04 93 33 56 98; fax 04 92 91 98 99; camping lerossignol@wanadoo.fr; www.campinglerossignol.com] Turn W off N7 Antibes-Nice at sp to Hospitalier de la Fontonne then bear L along Chemin des Quatres past hospital & traff lts junc. In 400m turn R at rndabt into Ave Jean Michard Pelissier, site 200m on R. NB Narr ent off busy rd. Med, hdg/mkd pitch, hdstg, terr, shd; wc; chem disp; mv service pnt; baby facs; shwrs inc; el pts (10A) €4.50; gas; lndtte; ice; shop 400m; tradsmn; bar; playgrnd; htd pool; shgl beach 1.5km; entmnt; games rm; TV rm; dogs €3; Eng spkn; adv bkg; quiet; cc acc; red long stay/CCI. "Conv Antibes & surrounding area; peaceful site." ♦ 8 Apr-30 Sep. € 19.40   2005*

See advertisement above

ANTIBES *10E4* (3.5km N Coastal) **Camping Antipolis, Ave du Pylone, La Brague**, 06600 Antibes [04 93 33 93 99; fax 04 92 91 02 00] Turn W off N7 Antibes-Nice on D4 to Biot; in 100m L to T-junc; turn R; in 500m 1st L to site. Lge, hdg/mkd pitch, shd; wc (some cont); chem disp; shwrs; el pts (10A) inc; gas; lndtte; ice; shop; tradsmn; rest; snacks; bar; BBQ; playgrnd; shgl beach 1km; htd pool; tennis; 95% statics; no dogs; phone; train 1km; quiet; adv bkg (dep req & bkg fee); cc acc; CCI. "Situated beside motorway, but pitches away fr rd; sm pitches; walk to beach along busy rds & across dual c'way; excel pool complex." ♦ 1 Apr-30 Sep. € 24.00   2002*

ANTIBES *10E4* (3.5km N Coastal) **Camping Les Embruns, 63 Route de Biot, La Brague, 06600 Antibes [04 93 33 33 35; fax 04 93 74 46 70]** Fr Antibes take N7 sp Nice, after 3.5km turn L at Camping sp. Ent immed on L. Med, pt shd; wc; shwrs inc; el pts (5-10A) €3-4; lndtte; ice; snacks; bar; shop; shgl beach adj; fishing & watersports adj; cycle hire; tennis; mini-golf; TV; dogs €1; bus & metro nrby; adv bkg; poss noise fr adj rd & rlwy; 5% red low ssn; cc acc. "Gd-sized pitches; well-supervised by owner; some pitches waterlogged in wet weather; v easy walking dist of bus & metro." 1 Jun-20 Sep. € 19.00   2003*

†**ANTIBES** *10E4* (4.5km N Coastal) **Camping du Pylone, Ave du Pylone, La Brague, 06600 Antibes [04 93 33 52 86 or 04 93 74 94 70; fax 04 93 33 30 54; contact@campingpylone.com; www.campingpylone.com]** Sp on N7. Turn inland at Biot rlwy marked D4 Biot, Campings, then 1st L 1st R & immed L. App on W of rlwy to avoid low bdge. NB Coast rd fr Antibes has height restriction. V lge, pt shd; htd wc; chem disp (wc); mv service pnt; shwrs inc; el pts (10A) inc; lndtte; shop; tradsmn in ssn; rest, snacks, bar in ssn; playgrnd; pool; paddling pool; sharply shelving shgl beach 200m; games area; TV; entmnt; 95% statics; no dogs; poss cr; no adv bkg; noisy; CCI. "Fair sh stay; narr rds on site - suitable sm vans only; conv Aquasplash & Marineland; rec train to Cannes, Nice, Monaco etc to avoid parking probs & v busy rd; payment cash only." € 18.00   2002*

ANTIBES *10E4* (5km N) **Camping L'Eden, Val de Pome, 06410 Biot [04 93 65 63 70; fax 04 93 65 54 22]** Turn W off N7 Antibes-Nice rd on D4 to Biot; site in 3km. Lge, shd; wc; mv service pnt; baby facs; shwrs inc; el pts (10A) €2.30; ice; gas; lndtte; shop; rest; snacks; BBQ; shgl beach 1.5km; fishing & watersports 1.5km; entmnts; playgrnd; TV; pool; many statics; poss cr; adv bkg ess; quiet. "Beautiful site but mostly statics." 1 Apr-31 Oct. € 19.05   2002*

ANTONNE ET TRIGONANT see Perigueux *7C3*

APREMONT *2H4* (2km N Rural) **Camping Les Charmes, Route de la Roussiere, 85220 Apremont [02 51 54 48 08 or 06 86 03 96 93 (mob); fax 02 51 55 98 85; lescharmes@cer85.cernet.fr; www.lescharmes.fr]** Fr D948 Challans to Aizenay turn W onto D94 sp Commequiers; after 2km L, sp Les Charmes. Med, mkd pitch, pt shd; wc (some cont); chem disp; 70% serviced pitches; fam bthrm; shwrs inc; el pts (6-10A) €2.60-3; gas; lndtte; ice; shop; tradsmn; playgrnd; pool; lake sw with beach 3km; sand beach 18km; TV rm; 4% statics; dogs €2; poss cr; Eng spkn; adv bkg (dep req); quiet; red long stay; cc acc; CCI. "Beautiful site; generous pitches; mod & v clean san facs; v helpful, friendly owners; immaculate; well appointed site; excel long/sh stay." ♦ 1 Apr-30 Sep. € 13.70   2005*

APREMONT *2H4* (E) **Camping Les Prairies du Lac, Route de Mache, 85220 Apremont [02 51 55 70 58; fax 02 51 55 76 04; infos@les-prairies-du-lac.com]** Fr Apremont take D40 twd Mache to site on N side of rd in 2km. Fr Aizenay D107 to Mache then D40 twd Apremont to site in 5km. Lge, mkd pitch, pt shd; wc (some cont); chem disp; 15% serviced pitches; shwrs inc; el pts (6-10A) €3-5; gas; lndtte; ice; tradsmn; snacks; bar; 2 htd pools; sand beach 17km; playgrnd; rv & lake sw/fishing 2km; mini-golf; entmnt in ssn; TV; dogs €2; phone; 60% statics; Eng spkn; adv bkg; quiet. "Friendly owners; facs v clean, poss ltd low ssn; access to cycle paths; many local attractions." 26 Jun-30 Aug. € 17.00   2004*

APT *10E3* (3km N Rural) **Aire Naturelle La Cle des Champs (Mayer-Abdallah), Quartier des Puits, 84400 Apt [04 90 74 41 41; fax 04 90 04 73 13]** Turn N off N100 in Apt by post office onto rd sp 'Camping La Cle des Champs/Residence St Michel. Care req not to miss sudden turnings. Access via steep, winding rd - not suitable lge o'fits. Sm, pt shd; wc; chem disp; shwrs; el pts (6-10A) inc; gas 3km; lndtte; shop 3km; 10% statics; dogs; adv bkg; quiet; CCI. "Pleasant, off-the-beaten-track site with nice views; v peaceful; vg." 1 Apr-30 Sep. € 10.60   2005*

APT *10E3* (9km N Rural) **Camping Les Chenes Blancs, Route de Gargas, 84490 St Saturnin-les-Apt** [04 90 74 09 20; fax 04 90 74 26 98; robert@ les-chenes-blancs.com; www.les-chenes-blancs.com] Exit A7 at Avignon-Sud, take D22-N100 twd Apt, at NW o'skts of Apt turn N on D101, cont approx 2km turn R on D83 into Gargas; thro Gargas & in 4km turn L at camp sp; site on R in 300m. Lge, shd; wc; mv service pnt; shwrs inc; el pts (6A) €4.80; lndry rm; shop; rest; snacks; bar; playgrnd; htd pool; lake fishing 5km; games area; entmnt; TV rm; dogs €2.10; poss cr; Eng spkn; adv bkg rec; quiet; red low ssn; cc acc. "Stony ground; need steel pegs for awnings; lge pitches amongst oaks; san facs poss stretched in high ssn; friendly staff; excel touring base." ♦ 15 Mar-31 Oct. € 15.20 (CChq acc) 2005*

APT *10E3* (500m NE Urban) **Camp Municipal Les Cedres, Route de Rustrel, 84400 Apt** [tel/fax 04 90 74 14 61; camping-apt@wanadoo.fr] In town turn N off N100 onto D22 twd Rustrel, site sp. Site on R in 200m immed after going under old rlwy bdge. Med, mkd pitch, pt shd; htd wc; chem disp; mv service pnt; shwrs inc; el pts (6-10A) €2.90-3.95; gas; lndtte; ice; shop; snacks; cooking facs; playgrnd; entmnt; TV rm; dogs €1.15; poss cr; adv bkg; CCI. "Excel, friendly site; clean san facs; lovely location; easy 5 min walk town; cycle tracks E & W; conv Luberon vills & ochre mines; lge mkt in town Sat." ♦ 15 Feb-15 Nov. € 10.00 2005*

APT *10E3* (8km NE Rural) **Camping Le Colorado, Route d'Apt, 84400 Rustrel** [tel/fax 04 90 04 90 37] Leave Apt on D22, site sp on R. Med, hdg/mkd pitch, pt shd; wc (cont); el pts (6A) €2.60; tradsmn; rest; bar; playgrnd; pool; adv bkg; Eng spkn; CCI. "Gloomy site in woodland adj gd mkd walks; steep, gravel path to pitches - suitable sm o'fits only; primitive facs; helpful, friendly warden; gd auberge in vill; Sat mkt in Apt." 15 Mar-15 Oct. € 11.00 2002*

APT *10E3* (2km SE Rural) **Camping Le Luberon, Route de Saignon, 84400 Apt** [04 90 04 85 40; fax 04 90 74 12 19; leluberon@wanadoo.fr; www. camping-le-luberon.com] Exit Apt by D48 sp Saignon & site on R in 2km. Med, mkd pitch, pt sl, pt shd; wc; chem disp; baby facs; shwrs inc; el pts (8A) €4; gas; lndtte; ice; shops 2km; tradsmn; rest; snacks; bar; BBQ; playgrnd; pool (proper sw trunks only); fishing, sailing 3km; TV; 20% statics; dogs €1.50; phone; poss cr; Eng spkn; adv bkg (dep req); quiet; red low ssn; cc acc; CCI. "Pitches well laid out in natural woodland; v helpful owners; well-run, clean site; gd all stays." ♦ ltd. 1 Apr-30 Sep. € 16.00 2003*

ARAGNOUET *8G2* (Rural) **Camp Municipal du Pont de Moudang, 65170 Aragnouet** [05 62 39 62 84 or 05 62 39 62 63 (Mairie); fax 05 62 39 60 47] Site on L of D929, 9km SW fr St Lary. Med, mkd pitch, hdstg; pt shd; wc; chem disp; shwrs; el pts (4-10A) inc; lndtte; shop 500m; playgrnd; TV rm; 25% statics; poss cr; quiet; CCI. "Jetons needed for use of hot water (no charge); superb surroundings; excel mountain walking area; conv for Aragnouet/Bielsa tunnel; gd long stay." 1 Dec-15 Sep. € 14.00 2003*

> We're having a great holiday - must fill in some site report forms and send them to The Club as soon as possible.

ARAMITS *8F1* (1km SW Rural) **Camping Baretous-Pyrenees, Quartier Ripaude, 64570 Aramits** [05 59 34 12 21; fax 05 59 34 67 19; atso64@hotmail.com; www.camping-baretous-pyrenees.com] SW fr Oloron-Ste Marie take D919 sp Aramits, Arette. Fr Aramits cont on D919 sp Lanne; site on R; well sp. Sm, mkd pitch, pt shd; wc; chem disp; mv service pnt; serviced pitches; shwrs inc; el pts (16A) €3.10; lndtte; ice; supmkt 500m; tradsmn; snacks, bar high ssn; playgrnd; htd pool high ssn; cycle hire; games rm; TV; 50% statics; dogs €1.50; poss cr; Eng spkn; adv bkg; CCI. "Friendly, helpful owner; well-kept, clean site; barrier clsd 2230-0800; twin-axles €9.15 extra per day; gd base for Pyrenees; easy day's journey into N Spain; poss unreliable opening dates - phone ahead low ssn." ♦ ltd. 3 Jan-16 Oct. € 16.50 2005*

ARBOIS *6H2* (1.5km E Urban) **Camp Municipal Les Vignes, Ave du General Leclerc, 39600 Arbois** [03 84 66 55 55 or 03 84 66 14 12 (Mairie); fax 03 84 66 25 50] Fr N or S, ent town & at rndabt in cent foll camp sp. Site located next to stadium & municipal pool. Med, some hdg pitch/mkd pitch, some hdstg, pt sl, terr, pt shd; wc; chem disp; serviced pitches; shwrs inc; el pts (10A) €3; gas; lndtte; shop & 1km; rest; snacks; bar; playgrnd; htd pool adj (sw trunks ess); tennis; fishing 1km; entmnts; TV; dogs €1; poss cr; Eng spkn; adv bkg; quiet; cc acc; CCI. "Some pitches no elec; spotless san facs but poss stretched high ssn; wine-growing area; pleasant sm town with vg rests, home of Louis Pasteur; Roman salt works, grottoes nr; lge fair 1st w/e in Sep; site clsd 2200-0800 in low ssn; free use of excel pool; excel site; ltd facs low ssn." ♦ 1 May-30 Sep. € 12.50 2005*

See advertisement opposite

FRANCE

ARC EN BARROIS *6F1* (W) **Camping Le Vieux Moulin** (formerly Camp Municipal), 52210 Arc-en-Barrois [03 25 02 51 33 (Mairie); fax 03 25 03 82 89] Fr Chaumont exit (24) on A5 take D10 S & site on L on exit vill. Or turn L onto D6 about 4km S of Chateauvillain fr D65. Site on R on D3 at ent to vill, adj rv. Sm, pt shd; htd wc; chem disp; mv service pnt; shwrs inc; el pts (3A) €1.70; gas in vill; shops 500m; snacks; BBQ; sm playgrnd; tennis adj; TV; dogs; phone in vill; quiet; cc not acc; CCI. "Well kept, attractive site adj vill tennis courts; immac san facs; warden calls am/pm; new rd fr A5 makes it gd NH; gd rests in vill." 1 Apr-30 Sep.
€ 9.00   2005*

ARCACHON *7D1* (10km E Coastal) **Camp Municipal de Verdalle, Allee de Verdalle, La Hume, 33470 Gujan-Mestras** [tel/fax 05 56 66 12 62] Fr A63 take A660 twd Arcachon. Turn R at rndabt junc with D652 sp La Hume. In vill at traff lts at x-rds with D650, go strt across & Allee de Verdalle clearly seen on R after rlwy line. Med, hdg pitch, pt shd; wc (some cont); chem disp (wc only); shwrs inc; el pts (4A) inc; lndtte; BBQ; sand beach adj; dogs; phone; poss cr; v little Eng spkn; CCI. "Friendly staff; €30 dep for barrier key; conv local attractions." ♦
1 May-15 Sep. € 14.40   2004*

†**ARCACHON** *7D1* (2km S Coastal) **Camping Club d'Arcachon, 5 Allee de la Galaxie, Les Abatilles, 33120 Arcachon** [05 56 83 24 15; fax 05 57 52 28 51; info@camping-arcachon.com; www.camping-arcachon.com]
Exit A63 ont A660/N250 dir Arcachon. Foll sp 'Hopital Jean Hameau' & site sp. Lge, terr, pt shd; htd wc; chem disp; mv service pnt; shwrs inc; el pts (10A) €3-4; gas; lndtte; shop; tradsmn; rest; snacks; bar; BBQ some pitches; playgrnd; pool; sand beach 1.5km; lake sw 10km; cycle hire; entmnt; child entmnt; TV rm; 40% statics; dogs; site clsd 12 Nov-11 Dec; adv bkg; Eng spkn; quiet; cc acc; CCI. "Excel touring base; vg site in pine trees." ♦
€ 27.00   2005*

ARCHIAC see Barbezieux St Hilaire *7B2*

ARCIS SUR AUBE *4E4* (300m N Urban) **Camp Municipal de l'Ile, Rue des Chalons, 10700 Arcis-sur-Aube** [03 25 37 98 79; fax 03 25 82 94 18; cha_99@club-internet.fr] Fr A26 junc 21 foll sp to Arcis. Fr town cent take N77 dir Chalons-en-Champagne. Turn R after rv bdge, site sp. Med, mkd pitch, shd, wc (some cont); chem disp; shwrs €1.60; el pts (4-10A) €2.20 (poss rev pol); rest, bar & shops 500m; playgrnd; rv adj; fishing; dogs €1.60; poss cr w/e & noisy; CCI. "Basic but clean san facs; narr site rds - diff to manoeuvre lge o'fits; gates locked at 2200 (2000 low ssn) - check; NH only." 15 Apr-30 Sep. € 11.70   2005*

†**ARCIS SUR AUBE** *4E4* (8km S Rural) **Camping La Barbuise (formerly La Porcherie), 10700 St Remy-sous-Barbuise** [03 25 37 50 95 or 03 25 37 41 11] Fr Arcis-sur-Aube, take N77 twd Voue; site on L bef vill of Voue, sp. Fr S on A26 exit junc 23, turn R onto N177, site on R after Voue. Sm, pt sl, pt shd; wc; chem disp (wc only); shwrs inc; el pts (5A) €1.40 (poss rev pol); lndtte; tradsmn; snacks; bar; pool 8km; dogs; phone; adv bkg; quiet but some rd noise; red facs low ssn; cc not acc; CCI. "Friendly owners; CL-type site with full, improved san facs but basic; el heaters not allowed; plenty of rm; site yourself & owner collects payment in eve; open all night; pleasant views; conv & pleasant NH/sh stay for Troyes & Champagne rtes/region; early arr rec; cash only." ♦ ltd. € 7.30   2005*

This site entry hasn't been updated for a while; we'd better fill in a site report form and send it to The Club.

ARDRES *3A3* (500m N Urban) **Camping Ardresien, 64 Rue Basse, 62610 Ardres** [03 21 82 82 32] On N43, N twds Calais; strt on at lights in town; site 500m on R; narr ent. Sm, hdg pitch, pt shd; wc; shwrs; el pts (2A) €2; 95% statics; CCI. "Basic site - poss cold shwrs; lge lakes at rear of site; NH only." 1 May-30 Sep. € 8.00   2004*

ARDRES *3A3* (9km NE) **Camping Les Pyramides, 1 Rue du Canal, 62370 Audruicq** [03 21 35 59 17] Fr Calais take A16 dir Dunkerque, after 8km exit S at junc 21 onto D219 to Audruicq; foll camp sp. Fr Ardres NE on D224 to Audruicq. Med, hdg pitch, unshd; wc; chem disp; shwrs inc, el pts (6A) €3.50; gas; lndtte; tradsmn; playgrnd; 80% statics; no cc acc; quiet; CCI. "Conv Calais; few sm pitches for tourers; rec phone ahead." ♦ ltd. 1 Apr-30 Sep.
€ 15.00   2005*

ARDRES *3A3* (9km SE) **Camping Le Relaxe, 318 Route de Gravelines, 62890 Nordausques** [tel/fax 03 21 35 63 77] Fr N on N43 in vill 25km S of Calais at beginning of vill, turn L at sp. Site 200m on R. Or fr S on A26, leave at junc 2 & take N43 S for 1km into Nordausques, then as above. Med, hdg pitch, pt shd; wc; chem disp; shwrs €1.50; el pts (6A) €2 (poss rev pol); lndry rm; shop 200m; tradsmn; snacks; playgrnd; 90% statics; poss cr; adv bkg ess; quiet; CCI. "Owner v obliging; v conv for A26 & Calais; not suitable lge o'fits as diff to manoeuvre; conv NH for ferry." 1 Apr-30 Sep.
€ 12.20   2005*

ARDRES *3A3* (10km SE Rural) **Bal Parc Camping-Caravaning, 500 Rue du Vieux Chateau, 62890 Tournehem-sur-la-Hem** [03 21 35 65 90; fax 03 21 35 18 57; balparc@wanadoo.fr; www. balparc.com] Fr S on A26 leave at exit 2 (ignore sp for Bal Parc Hotel) Turn R onto D217 then R onto N43 dir St Omer. Turn R in Nordausques onto D218 (approx 1km), pass under A26, site is 1km on L - ent thro Bal Parc Hotel gates. Fr N or S on N43, turn R or L in Nordausques, then as above. Med, hdg/mkd pitch, hdstg, pt sl, pt shd; htd wc (in hotel in winter); chem disp; shwrs inc; el pts (10A) inc (poss rev pol); gas; tradsmn; rest, snacks, bar in adj hotel; playgrnd; sand beach 20km; sports ground & leisure cent adj; tennis; entmnt; 80% statics; poss cr; Eng spkn; adv bkg; quiet; cc acc; red low ssn/CCI. "25km Cite Europe shopping mall; owner v helpful & friendly; gd NH." ♦ 1 Apr-31 Oct. € 19.00   2005*

ARDRES *3A3* (1km S) **Camping St Louis, 223 Rue Leulene, 62610 Autingues** [03 21 35 46 83; fax 03 21 00 19 78] Fr Calais S on N43 to Ardres; fr Ardres take D224 S twd Licques, after 2km turn L on D227; site well sp in 100m. Or fr junc 2 off A26 onto N43 dir Ardres. Turn L just after Total g'ge on R on app to Ardres. Well sp. If app fr S via Boulogne avoid Nabringhen & Licques as narr, steep hill with bends. Med, hdg/mkd pitch, pt shd, some hdstg; wc; chem disp; mv service pnt; shwrs €1; el pts (6-10A) €2.50-3.50 (50m lead req some pitches); gas; lndtte; sm shop & 1km; supmkt 3km; snacks; rest high ssn; BBQ; playgrnd; lake 1km; games rm; some statics; phone; poss cr; Eng spkn; adv bkg ess high ssn; quiet; cc acc; CCI. "Gd, peaceful, well-maintained & clean site 30 mins fr Calais; pleasant welcome; barrier clsd 2200-0700; ltd touring pitches high ssn - phone ahead to check any avail; gd for Cite Europe shopping & Calais or Eurotunnel; 10 new hdstg m'van-only pitches planned for 2006; san facs refurb planned end 2005; early dep/late arr area." ♦ 1 Apr-31 Oct. € 14.50   2005*

ARDRES *3A3* (1km SW Rural) **Caravaning La Fregate, 465 Ave du Lac, 62610 Ardres** [03 21 35 44 92; fax 03 21 85 81 26] Foll sp fr town cent heading S, turn R into Ave du Lac. Med, hdg pitch, pt shd; wc; chem disp; shwrs inc; el pts (6A) inc; lndtte; shop; supmkt 600m; rest, bar 200m; playgrnd; 90% statics; quiet; CCI. 1 Apr-31 Oct. € 20.00   2005*

ARES see Andernos les Bains *7D1*

ARFEUILLES see Chatel Montagne *9A1*

ARGELES GAZOST *8G2* (500m N Rural) **Camping Sunelia Les Trois Vallees, Ave des Pyrenees, 65400 Argeles-Gazost** [05 62 90 35 47; fax 05 62 90 35 48; 3-vallees@wanadoo.fr; camping-les-3-vallees.fr] S fr Lourdes on N21, site on L just past Champion Supmkt on app to Argeles-Gazost. Lge, mkd pitch, pt shd; htd wc; chem disp; sauna; shwrs inc; el pts (6A) inc; lndtte; supmkt opp; tradsmn; bar; playgrnd; htd pool; waterslide; games rm; cycle hire; games area; golf 11km; entmnt; TV rm; 30% statics; dogs €2; poss cr; adv bkg ess high ssn; some rd noise nr site ent; cc acc. "Interesting area; views of Pyrenees; conv Lourdes; excel touring base." ♦ 1 Apr-15 Oct. € 27.50 (CChq acc)   2005*

ARGELES GAZOST *8G2* (1km N Rural) **Camping La Bergerie, 65400 Ayzac-Ost** [tel/fax 05 62 97 59 99] Sp of N21. Sm, pt shd; wc; shwrs inc; el pts (6A) €3.20; lndtte; BBQ; playgrnd; htd pool; entmnt; some statics; dogs; Eng spkn; adv bkg; quiet. "V clean, friendly site." ♦ 1 May-30 Sep. € 10.00   2002*

ARGELES GAZOST *8G2* (2km N Rural) **Camping Bellevue, 24 Chemin de la Plaine, 65400 Ayzac-Ost** [05 62 98 58 11 or 05 62 97 58 81] Fr Lourdes on N21 S, foll sp for Ayzac-Ost then sp for 'Camping La Bergerie' but cont past ent for 200m. Site on R behind farm buildings. Sm, pt shd; wc; chem disp; shwrs inc; el pts (2-6A) €1.70-3.80; lndtte; shop, rest, snacks, bar 1km; tradsmn; playgrnd; fishing 300m; 2% statics; dogs; phone; quiet; CCI. "Surrounded by fields; gd san facs block; could be muddy; gd sh stay/NH." ♦ 1 Jun-30 Sep. € 6.70   2004*

†**ARGELES GAZOST** *8G2* (4km N Rural) **Camping Soleil du Pibeste, 65400 Agos-Vidalos** [05 62 97 53 23; fax 05 61 06 67 73; info@campingpibeste.com; www.campingpibeste.com] On N21, S of Lourdes. Exit at rndabt sp Agos-Vidalos, site on R on ent vill. Med, terr, pt shd; htd wc; chem disp; mv service pnt; shwrs inc; el pts (3-6A) €3; gas; lndtte; ice; shops adj; lndtte; tradsmn; rest; snacks; bar; playgrnd; sm pool; rv sw 500m; entmnt; TV; 10% statics; dogs €2; bus; Eng spkn; adv bkg rec high ssn; some rd noise; CCI. "Open outlook with views; beautiful area; warm, friendly welcome; guided mountain walks; excel, family-run site; gd." ♦ ltd. € 20.00   2005*

ARGELES GAZOST *8G2* (5km N Urban) **Camping de la Tour, 65400 Agos-Vidalos** [tel/fax 05 62 97 55 59; michel.dubie@wanadoo.fr] Fr Lourdes-Pyrenees on N21 for 9km. Med, pt shd; wc; chem disp; mv service pnt; baby facs; shwrs inc; el pts (3-10A) inc; gas; lndtte; shop 2km; playgrnd; htd pool; adv bkg; rd noise; cc acc; CCI. ♦ 1 May-1 Sep. € 18.00   2002*

ARGELES GAZOST *8G2* (5km N Rural) **Camping Le Viscos, 16 Route de Prechac,** 65400 Beaucens [05 62 97 05 45] Fr Lourdes S twd Argeles-Gasost on N21. Cont twd Luz & Gavarnie to L of Argeles town, & turn L within 500m, sp Beaucens. Turn R to D13, site 2.5km on L. Med, pt sl, shd; wc; chem disp; shwrs inc; el pts (2-6A) €1.85-3.05 (rev pol); gas; ice; lndtte; shops 5km; tradsmn high ssn; rest in hotel adj; snacks; BBQ; playgrnd; pool 4km; lake fishing 500m; dogs €1; quiet; adv bkg ess Jul-Aug; red long stay; cc not acc; CCI. "Sparkling san facs; landscaped grounds." 15 May-30 Sep. € 9.00   2003*

Some of these sites have changed their opening dates - we'd better fill in some site report forms and let the editor of the guide know.

ARGELES GAZOST *8G2* (1km SE Rural) **Camping La Prairie,** 65400 Lau-Balagnas [05 62 97 11 87] Foll N21 fr Argeles-Gazost twd Couterets. Site sp immed on L after Lau-Balagnas sp (behind Mairie). Med, mkd pitch, pt shd; wc (cont); chem disp (wc); shwrs inc; el pts (2A) inc; lndry rm; shops 1km; playgrnd; sw pool 500m; no dogs; phone adj; some Eng spkn; quiet but some rd noise & church bells; CCI. "Gd cent for mountains." 1 Jul-31 Aug. € 10.80   2002*

†ARGELES GAZOST *8G2* (2km S Rural) **Camp du Lavedan, 44 Route des Vallees,** 65400 Lau-Balagnas [05 62 97 18 84; fax 05 62 97 55 56; michel.dubie@wanadoo.fr; www.lavedan.com] Site on R of N21 twd S after sp Lau-Balagnas indicating end of vill. Med, pt shd; htd wc; chem disp; shwrs inc; el pts (2-6A) €2-6; gas; ice; lndtte; lndry rm; shops 2km; rest; snacks; bar; playgrnd; htd, covrd pool; paddling pool; TV rm; 30% statics; dogs €2; site clsd Nov & 1-14 Dec; adv bkg; rd noise if pitched adj to rd. "In beautiful green valley; v friendly staff; excel cycle rte to Lourdes." ♦ € 20.50 (CChq acc)   2005*

ARGELES GAZOST *8G2* (2.5km S Rural) **Camping du Lac, 29 Chemin d'Azun,** 65400 Arcizans-Avant [tel/fax 05 62 97 01 88; campinglac@camping lac65.fr; www.campinglac65.fr] Fr Lourdes cont S thro Argeles-Gazost on N21/D921. At 3rd rndabt take exit for St Savin/Arcizans-Avant. Cont thro St Savin vill & foll camp sp; site on L just thro Arcizans-Avant vill. NB: Dir rte to Arcizans-Avant is prohibited to c'vans. Med, hdg/mkd pitch, pt sl, pt shd; wc; chem disp; shwrs inc; el pts (5-10A) €5-6; gas; lndtte; ice; shop; tradsmn; rest 500m; snacks; htd pool; games rm; TV rm; dogs €2; adv bkg; quiet; CCI. "Excel, peaceful site; gd for touring; lovely views; gd size pitches." ♦ 15 May-30 Sep. € 16.50   2005*

See advertisement

ARGELES GAZOST *8G2* (3km S) **Camping Les Frenes,** 65400 Lau-Balagnas [05 62 97 25 12; fax 05 62 97 01 41] Site on R of N21 twd S. Med, pt terr, pt shd; htd wc; chem disp; baby facs; shwrs inc; el pts (2-12A) €1.80-10.80; gas; lndtte; ice; shop 100m; BBQ; playgrnd; pool; rv sw & fishing 1km; entmnt; TV; some statics; adv bkg rec; quiet; red long stay. ♦ 15 Dec-15 Oct. € 12.90   2005*

ARGELES GAZOST *8G2* (3km SW Rural) **Camping L'Ideal,** 65400 Arras-en-Lavedan [05 62 97 03 13 or 05 62 97 02 12; fax 05 62 97 94 16] Leave Argeles Gazost SW on D918. Site on N side of rd on E o'skts of Arras-en-Lavedan. Ent on bend. Med, terr, pt shd; wc; chem disp; shwrs inc; el pts (3-10A) €2.30-€7.60; sm shop; playgrnd; pool high ssn; tennis 1km; adv bkg; quiet; CCI. "Friendly owner, vg clean site/facs; mountain views; cooler than in valley; steel awning pegs rec; vg sh stay." ♦ 1 Jun-15 Sep. € 9.15   2002*

ARGELES GAZOST *8G2* (10km SW) **LES CASTELS Pyrenees Natura, Route du Lac, 65400 Estaing** [05 62 97 45 44; fax 05 62 97 45 81; info@camping-pyrenees-natura.com; www. camping-pyrenees-natura.com or www.les-castels.com] Fr Lourdes take N21 to Argeles Gazost. At 'Champion' supmkt rndabt take D101 to 'Centre Ville' then take D918 in dir Col d'Aubisque; after approx 6km turn L onto D13 to Bun; after Bun cross rv & turn R onto D198 to site. Med, mkd pitch, pt shd; wc; chem disp; mv service pnt; baby facs; sauna; shwrs inc; el pts (10A) inc; gas; lndtte; ice; shop; tradsmn; snacks; bar; BBQ (gas/elec/charcoal); playgrnd; pool 4km; solariumtennis; mini-golf; entmnt; internet; 15% statics; dogs €1.50; Eng spkn; adv bkg; quiet; red low ssn; cc acc; CCI. "V well-kept site; immac facs; no plastic ground-sheets allowed; friendly, helpful owners; wonderful scenery; adj National Park; bird viewing area; excel." ♦ 1 May-20 Sep. € 26.00 ABS - D22
2005*

ARGELES SUR MER *10 G1* (1km N Coastal) **Camping Le Pujol, Route du Tamariguer, 66700 Argeles-sur-Mer** [04 68 81 00 25; fax 04 68 81 21 21; www.campingdepujol.com] N114 exit 10 Perpignan S dir Argeles. L off slip rd foll sp Pujol, site on R wide entrance. Lge, mkd pitch, pt shd; wc (some cont); chem disp; mv service pnt; baby facs; shwrs inc; el pts (3-6A); gas 2km; lndtte; ice; shop; rest; snacks; bar; playgrnd; pool; beach 1km; rv sw 1km; mini-golf; car wash; 30% statics; dogs; phone; poss cr; Eng spkn; adv bkg rec high ssn; quiet but poss noisy disco; CCI. "Vg san facs but poss cold water shwrs only low ssn; vg pool; excel cycling." ♦ ltd. 1 Jun-30 Sep. € 24.00
2004*

ARGELES SUR MER *10 G1* (1km N) **Camping Les Galets, Route de Taxo d'Avall, 66701 Argeles-sur-Mer** [04 68 81 08 12; fax 04 68 81 68 76; lesgalets@wanadoo.fr; www.campmed.com] Fr Perpignan take N114 dir Elne, Argeles, 4km after Elne pass Municipal Camping on L sp listing many camp sites. Lge, pt shd; wc; baby facs; shwrs inc; el pts (10A) inc; gas; ice; lndtte; shop; rest; snacks; bar; playgrnd; htd pool; sand beach 1.5km; fishing, sailing & windsurfing 1.5km; rv sw 3km; equestrian cent nr; games area; entmnt; TV rm; dogs €3.50; poss cr; adv bkg rec all year; quiet; red low ssn. "Ltd touring pitches; gd for families." ♦ 3 Apr-2 Oct. € 29.00
2004*

ARGELES SUR MER *10 G1* (2km N) **Camping Le Dauphin, Route de Taxo d'Avall, 66701 Argeles-sur-Mer** [04 68 81 17 54; fax 04 68 95 82 60; camping.ledauphin66@wanadoo.fr] Fr Perpignan take N114 sp Elne & Argeles-sur-Mer. 4km after Elne, sp on L to Taxo d'Avall, turn L, site 2km on R. Lge, hdg/mkd pitches, shd; wc; chem disp; some serviced pitches; baby facs; shwrs inc; el pts (10A) €3.50; gas; ice; lndtte; shop; rest; snacks; bar; 3 pools; playgrnd; tennis; mini-golf; sand beach 3km; rv sw 1.5km; fishing; sailing; windsurfing; TV rm; entmnt; 80% statics; dogs €2; adv bkg; quiet. "Gd for families." 1 Jun-30 Sep. € 28.50   2004*

ARGELES SUR MER *10 G1* (2km N) **Camping L'Hippocampe, La Honors, Route de Taxo d'Avall, 66701 Argeles-sur-Mer** [04 68 81 10 10; fax 04 68 81 40 97; contact@camping-lasirene.fr] Exit junc 10 fr N114 onto Rte de Taxo. Camp about 1km on L adj lge campsite La Sirene. Med, shd; wc; baby facs; shwrs inc; el pts (5A) €3; lndtte; shop; rest; snacks; bar; playgrnd; pool; waterslide; sand/shgl beach 1.5km; entmnt; TV rm; poss cr; adv bkg; quiet. Easter-27 Sep. € 43.00 (3 persons)
2004*

Will you fill in the site report forms at the back of the guide, or shall I?

ARGELES SUR MER *10G1* (2km N Coastal) **Camping Paris Roussillon, Route de Tamariguer, Quartier Pujol, 66700 Argeles-sur-Mer** [04 68 81 19 71; fax 04 68 81 68 77; camping-parisroussillon@club-internet.fr; www.paris-roussillon.com] Fr Perpignan, take N114, junc 10 twds Pujol. Site 2km on R. Lge, mkd pitch, shd; wc; chem disp; shwrs inc; baby facs; el pts (4-10A) inc; lndtte; shop 1km; rest; snacks; bar; BBQ; playgrnd; pool; beach 1.5km; dogs; 10% statics; quiet; Eng spkn. ♦ 1 May-30 Sep. € 24.00   2004*

ARGELES SUR MER *10 G1* (2km NE Coastal) **Camp Municipal Roussillonnais, Blvd de la Mer, 66700 Argeles-sur-Mer** [04 68 81 10 42; fax 04 68 95 96 11; camping.rouss@infonie.fr] S fr Perpignan thro Elne to Argeles-sur-Mer, turn L in Argeles-sur-Mer foll coast rd & site on R in 1.5km. V lge, hdg/mkd pitch, pt shd; wc (some cont); chem disp; mv service pnt; baby facs; shwrs inc; el pts (5A) €3.10; gas; lndtte; ice; shop; rest; snacks; bar; playgrnd; sand beach; boating; watersports; games area; dogs €1.50; poss cr; Eng spkn; adv bkg; quiet; cc acc; CCI. "Test for firm sand on beach pitches; ltd facs low ssn." 15 Jun-15 Sep. € 24.00
2004*

ARGELES SUR MER *10 G1* (2km NE Coastal) **Camping du Stade, Route Nouvelle de la Plage, 66702 Argeles-sur-Mer** [04 68 81 04 40; fax 04 68 95 84 55; info@campingdustade.com; www.campingdustade.com] S on N114 thro traff lts at Argeles; turn L after 400m at clearly mkd turn sp 'A la Plage'. Site 800m on L. Lge, shd; wc; baby facs; shwrs inc; el pts (6A) €3.60; lndtte; shop 500m; rest; snacks; bar; playgrnd; sand beach 800m; sports complex adj; entmnt & child entmnt; TV rm; some statics; dogs €2; poss cr; adv bkg rec high ssn; red low ssn; quiet. "Lge pitches; gd walking area; nice mountain views; friendly owners." Easter & 1 Apr-30 Sep. € 18.00   2004*

FRANCE

Argelès sur Mer

In the Mediterranean, the Pyrenees have got their beach

Editions de l'Arbre ✆ 04 68 95 88 38

On the Mediterranean coast and at the foothills of the Pyrenees, Argelès sur Mer has everything to make your holiday complete : sun, golden sand, clear waters and numerous activities… not to mention the picturesque atmosphere of the Catalan way of life.

From ★★ to ★★★★, we have a superb range of camping and caravan parks ! Ask for our **free brochure** with detailed lists of camping sites.

OFFICE DU TOURISME
Place de l'Europe • F-66700 ARGELES SUR MER
✆ +33 4 68 81 15 85 • Fax +33 4 68 81 16 01
http://www.argeles-sur-mer.com

ARGELES SUR MER *10 G1* (2km NE Coastal) Camping La Marende, Ave de Littoral, 66702 Argeles-sur-Mer [04 68 81 12 09; fax 04 68 81 88 52; camp.marendel@altranet.fr; www.marende.com] Fr Perpignan S on N114 exit junc 10 Argeles-sur-Mer; foll sp Plage Nord; after Hippocampe (2km) L then R onto D81. In 800m turn L onto unmade rd; site on L in 200m. V lge, hdg/mkd pitch, shd; wc; chem disp; some serviced pitches; mv service pnt; baby facs; shwrs inc; el pts (6-10A) inc; gas; lndtte; ice shop; rest; snacks; bar; BBQ (el/gas); playgrnd; pool & paddling pool; jacuzzi; games area; sand beach adj; aquarobics, scuba-diving lessons Jul & Aug; 12% statics; internet; TV; phone; poss cr; Eng spkn; quiet; adv bkg; cc acc; CCI. "Beautiful site; lge pitches; friendly helpful family owners; 1st class facs; excel pool; gd area for cycling & walking." ♦ 18 May-28 Sep. € 23.00   2005*

ARGELES SUR MER *10 G1* (2km NE) **Camping La Sirene**, Route de Taxo, 66701 Argeles-sur-Mer [04 68 81 04 61; fax 04 68 81 69 74; camping.la. sirene@wanadoo.fr; www.camping-lasirene.fr] Take N114 fr Perpignan twd Argeles. Cross Rv Tech & take 1st L twd Taxo d'Avall, site 1 of many about 2.5km on R. Lge, shd; wc; baby facs; shwrs inc; el pts (5A) €3; gas; lndtte; ice; shop; rest; snacks; bar; BBQ; playgrnd; pool; waterslide; sand beach 1.5km; tennis; mini-golf; horseriding; archery; cycle hire; fishing, sailing & windsurfing 1km; dogs €4; adv bkg; quiet; red low ssn. "Noisy disco to front of site." 23 Mar-30 Sep. € 43.00   2004*

ARGELES SUR MER *10 G1* (2km NE Coastal) Camping Le Soleil, Route du Littoral, Plage-Nord, 66700 Argeles-sur-Mer [04 68 81 14 48; fax 04 68 81 44 34; camping.lesoleil@wanadoo.fr; www.campmed.com] Exit N114 junc 10 & foll sp Argeles Plage-Nord. Turn L onto D81 to site. Site among others. V lge, mkd pitch, pt shd; wc (some cont); chem disp; mv service pnt; baby facs; shwrs inc; el pts (6A) €3.10; gas; lndtte; ice; shop; rest; snacks; bar; no BBQ; playgrnd; pool; paddling pool; sand beach adj; rv fishing adj; tennis; cycle hire; horseriding; mini-golf; games area; entmnt; TV; 50% statics; no dogs; adv bkg (ess Aug); noisy nr disco; red low ssn; cc acc. "Lovely views; excel site suitable for partially-sighted; tel & fax nos swap when site clsd; visit to Collioure a must." ♦ 14 May-23 Sep. € 27.50   2005*

ARGELES SUR MER *10 G1* (2km NE Coastal) Camping Les Pins, Ave du Tech, Zone des Pins, 66700 Argeles-sur-Mer [04 68 81 10 46; fax 04 68 81 35 06; camping-les-pins@wanadoo.fr; www.les-pins.com] Exit N114 junc 10, foll sp Pujols & Plage-Nord, site sp. Lge, shd; wc (some cont); chem disp; baby facs; shwrs inc; el pts (6A) inc; gas; lndtte; shop; snacks; playgrnd; pool 2km; sand beach 200m; statics; dogs €2.50; poss cr; adv bkg (ess Jul/Aug); quiet; cc acc. ♦ 28 May-17 Sep. € 23.40   2004*

ARGELES SUR MER *10 G1* (2km NE Coastal) Camping-Caravaning Le Neptune, Chemin du Tamariquer, 66700 Argeles-sur-Mer [04 68 81 02 98; fax 04 68 81 00 41; neptune@parchemin.com; www.le-neptune.com] Fr Argeles Plage take D81 coast rd to Argeles-Plage Nord & site sp on L. Lge, mkd pitch, pt shd; wc (some cont); chem disp; baby facs; shwrs inc; el pts (10A) inc; gas; lndtte; shop 300m; rest; snacks; bar; playgrnd; pool; waterslide; sand beach 400m; dogs €3.50; golf 7km; cycle hire; entmnt; 15% statics; dogs; €3.50; Eng spkn; adv bkg ess; cc acc; CCI. "Well-maintained site; excel san facs." ♦ 1 May-30 Sep. € 26.00   2003*

ARGELES SUR MER *10 G1* (3km NE Coastal) Camping Beausejour, Ave de Tech, Argeles Plage, 66700 Argeles-sur-Mer [04 68 81 10 63; fax 04 68 95 75 08; hpabeausej@aol.com; www.campinglebeausejour.com] Fr Perpignan, foll N114 to Argeles-sur-Mer. Turn L after Champion supmkt & Shell g'ge; foll sp to Plage Nord. At coast rd turn R to Argeles-Plage cent. Site on R shortly after supmkt. Lge, mkd pitch, shd; wc; chem disp; shwrs inc; el pts (4A) inc; lndtte; shop adj; snacks, playgrnd; pool; sand beach 300m; 50% statics; dogs; phone; poss cr; Eng spkn; adv bkg rec; CCI. "Walking dist to beach; lots of shops, rests, takeaways nr." ♦ ltd.
1 Apr-15 Oct. € 32.00 (3 persons)   2004*

ARGELES SUR MER *10 G1* (500m E Coastal) Camping La Massane, Ave Moliere (Zone Pujol), 66700 Argeles-sur-Mer [04 68 81 06 85; fax 04 68 81 59 18; camping.massane@infonie.fr; www.camping-massane.com] Fr N114 exit junc 10, at traff island take 2nd exit, site sp further down rd. Site just bef municipal stadium on L Lge, hdg/mkd pitch, pt shd; wc (some cont); chem disp; baby facs; shwrs inc; el pts (6-10A) inc; gas; lndtte; ice; shop & 500m; snacks; bar; BBQ (gas/elec only); playgrnd; htd pool & children's paddling pool; sand beach 1km; mini-golf; tennis adj; entmnt, excursions high ssn; dogs €2; poss cr; Eng spkn; adv bkg rec high ssn; red long stay/low ssn; quiet; cc acc; CCI. "Vg site; friendly welcome; steel pegs req." ♦
15 Mar-15 Oct. € 24.00   2005*

ARGELES SUR MER *10 G1* (1km E Coastal) Camping Europe, Ave General de Gaulle, 66700 Argeles-sur-Mer [04 68 81 08 10; fax 04 68 95 71 84; camping.europe@wanadoo.fr] Fr Perpignan take N114 to Argeles-sur-Mer. Exit junc 12 to Argeles. At rndabt take last exit L to Argeles Ville. At next rndabt turn R, site on L after Dyneff g'ge. Med, mktd pitch, shd; wc; chem disp; baby facs; shwrs inc; el pts (3-10A) €2.75-3.20; gas; lndtte; shop; tradsmn; rest; snacks; bar; BBQ; playgrnd; pool 800m; sand beach 300m; 10% statics; dogs €1.60; phone; bus adj; poss cr; Eng spkn; adv bkg; quiet; CCI. "Friendly family-run; gd san facs." 1 Apr-30 Oct. € 17.00   2004*

ARGELES SUR MER *10 G1* (2km E Urban/Coastal) Camping La Chapelle, Place de l'Europe, 66702 Argeles-sur-Mer [04 68 81 28 14; fax 04 68 95 83 82] Fr A9 exit junc 42 onto N9/N114 to Argeles-sur-Mer. At junc 10 cont thro Argeles vill & foll sp Argeles-Plage. In 2.5km tun L at rndabt, bear L at Office of Tourism, site immed L. Lge, hdg/mkd pitch, shd; wc (mainly cont), shwrs inc; el pts (4-6A) €3.50; lndtte; shop; rests, snacks, bar 100m; playgrnd; pool 2km; beach 200m; tennis 200m; 33% statics; dogs €2.50; poss cr; Eng spkn; adv bkg; quiet; CCI. "Ltd facs low ssn; gd." ♦ 1 May-25 Sep.
€ 21.00   2004*

ARGELES SUR MER *10 G1* (3km E Coastal) Camping La Plage, Ave General de Gaulle, 66702 Argeles-sur-Mer [04 68 81 12 17]   Fr Perpignan take N114 to Argeles-sur-Mer. Exit junc 12 to port. Foll rd round to town. At the cent island turn L; site ent on L bef Dyneff g'ge in Argeles-Plage. Med, mkd pitch, pt shd; wc (some cont); chem disp; shwrs inc; el pts (6A) inc; gas; lndtte; shops 200m; rest, bar 500m; snacks; playgrnd; sand beach 200m; 5% statics; phone; poss cr; Eng spkn; quiet; CCI. "Friendly, helpful staff." Easter-30 Sep. € 16.50   2003*

ARGELES SUR MER *10 G1* (3km SE Coastal) Camping La Coste Rouge, Route de Collioure, Zone La Racou, 66700 Argeles-sur-Mer [04 68 81 08 94; fax 04 68 95 94 17] Exit junc 13 fr N114 dir Port-Argeles. At 2nd rndabt foll D114 to Racou, site on L. Med, shd; wc (some cont); chem disp; baby facs; shwrs inc; el pts (6A) €3.50; lndtte; ice; shop; rest; snacks; bar; no BBQ; playgrnd; pool; sand beach 1km; some statics; dogs €2.30; phone; adv bkg; quiet.cc acc. "Beautiful pool; gd cent for sea, Pyrenees & trips to Spain; aquarium at Banyuls-sur-Mer; cloisters at Elne." ♦
Easter-15 Oct. € 19.00   2003*

ARGELES SUR MER *10 G1* (4km SE Coastal) Camping Les Criques de Porteils, Route de Collioure, 66700 Argeles-sur-Mer [04 68 81 12 73; fax 04 66 95 85 76; criques.costa@wanadoo.fr; www.lescriques.com/camping] Fr A9/E15 take exit junc 42 onto N114 Argeles-sur-Mer. At exit 13 leave N114 sp Collioure. Site sp on L by Hotel du Golfe. Lge, mkd pitch, pt sl, terr, pt shd; wc; chem disp; mv service pnt; shwrs inc; el pts (6A) €4; gas; lndtte; ice; shop; rest; snacks; bar; playgrnd; shgl beach adj; boat excursions; fishing; watersports; dogs €4; phone; poss cr; Eng spkn; adv bkg; quiet; CCI. "Variable size pitches - not all suitable for lge o'fits; steps to beach, extra for sea view pitches." ♦
15 Mar-15 Nov. € 27.50 (3 persons)   2005*

FRANCE

ARGELES SUR MER *10 G1* (4km S Coastal/Rural) Camping Les Marsouins, Route du Tamariguer, 66702 Argeles-sur-Mer [04 68 81 14 81; fax 04 68 95 93 58; marsouin@campmed.com; www. campmed.com] Fr Perpignan take exit 10 fr N114 & foll sp for Argeles until Shell petrol stn on R & Total petrol stn on L. Take next L into Allee Ferdinand Buisson to T-junc, turn L at next rndabt dir Plage-Nord. Take 2nd R at next rndabt, site on L opp Spanish war memorial. V lge, hdg/mkd pitch, shd; wc; chem disp; mv service pnt; shwrs inc; el pts (5A) inc; gas; lndtte; ice; shops; rest; snacks; bar; BBQ; playgrnd; htd pool; sand beach 800m; entmnt; cycle hire; sailing & windsurfing 1km; dogs; poss cr; adv bkg (acc in writing Jan-May); quiet; red low ssn; cc acc. "Many sm coves; gd area for cycling; excel, well-run site; busy rd to beach, but worth it." 9 Apr-27 Aug. € 21.04   2004*

ARGELES SUR MER *10 G1* (2.5km SW) Camping Le Romarin, Route de Sorede, 66702 Argeles-sur-Mer [04 68 81 02 63; fax 04 68 56 62 33; camping-romarin@libertysurf.fr; www.camping-romarin.com] S fr Perpignon on N114; at rndabt junc with D618 foll sp St Andre on minor rd; in 500m L & immed L & foll sp to site. Or fr A9 exit junc 43; foll D618 to rndabt junc with N114; then as above. Med, pt sl, shd; wc (some cont); shwrs inc; el pts (4-6A) €2-3.50; gas; lndtte; shop; rest; snacks; bar; playgrnd; pool; waterslide; beach 4km; sports activities; entmnt; dogs €3; Eng spkn; adv bkg; quiet; red low ssn. "V pleasant site; conv Spanish border." 15 May-30 Sep. € 25.00   2005*

ARGELES SUR MER *10 G1* (5km SW Urban) Camping Les Micocouliers, Route de Palau, 66690 Sorede [04 68 89 20 27; fax 04 68 89 25 61; contact@camping-les-micocouliers.com; www. camping-les-micocouliers.com] A9 S dir Le Boulou exit 43 onto D618 dir Argeles-sur-Mer; R onto D11 to Sorede, sp to site. Lge, hdg/mkd pitch, pt sl, shd; wc; chem disp; shrws inc; el pts (6A) €3.50; gas; lndtte; ice; shops & in vill; tradsmn; snacks; bar; BBQ; playgrnd; pool; beach 20km; tennis adj; cycle hire; TV rm; 5% statics; dogs €1.80; poss v cr; ess adv bkg Jul-Aug (dep & bkg fee); no cc acc. "Lge pitches; conv N Spain eg Figueras, Dali museum." ♦ ltd. 26 Jun-15 Sep. € 19.50   2004*

ARGELES SUR MER *10G1* (8km W Urban) Camp Municipal Le Vivier, 31 Rue du Stade, 66740 Laroque-des-Alberes [04 68 89 00 93 or 04 68 89 21 13; fax 04 68 95 42 58] D2 fr Argeles-sur-Mer to Laroque-des-Alberes; foll sp in cent of vill. Lge, mkd pitch, pt sl, pt shd; wc; chem disp; shwrs inc; el pts (6A) €2.30; lndtte; ice; shop 300m; 5% statics; dogs €1.50; bus 300m; adv bkg; quiet; CCI. "Peaceful, simple site at edge of Pyrenees, in pleasant vill with shops & rests; vg." ♦ 1 Jun-30 Sep. € 10.20   2005*

ARGELES SUR MER *10 G1* (8km W Rural) Camping Les Alberes, 66740 Laroque-des- Alberes [04 68 89 23 64; fax 04 68 89 14 30; camping-des-alberes@wanadoo.fr; www.camping-des-alberes.com] Fr A9 exit junc 43 onto D618 dir Argeles-sur-Mer/Port Vendres. Turn R onto D50 to Laroque-des-Alberes. In vill at T-junc turn L, then turn R at rndabt & foll sp to site on D11. Lge, mkd pitch, terr, pt shd; wc (some cont); chem disp; mv service pnt; baby facs; shwrs inc; el pts (6-10A) €3.50; lndtte; shop; rest; snacks; bar; BBQ (gas only); playgrnd; pool; sand beach 8km; tennis 800m; TV; rm; entmnt; 5% statics; dogs €2; phone; quiet; poss cr; CCI. "V attractive site under slopes of Pyrenees; gd walking area; peaceful; friendly owners." ♦ ltd. 1 Apr-30 Sep. € 20.00   2005*

ARGELES SUR MER *10 G1* (8km W) Camping-Caravaning Las Planes, 117 Ave du Vallespir, 66740 Laroque-des-Alberes [04 68 89 21 36 or 04 68 95 43 76 (LS); fax 04 68 89 01 42; francois. camping.las.planes@libertysurf.fr] Fr Argeles take N114, D2 twd Sourede, thro Laroque des Alberes on D11, site sp. Med, pt sl, shd, mkd pitch; wc; chem disp; shwrs inc; el pts (4A) €3; gas; lndtte; ice; shop; snacks; bar; el/gas BBQ; playgrnd; 2 pools; sand beach 8km; cycle hire; dogs €2.30; poss cr; adv bkg rec high ssn; quiet. "C'van storage avail." 15 Jun-31 Aug. € 18.00   2004*

ARGELES SUR MER *10 G1* (2km NW) **Camping Etoile d'Or, Route de Taxo d'Avall, 66701 Argeles-sur-Mer** [04 68 81 04 34; fax 04 68 81 57 05; info@aletoiledor.com; www. aletoiledor.com] Fr N114 exit junc 10 dir Taxo-Plage. Site in 1km on R. Lge, shd; wc (cont); shwrs inc; el pts (4A) €3.50; gas; lndtte; ice; shop; rest; snacks; bar; el/gas BBQ; playgrnd; pool; sand beach 2.5km; tennis; mini-golf; games rm; entmnt; TV rm; many statics; dogs €2; adv bkg; quiet. ♦ 15 Mar-30 Sep. € 23.00   2004*

ARGELES SUR MER *10 G1* (3km NW) **Camping Le Canigou, Taxo-d'Amont, 66702 Argeles-sur-Mer** [tel/fax 04 68 81 02 55] N114 exit junc 10 dir Taxo d'Amont. Lge sp visible fr main rd. Med, shd; wc; shwrs; el pts (10A) €4.60; gas; lndtte; ice; shop; snacks; bar; BBQ; playgrnd; pool; sand beach 4.5km; cycle hire; entmnt; dogs €1.30; poss cr; adv bkg rec high ssn; quiet. 1 Apr-30 Sep. € 13.20
                    2003*

ARGENTAN *4E1* (S) **Camp Municipal du Parc de la Noe, 34 Rue de la Noe, 61200 Argentan** [02 33 36 05 69; fax 02 33 36 52 07] Heading S fr Caen on N158 foll camping sp fr by-pass (D15). Fr N on N158 foll sp Centre Ville or to 1st rndabt the R at lts, then R & foll sp to camp site. Sm, shd; wc (cont); chem disp; mv service pnt; shwrs; el pts (10A) €2.10; ice; lndtte; shop 1km; playgrnd; pool 1km; rv & pond; sports area; TV; few statics; poss cr; adv bkg ess high ssn; quiet. "Vg clean & tidy site; helpful warden; gd disabled facs." ♦ 1 Apr-30 Sep. € 8.00   2005*

†ARGENTAN *4E1* (2km S Rural) **Aire Naturelle du Val de Baize (Huet des Aunay), 18 Mauvaisville, 61200 Argentan** [02 33 67 27 11; fax 02 33 35 39 16] Take N158 fr Argentan twd Sees & Alencon. Turn R at Mauvaisville, site adj T-junc N of farm buildings. Sm, pt shd; wc; chem disp; mv service pnt; shwrs inc; el pts (6A) €2.50-4.60; gas; shops 1.5km; snacks; playgrnd; pool 2.5km; fishing adj; B&B; 10% statics; dogs; Eng spkn; adv bkg; quiet; cc not acc; CCI. "Lge pitches in orchard; well-kept site with clean but dated facs, ltd low ssn; friendly welcome." € 9.10   2005*

ARGENTAT *7C4* (10km N Rural) **Camp Municipal La Croix de Brunal, 19320 St Martin-la-Meanne** [05 55 29 11 91 or 05 55 29 12 75 (Mairie); fax 05 55 29 28 48] Fr Argentat take D18 to St Martin-la-Meanne. Site well sp on ent to vill. Sm, hdg pitch, pt shd; wc; shwrs inc; el pts (5A) €2.50; gas, lndtte; shop 1km; rest, snacks, bar; BBQ; htd pool 1km; sand beach 1km; rv sw 8km; tennis 1km; dogs; phone; quiet. "Simple country site; gd walking; fishing, horseriding, canoe hire, watersports within 15km; warden calls am & pm." ♦ ltd.
15 Jun-15 Sep. € 7.50   2003*

ARGENTAT *7C4* (4km NE Rural) **Camping Chateau de Gibanel, 19400 St Martial-Entraygues** [05 55 28 10 11; fax 05 55 28 81 62; contact@ camping-gibanel.com; www.camping-gibanel. com] Exit Argentat on D18 twd Egletons & fork R on lakeside past hydro-electric dam. Sp fr all dir. Site in grounds of sm castle on N bank of lake. App rd narr but satisfactory. Lge, mkd pitch, pt sl, pt shd; wc (some cont); chem disp; child/baby facs; fam bthrm; shwrs inc; el pts (6A) €3; gas; lndtte; ice; shop; tradsmn; rest; snacks; bar; BBQ; playgrnd; pool; paddling pool; lake sw; sports area; boating; fishing; entmnt; games rm; TV; 15% statics; dogs €1.50; Eng spkn; adv bkg; quiet; red low ssn; cc acc; CCI. "Excel site; v helpful owner; beautiful location, lovely sm town; gd rest in town; ltd facs low ssn; different sized pitches; lge shwr cubicles with washbasins; rms/apartments for rent; gd long/sh stay." ♦ ltd. 1 Jun-9 Sep. € 15.40 (CChq acc)
                    2005*

Mustn't forget to post our site report forms to The Club, otherwise sites might be deleted.

FRANCE

ARGENTAT *7C4* (3km SW) **Camping Europe, Le Chambon, 19400 Monceaux-sur-Dordogne** [05 55 28 07 70; fax 05 55 28 19 60; camping-europe@wanadoo.fr] Fr Argentat take D12 twd Beaulieu-sur-Dordogne. Site in 2km fr N120. Ent on L by awkward RH bend in Le Chambon. Med, mkd pitch, pt sl, pt shd; wc; chem disp; shwrs inc; el pts (5A) €2.60; gas; lndtte; shops 1km; rest 500m; snacks 1km; playgrnd; pool; tennis; games area; entmnt; child entmnt; some statics; dogs; poss cr; quiet. "Lovely rvside site; interesting town."
1 Apr-30 Oct. € 14.20   2004*

ARGENTAT *7C4* (4km SW Rural) **Sunelia Camping au Soleil d'Oc, 19400 Monceaux-sur-Dordogne** [05 55 28 84 84 or 05 55 28 05 97 (LS); fax 05 55 28 12 12; info@dordogne-soleil.com; www. dordogne-soleil.com] Fr Argentat foll D12 sp Beaulieu. At 4km turn L over narr single track bdge x-ing Dordogne (adj bar/tabac). Bear L over bdge. Site 2nd on L in 300m. Med, hdg/mkd pitch, terr, shd; wc (some cont); chem disp; mv service pnt; baby facs; shwrs inc; el pts (6A) €3; gas; lndtte; tradsmn; rest; snacks; bar; BBQ; playgrnd; pool & paddling pool high ssn; rv sw & shgl beach; canoe hire; games area; games rm; cycle hire; mini-golf; archery; entmnt; child entmnt; internet; sat TV; dogs €2; phone; Eng spkn; adv bkg; quiet; red low ssn/long stay/CCI. "Ideal family site; gd walking; lots beautiful vills in area; tours arranged." ♦
1 Apr-15 Nov. € 19.80 (CChq acc)   2005*

See advertisement opposite

SITES

ARGENTAT *7C4* (6km SW Rural) **Camping du Saulou, Vergnolles, 19400 Monceaux-sur-Dordogne [05 55 28 12 33; fax 05 55 28 80 67]** S on N120, turn R at N o'skts of Argentat on D12, sp Beaulieu. Foll rv L sp Vergnolles & camp sp. Lge, hdg/mkd pitch, pt shd; wc (some cont); chem disp; shwrs inc; el pts (10A) €3; gas; lndtte; ice; shop & 1km; tradsmn; rest; snacks; bar; htd pool; paddling pool; boating; fishing; games area; entmnt; TV rm; 10% statics; dogs; phone; poss cr; Eng spkn; adv bkg; quiet low ssn; red low ssn; cc acc; CCI. "Early dep should arrange disconnect el by warden night bef; facs constantly cleaned; v friendly, helpful owners; excel long/sh stay." 1 Apr-30 Sep. € 16.40
2004*

As we're travelling out of season, we'd better phone ahead to check that the site is actually open.

ARGENTAT *7C4* (9km SW Rural) **Camping Le Vaurette, 19400 Monceaux-sur-Dordogne [05 55 28 09 67; fax 05 55 28 81 14; info@vaurette.com; www.vaurette.com]** SW fr Tulle on N120; fr Argentat SW on D12 sp Beaulieu; site sp on banks of Rv Dordogne. Med, mkd pitch, pt shd; wc (some cont); chem disp; mv service pnt; baby facs; shwrs inc; el pts (6A) €3; gas; lndtte; ice; shop; snacks; bar; BBQ; playgrnd; pool; shgl beach & rv sw adj; tennis; badminton; fishing; canoe expeditions; games area; games rm; TV rm; statics; dogs €2.50; Eng spkn; adv bkg; quiet; cc acc; red low ssn; CCI. "V helpful, friendly owners; lovely setting; many sports avail; excel long stay." ♦ 1 May 21 Sep. € 20.00
2005*

ARGENTIERE LA BESSEE, L' *9C3* (6km N) **Camping de l'Iscle de Prelles, 05120 St Martin-de-Queyrieres [04 92 20 28 66; www.iscle-de-prelles.com]** S fr Briancon on N94 turn L after 5km over unguarded level x-ing (quiet line), track turns R & site in 500m. Med, mkd pitch, shd; wc (some cont); baby facs; shwrs inc; el pts (10A) €4.30; lndry rm; ice; sm shop; rest; snacks; htd pool; tennis; entmnt; TV; adv bkg; quiet. "Attractive mountain aspects; cable car." 15 May-15 Sep.
€ 13.35
2002*

ARGENTIERE LA BESSEE, L' *9C3* (2.5km S) **Camp Municipal Les Ecrins, 05120 L'Argentiere-la-Bessee [04 92 23 03 38; fax 04 92 23 07 71; camping-ecrins@wanadoo.fr]** Fr L'Argentiere on N94, turn R onto D104, site sp. Med, some mkd pitch, pt shd, htd wc (some cont); shwrs inc; el pts (10A) inc; lndtte; shop; snacks; playgrnd; walking; rafting; adv bkg; rd/rlwy noise. "Mountain scenery." ♦ Easter-30 Sep. € 12.15
2002*

†ARGENTIERE LA BESSEE, L' *9C3* (8km NW) **Camping Les Chambonnettes, 05290 Vallouise [tel/fax 04 92 23 30 26 or 06 82 23 65 09; camping.vallouise@free.fr]** Take N94 Briancon-Gap, on N o'skts of L'Argentierre-la-Bessee take D994 W dir Vallouise. In cent of Vallouise turn L over bdge & immed L, site in 200m. Lge, mkd pitch, pt sl, pt shd; htd wc (some cont); chem disp; shwrs inc; el pts (3-6A) €2.90; gas 1.5km; lndtte; shops 200m; tradsmn, rest, snacks, bar 500m; playgrnd; pool 3km; tennis; boules; TV; 10% statics; phone; poss cr; Eng spkn; adv bkg; quiet; red low ssn "Magnificent mountain scenery; basic facs; gd cent for walking, skiing, canoeing; white-water rafting at nrby rv; interesting vill." € 12.35
2005*

ARGENTON CHATEAU *4H1* (1km W Urban) **Camp Municipal du Lac d'Hautibus, Rue de la Sabliere, 79150 Argenton-Chateau [05 49 65 95 08 or 05 49 65 70 22 (Mairie); fax 05 49 65 70 84]** Well sp in town, on lakeside. Med, hdg pitch, pt sl, terr; wc (some cont); chem disp; shwrs inc; el pts (10A) €2.10; lndtte; shops in town; playgrnd; pool 100m; lake sw 500m; quiet; CCI. "Interesting town; excel site." ♦ 1 Apr-31 Oct. € 6.75
2004*

ARGENTON L'EGLISE see Thouars *4H1*

ARGENTON SUR CREUSE *7A3* (6km NE Rural) **Camp Municipal des Rives de la Bouzanne, 36800 Le Pont Chretien-Chabenet [02 54 25 80 53 or 02 54 25 81 40 (Mairie); fax 02 54 25 87 59]** Fr St Gaultier on D927 to Argenton-sur-Creuse, turn R in Pont Chretien-Chabenet, bef rv bdge, 50m on L. Med, pt shd; wc (some cont); chem disp (wc); shwrs inc; el pts €2.50; lndtte; shop, bar adj; playgrnd; rv sw adj; dogs €0.50; adv bkg; quiet; CCI. 15 Jun-15 Sep. € 7.00
2005*

ARGENTON SUR CREUSE *7A3* (12km SE) **La Chaumerette Camping Club a Tou Vert, 36190 Gargilesse-Dompierre [02 54 47 73 44; A.TOU.VERT@net-up.com]** Fr A20 take exit 17 for D48 to Badecon-le-Pin then R onto D40. Turn R sp Barsize then foll sp to site. Sm, shd; wc; chem disp; baby facs; shwrs; el pts (6A) inc; tradsmn; snacks; bar; playgrnd; rv sw; fishing; adv bkg; quiet; CCI. "Superb location in wooded valley adj rv; additional overflow area when site full; poor san facs." 1 May-31 Oct. € 14.50
2005*

ARGENTON SUR CREUSE *7A3* (12km SW Rural) **Camping La Petite Brenne (Naturist), La Grande Metairie, 36800 Luzeret [02 54 25 05 78; fax 02 54 25 05 97; www.lapetitebrenne.com]** Fr a'route A20 exit junc 18 sp Luzeret/Prissac; foll D55 to Luzeret vill. After bdge in vill turn L, then next L to site. Lge, pt sl, unshd; wc; chem disp (biodegradable only); sauna; shwrs inc; el pts (6A) €3 (long leads poss req); lndtte; ice; shop 12km; tradsmn; rest; bar; playgrnd; 2 pools; horseriding; dogs €4.60; Eng spkn; adv bkg rec high ssn; quiet; cc acc; red long stay/low ssn; INF cards ess. "V friendly Dutch owners; ideal for children; gd san facs; lge pitches." Easter-30 Sep. € 20.00
2005*

ARGENTON SUR CREUSE *7A3* (1km NW) **Camp Municipal Les Chambons, 36200 Argenton-sur-Creuse** [02 54 24 15 26] Exit A20 at junc 17 (twd Argenton) & foll camping sp. Best app fr N of town on D927 to avoid traff calming rd humps. At town sp turn R immed past LH turn for Roman archaeological museum; foll camping sp on narr, busy app rd (speed bumps). Med, mkd pitch, some hdstg, pt sl, shd; wc; chem disp; shwrs inc; el pts (10A) €3.20; gas; shop 1.5km; bar; rest 1km; playgrnd; quiet but some rlwy noise. "Beautiful site by rv; v muddy after heavy rain & poss uneven pitches by rv; archaeological Roman site nrby; no need to unhitch so useful for early start; helpful warden." 15 May-15 Sep. € 12.15 2005*

ARLANC *9C1* (1km W Rural) **Camping Le Metz, 63220 Arlanc** [04 73 95 15 62; fax 04 73 95 15 62; jardin-terre.arlanc@wanadoo.fr] Fr Ambert on D906 to Arlanc, turn R (W) onto D999A dir St Germain-l'Herm. Site on R in 800m, sp. Med, some hdg pitch, pt shd; wc (some cont); chem disp (wc); shwrs inc; el pts (6A) inc (long lead poss req); lndry rm; shop 800m; rest, snacks, bar 150m; playgrnd; pool 100m; games area; mini-golf; 10% statics; dogs; phone; adv bkg; quiet. "Trav cheques acc; lace-making museum in Arlanc." ♦ 1 May-30 Sep. € 11.40 2005*

ARLES *10E2* (8km NE) **Camp Municipal des Pins, Rue Michelet, 13990 Fontvieille** [04 90 54 78 69; fax 04 90 54 81 25] Take N570 fr Arles to Avignon; in 2km turn R on D17 to Fontvieille; at far end of vill turn R & foll sp. Med, pt sl, shd; wc; shwrs inc; el pts (6A) €2.30; gas fr Shell g'ge in vill; shops 1km; pool 500m high ssn; poss cr; Eng spkn; adv bkg; quiet; CCI. "Delightful site, quiet forest walks; friendly staff; poss mosquitoes; 10 mins walk to vill; vg facs; red long stay." 1 Apr-13 Oct. € 10.00 2005*

ARLES *10E2* (2km SE Urban) **Camping Le City, 67 Route de Crau, 13200 Arles** [04 90 93 08 86; fax 04 90 93 91 07; contact@camping-city.com; www.camping-city.com] Fr town cent foll rd to Pont de Crau. Site well sp on L in 2km. Med, mkd pitch, pt shd; wc (some cont); chem disp; mv service pnt; baby facs; shwrs inc; el pts (5A) €4; gas 1km; lndtte; shop; supmkt 1km; tradsmn; rest; snacks; bar; playgrnd; pool; paddling pool; sand beach 25km; tennis; cycle hire; entmnt; TV; many statics; dogs €2; bus; some Eng spkn; quiet; CCI. "Vg; 20 min walk to Arles town cent; basic san facs." ♦ 1 Mar-30 Oct. € 16.00 2005*

ARLES *10E2* (4km SE Urban) **Camping Les Rosiers, Pont de Crau, 13200 Arles** [04 90 96 02 12; fax 04 90 93 36 72] Exit Arles by N453 sp Pont de Crau (exit 7 on N113), 200m after exit vill take 1st exit at rndabt then R at Flor Hotel sp on D83E. Site in 50m on R adj hotel. Med, pt shd; wc (some cont); shwrs inc; chem disp; el pts (6A) €3.80-4.30; lndtte; shop 500m; rest; bar; playgrnd; pool; games area; entmnt; TV; bus fr rndabt; no vans over 5.50m allowed (but poss not enforced); poss cr; Eng spkn; some rd & rlwy noise; red facs low ssn. "Many mosquitoes; v muddy after rain; visit Les Baux citadel am bef coach parties arr; gd birdwatching, info at St Martin-de-Crau." 1 Mar-31 Oct. € 10.50 2003*

ARLES *10E2* (14km W) **Camping Caravaning Crin-Blanc, Hameau de Saliers, 13200 Arles** [04 66 87 48 78; fax 04 66 87 18 66; crin.blanc@free.fr; www.camping-crin-blanc.com] E fr St Gilles on N572 twd Arles; 4km E of St Gilles take R on D37 sp Saliers; site sp in 400m. Lge, pt shd; wc; chem disp; shwrs; el pts (10A) inc; gas; lndtte; shop; tradsmn; rest; snacks; bar; playgrnd; pool; tennis; horseriding; 70% statics; dogs €2; Eng spkn; adv bkg; quiet; red low ssn; cc acc; CCI. "Poss muddy; mosquitoes; sep men's & women's wc but no signs; park with bird reserve." ♦ 1 Apr-30 Sep. € 18.00 2003*

ARLES SUR TECH *8H4* (1.5km NE Rural) **Camping Le Vallespir, Route d'Amélie-les-Bains, 66150 Arles-sur-Tech** [04 68 39 90 00; fax 04 68 39 90 09; camping.le.vallespir@wanadoo.fr; www.campingvallespir.com] Site on D115 mid-way between Amelie-les-Bains & Arles-sur-Tech. Clearly sp on RH side of rd. Avoids narr vill. Med, some hdg pitch, pt shd; wc; chem disp; mv service pnt; child/baby facs; shwrs inc; el pts (6-10A) €3-4.15; lndtte; tradmn; rest; snacks; bar; playgrnd; pool; paddling pool; tennis; entmnt; golf 2km; TV rm; 50% statics; dogs €1.80; phone; poss cr; poss noisy by rd. "V pleasant site; lovely area for hiking & cycling; 2 attractive sm towns nrby; some facs poss clsd low ssn." ♦ 1 Apr-31 Oct. € 20.35 2004*

†**ARLES SUR TECH** *8H4* (1km W Urban) **Camping du Riuferrer, 66150 Arles-sur-Tech** [04 68 39 11 06; fax 04 68 39 12 09; www.campingduriuferrer.fr] Take D115 fr Le Boulou thro Arles-sur-Tech (v narr but poss). Twd town exit just bef rv bdge, turn R. Foll sp 500m to site. Ent across narr footbdge. O'fits width across wheels over 2.19m ask for guidance to rear ent. Med, pt sl, shd, mkd pitch, hdstg; wc (some cont); chem disp; shwrs inc; el pts (4A) inc; gas; lndtte; rest, snacks, bar in ssn; shops 500m; tradsmn; ice; playgrnd; pool adj; poss cr; adv bkg; 20% statics; dogs; quiet; cc not acc; red low ssn/long stay; Eng spkn; red CCI. "Gd sh/long stay; helpful owner; some sm pitches diff for manoeuvring." ♦ € 13.35 2002*

FRANCE

†ARMENTIERES *3A3* (3km E) **Camping L'Image, 140 Rue Brune, 59116 Houplines** [tel/fax 03 20 35 69 42 or 03 20 35 73 92; campimage@wanadoo.fr] Exit A25 junc 8 sp Armentieres, onto D945 N twd Houplines. After 4km at traff lts go strt on & take 1st R, site in 1km on R. Ent not v clearly sp. Med, hdg pitch, shd; wc; chem disp; mv service pnt; serviced pitches; shwrs €1.50; el pts (2-6A) €1.50-3; lndtte; shop high ssn & 4km; snacks; playgrnd; tennis; entmnt; 90% statics; poss cr; adv bkg; quiet; 5% red low ssn; CCI. "Turn R at ent for neighbouring site 'Les Alouettes' (more pitches for tourers); shwr block dark & old, but OK; NH only."
€ 9.50   2005*

ARNAY LE DUC *6H1* (1km E Rural) **Camping L'Etang de Fouche, Rue du 8 Mai 1945, 21230 Arnay-le-Duc** [03 80 90 02 23; fax 03 80 90 11 91; info@campingfouche.com; www.campingfouche.com] App by N6 to Arnay (site sp); turn E onto D17C, site on R in 2km. Lge, hdg/mkd pitch, hdstg, pt shd; htd wc; chem disp; shwrs inc; el pts (6A) €3.50; lndtte; shop; tradsmn; rest; snacks; bar; BBQ; playgrnd; lake sw & beach adj; waterslide; tennis; cycle hire; games rm; TV; entmnt; child entmnt; internet; dogs €1.50; Eng spkn; adv bkg; quiet; cc acc; red low ssn; CCI. "Wonderful site; clean & friendly; new san facs 2006; lge pitches; red facs low ssn; pleasant view & surroundings; attractive sm town & area; gd lakeside situation with fishing, pedalos & walks; gd touring base S Burgundy; short dist to town; gd for young families."
♦ 15 Apr-15 Oct. € 14.70   2005*

See advertisement above

ARRADON see Vannes *2F3*

ARRAS *3B3* (12km SE Rural) **Camping Paille Haute** (formerly Flandres-Artois), 145 Rue de Seilly, 62156 Boiry-Notre-Dame [03 21 48 15 40; fax 03 21 22 07 24; lapaillehaute@wanadoo.fr; www.la-paille-haute.com] Fr Calais take A26 a'route, A1 twd Paris, exit junc 15 onto D939 twd Cambrai; in 3km take D34 NE to Boiry-Notre-Dame & foll camp sp. Fr N50 Douai-Arras rd, at Fresnes turn S onto D43, foll sp to Boiry in 7km, site well sp in vill. Med, pt hdg pitch, hdstg, terr, pt shd; wc; chem disp; mv service pnt; shwrs inc; el pts (6A) €3 (poss rev pol); lndtte; ice; shop 500m; rest, snacks high ssn; bar; BBQ; playgrnd; htd pool; lake fishing; mini-golf; tennis; entmnt; 60% statics; dogs; quiet; cc acc; red 3+ days; CCI. "Busy, clean site; rec arr early; tight access lge o'fits; trout-fishing locally; friendly management; Calais under 2hrs; conv WW1 sites; site being upgraded 2005." ♦ 15 Mar-31 Oct.
€ 20.00   2005*

See advertisement opposite

ARRAS *3B3* (1km S Urban) **Camp Municipal Les Templiers, 166 Rue du Temple, 62000 Arras** [03 21 71 55 06] Exit A26 S at junc 7 onto N17; stay on this rd thro Arras town cent. 1km S of cent & just beyond Leclerc supmkt, turn L at traff lts. Site on L in 150m, not well sp. Sm, pt shd, mkd pitch, hdstg & grass; wc; chem disp (wc); shwrs inc; el pts (6A) €2.40; shops & supmkt nr; playgrnd; pool 1km; poss cr; adv bkg; quiet; CCI. "Basic, clean site; sm pitches; early arr rec high ssn; friendly warden; gd shopping in Arras; facs poss stretched in high ssn; poss itinerants on site; NH only." 1 Apr-30 Sep.
€ 6.60   2005*

†ARREAU *8G2* (Urban) **Camp Municipal Beuse Debat, 65240 Arreau** [05 62 98 65 56 (Mairie); 05 62 98 68 78] Foll sp fr D929 across bdge (D618 sp Luchon) immed turn E on D19 & foll sp into site on banks of Rv Neste. Sm, terr, pt shd; htd wc; chem disp; shwrs; el pts (4-10A) €2.80-4.10 (rev pol); lndtte; shops 1km; rest; snacks; playgrnd; rv fishing adj; tennis; entmnts; some statics; dogs €1; site clsd Oct; poss cr; adv bkg; quiet. € 11.90
                                                2004*

FRANCE

ARREAU *8G2* (7km N) **Camp Municipal d'Esplantas, 65410 Sarrancolin** [05 62 98 77 30 (Mairie)] Site on E side of D929 at N end of vill; ent by Total petrol stn, sp. Med, pt shd; wc; shwrs inc; el pts (10A) inc; shops; rest & gas in vill; pool; dogs; quiet. "Site on rv bank; warden calls am & pm; wc blocks v clean, gd facs for disabled." ♦ € 14.80
2004*

ARREAU *8G2* (12km SE Rural) **Camping Caravaning de Pene Blanche, 65510 Loudenvielle** [05 62 55 68 85; fax 05 62 99 98 20] S fr Arreau on D618 in dir of Avajan. Take D25 thro Genos. Site on W of D25 just bef turn over bdge to Loudenvielle. Avoid app fr E over Col de Peyresourde. Med, some mkd pitch, terr, pt shd; wc; chem disp; shwrs inc; el pts (3A); Indry rm; shop 500m; BBQ; playgrnd; pool opp; lake 1km; 20% statics; dogs €1.14; adv bkg; cc acc. "Lge sports/recreational complex opp; quiet out of main period." 1 Jan-31 Oct. € 14.50 2002*

†ARRENS MARSOUS *8G2* (800m E Rural) **Camping La Heche, 54 Route d'Azun, 65400 Arrens-Marsous** [05 62 97 02 64; laheche@free. fr; www. campinglaheche.com] Fr Argeles-Gazost foll D918. Site on L immed bef Arrens. If towing c'van do not app fr Col d'Aubisque. Lge, pt shd; wc; shwrs inc; el pts (3-6A) €2-3; gas; Indtte; ice; shops 500m; tradsmn; playgrnd; pool in vill high ssn; waterslide; tennis; 10% statics; dogs €0.50; phone; quiet; CCI. "Gd for wintersports; beautiful location; in low ssn only oldest facs block in use - own san rec; other facs block new & immac." € 6.10 2004*

ARROMANCHES LES BAINS *3D1* (3km E Coastal) **Camp Municipal Quintefeuille, 14960 Asnelles** [02 31 22 35 50] Site sp, but visible fr vill sq in Asnelles. Med, unshd; wc; chem disp; shwrs; el pts; Indtte; shops adj; rest; snacks; bar; playgrnd; sand beach 300m; sports area; tennis; fishing 300m; poss cr; quiet. "Facs dated but clean; tatty low ssn." ♦ 15 Jun-15 Sep. € 12.00 2004*

ARROMANCHES LES BAINS *3D1* (W Urban/ Coastal) **Camp Municipal, Ave de Verdun, 14117 Arromanches-les-Bains** [02 31 22 36 78; fax 02 31 21 80 22] App fr Bayeux on D516. Turn R on onto D65 on app to Arromanches to site on L. Med, pt sl, terr, pt shd; wc; shwrs €0.40; el pts (10A) €2.60; gas; sand beach 500m; poss cr. "Conv Mulberry Harbour Exhibition & invasion beaches; close to town & rests; levelling blocks req most pitches; ground soft when wet; €20 deposit for barrier card; friendly warden." 1 Apr-5 Nov. € 11.80 2005*

ARROU *4F2* (Rural) **Camp Municipal du Pont du Pierre, 28290 Arrou** [02 37 97 02 13 (Mairie); fax 02 37 97 10 28] Take D15 fr Cloyes. Site sp in vill of Arrou. Med, hdg/mkd pitch, pt sl, unshd; wc; chem disp; shwrs inc; el pts (6A) €2; Indry rm; supmkt nr; rest, bar, snacks in vill; BBQ; Iplaygrnd; pool adj; fishing; lake, sand beach; tennis; horseriding; cycle hire; 10% statics; phone; adv bkg; quiet; CCI. "Well-kept, peaceful site; dep for barrier key." ♦ 1 May-30 Sep. € 4.60 2004*

ARTAIX PAR MARCIGNY see Marcigny *9A1*

ARTEMARE see Virieu le Grand *9B3*

ARZAL *2G3* (6km W Rural) **Camping Kernejeune, 56190 Arzal** [02 97 45 01 60 or 06 13 42 06 98 (mob); fax 02 67 45 05 42; contact@camping-de-kerne jeune.com; www.camping-de-kernejeune.com] Fr E on N165 exit onto D139 sp Arzal. Opp town hall turn L sp Billiers & foll sp to site. Fr W on N165 exit onto D5 sp Billiers. Turn R at traff lts, site sp. Med, mkd pitch, pt shd; htd wc; shwrs; el pts (6-10A) €2.40; Indtte; ice; shop; tradsmn; BBQ; playgrnd; htd pool high ssn; fishing; games area; entmnt; TV; 30% statics; dogs €1.20; phone; red low ssn; quiet. "Gd touring base for interesting area; helpful, friendly owners; rec." ♦ 1 Apr-1 Oct. € 13.20 2005*

See advertisement on next page

Camping "Kernéjeune"

www.camping-de-kernejeune.com
contact@camping-de-kernejeune.com

welcomes you on a calm and shady site, situated between Arzal and Billiers close to the mouth of the river la Vilaine. Heated swimming pool, children's games, walking tracks, fishing. Rental of mobile homes, marked pitches.

RN 165 to Vannes-Nantes, exit Muzillac, direction Billiers and after Billiers direction Arzal

RN 165 to Nantes-Vannes, exit Arzal, direction Bourg d'Arzal, opposite of the town hall follow direction Billiers.

ARZON *2G3* (800m NE Coastal) **Camp Municipal Le Tindio, Kerners, 56640 Arzon** [02 97 41 25 59] Fr Vannes or Muzillac on D780 turn R at rndabt on o'skts of Arzon. Site clearly sp. Lge, pt sl, pt shd; wc; chem disp; shwrs; el pts (3A); lndtte; playgrnd; sand beach 1km; golf nr; poss cr; adv bkg; no statics. "Site overlooks Gulf of Morbihan." ♦ May-Oct. € 11.76   2004*

ASCAIN see St Jean de Luz *8F1*

ASCOU see Ax les Thermes *8G4*

ASNIERES SUR OISE *3D3* (Rural) **Domaine Les Princes, Route des Princes, 95270 Asnieres-sur-Oise** [tel/fax 01 30 35 40 92; www.g4s@ residence2000.com] Site sp fr D909, nr Abbaye de Royaumont. Med, hdg/mkd pitch, pt shd; htd wc; shwrs inc; el pts (10A) €3.50; playgrnd; fishing 500m; games area, golf, horseriding nr; BBQ; 50% statics; adv bkg; quiet; red long stay. "Pleasant, attractive site; conv Parc Asterix & Paris." 1 Apr-31 Oct. € 13.00   2005*

ASPET *8G3* (Rural) **Camp Municipal Le Cagire, 31160 Aspet** [05 61 88 51 55; fax 05 61 88 44 03; camping.aspet@wanadoo.fr] Exit A64 at junc 18 St Gaudens & take D5 S. In 14km, site sp on R in vill of Aspet. Sm, mkd pitch, shd; wc; chem disp; shwrs; el pts (6A) €4.20; lndtte; shop, rest, snacks, bar 500m; pool, tennis 300m; games area; quiet; adv bkg; CCI. 1 Apr-30 Sep. € 6.10   2005*

ASPRES SUR BUECH *9D3* (3km S) **Camping L'Adrech, Route de Sisteron, 05140 Aspres-sur-Buech** [04 92 58 60 45; fax 04 92 58 78 63; camping.ladrech@libertysurf.fr] Site on L of N75 fr Aspres. Med, hdg pitch, pt sl, pt shd; wc; shwrs €0.46; el pts (6-10A) inc; gas; lndtte; ice; shop & 1km; tradsmn; snacks; playgrnd; fishing; rv/lake 5km; entmnt; 50% statics; poss cr; Eng spkn; adv bkg; quiet; CCI. "Lge pitches; v helpful American owner; also open 21-31 Dec; ltd facs low ssn & poss unkempt; useful site." 1 Mar-31 Oct. € 13.00
2005*

ASPRES SUR BUECH *9D3* (8km NW Rural) **Camping La Source, 05140 St Pierre-d'Argencon** [tel/fax 04 92 58 67 81; info@lasource-hautesalpes.com; www.lasource-hautesalpes.com] Fr Aspres-sur-Buech on D993, thro vill, site sp. Sm, pt sl, pt shd; wc; chem disp; mv service pnt; shwrs inc; el pts €2.50; lndtte; tradsmn; playgrnd; dogs €1; adv bkg; quiet; cc acc; red long stay. "CL-type site; very clean; helpful British owners; chambre d'hote on site; beautiful area for walking, cycling, paragliding." 15 Apr-15 Oct. € 9.00
2005*

> This site entry hasn't been updated for a while; we'd better fill in a site report form and send it to The Club.

†ATTICHY *3C4* (Rural) **Camp Municipal Fleury, Rue de la Fontaine-Aubier, 60350 Attichy** [03 44 42 15 97] Fr Compiegne E on N31. After 16km turn L at traff lts sp Attichy & site. Over iron bdge & turn R to site on lakeside. Med, hdg pitch, pt shd; wc; chem disp; mv service pnt; shwrs €0.50; el pts (10A) €2.30-3.50; shop 1km; tradsmn; rests in town; BBQ; playgrnd; fishing; 80% statics; poss cr; quiet; CCI. "Attractive site in pleasant vill; many w/e statics; few touring pitches; shut 1200-1430; facs stretched high ssn; vg sh stay." € 7.30   2004*

ATTIGNY see Rethel *5C1*

ATUR see Perigueux *7C3*

AUBAGNE *10F3* (4km NE) **Camping Le Clos, 13420 Gemenos** [04 42 32 18 24; fax 04 42 32 03 56] On N96 immed exit Gemenos twd Toulon (LH side) sp. Med, pt shd; wc; shwrs; el pts (6A) inc; lndtte; ice; shop; rest; playgrnd; pool 500m; tennis; TV. "Friendly manager; sh drive to hypmkt; poss mosquitoes; frequent bus to Marseilles fr Gemenos." 1 Apr-20 Sep. € 17.90   2004*

AUBAZINES *7C3* (4km E Rural) **Camping Le Coiroux, Parc Touristique du Coiroux, 19190 Aubazines** [05 55 27 21 96; fax 05 55 27 19 16; arepos.coiroux@wanadoo.fr; www.camping-coiroux.com] Fr Brive-La-Gaillarde take N89 NE twd Tulle. At Cornil turn R onto D48 & foll sp. Site in 8km. Med, pt hdg/mkd pitch, pt shd; wc; chem disp; mv service pnt; shwrs inc; el pts (5A) €2.90; gas; lndtte; shop; rest; snacks; bar; playgrnd; htd pool; lake sand beach & sw 300m; lake fishing & boating; tennis; golf; cycle hire; entmnt; child entmnt; TV rm; 50% statics; poss cr; Eng spkn; adv bkg; quiet; CCI. "Excel, wooded site." ♦ 14 Apr-1 Oct. € 15.50
2005*

AUBENAS *9D2* (3km N Rural) **Camping Domaine de Gil, Route de Vals-les-Bains, 07200 Ucel** [04 75 94 63 63; fax 04 75 94 01 95; raf.garcia@wanadoo.fr; www.domaine-de-gil.com] Fr Aubenas NE on N304 to St Privat. Cross bdge over Rv Ardeche 1km. At Pont d'Ucel, turn L along D578 twds Ucel; site 3km on L. Med, hdg/mkd pitch, pt shd; wc; chem disp; mv service pnt; serviced pitch; baby facs; shwrs inc; el pts (6A) €3.70 (poss rev pol); lndtte; shop; tradsmn; rest; snacks; bar; playgrnd; htd pool; tennis; mini-golf; rv sw; canoeing; TV; entmnt; some statics; dogs €2.50; phone; adv bkg ess in Aug; quiet; red low ssn; cc acc; CCI. "Scenic area; v clean san facs; excel, family site." ♦ ltd. 16 Apr-18 Sep. € 25.00   2005*

AUBENAS *9D2* (6km N) **Camp Municipal Le Stade, 07600 Vals-les-Bains** [04 75 37 46 85] Clearly sp at N end of town; 1st turn L off Vals to Le Cheylard rd, D578. Med, shd; wc; mv service pnt; shwrs; el pts (6A) €2.45; lndtte; ice; shops 500m; playgrnd; entmnt; rv fishing adj; few statics; dogs €1; poss cr; quiet. 1 Apr-15 Oct. € 9.70   2002*

AUBENAS *9D2* (7km E Rural) **Ludocamping, Route de Lavilledieu, 07170 Lussas** [04 75 94 21 22; fax 04 75 88 60 60; ludocamping@infonie.fr; www.ludocamping.com] SE fr Aubenas on N102 twd Montelimar. Turn L after 10km in vill Lavilledieu onto D224 sp Lussas. Site sp on R in 4km. Med, mkd pitch, terr, pt shd; wc; chem disp; shwrs inc; el pts (6A) €3; gas; lndtte; ice; shop; rest in vill 600m; bar; playgrnd; htd pool; dogs €1.50; poss cr; Eng spkn; adv bkg; quiet. "Gd walking country; peaceful; facs poss stretched in high ssn; Dutch owned - all notices in Dutch only." ♦ 1 Apr-1 Oct. € 22.00
2005*

AUBENAS *9D2* (2km SE) **Camping La Chareyrasse, 07200 Aubenas** [04 75 35 14 59; fax 04 75 35 00 06] On app Aubenas on N102 take 1st turning on L after x-ing suspension bdge & foll sp. Site on R bank of Rv Ardeche, side rd clearly mkd. Narr app rd. Med, pt shd; wc; shwrs; el pts €3.10 inc; gas; ice; shop; snacks; bar; pool; tennis; TV; entmnt; quiet. "Simple, pleasant site; excel." 1 Apr-30 Sep. € 18.50   2004*

AUBENAS *9D2* (7km SE) **Camping Les Rives d'Auzon, Route de St Germain, 07170 Lavilledieu** [tel/fax 04 75 94 70 64] Fr Aubenas on N102 turn R immed after Lavilledieu, sp St Germain (D103) site on L. Sm, pt shd; wc (some cont); shwrs; el pts (4-6A) €2; lndry rm; ice; shop; rest; snacks; bar; playgrnd; TV rm; entmnt; dogs €1; Eng spkn; adv bkg; some rd noise. "Friendly owner, beautiful location, poss diff for lge o'fits due trees; conv for exploring Ardeche." 2 Apr-15 Sep. € 10.00   2002*

AUBENAS *9D2* (8km SE) **Camping a la Ferme Le Bardou, 07170 St Germain** [tel/fax 04 75 37 71 91; info@lebardou.com] On N102 Aubenas-Montelimar turn S at Lavilledieu on D103, site on L in 2km. Site ent fairly narr bet stone houses in St Germain. Med, unshd; wc (mainly cont); chem disp; shwrs inc; el pts (6A) €2.80; shops 150m; pool; fishing adj; adv bkg; quiet. "Lovely views; helpful owners; pleasant site low ssn; clean, basic facs but poss inadequate high ssn; gd sh stay." 1 Mar-31 Oct. € 11.50   2004*

AUBENAS *9D2* (3km S) **Camping Les Acacias, 07200 St Etienne-de-Fontbellon** [04 75 93 67 87; fax 04 75 93 71 77; camping-les-acacias@wanadoo.fr] Fr Aubenas travel thro cent of St Etienne. Turn 2nd R at rndabt S of Leclerc hypmkt & foll sps. Fr S turn off D104 N of Lachapelle to St Etienne. At next rndabt turn L & foll sp. Sm, pt shd; wc (cont); chem disp; baby facs; shwrs inc; el pts (6A) €2.45; lndtte; ice; shops 1.5km; rest, snacks, bar high ssn; BBQ; playgrnd; pool; entmnt; dogs €0.70; Eng spkn; adv bkg; quiet; red low ssn; CCI. "Gd touring cent." 1 Apr-24 Oct. € 9.90   2004*

AUBENAS *9D2* (8km S) **Camping Les Roches, 07200 Vogue** [tel/fax 04 75 37 70 45; camping.les.roches@free.fr] Fr Aubenas take N104 S. Then L onto D579 to Vogue. Site on L 1.5km past Vogue - do not turn twd Vogue, but cont in dir Vogue Gare. Med, pt sl, shd; wc (some cont); mv service pnt; baby facs; shwrs inc; el pts (6-10A) €3.20; lndtte; ice; shop; rest; snacks; bar; playgrnd; pool; tennis; games area; entmnt; TV; some statics; adv bkg; quiet. 1 Apr-30 Sep. € 16.00   2003*

AUBENAS *9D2* (10km S Urban) **Camping Les Peupliers, 07200 St Maurice-d'Ardeche** [04 75 37 71 47; fax 04 75 37 70 83; campingpeupliers@aol.com; www.camping-peupliers.com] Fr Aubenas take D104 S twd Ales. In 2km, turn L onto D579 dir Vogues/Vallon Pont d'Arc. In 9km, pass L turn to Vogue. Immed after crossing rv, turn R at rndabt. Site on R in 300m, (2nd site of 3 on rd). Lge, mkd pitch, pt shd; wc (some cont); chem disp; mv service pnt; shwrs inc; baby facs; el pts (6A) €3.30; gas; lndtte; ice; shop; rest; snacks; bar; BBQ; playgrnd; pool; rv sw; shgl beach adj; entmnt; dogs €1; phone; poss cr; adv bkg (dep & bkg fee); quiet; cc acc; CCI. "Gd touring base; access to rv for canoeing & fishing." 1 May-15 Sep. € 16.00   2003*

AUBENAS *9D2* (10km S) Domaine du Cros d'Auzon, 07200 St Maurice-d'Ardeche [04 75 37 75 86; fax 04 75 37 01 02; camping.auzon@wanadoo.fr; www.guideweb.com/ardeche /camping/cros-auzon] Take D104 S fr Aubenas for 2km; at island turn L onto D579. After 9km, pass L turn to Vogue vill, cross rv & turn R immed. Site 600m on R, 1km fr Vogue stn. Lge, hdg/mkd pitch, pt shd; htd wc; chem disp; mv service pnt; serviced pitch; child/baby facs; shwrs inc; el pts (4-6A) inc; gas; lndtte; ice; shop 1km; tradsmn; rest; snacks; bar; playgrnd; pool; waterslide; sand beach; rv sw; fishing; canoe hire; cycle hire; tennis; entmnt; games/TV rm; cinema; 70% statics; dogs €1.60; Eng spkn; adv bkg; quiet; red low ssn/long stay; cc acc; CCI. "Gd touring base; excel; office only open 0900-1200 & 1600-1900 high ssn, all other times check in at hotel at top of hill." ♦ Easter-15 Sep. € 21.60   2003*

AUBENAS *9D2* (7km NW Rural) **Camp Municipal du Pont des Issoux, Allee de Vals, 07380 Lalevade-d'Ardeche [04 75 94 14 09 or 04 75 38 00 51 (Mairie); fax 04 75 94 01 92]** Fr Aubenas, N102 sp Mende & Le Puy-en-Velay; Lalevade in 10km; R in vill; well sp. Med, mkd pitch, pt shd; wc (some cont); chem disp (wc); shwrs inc; el pts €0.90; gas; lndtte; ice; shop 50m; rest, snacks & bar 250m, playgrnd; lake sw & shgl beach adj; tennis & children's park nrby; dogs; bus 250m; poss cr; Eng spkn; adv bkg (dep req); quiet; CCI. "Quiet, shady beside Rv Ardeche; friendly, helpful warden; close to vill & supmkt; conv touring Ardeche region; no twin-axle c'vans; excel." ♦ 1 Apr-15 Oct. € 9.50   2005*

AUBENCHEUL AU BAC see Cambrai *3B4*

AUBERIVE *6F1* **Camp Municipal, 52160 Auberive [tel/fax 03 25 86 21 13 (Mairie)]** Leave A31 at junc 6 W twds Chatilion-sur-Seine on D428 (care uneven road) for 12km, site on L bef vill. Site sp. Sm, mkd pitch, sl, pt shd; htd wc (some cont); chem disp (wc); shwrs inc; el pts (6A) €1.60; lndry rm; shops in vill; rest in vill; playgrnd; phone; quiet; CCI. "Pleasant site in forestry area with gd walks; attractive vill adj; friendly warden calls; site yourself; ltd el pts; clean, well cared for site; gd long/sh stay." 15 Apr-30 Sep. € 7.00   2004*

AUBERIVES SUR VAREZE *9B2* (8km E Rural) **Camping Le Bontemps, 38150 Vernioz [04 74 57 83 52; fax 04 74 57 83 70; info@ campinglebontemps.com]** Take N7 S fr Vienne. After climbing hill & L bend, fork L at camping sp. Foll sps, thro Vernioz, site in approx 9km past Vernioz. Fr S, on N7 N of vill of Auberives R onto D37, site on R in 8km. Tight ent - rec swing wide. Med, mkd pitch; terr, pt shd; wc; shwrs inc; el pts (6A) inc; lndtte; shop; rest; snacks; bar; playgrnd; pool; games area; wildlife sanctuary; 30% statics; dogs €2; adv bkg; quiet; CCI. "Also sp Hotel de Plein Air; peaceful site; twin-axles welcome; excel." ♦ 1 Apr-30 Sep. € 21.00   2004*

†**AUBERIVES SUR VAREZE** *9B2* (1km S Rural) Camping des Nations, Clonas-sur-Vareze, 38550 Auberives-sur-Vareze [04 74 84 95 13 or 04 74 84 97 17; fax 04 74 79 93 75] S on W side of N7/E15 fr Vienne for 12km; site sp. Sm, hdg/mkd pitch, shd; htd wc; chem disp; shwrs inc; el pts (5A) inc; tradsmn; rest nr; snacks & pool high ssn; quiet; adv bkg; no cc acc; Eng spkn; CCI. "Useful transit site for Spain & Med; manager not always present; gd NH." € 15.00   2005*

AUBETERRE SUR DRONNE *7C2* (200m Urban) **Camp Municipal, 16390 Aubeterre-sur-Dronne [05 45 98 60 17 or 05 45 98 50 33 (Mairie); fax 05 45 98 57 82; mairie.aubeterre-sur-dronne@ wanadoo.fr]** On D2 fr Chalais, take D17 around S end of town. Turn R over rv & site on R adj sports ground. Med, pt shd; wc (cont); chem disp (wc); shwrs inc; el pts (6A) €2.20-2.40; shop 250m; rest in town; bar, café, beach & rv sw adj; playgrnd; fishing & boating adj; tennis; cycle hire; dogs €0.20; poss cr; Eng spkn; quiet. "Gd for children; conv touring Perigord; friendly staff; picturesque town; vg long/sh stay." 15 Jun-15 Sep. € 9.40   2003*

AUBIGNAN see Carpentras *10E2*

AUBIGNY SUR NERE *4G3* (1.5km E Rural) **Camp Municipal des Etangs, 18700 Aubigny-sur-Nere [02 48 58 02 37 or 02 48 81 50 07 (LS); fax 02 48 81 50 98; aubigny.mairie@wanadoo.fr]** D940 fr Gien, turn E in vill of Aubigny onto D923, foll sp fr vill; site 1km on R by lake. Med, mkd pitch, pt shd; wc; chem disp; shwrs inc; el pts (6-10A) €2.40-€4.20; ice; lndry rm; shop, rest & bar 1km; tradsmn; BBQ; playgrnd; fishing; dogs; phone; poss cr; adv bkg; quiet; 10% red CCI. "Well-kept site with lake views; plenty to see & do locally; pretty vill; excel mkt Sat." ♦ 1 Apr-31 Oct. € 9.00 (3 persons)   2005*

AUBURE see Ribeauville *6E3*

AUBUSSON *7B4* (10km N Rural) **Camping Les Genets, Forneaux, 23200 St Medard-la-Rochette [05 55 83 01 25]** On D942 N fr Aubusson dir Gueret; site on R bef Fourneaux. Sm, hdg/mkd pitch, terr, pt shd; wc; shwrs inc; el pts (6A) €3; lndtte; shops 10km; tradsmn; BBQ; playgrnd; sm htd pool; cycle hire; TV rm; few statics; Eng spkn; adv bkg; quiet; red low ssn; CCI. "Tapestry museum in Aubusson & other historical attractions; helpful owner; vg long/sh stay/NH." 1 May-30 Oct. € 9.00   2004*

AUBUSSON *7B4* (12km NE) **Camp Intercommunal La Naute, 23190 Champagnat [05 55 67 64 54; fax 05 55 67 30 36; secretariat. apoti@wanadoo.fr]** On D990 N fr Aubusson turn E onto D993, then R onto D24 dir Champagnat. Fr N turn E onto D9 at Letrieux & foll sp 'Plan d'Eau' to site. Sm, pt shd; wc; shwrs; el pts (10A) €2.30; lndry rm; tradsmn; snacks; bar; BBQ; playgrnd; sand beach; tennis; quiet. "Pleasant lakeside site." 15 Jun-15 Sep. € 6.10   2003*

AUBUSSON *7B4* (1.5km S Urban) **Camp Municipal La Croix Blanche, Route de Felletin, 23200 Aubusson [05 55 66 18 00]** Site on D982 on banks of Rv Creuse; sp fr all dir. Med, shd; wc (some cont); shwrs inc; el pts (10A) inc; lndry rm; tradsmn; snacks; playgrnd; pool 1km; phone; adv bkg; quiet; CCI. "Vg site in pleasant location; conv tapestry factories; facs adequate." Easter-30 Sep. € 10.80   2005*

AUCH *8F3* (7km N Rural) **Camping Le Talouch, 32810 Roquelaure [05 62 65 52 43; fax 05 62 65 53 68; info@camping-talouch.com; www.camping-talouch.com]** Head W on N124 fr Auch, then N on D148 for 7km to site. Med, mkd pitch, pt shd; wc; chem disp; mv service pnt; shwrs; baby facs; el pts (5A) inc; gas; lndtte; ice; shop; rest; snacks; bar; playgrnd; pool; paddling pool; tennis; golf driving range; games area; internet; entmnt; 25% statics; dogs €2.10; adv bkg; quiet; red low ssn; CCI. "Poss liable to flooding; gd walking & nature trails; run by Dutch couple; vg." ♦ 1 Apr-30 Sep. € 21.00 (CChq acc)   2005*

AUCH *8F3* (1.5km SW) **Camp Municipal d'Ile St Martin, Rue de Mouzon, Parc des Sports, 32000 Auch [05 62 05 00 22]** Fr S on N21 approx 750m after business area, turn R at traff lts into Rue General de Gaulle which runs into Rue du Mouzon, site in 500m adj rv. Med, hdg pitch, shd; wc; shwrs inc; el pts (5-10A) €2.30-4.60; shops 300m; pool 250m; 30% statics; poss cr; quiet but some rd noise. "Cathedral, ancient & modern architecture with museum in town; 10 min walk along rv to town; site not suitable for disabled with toilet facs up stairs; rec arr bef 1700 recep & barrier clsd 1200-1400." 15 Apr-15 Oct. € 6.40   2005*

AUCHONVILLERS see Albert *3B3*

AUDENGE *7D1* (1km E Rural) **Camping Le Braou, Route de Bordeaux, 33980 Audenge [tel/fax 05 56 26 90 03; info@camping-audenge.com; www.camping-audenge.com]** SW fr Bordeaux turn R off N250 twd Andernos onto D3; at traff lts in Audenge turn R; site 750m on R. Lge, mkd pitch, pt shd; wc; shwrs inc; el pts (3A) €4.50; ice; lndtte; shops 1km; tradsmn; pool nr; beach 1.5km; games area; entmnt; some statics; dogs €2.50; bus 1km; quiet; CCI. "Site being upgraded 2004." ♦ ltd. 1 May-30 Sep. € 14.00   2004*

AUDENGE *7D1* (10km SE Urban) **Camp Municipal de l'Eyre, Allée de la Plage, 33380 Mios [05 56 26 42 04; fax 05 56 26 41 69]** Fr N or S on A63, join A660 sp Arcachon; leave at junc 1 to Mios. After will turn L after traff lts (sm sp) bet tourist & post offices. Site adj Rv Eyre. Med, mkd pitch, pt shd; htd wc; shwrs inc; el pts (6A) €3; lndtte; shop 500m; sports hall adj; canoe hire; cycle hire for adj rte; CCI. "Excel touring base; v helpful warden; ltd facs low ssn; park outside site to book in; phone ahead low ssn to check if open; san facs poss stretched if site full; poss noisy at night." ♦ 1 Apr-30 Sep. € 11.00   2004*

AUDENGE *7D1* (5km S) **Camping Marache, 23 Rue Gambetta, 33380 Biganos [05 57 70 61 19; fax 05 56 82 62 60; jean-guerin/4@libertysurf.fr]** Fr Facture, take D3 twd Audenge, site clearly sp. Med, mkd pitch, pt shd; wc; mv service pnt; baby facs; shwrs inc; el pts (6A) €3.50; lndtte; ice; shops 1km; rest; snacks; playgrnd; htd pool; rv sw & fishing 1km; tennis 1km; entmnt; TV; dogs €2; adv bkg; quiet. "Pleasant management; twin-axles pay extra; ltd facs low ssn." ♦ 1 Apr-31 Oct. € 21.00   2004*

AUDIERNE *2F1* (700m SE Coastal) **Camping-Gite Le Loqueran, Bois de Loqueran, 29770 Audierne [02 98 74 95 06; fax 02 98 74 91 14; campgite. loqueran@free.fr; http://campgite.loqueran.free. fr]** Fr Quimper on D784 thro Plozevet & Plouhinec dir Audierne. Look out for sm, yellow/purple camping sp on R, site 500m on L. Sm, mkd pitch, pt shd; wc; chem disp; shwrs inc; el pts (6A) €2; lndtte; ice; shop & 600m; playgrnd; beach 1km; cc acc; quiet; CCI. "Gd sh stay." 15 May-30 Sep. € 10.50   2003*

AUDIERNE *2F1* (3km SE Coastal) **Camping de Kersiny, 1 Rue Nominoe, 29780 Plouhinec [02 98 70 82 44; mail@camping-kersiny.com; www.camping-kersiny.com]** Fr Audierne turn R at 2nd traff lts in Plouhinec. Med, hdg pitch, terr, pt shd; wc; chem disp; mv service pnt; shwrs; el pts (8A) €2.60; gas; lndtte; ice; tradsmn high ssn; snacks; BBQ; playgrnd; direct access to beach; dogs €1.50; quiet; barrier clsd 2300-0730; CCI. "Beautiful location; gate to beach, friendly warden; gd." 1 Apr-30 Sep. € 11.40   2004*

AUDIERNE *2F1* (8km W Coastal) **Camp Municipal de Kermalero, 29770 Primelin [tel/fax 02 98 74 84 75 or 02 98 74 81 19 (LS); camping kermalero@wanadoo.fr]** D784 Audierne-Pointe du Raz, after Ecomarche supmkt at Primelin turn L, site sp. Med, hdg pitch, terr, pt shd; wc; chem disp; mv service pnt; shwrs inc; el pts (6A) €2.30; lndtte; supmkt 1km; tradsmn; playgrnd; games area; sand beach 1km; tennis; TV; 5% statics; quiet. "Gd outlook/views; helpful warden; pleasant site; vg long/sh stay." ♦ 1 Mar-1 Dec. € 8.50   2005*

AUDRUICQ see Ardres *3A3*

AUGIGNAC see Nontron *7B3*

AUGIREIN *8G3* (E Rural) **Camping La Vie en Vert (formerly La Bellongue), 09800 Augirein [05 61 96 82 66; fax 05 61 04 73 00; earl@ lavieenvert.com; www.lavieenvert.com]** Fr St Giron on D618 twd Castillon. On app Castillon turn R foll sp to Luchon. 1km after vill Orgibet turn L into vill of Augirein. Site on L over bdge. Sm, hdg/mkd pitch; pt shd; wc; baby facs; shwrs inc; el pts (6A) inc; lndtte; ice; shop; tradsmn; rest in vill; playgrnd; dogs €1; Eng spkn; adv bkg; quiet; 5% red 5+ days; CCI. "Charming owners who own bar/cafe in vill; excel." ♦ 15 May-10 Sep. € 22.00   2003*

FRANCE

†AULUS LES BAINS *8G3* (Rural) **Camping Le Couledous, 09140 Aulus-les-Bains [05 61 96 02 26; fax 05 61 96 06 74]** Take D618 fr St Girons. After 13km cross rv; turn R onto D3 sp Aulus-les-Bains. On app to Oust turn L onto D32, site approx 17km on R at ent to vill. Med, mkd pitch, hdstg, sl, pt shd; wc (cont); chem disp; shwrs (inc) el pts (6A) €4.74; lndtte; shop 500m; bar 300m, playgrnd; some statics; site clsd last week Nov & 1st week Dec; poss cr; quiet; adv bkg; Eng spkn; CCI. "Gd walking & skiing (16km); sm spa in vill; excel." ♦ € 9.41
2002*

†AULUS LES BAINS *8G3* (9km NW Rural) **Camping Le Montagnou, Route de Seix, 09140 Le Trein-d'Ustou [05 61 66 94 97; fax 05 61 66 91 20; campinglemontagnou@ wanadoo.fr; www.lemontagnou.com]** Fr Aulus NW on D8 approx 13km by rd, site sp. Fr Seiz S on D3 & D8 dir Aulus. Med, pt shd; htd wc; shwrs inc; el pts (6A) inc; lndtte; tradsmn high ssn; snacks; rest nr; playgrnd; fishing; rv sw; tennis; dogs €1.10; quiet. "Beautifully situated rvside site surrounded by mountains; gd walking; skiing 9km; v friendly owners; highly rec; excel." ♦ € 14.50   2004*

AUMALE *3C3* (1km W) **Camp Municipal Le Grand Mail, 76390 Aumale [02 35 93 40 50; fax 02 35 93 86 79]** Clearly sp in town; long steep climb to ent. Med, pt shd; wc; mv service pnt; shwrs €1.50; el pts (7A) €2; lndtte; shops 1km; playgrnd; pool 1km; cycle hire €1; fishing 1km; dogs €1; noise fr rd. "Gd site; conv Channel ports; excel views; ltd no of pitches with el; set on valley side above town; gd range of shops in attractive town; 500m walk up steep slope fr town to site." ♦ 1 Apr-15 Sep. € 7.50   2003*

AUNAC see Mansle *7B2*

AUNAY SUR ODON see Villers Bocage *3D1*

†AUPS *10E3* (500m E) **Camping Les Pres, Quartier Les Faisses, 83630 Aups [04 94 70 00 93; fax 04 94 70 14 41; lespres.camping@wanadoo. fr]** 500m fr cent of Aups on rd to Tourtour, site on R. App on rutted rd. Med, pt shd; wc; shwrs inc; el pts (4-6A) €1.83-€2.60; gas; ice; lndtte; shop 1km; snacks; rest; bar; playgrnd; entmnt; TV rm; pool & tennis 200m; quiet; adv bkg. € 10.00   2002*

AUPS *10E3* (500m W) **International Camping, Route de Fox-Amphoux, 83630 Aups [04 94 70 06 80; fax 04 94 70 10 51; camping-aups@internationalcamping-aups.com; www. internationalcamping-aups.com]** Site on L on D60 nr vill cent. Med, hdg/mkd pitch; wc (few cont); chem disp; shwrs inc; el pts (16A) €4.50; lndtte; shop; tradsmn; snacks & rest high ssn; bar; pool; tennis; games rm; disco; entmnt; 30% statics; dogs €1; Eng spkn; rec adv bkg high ssn; quiet; cc acc. "Beautiful area; 10 min walk fr town; gd rest on site; excel long stay." 1 Apr-30 Sep. € 16.60
2005*

AUPS *10E3* (1km W Rural) **Camping St Lazare, Route de Moissac, 83630 Aups [04 94 70 12 86; fax 04 94 70 01 55]** NW fr Aups twd Regusse on D9, site sp. Med, pt sl, pt shd, hdg/mkd pitch; wc; chem disp; shwrs inc; el pts (10A) €3; gas; ice; lndtte; shop 1.5km; snacks; pool; playgrnd; dogs €2; phone; TV; entmnts; mountain bike hire; 10% statics; adv bkg rec; CCI. "Excel touring base; vg quiet site." 1 Apr-30 Sep. € 11.00   2005*

AURAY *2F3* (5km NE) **Camp Municipal du Motten, 56400 Ste Anne-d'Auray [02 97 57 60 27]** Fr W on N1675 Vannes take D17bis N to St Anne-d'Auray; then L onto D19 to town. This rte avoids Pluneret. Foll site sp. Med, pt shd; wc; chem disp; mv service pnt; shwrs inc; el pts (10A) €2.50; lndtte; shops 1km; snacks; playgrnd; sand beach 12km; sports area; tennis; TV adv bkg; poss cr; quiet; "Clean, peaceful & well-maintained; best pitches immed R after ent; san facs poss stretched high ssn; office open 0800-1000 & 1600-1900." ♦ 1 Jun-30 Sep. € 7.90   2005*

AURAY *2F3* (5km SE Coastal) **Camp Municipal Kergouguec, 56400 Plougoumelen [02 97 57 88 74]** Site is S of N165, 13km W of Vannes; sp fr vill sq 500m S on R, nr stadium. Med, pt sl, pt shd; wc (some cont); chem disp; shwrs; el pts (6A) €2.40; ice; playgrnd; beach & windsurfing 300m; tennis; dogs €1.20; adv bkg; quiet; CCI. "Good tour base, well-run site." ♦ 15 Jun-15 Sep. € 6.50   2005*

AURAY *2F3* (7km SE Rural) **Aire Naturelle La Fontaine du Hallate (Le Gloanic), La Hallate, 56400 Plougoumelen [02 97 57 84 12; clegloanic@campinghallate.com; www.camping hallate.com]** Fr N165 dir Auray, S thro Ploeren to Plougoumelen; watch for sp after Plougoumelen, site in La Hallate. Narr, bumpy app rd. Sm, hdg/mkd pitch, pt sl, pt shd; shwrs inc; el pts (6A) €2 (rev pol); lndtte; shops 2km; playgrnd; golf/tennis adj; 2% statics; dogs €1; phone; adv bkg ess Jul/Aug; CCI. "Gd alternative to lge/noisier sites; conv local boat trips; vg all stays." 1 Apr-30 Sep. € 9.00 2004*

AURAY *2F3* (8km SE) **Camping Mane Guernehue, 52 Mane er Groez, 56870 Baden [02 97 57 02 06; fax 02 97 57 15 43; mane-guerneheu@wanadoo. fr; www.mane-guernehue.com]** Exit N165 Auray-Vannes on D101 to Baden. In Baden vill turn R at camp sp immed after sharp L-hand bend. After 200m bear R at junc. Site on R, sp at both ends of vill. Lge, pt hdg pitch, pt sl, pt terr, pt shd; wc; chem disp; sauna; baby facs; shwrs inc; el pts (10A) €4.20; lndtte; ice; shop; snacks; BBQ; playgrnd; htd pool complex; waterslide; beach 2km; fishing; jacuzzi; tennis 600m; fitness rm; cycle hire; golf 1.5km; games/TV rm; 60% statics; dogs €3.40; phone; Eng spkn; quiet; red long stay. "Gd views; nice site." ♦ 3 Apr-30 Sep. € 30.80 (CChq acc)
2005*

AURAY *2F3* (5km S Rural) **Camping du Parc-Lann, Le Varquez, 56400 Le Bono** [02 97 57 93 93 or 02 97 57 83 91; campingdu parclann@minitel.net] S fr Auray on D101 sp Le Bono. Site well sp in Le Bono. Turn R after church; site in 600m after end vill sp on D101E. Med, unshd; wc; chem disp (wc); shwrs inc; el pts (6A) €2; lndtte; shop 2km; tradsm; rest; bar; playgrnd; pool 5km; sand beach 9km; dogs €0.50; phone; Eng spkn; adv bkg; quiet; red low ssn; CCI. "Excel; gd, clean san facs poss stretched high ssn; flat site in pretty area, nr rv & sea; ltd facs low ssn & warden only on site 1800-1900." ♦ 1 May-30 Sep. € 11.50   2004*

AURAY *2F3* (7km SW) **Camping Le Kergo, 56400 Ploemel** [tel/fax 02 97 56 80 66; campingde kergo@wanadoo.fr] Fr Auray take D768 SW sp Carnac. After 4km turn NW on D186 twd Ploemel & foll sp. Med, mkd pitch, pt shd; wc; chem disp; shwrs inc; el pts (6-10A) €2.40; lndtte; shops 2km; tradsmn; playgrnd; sand beach 5km; dogs €0.80; some statics; adv bkg rec high ssn; red low ssn/CCI. "Lovely, peaceful site, lots of trees; excel san facs, ltd low ssn." ♦ ltd. 1 May-15 Sep. € 12.00   2005*

†**AURAY** *2F3* (8km W) **Camping Le St Laurent, Kergonvo, 56400 Ploemel** [tel/fax 02 97 56 85 90; camping.saint.laurent@wanadoo.fr] Fr Auray on D22 twd Belz-Etel; after 8km turn L on D186 to Ploemel & site on L in 200m. Med, some hdstg, shd; wc; chem disp; baby facs; shwrs inc; el pts (10A) €2.30; lndtte; shop & 3km; rest; bar; BBQ; playgrnd; htd pool; sand beach 6km; dogs €0.80; adv bkg; quiet. "Peaceful site; friendly staff; red facs low ssn." € 12.60   2005*

AUREILHAN see Mimizan *7D1*

AURILLAC *7C4* (2km NE) **Camp Municipal de l'Ombrade, Chemin du Gue Bouliaga, 15000 Aurillac** [tel/fax 04 71 48 28 87]   Take D17 N fr Aurillac twd Puy Mary; site on banks of Rv Jordanne. Well sp fr town. Lge, pt shd; wc; shwrs inc; el pts (10A) inc; lndtte; ice; shops adj; TV & games rm; poss cr; quiet. "Generous pitches; well-managed site; facs clean but need refurb; rec arr early high ssn; interesting lge mkt town with gd rests; poss not well kept low ssn; conv for walking into town; unreliable opening dates." 1 May-30 Sep. € 9.80   2005*

AURILLAC *7C4* (2km S Urban) **Camp Municipal de la Cere, Rue Félix Ramond, 15130 Arpajon-sur-Cere** [tel/fax 04 71 64 55 07] Fr Rodez take D920 twd Aurillac. Site sp 2km bef Aurillac on S side of Arpajon. Med, hdg pitch, pt shd; wc; shwrs inc; el pts (10A) €2; gas; lndtte; shops adj; pool 4km; rv fishing adj; beach 20km; games area; golf 5km; adv bkg; some rd noise; cc acc; CCI. "Pretty area; public access to site - not secure." ♦ ltd. 1 Jun-15 Sep. € 11.00   2005*

AUSSOIS see Modane *9C4*

†**AUTERIVE** *8F3* (1km S) **Camp Municipal du Ramier, 31190 Auterive** [05 61 50 65 73] Turn E off N20, cross rv bdge & immed turn R. Site on R in 1km. Sm, pt shd; wc (cont); shwrs; el pts (6A) €2.60; shop 1km; pool adj; tennis; rv fishing; many statics; quiet but poss fr disco. "Rec arr by 1730; fair NH." € 5.00   2003*

†**AUTERIVE** *8F3* (7km NW) **Camp Municipal Le Ramier, 31810 Vernet** [05 61 08 39 98 or 05 61 08 50 47 (Mairie)] Site at S exit of Vernet, sp fr N20 Toulouse-Pamiers rd. Med, shd; wc (some cont); chem disp; shwrs; el pts (5A); shops adj; quiet. "Conv NH for Andorra; nice location by rv; rather run down." € 10.30   2002*

AUTHUILLE see Albert *3B3*

AUTRANS *9C3* (E Rural) **Camping au Joyeux Reveil, Le Chateau, 38880 Autrans** [04 76 95 33 44; fax 04 76 95 72 98; camping-au-joyeux-reveil@wanadoo.fr; www.camping-au-joyeux-reveil.fr] Fr Villard-de-Lans take D531 to Lans-en-Vercors & turn L onto D106 to Autrans. On E side of vill site sp at 1st rndabt. Med, mkd pitch, pt sl, pt shd; htd wc; chem disp; mv service pnt; baby facs; shwrs inc; el pts (2-10A) €2-7.70; gas; lndtte; ice; shop 300m; tradsmn; rest 100m; snacks; bar; BBQ; playgrnd; htd pool & paddling pool; waterslide; rv fishing; tennis 300m; cycle hire; golf 20km; games area; TV rm; cab TV to pitches; 60% statics; dogs; bus 300m; phone; quiet; adv bkg; Eng spkn; red low ssn; cc acc; CCI. "Site in Vercors National Park with excel views; winter sport facs, 1050m altitude; modern san facs." ♦ ltd. 17 Dec-30 Sep. € 25.00 (CChq acc)   2005*

AUTRECHE *4G2* Camp Municipal de l'Etang, Rue du Général de Gaulle, 37110 Autreche [02 47 29 59 64 or 02 47 56 22 03 (Mairie)] Exit A10 junc 18 onto D31 S to Autreche, turn L into vill for 600m, site sp. Sm, unshd; wc (cont for men); shwrs inc; el pts; playgrnd; tennis; poss cr; quiet; CCI. "Useful NH fr m'way." 8 May-18 Sep.   2004*

AUTRUY SUR JUINE see Angerville *4E3*

AUTUN *6H1* (1km N Urban) **Camp Municipal de la Porte d'Arroux, Les Chaumottes, 71400 Autun** [03 85 52 10 82; fax 03 85 52 88 56; contact@ camping-autun.com; www.camping-autun.com] Foll sp fr town on D980 to Saulieu & site on L; only site in Autun. Med, some hdg pitch, some hdstg, shd; wc (some cont); mv service pnt; baby facs; shwrs inc; el pts (6A) €2.80; (poss rev pol); gas high ssn; lndry rm; ice; shop; snacks; rest high ssn; playgrnd; rv sw & fishing; dogs €1.20; phone; Eng spkn; adv bkg; noisy nr rest; cc acc; CCI. "Lovely, quiet, clean site; friendly, helpful staff; no twin-axles; gd access to facs in town, inc 2 excel pools (1 covrd); perfect medieval architecture & Roman walls around town; mkt Wed/Fri; gd rest." 1 Apr-31 Oct. € 12.45   2005*

FRANCE

AUXERRE *4F4* (3km SE Urban) **Camp Municipal, 8 Rue de Vaux, 89000 Auxerre** [03 86 52 11 15; fax 03 86 51 17 54; camping.mairie@auxerre. com] Exit A6 at Auxerre Sud junc 20, at toll R twd Auxerre & R at 2nd junc. Thro 1st set traff lts & at no ent sp turn R & immed L. Thro next set lights & at next set bear L over rv bdge, turn sharp L foll sp to site opp stadium; site sp. Or fr N6 (N) take ring rd, site/stadium sp. Lge, mkd pitch, pt shd; wc; chem disp; mv service pnt; shwrs inc; el pts (6A) €2.35; lndtte; ice; shop; bar/café; playgrnd; pool 250m; fishing 300m; TV; 10% statics; dogs; adv bkg; quiet; cc acc; CCI. "Friendly staff; poss cr & noisy during football ssn; site poss flooded stormy weather; c'vans over 5m not allowed; no vehicles 2200-0700; lge pitches; pop NH." 1 Apr-30 Sep. € 10.70
2005*

AUXERRE *4F4* (10km S) **Camping Les Ceriselles, Route de Vincelottes, 89290 Vincelles** [tel/fax 03 86 42 39 39; lesceriselles@wanadoo.fr; www. campingceriselles.com] Leave A6 at Auxerre Sud. Fr Auxerre, take N6 S twd Avallon. 10km fr Auxerre turn L into vill. In 400m immed after 'Maxi Marche', turn L into site access rd, sp as Camping/Base de Loisirs. Site is approx 16km fr a'route exit. Med, mkd pitch, some hdstg, pt shd; htd wc; chem disp; mv service pnt; shwrs inc; el pts (6-10A) €1.80 (poss rev pol); gas adj; lndtte; ice; shops adj; tradsmn; rest; snacks; bar; BBQ; playgrnd; rv sw adj; cycle hire; TV rm; 10% statics; dogs €0.80; phone; no twin-axles; poss cr; some Eng spkn; adv bkg; quiet; red long stay/low ssn; CCI. "Excel site in lovely countryside; highly rec; friendly & helpful owner; v modern facs poss stretched high ssn & ltd low ssn; supmkt adj; gd cycle tracks. ♦ 1 Apr-30 Sep. € 13.00   2005*

AUXI LE CHATEAU *3B3* (Urban) **Camp Municipal des Peupliers, Rue de Cheval, 62390 Auxi-le-Chateau** [03 21 41 10 79] Take D928 S fr Hesdin. In 11km take D119 to Auxi-le-Chateau. Fr Doullens-Abbeville rd D925, turn N onto D933 at Bernaville to Auxi-le-Chateau, then take D938 twds Crecy, site sp on R in 300m by football stadium. Med, hdg pitch; unshd wc; chem disp; shwrs inc; el pts (3-6A) €1.50-2.50; lndtte; ice; shops, rest, snacks, bar 500m; playgrnd; fishing; sailing; dir access to rv; 80% statics; poss cr; adv bkg; quiet. 1 Apr-30 Sep. € 7.10   2004*

AUXONNE *6G1* (Urban) **Camping L'Arquebuse, Route d'Athee, 21130 Auxonne** [03 80 37 34 36 or 03 84 72 11 04] On N5 Dijon-Geneva, site sp on L bef bdge at ent to Auxonne. Med, pt shd; wc; chem disp; mv service pnt; shwrs inc; el pts (10A) inc; gas; lndry rm; shop 500m; rest; snacks; bar; playgrnd; pool adj; rv sw; fishing; sailing; windsurfing; entmnt; TV rm; 20% statics; adv bkg; quiet at night but poss noisy during day; clsd 2200-0700; CCI. "Site beside rv; sh walk to interesting town; gd sh stay." 15 Jun-15 Sep. € 13.20   2003*

AVAILLES LIMOUZINE see Pressac *7A3*

AVALLON *4G4* (2km SE) **Camp Municipal Sous Roches, 89200 Avallon** [tel/fax 03 86 34 10 39; campingsousroche@ville-avallon.fr] App town fr a'route or fr SE on N6. Turn sharp L at 2nd traff lts in town cent, L in 2km at sp Vallee du Cousin (bef bdge), site 250m on L. If app fr S care needed when turning R after bdge. Med, some hdstg pitches, terr, pt shd; wc; shwrs inc; el pts (9A) €3; ice; lndry rm; shop; tradsmn (to order); BBQ; playgrnd; pool 1km; rv sw & fishing adj; dogs; phone adj; Eng spkn; CCI. "Popular, cheerful site; helpful staff; new san facs 2004; conv Morvan National Park; poss flood warning after heavy rain." ♦ 15 Mar-15 Oct. € 10.00   2005*

AVANTON see Poitiers *7A2*

AVESNES SUR HELPE *3B4* (300m S Urban) **Camp Municipal Le Champs de Mars/La Rotonde, Rue Leo Legrange, 59440 Avesnes-sur-Helpe** [tel/fax 03 27 57 99 04] On SE edge of town. Sp fr all dir. Sm, pt sl, pt shd; htd wc (some cont); shwrs inc; el pts (6A) inc (poss rev pol); lndry rm; shop 500m; tennis; fishing adj; adv bkg; quiet some rlwy noise; CCI. "Well-kept facs; clean, neat site; gd facs for disabled." ♦ 15 Apr-30 Sep. € 15.00   2005*

AVIGNON *10E2* (2km N) **Camp Municipal La Laune, Chemin St Honore, 30400 Villeneuve-les-Avignon** [04 90 25 76 06 or 04 90 25 61 33; fax 04 90 25 91 55] Fr Avignon, take N100 twd Nimes over rv bdge. At W end of rv bdge, turn R onto N980 sp Villeneuve-les-Avignon. Site is 3km on R just past old walled town battlements on L. Adj sports complex. Med, hdg/mkd pitch, shd; wc; chem disp; mv service pnt; shwrs inc; el pts (6A) €2.30; lndtte; shop; snacks; bar; pool & sports complex adj (free to campers); dogs €0.75; phone; bus; Eng spkn; quiet but some rlwy noise; CCI. "Monuments & museum adj; lovely site; gd, v clean facs; facs poss run down/unclean low ssn; helpful staff; excel security; excel local mkt; Villeneuve lovely vill in walking dist; gd sh stay." ♦ ltd. 1 Apr-15 Oct. € 11.70   2005*

AVIGNON *10E2* (4km NE) **Camping du Grand Bois, Quartier La Tapy, 84130 Le Pontet** [04 90 31 37 44; fax 04 90 31 46 53] Exit A7/E714 at junc 23 onto D53 S. Site in approx 1km on R, sp. Med, hdg pitch, pt shd; wc; chem disp; shwrs inc; el pts (5A) €2.50; lndtte; shop; hypmkt 3km; tradsmn; rest; snacks; playgrnd; cycle hire; TV; dogs €1.50; phone; Eng spkn; adv bkg; quiet; cc acc; CCI. "Superb location; plenty of rm; family-run alt to main Avignon sites; ltd facs; v helpful staff; insects a problem." ♦ 1 May-15 Sep. € 18.00   2005*

AVIGNON *10E2* (9km NE Rural) **Camping Flory, Route d'Entraigues, 84270 Vedene [04 90 31 00 51; fax 04 90 23 46 19]** Nr junc of m'way & D942. After exit m'way NE on D942 twd Carpentras. In 3km foll sp on R for Camping Flory. Med, mkd pitch, pt sl, pt shd; wc (some cont); chem disp; shwrs inc; el pts (10A) inc (poss rev pol); gas; ice; lndtte; shop & 1km; tradsmn; rest & 3km; snacks; bar & 3km; playgrnd; pool (high ssn); dogs €1; phone; 15% statics; poss cr; quiet; adv bkg; Eng spkn; 10% red low ssn; CCI. "Gd long stay; ideal for visiting Vaucluse; superb shopping nr." ♦ 15 Mar-15 Oct. € 18.00   2004*

> Some of these sites have changed their opening dates - we'd better fill in some site report forms and let the editor of the guide know.

AVIGNON *10E2* (8km S Urban) **Camping de la Roquette, 746 Ave Jean Mermoz, 13160 Chateaurenard [tel/fax 04 90 94 46 81; contact@ camping-la-roquette.com; www.camping-la-roquette.com]** Exit A7/N7 Avignon S to Noves; take D28 to Chateaurenard 4km; foll sp to site & Piscine Olympic/Complex Sportiv. Poss awkward access/exit lge o'fits. Med, hdg/mkd pitch, pt shd; wc; chem disp; some serviced pitches; mv service pnt; baby facs; shwrs inc; el pts (6A) €2.80; lndtte; ice; shops 1.5km; tradsmn; rest; snacks; bar; playgrnd; pool; tennis; dogs €1; phone; Eng spkn; adv bkg; quiet but some rd noise; 5% red 30+ days; cc acc; CCI. "Gd touring cent; owners v kind, friendly & helpful; v clean facs; gd walks." ♦ ltd. 1 Mar-30 Oct. € 13.80   2005*

†**AVIGNON** *10E2* (12km W Rural) **Camping Le Bois des Ecureuils, Plateau de Signargues, 30390 Domazan [tel/fax 04 66 57 10 03; le.bois. des.ecureuils@wanadoo.fr]** Exit a'route A9/E15 at Remoulins exit 23, go twd Avignon on N100. In 6km site is on R. Fr S on N7 foll sp for Nimes onto N100. Go over 2 lge rndabts, site about 6km on L - need to ent R filter rd to turn safely across traff. Sm, mkd pitch, all hdstg, shd; htd wc (some cont); chem disp (wc); baby facs; shwrs inc; el pts (6A) €2.50; gas; lndtte; lndry area; ice; shop; rest adj; snacks; bar high ssn; BBQ; playgrnd; htd pool; entmnt; TV; 5% statics; dogs; phone; poss cr; Eng spkn; adv bkg (rec high ssn); quiet but some rd noise; red low ssn CCI. "Ideal for touring Avignon & Pont du Gard; friendly owners; spotless facs; steel awning pegs ess; gd sh stay." € 15.50   2004*

†**AVIGNON** *10E2* (500m NW Urban) **Camping Bagatelle, Ile de la Barthelasse, 84000 Avignon [04 90 86 30 39; fax 04 90 27 16 23]** Exit a'route A7 at Avignon Nord. After passing end of old bdge bear L, then onto new Daladier bdge & take immed R turn over bdge foll sp to Barthelasse & Villeneuve-les-Avignon. Caution - do not foll Nimes sp at more southerly bdge (Pont d'Europe). Lge, mkd pitch, pt shd; htd wc; mv service pnt; baby facs; shwrs inc; el pts (5A) €2.50; gas; lndtte; shop; rest; pool 100m; playgrnd; entmnt; TV; boating; fishing; tennis 2km; games area; TV rm; dogs €2.20; some traffic noise at night; cc acc; red CCI. "V helpful staff; on bank of Rv Rhone; walking distance to town, also free ferry; site is low lying & poss damp; poss o/night tented school parties; facs dated but clean; facs ltd low ssn; narr rds on site, suggest find pitch bef driving in; free ent to Olympic pool; if recep unmanned, go to bar or supmkt to check in; poor security." ♦ € 16.50   2005*

AVIGNON *10E2* (1km NW Urban) **Camping Le Pont d'Avignon, Ile de la Barthelasse, 84000 Avignon [04 90 80 63 50; fax 04 90 85 22 12; info@camping-avignon.com; www.camping-avignon.com]** Go round wall & under Pont d'Avignon; then cross rv dir Villeneuve, Ile de la Barthelasse. Turn R onto Ile de la Barthelasse. Lge, hdg/mkd pitch, pt shd; wc; chem disp; mv service pnt; shwrs inc; el pts (6A) inc; gas; lndtte; shop; rest; snacks; bar; BBQ; cooking facs; playgrnd; pool; paddling pool; tennis; rv adj; games area; games rm; entmnt; internet; TV; statics (sep area); dogs €2.10; phone; car wash; poss cr; Eng spkn; adv bkg ess high ssn; quiet but some rd/rlwy noise; red low ssn/7+ days; cc acc; CCI. "Superb site; Avignon festival Jul/Aug; many places of interest; magnificent views city & bdge; best site for Avignon (20 mins walk); some pitches with high kerbstones; floodlit at night; excel clean facs; pitches poss flooded low ssn; extra for c'vans over 5.50m." ♦ ltd. 14 Mar-30 Oct. € 20.50 (CChq acc)   2005*

AVIGNON *10E2* (5km NW Rural) **Camping Caravanning L'Ile des Papes, 30400 Villeneuve-les-Avignon [04 90 15 15 90; fax 04 90 15 15 91; contact@campeoles.fr; www.campeoles.fr]** Fr A9 exit sp Roquemaure; head S on D980. Site adj to rv 2km NW of city. Fr A7 exit Avignon Nord, twds Avignon cent & cross bdge twds Villeneuve. Turn off after x-ing rv before x-ing canal. Site bet rv & canal. Lge, pt shd; wc; shwrs; el pts (6A) €3.10; ice; lndtte; cooking facs; rest; supmkt; playgrnd; pool adj; mini-golf; archery; lake fishing adj; hiking; entmnt; TV; dogs €1.52; adv bkg; quiet but some rlwy noise; Eng spkn; red low ssn; cc acc; red CCI. "Lovely area; well-run site; gd staff; lge pitches; excel disabled facs & access to pool; gd rest on site; excel long/sh stay." ♦ 1 Apr-15 Oct. € 23.93   2004*

FRANCE

AVRANCHES *2E4* (6km S Rural) **Camping Rural Avallonn (Martinet), La Caufetiere, 50220 Ceaux** [02 33 68 39 47] Fr Avranches on N175 exit La Buvette & W onto D43. Site in approx 2km. Sm, pt shd; wc; shwrs inc; el pts inc; rest; snacks; sand beach 20km; Eng spkn; adv bkg; quiet. "In sm apple orchard; v helpful owner; rm for 3 c'vans; goats & horses in pens on site; 10km fr Mont St Michel; many activities, museums nrby; steep & narr ent but gd NH." ♦ 7 Jul-25 Aug. € 15.00   2005*

AVRANCHES *2E4* (10km W Rural) **Camping La Perame, 50530 Genets** [02 33 70 82 49] Fr Avranches on N176; in 1km L on D911 thro Genets. Turn R onto D35 immed after passing thro Genets, Site on R. Sm, pt shd; wc; shwrs inc; el pts (10A) €2.50 (rev pol); tradsmn; farm produce; playgrnd; 60% statics; dogs €0.70; phone; poss cr; red low ssn; quiet; CCI. "Rural CL-type site; gd views of Mont St Michel fr vill; poss ltd low ssn; v pleasant owner; guided walks to Mont St Michel; highly rec; gd long/sh stay." 1 Apr-31 Oct. € 10.50   2005*

AVRANCHES *2E4* (10km W Rural) **Camping Les Coques d'Or, Route du Bec-d'Andaine, 50530 Genets** [02 33 70 82 57 or 06 85 21 13 01 (LS); fax 02 33 70 86 83; information@campingles coquesdor.com; www.campinglescoquesdor. com] Fr Avranches foll Granville rd. In 1km L on N911 sp Vains to Genets. D35E for 500m & site on R. Med hdg/mkd pitch, pt shd; wc; shwrs inc; el pts (3-10A) €2.10-4.10; lndtte; shops 1km; tradsmn; snacks; bar; playgrnd; sm pool; sand beach 800m; fishing; TV rm; entmnt; 80% statics (sep area); dogs €1.50; poss cr; Eng spkn; quiet; red low ssn. "Gd views Mont St Michel nrby." ♦ ltd. 1 Apr-30 Sep. € 13.20   2004*

AVRANCHES *2E4* (10km NW Rural) **Camping Le Montviron, La Mesangere, 50530 Montviron** [02 33 60 43 26 or 02 33 58 67 02 (LS)] Exit N175 sp Granville. On D973 fr Avranches, in 6km turn R sp Montviron. In vill turn L sp Sartilly. Site in 2km on L. Well sp. Sm, hdg pitch, pt shd; wc; some serviced pitches; chem disp; shwrs inc; el pts (6A) €2; gas; lndtte; shops 500m; tradsmn; snacks; bar; playgrnd; sand beach 10km; golf; TV rm; 95% statics; poss cr; Eng spkn; adv bkg; quiet; CCI. "V friendly; wonderful rest nrby; gd 1st stop fr pm ferry Cherbourg or Le Havre; basic facs; poss tight pitches; conv Granville & Mont St Michel; fair." ♦ ltd. Easter-30 Sep. € 11.00   2005*

AVRILLE *7A1* (1km E) **Camping Le Beauchene, Ave du Marechal de Lattre de Tassigny, 85440 Avrille** [02 51 22 30 49 or 02 51 90 35 97; fax 02 51 90 39 31; www.lebeauchene.com] On E o'skts of Avrille, on D949, visible fr rd. Med, mkd pitch, shd, wc; chem disp; shwrs inc; el pts (6A) inc; ice; lndtte; shops 300m; tradsmn; rest adj; playgrnd; htd pool; sand beach 9km; dogs €1.50; TV rm; poss cr; adv bkg; CCI. "Friendly helpful owners; simple, roomy with gd facs." ♦ Easter-30 Sep. € 14.20   2004*

AVRILLE *7A1* (1km S Rural) **Camping Les Mancellieres, Route de Longeville-sur-Mer, 85440 Avrille** [02 51 90 35 97; fax 02 51 90 39 31; camping.mancellieres@tiscali.fr; www.les mancellieres.com] Fr Avrille take D105 S twd Longeville-sur-Mer. Site on L in 1.5km. Med, hdg/mkd pitch, pt sl; wc (some cont); chem disp; baby facs; shwrs inc; el pts (6A) inc; gas; lndtte; ice; shop; snacks; BBQ (charcoal/gas); playgrnd; htd pool; waterslide; beach 5km; watersports 5km; fishing 2km; tennis 800m; cycle hire, horseriding 3km; games rm; entmnt; 30% statics; recep 0900-1200 & 1400-2000; dogs €1.90; some Eng spkn; adv bkg; quiet; 30% red low ssn; cc not acc. "Friendly owners; peaceful; ent gates set on angle & poss diff lge o'fits." ♦ 1 May-15 Sep. € 18.70 ABS - A15   2005*

†**AX LES THERMES** *8G4* (2km NE Rural) **Camp Municipal La Prade, 09110 Sorgeat** [05 61 64 36 34 or 05 61 64 21 93; fax 05 61 64 63 38; sorgeat@ free.fr] In cent of Ax-les-Thermes turn E off N20 onto D613. In 5km in Sorgeat turn R & foll sp thro vill to site, 800m on R. Sm, hdg/mkd pitch, terr, pt shd; htd wc (some cont); chem disp; shwrs inc; el pts (5-10A) €2.70-5.20; gas 5km; lndtte; ice; shop 1km; rest 5km; snacks; playgrnd; pool 5km; 15% statics; dogs €0.60; phone; poss cr; adv bkg; quiet; cc not acc; CCI. "V clean; site is 1,150m high overlooking Ariege valley; ski lifts at Ax; gd walks; not suitable for lge o'fits; vg long/sh stay." € 9.40   2005*

AX LES THERMES *8G4* (7km E Rural) **Camping Ascou La Forge, 09110 Ascou** [05 61 64 60 03; fax 05 61 64 60 06; mountain.sports@wanadoo. fr; www.mountain-sports.net] On N20 S turn L at rndabt by church in Ax sp Ascou. In 4km turn R sp Ascou-Pailheres. Foll site sp to site on R in 3km after lake & hamlet Goulours. Rd narr & mountainous, not rec med/lge o'fits. Sm, mkd pitch; pt sl, pt shd; wc; chem disp; shwrs inc; el pts (4-6A) €3-4; lndtte; shop & 7km; tradsmn; bar; playgrnd; fishing; entmnt; dogs €1.50; adv bkg; CCI. "Immac facs; beautiful mountain scenery; gd walking, friendly, helpful owners." ♦ 1 Apr-31 Oct. € 14.70   2004*

†**AX LES THERMES** *8G4* (4km SE) **Camp Municipal d'Orlu, 09110 Orlu** [05 61 64 30 09 or 05 61 64 21 70; fax 05 61 64 64 23] On N20 S foll sp for Spain thro town cent. On exit town turn L immed bef bdge sp Orlu. Site on R in 3km. Med, mkd pitch, pt shd; htd wc; shwrs inc; el pts (3-10A) €1.80-5.25; gas; lndtte; shop 3km; tradsmn; rest, snacks, bar 500m; playgrnd; pool high ssn; rv adj; fishing; games area; entmnt; 30% statics; dogs €0.90; phone; poss cr; adv bkg; quiet; CCI. "Gd, friendly site; surrounded by beautiful mountain scenery; poss floods in bad weather; excel walks; conv Andorra or Spain." ♦ € 10.30   2005*

†AX LES THERMES *8G4* (1km NW Rural) **Camp Municipal Malazeou, 09110 Ax-les-Thermes [05 61 64 69 14; fax 05 61 64 05 60; camping. malazeou@wanadoo.fr]** Sp on N20 to Foix. Lge, hdg pitch, pt sl, shd; htd wc (some cont); chem disp; mv service pnt; baby facs; shwrs inc; el pts (6A) inc; gas; lndry rm; ice; shop 1km; tradsmn; playgrnd; 70% statics; dogs €2; train 500m; Eng spkn; adv bkg; quiet but some rd noise; CCI. "Fair NH; lovely scenery & gd fishing; rvside walk to town." ♦ ltd. € 19.50   2005*

†AX LES THERMES *8G4* (9km NW) **Camp Municipal Le Castella, 09250 Luzenac [05 61 64 47 53; fax 05 61 64 40 59]** Site on W of N20 bet Ax-les-Thermes & Foix. Med, mkd pitch; terr, pt shd; htd wc; shwrs inc; el pts (4-6A) €1.80-3.40; ice; lndtte; shop, bar 300m; playgrnd; pool in ssn; tennis; entmnt; archery; fishing quiet. "Gd walking; prehistoric caves at Niaux; mountain views." ♦ € 8.40   2002*

AXAT *8G4* (2km E Rural) **Camping La Cremade, 11140 Axat [tel/fax 04 68 20 50 64]** S fr Quillan on N117, cont 1km beyond junc with N118 twd Perpignan. Turn R into site, sp, narr access. Med, hdg pitch, pt sl, pt shd; wc; shwrs inc; el pts (6A) inc; lndtte; shop & 3km; 5% statics; dogs €1; Eng spkn; adv bkg; quiet; CCI. "Pleasant, well-maintained site in beautiful location; few level pitches." ♦ Easter-30 Sep. € 12.00   2004*

AYDAT *9B1* (Rural) **Camping Les Chadelas, 63970 Aydat [04 73 79 38 09; fax 04 73 79 34 12; reception@campingchadelas.com; www.camping chadelas.com]** Exit A75 S fr Clermont-Ferrand at junc 5 onto D13 W. Foll sp Lake Aydat. At x-rds at end of Rouillat Bas, turn L & foll site sp. Med, mkd pitch, some hdstg, terr, shd; wc (some cont); chem disp; mv service pnt; serviced pitches; shwrs inc; el pts (6-10A) €3-5; lndtte; shop 1km; tradsmn high ssn; rest 500m; snacks; bar 500m; playgrnd; lake sw 500m; fishing; entmnt; 30% statics; phone; poss cr; adv bkg; quiet; red low ssn; CCI. "On shore of Lake Aydat; quiet out of ssn but used as base for field work; gd rest by lake; gd for m'vans." ♦ 2 Apr-22 Oct. € 17.00   2003*

AYDAT *9B1* (3km W Rural) **Caming Les Volcans, La Garandie, 63970 Aydat [tel/fax 04 73 79 33 90; keith_harvey@compuserve.com]** Exit A73 junc 5 onto D213 W. In 16km turn S in Verneuge onto D5. After 2km turn W onto D788 sp La Garandie. In vill turn R just after phone box, site on L in 200m. Sm, mkd pitch, pt sl, pt shd; wc; chem disp; shwrs inc; el pts (4A) inc; lndtte; ice; sm shop; tradsmn; rest, snacks 4km; bar 3km; lake sw & sand beach 4km; dogs €0.60; phone adj; adv bkg; quiet. "Excel walking & cycle rtes nr; relaxing site; lge pitches; beautiful area; gd touring base." 1 Jun-31 Aug. € 11.20   2005*

AZAY LE FERRON *4H2* (Urban) **Camp Municipal Le Camp du Chateau, Rue Hersent-Luzarche, 36290 Azay-le-Ferron [02 54 39 21 91 (Mairie)]** D975 Chatillon-sur-Indre to Le Bland rd, turn R in vill onto D925, site on R in 100m. Sm, pt shd; wc (some cont); shwrs inc; el pts inc; shops 100m; rest; playgrnd; tennis; mini-golf; fishing; quiet. "Warden calls pm; casino & supmkt adj." 1 Apr-1 Oct. € 6.00   2004*

AZAY LE RIDEAU *4G1* (300m N Urban) **Camp Municipal Le Sabot, Rue du Stade, 37190 Azay-le-Rideau [02 47 45 42 72 or 02 47 45 42 11 (Mairie); fax 02 47 45 49 11; mairie. azaylerideau@free.fr]** Fr town cent foll D84 (N bank of rv) sp Artannes. After Chateau on R, cont to mini rndabt & turn sharp R. Parked cars hide ent to site. Lge, mkd pitch, pt shd; wc (some cont); chem disp; mv service pnt; shwrs inc; el pts (10A) €2.90 (poss rev pol); gas 1km; ice; shop, snacks, rest in town; BBQ; htd pool adj (caps ess); playgrnd; fishing; boat & canoe hire; TV; phone; dogs; poss cr fr Son et Lumiere in high ssn; Eng spkn; adv bkg rec; quiet, 10-15% red 14-30+ days; cc acc; CCI. "Well-kept, pleasant site by rv & chateau; recep open 0800-1200 & 1330-1930; security system; €20 deposit barrier pass; poss long dist to facs fr some pitches - central facs have steps; red facs low ssn; site prone to flooding; when site clsd m'vans can stay on car park by rv o'night - no facs but well lit (enq at tourist office)." ♦ 1 Apr-31 Oct. € 9.40   2005*

AZAY SUR THOUET see Parthenay *4H1*

AZUR see Soustons *8E1*

BACCARAT *6E2* (1km SE Rural) **Camp Municipal Pre de Hon, 54120 Baccarat [03 83 75 10 46; fax 03 83 75 36 76]** Fr Baccarat take D158 S twd Lachapelle & foll sp Tourist Office past church. Turn L after rv bdge at rndabt, site on L after 500m. Sm, pt shd, wc; chem disp; shwrs; el pts (10A); shop 200m; pool nr; bus 400m; poss cr; adv bkg; quiet, some rd noise; CCI. "Pleasant, quiet rvside site; if warden absent site yourself; interesting town with crystal factory; gd NH." ♦ ltd. 15 May-15 Sep. € 7.00   2005*

BADEN see Auray *2F3*

BAGNEAUX SUR LOING see Nemours *4F3*

BAGNERES DE BIGORRE *8F2* (1km E Urban) **Camping Les Fruitiers, 91 Route de Toulouse, 65200 Bagneres-de-Bigorre [tel/fax 05 62 95 25 97; daniellevillemur@wanadoo.fr]** On D938 fr town cent dir Toulouse. Site sp at traff lits at x-rds with D8. Site well sp on app; take care on final app to ent. Med, mkd pitch, pt sl, pt shd; htd wc; chem disp; baby facs; shwrs inc; el pts (2-6A) €2-5; lndtte; ice; shops 500m; rest 300m; snacks 200m; playgrnd; pool 200m; tennis; dogs €0.80; phone; bus; poss cr; adv bkg; quiet/some traff noise; red low ssn; CCI. "Attractive town; well-kept site; excel facs; helpful warden; sharp bends on site rds & overhanging trees poss diff lge o'fits." ♦ 1 May-30 Oct. € 13.30   2005*

FRANCE

Camping de la Vée ★★★

Situated between Paris and Brittany, at approx. 55 miles from the Mont Saint Michel and the landing beaches, in the heart of the Normandy, in green surroundings, with casino, golf, swimming pool, tennis, horseback riding, come and discover the charm of the countryside and the untouched magic of a 19th century touristic and thermal region. Open: April till October

250 pitches on offer.
F-61140 BAGNOLES DE L'ORNE
Phone : +33(0) 233 378 745
Fax : +33(0) 233 301 432
Booking of season : +33(0) 233 307 878
camping-de-la-vee@wanadoo.fr;
www.bagnoles-de-lorne.com

BAGNOLES
DE L'ORNE

Camping
Qualité

†BAGNERES DE BIGORRE 8F2 (3km E Urban) Camping Le Monloo, Quartier Monloo, 65200 Bagneres-de-Bigorre [tel/fax 05 62 95 19 65; www.lemonloo.com] Fr A64 exit junc 14 onto D20/D938 to Bagneres-de-Bigorre. At traff lts on ent turn R onto D8, site on L in 2km, sp at ent. Med, sl, pt shd; wc; chem disp; mv service pnt; shwrs inc; el pts (6A) €5; Indtte; shop 1km; playgrnd; pool; waterslide; tennis; TV; entmnt; 20% statics; phone; dogs €0.80; adv bkg; quiet; cc acc; CCI. "Friendly patron; gd facs; spacious, tidy & peaceful site away fr rds; pleasant town." € 15.00 (3 persons)   2004*

†BAGNERES DE BIGORRE 8F2 (7km S) Camping Le Layris, Quartier Bourg, 65710 Campan [05 62 91 75 34; lelayris@campan-pyrenees.com] Fr A64 or Tarbes avoid D935 by taking D938 to Bagneres. Fr Bagneres, take D935 S, site on R after ent to Campan, sp. Sm, mkd pitch, pt shd; htd wc (cont); chem disp; shwrs inc; el pts (2-10A) €2.15-6.10; Indtte; shops adj; playgrnd; pool 5km; fishing; tennis adj; wintersports 12km; dogs €1; poss cr; adv bkg; quiet; CCI. "Gd site for walkers. " € 10.70   2004*

BAGNERES DE LUCHON 8G3 (2km N Rural) Camping Pradelongue, 31110 Moustajon [05 61 79 86 44; fax 05 61 79 18 64]   Site is on D125c on W of D125 main rd fr Bagneres-de-Luchon. Ent at Moustajon/Antignac going S. Site adj Intermarche; sp. Lge, hdg/mkd pitch, pt shd; wc; chem disp; mv service pnt; baby facs; shwrs inc; el pts (10A) €4; Indtte; ice; shop 100m; BBQ; playgrnd; htd pool; games area; 10% statics; Eng spkn; adv bkg; quiet; cc acc; CCI. "Excel, well-run site with friendly, helpful owners; excel mountain views; rec; recep clsd 1230-1400." ♦ 1 Apr-30 Sep. € 13.50   2003*

†BAGNERES DE LUCHON 8G3 (4km N) Camping Le Pyreneen, 31110 Salles-et-Pratviel [05 61 79 59 19; fax 05 61 79 75 75] Fr Bagneres-de-Luchon, take N125 twd Montrejeau in 4km exit on D125 to Salles; thro vill & site sp on R. Med, pt shd; htd wc; chem disp; shwrs inc; el pts inc (10A); Indry rm; shops 4km; ice; pool; 50% statics; no dogs; adv bkg; quiet. "NH only; site run down; winter sports." ♦ ltd. € 17.25 (3 persons)   2004*

BAGNOLES DE L'ORNE 4E1 (3km SE) Camping Le Clos Normand, Bagnoles-de-l'Orne, 61410 Couterne [02 33 37 92 43 or 06 07 17 44 94] On D916 approx midway bet Couterne & La Ferte Mace; well sp. Med, hdg/mkd pitch, pt sl, shd; wc; chem disp; shwrs inc; el pts (5-10A) €2.40-3.35; gas; Indtte; ice; shops 2km; tradsmn; rest, bar 2km; snacks; BBQ; playgrnd; canoeing; entmnt; TV; 2% statics; dogs €0.50; phone; Eng spkn; adv bkg; some rd noise. "Attractive, well-maintained site; friendly; san facs in need of updating; in National Park Normandie-Maine; gd walks; poss long stay workers on site; close to thermal spa & excel sports facs, boating lake & casino; I hour fr car ferry." 1 May-30 Sep. € 6.70   2003*

BAGNOLES DE L'ORNE 4E1 (1.3km SW Rural) Camping de la Vee, Rue du President Coty, 61140 Bagnoles-de-l'Orne [02 33 37 87 45; fax 02 33 30 14 32; camping-de-la-vee@wanadoo.fr; www.bagnoles-de-lorne.com] Access fr D335 in vill of Tesse-la-Madeleine. Or fr La Ferte-Mace D916 6km sp Couterne. Well sp fr all dirs. Lge, hdg/mkd pitch, pt shd; htd wc (some cont); chem disp; mv service pnt; baby facs; shwrs inc; el pts (3-10A) €2.40-3.80 (poss rev pol); gas 1km; Indtte; ice; shop 1km; tradsmn; rest; snacks; bar; BBQ; playgrnd; htd pool 1.5km; rv & lake nrby; golf, archery, tennis & mini-golf nrby; TV; 2% statics; dogs €1.15; phone; poss cr; Eng spkn; no adv bkg; quiet; no cc acc; CCI. "Beautiful thermal spa town; excel situation; forest walks; vg, clean, refurbished facs; excel." ♦ Apr-Oct. € 11.20   2005*

See advertisement

BAGNOLS SUR CEZE 10E2 (1.5km N) Camping-Caravaning La Coquille, Route de Carmignan, 30200 Bagnols-sur-Ceze [04 66 89 03 05 or 04 66 89 59 86; fax 04 66 89 59 86] Head N fr Bagnols-sur-Ceze over rv bdge turn R at Total stn, site 2km on RH side. Sm, pt shd; wc (cont); chem disp; shwrs inc; el pts (3A); inc; gas in town; ice; Indtte; rest; shop 2.5km; pool; canoe hire; fishing; adv bkg rec high ssn; quiet; CCI. "Site under military aircraft flightpath, otherwise gd, friendly, family-run site." Easter-15 Sep. € 21.00   2004*

BAGNOLS SUR CEZE *10E2* (2km NE Rural) Camping Les Genets d'Or, Route de Carmigan, 30200 Bagnols-sur-Ceze [tel/fax 04 66 89 58 67; info@camping.genets-dor.com; www.camping-genets-dor.com] N fr Bagnols on N86 over rv bdge, turn R into D360 immed after Total stn. Foll sp to site on rv. Med, pt sl, pt shd; wc (some cont); shwrs inc; el pts (8A) inc (rev pol); gas; lndtte; shop; rest; snacks; bar; pool; playgrnd; sports area; canoeing, fishing 2km; games rm; poss cr; adv bkg ess; quiet. "V welcoming British owners; gd rest; highly rec." ♦ Easter-30 Sep. € 22.90   2004*

†**BAGNOLS SUR CEZE** *10E2* (7km S Rural) Camping Le Vieux Verger, 30330 Connaux [04 66 82 91 62] S fr Bagnols sur Ceze on N86 to Connaux. Look for green site sp 1km after turn. Med, hdg/mkd pitch, pt sl, terr, pt shd; wc; shwrs; el pts; lndtte; rest; shop & gas in vill; 2 htd pools; 25% statics; poss cr; adv bkg; quiet. "Excel san facs." ♦ € 15.00   2003*

BAGNOLS SUR CEZE *10E2* (8km NW) Camping Les Cascades, 30200 La Roque-sur-Ceze [04 66 82 72 97; fax 04 66 82 68 51; info@campinglescascades.com] Fr Bagnols take D6 W twd Ales. After 4km turn N on D143 & foll sp to La Roque-sur-Ceze. Site on R in 7km. App fr N not rec. Long narr bdge (2.3m). Med, pt sl, pt shd; wc (cont); chem disp; shwrs inc; el pts (6-10A) €3-3.50; gas; lndtte; ice; shop; rest; snacks; bar; playgrnd; pool; shgl beach & rv sw adj; tennis; fishing; boating; mini-golf; entmnt; TV; dogs €1; poss cr; adv bkg; quiet. "Tranquil site; poss ltd facs when full." 1 Apr-30 Sep. € 15.40   2003*

BAGUER PICAN see Dol de Bretagne *2E4*

BAIGNES STE RADEGONDE see Barbezieux St Hilaire *7B2*

BAILLEUL *3A3* (3km N Rural) Camping Les Saules (Notteau), Route du Mont Noir, 59270 Bailleul [03 28 49 13 76] N fr Lille on A25 exit junc 10 & head N on D10 to Bailleul. In town at traff lts turn R onto D23/N375. After 2km just bef Belgian border turn L onto D223. Site on L in 300m. Sm, pt shd; wc; chem disp; shwrs inc; el pts €3; lndtte; sm shop; BBQ; playgrnd; 90% statics; dogs; quiet; Eng spkn; CCI. "Conv Calais; facs old-fashioned but clean; visits to WW1 sites & Ypres; care on exit site as view to L restricted." 1 Apr-31 Oct. € 9.30
2004*

BAILLEUL *3A3* (4km N Rural) Domaine de la Sabliere, Mont Noir, 59270 St Jans-Cappel [03 28 49 46 34; fax 03 28 42 62 90] Fr A25 exit junc 10, N on D10 thro Bailleul to St Jans-Cappel. Thro vill turn R at x-rds onto D318 to Mont Noir. Site on R at top of hill. Med, shd, terr, hdg/mkd pitch, hdstg; wc; chem disp; some serviced pitches; shwrs €.70; el pts (6A) €3; lndtte; shop adj & 3km; tradsmn; rest adj; bar; playgrnd; tennis; mini-golf 100m; fishing 2km; 80% statics; phone. "Gd for WW1 battlefields; pitch acc poss diff for lge o'fits; steep gradients & tight turns; v clean san facs; well kept; vg sh stay." 15 Apr-15 Oct. € 7.50   2005*

BAIN DE BRETAGNE *2F4* (1km SE Urban) Camp Municipal du Lac, Route de Launay, 35470 Bain-de-Bretagne [02 99 43 85 67 or 02 99 43 70 24 (Mairie)] Take N772 E fr Bain-de-Bretagne twd Chateaubriant, foll sp. Site on R 300m down sm rd. Med, hdg/mkd pitch, pt shd; wc (chem closet); chem disp; shwrs inc; el pts (10A) inc; shop 1km; tradsmn; rest; snacks; bar; playgrnd; htd pool 500m; lake sw; sailing school nr; statics; phone; poss cr; Eng spkn; quiet; CCI. "Fees collected each eve, go to bar/cafe if gates locked on arr or phone warden on number displayed at office; poss itinerants; attractive sm town; many leisure facs within walking dist; excel value, nice outlook; gd sh/long stay." 1 Apr-21 Oct.
€ 8.20   2004*

> Will you fill in the site report forms at the back of the guide, or shall I?

BAIN DE BRETAGNE *2F4* (11km W Rural) Camp Municipal, Rue de Camping, 35480 Guipry [02 99 34 72 90 (Mairie) or 02 99 34 28 26] W fr Bain-de-Bretagne on D772, cross bdge at Messac. Under rlwy bdge, sharp 1st L bef Netto g'ge & Hardware. L. Site sp bef ent Guipry. Do not app after dark as rv is at end of app rd. Med, hdg/mkd pitch, pt shd; wc; mv service pnt; shwrs; el pts (8A) €2.20; rest nrby; shops 250m; lndry rm; playgrnd; pool nrby; fishing; rv walks; cycle paths; train noise; CCI. "Cruising & hire boats avail; warden on duty am & late pm; barrier 1.90m locked at times but phone for help or go to pitch 30; friendly, terrific value & clean; gd supmkt 1km; excel sh/long stay." Apr-1 Sep. € 6.50   2004*

BAINS LES BAINS *6F2* (1km N) Camping Les Pins, Rue des Creuses, 88240 Bains-les-Bains [03 29 36 33 51 or 03 29 36 20 49] Fr Neufchateau on D164, 1st L on ent town by ancient wash house. Ent on L in 400m. Fr S site sp fr town cent. Med, pt shd; wc; shwrs; el pts (5-10A) €2.20-2.30; rest, snacks; bar 1km; playgrnd; rv & fishing, golf, tennis 2km; dogs €1; quiet. "Fair sh stay; pleasant." 1 May-25 Oct. € 8.00   2004*

BAINS LES BAINS *6F2* (9km SW Rural) Camping Le Fontenoy, Route de la Vierge, 88240 Fontenoy-le-Chateau [03 29 36 34 74 or 03 29 30 43 88; fax 03 29 36 37 26; marliesfontenoy@hotmail.com] SE fr Bains-les-Bains, foll sp to Fontenoy-le- Chateau (6km). In cent of vill turn L onto D40 for 2km to site. Med, mkd pitch, pt shd; wc; chem disp; shwrs inc, el pts (4-11A) inc; lndtte; ice; tradsmn; rest; snacks; bar; playgrnd; pool 5km; 10% statics; dogs €0.60; poss cr; Eng spkn; adv bkg (dep & €15.20 bkg fee); quiet, cc not acc; red long stay; CCI. "Attractive, country site; lovely area; v tired facs; sh stay only." 15 Apr-30 Sep. € 12.80   2005*

BAIX *9D2* (Rural) **Camping Le Merle Roux, 07210 Baix** [04 75 85 84 14; fax 04 75 85 83 07; lemerleroux@hotmail.com; www.lemerleroux.com] Fr A7/E15 exit junc 16. Foll sp Le Pouzin, x-ing Rv Rhone. Turn L onto N86 (S), go thro Le Pouzin, in 2km immed bef rlwy x-ing, turn R twd Privas; in 500m turn L at sp & foll rd approx 2km. Med, pt sl, terr, pt shd; wc; chem disp; shwrs inc; el pts (4A); Indtte; shop; tradsmn; rest; snacks; bar; pool; playgrnd; 15% statics; adv bkg; quiet; CCI. "V helpful Dutch owners; gd site rest; excel." 1 Apr-30 Sep.   2005*

BALARUC LES BAINS see Sete *10F1*

BALBIGNY *9B1* (3km NW Rural) **Camping La Route Bleue, Route du Lac de Villerest, 42510 Balbigny** [04 77 27 24 97; fax 04 77 28 18 05; camping.balbigny@wanadoo.fr; www.laroutebleu.com] Fr N on N82, take 1st R after a'route (A89/72) junc N of Balbigny. Fr S on N82, turn L at RH bend on N o'skirts of Balbigny, sp Lac de Villerest. Well sp. Med, some hdg pitch, pt sl, pt shd; chem disp; mv service pnt; wc; shwrs inc; el pts (6-10A) €2.80-3.20; Indtte; ice; shops 1.5km; tradsmn; rest; snacks; bar; playgrnd; pool & paddling pool; rv sw adj; fishing; games rm; sports complex adj; adv bkg; quiet; red long stay; cc acc; CCI. "Excel site on rv bank; conv for A72; helpful & welcoming staff; higher charges for twin-axle vans." ♦ ltd. 15 Mar-30 Sep. € 9.90   2005*

BALLEROY *1D4* (5km SW Rural) **Camping L'Oree du Bois, 14490 Litteau** [02 31 22 22 08 or 06 62 54 47 22; fax 02 31 21 85 65; camping.loreedubois@wanadoo.fr] Fr St Lo, take D972 to Bayeux. After 14km, at La Malbreche, turn R onto D209 to Litteau. Site on L in approx 500m. Sm, some hdg/mkd pitch, pt sl, unshd; wc; chem disp (wc only); shwrs inc; el pts (6A) €2.80; Indtte; ice; shop & 4km; bar; playgrnd; htd pool; horseriding; lake fishing adj; sand beach 25km; dogs; adv bkg; quiet; CCI. "Vg long stay; forest adj; conv for D-Day beaches & museums & Bayeux tapestry." Easter-26 Oct. € 12.60   2002*

BANDOL *10F3* (6km NW) **Camping Le Clos, Route de Bandol, 83270 St Cyr-sur-Mer** [tel/fax 04 94 32 12 21; camping@clos-therese.com; www.clos-therese.com] Fr Bandol take N559 twd St Cyr & Marseilles. Site on R after 3km. Caution - site ent sharp U turn fr rd. Site service rds steep & narr; not suitable lge vans. Med, terr, shd; htd wc; chem disp; shwrs; el pts (2-10A) €2.60-4.70; gas; Indtte; ice; supmkt 1km; rest; snacks; bar; playgrnd; 2 pools (1 htd); paddling pool; sand beach 4km; golf, tennis, horseriding nr; entmnt; TV rm; 30% statics; dogs €2.10; adv bkg rec; some daytime rd noise. "Many beaches & beauty spots in area; tractor will site c'vans." ♦ Easter-30 Sep. € 20.00 (CChq acc)   2004*

BANDOL *10F3* (6km NW Coastal) **Camping Les Baumelles, Lecques, 83270 St Cyr** [04 94 26 21 27; fax 04 94 88 76 13; baumellesloisirs@aol.com] Fr Bandol take coast rd N559 NW to St Cyr. Turn L by statue on rd to La Madrague. Foll this coast rd 1.5km. Site on L at junc of coast rd. V lge, some mkd pitch; pt sl, shd; wc; baby facs; shwrs inc; el pts (10A) €3.50; gas adj; Indry rm; shop; rest; snacks; bar; playgrnd; sand beach adj; entmnt; TV; 60% statics; dogs €3; poss cr; quiet. "Facs clean but some in need refurb." 1 Apr-30 Oct. € 22.00   2005*

BANNALEC see Pont Aven *2F2*

BANNES see Langres *6F1*

BANON *10E3* (1km S) **Camping de l'Epi Bleu, Les Gravieres, 04150 Banon** [04 92 73 30 30; fax 04 92 73 31 10; epibleu@wanadoo.fr] Take N100 SW fr Forcalquier, take R on D5 N thro St Michel & Revest twd Banon. Turn L on D51 twds Simiane-la-Rotunde. Site on R in 500m immed bef town, sp at junc. Med, shd; wc; baby facs; shwrs inc; el pts (6-15A) €2.50-3.50; Indtte; gas; ice; shop; rest; snacks; pool; library; communal BBQs; dogs €2.50; adv bkg; quiet; red low ssn; CCI. "Vg with pleasant owners; gd walking & cycling tours; stony site, metal pegs rec; heavily wooded site." 1 Apr-30 Sep. € 14.00   2002*

BANYULS SUR MER *10H1* (2km S) **Camp Municipal La Pinede, 66650 Banyuls-sur-Mer** [04 68 88 32 13 or 04 68 88 00 62 (Mairie); fax 04 68 88 32 48; camp.banyuls@Banyulss/mer.com] On N114 foll sp to Banyuls-sur-Mer; turn R at camping sp at cent of sea-front by town hall; foll camping sp to site (2km fr sea-front). Care needed, narr access rds with sharp bends & trees. Lge, hdg/mkd pitch, pt sl, pt terr; pt shd; wc; chem disp; mv service pnt; shwrs; el pts (4A) €1.90; Indtte; snacks; supmkt 100m; playgrnd; shgl beach 2km; Eng spkn; quiet; cc acc; CCI. "Vg, clean facs; busy, friendly site; spacious pitches; gd views fr top; sh walk into Banyuls." ♦ 1 Apr-31 Dec. € 12.40   2005*

BAR LE DUC *6E1* (Urban) **Camp Municipal Parc de Marbeaumont, Rue de St Mihiel, 55000 Bar-le-Duc** [03 29 79 17 33 (Mairie)] Sm, pt shd; wc; shwrs; el pts €3.40 (poss long lead req); shops adj. "Pitch yourself if no warden; friendly & helpful warden locks/unlocks el pts; poss itinerants; new, clean san block; nice setting; gd NH/sh stay." 15 Apr-30 Sep. € 5.40   2005*

BAR SUR AUBE *6F1* (500m NW Urban) **Camp Municipal La Graviere, Ave du Parc, 10200 Bar-sur-Aube** [03 25 27 12 94] On N19 Chaumont-Troyes rd thro town; on o'skts turn L into Ave du Parc at sm supmkt on R; site in 100m on rvside. Sm, pt shd, some hdstdg; wc; chem disp; shwrs €1; el pts (6A) €2.50; gas; shop 100m; tradsmn; rest in town; playgrnd; pool; 20% statics; dogs; phone; poss cr; quiet; red 5+ days; no cc acc; CCI. "Haphazard pitching when site full; poss shabby low ssn; excel value but facs poss stretched high ssn; san facs need refurb; poss itinerants; no vehicle access 2200-0800; conv Champagne area & Parc Regional de Foret d'Orient; rec arr early as pop NH." ♦ ltd. 1 Apr-15 Sep. € 5.50   2005*

BAR SUR LOUP, LE see Vence *10E4*

BARBATRE see Noirmoutier en l'Ile *2H3*

BARBEZIEUX ST HILAIRE *7B2* (12km SW) **Camp Municipal, 16360 Baignes-Ste-Radegonde** [05 45 78 40 04 (Mairie); fax 05 45 78 47 41; baignes-charente@wanadoo.fr] W of N10, S of Barbezieux. Sm, pt shd; wc; chem disp; shwrs inc; el pts (5A) €1.55; shops 100m; pool adj; adv bkg; quiet. "Warden calls pm." 1 Jun-15 Sep. € 5.45   2004*

BARBEZIEUX ST HILAIRE *7B2* (12km NW) **Camp Municipal, 17520 Archiac** [05 46 49 10 46 or 05 46 49 10 82 (Mairie); tourisme.archiac@ wanadoo.fr] Fr Cognac turn L at rndabt sp Barbezieux, then 1st R immed past sm ind est. Site 100m past sw pool on D731. Sm, mkd pitch; pt sl, terr, pt shd; wc; shwrs €0.68; el pts (3A) €2.28; lndtte; tradsmn; shops 400m; 2 pools adj; tennis; games rm; warden calls daily; some noise fr local joinery works. "On arr check list on office door for allocated/free pitches." 15 Jun-15 Sep. € 4.26
          2003*

BARBIERES *9C2* (1km SE Rural) **Camping Le Gallo-Romain, Route de Col de Tourniol, 26300 Barbieres** [tel/fax 04 75 47 44 07; info@ legalloromain.net; www.legalloromain.net] Exit A49 junc 7 onto D149 dir Marches & Barbieres. Go thro vill & ascend Rte du Col de Tourniol for 2km, site on R, well sp. Med, mkd pitch, pt sl, terr, pt shd; wc; chem disp; baby facs; shwrs inc; el pts (6A) €2.70; lndry rm; ice; shop & 1km; rest; snacks; bar; BBQ; playgrnd; pool; entmnt; TV; 15% statics; dogs €1.80; phone; Eng spkn; adv bkg; quiet; no cc acc; CCI. "Friendly, helpful Dutch owners; warm welcome; beautiful mountain setting; ltd facs low ssn." ♦ 1 May-4 Sep. € 21.00   2004*

BARBOTAN LES THERMES see Gabarret *8E2*

BARCARES, LE *10G1* (Coastal) **Camping Les Bousigues, Ave des Gorbieres, 66420 Le Barcares** [04 68 86 16 19; fax 04 68 86 28 44; lasbousigues@wanadoo.fr] Fr A9/E15, take exit sp Perpignan Nord. Take D83 twd Le Barcares & exit junc 10. Turn R at rndabt, site sp on L. Lge, hdg/mkd pitch, shd; wc; chem disp; mv service pnt; serviced pitch; shwrs; el pts (6-10A) inc; lndtte; ice; shop; rest; snacks; bar; BBQ; playgrnd; pool; sand beach 5km; games area; entmnt; car wash; 50% statics; dogs; phone (card req); poss cr; €3.20; Eng spkn; adv bkg (dep req + bkg fee); quiet, poss noise fr music until midnight; CCI. "No twin-axles; v helpful staff; excel long stay." ♦ ltd. 1 Apr-2 Nov. € 25.75   2003*

BARCARES, LE *10G1* (Coastal) **Camping L'Oasis, Route de St Laurent, 66423 Le Barcares** [04 68 86 12 43; fax 04 68 86 46 83; camping. loasis@wanadoo.fr] Fr N on A9 take exit sp Perpignan Nord. Take D83 twds Le Barcares 11km. Foll site sp. Lge, shd; wc (some cont); chem disp; shwrs; el pts (10A) inc; lndry rm; lndtte; bar; snacks; supmkt; 3 pools; playgrnd; TV; entmnt; beach adj 800m; dogs €3; red low ssn; CCI. ♦ 13 Apr-14 Sep. € 23.00   2003*

†**BARCARES, LE** *10G1* (1km Coastal) **Camping L'Europe, Route de St Laurent, 66420 Le Barcares** [04 68 86 15 36; fax 04 68 86 47 88; reception@europe-camping.com; www.europe-camping.com] Exit A9 at Perpignan N & take D83 sp Le Barcares. After 9km turn R on D81 sp Canet Plage, L on D90 sp Le Barcares. Site on R. Lge, hdg/mkd pitch, shd; wc; shwrs inc; el pts (16A) €4.20; gas; lndtte; ice; shop & 2km; rest; snacks; bar; playgrnd; 2 pools high ssn; waterslides; rv & beach 500m; tennis; archery; entmnts; disco; 50% statics; dogs €5.60; Eng spkn; adv bkg; poss noisy; red long stay/low ssn; CCI. "Gd location; all pitches brick-built individual san facs; resident dogs (& mess) nuisance; gd value low ssn but ltd facs & unkempt pitches; gd cycle rte to beach & shops; vg winter NH/sh stay." ♦ ltd. € 34.00   2005*

BARCARES, LE *10G1* (2km S Coastal) **Camping California, Route de St Laurent, 66420 Le Barcares** [04 68 86 16 08; fax 04 68 86 18 20; camping-california@wanadoo.fr; www.camping-california.fr] Exit A9 junc 41 onto D83 dir Le Barcares, Canet. At junc 9 take D81 S &, then D90 & foll sp Le Barcares. Site on L. Lge, hdg/mkd pitch, shd; wc; chem disp; baby facs; shwrs inc; el pts (10A) inc; gas; lndtte; rest; shop high ssn; supmkt 1km; rest, snacks, bar high ssn; BBQ (gas/elec only); playgrnd; 3 pools; waterslide; sand beach 1.5km; watersports 1km; tennis; games area; entmnt; internet; 20% statics; dogs €5; Eng spkn; adv bkg; noisy high ssn; cc acc; red 7+ days in Jun & Sep; CCI. "Sm pitches poss diff; busy rd thro site; excel, modern san facs; highly rec; helpful, hardworking owners." ♦ 4 Apr-10 Sep. € 28.00 ABS - C02   2005*

BARCELONNETTE *9D4* (2km SE Rural) **Camping La Chaup, Route de Sauze, 04400 Enchastrayes** [04 92 81 02 82; fax 04 92 81 30 61] Fr W, go thro Barcelonnette on D900; just after vill go R onto D9 twds La Sauze & Enchastrayes; site sp. Sm, mkd pitch, sl, unshd; htd wc (some cont); shwrs; el pts (6A) €3.90; lndtte; shop & snacks nrby; BBQ; playgrnd; rv & lake 2km; dogs €1; poss cr; adv bkg; quiet; CCI. "Relaxing site with mountain views; friendly owners." 1 Jun-15 Sep. € 8.50   2004*

BARCELONNETTE *9D4* (1km S) **Camping Le Plan de Barcelonnette, 04400 Barcelonnette** [04 92 81 08 11] Exit town on D902 sp Col d'Allos & Col de la Cayolle. Site on R. Sm, pt shd; wc; shwrs inc; el pts (3-10A) €2.70-4 gas; shop; tradsmn; rest;dogs €1; quiet. "Lovely views; lovely walks; sh walk to town; helpful owners; unisex san facs; refurbed shwrs; excel." 25 May-30 Sep.
€ 12.45   2005*

BARCELONNETTE *9D4* (2km S) **Tampico Camping Caravaneige, Ave de Nice, 04400 Barcelonnette** [04 92 81 02 55; fax 04 92 81 02 55; le-tampico@wanadoo.fr] On ent town fr W turn R in square, sp Col d'Allos (D902). Foll Poids Lourdes sp fr town. Site on R in 2km after x-ing rv. Do not app fr Col d'Allos or Col de la Layotte. Med, pt shd; wc; shwrs; el pts (6A) €2.40-4.80; gas; lndtte; shop; rest; playgrnd; rv adj; games area; TV; dogs €1.10; poss cr; quiet. 15 Dec-30 Oct. € 9.30   2003*

BARCELONNETTE *9D4* (6km W) **Camping Le Fontarache, 04580 Les Thuiles** [tel/fax 04 92 81 90 42; reception@camping-fontarache.fr] On D900 W fr Barcelonnette in vill of Les Thuiles, sp. Med, shd; wc; chem disp; shwrs inc; el pts (6A) €2.50; lndtte; shop & 3km; snacks; playgrnd; pool; TV; entmnt; adv bkg; quiet. 1 Jun-15 Sep. € 13.00   2003*

†**BARCELONNETTE** *9D4* (6km W Rural) **Domaine Loisirs de l'Ubaye, Vallee de l'Ubaye, 04340 Barcelonnette.** [04 92 81 01 96; fax 04 92 81 92 53; info@loisirsubaye.com; www.loisirsubaye.com] Site on S side of D900. Lge, mkd pitch, terr, shd; wc; 10% serviced pitches; shwrs inc; el pts (6A) inc; lndry rm; gas; shop; rest; snacks; bar; playgrnd; htd pool; rv sw adj; watersports; cycle hire; entmnt; TV rm; 10% statics; phone; red 7 days; CCI. "Magnificent scenery." ♦ € 19.00   2002*

BAREGES see Luz St Sauveur *8G2*

†**BARFLEUR** *1C4* (1km N Coastal) **Camping La Ferme du Bord de Mer, 50760 Gatteville-le-Phare** [02 33 54 01 77; fax 02 33 54 78 99; fdbm@caramail.com] On D901 fr Cherbourg, on o'skts of Barfleur turn L for Gatteville-Phare. Site on R in 1km. Med, pt shd; wc; shwrs inc; some serviced pitches; el pts (3-10A); shop; lndry rm; gas; sand beach adj; playgrnd; entmnt; poss cr; 50% statics; quiet; Eng spkn. "Footpath to vill & lighthouse; WARNING: Sep 02 member reported site owner using high-strength poison against rodents in field adj site - no warning notices displayed; site not rec children or dogs." ♦   2002*

†**BARFLEUR** *1C4* (500m NW Urban/Coastal) **Camp Municipal La Blanche Nef, 50760 Barfleur** [02 33 23 15 40; fax 02 33 23 95 14; infos@lablanchenef.com; www.lablanchenef.com] Foll main rd to harbour; half-way on L side of harbour & turn L on mkd gap in car pk; cross sm side-street & foll site sp on sea wall; site visible on L in 300m. Med, pt sl, unshd; htd wc; chem disp; mv service pnt; shwrs inc; el pts (10A) €4.30; ice; lndtte; shops 1km; tradsmn; snacks; bar; playgrnd; sand beach adj; 45% statics; dogs €1.25; Eng spkn; quiet; adv bkg; red low ssn; cc acc; CCI. "Gd sized pitches; gd birdwatching, walking, cycling; excel position & facs; fine sea views; gd sandy beach but windy." ♦ € 10.70   2005*

BARJAC *9D2* (3km S Rural) **Domaine de la Sabliere (Naturist), 30430 St Privat-de-Champclos** [04 66 24 51 16; fax 04 66 24 58 69; contact@villagesabliere.com; www.camping sabliere.com] Fr Barjac S on D901 twd Bagnols. At 3km R onto D266, foll sp. Steep ent. Lge, hdg/mkd pitch, pt sl, shd; wc; chem disp; mv service pnt; sauna; shwrs; el pts (6-10A); €3.60; gas; lndtte; shop; rest; snacks; bar; playgrnd; 2 pools (1 htd, covrd); paddling pool; rv sw; fishing; canoeing; tennis; games area; archery; entmnt; 40% statics; dogs €2.50; bus; sep car park; Eng spkn; adv bkg; quiet. "Many naturist trails in forest; helpful owners; gd facs; card op barrier (€20 dep req); steep rds, narr bends & sm pitches - poss diff access lge o'fits; gd shopping & excel local mkt." 1 Apr-30 Sep.
€ 32.00 (CChq acc)   2004*

BARJAC *9D2* (9km S) **Naturissimo La Genese (Naturist), Route de la Genese, 30430 Mejannes-le-Clap** [04 66 24 51 73 or 04 66 24 51 82; fax 04 66 24 50 38; lagenese@aol.com; www. lagenese.com] Fr A7 exit junc 19, take dir Bagnols-sur-Ceze (D994 & N86) then in Bagnols head twd Ales on D6. Exit twd Lusanne onto D979 & foll sp for Mejannes-le-Clap. Site on banks of Rv Ceze. Lge, hdg/mkd pitch, pt sl, shd; wc; chem disp; shwrs inc; el pts (6A) inc; gas; lndtte; ice; shop & 5km; rest; snacks; bar; playgrnd; pool; rv sw; fishing; sailing; canoe & cycle hire; tennis; archery; entmnt; TV rm; 10% statics; dogs €3.80; phone; adv bkg; quiet; INF card req; cc acc; red low ssn. Easter-9 Oct. € 25.60   2004*

BARJAC (LOZERE) see Mende *9D1*

BARNEVILLE CARTERET *1C4* (6km N Coastal) **Camping Bel Sito, Le Caumont de la Rue, 50270 Baubigny** [02 33 04 32 74; fax 02 33 04 02 69; bel. sito@wanadoo.fr] Fr Cherbourg take D904 twd Coutances thro Les Pieux & on twd Carteret. 10km S of Les Pieux turn R onto D131 sp Baubigny to site 1km on L. Med, pt sl, pt shd; wc; shwrs inc; el pts (6A) €2.50; gas; ice; shop; sand beach 1km; dogs €2.50; quiet. 15 Apr-13 Sep. € 15.10   2004*

BARNEVILLE CARTERET *1C4* (2.5km S Coastal) Camping Les Vikings, St Jean-de-la-Riviere, 50270 Barneville-Cartaret [02 33 53 84 13; fax 02 33 53 08 19; campingviking@aol.com; www. campingviking.com] Fr D650 foll sp dir St Jean de-la-Riviere. Site well sp. Lge, hdg pitch, pt sl, pt shd; wc; chem disp; baby facs; shwrs inc; el pts (4A) €3 (poss rev pol); gas; lndtte; shop; rest; snacks; bar; BBQ; playgrnd; htd pool high ssn; sand beach 400m; games rm; games area; golf, tennis nr; entmnt high ssn; excursions; TV rm; 50% statics; dogs €1.71; Eng spkn; adv bkg; quiet; red low ssn; cc acc; CCI. "Nice site with v helpful owner; vg touring base; gd walking; vg rest." ◆ 15 Mar-15 Nov. € 23.73   2005*

See advertisement

BARNEVILLE CARTERET *1C4* (2.5km SW Coastal) Camping Les Bosquets, Rue du Capitaine Quenault, 50270 Barneville-Carteret [02 33 04 73 62; fax 02 33 04 35 82] Site sp fr D903. Lge, terr, pt shd; wc; chem disp; shwrs inc; el pts (10A) €3.20; lndtte; ice; shop; bar; playgrnd; htd pool; sand beach 400m; 50% statics; bus; poss cr; adv bkg; quiet; CCI. "Beach ideal for children; pleasant site." ◆ 1 Apr-15 Sep. € 13.60   2004*

BARNEVILLE CARTERET *1C4* (10km SW Coastal) Camping L'Esperance, 36 Rue de la Gamburie, 50580 Denneville-Plage [02 33 07 12 71; fax 02 33 07 58 32; camping.esperance@wanadoo. fr] On D903 Barneville-Carteret; in 7km R onto D650, sp Portbail & then R onto D137 sp Denneville-Plage & camping. Med, hdg/mkd pitch, pt shd; wc; chem disp; shwrs inc; el pts (6A) €3.40; gas; lndtte; ice; shop; snacks; bar; playgrnd; htd pool; sand beach 300m; entmnt; 50% statics; dogs €1.60; poss cr; Eng spkn; adv bkg; quiet; cc acc; CCI. "Helpful owners." 1 Apr-30 Sep. € 17.00
                                    2005*

BARNEVILLE CARTERET *1C4* (2.5km W Urban/Coastal) Camping du Bocage, Rue du Bocage, Carteret, 50270 Barneville-Carteret [02 33 53 86 91] Fr Cherbourg take D904 to Carteret, turn R onto D902, site by disused rlwy stn & nr Tourist Office. Med, hdg pitch, shd; wc (some cont); chem disp; shwrs inc; el pts (3-6A) €2.10-5; lndtte; shops adj; rest 200m; snacks; playgrnd; sand beach 500m; 20% statics; poss cr; adv bkg; quiet; CCI. "Pleasant seaside resort with excel beaches, daily boat in summer to Guernsey & Jersey; pitches soft in wet weather; well-kept site." 1 Apr-28 Sep. € 16.00   2004*

BARREME *10E3* (S Urban) Camping Napoleon, 04330 Barreme [04 92 34 22 70 or 04 92 34 24 91; fax 04 92 34 26 86] On N85 fr Nice, site sp at bdge on ent vill. Med, shd; wc; shwrs; el pts (10A) €2.50; ice; lndry rm; rest; playgrnd; rv fishing & sw adj; entmnt; TV; quiet; Eng spkn; CCI. "Gd long/sh stay; poss mosquitoes Jul; explore fossils locally; nice position by rv; narr gauge rlwy runs alongside camp so some noise; v helpful Belgian owners." 1 May-30 Sep. € 10.00   2002*

BARZAN PLAGE see Cozes *7B1*

BASTIDE DE SEROU, LA *8G3* (1km S Rural) Camping L'Arize, Route de Nescus, 09240 La Bastide-de-Serou [05 61 65 81 51; fax 05 61 65 83 34; camparize@aol.com; www. camping-arize.com] Fr Foix on D117 on ent La Bastide-de-Serou turn L at Gendarmerie on D15 sp Nescus, site 1km on R. Med, hdg/mkd pitch, pt shd; wc; chem disp; mv service pnt; baby facs; shwrs inc; el pts 6A) inc (poss rev pol); gas; lndtte; shop & 2km; tradsmn; rest adj; snacks; playgrnd; pool; lake sw 5km; fishing; golf 5km; horseriding adj; golf nr; 10% statics; dogs €1.50; poss cr; Eng spkn; adv bkg; cc acc; CCI. "V pleasant on bank Rv Arize; wonderful scenery; modern facs; gd walking/cycle rtes well mkd." ◆ ltd. 27 Mar-6 Nov. € 22.60   2005*

BAUBIGNY see Barneville Carteret *1C4*

FRANCE

BAUD *2F3* (1km Urban) **Camp Municipal, Ave Corbel du Squirio,** 56150 Baud [02 97 51 02 29; fax 02 97 39 07 22] D768 Auray-Baud; turn L on ent town at RH bend. Well sp. Sm, v sl, shd; wc (cont); chem disp; shwrs; el pts (10A) €1.83; shops adj. "Poss problem siting on uneven ground bet trees; fair sh stay." 15 Jun-15 Sep. € 5.30   2002*

BAUD *2F3* (3.5km S Rural) **Camp Municipal du Petit Bois, Route de Lambel-Camors,** 56330 Camors [02 97 39 18 36 or 02 97 39 22 06; fax 02 97 39 28 99] S fr Baud on D768 to Camors. Sp in vill. Sm, mkd pitch, pt sl, terr, unshd; wc; chem disp; mv service pnt; shwrs inc; el pts (6A) €1.75; lndry rm; lndtte; playgrnd; horseriding adj; adv bkg; quiet; CCI. "Pleasant surroundings; vg facs; well-managed site; vg long/sh stay." ♦ 1 Jul-31 Aug. € 6.10   2002*

BAUD *2F3* (7km W) **Camping de la Vallee du Blavet, Pont Augan,** 56150 Baud [02 97 51 04 74 or 02 97 51 09 37 (LS); fax 02 97 39 07 23] Fr Pontivy-Josselin join N24 to next junc; R on D172; foll sp Bubry-Quistinic; fr Auray N on D768 to Baud, W on D3, foll sp Bubry-Quistinic. Sm, hdg/mkd pitch, pt shd; htd wc; chem disp (wc only); mv service pnt; baby facs; shwrs inc; el pts (10A) €2; lndtte; rest, snacks & bar 500m; playgrnd; pool; fishing/canoeing in lake on site or in Rv Blavet adj; dogs; quiet; adv bkg; no cc acc; CCI. "V quiet & peaceful; barrier & office ltd opening hrs but parking area at end; excel long stay." ♦ ltd. 1 Apr-30 Sep. € 8.80   2003*

BAUGE *4G1* (1km E Rural) **Camp Municipal, Chemin du Pont des Fees,** 49150 Bauge [02 41 89 14 79 or 02 41 89 18 07 (Mairie); fax 02 41 84 12 19] Fr Saumur traveling N N147/D938 turn 1st R in Bauge onto D766. Foll camping sp to site by sm rv; ent bef rv bdge. Sm, hdg pitch, shd; wc; chem disp; shwrs inc; el pts (4A) €2.20; lndtte; shops 1km; BBQ; 2 pools & 2 tennis courts 150m; fishing; phone; adv bkg; quiet. "Excel countryside; office open 0700-1100 & 1700-2000." 15 May-15 Sep. € 8.00   2005*

BAULE, LA *2G3* (2km NE) **Airotel La Roseraie, 20 Ave Jean Sohier, Route du Golf,** 44500 La Baule-Escoublac [02 40 60 46 66; fax 02 40 60 11 84; camping@laroseraie.com; www.laroseraie.com] Take N171 fr St Nazaire to La Baule. In La Baule-Escoublac turn R at x-rds by church, site in 300m on R; sp fr La Baule cent. Lge, hdg/mkd pitch, pt shd; wc (some cont); chem disp; mv service pnt; baby facs; fam bthrm; shwrs inc; el pts (6A) €5; gas; lndtte; shop; tradsmn; rest; snacks; bar; BBQ; playgrnd; htd, covrd pool; paddling pool; waterslide; sand beach 2km; fishing; watersports; tennis; games area; games rm; entmnt; TV rm; 50% statics; dogs €4.50; phone; Eng spkn; adv bkg (dep req); quiet; cc acc; red long stay; CCI. "Well-kept, pleasant site." ♦ ltd. 1 Apr-30 Sep. € 23.00 (CChq acc)   2005*

†BAULE, LA *2G3* (5km NE Rural) **Camping Les Chalands Fleuris, Rue du Stade,** 44117 St Andre-des-Eaux [02 40 01 20 40; fax 02 40 91 54 24; chalfleu@club-internet.fr; www.chalandsfleuris.com] W fr St Nazaire on N171. Take 1st exit to St Andre-des-Eaux; fr town cent foll site sp 800m. Lge, hdg/mkd pitch, pt shd, serviced pitch; wc; mv service pnt; chem disp; serviced pitches; shwrs inc; el pts (3-6A) €2.75-3.30; gas; lndtte; ice, shop, tradsmn high ssn; snacks; bar; playgrnd; htd, covrd pool; sand beach 8km; fishing; tennis; golf 2km; games rm; TV; entmnt; child entmnt; 15% statics; dogs €2.30; adv bkg; quiet; red long stay/low ssn; cc acc; red CCI. "Site adj to 'Village Fleuris', v beautiful display all thro vill." ♦ ltd. € 20.00   2004*

BAULE, LA *2G3* (1km E Coastal) **Camping Le Bois d'Amour, Ave Capitaine R Flandrin & Allee de Diane,** 44500 La Baule [02 40 60 17 40; fax 02 40 60 10 01] Fr Ave du Bois d'Amour bear L & immed under rlwy bdge, turn R at traff lts. Ent to site on R. Lge, mkd pitch, pt shd; wc; shwrs inc; el pts (6A) inc; gas; ice; lndtte; shops & rest 500m; sand beach 1km; 50% statics; bus & railway adj; poss cr; adv bkg; quiet, but some rd/rlwy noise at site perimeter; CCI. "Useful NH, some pitches v sm; sm area for tourers." ♦ 15 Mar-30 Sep. € 18.45   2002*

BAUME LES DAMES *6G2* (12km N Rural) **Camping du Bois de Reveuge, Route de Rougemont, 25680 Huanne-Montmartin** [03 81 84 38 60; fax 03 81 84 44 04; info@campingduboisdereveuge. com; www.campingduboisdereveuge.com] Exit A36 junc 5 Baume-les-Dames onto D50 dir Rougemont-Villersexel. Foll camping sp for 9km. Site is 1km N of Huanne. Lge, mkd pitch, pt sl, terr, pt shd; wc (some cont); mv service pnt; chem disp; baby facs; shwrs inc; el pts (6A) inc; gas; ice; lndtte; shop & 4km; tradsmn; snacks; pizzeria; bar; playgrnd; 3 htd pools, (1 covrd); waterslides; fishing lake with pedaloes; sand beach 15km; sailing school; mini-golf; cycle hire; archery; horseriding; rockclimbing; fishing; games area; entmnt; child entmnt; excursions; TV rm; dogs €2; Eng spkn; adv bkg; quiet; cc acc; red low ssn; CCI. "Superb staff & management; lge pitches; wonderful countryside; gd walking, birdwatching, watersports; free activities; gd touring base." ♦ 22 Apr-16 Sep. € 30.00 (CChq acc)   2005*

See advertisement opposite

BAUME LES DAMES *6G2* (6km S Rural) **Camping L'Ile, 25110 Pont-les-Moulins** [03 81 84 15 23; info@campingdelile.fr] S fr Baume-les-Dames on D50, site on L on ent Pont-les-Moulins. Med, pt shd; wc (some cont); chem disp; shwrs inc; el pts (6A) €2.20; gas; lndtte; shops 6km; playgrnd; pool 6km; Eng spkn; adv bkg; rd noise; CCI. "Pleasant setting by Rv Cusancin; helpful, friendly owner; clean facs but basic, superb rest La Source Bleu 6km." 15 Apr-15 Sep. € 10.40   2005*

BAUME LES MESSIEURS see Lons le Saunier *6H2*

BAUME, LA *9A3* **Camp Municipal La Baume, 74430 La Baume** [04 50 72 10 06 (Mairie); fax 04 50 72 10 85] Take D902 twd Thonon-Les-Bains. Site on R after sp to La Baume vill. Sm, terr, pt shd; wc; shwrs; el pts (3-10A) €1.50-3.10; shops 5km; playgrnd; adv bkg; quiet. "Old but clean facs; gd sh stay/NH." 1 Jul-31 Aug. € 6.90   2002*

BAYEUX *3D1* (1km N Urban) **Camp Municipal, Blvd Peripherique d'Eindhoven, 14400 Bayeux** [tel/fax 02 31 92 08 43] Site sp off Peripherique d'Eindhoven (Bayeux by-pass, N13); fr W site almost opp Briconaut DIY store; fr E immed after ent Bayeux (town sp). Fr Bayeux, site N off inner ring rd. Lge, pt shd, some hdg pitch, some hdstg; wc (some cont); chem disp; mv service pnt; shwrs inc; el pts (5A) inc; gas; lndtte; ice; shop (Jul/Aug); playgrnd; indoor pool adj (caps ess); sand beach 10km; dogs; phone; some; adv bkg ess high ssn; rd noise; 10% red 5+ days; CCI. "Friendly helpful staff; gd, well-kept site; clean facs; avoid perimeter pitches (narr hdstgs & rd noise); no twin-axles; hdstgs problem for lge o'fits; conv for ferries; 10 min walk to town; lge mkt Sat; no access to site 1000-1400 low ssn." ♦ 1 May-30 Sep. € 12.63   2005*

BAYEUX *3D1* (6km SE Rural) **LES CASTELS Le Chateau de Martragny, 14740 Martragny** [02 31 80 21 40; fax 02 31 08 14 91; chateau. martragny@wanadoo.fr; www.chateau-martragny. com or www.les-castels.com] Fr Caen going NW on N13 dir Bayeux/Cherbourg, leave at Martragny/ Carcagny exit. Strt on & take 2nd R (past turn for Martragny/Creully) into site & chateau grounds. Fr Bayeux go SE on N13 take Martragny/Carcagny exit, turn L, cross bdge, L again, 2nd R into site. Lge, some mkd pitch, pt sl, pt shd; wc; chem disp (ltd in ssn); baby facs; shwrs inc; el pts (6A) inc (long lead poss req, poss rev pol); gas; lndtte; shop; snacks; bar; BBQ; playgrnd; htd pool; sand beach 10km; fishing; tennis; mini-golf; cycle hire; horseriding 500m; TV/games rm; entmnt; static tents; dogs; recep 0830-2000; Eng spkn; adv bkg; quiet; red low ssn; cc acc; CCI. "Busy site; attractive surroundings; friendly recep; helpful staff; poss long trek to san facs, stretched high ssn; nr Bayeux Tapestry, Calvados chateaux & D-Day beaches; Sat mkt in Bayeux; vg." ♦ 1 May-15 Sep. € 24.00 (CChq acc) ABS - N06   2005*

†BAYEUX *3D1* (8km SE Rural) **Manoir de l'Abbaye a la Ferme (Godfroy), 15 Rue de Creully, 14740 Martragny** [tel/fax 02 31 80 25 95; yvette.godfroy@libertysurf.fr] Take N13 Bayeux, Caen dual c'way for 7km, fork R sp Martagny & Creully site on R 500m. Sm, pt shd; wc; chem disp; shwrs; el pts (10A) inc (rev pol); lndtte; tradsmn; dogs €1; Eng spkn; adv bkg; CCI. "Conv for tapestry, D-Day museums; peaceful, well-kept site; helpful, friendly owners; meals & wine avail on request; winter storage; excel welcome." ♦ ltd. € 15.50   2005*

BAYEUX *3D1* (6km NW Rural) **Camping La Vignette, Route de Crouay, 14400 Tour-en-Bessin** [tel/fax 02 31 21 52 83; relais.vignette@ wanadoo.fr] Fr Bayeux take N13 sp Cherbourg. Leave N13 junc 38 sp Tour-en-Bessin. At end of vill turn L sp Crouay, at T-junc turn R & foll sp to site. Sm, unshd; wc; shwrs inc; el pts (5A) €2.50; supmkt 8km; sand beach 12km; v quiet. "Rustic facs; friendly owners, long lead req (1 el pts post only); gd CL-type site." Easter-31 Oct. € 8.50   2003*

BAYEUX *3D1* (9km NW) **Camping Reine Mathilde, 14400 Etreham** [02 31 21 76 55; fax 02 31 22 18 33; camping.reine.mathilde@ wanadoo.fr; www.campingreinemathilde.com] NW fr Bayeux on D6 turn L to Etreham (D100); site 3km (sp). Or W fr Bayeux on N13 for 8km, exist junc 38. At x-rds 1.5km after vill of Tour-en-Bessin turn R on D206 to Etreham & bear L at Etreham church. Med, hdg/mkd pitch, pt shd; wc; chem disp; shwrs inc; el pts (6A) €4.30; lndtte; ice; shop 4km; rest & snacks (high ssn); playgrnd; htd pool; sand beach 5km; cycle hire; fishing 1km; entmnts; TV; 15% statics; dogs €2.30; phone; adv bkg; quiet; CCI. "Helpful warden; conv for invasion beaches; vg long/sh stay." ♦ 1 Apr-30 Sep. € 17.30   2005*

FRANCE

BAYON *6E2* (Rural) **Camp Municipal du Passetemps, Rue de la Moselle, 54290 Bayon [03 83 72 51 52 (Mairie)]** Fr N57 N fr Charmes or S fr Nancy; turn onto D9 sp Bayon; in 2.5km strt on at x-rds & over bridge; site on L in 500m by Rv Moselle. Med, pt shd; wc (some cont); chem disp; shwrs; el pts; shop in vill; playgrnd; sports facs adj; rv adj; 50% statics; quiet. "Rv adj liable to dry out & also flood - care in wet weather; barrier clsd 2200-0700; conv sh stay in special area for tourers." € 11.15   2002*

> Mustn't forget to post our site report forms to The Club, otherwise sites might be deleted.

BAYONNE *8F1* (8km NE Rural) **Aire Naturelle (Barret), L'Arrayade, 40390 St Martin-de-Seignanx [05 59 56 10 60]** On D26 midway bet N10 & N117, 3km W of St Martin. (Opp tall crenellated building). Sm, pt sl, pt shd; wc; shwrs; el pts inc (long lead rec); quiet. "V helpful owner; gd welcome; simple facs poss facs stretched high ssn." 1 Apr-30 Sep. € 11.50   2002*

†**BAYONNE** *8F1* (10km NE) **Camping Le Ruisseau, 40390 St Andre-de-Seignanx [tel/fax 05 59 56 71 92; campingle@aol.com]** Fr Bayonne, take N117 dir Orthez. Turn L after 10km at traff lts in St Martin & foll sp for 5km to site. Sp fr all dir. Take care on ent - by rd junc. Med, hdg/mkd pitch, terr, pt shd; wc; chem disp; 15% serviced pitches; shwrs inc; el pts (6A) €3.20; ice; lndtte; shop; tradsmn; rest, snacks & bar 1km; playgrnd; pool; sand beach 10km; TV; 20% statics; dogs €1.20; adv bkg; quiet; red long stay/low ssn; CCI ess. "Away fr busy coastal area; owner v helpful; not suitable for long/wide vans." € 14.00   2003*

BAYONNE *8F1* (11km NE Rural) **Camping Lou P'tit Poun, 110 Ave du Quartier Neuf, 40390 St Martin-de-Seignanx [05 59 56 55 79; fax 05 59 56 53 71; contact@louptitpoun.com; www. louptitpoun.com]** Exit A63 junc 6 sp Bayonne Nord, take N117 dir Pau, site sp in 7km. Lge, mkd pitch, terr, pt shd; wc; chem disp; mv service pnt; serviced pitch; shwrs inc; el pts (6A) €3.50; gas; lndtte; ice; shop 4km; tradsmn; snacks; bar; BBQ (el/gas); playgrnd; pool; sand beach 10km; tennis; games area; cycle hire; entmnt; child entmnt; TV rm; 17% statics; dogs €4; phone; Eng spkn; adv bkg; quiet; red low ssn; cc acc; CCI. "V friendly, family-run site; conv Biarritz, St Jean-de-Luz." ♦ 1 Jun-16 Sep. € 23.50 ABS - A39   2005*

See advertisement

BAZAS *7D2* (2km E Rural) **Camping Le Grand Pre, Route de Casteljaloux, 33430 Bazas [05 56 65 13 17; fax 05 56 25 90 52; legrandpre@ wanadoo.fr]** Fr Bordeaux on A62 exit junc 3. Turn R onto D932 & R at 3rd rndabt. Then L at next rndabt onto D655 twd Bazas. Cont thro town cent. Site sp on R in 1km. Sm, hdg/mkd pitch, pt sl, pt shd; wc; chem disp; mv service pnt; baby facs; fam bthrm; shwrs inc; el pts (6-16A) €3.20-4.75; gas; lndtte; ice; shop 2km; tradsmn; bar; playgrnd; htd pool; TV rm; 6% statics; dogs €3; Eng spkn; adv bkg (dep req); quiet; red long stay/low ssn; CCI. "Friendly, relaxed site nr interesting, walled town; v helpful staff; well kept; san facs stretched high ssn; picturesque location, views of chateau & town; footpath to vill; vineyards nr; excel long/sh stay." ♦ 1 Apr-30 Sep. € 22.50   2005*

BAZINVAL see Blangy sur Bresle *3C2*

BAZOUGES SUR LE LOIR see Fleche, La *4G1*

BEAUCENS see Argeles Gazost *8G2*

BEAUGENCY *4F2* (Urban) **Camp Municipal du Val de Flux, Route de Lailly-en-Val, 45190 Beaugency [02 38 44 50 39 or 02 38 44 83 12; fax 02 38 46 49 10; mairie.de.beaugency@wanadoo. fr]** Exit A10 junc 15 onto N152. In Beaugency turn L at water tower onto D925 & again over rd bdge. Site sp on S bank of Rv Loire. Med, mkd pitch, pt shd; htd wc; chem disp; shwrs inc; el pts (6A) €3.05; Indry rm; ice; shop & 500m; rest 1km; snacks; bar; playgrnd; sand beach; rv sw forbidden; fishing; watersports; mini-golf; entmnts; 10% statics; poss cr w/e in ssn; quiet; Eng spkn; red long stay; CCI. "Basic facs stretched high ssn & poss unclean low ssn; pleasant views over Loire; helpful staff; poss itinerants & unruly youths; free 1 night site for m'vans over rv on other side of town." ♦ 1 Apr-31 Aug. € 10.70   2005*

†BEAUGENCY *4F2* (8km S Rural) **FFCC Camping de l'Amitie, Nouan-sur-Loire, 41220 St Laurent-Nouan [02 54 87 01 52; fax 02 54 87 09 93]** On D951 SW fr Orleans cont past power stn into Nouan-sur-Loire. Site on R sp Cmpg de Borg. Med, mkd pitch, pt shd; wc; mv service pnt; shwrs; el pts (10A) €2.30; Indtte; shop 500m; rest 500m; pools & sports activities nr; direct acc to rv; 50% statics; adv bkg; quiet; 10% red CCI. "Interesting area; workers resident on site; friendly staff; phone ahead low ssn to check open." € 8.80   2004*

†BEAULIEU SUR DORDOGNE *7C4* **Camping Les Iles, 19120 Beaulieu-sur-Dordogne [05 55 91 02 65; fax 05 55 91 05 19; jycastenet@aol.com; www. camping-des-iles.net]** On D940 fr Bretenoux, turn R in Beaulieu town sq, site about 200m on island in Rv Dordogne. 3m height limit at ent. Med, shd; wc; baby facs; shwrs inc; el pts (10A) €2.90 (poss long lead req); Indtte; Indry rm; ice; shops adj; snacks; bar; playgrnd; pool; rv sw; sports area; entmnt high ssn; cycle, canoe hire; archery; 15% statics; dogs €1.50; poss cr; Eng spkn; adv bkg rec; quiet; red long stay/low ssn. "Delightful, wooded site in beautiful surroundings; 3 mins walk fr cent of attractive vill; facs stretched high ssn; highly rec." € 17.90   2005*

BEAULIEU SUR LOIRE *4G3* (E Rural) **Camp Municipal Touristique du Canal, Route de Bonny, 45630 Beaulieu-sur-Loire [02 38 35 89 56; fax 02 38 35 86 57; beaulieu-sur-loire@ libertysurf.fr]** Exit A77 junc 21 Bonny-sur-Loire, cross rv to Beaulieu-sur-Loire on D296. On E o'skirts of vill on D926, nr canal. Sm, hdg/mkd pitch, pt shd; wc; chem disp; shwrs inc; el pts (6A) €2.50; Indry rm; shop 2km; rest adj; snacks, bar 500m; playgrnd; poss cr; adv bkg; CCI. "Mkt Wed; walking along canal/Loire; boat trips." ♦ Easter-1 Nov. € 5.60   2005*

BEAUMES DE VENISE see Carpentras *10E2*

BEAUMONT DE LOMAGNE *8E3* (E Urban) **Camp Le Lomagnol (formerly Municipal Le Lac), 82500 Beaumont-de-Lomagne [tel/fax 05 63 65 26 43]** On SE of D928 at E end of vill. Med, pt shd; wc; chem disp; jaccuzi; shwrs inc; el pts (10A) €3; Indtte; ice; shop; rest; snacks; bar; playgrnd; pool; sauna; waterslide; lake sw; tennis; cycle & canoe hire; golf; sailing; 25% statics; dogs €1.50; quiet. "Gd quality, modern site; v interesting old town; excel NH." ♦ Easter-30 Sep. € 11.00   2004*

BEAUMONT HAGUE *1C4* (5km N Rural/Coastal) **Camp Municipal du Hable, 50440 Omonville-la-Rogue [02 33 52 86 15 or 02 33 01 86 00; fax 02 33 01 86 01]** W fr Cherbourg on D901 to Beaumont-Hague; turn N onto D45 dir Omonville-la-Rogue. Med, hdg/mkd pitch, hdstg, pt shd; wc; chem disp; mv service pnt; shwrs inc; el pts (5-10A) €2.50-4; Indry rm; shop, gas adj; rest; bar; playgrnd; beach 100m; dogs €0.90; quiet; CCI. "In pretty vill with gd harbour, 30 mins fr Cherbourg; gd NH." 1 Apr-30 Sep. € 8.20   2004*

BEAUMONT SUR OISE *3D3* (8km SW Rural) **Parc de Sejour de l'Etang, Chemin des Bellevues, 95690 Nesles-la-Vallee [01 34 70 62 89; brehinier1@hotmail.com]** Fr D927 Meru-Pontoise rd, turn L onto D64 at sp L'Isle Adam. After passing thro Nesles-la-Vallee camp sp on L. Med, hdg pitch, pt shd; wc (cont); serviced pitches; shwrs inc; el pts (3A) €2.75 (rev pol); Indtte; ice; shops 1km; playgrnd; lake fishing adj; 90% statics; dogs €1; Eng spkn; quiet. "Lovely peaceful setting; helpful; conv day trips to Paris; gd sh stay." 1 Mar-31 Oct. € 12.00   2003*

BEAUMONT SUR SARTHE *4F1* (E Urban) **Camp Municipal du Val de Sarthe, 72170 Beaumont-sur-Sarthe [02 43 97 01 93; fax 02 43 97 02 21; beaumont.sur.sarthe@wanadoo.fr]** Fr N138 Alencon-Le Mans, turn L at traff lts in cent of Beaumont & foll site sp twd E of town. Fr Le Mans on A28 exit 21 onto D6, R onto N138 & R at traff lts & foll sp. Med, hdg/mkd pitch, pt shd; wc; chem disp; mv service pnt; shwrs inc; el pts (5A) €2.12; (long cable poss req); Indtte; shops & rest 500m; playgrnd; pool 500m; rv boating & fishing adj; dogs €0.32; poss cr w/e; adv bkg rec high ssn; cc acc; CCI. "Beautiful, peaceful site on bank of Rv Sarthe; immac san facs; dep req for barrier card; no twin-axle & poss no vans over 2,000 kg; barrier clsd 2200; close to pretty, sm town; excel." ♦ 1 May-30 Sep. € 5.40   2005*

FRANCE

BEAUNE *6H1* (1km NE Urban) **Camp Municipal Les Cent Vignes, 10 Rue Auguste-Dubois, 21200 Beaune** [03 80 22 03 91 or 03 80 22 20 80 (Mairie)] Fr N on A31 & fr S on A6 at junc with m'ways A6/A31 take A6 sp Auxerre-Paris; after 1km leave m'way at junc 24 to join N74 twd Beaune; after approx 1.5km, turn R at 2nd traff lts fr a'route to site (sp) in 200m. Site well sp fr inner ring rd & foll sp to Dijon (not Autoroute sps) Also sp fr Mersault/ L'Hopital x-rds. Med, hdg/mkd pitch, hdstg, pt shd; htd wc; chem disp; mv service pnt; shwrs inc; el pts (6A) €3.20 (some rev pol); gas; lndry rm; ice; shop; hypmkt 2km; rest; snacks; bar; playgrnd; pool 2km; extensive sports facs; TV; dogs; Eng spkn; adv bkg in writing only bef 30 May; quiet; red long stay; cc acc; CCI. "Excel base for wine country; well-run, clean & busy site; gd san facs; no twin-axles; a few pitches with high hdges for lge o'fits; reasonable sized pitches; narr access rds, tight turns & low trees poss diff for lge o'fits; walking dist of walled town; Beaune worth visit with medieval hospital; rest excel but opens for breakfast & evening meal only; rec arr early as site full by 1400 high ssn; recep open 0800-1230 & 1330-2200; highly rec." 1 Apr-31 Oct. € 11.80   2005*

As we're travelling out of season, we'd better phone ahead to check that the site is actually open.

†**BEAUNE** *6H1* (2km NE Rural) **Camping Les Bouleaux, 21200 Vignoles** [03 80 22 26 88] Do not leave A6 at new Beaune exit (24) but use old exit (junc 24.1); 500m after toll turn R at rndabt, in 1.5km turn R sp Dole rndabt. Immed after x-ing m'way turn L sp Vignoles. L again at next junc then R & foll yellow camping sp. In approx 1.5km in cent Chevignerot ignore ent to 1st chateau, after 100m turn L opp gates of 2nd chateau into Allee du Chateau. After 100m turn R, site in 200m. Fr town cent take D973 (E) sp Dole. In 2km cross a'route & 1st L (N) sp Vignoles. Sm, hdg/mkd pitch, pt shd; htd wc (some cont); chem disp; shwrs inc; el pts (3-6A) inc (rev pol altered on request); lndry rm; shop; tradsmn; supmkt 2km; dogs; adv bkg rec; quiet but some rd noise; red low ssn; CCI. "Arr early high ssn; helpful & friendly owners; pleasant site with tree-lined pitches, shrubs & flowers; some gd sized pitches; tidy & well-kept; superb san facs; poss muddy after rain - park on rdways; conv Beaune & a'route; excel; vg winter NH." ♦ ltd. € 14.20   2005*

BEAUNE *6H1* (8km SW Rural) **Camping La Grappe d'Or, 2 Route de Volnay, 21190 Meursault** [03 80 21 22 48; fax 03 80 21 65 74; info@camping-meursault.com; www.camping-meursault.com] SW on N74/D973 fr Beaune, fork R on D973 sp Autun, fork L on D111 at sp Monthelie & Mersault; camp at ent to Meursault, 300m past motel; care needed at ent - almost U-turn. Also sp fr N74 app Beaune/Meursault fr S. Med, mkd pitch; terr, pt shd; wc; chem disp; shwrs inc; el pts (15A) inc (check pol); gas; lndtte; ice; shop; tradsmn; rest; snacks; bar; playgrnd; pool; tennis; cycle hire; phone; dogs €1.30; poss cr; adv bkg ess in ssn (dep half total charge); some rd noise; red low ssn; CCI. "Facs ltd low ssn & well-used - 1 block in need of refurb; superb views over vineyards; gd food adj motel; barrier clsd 2200-0730; some pitches uneven & sm." ♦ 1 Apr-15 Oct. € 19.00 (CChq acc)   2004*

BEAUNE *6H1* (3km NW Rural) **Camp Municipal Premiers Pres, 21420 Savigny-les-Beaune** [03 80 26 15 06 or 03 80 21 51 21 (Mairie); fax 03 80 21 56 63] Fr Beaune ring rd turn N on N74 sp Dijon; in 200m at traff lts turn L sp Savigny; in 100m ignore camping sp & bear R to Savigny (3km); site 1km thro vill on L. Med, mkd pitch, pt shd; wc; chem disp; mv service pnt; shwrs inc; el pts (10-16A) €3.25 (some rev pol); gas 1.3km; ice; shops 1km; supmkt 3km; playgrnd; dogs; adv bkg; quiet; CCI. "V busy transit site; no twin-axle vans; pleasant site in beautiful area; excel rests in town; facs not adequate if site full & ltd low ssn; cr after 1700 high ssn; warden on site low ssn 0900-1000 & 1900-2000, site yourself; conv A6, A31 & A36; poss itinerant workers at time of grape harvest; excel sh stay/NH." ♦ ltd. 1 May-30 Sep. € 7.50   2005*

BEAURAINVILLE see Hesdin *3B3*

BEAURECUEIL see Aix en Provence *10F3*

BEAUREPAIRE *9C2* (Urban) **Camp Municipal, Ave de Gaulle, 38270 Beaurepaire** [04 76 84 64 89 or 04 74 79 22 60] Sp in town on L of Beaurepaire-Romans rd, adj pool. Med, shd; wc (some cont); shwrs inc; el pts (6A) €1.50; shops 250m; 2 supmkts nr; pool adj; rv fishing. 1 May-15 Sep. € 5.00   2002*

†**BEAUREPAIRE** *9C2* (12km NE Rural) **Camp Municipal des Eydoches, 38260 Faramans** [04 74 54 21 78 or 04 74 54 22 97 (Mairie); fax 04 74 54 20 00] Fr Beaurepaire take D73 to Faramans. Site sp. Med, pt shd; wc; chem disp; shwrs; el pts (5A) €2.80; snacks; shop 500m; lndtte; lake sw; fishing; dogs €1.50; quiet; adv bkg. 1 Apr-Oct. € 10.70   2003*

BEAUREPAIRE *9C2* (10km S) **Camp Municipal du Chateau, 26390 Hauterives** [04 75 68 80 19 or 04 75 68 83 10] Take D538 S to Hauterives, site sp in vill. Med, pt shd; wc; shwrs; el pts (4A); ice; lndtte; snacks; sm supmkt adj; playgrnd; htd pool; rv sw & fishing adj; adv bkg; quiet. "Gd NH; friendly; gd pool." ♦ 1 Apr-15 Oct. € 9.15   2005*

BEAUREPAIRE *9C2* (9km SW) **Camping Chateau de la Perouze, 26210 St Sorlin-en-Valloire [04 75 31 70 21 or 06 70 00 04 74 (mob); fax 04 75 31 62 74; www.lapeyrouse.free.fr]**
Exit Beaurepaire on D130A & D139 sp Manthes for approx 1km; bef St Sorlin turn L at site sp in 1.5km. Med, pt shd; shwrs; wc; shwrs inc; chem disp; baby facs; el pts (6-10A) €2.30-4.20; gas; lndtte; shop; tradsmn; bar; pool; tennis; fishing; sauna; jacuzzi; 30% statics; no dogs; quiet; adv bkg; CCI. "Excel long/sh stay; free sep shd car park; friendly, helpful warden; c'van storage in winter; in 14thC chateau grounds; gates clsd 2100-0900; access to pitches poss diff; narr ent." 15 Jun-15 Sep. € 18.90   2005*

BEAUVAIS *3C3* (Urban) **Camp Municipal, Rue Camard, 60000 Beauvais [03 44 02 00 22]**
On S edge of town. Take Paris rd fr town cent over Pont de Paris; after 200m turn R at Its up Rue Binet (steep). 1st R & site on R. Well sp. Diff steep app but can turn in car park at top of hill. Med, pt sl, pt shd; wc (some cont); shwrs inc; el pts (4A) €1.25; gas; shops in town; playgrnd; pool; tennis adj; poss cr; quiet; CCI. "Gd value; gd sh stay; friendly owner; site self when office clsd; height barrier clsd 1200-1700; phone ahead to check site open low ssn." 1 Jun-30 Aug. € 10.55   2005*

BEAUVAIS *3C3* (6km W) **Camping Le Clos Normand, 1 Rue de l'Abbaye, 60650 St Paul [03 44 82 27 30]**   Exit A16 Beauvais Nord & foll green Rouen sp & St Paul Parc onto N31. Drive thro vill, past abbey. Tight R turn into site. Med, pt sl, shd; htd wc; mv service pnt; shwrs inc; el pts (6A) inc; lndtte; shops 3km; tradsmn;fishing; 80% statics; dogs €2; poss cr; adv bkg; quiet. "Friendly; facs in need of updating; poss scruffy low ssn; fair NH." 1 Apr-30 Sep. € 15.00   2005*

BEAUVILLE *7D3* (500m Rural) **Camping Les Deux Lacs, 47470 Beauville [05 53 95 45 41; fax 05 53 95 45 31; camping-les-2-lacs@wanadoo.fr]**
Fr D656 S to Beauville, site sp on D122. Med, mkd/hdg, terr, shd; wc; chem disp; mv service pnt; shwrs inc; el pts (6A) €2.10; lndtte; rest; snacks; bar; shop 600m; playgrnd; lake sw; games area; fishing; watersports; 10% statics; dogs €1.90; Eng spkn; adv bkg; quiet; red long stay/low ssn; cc acc; CCI. "Peaceful; gd fishing; pleasant walk to vill; Eng newspapers avail; vg." ♦ 1 Feb-30 Nov. € 13.20   2005*

BEAUVOIR see Mont St Michel, Le *2E4*

BEAUVOIR SUR MER *2H3* (4km E Rural) **Camp Municipal St Gervais, 85230 St Gervais [02 51 68 73 14 (Mairie); fax 02 51 68 48 11]**
On D948, 1km E of St Gervais on R of rd. Sm, mkd pitch, pt shd; wc; chem disp; shwrs; el pts inc; gas; lndry rm; shop; BBQ; CCI. "Facs basic but clean; gd sh stay." ♦ 1 Jun-30 Sep. € 8.50   2004*

BEAUVOIR SUR MER *2H3* (4km E Rural) **Camping Le Fief d'Angibaud, 85230 St Gervais [02 51 68 43 08; davidleach1522@wanadoo.fr]**
Fr Beauvoir-sur-Mer E on D948 to St Gervais turn L after PO/Mairie onto D59 twd Bouin (narr ent easy to miss); in 2km pass sm chapel; take 2nd rd on L; site on R after 500m. Sm, unshd; wc; shwrs inc; chem disp; el pts (5A) inc; gas 4km; basic lndry rm; ice; shops 2km; tradsmn; sand beach 5km; fishing/golf nrby; adv bkg rec high ssn; quiet; red CCI. "On farm; v helpful British owners; lge pitches; premium pitches avail; clean facs; conv Ile de Noirmoutier; ferry to Ile d'Yeu, coastal resorts; free parking close to beach (blue flag); gd cycling area." ♦ Easter-31 Oct. € 15.00   2005*

BEC HELLOUIN, LE see Brionne *3D2*

BEDARIEUX *10F1* (8km N) **Camping La Sieste, 34260 La Tour-sur-Orb [04 67 23 72 96; fax 04 67 23 75 38]**   Fr Bedarieux, take D35 N twd Lodeve; site sp after La Tour-sur-Orb; site 3km N of La Tour-sur-Orbe at sm vill of Vereilles. Med, pt shd; wc; chem disp; shwrs inc; el pts (10A) €2.50; ice; lndtte; shop; tradsmn; rest; bar; BBQ; pool open June; rv sw; dogs €1.60; phone; adv bkg; Eng spkn; quiet; poss v cr high ssn; cc acc; 20% red low ssn; 5% red CCI. "V well-kept site; charming owners; unspoilt Languedoc countryside." ♦ 1 Jun-31 Aug. € 11.40   2004*

†**BEDENAC** *7C2* (1km E Rural) **Camping Louvrignac, 17210 Bedenac [05 46 70 31 88; lcarpenter@freenet.co.uk]**   Fr N10 exit sp Bedenac onto D145. Thro Bedenac vill take D158 sp Montguyon & in 500m take 1st L sp Bernadeau. Site on L in 100m - narr rd. Sm, pt shd; own san; chem disp; el pts (10A) inc; tradsmn; shop, rest, snacks, bar 10km; BBQ; htd pool; adv bkg; quiet. "CL-type site with 5 pitches; friendly British owners; rec phone in advance." € 10.00   2004*

BEDOIN see Malaucene *10E2*

BEDUER see Figeac *7D4*

BEGARD *2E2* (2km S Rural) **Camping du Donant, Gwenezhan, 22140 Begard [02 96 45 46 46; fax 02 96 45 46 48; camping.begard@wanadoo.fr; www.camping-donant-bretagne.com]**   Fr N12 at Guingamp take D767 dir Lannion, Perros-Guirec. S of Begard foll sp Armoripark, site sp. Med, hdg/mkd pitch, hdstg, terr, pt shd; wc; chem disp; mv service pnt; shwrs inc; el pts €2.60; gas 1km; lndtte; shop & bar adj; BBQ; playgrnd; htd pool & leisure facs adj; tennis adj; TV rm; statics; dogs; Eng spkn; adv bkg; quiet; cc acc. "In v pleasant countryside; conv coast; gd touring base." ♦ Easter-Mid Sep. € 12.10   2005*

FRANCE

BEGUDE DE MAZENC, LA *9D2* (Rural) **Camping a la Ferme des Roures (Gontard), Route de St Gervias, 26160 La Begude-de-Mazenc** [04 75 46 21 80; gontard.daniel@wanadoo.fr] Fr Montelimar E on D540 for 15km. Turn L onto D74 to St Gervais. Foll sp for site. Sm, pt sl, shd; wc; chem disp; shwrs inc; el pts (10A) €1.75; lndtte; gas & shop 4km; quiet; CCI. "Site in wood; friendly owners; fridge hire; pleasant area." ♦ 1 Apr-30 Sep. € 9.75   2003*

BELFORT *6G3* (1.5km N Urban) **Camping de l'Etang des Forges, 11 Rue Bethouard, 90000 Belfort** [03 84 22 54 92; fax 03 84 22 76 55; contact@campings-belfort.com] Fr A36, take junc 14 onto N83 twds Mulhouse; after 1.5km, turn L onto D22; thro Offermont; foll sp to site. After Belfort town town sp, turn L 10m bef 1st traff lts. Med, hdg/mkd pitch, pt shd; htd wc; chem disp; baby facs; shwrs inc; el pts (6A) €2.80; lndtte; ice; shop 500m; tradsmn high ssn; rest 200m; snacks; bar high ssn; playgrnd; pool; archery; fishing & watersports 50m; TV; entmnts; 10% statics; dogs €1.50; Eng spkn; adv bkg (dep req); quiet; red long stay; cc acc; CCI. "Clean modern san facs; friendly recep; conv for Corbusier's chapel at Ronchamp; vg rest in Belfort." ♦ 12 Apr-30 Sep. € 15.30   2005*

BELGENTIER see Cuers *10F3*

†**BELLAC** *7A3* (Urban) **Camp Municipal Les Rochettes, Rue des Rochettes, 87300 Bellac** [05 55 68 13 27; camping.bellac@wanadoo.fr] On N147 ent Bellac fr Poitiers take sharp L at 1st traff lts onto D675. Cont to rndabt & turn L Foll sp, site on L in 400m adj football pitch. Fr Limoges on N147 take R at 3rd traff lts after ent Bellac ont D675 then foll sp as above. Med, pt sl, pt shd, terr; htd wc; chem disp; mv service pnt; shwrs inc; el pts (10A) €2.50 (long lead poss req); gas; lndry rm; shops 500m; supmkt 1km; bar 500m; playgrnd; pool & waterslide 1km; games area; dogs €0.80; quiet; red long stay; cc not acc. "Pleasant guardian; poss diff if wet; v spacious, pleasant site; able to choose pitch; office clsd 1200-1500; coded barrier clsd 2000-0800; facs poss ltd; poss clsd low ssn - phone ahead." € 9.50   2005*

BELLAC *7A3* (9km SE Rural) **Camping Fontclaire, 87300 Blond** [tel/fax 05 55 60 88 26; fontclair@aol.com] Take D675 S twd St Junien. Site on L in approx 8km, 2km bef Mortemart. Sm, pt shd, wc; chem disp; shwrs inc; el pts (5A) €3 (poss rev pol); gas 1km; lndtte; ice; shop 2km; tradsmn; rest, bar 2km; sm htd pool; lake sw, sand beach 2km; fishing; dogs; phone 2km; Eng spkn; adv bkg (dep req); quiet. "CL-type site with v friendly, helpful British owners; gd facs; sm lake on site for carp fishing; close to Oradour-sur-Glane war-time martyr vill; excel base to explore local sights & Futuroscope." ♦ ltd. € 8.00   2005*

BELLEME *4E2* (Urban) **Camp Municipal Le Val, Route de Mamers, 61130 Belleme** [02 33 85 31 00 (Mairie); fax 02 33 83 58 85; mairie.belleme@wanadoo.fr] Fr Mortagne, take D938 S to Belleme; turn R ent town on D955 Alencon rd; site sp on L half-way down hill. Sm, pt sl, unshd; wc (mainly cont); shwrs inc; el pts (13A) inc; shops 1km by footpath; supmkt nrby; playgrnd, pool, tennis adj; fishing; adv bkg rec high ssn. "Pretty, park-like site; well-maintained; poor security; v long el cables req for many pitches; gd san facs; some pitches steep/v sl; cherry & lime trees; steep walk into town." 15 Apr-15 Oct. € 7.40   2005*

BELLENTRE see Aime *9B3*

BELLEY *9B3* (8km E Rural) **Camping Lac du Lit au Roi, 01300 Massignieu-de-Rives** [04 79 42 12 03; fax 04 79 42 19 94; acamp@wanadoo.fr] Fr N504 turn E onto D992 to Massignieu-de-Rives, site sp. Med, hdg/mkd pitch, terr, pt shd; htd wc; chem disp; shwrs inc; el pts (10A) €3; gas; lndtte; ice; shop 8km; tradsmn; snacks; bar; BBQ; playgrnd; pool; lake sw & beach; boating; tennis; TV rm; 20% statics; dogs €3.50; phone; Eng spkn; adv bkg (fee); red long stay; cc acc; CCI. "Many pitches on lake with lovely views; superb site; excel long/sh stay." ♦ Easter-27 Oct. € 16.00   2003*

BELMONT SUR RANCE *8E4* (Rural) **Camping Val Fleuri du Rance, Route de Lacaune, 12370 Belmont-sur-Rance** [05 65 99 95 13; fax 05 65 99 95 82] On D32 on ent vill fr SW; on L side of rd on sh unmade service rd. Sm, hdg/mkd pitch, pt shd; wc; chem disp; shwrs inc; el pts (6A); gas; lndry rm; shop 500m; rest; pool 500m; fishing; tennis; adv bkg; quiet; CCI. "Attractive valley setting; helpful staff; easy walk to attract sm town; diff ent/exit to/fr south." ♦ ltd. 1 Jun-15 Sep.   2004*

BELVES *7D3* (4km N) **Camping Le Port, 24170 Siorac-en-Perigord** [05 53 28 63 81 or 05 53 31 60 29] On D25 in vill turn down beside Intermarche supmkt. Site ent strt ahead. Med, mkd pitch, shd; wc; shwrs; el pts (10A) inc; lndtte; shops 1km; playgrnd; rv beach, sw & fishing; adv bkg rec; quiet. 15 May-30 Sep. € 15.00   2004*

BELVES *7D3* (7km SE Rural) **LES CASTELS Les Hauts de Ratebout, 24170 Belves** [05 53 29 02 10; fax 05 53 29 08 28; camping@hauts-ratebout.fr; www.hauts-ratebout.fr or www.les-castels.com] Turn E onto D54 2km S of Belves & foll camp sp. Lge, pt sl, terr, pt shd; htd wc; chem disp; shwrs inc; el pts inc (10A) inc; rest; snacks; bar; shop; gas; lndtte; covr'd pool & paddling pool; waterslide; tennis; golf; fishing; horseriding; entmnt; adv bkg Jul/Aug (dep req); Eng spkn; cc acc; CCI. "Excel hilltop site; adv bkg pitch requests poss not honoured; gd cent for touring." ♦ 24 Apr-4 Sep. € 31.00   2003*

BELVES *7D3* (2km S Rural) **Camping Le Moulin de la Pique, 24170 Belves [05 53 29 01 15; fax 05 53 28 29 09; camping@perigord.com; www. rcn-campings.fr]** Site sp S of Belves on L. Med, shd; wc; chem disp; shwrs inc; el pts (6A) inc; lndtte; shop; rest; snacks; bar; playgrnd; pools (1 htd) & paddling pool; waterslides; tennis; entmnt; TV; boating; fishing; some statics; dogs €2.50; Eng spkn; adv bkg; red low ssn. "Monpazier beautiful; expensive for sh stay but vg for children; clean & well-maintained site; poss soft in wet weather; expanding; gd Sat mkt." ♦ 17 Apr-19 Oct. € 25.00
2004*

BELVES *7D3* (4km SW Rural) **Domaine Les Nauves, Le Bos-Rouge, 24170 Belves [05 53 29 12 64 or 05 53 29 07 87; fax 05 53 29 07 87; camping-les-nauves@hotmail. com; www.campings-dordogne.com/les-nauves/]** On D53 fr Belves. Site on L just after junc to Larzac. Med, pt sl, pt shd; wc; chem disp; mv service pnt; shwrs inc; el pts (6A) €2.70; lndtte; ice; shop adj; snacks; bar; BBQ; playgrnd; pool; paddling pool; games rm; horseriding; cycle hire; entmnt; TV; some statics; dogs €2; adv bkg; quiet. "Excel site; Belves lovely town." ♦ 5 Apr-27 Sep. € 14.55   2003*

BELVES *7D3* (2km NW Rural) **Camping La Lenotte, 24170 Monplaisant [tel/fax 05 53 30 25 80 or 06 89 33 05 60; campinglanotte@libertysurf.fr; www.la-lenotte.com]** Fr Sarlat take D57 twds Beynac, turn R in vill onto the D703, at Siorac turn L onto the D710 twd Belves. Site on L in 2km. Med, hdg/mkd pitch, pt shd; wc; chem disp; mv service pnt; 80% serviced pitches; baby facs; shwrs inc; el pts (6A) €2.80; gas; lndtte; ice; shop; tradsmn; snacks; BBQ; playgrnd; pool; shgl beach 3km; mini-golf; cycling; rv sw & fishing 3km; 5% statics; dogs €2.50; phone; Eng spkn; adv bkg; quiet but some rd noise; red CCI. "Beautiful scenery; nr old castles & Bastide towns; Belves magnificent medieval town; helpful owner." ♦ ltd. 1 Apr-31 Oct. € 14.00   2004*

BENODET *2F2* (Urban/Coastal) **Camping Le Trez, 9 Rue des Peupliers, 29118 Benodet [tel/fax 02 98 57 15 94]** Fr N ent town on D34. At rndabt after junc with D44 (Pont l'Abbe) strt onto Rue Penfoul. At next rndabt (tourist info office on R after rndabt) go strt dir La Plage until reach seafront. Turn L at end of prom & L into Rue de Kersale, site sp. Fr E on N165 take D44 sp Fouesnant & foll rd to outskirts Benodet. After town sp, site is sp. Lge, pt shd; wc; chem disp; baby facs; shwrs inc; el pts (3-6A) €2-€3.05; snacks; ice; shops adj; htd pool; sand beach 200m; playgrnd; tennis; dogs €0.65; adv bkg; quiet. ♦ 1 Jun-15 Sep. € 15.55   2002*

BENODET *2F2* (500m SE Coastal) **Camping de la Plage, Rue du Poulquer, 29950 Benodet [02 98 57 00 55; fax 02 98 57 12 60; laplage benodet@aol.com]** Fr N ent town on D34. At rndabt after junc with D44 (Pont l'Abbe) strt onto Rue Penfoul. At next rndabt (tourist info office on R after rndabt) go strt dir La Plage until reach seafront. Turn L at end of prom twd Le Letty & L after Les Horizons development into Rue du Poulquer; site in 200m on L. Fr E on N165 take D44 sp Fouesnant & foll rd to outskirts Benodet. After town sp, site is sp. Lge, hdg pitch, pt sl, pt shd; wc; baby facs; shwrs inc; el pts (6-10A) €3.20-4; lndtte; ice; shop; bar; snacks; playgrnd; htd pool; waterslide; sand beach 300m; child entmnt; many statics; dogs €2.30; poss cr; adv bkg; red low ssn. 15 May-30 Sep. € 20.40
2003*

BENODET *2F2* (500m SE Coastal) **Camping du Poulquer, Route de Letty, 29950 Benodet [02 98 57 04 19; fax 02 98 66 20 30; campingdu poulquer@wanadoo.fr; www.campingdu poulquer.com]** Fr N ent town on D34. At rndabt after junc with D44 strt onto Rue Penfoul. At next rndabt (tourist info office on R after rndabt) go strt dir La Plage until reach seafront. Turn L at end of prom at camping sp; site in 100m on R. Fr E on N165 take D44 sp Fouesnant & foll rd to outskirts Benodet. After town sp, site is sp. Med, hdg/mkd pitch, pt sl, pt shd; wc (some cont); chem disp; shwrs inc; el pts (10A) inc (long lead poss req); gas; lndtte; shop, snacks, bar high ssn; BBQ; playgrnd; htd pool & paddling pool; waterslide; aqua park; sand beach adj; tennis; golf nr; cycle hire 1km; games rm; entmnt; dogs €1.22; recep 0830-2000; c'vans over 7.50m not acc high ssn; adv bkg; quiet; cc not acc; CCI. "Friendly, helpful owner; easy walk to beach & town; gd base; gd, clean san facs; pitches tight for lge o'fits; low branches on access rd; gd hotel rest 600m; mkt Mon; ideal for visiting Isles de Glenan." ♦ 15 May-30 Sep. € 25.00
ABS - B16   2005*

BENODET *2F2* (2km SE Coastal) **Camping Sunelia La Pointe St Gilles, Rue Poulmic, 29950 Benodet [02 98 57 05 37; fax 02 98 57 27 52; information@camping-stgilles.fr; www.camping-stgilles.fr]** Fr N ent town on D34. At rndabt after junc with D44 (Pont l'Abbe) strt onto Rue Penfoul. At next rndabt (tourist info office on R after rndabt) go strt dir La Plage until reach seafront. Turn L at end of prom twd Le Letty & L after Les Horizons development into Rue du Poulquer; site in 200m on L. Fr E on N165 take D44 sp Fouesnant & foll rd to outskirts Benodet. After town sp, site is sp. Lge, hdg pitch, pt shd; wc; shwrs inc; el pts (10A) inc; gas; lndtte; ice; shop; snacks; htd pool & paddling pool; jacuzzi; waterslide; sand beach adj; 90% statics; no dogs; phone; poss cr; adv bkg; quiet; red long stay; cc acc. "Pleasant town, gd beaches; rv trips; well-run site; helpful staff; ltd touring pitches in sep area." 13 Apr-18 Sep. € 38.00 (CChq acc)   2005*

FRANCE

BENODET *2F2* (7km W Coastal) **Camping Le Helles, 55 Rue du Petit-Bourg, 29120 Combrit-Ste Marine [02 98 56 31 46; fax 02 98 56 36 83; contact@le-helles.com; www.le-helles.com]** Exit D44 S dir Ste Marine, site sp. Med, mkd pitch, pt sl, pt shd; htd wc; chem disp; baby facs; shwrs; el pts (6-10A) €3.30-4.10; lndtte; tradsmn; snacks; BBQ; playgrnd; htd pool; paddling pool; sand beach 300m; some statics; dogs €2.50; Eng spkn; adv bkg; quiet; cc acc; red low ssn. "Vg site; friendly, helpful staff; excel beach." ♦ 1 May-16 Sep. € 17.50   2005*

See advertisement

BENODET *2F2* (1km NW) **Camping du Port de Plaisance, Route de Quimper, Clohars-Fouesnant, 29950 Benodet [tel/fax 02 98 57 02 38 or 02 98 57 14 69; info@campingbenodet.com]** Fr Benodet take D34 twd Quimper, site on R 200m bef rndabt at ent to town. Lge, hdg pitch; pt sl, pt shd; wc; chem disp; mv service pnt; shwrs inc; child/baby facs; el pts (6-10A) €2.30-3.10; lndtte; shop; tradsmn; rest; snacks; bar; playgrnd; htd pool; sand/shgl beach 1.5km; entmnt; 80% statics; dogs €2.30; phone; poss cr; Eng spkn; poss noisy (disco); adv bkg; red low ssn; cc acc.; CCI. "Many tour ops on site; some pitches poss diff lge o'fits; gd sh stay." ♦ ltd. 1 May-30 Sep. € 24.50   2003*

BENON see Courcon *7A2*

BENOUVILLE see Ouistreham *3D1*

BERAUT see Condom *8E2*

BERCK *3B2* (4km E Rural) **Camping L'Oree du Bois, Chemin Blanc, 62180 Rang-du-Fliers [03 21 84 28 51; fax 03 21 84 28 56; oree.du.bois@wanadoo.fr; www.loreedubois.com]** Exit A6 junc 25 onto D140 & D917. Thro Rang-du-Fliers, turn R bef pharmacy into Chemin Blanc, site sp. V lge, hdg/mkd pitch, pt shd; wc (some cont); mv service pnt; chem disp; mv service pnt; serviced pitches; shwrs inc; el pts (6A) inc; gas; shop adj; lndtte; tradsmn; rest; snacks; bar; playgrnd; sand beach 4km; tennis; gamea area; fishing lake; cycle hire; entmnt; 80% statics; dogs €2; Eng spkn; adv bkg; quiet; cc acc; red low ssn/long stay/CCI. "V conv Le Touquet; Boulogne; Montreuil; peaceful site in woodland; ltd facs low ssn; ltd space for tourers." ♦ 1 Apr-24 Oct. € 21.00   2005*

BERGERAC *7C3* (500m S Urban) **Camp Municipal La Pelouse, 8 bis Rue JJ Rousseau, 24100 Bergerac [tel/fax 05 53 57 06 67; tourisme-bergerac@aquinet.tm.fr]** On S bank of Rv Dordogne 300m W of old bdge opp town cent. Do not ent town, foll camping sp fr bdge, ent on R after L turn opp block of flats. Well sp. Med, mkd pitch, pt sl, pt shd; wc; own san; chem disp; mv service pnt; shwrs inc; el pts (6A) €2.50; gas; lndtte; ice; shop in town; playgrnd; fishing & rv sw adj; 90% statics; dogs €0.80; dep for barrier; poss cr; adv bkg; Eng spkn; quiet but some rlwy noise; cc not acc; CCI. "Twin-axle & c'vans over 6m not permitted; sh walk by rv into attractive old city; dated facs & poss stretched/dirty; sh stay/NH only." ♦ 15 Feb-31 Oct. € 9.00   2005*

BERGERAC *7C3* (8km SW Rural) **Camping Parc Servois Gardonne, 11 Rue du Bac, 24680 Gardonne [05 53 27 38 34]** Fr D936 Bergerac to Bordeaux, R in vill of Gardonne. Site 100m after traff lts. Sm, mkd pitch, pt shd; wc; chem disp; shwrs inc; el pts; ice; shops 200m; rest 300m; dogs €0.60; phone 200m; quet; CCI. "Pretty, CL-type site; facs immac but dated & poss stretched in ssn." 1 Apr-30 Sep. € 8.70   2005*

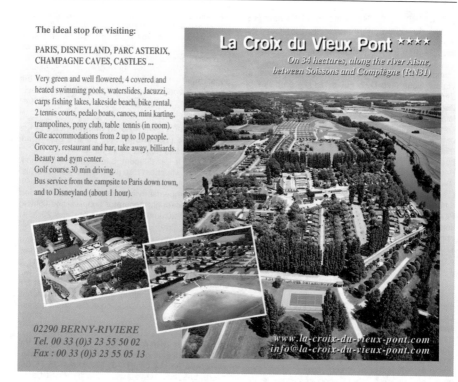

The ideal stop for visiting:

PARIS, DISNEYLAND, PARC ASTERIX,
CHAMPAGNE CAVES, CASTLES ...

Very green and well flowered, 4 covered and
heated swimming pools, waterslides, Jacuzzi,
carps fishing lakes, lakeside beach, bike rental,
2 tennis courts, pedalo boats, canoes, mini karting,
trampolines, pony club, table tennis (in room).
Gite accommodations from 2 up to 10 people.
Grocery, restaurant and bar, take away, billiards.
Beauty and gym center.
Golf course 30 min driving.
Bus service from the campsite to Paris down town,
and to Disneyland (about 1 hour).

La Croix du Vieux Pont ★★★★

*On 34 hectares, along the river Aisne,
between Soissons and Compiègne (RN31)*

02290 BERNY-RIVIERE
Tel. 00 33 (0)3 23 55 50 02
Fax : 00 33 (0)3 23 55 05 13

www.la-croix-du-vieux-pont.com
info@la-croix-du-vieux-pont.com

FRANCE

---

†BERGUES *3A3* (4km NE Rural) **Parc Residentiel de Loisirs la Becque, 791 Rue de l'Est, 59380 Warhem** [03 28 62 00 40; fax 03 28 62 05 65] Exit A25 at junc 16 sp Bergues. At top of slip rd turn L D916 then turn R at rndabt onto D110; L in 4km to Warhem. Site well sp in vill. Med, hdg/mkd pitch, hdstg, pt shd, wc (cont); own san; shwrs €1.50; el pts (6A) €2.30; gas; lndry rm; shop 1km; supmkt in Hoymille; playgrnd; rv fishing 2km; tennis; 95% statics; dogs €1.50; quiet; CCI. "Gd NH open till 2200; helpful owner; security barrier; san facs poss poor, cold water." € 18.30   2004*

BERGUES *3A3* (8km SW Rural) **Camping du 20ieme Siecle, 12 Cappelstraete, 59284 Pitgam** [tel/fax 03 28 62 14 44 or 06 11 26 41 33 (mob); campingdu20siecle@wanadoo.fr] Fr Dunkerque on N225 SE to Bierne/Steene, turn R onto D352. To junc of D52, turn R then L at camping sp; turn L at Cappelstraete; 2km to site down track; diff to find as not sp. Med, mkd pitch, pt shd, terr; htd wc; chem disp (wc); shwrs; el pts (3A) €2.30; gas; lndtte; ice; tradsmn; playgrnd; fishing & watersports 5km; tennis; 90% statics; dogs; noisy (dogs); CCI. "Conv for ferries; helpful, friendly owner; gd sized pitches; gd cycling." ♦ 1 Mar-30 Nov. € 11.20   2005*

BERNAY *3D2* (1.5km S Urban) **Camp Municipal, Rue des Canadiens, 27300 Bernay** [02 32 43 30 47] Site sp fr S'most (Alencon) rndabt off Bernay by-pass N138; twd France Parc Exposition then 1st L & on R. Well sp. Sm, hdg/mkd pitch, pt shd; wc; chem disp; mv service pnt; shwrs inc; el pts (16A) €3; lndry rm; shop 500m; tradsmn; rest, bar 1km; playgrnd; pool 300m; table tennis; TV rm; dogs; phone; adv bkg; quiet; no cc acc; CCI. "Clean facs; v helpful & friendly; 20 mins walk to town cent; plenty local tourist info avail; nice, well-maintained site; barrier clsd 2200-0700." ♦ 15 May-15 Sep. € 16.00   2004*

BERNERIE EN RETZ, LA see Pornic *2G3*

BERNEVAL LE GRAND *3B2* (Coastal) **Camp Municipal Le Val Boise, 76340 Berneval-le-Grand** [02 35 85 29 18 or 02 35 83 62 32 (Mairie); fax 02 35 06 07 20; camping-berneval@wanadoo.fr] Fr Dieppe take D925 for 6km, turn L at Graincourt onto D54 past Silo on R. Site sp. Sm, mkd pitch, hdstg, terr, pt shd; wc; chem disp; mv service pnt; shwrs; el pts (16A) €2.15; ice; shop 2km; playgrnd; shgl beach 400m; entmnt; some statics; dogs; Eng spkn; adv bkg rec; quiet; CCI. "Gd all stays; v hilly area; poss diff lge units; lovely quiet spot." 1 Apr-11 Nov. € 7.50   2002*

---

†BERNY RIVIERE *3C4* (1.5km S Rural) **Camping La Croix du Vieux Pont, 02290 Berny-Riviere** [03 23 55 50 02; fax 03 23 55 05 13; info@ la-croix-du-vieux-pont.com; www.la-croix-du-vieux-pont.com] On N31 bet Soissons & Compiegne. At site sp turn onto D13, then at Vic-sur-Aisne onto D91. Foll sp to site on o'skts of Berny. V lge, hdg pitch, hdstg, pt shd; htd wc; chem disp; mv service pnt; some serviced pitch; baby facs; shwrs inc; el pts (6A) €2.50 (poss rev pol & no earth); gas; Indtte; supmkt; tradsmn; rest; snacks; bar; playgrnd; 4 htd pools (1 covrd); waterslide; tennis; games rm; lake beach & sw; fishing; boating; horseriding; golf; cycle hire; gym; excursions to Paris & Disneyland; 5% statics; dogs; poss cr; Eng spkn; adv bkg rec; quiet; cc not acc; CCI. "Some sh stay pitches up steep bank; wine-growing area; coaches to Disneyland & Paris; popular w/e for Parisians; site well-controlled & quiet on rvside; some touring pitches liable to flood; gd family entmnt; excel." ♦ €20.00 (3 persons) (CChq acc) 2005*

See advertisement on previous page

†BERNY RIVIERE *3C4* (2km W Urban) **Camping La Halte de Mainville, Chemin de Routy, 02290 Ressons-le-Long** [03 23 74 26 69; fax 03 23 74 03 60] On L of N31 Soissons to Compiegne rd 10km W of Soissons, clearly sp. Lge, hdg/mkd pitch, pt shd; wc; chem disp; shwrs inc; el pts (6A) €2 (poss rev pol); Indtte; shop 4km; tradsmn; playgrnd; htd pool; fishing; tennis; 50% statics; dogs; phone; quiet but poss some rd noise; adv bkg rec; no cc acc; CCI. "Vg, pleasant site; friendly staff; 1 hr fr Disneyland." €14.00 2003*

BERRIAS ET CASTELJAU see Vans, Les *9D1*

BERT see Donjon, Le *9A1*

BERTANGLES see Amiens *3C3*

BESANCON *6G2* (5km NE Rural) **FFCC Camping La Plage, Route de Belfort, 25220 Chalezeule** [03 81 88 04 26; fax 03 81 50 54 62; laplage. besancon@ffcc.fr; www.ffcc.fr] Exit A36 junc 4; foll sp Montbeliard onto N83. Well sp fr N83. Fr Belfort 2.65m height restriction; foll sp to Chalezeule & 300m after supmkt turn L to rejoin N83, site in 200m. Med, mkd pitch, terr, pt shd; wc; chem disp; shwrs inc; el pts (6A) €3.15 (poss rev pol); Indry rm; supmkt 1km; snacks; playgrnd; htd pool; rv adj; gd kayaking; bus to city weekdays; poss cr; quiet but some rd & rlwy noise; cc acc; red CCI. "Vg site by rv; conv city, local rests & citadel; easy parking in town; twin-axles extra charge." ♦ 1 Apr-30 Sep. €12.05 2005*

BESANCON *6G2* (11km NW) **Camping Les Peupliers, 25870 Geneuille** [03 81 57 72 04] Fr Besancon take N57 towards Vesoul then take L into D1 & fork R to Geneuille. Site sp thro vill. Sm, mkd pitch, pt shd; wc (some cont); chem disp; el pts; shops 1km, rest, snacks, bar 500m; rv; 20% statics; dogs; quiet. "Fairly run down, old fashioned but peaceful, friendly site; fair sh stay." 15 May-30 Sep. €10.90 2004*

BESSANS *9C4* (2km N Rural) **Camping La Grange de Laverole (Vincendet), Rue de Pre de l'Huile, 73480 Bessans** [tel/fax 04 79 05 96 21] Take D902 fr Lanslebourg, site 2km past Bessans. Sm, unshd; wc; chem disp (wc); shwrs inc; no el pts; Indry rm; quiet. "Gd sh stay; spacious farm site with 12 pitches; mountain views; evening meals to order; access track rough; generator supplies site lighting 0600-2300." 20 Jun-20 Sep & Dec-Apr. €9.20 2002*

BESSANS *9C4* (1km S Rural) **Camping L'Illaz, Rue de l'Illette, 73480 Bessans** [04 79 05 83 31] Clearly sp on D902 fr Lanslebourg. Sm, unshd; wc; chem disp; shwrs €1; shops 1km; fishing; quiet but some rd noise. "Vg sh stay; undeveloped pitches among bushes; vg san facs; no el pts; direct access to rv & lake." €12.00 2002*

BESSE SUR BRAY *4F2* (Rural) **Camping Le Val de Braye, 25 Rue du Val de Braye, 72310 Besse-sur-Braye** [02 43 35 31 13; fax 02 43 35 58 86; mairie-bessesurbraye@wanadoo.fr] Fr St Calais on D303 turn L in cent of Besse-sur-Braye sp Troo; turn R immed over rlwy line (disused). Site on L in 300m. Or better rte fr St Calais ignore Centre Ville sp & cont on by-pass. Site on L 300m beyond traff lts. Med, pt shd; htd wc; chem disp; mv service pnt; shwrs inc; el pts (6A) €2 (some rev pol); Indtte; ice; shop adj; BBQ; playgrnd; htd, covrd pool adj; walking; fishing; TV; adv bkg; quiet; red long stay; CCI; "V helpful resident warden; pitch area ltd low ssn; dep req barrier key; well-kept, excel site." ♦ 15 Apr-15 Sep. €8.00 2005*

BESSEGES see St Ambroix *9D2*

†BESSINES SUR GARTEMPE *7A3* (4km N) **Camp Municipal, 87250 Morterolles-sur-Semme** [05 55 76 09 28 or 05 55 76 05 09 (Mairie); fax 05 55 76 68 45; ot.bessines@wanadoo.fr] S on A20 take exit 23.1 sp Chateauponsac. Take 1st turn R, site on L in vill of Morterolles by stadium. N on A20 take exit 24.2 sp Bessines, turn under a'route & take 1st R sp Chateauponsac to Morterolles in 3km. Sm, mkd pitch, pt shd; htd wc; shwrs inc; el pts (5A) €2 (poss rev pol); Indry rm; playgrnd; covrd pool 200m; cycle hire; dogs; poss cr; Eng spkn; quiet; CCI. "Delightful, farm site nr Limoges; a'route; gd low ssn as htd shwr blocks old-fashioned but clean; poss itinerants; if warden absent on arr, pitch yourself & will call later; gd NH." ♦ ltd. €6.50 2005*

BESSINES SUR GARTEMPE *7A3* (1.5km SW Urban) **Camp Municipal Lac de Sagnat, Route de St Pardoux,** 87250 Bessines-sur-Gartempe [05 55 76 17 69 or 05 55 76 05 09 (Mairie); fax 05 55 76 01 24; ot.bessines@wanadoo.fr] Fr A20 exit sp Bessines-sur-Gartempe onto D220; then D27 sp lake. Foll sp to Bellevue Restaurant. At rest, turn R foll site sp. Med, hdg/mkd pitch, pt sl, terr, pt shd; wc; chem disp; shwrs inc; el pts inc; lndtte; shops 1km; tradsmn high ssn; rest 500m; snacks high ssn; playgrnd adj; sand beach & lake sw adj; TV rm; Eng spkn; poss cr; quiet. "V friendly staff; lake views; peaceful location; sm boats for children; gd clean san facs." ♦ 15 Jun-15 Sep. € 12.00   2005*

BETHUNE *3B3* (1km E Urban) **Camp Municipal, Rue Victor Duteriez,** 62660 Beuvry [03 21 65 08 00 or 03 21 61 82 90 (Mairie); fax 03 21 61 82 91] Fr A26 exit junc 6 onto N41 dir Lille. At junc N41/N43 turn L to Beuvry, sp on R in town as 'Camping', also sp to 'Base de Loisirs'. Med, mkd pitches; some hdstg, pt sl, pt shd; wc (some cont); shwrs €1.10; el pts (2-6A) €2.30-4.60; lndry rm; shop 500m; tradsmn; snacks nr; htd, covrd pool 500m; fishing adj; 10% statics; adv bkg; cc not acc; CCI. "Unpleasant site; twin-axles prohibited; no recep facs after 1800 tho access allowed; buy jetons for shwrs on arr, as warden often absent; some el pts not working; conv ferries & WW1 battlefields at Loos & Vimy; poss noise fr football ground adj; san facs rudimentary; NH only if desperate." 15 May-15 Sep. € 6.35   2005*

BEUZEC CAP SIZUN see Douarnenez *2E2*

BEYNAC ET CAZENAC see Sarlat la Caneda *7C3*

BEYNAT *7C4* (4km W) **Centre Touristique L'Etang du Miel,** 19190 Beynat [05 55 85 50 66; fax 05 55 85 57 96; camping.lac.de.miel@ wanadoo.fr] On N680, 4km fr Beynat, & 2km fr Le Quatre rtes where D940 meets D121. Lge, mkd pitch, pt sl, pt shd; wc (some cont); chem disp; mv service pnt; shwrs; el pts (6A) inc; lndtte; gas 5km; ice; shop; snacks; rest 5km; BBQ; playgrnd; tennis; games rm; lake sw adj; beach adj; fishing; 2% statics; adv bkg; quiet; phone; CCI. "Gd long stay." ♦ ltd 15 Apr-15 Sep. € 16.00   2004*

BEZIERS *10F1* (10km NE) **Camping Le Rebau,** 34290 Montblanc [04 67 98 50 78; fax 04 67 98 68 63; gilbert@camping-lerebau.fr] NE on N9 fr Beziers-Montpellier, turn R on D18. Site sp, narr ent 2.50m. Med, pt shd; wc (some cont); chem disp; shwrs inc; el pts (5-6A) €4; gas; lndtte; ice; shop & in vill; snacks; sand beach 13km; pool; playgrnd; TV; entmnt; fishing; dogs €2.60; poss cr; Eng spkn; adv bkg; quiet; red low ssn. "Ltd facs low ssn, but v clean; tight ent & manoeuvring onto pitches; v helpful; low ssn stays fr Feb prior arrangement." 15 Jun-31 Aug. € 18.50   2005*

BEZIERS *10F1* (4km SE Urban) **Camping Les Berges du Canal,** 34420 Villeneuve-les-Beziers [04 67 39 36 09; fax 04 67 39 82 07; contact@ lesbergesducanal.com; www.lesbergesducanal. com] Fr A9 exit junc 35 & foll sp for Agde. Exit 1st rndabt for N112 dir Beziers then 1st L onto D37 sp Villneuve-les-Beziers. Foll site sp. Med, hdg/mkd pitch, shd; wc; chem disp; mv service pnt; baby facs; shwrs inc; el pts inc (poss rev pol); lndtte; shop; rest; snacks; playgrnd; htd pool; beach 10km; 45% statics; dogs €2; poss cr; Eng spkn; adv bkg dep req; red 5+ days; CCI. "Facs v clean but poss stretched in ssn; some pitches tight lge o'fits; expensive for long family holiday; vg long stay." 15 Apr-15 Sep. € 22.00   2005*

BEZIERS *10F1* (6km S) **Camping La Gabinelle,** 34410 Sauvian [04 67 39 50 87 or 04 67 32 30 79; info@lagabinelle.com; www.lagabinelle.com] Exit A9 at Beziers W, turn R twd beaches sp S to Sauvian. Site 500m on L thro town. Med, pt shd; wc; chem disp; shwrs inc; el pts €3; lndtte; shops, rest, snacks adj; bar; playgrnd; pool; sand beach 5km; sports area; entmnt; fishing 1km; canoeing 2km; games rm; TV; dogs €2; adv bkg; quiet. "Friendly; gd rest in vill." ♦ 10 Apr-11 Sep. € 17.00   2004*

†**BEZIERS** *10F1* (7km SW) **Camping Les Peupliers, 7 Promenade de l'Ancien Stade,** 34440 Colombiers [04 67 37 05 26; fax 04 67 37 67 87] SW fr Beziers on N9 turn R on D162E & foll sp to site using heavy vehicle rte. Cross canal bdge & fork R; turn R & site on L. Easier ent fr D11 (Beziers-Capestang), turn L at end of dual c'way sp Colombiers, in 1km turn L immed after rlwy bdge. Sm, pt shd; wc; shwrs inc; el pts (6-10A) €2.30-4.15; ice; shops & bar 1km; rest 3km; playgrnd; sand beach 15km; dogs €1.80; adv bkg; rlwy noise; CCI. "Nice location away fr busy beach sites; nr Canal du Midi; excel walking & cycling; dep req for barrier card; poss itinerants; poss san facs unclean low ssn." ♦ € 12.10   2005*

BEZINGHEM *3A3* (S) **Camping des Aulnes,** 62650 Bezinghem [03 21 90 93 88] S fr Desvres or N fr Montreuil on D127. Site at S end of vill on W side of rd, v narr app rds. Med, pt shd; wc (some cont); shwrs inc; el pts (6A) €2.40; gas; ice; shop; snacks; shop; some statics; rd noise; CCI. "Sm pitches; san facs poss unclean & in poor repair; NH only." Easter-15 Oct. € 13.40   2003*

BIACHE ST VAAST see Douai *3B3*

BIARRITZ *8F1* (3.5km E) **Camping Le Parme, Quartier Brindos,** 64600 Anglet [05 59 23 03 00; fax 05 59 41 29 55; campingdeparme@wanadoo. fr; www.campingdeparme.com] On N10 fr St Jean-de-Luz to Bayonne. Site sp on R bef Biarritz aerodrome, 500m down tarmac app rd. Lge, pt sl, terr, shd; htd wc (some cont); shwrs inc; el pts (6-10A) €3.70-4; gas; lndtte; ice; shops 3km; rest; snacks; bar; playgrnd; pool; paddling pool; sand beach 2.5km; tennis; TV; entmnt; dogs €3; cc acc. "Diff exit up steep slope & by blind corner - owner will advise alt R-turn rte." ♦ 15 Mar-15 Nov. € 23.00   2005*

BIARRITZ *8F1* (3km S Coastal) **Camping Residence des Pins, Ave de Biarritz, 64210 Bidart** [05 59 23 00 29; fax 05 59 41 24 59; contact@campingdespins.com; www.camping despins.com] S fr Bayonne on N10, by-pass Biarritz. 1km after A63 junc turn R at rndabt immed after Intermarche on R; sp to Pavillon Royal. Site 1km on R sp. Lge, mkd pitch, pt sl, terr, shd; wc; chem disp; shwrs inc; baby facs; el pts (10A) inc; gas; lndtte; shop; tradsmn; rest & snacks high ssn; bar; playgrnd; htd pool; sand beach 600m; tennis; games area; cycle hire; golf nr; horseriding; child entmnt; internet; TV; many statics & tour ops; dogs €2.10; phone; poss cr; Eng spkn; adv bkg over 15 days & high ssn; quiet; red low ssn; cc acc; CCI. "Gd beaches at Bidart, St Jean-de-Luz, Biarritz; attractive, mature site; site access rds narr - poss diff long o'fits." ♦ 15 May -30 Sep. € 28.50 (CChq acc)   2004*

BIARRITZ *8F1* (5km S Rural) **LES CASTELS Le Ruisseau des Pyrenees, Route d'Arbonne, 64210 Bidart** [05 59 41 94 50; fax 05 59 41 95 73; francoise. dumont@wanadoo.fr; www.les-castels.com & www.camping-le-ruisseau.fr] Exit N10 E in either dir, at Bidart take rd sp Arbonne, site sp. Rds twisty & narr. Lge, some hdg pitch, pt sl, terr, pt shd; wc; chem disp (wc only); mv service pnt; shwrs inc; el pts (6A) inc; gas; lndtte; ice; shop; rest; snacks; bar; playgrnd; 3 pools (1 covrd) & paddling pool; waterslide; lake fishing; boating; sand beach 2.5km; tennis; games area; cycling; mini-golf; 90% statics; dogs €1.50; poss cr; adv bkg ess high ssn; poss noisy; red low ssn; CCI. "Excel for children & teenagers; steep slope/short run to barrier poss diff; best pitches by lake; site muddy after rain; golf nr." 29 Apr-17 Sep. € 32.00   2005*

See advertisement above

BIARRITZ *8F1* (3km S Coastal) **Village Camping Sunelia Berrua, Rue Berrua, 64210 Bidart** [05 59 54 96 66; fax 05 59 54 78 30; contact@ berrua.com; www.berrua.com] S on N10 passing Biarritz at Bidart take rd sp Arbonne. Site on R in 400m. Lge, pt sl, pt shd; wc; chem disp; mv service pnt; shwrs inc; baby facs; el pts (6-10A) €4.50; (poss long lead req); gas; lndtte; ice; shop; tradsmn; rest; snacks; bar; BBQ; playgrnd; htd pool & paddling pool; waterslide; beach 1km; tennis; cycle hire; archery; golf 2km;TV; 40% statics; dogs €3.10; phone; bus 1km; poss cr; Eng spkn; adv bkg; poss cr & noisy; red 7+ days; cc acc; CCI. "Lots of trees; muddy after rain; sh walk to vill; excel, clean facs." ♦ 9 Apr-2 Oct. € 26.40 (CChq acc)   2005*

BIARRITZ *8F1* (6km S Coastal) **Camping Ur-Onea, Rue de la Chapelle, 64210 Bidart** [05 59 26 53 61; fax 05 59 26 53 94; contact@uronea.com or uronea@wanadoo.fr; www.uronea.com] Exit A63 junc 4 dir Bidart, fr Bidart on N10 sp St Jean de Luz, L at 2nd traff lts nr church, then immed R, site is 500m on L. Lge, mkd pitch, terr, pt shd; wc (some cont); chem disp; serviced pitches; baby facs; fam bthrm; shwrs inc; el pts (10A) €4.50; gas; lndtte; ice; shop high ssn; tradsmn; rest; snacks; bar, BBQ; playgrnd; pool; sand beach 600m; lake sw 12km; entmnt; TV; 20% statics; dogs €2; phone; Eng spkn; adv bkg; quiet; cc acc; red low ssn; CCI. "Conv Pays Basque vills; excel san facs." ♦ 8 Apr-16 Sep. € 22.50   2005*

See advertisement opposite

BIARRITZ *8F1* (3km SW Coastal) **Camping Biarritz, 28 Rue d'Harcet, 64200 Biarritz** [05 59 23 00 12; fax 05 59 43 74 67; biarritz. camping@wanadoo.fr; www.biarritz-camping.fr] S fr Bayonne on N10, by-pass Biarritz & cont to junc of N10 coast rd sp Bidart & Biarritz; double back on this rd, take 1st exit at next rndabt, 1st L dir Biarritz Cent, foll sp to site in 2km. Lge, mkd pitch, pt sl, terr, pt shd; wc; chem disp; mv service pnt; shwrs inc; el pts (6A) inc; gas; Indtte; shop; tradsmn; rest; snacks; bar; playgrnd; htd pool; sand beach 1km; entmnt; 10% statics; dogs; poss cr; adv bkg (dep req); cc acc; noisy in high ssn; red low ssn/CCI. "One of better sites in area espec low ssn." ◆ ltd. 10 May-20 Sep. € 22.50   2003*

BIARRITZ *8F1* (3.5km SW Coastal) **Camping Pavillon Royal, Ave du Prince-de-Galles, 64210 Bidart** [05 59 23 00 54; fax 05 59 23 44 47; info@ pavillon-royal.com; www.pavillon-royal.com] Leave A63 a'route at junc 4 sp Biarritz. After tolls turn L at rndabt onto N10. In approx 1.5km at 1st rndabt (just past Intermarche store) turn R onto D655 & in 1km turn R at T-junc. Turn L into narr rd & foll sp. Lge, hdg/mkd pitch, pt sl, pt shd, wc (some cont); chem disp; serviced pitch; baby facs; shwrs inc; el pts (5A) inc; gas; Indtte; ice; shop; tradsmn; rest; snacks; bar; BBQ; htd pool; playgrnd; pool & paddling pool; sand beach adj; tennis & mini-golf nr; games rm; cycle hire; golf 500m; horseriding 2km; internet; 30% statics; no dogs; recep 0800-2100; poss cr; Eng spkn; adv bkg (ess Jul/Aug); dep req & bkg fee €22.87; cc acc; red low ssn. "Direct access via steps to excel beach; clean, well-run, busy site; spacious pitches; friendly; excel family site; conv Spanish border & Pyrenees; mkt Sat." ◆ 15 May-25 Sep. € 36.90 ABS - A06   2005*

BIARRITZ *8F1* (5km SW Coastal) **Camping Erreka, 64210 Bidart** [05 59 54 93 64; fax 05 59 47 70 46; campingerreka@laposte.net; www.camping-erreka. com] Site at junc of N10 Biarritz by-pass & main rd into town cent; well sp. Lge, pt sl, pt shd; wc (some cont); chem disp; mv service pnt; baby facs; shwrs; el pts (6A) €3.15; gas; Indtte; shop; snacks; playgrnd; pool; sand beach 500m; TV; entmnt; dogs €1.50; red low ssn; adv bkg; cc acc; quiet; CCI. "Some pitches sl & poss v diff to get into, rec adv bkg to ensure suitable pitch; access rds v steep." ◆ 1 Jun-15 Sep. € 17.40   2003*

BIARRITZ *8F1* (5km SW Coastal) **Camping Oyam, Rue d'Eskola, 64210 Bidart** [tel/fax 05 59 54 91 61] Leave A63 at junc 4 onto N10; 150m after Bidart boundary sp, turn L at traff lts sp Arbonne. In 600m at brow of hill turn R & then immed L. Med, pt sl, terr, pt shd, mkd pitch; wc; chem disp; baby facs; shwrs inc; el pts (3A) €3.50; Indtte; shop; rest; snacks; playgrnd; pool; sand beach 1.2km; mini-golf; 70% statics; Eng spkn; adv bkg; some rd & rlwy noise; CCI. "A well-managed site in lovely surroundings." ◆ 15 Apr-30 Sep. € 22.00   2004*

BIDART see Biarritz *8F1*

BIERT see Massat *8G3*

BIESHEIM see Neuf Brisach *6F3*

BIGANOS see Audenge *7D1*

BIGNAC see Angouleme *7B2*

BILIEU see Abrets, Les *9B3*

BINIC *2E3* (500m N Urban/Coastal) **Camp Municipal des Fauvettes, 22520 Binic** [02 96 73 60 83 or 02 96 73 61 15 (Mairie); fax 02 96 73 72 38] Binic turn on St Quay rd; foll sp; 14km NW of St Brieuc. Site also sp fr rndabt on D786 N of Binic cent; ent narr. Med, mkd pitch, pt sl, terr, pt shd; wc; chem disp (wc); shwrs €1.50; el pts €3.20; Indtte; shop; snacks; BBQ; playgrnd; sand beach adj; some statics; dogs €2; Eng spkn; poss cr; quiet; CCI. "Clifftop site with gd sea views; vg long/sh stay." ◆ 1 Apr-30 Sep. € 14.10   2003*

BINIC *2E3* (1km S Coastal) **Camping Le Panoramic, Rue Gasselin, 22520 Binic** [02 96 73 60 43; fax 02 96 69 27 66; camping.lepanoramic@wanadoo. fr; www.lepanoramic.net] D786 St Brieuc-Paimpol. 1st slip rd for Binic & 1st R up hill 100m. Med, pt sl, terr, pt shd; htd wc; chem disp; shwrs; el pts (6A) €3.20 (poss rev pol); gas; Indtte; ice; shop; snacks; bar; BBQ; htd pool; sand beach 500m; golf adj; entmnt; many statics; dogs €1.80; quiet after 2230. "V clean facs; pleasant site; coastal path nr; ltd space for tourers." 1 Apr-15 Sep. € 16.00   2005*

FRANCE

BINIC *2E3* (4km S Coastal) **Camping Le Roc de l'Hervieu, 22590 Pordic** [02 96 79 30 12; le.roc.de.lhervieu@wanadoo.fr] Site on E side of vill off N786, Binic-St Brieuc rd. Turn E in cent of vill, sp to Les Madieres then sp Le Roc de l'Hervieu. Med, pt shd; wc (some cont); chem disp; shwrs inc; el pts (10A) €2.50; shop; lndtte; playgrnd; sand beach 2km; quiet. ♦ 19 May-30 Sep. € 14.00   2003*

BINIC *2E3* (4km S Coastal) **Camping Les Madieres, La Vau Madec, 22590 Pordic** [02 96 79 02 48; fax 02 96 79 46 67; campinglesmadieres@wanadoo.fr] Site at E end of Pordic vill, sp. Med, pt sl, shd; htd wc (mainly cont); shwrs inc; el pts (10A) €3.50; gas; lndtte; sm shop; rest; snacks; bar; htd pool; shgl beach 800m; sand beach & watersports 3km; entmnt; 10% statics; dogs €1.80; adv bkg; quiet; red CCI. "V pleasant, clean, child-friendly site; immac facs; friendly, helpful owners; poss diff access to shgl beach & not suitable children, Binic beach 3km OK; highly rec." ♦ 1 Apr-3 Nov. € 16.50   2005*

BINIC *2E3* (8km SW Rural) **Camping a la Ferme** (Hello), La Corderie, 22170 Plelo [02 96 74 21 21; fax 02 96 74 31 64; hello.odile@22.cernet.fr] Fr Binic take D4 dir Chatelaudren, site on R at La Corderie. Sm, pt shd; wc; chem disp; shwrs inc; el pts (6A) €2; lndtte; sand beach 8km; 20% statics; quiet. "CL-type site; gd long/sh stay." 25 Jun-10 Sep. € 8.00   2003*

BINIC *2E3* (6km W) **Camping Les Etangs**, 22410 Lantic [02 96 71 95 47; lesetangs@caramail.com] D786 fr Binic twd Paimpol; turn L approx 1km on D4 sp Chatelaudren & Lantic; in 3km at x-rds turn L foll camping sp; site in 50m on R. Fr N12 Guingamp-St Brieuc take D4 at Chatelaudren. Med, mkd pitch, pt sl, pt shd; wc (cont); chem disp; mv service pnt; shwrs inc; el pts (6A) €2.50; gas; lndtte; ice; sm shop; tradsmn; snacks; playgrnd; pool; beach 3km; TV; 2% statics; dogs €1; phone; poss v cr; Eng spkn; adv bkg (dep req); quiet; cc acc; CCI. "Gd base slightly away fr cr coast sites; helpful, friendly owners; gd pool; boat excursions fr St Brieuc; excel long stay." ♦ 1 Apr-30 Sep. € 10.50   2003*

BIOT see Antibes *10E4*

BIRON *7D3* (W Rural) **Aire Communale**, Route de Vergt de Biron, 24540 Biron [05 53 63 15 04; fax 05 53 24 28 12] Fr Villereal or Monpazier on D104/D2 turn onto D53 to Biron, foll sp for Information. M'vans only. Sm, unshd; own san; chem disp; mv service pnt; water €2; shop 8km; rest, snacks, bar 100m; dogs; poss cr; quiet. "Extensive views fr site; gd NH." 1 Apr-31 Oct.   2003*

BIRON *7D3* (4km S Rural) **Camping Sunelia Le Moulinal**, 24540 Biron [05 53 40 84 60; fax 05 53 40 81 49; lemoulinal@perigord.com; www.lemoulinal.com] Fr Bergerac S dir Agen, then E Issigeac & Villereal; fr Villereal dir Lacapelle-Biron, site sp. Fr Monpazier take D104 twd Villereal; in 4km S on D53 thro Biron & onto Lacapelle-Biron. Head W twd Villereal for 2km to site. Lge, mkd pitches, terr, pt shd; htd wc (some cont); baby facs; shwrs; el pts (6A) inc; gas; lndtte; ice; shop; rest; snacks; bar; BBQ; playgrnd; htd pool; sand beach for lake sw; boating; tennis; games area; games rm; internet; entmnt; dogs €5; poss cr; Eng spkn; adv bkg; quiet; cc acc; red low ssn; CCI. "Lovely site; extra for lakeside & 'super' pitches." ♦ 1 Apr-15 Sep. € 35.00   2005*

BIRON *7D3* (4km SW Rural) **Camping Laborde** (Naturist), 47150 Paulhiac [05 53 63 14 88; fax 05 53 61 60 23; www.domainelaborde.com] Leave Montpazier on D2 sp Monflanquin/Villereal; in 5.6km at Source de la Brame turn L onto D2E sp Monflanquin. Turn R onto D255 at sp Laborde FFN dir Lacapelle-Born. Med, pt sl, pt shd; wc; chem disp; sauna; shwrs inc; el pts (3-10A) €3-4 (poss long lead req); gas; ice; lndtte; tradsmn; shop; rest; snacks; bar; playgrnd; 2 tropical indoor pools & outdoor pool; lake sw adj; tennis; games rm; dogs €3; Eng spkn; adv bkg; quiet; cc acc; INF card not req. "A perfect site; excel long stay." ♦ 15 Apr-1 Oct. € 19.00   2004*

BISCARROSSE *7D1*. **See also sites listed under Gastes, Sanguinet and Parentis en Born.**

BISCARROSSE *7D1* (3km N) **Aire Naturelle Camping Les Bruyeres**, 3725 Route de Bordeaux, 40600 Biscarrosse [05 58 78 79 23] N fr Biscarrosse on D652 twd Arcachon; site on L behind 2 bungalows (1 new 1 old) 3km fr town; visible fr rd. Sm, shd; wc; chem disp (wc); shwrs €1.10; baby facs; el pts (3-10A) inc, rev pol; ice; shop adj; cooking facs; BBQ; sand beach 10km; lake sw & watersports 3km; adv bkg; quiet. "Helpful owners; CL-type site; teens facs; beach 10km excel for surfing." Apr-Sep. € 11.00   2004*

BISCARROSSE *7D1* (5km N Rural) **Aire Naturelle Le Frezat (Dubourg)**, 2583 Chemin de Mayotte, 40600 Biscarrosse [06 22 65 57 37] Fr Biscarrosse on D652 dir Sanguinet; after 5km L at water tower onto D333; site 2nd on R in 1km. Med, shd; wc (some cont); chem disp (wc); shwrs €1; el pts (6A) inc; shops 5km; tradsmn; BBQ; playgrnd; lake & sand beach 3km; dogs; phone 1km; Eng spkn; quiet; adv bkg; CCI. "Vg site; friendly owners; cycle paths." 15 Apr-15 Oct. € 12.50   2005*

BISCARROSSE *7D1* (5km N Rural) **Yelloh! Village Mayotte**, Chemin des Roseaux, 40600 Biscarrosse [05 58 78 00 00; fax 05 58 78 83 91; mayotte@yellohvillage.com; www.mayottevacances.com] Twd NE fr Biscarrosse on D652 L sp Navarosse & at 1st fork R to Mayotte, foll camping sp. V lge, mkd pitch, hdstg, pt shd; wc; chem disp; mv service pnt; shwrs inc; el pts (10A) inc; snacks; gas; lndtte; shop; rest; snacks; bar; BBQ; playgrnd; pool; waterslide; jacuzzi; lake sw adj; sailing school; sand beach 9km; tennis; cycle hire; games rm; entmnt; child entmnt; TV; 25% statics; dogs €5; Eng spkn; adv bkg (ess Jul/Aug); quiet; cc acc; red low ssn/CCI. "Excel leisure facs; vg for families; rec." ♦ 29 Apr-23 Sep. € 38.00   2005*

See advertisement opposite (top)

BISCARROSSE *7D1* (8km NE Rural) **Camping Domaine de la Rive**, Route de Bordeaux, 40600 Biscarrosse [05 58 78 12 33; fax 05 58 78 12 92; info@camping-de-la-rive.fr; www.larive.fr] S on D652 fr Sanguinet to Biscarrosse. Site sp on R in 6km. V lge, hdg/mkd pitch, pt shd; wc; chem disp; baby facs; shwrs inc; el pts (6A) inc; gas; lndtte; ice; shop; rest; snacks; bar; BBQ (gas & charcoal); playgrnd; 2 pools (1 htd, covrd); waterslide; jacuzzi; lake sw & private, sand beach adj; ocean beach 18km; watersports; tennis; cycle, canoe, surf hire; archery; games area; organised activities; entmnt; child entmnt; internet; TV; 30% statics; dogs €4; phone; Eng spkn; adv bkg (dep req); cc acc; red low ssn; CCI. "Lakeside site; delightful area; some pitches diff lge o'fits due trees; excel." ♦ 1 Apr-24 Sep. € 41.00 (CChq acc) ABS - A38   2005*

See advertisement opposite (bottom)

FRANCE

BISCARROSSE *7D1* (1.5km S) **Camp Municipal de Latecoere, 40600 Biscarrosse** [05 58 78 13 01; fax 05 58 78 16 26; latecoere.biscarrosse@ wanadoo.fr] S on D652 Sanguinet-Biscarrosse rd to cent of town. Strt in front of church by mkt sq; site in 1.5km. Lge, mkd pitch, pt shd; wc; shwrs inc; el pts inc; lndtte; shop; rest; snacks; bar; BBQ; playgrnd adj; pool; lake sand beach; 40% statics; quiet. "Yacht club adj; museums opp; seaplanes; gd sh stay." Apr-Sep. € 12.80   2002*

BISCARROSSE *7D1* (8km NW Coastal) **Campeole Le Vivier, 681 Rue du Tit, 40600 Biscarrosse-Plage** [05 58 78 25 76; fax 05 58 78 35 23; www. campeoles.fr] Fr Arcachon & Pyla-sur-Mer, take D218, D83 to Biscarrosse Plage. Town o'skts site sp to R. Foll sps. Lge, pt shd; wc; chem disp; shwrs; el pts €3.20; shop; snacks; playgrnd; pool; sand beach 800m; tennis; boating; fishing; horseriding; dogs €3; quiet. "Access to beach via path thro dunes." 1 May-14 Sep. € 19.80   2003*

BISCARROSSE *7D1* (9km NW Coastal) **Campeole Plage-Sud, 230 Rue des Becasses, 40600 Biscarrosse-Plage** [05 58 78 21 24; fax 05 58 78 34 23] Clearly sp on D146 on ent to Biscarrosse-Plage in pine forest. V lge, mkd pitch, pt sl, pt shd; wc; chem disp; baby facs; shwrs inc; el pts (6A) €3.05; lndtte; ice; shop adj; tradsmn; snacks; bar; BBQ; playgrnd; htd pool; sand beach 800m; cycle hire; entmnt; 20% statics; dogs €1.50; Eng spkn; adv bkg; noise fr disco high ssn; CCI. "Sm, modern town; lots of rests; gd beach inc surfing." 1 May-30 Sep. € 18.00   2002*

BIZANET see Narbonne *10F1*

BLAIN *2G4* (1km S) **Camp Municipal du Chateau Le Gravier, Route de St Nazaire, 44130 Blain** [02 40 79 11 00 or 02 40 79 00 08 (Mairie); fax 02 40 79 83 72] Fr N on N137 turn W onto N171; fr S on N137 turn W onto D164 to Blain. On app town, take L at rndabt on N171 dir St Nazaire/ Bouvron. Immed after x-ing Brest-Nantes canal bdge, site on L adj to chateau. Sm, mkd pitch, pt shd; wc; shwrs; chem disp; el pts (6A) inc; lndry rm; ice; shops 500m; tradsmn; rest, bar 500m; playgrnd; pool 1km; fishing; boating; dogs €0.70; phone adj; Eng spkn; adv bkg; quiet but some rd noise; CCI. "Well-managed site; immac san facs; gd pitch size; chateau museum adj; no twin-axles; no vehicular ent after 2000 high ssn; excel long/sh stay." ♦ 1 May-30 Sep. € 8.50   2005*

BLAMONT *6E3* (E Rural) **Camp Municipal de la Vezouze, Route de Cirey, 54450 Blamont** [03 83 76 28 28 (Mairie)] Fr Sarrebourg on N4 dir Blamont then D993 dir Cirey-sous-Vezouze & foll sp for site. Sm, pt shd; wc; shwrs inc; el pts (16A) €2; ice; shop, rest, snacks, bar 300m; playgrnd; sports area; sw, fishing adj. "Gd site beside lake; gd walking, cycling; phone ahead bef arrival." 1 Jun-15 Sep. € 6.50   2004*

BLANC, LE *4H2* (2km E Urban) **Camp Municipal L'Ile d'Avant a Tou Vert, 36300 Le Blanc** [02 54 37 88 22 or 02 54 22 26 61(LS)] Fr town cent take N151 twd St Gaultier/Argenton; site on R 1km after supmkt. Med, hdg/mkd pitch, pt shd; wc; shwrs inc; el pts (5-6A) €3.30-3.50; gas 3km; lndtte; shops 1km; rest, snacks, bar 3km; playgrnd; pool adj; rv sw; tennis adj; fishing; BBQ; adv bkg; quiet but some rd noise. "Site yourself, list of mkd pitch on office door; diff to manoeuvre lge vans; muddy uneven pitches; next to sports field & club house; fair NH only." 1 Mar-31 Oct. € 11.00   2004*

> This site entry hasn't been updated for a while; we'd better fill in a site report form and send it to The Club.

BLANDY *4E3* (1.5km E) **Camping Le Pre de l'Etang, 34 Rue St Martin, 77115 Blandy-les-Tours** [tel/fax 01 60 66 96 34] Fr Paris on A5 take exit 16 onto D47 dir Blandy, or fr D215 take D68. In Blandy foll dir St Mery, site on R in 200m. Site is 2.5km fr a'route. Med, hdg/mkd pitch, pt sl, pt shd; htd wc (some cont); chem disp; shwrs inc; el pts (5A) inc; bar, shop, rest 500m; BBQ; playgrnd 500m; 60% statics; dogs €1; phone; adv bkg; quiet; CCI. "Lge pitches but poss unkempt & overgrown grass; v picturesque; pond on site; conv Fontainebleau, Disneyland; trains for Paris 10km; vg long/sh stay." ♦ 15 Feb-15 Dec. € 12.00   2004*

BLANGY LE CHATEAU *3D1* (Rural) **Camping Domaine du Lac, 14130 Blangy-le-Chateau** [02 31 64 62 00; fax 02 31 64 15 91] Fr Pont-l'Eveque & A13 S on D579 twd Lisieux. In 5km turn L onto D51 to Blangy where at fountain (rndabt) turn L, taking care. In 200m at end of vill turn L onto D140 Rte de Mesnil & site 200m on R. Site is 5km SE of Pont-l'Eveque. Med, mkd pitch, pt sl, pt shd; wc; chem disp; shwrs; el pts (5A) inc (rev pol & long lead poss req); lndtte; ice; shop & 1km; rest; snacks; bar; BBQ; beach 22km; lake fishing; tennis; games rm; 70% statics; recep 0830-2130; adv bkg; cc acc; CCI. "Nice, peaceful site; friendly British owner; poss uneven pitches; access to pitches diff when wet; allow 1hr to Le Havre for ferry; gd rest; pretty vill; gd local walks." 1 Apr-31 Oct. € 20.50 ABS - N03   2005*

BLANGY LE CHATEAU *3D1* (3km SE) **LES CASTELS** Le Brevedent, 14130 Le Brevedent [02 31 64 72 88 or 02 31 64 21 50 (LS); fax 02 31 64 33 41; contact@campinglebrevedent. com; www.campinglebrevedent.com or www. les-castels.com] Fr Pont l'Eveque & A13 go S on D579 twd Lisieux; after 5km turn L onto D51 twd Blangy-le-Chateau. In Blangy bear R at rndabt to stay on D51 & foll sp to Le Brevedent; site on L in 3km. Med, mkd pitch, pt sl, pt shd; wc; chem disp; mv service pnt; baby facs; shwrs inc; el pts (5-10A) inc; gas; lndtte; ice; shop & 3km; tradsmn; rest; snacks; bar; BBQ; playgrnd; 2 htd pools; sand beach 22km; lake fishing; tennis 100m; sports area; mini-golf; archery; cycle hire; horseriding 2km; golf 11km; entmnt; TV rm; many statics & tour ops; no dogs; sep car park after 2230; poss cr; Eng spkn; adv bkg (dep req); quiet; cc acc; CCI. "Superb setting; v welcoming & helpful staff; recep 0830-2000; sm pitches; no c'vans over 8m acc; wc blocks clean but ltd no; facs stretched low ssn; no site lighting at night; long elec cables poss req; excursions bkd; excel." ♦ 29 Apr-24 Sep. € 24.00 (CChq acc) ABS - N01   2005*

BLANGY SUR BRESLE *3C2* (2.5km E Rural) Camp Municipal Les Etangs, 76340 Blangy-sur-Bresle [02 35 94 55 65; fax 02 35 94 06 14] Leave A28 at junc 5, R at T-junc onto D49, site on L in less than 1km. Med, mkd pitch; unshd; wc; chem disp; shwrs inc (clsd 2100-0700); el pts (5-10A) €1.30-2.25 (rev pol); lndry rm; rest, snacks bar 2km; BBQ; playgrnd; tennis & mini-golf nrby; CCI. "Clean, attractive & well-run site; cramped pitches; lakes adj; conv Calais; vg NH." ♦ 15 Mar-15 Oct. € 7.75   2005*

BLANGY SUR BRESLE *3C2* (8km W Urban) Camp Municipal de la Foret, 76340 Bazinval [tel/fax 02 32 97 04 01] NW fr Blangy on D49 for 6km, then D149 to Bazinval. Site sp fr rd. Sm, hdg pitch, pt shd; wc; chem disp (wc); shwrs inc; el pts (10A) inc (poss rev pol); Eng spkn; quiet; CCI. "Beautiful flower beds; early am tractor noise; immac san facs, poss stretched high ssn; site yourself, warden calls early eve; poss itinerants on site; NH only." 1 Apr-31 Oct. € 9.05   2005*

BLAUVAC see Carpentras *10E2*

BLAVOZY see Puy en Velay, Le *9C1*

BLAYE *7C2* (Urban) Camp Municipal, La Citadelle, 33390 Blaye [05 57 42 00 20 or 05 57 42 16 79 (LS)] Fr N ent town, over x-rds, sp in town; ent thro narr gateways in fortifications; access by narr track, single in places. NB Site access unsuitable m'vans higher than 2.7m due to narr, curved arches. Sm, terr, pt shd; wc (some cont); serviced pitches; shwrs inc; el pts (15A) inc; ice; shops 500m; tradsmn high ssn; pool 250m; phone adj; poss cr; quiet; no cc acc. "Lovely site; vineyards at Blaye & Bourg; part overlooks rv; pleasant recep; spacious pitches; pitch yourself; warden visits pm; clean but basic san facs." 1 May-30 Sep. € 10.00   2003*

BLAYE *7C2* (5km NE Rural) Camping Les Tilleuls, Chateau Les Alberts, 33390 Mazion [05 57 42 18 13; fax 05 57 42 13 01] Fr Blaye D937 N, sp to site on L. Sm, pt sl, pt shd; wc; shwrs inc; el pts (3-10A) €2.50; ice; BBQ; dogs; rd noise; CCI. "Pleasant site in cent of vineyards; wine-tasting; cycle track to Blaye; gd sh stay." 1 Apr-31 Oct. € 12.00   2003*

BLENEAU *4G3* Camp Municipal La Perpiniere, Route de Champcevrais, 89220 Bleneau [03 86 74 93 73 or 03 86 74 91 61 (Mairie); fax 03 86 74 86 74; mairiedebleneau@wanadoo.fr] At junc of D47/D22 & D90 in Bleneau take D64 twd Champcevrais & site. Sp in Bleneau. Sm, hdg pitch, shd; wc (cont); chem disp; shwrs inc; el pts (10A) €1.90; shops 500m; pool adj; games rm; fishing adj; poss cr; adv bkg; quiet; CCI. "Set in orchard; gd." 1 Apr-15 Oct. € 4.68   2003*

†**BLENEAU** *4G3* (12km NE Rural) Camping Le Bois Guillaume, 89350 Villeneuve-les-Genets [03 86 45 45 41; fax 03 86 45 49 20; camping@bois-guillaume.com; www.bois-guillaume.com] Fr Toucy take D965 dir St Fargeau. At Mezilles take D7 twd Tannerre-en-Puisaye & foll sp for site. 2.5km fr Villeneuve-les-Genets. Med, hdg/mkd pitch, some hdstg, shd; htd wc; chem disp; mv service pnt; shwrs inc; el pts (5A) €3.80; gas; rest; bar; playgrnd; htd pools; sports area; cycle hire; tennis; poss cr; Eng spkn; CCI. "Friendly staff; clean, tidy site; facs ltd low ssn; vg rest." € 15.30   2004*

BLERE *4G2* (500m NE Urban) Camp Municipal La Gatine, Rue de Cdt Lemaitre, 37150 Blere [tel/fax 02 47 57 92 60; marie@blere-touraine.com] Site sports cent on S side of Rv Cher. Lge, mkd pitch, shd; wc; chem disp; mv service pnt; shwrs inc; el pts (5-10A) €3.20-3.80 (long lead poss req); lndtte; ice; shops 300m; supmkt 400m; htd pool adj; rv fishing adj; dogs €1.90; no adv bkg; quiet; cc not acc; CCI. "Gd, well-maintained site; excel san facs; helpful wardens; gates clsd 1200-1400 (1500 Sun); sm pitches; sh walk into town; towpath walks; gd cent for wine rtes (Touraine) & chateaux; excel tourist office in town." ♦ Easter-15 Oct. € 8.60   2005*

BLESLE see Massiac *9C1*

BLET *4H3* (Urban) Camp Municipal, 18350 Blet [02 48 74 78 24 or 02 48 74 71 04 (Mairie)] Take N76 twd Sancoins SE fr Bourges. In 35km turn R on D6 in cent of Blet sp Chalivoy/St Amand. Site 400m on R just past lake. NB no sp at ent. Med, pt shd; wc; shwrs; el pts €2.70; shop 500m; dogs €1; quiet. "Gd NH; facs basic but adequate." ♦ 1 Apr-1 Nov. € 5.70   2004*

BLIGNY SUR OUCHE *6H1* (Urban) Camp Municipal des Isles, 21360 Bligny-sur-Ouche [03 80 20 11 21; fax 03 80 20 17 90] On D17 fr Arnay-le-Duc, site on L on ent vill. Med, pt shd; wc; shwrs inc; el pts (15A) €2.50; shop 500m; rest 300m; playgrnd; quiet. "Site yourself, fees collected each evening; in reach of Cote d'Or wine areas; steam rlwy 100m; peaceful, clean & tidy; noise fr cornmill at harvest time; gd." 15 May-15 Sep. € 7.00   2003*

FRANCE

BLOIS *4G2* (15km NE) **LES CASTELS Le Chateau de la Grenouillere**, 41500 Suevres [02 54 87 80 37; fax 02 54 87 84 21; la.grenouillere@wanadoo.fr; www.camping-loire.com or www.les-castels.com] On N152 bet Blois & Orleans, thro Mer, site on R, 2km NE of Suevres; sp. Lge, mkd pitch, pt shd; wc; chem disp; mv service pnt; sauna; baby facs; shwrs inc; el pts (6A) inc; gas; lndtte; ice; shop; rest; snacks; bar; BBQ (gas/charcoal); playgrnd; 2 pools (1 covrd); paddling pool; waterslide; boating; fishing; tennis; cycle hire; entmnt; TV; statics (tour ops); dogs €4; Eng spkn; adv bkg (min 3 nts); some rd & rlwy noise; cc acc; CCI. "Ideal for touring Loire area, particularly visiting the chateaux; gates clsd 2230-0700; recep open 0830-2100 high ssn; mkt Tue & Sat Blois. " ♦ 28 Apr-9 Sep. € 35.00 ABS - L04   2005*

BLOIS *4G2* (10km E Rural) **Aire Naturelle (Delaboissiere)**, 6 Rue de Chatillon, 41350 Huisseau-sur-Cosson [02 54 20 35 26] Fr Blois cr Rv Loire to Vineuil. 1km S turn L onto D33. Site at E end of vill of Huisseau, turn R into Rue de Chatillon. Sm, hdg/mkd pitch, pt sl, pt shd; wc ltd; own san; chem disp; mv service pnt; shwrs inc; el pts (6A) inc (poss rev pol); gas; shops 400m, supmkt 4km; rv 10km; dogs; poss cr; adv bkg; quiet; cc not acc; CCI. "Sm garden site with ltd facs; peaceful; immac kept; friendly owner, takes keen interest in all activities; local wine & fruit for sale; conv Loire Valley chateaux; cycle rte thro forest to Chambord Chateau." 1 May-1 Oct. € 13.00   2005*

BLOIS *4G2* (8km S Rural) **Camp Municipal**, 41120 Cellettes [02 54 70 48 41 or 02 54 70 47 54 (Mairie)] On D956, Blois to Chateauroux rd, pass almost thro Cellettes, site 120m fr D956 down 1st L after rv bdge, site on L in 100m, well sp. Med, pt shd; wc; chem disp; shwrs inc; el pts (6-10A) inc; shops, pool, playgrnd & tennis adj; fishing; phone; quiet; some daytime rd noise; cc acc; CCI. "V friendly manager; excel for touring Loire chateaux; pleasant rvside location; poor shwrs; security gates." ♦ ltd. 1 Jun-11 Sep. € 11.00   2005*

BLOIS *4G2* (6km SW) **Camping Le Cosson**, 1 Rue de la Foret, 41120 Chailles [02 54 79 46 49] Fr Blois foll sp dir Montrichard (D751); after x-ing rv bdge site ent on L 100m after rv bdge, sm sp easily missed. Sm, hdg pitch, terr, shd; wc (some cont); chem disp (wc); shwrs inc; baby facs; el pts (6A) €3.05; gas; ice; snacks; bar; shops 1km; rv sw & fishing; games area; playgrnd; dogs; phone; quiet; adv bkg; CCI. "Well-maintained site nr chateaux; v pleasant, helpful owner; walks in local forest." 15 Jun-10 Sep. € 9.80   2005*

BLOND see Bellac *7A3*

BOIRY NOTRE DAME see Arras *3B3*

BOIS DE CENE *2H4* (S Urban) **Camping Le Bois Joli**, 85710 Bois-de-Cene [02 51 68 20 05; fax 02 51 68 46 40; campingboisjoli@free.fr; www.camping-leboisjoli.com] Fr D21 turn R at church in cent of vill, site on R in 500m on rd D28. Med, mkd pitch; shd; wc; chem disp; shwrs inc; el pts (6A) inc; gas; lndtte; ice; shop adj; snacks; playgrnd; pool; sand beach 10km; tennis; fishing; Eng spkn; adv bkg; ltd facs low ssn; CCI. "Exceptionally friendly, helpful owner; clean san facs; washing facs for vehicles avail; friendly vill; gd walks." Easter-15 Sep. € 15.90   2004*

BOISSET PENCHOT see Decazeville *7D4*

BOISSIERE DU MONTAIGU, LA see Montaigu *2H4*

BOLLENE *9D2* (500m Urban) **Camp Municipal du Lez**, Quartier des Jardin, 84500 Bollene [tel/fax 04 90 30 16 86; info@bollenetourisme.com; www.bollenetourisme.com] Exit A7 junc 19 to Bollene town cent; strt on over rv bdge; L & foll sp to site. Sm, hdg/mkd pitch, hdstg, pt shd; wc; chem disp; shwrs inc; el pts (15A) €2; lndtte; shop, rest, snacks & bar 800m; playgrnd; covrd pool 1km; rv sw; dogs €1; phone; Eng spkn; adv bkg; quiet; red 15+ days; CCI. "V clean, well-kept; helpful & friendly manager; excel touring base; no twin-axles; office closed 1200-1500; vg." ♦ ltd. 1 Apr-31 Aug. € 9.00   2005*

†**BOLLENE** *9D2* (1.5km N) **Camping Le Barry**, 84500 Bollene [04 90 30 13 20; fax 04 90 40 48 64; lebarry@avignon.pacwan.net] Exit a'route A7 at Bollene, D26 twd Pierrelatte. Site 1km off D26. Med, mkd pitch, terr, pt shd; htd wc (some cont); baby facs; shwrs inc; el pts (6A) inc; gas; lndtte; ice; shop; rest; snacks; bar; BBQ (gas); playgrnd; pool; rv 2.5km; lake fishing & watersports 3km; entmnt; TV; dogs €1; poss cr; Eng spkn; adv bkg ess; poss noisy; red low ssn. "V ltd facs low ssn; low ssn office open 1030-1200. & 1630-1900 only; access to pool up steep slope; vg" € 18.50   2003*

†**BOLLENE** *9D2* (5.5km E Rural) **Camping de la Simioune**, Quartier Guffiage, 84500 Bollene [04 90 30 44 62; fax 04 90 30 44 77; la-simioune@wanadoo.fr; www.la-simioune.fr] Exit A7 junc 19 onto D994/D8 dir Carpentras (Ave Salvatore Allende D8). At 3rd x-rd 900m bef fire stn take L turn (Ave Alphonse Daudet) foll rd 3k to sp for camping on L, then site 1km. Sm, pt sl, shd; wc; chem disp; baby facs; shwrs €1; el pts (6A) €3.10; lndtte; shops & supmkt 4km; tradsmn; rest; bar; playgrnd; pool; horseriding; BBQ evenings; 10% statics; dogs €1.50; adv bkg rec high ssn; quiet; red CCI. "In pine forest; facs need upgrading - ltd in winter; excel pony club for children & adults; NH only." € 13.00   2004*

BOLLENE *9D2* (7km E) **Camping Le Lez**, La Bourgade, 26790 Suze-la-Rousse [tel/fax 04 75 98 82 83] E fr Bollene on D94 to Suze-la-Rousse; L in vill sq; R immed bef rv bdge. Sm, pt shd; wc; shwrs inc; el pts (6-10A) €2.60-3; lndtte; shop 300m; snacks; bar; playgrnd; pool; fishing; games area; TV; dogs €1; CCI. "No twin-axle vans; site poss untidy, but facs clean." Easter-30 Sep. € 10.70   2005*

†BOLLENE *9D2* (6km SW Rural) **Camp Municipal La Pinede, Quartier des Massanes, 84430 Mondragon [04 90 40 82 98; fax 04 90 40 94 82]** Exit A7 junc 19 dir Bollene & take D26 S, site 1.5km N of Mondragon. Steep access. Med, mkd pitch, pt sl, terr, pt shd; wc; chem disp; shwrs inc; el pts (5-8A) inc; Indtte; ice; shop; BBQ; playgrnd; htd, covrd pool 5km; some statics; dogs €1.20; adv bkg; quiet; CCI. "Full by 1700, early arr rec; no twin-axle vans over 6m; gd, clean site but basic facs & poss cold shwrs; code operated barrier; gd touring base; conv Ardeche Gorge." € 11.00   2005*

BONLIEU see St Laurent en Grandvaux *6H2*

BONNAC LA COTE *7B3* (1km S Rural) **LES CASTELS Le Chateau de Leychoisier, 1 Route de Leychoisier, Domaine de Leychoisier, 87270 Bonnac-la-Cote [tel/fax 05 55 39 93 43; contact@ leychoisier.com; www.leychoisier.com or www. les-castels.com]** N'wards on A20 exit junc 27 & L at T-junc onto D220. At rndabt take 3rd exit then 1st L onto D97 sp Bonnac-la-Cote. Turn L in the vill & foll sp to site. Med, mkd pitch, pt sl, shd; wc; chem disp; baby facs; shwrs inc; el pts (10A) inc; Indtte; shop; rest; snacks; bar; BBQ (gas & charcoal); playgrnd; pool; lake sw; tennis; cycle hire; games rm; dogs €0.80; Eng spkn; adv bkg; red low ssn; cc not acc; CCI. "Excel, peaceful site; welcoming, friendly & helpful staff; excel rest; conv NH nr m'way; recep 0830-2100; gd san facs; much improved site; extra for m'vans." ♦
15 Apr-20 Sep. € 27.00 ABS - L11   2005*

BONNAL *6G2* (3.5km N Rural) **LES CASTELS Le Val de Bonnal, 25680 Bonnal [03 81 86 90 87; fax 03 81 86 03 92; val-de-bonnal@wanadoo.fr; www.les-castels.com]** Leave a'route A36-E60 at junc 5 onto D50 N twd Vesoul. After 11km turn L on D49 then foll sp to Bonnal & site. Lge, mkd pitches, pt shd; wc; chem disp; baby facs; shwrs inc; el pts (6A) inc; gas; Indtte; shop; rest; snacks; bar; BBQ; playgrnd; pool; waterslide; lake sw & sand beach adj; fishing (permit); canoeing; watersports; cycle hire; gym; golf 6km; entmnt high ssn; child entmnt; internet; TV; 40% statics; dogs; poss cr; Eng spkn; adv bkg; quiet; red low ssn; cc acc; CCI. "Attractive site; busy & popular high ssn; excel welcome; lge accessible pitches; clean facs; gd child activities; ltd facs low ssn." ♦ 6 May-10 Sep. € 32.30 ABS - J01   2005*

BONNES see Chauvigny *7A3*

BONNEUIL MATOURS *4H2* (1km Rural) **Camp Municipal de Cremault, 8 Allee du Stade, 86210 Bonneuil-Matours [05 49 85 20 47]** Fr N10 20km N of Poitiers take D82 E to Bonneuil-Matours. Site sp in vill next to Stade & rv but site ent not well sp. Med, shd; htd wc; chem disp; shwrs inc; el pts €2.70; Indry rm; ice; shops 1km; tradsmn; snacks; rest; bar; BBQ; playgrnd; entmnts; cycling; tennis; mini-golf; archery; rv sw & fishing; quiet. "Nature reserve adj; clean facs; lovely site." 1 May-30 Sep. € 8.70   2003*

BONNEVAL *4F2* (1km SE Rural) **Camp Municipal Le Bois Chievre, Route de Vouvray, St Maurice, 28800 Bonneval [02 37 47 54 01; fax 02 37 96 26 79; camping.bonneval@wanadoo.fr; www.bonneval tourisme.com]** Rec app fr N (Chartres), or SE (D27 fr Patay/Orleans) as app fr S thro town is narr & diff. Fr Chartres take N10 into Bonneval & foll camp sp (mainly to L). Med, mkd pitch, hdstg, pt sl, shd; htd wc; chem disp; shwrs inc; el pts (6A) inc (rev pol); Indtte; ice; shop 1km; tradsmn; rest; snacks, bar, BBQ; playgrnd; htd pool adj; some statics; Eng spkn; adv bkg; quiet; red long stay; CCI. "Well-maintained site in woodland; vg facs but poss stretched in ssn; friendly, helpful staff; wooded walk to rv & picnic site; lge pitches; no twin-axle vans or c'vans over 5.60m; vg NH for Le Havre or Dieppe."
♦ 1 Mar-30 Nov. € 11.60   2005*

BONNEVILLE *9A3* (Urban) **Camp Municipal du Bois du Tours, Rue des Bairiers, 74130 Bonneville [04 50 97 03 31 or 04 50 25 22 14 (Mairie)]** Fr A40 junc 16 take N203, or fr Cluses take N205 to Bonneville. Cross rv bdge into town cent; site sp. Med, pt shd; wc (some cont); chem disp; shwrs; el pts (10A); shops 500m; poss cr; adv bkg; quiet. "Well-maintained, immac site; refurbished san facs; 15 Jun-15 Sep. € 6.10   2003*

BONNIEUX *10E2* (1km W Rural) **Camp Municipal du Vallon, Route de Menerbes, 84480 Bonnieux [tel/fax 04 90 75 86 14]** Fr Bonnieux take D3 twd Menerbes, site sp on L on leaving vill. Med, mkd pitch, terr, pt shd; wc (some cont); shwrs inc; el pts (10A) inc; Indtte; shop; tradsmn; snacks; bar; playgrnd; dogs €1; quiet; CCI. "Beautiful wooded area; attractive hilltop vill; quaint, 'olde worlde' site in gd touring area; gd walking & moutain bike area."
15 Mar-20 Oct. € 11.90   2005*

BONO, LE see Auray *2F3*

BONZEE *5D1* (E Rural) **Base de Loisirs du Col Vert Les Eglantines, 55160 Bonzee [03 29 87 31 98; fax 03 29 87 30 60; base-de-loisirs-du-col-vert@wanadoo.fr]** Fr Verdun take D903 twd Metz for 18km; in Manheulles, turn R to Bonzee in 1km; at Bonzee turn L for Fresnes; site on R. Med, hdg/mkd pitch, pt shd; wc; chem disp; mv service pnt; shwrs inc; el pts (4-6A) €3.50-6.63; gas & 1km; Indtte; shop & 1km; tradsmn; BBQ; rest; snacks; bar; playgrnd; lake sw & boating adj; fishing; tennis 1.5km; many statics; phone; adv bkg; noisy high ssn; cc acc; CCI. "Spacious pitches in well planned sites; 2 sites together; sh stay/NH only." ♦ 1 Apr-30 Sep. € 12.10   2004*

BOOFZHEIM see Rhinau *6E3*

FRANCE

†BORDEAUX *7C2* (10km E Rural) **Camping Caravanning Bel Air, 33670 Sadirac [05 56 23 01 90; fax 05 56 23 08 38; info@camping-bel-air.com; www.camping-bel-air.com]** Fr A10 at junc 24 take D936 E fr Bordeaux sp Bergerac. Approx 15km E turn SE onto D671 sp Creon. Site on L, 1.5km after Lorient. Med, hdg/mkd pitch, hdstg, pt shd; wc (some cont); chem disp; shwrs inc; el pts (5A) inc; gas; lndry rm; shop high ssn; tradsmn; supmkt 1km; rest; snacks; bar; playgrnd; pool; 10% statics; dogs €1.55; clsd to vehicles 2200-0800; Eng spkn; adv bkg (no dep, no fee); quiet; red 4+ wks; CCl. "Helpful owners; plenty to do in area; no twin-axle vans; sep car park low ssn; phone ahead to check open low ssn; rest sm & ltd; facs v ltd low ssn & poss itinerants; rec sh stay/NH only." ♦ ltd. € 14.45
2003*

†BORDEAUX *7C2* (4km S Urban) **Camping Beau Soleil, Cours General de Gaulle, 33170 Gradignan [tel/fax 05 56 89 17 66; campingbeausoleil@wanadoo.fr]** Fr N take exit 16 Bordeaux ring rd-Gradignan (N10). Site S of town on N10 100m on R after Beau Soleil complex. Sm, mkd pitch, hdstg, pt sl, pt shd; htd wc; chem disp; shwrs inc; el pts (6-10A) €1.50-3; lndtte; ice; shops adj; snacks; bar; gas/elec BBQ; rv/lake sw 2km; 70% statics; dogs €1; bus 100m; poss cr; Eng spkn; adv bkg rec; quiet; CCl. "Pleasant, clean, family-run site; v helpful; conv for Bordeaux; ltd but vg san facs; few touring pitches means poss cr w/e even low ssn; some pitches poss unsuitable for c'vans; adv bkg rec; vg sh stay." ♦ € 14.50
2005*

BORMES LES MIMOSAS see Lavandou, Le *10F3*

BORT LES ORGUES *7C4* (4km N Rural) **Escapades Terre Oceane Camping La Siauve, Rue du Camping, 15270 Lanobre [04 71 40 31 85 or 05 46 55 10 01; fax 04 71 40 34 33 or 05 46 55 10 10; info@campingterreoceane; www.campingterreoceane.com]** On D992 Clermont-Ferrand to Bort-les-Orgues, site on R 3km S of Lanobre. Site sp. Lge, hdg/mkd pitch, terr, pt shd; wc; chem disp; mv service pnt; shwrs inc; el pts (6A) €3; lndtte; shop & 3km; tradsmn; rest; snacks; bar; playgrnd; lake sw adj; fishing; tennis nr; games area; cycle hire; entmnt; TV rm; dogs; phone; Eng spkn; adv bkg (dep req); noisy high ssn; cc acc; CCl. "Footpaths (steep) to lake; gd sw, boating etc; excel touring base; v scenic." 17 Jun-16 Sep.
€ 14.00
2005*

†BORT LES ORGUES *7C4* (7km SW Rural) **Camping a la Ferme (Chanet), Domaine de la Vigne, 15240 Saignes [tel/fax 04 71 40 61 02]** Take D922 S fr Bort sp Mauriac. After 5.5km at junc with D22 take sharp L sp Saignes. In cent of Saignes turn L at T-junc onto D30. After 200m turn L onto C14 sp La Vigne & Camping. Farmhouse on L after 400m, site on R. Sm, pt sl, pt shd; wc; cold shwrs inc; el pts (6A) €2 (rev pol); shops 800m; sm pool; poss cr; adv bkg; quiet. "Beautiful, peaceful setting; CL-type site; friendly owners; adv bkg rec otherwise have to pay extra; ltd facs; san facs poss neglected low ssn; gd sh stay." € 10.00   2004*

BORT LES ORGUES *7C4* (10km SW) **Camp Municipal de la Champ, 15350 Champagnac-les-Mines [04 71 69 61 55 (Mairie)]** Exit Bort twd Mauriac on D922. After 5km turn R for Champagnac-les-Mines on D15 & foll sp. Sm, pt shd; wc; shwrs; el pts; shops 1km; shgl beach 16km; pool 7km; fishing; sailing; windsurfing; adv bkg; quiet.   2003*

BOUCHEMAINE see Angers *4G1*

BOUGE CHAMBALUD see St Rambert d'Albon *9C2*

BOULANCOURT see Malesherbes *4F3*

BOULOGNE SUR GESSE *8F3* (6km NE Rural) **Camping Le Canard Fou, 31350 Lunax [05 61 88 26 06]** Fr Boulogne-sur-Gesse N on D632 sp Toulouse. In 6km turn L sp Lunax, foll site sp for 1km. Turn L at x-rds, site 300m on R. Sm, pt sl, pt shd; wc; chem disp (wc); shwrs inc; el pts (9A) inc; gas; lndtte; shop 6km; BBQ; pool 6km; reservoir adj; 40% statics; phone 800m; Eng spkn; adv bkg; quiet. "Peaceful CL-type site; v friendly owners; breakfast & eve meals avail; perfect site for walking, cycling." ♦ 15 Mar-15 Dec. € 11.00 (4 persons)   2005*

BOULOGNE SUR GESSE *8F3* (1.3km SE) **Camp Municipal du Lac, Ave du Lac, 31350 Boulogne-sur-Gesse [05 61 88 20 54 or 05 61 62 39 30; fax 05 61 88 62 16]** Fr Boulogne-sur-Gesse, take D633 for 1km. Foll sp, turn L to site. Lake (watersports cent) adj ent. Lge, mkd pitch, pt sl, pt shd; wc (some cont); chem disp; shwrs inc; el pts (10A) inc; gas; shops 1km; rest; bar; playgrnd; htd pool 300m; boating; fishing; tennis; golf; entmnt; 90% statics; dogs; phone; Eng spkn; quiet. "High kerbs mean site poss unsuitable for lge o'fits; friendly site; clean facs; sh walk into town." ♦ 1 Apr-30 Sep. € 12.75   2005*

†BOULOGNE SUR MER *3A2* (6km E Rural) **Camping Manoir de Senlecques, 45 Rue de la Fontaine, 62126 Pernes-lez-Boulogne [03 21 83 35 96; fax 03 21 33 83 85; manoirdesenlecques@wanadoo.fr; http://perso.wanadoo.fr/..manoirdesenlecques]** Exit A16 junc 33 sp to Wimille. Turn under m'way onto D233 (pt of rd is narr) to Pernes & site is E of vill. Alt rte for longer o'fits (rds wider): exit A16 onto N42 dir St Omer. Turn R for La Capelle, then L on D233E for Pernes. Sm, some hdstg, pt shd; wc; chem disp; mv service pnt; shwrs €1.40; el pts (6A) €2.50 (some rev pol); lndtte; ice; shop, supmkt 5km; BBQ; sand beach 6km; fishing; 10% statics; dogs €1; some Eng spkn; adv bkg; quiet; cc not acc; red CCl. "Warm welcome fr helpful owners; delightful site in manor house grounds; B&B also avail; free elec NH; gd vet within 3km; ltd el pts high ssn; conv Calais, Tunnel & Nausica Seaworld; busy NH; excel." € 13.50   2005*

BOULOGNE SUR MER *3A2* (8km E) **Camp Municipal Les Sapins, 62360 La Capelle-les-Boulogne** [03 21 83 16 61] Exit A16 junc 31 E onto N42 to La Capelle vill; cont to next rndabt & take sp Cremarest; site on L. Sm, pt shd; wc; shwrs inc; el pts (4A) €2.25-6.45; lndtte; shops 500m; hypmkt 2km; playgrnd; sand beach 10km; 50% statics; poss cr; adv bkg; poss rd noise & fr adj horseriding school; no cc acc; CCI. "Clean but basic; helpful warden; gd for Calais; gd NH/sh stay." 15 Apr-15 Sep. € 10.00
2005*

†**BOULOGNE SUR MER** *3A2* (16km E Rural) **Camping a la Ferme Le Bois Groult, Le Plouy, 62142 Colembert** [03 21 33 32 16] Take N42 fr Boulogne twd St Omer, take exit S to Desvres (D127). At rndabt foll sp Colembert. On ent Le Plouy foll sp to site. Sm, pt sl, pt shd; wc; shwrs €2; el pts inc; shops 6km; dogs; adv bkg; quiet; cc not acc. "Conv for ferry port; pleasant owner; v basic facs ltd in winter; CL-type site; twin-axles acc."
€ 10.00
2004*

BOULOGNE SUR MER *3A2* (6km S Coastal) **Camp Municipal La Falaise, Rue Charles Cazin, 62224 Equihen-Plage** [03 21 31 22 61; fax 03 21 80 54 01; mairie.equihen.plage@wanadoo.fr] Exit A16 junc 29 onto N1 S, foll sp Equihen-Plage & site. Med, pt sl, pt shd; wc; mv service pnt; shwrs inc; el pts (10A) €3.30; lndtte; playgrnd; sand beach 200m; watersports; games rm; statics; dogs €1.60; phone; adv bkg; quiet. "Pleasant, clean, well-run site in excel location." 28 Mar-4 Nov. € 13.50   2003*

BOULOGNE SUR MER *3A2* (6km S Urban) **Caravaning du Chateau d'Hardelot, 21 Rue Nouvelle, 62360 Condette** [tel/fax 03 21 87 59 59 or 03 21 31 74 01; campingduchateau@libertysurf.fr; www.camping-caravaning-du-chateau.com] Take N1 S fr Boulogne, R turn onto D940 to Le Touquet; then R at rndabt on D113 to Condette; take 2nd turning to Chateau Camping, R at next rndabt & site 400m on R. Fr S leave A16 at exit 27 to Neufchatel Hardelot then take D940 twd Condette & turn L at 1st rndabt onto D113 then as above. Med, hdg/mkd pitch, pt sl, pt shd; wc; chem disp; mv service pnt; baby facs; shwrs inc; el pts (10A) €4.30 (poss rev pol); lndtte; shop 500m; playgrnd; sand beach 3km; tennis 500m; sm multi-gym; horseriding; games rm; golf; poss cr; some statics; dogs; some Eng spkn; adv bkg; quiet but some rd noise; red low ssn; no cc acc; CCI. "Lovely site in wooded surroundings; gd value; bar & gd rest walking dist; immac san facs; nr chateau & lake; v helpful & friendly owner; conv for Calais & Cite Europe but barrier only opens at 0800; v busy high ssn; sm pitches." ♦ 1 Apr-31 Oct. € 16.80   2005*

BOULOGNE SUR MER *3A2* (7km S Urban) **Camping Les Cytises, Rue de l'Eglise, 62360 Isques** [tel/fax 03 21 31 11 10] S fr Boulogne on N1 to Isques; site 150m fr N1. Or on A16 exit junc 28 & foll sp Isques N1. Foll camp sp. Med, hdg pitch, terr, pt shd; htd wc; chem disp; baby facs; shwrs inc; el pts (3-6A) inc; gas; lndtte; ice; shop 100m; snacks; playgrnd; pool & sand beach 4km; rv adj; archery; dogs; Eng spkn; adv bkg; some rlwy noise; cc not acc; CCI. "Gd site; v clean san facs; poss sm pitches; 30 mins fr Channel Tunnel & 5 mins fr Nausica; vg NH nr m'way." ♦
1 Apr-15 Oct. € 15.00   2005*

BOULOIRE *4F2* (1km E) **Camp Municipal, Chemin des Ruelles, 72440 Bouloire** [02 43 35 52 09 or 02 43 35 40 25 (Mairie)] On N157 Le Mans dir Orleans rd. At supmkt in Bouloire turn R then L, across N157 at traff lts. Sm, pt sl, pt shd; wc; chem disp; shwrs inc; el pts (5A) €4; shops & pizzeria adj; CCI. "Conv Le Mans; excel sh stay." Easter-1 Sep.
€ 9.00   2003*

BOULOU, LE *8G4* (Urban) **Camping L'Olivette, Les Thermes du Boulou, Route du Perthus, 66160 Le Boulou** [04 68 83 48 08; fax 04 68 87 46 00] N9 twd Spanish border site on R alongside main N9, v busy rd. Med, hdg/mkd pitch; pt sl, pt shd; wc; baby facs; shwrs inc; el pts (10A) €2.30; ice; lndtte; shops; snacks; bar; many statics; dogs €1.60; poss cr; Eng spkn; some rd noise. "Conv for Salvador Dali Museum & ruins at Empurias; security gate; poss tired pitches; clean san facs; v helpful owners; gd NH." 15 Mar-31 Oct. € 12.60   2005*

BOULOU, LE *8G4* (2km N) **Camping Le Mas Llinas, 66160 Le Boulou** [04 68 83 25 46; info@camping-mas-llinas.com; www.camping-mas-llinas.com] Fr Perpignan, take N9 S; 1km N of Le Boulou turn R at Intermarche supmkt 100m to mini rndabt, turn L & foll sp to Mas-Llinas to site in 2km. Or fr A9 exit 43 & foll sp dir Perpignan thro Le Boulou. L at rndabt adj Le Clerc, site well sp. Med, terr, pt shd; wc; shwrs inc; chem disp; el pts (5-10A) €3-4; gas; lndtte; shops adj; tradsmn; snacks; playgrnd; pool; some statics; dogs €2; phone; adv bkg; Eng spkn; quiet; red low ssn; CCI. "Friendly, welcoming owners; peaceful in hillside setting with gd views fr top levels; beware poss high winds on high plateau pitches; ltd water points at top levels; ltd facs low ssn; facs clean; gd sized pitches." ♦ ltd.
1 Feb-30 Nov. € 15.40   2005*

BOULOU, LE *8G4* (6km E Urban) **Camping Soleil d'Or, 66740 Villelongue-dels-Monts** [04 68 89 72 11] Fr Le Boulou D618 sp Argeles-sur-Mer; in 7km at rndbt turn R sp Villelongue. Foll yellow camping sp. Sm, hdg/mkd pitch, hdstg, pt sl, pt shd; wc; chem disp; shwrs inc; el pts (10A) €4; lndtte; shops adj; playgrnd; bus 500m; quiet; no cc acc; CCI. "Helpful owner; ltd pitches for lge o'fits."
15 May-30 Sep. € 13.00   2002*

†BOULOU, LE *8G4* (1.5km SE Rural) Camping Les Oliviers, Route d'Argeles, 66160 Le Boulou [04 68 83 12 86; fax 04 68 87 60 08; campingles oliviers@wanadoo.fr] Exit A9 junc at Le Boulou. Foll sp onto D618 twds Argeles-sur-Mer. Site on R in 1km, well sp fr D618. Med, pt shd, mkd pitch; htd wc; chem disp; mv service pnt; shwrs inc; el pts (6A) €2.60; gas 1km; lndry rm; shop & 1km; tradsmn; playgrnd; shgl beach 12km; 10% statics; dogs €0.80; site clsd 15 Dec-15 Jan; poss cr; adv bkg; quiet but some rd noise; red low ssn; CCI. "V clean facs; site nr juncs of A9 & N9, gd touring base or NH en rte Spain; v helpful owner; gd facs & v popular low ssn; dog-friendly." ♦ ltd. € 12.20   2005*

†BOULOU, LE *8G4* (5km S Rural) Camping Le Congo, Route de Ceret, 66480 Maureillas-las-Illas [04 68 83 23 21; fax 04 68 87 47 15; campinglecongo@hotmail.com; www.camping lecongo.com] Fr Le Boulou take N9 S, fork R after 2km onto D618 dir Ceret. Site on L 500m after Maureillas. Med, hdg pitch, shd; htd wc (cont); chem disp (wc); shwrs inc; el pts (10A); gas; lndtte; ice; shop 500m; tradsmn; rest; snacks; BBQ; playgrnd; pool; sand beach 20km; 10% statics; dogs; phone; adv bkg; Eng spkn; cc acc. ♦ € 21.00   2005*

BOULOU, LE *8G4* (4km SW) Camping de la Vallee/Les Deux Rivieres, Route de Maureillas, 66490 St Jean-Pla-de-Corts [04 68 83 23 20; fax 04 68 83 07 94] Exit a'route A9 at Le Boulou exit. Turn W on D115. Turn L after 3km at rndabt, into St Jean-Pla-de-Corts, thro vill, over bdge, site on L. Med, mkd pitch, pt shd, wc; chem disp; mv service pnt; shwrs inc; baby facs; el pts (5A) €3; gas 800m; lndtte; ice; shop 800m; tradsmn; rest; snacks; bar; playgrnd; pool; sand beach 20km; lake sw & fishing 1km; archery; mini-golf; entmnt; TV; phone; dogs €2; 5% statics; poss cr; Eng spkn; adv bkg (bkg fee & dep req); quiet; cc acc; red 10 days CCI. "Lge pitches; excel san facs." ♦ 1 Mar-31 Oct. € 14.50   2004*

BOULOU, LE *8G4* (5km SW Rural) Camping La Clapere (Naturist), Route de Las Illas, 66400 Maureillas-las-Illas [04 68 83 36 04; fax 04 68 83 34 44; info@clapere.com; www.clapere. com] Exit Boulou S on N9 twd Le Perthus; after 3km take N618 twd Maureillas, D13 for 2km twd Las Illas. Lge, terr, pt shd; wc; chem disp; shwrs inc; el pts (3-6A) €3.20-4.80; lndtte; ice; shop; rest; snacks; bar; playgrnd; pool; rv adj; fishing; tennis; archery; games area; entmnt; TV; dogs €1.20; poss cr; Eng spkn; adv bkg; quiet. "Excel with easy access for c'vans; INF card req or may be purchased; vg for children; friendly recep." ♦ Easter-31 Oct. € 19.50   2002*

†BOULOU, LE *8G4* (3km W Rural) Camping Les Casteillets, 66490 St Jean Pla-de-Corts [04 68 83 26 83; fax 04 68 83 39 67; jc@campingles casteillets.com; www.campinglescasteillets.com] Exit A9 at Le Boulou; turn W on D115; after 3km turn L immed after St Jean-Pla-de-Corts; site sp on R in 400m. NB Narr app last 200m. Med, mkd pitch, pt shd; wc; chem disp; some serviced pitches; shwrs inc; el pts (6A) €3; gas; lndtte; ice; shop; rest; snacks; bar; playgrnd; pool; tennis; sand beach 20km; TV; entmnt; 10% statics; poss cr; Eng spkn; adv bkg ess high ssn; quiet. "Friendly site; conv for touring NE Spain; site clsd early Dec to early Jan; lge pitches; views of mountains; gd rest." ♦ € 15.50   2005*

BOULOU, LE *8G4* (8km W Rural) Camping Al Comu, Route de Fourques, 66300 Llauro [04 68 39 42 08; alcomu@wanadoo.fr] Fr N on A9 exit junc 43. Take D115 dir Ceret. Bef bdge R onto D615 to Llauro. Site on L after vill. Sm, mkd pitch, terr, pt shd; wc; chem disp (wc); shwrs inc; el pts (16A) inc; ice; shop 6km; playgrnd; pool 10km; lake sw 6km; dogs; Eng spkn; quiet. "Attractive setting in lower Pyrenees; friendly & helpful owners; gd." ♦ ltd. 1 Apr-1 Nov. € 13.85   2005*

BOURBON LANCY *4H4* (Urban) Camping St Prix, Rue de St Prix, 71140 Bourbon-Lancy [tel/fax 03 85 89 20 98 or 03 86 37 95 83; aquadist@ wanadoo.fr; www.camping-chalets-bourbon-lancy.com] Fr N turn L fr D979 on D973 & foll into Bourbon-Lancy. Where D973 veers L (sp Autun) strt on to x-rds in about 100m. Turn R, then next R, site sp. Med, hdg pitch, hdstg, terr, pt sl, shd; wc; chem disp; shwrs inc; el pts (10A) inc; lndry rm; ice; shop; snacks; playgrnd; htd pool adj; lake sw/fishing; 20% statics; Eng spkn; quiet; CCI. "Well-managed site in gd condition; helpful staff; lovely old town 10 min walk; gd long/sh stay; rec." 1 Apr-31 Oct. € 15.00   2005*

BOURBON L'ARCHAMBAULT *9A1* (10km NE Rural) Camping Les Fourneaux (Naturist), Route Limoise, 03160 Couzon [tel/fax 04 70 66 23 18] Fr Bourbon NE on D139 to Couzon, then L onto D13, site in 2km on L. Med, pt sl, pt shd; wc; chem disp; shwrs el pts (2-4A) €2.50-4; tradsmn; bar; playgrnd; pool; cycle hire; phone; Eng spkn; quiet; red 3+ days; INF card req. "V lge pitches; helpful Dutch owners; conv touring base." ♦ ltd. 1 Jun-15 Sep. € 22.00   2005*

BOURBON L'ARCHAMBAULT *9A1* (1km W Rural) Camp Municipal de Bignon, 03160 Bourbon-l'Archambault [04 70 67 08 83; mairie-bourbon-archambault@wanadoo.fr] Take D953 (sp) to Montlucon fr town cent. Turn R nr top of hill at camping sp bef town cancellation sp. Lge, sl, pt shd; wc (some cont); shwrs inc; el pts (6-10A) inc; shops 1km; htd pool & waterslide 300m; tennis nr; 75% statics; poss cr; quiet. "Beautifully laid-out in park surroundings; dated san facs; gd pitches; charming town; excel." 1 Mar-31 Oct. € 8.50   2005*

BOURBONNE LES BAINS *6F2* (NW) **Camping Caravaning Le Montmorency, Rue du Stade,** 52400 Bourbonne-les-Bains [03 25 90 08 64] Sp on ent town either way on D417. After exit D417, sp at 1st turn L at telephone box. Site adj to pool. Med, pt sl, unshd; wc; mv service pnt; shwrs inc; el pts (6A) inc; gas; lndry rm; shops 500m; snacks; pool adj; tennis; adv bkg; quiet. "Pleasant site; helpful warden; popular with visitors to spa cent; gd NH." 1 Apr-15 Oct. € 11.60   2003*

†**BOURBOULE, LA** *7B4* (2km E) **Camping Les Clarines, 1424 Blvd Marechal Leclerc, Les Planches,** 63150 La Bourboule [04 73 81 02 30; fax 04 73 81 09 34] Fr La Bourboule take D996 (old rd sp Piscine & Gare); fork L at exit fr town. Site sp on R. Lge, terr, pt shd; wc (some cont); baby facs; shwrs inc; el pts (3-10A) €2.13-€5.79; gas; lndtte; ice; shop & adj; bar; BBQ; htd pool; playgrnd; entmnt; TV; dogs €1.37; poss cr; adv bkg (ess high ssn); quiet; 15% red low ssn. "Gd winter sports cent (open for ski Xmas-Easter); clsd 14 Nov-18 Dec." ♦ € 12.50   2005*

BOURBOULE, LA *7B4* (3km E) **Camp Municipal des Vernieres, Blvd des Vernieres,** 63150 La Bourboule [04 73 81 10 20 or 04 73 81 31 00; fax 04 73 65 54 98] Fr N on N89 or S on D922 turn E onto D130 dir Le Mont-Dore, site sp. Lge, pt terr, pt shd; wc (some cont); shwrs inc; el pts (6-10A) €2.50-5; lndtte; supmkt nr; playgrnd; pool nr; fishing nr; poss cr; no adv bkg; some rd noise. "Rec; gd clean facs." ♦ Easter-30 Sep. € 9.30   2004*

†**BOURBOULE, LA** *7B4* (3km NW Urban) **Camping Le Poutie, Ave de Marechal Leclerc,** 63150 Murat-le-Quaire [04 73 81 04 54] Fr La Bourboule on D996, just past stn. Med, mkd pitch, hdstg, terr, pt shd; wc (some cont); chem disp; shwrs inc; el pts (6A) €3 (poss rev pol); lndtte; supmkt 600m; htd pool 300m; many statics; dogs €1.50; poss cr; adv bkg; quiet; CCI. "Helpful owner; ltd space for tourers." € 11.00   2004*

BOURDEAU see Yenne *9B3*

BOURDEAUX *9D2* (1.5km SE Rural) **Camping Les Bois du Chatelas,** 26460 Bourdeaux [04 75 00 60 80; fax 04 75 00 60 81; bois.du. chatelas@infonie.fr; www.chatelas.com] A7 m'way exit at Valence Sud, head twd Crest then twd Bourdeaux. In Bourdeaux sp Dienlefit, site in 1km on L. Med, mkd pitch, terr, pt shd; htd wc; chem disp; mv service pnt; baby facs; shwrs inc; el pts (10A) €4; gas; lndtte; ice; shop; tradsmn; rest; snacks; bar; cooking facs; playgrnd; htd covrd pool; rv sw 5km; entmnt; TV rm; 30% statics; dogs €4; phone; Eng spkn; adv bkg ess high ssn (dep req + bkg fee); red low ssn; cc acc; CCI. "In lovely area; stunning views; gd walking; on steep slope." 15 Apr-2 Oct. € 17.50   2005*

BOURDEAUX *9D2* (300m S) **Camp Municipal Le Gap des Tortelles,** 26460 Bourdeaux [tel/fax 04 75 53 30 45] Foll camping/piscine sp in vill. Gd app fr S via D94 & D70 fr Nyons. Sm, terr, pt shd; wc; shwrs inc; el pts (6A) €2.60; lndtte; shop, 600m; rest 300m; pool; sw rv; tennis adj; few statics; adv bkg; quiet. "V attractive area away fr tourist scene; sh path into vill." ♦ 1 Apr-30 Sep. € 9.20   2004*

BOURDEAUX *9D2* (10km W) **Camp Municipal Le Parc,** 26160 Pont-de-Barret [04 75 90 47 64 or 04 75 90 12 38; fax 04 75 90 10 64] Fr N (Crest) take D538. In 5km at La Repara take D6, in 11km at Cleon d'Andran turn S on D9 (sp Charols & La Begude). In 1km fork E foll sps to Manas & Pont-de-Barret. Diff ent, narr, uneven site. Sm, shd; wc; shwrs inc; el pts (15A) inc; shops 200m in vill; pool 7km; playgrnd; rv sw; quiet; adv bkg. Easter-31 Oct. € 6.40   2002*

BOURDEAUX *9D2* (4km NW Rural) **Camping Le Couspeau, Quartier Bellevue,** 26460 Le Poet-Celard [04 75 53 30 14; fax 04 75 53 37 23; info@couspeau.com; www.couspeau.com] Fr D538 Crest-Bourdeaux; pass thro Saou & after several kms turn R over bdge to Le Poet-Celard, site sp in vill. Med, terr, mkd pitch, sl, pt shd; wc; chem disp; serviced pitches; shwrs inc; el pts (6A) €3 (poss rev pol); gas; lndtte; sm shop; tradsmn; rest, snacks, bar high ssn; playgrnd; 2 htd pools (1 covrd); rv sw & fishing; canoeing; tennis; horseriding 4km; TV rm; 20% statics; dogs €1; Eng spkn; adv bkg; quiet; cc acc; red low ssn; CCI. "On steep hillside; stunning scenery; peaceful even in high ssn; facs for disabled but site rds steep; tractor assistance avail on arr/dep; red low ssn." ♦ 16 Apr-30 Sep. € 24.00 (CChq acc)   2005*

BOURG see Langres *6F1*

BOURG ACHARD *3D2* (1km W) **Camping Le Clos Normand, 235 Route de Pont Audemer,** 27310 Bourg-Achard [02 32 56 34 84 or 06 03 60 36 26] 1km W of vill of Bourg-Achard, N175 Rouen-Pont Audemer or exit a'route A13 at Bourg-Achard junc. Med, hdg/mkd pitch, pt sl, pt shd; wc (chem clos); shwrs inc; el pts (6A) €2.50 (poss rev pol); gas; ice; shop; supmkt nr; pool; playgrnd; mini-golf; 10% statics; poss cr; quiet; adv bkg; cc acc; CCI. "Gd sh stay; clean facs." ♦ 1 Apr-30 Sep. € 12.30   2003*

BOURG ARGENTAL *9C2* (7km NE Rural) **Camping a Tou Vert du Val Ternay, Le Pre Battoir,** 42220 St Julien-Molin-Molette [04 77 51 50 76; fax 04 71 59 65 56; a.tou.vert@net-up.com] N fr Annonay on D206/N82, turn R onto D306 to vill, site sp. Med, pt shd; shwrs inc; el pts (10A) €2.30; lndtte; ice; shop; bar; BBQ; playgrnd; TV; fishing; entmnt; dogs €0.75; adv bkg; quiet; red low ssn. 1 Mar-30 Oct. € 8.40   2002*

FRANCE

†BOURG ARGENTAL 9C2 (S Rural) Camp Municipal L' Astree, Parc Residentiel de Loisir Les Rivets, 42220 Bourg-Argental [tel/fax 04 77 39 72 97] S fr St Etienne on N82 to Bourg-Argental, thro town, site well sp on R soon after rndabt & opp filling stn. Fr Annonay or Andance site on L of N82 at start of Bourg-Argental, adj rv. Sm, pt shd; wc; chem disp (wc); shwrs inc; el pts (4-6A) €3-4 (long cable poss req); gas; lndtte; shop 250m; snacks; playgrnd; rv sw adj; waterslide; fishing; 60% statics; dogs €1.50; phone; poss cr; some rd noise; red low ssn; CCI. "Pleasant site with modern facs; vg NH." ♦ € 15.00   2005*

BOURG DES COMPTES see Guichen 2F4

BOURG D'OISANS, LE 9C3 (Rural) Camping Le Colporteur, Le Mas du Plan, 38520 Le Bourg d'Oisans [04 76 79 11 44 or 06 85 73 29 19; fax 04 76 79 11 49; info@colporteur.com; www. camping-colporteur.com] W fr Briancon on N91 to Le Bourg d'Oisans. Ent town, pass Casino supmkt, site sp on L; 150m to sw pool - 2nd site sp, site 50m - sp on side of house. Fr Grenoble on A480 exit 8 onto N85, cont on N91 to Le Bourg d'Oisans. Foll sp R in cent of town after Total service stn. Med, hdg/mkd pitch, hdstg, shd; htd wc; chem disp; baby facs; shwrs inc; el pts (6-15A) €3.90; lndtte; shops 500m; tradsmn; rest; snacks; bar; BBQ; playgrnd; htd pool 150m; waterslide; lake sw 10km; fishing; tennis 150m; mountain bikes; rockclimbing; horseriding; cycle hire 200m; entmnt; games rm; TV; 10% statics; dogs €1.50; Eng spkn; adv bkg (dep req); quiet; red long stay/low ssn; cc acc; red long stay; CCI. "Site to v high standard; well-organised; lge indiv pitches; gd security; mountain scenery; many activities; conv National Park des Ecrins." ♦ 15 May-17 Sep. € 21.00   2005*

See advertisement

BOURG D'OISANS, LE 9C3 (1.5km NE Rural) Camping a la Rencontre du Soleil, Route de l'Alpe-d'Huez, La Sarenne, 38520 Le Bourg-d'Oisans [04 76 79 12 22; fax 04 76 80 26 37; rencontre.soleil@wanadoo.fr; www.joliefrance.com/ars] Fr N91 approx 800m E of town turn on D211, sp Alpe d'Huez. In approx 500m cross sm bdge over Rv Sarennes, then turn immed L to site. (Take care not to overshoot ent, as poss diff to turn back.) Med, mkd pitch, pt shd; wc (some cont); chem disp; mv service pnt; baby facs; shwrs inc; el pts (2-10A) inc; lndtte; ice; supmkt 300m; rest; snacks; bar; BBQ; playgrnd; htd pool; fishing; tennis; horseriding 10km; child entmnt high ssn; internet; TV/games rm; 45% statics; dogs €0.80; adv bkg ess; rd noise; red low ssn; cc acc; CCI. "Wonderful scenery; Ecrins National Park; Tour de France usually passes thro area & access may be restricted; mkt Sat; organised walks; pitches poss flooded after heavy rain, but staff excel at responding." 10 May-15 Sep. € 24.00 (CChq acc) ABS - M01   2005*

Some of these sites have changed their opening dates - we'd better fill in some site report forms and let the editor of the guide know.

BOURG D'OISANS, LE 9C3 (1.5km NE Rural) Camping La Cascade, Route de l'Alpe d'Huez, 38520 Le Bourg-d'Oisans [04 76 80 02 42; fax 04 76 80 22 63; lacascade@wanadoo.fr] Drive thro Le Bourg-d'Oisans & cross bdge over Rv Romanche. Approx 800m E of town turn onto D211, sp Alpe-d'Huez. Site on R in 600m. Med, mkd pitch, pt shd; htd wc; chem disp; baby facs; shwrs; el pts (16A) €3.70; lndtte; supmkt 1km; snacks; bar high ssn; playgrnd; htd pool high ssn; some statics; poss cr; Eng spkn; adv bkg; quiet; cc acc; CCI. "Friendly site; discounts for ski passes fr recep; nr Les Deux-Alpes, L'Alpe-d'Huez, Pelvoux National Park." 15 Dec-30 Sep. € 23.30   2005*

†BOURG D'OISANS, LE *9C3* (1.5km NE) Camping La Piscine, Route de l'Alpe d'Huez, 38520 Le Bourg-d'Oisans [04 76 80 02 41; fax 04 76 11 01 26; infos@camping-piscine.com; www.camping-piscine.com] Fr N91 approx 800m E of town, take D211 sp Alpe d'Huez. After 1km turn L into site. Fountains at ent. Med, mkd pitch, pt shd; htd wc (some cont); chem disp; shwrs inc; el pts (16A) €3.40; lndtte; ice; shops 1.5km; tradsmn; rest, snacks, bar 1.5km; BBQ; playgrnd; htd pool (summer); rv adj; tennis 2km; entmnts; TV; 10% statics; dogs €1; phone; poss cr; Eng spkn; adv bkg; quiet but with some rd noise; 10% red 7+ days/low ssn; cc acc; CCI. "Excel site; excel lge pool; conv town cent; gd for mountain drives & walks; facs stretched high ssn & when Tour de France in area; ski slopes 10-18km; vg long stay." ♦ € 20.00   2004*

BOURG D'OISANS, LE *9C3* (4km SE) Camping Le Vernis, 38520 Le Bourg d'Oisans [04 76 80 02 68; camping.levernis@online.fr; www.oisans.com/levernis] On N91. L of rd on main rte to Col du Lautaret (Briancon). Med, pt shd; htd wc; mv service pnt; shwrs inc; el pts; lndtte; ice; shops 3km; BBQ; playgrnd; htd pool 1.5km; boating; fishing; ski stn; no dogs; quiet; adv bkg rec summer & winter. "Beautiful scenery; conv touring & walking." 15 Dec-30 Apr & 15 Jun-Sep. € 14.50   2002*

BOURG D'OISANS, LE *9C3* (13km SE Rural) Camping Le Champ du Moulin, Bourg d'Arud, 38520 Venosc [04 76 80 07 38; fax 04 76 80 24 44; christian-avallet@wanadoo.fr; www.champ-du-moulin.com] On N91 SE fr Le Bourg d'Oisans sp Briancon for about 6km; turn R onto D530 twd Le Berarde & after 8km foll sp to site. Turn R to site 350m after cablecar stn beside Rv Veneon. NB Site bef vill; do not cross rv on D530; sp on R of rd at turn with 'Caravaneige' in lge letters. Med, mkd pitch, pt shd; wc; chem disp; baby facs; shwrs inc; el pts (3-10A) inc (extra charge up to 10A & in winter; poss rev pol); gas; lndtte: lndry rm; ice; shop; rest; snacks; bar; BBQ; playgrnd nr; htd pool adj; tennis, rafting, horseriding, archery nr; games rm; internet; 20% statics; dogs €1; recep 0800-1200 & 1400-1800; barrier (dep €20 req); poss cr; Eng spkn; adv bkg ess; quiet; cc acc; red long stay/low ssn; CCI. "Ideal cent for walking, climbing, touring; telecabins to Les Deux Alpes adj; magnificent scenery; beautifully situated by Alpine torrent (unguarded); 25% off day ski lift pass for residents; owners friendly & helpful; clean site; during May & Jun v ltd facs; mkt Tue Venosc." ♦ 15 Dec-30 Apr & 1 Jun-15 Sep. € 23.50 ABS - M03   2005*

BOURG D'OISANS, LE *9C3* (7km NW Rural) Camping Belledonne, Rochetaillee, 38520 Le Bourg d'Oisans [04 76 79 12 95; belledon@club-internet.fr; www.le-belledonne.com] Fr S of Grenoble take N85 to Vizille then N91 twd Le Bourg-d'Oisans; about 25km after Vizille in Rochetaillee bef Le Bourg-d'Oisans turn L onto D526 sp Allemont. Site 100m on R. Med, hdg pitch, shd; wc (some cont); chem disp; sauna; baby facs; shwrs inc; el pts (6A) inc; gas; lndtte; shop; rest; snacks; bar; BBQ; playgrnd; 2 htd pools & paddling pool; tennis; horseriding, fishing 500m; entmnt; TV rm; dogs €1.10; recep 0830-2000; Eng spkn; quiet; cc acc; CCI. "Excel mountain scenery; gd recep; Tour de France usually passes thro area & access may be restricted at certain times; rafting, climbing, paragliding, walks etc. organised by site - gd for families with teenagers; mkt Sat." ♦ 15 May-9 Sep. € 26.90 (CChq acc) ABS - M02   2005*

†BOURG D'OISANS, LE *9C3* (7km NW Rural) Camping Le Grande Calme, 38114 Allemont [04 76 80 70 03; fax 04 76 80 73 13; hotel-ginies@wanadoo.fr] Fr Grenoble on N91, at Rochetaillee turn L (N) on D526 to Allemont. Site on R in 1.5km opp Hotel Ginies. Med, pt shd; pt htd wc; chem disp; shwrs €1; el pts (10A) inc; lndtte; shops 500m; tradsmn; rest; bar; playgrnd; 10% statics; dogs; phone nr; poss cr; Eng spkn; adv bkg; quiet; cc acc; CCI. "Vg site run by hotel opp; well-maintained; beautiful area - lots to explore; gd rest in hotel; v quiet in wonderful scenery; gd for skiers & walkers; site poss neglected low ssn; call at hotel recep if site recep clsd low ssn; phone ahead to check site open low ssn." ♦ € 13.20   2005*

BOURG D'OISANS, LE *9C3* (7km NW Rural) Camping Les Bouleaux, 38114 Allemont [04 76 80 71 23; fax 04 76 80 70 75] Take N91 fr Bourg d'Oisans, then turn onto D526 dir Allemont. After crossing 2nd bdge, turn immed L down narr lane beside stream to recep on R. Med, pt shd; wc; chem disp; shwrs inc; el pts inc; tradsmn; pool 2km; poss cr; Eng spkn; quiet; red 7+ days & low ssn; CCI. "Vg sheltered site but v basic; v helpful owners; gd sh stay." ♦ ltd. 15 Jun-15 Sep. € 11.82   2003*

BOURG D'OISANS, LE *9C3* (7km NW) LES CASTELS Le Chateau Bourg d'Oisans, Chemin de Boutheon, 38520 Rochetaillee [04 76 11 04 40; fax 04 76 80 21 23; www.camping-le-chateau.com or www.les-castels.com] On N91 fr Grenoble turn 7km bef Le Bourg d'Oisans onto D526 sp Allemont. Site is 50m on L. Med, pt shd; wc; chem disp; baby facs; shwrs inc; el pts (6A) inc; lndtte; shop; rest; snacks; bar; BBQ; playgrnd; sports area; pool; dogs €0.80; 5% statics; quiet; CCI. "Vg; san facs clean & new; helpful staff; beautiful mountain views fr site." ♦ 14 May-10 Sep. € 25.60   2005*

BOURG D'OISANS, LE *9C3* (8km NW Rural) **Camp Municipal Le Plan, 38114 Allemont** [04 76 80 76 88 or 04 76 80 70 30 (Mairie); fax 04 76 79 80 28] At Rochetaillee on N91 fr Grenoble turn N 7km bef Le Bourg-d'Oisans on D526 sp Allemont site on R at N end of vill below dam. Med, mkd pitch, pt shd; htd wc; chem disp; serviced pitches; shwrs; el pts inc; lndry rm; shops in vill; pool adj high ssn only; no statics; adv bkg; quiet; cc acc high ssn only; CCI. "In quiet vill with lovely mountain scenery; v clean facs." ♦ 7 May-Sep. 2004*

BOURG DUN, LE see Veules les Roses *3C2*

BOURG EN BRESSE *9A2* (1km NE Urban) **Camp Municipal de Challes, Ave de Bad Kreuznach, 01000 Bourg-en-Bresse** [04 74 45 37 21; fax 04 74 22 40 32; camping-municipal-bourgen bresse@wanadoo.fr; www.bourg-en-bresse.org] Fr N or S on N83 foll sp Camping/Piscine/Stade. Site opp stadium. Med, hdstg, shd; wc (most cont); chem disp; shwrs; el pts (6A) inc; ice; lndry rm; hypermkt nr; snacks; rest; BBQ; htd, covrd pool & sports ground adj; 10% statics; bus adj; poss cr; adv bkg; some rd noise; red long stay; cc acc; 10% red CCI. "Many lge twin-axle vans; gd shwr block; gd touring base; easy walk to town for rests." 1 Apr-15 Oct. € 13.60 2005*

BOURG EN BRESSE *9A2* (8km E Rural) **Camp Municipal Le Domagne, 01250 Ceyzeriat** [04 74 25 02 31; fax 04 74 36 41 78] On W side of Ceyzeriat at rndbt on D979; site part of sm sports complex. Sm, mkd pitch, pt shd; wc; shwrs inc; el pts (5A); shops 500m; sm bar; quiet. "Gd NH." ♦ 15 Apr-30 Sep. 2002*

BOURG EN BRESSE *9A2* (13km SE) **Camp Municipal de Journans, 01250 Journans** [04 74 51 66 86 or 04 74 51 64 45] Exit A40 junc 7, turn L onto N75, then L onto D64 dir Tossiat & Journans. Or SE fr Bourg-en-Bresse on N75 for 9.5km E onto D64 to Journans. sp. Sm, mkd pitch, sl terr, pt shd; wc (some cont); shwrs inc; el pts €2.35; shops 1km (Tossiat); dog €0.80; poss cr; quiet; CCI. "Helpful warden calls pm; excel value; some pitches diff for c'vans; gd views; poss mkt traders." 1 Apr-15 Sep. € 8.60 2005*

BOURG EN BRESSE *9A2* (14km SE Rural) **Camping de l'Ile Chambod, 01250 Hautecourt-Romaneche** [04 74 37 25 41; fax 04 74 37 28 28; camping.chambod@free.fr] Turn S off D979 in Hautecourt at x-rds. Site sp in 4km off D59. At rvside cont for 500m. Med, mkd pitch; pt shd; wc; mv service pnt; baby facs; shwrs inc; el pts (5-10A) €2.50-3.50 (poss rev pol); gas; lndtte; ice; shop; snacks; BBQ; playgrnd; pool; lake 100m; fishing/boat hire 400m; games area; cycle hire; internet; entmnt; 10% statics; dogs €1; poss cr; Eng spkn; adv bkg; quiet; cc acc. "Excel site; clean; superb san facs; picturesque; peaceful; close enough to visit Geneva; helpful manager; highly rec." ♦ 1 May-30 Sep. € 14.50 2005*

BOURG EN BRESSE *9A2* (12km SW Rural) **Base de Plein Air, Etang du Moulin, 01240 St Paul-de-Varax** [04 74 42 53 30; fax 04 74 42 51 57] Fr N on N83 fr Bourg-en-Bresse turn L into St Paul-de-Varax under narr rlwy bdge, thro vill on D70B twd St Nizier-le-Desert. In 2km turn L into lane with 45km/h speed limit, site on R in 2km. Lge, hdg/mkd pitch, pt shd; wc (mainly cont); mv service pnt; baby facs; shwrs inc; el pts (5A) inc; lndtte; ice; shops; rest; snacks; bar; BBQ; playgrnd; pool; shgl beach on lake; fishing; watersports; mini-golf; tennis; archery; TV rm; 10% statics; dogs €2.40; quiet low ssn; dep req; cc acc; red 30 days; 10% red CCI. "Rec sh stay, excel for bird-watching." 1 May-15 Sep. € 16.20 2002*

BOURG EN BRESSE *9A2* (13km SW) **Camp Municipal, 01249 Dompierre-sur-Veyle** [04 74 30 31 81; fax 04 74 30 36 61] S fr Bourg on N83, fork L after 5km on D22. Site sp on L after 10km on vill o'skts just after vill sign. Sm, pt shd; wc; shwrs inc; el pts (10A) €1.50; shops 500m; playgrnd; adv bkg. "Gd cent for fishing, birdwatching, many lakes & marshes; v well-maintained site; facs clean but stretched high ssn." 1 Apr-30 Sep. € 8.00 2005*

†**BOURG MADAME** *8H4* (1km Urban) **Camping Mas Piques, Rue du Train Jaune, 66760 Bourg-Madame** [04 68 04 62 11; fax 04 68 04 68 32] Last camp site in France bef Spain & Cadi Tunnel. App via N20 or N116. Med, pt shd; wc; chem disp; shwrs; el pts (6A) inc; shop 500m; lndry rm; playgrnd; gas; ice; pool 500m; 75% statics; adv bkg ess high ssn. "Vg; organised rambling; gd san facs & el pts." ♦ ltd. € 14.70 2004*

†**BOURG MADAME** *8H4* (5km NE) **Camping L'Enclave, 66800 Estavar** [04 68 04 72 27; fax 04 68 04 07 15; lenclave@camping-lenclave.com; www.camping.lenclave.free.fr] Leave Saillagouse on D33 sp Estavar vill. Lge, pt sl, terr, pt shd; htd wc; chem disp; mv service pnt; baby facs; shwrs inc; el pts (3A) inc; gas; lndtte; ice; shop adj; rest adj; snacks; bar; playgrnd; htd, covrd pool; tennis; cycle hire; guided walks; entmnt; dogs €1.52; site clsd 1-24 Oct; adv bkg; quiet; red low ssn; CCI. "Nr ski resorts & Spanish border, friendly." ♦ € 22.00 2005*

BOURG MADAME *8H4* (7km NE Rural) **Camping La Riberette, 20 Rue de la Riberette, 66800 Err** [04 68 04 75 60] Fr Bourg-Madame on N116 to Saillagouse turn off onto rd C2 dir Err, site in 300m. Sm, mkd pitch, pt shd; wc (some cont); chem disp; shwrs inc; el pts (15A) €3.50; lndtte; shop, rest, snacks, bar 300m; playgrnd; fishing, tennis nr; some statics; dogs €1; adv bkg; quiet. "Pleasant owners; simple, quiet site; beautiful situation." ♦ 10 Jun-30 Sep. € 8.70 2004*

†BOURG MADAME *8H4* (7km NE) **Camping Las Closas, 66800 Err [04 68 04 71 42; fax 04 68 04 07 20; camping.las.closas@wanadoo.fr]** On N116 fr Bourg Madame take D33A on R immed after vill to Err. Site well sp. Med, pt sl, unshd; htd wc; shwrs; el pts (3-10A) €3-6.10; gas; lndtte; shop; playgrnd; entmnt; dogs €1.25; adv bkg; quiet; red low ssn. € 10.70   2003*

†BOURG MADAME *8H4* (11km NE Rural) **Camping Le Cerdan, 11 Route d'Estavar; 66800 Saillagouse [04 68 04 70 46; fax 04 68 04 05 26; lecerdan@ lecerdan.com; www.lecerdan.com]** Fr Mont Louis take N116 twd Bourg Madame; turn R in Saillagouse cent; past church & foll sm sp. Sm, pt sl, shd; htd wc; chem disp; shwrs inc; el pts (3-6A) €3-3.70; gas; lndtte; shop 250m; playgrnd; BBQ; games area; 10% statics; dogs €1; Eng spkn; adv bkg rec; quiet; CCI. "Helpful managers; organised walks; orchard site." ♦ € 12.00   2005*

†BOURG MADAME *8H4* (6km NW Rural) **Camping Le Robinson, Ave Gare Internationale, 66760 Enveitg [tel/fax 04 68 04 80 38; www.robinson-cerdagne.com]** Fr Bourg-Madame, take N20 N twd Foix. Thro vill of Enveitg & turn L down Chemin de la Gare & L at camping sp. Lge, mkd pitch, pt sl, shd; wc; chem disp; baby facs; shwrs inc; el pts (4-13A) €3-9; gas; ice; lndtte; shops adj; tradsmn; rest adj; snacks; BBQ; playgrnd; mini-golf; pool; games rm; entmnt; TV rm; some statics; dogs €1.50; phone; adv bkg; quiet. "Beautiful setting; wintersports cent; conv Barcelona, Andorra." ♦ € 14.00   2005*

BOURG ST ANDEOL *9D2* (1.5km N Rural) **Camping Le Lion, Chemin du Chenevrier, 07700 Bourg-St Andeol [tel/fax 04 75 54 53 20; contact@ campingdulion; www.campingdulion.com]** Exit A7 at junc 18 or 19 onto N7. At Pierrelatte turn W on D59 to Bourg-St Andeol. Site sp fr cent town dir Viviers. Med, mkd pitch, shd; wc; own san rec; shwrs inc; el pts (6A) €3; lndtte; ice; shop; snacks; bar; playgrnd; pool; games area; games rm; dir access to rv; dogs €1.70; poss cr; adv bkg; quiet; red low ssn. "Peaceful site in woodland setting; new modern facs highly rec." 1 Apr-15 Sep. € 16.50
                                            2004*

†BOURG ST MAURICE *9B4* (2km NE Rural) **Camp Municipal Le Reclus, 73700 Seez [04 79 41 01 05; fax 04 79 41 01 05; campinglereclus@wanadoo.fr]** Site on R of N90 bet Bourg-St Maurice & St Bernard Pass, bef vill of Seez. Med, sl, shd; htd wc; chem disp; shwrs inc; el pts (4-10A) €3-4.15; lndtte; shops 300m; BBQ; playgrnd; pool 1.5km; quiet; site clsd 4-24 Nov; CCI. "Diff exit fr site due to slope up to rd & on a bend." € 10.60   2002*

BOURG ST MAURICE *9B4* (1km E Rural) **Camping Le Versoyen, Route des Arcs, 73700 Bourg-St Maurice [04 79 07 03 45; fax 04 79 07 25 41; leversoyen@wanadoo.fr; www.leversoyen.com]** Fr SW on N90 thro town turn R to Les Arcs. Site on R in 1km. Do not app fr any other dir. Lge, hdstg, pt shd; wc; chem disp; mv service pnt; sauna; shwrs inc; el pts (4-10A) €4.20-5; lndtte; shops 200m; playgrnd; 2 pools adj; tennis adj; games area; entmnt; fishing, canoeing; dogs €1; Eng spkn; quiet; red low ssn; red CCI. "Excel for touring mountains & wintersports; mountain views; mkd walks fr site; rvside walk to town; well-organised site; dated but v clean facs." ♦ 15 Dec-1 May & 26 May-3 Nov. € 15.30   2005*

BOURG ST MAURICE *9B4* (8km S Rural) **Camping Les Lanchettes, 73210 Peisey-Nancroix [04 79 07 93 07; fax 04 79 07 88 33; lanchettes@ free.fr; www.camping-lanchettes.com]** Fr Moutier foll N90 NE twds Bourg-St Maurice. In 20km turn R sp Landry & Peisey-Nancroix. Up v steep rd with hairpin bends for 6km. Site 1km beyond Nancroix. Med, pt sl, terr, pt shd; htd wc; chem disp; mv service pnt; shwrs inc; el pts (3-10A) €3-7.30; gas adj; lndtte; ice; shop 200m (summer); rest; snacks; bar; playgrnd; tennis 100m; ski cent in winter; dogs €1.20; adv bkg (dep req + bkg fee); CCI. "Lovely setting in National Park; long steep ascent with many hairpin bends, not rec for closely rated o'fits; superb location for outdoor pursuits; excel walking." ♦ 15 Dec-15 Oct. € 12.80 (CChq acc)   2005*

BOURG ST MAURICE *9B4* (6km SW Urban) **Camping L'Eden, 73210 Landry [04 79 07 61 81; fax 04 79 07 62 17; info@camping-eden.net; www.camping-eden.net]** Fr N90 Moutiers to Bourg-St Maurice at 20km turn R onto D87 sp Landry & Mont Chavin; site on L after 500m adj Rv Isere. Med, mkd pitch, hdstg, pt shd; htd wc; chem disp; shwrs inc; el pts (10A) €4-6; gas; lndtte; shop; tradsmn; snacks; bar; playgrnd; htd pool; dogs €1.50; poss cr; quiet; adv bkg; cc acc; Eng spkn; CCI. "Gd cent mountain sports; helpful, friendly owner; free ski bus." 20 Dec-8 May & 1 Jun-15 Sep. € 21.40   2005*

BOURG SUR GIRONDE *7C2* (Urban) **Camp Municipal La Citadelle (formerly Halte Nautique), 33710 Bourg-sur-Gironde [05 56 68 40 06; fax 05 57 68 39 84]** Take D669 fr St Andre-de-Cubzac (off A10) to Bourg. Foll sp Halte Nautique & Le Port into Rue Franklin on L app town cent & foll sp to site. Or fr Blaye, ignore other camping dir sp on app Bourg owing to narr streets & cont to other end of town. Sm, mkd pitch, pt shd; wc (own san rec); chem disp (wc); shwrs inc; el pts (3-10A) inc; shops in town; BBQ; pool; playgrnd adj; dogs; no statics; adv bkg; quiet; CCI. "Excel site; gd clean facs; rvside site; tourist office in town with Eng info; gd for vineyards; poss variable opening dates." ♦ ltd. 2 May-27 Sep. € 11.00   2004*

FRANCE

Camping Municipal DES CHATEAUX ★★★ F-41250

In Sologne, in the heart of the castles region of the Loire: Chambord, Cheverny, Blois, Villessavin region of gastronomy. Relax (rivers, forests), cycling tracks (Velocamp label), hiking tracks. Station verte de vacances (green holidays label). Swimming pool, tennis, fishing All shops at 300 metres. Security surveillance day and night..

Phone: 00.33/02.54.46.41.84
Fax: 00.33/02.54.46.41.21
campingdebracieux@wanadoo.fr
www.campingdeschateaux.com

Rental of chalets and mobile homes.
Open from 17/03 till 13/11

BOURGANEUF 7B4 (10km S Rural) **Camping Les Chenauds,** 23400 St Junien-la-Bregere [05 55 54 91 87; susan.owen1@worldonline.fr] Fr Bourganeuf S on D940 twd Peyrat; site on R approx 2km past x-rds fr St Junien vill; well sp. NB sharp L turn when ent site fr S. Sm, mkd pitch, pt sl, pt shd; wc; chem disp; shwrs inc; el pts (6A) €3; lndtte; tradsmn; rest, snacks, shops 10km; playgrnd; htd pool 15km; sand beach 6km; lake sw 15km; cycle hire; dogs; poss cr; adv bkg (25% dep); quiet; 20% red +7 days; cc acc. "Pleasant, well appointed CL-type site; Eng owners; gd base for walking, fishing, golf & all watersports at Lac de Vassiviere 15km; B&B & eve meal avail on site. ♦ ltd. 1 Apr-Oct. € 7.00   2002*

BOURGES 4H3 (1km S Urban) **Camp Municipal de Bourges,** 26 Blvd de l'Industrie, 18000 Bourges [02 48 20 16 85; fax 02 48 50 32 39; www.ville-bourges.fr] Exit A71/E11 at junc 7, foll sp Bourges Cent & bear R at Autres Directions sp; foll site sp; site situated at traff lts on N side of S section of inner ring rd half-way bet junc with N144 & N76. NB: site access is via a loop - no L turn at traff lts, but rndabt just past site if turning missed. If on new outer ring rd D400, app city on N144 & then as above. Med, hdg/mkd pitch, hdstg, pt shd; htd wc; chem disp; shwrs inc; el pts (6-10A) €2.80- €4.30 (rev pol); gas 3km; lndtte; shops 100m; supmkt 1km; playgrnd; pool 1km; dogs; poss cr; Eng spkn; quiet but some rd noise; poss no vans over 5m, €24.10 extra twin-axle; cc acc; red long stay; CCI. "Excel site; spotlessly clean; gd facs for disabled; attractive & well-kept; busy; free access to sw pool; rv side; some lge pitches & some poss tight pitches; gates controlled by barrier, code issued by bureau on arr; sh walk chateau & cathedral; excel sightseeing." ♦ ltd. 15 Mar-15 Nov. € 11.20   2005*

BOURGNEUF EN RETZ 2H3 (1km NW Rural) **Camping Les Chenes Verts, Les Rigaudieres,** Route de Pornic, 44580 Bourgneuf-en-Retz [02 40 21 48 16; fax 02 40 21 48 19] Fr Bourgneuf-en-Retz on D13 twd Pornic. Site ent marked 1km NW on L. Lge, mkd pitch, unshd; wc; shwrs inc; el pts; ice; shop; tradsmn; playgrnd; pool; sand beach 3.5km; 20% statics; quiet but some rd/rlwy noise; CCI. "Facs run down & unkempt." 1 Jun-30 Sep. € 10.50   2002*

BOURGUEIL 4G1 (Rural) **Parc Municipal Capitaine,** 37140 Bourgueil [02 47 97 85 62 or 02 47 97 25 00 LS] N on D749 fr junc 5 of A85, site 1km on R. Fr W (Longue) via D10 & by-pass, S at rndabt on D749 to site on L in 200m. Do not app fr N via D749 thro town cent. Med, hdg/mkd pitch, pt shd; wc; chem disp; mv service pnt; shwrs inc; el pts (10A) €1.80; gas; lndtte; shops 1km; supmkt nrby; rest; playgrnd; sw lake; dogs €1.15; quiet; CCI. "Gd san facs; ideal cent Loire Chateaux & wine rtes; long el cable req some pitches; take care with electrics - poss lack of earth; 2 sites - one on R for tourers." ♦ ltd. 15 May-15 Sep. € 9.20   2005*

BOURNEZEAU 2H4 (500m N Rural) **Camp Municipal Les Humeaux, Rue de la Gare,** 85480 Bournezeau [02 51 40 01 31 or 02 51 40 71 20 (Mairie); fax 02 51 40 79 30; mairie@bournezeau.fr] Exit A83 junc 6 to Bournezeau cent. Take D7 sp St Martin-des-Noyes. Site on R in 500m, well sp. Sm, mkd pitch, pt shd; wc; chem disp; mv service pnt; shwrs; el pts (6A) €2.70; lndtte; shop, rest, snacks, bar 500m; playgrnd; dogs; adv bkg; quiet. "Vg, conv NH; modern, clean san facs; easy walk to town." 1 Jun-15 Sep. € 8.00   2004*

BOURGET DU LAC, LE see Aix Les Bains 9B3   **BOURRIOT BERGONCE see Roquefort** 8E2

BOUSSAC *7A4* (2km NE Rural) **LES CASTELS Le Chateau de Poinsouze, Route de la Chatre, 23600 Boussac-Bourg** [05 55 65 02 21; fax 05 55 65 86 49; info@camping-de-poinsouze. com; www.camping-de-poinsouze.com or www. les-castels.com] Fr junc 10 on A71/E11 by-pass Montlucon via N145 dir Gueret. After 22km take D917 NW to Boussac, then La Chatre, site 3km on L. Or fr Gueret on N145, exit Gouzon, at rndabt take D997 to Boussac, then as above. Med, mkd pitch, pt sl, unshd; wc; chem disp; mv service pnt; serviced pitch; baby facs; shwrs inc; el pts (6-10A) inc; gas; lndtte; shop & 3km; tradsmn; rest; snacks; bar; playgrnd; htd pool; paddling pool; waterslide; course-fishing lake; boating; tennis; horseriding; golf 20km; entmnt; 10% statics; dogs €3 (max 2 nights in high ssn; Eng spkn; adv bkg ess high ssn & booking fee; quiet; cc acc; CCI. "Excel site; helpful owners; lovely setting; lge pitches; lake with canoes/windsurfers; immac facs; pools away fr camp area." ♦ 13 May-18 Sep. € 31.00 (CChq acc) 2005*

Will you fill in the site report forms at the back of the guide, or shall I?

BOUSSAC *7A4* (3km W) **Camping Creuse-Nature (Naturist), Route de Betete, 23600 Boussac** [05 55 65 18 01; fax 05 55 65 81 40; creuse-nature@ wanadoo.fr] Fr Boussac take D917 N twd La Chatre. In 500m turn L (W) on D15 sp Betete. Site on R in 2.5km, clearly sp. Med, hdg/mkd pitch, pt sl, pt shd; wc; shwrs; el pts (10A) €3.50; lndtte; sm shop; rest; snacks; bar; playgrnd; 2 htd pools (1 covrd); fishing; games area; entmnt; dogs €5.50; Eng spkn; adv bkg; v quiet; red low ssn; cc acc; INF card req. "Vg facs; recep open 1030-1300 & 1500-1900; insect prob; interesting chateau in town." ♦ 20 Apr-31 Oct. € 19.00 2003*

BOUZONVILLE AUX BOIS see Pithiviers *4F3*

BOZEL see Pralognan la Vanoise *9B4*

BRACH *7C1* (SW Rural) **Aire Naturelle Le Bois de Geai (Douat), Route de Lacanau, 33480 Brach** [05 56 58 70 54] N on D1 fr Bordeaux. L onto D207 in Castelnau-de-Medoc cent. After 11km in vill of Brach fork L. Sm, pt shd; own san; shwrs; el pts (6A) €2.29; gas; lndtte; ice; shop; tradsmn; playgrnd; fishing; sailing & beaches nr; adv bkg; CCI. "Poss v cr with pickers at wine harvest time; NH only." 15 Jun-15 Oct. € 9.10 2003*

BRACIEUX *4G2* (N Rural) **Camp Municipal des Chateaux, 11 Rue Roger Brun, 41250 Bracieux** [02 54 46 41 84; fax 02 54 46 41 21; camping debracieux@wanadoo.fr; www.campingdes chateaux.com] Fr S take D102 to Bracieux fr Cour-Cheverny. Fr N exit Blois on D765 dir Romorantin; after 5km take D923 to Bracieux & site on R on N o'skts of town opp church, sp. Lge, pt hdg/mkd pitch, hdstg, pt shd; wc (some cont); chem disp; shwrs inc; el pts (3A) €2.35 (poss long lead req); gas 300m; lndtte; shop 300m; supmkt 1km; tradsmn; snacks; rest, bar 300m; playgrnd; htd pool high ssn; tennis; cycle hire & tracks; games rm; entmnt; TV; some statics; dogs; Eng spkn; adv bkg; quiet; red long stay; cc acc; CCI. "Excel; peaceful spot; excel disabled facs; gd security; card operated barrier; uneven ground tho level; attractive forest area; gd base for touring chateaux." ♦ 17 Mar-13 Nov. € 13.95 2005*

See advertisement opposite

BRAIN SUR L'AUTHION see Angers *4G1*

BRAMANS LE VERNEY see Modane *9C4*

BRANTOME *7C3* (1km E Rural) **Escapades Terre Oceane Camping Peyrelevade, Ave Andre Maurois, 24310 Brantome** [05 53 05 75 24 or 05 46 55 10 01; fax 05 46 55 10 00; info@campingterreoceane.com; www.campingterreoceane.com] Fr N on D675 foll sp Centre Ville; ent vill & turn L onto D78 Thiviers rd, site sp at turn; in 1km on R past stadium adj g'ge. Fr S D939 foll sp Centre Vill fr rndabt N of town. Then L onto D78 Thiviers rd & foll sp. Do not foll Centre Vill fr rndabt S of town, use by-pass. Med, mkd pitch, pt shd; wc; chem disp; mv service pnt; baby facs; shwrs inc; el pts (6A) €3; lndtte; shop 1km; tradsmn; snacks; bar; BBQ; playgrnd; htd pool; paddling pool; tennis nr; entmnt; 20% statics; dogs €2; adv bkg; quiet; red low ssn; cc acc; CCI. "Nice town; beautiful countryside; site in gd position on rvside; spacious pitches; interesting abbey & grottoes; 15 min walk to town; pleasant, helpful staff; excel." ♦ 13 May-16 Sep. € 16.00 2005*

See advertisement on next page

BRANTOME *7C3* (4km SW) **Camping Le Bas Meygnaud, 24310 Valeuil** [05 53 05 58 44; camping-du-bas-meygnaud@wanadoo.fr] Fr Brantome, take D939 S twd Perigueux; in 4.5km turn R at sp La Serre. In 1km turn L to in 500m, well sp. Sm, pt sl, pt shd; wc; chem disp; shwrs inc; el pts (6A) inc; gas 4km; ice; lndtte; shop; tradsmn; rest 4km; snacks; bar; BBQ; playgrnd; pool; entmnt; dogs €2; phone; Eng spkn; quiet; CCI. "Helpful & friendly owner; unspoilt countryside; winding, narr app thro lanes; poss diff lge o'fits; conv for Brantome; gd sh stay." 1 Apr-30 Sep. € 13.50 2004*

BRASSAC *8F4* (Urban) **Camp Municipal La Lande,** 81260 Brassac [05 63 74 09 11; fax 05 63 74 57 44] Fr Castres on D622, turn sharp L just bef rv bdge in Brassac. Sm, pt shd; wc; shwrs inc; el pts €1.50; lndry rm; ice; shops & rest 500m; BBQ; playgrnd; fishing; dogs; quiet; CCI. "Pleasant site with gd, clean san facs; vg sh/long stay." ♦ ltd. 1 Apr-31 Oct. € 5.90   2004*

Mustn't forget to post our site report forms to The Club, otherwise sites might be deleted.

BRASSAC *8F4* (8km SE) **LES CASTELS Le Manoir de Boutaric, Route de Lacabarede,** 81260 **Angles-du-Tarn** [05 63 70 96 06; fax 05 63 70 96 05; manoir.boutaric.com; www.boutaric.com or www. les-castels.com] Fr Brassac take D53 to Angles. Opp vill sq turn R onto D52 Lacabarede, site on L in 100m thro high iron gates, well sp; tight fit for long o'fits. Lge, hdg pitch, pt sl, terr, shd, wc; chem disp; mv service pnt; serviced pitch; shwrs inc; el pts (5A) inc (rev pol); lndtte; shops 1km; rest on E edge of vill; snacks; bar; playgrnd; pool; lake 3km; boating; fishing; tennis; horseriding; entmnt; many statics; dogs €4; adv bkg; quiet; CCI. "Beautiful countryside with lakes & gentle hills; some v sm pitches in main area." ♦ 11 Apr-30 Sep. € 25.00   2005*

BRASSAC *8F4* (11km SE Rural) **Camping Le Rouquie, Lac de la Raviege,** 81260 Lamontelarie [05 63 70 98 06; fax 05 63 50 49 58] Fr Brassac take D62 to N side of Lac de la Raviege; site on lakeside. Med, mkd pitch, terr, pt shd; wc; baby facs; shwrs; el pts (3-6A); lndtte; shop; tradsmn; snacks; bar; playgrnd; lake sw; fishing; sailing & watersports adj; games area; cycle hire; entmnt; TV; poss cr; quiet; CCI. "Ltd facs low ssn; gd lake views." 1 Mar-31 Oct.   2003*

BRAUCOURT *6E1* (3km W Rural) **Camp Municipal Presqu'ile de Champaubert,** 52290 Eclaron [03 25 04 13 20; fax 03 25 94 33 51; camping-de-braucourt@wanadoo.fr] Fr St Dizier take D384 SW twd Montier-en-Der & Troyes. In Braucourt R onto D153 sp Presq'ile de Champaubert, site on L in 2km. Site situated on Lac du Der-Chantecoq. Lge, hdg/mkd pitch, pt shd; wc; chem disp; mv service pnt; serviced pitch; shwrs inc; el pts (10A) €4 (rev pol); gas; lndtte; ice; basic shop; tradsmn; snacks; bar in ssn; playgrnd; lake sw nrby; sand beach; watersports, boating, fishing, bird-watching; TV; dogs €1; poss cr; quiet; 15% statics; Eng spkn; cc acc; CCI. "Gd watersports; beautiful lge lakeside beach; lge pitches; improved san facs; gates clsd 2230; efficient staff." 1 Apr-30 Sep. € 17.10   2005*

†BRAUCOURT *6E1* (9km W Rural) **Camping Le Clos du Vieux Moulin, 33 Rue du Lac,** 51290 Chatillon-sur-Broue [tel/fax 03 26 41 30 43] Fr N take D13 fr Vitry-le-Francois. Turn R at sp for Chatillon-sur-Broue. Fr S 2nd L fr Giffaumont (1km). Site under 100m on R. Med, hdg/mkd pitch, hdstg, pt sl, pt shd; htd wc; chem disp; baby facs; shwrs inc; el pts (5A) €2; gas; lndtte; ice; shops; tradsmn; rest; snacks; bar; playgrnd; pool; sand beach 16km; lake 300m; watersports; birdwatching; 50% statics; dogs; phone; quiet; CCI. "2004 under new ownership; new san facs; paths for disabled." ♦ € 10.00   2004*

BRAY DUNES see Dunkerque *3A3*

BRAY SUR SEINE *4E4* (Rural) **Camping La Peupleraie, Rue des Patures,** 77480 Bray-sur-Seine [01 60 67 12 24 or 06 83 93 33 89; camping. lapeupleraie@wanadoo.fr] Exit A5 at junc 18 onto D41, in 20km turn N to Bray. Turn L bef bdge, foll rd down under bdge, cont on rvside to site. Foll 'complex sportif' & camping sp. Lge, hdg/mkd pitch, pt shd; wc (cont); shwrs inc; el pts (6A) €3.50; lndtte; supmkt adj; snacks; playgrnd; pool adj; boating; tennis; 40% statics; dogs €1.50; adv bkg; quiet. "Diff to exit bef 0900 when office opens; v clean with helpful warden." ♦ 1 Apr-31 Oct. € 10.00   2005*

BRECEY *2E4* (1km S Rural) **Camp Municipal Le Pont Roulland, 50370 Brecey [02 33 48 60 60; fax 02 33 89 21 09]** Fr Villedieu-les-Poeles S on D999. In Brecey cent L by church E on D911; after 1km turn S on D79 sp Les Cresnays. Site in 50m on L thro car park. Med, pt sl, pt shd; wc; chem disp; shwrs; el pts (16A) (rev pol); shops 1km; tradsmn; lndtte; tennis; playgrnd; htd pool adj; dogs €0.38; adv bkg; quiet; CCI. "Excel facs; friendly staff; nr fishing lake; adj stables attract flies in hot weather." 1 Jun-30 Sep. € 8.70   2002*

BRENGUES *7D4* (Rural) **Camp Municipal de Brengues, 46320 Brengues [tel/fax 05 65 40 06 82 or 05 65 40 05 71 (Mairie)]** W fr Figeac on D13. After 6km turn L onto D41. After 17km, turn L at x-rds with D38, site ent 100m on R bef bdge over Rv Cele. Sm, mkd pitch, pt shd; wc; shwrs; el pts (10A) inc (rev pol); ice; lndtte; shop 300m; playgrnd; tennis; CCI. "Warden visits 0900 & 2100 week days." 1 Jun-30 Sep. € 10.75   2003*

BRENGUES *7D4* (1.5km N Rural) **Camping Le Moulin Vieux, Route de Figeac, 46320 Brengues [05 65 40 00 41; fax 05 65 40 05 65; blasquez.a@wanadoo.fr]** Fr Figeac on D13, in 6km L onto D41. In approx 17km site well sp on L bef Brengues vill. Med, shd; wc; chem disp; shwrs inc; el pts (10A) inc; lndtte; ice; shop; rest; bar; playgrnd; pool; rv sw; entmnt; archery; mini-golf; some statics; adv bkg; some rd noise; cc acc; CCI. "Helpful owners; beautiful site; facs stretched high ssn; excel sh stay." ♦ 1 Apr-30 Sep. € 14.70   2004*

BRENGUES *7D4* (2km W Rural) **Camp Municipal, 46160 St Sulpice [05 65 40 64 64 or 05 65 40 62 05; fax 05 65 40 71 17]** Take D13 Figeac to Cahors rd. In 3km turn L on D41. Site on L in St Sulpice on rv bank. Poss diff to turn into site fr dir Figeac. Sm, pt shd; wc; chem disp; shwrs inc; el pts (4A) €2.60; shop & snacks adj; playgrnd; rv sw; fishing; tennis; phone adj; poss cr; adv bkg; quiet. "Gd base for Figeac, Cahors, Conques, St Cere." 15 Mar-30 Sep. € 8.00   2005*

†**BRESSE, LA** *6F3* (3km E Urban) **Camp Municipal Le Haut des Bluches, 5 Route des Planches, 88250 La Bresse [03 29 25 64 80; fax 03 29 25 78 03; domaineduhautdesbluches@labresse.fr]** Leave La Bresse on D34 Rte de la Schlucht. Site on R in 3km. Med, mkd pitch, terr, pt shd; htd wc; chem disp; shwrs; el pts (4-13A) €1.50-4.50; lndtte; ice; shop 2km; tradsmn; rest; snacks; bar; BBQ; playgrnd; pool in vill; games rm; TV; 10% statics; dogs; Eng spkn; adv bkg; some rd noise; red low ssn; cc acc; CCI. "Excel site in v attractive setting; excel san facs; many gd walks fr site & further afield; conv winter sports." ♦ € 11.00   2005*

†**BRESSUIRE** *4H1* (S Rural) **Camping Le Puy Rond, Cornet, 79300 Bressuire [05 49 72 43 22 or 06 85 60 37 26 (mob); info@puyrondcamping.com; www.puyrondcamping.com]** Fr N149 foll site sp on rte Poids Lourds to site on D38. V well sp. Fr 'Centre Ville' foll sp for Fontenay-Le-Comte; turn R 100m after overhead bdge & go across junc to site. Sm, mkd pitch, pt sl, pt terr, pt shd; htd wc (some cont); chem disp (wc); mv service pnt; baby facs; shwrs inc; el pts (10A) €3; gas 1.50m; lndtte; ice; shop & 1.5km; tradsmn; snacks; rest, bar 1.5km; BBQ; playgrnd; pool; fishing 1km; 15% statics; dogs €2; bus 2km; phone 500m; adv bkg (50% dep req); quiet; red long stay; cc acc; CCI. "Gd base for exploring area; British owners; basic facs, improvements in hand; adv bkg ess for twin-axles; winter storage avail." ♦ € 15.50   2005*

BREST *2E2* (4km E Coastal) **Camp Municipal de Camfrout, 29480 Le Relecq-Kerhuon [02 98 28 37 84 or 02 98 28 14 18 (Mairie); fax 02 98 28 61 32; secretariat.mairie@mairie-relecq- kerhuon.fr]** Fr Brest take N165 dir Quimper, at city o'skts becomes Relecq-Kerhuon. In 2km turn L onto D67, site on L opp foreshore. Fr S on N165, cross Rv Elorn twd Brest & R onto D67. Med, hdg pitch, pt shd; wc; chem disp; shwrs; el pts (6A) €1.65; lndtte; shops 3km; playgrnd; sand beach adj; fishing; boating; dogs €1.25; quiet. "Many places of interest in area." ♦ 24 Jun-10 Sep. € 8.50   2004*

†**BREST** *2E2* (6km W Coastal) **Camping Le Goulet, Ste Anne-du-Porzic, 29200 Brest [02 98 45 86 84; campingdugoulet@wanadoo.fr; www.campingdugoulet.com]** On D789 turn L at site sp approx 4km fr Brest; turn L at x-rd, site on R in 200m. Med, pt sl, terr, unshd; htd wc; chem disp; shwrs inc; el pts (6A) €2.50; lndtte; shop high ssn; playgrnd; sand beach 1km; 15% statics; quiet; adv bkg; CCI. "Gd NH; friendly warden." ♦ € 10.21
2002*

BRETENOUX *7C4* (Urban) **Camp La Bourgnatelle, 46130 Bretenoux [tel/fax 05 65 38 44 07; bourgnatel@aol.com]** In town 100m fr D940. Lge, pt shd; wc; mv service pnt; shwrs inc; el pts (5-10A) €2.40; lndtte; ice; shops adj; playgrnd; pool 250m; rv sw & fishing; canoe hire; entmnt; dogs €1; adv bkg; quiet. "Site on banks of Rv Cere; gd fishing; clean site; lovely town." 1 May-30 Sep. € 12.00
2005*

BRETENOUX *7C4* (4km W Rural) **Camping Les Chalets sur La Dordogne, Pont de Puybrun, 46130 Girac [05 65 10 93 33; fax 05 65 38 44 42; contact@camping-leschalets.com; www.camping-leschalets.com]** Fr Bretenoux on D803 dir Puybrun. Site on L on rvside - sp on rd barrier easily missed. Sm, mkd pitch, shd; wc; chem disp; shwrs inc; el pts (10A) €3; lndtte; ice; shop; tradsmn; rest; snacks; bar; playgrnd; pool; rv sw & shgl beach adj; TV rm; 20% statics; dogs; Eng spkn; quiet. "Gd, clean family site; helpful owners." ♦ 1 May-15 Sep. € 14.00   2005*

FRANCE

BRETEUIL *3C3* (Urban) **Camp Municipal du Moulin d'Orgissel, 68 Rue Basse, St Cyr, 60120 Breteuil** [03 44 80 94 73 or 03 44 07 00 12 (Mairie); fax 03 44 80 16 33; breteuil60@wanadoo.fr] Foll sp on N1 & D930 fr o'skts of town. Also sp fr town cent. Sm, pt sl, pt shd; wc (some cont); shwrs inc; el pts (13-26A) €2.10-3.60; tradsmn; quiet. "Park nrby with cycling, walking & tennis; excel san facs; 15 mins walk town cent; vg sh stay/NH." € 9.00   2005*

BRETIGNOLLES SUR MER *2H3* (Coastal) **Camping La Motine, 4 Rue des Morinieres, 85470 Bretignolles-sur-Mer** [02 51 90 04 02; fax 02 51 33 80 52; campinglamotine@wanadoo.fr] Foll sp fr D38 in Bretignolles-sur-Mer dir Plage de la Paree along Ave de la Plage, then turn R into Rue des Morinieres. Med, hdg pitch, pt sl, pt shd; wc; chem disp; mv service pnt; serviced pitches; baby facs; shwrs inc; el pts (6A) inc; lndtte; rest; bar; playgrnd; htd, covrd pool; sand beach 600m; 60% statics; dogs €3; adv bkg; quiet; cc acc; CCI. "Unisex san facs low ssn; vg site." ♦ 1 Apr-30 Sep. € 25.30
                                                                     2005*

BRETIGNOLLES SUR MER *2H3* (2km N Coastal) **Camping Les Vagues, 85470 Bretignolles-sur-Mer** [02 51 90 19 48 or 02 40 02 46 10; fax 02 40 02 49 88; les vagues@free.fr] Well sp on D38. Lge, hdg pitch, pt shd; wc; chem disp; shwrs; el pts (6A) €3.50; lndtte; ice; snacks; playgrnd; pool; waterslide; sand beach 900m; games rm; TV; entmnt; 50% statics; dogs €2.50; adv bkg; red low ssn; CCI. "Vg sh stay; gd sized pool; close to town cent with shops & rests; office closes 1830 low ssn." ♦ 1 Apr-30 Sep. € 20.00   2005*

BRETIGNOLLES SUR MER *2H3* (1km E Coastal) **Camping La Haute Rivoire, 85470 Bretignolles-sur-Mer** [02 51 33 80 34] Fr St Gilles Croix-de-Vie take D38 S twd Les Sables. Cross bdge over Rv Jaunay. Turn L on D12 sp Chaize-Giraud. Site 3rd turning on R sp Chambres. Site in 300m. Take ent after barns. Sm, unshd; wc; chem disp; shwrs inc; el pts (6A) €4.50 (poss rev pol); snacks; shop 2km; sand beach 2km; pool; golf; fishing; horseriding; watersports adj; sep car park; adv bkg; red low ssn. "San facs v clean; British-owned (ex Club member) CL-type farm site; no children under 10yrs/no visitors/no pets; ssn open 0830-2030; only 6 tourer pitches; €4-7 extra twin-axle vans; phone bef arrival to check opening; san facs mixed & poss stretched ssn; payment on arr." € 22.00   2004*

BRETIGNOLLES SUR MER *2H3* (1km E Urban) **CHADOTEL Camping La Trevilliere, Route de Bellevue,   85470   Bretignolles-sur-Mer** [02 51 90 09 65 or 02 51 33 05 05 (LS); fax 02 51 33 94 04; chadotel@wanadoo.fr; www.camping-chadotel.fr] S along D38 fr St Gilles Croix-de-Vie twd Olonne-sur-Mer, site is sp to L in Bretignolles-sur-Mer 1km fr town cent. Sp from town cent. Foll sp 'Ecole'. Lge, hdg/mkd pitch, shd; wc; chem disp (wc); 50% serviced pitches; baby facs; shwrs inc; el pts (6A) inc (rev pol); gas; lndtte; shop; tradsmn; rest; snacks; bar; BBQ (gas); playgrnd; htd pool; paddling pool; waterslide; sand beach 2km; fishing; watersports 3km; horseriding 5km; mini-golf; cycle hire; games rm; entmnt; child entmnt; 70% statics; dogs €2.90; phone; recep 0800-2000; c'van max 8m high ssn; Eng spkn; adv bkg (dep req); cc acc; red long stay/low ssn; CCI. "Friendly & helpful; gd family site; poss unkempt pitches low ssn; pleasant walk to local shops & rests; thoroughly rec; mkt Thu & Sun; salt marshes worth a visit." ♦ 1 Apr-23 Sep. € 27.50 ABS - A26   2005*

> As we're travelling out of season, we'd better phone ahead to check that the site is actually open.

BRETIGNOLLES SUR MER *2H3* (5km E Rural) **Camping L'Evasion, Route des Sables, 85220 Landevieille** [tel/fax 02 51 22 90 14] Site sp in Landevieille. Med, hdg/mkd pitch, pt shd; wc; chem disp; baby facs; shwrs inc; gas; lndtte; ice; shop; supmkt 750m; rest; snacks; bar; BBQ; playgrnd; 3 htd pools; waterslide; jacuzzi; beach 5km; fishing lake; games area; 75% statics; dogs; dog exercise area; phone; some Eng spkn; quiet except for bar/disco high ssn; cc acc; CCI. "Vg long stay." 1 Apr-1 Nov. € 13.50   2003*

BRETIGNOLLES SUR MER *2H3* (5km E Urban) **Camping L'Oree de l'Ocean, Rue Capitaine de Mazenot, 85220 Landevieille** [02 51 22 96 36; fax 02 51 22 29 09] Take D12 fr La Mothe-Achard to St Julien-des-Landes & cont to x-rds bef La Chaize-Giraud. Turn L onto D32, take 1st R in Landevieille to site on L in 50m. Adj Mairie. Med, hdg/mkd pitch, pt sl, pt shd; wc; chem disp; shwrs inc; el pts (10A) inc; ice; lndtte; lndry rm; shops 500m; bar; playgrnd; htd pool; tennis; sand beach 4km; TV rm; phone; 40% statics; dogs; phone; poss cr; quiet; adv bkg; Eng spkn; 15% red 7+ days; cc acc; CCI. "Gd, friendly family site; many gd beaches nr; mkd cycle tracks in surrounding area; gd all stays." ♦ 25 Jun-5 Sep. € 22.00   2004*

BRETIGNOLLES SUR MER *2H3* (5km E) **Camping Pong, Rue du Stade,** 85220 Landevieille [02 51 22 92 63; fax 02 51 22 99 25; info@lepong. com; www.lepong.com] Fr Challans S on D32. Pass Landevieille church on L, then rd bends R; turn L after sm bdge into Rue de la Stade; foll rd, site on L. Fr Vaire N on D32, soon after ent Landevieille & immed bef sm bdge turn R into Rue de la Stade, then as above. Lge, pt sl, pt shd; wc (some cont); chem disp; serviced pitches; baby facs; shwrs inc; el pts (6A) inc; gas; lndtte; ice; shop; rest; snacks; bar; BBQ (charcoal/gas); playgrnd; pool & paddling pool; sand beach 4km; lake 2.5km; fishing; tennis; mini-golf; cycle hire; games rm; entmnt; some statics; dogs €2; recep 0900-1300 & 1400-1900; adv bkg; quiet; cc acc. "Lac d'Apremont with 16thC chateau 13.5km; v pleasant & extremely helpful staff; beautiful site with great facs; extra charge for lger pitches; highly rec; vineyards & winetasting in area." ♦
1 Apr-15 Sep. € 24.50 ABS - A24   2005*

BRETIGNOLLES SUR MER *2H3* (4km S Coastal) **Camping Le Chaponnet, Rue du Chaponnet,** 85470 Brem-sur-Mer [02 51 90 55 56; fax 02 51 90 91 67; chaponnet@free.fr; www.le-chaponnet.com] Fr Bretignolles, take the D38 S & foll sp to Brem-sur-Mer. Site 1km W of town cent on one-way system. Lge, hdg pitch, pt shd; wc; chem disp; baby facs; sauna; shwrs inc; el pts (6A); gas; lndtte; ice; sm shop on site & shops & supmkt 200m; rest; snacks; bar; BBQ; playgrnd; htd & covrd pool with water slides; sand beach 1km; jacuzzi; gym; games area; tennis; cycle hire; entmnt; games rm; TV rm; 75% statics; dogs; €1.50; phone; poss cr; adv bkg; quiet; red low ssn; cc acc; CCI. "Gd beaches adj; excel long/sh stay." ♦
1 Apr-30 Oct. € 28.70 (3 persons)   2003*

BRETIGNOLLES SUR MER *2H3* (4km S Coastal) **Camping Les Dunes,** 85470 Bretignolles-sur-Mer [02 51 90 55 32; fax 02 51 90 54 85] Fr N foll D178 fr Nantes as far S as Aizenay. Fr Aizenay foll D6 to Coex; turn L at Coex onto D40 & foll sp to Bretignolles-sur-Mer; at Bretignolles turn L onto D38 twd Les Sables d'Olonne; in 3km turn R at sp to Camp Les Dunes; site in 1km. V lge, pt shd; wc (some cont); shwrs inc; el pts (10A) inc; lndtte; gas; shop; rest; bar; playgrnd; 2 pools; jacuzzi; sand beach 100m; TV; entmnt; 90% statics; bus 1km; poss cr; adv bkg. "Rest, casino in Les Sables; Croix-de-Vie interesting fishing port; tourer pitches scattered among statics; poor disabled facs." ♦ ltd.
Easter-11 Nov. € 32.00   2004*

BRETTEVILLE see Cherbourg *1C4*

BREUILLET *7B1* **Camping Transhumance, Route de Royan,** 17920 Breuillet [05 46 22 72 15; fax 05 46 22 66 47; contact@transhumance.com; www.transhumance.com] Fr Saujon take D14 NW dir St Sulphice-de-Royan & La Tremblade. After approx 8km turn L at junc with D140 sp Breuillet & Camping Transhumance; site well sp on L. Or fr Rochefort S on D733; turn R onto D14 to Breuillet & as above. Lge, hdg pitch, unshd; wc; chem disp; baby facs; shwrs inc; el pts (6A) inc; gas; lndtte; ice; shop; rest; snacks; bar; BBQ; playgrnd; 2 pools; paddling pool; beach 3.5km; watersports 6km; fishing; tennis; games rm; table tennis; cycle hire; archery; horseriding 4km; golf 7km; entmnt; statics; dogs €3; recep 0900-1200 & 1400-2000; adv bkg; quiet; cc acc; CCI. "Excel; gd facs, poss stretched high ssn; vg rest in vill." ♦ 13 May-10 Sep. € 20.50 ABS - A18   2005*

BREUILLET *7B1* (1.5km NW Rural) **Camping a la Belle Etoile, 27 Route des Renouleaux,** 17920 Breuillet [tel/fax 05 46 02 14 07; camping.a.la. belle.etoile@wanadoo.fr] Fr Saujon on D14 W dir La Tremblade, turn L onto D242 dir St Augustin then 1st R after 700m. Site sp. Med, mkd pitch, pt shd; wc (cont); chem disp; mv service pnt; shwrs inc; el pts (10A) €3.10; gas; lndtte; ice; shop 1.5km; tradsmn; rest 500m; snacks; bar 1.5km; playgrnd; pool; sand beach 10km; 35% statics; dogs €0.90; adv bkg; quiet; cc acc; red CCI. "Gd cycle rtes nr; conv Royan, Ile d'Oleron, La Rochelle; excel long/sh stay." ♦ ltd. 1 Apr-3 Oct. € 10.50   2003*

BREVEDENT, LE see Blangy le Chateau *3D1*

BREVILLE SUR MER see Granville *1D4*

†BRIANCON *9C4* (3km NE Rural) **Camping Les Gentianes, La Vachette,** 05100 Val-des-Pres [02 92 21 21 41; fax 04 92 21 24 12] Fr Briancon take N94 dir Montgenevre. At La Vachette site sp in vill. Med, pt sl, pt shd; htd wc; chem disp; mv service pnt; shwrs inc; el pts (6-10A) €2.75-4; lndtte; shops, rest in vill; snacks; bar; playgrnd; pool; canoeing; fishing; x-country skiing; 40% statics; dogs €1; adv bkg; quiet; CCI. "Renovations under way 2004; mountain streams runs thro site; NH only."
€ 14.40   2003*

BRIANCON *9C4* (5km NE Rural) **Camping de l'Iscle du Rosier, Le Rosier,** 05100 Val-des-Pres [04 92 21 06 01; fax 04 92 21 46 46; www.ifrance. com/campingdurosier] Fr Briancon N94 E & take 3rd L after leaving Briancon (5km) sp Le Rosier. Foll rd thro until Le Rosier, site on L after bdge. Med, pt shd; wc (some cont); chem disp; shwrs inc; el pts (5A) inc; gas; lndry rm; shops; snacks; bar; BBQ; playgrnd; 5% statics; dogs €1.70; phone; Eng spkn; quiet. "Clean & tidy site with friendy helpful staff; nr rv." ♦ 15 Jun-15 Sep. € 13.00   2004*

†BRIANCON *9C4* (6km NE Rural) **Camp Municipal du Bois des Alberts, 05100 Montgenevre** [04 92 21 16 11 or 04 92 21 92 88; fax 04 92 21 98 15] Take N94/D201 fr Briancon sp Italie. In 4km turn L onto D994, site 200m past Les Alberts vill on L. Lge, hdstg, shd; htd wc (some cont); chem disp; mv service pnt; baby facs; shwrs inc; el pts (6-10A) inc (rev pol); lndtte; shop; tradsmn; rest, snacks, bar high ssn; playgrnd; tennis; games area; kayak tuition; cycle & walking paths; fishing; x-country skiing; 30% statics; adv bkg; quiet; cc acc; CCI. "Clean site set in pine trees; random pitching in lge forest area; relaxed & friendly; gd touring base; facs dated but v clean; ltd facs low ssn." ♦ € 12.20   2005*

We're having a great holiday - must fill in some site report forms and send them to The Club as soon as possible.

BRIANCON *9C4* (2km S Rural) **Camping Les Cinq Vallees, St Blaise, 05100 Briancon** [04 92 21 06 27; fax 04 92 20 41 69; infos@camping5vallees.com; www.camping5vallees.com] S of Briancon by N94 to vill St Blaise. Ent on L. Med, pt shd; wc; shwrs inc; el pts (10A) inc; lndtte; shop; snacks; playgrnd; htd pool; games rm; TV rm; many statics; some noise fr by-pass. ♦ 1 Jun-30 Sep. € 21.20   2005*

BRIARE *4G3* (7km S) **Camp Municipal des Combes, 45360 Chatillon-sur-Loire** [02 38 31 42 92] SE fr Briare on N7, in 4km turn SW onto D50. Site immed bef rv bdge on R. Care needed over bdge after ent. Med, terr, pt shd; wc (some cont); chem disp; shwrs inc; el pts (3-6A) €1.50-3; gas; lndry rm; shops 2km; playgrnd; fishing; many statics; quiet; CCI. "Pleasant, quiet by Loire; friendly staff; mkt day 2nd Thurs of each month; close to historical canals & Pont-Canal de Briare; no twin-axles; vg sh stay/NH." ♦ 1 Mar-31 Oct. € 7.00   2005*

BRIARE *4G3* (W Urban) **Camping Le Martinet, Quai Tchékof, 45250 Briare** [02 38 31 24 50 or 02 38 31 24 51; fax 02 38 31 39 10] Exit N7 into Briare. Fr N immed R after canal bdge; fr S L bef 2nd canal bdge; sp. Lge, mkd pitch, shd; wc (cont); shwrs; el pts (10A) inc; lndry rm; shops 500m; rest, snacks, bar 500m; fishing adj; poss cr; adv bkg; quiet. "Gd views some pitches; gd walking & cycling; gates close 2200; pretty bars & rests along canal." ♦ 1 Mar-31 Oct. € 16.65   2005*

†BRIENNE LE CHATEAU *6E1* (6km S Rural) **Camping Le Colombier, 8 Ave Jean-Lanez, 10500 Dienville** [tel/fax 03 25 92 23 47] On D443 S fr Brienne; in Dienville town cent turn L immed after church & bef bdge, site on R thro archway. Sm, hdg pitch, pt shd; htd wc; chem disp; mv service pnt; shwrs inc; el pts (12A) €3; gas; lndry rm; shop 400m; rest; snacks (high ssn); bar; playgrnd; rv adj; lake 500m; watersports; dogs €1.50; Eng spkn; adv bkg; quiet. "Facs poss stretched high ssn; access poss diff lge vans if site busy; some sm pitches; pretty rvside site - pitches away fr bdge quieter, pitches next to rv extra charge; church clock strikes 24 hrs; rooms avail; excel watersports on lake; red facs low ssn; pleasant, friendly owner." ♦ ltd. € 15.00   2005*

BRIENNE LE CHATEAU *6E1* (5km SW Rural) **Camping Le Garillon, Rue des Anciens Combattants, 10500 Radonvilliers** [03 25 92 21 46 or 03 25 92 21 34 (Mairie); fax 03 25 92 21 34] Exit Brienne S on D443 & at Brienne Le Ville turn R onto D11B to Radonvilliers. Site well sp. Med, pt shd; wc (some cont); chem disp; shwrs inc; el pts (3-10A) inc; lndry rm; shops 2km; tradsmn; snacks, bar 2km; playgrnd; lake 1.5km; statics; poss cr Jul/Aug; Eng spkn; adv bkg; quiet; red CCI. "Pleasant, friendly, family site; relaxed feel; 2 golf courses within 40km; site surrounded by Parc Regional de la Foret d'Orient; Nigoland theme park 5km S; modern, clean facs block but unisex washbasin/wc area; gd cycle track around lake; some pitches boggy when wet." ♦ ltd. 1 May-15 Sep. € 15.00   2005*

BRIGNOGAN PLAGES *1D2* (Coastal) **Camping de la Cote des Legendes, Keravezan, 29890 Brignogan-Plages** [02 98 83 41 65; fax 02 98 83 59 94; camping-cote-des-legendes@ wanadoo.fr; www.campingcotedeslegendes.com] Fr Roscoff on D10, fr Brest on D788/770 or fr N12 exit dir Lesneven. In Brignogan foll sp Brignogan-Plages & 'Centre Nautique'. Lge, hdg/mkd pitch, pt shd; wc; chem disp; mv service pnt; baby facs; shwrs inc; el pts (5-10A) €2.20-3 (poss rev pol); lndtte; ice; shop; tradsmn; snacks; BBQ; playgrnd; pool; dir access to sand beach adj; watersports; sailing; entmnt; child ent; site guarded 24 hrs; 10% statics; dogs €1; phone; Eng spkn; adv bkg; quiet; cc acc; red long stay/low ssn; red CCI. "Excel san facs; on beautiful sandy cove; some seaview pitches; wonderful site." ♦ Easter-1 Nov. € 12.00   2005*

BRIGNOGAN PLAGES *1D2* (2km SE Coastal) **Camp Municipal de Kerurus, 29890 Plouneour-Trez** [02 98 83 41 87 or 02 98 83 41 03; fax 02 98 83 46 30] Fr cent of town foll sp to beaches. Lge, hdg/mkd pitch, terr, unshd; wc; shwrs inc; el pts (10A); ice; lndry rm; shops 200m; rest, snacks & bar nrby; sand beach adj; no statics; quiet; some Eng spkn; CCI. "Facs clean; vg sh stay." ♦ 15 Jun-15 Sep.   2002*

BRIGNOGAN PLAGES *1D2* (1km NW Coastal) **Camping du Phare, Plage du Phare, 29890 Brignogan-Plages [tel/fax 02 98 83 45 06 or 02 98 83 52 19 (LS); camping_du_phare@ caramail.com]** Take D770 N fr Lesneven to Brignogan-Plages; take L fork in town cent & foll site sp. Med, some hdg pitch, pt shd; wc; chem disp; mv service pnt; shwrs €1; el pts €2.50; gas; lndtte; shop 1km; tradsmn; snacks; playgrnd; sand beach adj; 10% statics; dogs €1.50; poss cr; adv bkg; quiet; red facs low ssn; CCI. "Next to pretty bay & gd beach; helpful owner; vg." 1 Apr-30 Sep. € 10.50
                                                                    2005*

BRIGNOLES *10F3* (500m E) **Camp Municipal, 786 Route de Nice, 83170 Brignoles [tel/fax 04 94 69 20 10; campingbrignoles@aol.com; www.campingbrignoles.ifrance.com]** Exit A8 junc 35 onto N7 dir Le Luc/Nice. Site on L of N7 immed after exit Brignoles. Med, hdg pitch, pt shd; wc; chem disp; shwrs inc; el pts (10A) €3; gas; lndtte; supmkt 100m; tradsmn; snacks; playgrnd; municipal pool adj; 10% statics; phone; dogs €1.60; Eng spkn; some rd noise; adv bkg; CCI. "NH; well-managed site by friendly family."
15 Mar-15 Oct. € 12.50   2005*

BRIGNOLES *10F3* (9km SE Rural) **Camping La Vidaresse, 83136 Ste Anastasie-sur-Issole [04 94 72 21 75; fax 04 98 05 01 21; lavidaresse@ wanadoo.fr; www.campinglavidaresse.com]** On N7 2km W of Brignoles at rndabt take D43 dir Toulon. In about 10km turn L at rndabt to D15. Do not ent vill, go strt & site is approx 250m on R. Med, hdg pitch, terr, pt shd; wc (some cont); chem disp; mv service pnt; shwrs inc; el pts (6A) inc (poss rev pol); gas; lndtte; ice; shop in vill 1km & 5km; rest high ssn; snacks; bar; BBQ (gas/elec only); playgrnd; htd, covrd pool; paddling pool; sand beach 40km; tennis; games area; fishing 200m; 40% statics; dogs €1.80; poss cr; Eng spkn; adv bkg; red long stay; cc acc; CCI. "Rec; helpful owners; facs adequate; excel pool; gd touring base Haute Provence; conv Gorges du Verdon & Riviera; wine at Carbasson vineyard adj."
♦ 1 Apr-15 Oct. € 23.90 ABS - C29   2005*

BRILLANE, LA *10E3* (6km NE Rural) **Camping Les Matherons, 04700 Puimichel [tel/fax 04 92 79 60 10; lesmatherons@wanadoo.fr]** Exit N96 or A51 at La Brillane. Take D4B to Oraison. Foll camp sps on D12 twd Puimichel; site on L 6km. Sm, pt sl, terr, pt shd; wc; chem disp; shwrs inc; el pts (3A) €2; shop 6km; tradsmn; snacks; playgrnd; dogs €1.10; Eng spkn; adv bkg ess; quiet; red low ssn; CCI. "Unspoilt natural site; gd walks." 20 Apr-30 Sep. € 12.50
                                                                    2003*

BRILLANE, LA *10E3* (3km W) **Camping Le Moulin de Ventre, 04300 Niozelles [04 92 78 63 31; fax 04 92 79 86 92; moulindeventre@free.fr; www. moulindeventre.com]** Leave A51 at La Brillane; in La Brillane turn L onto N100 sp Niozelles & Forcalquier. Site in 2km on L. Med, mkd pitch, pt shd; htd wc; chem disp; mv service pnt; serviced pitches; shwrs inc; el pts (6-10A) inc; gas; lndtte; ice; shop 2km; tradsmn; rest; snacks; bar; playgrnd; pool; lake sw, fishing, boat hire & beach; child entmnt; TV rm; 10% statics; dogs €3; phone; Eng spkn; adv bkg (bkg fee + 30% dep); quiet; red long stay; cc not acc; CCI. "Well-run, pleasant site; some pitches adj stream; excel touring base." ♦
1 Apr-30 Sep. € 25.00 (CChq acc)   2005*

BRIONNE *3D2* (Urban) **Camp Municipal La Vallee, Rue Marcel Nogrette, 27800 Brionne [02 32 44 80 35; fax 02 32 46 25 61]** Fr N138 N or S on by-pass, leave at Champion Supmkt onto D130. Site on R 250m. Sm, hdg pitch, unshd; wc; chem disp; mv service pnt; shwrs inc; el pts (5A) €3; gas; lndtte; shop, rest etc nrby; BBQ; playgrnd; many statics; dogs; poss cr; quiet; CCI. "Excel site, highly rec; poss ltd facs low ssn; barrier open 1000-1200 & 1700-2000 Tues to Sun only."
1 Apr-30 Sep. € 8.80   2005*

BRIONNE *3D2* (5km N Urban) **Camp Municipal St Nicolas, 27800 Le Bec-Hellouin [tel/fax 02 32 44 83 55 or 02 32 44 86 40 (Mairie)]** Heading S fr Montfort-sur-Risle on D130 fork L to Le Bec-Hellouin; in vill foll camping sp up hill; site 2km fr vill. Med, pt shd; htd wc; chem disp (wc); mv service pnt; shwrs inc; el pts (10A) €2.80; lndtte; ice; tradsmn; rest, snacks, bar in vill; BBQ; playgrnd; tennis; horseriding nr; 50% statics; dogs €0.90; poss cr; Eng spkn; quiet; CCI. "Excel site; lots of roses; vg san facs; v friendly warden; cider sold on site; pleasant & interesting area; gd cycling; Benedictine Abbey 10 mins walk down but steep on return; gate clsd 2200; €2.10 for use of m'van services." ♦ ltd. 1 Apr-30 Sep. € 7.40   2005*

†**BRIONNE** *3D2* (6km N) **Camp Municipal Les Marronniers, 27290 Pont-Authou [tel/fax 02 32 42 75 06 or 02 32 42 72 07]** Heading S on N138 take D130 just bef Brionne sp Pont-Audemer (care req at bdge & rndabts). Site on L in approx 5km, well sp on o'skts of Pont-Anthou. Med, mkd pitch, some hdstg, pt shd; wc; chem disp; mv service pnt; shwrs; el pts (10A) €2.75 (poss rev pol); lndtte; shops 500m; tradsmn; rest, bar in vill; BBQ; playgrnd; fishing; 50% statics; dogs €1.10; adv bkg; quiet; CCI. "Useful, pleasant, clean stop nr Rouen; friendly recep; beautiful valley with many historic towns & vills; best pitches far side of lake; excel walking; vg sh stay/NH." € 8.90   2005*

BRIOUX SUR BOUTONNE see Melle *7A2*

FRANCE

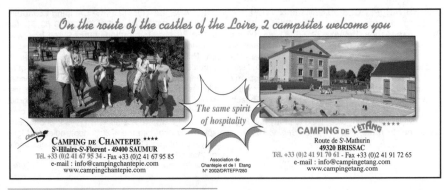

BRISSAC QUINCE *4G1* (2km NE Rural) **Camping Domaine de l'Etang, Route de St Mathurin, 49320 Brissac-Quince** [02 41 91 70 61; fax 02 41 91 72 65; info@campingetang.com; www.campingetang.com] Fr N on A11, exit junc 14 onto N260 passing E of Angers, following sp for Cholet-Poitiers. After x-ing Rv Loire, foll sp Brissac-Quincé on dual c'way way D748. Leave D748 to Brissac-Quince vill. Foll sp for St Mathurin-Domaine de l'Etang & site is on D55 2 km fr vill. Med, hdg/mkd pitch, hdstg, pt shd; htd wc; mv service pnt; chem disp; baby facs; some serviced pitches; shwrs inc; el pts (10A) inc; gas; lndtte; ice; shop; tradsmn; rest; snacks; bar; BBQ; playgrnd; htd, covrd pool; paddling pool; waterslide; lake fishing; games rm; cycle hire; golf 3km; horseriding 200m; entmnt; TV; dogs €2.50; recep 0800-1900; Eng spkn; adv bkg; quiet; cc acc; red long stay/low ssn; CCI. "Excel; spotless modern facs; lge pitches; gd touring base Loire valley; wine-tastings & visits; leisure facs gd for children; mkt Thu." ♦ 15 May-15 Sep. € 29.00 ABS - L15
2005*

See advertisement above

This site entry hasn't been updated for a while; we'd better fill in a site report form and send it to The Club.

BRISSAC QUINCE *4G1* (1km S Rural) **Camping a la Ferme Domaine de la Belle Etoile, La Belle Etoile, 49320 Brissac-Quince** [02 41 54 81 18] Take D748 S fr Angers to Poitiers. 1km fr Brissac-Quince & after D761 rndabt, take 3rd rd on R. Site in 600m Sm, pt shd; wc; chem disp (wc only); shwrs €1; el pts (5A) €2; lndtte; ice; BBQ; playgrnd; quiet. "CL-type site at vineyard with wine-tasting & farm produce; clean facs; troglodyte caves, mushroom farms & Brissac-Quince chateau nrby; vg sh stay." 1 Apr-30 Nov. € 6.50   2003*

†BRIVE LA GAILLARDE *7C3* (8km S Rural) **Camping a la Ferme (Delmas), Malfarges, 19600 Noailles** [tel/fax 05 55 85 81 33] Fr A20/E9 take exit 52 sp Noailles; foll sp to vill; 200m & take 1st R at vill shop (to avoid steep dangerous hill). Sp fr m'way. Sm, mkd pitch, terr, pt shd; wc; chem disp; mv service pnt; shwrs inc; el pts (6A) €4.40 (poss rev pol); shop 500m; farm meals & produce; rv sw 5km; fishing 200m; dogs €1.80; few statics; adv bkg; quiet; CCI. "V conv NH/sh stay adj to A20; friendly, helpful farmer; meals avail at farmhouse; gd value; if owner not around choose a pitch; basic san facs, poss unclean; parking on terraces poss awkward; strict silence after 2200; excel." € 13.00
2005*

†BRIVE LA GAILLARDE *7C3* (6km SW Rural) **Camping La Prairie, 19600 Lissac-sur-Couze** [tel/fax 05 55 85 37 97 or 04 73 34 75 53 LS] A20 exit 51; N89 to Larche; L onto D19 sp Lissac; L onto D59 round N side of lake, then bear L over dam; R to site in 2km. Med, mkd pitch, hdstg, terr, pt shd; wc; 70% pitches serviced; shwrs inc; el pts (10A) €3; gas 4km; lndtte; snacks; bar; shop; playgrnd; lake sw; boating; windsurfing; 5% statics; dogs €3; quiet; adv bkg; no cc acc; CCI. "Beautiful setting overlooking lake; gd long/sh stay; poss poor san facs; red facs low ssn." ♦ € 11.00   2005*

BROU *4F2* (1.5km W) **Parc de Loisirs de Brou, Route des Moulins, 28160 Brou** [02 37 47 02 17; fax 02 37 47 86 77] Sp in town on D13. Lge, hdg/mkd pitch, shd; wc; chem disp; shwrs inc; el pts (10A) €5.50; lndtte; shops 2km; rest; playgrnd; htd pool; waterslide; lake adj; fishing; golf; many statics; quiet; red low ssn; CCI. "Ent to site by card, so no ent when office clsd (winter office clsd Tues & Wed); excel new san facs 2004." ♦ 16 Feb-14 Dec.
€ 11.00   2005*

BROUSSES ET VILLARET *8F4* (500m S) **Camping Le Martinet Rouge, 11390 Brousses-et-Villaret** [tel/fax 04 68 26 51 98; martinet.bv.free.fr] Fr D118 Mazamet-Carcassonne, turn R 3km after Cuxac-Carbades onto D103; turn L in Brousses & foll sp. Sm, pt sl, shd; wc; baby facs; shwrs inc; el pts €2.50; lndtte; ice; shop; snacks; bar; playgrnd; pool; trout-fishing; horseriding; canoeing; 20% statics; adv bkg; quiet; CCI. "Helpful owners." ♦ 1 Apr-15 Oct.
€ 12.00   2004*

FRANCE

BRUERE ALLICHAMPS see St Amand Montrond *4H3*

BRUGHEAS see Vichy *9A1*

BRULON *4F1* (Urban) **Camping Le Septentrion** (formerly Brulon Le Lac), 72350 Brulon [02 43 95 68 96; fax 02 43 92 60 36; le.septentrion@ wanadoo.fr] Exit A81 junc 1; foll D4 S to Brulon, site on L on ent town, clearly sp. Sm, pt sl, shd; wc; mv service pnt; shwrs inc; el pts (6A) €2; lndtte; ice; shop 600m; tradsmn; rest; snacks; bar; BBQ; playgrnd; pool; lake sw; boating; fishing; cycle hire; games TV rm; phone; dogs €1; Eng spkn; adv bkg; quiet; red long stay/low ssn. "Gd cycling & walking area; v spacious pitches; gd welcome fr owners." 1 May-30 Sep. € 13.00   2005*

BRUNIQUEL *8E3* (4km NW) **Camping Le Clos Lalande**, Route de Bioule, 82800 Montricoux [tel/fax 05 63 24 18 89; contact@camping-lecloslalande. com; www.camping-lecloslalande.com] Fr A20 exit junc 60 for N20 dir Caussade. At Caussade take D964 dir Montricoux. Foll sp. Med, pt shd; wc; chem disp; el pts (6A) €2.50; lndtte; shop 300m; snacks; bar; playgrnd; pool; tennis; basketball; fishing; water sports; dogs €1; poss cr; adv bkg; quiet. "Lovely vill; vg for touring; mkt Weds. ♦ 1 May-15 Sep. € 11.60   2005*

BRUSQUE *10E1* (6km W Rural) **Aire Naturelle de la Bouyssiere de Blanc**, 12360 Peux-et- Couffouleux [05 65 49 55 17; vacances@labouyssiere.com; www.labouyssiere.com] Fr N or S on D12 to Brusque. At Brusque cross Rv Dordou & take D119 local rd dir Murat, site in 6km. Sm, mkd pitch, terr, shd; wc (cont); shwrs inc; el pts (16A) €3; lndtte; ice; tradsmn; rest 6km; snacks; bar; BBQ; playgrnd; pool; no dogs; adv bkg; quiet; red long stay. "Gd walking paths; 9thC vill adj; beautiful, unspoilt location; warm welcome fr British owners." 1 May-30 Sep. € 13.00   2005*

BRUYERES *6E2* (6km SE) **Camping Les Pinasses**, La Chapelle-devant-Bruyeres, 88600 Bruyeres [03 29 58 51 10; pinasses@dial.oleane. com; www.camping-les-pinasses.com] Fr Bruyeres, take D423 twd Gerardmer. In 3km turn L on D60 sp Corcieux, Site on R in 3km at La-Chapelle-devant-Bruyeres. Med, hdg/mkd pitch, pt shd; wc (some cont); chem disp; shwrs inc; el pts (4-6A) €3.30-4.30; gas; lndtte; shop; tradsmn; rest; snacks; bar; BBQ; playgrnd; entmnt; pool; minigolf; tennis & table tennis; 10% statics; dogs €1.30; adv bkg; some rlwy noise; CCI. "Beautiful area; vg long stay." Apr-15 Sep. € 17.20   2004*

BRUYERES *6E2* (6km S Rural) **Domaine des Messires**, La Feigne, 88600 Herpelmont [03 29 58 56 29 or 0031 321 331456 (N'lands); fax 03 29 51 62 86; mail@domainedesmessires.com; www.domainedesmessires.com] SE fr Bruyeres on D423; at Laveline turn R sp Herpelmont & foll site sp. Site 1.5km N of Herpelmont. Med, pt shd; wc; mv service pnt; chem disp; serviced pitches; child/baby facs; shwrs inc; el pts inc (6A) inc; lndtte; ice; shop; tradsmn; rest; snacks; bar; BBQ; playgrnd; lake sw; fishing; boating; dogs €3; Eng spkn; adv bkg; quiet; cc acc; red low ssn/long stay; CCI. "Attractive, peaceful lakeside site; gd touring base Alsace & Vosges." ♦ 29 Apr-16 Sep. € 23.00   2005*

See advertisement above

BUGEAT *7B4* (3km NW Rural) **Camp Municipal Puy de Veix**, 19170 Viam [05 55 95 52 05 (Mairie); fax 05 55 95 21 86; viam.mairie@wanadoo.fr] Fr Bugeat NW on D979; in 4km L onto D160; foll sp to Viam. Sm, mkd pitch, pt sl, terr, pt shd; wc; chem disp; mv service pnt; el pts (6-10A) €1.80; lndtte; shop 4km; rest 500m; playgrnd; lake sw & shgl beach adj; phone; poss cr; Eng spkn; adv bkg; CCI. "On lakeside; beautiful views; sw, boating, fishing; vg." 15 Jun-30 Sep. € 7.30   2005*

BUGUE, LE *7C3* (4km NE Rural) **Camping La Linotte, Route de Rouffignac, 24260 Le Bugue** [05 53 07 17 61; fax 05 53 54 16 96; campinglalinotte@wanadoo.fr] E off D710 onto D32E after passing thro town heading N twd Perigueux on rd to Rouffignac. Site sp fr D710. Med, hdg pitch, pt sl, terr, pt shd; wc; chem disp; baby facs; fam bthrm; shwrs inc; el pts (10A) inc; lndtte; shop; rest; snacks; playgrnd; htd pool; entmnt; quiet; adv bkg; CCI. "Splendid views; lovely site; vg long/sh stay; gd mkt Le Bugue Tues." 1 Apr-30 Sep. € 23.65   2004*

BUGUE, LE *7C3* (1km SE Urban) **Camping Les Trois Caupain** (formerlly Municipal Le Port), 24260 Le Bugue [05 53 07 24 60; info@camping-bugue.com; www.camping-des-trois-caupain.com] Exit Le Bugue town cent on D703 twd Campagne. Turn R at sp after 400m to site in 600m. Med, mkd pitch, unshd; wc; chem disp; mv service pnt; shwrs inc; el pts (6-10A) €2.80-3.40; gas; shops 1km; rest; snacks; bar; playgrnd; covrd pool; rv sw & games area adj; 20% statics; Eng spkn; adv bkg; quiet. "Pleasant, helpful owners; beautiful site; 15 mins walk to pretty town; excel long stay." 26 Mar-30 Oct. € 14.95   2004*

BUGUE, LE *7C3* (3km SE Rural) **Camping Le Val de la Marquise, 24260 Campagne** [05 53 54 74 10; fax 05 53 08 85 38; contact@val-marquise.com; www.val-marquise.com] Site 4km outside of Le Bugue in dir of Les Eyzies. Med, mkd pitch, terr, pt shd; wc; chem disp; shwrs inc; el pts (15A) €3; lndtte; shops 4km; tradsmn; rest; playgrnd; pool; 5% statics; dogs €1.50; phone; Eng spkn; adv bkg; quiet; CCI. "Highly rec; peaceful, friendly esp out of ssn; poss diff access to pitches for lge vans due narr site rds & low terrs; spotless san facs; beautiful pool; excel long stay." 1 Apr-15 Oct. € 14.80   2003*

BUGUE, LE *7C3* (7km SE Rural) **Camping Le Clou, Meynard, 24220 Coux-et-Bigaroque** [05 53 31 63 32; fax 05 53 31 69 33; info@camping-le-clou.com; www.camping-le-clou.com] S fr Le Bugue on D703 twd Belves; site 8km on R. Med, mkd pitch, pt sl, pt shd; htd wc; chem disp; mv service pnt; serviced pitches; baby facs; fam bthrm; shwrs inc; el pts (6A) €3.10; gas; lndtte; ice; tradsmn; rest; snacks; bar; BBQ; playgrnd; 2 pools & paddling pool; rv sw 5km; fishing; canoeing; horseriding; entmnt; child entmnt; games rm; TV; phone; 10% statics; dogs €1.50; Eng spkn; adv bkg; quiet; cc acc; red long stay/low ssn/CCI. "Pleasant owners; ideal base for Dordogne; BBQs arranged; lovely wooded site with much wildlife; vg long/sh stay." ♦ Easter-30 Sep. € 17.20   2003*

BUGUE, LE *7C3* (10km SE) **Camping La Faval, 24220 Coux-et-Bigaroque** [05 53 31 60 44; fax 05 53 28 39 71] On N side of Rv Dordogne at junc of D703 & D710, approx 300m fr rv. Med, shd, mkd pitch; wc; shwrs inc; el pts (3-6A) €2.60-2.80; lndtte; ice; rest; shop; playgrnd; sm pool; entmnt; golf & tennis adj; TV rm. "Run by friendly couple; indiv washrms; gd sized pitch; rd noise but quiet at night; helpful manager." ♦ 1 Apr-30 Sep. € 15.24   2004*

BUGUE, LE *7C3* (8km S Rural) **Camping Le Pont de Vicq, 24480 Le Buisson-de-Cadouin** [05 53 22 01 73; fax 05 53 22 06 70; le.pont.vicq@wanadoo.fr; www.campings-dordogne.com/pontdevicq] Fr Le Bugue foll sp to Le Buisson. Site immed S of bdge over Rv Dordogne on rd D51E. Sp fr all dir in Le Buisson. Med, hdg/mkd pitch, pt shd; wc; shwrs inc; el pts (6A) €3 (rev pol); lndtte; shops 1.5km; rest adj; snacks in ssn; playgrnd; shgl beach for rv sw; TV; 60% statics; dogs €1; phone adj; poss cr; adv bkg; quiet; CCI. "Pleasant site on rv but ltd facs; poss mosquitoes." 1 Apr-15 Oct. € 12.70
                    2005*

BUGUE, LE *7C3* (5km SW Rural) **Camping La Ferme des Poutiroux, 24510 Limeuil** [05 53 63 31 62; fax 05 53 58 30 84; camping.les.poutiroux@tiscali.fr; www.poutiroux.com] W fr Le Bugue on D703 twd Bergerac; in 2km take D31 S for 4km; bef bdge take R fork twd Tremolat/Lalinde; in 300m fork R (sp), site well sp. Sm, mkd, pt sl, terr, pt shd; wc; chem disp; mv service pnt; shwrs; el pts (6A) €3; lndtte; ice; shops 2km; playgrnd; pool (no shorts); canoes & rv sw nrby; some statics; dogs €1; phone; Eng spkn; adv bkg (dep req); quiet; cc not acc; CCI. "Friendly, helpful farmer; well-positioned; peaceful, family-run site; highly rec." ♦ 1 Apr-30 Sep. € 13.50   2004*

BUGUE, LE *7C3* (6km SW Rural) **Camping du Port de Limeuil, 24480 Alles-sur-Dordogne** [05 53 63 29 76; fax 05 53 63 04 19; didierbonvallet@aol.com] Exit Le Bugue on D31 sp Le Buisson; in 4km turn R on D51 sp Limeuil; at 2km turn L over rv bdge; site on R after bdge. Med, hdg/mkd pitch, pt sl, pt shd; wc; chem disp; 50% serviced pitches; shwrs inc; el pts (5A) €3.20; gas; lndtte; shop & 1km; bar; snacks; BBQ; playgrnd; htd pool; shgl beach & rv sw adj; games rm; mini-golf; canoe & cycle hire; 40% statics; dogs €2; poss cr; Eng spkn; adv bkg; quiet; red low ssn; CCI. "Superb location & site; excel for young or old; v clean san facs; gd sw in clean rv; lge pitches; conv for exploring region at confluence of Dordogne & Vezere rvs; ltd facs low ssn; gd long stay." ♦ ltd. 1 May-30 Sep. € 19.90   2005*

BUGUE, LE *7C3* (9km SW Rural) **Camping Nautique Departemental, Route de Mauzac, 24510 Tremolat** [05 53 22 81 18 or 05 53 05 65 65 (res); fax 05 53 06 30 94; semitour@perigord.tm.fr] Fr Le Bugue, take D703 W twd Pezuls. In vill, turn L onto D30 twd Tremolat. Site 700m W of Tremolat, well sp fr all directions. Med, hdg pitch, pt shd; wc; chem disp; shwrs inc; el pts (10A) inc; lndtte; ice; shops 700m; rest; snacks; BBQ; pool; rv adj; fishing; canoeing; 20% statics; dogs; phone; poss cr; adv bkg; quiet; CCI. "Most touring pitches have rv frontage, excel for fishing & canoeing; facs poss stretched high ssn; excel long stay." ♦ ltd. 1 May-30 Sep. € 20.00   2003*

BUGUE, LE *7C3* (10km W) **Camping La Foret,** Ste Alvere, 24510 Pezuls [05 53 22 71 69; fax 05 53 23 77 79; camping.laforet@wanadoo.fr; www.camping-la-foret.com] Off D703 fr Le Bugue to Lalinde rd, sp on L 1.5km bef Pezuls. In Le Bugue do not foll sp to Lalinde but cont thro town on D703, turn R, L & R, passing fire stn. Med, pt sl, pt shd; wc; chem disp; baby facs; shwrs inc; el pts (4A) inc; gas; lndtte; sm shop; snacks; BBQ (gas/charcoal only); playgrnd; pool; tennis; games area; games rm; disco weekly high ssn away fr vans; dogs free; recep 0830-1030 & 1500-1900; no c'vans over 6m high ssn; adv bkg; quiet; cc not acc; CCI. "Simple, peaceful site; nature lovers' paradise - wild orchids, butterflies, etc; friendly staff; gd san facs, ltd low ssn; mkt Le Bugue Tue." ♦ 1 Apr-15 Oct. € 18.20 ABS - D03   2005*

BUGUE, LE *7C3* (5km NW) **Camping St Avit Loisirs,** 24260 St Avit-de-Vialard [05 53 02 64 00; fax 05 53 02 64 39; contact@saint-avit-loisirs.com; www.saint-avit-loisirs.com] Leave N89/E70 SE of Perigueux & turn S onto D710. Approx 6km bef Le Bugue turn R onto D42 sp Journiac, then immed L onto C206 for Ste Alvere. In 3km turn R for St Alvere, site on R. Narr, twisting app rd. Lge, hdg pitch, pt sl, pt shd; wc; chem disp; baby facs; shwrs inc; el pts (6A) inc; gas; lndtte; shop; rest; snacks; bar; BBQ; playgrnd; 2 pools (1 htd, covrd); waterslide; tennis; crazy golf; golf, watersports, archery & horseriding nr; cycle hire; games rm; excursions; entmnt; TV/games rm; dogs €3.80; many static tents/vans; poss cr; adv bkg (bkg fee); quiet; cc acc; CCI. "Excel site & san facs; lovely; friendly welcome; well-run, busy site; conv for mkts, countryside & Lascaux" ♦ 1 Apr-30 Sep. € 34.30 ABS - D10   2005*

BUIS LES BARONNIES *9D2* (3km N Rural) Camping Le Romecas (Naturist), 26170 Buis-les-Baronnies [tel/fax 04 75 28 10 78] S fr Nyons on D938, E on D46/D4/D5 to Buis-les-Baronnies. On D546 turn N on D108 sp St Jalle. Site on L bef summit of Col d'Ey. Rd access gd although high. Med, terr, pt shd; wc (some cont); shwrs; el pts (6A) €2.70; lndtte; shop; rest; playgrnd; pool & paddling pool; TV; some statics; dogs €2.30; no adv bkg; quiet; CCI. "Beautiful situation; gd walking; friendly staff; access round site diff due tight bends & steep hillside." Easter-30 Sep. € 22.70 (3 persons)   2004*

BUIS LES BARONNIES *9D2* (7km E Rural) Camping/ Gite du Lievre (Taponnier), La Roche-sur-les-Buis, 26170 Buis-les-Baronnies [04 75 28 11 49; fax 04 75 28 19 26; gitedulievre@wanadoo.fr] In Buis-les-Baronnies travel N on D546; at edge of town after x-ing rv turn R onto D159; foll for 10km to Poet-en-Percip; site sp on L; 3km down unmade rd. Sm, mkd pitch, hdstg, terr, pt shd; wc (some cont); chem disp (wc); shwrs inc; el pts (10A) €1.70 (poss long lead req); tradsmn; rest; snacks; bar; playgrnd; pool; mountain bike trails; horseriding; quiet; adv bkg; no cc acc; CCI. "Site on farm; bread avail to order; v isolated; 3,000 feet high; views of Mt Ventoux; walks; climbing." 1 May-Oct. € 12.00   2003*

BUIS LES BARONNIES *9D2* (1.5km S) **Camping Les Ephelides,** Quartier Tuves, 26170 Buis-les-Baronnies [04 75 28 10 15; fax 04 75 28 13 04] Fr S of Vaison D54 or D13 E to Entrechaux, then D5 & D147 to vill. Sp in main rd S across rv, turn R, site in 1.5km. Normal exit in main rd blocked; access fr SW end of town to 'Parking Sud' by rv. Med, pt shd; wc; shwrs; el pts (3-10A) €2.50-3.10; lndtte; snacks; tennis adj; phone; adv bkg; quiet; red low ssn; cc acc. "Sited in old cherry orchard; excel views; mkt in town Wed; take care when x-ing bdge." 20 May-5 Sep. € 14.50   2003*

BUISSON DE CADOUIN, LE see Bugue, Le *7C3*

BUJALEUF see St Leonard de Noblat *7B3*

BUNUS *8F1* (1km W Rural) **Camping Inxauseta,** 64120 Bunus [tel/fax 05 59 37 81 49] Fr St Jean-Pied-de-Port twd St Palais on D933; turn R on D918 at Larceveau. In 4km turn L bef Bunus (school & town hall), down narr lane. Site sp fr D933. Med, pt sl, terr, pt shd; wc; shwrs inc; el pts (5A) €2; shops 1.5km; playgrnd; games rm; quiet; red low ssn. 20 Jun-10 Sep. € 9.00   2003*

BURNHAUPT LE HAUT see Cernay *6F3*

BURTONCOURT *5D2* (1km Rural) **Camping La Croix du Bois Sacker,** 57220 Burtoncourt [tel/fax 03 87 35 74 08; camping.croixsacker@wanadoo.fr; www.campingcroixsacker.com] Exit A4 junc 37 onto D3 to Burtoncourt for 12km dir Bouzonville. Lge, mkd pitch, some hdstg, terr, pt shd; wc; shwrs €0.80; el pts inc; lndtte; shop; rest, snacks 1km; bar; playgrnd; lake fishing; tennis; entmnt; TV; dogs €1.50; Eng spkn; adv bkg; quiet. "Lovely, wooded site; pleasant, friendly owners making improvements; gd security; gd NH or sh stay en rte Alsace/Germany." ♦ 1 Apr-31 Oct. € 13.00   2004*

†**BUSSIERE POITEVINE** *7A3* (Urban) **Camp Municipal La Croix de L'Hozanne,** 87320 Bussiere-Poitevine [05 55 60 08 17 or 05 55 68 40 83 (Mairie); fax 05 55 68 40 72] NW fr Bellac on N147, 8km after St Bonnet-de-Bellac turn R onto D4 sp Bussiere-Poitevine. Site 500m on R opp water tower. Sm, hdg pitch, pt shd; htd wc (some cont); shwrs inc; el pts (10-15A) €1.85-2.75; shops, rest & bar 500m; snacks; playgrnd; CCI. "Gd CL-type site; old but v clean facs; grass pitches poss water-logged in winter but can pitch in rd; ltd facs in low ssn; gd NH." € 5.70   2004*

BUYSSCHEURE see St Omer *3A3*

BUZANCAIS *4H2* (S Urban) **Camp Municipal La Tete Noire,** 36500 Buzancais [02 54 84 17 27 or 06 15 85 53 04 (mob); fax 02 54 02 13 45; buzancais@wanadoo.fr] N143 fr Chateauroux thro town cent, cross rv, immed turn R into sports complex. Lge, some hdstg, pt shd; wc (some cont); shwrs inc; el pts (6-10A) €1.70-2.50; ice; lndtte; shop, rest, snacks, bar 500m; playgrnd; pool 500m; entmnt; some statics; adv bkg; quiet; red 2+ night; CCI. "Pleasant peaceful situation on rv, gd fishing; clean, well-kept site; clean facs, red low ssn; no twin-axle vans; office clsd 1200-1600 & no access; gd disabled facs." ♦ 1 May-30 Sep. € 9.80   2005*

BUZANCY *5C1* (1.5km SW) **Camping La Samaritaine**, 08240 Buzancy [03 24 30 08 88; fax 03 24 30 29 39; info@campinglasamaritaine.com; www.campinglasamaritaine.com] Fr Sedan take D977 dir Vouziers for 23km. Turn L onto D12, cont to end & turn L onto D947 for Buzancy. On ent Buzancy in 100m turn 2nd R immed after g'ge on R sp Camping Stade. Foll sp to site on L past football pitches. Med, hdg/mkd pitch, some hdstg; pt shd; wc; chem disp (wc); mv service pnt; 45% serviced pitches; mv service pnt; baby facs; shwrs inc; el pts (10A) inc; lndtte; lndry rm; ice; sm shop; tradsmn; rest 1.6km; snacks, bar high ssn; BBQ (gas/charcoal); playgrnd; lake sw & sand beach adj; fishing; tennis 800m; games rm; child entmnt; TV rm; 10% statics; dogs €2.50; phone; Eng spkn; adv bkg (dep €10 req); quiet; red low ssn; cc acc; CCI. "Excel renovated site; no site lighting low ssn; lovely area for walking/cycling; helpful, pleasant staff." ♦ 14 Apr-30 Sep. € 19.50 ABS - P10   2005*

CABOURG *3D1* (1km E Coastal) **Camp Municipal Les Tilleuls**, 14160 Dives-sur-Mer [02 31 91 25 21; fax 02 31 91 72 13] Fr Cabourg cross bdge to Dives-sur-Mer, turn R at traff lts (Rue Gaston Manneville) & foll camping sp past church at bottom of hill up to D45. Turn L, site on R in 300m. Or fr A13 take D400 sp Cabourg, pass Super U & Intermarche supmkts & turn R sp Camping Touristique, site on R in 1.2km. Lge, pt sl, pt shd; wc (mainly cont); shwrs inc; el pts (9A) €3.40; ice; lndry rm; shops 500m; sand beach 1km; horseriding; boules; playgrnd; quiet. Easter-15 Sep. € 10.40   2005*

CABOURG *3D1* (8km SW) **Camping Le Clos Tranquille**, Gonneville-en-Auge, 14810 Merville-Franceville-Plage [02 31 24 21 36; fax 02 31 24 28 80; leclostranquille@wanadoo.fr; www.leclostranquille.com] Fr Cabourg, take D513 twd Caen. 2km after Varaville turn R to Gonneville-en-Auge (by garden cent) D95A. Foll sp to vill, site ent on R after LH bend. Med, pt shd; wc; chem disp; el pts (4-10A) €2.40-€4.60; shwrs inc; gas; lndtte; tradsmn; snacks; shop; playgrnd; cycle hire; sand beach 5km; 12% statics poss cr; Eng spkn; adv bkg; quiet; CCI. "Excel." 9 Apr-19 Sep. € 12.00   2004*

CABOURG *3D1* (1km W Coastal) **Camping La Pommeraie, Le Bas Cabourg**, 14390 Cabourg [02 31 91 54 58] Take D513 fr Cabourg twd Caen. Site on L 1km after Bas Cabourg sp. Med, pt shd; wc; shwrs €1; el pts (5A) €3.80; gas; lndtte; shop; ice; sand beach 800m; dogs €1.52; adv bkg; cc acc. "Mkt Sat." 9 Apr-19 Sep. € 15.30   2004*

CABOURG *3D1* (2km W Coastal) **Camping Les Peupliers, Allee des Pins**, 14810 Merville-Franceville-Plage [tel/fax 02 31 24 05 07; asl-mondeville@wanadoo.fr; www.asl-mondeville.com] Exit A13 to Cabourg, take D514 W, turn R sp La Home, site sp, 2km E of Merville-Franceville. Med, mkd pitch, pt shd; htd wc; baby facs; shwrs inc; el pts (10A) €5; lndtte; shop 2km; tradsmn; rest high ssn; snacks; bar; BBQ; playgrnd; htd pool; beach 300m; games area; entmnt; child entmnt; TV; 12% statics; dogs €2.60; Eng spkn; adv bkg; quiet; cc acc; CCI. "Vg facs for children; pleasant site." ♦ 1 Apr-31 Oct. € 20.00   2005*

See advertisement

CABOURG *3D1* (6km W Coastal) **Camp Municipal Le Point du Jour, Route de Cabourg**, 14810 Merville-Franceville-Plage [02 31 24 23 34 or 02 31 24 21 83 (Mairie); fax 02 31 24 15 54; camp. lepointdujour@wanadoo.fr] Fr Ouistreham on D514/515 turn E at Benouville, cross bdge onto D514, site on L dir Cabourg. Med, hdg/mkd pitch, pt sl, pt shd; htd wc; chem disp; baby facs; shwrs inc; el pts (10A) €5 (poss rev pol); lndtte; shop, rest, snacks, bar 2km; playgrnd; sand beach adj; few statics; no dogs; bus; poss cr; adv bkg; quiet; CCI. "Excel site; easy access D-Day beaches." ♦ 1 May-22 Sep. € 16.40   2005*

CABRERETS *7D3* (1km Rural) **Camping Cantal**, 46330 Cabrerets [05 65 31 26 61; fax 05 65 31 20 47] Fr Cahors take D653 E for approx 15km bef turning R onto D662 E thro Vers & St Gery. Turn L onto D41 to Cabrerets. Site 1km after vill on R. Sm, pt sl, pt shd; wc; chem disp (wc only); 50% serviced pitch; shwrs inc; el pts €2; quiet; CCI. "Superb situation; v peaceful; warden calls; ground conditions rough; facs old but fair condition; elec unreliable; conv Pech Merle; excel sh stay." 1 Apr-30 Oct. € 9.30   2005*

CABRIERES D'AIGUES see Pertuis *10E3*

CADENET *10E3* (10km NE Rural) **Camping Le Moulin a Vent, Chemin de Gastoule, 84160 Cucuron** [04 90 77 25 77; fax 04 90 77 28 12; bressier@aol.com] Fr A51 exit junc 15 to Pertuis. N on D56 fr Pertuis to Cucuron. Site sp S fr Cucuron vill dir Villelaure. Sm, mkd pitch, terr, pt shd; wc; shwrs inc; el pts inc (2-10A) €1.60-4; shop; tradsmn; snacks; lndtte; playgrnd; htd pool 4km; dogs €2; quiet; Eng spkn; 10% statics; 5% red; cc not acc; CCI. "Gd sh stay; spacious pitches, but access poss diff; friendly, helpful staff." ♦ 1 Apr-30 Sep. € 13.00   2004*

> Some of these sites have changed their opening dates - we'd better fill in some site report forms and let the editor of the guide know.

CADENET *10E3* (10km NE Rural) **Camping Lou Badareu, La Rasparine, 84160 Cucuron-en-Luberon** [04 90 77 21 46] Take D45 then D27 NE fr Cadenet twds Cucuron. S of Cucuron turn onto D27 (do not go into town), site is E 1km. Well sp fr D27. Med, mkd pitch, pt sl, pt shd; ltd wc (own san rec); chem disp; shwrs inc; el pts (4-6A) €2.20-3 (long lead poss req); shop & 1km; lndtte; playgrnd; pool; quiet; 20% statics; phone; dogs €1.50; CCI. "In cherry orchard, sep access for high vans; pretty & comfortable." ♦ 20 Mar-30 Oct. € 9.00   2002*

CADENET *10E3* (2km SW Rural) **Camping Val de Durance, Les Routes, 84160 Cadenet** [04 90 68 37 75 or 04 42 20 47 25 (LS); fax 04 90 68 16 34; info@homair-vacances.fr; www.homair-vacances.fr] Exit A7 at Cavaillon onto D973 dir Cadenet. In Cadanet take D59, site sp. Lge, hdg pitch, pt shd; wc; chem disp; shwrs inc; el pts (6-10A) €4; gas; lndtte; ice; shop & 2km; rest; snacks; bar; playgrnd; pool; rv sw & beach; archery; canoeing; cycling; games area; entmnt; TV; 30% statics; dogs €4; adv bkg; red low ssn; cc acc; CCI. "Dir access to lake; adj Luberon Park." ♦ 4 Apr-2 Oct. € 28.00
                                          2004*

CADENET *10E3* (5km SW Rural) **Camping Sylvacane-en-Provence, 13640 La Roque-d'Antheron** [04 42 50 40 54; fax 04 42 50 43 75; campoclub@wanadoo.fr] Fr A7 take Senas exit onto N7 twd Aix-en-Provence. In 10km take D561 E to La Roque-d'Antheron. Site sp & visible fr rd. Med, terr, shd; wc; shwrs; el pts (10A) inc; lndtte; shop; supmkt nr; snacks; bar; BBQ; playgrnd; pool; waterslide; tennis; fishing; entmnt; TV; many statics; dogs €2.30; poss cr; adv bkg; quiet but some rd noise; red low ssn; cc acc; CCI. "Beautiful scenery in Durance Valley." ♦ 15 Mar-30 Sep. € 20.00   2002*

CADENET *10E3* (5km SW Rural) **Caravanning Domaine des Iscles, 13640 La Roque-d'Antheron** [04 42 50 44 25; fax 04 42 50 56 29; campoclub@wanadoo.fr; www.campoclub.com] Fr A7 at junc 26 take N7 sp Lambesc; At Pont Royal turn L onto D561 to La Roque-d'Antheron; at rndabt on edge of vill stay on D561; immed R on slip rd, foll sp thro tunnel under canal. Lge, hdg pitch, pt shd; wc (cont); chem disp; mv service pnt; shwrs inc; el pts (10A) inc; ice; lndtte; shop; tradsmn; rest; snacks; bar; playgrnd; pool; lake adj; fishing; golf; tennis; games area; 4% statics; dogs €2.30; poss cr; Eng spkn; adv bkg (dep req); red low ssn; CCI. "Gd site for children; lge pitches; pleasant setting; san facs clean; rec extension leads." ♦ 1 Mar-15 Oct.
€ 21.00   2002*

†**CADENET** *10E3* (10km W Rural) **Camping L'Oree du Bois, 13350 Charleval** [04 42 28 41 75; fax 04 42 28 47 48; campoclub@wanadoo.fr] Fr Cadenet take D561 to Roque-d'Antheron, cont to Charleval. Site sp in vill. Lge, hdg/mkd pitch, pt sl, pt shd; wc (cont, own san rec); chem disp; shwrs inc; el pts (10A) inc; gas; lndtte; shop high ssn; rest; snacks, bar 500m; playgrnd; pool adj; entmnt; 30% statics; dogs; phone; poss cr; Eng spkn; adv bkg (dep req, bkg fee); poss noisy; cc acc; CCI. € 16.80   2002*

CADEUIL *7B1* (2km N) **Camping Lac Le Grand Bleu, Route des Saintes, 17250 Ste Gemme** [05 46 22 90 99 or 06 81 04 41 68; fax 05 46 22 14 95; campinglegrandbleu@hotmail.com] Site 22km S of Rochefort, 16km N of Royan on D753. In Cadeuil take D728 twd Saintes to site sp on L. Med, pt shd, mkd pitch; wc; shwrs; el pts (6A) inc; lndtte; ice; shop; rest; snacks; bar; BBQ; playgrnd; pool; cycle hire; lake adj; canoeing; games area; mini-golf; entmnts; TV; child entmnt; some statics; dogs €2.30; adv bkg; red low ssn; quiet; cc acc. 5 Apr-27 Sep. € 20.00   2003*

CADEUIL *7B1* (9km NE) **Camping Parc de la Garenne, 24 Ave Bernard Chambenoit, 17250 Pont-l'Abbe-d'Arnoult** [05 46 97 01 46 or 06 09 43 20 11 (mob); info@lagarenne.net; www.lagarenne.net] N fr Saintes on N137. In 18km turn L onto D18 to Pont-l'Abbe. In town turn L, foll camp sp to site adj sw pool. Med, shd; wc; chem disp; mv service pnt 150m; baby facs; shwrs inc; el pts (6-10A) €3.90-4.20; gas; lndtte; ice; shop, rest, snacks & bar 500m; snacks; BBQ (elec only); playgrnd; pool adj; tennis; games area; TV rm; 10% statics; dogs €2; phone; Eng spkn; adv bkg; quiet; CCI. "Well-run site, conv coast, inland touring; gd san facs; €50 dep for barrier disk, cash only; gd." ♦ 15 May-25 Sep. € 15.00   2005*

CADEUIL *7B1* (4km NW Rural) **Camping Le Valerick, La Mauviniere, 17600 St Sornin [tel/fax 05 46 85 15 95; camplevalerick@aol.com]** Fr Marennes take D728 sp Saintes for 10km; L to St Sornin; site sp in vill. Fr Saintes D728 W for 26km; turn R to vill. Med, mkd pitch, pt sl, pt shd; wc; chem disp (wc); shwrs inc; el pts (4-6A) €2.80-€3.20 (poss rev pol); lndtte; shop; rest; snacks; bar; BBQ; playgrnd; sand beach 18km; entmnt; dogs €1.30; adv bkg; CCI. "Nice site; friendly; insufficient facs high ssn but v clean; washroom area open to full view of site; plenty of bird life - herons, storks etc; poss mosquito probem." 1 Apr-30 Sep. € 10.50   2005*

> Will you fill in the site report forms at the back of the guide, or shall I?

CAEN *3D1* (14km N Coastal) **Yelloh! Village Cote de Nacre, Rue General Moulton, 14750 St Aubin-sur-Mer [02 31 97 14 45; fax 02 31 97 22 11; camping-cote-de-nacre@wanadoo.fr; www.camping-cote-de-nacre.com]** Fr Caen on D7 dir Douvres-la-Delivrande, Langrune-sur-Mer & St Aubin. Site in St Aubin-sur-Mer on S side of D514; clearly sp on o'skts. Lge, mkd pitch, hdstg, unshd; wc; chem disp; mv service pnt; baby facs; shwrs inc; el pts (10A) inc; gas; lndtte; shop high ssn; tradsmn; rest; snacks; bar; BBQ; playgrnd; htd pool; waterslide; sand beach 500m; tennis 200m; cycle hire; games rm; entmnt; TV; internet; 15% statics; dogs €4; quiet; phone; poss cr; Eng spkn; adv bkg rec; red low ssn; cc acc; CCI. "Conv Normandy beaches, Mont St Michel, Honfleur; v helpful staff; vg." ♦ 1 Apr-17 Sep. € 38.70   2005*

See advertisement above

CAGNES SUR MER *10E4* (3km N) **Camping Green Park, 159 Vallon-des-Vaux, 06800 Cagnes-sur-Mer [04 93 07 09 96 or 06 80 48 25 74; fax 04 93 14 36 55; info@greenpark.fr; www.greenpark. fr]** Fr Aix on A8 exit junc 47 & foll dir Cagnes-ur-Mer/Nice on N7 (do not foll sp Centre Ville). After 1st traff lts beside racecourse strt on for 2km, then turn L dir Val Fleuri, site in 3km. Fr Nice take N98 coast rd dir Cannes. Shortly after Cagnes turn R opp Le Port & foll sp Camping. Turn R then L at traff lts, site 3rd on L in 3km. Med, mkd pitch, pt shd; wc (some cont); chem disp; mv service pnt; baby facs; shwrs inc; el pts (10A) inc; lndtte; ice; shop; rest; snacks; bar; BBQ (gas/elec); playgrnd; 2 htd pools; shgl beach 4.3km; tennis 400m; sports area; cycle hire; disco; entmnt; internet; TV rm; dogs €2.50; adv bkg; quiet; red low ssn; CCI. "Friendly; well run; rec." ♦ 1 Apr-30 Sep. € 38.40 (CChq acc) ABS - C28   2005*

†**CAGNES SUR MER** *10E4* (3km N Urban) **Camping-Caravaning Le Val de Cagnes, 179 Chemin des Salles, 06800 Cagnes-sur-Mer [tel/fax 04 93 73 36 53; valdecagnes@wanadoo.fr]** On A8 exit Cagnes sur Mer, foll sp for Centre Ville. In town foll sp 'Haut de Cagnes' to Rue Jean Ferraud, then R fork onto Chemin des Salles & foll for approx 2km to site on L. Sm, hdg/mkd pitch, terr, pt shd; wc; chem disp; shwrs; el pts (6A) €3.30; lndtte; sm shop; snacks; bar; playgrnd; pool; shgl beach 3.5km; dogs €2.30; Eng spkn; adv bkg (dep req); quiet; red low ssn; CCI. "San blocks v clean but tired; family-run site; v helpful owners; close to beaches & town; trains to Monaco & Italy fr town; sm pitches; v ltd facs low ssn." € 16.30   2004*

†**CAGNES SUR MER** *10E4* (3.5km N) **Camping La Riviere, 06800 Cagnes-sur-Mer [tel/fax 04 93 20 62 27]** Sp fr cent town. Med, mkd pitch; pt shd; wc; shwrs inc; el pts (3-6A) €2.50-€3; shwrs inc; gas; lndtte; shop; bar; rest; sand beach 5km; playgrnd; pool; 70% statics; dogs €1.50; poss cr; quiet; adv bkg; cc acc. "Site clsd 11 Oct-14 Nov." ♦ € 12.40   2004*

FRANCE

†CAGNES SUR MER *10E4* (3.5km N) **Camping Le Val Fleuri**, 139 Vallon-des-Vaux, 06800 Cagnes-sur-Mer [tel/fax 04 93 31 21 74] Fr Nice take N7 W twd Cannes. On app Cagnes turn R & foll sp Camping; site on R after 3km, well sp. Sm, terr, pt shd; wc (some cont); shwrs; el pts (3A) inc; shop 3km; rest; shgl beach 4km; playgrnd; sm pool; entmnt; poss cr; Eng spkn; adv bkg; red low ssn. "Site divided by rd (not busy); helpful owners; gd." € 17.00   2004*

CAGNES SUR MER *10E4* (8km NE) **Camping Magali**, 1814 Route de la Baronne, 06700 St Laurent-du-Var [04 93 31 57 00; fax 04 92 12 01 33; www.camping-magali.com] Exit A8 junc 49 to St Laurent-du-Var. Site sp fr town cent. Or Fr Digne S on N202, turn R onto D2210 at Pont-de-la-Manda; foll sp to St Laurent-du-Var on D2209 approx 7km, site on L. Med, mkd, pitch pt shd; htd wc (mainly cont); chem disp; shwrs inc; baby facs; el pts (2-4A) €2.70-3.20; gas; ice; lndtte; shop; rest; snacks; bar; pool; shgl beach 6km; sailing; fishing; horseriding; tennis; some statics; dogs €1.90; bus nrby; poss cr; adv bkg; quiet; red low ssn; cc acc. "Conv Nice ferry (25 mins to port), Nice carnival/Menton Lemon Fair; sm pitches; v helpful warden." ♦ 1 Feb-31 Oct. € 22.30   2005*

CAGNES SUR MER *10E4* (2km S Coastal) **Parc des Maurettes**, 730 Ave du Docteur Lefebvre, 06270 Villeneuve-Loubet [04 93 20 91 91; fax 04 93 73 77 20; info@parcdesmaurettes.com; www.parcdesmaurettes.com] N fr Cannes on A8 exit Villeneuve-Loubet-Plage, then N7 exit 46 twds Antibes for 1km. Turn inland off N7 at SE corner of Intermarche, site in 300m. Med, mkd pitch, terr, pt shd; some serviced pitches; htd wc; chem disp; shwrs inc; el pts (3-10A) €3-5; gas; ice; lndtte; shops adj; supmkt 100m; snacks; playgrnd; htd, covrd pool; shgl beach 500m; sat TV; dogs €1.75; train Nice 400m; poss cr; Eng spkn; adv bkg; quiet; 10-40% red long stay; cc acc; CCI. "Marineland Zoo 1km; Cannes, Nice 20 mins by train; well-kept site with clean facs." ♦ 10 Jan-15 Nov. € 25.40   2004*

†CAGNES SUR MER *10E4* (4km S Coastal) **Camping La Vieille Ferme**, 296 Blvd des Groules, 06270 Villeneuve-Loubet-Plage [04 93 33 41 44; fax 04 93 33 37 28; camping.vieilleferme@wanadoo.fr; www.vieilleferme.com] Fr W (Cannes) take Antibes exit 44 fr A8, foll D35 dir Antibes. At lge junc turn onto N7 twd Biot & Villeneuve-Loubet (rlwy line on R). Just after Marineland turn L onto Blvd des Groules. Fr E (Nice) leave A8 at junc 47 to join N7 twd Antibes, take 3rd turning after Intermarche supmkt; site well sp fr N7. Med, hdg/mkd pitch, pt terr, pt sl, pt shd; htd wc; chem disp; mv service pnt; serviced pitches; baby facs; shwrs inc; el pts (10A) inc; gas; lndtte; ice; sm shop; supmkt 800m; rest; snacks; BBQ (gas/elec only); playgrnd; htd/covrd pool; shgl beach 1km (busy rd & rlwy to cross); archery; games rm; TV rm; internet; 40% statics; dogs €1.50; recep 0800-1200 & 1400-2000; c'vans over 8m not acc; Eng spkn; adv bkg; some aircraft & rd noise; red long stay & low ssn; cc acc; CCI. "Well-kept, family-run site; beach not suitable children & non-swimmers; excel pool; gd for walking, cycling & dogs as lge park adj; poss mosquito problem; well-drained, lge pitches; buses & trains for Nice & Cannes/Menton/Monaco 5 min walk; excel." ♦ € 34.00 ABS - C22   2005*

CAGNES SUR MER *10E4* (4km SW Rural) **Parc Saint James Le Sourire**, Route de Grasse, 06270 Villeneuve-Loubet [04 93 20 96 11; fax 04 93 22 07 52; info@camping-parcsaintjames.com; www.camping-parcsaintjames.com] Exit A8 at exit 47; take D2 to Villeneuve; at rndbt take D2085 sp Grasse. Site on L in 2km. Sp Le Sourire. Med, hdg pitch, pt shd; wc (some cont); chem disp; mv service pnt; shwrs inc; el pts (6A) inc; gas; lndtte; ice; shop; tradsmn; rest; snacks; bar; playgrnd; 2 htd pools; shgl beach 4km; tennis, golf & horseriding nr; table tennis; mini-golf; sauna; rv 2km; 70% statics; dogs €5; some rd noise; Eng spkn; adv bkg; 10% red long stay & w/e low ssn; cc acc; CCI. "Vg; red facs low ssn; park in visitors' car park bef registering; conv Nice, Cannes." ♦ ltd. 8 Apr-30 Sep. € 27.50   2005*

See advertisement above

CAGNES SUR MER *10E4* (1km NW Urban) **Camping Le Colombier, Collines de la Route de Vence, 35 Chemin de Ste Colombe, 06800 Cagnes-sur-Mer** [tel/fax 04 93 73 12 77; campinglecolombier06@wanadoo.fr; www.campinglecolombier.com] N fr Cagnes cent foll 1-way system dir Vence. Half way up hill turn R at rndabt dir Cagnes-sur-Mer & R at next island. Site on L 300m, sp fr town cent. Sm, hdg/mkd pitch, pt shd; htd wc; chem disp; mv service pnt; shwrs inc; el pts (6A) €3; lndry rm; shop 400m; rest 800m; snacks; bar; no BBQ; playgrnd, sm pool adj; TV; beach 2.5km; cycle hire; some statics; no dogs Jul/Aug; phone; Eng spkn; quiet; red long stay/CCI. "V friendly, family-run site." 1 Apr-30 Sep. € 22.00   2004*

CAGNES SUR MER *10E4* (4km NW) **Camping Le Vallon Rouge, Route de Greolieres, 06480 La Colle-sur-Loup** [04 93 32 86 12; fax 04 93 32 80 09; auvallonrouge@aol.com; www.auvallonrouge.com] Leave A8 at junc 47 Cagnes-sur-Mer, foll dir Villeneuve-Loubet vill. At vill turn L at traff lts onto D6 to La Colle-sur-Loup, site on R. NB Lge o'fits park in lay-by & ask at recep for advice on tackling steep ent driveway. Med, mkd pitch, pt shd; wc; chem disp; baby facs; shwrs inc; el pts (10A) inc; gas; lndtte; ice; shop; rest; snacks; bar; BBQ (gas/elec); playgrnd; pool; shgl beach 7km; rv sw nrby; fishing; games area; entmnt; TV rm; dogs; c'vans over 7m not acc; adv bkg; red low ssn; cc acc; CCI. "Conv Nice, Cannes, St Paul-de-Vence & Grasse; Sat mkt." ♦ 1 Apr-30 Oct. € 31.80 ABS - C20   2005*

CAGNES SUR MER *10E4* (4km NW) **Camping Les Pinedes, St Donat, Route de Pont de Pierre, 06480 La Colle-sur-Loup** [04 93 32 98 94; fax 04 93 32 50 20; campinglespinedes06@aol.com; www.lespinedes.com] Exit A8 junc 47 or 48 dir Vence to La Colle-sur-Loup. Site is on D6 1.5km W of La Colle, foll sp Gorges du Loup & Site. Lge, mkd pitch, hdstg, pt sl, terr, pt shd; wc; chem disp; mv service pnt; serviced pitches; shwrs inc; el pts (3-10A) €2.70-4; lndtte; ice; sm shop & 1.5km; tradsmn; rest adj; snacks; bar; pool; beach 3km; rv sw adj; 20% statics; dogs €2.60; Eng spkn; adv bkg; quiiet; cc acc; red long stay/low ssn; CCI. "V helpful, friendly manager; steep access to pitches but gd rd surface; not suitable for disabled; excel for touring Cote d'Azur; excel site." 15 Mar-5 Oct. € 20.80   2002*

CAHORS *7D3* (8km N Rural) **Camping Les Graves, 46090 St Pierre-Lafeuille** [tel/fax 05 65 36 83 12; infos@camping-lesgraves.com; www.camping-lesgraves.com] Leave A20 at junc 57 Cahors Nord onto N20. Foll sp St Pierre-Lafeuille; at N end of vill, site is opp L'Atrium wine cave. Med, hdg pitch, pt sl, pt shd; wc, chem disp; mv service pnt; shwrs inc; el pts (6-10A) €2.50-3.50 (poss rev pol); lndtte; ice; shop 10km; rest; snacks; bar; playgrnd; pool; cycle hire; 5% statics; dogs €1; adv bkg rec high ssn; quiet but some rd noise; CCI. "V clean; lge pitches; lovely views; guided walks; poss clsd during/after wet weather due boggy ground; conv access to a'route; handy for Cahors & Lot valley; gd sh/long stay." ♦ 1 Apr-15 Oct. € 12.50   2005*

CAHORS *7D3* (8km N Rural) **Quercy-Vacances, 46000 St Pierre-Lafeuille** [05 65 36 87 15; fax 05 65 36 02 39; quercyvacances@wanadoo.fr] Head N on N20 Souillac-Brive rd, turn L at N end of St Pierre-Lafeuille turn W at site sp N of vill, site in 700m down lane; new site opened adj so care needed to spot correct sp. Med, pt sl, pt shd; wc; chem disp; baby facs; shwrs inc; el pts (6-10A) €3.30-5.30; gas; lndtte; shops 10km; tradsmn; rest; snacks; bar; playgrnd; pool; tennis; TV; dogs €2.50; phone; Eng spkn; adv bkg; quiet; ltd facs low ssn; cc acc; CCI. "Most pitches slightly sloping; pretty site; spotlessly clean; v helpful owner; much to do/see locally; conv N20." ♦ 1 May-19 Sep. € 18.80   2005*

CAHORS *7D3* (1.5km E Urban) **Camping Riviere de Cabessut, Rue de la Riviere, 46000 Cahors** [05 65 30 06 30; fax 05 65 23 99 46; camping-riviere-cabessut@wanadoo.fr; www.cabessut.com] Fr E on D911 R bef Cabessut bdge at traff lts. Site in 1km & sp. Fr N on N20 turn onto by-pass (S); at end of by-pass at island foll sp Cahors Centre; at traff lts at Louis Philippe bdge cont onto D911 dir Rodez; in 1km at site sp turn L. Site on E bank of Rv Lot, ent on R. Site well sp fr town. Med, hdg/mkd pitch, pt shd; wc; chem disp; mv service pnt; some serviced pitches; baby facs; shwrs inc; el pts (10A) inc (rev pol); gas; lndtte; ice; shop 2km; tradsmn; rest; snacks; bar; BBQ (gas only); playgrnd; pool (no shorts); rv adj; 5% statics; €20 dep for barrier card; dogs €2; phone; poss cr; Eng spkn; adv bkg rec - ess high ssn; quiet but dawn cockerel; CCI. "Excel, well-managed site with efficient & courteous staff; rv trips; prehistoric caves & medieval vill nr; gd mkt Sat." ♦ 1 Apr-30 Sep. € 16.60   2005*

CAHORS *7D3* (7km E) **Camp Municipal Lamagdelaine,   46090   Lamagdelaine** [05 65 35 05 97 (Mairie); fax 05 65 22 64 93] Fr Cahors take D653 sp Figeac; site on R at Lamagdelaine rndabt. Fr Figeac on D653 sp Cahors; rndabt is 9km after Vers. Sm, pt shd; wc (some cont); shwrs inc; el pts €1.80; shops 1.5km; pool 7km; dogs €1; quiet; CCI. "Warden calls bet 0700-0800 & 2000-2200; chain across ent 2200; key fr Mairie adj if warden absent." 15 Jun-Aug. € 9.50   2005*

CAHAGNES see Villers Bocage *3D1*

CAJARC *7D4* (300m SW Urban) **Camp Municipal Le Terriol, Rue Le Terriol, 46160 Cajarc** [05 65 40 72 74; fax 05 65 40 39 05] Fr Cahors dir Cajarc on D662 on L foll sp to site. Sm, hdg/mkd pitches, some hdstg, pt shd; wc (cont); chem disp; baby facs; fam bthrm; shwrs inc; el pts (10A) inc; lndtte; shop, rest, bar in vill; BBQ; playgrnd; pool; tennis; dogs; phone; poss cr; Eng spkn; adv bkg; quiet but some rd noise; CCI. "Medieval vill has gd rests & facs; Lot valley scenery; fair sh stay." 1 May-30 Sep. € 10.40   2004*

CAJARC *7D4* (6km SW Rural) **Camp Municipal le Grand Pre, 46330 Cenevieres** [05 65 30 22 65 or 05 65 31 28 16 (Marie); fax 05 65 31 37 00] Fr Villefranche on D911 twd Cahors turn R onto D24 at Limogne for Cenevieres. Foll sp. Fr St Cirq-Lapopie on D24 thro vill & over rlwy. Sm, hdg/mkd pitch, pt shd; wc; chem disp (wc); mv service pnt; shwrs inc; el pts (10A) €2.20; rest, snacks, bar 1km; BBQ; rv sw; dogs; bus; phone; quiet. "Peaceful site with vg san facs; site self & warden calls pm; wonderful views of cliffs; pitch adj; vg long/sh stays." Jun-Sep. € 8.80   2005*

CAJARC *7D4* (9km NW Rural) **Camping Mas de Nadal (Naturist), 46330 Sauliac-sur-Cele** [05 65 31 20 51; fax 05 65 31 20 57; info@ masdenadal.com; www.masdenadal.com] Fr Cahors take Cele rv scenic rd or D653 E. After 35km turn R onto D40 S, sp Blars. Fr Blars cont S for 2km to site ent on R. Sm, mkd pitch, pt sl, pt shd; wc; shwrs inc; el pts (9A) €3.50; ice; shops 2km; tradsmn; rest; bar; pool; canoe hire; dogs €3.50; phone; poss cr; Eng spkn; adv bkg (dep req €16); quiet; CCI/INF card req. "Secluded wooded hillside; ltd rough pitches not suitable lge o'fits; rec phone ahead to check avail; suitable for m'vans." 1 Apr-1 Oct. € 19.00   2005*

†**CALAIS** *3A3* (8km E Rural) **Camping Bouscarel, 448 Rue du Lac, 62215 Oye-Plage** [03 21 36 76 37; fax 03 21 35 68 19; bouscarel62@aol.com] Fr W exit A16 at junc 50 & foll D940 twd Oye-Plage; at traff lts in cent of Oye-Plage turn L; at junc with D119 turn R, site on R in 200m. Fr E exit A16 junc 50 onto D219 to Oye-Plage. At traff lts strt on then R onto D119, site on R in 200m. Med, hdg/mkd pitch, hdstg, pt shd; wc; chem disp; mv service pnt; shwrs inc; el pts (4A) inc (poss rev pol); lndtte; shops 1.5km; playgrnd; sand beach 2km; games rm; 50% statics; dogs €1.70; phone; poss cr; adv bkg rec; cc not acc; CCI. "Excel, friendly owners; immac facs poss stretched high ssn; sizeable & v sm pitches; neat, well-maintained site but poss untidy low ssn; conv for Calais & Dunkerque ferries/tunnel/Cite Europe (20 mins to ferry terminal) or to tour area; late arrivals welcome; poss noisy high ssn due to constant arr/dep of campers & cockerel; excel NH/sh stay, esp low ssn." ♦ € 15.60   2005*

CALAIS *3A3* (8km E) **Camping Les Petit Moulins, 1634 Rue des Petit Moulins, 62215 Oye-Plage** [03 21 85 12 94] Fr A16 junc 21 proceed to Oye Plage. Strt thro traff lts & take 2nd L to site past derelict windmill. Sm, unshd; wc; chem disp (wc); shwrs inc; el pts (10A) inc; shops 2km; playgrnd; sw beach 2km; 90% statics; dogs; poss cr; quiet. "Open view; friendly, helpful owner; gd sized pitch but ltd in number; well-kept CL-type site; but inadequate facs & poss neglected when busy; find pitch, book in house adj; phone ahead; gd sh stay/NH." 15 Apr-30 Sep. € 8.00   2005*

†**CALAIS** *3A3* (12km E Coastal) **Camping Clairette, 525 Route des Dunes, 62215 Oye-Plage** [tel/fax 03 21 35 83 51] Exit A16 junc 21 & foll sp Oye-Plage. At traff lts at D940 cont strt. At junc with D119 turn R then L, site on L in 2km. Med, pt shd; htd wc; chem disp; mv service pnt; shwrs inc; el pts (6-10A) €3-3.65; gas 5km; shops 5km; tradsmn; sm playgrnd; htd, covrd pool 5km; beach 500m; 90% statics; dogs €1.10; poss cr; Eng spkn; adv bkg; quiet; cc acc; CCI. "Clsd 16 Dec-14 Jan; basic, dated facs; fresh water pipe also used for flushing toilet cassettes; not suitable for young family hols; security barrier; owners v friendly, helpful; nature reserve nrby; conv for ferries; gd NH/sh stay." € 11.60   2004*

†**CALAIS** *3A3* (12km E Rural) **Camping Le Pont d'Oye, Rue de la Riviere, 62215 Oye-Plage** [03 21 35 81 25 or 06 67 56 43 46 (mob)] Exit A16 at junc 50 onto D219 to Oye-Plage; cross rv & turn R sp camping; site on L. Sm, unshd; wc; chem disp (wc); shwrs €0.80; el pts (6A) €2.20; lndtte; shop 2km; tradsmn; playgrnd; dogs; CCI. "Basic CL-type site; grassed field for c'vans; open views; friendly owners; toilet block adj statics park; fair NH." ♦ ltd. € 9.00   2005*

†**CALAIS** *3A3* (1km SW Coastal) **Aire Communale, Plage de Calais, Ave Raymond Poincare, 62100 Calais** [03 21 46 66 41; tourisme-patrimonie@ marie-calais.fr] A16 exit junc 43 dir Bleriot-Plage/Calais cent & foll sp for beach (plage). Site nr harbour wall & Fort Risban. Well sp fr town cent. Med; wc; water; shop, rest nrby; obtain token/pass fr Camp Municipal adj; m'vans only. € 7.00   2005*

†**CALAIS** *3A3* (1km SW Coastal) **Camp Municipal, Plage de Calais, Ave Raymond Poincare, 62100 Calais** [03 21 34 73 25 or 03 21 97 89 79 (Mairie); www.calais.fr] A16 exit junc 43 dir Bleriot-Plage/ Calais cent & foll sp for beach (plage). Site nr harbour wall & Fort Risban. If barrier down during day, call at building adj site office. Lge, unshd; wc; own san rec; shwrs; el pts (10A) inc (poss rev pol); lndtte; sand beach 200m; 70% statics; poss cr; Eng spkn; adv bkg for 5+ nights only; noise fr ferries daytime but quiet at night. "Conv ferries; gd rests nr; some sm pitches; rec arr early to secure a pitch high ssn; barrier opens 0600 but poss down low ssn at w/e & warden poss diff to find after 1730 or absent altogether; san facs & site poss v dirty with dangerous elecs (Sep 05); many itinerants." € 11.20   2005*

FRANCE

CALAIS *3A3* (4km SW Coastal) **Camp Municipal du Fort Lapin, 62231 Bleriot-Plage** [03 21 97 67 77 or 03 21 97 89 79 (Mairie)] Exit junc 44 fr A16 to Calais cent, dir beach (Bleriot Plage). Turn L along coast onto D940 at 4th rndabt dir Sangatte. Site on R in dunes shortly after water tower, opp sports cent. Site sp fr N40. Lge, mkd pitch, pt sl, unshd; htd wc (some cont); own san high ssn; chem disp; baby facs; shwrs inc poss clsd 2130; el pts (10A) inc (poss rev pol); lndtte; poss 1km; rest; snacks; bar; BBQ; playgrnd; sand beach adj; 20% statics; dogs; phone; bus; poss cr; adv bkg; quiet; CCI. "Warden lives on site - if recep unmanned; rec arr bef 1700 high ssn or phone ahead to book; security code for ent; poss youth groups high ssn & poss security probs; conv Auchan & Cite Europe shops; gate clsd 2300-0700; conv NH." ♦ 4 Apr-10 Oct. € 17.60
2005*

Mustn't forget to post our site report forms to The Club, otherwise sites might be deleted.

CALAIS *3A3* (8km SW Rural) **Camping Les Epinettes, Mont-Pinet, 62231 Peuplingues** [03 21 85 22 24 or 03 21 85 21 39; fax 03 21 85 26 95] A16 fr Calais to Boulogne, exit junc 40 W on D243 sp Peuplingues, go thro vill & foll sp; site on L in 3km. Med, hdg pitch, pt sl, unshd; wc; own san; chem disp; shwrs €0.80; el pts (10A) inc; lndtte; ice; sm shop & 3km; hypmkt 5km; tradsmn; rest 1.5km; playgrnd; sand beach 3km; 80% statics; dogs €1; phone; poss cr; adv bkg; cc acc; CCI. "Pleasant, quiet site; conv ferries, tunnel & Calais supmkts; adv bkg doesn't guarantee pitch high ssn; when bureau clsd, site yourself - warden calls eve or call at cottage to pay; if arr late, park on grass verge outside main gate; use facs excl elec - pay half price; some pitches sm; excel san facs but insufficient for site size; friendly staff; NH only." 1 Apr-31 Oct. € 11.60
2005*

CALAIS *3A3* (5km W Coastal) **Camping Cassiopee** (formerly Les Noires Mottes), **Rue Pierre Dupuy, 62231 Sangatte** [tel/fax 03 21 82 04 75; cassiopee. tourisme@wanadoo.fr] Fr A16 (Boulogne-Calais) exit junc 41 sp Sangatte, at T-junc in vill turn R then R again bef monument. Lge, hdg/mkd pitch, pt sl, pt shd; wc (some cont); chem disp; mv service pnt; shwrs inc (clsd 2130-0800); el pts (6-10A) €3.10 (poss rev pol); lndtte; shop 200m; tradsmn; playgrnd; sand beach 500m; many statics; dogs €1.25; poss cr; adv bkg rec high ssn; quiet; red low ssn; no cc acc; CCI. "No longer municipal site; pitches lger than average; conv ferries & Eurotunnel; poss itinerants; office clsd 1200-1600 but site yourself; gd NH." 15 Mar-15 Nov. € 10.20
2005*

CALLAC *2E2* (1km W) **Camp Municipal La Verte Vallee, 22160 Callac** [02 96 45 58 50 or 02 96 45 81 30 (Mairie); fax 02 96 45 91 70] Sp fr all town app rds, on D28 to Morlaix. Med, terr, unshd; wc; shwrs; el pts inc; gas; shop 1km; lake sw 500m; fishing; quiet but some traff noise. "One hour to beaches of Corniche de l'Amorique." 15 Jun-15 Sep. € 8.69
2003*

CALLAS see Draguignan *10F3*

CALVIAC *7C4* (NE Rural) **Camping & Caravaning Les Trois Sources, 46190 Calviac** [05 65 33 03 01; fax 05 65 33 06 45] Take D673 E fr St Cere. At Sousceyrac take D653 NE, after 6km turn L on D25, sp fr main rd in both dir. Lge, pt sl, pt shd, mkd pitch, terr; serviced pitches; wc; chem disp; shwrs inc; baby facs; el pts (6A); gas; ice; rest; snacks; bar; shop; pool with slide & children's pool; entmnt high ssn; children's club; disco; tennis; games area; adv bkg; no statics; red long stay; cc acc. 1 May-1 Oct. € 15.40
2003*

CALVIAC EN PERIGORD see Sarlat la Caneda *7C3*

CAMARET SUR MER *2E1* (Urban) **Camping Municipal du Lannic, Rue du Grouanoch, 29129 Camaret** [02 98 27 91 31 or 02 98 27 94 22]
On ent town foll sp to Port, on quayside to L turn marked Camping-Golf Miniature. Foll sp to site in 500m. Med, pt sl, pt shd; wc; chem disp; mv service pnt; shwrs €2; shops 500m; el pts; sand beach 1km; poss cr; quiet. "Excel site; 24 hr surveillance bet town/port & beaches; sections for vans & tents." 1 May-30-Sep. € 8.40   2004*

CAMARET SUR MER *2E1* (2km NE Coastal) **Camping Le Grand Large, Lambezen, 29570 Camaret-sur-Mer** [02 98 27 91 41; fax 02 98 27 93 72; contact@campinglegrandlarge.com; www.campinglegrandlarge.com]
On D8 bet Crozon & Camaret, turn R at ent to Camaret onto D355, sp Roscanvel. Foll sps to site in 3km. Med, hdg/mkd pitch, pt sl, pt shd; wc; chem disp; baby facs; shwrs inc; el pts (5A) €3.50; gas; lndtte; shop; snacks; bar; BBQ; playgrnd; htd pool; sandy & shgl beach 450m; tennis; boating; TV; dogs €3; Eng spkn; adv bkg; quiet; cc acc; red low ssn. "Superb coastal views; pleasant, helpful owners; cliff top walk to town; excel." ♦ 1 Apr-30 Aug. € 21.000 (CChq acc)   2005*

See advertisement

CAMARET SUR MER *2E1* (3.5km NE Coastal) **Camping Plage de Trez-Rouz, 29129 Camaret-sur-Mer** [02 98 27 93 96; fax 02 98 27 84 54; camping-plage-de-trez-rouz@wanadoo.fr]
Foll D8 to Camaret-sur-Mer & at rndabt turn N sp Roscanvel/D355. Site on R in 3km. Med, pt sl, pt shd; wc; chem disp; mv service pnt; shwrs inc; el pts (10A) inc; lndtte; ice; shops 3.5km; bar; playgrnd; sand/shgl beach; tennis 500m; horseriding 2km; poss cr; Eng spkn; adv bkg; poss cr; quiet;. "Boat trips fr Camaret in ssn; conv for Presqu'Ile de Crozon; san facs stretched high ssn; site scruffy low ssn." Easter-30 Sep. € 17.50   2005*

CAMBO LES BAINS *8F1* **Camping Bixta-Eder, Route de St Jean-de-Luz, 64250 Cambo-les-Bains** [05 59 29 94 23; fax 05 59 29 23 70; camping.bixtaeder@wanadoo.fr] Fr Bayonne on D932 (ignore 1st sp Cambo-les-Bains) exit at junc with D918 L twd Cambo. Site on L nr top of hill (Intermarche supmkt at by-pass junc). Med, pt sl, pt shd; wc; baby facs; shwrs inc; el pts (6A); lndtte; shops 500m; sand beach 20km; pool adj; playgrnd; poss cr; adv bkg; cc acc. ♦ 15 Apr-15 Oct. € 11.90   2002*

CAMBO LES BAINS *8F1* (Urban) **Camping Ur Hegia, Route des Sept Chenes, 64250 Cambo-les-Bains** [05 59 29 72 03] Fr Bayonne, on D932 - ignore 1st sp Cambo/Arnaga - exit at junc with D918 L twd Cambo across traff lts twd Gare & Bas-Cambo. Rd twists & descends bef x-ing narr rv bdge. Pass stn on R & thro Bas-Cambo. Site on R at exit fr Bas-Cambo. Med, pt sl, pt shd; wc; chem disp (wc); shwrs inc; el pts (6A) €2.74; lndry rm; rest; gas; ice; shops, bar, snacks 1.5km; tradsmn; pool 1.5km; dogs; phone 50m; adv bkg; quiet; poss cr; red long stay. "Gd long/sh stay; close to rack & pinion rlwy; gd for touring Basque Region." € 10.37   2002*

CAMBO LES BAINS *8F1* (10km E) **Camping Chapital, Route de Cambo, 64240 Hasparren** [05 59 29 62 94; fax 05 59 29 69 71] Fr A64 exit onto D21 to Hasparren, site sp off D22/D10 dir Cambo-les-Bains, on L 1km fr Hasparren. Med, mkd pitch, pt sl, shd; wc; chem disp (wc); serviced pitches; shwrs inc; el pts (10A) inc; gas 500m; lndtte; shop 500m; rest & bar 1km; playgrnd; pool adj; 10% statics; dogs; phone; adv bkg; quiet; cc acc; gd. "Gd for exploring French Basque coutry & coast nr Biarritz." 1 May-30 Sep. € 9.00   2005*

CAMBO LES BAINS *8F1* (3km SW Rural) **Camping L'Hiriberria, 64250 Itxassou** [05 59 29 98 09; fax 05 59 29 20 88; hiriberria@wanadoo.fr] Fr Cambo-les-Bains on D932 to Itxassou. Site on L 200m fr D918. Lge, hdg/mkd pitch, hdstg, pt sl, pt shd; htd wc (some cont); chem disp; mv service pnt; shwrs inc; baby facs; el pts (5A) €2.20; gas; ice; lndtte; shops 24m; tradsmn; rest, bar 1km; snacks 3km; BBQ; playgrnd; pool; TV rm; 20% statics; dogs €1; rv 2km; Eng spkn; phone; quiet; 10% red 21+ days; CCI. "Excel all stays; popular, phone ahead rec; gd views Pyrenees; pretty vill in 1km." ♦ 1 Mar-30 Nov. € 15.10   2005*

CAMBO LES BAINS *8F1* (5km W Rural) **Camping Alegera, 64250 Souraide** [05 59 93 91 80]
Fr St Jean-de-Luz take D918 to Souraide, site sp on L on rvside. Lge, shd; wc; chem disp; baby facs; shwrs inc; el pts (10A) €2.75; gas; lndtte; ice; shops adj; snacks; BBQ; playgrnd; pool; tennis; golf; fishing 4km; games rm; dogs; poss cr; adv bkg; quiet. 15 Mar-31 Oct. € 11.40   2003*

CAMBRAI *3B4* (11km NW Rural) **Camping Les Colombes, Route de Fressies, 59265 Aubencheul-au-Bac** [03 27 89 25 90; fax 03 27 94 58 11]
On N43 Cambrai to Douai rd, on ent vill of Aubencheul-au-Bac, turn R at camp sp & site on L down lane. Med, hdg pitch, pt shd; wc; chem disp; shwrs inc; el pts (4-6A) €2-€3.45; ice; shops 1km; tradsmn; BBQ; playgrnd; lake fishing; 90% statics; dogs; poss cr; adv bkg; quiet; CCI. "V pretty, clean site; friendly & helpful staff; excel facs; ltd touring pitches; poss aircraft noise; gate locked 2200-0700; gd NH/sh stay." ♦ 1 Apr-31 Oct. € 12.20   2005*

CAMBRAI *3B4* (12km NW Rural) **Camping aux Roubaisiens, Rue de l'Abbeye, 62860 Oisy-le-Verger [03 21 59 51 54; pascallage@aol.com]** Fr Cambrai take N43 NW twd Douai. In 10km immed bef canal bdge turn L (W) twd Oisy-le-Verger. Go under rlwy bdge after 100m then R in 1km: cross canal & site on L in 200m. Sm, pt shd; wc; own san rec; chem disp; shwrs; el pts (10A) inc; shop; fishing; 90% statics; quiet. "Fair NH." 1 Apr-15 Oct. € 10.00   2004*

CAMBRAI *3B4* (12km NW Rural) **Camping de l'Epinette, 7 Rue du Calvaire, 62860 Sauchy-Lestree [03 21 59 50 13; epinette62@aol.com; www.epinette62.com]** Fr Cambrai take D939 twd Arras; on ent Marquion turn R at x-rds to Sauchy-Lestree; on ent vill turn R at 1st T-junc & site on L in 100m; fr a'route A26 exit junc 8 to Marquion as above. Sm, pt sl, pt shd; wc (own san rec); chem disp; shwrs €1.50; el pts (10A) €2.50-3; gas; lndtte; shops 3km; playgrnd; games area; many statics; dogs; adv bkg; quiet but some military aircraft noise; cc not acc; CCI. "Conv Calais/Dunkerque; v clean with helpful owner; well-kept homely site; simple but adequate facs; must ask recep for key to shwrs; CL-type area for tourers; levelling blocks ess for m'vans; WW1 cemetary nr; ltd space for tourers; excel sh stay/NH." 1 Apr-31 Oct. € 9.50   2005*

CAMIERS see Touquet Paris Plage, Le *3B2*

CAMON see Mirepoix (Ariege) *8F4*

CAMPOURIEZ see Entraygues sur Truyere *7D4*

CAMPSEGRET *7C3* (S Rural) **Camping Le Bourg, 24140 Campsegret [05 53 61 87 90; fax 05 53 24 22 36]** On N21, sp & clearly visible on E of main rd. Sm, mkd pitch, pt shd; wc; shwrs inc; el pts (6A) inc; shop; playgrnd; paddling pool; fishing; tennis; dogs €0.50; rd & farm noise, church bells. "NH only." ♦ 1 Jun-30 Sep. € 8.00   2003*

CANCALE *2E4* (3km N Coastal) **Camp Municipal a la Pointe du Grouin, 35260 Cancale [02 99 89 63 79 or 02 99 89 60 15]** Take D76 twd Cancale & cont on D201 sp Pointe de Grouin; site on R in 3km on cliffs above sea, on N side of Cancale (diff to see, on RH bend marked with chevrons); sp 'Camp Municipal'. Care req at ent. Lge, pt sl, terr; wc (mainly cont); mv service pnt; shwrs inc; el pts (3-10A) €3-4 (poss long lead req); lndtte; ice; shop; rest in town; BBQ; playgrnd; rocky beach adj; watersports; fishing; dogs €1.20; Eng spkn; quiet. "Conv Dinan, Mont St Michel; excel views; gd walking; excel san facs; gd, well-maintained site; some pitches uneven." 1 Mar-31 Oct. € 11.50   2004*

CANCALE *2E4* (6km S Coastal) **Camp Municipal, Rue Bord de la Mer, 35114 St Benoit-des-Ondes [02 99 58 65 21; fax 02 99 58 70 30]** In vill cent on D155. Med, unshd; wc; chem disp (wc only); mv service pnt; shwrs inc; el pts (6A) €2.31; lndtte; snacks, rest, shop, bar adj; playgrnd; sand/shgl beach adj; dogs €0.82; Eng spkn; phone; CCI. "Gd sh stay; barrier site key; gd san facs; gd walking & cycling." 15 Jun-15 Sep. € 11.17   2005*

CANCALE *2E4* (6km S Coastal) **Camping de l'Ile Verte, 35114 St Benoit-des-Ondes [02 99 58 62 55]** Site on S side of vill. Fr Cancale, take D76 SW for approx 4km, then turn L onto D155 into St Benoit. Foll site sp. Sm, hdg pitch, pt shd; htd wc (cont); chem disp; mv service pnt; shwrs inc; el pts €3 (poss rev pol); gas; lndtte; shop; rest, bar adj; playgrnd; sand beach adj; 3% statics; phone; adv bkg; quiet; CCI "Well-kept site on edge of coastal vill; excel long/sh stay." 31 May-12 Sep. € 17.00   2005*

CANCALE *2E4* (4km SW Urban) **Camp Municipal de la Vallee Verte, 35350 St Meloir-des-Ondes [02 99 89 10 23 or 02 99 89 10 78 (Mairie)]** Take D76 fr Dol de Bretagne, site sp in vill adj sports ground. Med, hdg/mkd pitch, pt sl, unshd; wc (mainly cont); chem disp; mv service pnt; shwrs inc; el pts (4A) inc; shops in vill; tradsmn; lndry rm; sand beach 5km; quiet but some rd noise; Eng spkn; CCI. Jul-Aug. € 12.20   2002*

SITES

CANCALE 2E4 (1km W Coastal) Camping Les Genets, La Ville Gueurie, 35260 Cancale [02 99 89 76 17; fax 02 99 89 96 31; les.genets. camping@wanadoo.fr] Fr Cancale take the D355 St Malo rd; go across supmkt rndabt; then take 1st rd on R (about 200m) & site on R in 200m. Med, mkd pitch, pt shd; wc; chem disp (wc); shwrs inc; el pts (6A) €3.50; gas 500m; lndtte; ice; shop & supmkt 500m; rest in town; snacks; bar; playgrnd; sand beach 1.5km; 70% statics; dogs €1.70; phone; adv bkg (bkg fee & dep req); CCI. "V clean, well-kept site; half way bet town & beach; gd sh stay." ♦ 1 Apr-15 Sep. € 13.90   2003*

CANCALE 2E4 (7km NW Coastal) Camping Le Bois Pastel, 13 Rue de la Corgnais, 35260 Cancale [02 99 89 66 10; fax 02 99 89 60 11; camping.bois-pastel@wanadoo.fr; www.campingboispastel.fr.] Fr Cancale take D201 dir Pointe du Grouin & St Malo by Rte Touristique. Site sp on L 2.5km after Pointe du Grouin. Med, pt shd; wc; shwrs inc; mv service pnt; shwrs inc; el pts (6A) €4; lndtte; ice; shop; bar; BBQ; playgrnd; htd, covrd pool; sand beach 800m; 25% statics; dogs €2.50; adv bkg; quiet; red long stay/low ssn. "Conv Mont St Michel, St Malo; gd touring base." 1 Apr-1 Oct. € 22.80   2005*

See advertisement opposite

CANCALE 2E4 (2km W Rural) Camping La Ville es Poulain, 35260 Cancale [02 99 89 87 47] Leave Cancale town cent on D355; after 1km cross the D201 & turn immed R by bar & foll sp; site in 1km. Sm, hdg pitch, pt shd; wc; chem disp; shwrs; el pts (10A); lndry rm; supmkt 1.5km; sand beach 2km; quiet; no cc acc; CCI. "CL-type site; lge pitches; gd base but no views - entire site surrounded by high hedge; conv for oyster beds, St Malo & Mont St Michel; excel fish rests in port." Jun-Sep.   2005*

CANCON 7D3 (5km N) Camp Municipal de St Chavit, 47290 Lougratte [05 53 01 70 05; fax 05 53 41 18 04] N on N21 fr Cancon, site at lake, L turn 50m bef church, site seen fr rd 500m fr turn. Sm, pt shd; wc; shwrs; el pts inc; shop 500m; bar; ice; sand beach; lndtte; playgrnd; games rm; boating; fishing; tennis nr; v quiet. ♦ 15 Jun-15 Sep. € 9.50   2004*

CANCON 7D3 (2km E Rural) Camp Municipal du Lac, 47290 Cancon [05 53 36 54 30 or 05 53 01 60 24 (Mairie); fax 05 53 01 64 70; mairie.cancon@wandaoo.fr] Sp fr N21 on both sides of Cancon & in town. Med, mkd pitch, pt sl, shd; wc; shwrs inc; el pts (10A) €3; shop 2 km; rest, snacks; bar; playgrnd; pool; fishing; games area; dogs; Eng spkn; CCI. "Gd site; peaceful in beautiful woodland & lake setting." 15 Jun-15 Sep. € 7.70   2005*

†CANCON 7D3 (8km W Rural) Camping Le Moulin, Lassalle, 47290 Monbahus [05 53 01 68 87; fourbears@theporridgetable.freeserve.co.uk] Fr N21 turn W at Cancon on D124 sp Miramont. In 7.5km at Monbahus pass thro vill cent take L turn, still on D124 sp Tombeboeuf. In 3km lge grain silos on L, site next on R. Sm, pt shd; wc; chem disp; shwrs; el pts (10A) €4; lndtte; shop; bistro; snacks; playgrnd; pool; lake 5km; cycle hire; dogs €2; quiet; "CL-type site; friendly British owners; excel meals; B & B avail; facs spotless; extra for twin-axles over 5m." € 13.00   2005*

CANCON 7D3 (12km NW Rural) Camping La Vallee de Gardeleau, 47410 Serignac-Peboudou [tel/fax 05 53 36 96 96] Fr Cancon take the N21 N; turn L twds Montauriol & Serignac-Peboudou; foll camping sp. Sm, hdg pitch, pt sl, pt shd; wc; chem disp; shwrs inc; el pts (5A) inc; gas 5km; lndtte; ice; shop & 5km; tradsmn; rest; snacks; bar; playgrnd; pool; lake fishing 2km; entmnt; 8% statics; dogs; phone; poss cr; Eng spkn; adv bkg (bkg fee & dep req); quiet; cc acc; CCI. " Calm & peaceful atmosphere"; friendly owners; close to Bastide towns; excel long/sh stay." ♦ 18 May-20 Sep. € 14.70   2002*

CANDE 2G4 (5km SW) Camp Municipal de l'Erdre, Route de Cande, 44540 St Mars-la-Jaille [02 40 97 00 34] Fr Ancenis N take N23 & N178. In town cent take D33 sp Cande. Site lies immed over bdge on L in St Mars-la-Jaille. Sp on all app rds. Med, pt shd; wc; shwrs inc; el pts (5A) €1.70; pool 500m; poss noise fr by-pass. "Warden calls daily; ltd facs low ssn." Easter-15 Sep. € 4.35   2002*

CANDE SUR BEUVRON 4G2 (500m S Rural) Camping La Grande Tortue, 3 Route de Pontlevoy, 41120 Cande-sur-Beuvron [02 54 44 15 20; fax 02 54 44 19 45; info@la-grande-tortue.com; www. la-grande-tortue.com] Exit A10 at Blois dir Vierzon. Cross rv on D751 (sp Chaumont/Amboise). In 14km cross Rv Beuvron at Cande-sur-Beuvron & 400m after bdge take L fork & site immed on L. Fr Onzain cross rv to Chaumont, then NE on D751; in 4km turn sharp R (S) & site on L. Lge, hdg/mkd pitch, pt shd; wc; chem disp; mv service pnt; some serviced pitches; baby facs; shwrs inc; el pts (10A) inc; gas; lndtte; shop; tradsmn; rest; snacks; bar; BBQ; playgrnd; htd, covrd pool; paddling pool; canoe & cycle hire; tennis; horseriding; games rm; entmnt; internet; dogs €3.50; Eng spkn; adv bkg; quiet; cc acc; red low ssn/CCI. "Excel site amongst trees; poss diff access due to trees; helpful staff; gd cycling; conv Loire chateaux; gd for children; vg, clean, modern san facs & gd pool." ♦ 9 Apr-26 Sep. € 28.50 (CChq acc)   2005*

See advertisement on next page

CANET DE SALARS see Pont de Salars 7D4

CANET EN ROUSSILLON see Canet Plage 10G1

FRANCE

Site report forms at back of Guide   231   *Last year of report

Loire Valley
3, route de Pontlevoy - 41120 Candé-sur-Beuvron
Tel: 00 33 (0) 2 54 44 15 20-Fax: 00 33 (0) 2 54 44 19 45
info@la-grande-tortue.com - www.la-grande-tortue.com

La Grande Tortue

Camping ★★★★
Caravanning

This pleasant,rusticsite has been tastefully developed in an old forest. 169 touring pitches (more than 100 sq.m) set among trees, with some shade and some sunshine. In July and August, the family owners organize a programme of trips including wine and cheese tasting, canoeing, and all-day visits to the Loire Valley.

La Clef Verte

Camping Qualité

3 sanitary blocks - laundry - washing/drying machine - shop - terraced bar and restaurant - trampolines - bouncy castle - ball crawl with slide and climbing wall - table tennis - covered and heated swimming pool - padding pool. Nearby: golf course, walking, cycling, fishing, horseback riding.

CANET PLAGE *10G1* (Urban) **Camping Domino, Rue des Palmiers, 66140 Canet-Plage** [04 68 80 27 25; fax 04 68 73 47 41] Fr Perpignan dir 'Plage'; foll sps to cent; L twds port & 1st L. Med, shd; wc (some cont); shwrs inc; shops adj; el pts (3-10A) €2.50-3.50; ice; lndtte; snacks (high ssn); bar in town; shop adj; playgrnd; sand beach 50m; dogs €1.52; 20% statics; poss cr; quiet; adv bkg; dep req; red low ssn; 10% red CCI. "Gd long stay." 1 Apr-30 Sep. € 26.00   2004*

As we're travelling out of season, we'd better phone ahead to check that the site is actually open.

CANET PLAGE *10G1* (4km W Urban) **Camping Ma Prairie, Ave des Coteaux, 66140 Canet-en-Roussillon** [04 68 73 26 17; fax 04 68 73 28 82; ma.prairie@wanadoo.fr; www.maprairie.com] Leave A9/E15 at junc 41, sp Perpignan Centre/ Canet-en-Roussillon. Take D83, then D81 until Canet-en-Roussillon. At rndabt, take D617 dir Perpignan & in about 500m leave at exit 5. Take D11 dir St Nazaire, pass under the bdge & at rndabt turn R. Site on L. Lge, hdg pitch, shd; wc (Eng & cont); serviced pitches; chem disp; baby facs; shwrs inc; el pts (10A) inc; gas; lndtte; ice; supmkt adj; tradsmn; rest; snacks; bar; BBQ (gas/elec); playgrnd; pool; paddling pool; waterslide; solarium; sand beach 2km; waterskiing; sailing, canoeing, tennis; cycle hire; games rm; entmnt; internet; 20% statics; dogs €2.80; no c'vans over 7m high ssn; poss cr; Eng spkn; adv bkg ess Aug; quiet; cc acc; red low ssn; CCI. "Staff friendly & helpful; some pitches sm; well kept; gd san facs; shuttle bus to beach; cycle track to beach & along sea front; recep clsd 1230-1400 & after 1830; daily mkt Perpignan." ♦ 5 May-25 Sep. € 32.00 (CChq acc) ABS - C05
                                                                    2005*

CANET PLAGE *10G1* (2km N Coastal) **Camping Le Palais de la Mer, 66470 Ste Marie-Plage** [04 68 73 07 94; fax 04 68 73 57 83; contact@ palaisdelamer.com; www.palaisdelamer.com] Exit A9 at Perpignan Nord dir Canet. Fr Canet take D81 N to Ste Marie & foll sp to Ste Marie-Plage. At seafront turn L, site in 300m. Lge, hdg pitch, shd; htd wc (some cont); chem disp; serviced pitches; mv service pnt; baby facs; shwrs inc; el pts (6A) inc; gas 1km; shop; ice; lndtte; rest; snacks; bar; BBQ; playgrnd; pool; sand beach adj; games area; tennis; entmnt; TV rm; 20% statics; dogs €4; phone; poss cr; Eng spkn; adv bkg (dep & booking fee req); CCI. "Sm pitches poss diff lge o'fits." ♦ 15 May-22 Sep. € 29.50   2005*

CANET PLAGE *10G1* (3km N Coastal) **Camping Le Brasilia, 66140 Canet-en-Roussillon** [04 68 80 23 82; fax 04 68 73 32 97; camping-le-brasilia@wanadoo. fr; www.brasilia.fr] Avoid Perpignan when towing. Fr A9 or N9 take exit sp Leucate, foll D627 & D81 along coast to junc with D617. Circle rndabt under flyover, take A81 N to turn off on rd sp Zone Artisanal/Champs de Fois/Les Bigues. Cont twd coast, foll sp to site in Zone Technique du Port du Canet Plage. V lge, hdg/mkd pitch, pt shd, wc (some cont); chem disp; baby facs; shwrs inc; el pts (10A) inc; gas; lndtte; shops; tradsmn; rest; snacks; bar; BBQ (gas/elec); playgrnd; htd pool high ssn; sand beach 150m; tennis; games rm; cycle hire; entmnt; excursions; internet; 35% statics; dogs €3.80; recep 0800-2000; bus to Canet; Eng spkn; quiet but poss noisy disco & entmnt on adj campsite; cc acc; CCI. "V well-managed; gardens immac; pool spotless; staff v friendly; excel facs; in Jul & Aug identity card for pool - passport size photo needed; conv day trips to Andorra; daily mkt in Canet except Mon." ♦ 29 Apr-30 Sep. € 45.30 ABS - C01   2005*

FRANCE

CANET PLAGE *10G1* (4km N Coastal) **Camp Municipal de la Plage,** 66470 Ste Marie-Plage [04 68 80 68 59; fax 04 68 73 14 70; camping-sainte-mairie-la-mer@wanadoo.fr] Exit A9 junc 41 onto D83, then D81 to Ste Marie-Plage. Look for sm red sp, site adj Camping La Palais de la Mer. Lge, hdg pitch, pt shd; wc; chem disp; mv service pnt; shwrs; el pts (6A) €2.80; lndtte; shop; rest; snacks; bar; playgrnd; pool; sand beach adj; games area; cycle hire; child entmnt; TV; 30% statics; dogs €2.40; poss cr; Eng spkn; adv bkg (dep req); quiet; CCI. "Direct access to beach; v busy high ssn, quiet otherwise." ♦ ltd. 1 Mar-31 Oct. € 20.50   2005*

We're having a great holiday - must fill in some site report forms and send them to The Club as soon as possible.

CANET PLAGE *10G1* (500m S Coastal) **Camping Club Mar Estang,** Route de St Cyprien, 66140 Canet-en-Roussillon [04 68 80 35 53; fax 04 68 73 32 94; marestang@wanadoo.fr; www.marestang.com] Exit A9 junc 41 Perpignan Nord dir Canet, then foll sp St Cyprien, site sp. V lge, mkd pitch, hdstg, pt shd; wc; chem disp; mv service pnt; baby facs; shwrs inc; el pts (5A) €6; gas; lndtte; ice; shop; tradsmn; rest; snacks; bar; playgrnd; htd pool; waterslide; private sand beach adj; tennis; cycle hire; fitness rm; TV rm; 50% statics; dogs €5; Eng spkn; adv bkg; quiet; cc acc; red low ssn/long stay/low ssn/CCI. "V conv Spanish border & Pyrenees; gd birdwatching." ♦ 29 Apr-23 Sep. € 30.00   2005*

See advertisement above

CANNES *10F4* (3km NE Urban) **Camping Parc Bellevue,** 67 Ave Maurice Chevalier, 06150 Cannes [04 93 47 28 97; fax 04 93 48 66 25; contact@parcbellevue.com; www.parcbellevue.com] A8 exit 41 twrd Cannes. Foll R N7 & at junc controlled by traff lts, get in L lane. Turn L & in 100m turn L across dual c'way, foll sp for site. Site in 400m on L after sports complex - steep ramp at ent. Lge, mkd pitch, pt sl, terr, pt shd; wc; chem disp; shwrs; el pts (6A) €3; gas; lndtte; shops; rest; snacks; bar; pool; sandy beach 1.8km; sat TV; 50% statics; dogs €2; phone; bus/train nr; poss cr; Eng spkn; adv bkg; rd noise; red 7 days; CCI. "Gd, flat site; gd security; san facs old but clean; some pitches long way fr facs; helpful, friendly staff; conv beaches & A8; green oasis in busy area; no m'van facs." ♦ ltd. 1 Apr-30 Sep. € 19.00 (CChq acc)   2005*

CANNES *10F4* (4km NW Urban) **Ranch Camping,** Chemin de St Joseph, 06110 Le Cannet [04 93 46 00 11; fax 04 93 46 44 30] Exit A8 at junc 42 Le Cannet. Foll sp L'Aubarede & then La Bocca. Site well sp via D9. Med, hdg pitch, pt sl, terr, pt shd; wc (some cont); shwrs inc; el pts (4-6A) inc; lndtte; ice; shop; tradsmn; playgrnd; covrd pool; sand beach 2km; 10% statics; dogs €1; bus; adv bkg summer ssn ess by Mar with deposit; some rd noise; quiet. "Gd long/sh stay; pitches at cent or top of site quieter." 1 Apr-30 Oct. € 36.60   2002*

CANNES *10F4* (5.5km NW) **Camping St Louis,** Domaine des Chenes, 06580 Pegomas [04 92 19 23 13; fax 04 92 19 23 14; caravaning.stlouis@free.fr; www.homair-vacances.fr & www.campingsaintlouis.com] Exit a'route at Cannes/Mandelieu & take N7 twd Cannes to Mandelieu. Fr Mandelieu take D109 twd Grasse. Turn R in Pegomas, site on L on leaving vill. Med, mkd/hdg pitch, v sl, terr, pt shd; wc; chem disp; shwrs inc; el pts (6A) inc; gas; lndtte; shop; supmkt 100m; pizzeria; snack; bar; pool; waterslide; & beach 6km; pool; tennis nr; 25% statics; dogs; adv bkg; quiet; red low ssn. "Friendly staff; sm, sl pitches; facs ltd low ssn; conv Nice, Cannes." ♦ 5 Apr-27 Sep. € 33.50 (3 persons)   2004*

CANNES *10F4* (9km NW) **Camping Le Cabrol,** 305 Chemin de Cabrol, 06580 Pegomas [04 93 42 21 56; fax 04 92 97 52 63; campinglecabrol@ifrance.com] Fr A8 exit junc 40 onto D109 to Pegomas. Turn L bef rv bdge just bef town. Fr Grasse by N85, turn onto D9 for Pegomas. On ent Pegomas turn R sp 'camping' & Mandelieu. Foll D109 over rv bdge, then R to site. Sp on all rds. Med, hdg/mkd pitch, pt shd; wc; chem disp; mv service pnt; baby facs; shwrs inc; el pts (6A) €3; gas; lndtte; ice; shop 500m; rest 1km; snacks; playgrnd; pool; sand beach 9km; lake sw 12km; entmnt; TV rm; 50% statics; dogs €1; phone; poss cr; quiet; cc acc; CCI. "Gd sh stay." ♦ ltd. Easter-15 Sep. € 19.00   2003*

CANNES *10F4* (9km NW) **Caravaning Les Mimosas,** Quartier Cabrol, 06580 Pegomas [04 93 42 36 11; fax 04 93 60 92 74] Site on L of D109 Mandelieu to Grasse. Exit A8 junc 41 at Mandelieu turn R & foll sp to Pegomas on D9. Turn L immed bef rv bdge app Pegomas. Med, hdg/mkd pitch, shd; wc; chem disp; mv service pnt; baby facs; shwrs inc; el pts (5A) inc; lndtte; ice; shop; rest, bar 1km; snacks; playgrnd; pool; sand beach 8km; fishing in rv adj; games area; entmnt; 40% statics; dogs €1.60; adv bkg; quiet; cc acc; CCI. "Pleasant; convenient for Cannes, Cote d'Azur & mountain vills; excel mod shwr block; night security guard in ssn; barrier clsd 2300-0600." ♦ ltd. Easter-31 Oct. € 20.00   2005*

CANOURGUE, LA *9D1* (2km E Rural) **Camping Le Val d'Urugne,** Route des Gorges-du-Tarn, 48500 La Canourgue [04 66 32 84 00; fax 04 66 32 88 14; lozereleisure@wanadoo.fr; www.lozereleisure.com] Exit A75 junc 40 dir La Canourgue; thro vill dir Gorges-du-Tarn. In 2km site on R 600m after golf clubhouse Sm, hdg pitch, pt shd; wc; chem disp; mv service pnt; shwrs inc; el pts (6A) €3; lndtte; ice; shop (high ssn) & 2km; tradsmn; rest, snacks; bar at golf club; TV rm; some chalets adj; dogs; Eng spkn; adv bkg; quiet; cc acc; CCI. "Vg site; 16-hole golf course adj; conv A75 & Gorges-du-Tarn; low ssn stop at golf club for key to site." ♦ ltd. 15 May-15 Sep: € 11.50   2005*

CANOURGUE, LA *9D1* (1km SE) **Camping La Mothe,** 75 Route d'Espagne, 48500 Banassac [04 66 32 88 11 or 04 66 32 97 37; fax 04 66 32 97 37] Leave A75 at junc 40, foll sp D998 La Canourgue. Take 2nd exit at each of 2 rndabts sp St Geniez-d'Olt N9 twds La Mothe. Site on L in 300m immed over Rv Lot. Med, shd; wc (some cont); chem disp (wc); shwrs inc; el pts (6A) €2.50; lndtte; ice; supmkt 1.5km; rest 2km; snacks; bar; BBQ; playgrnd; pool; rv sw & fishing 1.5km; dogs €0.50; some rd noise; CCI. "Basic site; gd for birdwatchers & fishing; interesting area; phone ahead to check opening dates; no warden on site end ssn." ♦ 1 Apr-30 Oct. € 10.00   2005*

CANY BARVILLE *3C2* (500m S Urban) **Camp Municipal,** Route de Barville, 76450 Cany-Barville [02 35 97 70 37; fax 02 35 97 72 32; mairie-de-cany-barville@wanadoo.fr] Sp fr town cent, off D268 to S of town, adj stadium. Med, hdg/mkd pitch, hdstg, pt shd; htd wc; chem disp; mv service pnt; shwrs inc; el pts (10A) €2.80 (poss rev pol); lndtte; shop 500m; playgrnd; pool 1km; lake 2km; 25% statics; adv bkg; poss noisy; 10% red 14+ days; cc acc; CCI. "Lovely valley for cycling; excel facs but poss stretched at high ssn; within reach of Dieppe & Fecamp Benedictine chateau." ♦ Easter-30 Sep. € 9.65   2005*

CAPELLE LES BOULOGNE, LA see Boulogne sur Mer *3A2*

CAPESTANG *10F1* (Rural) **Camp Municipal,** 34310 Capestang [04 67 49 85 95 or 04 67 93 30 05 (Mairie)] Fr Beziers on D11, turn R twd vill of Capestang, approx 1km after passing supermarket. Site on L in leisure park opp Gendamarie. Med, hdg pitch, pt shd; wc (cont only); shwrs; el pts (6A) €2.85; shops, rest 500m; playgrnd; quiet. "300m fr Canal de Midi, excel walks or cycle rides; lovely rest in vill; low ssn site yourself, fees collected; gd sh stay." 1 May-30 Sep. € 11.40   2004*

CAPPY see Albert *3B3*

CAPVERN LES BAINS see Lannemezan *8F2*

CARAMAN *8F4* (1.5km S Rural) **Camp Municipal L'Orme Blanc,** 31460 Caraman [05 62 18 81 60 or 05 61 83 10 12 (Mairie); mairie-caraman@wanadoo.fr] Site sp on D1 & D11 fr all dirs. Steep, narr, unfenced app track & sharp R turn not rec lge o'fits or lge m'vans. Sm, mkd pitch, pt sl, shd; wc; chem disp; shwrs; el pts €2.50; gas, ice; shop 1km; rest, snacks, bar 1km; BBQ; lake fishing, sw & watersports adj; tennis; phone; adv bkg; quiet; CCI. "Rural site 20km fr Toulouse." ♦ 20 Jun-15 Sep. € 9.00   2004*

CARANTEC see St Pol de Leon *1D2*

CARCANS *7C1* (8km W Rural) **Camping Le Maubuisson,** 81 Ave de Maubuisson, 33121 Carcans [05 56 03 30 12; fax 05 56 03 47 93; camping-maubuisson@wanadoo.fr; www.camping-maubuisson.com] Fr N215 to Castelnau-de-Medoc turn W onto D207 to Carcans & onto Maubuisson, in vill camp ent on L, sp. V lge, pt sl, shd; wc; baby facs; shwrs inc; el pts (5A) inc; gas; lndtte; shop; rest; snacks; bar; playgrnd; sand beach 3km; lake sw 100m; fishing; watersports; windsurfing; tennis; mini-golf; statics; dogs; poss cr; adv bkg; quiet. "Site in wooded park; conv Medoc wine region & many sandy beaches; vg long/sh stay." ♦ 1 Mar-30 Nov. € 22.00   2003*

CARCASSONNE *8F4* (5km N Rural) **Camping Das Pinhiers, 11620 Villemoustaussou [04 68 47 81 90; fax 04 68 71 43 49; campingdaspinhiers@ wanadoo.fr]** Exit a'route A61 at junc 23 Carcassonne Ouest, & foll sp Mamazet on D118; R at rndabt with filling stn, turn R & foll camping sp. Med, hdg pitch, pt sl, pt shd; wc; chem disp; shwrs inc; el pts (10A) €3.10; shop & 1km; rest; snacks; bar; playgrnd; pool; 10% statics; dogs; eng spkn; adv bkg; quiet; CCI. "Diff to pitch lge vans due to hdg pitches & slope; san facs in need of renovation & pool showing signs of neglect; fair long stay." 1 Apr-30 Sep. € 10.90   2004*

This site entry hasn't been updated for a while; we'd better fill in a site report form and send it to The Club.

CARCASSONNE *8F4* (10km NE Rural) **Camping Le Moulin de Ste Anne, Chemin de Ste Anne, 11600 Villegly-en-Minervois [04 68 72 20 80; fax 04 68 72 27 15; campingstanne@wanadoo.fr; www.moulindesainteanne.com]** Leave A61 junc 23 Carcassonne Ouest dir Mazamet; after approx 14km onto D620 to Villegly, site sp at ent to vill. NB Turning off D620 hidden by trees, then over narr bdge; long o'fits need wide swing in. Med, hdg/mkd pitch, terr, unshd; htd wc; chem disp; serviced pitches; mv service pnt; shwrs inc; el pts (10A) inc; lndtte; shop 300m; tradsmn; snacks; bar; playgrnd; pool; sand beach 60km; 20% statics; dogs €1.50; adv bkg; Eng spkn; quiet; red long stay & low ssn; CCI. "Gd touring base; conv Carcassonne; Canal du Midi; v friendly, helpful owner; spotless san facs." ♦ 1 Mar-31 Dec. € 15.00   2005*

CARCASSONNE *8F4* (6km E) **Camp Municipal A L'Ombre des Micocouliers, Chemin de la Lande, 11800 Trebes [04 68 78 61 75 or 04 68 78 88 77 (LS); fax 04 68 78 88 77; campingmunicipalm@tele2.fr]** Fr Carcassonne, take the N113 E for 6km to Trebes. In vill, turn L immed bef bdge. Site on L in 200m. Med, mkd pitch, shd; wc (cont); chem disp; shwrs (up steps); el pts (16A) €2; lndry; shop; rest; snacks; BBQ; htd, covrd pool nr; rv fishing; TV; no statics; dogs €1; phone; poss cr; some Eng spkn; red low ssn; CCI. "V sandy site; friendly; clean but old facs; fair rest; pool is public but free entry for site guests, also poss cr; walking dist to sm town; gd base for seeing/cycling Canal du Midi; some theme nights; basic but gd site." ♦ 1 Apr-30 Sep. € 13.50   2005*

CARCASSONNE *8F4* (1.5km SE Urban) **Campeole La Cite, Route de St Hilaire, 11000 Carcassonne [04 68 25 11 77; fax 04 68 47 33 13; cpllacite@ atciat.com; www.campeoles.fr]** Fr N & W exit Carcassonne by N113 twd Narbonne; cross rv & turn S on D104 foll sp. Fr S (D118) take D104 to E & foll sp. Fr E (N113) take D342 S to D104; foll sp. NB Site (La Cite) well sp fr all dir & easy access fr A61 a'route, exit 23. Final app rd uneven. Lge, hdg/mkd pitch, pt shd; wc (cont); chem disp; mv service pnt; shwrs inc; el pts (10A) inc (poss rev pol); lndry rm; ice; shops 1.5km; tradsmn; rest; snacks; bar; playgrnd; pool; tennis; internet; some statics; dogs €3.10; Eng spkn; adv bkg rec high ssn; quiet with some rd noise; 25% red low ssn; cc acc; CCI. "Excel base adj woods; friendly, helpful staff; mixed pitch sizes & types; facs stretched high ssn; popular site, rec arr bef 1600; reg bus service to town with medieval castle; poss unkempt low ssn; pool poss clsd low ssn; pleasant walk to town by stream." ♦ 15 Mar-10 Oct. € 22.50   2005*

†CARCASSONNE *8F4* (5km S) **Camping a l'Ombre des Oliviers, 11570 Cazilhac [tel/fax 04 68 79 65 08 or 06 81 54 96 00]** Fr N & W exit Carcassonne by N113 dir Narbonne. Cross rv & turn S onto D104, then D142/D56 to Cazilhac, site sp. Sm, pt shd; wc; baby facs; shwrs inc; el pts (6-10A) €2 (poss rev pol); lndry rm; ice; supmkt in vill; bar; BBQ; playgrnd; tennis; games area; TV; 10% statics; poss v cr; adv bkg; quiet; red low ssn. "Site in pleasant position; pitches poss muddy/soft & diff for med/lge o'fits to manoeuvre; few water points; v ltd facs low ssn; long c'vans check with recep, then ent via exit, as corners tight; if office clsd on arr phone owner on mobile, or site yourself; insufficient san facs when site full & ltd other facs; bus to old city nrby; v helpful owners." € 14.00   2005*

CARCASSONNE *8F4* (8km S Rural) **Camping Airotel Grand Sud, Route de Limoux, 11250 Preixan [04 68 26 88 18; fax 04 68 26 85 07; air. hotel.grand.sud@wanadoo.fr; www.camping-grandsud.com]** A61 exit junc 23 at Carcassonne Ouest onto D118 dir Limoux. Site visible fr rd on lakeside. Med, hdg/mkd pitch, hdstg, pt shd; wc; chem disp; mv service pnt; baby facs; shwrs inc; el pts (4A) inc; lndtte; ice; tradsmn; rest; snacks; bar; BBQ; playgrnd; pool high ssn; waterslide; fishing; boating; horseriding; tennis; cycle hire; games area; games rm; internet; entmnt; TV; 50% statics; dogs €3.50; Eng spkn; adv bkg; quiet; cc acc; CCI. "Wild fowl reserve; conv beautiful city of Carcassonne; gd walking; helpful owners; attractive site." ♦ 13 Mar-15 Oct. € 25.00   2005*

See advertisement on next page

FRANCE

CARCASSONNE *8F4* (14km SW) **Domaine d'Arnauteille**, 11250 Montclar [04 68 26 84 53; fax 04 68 26 91 10; arnauteille@mnet.fr; www.arnauteille.com] Fr Carcassonne take D118 S twd Limoux. Turn R bef end of sm section dual c'way (not 1st section) & foll sp to Montclar. Site approx 3km on L. NB Site app along 3km single track - site ent steep & narr. Vlge, hdg/mkd pitch, pt sl, terr, pt shd; htd wc; chem disp; mv service pnt; some serviced pitches; baby facs; shwrs inc; el pts (6A) €4 (10A extra); gas; lndtte; shop; tradsmn; rest; snacks; bar; playgrnd; pool; waterpark; horseriding; fishing 2km; golf 14km; games rm; games area; entmnt; internet; TV rm; 20% statics; dogs €3; Eng spkn; adv bkg; v quiet; cc acc; CCI. "Expanded in 2005, now huge & impersonal; grandiose pool; level & sloping pitches; excel rest; superb facs but siting can be diff in wet weather; muddy after rain; stunning views of Corbieres; vg site." ♦ 7 Apr-26 Sep. € 27.00 (CChq acc)   2005*

> Some of these sites have changed their opening dates - we'd better fill in some site report forms and let the editor of the guide know.

CARCASSONNE *8F4* (4km NW) **Camping Chateau de Pennautier**, 11610 Pennautier [04 68 25 41 66; fax 04 68 47 11 23; camping@chateaudepennautier.com; www.chateaudepannautier.com] Exit A61 Carcassonne W; site sp on R 4km fr Carcassonne on N113 dir of Toulouse. On D203 sp Pennautier, site on rvside. Sm, hdg pitch, shd; wc; chem disp; mv service pnt; shwrs inc; el pts (8A) €2.70; lndry rm; ice; shop 1.5km; tradsmn; rest; playgrnd; pool; fishing; lake sw 15km; 11% statics; dogs €1; Eng spkn; adv bkg (25% dep); quiet but some rd noise; cc acc; CCI. "Lovely location; no twin-axle vans; friendly, helpful staff; clean facs; barrier clsd 2200-0700; local Chateau Pennautier wine sold; excel vineyards nrby; pool superb; rec." ♦ 1 May-30 Sep. € 12.00   2005*

CARCASSONNE *8F4* (15km NW Rural) **Camping Les Oliviers**, 11170 Montolieu [04 68 24 88 08; fax 04 68 77 42 79] Fr N113 4km W Carcassonne, take the D629 twd Montolieu; site on R in 2.5km after Moussoulens; sp fr N113, approx 5km dist. App thro Montolieu not rec. Sm, hdg/mkd pitch, pt shd; wc; chem disp; shwrs inc; el pts (6A) inc; gas; lndtte; shops 1.5km; tradsmn; rest, snacks, bar 100m; BBQ; pool 100m; few statics; no dogs; phone; adv bkg; quiet; cc not acc; CCI. "V clean, well-managed site in lovely countryside & v under-used; gd, modern san facs; friendly, helpful owners; conv for Carcassonne & Montagnes Noir; St Ferreol geyser & Durford worth visit." ♦ 15 Jun-15 Sep. € 16.50   2005*

CARDET *10E1* (Rural) **Camping Beau Rivage**, 22 Chemin du Bosquet, 30350 Cardet [04 66 83 02 48; fax 04 66 83 80 55; receptie@campingbeaurivage.com; www.CampingBeauRivage.com] Fr Ales take N106 dir Nimes. Exit at sp Ledignan onto D982 dir Anduze & cont for 7km. On app Cardet take 3rd exit to site to avoid narr rds in vill. Med, level, shd; htd wc; chem disp; baby facs; shwrs inc; el pts (6A) €2.75; gas; lndry rm; ice; tradsmn; rest; snacks; BBQ; playgrnd; pool; rv sw adj; canoe hire; games rm; TV rm; disco; dogs €1.50; poss cr; Eng spkn; adv bkg; quiet; red low ssn; red CCI. "Excel site; well-organised; v helpful staff; gd pizzeria; untidy waste collection point; gd camping store nrby." 1 Apr-30 Sep. € 15.00   2003*

CARENTAN *1D4* (10km NE Coastal) **Camping Utah Beach**, La Madeleine, 50480 Ste Marie-du-Mont [02 33 71 53 69; fax 02 33 71 07 11; utah.beach@wanadoo.fr; www.camping-utahbeach.com] 50km S of Cherbourg on N13 turn L onto D70 to Ste Marie-du-Mont. Foll D913 to coast & sp to Utah Beach Memorial - approx 4km. Site on beach rd D421. Med, hdg/mkd pitch, pt sl, pt shd; wc; chem disp; mv service pnt; shwrs inc; el pts (6A) €3.70; gas; lndtte; ice; shop; tradsmn; snacks; bar; playgrnd; htd pool; sand beach 50m; water/beach sports; tennis; games rm; mini-golf; archery; entmnt; 55% statics; dogs €2.90; phone; quiet; adv bkg; red low ssn; cc acc; red CCI. "Gd touring base; site of US landing in 1944; well-kept; gd birdwatching; excursions." 1 Apr-30 Sep. € 16.40   2004*

CARENTAN *1D4* (500m E Urban) **Camp Municipal Le Haut Dick, 30 Chemin du Grand-Bas Pays, 50500 Carentan [tel/fax 02 33 42 16 89; lehautdick@ aol.com; www.camping-municipal.com]** Fr N13 Cherbourg - Caen a'route; clearly sp in town cent, nr pool, on L bank of canal, close to marina. Med, hdg/mkd pitch, pt shd; wc; chem disp; mv service pnt; shwrs inc; el pts (6A) inc (rev pol); gas; lndtte; ice; shop 500m; tradsmn; rest, snacks, bar 500m; BBQ; playgrnd; htd pool; sand beach 10km; cycle hire; mini-golf; games rm; 5% statics; dogs; phone; poss cr; Eng spkn; adv bkg ess high ssn (dep req); quiet; cc not acc; CCI. "Immac site, clean facs; san facs poss ltd in low ssn; some pitches tight for lge o'fits; gd security; gates locked 2200-0700; mkt Mon; conv Cherbourg ferry & D-Day beaches; gd bird-watching on marshes; gd cycling area." ♦ 15 Jan-1 Nov. € 14.30   2005*

CARENTAN *1D4* (6km SE) **Camping a la Ferme (Duval), 50620 Montmartin-en-Graignes [02 33 56 84 87]** On N13 by-pass Carantan going S; join N174; site on L in 4km. Sm, unshd; wc; shwrs inc; el pts inc; chem disp; playgrnd; adv bkg; quiet. "Pleasant owner; CL-type site; also B&B; easy 1 hr drive fr Cherbourg; obliging & helpful owner; gd sh stay." 15 Jun-15 Sep. € 9.30   2004*

CARHAIX PLOUGUER *2E2* (1.5km W Rural) **Camp Municipal La Vallee de l'Hyeres, Rue de Kerniguez, 29270 Carhaux-Plouguer [02 98 99 10 58; fax 02 98 99 15 92; www.ville-carhaix.com]** SE fr Huelgoat on D794 for 17km, sm site sp on all apps to Carhaix Med, pt shd; wc (some cont); chem disp (wc); shwrs inc; el pts (10A) €2; lndtte; shop 1.5km; tradsmn, snacks; bar; playrnd nr; pool 1.5km; canoe/kayak hire; 5% statics; adv bkg; quiet; CCI. "Pleasantly situated in parkland on rv." ♦ ltd. 1 Jun-30 Sep. € 6.65   2004*

CARLEPONT see Noyon *3C3*

CARLUCET *7D3* (1.5km NW Rural) **Camping Chateau de Lacomte, 46500 Carlucet [05 65 38 75 46; fax 05 65 33 17 68; chateau lacomte@wanadoo.fr; www.camping chateau lacomte]** Fr Gramat SW on D677/ D807. After approx 14km turn R onto D32 sp Carlucet, foll site sp (narr rd). Or fr A20 exit junc 56 & foll D802/D807 sp Gramat. In 5km turn L onto D32 as bef. Med, hdg pitch, some hdstg, pt sl, terr, pt shd; wc; chem disp; all serviced pitches; shwrs; el pts (10A) €4.50; gas 7km; ice; lndtte; shops 12km; rest; snacks; bar; playgrnd; 3 pools; tennis; cycle hire; golf 9km; 5% statics; dogs €3; adv bkg; quiet; cc acc; red low ssn/CCI. "British owners; excel facs & rest, superb food; conv Rocamadour & Lot & A20; excel walking in area; 'freedom' pitches for m'vanners €45 per night inc use of sm car, bookable daily." ♦ 15 May-15 Sep. € 20.00   2005*

CARLUX see Sarlat la Caneda *7C3*

CARMAUX *8E4* (10km N Rural) **Camping Les Clots, 81190 Mirandol-Bourgnounac [tel/fax 05 63 76 92 78; campclots@wanadoo.fr; www. tron.be/clots]** Fr Carmaux N on N88; L on D905 to Mirandol, site sp; last 2-3km narr private rd - rough with steep hairpin. Sm, terr, pt shd; wc; chem disp; shwrs inc; el pts (6-10A) €2.40; gas; lndtte; sm shop, tradsmn, bar high ssn; playgrnd; 2 pools; rv sw & fishing adj; games rm; TV; 10% statics; adv bkg; quiet; red 5+ days; CCI. "Very helpful Dutch owners; v diff ent to site - not rec for towed c'vans; sh stay/NH only." 1 May-1 Oct. € 16.40 (3 persons)   2003*

CARNAC *2G3* (1km N) **Camping Les Ombrages, Kerlann, 56340 Carnac [02 97 52 16 52 (Jul & Aug) or 02 97 52 14 06]** Exit Auray SW on N168. After 9.5km L on D119. After 3km R at carwash, site 600m on R sp fr D119. Med, shd; wc; shwrs; el pts (6A) €2.30; lndtte; shops 500m; playgrnd; sand beach 3km; tennis; dogs €1; poss cr; quiet. "Well-kept site in wooded area." 1 May-15 Sep. € 13.00   2003*

CARNAC *2G3* (1km N) **Camping Les Pins, Kerlann, 56340 Carnac [02 97 52 18 90]** On main Carnac-Auray rd; turn L at alignments; 1st R at fork site 500m on L. Lge, pt shd; wc; baby facs; shwrs inc; el pts (6-10A) €2.30; lndtte; ice; shop; snacks; BBQ; playgrnd; htd pool; sand beach 3km; entmnt; TV; dogs €0.60; red low ssn. 1 Apr-30 Sep. € 13.20   2003*

CARNAC *2G3* (1km N Rural) **Camping Moulin de Kermaux, Route de Kerlescan, 56340 Carnac [02 97 52 15 90; fax 02 97 52 83 85; moulin-de-kermaux@wanadoo.fr; www.camping-moulin kermaux.com]** Fr Auray take D768 S sp Carnac, Quiberon. In 8km turn L onto D119 twds Carnac. 1km bef Carnac take D196 (Rte de Kerlescan) L to site in approx 500m opp round, stone observation tower for alignments. Med, hdg/mkd pitch, pt shd; htd wc; chem disp; mv service pnt; baby facs; shwrs inc; el pts (6A) €3; gas; lndtte; ice; shop; snacks; bar; BBQ; playgrnd; htd pool; jacuzzi; sand beach 3km; games area; TV; 30% statics; dogs €3; phone; bus (Auray); Eng spkn; adv bkg; quiet; cc acc; CCI. "Well-kept, friendly site; attractive location nr standing stones; quiet & comfortable low ssn; many repeat visitors; excel long/sh stay." ♦ 6 Apr-15 Sep. € 22.00   2005*

CARNAC *2G3* (1km N) **LES CASTELS La Grande Metairie, Route des Alignements de Kermario, 56342 Carnac [02 97 52 24 01; fax 02 97 52 83 58; grande.metairie@wanadoo.fr; www.les-castels. com or www.lagrandemetairie.com]** Fr Auray take N768 twd Quiberon. In 8km turn L onto D119 twd Carnac. La Metairie site sp 1km bef Carnac (at traff lts) turn L onto D196 to site on R in 1km. Lge, pt sl, pt shd; wc; mv service pnt; shwrs inc; el pts (6A) inc; gas; lndtte; ice; shop; rest; snacks; bar; playgrnd; 2 pools (1 htd, covrd); paddling pool; waterslide; sand beach 3km; tennis; mini-golf; entmnt; sailing 3km; 80% statics; dogs; adv bkg; quiet; cc acc. ♦ 2 Apr-10 Sep. € 41.80   2005*

FRANCE

E-mail : ebideau@camping-kervilor.com
Internet : www.camping-kervilor.com

Camping de KERVILOR
F-56470 La Trinité sur Mer
Tel.: 00 33 (0)2 97 55 76 75
Fax: 00 33 (0)2 97 55 87 26

Close to the harbour and the beaches, rental of mobile homes, heated swimming pools, waterslides, slide with several tracks, thermal waters, bar, animations, tennis, billiards, all services at the site.

CARNAC *2G3* (2km N) **Camping de l'Etang**, Route de Kerlann, 56340 Carnac [02 97 52 14 06; fax 02 97 52 23 19] Exit Auray on D768 Carnac-Quiberon. In 9.5km L onto D119 & in 3km R immed after petrol stn to site in 700m on R. Sp Les Ombrages, de l'Etang & Les Pins. Lge, hdg/mkd pitch, pt shd; wc (cont); shwrs inc; el pts (6A) inc; gas; lndtte; ice; tradsmn; snacks; pool; waterslide; playgrnd; TV; sand beach 3km; sailing; fishing; dogs €0.76; Eng spkn; adv bkg; quiet; CCI. "Lge pitches." ♦ 1 Apr-30 Oct. € 18.00   2002*

CARNAC *2G3* (3km N) **Camping Le Rosnual**, Route d'Auray, 56340 Carnac [02 97 52 14 57 or 02 51 27 37 80 (reservation); fax 02 97 52 86 44 or 02 51 28 84 09; vagues.oceanes@wanadoo.fr; www.camping-vagues-oceanes.com] Fr Auray take N768 sp Quiberon. In 8km turn L for Carnac & foll site sp. Site on both sides of rd. Lge, mkd pitch, pt shd; wc; chem disp; shwrs; el pts; gas; lndtte; shop; rest; snacks; bar; playgrnd; 3 htd pools; sand beach 3km; 60% statics; no dogs; Eng spkn; adv bkg; cc acc; CCI. "Close to megalithic alignments; gd sh/long stay." ♦ ltd. 1 Apr-30 Sep.   2002*

CARNAC *2G3* (1.5km NE Rural) **Camping de Kervilor**, 56470 La Trinite-sur-Mer [02 97 55 76 75; fax 02 97 55 87 26; ebideau@camping-kervilor. com; www.camping-kervilor.com] Sp fr island in cent of Trinite-sur-Mer. Lge, hdg/mkd pitch, hdstg, pt shd; wc; chem disp; mv service pnt; chem disp; shwrs inc; el pts (6-10A) €3.30-3.80; gas; lndtte; ice; shop; snacks; bar; playgrnd; htd pool & paddling pool; waterslides; solarium; sand beach 2km; tennis; cycle hire; entmnt; 30% statics; dogs €2.80; poss cr; Eng spkn; adv bkg (dep & bkg fee); cc acc; red long stay/low ssn; CCI. "Busy family site; vg facs." ♦ 1 May-10 Sep. € 25.70   2005*

See advertisement above

CARNAC *2G3* (3km NE) **Camping du Moustoir**, Route du Moustoir, 56340 Carnac [02 97 52 16 18; fax 02 97 52 88 37; info@lemoustoir.com; www. lemoustoir.com] On D768 Auray-Carnac rd turn L at sp approx 3km N of Carnac. Lge, hdg/mkd pitch, pt sl, pt shd; wc; chem disp; mv service pnt; shwrs inc; el pts (6A) €3.10; lndtte; ice; shop; tradsmn; snacks; bar; BBQ; playgrnd; 2 htd pools; paddling pool; waterslide; sand beach 3km; tennis; games area; cycle hire; child entmnt; internet; 30% statics; dogs €1.50; phone; poss cr; Eng spkn; adv bkg; red low ssn; cc acc; CCI. "V attractive & well-run site; facs clean but stretched; many tour ops; Sun mkt nrby; bins outside site." ♦ 2 May-17 Sep. € 22.80 (CChq acc)   2004*

CARNAC *2G3* (8km NE) **Camping Le Fort Espagnol**, Route de Fort Espagnol, 56950 Crac'h [02 97 55 14 88; fax 02 97 30 01 04; fort-espagnol@wanadoo.fr; www.fort-espagnol.com] Fr Auray take D28 S; in Crac'h turn L at rndabt; site sp in 1km on R. Lge, pt shd; htd wc (some cont); chem disp; baby facs; shwrs inc; el pts (10A) €3.50; gas; lndtte; shops 1km; tradsmn; snacks; bar; playgrnd; pool; waterslide; sand beach 5km; tennis; sports facs; entmnt; 30% statics; poss cr; adv bkg rec high ssn; quiet; cc acc; CCI. "Helpful, pleasant management; pop with British; some lge pitches." 1 May-10 Sep. € 20.00   2005*

†**CARNAC** *2G3* (8km NE) **Camping Lodka**, 56950 Crac'h [tel/fax 02 97 55 03 97] Fr Auray take D28 S twd Locmariaquer; at rndabt in Crac'h turn L sp Port Espagnol & foll site sp. Sm, pt shd; wc; chem disp; shwrs inc; el pts €2.29; lndtte; shop; playgrnd; sand beach & watersports; 6km; pool; TV rm; 80% statics; dogs €1.52; poss cr; adv bkg; quiet. "Lge pitches; interesting archaeological area; ltd san facs low ssn." ♦ € 15.24   2004*

CARNAC *2G3* (2km E Rural/Coastal) **Camping Les Druides**, Beaumer, 56340 Carnac [02 97 52 08 18; fax 02 97 52 96 13; campingl-les-druides@wanadoo.fr] Go E on seafront Carnac Plage to the end; turn N onto Ave d'Orient; at junc with Rte de la Trinite-sur-mer, turn L, then 1st R; site 1st on L in 300m. Med, hdg pitch, pt sl, pt shd; wc; chem disp; mv service pnt; baby facs; shwrs inc; el pts (6A) €3.90; lndtte; ice; shop 1km; rest adj; playgrnd; htd pool; sand beach 300m; entmnts; games/TV rm; 5% statics; dogs €2.60; phone adj; Eng spkn; adv bkg; quiet; cc acc; CCI. "Friendly welcome; barrier key dep; vg long stay." ♦ ltd. 9 May-10 Sep. € 27.00   2004*

CARNAC *2G3* (3km E) **Camping du Lac**, 56340 Carnac [02 97 55 78 78 or 02 97 55 82 60; fax 02 97 55 86 03; camping.dulac@wanadoo.fr] Fr E end of quay-side in La Trinite-sur-Mer take main Carnac rd & in 100m turn R onto D186; in 2km R on C105, R on C131; sp. Fr Auray (by-pass) take D768 sp Carnac; in 4km turn L on D186; after 4km look for C105 on L & foll sp to site. Med, pt shd; wc; chem disp; mv service pnt; serviced pitches; baby facs; shwrs inc; el pts (4-6A) €3; lndtte; ice; shop; rest 3km; playgrnd; pool; sand beach 3km; cycle hire; exercise equip rm; TV rm; entmnt; 15% statics; dogs €1.50; Eng spkn; adv bkg; quiet; cc acc; CCI. "Excel woodland site overlooking tidal lake; gd cycling & walking; v helpful owner; clean, well cared for." 1 Apr-20 Sep. € 14.63   2005*

CARNAC *2G3* (2km SE Coastal) **Camping Le Men Du**, 56340 Carnac [02 97 52 04 23; mendu@wanadoo.fr; www.camping-du-mendu.com] Go E on seafront (Carnac Plage) to end; N on Ave d'Orient; at junc with Rte de la Trinite-sur-Mer turn L & 1st R; 2nd site on R. Med, hdg/mkd pitch, pt sl, pt shd; wc; chem disp; shwrs inc; el pts (6-10A) €3; gas; lndtte; ice; shop 1km; rest, snacks, bar high ssn; sand beach 200m; 50% statics; bus 100m; poss cr; poss noisy; adv bkg (dep req); some Eng spkn; CCI. "Friendly staff; mkd pitches not rec for manoeuvring twin-axles; manhandling req for long or heavy vans; narr rds on site; yachting (inc school)." ♦ ltd. 1 Apr-30 Sep. € 20.00   2004*

CARNAC *2G3* (2km E Coastal) **Camping Park Plijadur**, 94 Route de Carnac, 56470 La Trinite-sur-Mer [02 97 55 72 05; fax 02 97 55 83 83; parkplijadur@hotmail.com; www.parkplijadur.com] Take D781 Route de Carnac W fr La Trinite-sur-Mer, site 1km on R. Lge, hdg/mkd pitch, pt shd; wc; chem disp; mv service pnt; baby facs; sauna; shwrs inc; el pts (6-10A) €2.50-3.50; lndtte; ice; shop; tradsmn; supmkt nr; rest 1km; snacks; bar; BBQ; playgrnd; htd pool; paddling pool; jacuzzi; sand beach 1km; games rm; fitness rm; mini-golf; cycle hire; golf 10km; entmnt; TV rm; 3% statics; dogs €2; phone; poss cr; Eng spkn; adv bkg; quiet; cc acc; red low ssn/long stay/CCI. ♦ Easter-1 Oct. € 21.55   2005*

See advertisement above

CARNAC *2G3* (3km SE Coastal) **Camping de la Plage**, Plage de Kervillen, 56470 La Trinite-sur-Mer [02 97 55 73 28; fax 02 97 55 88 31; laplage@clubinternet.fr; www.camping-plage.com] Fr Auray on D28 & D781 dir La Trinite. Foll sp Kervillen Plage to S. Lge, hdg pitch, pt shd; wc; mv service pnt; chem disp; serviced pitches; baby facs; shwrs inc; el pts (6A) €3.10; gas; lndtte; ice; shop 200m; rest; snacks; bar; BBQ; playgrnd; htd pool; waterslide; jacuzzi; sand beach adj; fishing; tennis adj; boat hire; mini-golf; cycle hire; 25% statics; dogs €1.20; Eng spkn; adv bkg; quiet; red long stay/low ssn; cc acc; CCI. "Pleasant site; friendly staff." ♦ 29 Apr-17 Sep. € 33.70   2005*

CARNAC 2G3 (4km SE Coastal) Camping La Baie, Plage de Kervillen, 56470 La Trinite-sur-Mer [02 97 55 73 42; fax 02 97 55 88 81; contact@campingdelabaie.fr; www.campingdelabaie.fr] Fr Carnac take D186. Turn R after causeway, keep R, past Camping de la Plage site, & site on L. Fr E app vill along seafront sp Carnac, cont strt thro traff lts, after 2nd traff lts take 1st L & foll rd for 1km. Site ent on L. Lge, hdg/mkd pitch, hdstg, pt shd; wc; chem disp; mv service pnt; baby facs; serviced pitches; shwrs inc; el pts (6-10A) €2.20-3.25; ice; lndtte; shops, snacks, rest, bar 500m; playgrnd; entmnt; htd pool; sand beach 50m; fishing; boat hire, mini-golf & tennis 250m; TV rm; 30% statics; dogs €1.20; phone; Eng spkn; poss cr; adv bkg (dep req & bkg fee); quiet; red low ssn; cc acc. "Excel site; highly rec; superb recep & san facs; well maintained; some narr site rds - pitching poss diff lge o'fits; vg family beach." ♦ 20 May-17 Sep. € 35.35   2005*

See advertisement

CARNAC 2G3 (9km SW Coastal) Camp Municipal Les Sables Blancs, 56340 Plouharnel [02 97 52 37 15 or 02 97 52 30 90 (Mairie); fax 02 97 52 48 49] Fr Auray take by-pass to Quiberon (clearly mkd), cont thro Plouharnel (D768) twd Quiberon - site clearly mkd after passing thro Plouharnel. Lge, unshd; wc; shwrs inc; el pts (4-13A) €2.45-3.45; gas; lndtte; ice; shops; rest in ssn; sand beach; 30% statics; dogs €1.05; Eng spkn; quiet. "Situated on a sand spit, care needed over soft sand." 31 Mar-30 Sep. € 12.00   2005*

CARNAC 2G3 (1.5km NW) Camping Les Goelands, Kerbachic, 56340 Plouharnel [02 97 52 31 92; michelinealloux@aol.com] Take D768 fr Auray twd Quiberon. In Plouharnel turn L at rndabt by supmkt onto D781 to Carnac. Site sp to L in 500m. Med, pt shd; wc (some cont); chem disp; shwrs €0.80; el pts (3-5A) €1.80-2.80; gas; lndtte; ice; shops 1km; playgrnd; sand beach 3km; dogs €0.80; poss cr; adv bkg. "V friendly owners; excel facs; gd-sized pitches; gate clsd at 2200; nr beaches with bathing & gd yachting; bells fr adj abbey not too intrusive; conv for megalithic sites; high standard; gd all stays." 1 Jun-15 Sep. € 10.30   2005*

CARNAC 2G3 (6km NW) Camping Le Chat Noir, Route de la Trinite-sur-Mer, 56470 St Philibert [tel/fax 02 97 55 04 90; chatnoir@camping-lechatnoir.com] Exit Auray on D28 S to junc with D781. Turn R & site on R in 500m. Med, hdg/mkd pitch, shd; wc; chem disp; baby facs; shwrs inc; el pts (6A) €2.50; lndtte; tradsmn; snacks; playgrnd; htd pool; beach 1.5km; games area; entmnt; TV; some statics; dogs €2; adv bkg; quiet; cc acc. Easter-30 Sep. € 16.00   2003*

CARNAC 2G3 (8km NW Rural) Camping Kerzerho, 56410 Erdeven [tel/fax 02 97 55 63 16; info@camping-kerzerho.com; www.camping-kerzerho.com] N fr Carnac on D781, site sp 400m S of Erdeven. Med, hdg/mkd pitch, pt shd; wc; baby facs; sauna; shwrs; el pts; lndtte; shop; tradsmn; rest; snacks; bar; playgrnd; htd pool; paddling pool; waterslide; beach 2.5km; cycle hire; entmnt; child entmnt; mini-golf; excursions; some statics; dogs €1.30; adv bkg; quiet; red low ssn. € 19.00   2002*

CARNAC 2G3 (8km NW Rural) Camping La Croez Villieu, Route de Kerhilio, 56410 Erdeven [02 97 55 90 43; fax 02 97 55 64 83; la-croez-villieu@wanadoo.fr] Fr Carnac take D781 to Erdeven, turn L opp Marche des Menhirs. Site 1km on R. Med, hdg pitch, pt shd; wc; chem disp (wc); baby facs; shwrs inc; el pts (4-6A) €2.50-3.50; gas; lndtte; ice; shops 1km; snacks; bar; playgrnd; htd pool; sand beach 2km; 65% statics; dogs €1.10; poss cr; Eng spkn; adv bkg; quiet; red low ssn; CCI. "Friendly & helpful owners." ♦ 1 May-15 Sep. € 15.00   2003*

CARNAC 2G3 (8km NW) Camping Les Megalithes, Kergouet, 56410 Erdeven [02 97 55 68 76 or 02 97 55 68 09] Fr Carnac take D781 thro Plouharnel after further 4km; site on L opp sm cafe in 500m. Med, hdg/mkd pitch, pt sl, pt shd; wc; shwrs inc; el pts (10A) inc; lndtte; shop; snacks; playgrnd; sand/shgl beach 3km; dogs €1; quiet. "Conv for megalithic alignments; nice site with lge pitches but poorly lit." 1 Apr-15 Oct. € 17.60   2002*

CARNAC *2G3* (8km NW Coastal) **Ideal Camping, Route de la Plage de Kerhilio, Lisveur, 56410 Erdeven [02 97 55 67 66; idealcamping@ wanadoo.fr]** Fr Carnac take D781 to Erdeven, turn L opp Marche des Menhirs. Site 2km on R. Med, hdg pitch, pt shd; wc; chem disp; shwrs inc; el pts (6A) inc; gas; lndtte; rest; ice; shops 500m; tradsmn; snacks; bar; playgrnd; htd, covrd pool; sand beach 800m; 25% statics; dogs €2; adv bkg (30% bkg fee); quiet; cc acc; CCI. "Sm peaceful site nr to magnificent beach & cent of mkt town; fluent Eng-spkg owners; gd rest & takeaway; vg long stay." ♦ Easter-30 Oct. € 17.00 (3 persons) 2002*

Mustn't forget to post our site report forms to The Club, otherwise sites might be deleted.

CARNAC *2G3* (12.5km NW) **Camping Les Sept Saints, 56410 Erdeven [02 97 55 52 65; fax 02 97 55 22 67; info@septsaints.com; www. septsaints.com]** On D781 NW almost 2km fr Erdeven twd Lorient, site on L. Lge, hdg/mkd pitch, pt sl, pt shd; wc; chem disp; baby facs; shwrs inc; el pts (10A) inc; gas; lndtte; ice; shop; snacks; bar; BBQ (charcoal/gas); playgrnd; htd pool; paddling pool; waterslide; sand beach 4km; watersports 1.5km; cycle hire; games rm; entmnt; many statics; dogs €2.80; c'vans over 8m not acc high ssn; adv bkg; quiet; cc acc; red low ssn; CCI. "Lge areas for touring; gd lge pitches; v pleasant site; excursions booked." ♦
15 May-15 Sep. € 35.00 ABS - B26 2005*

CAROMB see Malaucene *10E2*

CARPENTRAS *10E2* (5km N Rural) **Camping Le Bregoux, Chemin du Vas, 84810 Aubignan [04 90 62 62 50 or 04 90 67 10 13 (LS); fax 04 90 62 65 21; camping-lebregoux@wanadoo.fr; www.camping-lebregoux.fr]** Exit Carpentras on D7 sp Bollene. In Aubignan turn R immed after x-ing bdge, R again in approx 250m at Office du Tourisme & foll site sp. Lge, hdg/mkd pitch, shd; wc; chem disp; mv service pnt; baby facs; shwrs inc; el pts (6A) inc; gas 1km; lndtte; shops, rest, bars etc 1km; BBQ; playgrnd; pool 5km in ssn; go-karting & golf nrby; entmnt; games rm; TV; dogs €1.30; phone; poss v cr; some Eng spkn; adv bkg; poss noisy high ssn; red low ssn; cc acc; CCI. "1st class, popular site; vg value for money; gates clsd 2200-0800; poss flooding in heavy rain; guarded day & night; prefers stays of 4+ nights; office clsd 1200-1430; some lge pitches but poss obstructed by lge trees; beautiful area; excel walking nrby." ♦ ltd. 1 Mar-31 Oct. € 11.55 2005*

CARPENTRAS *10E2* (7km N) **Camp Municipal de Roquefiguier, 84190 Beaumes-de-Venise [04 90 62 95 07 or 04 90 62 94 34 (Mairie)]** Leave A7 exit 22, take N7 S then L onto D950 sp Carpentras. At traff lts N of Sarrians turn L onto D21 to Beaumes-de-Venise. Cross Beaumes & foll site sp. Turn L bef Credit Agricole to site on R. Med, hdg/mkd pitch, pt sl, terr, pt shd; wc (some cont); chem disp; mv service pnt; shwrs inc; el pts (6A) inc; lndtte; ice; shops 250m; BBQ; pool in vill; wine caves adj; dogs €1.15; phone; no adv bkg; quiet; cc acc; CCI. "Facs clean but basic; steel pegs req for pitches; poss diff access lge o'fits; steep access some pitches; gate clsd 1900-0900, key avail dep €15; 5 mins walk to town; attractive views; plenty of mkd walks & cycle ways; conv for Mt Ventoux, Orange & Avignon; vg long stay." ♦ 1 Apr-31 Oct. € 10.55
2005*

CARPENTRAS *10E2* (7km E Rural) **Camping Le Ventoux, Route de Bedoin, 84380 Mazan [tel/fax 04 90 69 70 94 or 06 80 84 01 65; camping.le. ventoux@wanadoo.fr]** Take D974 twd Bedoin; after 7km turn R at x-rds on D70 sp Mazan. Site on R in 300m. Sm, pt shd; wc (some cont); chem disp; shwrs inc; el pts (6A) inc (poss rev pol); gas; lndtte; ice; shop (high ssn) & 3km; tradsmn; snacks high ssn; bar; BBQ; playgrnd; pool; lake fishing 4km; dogs €1.07; phone; poss cr; entmnts; adv bkg (ess high ssn); quiet, poss noise fr farm machinery; cc acc; CCI. "Gd; ltd facs low ssn; friendly warden; wine-tasting area; fair sh stay/NH." ♦ ltd
15 Feb-15 Nov. € 17.70 2003*

CARPENTRAS *10E2* (12km E Rural) **Camp Municipal Aeria, 84570 Blauvac [04 90 61 81 41 (Mairie)]** E fr Carpentras on D942; E of Mazan fork onto D150. Site 100m N of Blauvac vill cent. Sm, pt shd; wc (some cont); shwrs; el pts (6A) €1.70; shop 7km; playgrnd. "Basic facs on quiet site; gd views; site on hilltop & may be exposed in bad weather; warden calls am & pm." 15 Mar-15 Oct. € 7.50
2003*

CARPENTRAS *10E2* (10km SE Rural) **Camping Font Neuve, Rue de Methamis, 84570 Malemort-du-Comtat [tel/fax 04 90 69 90 00 or 04 90 69 74 86; camping.font-neuve@libertysurf.fr]** Fr Malemort take Methanis rd D5; as rd starts to rise look for sp on L to site. Med, hdg pitch, terr, pt shd; wc (some cont); chem disp; serviced pitches; baby facs; shwrs inc; el pts (6A) €3; lndtte; tradsmn; rest; bar; pool; tennis; adv bkg req high ssn; cc not acc. "V friendly & helpful family-run site; gd rest; immac wcs; many pitches now looking tired." ♦
1 May-30 Sep. € 11.60 2003*

CARPENTRAS *10E2* (6km S Urban) **Camp Municipal Coucourelle, Ave Rene Char, 84210 Pernes-les-Fontaines [04 90 66 45 55 or 04 90 61 31 67 (Mairie); fax 04 90 61 32 46]** Take D938 fr Carpentras to Pernes-les-Fontaines for 6km. Site well sp, Foll sports complex, site at rear of sw pool. Sm, hdg/mkd pitch, pt shd; wc; chem disp; mv service pnt; shwrs inc; el pts (6A) €2.80; gas 1km; lndtte; clean facs; lndry rm; BBQ; shops & rests 1km; playgrnd; pool, sw & fishing 2.5km; tennis adj; dogs €0.50; quiet; cc not acc; CCI. "V attractive old town; some pitches poss sm & narr; gd clean facs; m'vans can park adj to mv point free when campsite clsd; no twin-axle c'vans; pleasant, functional site." ♦ 1 Apr-30 Sep. € 10.20   2005*

CARPENTRAS *10E2* (4km SW Rural) **Camp Municipal de Bellerive, 54 Chemin de la Ribiere, 84170 Monteux [04 90 66 81 88]** Site on N edge of Monteux cent, sp off ring rd Monteux N, immed after rlwy x-ing. Sm, hdg/mkd pitch, pt shd; some serviced pitches; wc; chem disp; shwrs inc; el pts (6A) €2; lndry rm; shops 500m; rest, snacks, bar 500m; playgrnd; pool 4km; poss cr; quiet; CCI. "Conv wine region; gd local mkts; excel, quiet site; 5 min walk into vill; pleasant manager; excel value; rec arr early; poss poor security." 1 Apr-31 Oct. € 9.00   2005*

CARPENTRAS *10E2* (11km NW) **Camp Municipal Les Queirades, 84190 Vacqueyras [04 90 65 84 24 (Mairie); fax 04 90 65 83 28; tourisme.vacqueyras@wanadoo.fr]** Site on W of D7 at N end of Vacqueyras, clearly sp. Sm, pt shd, hdg pitch; wc; shwrs inc; el pts (6A) €3; ice; shops 1km; playgrnd; rv sw 3km; tennis adj; adv bkg; quiet, but some rd noise; CCI. "Clean, popular site, with wine caves opposite; D7 v fast & busy; gd long stay." 1 Apr-31 Aug. € 9.40   2003*

CARQUEIRANNE see Hyeres *10F3*

†**CARRY LE ROUET** *10F2* (Coastal) **Camping Lou Soulei, 13620 Carry-le-Rouet [04 42 44 75 75; fax 04 42 44 57 24; lousoulei@wanadoo.fr]** Fr Martigues take A55 & exit dir Carry-le-Rouet. Site on beach rd. V lge, hdg/mkd pitch, hdstg, pt shd; wc; chem disp; serviced pitch; shwrs inc; el pts (6A) inc; lndtte; shop adj; rest; snacks; bar; playgrnd; htd pool; beach adj; TV rm; 75% statics; dogs; phone; poss cr; Eng spkn; adv bkg; red low ssn. "Gd base for Marseille, Camargue, Aix, etc; red facs low ssn; gd long stay." € 36.00 (4 persons)   2003*

CARSAC AILLAC see Sarlat la Caneda *7C3*

CASSAGNABERE TOURNAS *8F3* (Rural) **Camping Pre Fixe, 31420 Cassagnabere-Tournas [tel/fax 05 61 98 71 00; camping@instudio4.com; www.instudio4.com/pre-fixe]** Exit A64 at junc 21 onto D635 dir Aurignac. Cont thro vill on D635 sp Cassagnabere for 8km, sp in vill. Sm, hdg/mkd pitch, terr, pt shd; wc (some cont); chem disp; mv disposal; baby facs; shwrs inc; el pts (6-10A) €2.80-3.40; gas; ice; lndtte; shop 500m; tradsmn; rest; snacks; bar; BBQ; playgrnd; pool; sw 8km; entmnt; TV rm; 10% statics; no dogs; phone; Eng spkn; adv bkg; dep req; quiet; CCI. "V friendly owners; beautiful landscape; gd touring base for Haute-Garonne; rec; excel." ♦ 15 Apr-30 Sep. € 12.80   2005*

CASSANIOUZE *7D4* (10km SW Rural) **Camping Le Coursavy, 15340 Cassaniouze [tel/fax 04 71 49 97 70; camping.coursavy@wanadoo.fr; www.campingcoursavy.com]** Fr Entraygues (E) foll D107 along Rv Lot dir Conques. 6km after Vieillevie, site is on L on rvside. Cont to next rd junc (500m) after site ent to turn & return. Sm, mkd pitch, pt sl, pt shd; wc; chem disp, shwrs inc; el pts (5A) €2.20; lndtte; ice; shop 2km; tradsmn; playgrnd; pool; rv sw; TV rm; dogs €1.20; phone adj; Eng spkn; adv bkg; quiet; red low ssn; CCI. "Excel site in beautiful, unspoilt area; gd touring base; friendly Dutch owners." ♦ 20 Apr-20 Sep. € 14.60   2003*

CASSIS *10F3* (1.5km N Coastal) **Camping Les Cigales, Route de Marseille, 13260 Cassis [04 42 01 07 34; fax 04 42 01 34 18]** App Cassis on D41E, then at 2nd rndabt exit D559 sp Cassis, then turn 1st R sp Les Calanques into Ave de la Marne, site immed on R. Avoid town cent as rds narr. Lge, hgd/mkd pitch, hdstg, pt sl, pt shd; wc (some cont); chem disp; mv service pnt; shwrs inc; el pts (3A) inc; gas; lndtte; ice; shop; tradsmn; rest; snacks; bar; playgrnd; shgl beach 1.5km; 30% statics; dogs; phone; quiet, but some rd noise; Eng spkn; cc acc; CCI. "Tired san facs end ssn; gd base for Calanques; attractive resort, but steep walk to camp site; poss diff lge o'fits due trees; gd long/sh stay." 15 Mar-15 Nov. € 20.00   2005*

CASTELFRANC *7D3* (9km N) **Camping La Pinede, 46250 Goujounac [05 65 36 61 84]** Fr Gourdon take D673 SW. At Frayssinet-le-Gelet turn L onto D660 for 2.5km. Site on L at ent to vill. Sm, mkd pitch, terr, pt shd; wc; chem disp; shwrs inc; el pts (20A) €2; lndtte; shop 1km; bar; pool; tennis; quiet. "Attractive vill & site in pine wood; gd rest 1km." 15 Jun-15 Sep. € 10.50   2004*

CASTELFRANC *7D3* (4km SE) **Camp Municipal Pech del Gal, 46140 Albas [05 65 36 70 75 or 05 65 20 12 21 (Mairie); fax 05 65 33 99 55]** Fr Castelfranc cross rv on D45 & L on D8 to Albas. Site sp. Sm, pt shd; wc; shwrs; el pts; shop 500m; playgrnd; rv fishing; boat hire. "Beautiful area & pleasant pool 4km." 15 Jun-15 Sep.   2002*

CASTELFRANC *7D3* (6km SE Rural) **Camp Municipal de l'Alcade (Naturist), 46140 Luzech [05 65 30 72 32 (Mairie); fax 05 65 30 76 80; mairie.luzech&wanadoo.fr]** Fr Cahors take D811 NW, turn L onto D8 foll sp to Luzech; cross both bdges in Luzech; site on R in 1km on D8; do not foll camp sp on D88 to Sauzac. Sm, pt shd; wc (cont); sauna; shwrs inc; el pts (6-10A) €3 (rev pol); shops 1km; bar; playgrnd; dogs €2; some rd noise; red low ssn. "On banks of Rv Lot; rv not suitable for sw, sluice gates of dam upstream liable to be opened, causing rv to rise sharply; warden visits 0800-0900 & 1830-1930 - arrange for barrier to be open; peaceful site." 1 Jul-30 Sep. € 16.00   2003*

CASTELFRANC *7D3* (2km SW Rural) **Camping Base Nautique Floiras, 46140 Anglars-Juillac [05 65 36 27 39; fax 05 65 21 41 00; camping floiras@aol.com]** Fr Castelfranc head S on D45; cross rv W on D8; site on W of rd thro Juillac, sp. Or fr W on D811 (formerly D911) turn R at main sq Prayssac sp Mont Cuq. In 2km cross rv at Pont Juillac, turn 1st R & foll sp to site. Sm, mkd pitch, pt shd; htd wc; chem disp; mv service pnt; shwrs inc; el pts (10A) inc (rev pol); gas; lndtte; ice; shop 3km; tradsmn; rest adj; snacks; sm bar; BBQ; playgrnd; pool 2km; rv sw; cycle & canoe hire; entmnt; TV rm; dogs €1.25; phone adj; Eng spkn; adv bkg ess high ssn (bkg fee); quiet; cc acc; CCI. "Helpful owner; well-kept site on Rv Lot set in vineyards; nr mkts & rests; highly rec." ♦ Easter-31 Oct. € 15.50   2005*

CASTELJALOUX *7D2* (N Urban) **Camp Municipal de la Piscine, 47700 Casteljaloux [05 53 93 54 68; fax 05 53 89 13 25]** On N side of town on D933 visible fr rd. Sm, pt shd; wc; shwrs inc; el pts (10A) inc; ice; shops 750m; rest; pool; rv & lake sw; fishing; rd noise. ♦ 1 Apr-30 Oct. € 8.15   2003*

CASTELJALOUX *7D2* (8km SE Rural) **Camping Moulin de Campech, 47160 Villefranche-du-Queyran [05 53 88 72 43; fax 05 53 88 06 52; campech@wanadoo.fr; www.moulindecampech. co.uk]** Fr a'route A62 exit junc 6 sp Damazan. Fr toll booth take D8 sp Mont-de-Marsan. In 3km turn R in Cap-du-Bosc onto D11 twd Casteljaloux. Site on R in 4km. Or fr Casteljaloux S on D655 then SW on D11 after 1.5km. Site on L after 9.5km. Med, hdg/mkd pitch, pt shd; wc (some cont); chem disp; shwrs inc; el pts (6A) inc; lndtte; sm shop; tradsmn; rest; snacks; bar; BBQ; htd pool; lake fishing; games area; golf nr; guided tours; dogs €2.40; phone; recep 0800-2200; poss cr; British owners; adv bkg; quiet; cc acc; CCI. "Superb, rvside site; gd facs & helpful, friendly staff; ideal for nature lovers." 1 Apr-23 Oct. € 24.00 ABS - D16   2005*

CASTELLANE *10E3* (1km N) **Camping Le Provencal, Route de Digne, 04120 Castellane [tel/fax 04 92 83 65 50; accueil@camping-provencal.com]** Fr N on N85 at foot of Col de Lecques site on R on LH bend. Fr Castellane site on N85 in 1km on L. Med, mkd pitch, pt sl, pt shd; wc; chem disp; baby facs; shwrs inc; el pts (3-6A) €2-3; lndtte; shop; supmkt 500m; tradsmn; snacks; bar; pool 1.5km; dogs €2; some rd noise; red low ssn. "Gd, clean site; fine scenery, friendly owners; conv Gorges du Verdon." 1 May-15 Sep. € 12.00   2005*

CASTELLANE *10E3* (8km N Rural) **Camping Castillon de Provence (Naturist), La Grande Terre, La Baume, 04120 Castellane [04 92 83 64 24; fax 04 92 83 68 79]** Fr Castellane take D955 at Casino supmkt & after 5km turn L on D402 (up narr mountain rd) site in 7km. NB up access for car & vans only after 1400, down before 1300. Med, pt sl, pt shd; wc (some cont); chem disp (wc); shwrs inc; el pts (2-6A) €2.20; gas; ice; lndtte; shop; tradsmn; rest; snacks; bar; playgrnd; paddling pool; lake sw, fishing, watersports 2km; TV rm; 20% statics; dogs; phone; poss cr; Eng spkn; adv bkg (dep req); quiet; cc not acc; INF card. "Site 1000m high & cold at night; fantastic mountain views overlooking Lac de Castillon; v lge pitches." ♦ Easter-30 Sep. € 21.00   2004*

CASTELLANE *10E3* (5km SE Rural) **Camping Les Collines de Castellane, Route de Grasse, 04120 Castellane [04 92 83 68 96; fax 04 92 83 75 40; info@rcn-lescollinesdecastellane.fr; www.rcn-campings.fr]** Fr Castellane, take the RN85. After 5 km is La Garde, go thro vill & foll sp. Site on R just past this vill. Lge, terr, pt shd; wc; mv service pnt; baby facs; shwrs inc; el pts inc; gas; lndtte; ice; shop; rest; snacks; bar; playgrnd; pool; lake sw 5km; games area; organised activites inc variety of watersports, rock climbing, paragliding, hiking; entmnt, TV; Eng spkn; adv bkg. "Friendly owners; set on steep hillside with stunning views; peaceful; main site rd v steep; m'vans arr after 1500, dep before 1000; campers arr after 1200, dep bef 1200." ♦ 15 May-15 Sep. € 24.00   2004*

CASTELLANE *10E3* (SW Urban) **Camping Le Frederic Mistral, Route des Gorges-du-Verdon, 04120 Castellane [04 92 83 62 27]** In town turn onto D952 sp Gorges-du-Verdon, site on L in 100m. Med, mkd pitch, pt shd; htd wc; chem disp; some serviced pitches; shwrs inc; el pts (6A) €3 (poss earth & polarity probs); gas 200m; shops adj; supmkt nr; bar; snacks; pool 200m; 2% statics; poss cr; adv bkg; quiet; CCI. "Friendly owners; conv town cent; unltd free hot water; gd new san facs but poss stretched in ssn; gd base for gorges etc." ♦ 1 Mar-30 Nov. € 12.40   2005*

FRANCE

CASTELLANE *10E3* (500m SW Rural) **Camping Notre Dame, Route des Gorges du Verdon, 04120 Castellane** [tel/fax 04 92 83 63 02]
N fr Grasse on N85, turn L in Castellane at sq onto D952 to site on R in 500m. Sm, pt shd; wc; chem disp; mv service pnt; shwrs inc; el pts (6A) inc; gas; ice; lndtte; sm shop; rest 600m; playgrnd; 5% statics; phone; poss cr; adv bkg; quiet; red low ssn; CCI. "Helpful owners." ♦ ltd. 1 Apr-15 Oct. € 18.50   2005*

CASTELLANE *10E3* (1.5km SW Rural) **LES CASTELS Le Camp du Verdon, Domaine de La Salou, 04120 Castellane** [04 92 83 61 29; fax 04 92 83 69 37; contact@camp-du-verdon.com; www.camp-du-verdon.com or www.les-castels. com] Fr Castellane take D952 SW twd the Grand Canyon du Verdon & Moustiers-Ste Marie. After 1.5km turn L into site. (NB To avoid Col de Leques with hairpins use N202 & D955 fr Barreme instead of N85.) Lge, hdg/mkd pitch; pt shd; wc (some cont); chem disp; mv service pnt; ltd baby facs; shwrs inc; el pts (6A) inc; gas; lndtte; shop; rest; snacks; bar; BBQ (gas only); playgrnd; htd pool; waterslides; rv adj; fishing; canoeing, kayaking, rafting, horseriding nrby; cycle hire; archery; mini-golf; games rm; games area; entmnt; dogs €2.50; poss cr; Eng spkn; poss noisy; cc acc; CCI. "Vg site; mkt Wed & Sat am; guided walks to gorge." ♦ 13 May-15 Sep. € 22.00 (CChq acc) ABS - C15   2005*

CASTELLANE *10E3* (2km SW Rural) **Camping de la Colle, Quartier de la Colle, 04120 Castellane** [tel/fax 04 92 83 61 57; camping.la.colle@freesbee.fr]
Leave Castellane on D952 heading W. In 2km, take R at fork in rd. Site is on a narr rd. Foll sp 'Camping de la Colle.' Sm, terr, shd; wc; chem disp; shwrs inc; el pts (6-10A) €3; gas 2km; lndtte; ice; sm shop on site & shops 2km; tradsmn; snacks; bar 2km; playgrnd; pool 2km; lake & rv sw 5km; 15% statics; dogs; phone; adv bkg; quiet; CCI. "Not suitable for v lge c'vans or m'vans; family-run; unspoilt natural setting well above town; dir access to Gorges du Verdon; vg long stay." ♦ 1 Apr-30 Oct. € 14.50
                                                      2003*

CASTELLANE *10E3* (8km SW Rural) **Domaine de Chasteuil-Provence, Route de Moustiers, Chasteuil, 04120 Castellane** [04 92 83 61 21; fax 04 92 83 75 62; contact@chasteuil-provence. com; www.chasteuil-provence.com]
Take D952 W fr Castellane, site by rv on R. Lge, mkd pitch, pt terr, shd; wc; chem disp; shwrs inc; el pts (6A) inc; gas; lndtte; ice; shop; tradsmn; rest; snacks; bar; playgrnd; pool; rv beach; boating; fishing; 10% statics; poss cr; adv bkg; quiet; red low ssn; CCI. "Excel touring & walking base; beautiful surroundings; more spacious & better located site than some nearer Castellane." 5 May-20 Sep. € 23.20 (3 persons)   2002*

CASTELLANE *10E3* (12km SW Rural) **Camp Municipal de Carajuan, 04120 Roujon** [04 92 83 70 94 or 04 92 83 66 32 (Mairie); fax 04 92 83 66 49; mairie.rougon@wanadoo.fr]
S fr Digne on N85 turn R on D952 & foll sps for 16km to rv bank of Gorges du Verdon nr Carajuan bdge. Sm, mkd pitch, pt sl, pt shd; wc; shwrs inc; el pts (6A) €2.30; shop 10km; playgrnd; rv sw; 10% statics; dogs €0.80; quiet; Eng spkn; CCI. "Natural, unspoilt; conv for Gorges du Verdon; gd walking." ♦ 1 Apr-31 Oct. € 12.00   2003*

CASTELLANE *10E3* (W Urban) **Camping Les Lavandes, Route des Gorges du Verdon, 04120 Castellane** [04 92 83 68 78 or 04 92 78 33 51 (LS); fax 04 92 83 69 92; accueil@camping-les-lavandes.com; www.camping-les-lavandes.com]
Head W on D952 sp Gorges du Verdon to site on R. Med, pt shd; wc; chem disp; sauna, solarium; baby facs; shwrs €1; el pts (3-10A) €2.90-3.90; supmkt 500m; playgrnd; entmnt; rv adj; some statics; poss cr; adv bkg; quiet; red low ssn; no cc acc. "Lovely site; sm pitches; beautiful mountain scenery; excel view of Notre Dame du Roc; conv town cent; office open 0900-1000 & 1800-1900, site yourself; poss unkempt low ssn." 1 Apr-15 Oct. € 12.50   2003*

CASTELLANE *10E3* (8km W Rural) **Camp des Gorges du Verdon, Clos d'Aremus, 04120 Castellane** [04 92 83 63 64; fax 04 92 83 74 72; aremus@camping-GorgesDuVerdon.com] N85 fr Grasse turn L on D952 in Castellane. Camp in 8km on L. Look for sp Casteuil on R of rd; camp is 500m further on. Lge, shd, poss boggy in wet; wc; serviced pitch; chem disp; shwrs inc; el pts (6A) €3.70; rest; gas; lndtte; ice; sm shop; playgrnd; htd pool; fishing; boating; canoeing; poss cr; Eng spkn; adv bkg ess; red low ssn; CCI. "Some sm pitches; rd along Gorges du Verdon poss diff for lge o'fits; conv town cent." ♦ 1 May-15 Sep. € 19.20 (3 persons) 2003*

CASTELLANE *10E3* (1km NW Rural) **Camping International, Route Napoleon, La Palud, 04120 Castellane** [04 92 83 66 67; fax 04 92 83 77 67; info@campinginternational.fr; www.camping international.fr & www.homair-vacances.fr] Site sp fr N85. Lge, hdg pitch, pt sl, pt shd; wc; chem disp; mv service pnt; serviced pitches; baby facs; shwrs inc; el pts (6A) €5; gas; lndtte; ice; shop; supmkt 800m; tradsmn; rest; snacks; bar; playgrnd; pool; lake sw, sand beach 5km; games area; golf; horseriding; entmnt; child entmnt; internet; TV rm; 50% statics; dogs €4; quiet; adv bkg (dep req); Eng spkn; cc acc; red low ssn; CCI. "Friendly, helpful owners; conv Gorges de Verdon; gd walking." ♦ Easter-30 Sep. € 21.00 (CChq.acc) 2005*

See advertisement

CASTELLANE *10E3* (8km NW Rural) **Camping des Sirenes (formerly Camp Municipal L' Oasis), Col des Leques, Route Napoleon, 04120 Castellane** [04 92 83 70 56; www.camping-des-sirenes.com] On N85 8km NW of Castellane. Sm, pt sl, shd; wc; shwrs; el pts (10A) inc; shop 8km; rest; bar; playgrnd; pool; quiet; adv bkg; CCI. "Gd views, scenic walks; conv heritage fossil site." May-Sep. € 12.90 2003*

CASTELNAU MAGNOAC *8F2* (2km SE Rural) **Camping L'Eglantiere (Naturist), 65330 Aries-Espenan** [05 62 99 83 64 or 05 62 39 88 00; fax 05 62 39 81 44; infos@leglantiere.com; www.leglantiere.com] Fr Castelnau-Magnoac take D929 S sp Lannemezan; in 2.5km L on D9 sp Monleon; in 1km L on unclass rd for 500m; L at T-junc & foll L'Eglantiere sp to site; app fr D632 not rec. Lge, hdg/mkd pitch, pt sl, pt shd; wc; chem disp; mv service pnt; serviced pitch; sauna; shwrs inc; el pts (10A) €4.20 (rev pol); gas; lndtte; ice; shop; tradsmn; rest; snacks; bar; playgrnd; htd pool; paddling pool; rv sw; fishing; canoeing; archery; cycle hire; 15% statics; dogs; adv bkg; Eng spkn; quiet; red low ssn; cc acc; CCI. "Helpful staff; beautiful site on rv; conv Pyrenees; golf courses nrby." ♦ 3 Apr-26 Sep. € 30.00 (CChq acc) 2005*

CASTELNAUD LA CHAPELLE see Sarlat la Caneda *7C3*

CASTELNAUDARY *8F4* (4km E Rural) **Camping La Capelle, 11400 St Papoul** [04 68 94 91 90] Fr N113, take D103E at rndabt to St Martin-Lalande, foll sp to St Papoul & site in 2km. Sm, pt hdg pitch, pt sl, pt shd; wc; chem disp (wc); mv service pnt; shwrs inc; el pts €2; BBQ; shop 5km; tradsmn; playgrnd; no statics; dogs; phone; Eng spkn; quiet; CCI. "Attractive site; helpful owners; v clean facs; 12C abbey at St Papoul; gd walking; ideal NH for Spain; vg sh stay/NH." 1 Apr-30 Sep. € 10.00 2005*

As we're travelling out of season, we'd better phone ahead to check that the site is actually open.

CASTERA VERDUZAN *8E2* (Rural) **Camping La Plage de Verduzan, 32410 Castera-Verduzan** [05 62 68 12 23; fax 05 62 68 18 95; la-plage-de-verduzan@wanadoo.fr] Fr Condom take D930 S twds Auch; site on L after 19km; visible fr rd & sp in vill. Med, hdg pitch, pt shd; wc; chem disp; shwrs inc; el pts (5A) inc; lndtte; shops in vill; snacks; bar; playgrnd; beach; adj lake; archery; cycle hire & tennis nrby; fishing; boat hire; adv bkg; 10% statics; cc acc; CCI. ♦ Easter-29 Sep. € 18.60 2002*

CASTETS *8E1* (1km E Urban) **Camp Municipal de Galan, 73 Rue du Stade, 40260 Castets** [05 58 89 43 52 or 05 58 89 40 09; fax 05 58 55 00 07; campinglegalan@wanadoo.fr] Site sp N & S of town on N10. Lge, pt sl, shd; wc; hot water & shwrs inc; el pts (6A) inc; gas; lndtte; shop high ssn & 1km; tradsmn; playgrnd; paddling pool; tennis; few statics; dogs €1.50; bus; adv bkg; quiet but some rd noise; CCI. " Excel, v clean site in nice vill; extra charge for twin-axle; rv walks." ♦ 1 Feb-30 Nov. € 13.60 2005*

CASTILLON LA BATAILLE *7C2* (400m Urban) **Camp Municipal La Pelouse, 33350 Castillon-la-Bataille** [05 56 40 04 22 or 05 56 40 00 06 (Mairie)] Site in town by Rv Dordogne; sp. Sm, shd; wc; shwrs inc; el pts (15A) inc; shop; rv sw; adv bkg; quiet; CCI. "Conv for wine area; conv St Emillion; clean facs; helpful warden; rec; gd NH." 1 May-30 Sep. € 10.00 2005*

CASTILLONNES *7D3* (N Urban) **Camp Municipal La Ferrette, Route de Bergerac, 47330 Castillonnes** [05 58 36 80 49 (Mairie)] On N21, 27km S of Bergerac, on N side of Castillonnes. Easily seen fr main rd. Med, pt sl, pt shd; wc (cont); el pts (6A) €2.50; shops 300m; playgrnd; tennis adj; quiet. "Beautiful situation; interesting town; beautiful san facs; gd sh stay." ♦ 1 Jul-31 Aug. € 7.00 2003*

FRANCE

CASTRES *8F4* (3km NE Urban) **Camping Gourjade** (formerly Municipal), Ave de Roquecourbe, 81100 Castres [tel/fax 05 63 59 33 51; contact@ campingdegourjade.com; www.campingde gourjade.com] App Castres fr S, after x-ing rv bdge turn NE onto D89 at traff lts sp Rocquecourbe; site after 3.2km at lge wooded traff island. Med, hdg pitch, pt terr, pt shd; wc; chem disp; mv service pnt; shwrs; el pts (6A) inc; gas; lndtte; shop in ssn; rest adj; snacks; bar; BBQ; playgrnd; pool adj; 9 hole golf course adj; cycling; boat fr site to town; 5% statics; dogs €1; bus €1; v quiet; cc acc; CCI. "Castres worth visit; lovely site set in beautiful park; gd, spotless san facs; gd security; helpful staff, extra charge for twin-axle vans; vg cycling; some lower pitches sl & poss soft; poss groups of workers on site low ssn; highly rec." ♦ 31 Mar-31 Oct. € 12.50
2005*

†CASTRIES *10E1* (1.5km NE Rural) **Camping Domaine de Fondspierre, 275 Route de Fontmarie, 34160 Castries [04 67 91 20 03; fax 04 67 16 41 48; pcomtat@free.fr]** Fr A9 exit junc 28 dir Castries onto N110; site 1.5km after vill on L. Med, hdg/mkd pitch, terr, pt shd; wc; chem disp; mv service pnt; baby facs; shwrs inc; el pts (10A) €3; gas 5km; lndtte; shops 1.5km; tradsmn; rest, snacks 1.5km; bar; playgrnd; pool; lake sw 5km; 20% statics; dogs €3; phone; site clsd Jan; Eng spkn; quiet; cc acc; 15% red CCI. "Tennis 50m, golf 2.5km; mountain bike hire nrby; excel touring base." € 19.00
2005*

CAUDECOSTE see Agen *8E3*

CAUNES MINERVOIS *8F4* (Urban) **Camp Municipal du Haut-Minervois, 11160 Caunes-Minervois [04 68 78 00 28 (Mairie)]** In town 200m fr D620 at stadium. Sm, pt shd; wc; shwrs; el pts (4A); shops adj; pool 6km; quiet. "Pleasantly situated."
2003*

CAUREL see Mur de Bretagne *2E3*

CAUSSADE *8E3* (750m NE Urban) **Camp Municipal de la Piboulette, 82300 Caussade [05 63 93 09 07]** S on N20 fr Cahors (40km), turn L off N20 on ent Caussade onto D17 (Rte de Puylaroque). About 750m turn L (sp), site on R in 100m; lge grass stadium. Med, mkd pitch, pt shd; wc (some cont); chem disp; serviced pitches; shwrs inc; el pts (6A) inc; lndtte; shop 500m; tradsmn; playgrnd; pool on far side of stadium; adv bkg; quiet; CCI. "Interesting town; mkt Mon; vg san facs; pleasant warden; conv for Gorges de l'Aveyron; gd sh stay." ♦ 1 May-30 Sep. € 7.30   2004*

†CAUSSADE *8E3* (10km NE Rural) **Camping Le Clos de la Lere, Route de Septfonds, 82240 Cayriech [05 63 31 20 41; le-clos-de-la-lere@ wanadoo.fr; www.camping-leclosdelalere.com]** Take the D17 fr Caussade. Turn R at junc with D103 (sp Cayriech/Septfonds). In Cayriech vill tunr R at T-junc by church, site on R. Foll sp only for Camping Le Clos de la Lere. Sm, hdg/mkd pitch, hdstg, pt shd; htd wc; mv service pnt; baby facs; shwrs inc; el pts (6-10A) €1.80-3.50; gas; lndtte; shop 4km; tradsmn; snacks; playgrnd; pool; few statics; dogs €1; site clsd 20-30 Dec; adv bkg (dep req); quiet; red long stay; CCI. "Excel games facs; helpful staff; excel winter site." ♦ € 11.10   2005*

CAUSSADE *8E3* (11km SW) **Camp Municipal Le Colombier, 82800 Negrepelisse [05 63 64 20 34; fax 05 63 30 38 01]** Fr A20 exit junc 59 dir Negrepelisse. Fr Montauban, take D958 to Negrepelisse, turn L into vill then 1st L after Total/Citroen g'ge, foll sp to site. Site nr prominent water tower in town. Med, mkd pitch, pt shd; wc; shwrs inc; el pts (6A) €2; supmkt 300m; gas; pool adj; playgrnd; quiet. "Pool open school hols - free with 3+ days stay; code operated barrier." 1 Jun-15 Sep. € 8.00   2002*

CAUSSADE *8E3* (10km NW) **Camp Municipal Le Faillal, 82270 Montpezat-de-Quercy [tel/fax 05 63 02 07 08; montpezat-accueil@wanadoo.fr]** N on N20, turn L onto D20, site clearly sp on R in 2km. (Do not take D38 bef D20 fr S). Med, hdg pitch, pt sl, terr, pt shd; wc; chem disp; shwrs inc; el pts (10A) €2.50; lndtte; shops 200m; playgrnd; pool high ssn; few statics; phone; adv bkg; quiet; red CCI. "Old town is a must; pretty site, gd, clean san facs but poss ltd; rec pay night bef departure; gd sh/long stay." ♦ 1 Apr-31 Oct. € 12.00   2004*

†CAUTERETS *8G2* (500m N Urban) **Camping Les Gleres, 19 Route de Pierrefitte, 65110 Cauterets [05 62 92 55 34; fax 05 62 92 03 53; camping-les-gleres@wanadoo.fr; www.gleres. com]** Fr N on N920 ent town; site on R with sharp turn but sp. Med, hdg/mkd pitch, hdstg, pt shd; htd wc; chem disp; mv service pnt nr; some serviced pitches; shwrs inc; el pts (6A) inc; gas; lndtte; rest, snacks, bar, shop, pool 500m; playgrnd; 10% statics; dogs €1.10; phone; site clsd 21 Oct-30 Nov; Eng spkn; quiet; red low ssn; CCI. "Conv town cent; gd walking area with cablecar 500m; recep/gate clsd 1230-1500; excel san facs; municipal m'van site adj." € 17.65   2005*

CAUTERETS *8G2* (1km N) **Camping Le Peguere, 65110 Cauterets [tel/fax 05 62 92 52 91; camping peguere@wanadoo.fr; www.lescampings.com]** Fr Lourdes on N21 foll sp for Cauterets. On app to Cauterets site on R immed after rv bdge, by rd. Med, pt sl, pt shd; wc; shwrs inc; el pts (6A) inc; lndtte; ice; tradsmn; snacks; playgrnd; rv fishing adj; disco; TV rm; dogs €0.75; adv bkg; cc acc; CCI. "Noisy disco; late night arrivals; clean facs; beautiful setting; ideal base for walking in Pyrenees." ♦ 10 Apr-30 Sep. € 12.65   2004*

CAUTERETS *8G2* (1.5km N) **Camping Le Cabaliros, Pont de Secours,** 65110 Cauterets [tel/fax 05 62 92 55 36; chantal.boyrie@wanadoo.fr] App Cauterests fr Argeles, site 1st one on R over bdge. Med, pt sl, pt shd wc; chem disp; shwrs inc; el pts (3A) €2.30; lndtte; ice; shop 500m; snacks adj; pool 1km; fishing; 10% statics; dogs €0.80; poss cr; adv bkg ess; quiet. "Conv Pyrenees National Park; gd walking." ♦ 1 Jun-30 Sep. € 10.00   2003*

CAVAILLON *10E2* (8km E) **Camp Municipal,** 84660 Maubec [04 90 76 50 34; fax 04 90 76 73 14] Heading E on Cavaillon-Apt rd D2 thro vill Robion, 400m end vill sp turn R to Maubec. Site on R in 1km bef old vill. (Avoid any other rte with van). Diff access at ent, steep slope. Sm, terr, pt shd; wc (mainly cont); shwrs inc; shops 1km; el pts (3A) €2.30; lndtte; playgrnd; quiet; secluded; poss cr; 30% statics; CCI. "Awkward site for lge o'fits - otherwise v gd; san facs stretched high ssn; conv A7." 1 Apr-30 Sep. € 14.78   2005*

CAVAILLON *10E2* (10km E Rural) **Camping Les Boudougnes, Les Chenes, Petit-Coustellet,** 84580 Oppede [tel/fax 04 90 76 96 10]   Fr   N180   in Coustellet, take D2 dir Cavaillon. After 1km turn L onto D3 sp Menerbes. Site on L in approx 2km just after hamlet of Petit-Coustellet. Take care, hump at ent to lane leading to site, danger of grounding. Sm, pt shd; wc; shwrs inc; el pts (16A); ice; shop 700m; snacks; playgrnd; adv bkg; CCI. "Pleasant, farm site on edge of Luberon National Park; quiches made to order & fresh fruit fr orchards; old facs; close to lavender museum." 10 Apr-1 Oct. € 5.40   2005*

CAVAILLON *10E2* (1km S) **Camping de la Durance,** 84300 Cavaillon [tel/fax 04 90 71 11 78; camping.cavaille@wanadoo.fr] S of Cavaillon, nr Rv Durance. Fr m'way exit foll sp to town cent. In 200m R immed after x-ing rv. Site sp (Municipal Camping) on L. Lge, pt shd; wc; chem disp; shwrs; el pts (4A) €2.20; shops 1.5km; pool 100m (free to campers); dogs; poss cr; adv bkg; some noise during early am. "NH only; token for pool at recep." 1 Apr-30 Sep. € 13.00   2002*

†CAVAILLON *10E2* (7km W) **Camp Municipal St Andiol,** 13670 St Andiol [tel/fax 04 90 95 01 13] Exit Avignon on N7 to St Andiol, site on R of N7 past vill. Sm, hdg pitch, pt shd; wc; shwrs inc; el pts (6-10A) €3.50-4.50; gas; ice; lndtte; snacks; shop in vill; bar; pool; tennis 1km; golf 15km; dogs €1; some rd noise; CCI. "Gd sh stay." € 13.00   2005*

CAVALAIRE   SUR   MER   *10F4*   (Urban/Coastal) Camping   La   Baie,   Blvd   Pasteur,   83240 Cavalaire-sur-Mer [04 94 64 08 15 or 04 94 64 08 10; campbaie@club-internet.fr;   www.camping-baie. com] Exit A8 sp Ste Maxime/St Tropez & foll D25 & D559 to Cavalaire. Site sp fr seafront. Lge, pt sl, pt shd; wc; baby facs; shwrs inc; el pts (10A) €4; lndtte; ice; shop; rest; snacks; bar; BBQ; playgrnd; pool; sand beach 400m; sailing; watersports; diving 500m; games area; games rm; internet; 10% statics; dogs €3; poss cr; Eng spkn; adv bkg; quiet; red low ssn. ♦ 15 Mar-15 Nov. € 31.00 (3 persons)   2002*

CAVALAIRE   SUR   MER   *10F4*   (1.5km   NE) Camping/Caravaning du Cros de Mouton, 83240 Cavalaire-sur-Mer [04 94 64 10 87 or 04 94 05 46 38; fax 04 94 64 10 87; campingcrosdemouton@ wanadoo.fr; www.crosdemouton.com] Exit A8 dir Maxime to Cavalaire-sur-Mer. Site sp on coast app fr Grimaud/St Tropez & Le Lavandou; diff access. Lge, mkd pitch, terr, mainly shd; wc; chem disp; mv service pnt; 20% serviced pitches; shwrs inc; el pts (10A) €4; gas; ice; lndtte; shop; rest; snacks; bar; playgrnd; htd pool; paddling pool; sand beach 1.5km; TV; dogs €2; phone; quiet; adv bkg (ess Jul/Aug book by Jan; bkg fee & dep req); Eng spkn; red low ssn; cc acc; CCI. "Lge indiv pitch; situated in hills behind town; excel, well-run, popular site - rec adv bkg even low ssn." ♦ 15 Mar-31 Oct. € 21.30 (CChq acc)   2004*

CAVALAIRE SUR MER *10F4* (3km NE Coastal) Selection Camping, 12 Blvd de la Mer, 83420 La Croix-Valmer [04 94 55 10 30; fax 04 94 55 10 39; camping-selection@wanadoo.fr;   www.selection camping.com] Off N559 bet Cavalaire & La Croix-Valmer, 2km past La Croix at rndabt turn R sp Barbigoua, site in 200m. Lge, hdg/mkd pitch, terr, shd; wc; chem disp; mv service pnt; baby facs; shwrs inc; el pts (10A) €5; gas; lndtte; shop; tradsmn; rest; snacks; bar; playgrnd; htd pool; paddling pool; sand beach 400m; games area; entmnt; TV rm; 20% statics (not Jul/Aug) €3.20; phone; bus; poss cr; Eng spkn; adv bkg ess high ssn (dep & bkg fee); quiet. "In excel location; sm pitches." ♦ 15 Mar-15 Sep. € 31.50 (CChq acc)   2005*

CAVALAIRE SUR MER *10F4* (1km W Coastal) Camping La Pinede, Route de Mannes, 83240 Cavalaire-sur-Mer   [04   94   64   11   14;   fax 04 94 64 19 25] Sp on R (N) of N559 on o'skts of Cavalaire to SW. Lge, mkd pitch, shd; wc; shwrs inc; el pts (5A) €3; shop; gas; ice; lndtte; sand beach 500m; playgrnd; poss cr; adv bkg ess; quiet but noisy nr rd; red low ssn. "Cavalaire pleasant, lively resort." ♦ 15 Mar-15 Oct. € 19.00   2003*

CAVALAIRE SUR MER *10F4* (1km W Coastal) Camping La Treille, 83240 Cavalaire-sur-Mer [04   94   64   31   81;   fax   04   94   15   40   64; campingdelatreille@wanadoo.fr] Fr St Tropez foll promenade into Cavalaire to rndabt. Take Toulon/Lavandou exit, 1 way rd. 50m after passing x-rd sp Pompiers Camping Pinede, turn R at next junc; phone box on corner. Site on R in 50m. Lge, mkd pitch, terr, pt shd; wc; chem disp; baby facs; shwrs; el pts (5A) €3.50; gas; lndtte; shop; supmkt; rest; snacks; bar; BBQ (gas only); playgrnd; pool 2km; sand beach 1km; some statics; phone; Eng spkn; adv bkg; poss noisy; red long stay/low ssn; CCI. "Well-run, friendly family site; nr sandy cove & lively town with lots of facs; take metal pegs for awning - ground v hard; vg long stay." ♦ ltd. 15 Mar-15 Oct. € 19.50   2003*

FRANCE

CAVALAIRE SUR MER *10F4* (2km W Coastal) Camping Bonporteau, 83240 Cavalaire-sur-Mer [04 94 64 03 24; fax 04 94 64 18 62; www. homair-vacances.fr] Sp on S side of N559 Cavalaire-Toulon rd, approx 100m on R after rndabt. Lge, sl, terr, shd; wc; shwrs inc; el pts (10A) €4.50; gas; ice; lndtte; shop; supmkt 500m; rest; snacks; bar; playgrnd; htd pool; jacuzzi; sand beach 250m; cycle hire; TV; some statics; dogs €4; adv bkg; red low ssn; quiet. 20 Mar-9 Oct. € 30.00 (3 persons) 2002*

CAYLAR, LE *10E1* (4km SW Rural) Aire Naturelle Mas de Messier, St Felix de l'Heras, 34520 Le Caylar [tel/fax 04 67 44 52 63] Fr N exit A75 junc 49 onto D9 thro Le Caylar. Turn R sp St Felix & foll sp St Felix de l'Haras. At x-rds in St Felix turn R, site 2.5km on L. Sm, hdg pitch, pt sl, pt shd; wc; chem disp; mv service pnt; shwrs; el pts (5A) inc; shop 4km; tradsmn; pool; adv bkg; quiet; Eng spkn; CCI. "Friendly & helpful Dutch owner; many; caves, country towns in area; gd walking; excel views; facs fair; adv bkg ess high ssn." ♦ ltd. 15 Apr-15 Oct. € 10.40 2005*

CAYLUS *8E4* (NE Rural) Camping La Vallee de la Bonnette, 82160 Caylus [tel/fax 05 63 65 70 20] In vill by rv. Med, hdg/mkd pitch, pt shd; wc; chem disp; mv service pnt; baby facs; shwrs inc; el pts (6A) inc; lndtte; ice; shop 1km; tradsmn; snacks; BBQ; playgrnd; pool 1km; rv sw & fishing 500m; games area; entmnts; dogs €1.50; Eng spkn; adv bkg (rec high ssn); quiet; red 7 days; CCI. "Nice, tidy site on edge of medieval vill; v friendly warden; scenic & historic area; gd sh stay." ♦ 1 Mar-31 Oct. € 17.00 2004*

CAYRIECH see Caussade *8E3*

CAZALS see Villefranche du Perigord *7D3*

CAZOULES see Souillac *7C3*

CELLES SUR BELLE see Melle *7A2*

CELLES SUR PLAINE see Raon l'Etape *6E3*

CELLETTES see Blois *4G2*

CENAC ET ST JULIEN see Sarlat la Caneda *7C3*

CENDRAS see Ales *10E1*

CENEVIERES see Cajarc *7D4*

CERET *8H4* (500m E Urban) Camp Municipal Bosquet de Nogarede, Ave d'Espagne, 66400 Ceret [04 68 87 26 72] Exit A9 junc 43 onto D115 twd Ceret, then foll sp Maureillas D618. Site clearly sp 500m fr cent Ceret. Med, mkd pitch, terr, shd; wc; chem disp; shwrs inc; el pts (6A) €2.50; gas 1km; lndtte; shop 1km; rest; snacks; bar 1km; BBQ; playgrnd; htd, covrd pool 800m; sand beach 27km; 10% statics; dogs; phone; poss cr; some rd noise; CCI. "Ceret attractive town with modern art museum; gd san facs; gd NH." ♦ ltd. 1 Apr-30 Oct. € 11.00 2004*

†**CERET** *8H4* (1km E Rural) Camping Les Cerisiers, Mas de la Toure, 66400 Ceret [04 68 87 00 08] Exit A9 junc 43 onto D115, turn off for cent of Ceret. Site is on D618 approx 800m E of Ceret twd Maureillas, sp. Med, mkd pitch, shd; wc; chem disp; baby facs; fam bthrm; shwrs inc; el pts (4A) €2.75; gas; lndtte; ice; shop, rest, snacks, bar 1km; playgrnd; pool 600m; lake sw 2km; sand beach 28km; 99% statics; dogs; phone; site clsd Jan; quiet; CCI. "Site in cherry orchard; footpath to attractive vill; excel modern art gallery; conv Andorra, Perpignan, Collioure." ♦ € 10.10 2004*

CERILLY *4H3* (8km N) Camping des Ecossais, 03360 Isle-et-Bardais [04 70 66 62 57 or 04 70 67 55 89 (LS); fax 04 70 66 63 99] Fr Lurcy-Levis take D978A SW, turn R onto D111 N twd Isle-et-Bardais & foll camp sp. Ent tight. Med, pt sl, pt shd; wc; shwrs inc; el pts (10A) €2.80; lndtte; playgrnd; lrest nr; ake sw; fishing; dogs €0.70; adv bkg; quiet; red low ssn; CCI. "V busy high ssn; ltd facs low ssn; gd cycling; site in oak forest; rec." 1 Apr-30 Sep. € 10.00 2005*

CERILLY *4H3* (11km NW Rural) Camping de Champ Fosse, 03360 St Bonnet-Troncais [04 70 06 11 30; fax 04 70 06 15 01] After 14km on N144 St Amand-Montlucon rd, turn L on D978 sp Foret de Troncais; after 8km foll sp to vill of St Bonnet-Troncais. Med, sl, pt shd; wc (some cont); shwrs inc; el pts (10A) inc; ice; lndry rm; shops 1km; snacks; playgrnd; sand beach; bathing; boat hire; fishing; walking; dogs €0.80; quiet; adv bkg. "Poor supervision; sl, so blocks req; idyllic location; excel walks; sh walk to vill." 1 Apr-30 Sep. € 10.30 2004*

CERNAY *6F3* (5km N Rural) Camping Les Sources, Route des Cretes, 68700 Wattwiller [03 89 75 44 94; fax 03 89 75 71 98; camping.les.sources@ wanadoo.fr; www.camping-les-sources.com] Fr Cernay take D5 NE two Soultz; thro Uffholtz & turn L foll sp to Wattwiller; turn L immed after vill sp & foll camp sp. Park outside bef check-in. Some site rds steep. Lge, mkd pitch, hdstg, terr, pt shd; wc (v steep app to facs - gradient 1:4); chem disp; mv service pnt; serviced pitches; baby facs; shwrs inc; el pts (5A) inc (poss rev pol); gas; lndtte; ice; shop; tradsmn; rest; BBQ (gas/charcoal only); playgrnd; htd, covrd pool; tennis; games rm; games area; badminton; horseriding adj; entmnt; internet; 25% statics; dogs €1.70; recep 0730-1200 & 1300-21.30; barrier pass; Eng spkn; adv bkg ess high ssn (dep req & bkg fee); quiet; cc acc; CCI. "Rest, snacks open all year; v steep wooded app to site; diff getting on & off some pitches; tractor to position o'fits on high pitches; not suitable lge o'fits; on 'wine rte'; cc only acc for balance of bill not dep; barrier clsd 2200; excursions booked at recep; mkt Tue & Fri Cernay." ♦ 9 Apr-30 Sep. € 25.90 (CChq acc) 2004*

CERNAY *6F3* (S Urban) **Camping Les Acacias, 16 Rue Rene Guibert, 68700 Cernay [03 89 75 56 97; fax 03 89 39 72 29; lesacacias.cernay@ffcc.asso.fr]** Fr N on N83 by-pass, exit Cernay Est. Turn R into town at traff lts, immed L bef rv bdge, site sp on L; well sp. Lge, mkd pitch, pt shd; wc; shwrs inc; el pts (5A) €3.20 (poss rev pol); lndtte; shop, rest, bar & pool adj; entmnt; 25% statics; dogs €0.95; poss cr; quiet; red long stay; 10% red CCI (pitch only). "Friendly staff; storks nesting over some pitches; site clean, tidy; new san facs 2004; €20 dep barrier key; sh walk to town." ♦ 1 Apr-10 Oct. € 10.70   2005*

CERNAY *6F3* (6km S Rural) **Camping Les Castors, 4 Route de Guewenheim, 68520 Burnhaupt-le-Haut [03 89 48 78 58; fax 03 89 62 74 68; camping.les.castors@wanadoo.fr]** Exit A36 junc 15 sp Burnhaupt-le-Haut onto N83, then D466 sp Masevaux. Site on R. Med, mkd pitch, pt shd; htd wc; chem disp; baby facs; shwrs inc; el pts (5A) inc; gas; lndtte; ice; tradsmn; rest; bar; BBQ; playgrnd; games rm; 40% statics; dogs €1.20; phone; poss cr; Eng spkn; adv bkg; quiet; CCI. "Conv German & Swiss borders, Black Forest; wine route; Mulhouse motor museum; vg sh stay/NH." ♦ 14 Feb-31 Dec. € 13.90   2003*

CESSERAS see Olonzac *8F4*

CEYRAT see Clermont Ferrand *9B1*

CEYZERIAT see Bourg en Bresse *9A2*

CHABANAIS see Rochechouart *7B3*

CHABEUIL see Valence *9C2*

CHABLIS *4F4* (Urban) **Camp Municipal Le Serein, 89800 Chablis [03 86 42 44 39; fax 03 86 42 49 71; ot-chablis@chablis.net]** On D965 Tonerre-Chablis turn L at camping sp bef x-ing rv. Fr a'route A6 thro Chablis & turn R after x-ing 2nd rv. Site in 300m. Med, hdg/mkd pitch, shd; wc (some cont); el pts (3-5A) inc; gas, shops, rest, snacks 1km; rv adj; poss cr; Eng spkn; adv bkg; quiet; CCI. "Vineyards & cellars nrby; facs stretched high ssn; vg sh stay." ♦ ltd. 1 Jun-30 Sep. € 10.00   2004*

CHAGNY *6H1* (W) **Camp Municipal du Paquier Fane, Rue du Paquier Fane, 71150 Chagny [03 85 87 21 42]** Clearly sp in town. Med, hdg pitch, pt shd; wc; chem disp; shwrs; el pts (6A) €3.60 (rev pol); gas; lndtte; shop; snacks; playgrnd; pool adj; fishing; tennis; dogs €1; adv bkg (ess Jul/Aug); quiet except rlwy noise adj. "Well laid-out site; poss neglected san facs; gd night lighting; on wine rte; somewhat dictatorial management." ♦ 15 Apr-31 Oct. € 11.40   2005*

CHAGNY *6H1* (6km W) **Camping des Sources, Ave des Sources, 21590 Santenay [03 80 20 66 55; fax 03 80 20 67 36; dessources.santenay@wanadoo.fr; www.campingsantenay.com]** Site sp fr N6 & at N74 junc, foll sp adverts for Santenay Casino & campsite. Do not drive into Chagny. Med, mkd pitch, pt shd; wc; chem disp; mv service pnt; shwrs inc; el pts (6A) €3.50 (poss rev pol; long lead poss req); gas; lndtte; shop & 1km; rest; snacks; bar; playgrnd; htd pool adj; tennis adj; 60% statics; dogs €1.30; phone; Eng spkn; adv bkg; cc acc; CCI. "Vill surrounded by vineyards; lovely walks; no twin-axles; tour ops on site; v clean facs; gates clsd 2200-0730; recep clsd 1100-1400; v helpful owner." ♦ 15 Apr-31 Oct. € 15.50 (CChq acc)   2005*

†CHAILLAC *7A3* (SW Rural) **Camp Municipal Les Vieux Chenes, 36310 Chaillac [02 54 25 61 39; fax 02 54 25 65 41]** Exit N20 S of Argenton-sur-Creuse at junc 20 onto D36 to Chaillac. Thro vill, site 1st L after sq by 'Mairie.' Sm, hdg/mkd pitch, pt sl, pt shd; wc (some cont); chem disp; shwrs inc; el pts (6-16A) €2.50-2.70; lndry rm; BBQ; playgrnd; lake sw adj; waterslide; tennis adj; 35% statics; dogs; phone adj; poss cr; adv bkg; quiet; CCI. "Well-maintained site; beautiful setting with lakes; v clean facs; friendly warden on site; rest within walking dist; conv fr a'route; ideal base for exploring Creuse valley; excel walks. " ♦ € 6.00   2005*

CHAILLES see Blois *4G2*

CHAISE DIEU, LA *9C1* (2km N Rural) **Camp Municipal Les Prades, 43160 La Chaise-Dieu [04 71 00 07 88]** Site well sp. Med, pt sl, shd; wc (some cont); chem disp; shwrs inc; el pts (10A) €2.90; lndtte; shops 2km; playgrnd; lake sw 300m; 10% statics; quiet. "Fair sh stay/NH; tourist info office in vill; 14thC church; vg for mushrooms in ssn!" 1 Jun-30 Sep. € 9.00   2002*

CHALANDRAY *4H1* (Rural) **Camping du Bois de St Hilaire, Rue de la Gare, 86190 Chalandray [tel/fax 05 49 60 20 84 or 01773 873068 (UK); acceuil@camping-st-hilaire.com; www.camping-st-hilaire.com]** Foll N149 bet Parthenay & Vouille; upon ent to Chalandray vill, turn before Spar shop; site 750m on R over rlwy line. Sm, mkd pitch, pt shd; wc; chem disp; shwrs inc; el pts (10A) €3.10; lndtte; ice; shop; rest, snacks, bar in vill; BBQ; playgrnd; pool; tennis; mini-golf; games rm; TV rm; dogs; bus 750m; c'van storage; Eng spkn; adv bkg (25% dep req); cc acc; quiet; CCI. "Friendly, helpful British owners; situated in mature forest area, sh walk fr vill; 20 mins fr Futuroscope; lge pitches; excel, clean site & pool." ♦ 16 Apr-20 Sep. € 14.50   2005*

CHALARD, LE see St Yrieix la Perche *7B3*

FRANCE

†CHALLANS *2H4* (3km S Rural) **Camping Le Ragis, Chemin de la Fradiniere, 85300 Challans.** [tel/fax 02 51 68 08 49; leragis@free.fr]
Fr Challans go S on D32 Rte Les Sables, turn R onto Chemin de la Fradiniere & foll sp. Med, hdg/mkd pitch, pt sl, pt shd; wc; chem disp (wc); shwrs inc; el pts (6A) €3; gas; lndtte; shop; tradsmn, rest, snacks high ssn; bar 3km; playgrnd; pool (caps ess); sand beach 12km; mini-golf; games area; entmnt; TV; 60% statics; dogs €1.50; phone; Eng spkn; adv bkg (dep req); quiet. "Vg long/sh stay." ♦ ltd. € 15.00   2002*

CHALLES LES EAUX see Chambery *9B3*

†CHALON SUR SAONE *6H1* (2km E Urban) **Camp Municipal La Butte, Rue Leneveu, 71380 St Marcel-les-Chavannes** [03 85 48 26 86 or 03 85 48 38 86]
Fr A6 exit Chalon-sur-Saone. SE bank of rv nr town cent, then cross rv by masonry bdge (nr sw pool) & take 1st turn to N (L); foll sp for Lons-le-Saunier or Roserai St Nicholas when ent town. Site sp on L. Med, hdg/mkd pitch, terr, pt shd; wc; chem disp; shwrs inc; el pts (6-10A) €4.75; gas; lndry rm; shop; rest; snacks; bar; playgrnd; pool 500m; rv fishing; tennis; TV; 20% statics; noisy; CCI. "Facs dated; generally a bit scruffy; rv walks; v lge pitches & some by rv; poss itinerants." € 6.00   2004*

CHALON SUR SAONE *6H1* (12km SE Rural) **Mini Camping aux Tantes, 29 Route de Gigny, 71240 Marnay** [03 85 44 23 88] On D978 SE fr Chalon-sur-Saone, turn R in vill of Ouroux-sur-Saone onto D6 twd Marnay. Over bdge, foll site sp. Sm, hdg pitch, shd; wc; chem disp; el pts; lndtte; tradsmn; BBQ; sm playgrnd; 50% statics; dogs; phone; quiet.
♦ 1 May-31 Oct. € 10.00   2003*

CHALONNES SUR LOIRE *2G4* (1km E) **Escapades Terre Oceane Camping Le Candais, Route de Rochefort, 49290 Chalonnes-sur-Loire** [02 41 78 02 27 or 05 46 55 10 01; fax 02 41 78 02 27; info@campingterreoceane.com; www.campingterreoceane.com]
Turn E in Chalonnes to D751. Site on L in 1km on S bank of Loire. Lge, mkd pitch, pt shd; wc; shwrs inc; mv service pnt; el pts (5A) inc; gas; lndtte; ice; shop 1km; snacks; bar; playgrnd; pool; fishing; entmnt; statics; dogs; Eng spkn; adv bkg; quiet; CCI. "Peaceful site in beautiful location; liable to flooding; lge pitches; gd touring base." ♦ 17 Jun-16 Sep.
€ 12.00   2005*

CHALONNES SUR LOIRE *2G4* (8km SE Rural) **Camp Municipal, 49290 Chaudefonds-sur-Layon** [02 41 78 04 10 (Mairie); fax 02 41 78 66 89]
Fr Chalonnes on D961 S dir Cholet. Turn L onto D125. At narr rlwy bdge after 3km, foll sp to site. Sm, pt shd; wc; shwrs €1; el pts €1.50; shop; quiet. "V basic, clean site nr rv; lots of interest in area; vg sh stay." € 5.50   2003*

CHALONNES SUR LOIRE *2G4* (9km SE Urban) **Camp Municipal du Layon, 49190 St Aubin-de-Luigne** [02 41 78 33 28; fax 02 41 78 68 55]
Exit N160 Angers-Chemille at sp St Aubin or turn S off D751 at sp St Aubin. Site sp in vill. Sm, hdg/mkd pitch, pt shd; wc; shwrs; el pts €2.10; shop 150m; playgrnd; quiet. "Gd walking/wine-tasting area." ♦ 1 May-30 Oct. € 7.55   2003*

CHALONNES SUR LOIRE *2G4* (9km NW) **Camping La Promenade, Quai des Mariniers, 49570 Montjean-sur-Loire** [02 41 39 02 68; fax 02 40 83 16 19; efberthelot@wanadoo.fr]
Exit Angers on N23 twd Nantes. Exit 1km beyond St Germain-des-Pres dir Montjean-sur-Loire. Cross rv then R on D210 to site in 500m. Med, pt shd; wc (some cont); shwrs inc; el pts (6-9A) €2; gas 5km; lndtte; shops adj; rest; snacks; BBQ; playgrnd; pool; sand beach 600m; entmnt; TV; 30% statics; dogs; Eng spkn; adv bkg; quiet; CCI. "Friendly, new, young owners (2004); interesting sculptures in vill & at Ecomusee." 26 Mar-13 Oct. € 11.60   2005*

CHALONS EN CHAMPAGNE *5D1* (3km S Urban) **Camp Municipal, Rue de Plaisance, 51000 Chalons-en-Champagne** [tel/fax 03 26 68 38 00; camping.mairie.chalons@wanadoo.fr]
Fr N on A26 exit junc 17 take D3 to Chalons, site sp. Fr S exit junc 18 onto D5 & foll sp. Fr N44 S of Chalons sp St Memmie; foll site sp. D977 fr N into Chalons, cont on main rd to traff lts at 6 x-rds & turn R, site well sp. Or exit A4 junc 27 onto N44; turn R at St Memmie; site sp. NB some sps in area still show old town name 'Chalons-sur-Marne'. Med, hdg/mkd pitch, some hdstg (pebbled), pt shd; htd wc; chem disp; mv service pnt; shwrs inc; el pts (10A) €3 (poss long lead req) gas; lndtte; ice; shop 100m; hypmkt 1km; tradsmn; rest high ssn; snacks; bar; BBQ; playgrnd; pool 2km; sm lake; TV rm; dogs; bus; poss cr; little Eng spkn; adv bkg; quiet but poss noisy high ssn; cc acc; CCI. "Generous pitches; helpful & efficient management; clean & tidy; gd facs; c'van cleaning area; v popular site; rec phone ahead; 4.30m height limit at bdge on app to site; recep clsd 1200-1315; gates shut 2130 low ssn & 2300 high ssn; interesting town; excel." ♦ 1 Apr-31 Oct. € 16.90   2005*

CHALUS *7B3* (12km S Rural) **Camping Le Perigord Vert, Fardoux, 24450 La Coquille** [05 53 52 85 77; fax 05 53 55 14 25; denyse michel@aol.com; www.aubergeetfermeauberge.com] On N21 Perigueux/Chalus rd bet Thiviers & Chalus, turn L in vill of La Coquille at traff lts foll sps for Mialet. In 1.5km turn R, site 500m on L; sp. Sm, pt shd, pt sl; wc; chem disp (wc); shwrs inc; el pts (6A) €1.90; gas; lndtte; shops 2km; tradsmn; rest, snacks, bar high ssn; playgrnd; pool high ssn; free fishing; tennis; 5% statics; dogs; phone; poss cr; Eng spkn; adv bkg; quiet; red low ssn; CCI. "Nice, clean, happy site; ltd facs low ssn; helpful staff; choice of meadow or woodland pitch; gd long/sh stay." ♦ Easter-1 Nov. € 9.00   2004*

CHAMBERET see Treignac *7B4*

CHAMBERY *9B3* (5km E Urban) **Camp Municipal Le Savoy, Chemin des Fleurs, 73190 Challes-les-Eaux [04 79 72 97 31]** On o'skts of town app fr Chambery on N6. Pass airfield, lake & tennis courts on L, L at traff lts just before cent of Challes-les Eaux sp Parc de Loisirs, at Les Neiges de France hotel foll camp sp to site in 100m. Fr A41 exit junc 20, foll sp Challes-les-Eaux, then Centre Ville, then N6 N. Med, mkd pitch, shd; wc; chem disp; serviced pitches; shwrs; el pts (6-10A) inc; gas; lndtte; lndry rm; ice; shop, rest adj; snacks in ssn; lake sw adj; tennis adj; quiet but some rd noise; cc acc; adv bkg. "Well-run site; beautiful setting; clean; friendly staff; excel walking." 1 May-30 Sep. € 13.00
2005*

CHAMBERY *9B3* (10km SW Rural) **Camping Les Peupliers, Lac d'Aiguebelette, 73610 Lepin-le-Lac [04 79 36 00 48; fax 04 79 44 12 48; info@camping-lespeupliers.net; www.camping-les peupliers.net]** Exit A43 junc 12 & foll sp Lac d'Aiguebelette (D921). Turn L at rndabt & foll rd on L of lake. Site on R after sm vill. Lge, hdg/mkd pitch, pt shd; wc; chem disp; shwrs inc; el pts (6A) €3.10; shop 2km; tradsmn; rest; lake sw adj; fishing; poss cr; quiet; cc acc; CCI. "Friendly, helpful owner; beautiful setting; gd long stay." 1 Apr-31 Oct.
€ 10.80
2004*

CHAMBERY *9B3* (11km SW Rural) **Camping Le Curtelet, 73610 Lepin-le-Lac [tel/fax 04 79 44 11 22; lecurtelet@wanadoo.fr]** Fr A43 E to Chambery exit junc 12 onto D921 bef Tunnel L'Epine sp Lac d'Aiguebelette. Foll rd round lake, turn L on D921D to Lepin-le-Lac. Site sp after stn on L over level x-ing. Med, mkd pitch, pt sl, pt shd; wc; chem disp; baby facs; shwrs inc; el pts (2-6A) €2.15-2.75; lndtte; ice; shop 1km; tradsmn; bar; BBQ; playgrnd; lake sw; sand beach adj; dogs €1.20; Eng spkn; adv bkg; some rlwy noise; red low ssn; CCI. "Beautiful scenery; well-maintained site; poss some rlwy noise at top of site; excel long stay."
15 May-30 Sep. € 10.70
2005*

CHAMBERY *9B3* (12km W Rural) **Camping Le Sougey, 73610 St Alban-de-Montbel [04 79 36 01 44; fax 04 79 44 19 01; info@camping-sougey.com; www.camping-sougey.com]** Fr A43 E to Chambery take D921 sp Lac d'Aiguebelette. On W side of lake 3km to site on L. Med, hdg/mkd pitch, some hdstg, pt sl, pt shd; wc; chem disp; 30% serviced pitches; baby facs; shwrs inc; el pts (6A) inc; gas; lndtte; ice; shop; rest; snacks; bar; playgrnd; tennis; horseriding; cycle hire; mini-golf; archery; lake sw & fishing adj; TV; entmnts; 20% statics; dogs €1.50; Eng spkn; adv bkg rec high ssn; quiet; red low ssn; cc acc. "Attractive area; spacious site; helpful staff."
♦ 1 May-15 Sep. € 17.40
2002*

CHAMBON SUR LIGNON, LE see Tence *9C2*

CHAMONIX MONT BLANC *9B4* (2km NE Rural) **Camping Les Rosieres, 74400 Chamonix [04 50 53 10 42 or 06 07 44 79 95 (mob); fax 04 50 53 29 55; info@campinglesrosieres.com; www.campinglesrosieres.com]** Fr W on N205 past Mt Blanc tunnel & Chamonix, L 300m bef boundary sp 'Les Praz de Chamonix'. Foll sp Les Rosieres. Fr N by N506 turn R 300m after boundary sp to Les Rosieres. Thro vill, 1st L after garden cent. Med, pt shd; htd wc (some cont); baby facs; shwrs inc; el pts (4-10A) €2.90-3.30; gas; lndtte; ice; sm shop adj; supmkt 1.5km; snacks; bar; htd pool 2km; cable cars, rlwy, sports cent nr; some statics; bus fr ent; phone adj; poss cr; Eng spkn; adv bkg; red low ssn; CCI. "Clean but dated san facs; gd location with rvside path to town; superb views; all attractions within walking dist; phone ahead to check if open low ssn; excel long stay." ♦
27 May-18 Sep. € 18.20
2005*

CHAMONIX MONT BLANC *9B4* (3km NE) **Camping La Mer de Glace, Praz de Chamonix, 74400 Chamonix [04 50 53 08 63 or 04 5 53 44 03; fax 04 50 53 60 83; www.chamonix-camping. com]** Foll sp thro Chamonix to Argentiere & Swiss Frontier. Site well sp on R in 3km. Ent under bdge 2.6m. To avoid low bdge cont to rndabt Praz de Chamonix, R over rlwy; strt 400m. Lge, pt shd; htd wc (some cont); chem disp; shwrs inc; el pts (3-10A) inc; lndtte; shops, bar, snacks 2km; tradsmn; pool 3km in Chamonix; dogs; poss cr; Eng spkn; quiet but helicopter noise; CCI. "Superb views; vg facs; helpful warden; excel." 7 Jun-15 Sep. € 22.00
2003*

CHAMONIX MONT BLANC *9B4* (3.5km NE Rural) **Camping Les Drus, Les Bois, 74400 Les Praz-de-Chamonix [04 50 53 49 20 or 04 50 53 16 59 (LS)]** NE foll by-pass & sps for Argentiere & N Suisse. App vill of Les Praz at x-rds turn R foll sps. SW fr Argentiere foll sps for Chamonix. Camp sp at Les Tines vill, level x-ing. Med, unshd; htd wc; shwrs inc; el pts (3-5A) €2.20-2.70; gas; ice; shop; pool 3km; Eng spkn; quiet. "Beautiful surroundings; great views; poss cr in ssn with pressure on facs; friendly welcome; helpful owners; gd walking; unreliable opening dates, phone ahead low ssn; gd value; great for families." 27 May-18 Sep. € 10.80
2005*

CHAMONIX MONT BLANC *9B4* (7km NE Rural) **Camping Le Glacier d'Argentieres, Les Chosalets, 74400 Chamonix [04 50 54 17 36; fax 04 50 54 03 73]** On Chamonix-Argentiere rd bef Argentiere take R fork twd Argentiere Cable Car Stn. Site immed on R. Med, pt sl, pt shd; wc; chem disp; shwrs inc; el pts (2-6A) €2.40-3.60; lndtte; ice; shops 1km; tradsmn; BBQ; dogs; phone adj; poss cr; adv bkg; quiet; CCI. "Alpine excursions; cable cars adj; v beautiful area, mountain views; friendly, helpful owners." ♦ 14 May-30 Sep. € 14.00
2005*

FRANCE

CHAMONIX MONT BLANC *9B4* (1km SW) **Camping Iles des Barrats**, 185 Chemin de l'Ile, 74400 Chamonix [tel/fax 04 50 53 51 44] Fr Mont Blanc tunnel take 1st L on app Chamonix, foll sp to hospital, site opp hospital. Do not go into town. Sm, mkd pitch, pt sl, unshd; wc; chem disp; mv service pnt; shwrs inc; el pts (5-10A) €3-4.20; gas; lndtte; shops 1km; sw 250m; dogs €1; poss cr; Eng spkn; adv bkg (dep req); quiet; CCI. "Great little site; clean facs; friendly, family owners; 10 mins level walk to town; 10 mins cable car Mont Blanc; lovely mountain views."
8 May-29 Sep. € 18.70   2004*

CHAMONIX MONT BLANC *9B4* (2km SW) **Camping Les Marmottes**, Chemin des Deux, Les Bossons, 74400 Chamonix [04 50 53 61 24] On N205 4km SW of Chamonix turn N off dual c'way sp Les Bossons & Campings. Site after narr rlwy bdge turn R. Care needed under narr rlwy tunnel. Gradient at junc with main rd fr side rd diff. Sm, unshd (trees planted); wc; shwrs; el pts inc (6A) inc; lndtte; shop; adv bkg; quiet, but some train noise. ♦ 15 Jun-Sep. € 14.50   2002*

CHAMONIX MONT BLANC *9B4* (3km SW Rural) Camping Les Ecureuils, Rue Chemin des Deux, Les Bossons, 74400 Chamonix [tel/fax 04 50 53 83 11; roghis@wanadoo.fr] Fr St Gervais on N205 twd Chamonix. L fork to vill. L at x-rd. Under rlwy, sharp R. Site at end of rd. Sm, pt shd, mkd pitch, hdstg; wc; shwrs inc; el pts (6A) inc; lndtte; shop 3km tradsmn; poss cr; quiet; adv bkg; cc acc; CCI. "Warm welcome; many old c'vans on site; vg."
1 Apr-30 Sep. € 13.90   2004*

†**CHAMONIX MONT BLANC** *9B4* (3.5km SW Rural) Camping Les Deux Glaciers, 80 Route des Tissieres, Les Bossons, 74400 Chamonix [04 50 53 15 84; fax 04 50 55 90 81; glaciers@ clubinternet.fr] Exit Mont Blanc tunnel foll sps Geneva turn L on N506 (Chamonix-Geneva rd), in 2km turn R for Les Bossons & L under bdge. Fr W foll sps Chamonix & Mont Blanc tunnel. On dual c'way turn R at sp 'Les Bossons' & site after Novotel; adj Les Cimes site; site clearly sp from N205. Med, terr, pt shd; htd wc; chem disp; shwrs inc; el pts (2-10A) €2.40-6.70; shop; lndry rm; rest; snacks; bar; sm shop; tradsmn; playgrnd; pool 4km; Eng spkn; quiet but some rd noise; site clsd 15/11- 15/12; CCI. "Diff site for lge o'fits over 6m; old but v clean facs; pleasant site just under Mont Blanc; funicular adj to Mer de Glace; rec arr under early high ssn; gd long stay." ♦ € 12.70   2005*

CHAMONIX MONT BLANC *9B4* (3.5km SW) **Les Cimes Camping**, Route du Treplin Olympique, Les Bossons, 74400 Chamonix [04 50 53 19 00 or 04 50 53 58 93; infos@campinglescimesmont blanc.com] Exit Mont Blanc tunnel foll sps Geneva turn L on N506 (Chamonix-Geneva rd), in 2km turn R for Les Bossons & L under bdge. Fr Sallanches foll sps Chamonix & Mont Blanc tunnel. On dual c'way turn R at sp 'Les Bossons' & site after Novotel adj to Les Deux Glaciers site. Med, pt sl, pt shd; wc (cont); shwrs inc; el pts (3A) €2.50; lndtte; shop 4km; tradsmn; rest 500m; snacks; BBQ; playgrnd; dogs; poss cr; adv bkg; rd noise; CCI. "Fair site; rec sh stay; poss diff lge o'fits." 1 Jun-30 Sep. € 13.80
                                                        2005*

CHAMOUILLE *3C4* (Rural) **Camping de l'Ailette**, 02860 Chamouille [03 23 24 66 86 or 03 23 24 83 03; fax 03 23 24 66 87; ailette@wanadoo.fr; http:// perso.wanadoo.fr/ailette] Fr Laon take D967 S to Fismes (avoid R turn onto D967 fr N2, low bdge). Foll sp Parc Nautique de l'Ailette. In 13km at Chamouille turn L onto D967E. Site sp on R in 2km. Lge, hdg/mkd pitch, some hdstg, pt sl, pt terr, pt shd; wc; chem disp; shwrs inc; el pts (10A) €3.50; gas; lndtte; rest & snacks adj; bar; playgrnd; sand beach & lake adj; 30% statics; dogs €2.50; poss cr; Eng spkn; adv bkg (dep req + bkg fee); cc acc; red long stay; CCI. "Ideal for families; many activities in adj leisure park on lakeside (high ssn); gd walking."
♦ ltd. 1 Apr-30 Sep. € 15.00   2005*

CHAMPAGNAC LES MINES see Bort les Orgues *7C4*

CHAMPAGNAT (SAONE ET LOIRE) see Cuiseaux *9A2*

CHAMPAGNE SUR LOUE see Mouchard *6H2*

CHAMPAGNOLE *6H2* (1km NW Urban) **Camp Municipal de Boyse**, Rue Georges Vallerey, 39300 Champagnole [03 84 52 00 32; fax 03 84 52 01 16; boyse@free.fr] Turn W onto D5, N of town off main rd to Dijon (N5). Look for sp. Site adj to sw pool. Lge, mkd pitch, pt sl, pt shd; wc (cont); chem disp; shwrs inc; el pts (5A) inc; lndtte; shops 5km; tradsmn; rest; snacks; bar; sw pools adj; dogs; quiet; adv bkg; phone; free hot water; early arrival rec; barrier card €23; no admissions 1200-1400; cc acc; CCI. "Friendly warden; poss ltd facs low ssn; vg rest; vg long/sh stay." ♦
1 Jun-30 Sep. € 15.80   2004*

†**CHAMPDOR** *9A3* **Camp Municipal Le Vieux Moulin**, 01110 Champdor [04 74 36 01 72 or 04 74 36 01 79] Exit junc 8 on A404 & foll sp for St-Martin-du-Frene. At ent to St-Martin-du-Frene turn R onto D31 sp Brenod. After 10km turn R onto D21. Site 7km on R on o'skts of Champdor. Med, mkd pitch, some hdstg, unshd; wc; chem disp; mv service pnt; shwrs; €0.90; el pts (4-16A) €1.50; gas; lndry rm; shop, snacks, bar 1km; playgrnd; rv sw & fishing nrby; 20% statics; phone; quiet; CCI. "Gd sh stay; modern san facs; gd walks adj; height restricted - 5m." € 8.70   2004*

CHAMPFROMIER *9A3* (Rural) **Camp Municipal Les Georennes**, 01410 Champfromier [04 50 56 92 40 (Marie); fax 04 50 56 96 05; marire. champfromier@wanadoo.fr] Fr Bellegarde foll N84 twds Nantua. In 8km turn sharp R onto D14 sp Pont des Pierres/Mont Rond. Site sp R on ent vill of Champfromier. Sm, terr, pt shd; wc; shwrs; el pts (16A) €2; shop 500m; playgrnd; fishing; quiet; CCI. "Gd walking & scenery; vg." ♦ 1 Jun-15 Sep. £11.00
                                                        2004*

CHAMPIGNY SUR MARNE see Paris *3D3*

CHAMPS ROMAIN see Nontron *7B3*

CHANCEAUX *6G1* (12km SE) **Camp Municipal,** 21440 St Seine-l'Abbaye [03 80 35 01 64 or 03 80 35 00 09] On N71 in vill of St Seine-l'Abbaye, turn N onto D16. Turn R uphill, sp camping & turn R thro gateway in high stone wall. Narr streets in vill. Or fr N on N74, avoiding Dijon, turn R onto D959 at Til-Chatel, then D6 & D901 Moloy/Lamargelle. Turn L in Lamargelle onto D16 St Seine L'Abbaye. Turn L uphill at edge of vill & as above (avoids narr streets). Sm, pt sl, unshd; wc (cont); chem disp; shwrs inc; el pts (10A) inc (rev pol); shops 500m; pool 4km; rv 500m; v quiet; CCI. "Vg sh stay/NH; very pleasantly situated site; conv for Dijon or as NH; fees collected at 2000 hrs; basic but immac clean facs; poss itinerants." 1 May-1 Oct. € 7.65   2002*

CHANCEAUX *6G1* (NW Urban) **Camp Municipal,** 21440 Chanceaux [03 80 35 02 80 or 03 80 35 02 66 (Mairie)] Heading SE fr Troyes twd Dijon site on L on N71 on NW o'skts of Chanceaux. Sm, pt shd; wc (some cont); chem disp (wc); shwrs €0.76; el pts (4-5A) €1.52; shop nr; BBQ; quiet tho some rd noise; cc acc; CCI. "Site yourself - warden calls pm; poss itinerants; no security; vg sh stay/NH." 15 Apr-30 Sep. € 6.10   2002*

CHANTEMERLE LES BLES see Tain l'Hermitage *9C2*

CHANTILLAC see Montlieu la Garde *7C2*

†**CHANTILLY** *3D3* **Camping L'Abbatiale,** 60340 St Leu-d'Esserent [tel/fax 03 44 56 38 76] S twds Paris on A1 exit Senlis; cont W fr Senlis on D44 thro Chantilly x-ing Rv Oise to St Leu-d'Esserent; leave town on D12 NW to Cramoisy; foll site sps; avoid rv x-ing on D17 fr SW; v narr bdge. Lge, pt shd; wc; shwrs €1; el pts (3A) €1.60; lndry rm; shop; playgrnd. "Chantilly & chateau interesting. € 10.20   2004*

CHANTILLY *3D3* (5km NW Rural) **Camping Campix,** 60340 St Leu d'Esserent [03 44 56 08 48; fax 03 44 56 28 75; campixfr@aol.com; www.campingcampix.com] S twds Paris on A1 exit Senlis; cont W fr Senlis on D44 thro Chantilly, x-ing Rv Oise to St Leu-d'Esserent; leave town on D12 NW twd Cramoisy thro housing est; foll site sp for 1km. Med, mkd pitch, hdstg, terr, shd; htd wc; chem disp; mv service pnt; baby facs; shwrs inc; el pts (6A) €3.50 (min 25m cable poss req); gas; lndtte; tradsmn; rest & shops 500m; snacks; bar; BBQ; playgrnd; pool complex; sand beach & lake sw 1km; fishing; games rm; some statics; dogs €2; phone; Eng spkn; adv bkg (25% dep); quiet; red long stay/low ssn; cc acc; CCI. "Helpful owner & friendly staff; easy access to Paris; conv Parc Asterix & Disneyland (Asterix tickets fr recep); poss diff use of mv service pnt facs for lge vans; site in former quarry; excel san facs; wide variety of pitches; some pitches narr access & overhanging trees; excel site; highly rec." ♦ 7 Mar-30 Nov. € 15.00   2005*

See advertisement

CHANTONNAY *2H4* (4km S) **Camping Les Asphodeles, Le Moulin Neuf,** 85110 Chantonnay [02 51 94 30 27 or 02 51 94 46 51 (Mairie); fax 02 51 94 57 76] Sp as 'Le Moulin Neuf' on N137. App rd winding & narr. Sm, terr, pt shd; wc (cont); shwrs inc; el pts inc; shop 4km; tradsmn; snacks; pool; lake sw; tennis; quiet. "Logis Hotel adj; excel value; not rec low ssn if site empty - v isolated; vg sh stay." 1 Jun-30 Sep. € 12.20   2002*

CHANTONNAY *2H4* (7km NW Rural) **Camping-Residence La Riviere, Rue du Stade,** 85110 Ste Cecile [06 86 67 39 51 or 02 51 40 24 07; fax 02 51 40 25 59] Fr Chantonnay NW on N137; in St Vincent-Sterlanges turn onto D39 to Ste Cecile (2.5km); site sp clearly fr main rd. Sm, hdg/mkd pitch, pt shd; wc; shwrs inc; el pts (6A) €2.30; ice; lndtte; playgrnd; rv fishing adj; tennis; adv bkg rec high ssn; quiet. "V clean; excel facs but stretched if site full; warden calls am & pm; no twin-axles; barrier clsd after 2000 but phone no. to call; vg long/sh stay." 1 Jun-15 Sep. € 7.00   2002*

CHAPELLE AUX FILTZMEENS, LA see Combourg *2E4*

FRANCE

CHAPELLE D'ANGILLON, LA *4G3* (1 km SE) Camp Municipal Les Murailles, Route d'Henrichemont, 18380 La Chapelle-d'Angillon [02 48 73 40 12 (Mairie); fax 02 48 73 48 67] Fr Bourges or Aubigny-sur-Nere on D940, turn onto D12 in vill, site on R, sp. Sm, pt sl, pt shd; wc (some cont); chem disp (wc); shwrs inc; el pts (6A) €3; shop 1km; BBQ; fishing in lake adj; some statics; quiet. "Excel san facs; huge castle overlooking lake; vg." 1 Jun-15 Sep. € 6.65   2005*

CHAPELLE EN VERCORS, LA *9C3* (1km Rural) Camp Municipal Les Bruyeres, Ave Bruyeres, 26420 La Chapelle-en-Vercors [04 75 48 20 12; fax 04 78 48 10 44] Take D518 N fr Die over Col de Rousset. Fr N on A49 exit 8 to N532 St Nazaire-en-Royans, then D76 thro St Thomas-en-Royans, then D216 to St Laurent-en-Royans. Take D2 round E flank of Combe Laval (2 short 2-lane tunnels). Fr Col de la Machine foll D76 S 1km, then D199 E over Col de Carri to La Chapelle. (D531 fr Villard de Lons, D76 over Combe Laval & D518 Grandes Goulet not suitable for c'vans & diff lge m'vans, narr rds & tunnels in 5km of overhanging ledges.) Med, pt sl, pt shd; wc; chem disp; shwrs inc; el pts; lndtte; shops adj; rest, snacks, bar 200m; playgrnd; pool 2km; fishing; climbing; horseriding; cycling; TV; adv bkg; quiet; CCI. "Excel base for beautiful Vercors plateau." ♦ 1 May-1 Oct. € 12.00
2004*

CHAPELLE EN VERCORS, LA *9C3* (6.5km N Rural) **Camping La Porte St Martin**, 26420 St Martin-en-Vercors [04 75 45 51 10; www. camping-laportestmartin.com] Sp 200m N of vill on D103. (D531 fr Villard-de-Lans W not rec for c'vans.) Med, mkd pitch, pt terr, pt shd; wc; shwrs inc; el pts €2.15; lndry rm; shops, rest, snacks & bar 500m; dogs; quiet; Eng spkn; phone; red low ssn; CCI. "Superb mountain views fr most pitches; excel walking." ♦ 1 May-30 Sep. € 9.50   2002*

CHAPELLE EN VERCORS, LA *9C3* (2km E Rural) Camping Les Myrtilles, Les Chaberts, 26420 La Chapelle-en-Vercors [tel/fax 04 75 48 20 89; camping.des.myrtilles@wanadoo.fr] Fr A49/E713 exit 8 to N532 St Nazaire-en-Royans, then D76 thro St Thomas-en Royans, then D216 to St Laurent-en-Royans. Take D2 around E flank of Combe Laval (2 short 2-lane tunnels). Fr Col de la Machine foll D76 S 1km, then D199 E over Col de Carri to La Chapelle. Fr S fr Die, foll D518 over Col de Rousset. (D76 over Combe Laval, D531 fr Villard-de-Lans & D518 fr Pont-en-Royans over Grandes Goulet not suitable for c'vans.) Med, pt sl, pt shd; wc; chem disp; shwrs inc; el pts (5A) €2.65; lndtte; shop 1km; snacks; bar; playgrnd; htd pool; rv fishing 2km; 20% statics; dogs €1.30; adv bkg; v quiet; CCI. "Beautiful setting; excel walking, caves & gorges; gates locked 2200-0700." ♦ 1 May-15 Sep. € 12.20   2005*

CHAPELLE HERMIER, LA *2H4* (3.5km SW Rural) Camping Le Pin Parasol, Chateaulong, 85220 La Chapelle-Hermier [02 51 34 64 72; fax 02 51 34 64 62; campingpinparasol@free.fr; http://campingpinparasol.free.fr] Exit A83 junc 4 onto D763/D937 dir La Roche-sur-Yon. Turn R onto D948 & at Aizenay turn L onto D6 twd St Gilles Croix-de-Vie; after 10km turn L onto D21; in La Chapelle-Hermier foll D42 twds L'Aiguillon-sur-Vie & site sp to Lac-du-Jaunay. Med, hdg/mkd pitch, pt sl, terr, unshd; wc; chem disp; mv service pnt; baby facs; shwrs inc; el pts (10A) inc; lndtte; ice; shop; tradsmn; rest 5km; snacks; bar; playgrnd; htd pool; sand beach 10km; lake sw; boating, fishing, canoeing 200m; cycle hire; entmnt; internet; TV; 10% statics; dogs €2.20; poss v cr; Eng spkn; adv bkg; quiet; CCI. "Excel facs; lge pitches; away fr crowds but close to beaches; extensive network of cycle tracks; 5km to sm town; many British tourers." ♦ 28 Apr-25 Sep. € 27.00 ABS - A36   2005*

CHAPELLE TAILLEFERT, LA see Gueret *7A4*

CHARETTE VARENNES *6H1* (Rural) **Aire Naturelle Municipal La Jeanette**, 71270 Charette-Varennes [tel/fax 03 85 76 23 58] Exit N73 by bdge SW of Navilly onto D996. In 1km, turn L sp camping onto sm rd. Site on L in 1km. Sm, pt sl, pt shd; wc (one cont); chem disp (wc only); shwrs inc; el pts (16A); lndry rm; shop 10km; BBQ; phone; quiet. "Peaceful CL-type site adj rv; v helpful warden in c'van at ent; poss problem with flooding in wet weather low ssn; vg sh stay." 1 Jun-15 Sep. € 8.00
2003*

CHARITE SUR LOIRE, LA *4G4* (500m W Urban) Camp Municipal La Saulaie, Quai de la Saulaie, 58400 La Charite-sur-Loire [03 86 70 00 83 or 03 86 70 16 12; fax 03 86 70 32 00; Sl.LaCharite@ wanadoo.fr] Fr old N7 (Montargis-Nevers) turn W over bdge sp Bourges; take 2nd R bef next bdge. Fr Bourges on N151, turn L immed after x-ing 1st Loire bridge. Foll sp. Med, mkd pitch, pt shd; wc; chem disp; shwrs inc; el pts (16A) €2.70; lndtte; ice; shop 500m; tradsmn; snacks; playgrnd & pool adj; rv beach & sw adj; no twin-axle vans; some noise; cc not acc; CCI. "Gd value site; gd, well-maintained, modern facs, ltd low ssn; gd security; friendly warden & helpful staff; sh walk into pleasant old town; low ssn phone to check open." ♦ 15 Apr-9 Sep. € 9.50   2005*

CHARITE SUR LOIRE, LA *4G4* (2km NW) Camping Belle Rive, 18140 La Chapelle-Montlinard [02 48 79 54 06] Fr La Charite N151 W over bdge. Immed after bdge turn R onto D7 dir Herry, site on R adj Rv Loire. Sm, pt shd; wc (cont); shwrs inc; el pts (5A) €2.70; shop 2km; tradsmn; playgrnd; quiet. "Friendly owners; gd sh stay/NH." 1 Jun-30 Sep. € 9.00   2002*

CHARLEVAL see Cadenet *10E3*

CHARLEVILLE MEZIERES *5C1* (500m N Urban) Camp Municipal Mont Olympe, Rue des Paquis, 08000 Charleville-Mezieres [03 24 33 23 60 or 03 24 32 44 80; fax 03 24 33 37 76; camping-charlevillemeziers@wandadoo.fr] Fr N43/E44 head for Hotel de Ville, with Hotel de Ville on R, cont N along Ave des Arches, turn R at 'Gare' sp & cont ahead & cross rv bdge. Turn sharp L immed along Rue des Paquis, site on L in 500m, visible fr rd. Well sp from city centre. Med, hdg/mkd pitch, pt shd; htd wc (some cont); chem disp (wc); mv service pnt; all serviced pitches; baby facs; fam bthrm; shwrs inc; el pts (10A) €3.60; gas; lndtte; ice; shops 500m over suspension bdge; tradsmn; bar; playgrnd; htd covrd pool adj; fishing & boating; TV; some statics; dogs €1.40; poss cr; Eng spkn; quiet; cc acc; CCI. "Next to Rv Meuse; well-kept; excel san facs; vg site." 1 Apr-15 Oct. € 11.00   2005*

CHARLEVILLE MEZIERES *5C1* (12km N Urban) Camp Municipal au Port a Diseur, Rue A Combain, 08800 Montherme [03 24 53 01 21; fax 03 24 53 01 15] Leave Charleville N on N43 turn R sp Nouzonville. Turn on D988 sp Montherme (D989). In town cross rv bdge, stay on D989 thro town, site 300m on R after supmkt on L. Med, pt sl, pt shd; wc (some cont); chem disp (wc); shwrs inc; el pts (4-10A) €2.50-3.70; gas 100m; lndtte; ice; shop 100m; rest, snacks, bar 1km; few statics; dogs; phone; poss cr; quiet but some rd noise; CCI. "Pleasant, well-maintained rvside site; popular with fishermen & canoeists." Easter-28 Aug. € 7.50
                    2005*

†**CHARLEVILLE MEZIERES** *5C1* (12km NE Rural) Camping Departemental d'Haulme, 08800 Haulme [03 24 32 81 61; fax 03 24 32 37 66] Fr Charleville, take N43 & turn R at sp to Nouzonville. Turn onto D988, D989 to Montherme. In town turn R over bdge onto D31. In 5km turn R sp Haulme, site in 1.5km. Lge, pt shd; wc (cont); shwrs inc; el pts (10A) inc; gas; ice; tradsmn; rv sw; fishing; tennis; cycle hire; dogs €0.90; poss cr; adv bkg; fairly quiet; cc acc. "Vg; excel for fishing; top end of site noisy due to semi-perm tents for youths; rec pitch mid-site as lower site is adj public park; v wet pitches in rain; vg, modern san facs; sh walk to town cent." ♦ € 11.30   2005*

CHARLIEU see Pouilly sous Charlieu *9A1*

CHARLY *3D4* (Urban) Camp Municipal Les Ilettes, Route de Pavant, 02310 Charly [03 28 82 12 11 or 03 23 82 00 32 (Mairie); fax 03 23 82 13 99] Fr A4 exit Montreuil-aux-Lions or Chateau Thierry. Foll sp. Sm, hdg pitch, pt shd; wc; chem disp; shwrs inc; el pts (5-10A) €1.60; lndry rm; ice; supmkt adj; quiet; red long stay. "Excel clean site; well-ordered; pleasant warden; conv town cent; steep access to some pitches." ♦ 1 Apr-1 Oct. € 9.40   2005*

CHARMES *6E2* (500m NE Rural) Camp Municipal Les Iles, 20 Rue de l'Ecluse, 88130 Charmes [tel/fax 03 29 38 87 71 or 03 29 38 85 85; andre.michel@tiscali.fr] Exit N57 for Charmes, site well sp on Rv Moselle. Do not confuse with sp for 'Camping Cars'. Med, mkd pitch, pt shd; wc; chem disp (wc); shwrs inc; el pts (10A) €3; gas; lndtte; ice; shop 300m; tradsmn; rest; snacks; bar; BBQ; playgrnd; fishing; mini-golf; kayak hire; dogs; phone; Eng spkn; adv bkg; quiet; red after 1 night; CCI. "Gd sh stay/NH; pleasant spot." 15 Apr-30 Sep. € 7.90
                    2005*

CHARMES SUR L'HERBASSE see Romans sur Isere *9C2*

CHARNY *4F3* (500m N Rural) Camping des Platanes, 41 Route de la Mothe, 89120 Charny [tel/fax 03 86 91 83 60; campingdesplatanes@wanadoo.fr; www.campingdesplatanes.com] Fr D943 turn S onto D950 dir Charny, site sp. Med, hdg/mkd pitch, pt shd; htd wc; shwrs inc; el pts (6-10A) €3.50; gas; lndtte; shop 500m; tradsmn; snacks; playgrnd; pool 500m; rv fishing 150m; tennis, cycle hire 500m; 20% statics; dogs €1; adv bkg; quiet; red low ssn; CCI. "Pleasant site; vg touring base; gd walking." ♦ 15 Mar-15 Oct. € 11.00   2005*

See advertisement on next page

CHAROLLES *9A2* (500m E Rural) Camp Municipal, Route de Viry, 71120 Charolles [03 85 24 04 90; fax 03 85 24 08 20] Exit N79 at E end of by-pass (Macon); sharp R bottom hill bef town; ent town & site on L (1- way system via Rue Gambetta). Med, hdg/mkd pitch, hdstg, pt shd; wc; chem disp; shwrs inc; el pts (10A) inc; lndtte; shops 300m; rest; snacks; bar; playgrnd; pool adj high ssn (proper sw trunks req); adv bkg rec; quiet; CCI. "Helpful warden; clean & well-maintained; lge pitches; facs downstairs under office; conv Rte des Vins; easy walk to lovely town; hdstg for 10 m'vans outside site ent." 1 Apr-30 Sep. € 9.70   2005*

CHARRIN see Decize *4H4*

CHARTRE SUR LE LOIR, LA *4F2* (500m W Urban) Camp Club a Tou Vert Le Vieux Moulin (Part Municipal), Ave des Deportes, Chemin des Bergivaux, 72340 La Chartre-sur-le Loir [02 43 44 41 18 or 02 43 38 16 16 (Mairie); fax 02 43 44 41 18; camping@lachartre.com; www.lachartre.com/campinglachartre.htm] Sp fr D305 in town. Med, hdg/mkd pitch, pt shd; htd wc; chem disp; mv service pnt; baby facs; fam bthrm; shwrs inc; el pts (6A) €4; lndtte; ice; shop; tradsmn; snacks; bar; BBQ; playgrnd; htd pool; rv fishing adj; cycle hire; entmnt; TV; 80% statics; dogs €1; phone; poss cr; Eng spkn; adv bkg rec high ssn; quiet; red low ssn; CCI. "Pleasant rvside site; gd base for Chateaux, forest & Loir Valley; well-kept; helpful & friendly staff; facs gd but stretched high ssn; excel pool; pitches vary in size; gd for dogs; v lge m'vans acc (over 3.50t); excel." ♦ 1 Apr-30 Sep. € 11.20   2005*

FRANCE

CHARTRES *4E2* (1km SE Urban) **Camping Les Bords de l'Eure, 9 Rue de Launay, 28000 Chartres [tel/fax 02 37 28 79 43; campingroussel-chartres@wanadoo.fr; www.auxbords deleure.com]** Exit N123 ringrd at D935, R at T-junc dir Chartres; then R at 2nd traff lts dir Chartres immed after rlwy bdge; site on L in 400m; inside of ring rd. Also sp fr town cent on N154 fr N, foll sp town cent under 2 rlwy bdges, L at traff lts sp Orleans, site sp. Fr SE on N154 cross ringrd, foll site sp; site on L. Med, hdg/mkd pitch, pt shd; htd wc (some cont); mv service pnt; baby facs; shwrs inc; el pts (3-10A) €3 (poss rev pol); lndry rm; ice; shop; tradsmn; BBQ; shop in ssn; supmkt 1km; playgrnd; fishing; some statics; dogs €1; poss cr; Eng spkn; adv bkg (dep req); quiet; CCI. "Conv Chartres Cathedral & Channel ports; well laid-out & well-maintained site; facs poss stretched high ssn & need refurb; some pitches diff lge o'fits; 3km walk thro woods to Cathedral; conv town; office shut 1200-1500 low ssn; gates shut 2200-0700; friendly, helpful staff." ♦ Easter-30 Oct. € 11.80   2005*

CHARTRES *4E2* (9km S Rural) **Camp Municipal, 28630 Morancez [02 37 30 02 80 or 02 37 28 49 71 (Mairie)]** S on Chartres by-pass (N123) take exit D935; L at T-junc twd Morancez; R on D114/Base de Loisirs at S end of vill (abrupt turn); cross bdge; after 200m turn R onto track, site at end of lake 300m. Travelling N on N10 turn R onto D114 sp Morancez. Strt over at x-rds, site down narr track. Sm, hdg/mkd pitch, pt shd; wc (cont); chem disp (wc); shwrs inc; el pts (6A) €2.50 (poss rev pol); shops 2km; rest 500m; playgrnd adj; fishing adj; 20% statics; adv bkg; quiet; CCI. "Site locked 2200-0700; v peaceful; surrounded by woods, lakes & rvs; helpful warden; ltd number san facs, dated but clean; excel rest 10 mins walk." 1 Jun-30 Aug. € 8.00   2005*

CHASSENEUIL DU POITOU see Jaunay Clan *4H1*

CHASSENEUIL SUR BONNIEURE *7B3* (Urban) **Camp Municipal, Rue des Ecoles, 16260 Chasseneuil-sur-Bonnieure [05 45 39 55 36]** On N141 Angouleme-Limoges leave by-pass sp Chasseneuil. In town turn L onto D27 sp Memorial de la Resistance. Turn R at camping sp, site ahead. Med, hdg pitch, pt shd; wc; chem disp; shwrs inc; el pts (6A) €2; lndtte; gas, shop, rest, snacks, bar 200m; playgrnd; htd, covrd pool adj; dogs; quiet. "Warden calls pm or key fr Office de Tourisme; diff to ent/leave site without key to bollard." 1 Apr-31 Oct. € 6.10   2005*

This site entry hasn't been updated for a while; we'd better fill in a site report form and send it to The Club.

†CHASSENEUIL SUR BONNIEURE *7B3* (9km E Rural) **Camping Le Paradis, Mareuil, 16270 Mazieres [05 45 71 12 32 or 05 45 84 62 06]** Fr Limoges W on N141 twd Angouleme, turn L at Roumazieres-Loubert or Fontafie to Mazieres, site sp in 10km. Sm, hdg/mkd pitch, hdstg, pt shd; htd wc; chem disp; mv service pnt; baby facs; shwrs inc; el pts (16A) inc; gas; 1km; lndtte; ice; shop & 1km; tradsmn; rest, snacks, bar 1km; BBQ; playgrnd; tennis; lake sw & fishing 5km; 20% statics; dogs; Eng spkn; adv bkg; quiet; CCI. "New san facs, pool & games rm planned for 2005; Futuroscope nrby; welcoming British owners; clean & tranquil; gd touring base; excel." € 15.00   2004*

CHATAIGNERAIE, LA *2H4* (5km E Rural) **Camping La Violliere, 85120 Breuil-Barret [02 51 87 44 82; familywoodman@aol.com]** Take D949 E dir Poitiers thro Chataigneraie 5km. Cont thro Breuil-Barret & site 2nd R after rlwy bdge. Sm, pt sl, pt shd; wc; chem disp; shwrs inc; el pts (ltd) €3; tradsmn; playgrnd; Eng spkn; adv bkg; quiet. "V peaceful & relaxing site; 6 pitches & 4 el pts only; gd sh stay." 1 May-30 Sep. € 11.00 2003*

FRANCE

†CHATEAU ARNOUX *10E3* (N Urban) FFCC Camping Les Salettes, Rue Victor in Maurel, 04160 Chateau-Arnoux [04 92 64 02 40 or 06 87 33 37 73 (mob); fax 04 92 64 25 06; infos@ lessalettes.com; www.lessalettes.com] Exit A51 for Peyruis or Aubignosc. Site well sp fr both dirs on N85 to N of town. Lge, hdg/mkd pitch, pt shd; htd wc (some cont); chem disp; mv service pnt; fam bthrm; shwrs inc; el pts (4-10A) €4-6; gas; lndtte; ice; shop; rest; snacks; bar; BBQ; playgrnd; pool; lakes adj & 100m; boating & fishing on lake; games area; mini-golf; entmnt; TV rm; carwash; 5% statics; dogs €1; phone; train 1km; extra charge for twin-axle vans; Eng spkn; adv bkg (dep €69); quiet; cc acc; 10% red CCI. "Nr Gorges du Verdon & Rte Napoleon; vg." € 17.00   2005*

CHATEAU ARNOUX *10E3* (3km NE Rural) Camping L'Hippocampe, Route Napoleon, 04290 Volonne [04 92 33 50 00; fax 04 92 33 50 49; camping@ l-hippocampe.com; www.l-hippocampe.com] Exit A51 junc 21 onto N85 12km S of Sisteron twd Volonne vill over rv. Turn R on D4 on ent vill & foll camp sp 1km. Lge, hdg/mkd pitch, hdstg, pt shd; wc; chem disp; mv service pnt; child/baby facs; serviced pitches; shwrs inc; el pts (10A) €5 (poss rev pol); lndtte; ice; shop; tradsmn; rest; bar; BBQ (elec/gas); playgrnd; htd pool planned 2006; fishing; canoeing; rafting; tennis; cycle hire; games rm; entmnt; internet; TV rm; some statics; dogs €4; Eng spkn; adv bkg; quiet but poss noisy nr recep; red low ssn/long stay; cc acc; red low ssn; CCI. "Excel site; busy but well-run; recep open 0700-2000; spacious, well-screened pitches; pitching poss diff on some pitches due trees." ♦ 25 Mar-30 Sep. € 27.00 (CChq acc)   2005*

CHATEAU ARNOUX *10E3* (10km SW Rural) FFCC Camping Les Cigales, Chemin de la Digue du Bevon, 04310 Peyruis [tel/fax 04 92 68 16 04; lescigales@mageos.com] Site sp fr N96. Sm, hdg pitch, terr, pt shd; wc; chem disp; shwrs inc; el pts (6A) €3.80; ice; lndtte; shop; snacks; bar; BBQ; playgrnd; pool & sports complex nr (tickets fr site recep); entmnt; 5% statics; dogs €1; adv bkg; quiet; 10% red CCI. "Pretty 'garden' site; excel, modern, well-maintained; immac san facs; friendly, helpful manager; interesting old town 15 mins walk; highly rec." ♦ 1 Apr-30 Sep. € 11.55   2004*

CHATEAU CHINON *4H4* (1km S Urban) Camp Municipal du Gargouillat, Rue de Pertuy d'Oiseau, 58120 Chateau-Chinon [03 86 85 08 17; fax 03 86 85 15 05] Sp fr D978 rndabt at E end town. Med, hdg/mkd pitches, sl, pt shd; wc (some cont); shwrs inc; el pts (10A) inc; shops 1km; tradsmn; poss cr; quiet. "Facs ltd low ssn; poss itinerants; conv Morvan National Park; levelling blocks rec; gd NH." 1 May-30 Sep. € 10.50   2003*

CHATEAU D'OLONNE see Sables d'Olonne, Les *7A1*

CHATEAU DU LOIR *4G1* (6km E Rural) Camping Le Lac des Varennes, Les Varennes, 72340 Marcon [02 43 44 13 72; fax 02 43 44 54 31; camping.des. varennes.marcon@wanadoo.fr; www.ville-marcon. fr] S on N138 fr Chateau-du-Loir dir Vendome for 3km. Turn L onto D305 sp Marcon. In vill turn L onto D61 over bdge. Site on R by lake. Lge, hdg/mkd pitch, hdstg, pt shd; htd wc (some cont); chem disp; mv service pnt; baby facs; shwrs inc; el pts (6A) €2 (poss rev pol); lndtte; shop high ssn; tradsmn; rest, snacks & bar high ssn; BBQ; playgrnd; lake sw & sand beach adj; boat hire; watersports; tennis; cycle hire; horseriding; mini-golf; cycle hire; entmnt; 20% statics; dogs €1.20; Eng spkn; adv bkg rec; quiet; cc acc; red low ssn; CCI. "Pretty site in lovely situation; gd security." ♦ 25 Mar-10 Oct. € 12.00   2005*

See advertisement above   *See advertisement on next page*

LAC DES VARENNES ★★★
72340 Marçon
Tel.: 00 33 (0)2 43 44 13 72
Fax: 00 33 (0)2 43 44 54 31

Pitches
TRIGANO Bungalows and MOBILE HOMES
Quiet, shady park with private beach
and leisure area.
Sailing, Tennis, fishing, hiking paths.
Fast food, grocery.

Le Mans-Tours via RN 138, Chateau-du-Loir direction Vendôme via D305

E-mail: camping.des.varennes.marcon@wanadoo.fr   **Open from 25/3 till 10/10**

CHATEAU GONTIER *4F1* (1km N Urban) **Camping Le Parc**, Route de Laval, 53200 Chateau-Gontier [02 43 07 35 60; fax 02 43 70 38 94; tourisme@ ccchateau-gontier.fr; www.ville-chateau-gontier. fr] Fr Angers on N162 at rndabt sp A81/Laval (opp Elan g'ge). Take 1st exit. At rndabt at end of short dual c'way take 3rd exit with Laval sp, sp La Gare/Office de Tourisme. Turn R over rv bdge sp Toutes Directions, Laval/Chateauneuf then 1st L into Quai Pasteur sp Laval/Evron & Camping. Sp for camping in 1.5km at ent on L. Med, mkd pitch, pt sl, pt shd; wc; chem disp; mv service pnt; shwrs inc; el pts (10A) inc (rev pol); lndtte; shops 1km; tradsmn; bar; playgrnd; pool 800m; fishing; entmnt; 20% statics; quiet; red low ssn; CCI. "Easy walk to town via rvside path; lovely floral displays in town; excel san facs; lge pitches; mkt Thurs; free access to local pool inc." ♦ 1 Apr-30 Sep. € 11.50   2005*

CHATEAU GONTIER *4F1* (11km SE Rural) **Camp Municipal de Daon**, 53200 Daon [02 43 06 94 78 or 02 43 06 94 10; fax 02 43 06 91 35; mairie. daon@cc-chateau-gontier.fr] On town side of rv bdge, turn down lane & site ent on R at bottom of hill. Med, some terr, pt shd; wc; chem disp; shwrs inc; el pts (10A) inc; lndtte; shop in town; playgrnd; tennis, mini-golf & sw nrby; adv bkg; quiet; CCI. "Vg clean & well cared for site; boating on adj Rv Mayenne; noise fr rv." ♦ 1 Apr-30 Sep. € 8.60   2004*

CHATEAU GONTIER *4F1* (6km S Rural) **Camping du Bac**, Rue de Port, 53200 Menil [tel/fax 02 43 70 24 54 or 02 43 70 25 25; menil@ cc-chateau-grontier.fr] On N162 dir Chateau Gontier, turn off at Menil & foll sp. Sm, hdg pitch, pt shd; wc; shwrs inc; el pts (10A) €1.75; lndry rm; snacks; bar 250m; playgrnd; 5% statics; dogs; phone; bus; Eng spkn; adv bkg; CCI. "Edge of rv Mayenne; gd fishing, walks, cycling; lge vans by request; vg all stays." ♦ 15 Apr-15 Sep. € 7.45   2004*

CHATEAU LA VALLIERE *4G1* (Rural) **Camp Municipal du Val Joyeux**, 37330 Chateau-la-Valliere [02 47 24 00 21 or 02 47 24 04 93; fax 02 47 24 06 13] Turn L off D959, in vill 1km S on D749. Site on R after x-ing bdge with lake on L. Med, hdg/mkd pitch, pt shd; wc; chem disp; mv service pnt; serviced pitch; shwrs inc; el pts €2.50; shops 1km; tradsmn; playgrnd; lake beach & fishing adj; dogs; Eng spkn; adv bkg rec high ssn; quiet; CCI. "Friendly welcome; handy for Loire chateaux; mkd walks; modern, spotless san facs; v soft ground after heavy rain; excel long stay. ♦ 15 May-15 Sep. € 8.50   2004*

CHATEAU RENAULT *4G2* (Urban) **Camp Municipal du Parc de Vauchevrier, Rue Paul-Louis-Courier**, 37110 Chateau-Renault [02 47 29 54 43 or 02 47 29 85 50 (LS); fax 02 47 56 87 50] At Chateau-Renault foll sp to site 800m fr N10. If app fr a'route turn L on ent town & site on R of main rd. Med, mkd pitch, pt shd; wc; chem disp; mv service pnt; shwrs inc; el pts (6A) €1.85; shops 800m; rest 600m; bar 300m; playgrnd; htd pool; fishing; tennis; some rd noise; cc not acc; CCI. "Part of municipal park; no c'vans over 5.50m; office clsd 1230-1430; v pleasant site & staff; adj Rv Brenne." ♦ 1 May-15 Sep. € 6.05   2004*

CHATEAU RENAULT *4G2* (6km S) **Camp Municipal de Moulin, Rue du Lavoir**, 37110 Villedomer [02 47 55 05 50 or 02 47 55 00 04 (Mairie); fax 02 47 55 06 27] Take N10 SW fr Chateau-Renault. Site sp at 3km & 6km to Villedomer. Site 2km fr N10. Also easy access fr A10 & D31; foll sp to Auzouer & Villedomer. Sm, hdg pitch, shd; wc (cont for men); chem disp; shwrs inc; el pts (10A) €3; shops adj; rv fishing; lake 3km; adv bkg. "Gd, clean facs but old-fashioned; pitch yourself if warden not present - comes to collect fees at 2000 hrs." 15 Jun-15 Sep. € 5.90   2003*

CHATEAU SALINS *5D2* (1km E Urban) **Camp Municipal des Salines**, 57170 Chateau-Salins [03 87 05 10 52; fax 03 87 05 16 34] Foll D955 twds Luneville; well sp. Sm, mkd pitch, pt sl, pt shd; wc; chem disp; shwrs inc; el pts; shop 1km; gas 1km; no cc acc; quiet; CCI. "Gd sh stay." 1 May-30 Oct.   2004*

CHATEAU THIERRY *3D4* (E Urban) **Camp Municipal, 70 Ave d'Essomes, 02400 Chateau-Thierry [03 23 83 48 23]** Fr A4/E50 take junc 20 onto D1 into town. At junc prior to rv bdge, turn R & foll sp Camping/Piscine. Site on L next to McDonalds. Sm, mkd pitch, unshd; wc; chem disp; shwrs inc; el pts (8A) €2.60; gas; lndtte; BBQ; rest, bar & shops 1.6km; snacks adj; pool adj; 30% statics; dogs €0.84; poss cr; some rd noise; CCI. "Fast-food rest & drive thro immed adj to site - traff noise until 2300; conv trains Paris & Disneyland Paris; gd walks along rv; WW1 US memorial overlooks town; facs clean but worn; phone ahead to check open low ssn; office open 0830-1000 & 1730-2000 - access for vehicles over 1.90m only during these times; gd sh stay/NH." 15 May-30 Sep. € 8.85   2005*

CHATEAUBRIANT *2F4* (1.5km S) **Camp Municipal, Les Briotais, Rue de Tugny, 44110 Chateaubriant [02 40 81 14 38 or 02 40 81 02 32]** App fr Nantes (D178) site sp on S end of town or Angers (D163) foll sp at 1st rndabt; fr town cent, foll sps thro town. Sm, hdg pitch, pt shd; wc; shwrs; el pts inc; shops, rest, snacks, bar 500m; pool in town; dogs; €0.33; quiet. "11thC chateau in town; site locked overnight; site on municipal playing field; gd NH." ♦ 1 May-30 Sep. € 9.50   2004*

CHATEAUDUN *4F2* (2.5km NW) **Camp Municipal Le Moulin a Tan, Rue de Chollet, 28200 Chateaudun [02 37 45 05 34 or 02 37 45 11 91 (LS); fax 02 37 45 54 46]** App Chateaudun fr N on N10; turn R at rndabt (supmkt on L); L at next rndabt & foll site sp. Site adj Rv Loir. Med, mkd pitch, pt shd; wc (some cont); chem disp; shwrs inc; el pts (6A) €1.75; lndtte; ice; shops, rest, snacks 2km; playgrnd; htd, covrd pool 2km; fishing; canoeing; games area; TV; 5% statics; CCI. "Continuous traff noise fr N10; gd base for touring; some night flying fr nrby military airfield; security gate 2.10m height; no twin-axle vans; helpful warden." 15 Mar-15 Oct. € 7.00   2004*

CHATEAULIN *2E2* (1.5km S Rural) **La Pointe Superbe Camping, 29150 St Coulitz [tel/fax 02 98 86 51 53; lapointecamping@aol.com]** Fr N165 foll sp to Chateaulin; in town cent, cross bdge & turn L along rv on D770. After approx 750m, turn L at sp for St Coulitz; 100m turn R into site. If travelling N on D770 do not turn R (tight turn), go into town & turn round. Med, hdg/mkd pitch, pt sl, pt shd; wc; chem disp; mv service pnt; baby facs; shwrs inc; el pts (10A) €2; gas 1km; lndry rm; ice; shop 1km; rest, snacks & bar 500m; BBQ; playgrnd; games rm; sand beach 15km; rv nr; dogs €1; adv bkg (dep req); quiet; no cc acc. "Best site in Brittany if you don't req a pool; immac facs; gd pitches; sm shwr rms; well-organised; delightful, peaceful, rural setting yet close to town; v helpful & friendly British owners; gd base for Crozon peninsula." ♦ 15 Mar-31 Oct. € 14.00   2005*

CHATEAULIN *2E2* (500m SW) **Camp Municipal Rodaven, 29150 Chateaulin [02 98 86 32 93 or 02 98 86 10 05 (Mairie); fc-ssport@chateaulin.fr]** Fr canal/rv bdge in town cent take Quai Moulin (SE side of rv) for about 350m & site down track on R opp indoor pool. Med, pt shd; wc; chem disp; shwrs inc; el pts (10A) €2; shops 200m; playgrnd; htd indoor pool 300m; direct rv access, fishing; sand beah 5km; entmnt; dogs €1; phone; poss cr; adv bkg; quiet; CCI. "Well-managed site; gd touring base; gd sh stay." ♦ ltd. 1 Jun-14 Sep. € 10.00   2004*

CHATEAUMEILLANT see Culan *7A4*

CHATEAUNEUF DE GALAURE *9C2* (800m SW) **Camping Le Chateau de Galaure, Route de St Vallier, 26330 Chateauneuf-de-Galaure [04 75 68 65 22; fax 04 75 68 60 60]** Site sp at Chateauneuf-de-Galaure on D51. Med, pt shd; wc; chem disp; shwrs inc; el pts (5A) inc; gas adj; lndtte; shops 750m; pool; tennis; games rm; TV; quiet; adv bkg; Eng spkn. "Lge pitches; facs for most sports; excel rest Yves Leydier in vill; conv Palais Ideal." 1 Jun-1 Sep. € 22.00   2002*

CHATEAUNEUF D'ILLE ET VILAINE *2E4* (1.5km NE Rural) **Camping Bel Event, 35430 St Pere [02 99 58 83 79; fax 02 99 58 82 24; contact@camping-bel-event.com]** Fr terminal at St Malo, at 1st rndabt foll sp Toutes Directions; at 2nd traff lts turn R & cont foll dir Toutes Directions, then sp Rennes; cont twd Rennes for approx 10km & take exit for Dinan/Chateauneuf; take immed L twds Cancale; past an old rlwy stn on R & take 1st little rd on L (500m fr stn) opp rest; site 100m further on L. Fr S on N137 at Chateauneuf junc turn R onto D74 sp Cancale, then as above. Med, mkd pitch, pt sl, pt shd; wc; chem disp; shwrs inc; el pts (10A) €4 (rev pol poss); lndtte; ice; tradsmn; sm shop; snacks; bar; htd pool (Jun-Sep); playgrnd; lake sw, fishing & watersports adj; sand beach 5km; cycle hire; tennis; TV; 75% statics (sep area); dogs €2; adv bkg; quiet, some rd noise. "Vg NH for St Malo & ferry; immac facs; sm pitches - 4 per enclave; gd touring base." 1 Apr-30 Sep. € 18.00   2005*

CHATEAUNEUF DU FAOU *2E2* (4km SE) **Camp Municipal du Goaker, Moulin du Pre, 29520 St Goazec [02 98 26 84 23]** D36 out of Chateauneuf, turn L sp St Goazec & foll sps. Sm, pt shd; wc (cont); shwrs inc; el pts; shops 2km; quiet. "Pleasantly situated."   2003*

CHATEAUNEUF LES BAINS see St Gervais d'Auvergne *7A4*

CHATEAUNEUF SUR LOIRE *4F3* (500m S Urban) **Camping La Maltournee, Sigloy, 45110 Chateauneuf-sur-Loire [02 38 58 42 46; fax 02 38 58 54 11]** On L side of D11 on S bank of Rv Loire, sp fr town. Lge, pt shd; htd wc; shwrs inc; el pts (10A) €3; lndtte; shops 1km; snacks; pool 2km; canoeing; 75% statics; dogs; security barrier; adv bkg; quiet; CCI. "Superb views of rv fr some pitches; well kept site; clean, modern san facs; m'van pitches beside rv; helpful, pleasant staff." ♦ 1 Apr-31 Oct. € 7.00   2005*

FRANCE

CHATEAUNEUF SUR LOIRE *4F3* (7km W Urban) Camping de l'Isle aux Moulins, 45150 Jargeau [02 38 59 70 04; fax 02 38 59 92 62] On D952 thro Chateauneuf & N60 twd Orleans. At St Denis-de l'Hotel take sharp L onto D921 to Jargeau over Loire bdge. Site clearly visible on R of bdge on W bank. Turn R immed at end of bdge. Lge, shd; wc (mainly cont); own san rec; chem disp; shwrs inc; el pts (10A) inc; gas; ice; lndtte; shops 1km; tradsmn; playgrnd; pool adj; rv fishing adj; cycle hire; mini-golf; archery; entmnt; quiet; adv bkg; Eng spkn; cc acc; CCI. "Poor NH; use only if desperate; alongside rv; friendly farming family." 1 Mar-31 Oct. € 12.70   2005*

CHATEAUNEUF SUR SARTHE *4G1* (E Rural) Camp Municipal du Port, Rue de la Gare, 49330 Chateauneuf-sur-Sarthe [02 41 69 82 02 or 02 41 96 15 20; fax 02 41 96 15 29; tourisme chateauneufsursarthe@wanadoo.fr] Site clearly sp in vill, 18km E of Le Lion d'Angers. Access to site fr bdge. Sm, pt shd; wc; chem disp; shwrs inc; el pts (10A) €2.35 (long lead poss req); lndtte; shops & rest in vill; playgrnd; rv adj; fishing; sailing; v quiet but some rd noise; CCI. "Boating on Rv Sarthe, attractive area, clean facs but poss stretched high ssn; sm pitches; warden on site Jul/Aug only; clsd to vans 1230-1600 but 24hr access for cars fr rear of site." 1 May-30 Sep. € 6.50   2003*

†CHATEAUPONSAC *7A3* (200m SW) Camp Municipal La Gartempe, Villages de Vacances, 87290 Chateauponsac [05 55 76 55 33 or 05 55 76 31 55 (Mairie); fax 05 55 76 98 05; chateauponsac.tourisme@wanadoo.fr] Fr N20 N of Bessines-sur-Gartempe take D711 W for 7km to Chateauponsac, well sp. Sm, hdg/mkd pitch, terr, pt shd; wc; chem disp; shwrs inc; el pts (6A) €2.50; lndtte; ice; supmkt 500m; rest, snacks, bar (Jul.Aug); playgrnd; pool; rv adj; lake 10km; mini-golf; kayak; archery; children's activites; adj to holiday bungalows/gites; dogs €1; poss cr; Eng spkn; adv bkg; red low ssn; CCI. "Pleasant site; v helpful staff; facs somewhat worn; htd bthrm avail for winter guests; not suitable lge m'vans; sh walk to town for shops, museum & historic sites; activities down steep hill; many sports avail in area." € 15.00   2005*

CHATEAUROUX *4H2* (1km N) Camp Municipal Le Rochat-Belle Isle, Rue du Rochat, 36000 Chateauroux [02 54 34 26 56 or 02 54 08 33 00; fax 02 54 07 03 11] Site on banks of Rv Indre, sp in town. Med, pt shd; wc (cont); chem disp; mv service pnt; baby facs; shwrs inc; el pts (10A) €4.80; gas; lndtte; shops 300m; rest, snacks, bar 100m; playgrnd; Eng spkn. "Leisure park adj with pool & windsurfing on lake; poss music noise till late w/e high ssn; poss itinerants; gd san facs." ♦ 1 May-30 Sep. € 13.60   2005*

†CHATEAUROUX *4H2* (9km SW Rural) Camping Les Grands Pins, Les Maisons-Neuves, 36330 Velles [02 54 36 61 93; fax 02 54 36 10 09; contact@les-grands-pins.fr; www.les-grands-pins.fr] Fr N exit A20 junc 14 dir Chateauroux; in 500m turn R onto D20 parallel with m'way. Foll sp Maisons-Neuves & site. Fr S exit A20 junc 15, turn R then L onto D920, site on R. Med, pt sl, pt shd; wc (some cont); chem disp; some serviced pitches; shwrs inc; el pts (10A) €3.50 (poss rev pol); lndtte; shop 8km; rest; snacks; bar; playgrnd; pool; tennis; mini-golf; dogs €1.50; site clsd w/e 15 Nov-15 Mar; Eng spkn; adv bkg; quiet; CCI. "Gd, tidy site in pine forest; vg rest; max weight m'van 4 tons; phone to check open if travelling low ssn; vet in Chateauroux; excel NH." ♦ € 12.90   2005*

See advertisement

CHATEL *9A4* (2km Rural) Camping Caravaneige L'Oustalet, 74390 Chatel [04 50 73 21 97; fax 04 50 73 37 46; oustalet@valdabondance.com; www.oustalet.com] Fr Thonon-les-Bains, take D902 & D22 to Chatel. Site sp fr church in cent. Med, pt shd; wc; mv service pnt; shwrs inc; el pts (2-10A) inc; gas; lndtte; shop, rest, bar 100m; playgrnd; htd, covrd pool high ssn; tennis; games rm; entmnt; dogs €1.60; adv bkg rec winter; quiet. "Excel site; conv fr ski lifts; gd mountain walks; vg." ♦ 20 Jun-1 Sep & 15 Dec-30 Apr. € 25.00   2003*

CHATEAURENARD see Avignon *10E2*

CHATEL CENSOIR see Coulanges sur Yonne *4G4*

CHATEL DE NEUVRE *9A1* (Rural) **Camping Deneuvre, 03500 Chatel-de-Neuvre [tel/fax 04 70 42 04 51; campingdeneuvre@wanadoo.fr]** S fr Moulins on N9; sp N of vill on E side of N9. Med, mkd pitch, hdstg, pt shd; wc; chem disp; mv service pnt; baby facs; shwrs inc; el pts (4A) €2.35; ice; gas; lndtte; tradsmn; rest; snacks; bar; playgrnd; rv sw; canoe hire; dogs; adv bkg (dep req); Eng spkn; quiet; cc not acc; CCI. "Excel, clean facs; Dutch management; v friendly welcome; at border of Rv Allier in nature reserve; splendid place for walking, fishing, biking & birdwatching; ltd facs low ssn; diff ent/exit for lge o'fits; no twin-axles." ♦ 1 Apr-1 Oct. € 11.60   2005*

> Some of these sites have changed their opening dates - we'd better fill in some site report forms and let the editor of the guide know.

†CHATEL DE NEUVRE *9A1* (400m W Rural) **Camping de la Courtine, 7 Rue de St Laurant, 03500 Chatel-de-Neuvre [04 70 42 06 21; fax 04 70 42 82 89; camping-lacourtine@ club-internet.fr]** Fr N on N9 to cent of vill, turn L at x-rds onto D32; site in 500m. Sm, mkd pitch, pt shd; htd wc; chem disp; mv service pnt; baby facs; shwrs inc; el pts (6A) €2 (poss rev pol); lndtte; shop 400m; tradsmn; rest 400m; snacks; bar; playgrnd; dogs €0.50; poss cr; Eng spkn; adv bkg; quiet; CCI. "Friendly welcome; facs poss poorly maintained & site unkempt low ssn; site vulnerable to flooding & poss clsd low ssn, phone ahead to check; access to Rv Allier for canoeing, fishing; walking in nature reserve; NH only." ♦ € 8.70   2005*

CHATEL MONTAGNE *9A1* **Camping La Croix Cognat, 03250 Chatel-Montagne [tel/fax 04 70 59 31 38; campinglacroixcognat@ wanadoo.fr]** SW fr Lapalisse on D7; in 15km L on D25 to Chatel-Montagne in 5km & foll sp; site on L on ent vill. 'Sleeping policemen' at ent. Sm, terr, sl, pt shd; wc (some cont); chem disp; baby facs; shwrs inc; el pts (6A) €3; gas; lndtte; supmkt 6km; rest; snacks; playgrnd; pool (high ssn); mountain bike hire; fishing; horseriding & windsurfing adj; 5% statics; dogs €0.50; adv bkg; quiet; CCI. "Sm pitches poss diff o'fits over 6m." 1 May-1 Oct. € 11.00   2005*

CHATEL MONTAGNE *9A1* (10km NE Rural) **Camp Municipal, 03120 Arfeuilles [04 70 55 50 11 (Mairie); fax 04 70 55 53 28]** Site off D207 at NE exit to Arfeuilles 50m fr town name sp. 8km fr N7. Sm, pt sl, pt shd; wc; chem disp; fam bthrm; shwrs inc; el pts (6-10A) €2-2.30; lndry rm; shops 250m; dogs; Eng spkn; quiet; CCI. "Set in beautiful countryside; local fishing & bowls; peaceful." ♦ 1 May-30 Sep. € 6.80   2003*

CHATELAILLON PLAGE *7A1* (1km N Urban) **Camping L'Ocean, Ave d'Angoulins, 17340 Chatelaillon-Plage [05 46 56 87 97]** Fr La Rochelle take D602 to Chatelaillon-Plage, site sp on L in 300m (after passing g'ge & L'Abbaye camp site). Med, part hdg/mkd pitch, pt shd; wc (some cont); chem disp (wc only); mv service pnt; shwrs inc; el pts (10A) inc; lndtte; ice; tradsmn; shops, rest, snacks, bar 1km; BBQ; waterslide; sand beach 600m; dogs €1.52; poss cr. "Gd, clean san facs; daily covrd mkt in town; occasional noise fr rlwy & clay pigeon range." 15 Jun-15 Sep. € 16.00   2002*

CHATELAILLON PLAGE *7A1* (2.5km SE Coastal) **Camping Port Punay, Les Boucholeurs, Allee Bernard Moreau, 17340 Chatelaillon-Plage [05 46 56 01 53; fax 05 46 56 86 44; camping. port-punay@wanadoo.fr; www.camping-port-punay.com]** S fr La Rochelle on N137, turn R at 15km sp Chatelaillon-Plage. At 500m turn L on Ave de L'Hippodrome. Cont for 2km (x-ing rlwy) to shore at Port Punay. Turn L & foll sp to site. Lge, pt shd; wc; serviced pitches; baby facs; shwrs inc; el pts (6-10A) €3.70-5.70; gas; lndtte; lndry rm; ice; shops adj; rest; snacks; bar; playgrnd; pool; sand beach 500m; games area; entmnt; TV; 25% statics; dogs €1; Eng spkn; adv bkg; quiet. "Immac san facs; helpful owners." Easter-30 Sep. € 19.00 (3 persons)   2004*

CHATELAILLON PLAGE *7A1* (S Coastal) **Camping Le Clos des Rivages, Ave des Boucholeurs, 17340 Chatelaillon-Plage [05 46 56 26 09]** 10km S of La Rochelle on N137 turn R twd Chatelaillon. Take 1st L & site at rndabt in 500m. Med, hdg pitch, pt shd; wc; shwrs inc; el pts (6-10A) inc; gas; BBQ; ice; lndtte; shops 500m; bar; pool; playgrnd/ball games area; sand beach 300m; sm fishing lake; dogs €1.50; poss cr; adv bkg rec high ssn; quiet; some Eng spkn; CCI. "Vg long/sh stay; san facs poss not regularly cleaned; daily covrd mkt & lge street mkt on Tue & Fri; long promenade; rec." 15 Jun-5 Sep. € 22.00   2002*

CHATELGUYON see Riom *9B1*

CHATELLERAULT *4H1* (N Rural) **Le Relais du Miel, Route d'Antran, 86100 Chatellerault [05 49 02 06 27; fax 05 49 93 25 76; camping@ lerelaisdumiel.com; www.lerelaisdumiel.com]** On A10 exit junc 26 at Chatellerault-Nord. Foll sp twd Antran; site on R fr rndabt, well sp. Med, hdstg, terr, shd; wc; chem disp; mv service pnt; serviced pitches; shwrs inc; el pts (10A) inc; lndtte; ice; shop 400m; tradsmn; bar; BBQ; playgrnd; pool; tennis; boules; dogs €3; Eng spkn; adv bkg; some rd noise; red long stay; cc acc; CCI. "Friendly owners; conv Futuroscope, Chinon, Loches; rvside site in Chateau de Valette park; gd long/sh stay; handy to A10; excel." ♦ 12 May-3 Sep. € 24.00   2005*

FRANCE

CHATILLON COLIGNY *4F3* (S Rural) **Camp Municipal de la Lanciere, Rue Andre Henriat, 45230 Chatillon-Coligny [02 38 92 54 73 or 06 16 09 30 26; lalanciere@wanadoo.fr]** N fr Briare twd Montargis on N7; E fr Les Bezards on D56 twd Chatillon-Coligny; site sp on ent town on R immed bef canal bdge. Fr town cross Canal de Briare on D93 twd Blenau; immed turn S along canal rd sp Camping & Marina. Sm, pt shd; wc (some cont); chem disp (wc); shwrs inc; el pts (3-6A) €1.80-2.80 shops adj; pool high ssn; rv fishing; quiet; 25% statics; no cc acc; CCI. "Clean facs; attractive, peaceful site; excel value; friendly warden; gd walking/cycling along canal." 1 Apr-30 Sep. € 8.20   2005*

CHATILLON EN DIOIS *9D3* (Urban) **Camp Municipal Les Chaussieres, 26410 Chatillon-en-Diois [04 75 21 10 30 or 04 75 21 14 44 (Mairie); fax 04 75 21 18 78]** Fr Die take the D93 S for 6km then L on D539 to Chatillon (8km) site sp on R on ent to town. Lge, mkd pitch, pt shd; wc (some cont) chem disp (wc); mv service pnt; shwrs; el pts (10A) €2.45 ice; shop 200m; snacks; rest, bar 200m; BBQ; playgrnd; pool; canoeing; horseriding; cycling; entmnts; 30% statics; dogs €1.45; phone; Eng spkn; adv bkg; quiet; cc acc; CCI. "On rv bank; attractive old town; gd walking; spectacular mountain scenery; helpful, friendly staff; facs basic but clean; low branches on some pitches; vg long stay." 1 Apr-1 Nov. € 9.65   2005*

CHATILLON EN DIOIS *9D3* (1km W Urban) **Camping Les Ilas, 26410 Chatillon-en-Diois [04 90 59 07 77]** S fr Die on D93, after 6km take D539 to Chatillon. At far end of vill L onto D120, site in 200m. Sm, pt shd; wc; shwrs; el pts; shop 1km; rest adj; 20% statics; phone; quiet. "Friendly staff; interesting old town; 1 modern san facs block; 1 in need of refurb; fair sh stay/NH." 1 Jul-31 Aug. € 9.00   2002*

CHATILLON EN VENDELAIS see Vitre *2F4*

CHATILLON SUR CHALARONNE *9A2* (500m E Urban) **Camp Municipal du Vieux Moulin, Route de Chalamont, 01400 Chatillon-sur-Chalaronne [04 74 55 04 79; fax 04 74 55 13 11]** Take D936 SW out of Bourg to Chatillon-sur-Chalaronne. Site clearly sp on ent next town. Med, hdg pitch, shd; wc (mainly cont); baby facs; shwrs inc; el pts (10A) €3.50; lndry rm; supmkt adj; rest adj; snacks; playgrnd; pool adj; fishing; leisure cent adj; 50% statics; dogs €1.60; phone; adv bkg; quiet; cc acc; 10% red CCI. "Immac facs; lovely town; helpful warden; some facs closed low ssn; excel long/sh stay/NH." ♦ 15 Apr-15 Sep. € 13.90   2005*

CHATILLON SUR INDRE *4H2* (N Rural) **Camp Municipal de la Menetrie, Rue de Moulin la Grange, 36700 Chatillon-sur-Indre [06 78 27 16 39 or 02 54 38 75 44 (Mairie)]** Site well sp in vill. N twd Loches then turn R twd rlwy stn. Med, hdg/mkd pitch, pt shd; wc; chem disp; shwrs inc; el pts (6A) €1.80; gas, shop & rest 400m; BBQ; playgrnd adj; paddling pool; htd pool adj (proper sw trunks only); dogs; phone; no adv bkg; quiet; CCI. "Lovely relaxed site; gd bird-watching area; sh walk to interesting old town, church, chateau; conv Loire chateaux; mkt Fri; barrier locked when warden out but lives opp; recep 0900-1000 & 1900-2000; barrier key dep €50; no twin-axle vans; vg all stays." ♦ 15 May-15 Sep. € 5.80   2005*

CHATILLON SUR LOIRE see Briare *4G3*

CHATILLON SUR SEINE *6F1* (1km Urban) **Camp Municipal Louis Rigoly, 21400 Chatillon-sur-Seine [03 80 91 03 05 or 03 80 91 13 19 (LS); fax 03 80 91 21 46; tourism-chatillon-sur-seine@wanadoo.fr]** Fr N, cross rv bdge (Seine); cont approx 400m twd town cent; at lge fountain forming rndabt turn L into street with Bureau de Tourisme on corner; foll sp to site. Fr S ignore all camping sp & cont into town cent to fountain, turn R & cont as above. Med, hdg/mkd pitch, pt sl, pt shd; wc; chem disp; shwrs inc; el pts (4-6A) €2.15-4.30 (rev pol); gas; lndtte; ice; shops 500m; tradsmn; snacks high ssn; playgrnd; htd pool adj; dogs; Eng spkn; quiet; cc acc; CCI. "Ancient town, museum, ruined chateau; gd rest adj; helpful warden; clean, tidy, well-spaced pitches; sm, clean san facs block; easy walk to town; poss diff twin-axle vans." ♦ ltd. 1 Apr-30 Sep. € 10.20   2005*

†**CHATILLON SUR SEINE** *6F1* (6km S Rural) **Camping de la Forge, La Forge, 21400 Ampilly-le-Sec [tel/fax 03 80 91 46 53; campinglaforge@wanadoo.fr; www.campingla forge.com]** S on N71, on leaving Buncey take 1st turn R immed after layby (narr rd). Site on R in 1km, on bend immed bef rv bdge, sp. Sm, pt shd; wc; chem disp; shwrs inc; el pts (16A) inc; lndtte; ice; shop 2km; tradsmn; rest 2.5km; BBQ; playgrnd; rv sw adj; dogs; phone; Eng spkn; adv bkg rec high ssn (dep req); quiet; red long stay; cc acc; CCI. "Helpful & friendly British owners; clean, modern san facs; CL-type site in lge garden; 5 acres of parkland bounded on one side by Rv Seine; much bird & wildlife; gd historic area; conv 3 wine-producing areas; area for lge m'vans across rd; vg." ♦ ltd. € 13.80   2005*

CHATONRUPT SOMMERMONT see Joinville *6E1*

CHATRE, LA *7A4* (5km SE Rural) **Intercommunal Le Val Vert, Vavres, 36400 La Chatre** [02 54 48 32 42; fax 02 54 48 32 87] Fr La Chatre take D943 dir Montlucon. On o'skts La Chatre turn R to Briantes, site sp at this junc. Or fr Montlucon on D943, turn L just bef La Chatre; site sp at this junc. Sm, hdg pitch, terr, pt shd; wc; chem disp; mv service pnt; shwrs inc; el pts (10A) inc; lndry rm; shop 1km; tradsmn; BBQ; playgrnd; htd pool 5km; statics; adv bkg; quiet; cc not acc; CCI. "Spacious, pleasant site; excel grounds; san facs poor quality & looking old; walk/cycle to shops; poss itinerants." ♦ 1 Jun-30 Sep. € 10.55   2004*

CHATRE, LA *7A4* (3km NW) **Camp Municipal Solange-Sand, Rue du Pont, 36400 Montgivray** [02 54 06 10 34 or 02 54 06 10 36; fax 02 54 06 10 39; mairie.montgivray@wanadoo.fr] Fr La Chatre take rd to Montgivray, foll camping sp. Fr Chateauroux on D943 SE twd La Chatre turn R 2km S of Nohant on D72. Site behind church. Med, mkd pitch, pt shd; wc; chem disp; shwrs inc; el pts (3-10A) €1.55-5.25 (poss rev pol); lndry rm; BBQ; dogs; quiet; CCI. "Pleasant site in chateau grounds; san facs old but v clean; gd access; warden needs to connect el pts but not disconnect (calls am & pm); gd rest adj; gd walks." ♦ 15 Mar-15 Oct. € 6.50   2005*

CHATRES SUR CHER see Villefranche sur Cher *4G3*

CHAUDEFONDS SUR LAYON see Chalonnes sur Loire *2G4*

CHAUDES AIGUES *9C1* (5km N) **Camping Le Belvedere, Le Pont-de-Lanau, 15260 Neuveglise** [04 71 23 50 50; fax 04 71 23 58 93; belvedere.cantal@wanadoo.fr; www.campinglebelvadere.com] S on A75/E11 exit junc 28 at St Flour; take D921 S twd Chaudes-Aigues; site at Pont-de-Lanau 300m off D921. Steep acc poss diff lge o'fits. Med, terr, pt shd; wc (some cont); chem disp; baby facs; sauna; shwrs inc; el pts (6A) inc; gas; lndtte; shop; rest; bar; BBQ; pool; rv sw; canoeing; fishing; sailing 15km; fitness rm; games rm; climbing; horseriding 20km; entmnt; 25% statics; dogs free; adv bkg; quiet; cc acc; CCI. "Views over Rv Truyere; nr mkt Neuveglise Fri; v friendly, peaceful, family-run site; steep terrs & tight pitches poss diff; not rec for disabled." ♦ 15 Apr-15 Oct. € 21.00 ABS - D12   2005*

CHAUDES AIGUES *9C1* (3km SW Rural) **Camp Municipal Le Chateau du Couffour, 15110 Chaudes-Aigues** [tel/fax 04 71 23 57 08 or 04 71 23 52 47 (Mairie)] Sp on L of D921 N dir Laguiole. Lge, pt shd; wc; shwrs inc; el pts (6A) €2.50; lndtte; shops, rest, snacks, bar 2.5km; playgrnd; pool 3km; sports area; tennis; fishing 1km; golf 2km; quiet. "V picturesque area; nice family-run site; 1000m altitude; attractive site wth fine views." ♦ 1 May-20 Oct. € 7.60   2004*

CHAUFFAILLES see Clayette, La *9A2*

CHAUMONT *6F1* (800m NW Urban) **Camp Municipal Parc Ste Marie, Rue des Tanneries, 52000 Chaumont** [03 25 32 11 98 or 03 25 30 60 27; fax 03 25 03 92 80; sports@ville-chaumont.fr] Site on Chaumont W by-pass joining N19 Troyes rd to N67 St Dizier rd. Do not try to app fr town cent. Sm, hdg pitch, pt sl, pt shd; wc (cont); chem disp; shwrs inc; el pts (10A) €2.20 (poss long lead req); shops 1km; tradsmn; snacks; playgrnd; 20% statics; dogs €1; poss cr; some traff noise; CCI. "Rec arr early; care needed with steep access to some sl pitches; ent barrier under warden control at all times; sh stay/NH." 2 May-30 Sep. € 9.00   2005*

CHAUMONT SUR LOIRE *4G2* (Rural) **Camp Municipal Grosse Greve, 41150 Chaumont-sur-Loire** [02 54 20 95 22 or 02 54 20 98 41 (Mairie); fax 02 54 20 99 61] Site sp in vill on D751. Med, pt shd; wc; chem disp; shwrs inc; el pts €1.80; lndry rm; BBQ; playgrnd; no twin-axle c'vans; quiet; CCI. "Easy walk to vill; interesting chateau." ♦ 15 May-30 Sep. € 8.10   2005*

CHAUNY *3C4* (2km NW) **Camp Municipal, Auberge de Jeunesse, Boulevard de Bad-Köstritz, 02300 Chauny** [03 23 52 09 96; fax 03 23 38 70 46] Travel N on D1 until junc with N32 sp Compiegne. Take N32 SW until junc with D56. Site sp 100m on L. Sm, hdg/mkd pitch, hdstg; pt sl, pt shd; wc (cont); shwrs inc; el pts (4-10A) €2-50-6.50; ice; shop 1km; playgrnd; sports area; water sports 2km; adv bkg; quiet; cc not acc. "Fair NH only; poss itinerant workers on site." ♦ 1 Jul-31 Aug. € 7.77   2004*

CHAUVIGNY *7A3* (1km Urban) **Camp Municipal de la Fontaine, Rue de la Fontaine, 86300 Chauvigny** [05 49 46 31 94; fax 05 49 46 40 60; chauvigny@cg86.fr] Fr N on D749. Site well sp fr Chauvigny. On ent vill turn L into Rue Vital Guerin & site on R. Med, hdg/mkd pitch, pt shd; wc (some cont); chem disp; mv service pnt; baby facs; shwrs; el pts (15A) inc; lndtte; shop 500m; tradsmn; BBQ; playgrnd; pool & tennis 1km; rv 1km; cycle hire; dogs; €0.76; adv bkg; CCI. "Popular; adj to park with lake; excel views of castle; access old town via steps; immac facs; el connected by warden; recep clsd 1200-1530; €8 extra for twin-axles." ♦ 15 Apr-10 Oct. € 11.00   2005*

CHAUVIGNY *7A3* (7km NW Rural) **Camp Municipal, 13 Rue de la Varenne, 86300 Bonnes** [05 49 56 44 34 or 05 49 56 41 17 (Mairie); fax 05 49 56 48 51; camping_bonnes86@hotmail.com] Sp fr N151 rd. Sp to site easily missed in vill. Med, pt shd; wc; chem disp; mv service pnt; shwrs inc; el pts (10A) inc; lndtte; ice; shop adj in vill; tradsmn; rest & bar 500m; pool adj; waterslide; playgrnd; rv adj; sand beach adj; dogs €1.05; poss cr; adv bkg; quiet; Eng spkn; dogs; CCI. "Old vill, attractive rv; friendly, helpful staff; barrier key dep €20; v clean & welcoming; vg value rest adj; poss itinerants on site." 15 May-15 Sep. € 10.65   2005*

FRANCE

CHAVANNES SUR SURAN *9A2* (500m E Rural) Camp Municipal, 01250 Chavannes-sur-Suran [04 74 51 70 52; fax 04 74 51 71 83] Turn E off N83 at St Etienne-du-Bois onto D3, cross D52 bef Treffort (v narr rds). Then steep climb & bends & after 6km turn N onto D936 sp Chavannes. Turn E at town hall (Mairie), site sp. Fr Bourg-en-Bresse turn E onto D936 sp Jasseron about 1km after joining N83 in Bourg. Foll D936 for approx 18km to Chavannes. Sm, hdg/mkd pitch, pt shd; wc; chem disp (wc); shwrs inc; el pts (5-10A) inc (poss rev pol); shop 500m; BBQ; quiet. "Spotless san facs; excel sycling, fishing; v pretty rvside site; gd touring base; gd walking; attractive vill; site self, warden calls; lge pitches; highly rec." ♦ ltd. 1 May-30 Sep. € 8.10   2004*

†**CHEF BOUTONNE** *7A2* (2km W Rural) Camping Le Moulin, Route de Brioux, 79110 Chef Boutonne [tel/fax 05 49 29 73 46; camping lemoulin.chef@tiscali.fr; www.campingchef.com] Fr D950 to or fr Poitiers, turn E onto D740 to Chef-Boutonne, site on R. Fr N10 turn onto D948 to Sauze-Vaussais then L onto D1 to Chef-Boutonne. Sm, hdg/mkd pitch, hdstg, pt shd; htd wc; chem disp; shwrs inc; el pts (6-10A) €2; lndtte; ice; shop 2km; rest; snacks; bar; playgrnd; pool & terr; dogs €1; poss cr; adv bkg; quiet; cc acc; red long stay/low ssn; CCI. "Friendly, British owners; conv Futuroscope & La Rochelle; htd san facs ltd low ssn; gd rest on site." ♦ € 12.80   2005*

CHEMERY see Contres *4G2*

CHEMILLE *2G4* (1km SW Rural) Camping de Coulvee, Route de Cholet, 49120 Chemille [02 41 30 42 42 or 02 41 30 39 97 (Mairie); fax 02 41 30 39 00] Fr Chemille dir Cholet, 1km on R on N160. Sm, hdg pitch, terr, pt shd; wc; chem disp; mv service pnt; shwrs inc; el pts (3-10A) €2.80-3.80; lndtte; ice; tradsmn; bar; BBQ on lakeside or on pitch with disclaimer; playgrnd; sm sand beach; lake sw; pedaloes; activities; dogs €1.40; quiet; adv bkg; ltd Eng spkn; cc not acc; 10% red 28 days; CCI. "V clean facs; v helpful; lovely pitches; office clsd 1230-1500; mkt Thu." ♦ 1 May-15 Sep. € 9.20   2004*

CHENAC ST SEURIN D'UZET see Cozes *7B1*

CHENONCEAUX *4G2* (1.5km E Rural) Camp Municipal, Rue de l'Ecluse, 37150 Chisseaux [02 47 23 87 10 or 02 47 23 90 75 (Mairie); fax 02 47 23 95 70] E fr Chenonceaux on D176; cross bdge; immed hard R & foll rv bank; site in 300m. Med, mkd pitch, pt shd; wc; shwrs inc; el pts (6A) inc (rev pol); lndtte; shop 1km; supmkt 6km; tradsmn; playgrnd; tennis; adv bkg; quiet tho some rd/rlwy noise; CCI. "Dep req for security card; many itinerants." ♦ 1 May-30 Aug. € 11.80   2004*

CHENONCEAUX *4G2* (1.5km S) Camping Le Moulin Fort, 37150 Francueil [02 47 23 86 22; fax 02 47 23 80 93; lemoulinfort@wanadoo.fr; www. lemoulinfort.com] Site on S bank of Rv Cher just of N76. Fr Tours take N76 signposted Vierzon. Keep on N76 by-passing Bléré. In 5km turn N to cross rv but take sm rd on R to site, bef actually x-ing bdge. Site well sp. Med, hdg/mkd pitch, pt shd; wc; chem disp; baby facs; shwrs inc; el pts (6A) inc (long lead poss req); gas; lndtte; ice; shop; tradsmn; rest; snacks; bar; BBQ (gas/charcoal); playgrnd; pool & paddling pool; fishing; cycle hire; TV rm; dogs €3; office clsd 1200-1500; Eng spkn; adv bkg ess (min 3 nts); a little noise fr rlwy; red low ssn; cc acc; CCI. "Lovely, well-kept site; beautiful setting; v friendly & helpful British owners; some sm pitches; poss security prob due access to site fr rv bank; gd facs." ♦ 1 Apr-30 Sep. € 24.00 ABS - L08   2005*

CHENONCEAUX *4G2* (2km W Rural) Camp Municipal de l'Isle, Route de Blere, 37150 Civray-de-Touraine [02 47 23 62 80 or 02 47 29 90 75 (Mairie); fax 02 47 23 62 88; civraydetouraine@ wanadoo.fr] On N76 bet Blere & Montrichard site on N bank of Rv Cher, sp fr both dirs; ent 100m after x-ing narr bdge. V diff for car & c'van to make R turn into narr ent. Instead pass ent, turn around & turn L into ent. Sm, pt shd; wc; chem disp; mv service pnt; shwrs inc; el pts (5A) €2.50; shop 1km; tradsmn; pool 3km; rv adj; quiet but poss noise fr nrby rd & rlwy; CCI. "Gd well-maintained site; v attractive rv lock & weir 500m; gd sh stay." ♦ 19 Jun-31 Aug. € 8.50   2004*

CHENS SUR LEMAN see Douvaine *9A3*

†**CHERBOURG** *1C4* (12km NE Coastal) Camping La Plage, 2 Village de Freval, 50840 Fermanville [02 33 54 38 84; fax 02 33 54 74 30] Fr Cherbourg on D116 dir Barfleur, site in 12km on L. Med, some hdg pitch, unshd; wc; chem disp; shwrs inc; el pts (6A) €3.50; snacks; bar; playgrnd; beach 300m; 70% statics; dogs €1.60; poss cr; adv bkg ess summer, rec winter; quiet. "Friendly owner; conv for ferry & D-Day landing beaches; gd sh stay/NH." € 11.50   2004*

CHERBOURG *1C4* (5km E Urban/Coastal) Camping Espace Loisirs de Collignon, 50110 Tourlaville [02 33 20 16 88; fax 02 33 20 53 03; VPT50@wanadoo.fr] Foll sp fr new terminal for Espace Loisirs Collignon or Tourlaville Plage; site on D116; turn L at new lge rndabt beyond Tourlaville boundary. Med, mkd pitch, unshd; wc; chem disp; shwrs inc; el pts (10A) inc; gas; lndry rm; shops 1.5km; pool; sand beach adj; fishing, sw & watersports adj; games rm; entmnt; TV; 30% statics; poss cr; adv bkg (rec high ssn); noisy high ssn (youth groups); some rd noise; cc acc; CCI. "Lge landscaped complex; generous pitches; poor security, open to public; conv ferries but check exit barrier key works if leaving early morning; NH/sh stay only." ♦ 23 May-30 Sep. € 16.85   2004*

CHERBOURG *1C4* (8km E Coastal) **Camp Municipal du Fort, 50110 Bretteville [02 33 22 27 60]** Immed exit car ferries in Cherbourg, turn L on D116. On leaving Bretteville turn sharp L at junc of D116 & D611, 1st turn R. App poss diff lge o'fits. Med, pt sl, unshd; wc; chem disp; shwrs; el pts (10A) €2.30; shops 4km; BBQ; playgrnd; shgl beach adj; 90% statics; quiet. "Sep area tourers, sm pitches; some pitches view of coast; locked 2200-0700; poss diff in wet; some pitches diff lge o'fits; sh stay only."
1 May-30 Sep. € 8.50   2003*

CHERBOURG *1C4* (10km E Coastal) **LES CASTELS L'Anse du Brick, Route du Val de Saire, 50330 Maupertus-sur-Mer [02 33 54 33 57; fax 02 33 54 49 66; welcome@anse-du-brick. com; www.anse-du-brick.com]** Fr Cherbourg ferry take 1st L onto Rue du 8 Mai which becomes D116 twd Barfleur. Cont past Le Becquet & Bretteville for approx 9km to site ent on R. Fr S on N13 turn R twd ferry port at 1st lge rndabt. At 2nd rndabt in Tourlaville cont strt sp Tourlaville. Cont thro 4 set traff lts then turn R onto D116 coast rd twd Collignon/Barfleur. Pass Le Becquet & Bretteville for approx 8km, site on R. Sh, steep hill to site ent. Med, hdg/mkd pitch, terr, shd; wc; mv service pnt; chem disp; serviced pitches; baby facs; shwrs inc; el pts (10A) inc (poss rev pol); gas; lndtte; shop & 3km; tradsmn; rest; snacks; bar; BBQ; playgrnd; 2 htd pools; paddling pool; waterslide; sand beach adj; tennis; cycle hire; archery; games/TV rm; golf 10km; internet; dogs €2.10; poss cr; recep 0800-1900; adv bkg; quiet; cc acc; CCI. "Well-kept, clean site; excel for dogs - allowed on adj beach; some pitches for lge o'fits; cliff behind so no sat TV recep; plenty to do in area; conv Landing Beaches." ♦
1 Apr-30 Sep. € 26.40 (CChq acc) ABS - N14   2005*

†CHERBOURG *1C4* (6km S Rural) **Camping Le Village Vert (formerly Les Pins), 50470 Tollevast [02 33 43 00 78; fax 02 33 43 03 38; www. le-village-vert.com]** S'bound take N13 sp Caen out of town. Cont on N13 fr Auchan rndabt for approx 5km to D56 slip rd sp Delasse. Turn L at x-rds over N13 onto N13 sp Cherbourg. Site on R approx 3.5km, sp nr Auchan hypmkt. N'bound exit sp Tollevast & site. Lge, some hdstg, pt sl, pt shd; wc; chem disp; mv service pnt; shwrs inc; baby facs; el pts (6A) inc (check rev pol); gas; lndry rm; sm shop & 1km; tradsmn; rest 200m; playgrnd; tennis; golf & horseriding 2km; 95% statics (sep); dogs €1; Eng spkn; adv bkg; quiet but poss rd noise at front of site; cc acc; red CCI. "Mainly permanent statics; poss itinerants; ltd space for tourers but spacious pitches; woodland setting; coded security barriers; poss waterlogged pitches in wet weather; open san facs block poss cold in winter; v conv ferries 10km; friendly & efficient; night arrivals area; conv NH for ferries." ♦ € 13.50   2005*

†CHERBOURG *1C4* (3km NW Coastal) **Camp Municipal de la Saline, 50120 Equeurdreville-Hainneville [02 33 93 88 33 or 02 33 53 96 00 (Mairie); fax 02 33 93 12 70; mairie-equeur dreville@dialoleane.com]** Fr ferry terminal foll D901 & sp Beaumont-Hague. On dual c'way beside sea look out for site sp to L. Med, hdg pitch, hdstg, pt sl, terr, pt shd; htd wc (male cont); chem disp; shwrs inc; el pts (6A) inc; shop; beach adj; fishing; 30% statics; rd noise; CCI. "Sea view; sandy beach & pier; bowls & skateboard park adj; cylce path to town; gd shwrs; site unmanned w/e low ssn."
€ 12.20   2005*

CHERRUEIX see Dol de Bretagne *2E4*

CHERVEUX see Niort *7A2*

†CHESNE, LE *5C1* (2km NE Rural) **Camp Departmental du Lac de Bairon, 08390 Le Chesne [03 24 30 11 66]** Leave A203 exit Sedan, W on D764, in 500m L on D977 sp Vouziers. 2km bef Le Chesne R on D12, in 500m L on D312. Site 2km on L. Lge, mkd pitch, hdstg, pt shd; wc; chem disp; shwrs inc; el pts (6-10A) €2.50-4.20; ice; lndtte; shop 2km; tradsmn; snacks; bar; playgrnd; tennis; cycle hire; watersports; entmnts; lake sw, sand beach, fishing, boat & canoe hire; TV rm; entmnt; phone; dogs €1; poss cr; noisy; forest walks; CCI. "Excel site; modern, clean san facs; poss diff site ent with lge o'fits." ♦ € 8.10   2005*

CHEVENON see Nevers *4H4*

CHEVERNY *4G2* (Rural) **Camping Les Saules, 102 Route de Contres, 41700 Cheverny [02 54 79 90 01; fax 02 54 79 28 34; contact@camping-cheverny. com; www.camping-cheverny.com]** Exit A10 junc 17 dir Blois Sud onto D765 to Romorantin. At Cour-Cheverny foll sp Cheverny & chateau. Fr S on D956 turn R onto D102 just N of Contres, site on L just bef Cheverny. Lge, mkd pitch, hdstg, pt shd; wc; chem disp; mv service pnt; baby facs; shwrs inc; el pts (6A) €3.50; gas; lndtte; shop; rest; snacks; bar; BBQ; playgrnd; pool; fishing; tennis; golf nr; excursions; games rm; cycle hire; TV; dogs €2; adv bkg rec high ssn; Eng spkn; quiet; cc acc; red long stay/low ssn; CCI. "Site conv many chateaux; in Vallee des Rois; many cycle & walking routes nr; vg." ♦ 1 Apr-15 Oct. € 25.00   2005*

See advertisement on next page

CHEVERNY *4G2* (3km N Urban) **Camping Essi Le Casseux, 41700 Cour-Cheverny [02 54 79 95 63]** Well sp fr all dirs; foll 'camping' sp around Cour-Cheverny. Sm, shd; wc; chem disp; shwrs; el pts (5A) €1.50; no adv bkg; quiet. "Warden calls am & pm; footpath fr site to town; NH only."
1 Jun-15 Sep. € 6.60   2004*

CHEYLARD, LE see St Agreve *9C2*

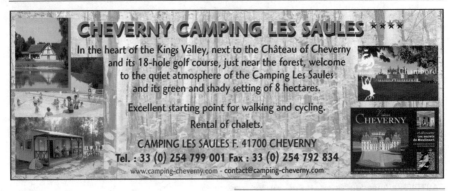

CHEZERY FORENS *9A3* (500m S Rural) **Camp Municipal de la Valserine, 01410 Chezery-Forens** [tel/fax 04 50 56 20 88] Site off D991 on app to vill. Sm, pt shd; wc; chem disp; shwrs inc; el pts (6-10A) inc; shops adj; rv adj; quiet. "Gd walks." 15 Apr-30 Sep. € 8.60   2004*

CHILLY LE VIGNOBLE see Lons le Saunier *6H2*

CHINON *4G1* (500m SW Urban) **Camp Municipal de L'Ile Auger, Quay Danton, 37500 Chinon** [02 47 93 08 35 or 02 47 93 53 00; fax 02 47 98 47 92] On S side of rv at bdge. Fr S foll sp Chinon St Jacques; when app bdge on 1-way 'loop', avoid R lane indicated for x-ing bdge & cont strt past S end of main bdge to site on R. Fr N foll sp 'Centre Ville' round castle, cross bdge, site on R. Well sp in town & opp castle. Lge, mkd pitch, pt shd; wc (some cont); chem disp; mv service pnt; baby facs; shwrs inc; el pts (4-12A) €1.80-3.10 (poss rev pol) lndtte; ice; shop 200m; snacks adj; playgrnd; htd pool 300m; sat TV; dogs €0.85; phone; quiet; cc acc; CCI. "Gd base for town, chateaux, wine caves & vineyards; vg value; delightful position; beautiful views of chateau; excel, well-maintained; plenty san facs both modern & dated; if clsd site yourself; elec connected by warden; twin-axles discretionary; poss midge problem; town walking dist." ◆ 15 Mar-15 Oct. € 11.80   2005*

CHINON *4G1* (14km NW) **Camping Belle Rive formerly (Intercommunal Bellerive), 37500 Candes-St Martin** [02 47 95 98 11; fax 02 47 95 80 95; cte.de.cnes.RGV@wanadoo.fr] Fr Chinon take D751. Site on R bef junc with D7, on S bank of Rv Vienne. Med, mkd pitch, pt shd; wc; shwrs; el pts (10A) inc; lndtte; ice; shops 1km; tradsmn; rv sw 1km; playgrnd; fishing adj; dogs €0.80; adv bkg; quiet; CCI. "Pleasant rvside site, conv Saumur & chateaux; san facs on two floors." ◆ 12 Jun-12 Sep. € 8.51   2004*

CHIRAC see Marvejols *9D1*

CHOISY see Annecy *9B3*

CHOLET *2H4* (5km SE Rural) **Camping Village Vacances Le Lac de Ribou, Allee Leon Mandin, 49300 Cholet** [02 41 49 74 30; fax 02 41 58 21 22; lacderibou@cholet-sports-loisirs.fr; www.cholet-sports-loisirs.com] Fr Cholet ring rd foll sp Parc des Loisirs de Ribou. Sp fr Cholet. Lge, hdg/mkd pitch, hdstg, terr, pt shd; htd wc; chem disp; mv service pnt; serviced pitches; shwrs inc; el pts (10A) €5.10 (long lead req); lndtte; tradsmn; shop; hypmkt 1.5km; rest; snacks; bar; BBQ; playgrnd; 2 htd pools; waterslides; lake sw & sand beach 500m; fishing; boating; windsurfing; skating; tennis; archery; golf nr; entmnt; child entmnt; TV rm; dogs €1.70; Holiday Village open all year; poss cr; Eng spkn; adv bkg ess; quiet; cc acc; 5% red CCI. "Excel touring area; excel site." ◆ 1 Apr-30 Sep. € 18.90   2005*

See advertisement opposite

CHOLET *2H4* (8km SE) **Camping du Verdon, Le Bois Neuf, Route du Verdon, 49280 La Tessoualle** [02 41 49 74 61; fax 02 41 58 21 22] D258 fr Cholet ring rd, turn L in 6km. Site well sp at Barrage du Verdon. Sm, hdg pitch, pt shd; wc; chem disp; shwrs; el pts (5A) €2.86; shop; rest, snacks, bar adj; lake sw & land beach; dogs; Eng spkn; adv bkg; quiet; CCI. "Windsurfing on Lac du Verdon; excel walking, cycling; gd value; helpful wardens at bar adj; san facs not the best; gd long/sh stay." 1 Jul-31 Aug. € 9.98   2005*

CHORGES *9D3* (2.5km E Rural) **Camping Le Rio Claret, Les Chabes, 05230 Chorges** [tel/fax 04 92 50 62 16; rio-claret@wanadoo.fr; www.camping-lerioclaret.com] Fr Gap foll N94 E dir Embrun; take main rd by-passing Chorges & 4km past traff lts look for sp to site. Turn L at junc (narr lane), turn R & R again to site. Sm, mkd pitch, pt shd; wc (some cont); chem disp; mv service pnt; shwrs inc; el pts (3-10A) €2.50-3.80; lndry rm; tradsmn; shop 2.4km; rest; snacks; bar; playgrnd; lake sw & beach 2km; TV; 10% statics; dogs €2; phone; adv bkg; some rd noise at lower level. "Conv touring base; day trip to Italy via Briancon; boat excursions; spectacular views; gd san facs; excel meals; v helpful, pleasant owners; vg long/sh stay." ◆ 1 May-30 Sep. € 12.00   2004*

Camping ★★★★ Lac de Ribou
Village Vacances 49300 - CHOLET lacderibou@cholet-sports-loisirs.fr

Information and reservations: Tel.: 33 (0) 241 49 74 30 - Fax: 33 (0) 241 58 21 22

Cholet Sports loisirs • www.cholet-sports-loisirs.com
Campingsite**: 162 pitches. 15 chalets, 14 mobile homes • Holiday center: 30 cabins, simple rent, but also half and full pension possible. Bar - Restaurant - Take away meals - Situated in a rural park of 8 ha. 2 supervised swimming pools with waterslides security staff, tennis, volleyball, table football, table tennis, etc. Daytime entertainment: for adults and children from 3 years on. Nighttime entertainment: shows, cabaret, games, dancing nights, etc. • 1,5 km from the supermarket. • At 500 m. from a recreation park: water sports, archery, climbing, mountainbikes, horseback riding, and swimming with supervision. • 18 holes golf course nearby • Region of wine culture. • 1 hour from the Atlantic Ocean • 20 km from Puy du Fou. Holiday Village open all year, campsite open from 1.4 till 30.9.**

FRANCE

CHORGES *9D3* (5km E Rural) **Camping Club Le Roustou**, 05230 Prunieres [04 92 50 62 63; fax 04 92 50 90 48; info@campingleroustou.com; www.campingleroustou.com] E fr Gap on N94. Site on side of Lac de Serre-Poncon. Do not attempt to go to Prunieres vill, always stay on N94. Lge, mkd pitch, hdstg, terr, pt shd; wc; own san rec; chem disp; mv service pnt; baby facs; shwrs inc; el pts (4A) inc; lndtte; shops 10km; tradsmn; snacks; bar; playgrnd; pool (no shorts); beach addition; lake sw; canoe hire; tennis; cycle hire; games area; TV; dogs €0.80; poss cr; Eng spkn; quiet; cc acc; CCI. "Beautiful views; excel scenery; relaxing area; always park on E side in case of poss prob with wind; gd long/sh stay." 1 May-30 Sep. € 20.70
2004*

CHORGES *9D3* (6km SE) **Camping Le Nautic, Lac de Serre-Poncon**, 05230 Prunieres [04 92 50 62 49; fax 04 92 53 58 42; campinglenautic@wanadoo.fr; www.campinglenautic.com] Fr Gap or Embrun take N94, site sp bet Savines & Chorges. Med, terr, shd; wc; chem disp; shwrs; el pts (6A) €3; gas; ice; shop; snacks; playgrnd; pool; shgl beach & lake sw; boating; dogs €1.50; adv bkg; quiet. "Lake sw excel in sheltered bay; vg san facs." 15 Jun-15 Sep.
€ 17.20 (CChq acc)
2005*

CHORGES *9D3* (10km SW Rural) **Camping La Viste, Le Belvedere de Serre-Poncon, Rousset, 05190 Espinasses** [04 92 54 43 39; fax 04 92 54 42 45; camping@laviste.fr; www. laviste.fr] N on A51 or N85 twds Gap; take the D942 sp Barcelonnette; after Espinasses turn L onto D3 to Barrage de Serre-Poncon; then L onto D103. Site on L. NB D3 long, v steep climb, hairpin bends. Med, hdg/mkd pitch, pt sl, pt shd; wc (cont); chem disp; mv service pnt; shwrs inc; el pts (5A) €2.90; gas; lndtte; shop & 4km; tradsmn; rest; snacks; bar; BBQ; playgrnd; pool; lake sw 2km; phone; adv bkg; quiet; cc acc; CCI. "Gd long stay; ltd facs low ssn; site o'looks Lac de Serre-Poncon (amenity area); cool at night; height 770m; gd for walking & touring by rd; site rds narr; access diff lge o'fits." ♦ ltd.
15 May-15 Sep. € 16.60
2005*

CIOTAT, LA *10F3* (2km NE Coastal) **Camping Le St Jean, 30 Ave de St Jean**, 13600 La Ciotat [04 42 83 13 01; fax 04 42 71 46 41; stjean@easynet.fr] E on La Ciotat-Plage to far end & foll sp to site on old D559, not new town by-pass. Med, shd; wc; shwrs; el pts (6A) inc; gas; rest; snacks; lndtte; ice; shop; playgrnd; direct access to beach adj; tennis; dogs €4; poss cr; quiet. "Sm pitches." ♦ 3 Apr-30 Sep. € 25.30 (3 persons)
2003*

CIOTAT, LA *10F3* (3km NE Coastal) **Camping Les Oliviers, Route de Bord de Mer**, 13600 La Ciotat [04 42 83 15 04; fax 04 42 83 94 43] Fr La Ciotat, foll D559 coast rd sp Bandol & Toulon. Site in 4km, look for lge sp on L. Caution x-ing dual c'way. V lge, pt sl, terr; pt shd; wc; chem disp; shwrs inc; el pts (3-6A) €2.60-6.10; gas; lndtte; ice; shops 300m; rest, snacks, bar 300m; playgrnd; pool; sand/shgle beach 3km; tennis; 5% statics; dogs €1; bus 300m; Eng spkn; adv bkg; quiet but some noise fr main rd & rlwy adj; cc acc; CCI. "Many pitches have sea view; friendly staff; care on ent due to lge boulders; vg long stay." ♦ ltd 15 Mar-15 Sep. € 15.50   2003*

†**CIOTAT, LA** *10F3* (3km E Coastal) **Camping Santa Gusta, Fontsainte**, 13600 La Ciotat [04 42 83 14 17; fax 04 42 08 90 93] Foll D559 coast rd fr La Ciotat twd Les Lecques to Total filling stn on R. Site down by filling stn. Lge, pt sl, pt shd; wc (cont); chem disp (wc); shwrs inc; el pts (5A) €2.90; lndtte; shop; rest, snacks, bar high ssn; playgrand; rocky beach adj; boat-launching facs; entmnt; 95% statics; poss cr; quiet; CCI. "San facs open 0730-2000; adj beach not suitable for bathing; v basic facs low ssn; smart card access; NH only." € 18.00
2002*

CIVRAY *7A2* (1km NE Urban) **Camp Municipal Les Aulnes, Les Coteaux de Roche**, 86400 Civray [05 49 87 17 24] Civray 9km E of N10 halfway bet Poitiers & Angouleme. Site outside town SE of junc of D1 & D148. Sp on D148 & on S by-pass. Avoid town cent narr rds. Med, mkd pitch, pt sl, pt shd; wc (cont); chem disp (wc); shwrs; el pts (6-10A) €1.80; lndry rm; shop 500m; snacks; bar; BBQ; playgrnd; htd pool 1km; rv sw & fishing adj; cycle hire; golf; few statics; dogs; Eng spkn; quiet; cc acc; CCI. "V pleasant by rv but spoilt by old san facs; conv town cent; pitches soft when wet." Easter-15 Oct.
€ 10.50
2005*

Will you fill in the site report forms at the back of the guide, or shall I?

CLAIRVAUX LES LACS *6H2* (Rural) **Camp Municipal Le Lac de Narlay, Le Frasnois, 39130 Clairvaux-les-Lacs [03 84 25 58 74 (Mairie)]** On N5 fr Champagnole to St Laurent turn R onto D75 at Pont de Chaux; go to Le Frasnois & site sp in vill. Med, pt sl, pt terr, pt shd; wc (some cont); chem disp (wc only); shwrs inc; el pts inc; lndry rm; snacks; shops 500m; playgrnd; tennis; cycle hire; lake sw adj; dogs; phone; 5% statics; poss cr; noisy; Eng spkn; CCI. "Site yourself warden calls each pm; splendid Cascades du Herisson in 3 mins drive; many walks in vicinity; only terr pitches have el pts; many teenage campers; pizza van calls Wed & Sat; bread avail fr adj farm." 15 May-15 Sep. € 13.00
2004*

CLAIRVAUX LES LACS *6H2* (1.2km SE Rural) **Yelloh! Village Le Fayolan, Chemin de Langard, 39130 Clairvaux-les-Lacs [03 84 25 26 19 or 08 20 00 55 93; fax 03 84 25 26 20; relais.soleil.jura@ wanadoo.fr or reservation@rsl39.com; www. campingfayolan.com or www.vacances-nature.com]** Fr town foll campsite sp, last site along lane adj to lake. V lge, hdg/mkd pitch, terr, pt shd; wc; serviced pitches; chem disp; shwrs inc; el pts (6A) inc; gas; lndtte; ice; shop; rest; snacks; bar; playgrnd; htd pool; sand lake beach adj; games rm; tennis 1km; cycle hire; entmnt; child entmnt; TV; 16% statics; dogs €3.50; Eng spkn; adv bkg rec (dep req + bkg fee); quiet; red low ssn; cc acc; CCI. "Excel, clean site; extra for lakeside pitches high ssn; v pleasant sm town in easy walking dist; lovely area." ♦ 5 May-10 Sep. € 30.00   2005*

See advertisement above

CLAIRVAUX LES LACS *6H2* (1km S Rural) **Camping La Grisiere et Europe Vacances, Chemin Langard,** 39130 Clairvaux-les-Lacs [03 84 25 80 48; fax 03 84 25 22 34; bailly@la-grisiere.com; www.la-grisiere.com] Turn S off N78 in Clairvaux opp church onto D118 sp St Claude. Fork R in 500m & foll site sps to lake. V lge, mkd pitch, pt sl, pt shd; htd wc (some cont); chem disp; mv service pnt; shwrs inc; el pts (6-10A) €2.50; gas; lndtte; ice; shop; tradsmn; snacks; bar; BBQ; playgrnd; lake sw & beach adj; rv sw 5km; fishing; watersports; tennis 1km; games rm; cycle hire; internet; TV; 3% statics; dogs €0.80; phone; Eng spkn; no adv bkg; cc acc; red low ssn; CCI. "Lovely views in beautiful area; sm pitches; vg site." ♦ 1 May-30 Sep. € 17.30   2005*

See advertisement above

CLAIRVAUX LES LACS *6H2* (1km S Rural) Camping Le Grand Lac, Chemin du Langard, 39130 Clairvaux-les-Lacs [03 84 25 22 14; fax 05 34 25 26 20; reservation@rsl39.com; www.vacances-nature.com] SE on N78 fr Lons-le-Saunier; in Clairvaux vill turn R opp church on L, 1st R then fork R, foll sp. Ent 2.7m wide. Lge, pt shd; wc; mv service pnt; baby facs; shwrs inc; el pts (6A) inc; lndtte; shop; tradsn; BBQ; sand beach; fishing; boating; 30% statics; Eng spkn; cc acc. "Lovely country nr Jura mountains; gd site." 5 May-4 Sep. € 19.00   2004*

CLAIRVAUX LES LACS *6H2* (10km S Rural) Camping Le Val d'Ete, 39130 Etival [tel/fax 03 84 44 87 31] E fr Lons-le-Saunier on N78 to Clairvaux-les-Lacs. In Clairvaux foll camping sp thro town. Then ignore them & take D118 to Chatel-de-Joux & Etival. Site on L on ent to vill. Sm, mkd pitch, sl, pt shd; htd wc (cont); chem disp (wc); shwrs inc; el pts (6A) €2.50; gas 10km; lndtte; shops 10km; tradsmn; snacks; bar 10km; playgrnd; lake sw 500m; games area; 30% statics; adv bkg; quiet; red low ssn. CCI. "Guided walks, superb wild flowers; lovely position; helpful owner; site untidy with old statics." 5 Jul-31 Aug. € 8.20   2003*

CLAIRVAUX LES LACS *6H2* (10km SW Rural) Camping Surchauffant, Pont de la Pyle, 39270 La Tour-du-Meix [03 84 25 41 08; fax 03 84 35 56 88; surchauffant@chalain.com; www.chalain.com] Fr Clairvaux S on D27 or D49 to D470. Foll sp Lac de Vouglans, site sp. Lge, pt sl, pt shd; wc; shwrs inc; el pts (5A) €2.60; lndtte; shops adj; rest, snacks & bar; BBQ; playgrnd; pool; paddling pool; dir access to lake 120m; sailing; watersports; entmnt; TV rm; statics; dogs €1.55; Eng spkn; adv bkg; quiet; cc acc. "Vg facs; lovely location; hiking trails." ♦ 1 May-12 Sep. € 20.00   2005*

See advertisement on page 300

CLAIRVAUX LES LACS *6H2* (4km W Rural) Camping Le Moulin, 39130 Patornay [03 84 48 31 21; fax 03 84 44 71 21; contact@camping-moulin.com; www.camping-moulin.com] Exit A39 junc 9 dir Lons-le-Saunier, on N78 SE to Pont-de-Poitte. After x-ing bdge over Rv Ain, ent to site on L. Lge, hdg pitch, hdstg, pt terr, shd; wc; chem disp; mv service pnt; baby facs; shwrs inc; el pts (6A) inc; gas; lndtte; ice; shop; tradsmn; snacks; bar; playgrnd; pool; waterslide; rv sw & sand beach 5km; fishing; games area; games rm; entmnt; child entmnt; TV; dogs €1.50; phone; poss cr; Eng spkn; adv bkg; cc acc; red low ssn; CCI. "Site clsd 1200-1400, do not arr during this time as narr app rd poss blocked with queuing traff; excel cent for touring Jura; vg site." ♦ 20 May-17 Sep. € 26.00   2005*

See advertisement on next page

CLAIRVAUX LES LACS *6H2* (7km W Rural) Camping Beauregard, 2 Grande Rue, 39130 Mesnois [tel/fax 03 84 48 32 51; reception@ juracampingbeauregard.com; www.juracamping beauregard.com] Fr Lons on N78 about 1km bef Pont de Poitte turn L on D151. Site 1km on L opp rd junc to Pont de Poitte. Med, hdg/mkd pitch, hdstg, pt sl, pt shd; wc (some cont); chem disp; baby facs; shwrs inc; el pts (6A) €2.60; gas; lndtte; shop 5km; tradsmn; rest; bar; playgrnd; htd pool high ssn; sand beach 500m; lake sw 7km; kayaking nr; tennis; cycle hire; games rm; 10% statics; dogs €0.60; poss cr; Eng spkn; adv bkg (dep req); quiet; cc acc. "Excel san facs; gd size plots; poss req long elec lead; well-run, v clean; excel info map fr recep for touring many beautiful lakes & waterfalls nrby; excel rest; v narr site rds; vg long/sh stay." ♦ 1 Apr-30 Sep. € 20.00   2005*

See advertisement below

As we're travelling out of season, we'd better phone ahead to check that the site is actually open.

CLAMECY *4G4* (5km NE) Camping Le Bois Joli, Route de Villeprenoy, 89480 Andryes [tel/fax 03 86 81 70 48; info@campingauboisjoli.com; www.campingauboisjoli.com] S on N151 fr Auxerre to Coulanges-sur-Yonne. W on D39 sp Andryes, foll sps 'Camping Andryes', site 1km after vill. Med, mkd pitch, hdstg, terr, shd; htd wc; chem disp; mv service pnt; baby facs; baby facs; fam bthrm; shwrs inc; el pts (6A) inc; gas; lndry rm; shop; tradsmn; snacks; bar; BBQ; playgrnd; pool inc; rv sw, fishing & boat hire 2km; tennis; cycle hire; internet; TV; 10% statics; dogs €2; phone; Eng spkn; quiet; CCI. "New Dutch owners 2005; beautiful countryside; excel wine region; gd pitches; excel facs." ♦ 1 Apr-31 Oct. € 17.50   2005*

CLAMECY *4G4* (S Urban) Camp Municipal du Pont-Picot, Rue de Chevroche, 58500 Clamecy [03 86 27 05 97] Fr S via Nevers, Varzy Nisi turn R immed after level x-ing 1km bef Clamecy. Site sp 2.4km. Fr N Auxerre, Avallon cross rv foll camping sp. Sp but rte takes out of town & doubles back. App satisfactory, but single lane rd. Med, pt sl, pt shd; wc; chem disp; shwrs inc; el pts (5A) inc; lndry rm; shops 1km; tradsmn; playgrnd; sw; poss cr; Eng spkn; quiet; CCI. "Pleasant site; facs poss inadequate when busy; not rec as NH - access tortuous & narr; town 10 min walk on towpath; quiet site bet rv & canal with beautiful surroundings; Vezelay (20km) worth a visit; gd long stay." ♦ 1 May-30 Sep. € 14.40   2005*

CLAYETTE, LA *9A2* (8km NE Rural) **Camping Chateau de Montrouant, 71800 Gibles** [03 85 84 54 30; fax 03 85 84 52 80]
Fr N79 at Trivy take D41 to Dompierre-les-Ormes & Montmelard, then Gibles. Site sp fr Gibles. Sm, mkd pitch. Pt sl, pt shd; wc; chem disp; shwrs inc; el pts (6A) €3.50; lndry rm; basic shop 4km; rest 1.5km; snacks; bar; playgrnd; pool; paddling pool; fishing lake; sh tennis; TV; dogs; v quiet. "Vg; v hospitable owners; site unsuitable for lge o'fits/m'vans due steep rds." ♦ ltd. 1 Jun-4 Sep. € 15.70 (CChq acc)
2004*

†**CLAYETTE, LA** *9A2* (500m E Urban) **Camp Municipal Les Bruyeres, Route de St Bonnet-de-Joux, 71800 La Clayette** [03 85 28 09 15; fax 03 85 28 17 16] Site on D79, 100m fr D987 & lake. Med, hdg/mkd pitch, hdstg, pt sl, shd; htd wc; chem disp; mv service pnt; shwrs inc; el pts (6A) inc; gas; lndtte; shops adj; tradsmn; snacks, bar 500m; BBQ; playgrnd; htd pool adj Juln, Jul, Aug; tennis; games area; boating; mini-golf; entmnt; 10% statics; dogs; phone; poss cr; adv bkg; quiet; CCI. "Excel site; v clean, pleasant & well-maintained; friendly, helpful staff; gd-sized pitches; attractive sm town in Beaujolais area; 3 min walk fr supmkt; numerous wine cellars; overlooks lake with chateau." ♦
€ 14.40   2004*

CLAYETTE, LA *9A2* (13km S) **Camp Municipal Les Feuilles, Rue de Chatillon, 71170 Chauffailles** [03 85 26 48 12; fax 03 85 26 55 02; st.marie.chauffailles@wanadoo.fr]
S fr La Clayette on D985 (dir Les Echarmeaux), turn R at camp sp down hill & cross Rv Botoret to site. Med, hdg/mkd pitch, hdstg, pt shd; wc; chem disp; shwrs; el pts (5-10A) €2.56-5.12; lndry Rm; supmkt 500m; playgrnd; pool adj; fishing; tennis; games rm; TV; 30% statics; Eng spkn; adv bkg ess; quiet; 10% red CCI. "Walking & wine area, easy walk to interesting town; gd san facs but hot water to shwrs & dishwashing only; attractive site." 1 May-30 Sep.
€ 8.20   2005*

CLECY see Thury Harcourt *3D1*

CLELLES *9C3* (4km N Rural) **Camp Municipal de la Chabannerie, 38930 St Martin-de-Clelles** [tel/fax 04 76 34 00 38; sylvaincouetoux@ clubinternet.fr] N75 fr Grenoble, after St Michel-les-Portes look for rest on R. Turn L after 300m to St Martin-de-Clelles, site sp. Site well sp fr N & S. Sm, mkd pitch, hdstg, terr, pt shd; wc; chem disp; shwrs inc; el pts (10A) €2.40; gas; lndtte; sm shop; tradsmn; snacks; bar; no BBQs; playgrnd; pool; TV rm; dogs €1.50; phone; Eng spkn; adv bkg; quiet; CCI. "Conv Vercours National Park & mountains; gd walking; v quiet site with 38 species of orchids in ssn." ♦ 1 Apr-30 Oct. € 15.00   2004*

CLELLES *9C3* (6km SE Rural) **Camping a la Ferme (Gabert), 38930 Clelles** [04 76 34 42 51]
Fr N75 take D526 thro vill of Clelles. At statue turn sharp R then next L in 1km. Farm on L in 200m. Sm, unshd; wc; shwrs inc; el pts €2; lndry rm; cooking facs; ice; farm produce. "Splendid mountain scenery all round; pleasant town of Mens 14km; gd walking." 1 May-31 Oct. € 10.00   2004*

CLEON D'ANDRAN *9D2* (Rural) **Camp Municipal Les Cigales, Rue de Piscine, 26450 Cleon-d'Andran** [04 75 90 12 73 (Mairie)] Fr A7 leave at junc 16 sp Privas/Crest. S fr Crest on D538. In 5km take D6. In 11km at Cleon-d'Andran turn L in vill, in 100m turn R. Sm, shd; wc (cont); shwrs inc; el pts €2.50; lndtte; shop 500m; pool; quiet; CCI. 1 Jun-31 Aug. € 10.80   2003*

CLERE SUR LAYON see Vihiers *4G1*

CLEREY see Troyes *4E4*

CLERGOUX *7C4* (300m E Rural) **Camping La Petite Riviere, 19320 Clergoux** [tel/fax 05 55 27 68 50; jcbakker@xs4all.nl; www.compumess.nl/lapetite riviere] Site in 20km on D978 fr Tulle. Sm, mkd pitch, pt sl, pt shd; wc; chem disp; baby facs; shwrs inc; el pts (6A) €2.20; lndtte; ice; tradsmn; lake sw & sand beach 1.5km; 20% statics; dogs €1.20; Eng spkn; adv bkg (dep req + bkg fee); quiet; CCI. "V helpful Dutch owner; 25 planned walks in area; excel long stay." 15 Apr-30 Sep. € 9.00   2003*

CLERMONT EN ARGONNE *5D1* (6km SW Rural) **Camp Municipal Futeau, 55120 Futeau** [03 29 88 27 06 (Mairie)] Leave A4 at Ste Menehould & proceed E on N3 for 9km to Les Islettes; turn S on D2 for 4km to Futeau; site behind church. Sm, pt shd; htd wc (some cont); chem disp (wc); shwrs inc; el pts (10A) inc (poss rev pol); shops 4km; tradsmn; BBQ; dogs; phone; quiet but cockerel in vill & church bells; CCI. "Site yourself; warden calls; gd for walking." ♦ 30 Apr-1 Oct.
€ 10.00   2005*

†**CLERMONT FERRAND** *9B1* (7km SE Rural) **Camping Le Clos Auroy, Rue de la Narse, 63670 Orcet** [tel/fax 04 73 84 26 97; camping.le.clos. auroy@wanadoo.fr; www.camping-le-clos-auroy. com] S on A75 fr Clermont-Ferrand, take exit 5 sp Orcet; foll D213 to Orcet for 2km, at rndabt onto the D52, take 1st L, site on R, sp. Med, hdg/mkd pitch, terr, pt shd; htd wc; chem disp; mv service pnt; shwrs inc; el pts (5-10A) €2.90-€4.40 (poss rev pol); gas; lndtte; ice; shop 500m; tradsmn; snacks; bar; playgrnd; htd pool; rv sw, fishing 500m; tennis; archery, horseriding, entmnt; 15% statics; dogs €1.50; phone; Eng spkn; adv bkg; quiet; red low ssn/long stay; CCI. "Tidy, well-maintained site; easy access; lge, well mkd pitches, poss v high hedges; pitches by rv poss liable to flood; additional charge for m'vans staying 1-3 nights; waste disp points not at ground level - diff to use; ltd facs low ssn; Orcet v interesting; conv touring base Auvergne." ♦ € 16.50
2005*

FRANCE

†CLERMONT FERRAND *9B1* (9km SE Urban) **Camp Municipal Le Pre des Laveuses, Rue des Laveuses, 63800 Cournon-d'Auvergne** [04 73 84 81 30; fax 04 73 84 90 65; camping@cournon-auvergne.fr; www.cournon-auvergne.fr/camping] Fr S o'skts Clermont-Ferrand take D212 E to Cournon & foll sp in town; by Rv Allier, 1km E of Cournon. Lge, mkd pitch, pt shd; wc (some cont); chem disp; baby facs; shwrs inc; el pts (5-10A) €2.95-4.45; lndtte; shop; snacks; bar; playgrnd; pool nrby; paddling pool; rv sw/lake adj; fishing & boating; dogs €1.70; poss cr; Eng spkn; quiet; red low ssn; cc acc; CCI. "Excel, well-kept site - even low ssn; lge pitches; helpful manager; excel long/sh stay." ♦ € 10.95   2005*

We're having a great holiday - must fill in some site report forms and send them to The Club as soon as possible.

†CLERMONT FERRAND *9B1* (15km SE Rural) **Camping La Font de Bleix, 63730 Les Martres-de-Veyre** [04 73 39 26 49; fax 04 73 69 40 27; ailes-libres@infonie.fr] Fr Clermont-Ferrand exit A75 junc 5. Turn E onto D213, then R onto D978 at rndabt & thro vill. Site on L 100m after traff lts over rlwy x-ing. Sm, mkd pitch, pt sl, unshd; wc (cont); chem disp; shwrs inc; el pts (10A) €3.50; lndtte; shop 1km; snacks; rv adj; dogs €1.50; quiet; adv bkg; CCI. "Dated facs; gd sh stay." ♦ € 7.80   2004*

†CLERMONT FERRAND *9B1* (6km SW Urban) **Camp Municipal Le Chanset, Ave Marrou, 63122 Ceyrat** [tel/fax 04 73 61 30 73 or 04 73 61 42 55 (Mairie); camping.lechanset@wanadoo.fr] Exit A75 junc 2 onto N189 then foll sp uphill into Ceyrat. Curve R to traff lts; cross main street & take L fork up hill. Site at top on R - turn poss diff so cont 50m for U-turn back to site. Lge, hdg/mkd pitch, pt sl, pt shd; wc (some cont); chem disp; baby facs; shwrs inc; el pts (6-10A) inc; gas; lndtte; ice; shop; rest; snacks; bar; BBQ; playgrnd; htd pool high ssn; games & TV rm; 10% statics; dogs €1.20; bus; phone; security barrier; poss cr; some Eng spkn; adv bkg; poss noisy when cr; red + 7 days/low ssn; cc acc; CCI. "Excel views; busy site but vg for families with children; friendly staff; gd base for exploring Auvergne & visiting Puy de Dome & amazing Volcania Park; gd bus to Clermont- Ferrand; pool used by public at w/end (poss cr); some sm pitches; vg long stay." ♦ € 17.00   2004*

CLERMONT FERRAND *9B1* (3km W Rural) **Camping Indigo Royat, Route de Gravenoire, 63130 Royat** [04 73 35 97 05; fax 04 73 35 67 69; royat@camping-indigo.com; www.camping-indigo.com] Site diff to find fr Clermont-Ferrand cent. Fr N, leave A71 at Clermont-Ferrand. Foll sp Chamalieres/Royat, then sp Royat. Go under rlwy bdge & pass thermal park on L. At mini-rndabt go L & up hill. At statue, turn L & go up long hill. Look for site sp & turn R. Site on R. NB Do not go down steep rd with traff calming. Lge, hdg/mkd/hdstg pitch, terr, pt shd; wc; chem disp; mv service pnt; serviced pitch; baby facs; shwrs inc; el pts (6-10A) €4.10-5.60; gas; lndtte; ice; shop; tradsmn; rest; snacks; bar; BBQ; playgrnd; pool; tennis; TV rm; some statics; dogs €2; phone; poss cr; Eng spkn; adv bkg; quiet; red low ssn; cc acc; CCI. "Excel, clean site with quiet families taking cure at Royat; spacious; lovely views at top levels over Clermont; facs need refurb & poss stretched." ♦ 8 Apr-28 Oct. € 18.00   2005*

CLERMONT L'HERAULT *10F1* (7km SE Rural) **Camping Les Rivieres, Route de la Sabliere, 34800 Canet** [04 67 96 75 53; fax 04 67 96 58 35; info@camping-les-rivieres.com; www.camping-les-rivieres.com] On D2 sp Clermont-l'Herault/ Canet. At Canet foll sp approx 2km. Med, hdg/mkd pitch, pt shd; wc; shwrs inc; el pts (5A) inc; lndtte; tradsmn; rest; snacks; playgrnd; pool; solarium; rv fishing; 5% statics; sm dogs only €2.50; Eng spkn; quiet. "Well-laid out; nice pool with rest/bar; friendly, helpful staff; gd area for touring; nr to Lac du Salagou." 1 May-15 Sep. € 23.00   2005*

†CLERMONT L'HERAULT *10F1* (5km NW Rural) **Camp Municipal du Lac du Salagou, 34800 Clermont-l'Herault** [04 67 96 13 13; fax 04 67 96 32 12] Fr N9 S take D909 to Clermont-l'Herault, foll sp to Lac du Salagou 1.5km after town sp. Fr by-pass foll sp Bedarieux. Well sp. Lge, mkd pitch, pt sl, pt shd; htd wc (some cont); chem disp; mv service pnt; shwrs inc; el pts (10A) inc; lndtte; ice; shops 4km; tradsmn; rest; snacks; BBQ; playgrnd; shgl beach & lake 300m; fishing; watersports; entmnt; TV; many statics; dogs €1.55; phone; poss cr; adv bkg; noise fr disco some nights; CCI. "Unique location; gd undeveloped beaches around lake; poss muddy low ssn & poss windy." ♦ € 15.60   2004*

CLISSON *2H4* (S Urban) **Camp Municipal du Vieux Moulin, Route de Nantes, 44190 Clisson** [02 40 54 44 48 or 02 40 54 02 95 (LS)] 1km NW of Clisson cent on main rd to Nantes, at rndabt. Look for old windmill nr ent on L of rd. Leclerc hypmkt on opp side of rd; site sp fr town cent. Narr ent. Sm, hdg pitch, pt sl, pt shd; wc; chem disp; shwrs inc; el pts (10A) inc; hypmkt, rest, snacks, bar 500m; tradsmn; fishing, tennis, horseriding adj; boating; phone (card only); Eng spkn; adv bkg; quiet but some rd noise. "Gd municipal site; v clean facs; lge pitches; gate clsd 1030-1500 (low ssn) but can phone warden; picturesque town 15 min walk fr site; gd sh stay." 15 May-15 Oct. € 12.00   2004*

CLOHARS CARNOET see Pouldu, Le *2F2*

CLOYES SUR LE LOIR *4F2* (1km N) **Parc de Loisirs de Cloyes, Route de Montigny, 28220 Cloyes-sur-le-Loir** [02 37 98 50 53; fax 02 37 98 33 84; info@parc-de-loisirs.com] Located on L bank of Loir off N10; site sp. Med, pt shd; wc (some cont); chem disp; shwrs inc; el pts (5A) €3.25; ice; shop; rest; snacks; bar; playgrnd; pool; waterslide; cycle hire; 50% statics; dogs €1.65; adv bkg. "Facs gd for children but ltd low ssn; well-run; pleasant & quiet in wooded valley; site fees inc use of sm leisure park, pedaloes & rowing boats on Rv Loir." 15 Mar-15 Nov. € 18.90   2005*

CLOYES SUR LE LOIR *4F2* (4km S Rural) **Camping Les Fouquet (formerly Camping Aire Naturelle (Fetter)), 41160 St Jean-Froidmentel** [02 54 82 66 97] Off N10 twd Vendome. Sp Les Fouquets 200m SE of N10. Sm, shd; wc; shwrs inc; el pts; lndry rm; shop 3km; pool; fishing, tennis & sailing 2km; 10% statics; quiet; CCI. "Lovely family-run site; v friendly owner." ♦ 1 Apr-30 Sep. € 9.50   2004*

CLUNY *9A2* (E Urban) **Camp Municipal St Vital, Rue de Griottons, 71250 Cluny** [tel/fax 03 85 59 08 34; cluny-camping@wanadoo.fr] Fr Cluny take D15 sp Aze, cross narr rv bdge. Site 1st R adj to pool. Lge, mkd pitch, sl, pt shd; wc; chem disp; shwrs inc; el pts (6A) inc; gas; ice; lndtte; shops 500m; playgrnd; pool adj; poss cr; adv bkg rec high ssn; frequent rlwy noise daytime. "Clean, well-kept facs; helpful staff; avoid end Sep/beg Oct when site taken over for dog show (600+ lge dogs!); cycle & walking rte adj; interesting town & abbey in walking dist." ♦ 1 May-30 Sep. € 14.20   2005*

CLUNY *9A2* (11km S Rural) **Camping du Lac de St Point, Route Lamartine, 71520 St Point** [03 85 50 52 31 or 03 85 50 51 18 (Mairie); fax 03 85 50 51 92; campingstpoint@wanadoo.fr] Turn S off N79, Macon/Paray-le-Monial rd, turn L bef Ste Cecile on D22; site sp at junc; site 100m on R after St Point vill. Med, hdg/mkd pitch, pt terr, pt sl (gd blocks needed), pt shd; wc; chem disp; shwrs inc; el pts (4-13A) €3-5.50; gas 800m; lndtte; ice; shop 800m; rest; snacks; bar; BBQ; playgrnd; TV; lake sw adj; fishing; boat hire; tennis 4km; 30% statics; dogs €1.50; phone; Eng spkn; adv bkg; quiet; CCI. "Lovely scenery & pleasant lake; on edge of Beaujolais; sp walks fr site; poss no hot water for washing up; ltd facs low ssn; Cluny attractive town & abbey; gd long/sh stay." 1 Apr-31 Oct. € 12.10 (4 persons)   2004*

CLUNY *9A2* (11km NW Rural) **Camp Municipal de la Clochette, 71250 Salornay-sur-Guye** [03 85 59 90 11; fax 03 85 59 47 52; mairie. salornay@wanadoo.fr] Sp fr N or S on D980; turn E on D14 sp Cormatin & Taize. Ent opp PO within 300m. Med, mkd pitch, pt shd; wc; shwrs €0.80; chem disp; mv service pnt; el pts (8-10A) €1.60-2.40; lndry rm; ice; shop adj; BBQ; playgrnd; rv adj; fishing; adv bkg; quiet; CCI. "Pleasant, tidy site on sm rv & mill pond; site yourself, recep open morning & evening; well sp walks around vill; rvside pitches poss subject to flooding if rv rises." 21 May-4 Sep. € 5.20   2005*

CLUSAZ, LA *9B3* (6km N) **Camping Le Clos du Pin, 74450 Le Grand-Bornand** [04 50 02 70 57 or 04 50 02 27 61] Foll sps fr La Clusaz &/or St Jean-de-Sixte to Grand Bornand. Thro vill dir Vallee du Bouchet; site on R in 1km. Med, mkd pitch, unshd; htd wc; chem disp; shwrs inc; el pts (2A) inc; gas 1km; lndtte; ice; shops 1km; BBQ; playgrnd; rv sw & fishing 100m; pool 1km; TV/games rm; 30% statics; dogs €1.10; adv bkg; quiet; cc acc; CCI. "Excel long stay; base for ski stn; ski & boot rm; friendly owner; barrier key; high ssn is Feb when fees are higher." ♦ 15 Jun-20 Sep & 1 Dec-10 May. € 14.10   2004*

CLUSAZ, LA *9B3* (6km N) **Camping L'Escale, 74450 Le Grand-Bornand** [04 50 02 20 69; fax 04 50 02 36 04; contact@campinglescale.com; www.campinglescale.com] Exit A41 junc 17 onto D16/D909 E dir La Clusaz. At St Jean-de-Sixt turn L at rndabt sp Le Grand Bornand. After 1.5km foll camping sp on main rd & at junc turn R sp for site & 'Vallee du Bouchet'. Site is 1st exit R at rndabt at end of this rd. D4 S fr Cluses not rec while towing as v steep & winding. Med, mkd pitch, pt sl, terr, pt shd; htd wc; chem disp; mv service pnt; serviced pitch in summer; baby facs; shwrs inc; el pts (3-10A) inc (poss rev pol); gas; lndtte; ice; shop 300m; tradsmn; rest; snacks; bar; BBQ; playgrnd; 2 pools (1 htd, covrd); fishing; wintersports; tennis; games rm; internet; TV rm; 20% statics; dogs €2.30; skibus; recep 0830-2100; poss cr; adv bkg ess (dep & bkg fee req); red low ssn; cc acc; CCI. "Helpful owner; free use htd ski/boot rm in winter; vg rest; gd scenic area; excel sports facs in town; mkt Wed; boggy in wet weather." ♦ 2 Dec-23 Apr & 20 May-24 Sep. € 26.50 (CChq acc) ABS - M07   2005*

CLUSAZ, LA *9B3* (12km NE) **Camp Municipal Les Marroniers, 74130 Le Petit-Bornand-Les-Glieres** [04 50 03 54 74] E fr Annecy on D909 for 28km to St Jean-de-Sixt. N on D4 for 1km, turn W on D12 for 11km to Le Petit Bornand. Site thro vill on L. Sm, pt sl, pt shd; wc; chem disp; shwrs; el pts (3A) inc; lndtte; shop adj; rv sw; fishing; tennis nr; adv bkg; quiet; CCI. "Vg site in National Park." 1 Jun-15 Sep. € 8.30   2002*

CLUSAZ, LA *9B3* (2km E Rural) **Caravaning Le Plan du Fernuy, Route des Confins, 74220 La Clusaz** [04 50 02 44 75; fax 04 50 32 67 02] Fr Annecy take D909 to La Clusaz (32km). Turn L for Les Confins & site on R in 2km. Med, pt sl, unshd; wc; chem disp; shwrs inc; baby rm; el pts (4A) inc; gas; lndtte; snacks; shop; bar; paddling pool & pool (htd & covrd); playgrnd; TV; free ski bus; poss cr; quiet. "Site at 1050m alt; excel site & facs; poss diff lge o'fits." ♦ 3 Jun-10 Sep. € 19.90   2002*

FRANCE

†CLUSES *9A3* (1km N) **Camping La Corbaz, Ave des Glieres, 74300 Cluses** [04 50 98 44 03; fax 04 50 96 02 15] Take N205 W fr Chamonix or fr Annecy N203 NE to Bonneville & N205 E to Cluses. Med, pt shd; htd wc; chem disp; mv service pnt; shwrs; el pts (4-10A) €3.15; ice; shop; rest; lake sw 2km; pool 1km; TV; adv bkg; 70% statics; quiet but some rd & rlwy noise. "Excel base for touring Haute Savoie; lge pitches; helpful owners" € 13.15   2002*

†CLUSES *9A3* (6km N) **Camp Municipal Essi Les Thezieres, 74440 Taninges** [04 50 34 25 59; fax 04 50 34 39 78; camping.taninges@wanadoo.fr] Take D902 N fr Cluses; site 1km S of Taninges on L - just after 'Taninges' sp on ent town boundary; sp Camping-Caravaneige. Lge, pt shd; htd wc; chem disp; mv service pnt; shwrs inc; el pts (6-10A) €2.05-3.60; lndtte; shops, rest, snacks, bar 1km; playgrnd; pool at Samoens 11km; tennis; dogs €0.90; phone; poss cr; Eng spkn; quiet; CCI; "Conv for N Haute Savoie & Switzerland to Lake Geneva; splendid site with magnificent views; lge pitches; excel facs; friendly & helpful British warden; excel long/sh stay." € 7.35   2005*

COGNAC *7B2* (1km NE Urban) **Camp Municipal de Cognac, Blvd de Chatenay, Route de Ste Severe, 16100 Cognac** [05 45 32 13 32 or 05 45 36 64 30; fax 05 45 32 15 82; ccdc. camping@wanadoo.fr] Foll 'Camping ***' sp fr town cent, on D24 by Rv Charente on just S of rv. Med, hdg/mkd pitch, pt shd; wc (some cont); chem disp; mv service pnt; shwrs inc; el pts (6A) inc (poss long leads req); lndtte; ice; shop high ssn & 2km; tradsmn; rest, snacks high ssn; bar; BBQ; playgrnd; htd pool; rv boating & fishing; dogs €1.50; phone; poss cr; Eng spkn; adv bkg; cc acc; red long stay/low ssn; CCI. "Gd value; conv Cognac distilleries (ask for free vouchers at site recep); site yourself 1200-1500 as recep clsd; some facs clsd low ssn; footpath to town cent along rv; excel lge park with many facs 10 mins walk along rv; no twin-axles; gates clsd 2200-0700." ♦ 1 May-15 Oct. € 16.00   2005*

COGNAC *7B2* (10km E Rural) **Camp Municipal, 16200 Bourg-Charente** [05 45 80 30 25 (Mairie); fax 05 45 81 64 20] Fr Cognac E603, site sp on D158. NB Care req thro chicane on ent esp for lge o'fits. Sm, pt sl, pt shd; wc (some cont); chem disp; mv service pnt; shwrs €1; el pts (6A) €1.50; rest, shop 500m; fishing; poss cr; cc acc; red long stay. "Delightful little site on banks of Rv Charante; gd clean facs; gd walks & cycle path to Jarnac & Cognac; poss itinerants; warden calls pm; facs poss stretched in high ssn." 15 Jun-15 Sep. € 6.00 2005*

COGNAC *7B2* (14km E Urban) **Camping de l'Ile Madame, 16200 Jarnac** [05 45 81 18 54 or 05 45 81 68 02; fax 05 45 81 24 98; camping-jarnac@wanadoo.fr] Turn E at S end of rv bdge at S end of town. Lge, pt shd; wc; shwrs inc; el pts (10A) €2.20 (rev pol); ice; lndtte; shops & rest adj; playgrnd; pool; games area; golf, canoe & cycle hire nrby; entmnt; TV; dogs €0.50; poss cr; adv bkg; poss noise fr adj sports ground & disco; CCI. "Well-run site; clean facs; gd sized pitches; nr Courvoisier bottling plant." 1 Apr-30 Sep. € 11.60   2005*

COGNAC *7B2* (8km S Rural) **Camping a la Ferme d'Acceuil (Chainier), Le Chiron, Celles, 16130 Salles d'Angles** [05 45 83 72 79; fax 05 45 83 64 80] Fr Cognac D731 Barbezieux to Salles d'Angles, R at bottom hill then in 3km turn L & 1km on R (foll Chambres d'Hote sps). Sm, pt sl, pt shd; htd wc (1 cont); chem disp; shwrs inc; el pts (10A) (rev pol); shop 3km; quiet; cc not acc. "Vg sh stay; meals avail at farm."   2002*

COGNAC LA FORET *7B3* (1.5km W Rural) **Camping Les Alouettes, Route des Alouettes, 87310 Cognac-la-Foret** [05 55 03 80 86] Fr Aixe on D10, site W of Cognac-la-Foret on D10, sp to L. Med, mkd pitch, pt sl, unshd; wc; chem disp; shwrs inc; el pts (6A) €1.80; shop 1.5km; snacks; playgrnd; leisure facs 1km; 10% statics; dogs €1.60; quiet; CCI. "Friendly warden; conv war vill Oradour-sur-Glane; poss overgrown, untidy low ssn; old facs." ♦ ltd. Easter-30 Sep. € 9.40   2004*

COGNIN LES GORGES *9C3* (E Rural) **Aire Naturelle La Chatonniere, Route de Malleval, 38470 Cognin-les-Gorges** [04 76 38 18 76; info@la-chato.com; www.la-chato.com] Exit A49 junc 10 S onto N532, turn 1st L after Cognin-les-Gorges sp at service stn. Fr vill cent, take 1st R past church. In 50m turn L at stop sp, site 100m on L. Sm, pt shd; wc; chem disp; mv service pnt; child/baby facs; shwrs inc; el pts (10A) €2 (rev pol); ice; shop 500m; tradsmn; pool 6km; rv sw; no statics; dogs; bus; phone 100m; Eng spkn; adv bkg; quiet; red +7 days; CCI. "Welcoming, helpful owners; bread baked on site; meals avail; picturesque mountain setting; conv Grenoble & Vercours; excel all stays." 1 Apr-31 Oct. € 14.00   2005*

COGOLIN see Grimaud *10F4*

COLEMBERT see Boulogne sur Mer *3A2*

COLLE SUR LOUP, LA see Cagnes sur Mer *10E4*

COLLIAS see Remoulins *10E2*

COLMAR *6F3* (2km E Urban) **Camp Intercommunal de l'Ill, Route de Neuf Brisach, Pont de Harbourg, 68000 Colmar** [tel/fax 03 89 41 15 94] Exit A35 junc 25, foll Freibourg sp. At 2nd rndabt turn L to Colmar cent, site on L bef bdge. Lge, hdg/mkd pitch, hdstg, terr, shd; wc; chem disp; mv service pnt; shwrs; el pts (3-6A) €2.50-4.60 (poss rev pol); lndtte; shop; tradsmn; supmkt 500m; rest; snacks; bar; playgrnd; pool 8km; rv sw adj; 10% statics; dogs €1.60; bus to city cent; poss cr; some Eng spkn; adv bkg; noise fr a'route; cc acc (over €20); CCI. "On rv bank; recep shut 1100-1400 & 2100-0800; beautiful city with 'Little Venice' canals; conv Alsace wine district; san facs clean but dated, poss stretched high ssn; some pitches req steel pegs; sep area for NH; gd Italian rest across rv; conv town centre; gd long/sh stay." ♦ 1 Mar-30 Nov. € 9.30   2005*

COLMAR *6F3* (7km S Rural) **Camping Clairvacances, Route de Herrlisheim, 68127 Ste Croix-en-Plaine** [03 89 49 27 28; fax 03 89 49 21 55; clairvacances@wanadoo.fr] Exit N83 at sp Herrlisheim onto D1 bis. Take 2nd rd to vill sp camping, foll site sp thro vill. NB Rd thru vill narr with traff calming bollards. Fr A35 turn off at junc 27 sp Herrlisheim/Ste Croix en Plaine onto D1 dir Herrlisheim to site in 1km. Med, some hdg/mkd pitch, some hdstg, pt shd; htd wc; chem disp; mv service pnt; baby facs; shwrs inc; el pts (8-13A) €3-5 (long lead poss req); gas; lndtte; shop 2km; tradsmn; BBQ; playgrnd; pool; cycle hire; 10% statics; no dogs; phone; poss cr; Eng spkn; adv bkg dep req; quiet; cc acc; red low ssn; CCI. "V helpful & friendly owners; gd size pitches; gd touring base Alsace wine rte; weekly wine-tasting; 1st class san facs; wonderful site; well-maintained & regularly supervised; sep area for tents; barriers in place." ♦ Easter-17 Oct. € 16.00   2005*

COLMAR *6F3* (7km SW Rural) **Camp Municipal Les Trois Chateaux, 10 Rue du Bassin, 68420 Eguisheim** [03 89 23 19 39; fax 03 89 24 10 19] Foll N83 S (Colmar by-pass) R at sp Eguisheim. R into vill to site at top of vill, foll camp sp. Med, mkd pitch, pt sl, terr, pt shd; wc; chem disp; mv service pnt; shwrs inc; el pts (6A) €3.40 (poss rev pol); gas; lndtte; ice; shops, rest & bars in vill 300m; hypmkt 5km; playgrnd; phone adj; poss cr; clsd 1230-1400; adv bkg (tel 2 days bef arr); poss noisy; cc not acc; CCI. "No c'vans over 7m (inc draw bar); stork park adj; delightful area; sm pitches poss cramped; v busy; many local attractions; wine-tasting & cellars in vill; rec arr early; mv pitches flat but some c'van pitches sl & poss diff; excel." ♦ ltd. Easter-30 Sep. € 10.70   2005*

COLMAR *6F3* (7km W) **Camp Municipal Les Cigognes, Quai de la Gare, 68230 Turckheim** [03 89 27 02 00; fax 03 89 80 86 93; www.turckheim-alsace.com] Fr N83 twd Turchkeim turn W onto D11 to Turckheim. On ent vill, turn immed L down 1-way rd after x-ing rlwy lines. Do not cross rv bdge. Site on L bef bdge, adj stadium. Med, hdg pitch, pt shd; wc; chem disp; mv service pnt; baby facs; shwrs inc; el pts (6-10A) €3.10-4.80; lndtte; shop 500m; playgrnd; entmnt; TV; 50% statics; dogs €1.10; bus 500m; train 250m; poss cr; quiet; red low ssn; CCI. "Lovely site with OK san facs; cycle rtes nr; storks nesting; interesting town; gd wine co-operative 500m." ♦ 15 Mar-31 Oct. € 11.60   2005*

COLMARS *9D4* (500m S Rural) **Aire Naturelle Les Pommiers, 04370 Colmars** [04 92 83 41 56; fax 04 92 83 40 86] Fr N on D908 on ent Colmars take 1st R over rd bdge & foll site sp. Sm, pt terr, pt shd; wc (some cont); chem disp (wc); shwrs inc; el pts (10A) €2; lndry rm; shop 500m; tradsmn; rest, snacks, bar 500m; BBQ; pool 500m; dogs €0.65; phone; adv bkg; CCI. "Beautifully situated, well-maintained CL-type site; friendly owner; Colmars fascinating medieval walled town; ideal for walking in Haute-Provence." ♦ ltd. 14 Apr-30 Sep. € 10.00   2005*

COLMARS *9D4* (1km S) **Camping Le Bois Joly, 04370 Colmars** [04 92 83 40 40; fax 04 92 83 50 60] Fr S on D955 & D908 twds Colmars, go thro Beauvezer & Villars-Colmars. Ignore two other sites en rte. Site sp. Sm, mkd, hdstg, shd; wc (some cont); chem disp (wc); mv service pnt; shwrs inc; el pts (6A) €2.43; gas; lndtte; ice; rest, snacks, bar & shop 1km; BBQ; tradsmn high ssn; rv fishing adj; no dogs; phone; adv bkg; quiet; CCI. "Beautifully-maintained wooded site; ideal base for superb walking in Haute Provence; friendly owners; wonderful atmosphere; excel long or sh stay." 1 May-30 Sep. € 10.37   2003*

COLMARS *9D4* (2km SW Rural) **Camping Le Haut Verdon, 04370 Villars-Colmars** [04 92 83 40 09; fax 04 92 83 56 61; campinglehaut verdon@wanadoo.fr; www.lehautverdon.com] Only app fr S on D955 & D908 fr St Andre-les-Alps thro Beauvezer. Clearly sp on ent Villars-Colmars on R. (Do not confuse with Municipal site approx 5km bef this site). Med, hdg/mkd pitch, pt shd; htd wc; chem disp; mv service pnt; shwrs inc; el pts (6-10A) €3-4; gas; lndtte; ice; shop & 2km; tradsmn; rest 1km; snacks; bar; playgrnd; pool; rv fishing; TV rm; dogs €2; poss cr; Eng spkn; adv bkg; quiet; CCI. "Superb setting on Rv Verdon; conv Colmars, flower meadows, Allos Lake; v helpful staff." ♦ 30 Apr-2 Oct. € 20.00 (CChq acc)   2005*

COMBOURG *2E4* (1.5km Urban) **Camp Municipal Le Vieux Chatel**, 35270 Combourg [02 99 73 00 18] Fr W, N & E foll sp fr town cent. Fr S on D795, turn R at lake. Site on L in approx 500m. Med, hdg pitch, pt shd; wc; chem disp; shwrs; el pts (5A) inc; lndtte; BBQ; playgrnd; pool 1km; lake fishing nrby; no statics; phone; Eng spkn; adv bkg; quiet; CCI. "Forests, chateaux & churches nrby; 20 mins to Emerald Coast; castle in Combourg; vg long/sh stay." 6 Jun-29 Aug. € 9.85   2003*

COMBOURG *2E4* (8km NE Rural) **Camping Le Bois Coudrais**, 35270 Cuguen [02 99 73 27 45; fax 02 99 73 13 08; info@vacancebretagne.com; www.vacancebretagne.com] Fr Combourg take D796 twd Pleine-Fougeres, 5km out of Combourg turn L on D83 to Cuguen; 500m past Cuguen, turn L, site sp. Or fr Dol de Bretagne, take D795 then turn L onto D9 to Cuguen. Sm, hdg/mkd pitch, pt sl, pt shd; wc; chem disp; shwrs inc; el pts (6A) inc; ice; shop 500m; snacks; bar; BBQ; playgrnd; pool; fishing, watersports, golf, zoo, adventure park nr; cycle hire; dogs €1; Eng spkn; adv bkg (dep req); v quiet; red long stay; no cc acc; CCI. "CL-type site surrounded by fields & trees; British owners; gd facs; sm animal-petting area; central to major attractions; gd touring base." ♦ 1 Apr-30 Sep. € 14.50   2005*

COMBOURG *2E4* (6km SW Rural) **Domaine du Logis**, 35190 La Chapelle-aux-Filtzmeens [02 99 45 25 45; fax 02 99 45 30 40; domainedu logis@wanadoo.fr; www.domainedulogis.com] Fr N176 at junc for Dol-de-Bretagne branch R onto D155 sp Dol & take D795 S to Combourg. Then take D13 twd St Domineuc, go thro La Chapelle-aux-Filtzmeens & site on R in 1km. Lge, mkd pitch, pt shd; wc; chem disp; mv service pnt; shwrs inc; el pts (10A) inc; gas; lndry rm; lndtte; ice; sm shop & 5km; tradsmn; rest; snacks; bar; BBQ; playgrnd; 2 htd pools; sand beach 20km; canoes 800m; fishing nr; cycle hire; mini-golf; golf 15km; games area; games rm; TV rm; 45% statics; dogs €3 (some breeds not acc - check with site); phone; Eng spkn; adv bkg; cc acc; red low ssn/long stay/CCI. "Helpful staff; mkt in Combourg Mon; conv St Malo, Mont St Michel, Dinan & Channel Islands." ♦ 1 Apr-30 Sep. € 30.00 ABS - B02   2005*

See advertisement

COMBRIT STE MARINE see Benodet *2F2*

COMPREIGNAC *7B3* (2.5km N Rural) **Camp Municipal de Montimbert**, 87140 Compreignac [05 55 71 04 49 or 05 55 71 00 23 (Mairie)] S on A20 to Limoges, turn W at exit 26 Le Crouzill. Foll D5 W to Compreignac, turn N by church onto D60, fork L, foll sp 'Montimbert' for site. Sm, pt sl, pt shd; wc; chem disp; shwrs inc; el pts (5A) €2.30 (rev pol); shop in vill; playgrnd; lake sw, fishing & boating 1km; CCI. "Excel long stay; facs ltd; unreliable opening dates." 1 Jun-15 Sep. € 5.80   2005*

COMPREIGNAC *7B3* (6km N Rural) **Site de Santrop, Lac de St-Pardoux**, 87640 Razes [05 55 71 08 08 or 05 55 71 04 40 (LS); fax 05 55 71 23 93; www.lac-saint-pardoux.com] N fr Limoges on A20, exit 25 Razes; foll sp 4km to site. (NB If no sp to Razes foll sp to Lac de St Pardoux). Lge, hdg pitch, pt sl, shd; wc; baby facs; shwrs inc; el pts (6A) €3; lndtte; shop; rest; bar; playgrnd; pool; waterslide; lake adj; watersports; games area; entmnt; TV rm; dogs €1.10; poss cr; Eng spkn; poss noisy. "Popular, busy site on lake beach; random pitching under trees in woodland; gd rest on lakeside; poss late night noise fr revellers on beach; excel long/sh stay." 4 May-18 Sep. € 15.80   2005*

CONCARNEAU *2F2* (4km SE Coastal) **Camping Caravanning La Plage Loc'h Ven, Plage de Pendruc**, 29910 Tregunc [02 98 50 26 20; fax 02 98 50 27 63] Fr N165 exit at Kerempaou sp Tregunc. At rndbt W of Tregunc foll Loc'h Ven sp thro Lambell, site on coast. Med, hdg/mkd pitch, pt sl, pt shd; htd wc; chem disp; shwrs inc; el pts (4-6A) €2.60-3.20; gas; lndtte; shop 4km; tradsmn; rest, snacks, bar 4km; playgrnd; sand/shgl beach adj; games area; TV; 40% statics; dogs; poss cr; Eng spkn; adv bkg; quiet. "Easy walk to beach, rock pools & coastal footpath; v helpful owners." 1 Apr-30 Sep. € 12.00   2004*

CONCARNEAU *2F2* (6km SE Coastal) **Camping des Etangs de Trevignon, Kerlin, 29910 Tregunc** [02 98 50 00 41; fax 02 98 50 04 09; camp. etangdetrevignon@wanadoo.fr; www.camping-etangs.com] Exit N165/E60 at Kerampaou. S on D122 to Tregunc, then cont S on D1 to Trevignon. Site in 3km W. Foll sp. Lge, hdg/mkd pitch, pt shd; wc (some cont); chem disp; baby facs; shwrs inc; el pts (5A) €3.10; gas; lndtte; ice; shop 2km; tradsmn; rest 3km; snacks; bar; BBQ; playgrnd; htd, covrd pool high ssn; waterslide; sand beach 800m; mini-golf; cycle hire; TV rm; 5% statics; dogs €1.80; phone; Eng spkn; adv bkg; quiet; red low ssn/long stay; cc acc; red CCI. "In nature res with bird sanctuary nr; close to fishing ports, islands; excel." ♦ 25 May-15 Sep. € 19.85   2005*

This site entry hasn't been updated for a while; we'd better fill in a site report form and send it to The Club.

CONCARNEAU *2F2* (7km SE Coastal) **Camping La Pommeraie, St Philibert, 29910 Tregunc** [02 98 50 02 73; fax 02 98 50 07 91; pommeraie@ club-internet.fr; www.campingdelapommeraie. com] Fr D783 bet Concarneau & Pont-Aven, turn S in Tregunc onto D1 twd Pointe de Trevignon. In 5.5km look for site sp. Turn L to Philibert & Nevez. Ent immed on L. Lge, hdg/mkd pitch, pt shd; wc (some cont); chem disp; shwrs inc; mv service pnt; some serviced pitches; el pts (6-10A) €3.20-4.20; gas; lndtte; ice; shop & 250m; rest; snacks; bar; playgrnd; htd pool; paddling pool; sand beach 1km; boating; fishing; games rm; cycle hire; entmnt; TV; 60% statics; dogs €1.60; Eng spkn; adv bkg; quiet; cc acc; red low ssn; CCI. "Sale of farm produce; pleasant site in apple orchard; warm welcome." ♦ 1 May-4 Sep. € 19.00   2005*

CONCARNEAU *2F2* (3km W Coastal) **Camping Les Pres Verts, Kernous-Plage, 29900 Concarneau** [02 98 97 09 74; fax 02 98 97 32 06; info@presverts.com; www.presverts.com] Fr N165 take exit Concarneau onto D70. At rndabt by Leclerc supmkt foll sp Centre Ville with Leclerc on L. At x-rds with traff lts go strt over, then fork R into Rue de Kerneach & down slope. Bear L at 1st rndabt & R at next. Keep R to join coast rd foll sp La Foret-Fouesnant; pass Hotel Oceans; site 3rd rd on L in 1.5km. Med, hdg/mkd pitch, pt sl, pt shd; wc; chem disp; mv service pnt; serviced pitch; shwrs inc; el pts (2-6A) inc (poss rev pol & long lead req); gas 2km; lndtte; shop; rest 3km; bar; BBQ (charcoal/gas); playgrnd; htd pool; dir access to sand beach 300m; sailing 1km; horseriding, 10% statics; €1.30; recep 0900-1200 & 1400-2000; c'vans over 8m not acc high ssn; poss cr; adv bkg; quiet; red low ssn; cc acc. "Rec; friendly staff; gd facs; dir access to beach; excursions booked; mkt Mon & Fri; gd touring base." ♦ 1 May-22 Sep. € 27.60 ABS - B24   2005*

CONCARNEAU *2F2* (1km NW Urban/Coastal) **Camping Les Sables Blancs, Le Dorlett, 29900 Concarneau** [tel/fax 02 98 97 16 44; contact@ camping-lessablesblancs.com; www.camping-lessablesblancs.com] Exit N165 to Concarneau dir 'Centre Ville'. Then foll sp 'La Cote' 300m after traff lts. Site on R, sp. Med, hdg/mkd pitch, hdstg, pt sl, terr, pt shd; wc; chem disp; mv service pnt; baby facs; shwrs inc; el pts (10A) €2; gas; lndtte; shop 1.5km; tradsmn; rest, snacks & bar in ssn; BBQ; playgrnd; htd pool; sand beach 200m; games area; entmnt; TV rm; 3% statics; dogs €1; phone; poss cr; Eng spkn; adv bkg; quiet; red low ssn/long stay; cc acc; CCI. "Family site in sheltered woodland; v clean; excel san facs; 20 mins walk into town; vg." ♦ 8 Apr-30 Sep. € 15.00   2005*

See advertisement

CONCHES EN OUCHE *3D2* (8km NE Urban) **Camping sous Les Sapins, 27190 La Bonneville-sur- Iton** [02 32 37 11 03] Fr cent of Evreux W on N13, L on D830 twd Conches, site on R after 6km (sp). Sm, pt shd; wc; shwrs; el pts (6A); lndtte; shop; snacks; playgrnd; fishing; rv sw; poss cr; quiet. "Rv 900m, lake 1km; rec sh stay/NH only." € 11.43   2003*

CONCORET *2F3* (500m S Rural) **Camp Municipal du Val-aux-Fees, 56430 Concoret** [02 97 22 64 82 or 02 97 22 61 19 (Mairie); fax 02 97 22 93 17] Site sp fr cent of Concoret. Lge, pt sl, pt shd; wc; chem disp (wc only); shwrs inc; el pts (10A) €2.30; ice; shops 500m; playgrnd; fishing; 5% statics; dogs; Eng spkn; quiet. "V basic; san facs clean but dated, poss stretched high ssn; fishing on site €1.50 per day; 'Enchanted Forest' of King Arthur adj; gd all stays." € 8.70   2003*

CONDAMINE CHATELARD, LA *9D4* (1km W Rural) **Camping Base de Loisirs Champ Feleze, 04530 La Condamine-Chatelard** [04 92 84 39 39; fax 04 92 84 37 90; syflor@infonie.fr] 15 km NE of Barcelonnette on D900. Lge sp on D900 1km E of La Condamine visible fr rd. Sm, pt shd; wc; chem disp; serviced pitch; shwrs inc; el pts (4-6A) €2.20-3.10; lndtte; shops 1km; rest; snacks; bar; playgrnd; lake & rv adj; canoe hire; 5% statics; dogs €0.50; Eng spkn; adv bkg; quiet; CCI. "Gd site; lge pitches; easy access to sm private lake; gd base for touring Alps, fishing & walking; gd long/sh stay. 1 Jan-30 Sep. € 11.60   2003*

CONDE SUR NOIREAU *3D1* (10km E) **Camp Municipal, Route de Flers, 14690 Pont-d'Ouilly** [02 31 69 80 20 or 02 31 69 46 12] Fr Cherbourg take N13 to Vire, D512 for Conde-sur-Noireau & D562/D1 twd Falaise to site in 11km on W side of vill. On ent Pont-d'Ouilly turn R, site bef bdge over rv. Well sp in vill. Med, hdg/mkd pitch, pt sl, pt shd; wc (some cont); own san rec; chem disp; shwrs inc; el pts (7A) inc; ice; shops, rest, snacks, bar in vill; BBQ; playgrnd; tennis; canoeing & leisure cent adj; phone; poss cr; adv bkg; quiet; CCI. "Excel long/sh stay; gd cent for walking; conv WW2 battle areas; Museum of Automata, Falaise; helpful warden; facs poss stretched high ssn." Easter-15 Sep. € 10.20   2005*

CONDE SUR NOIREAU *3D1* (500m W Urban) **Camp Municipal du Stade, Rue de Vire, 14110 Conde-sur-Noireau** [02 31 69 45 24] On D562 (Flers to Caen rd). In town, turn W on D512 twd Vire. After Zone Industrielle, sports complex on L, no L turn. Go 1 block further & foll lge white sp 'Espace Aquatique' to site. Site 500m on R in grounds of sports cent. Sm, pt shd; wc; chem disp; shwrs inc; el pts (6-10A) €1.70; lndry rm; shops, rest, snacks, bar 500m; playgrnd; htd pool adj; tennis; dogs; quiet; CCI. "Well-maintained, clean site in grounds of leisure cent; gd size pitches; vg san facs; staff friendly & helpful; pleasant town; office open 1100-1200 & 1700-1800; gd sh stay/NH." 1 May-30 Sep. € 7.10   2003*

CONDETTE see Boulogne sur Mer *3A2*

CONDOM *8E2* (4km NE Rural) **Camping a la Ferme (Rogalle), Guinland, 32100 Condom** [05 62 28 17 85] NE fr Condom on D931, turn R onto D41. Pass water tower on R, site ent on L at bottom of hill just bef sm lake on R. Sm, shd; wc; chem disp; shwrs inc; el pts; shop, rest etc 4km; BBQ; playgrnd; tennis & canoe hire nrby; 10% statics; dogs; quiet. "Vg CL-type site in pine grove; friendly owner; gd value; clean facs." 1 Apr-30 Nov. € 9.00   2003*

†**CONDOM** *8E2* (6km SE) **Camping a la Ferme (Vignaux), Bordeneuve, 32100 Beraut** [05 62 28 08 41] E fr Condom on D7 to Caussens; far end of vill turn R on D204, sp St Orens; in 1.2km turn R sp Beraut, bear R at fork, site ent on L in 400m. Also sp fr D654. Sm, pt sl, pt shd; wc; chem disp; shwrs inc; el pts (12A) inc; lndry rm; shops 2km; adv bkg; quiet. "Waymkd trails nr; helpful owner; peaceful & secluded; vg long stay." € 8.00   2004*

CONDOM *8E2* (1.5km SW) **Camp Municipal de l'Argente, Chemin de l'Argente, 32100 Condom** [tel/fax 05 62 28 17 32] Fr Condom, take D931 twd Eauze; site ent on L opp municipal sports grnd. Med, pt shd, wc; chem disp (wc); baby facs; shwrs inc; el pts (6A) inc; shop 500m; tradsmn; rest & bar adj; playgrnd; pool 200m; fishing; tennis adj; dogs €1.05; phone; red low ssn. "Friendly staff; excel san facs but ltd low ssn; levelling blocks useful - bumpy surface; lge pitches; no twin-axle c'vans; dep on barrier card; free access to public pool; lots for older children to do; roomy with lovely walks by rv; unspoilt town; rec visit Armagnac distilleries; check bill on departure!" 1 Apr-30 Sep. € 15.36   2005*

†**CONDOM** *8E2* (2km SW Rural) **Camping La Ferme de Laillon (Danto), Route d'Eauze, 32100 Condom** [tel/fax 05 62 28 19 71] Site sp fr D931 dir Vopillon. Bumpy lane to site. Sm, pt sl, shd; wc; chem disp; shwrs inc; el pts inc; lndry rm; farm produce; playgrnd; Eng spkn; quiet. "Delightful, wooded site; helpful owner; pleasant area; fair sh stay." € 8.50   2003*

CONDORCET see Nyons *9D2*

CONDRIEU *9B2* (1km NE) **Camping Belle Rive, Chemin de la Plaine, 69420 Condrieu** [tel/fax 04 74 59 51 08] Heading S on N86 fr Vienne after ent vill turn L immed bef Elf g'ge on R. Site in 600m. NB Headroom under rlwy 2.60m. Alt rte avoiding bdge after vill. Lge, mkd pitch, unshd; wc; shwrs; el pts (3-6A) €2-4; gas; lndtte; ice; shop; rest adj; snacks; bar; BBQ; playgrnd; pool; paddling pool; waterslide; lake fishing 2km; tennis; cycle hire; games area; 60% statics; dogs €1.20; poss cr; some rlwy noise. "C'vans over 6.50m poss need manhandling." 1 Apr-30 Sep. € 12.40   2005*

CONDRIEU *9B2* (2km SE) **Camping Le Daxia,** 38370 St Clair-du-Rhone [04 74 56 39 20; fax 04 74 56 93 46] S fr Vienne on N86, turn E in Chavanay onto D7, under rlwy then over Rhone, in 5km turn N on D4, site on R in 500m. Med, hdg/mkd pitch, pt shd; wc (cont); chem disp; mv service pnt; baby facs; shwrs inc; el pts (5A) €2.80; lndtte; ice; shop 1km; snacks; BBQ; playgrnd; pool 3km; adv bkg; quiet; CCI. "Vg site." ♦ ltd. 1 Apr-30 Sep. € 13.60   2002*

CONFOLENS *7A3* (1km N Rural) **Camp Municipal des Ribieres, Ave de St Germain,** 16500 Confolens [05 45 85 35 27 or 05 45 84 01 97 (Mairie); fax 05 45 85 34 10] Fr N foll D951 dir Confolens turn L sp St Germain-de-Confolens, site on R in 7km at edge of town bet rd & rv. Med, mkd pitch, pt shd; wc (some cont); shwrs inc; gas; ice; el pts (16A) €2; lndry rm; shop 700m; tradsmn; BBQ; pool 200m; rv sw adj; fishing & boating; some statics; dogs; phone; quiet; cc not acc; CCI. "Relaxing site by pretty town; excel, clean site." ♦ 17 May-11 Sep. € 7.00   2005*

CONFOLENS *7A3* (7km S Rural) **Camp Municipal Moulin de la Cour,** 16500 St Maurice-des-Lions [05 45 85 55 99; fax 05 45 85 52 89] Fr Confolens take D948 S. In 6.5km turn L thro vill, site 500m, well sp. Sm, hdg/mkd pitch, pt sl, pt shd; wc (some cont); chem disp (wc); shwrs inc; el pts (6A) €1.60; shop, rest, bar 1km; BBQ; adv bkg; quiet. "Delightful sm site nr pretty vill, 12thC church & old houses; conv Confolens folk festival mid-Aug; warden calls am & pm; pitch yourself; basic facs, more like a CL site; v quiet low ssn; height limitations only in place out of ssn (see sp at ent to sports cent & site); ent thro stone pillars - care req with wide o'fits; site yourself, warden calls evenings; excel sh stay." 1 Jun-30 Sep. € 5.34   2004*

CONLIE see Sille le Guillaume *4F1*

CONNANTRE see Sezanne *4E4*

CONNERRE *4F1* (8km SE) **Camp Municipal, Route de Lavare,** 72390 Dollon [02 43 93 42 23; fax 02 43 71 53 88; mairie.dollon@wanadoo.fr] Fr Connerre take D302 sp Vibraye & Thorigney-sur-Due. In Dollon foll 'La Piscine' sp to sports complex at end of vill. Sm, pt shd; wc; chem disp; shwrs; el pts (10A) inc; gas; ice; shops 300m; playgrnd; pool; tennis; fishing; adv bkg rec; quiet. "Site part of sports complex; popular - likely to be full high ssn." 1 May-15 Sep. € 9.00   2003*

CONNERRE *4F1* (6km S) **Camp Municipal de Landon,** 72370 Le Breil-sur-Merize [02 43 89 83 13 (Mairie)] Take D33 sp Le Grand Luce. S fr Connerre to Le Breil. Site on D20 at junc with D33 on L adj to sports stadium. Sm, pt shd; wc; shwrs inc; el pts; playgrnd; games area; shops 1km; quiet. "Off beaten tracks; site yourself; warden calls each evening; poss itinerants." 2003*

CONQUES *7D4* (8km SE Rural) **Camp Municipal,** 12320 Cyprien-sur-Dourdou [05 65 72 80 52 or 05 65 69 83 16 (Mairie)] Fr Conques on D901 S, turn L onto D46 to St Cyprien-sur-Dourdou & foll sp to site. Sm, hdg pitch, shd; wc; shwrs inc; el pts €1.80; lndry rm; shops, rest, snacks, bar 500m; playgrnd; htd pool adj; dogs; phone; adv bkg; CCI. "Well maintained; sports field nrby; sh walk to vill; gd shops, bars in vill; gd walking, touring area close to Lot Valley." ♦ 15 Jun-15 Sep. € 7.00   2004*

CONQUES *7D4* (1km S Rural) **Camping Beau Rivage,** 12320 Conques [05 65 69 82 23 or 05 65 72 89 29 (LS); fax 05 67 72 89 29] Site on D901 Rodez-Aurillac rd, 1km S of Conques. Med, mkd pitch, pt sl, pt shd; wc (some cont); chem disp; shwrs inc; el pts (6-10A) €3; gas; lndry rm; shop; tradsmn; rest; snacks; bar; playgrnd; pool; fishing; rv adj; some statics; adv bkg; quiet; red low ssn; CCI. "Gd san facs but poss stretched high ssn; charming wardens cook reg menu eves; superb position, nr medieval town." ♦ 1 Apr-30 Sep. € 14.50   2004*

CONQUES *7D4* (5km NW Rural) **Camping Le Moulin,** 12320 Grand-Vabre [05 65 72 87 28] N fr Conques on D901, site sp. Sm, mkd pitch, terr, shd; wc; shwrs; el pts (10A) €1.60; tradsmn; snacks; bar; playgrnd; tennis 1km; poss cr; quiet. "Pleasant lakesite site; gd sh stay." € 8.10   2002*

CONQUET, LE *2E1* (2km N Coastal) **Camping Les Blancs Sablons (formerly Municipal Le Theven),** 29217 Le Conquet [tel/fax 02 98 89 06 90; www. lescledelles.com] Exit Brest on D789 to Le Conquet. Turn R after 22km (1.8km bef Le Conquet) on D67 twd St Renan, turn L after 700m on D28 twd Ploumoguer. After 2km, turn L at x-rds twd Plage des Blancs Sablons, site on L in 1km sp Blancs Sablons. Lge, mkd pitch, unshd; wc; chem disp; mv service pnt; shwrs inc; el pts (16A) €3 (long lead poss req); lndtte; shop in ssn & 1km; rest, snacks 1km; bar 500m; playgrnd; pool; sand beach 100m; adv bkg; cc acc; CCI. "Vg; gd views fr some pitches; some soft pitches; lovely old fishing town; excel shwrs." ♦ 1 Apr-30 Sep. € 14.50   2005*

CONTIS PLAGE *8E1* (Coastal) **Camping Lous Seurrots,** 40170 Contis-Plage [05 58 42 85 82; fax 05 58 42 49 11; info@lous-seurrots.com; www. lous-seurrots.com] S fr Mimizan take D652; 14km turn R onto D41 sp Contis-Plage; site on L. Or fr N10/E5/E70 exit junc 14 onto D38/D41 to Contis. V lge, shd; htd wc; chem disp; baby facs; fam bthrm; shwrs inc; el pts (6A) €4; gas; lndtte; ice; shop; rest; snacks; bar; playgrnd; pools; sand beach 400m; tennis; cycle hire; games area; entmnt; internet; TV; 30% statics; dogs €3; adv bkg; quiet; Eng spkn; cc acc. "Pitches vary in size; some pitches req levelling blocks; excel." ♦ 23 Apr-30 Sep. € 30.00   2004*

FRANCE

CONTRES *4G2* (9km S) **Camp Municipal, Le Gue,
41700 Chemery** [02 54 71 37 11 or 02 54 71 31 08;
fax 02 54 71 37 11] S fr Contres on D956 turn NW
in town cent sp Couddes. Site on R over bdge. Med,
pt shd; wc; chem disp; mv service pnt; shwrs inc; el
pts (6A) €2.30 (rev pol); ice; shops 500m; tradsmn;
playgrnd; pool high ssn; cycle hire; rv fishing adj;
m'van 'aire de service'; many statics; dogs €0.50;
quiet; adv bkg; CCI. "Friendly management; gd
value; warden only on site Mon-Fri low ssn, ensure
arr bef w/e because of ent barrier, otherwise can
find warden's home in vill; rec; gd sh stay."
19 Apr-19 Sep. € 6.10   2003*

CONTRES *4G2* (4km SW Rural) **Camping a la
Ferme (M Boucher), La Presle, 41700 Oisly**
[02 54 79 52 69] Fr Contres take D675 SW for 3km
D21 to Oisly. Well sp. Sm, pt sl, pt shd; wc; shwrs; el
pts (4A) inc; shops 1.5km; lake fishing; v quiet.
"Excel CL-type; owner helpful; wine sold by site
owner." Easter-1 Nov. € 8.80   2002*

CONTREXEVILLE *6F2* (1km SW Urban) **Camp
Municipal du Tir aux Pigeons, Rue du Onze
Septembre, 88140 Contrexeville** [03 29 08 15 06]
Off D164. App town fr NW on D164 turn R onto D13
& foll sp. 200m W of level x-ing, adj to stadium. Med,
mkd pitch, pt shd; wc; chem disp; shwrs inc; el pts
(5A) €2.30; lndtte; shops 1km; tradsmn; paddling
pool; lake fishing 2km; tennis adj; poss cr; some rd
noise. "Popular NH." ♦ 1 Apr-31 Oct. € 6.00
                                         2005*

COQUILLE, LA see Chalus *7B3*

CORBIGNY *4G4* (3.5km W) **Camp Intercommunal
L'Ardan, Route de Germeney, 58800 Chaumot**
[03 86 20 07 70] D977 fr Corbigny to Chaumot.
Turn on D130 sp Germenay. Site on R after 50m.
Med, shd; wc (some cont); chem disp; shwrs inc; el
pts; ice; shop 3.5km; playgrnd; lake adj; fishing; boat
hire; adv bkg; quiet. Easter-15 Sep.   2002*

†CORCIEUX *6F3* (Rural) **Camping Le Domaine des
Bans, La Rochotte, 88430 Corcieux** [03 29 51 64 67;
fax 03 29 51 64 65; les.bans@domaine-des-bans.
com; www.domaine-des-bans.com]
Fr St Die by-pass join N415 S to Anould. After
approx 10km turn R on D8 & in 5km R on D60 to
Corcieux. Or fr S take D8 N fr Gerardmer thro
Gerbepal. In 2km turn L onto D60 twd Corcieux, site
on L. V lge, hdg/mkd pitch, terr, pt shd; wc; chem
disp; baby facs; shwrs inc; el pts (6A) inc; gas;
lndtte; sm shop, rest, snacks, bar high ssn; BBQ;
playgrnd; pool high ssn; tennis; games rm;
horseriding; sm lake; entmnt; 75% tour ops static
tents/vans; dogs; recep 0900-2200; poss cr; Eng
spkn; adv bkg ess high ssn (min 7 days); poss
noisy; cc acc; CCI. "Pitches by lake quieter than nr
vill; gd site with gd facs, poss stretched high ssn;
care needed on narr site rds with speed control
ditches (warning sps faded); check el pts; mkt Mon."
♦ 24 Apr-23 Oct. € 30.00   2004*

CORCIEUX *6F3* (600m Rural) **Camping Le Clos de
la Chaume, 21 Rue d'Alsace, 88430 Corcieux**
[tel/fax 03 29 50 76 76 or 06 85 19 62 55; info@
camping-closdelachaume.com; www.camping-
closdelachaume.com] Take N145 fr St Die, then
D8 thro Anould onto D60. Site in 3km on R at ent to
vill. Med, mkd pitch, hdstg, pt shd; wc (some cont);
chem disp; mv service pnt; some serviced pitches;
fam bthrm; shwrs inc; el pts (6A) €2.80; gas; lndtte;
ice; shop 800m; tradsmn, rest, snacks, bar 600m;
BBQ; playgrnd; pool; beach & rv sw 12km; fishing;
cycle hire 800m; games area; games rm; cycle hire
800m; 15% statics; dogs €1.20; phone; Eng spkn;
adv bkg; quiet; cc acc; red low ssn/long stay; CCI.
"Beautiful area; conv Gerardmer & Alsace wine rte;
excel quality site." ♦ 30 Apr-16 Sep. € 11.20
                                         2005*

See advertisement

CORCIEUX *6F3* (1km Rural) **Camping au Mica, 8 Route de Gerardmer, 88430 Corcieux [tel/fax 03 29 50 70 07; info@campingaumica.com; www.campingaumica.com]** Take N145 fr St Die, then D8 thro Anould onto D60. Site in 5km on L. Med, hdg/mkd pitch, shd; wc (come cont); chem disp; mv service pnt; serviced pitches; shwrs inc; el pts (6A) €2.50; gas; ice; lndtte; shop; tradsmn; bar; BBQ; pool 150m; playgrnd; games rm; TV; cycle hire; rv fishing adj; phone; adv bkg; Eng spkn; quiet; red low ssn/long stay; cc acc; CCI. "Walking rtes; beautiful area in National Park." 1 May-23 Sep. € 10.00   2002*

CORCIEUX *6F3* (8km NE Urban) **Camping Les Acacias, 191 Rue L de Vinci, 88650 Anould [tel/fax 03 29 57 11 06; contact@acaciascamp. com; www.acaciascamp.com]** Site in vill of Anould sp fr all dir; just off main rd. (Annexe Camping Nature Les Acacias 800m fr this site open 15 Jun-15 Sep, terr in woods - new facs.) Med, pt shd; wc (some cont); chem disp; mv service pnt; baby facs; shwrs inc; el pts (3-6A) €2.60-3; gas; lndtte; ice; shops 500m; supmkt 2km; rest; snacks; sm bar; playgrnd; sm pool; rv fishing nrby; games rm; tennis & karting 2km; cycle trails; excursions; 10% statics; dogs €1; poss cr; Eng spkn; adv bkg rec; quiet; CCI. "Gd standard; helpful proprietors; excel; san facs clean; gd sh stay." ♦ 1 Dec-10 Oct. € 10.60   2005*

CORDELLE see Roanne *9A1*

CORDES *8E4* (1.5km SE) **Camping Moulin de Julien, 81170 Cordes [tel/fax 05 63 56 11 10; www.cordes-sur-ciel.org]** Exit Cordes E on D600 in Albi dir. Turn R on D922 Gaillac. Site on L in 100m. Fr Gaillac heading N site on R 100m bef junc with D600 & site sp bef red shield on R advertising Hotel Ecuyer. Med, pt sl, pt shd; wc; chem disp; shwrs inc; el pts (5A) €3.60; ice; lndtte; shop 2km; snacks & bar in ssn; playgrnd; 2 pools in ssn, 1 with chute; sm lake for fishing; CCI. "V pleasant, peaceful site in interesting area; friendly owners; conv Albi Cathedral, Bastide towns/vills & medieval town of Cordes; excel long stay." 15 May-15 Sep. € 17.00   2005*

CORDES *8E4* (5km SE) **Camping Redon, Livers-Cazelles, 81170 Livers-Cazelles [tel/fax 05 63 56 14 64; campingcampredon@wanadoo. fr]** Off D600 Albi to Cordes rd. Exit on D107 to E nr water tower. Site sp. Sm, hdg pitch, pt sl, pt shd; wc; shwrs inc; el pts (6A) inc; snacks; gas; shops 5km; tradsmn; pool; sm playgrnd; quiet; adv bkg; Eng spkn; CCI. "Friendly, helpful Dutch owner; excel san facs; lovely countryside views fr some pitches; conv Bastides in area." Apr-22 Oct. € 16.50   2005*

CORDES *8E4* (2km W Rural) **Camping Le Garissou, 81170 Cordes [05 63 56 27 14; fax 05 63 56 26 95; legarissou@wanadoo.fr]** Take D600 fr Cordes thro Les Cabanes, site sp on L. Med, terr, pt shd; wc; shwrs inc; el pts (5A) inc; lndtte; sm shop; playgrnd; pool complex adj; no dogs; quiet. "Hilltop site; excel views; clean facs." 1 May-30 Sep. € 13.00   2005*

†CORDES *8E4* (10km NW Rural) **Lissart Centre Naturiste (Naturist), 81170 Marnaves [tel/fax 05 63 56 37 30 or 05 63 56 39 04; info@lissart. com; www.lissart.com]** Fr Cordes take D600 NW twd St Antonin Noble-Val, site on L in 8km bef Marnarves; (sharp turn fr this dir; warning sp on main rd - rec lge o'fits app fr St Antonin.) Sm, mkd pitch, hdstg, terr, unshd; wc; chem disp; shwrs inc; el pts inc (5-10A) inc; gas; lndtte; ice; shop 12km; tradsmn; bar; playgrnd; 2 pools (1 htd); TV rm; 5% statics; no dogs; Eng spkn; adv bkg; quiet; cc not acc. "Levelling blocks req; steel pegs rec; v caring Eng owners; only green san chemical permitted; restored house for use of campers with kitchen, lounge with fire, sauna & jacuzzi; interesting area; woodland walks; delightful site." ♦ € 25.00   2005*

CORMATIN *9A2* (500m N Rural) **Camping Le Hameau des Champs, 71460 Cormatin [03 85 50 76 71; fax 03 85 50 76 98; camping. cormatin@wandoo.fr; www.le-hameau-des-champs.com]** Fr Cluny N on D981 dir Cormatin for approx 14km, site N of town sp on L, 300m after chateau. Look for line of European flags. Sm, hdg/mkd pitch, pt sl, pt shd; htd wc; chem disp; mv service pnt; shwrs inc; el pts (13A) €3 (long lead poss req); gas 500m; lndtte; ice; shop 500m; tradsmn; rest; snacks; bar; BBQ (gas/elec); cooking facs; playgrnd; rv sw 1km; shgle beach 7km; cycle hire; TV rm; 10% statics; dogs €1; phone; Eng spkn; adv bkg; dep 25%; quiet; cc acc; CCI. "Clean, secure site; welcoming, friendly staff; nrby bicycle museum, cycle route (Voie Verte) Givry to Cluny adj, chateau, church, wine route; lge grassy pitches; resident warden." ♦ 1 Apr-30 Sep. € 11.60   2005*

CORMATIN *9A2* (6km NW Rural) **Camping Le Gue, Messeugne, 71460 Savigny-sur-Grosne [03 85 92 61 88]** Fr Cluny N on D981, 2km N of Cormatin fork L sp Malay. Site 3km on R bef rv bdge. Med, mkd pitch, shd; htd wc; chem disp (wc); shwrs €0.80; el pts €2; tradsmn; snacks; bar; BBQ; playgrnd; games area; dir access to rv; fishing; 50% statics; dogs; CCI. "Gd sh stay; nr St Genoux-le-National (national monument), Cluny & Taize; on Burgundy wine rd; friendly site." Mar-Oct. € 8.20   2002*

CORMEILLES *3D1* (4km E Rural) **Camping Les Pommiers (formerly La Febvrerie), 27260 St Sylvestre-de-Cormeilles [02 32 42 29 69]** Exit A13 junc 28 Beuzeville onto N175 then D27 S sp Epaignes & Bernay twds Lieurey. Cont on D27 for approx 15km & at rndabt with D139 at Epaignes strt on for 5.6km, turn off R down narr lane sp St Sylvestre, Camping. Site on R in 1.5km. Sm, hdg pitch, pt shd; wc; chem disp (wc); shwrs inc; el pts inc (6A) inc (poss rev pol); lndry rm; shops 4km, rest, snacks, bar 4km; BBQ; playgrnd; some statics; dogs; phone; poss cr; Eng spkn; adv bkg; quiet. "Pleasant, friendly, family-run site in orchard; secluded with excel clean facs; gd rests Cormeilles." 1 Apr-1 Oct. € 10.35   2005*

CORNY SUR MOSELLE see Metz *5D2*

CORPS *9C3* (W Rural) **Camping La Rouilliere, Route du Coin, 38970 Corps** [04 76 30 03 34; fax 04 76 43 72 34] Sp off D537 dir Veynes. Sm, shd; wc; shwrs; el pts €3.04; shops in town; lake fishing & watersports 3km; quiet. "Basic, clean site; gd sh stay." 30 Jun-30 Aug. € 8.20   2002*

CORPS *9C3* (2.5km W) **Camping Indigo - Lac du Sautet, Route du Lac, 38970 Corps** [04 76 30 00 97; www.camping-indigo.com] Heading S turn R sp Veynes & Le Sautet & Centre Nautique bef ent Corps at top of hill. Rd fr town descends to lakeside. In 2km turn L sp Centre Nautique, to site. Acute ent so cont to car park & turn. Sm, sl, pt shd; wc (cont); shwrs inc; el pts €2.50; lndtte; shops 2.5km; playgrnd; pool; shgl beach; lake sw; fishing; dogs €1; quiet. "CL-type with basic facs." 1 Jun-15 Sep. € 11.00   2002*

CORREZE *7C4* (400m E Urban) **Camp Municipal La Chapelle, 19800 Correze** [05 55 21 29 30 or 05 55 21 25 21 (Mairie)] N fr Tulle on N89 twd Egletons or halfway fr Seillhac & Tulle on N120, foll sp to Correze. Site 400m fr town cent on D143. Med, mkd pitch, pl sl, terr, pt shd; wc; chem disp; shwrs inc; el pts (5A) €2; gas; lndtte; shop, rest, shops; snacks; playgrnd; htd pool 500m; canoeing & rv fishing; phone; Eng spkn; quiet; CCI. "Lovely area; old vill." ♦ ltd. 15 Jun-15 Sep. € 6.10   2005*

COSNE COURS SUR LOIRE *4G3* (2km S) **Camping de l'Ile, Ile de Cosne, 18300 Bannay** [03 86 28 27 92; fax 03 86 28 18 10; campingile18@aol.com; www.camping-de-l-ile. com] Fr Cosne take Bourges rd, D955, over 1st half of bdge, ent immed on L, 500m strt. On rv island. Lge, shd; htd wc (cont); chem disp; shwrs inc; el pts (10A) €3.80; lndtte; ice; ltd shop; rest; snacks; bar; BBQ; playgrnd; paddling pool; entmnts; cycle hire; TV; dogs €0.90; quiet; cc acc; CCI. "Helpful staff; site flooded 2004; poss still unkempt; poss san facs unclean; gd NH." ♦ 1 Apr-15 Sep. € 13.50   2004*

COUBON see Puy en Velay, Le *9C1*

COUCHES see Nolay *6H1*

COUCOURDE DERBIERES, LA see Montelimar *9D2*

COUHE *7A2* (1km N Rural) **Camping Les Peupliers, 86700 Couhe** [05 49 59 21 16; fax 05 49 37 92 09; info@lespeupliers.fr; www.lespeupliers.fr] Site 35km S of Poitiers on N10 bis (old rd off by-pass); ent by bdge over Rv Dive. Fr N or S on N10 take N exit for Couhe. Site on R in 800m. Lge, hdg/mkd pitch, pt shd; wc; 30% serviced pitch; chem disp; mv service pnt; shwrs inc; el pts (10A) €4; gas; lndtte; ice; shop & 1.5km; tradsmn; rest; snacks; bar; BBQ; playgrnd; 3 htd pools & 2 paddling pools high ssn; waterslides; fishing; sports area; pedaloes; entmnt; child entmnt; games rm; TV rm; some statics; dogs; Eng spkn; adv bkg; quiet; cc acc; red low ssn/long stay/CCI. "Well-organised; excel site in every way; poss inadequate el pnts; conv & easy access fr N10; conv Futuroscope." ♦ 2 May-30 Sep. € 21.50 (CChq acc)   2005*

See advertisement

COULANGES SUR YONNE *4G4* (Rural) **Camping des Berges de l'Yonne, 89480 Coulanges-sur-Yonne** [03 86 81 76 87] On N151 dir Nevers. Med, pt shd; wc; chem disp; shwrs; el pts (10A) inc; shop; snacks; playgrnd; rv sw; tennis. "V pleasant; old-fashioned facs but v adequate; excel bakery in Coulanges, sh walk fr site; useful NH." 1 May-15 Sep. € 12.20   2003*

COULANGES SUR YONNE *4G4* (9km E Rural) **Camp Municipal Le Petit Port, 89660 Chatel-Censoir** [03 86 81 01 98 (Mairie) or 03 86 81 06 35; fax 03 86 81 08 05] Fr Auxerre or Clamecy on N151 at Coulanges turn E onto D21, S side of rv & canal to Chatel-Censoir; site sp. Med, pt shd; wc (some cont); chem disp (wc); shwrs €0.75; el pts (16A) €1.90 (poss rev pol); lndry rm; shop, rest, & bar 400m; BBQ; playgrnd; rv sw & fishing adj; phone; some rlwy noise; CCI. "V attractive, peaceful site bet rv & canal; clean, modern san facs; beautiful area with gd cycling; superb value; no twin-axle vans but poss itinerants/mkt traders (with twin-axles!); warden calls am & pm." 1 May-30 Sep. € 5.40   2005*

COULLONS *4G3* (1km W Rural) **Camp Municipal Plancherotte,** 45720 Coullons [02 38 29 20 42; fax 02 38 29 23 07] Fr cent of Coullons foll sp twd Cerdon (D51). Bef leaving vill & after passing lake, take 1st rd on L. Site in 500m on L side of lake. Med, pt shd, hdg/mkd pitch; wc (cont); chem disp; some serviced pitches; shwrs; el pts inc; gas 1km; shop 1km; playgrnd; lake sw adj; 50% statics; phone; adv bkg; CCI. "Vg long/sh stay." ◆ 1 Apr-31 Oct. € 8.30   2002*

COULON *7A2* **Camp Municipal La Niquiere, Route de Benet,** 79510 Coulon [05 49 35 81 19 or 05 49 35 90 26 (Mairie); fax 05 49 35 82 75] Take D1 fr Benet to Coulon to site on L at ent to Coulon. Sm, pt shd; wc (cont); shwrs inc; el pts (10A) inc; gas; ice; shops 1km; sports facs adj; boats for hire; poss cr. "Well-kept site; ent only with barrier card; office open 1030-1200 & 1500-1630 outside Jul/Aug, open 0730-2000 Jul/Aug; Coulon rec." 1 Apr-30 Sep. € 9.00   2005*

COULON *7A2* (3km N) **Camping a la Ferme La Planche,** 79510 Coulon [05 49 35 93 17] Fr N148, foll main rd thro Benet, then foll sp (bus & lorry) Coulon. Take 1st L sp Coulon, then 1st R sp 'Camping a la Planche'. Site on L in 1.5km. Sm, pt shd; wc; shwr; el pts (10A) inc; supmkt 1.5km; tradsmn; rest 1.5km; BBQ; horse & carriage rides; some statics; adv bkg; quiet. "Excel CL-type farm site; friendly owners; ltd but clean facs; busy high ssn; sm pitches; gd long stay." € 8.20   2004*

COULON *7A2* (2km S Rural) **Camping de La Garette, Rue des Gravees,** 79270 La Garette [05 49 35 00 33; fax 05 49 35 00 31] Fr Niort take dir to Coulon & La Venise Verte; at Coulon rndbt turn L; site thro vill on R. Med, mkd pitch, pt shd; wc; shwrs inc; el pts (6A) €2.50; rest/bar 300m; shop & 3km; tradsmn; pool; mini-golf; tennis; fishing; boat rides; cc acc; 15% red +7 days; quiet; CCI. "Many rests within 1km; vg long stay." ◆ € 10.00   2003*

COULON *7A2* (2km W) **Camping La Venise Verte, 178 Route des Bordes de Sevre,** 79510 Coulon [05 49 35 90 36; fax 05 49 35 84 69; accueil@camping-laveniseverte.com; www.camping-laveniseverte.com] Do not app thro Benet. Exit A83 junc 9 onto N148. At x-rds with D123 turn R dir Coulon, (vill in approx 5km). Site 2km W of Coulon on D123, sp Med, mkd pitch, pt shd; wc; chem disp; shwrs inc; el pts (10A) inc (rev pol); gas; lndtte; ice; shop; tradsmn; rest high ssn; snacks; BBQ (charcoal/gas); playgrnd; htd pool; boating; fishing; canoe/cycle hire; entmnt & excursions; internet; TV rm; 25% statics; dogs €1.50; phone; Eng spkn; poss cr; adv bkg; poss noisy high ssn; red low ssn; CCI. "Excel site in park-like setting; helpful owner; gd facs; excel touring base for nature lovers; gd cycle rtes." 1 Apr-31 Oct. € 20.00 ABS - A37   2005*

COULON *7A2* (6km W Rural) **Camping Le Relais du Pecheur,** 85420 Le Mazeau [02 51 52 93 23 or 02 51 52 91 14 (Mairie); fax 02 51 52 97 58] Fr Fontenay-le-Comte take N148 SE. At Benet turn R onto D25 & foll sp to vill. Turn L in vill then R over canal bdge. Site on L in 500m. Med, hdg pitch, pt shd; wc; chem disp; shwrs inc; el pts (16A) €2; lndtte; shop 500m; supmkt 5km; playgrnd; paddling pool; adv bkg; CCI. "Modern, clean san facs; delightful location; gd touring base Vendee; gd cycling & walks; facs v ltd low ssn." ◆ ltd. 1 Apr-15 Oct. € 7.80   2005*

COULONGES SUR L'AUTIZE *7A2* (500m S) **Camp Municipal Le Parc, Rue du Calvaire,** 79160 Coulonges-sur-l'Autize [05 49 06 10 72 or 05 49 06 10 86; fax 05 49 06 13 26] Fr Fontenay take D745 sp Parthenay/St Hilaire E to Coulonges where site sp. Fr Niort take D744 N to Coulonges. Sm, hdg/mkdch, pt shd; wc; chem disp (wc only); shwrs inc; el pts inc; lndry rm; ice; shop adj; tradsmn; playgrnd; pool; cycle hire; rv sw & fishing 4km; 80% statics; dogs; phone; quiet; CCI. "Gd sh stay; site yourself; warden will call." ◆ Jun-Sep. € 7.40   2004*

COURBIAC see Fumel *7D3*

COURCON *7A2* (6km N Rural) **Camping Le Port, Rue du Port,** 17170 La Ronde [05 46 27 82 78 or 05 46 27 87 92] Fr Marans E on D114, bef Courcon head N on D116 sp Maillezais. Site on R after leaving vill of La Ronde. Sm, hdg/mkd pitch, hdstg, pt shd; wc; chem disp; shwrs inc; el pts (5-10A) €2.20-4; gas; lndtte; ice; shops adj; BBQ; playgrnd; pool high ssn; sand beach 30km; few statics; dogs; poss cr; adv bkg; quiet. "V helpful owner; excel quiet sm site; well looked-after; facs clean." ◆ 1 May-30 Sep. € 9.00   2005*

COURCON *7A2* (500m S) **Camp Municipal,** 17170 Courcon [05 46 01 60 19 or 05 46 01 60 50 (Mairie); fax 05 46 01 63 59] Fr N11 Mauze-La Rochelle turn N at La Laigne on D114 to Courcon. Site on L on app to vill. Sm, pt shd; wc (cont); shwrs; el pts (3A); lndtte; shops 1km; htd pool adj; rv sw 5km; fishing 5km; adv bkg rec high ssn; quiet.   2003*

COURCON *7A2* (5km S) **Camp Municipal du Chateau,** 17170 Benon [06 66 90 35 59 or 05 46 01 61 48 (Mairie); fax 05 46 01 01 19; benon@mairie17.com] Fr N11 turn S to Benon onto D116. On S side of Benon turn E onto D206 twd St George-du-Bois, site immed on R thro tall, narr, metal gateway; take wide sweep on ent. Site also sp in Benon. Sm, pt sl, pt shd; wc; chem disp; shwrs inc; el pts (6A) €2.10; lndtte; shop 300m; tradsmn; playgrnd; pool 6km; tennis; dogs €0.80; quiet; adv bkg; cc acc; CCI. "Attractive site with mature trees in walled area adj Mairie; helpful warden; no lighting; excel rest 2km N nr N11 & gd value rest 150m in vill; oyster beds at Chatelaillon; gd cycling area; 20 mins La Rochelle; poss itinerants; vg long/sh stay." 1 May-30 Sep. € 8.20   2004*

COURNON D'AVERGNE see Clermont Ferrand *9B1*

COURSEULLES SUR MER *3D1* (E Coastal) **Camp Municipal Le Champ de Course, Ave de la Liberation, 14470 Courseulles-sur-Mer** [02 31 37 99 26; fax 02 31 37 96 37]
Fr N814 by-pass thro Caen, take exit 5 onto D7 & D404 dir Courseulles-sur-Mer. On ent to town, foll sp 'Campings' at 1st rndabt, then sp 'Centre Juno Beach'. Site on D514 on R. App rds poor. Lge, hdg pitch; unshd; wc; chem disp; serviced pitch; shwrs inc; el pts (6-9A) 3.35-4.40; lndtte; tradsmn; rest, snacks, bar adj; playgrnd; pool adj; sand beach; sports area; boat hire; tennis, mini-golf & horseriding nr; TV rm; 15% statics; poss cr; Eng spkn; adv bkg; quiet; cc acc; CCI. "Friendly staff; smart entrance & bureau; slightly run-down facs; conv Juno (D-Day landings) beach; gd long stay." ♦ Easter-30 Sep. € 14.50   2004*

COURSEULLES SUR MER *3D1* (2km E Coastal) **Camping Le Havre de Bernieres, Chemin de Quintefeuille, 14990 Bernieres-sur-Mer** [02 31 96 67 09; fax 02 31 97 31 06; camping normandie@aol.com] W fr Ouistreham on D514 for 20km. Site well sp. Lge, mkd pitch, pt sl, pt shd; wc; chem disp; 50% serviced pitches; shwrs inc; el pts (6-10A) €3.90-5.30; lndtte; shop; rest; playgrnd; pool; sand beach adj; tennis; many statics; dogs €3.60; poss cr; Eng spkn; adv bkg; quiet; red low ssn; CCI. "Excel site; gd beaches & watersports; conv Ouistreham ferries; site poss untidy in low ssn; poss ltd facs low ssn; when site cr c'vans poss need manhandling; gates clsd 2200-0730." ♦
1 Apr-31 Oct. € 23.80   2005*

COURSEULLES SUR MER *3D1* (8km SW Rural) **Camp Municipal des Trois Rivieres, Route de Tierceville, 14480 Creully** [tel/fax 02 31 80 12 00 or 02 31 80 90 17] Fr Caen ring rd, exit junc 5 onto D7 twd N; at rndabt at Courseulles-sur-Mer turn L onto D12 dir Bayeux. At Tierceville turn S, sp Creully; site 1km on L on D93 to Creully. NB only app is fr Tierceville as c'vans not permitted on other rds. Med, hdg pitch, pt sl, pt shd; htd wc; chem disp (wc); shwrs inc; chem disp; el pts (5-10A) €3.50 (long leads adv); lndtte; shops, rest, snacks, bar 1km; BBQ; playgrnd; pool 5km; games area; games rm; sand beach 5km; dogs €1; Eng spkn; adv bkg; quiet; cc acc; CCI. "Well-maintained, clean site; conv D-Day beaches, Bayeux; no ent poss when barrier clsd 1200-1500 & at 2200; facs stretched high ssn; picturesque vills in area." ♦ 1 Apr-30 Sep.
€ 9.45   2005*

COURTILS see Mont St Michel, Le *2E4*

COURVILLE SUR EURE *4E2* (S Urban) **Camp Municipal, Ave Thier, 28190 Courville-sur-Eure** [02 37 23 76 38 or 02 37 18 07 90 (Mairie); fax 02 37 18 07 99; jean-claude.larcher@courville-sur-eure.fr] Turn N off N23 19km W of Chartres. Site on bank of rv. Foll sp. Med, hdg pitch, unshd; wc (some cont); chem disp (wc); shwrs; el pts (6A) €2.60; shops 2km; rest in town; pool 200m; dogs; poss cr; quiet. "Fair NH; facs stretched all year; conv Chartres." 1 Jun-15 Sep. € 6.50   2005*

COUTANCES *1D4* (6km N Rural) **Camping La Raisiniere, 50200 Ancteville** [02 33 45 11 53; terencedearman@hotmail.com] Fr Cherbourg S on N13, D900 & D2 dir Le Mont-St Michel, 1km S of Montsurvent turn L onto D393 to Ancteville, site 1.5km on L. Sm, pt shd; wc; chem disp; shwrs inc; el pts (6A) inc; shop, rest, bar 2km; Eng spkn; quiet; red long stay. "Gd, clean, simple CL-type site 1 hr fr Cherbourg; ltd facs; excel walking & cycling; British owners." 1 Apr-31 Oct. € 14.00   2005*

> Some of these sites have changed their opening dates - we'd better fill in some site report forms and let the editor of the guide know.

COUTANCES *1D4* (9km NE) **Camp Municipal, 50490 St Sauveur-Lendelin** [02 33 76 52 00; fax 02 33 76 52 01] Fr Coutances take D971 NE. Site lies on L of rd bef rd junc on ent vill. Lge o'fits take care at ent. Sm, pt shd, hdg pitch; wc; shwrs inc; el pts inc; shops & rest 500m; some rd noise. "Warden calls am & pm; generous pitches; basic san facs but clean; 75 min fast rd Cherbourg; conv NH."
1 Jun-15 Sep. € 10.00   2004*

†**COUTANCES** *1D4* (1km W Urban) **Camp Municipal Les Vignettes, 27 Rue de St Malo, 50200 Coutances** [02 33 45 43 13; fax 02 33 45 74 98] Fr N on D971 or D2 turn R onto Coutances by-pass, sp St Malo & Avranches. At rndabt turn L. Site 200m on R after Cositel ent. Fr S foll sp for Valognes or Cherbourg. Site in Coutances on L immed after Logis sp. Med, hdg/mkd pitch, pt sl, pt shd; wc (some cont); chem disp; shwrs inc; ltd el pts (2-6A) €2.10; shops 500m; snacks; bar; BBQ; playgrnd; htd pool adj (caps ess); sports stadium adj; few statics; dogs €1; poss cr; some rd noise; CCI. "Access poss diff to some pitches; pretty site; san facs poss unclean low ssn; warden calls 0800; gd sh stay/NH for Cherbourg." € 8.60   2004*

COUTRAS *7C2* (Urban) **Camp Municipal Frais Rivage, Route de Guîtres, 33230 Coutras** [05 57 49 12 00; fax 05 57 56 09 04] In Coutras on D674 turn onto D10, over new bdge. Site on L. Fr S on D674 turn L onto D10. Well sp. Sm, pt shd; wc; shwrs; el pts (6A) €2 (poss rev pol); shop 300m; pool 1km; fishing; quiet. "Pleasant rvside site; clean san facs." ♦ 1 Jun-12 Sep. € 8.40   2004*

COUTRAS *7C2* (3km SW Rural) **Camping Le Paradis, Port-du-Mas, 33230 Abzac** [05 57 49 05 10; fax 05 57 49 18 88; campingle paradis@free.fr] Fr Coutras on S on D17 to Abzac, site well sp. Sm, pt shd; htd wc; mv service pnt; baby facs; shwrs inc; el pts (6A) €3; gas; ice; lndtte; shop; rest; BBQ; playgrnd; TV rm; lake sw; fishing; entmnt; 50% statics; dogs €1.30; cc acc; CCI. "Excel site, gd for vineyards; rec long stay." 1 Apr-30 Sep. € 14.80   2005*

COUTURES *4G1* (1km NE Rural) **Camping Parc de Montsabert (formerly L'Europeen), 49320 Coutures** [02 41 57 91 63; fax 02 41 57 90 02; camping@parcdemontsabert.com; www.camping -europeen.com] Easy access on R side of Rv Loire bet Angers & Saumur. Take rte D751 to Coutures. Fr town cent foll sp for site. First R after 'Tabac' & foll rd to site (first on R bef chateau). Med, hdg/mkd pitch, hdstg, pt sl, pt shd; htd wc; chem disp; 50% serviced pitches; child/baby facs; shwrs inc; el pts (5-10A) €2.80-4; lndtte; ice; shop 1.5km; tradsmn; rest; snacks; bar; playgrnd; htd, covrd pool; paddling pool; tennis; games area; games hall; cycle hire; crazy golf; gym; entmnt; child entmnt; TV; 15% statics; dogs €3; phone; bus 1km; Eng spkn; adv bkg (dep req); quiet; cc acc; CCI. "Ideal for Caves Champignon, chateaux & wine cellars; lge pitches; excel all stays." ♦ 29 Apr-15 Sep. € 23.80
2005*

COUX ET BIGAROQUE see Bugue, Le *7C3*

COUZON see Bourbon L'Archambault *9A1*

COZES *7B1* (8km NE Rural) **Camping Vacances St Jacques, La Mirolle, 17260 St Andre-de-Lidon** [tel/fax 05 46 90 11 05; vacances_st_jacques@ compuserve.com] D129 fr St Andre-de-Lidon dir Montpellier-de-Medillan, just off rd to Cravans. Sm, mkd pitch, pt shd; wc; shwrs; el pts (16A) inc; gas 7km; lndtte; shops, rest, snacks 2km; bar; BBQ; playgrnd; paddle pool; sand beach 20km; TV rm; quiet; adv bkg (dep req); Eng spkn; no cc acc. "Friendly British owners; CL-type site; gd for disabled; gd cycling; gd rests in vill; nrby beaches, medieval towns; vg all stays." ♦ May-Oct. € 12.00
2004*

COZES *7B1* (9km S Rural) **Camp Municipal St Seurin-d'Uzet, 17120 Chenac-St Seurin-d'Uzet** [05 46 90 45 31 or 05 46 90 44 03 (Mairie); fax 05 46 90 40 02] SE fr Royan take D25/D145 thro St Georges-de-Didonne, Meschers-sur-Gironde & Talmont to St Seurin-d'Uzet. Site sp in vill. Med, hdg/mkd pitch, pt shd; wc; chem disp (wc); shwrs inc; el pts €2.20 (rev pol) (poss long lead req); lndtte; shop 100m; playgrnd; rv sw & sand beach adj; dogs €0.75; adv bkg rec high ssn; quiet. "Rec; pretty site beside creek; gd views & walks; gd vill shop; pleasant staff; mosquitoe problem."
1 May-30 Sep. € 6.80   2005*

COZES *7B1* (4km SW) **Camping Fleur des Champs, Le Coudinier, 17120 Arces-sur-Gironde** [05 46 90 40 11; fax 05 46 97 64 45] Site on D114 on R 1km fr Arces to Talmont. Sm, mkd pitch, pt sl, pt shd; wc; shwrs inc; el pts (4-6A) €2-3; gas; ice; tradsmn; lndtte; shop 1km; tradsmn; pool 4km; cycle hire; playgrnd; entmnts; archery; lake beach, sw & fishing 2km; dogs €1.22; 70% statics; quiet. "Gd; nice, quiet rural site; ideal for seaside holiday away fr typical coastal sites." 1 Jun-15 Sep. € 8.70
2004*

COZES *7B1* (10km SW Coastal) **Camping Bellevue, 220 Route Verte, 17120 Barzan-Plage** [05 46 90 45 91] Fr Cozes W D114 thro Arces to Talmont-sur-Gironde L onto D145, site 2km on L. Sm, mkd pitch, pt sl, pt shd; wc (some cont); shwrs inc; el pts €3; lndtte; rest 500m; pool & beach adj; 50% statics; dogs; quiet; CCI. "Fair sh stay." ♦ ltd. 15 May-15 Sep. € 10.00   2002*

COZES *7B1* (W Urban) **Camp Municipal Le Sorlut, Rue de Stade, 17120 Cozes** [05 46 90 75 99 or 05 46 90 90 97 (Mairie)] Clearly sp in Cozes, 150m fr N730. Turn into app rd on R of Champion supmkt. Med, mkd pitch, pt shd; wc; chem disp; shwrs inc; el pts (5A) €2.25; lndry rm; shops adj; supmkt 500m; playgrnd; pool; sand beach 6km; tennis; quiet; CCI. "Helpful warden calls 0830-0930 & 1800-1900 otherwise phone for ent; barrier erected to prevent itinerants; no twin-axles; v pleasant site close to Royan; ltd facs when only few vans; no arr 1200-1500; excel long/sh stay." 15 Apr-15 Oct.
€ 6.45   2004*

CRAC'H see Carnac *2G3*

CRAON *2F4* (Urban) **Camp Municipal du Murier, Rue Alain Gerbault, 53400 Craon** [02 43 06 96 33 or 02 43 06 13 09 (Mairie); fax 02 43 06 39 20] Fr Laval take N171 S to Craon. Site off town cent. Med, hdg pitch, pt shd; wc; shwrs inc; el pts (6A) €1.86; lndtte; snacks; playgrnd; pool 200m; tennis; entmnt; no twin-axles; adv bkg; quiet; 10% red long stays. 1 May-15 Sep. € 8.72   2004*

CRAZANNES see St Savinien *7B2*

CRECHES SUR SAONE see Macon *9A2*

CREISSAN *10F1* **Camp Municipal Les Oliviers, 34370 Creissan** [04 67 93 81 85 or 04 67 93 75 41 (Mairie); fax 04 67 93 85 28] Fr N112 foll sp Creissan & site. Sm, mkd pitch, pt shd; shwrs inc; el pts €2.30; lndtte; shop, rest, bar in vill; BBQ; playgrnd; pool; tennis; entmnt; adv bkg; quiet. "Pleasant site." 1 Apr-30 Sep. € 7.80   2002*

CREON D'ARMAGNAC see St Justin *8E2*

CRESPIAN *10E1* (Urban) **Camping Le Mas de Reilhe, 30260 Crespian** [04 66 77 82 12; fax 04 66 80 26 50; info@camping-mas-de-reilhe.fr; www.camping-mas-de-reilhe.fr] Exit A9 at Nimes Ouest N onto N106 dir Ales for 5km. From L over bdge onto D999 dir Le Vigan. Foll rd for 24km, R at x-rds onto N110 to site on R just on ent Crespian. Take care - ent on a bend on busy rd. Med, mkd pitch, pt sl, terer, pt shd; wc; chem disp; baby facs; shwrs inc; el pts (6A) inc; lndtte; shop; rest; bar; BBQ (gas/elec); playgrnd; pool & paddling pool; tennis; fishing & horseriding 3km; organised walks; games rm; entmnt high ssn; dogs €2.30; recep 0830-2200; poss cr; Eng spkn; quiet but some rd noise; cc acc; CCI. "Quiet & relaxing; friendly wardens; conv Nimes, Uzes & Cevennes National Park; excel." ♦ 8 Apr-24 Sep. € 22.30 (CChq acc) ABS - C10   2005*

CREST *9D2* (5km E Rural) **Gervanne Camping, 26400 Mirabel-et-Blacons [04 75 40 00 20; fax 04 75 40 03 97; info@gervanne-camping.com; www.gervanne-camping.com]** Exit A7 junc 16 Loriol onto D104/D164, turn off onto D93. Site 2km E of Mirabel-et-Blacons on both sides or rd. Recep by shop. Med, pt sl, pt shd; wc; shwrs inc; baby facs; el pts (4-6A) €2.60-3.20; lndtte; shop adj; rest; snacks; bar; BBQ; playgrnd; htd pool; rv sw adj; child entmnt; 20% statics; dogs €2; poss cr; Eng spkn; adv bkg (ess high ssn); quiet; cc acc; red low ssn; CCI. "Excel, family-run site in beautiful area; gd size pitches in upper & lower site; dep for security barrier key." 1 Apr-3 Nov. € 16.60   2005*

CREST *9D2* (500m S Urban) **Camping Les Clorinthes, 26400 Crest [04 75 25 05 28; fax 04 75 76 75 09; lecampinglesclorinthes@minitel. net]** S fr Crest twd Nyons on D538 turn L immed after x-ing bdge over rv. Site sp. Lge, hdg/mkd pitch, pt sl, pt shd; wc (some cont); own san rec; chem disp; shwrs; el pts (6A) inc; gas; ice; lndtte; shop & 500m; tradsmn; snacks; bar; pool; rv sw adj; sports complex 500m; TV; entmnt; fishing; 20% statics; dogs; phone; poss cr; adv bkg; poss cr; quiet, some train noise; CCI. "Security barrier with dep for key; dir access rv; beautiful situation; much improved; muddy when wet; fair sh stay." ♦ ltd. 1 May-30 Sep. € 20.43   2004*

†CREST *9D2* (8km W) **Camping Les Quatre Saisons, Route de Roche-sur-Grane, 26400 Grane [04 75 62 64 17; fax 04 75 62 69 06; camping.4saisons@wanadoo.fr]** Exit A7 at junc for Loriol or Crest, take D104 E for 18km. Turn R thro vill twd Roche-sur-Grane, site well sp. If a lge unit, access thro 4th junc to Grane. Site well sp fr Crest. Med, pt sl, terr, shd; wc; chem disp; mv service pnt; baby facs; shwrs inc; el pts (10A) €4; lndtte; ice; shop; tradsmn; snacks; bar; BBQ; pool; tennis; games area; dogs €3; phone; poss cr; adv bkg; quiet; red long stay/low ssn; cc acc; CCI. "Beautiful views; friendly owners; excel modern facs but poss lukewarm shwrs; sm pitches; chem disp v primitive; many holiday facs in Drome valley; excel walk to Grane (supmkt, rest etc.); excel long/sh stay." ♦ € 15.00   2005*

CREULLY see Courseulles sur Mer *3D1*

CREVECOEUR EN BRIE see Fontenay Tresigny *4E3*

†CREVECOEUR LE GRAND *3C3* (7km SE Rural) Camping a la Ferme (Fontana), 8 Hameau de la Neuve Rue, 60480 Ourcel-Maison [03 44 46 81 55] NE fr Beauvais on N1 to Froissey; turn W at traff lts onto D151. Avoid 1st sp to Francastel but cont to x-rds & turn into vill on D11. Francastel adjoins Ourcel-Maison & site at far end. Or fr A16 exit junc 16 W onto D930 & foll sp. Sm, pt shd; wc (some cont); chem disp; shwrs inc; el pts (3A) inc (rev pol); shop 6km; rest; tradsmn; BBQ; playgrnd; quiet; cc not acc. "Vg, quiet site with farm produce & occasional eve meals; no hdstg & poss muddy/diff in wet weather; san facs need attention." € 7.00 2005*

CREYSSE see Martel *7C3*

CRIEL SUR MER *3B2* (2km N Coastal) **Camping Les Mouettes, Rue de la Plage, 76910 Criel-sur-Mer [tel/fax 02 35 86 70 73; camping-lesmouettes.com; www.camping-lesmouettes. com]** Fr D925 take D222 thro Criel to coast, site sp. Sm, terr, pt shd; wc; shwrs; el pts (6A) €3; lndtte; ice; shop; rest; bar; BBQ; playgrnd; games area; some statics; adv bkg; quiet. "V nice little site; sea views." Easter-1 Nov. € 12.00   2002*

CRIQUETOT L'ESNEVAL see Etretat *3C1*

CROISIC, LE *2G3* (1km SE Coastal) **Camping Le Paradis, 44490 Le Croisic [02 40 23 07 89]** Fr La Baule take rd to Le Croisic, past Batz-sur-Mer, ent to Le Croisic fork L on coast rd & take long way round to town cent. About 6km fr Batz turn R at strange-looking chapel & L at T-junc. Site on R. Med, pt sl, pt shd; wc; shwrs inc; el pts (3-5A) €2.30-€2.90; gas; lndry rm; ice; shop 1km; rest; snacks; bar; BBQ; sand beach 400m; dogs €1.25; adv bkg. 15 May-30 Sep. € 11.30   2002*

†CROISIC, LE *2G3* (2km S Coastal) **Camping La Pierre Longue, Rue Henri Dunant, 44490 Le Croisic [02 40 23 13 44; fax 02 40 23 23 13]** Turn L off Le Pouligan-Le Croisic rd at g'ge at Le Croisic sp foll camp sps. Med, hdg/mkd pitch, pt shd; htd wc; chem disp; mv service pnt; baby facs; shwrs inc; el pts (6-10A) €3.50-5; gas; lndtte; ice; shop; rest; snacks; bar; BBQ; playgrnd; htd pool; sand beach 400m; entmnt; TV; 60% statics; phone; dogs €2; Eng spkn; adv bkg; quiet; cc acc; red low ssn; CCI. "Warm welcome; excel facs; excel beaches." ♦ € 19.50   2005*

CROISIC, LE *2G3* (1km W Coastal) **Camping de l'Ocean, 15 Route de la Maison Rouge, Le Pre Brule, 44490 Le Croisic [02 40 23 07 69; fax 02 40 15 70 63; info@camping-ocean.com; www. camping-ocean.com]** Foll N171 to Guerande. At junc take D774 to La Baule, Batz-sur-Mer. Back on old N171 to Le Croisic. At rndabt foll site sp. Lge, hdg/mkd pitch, pt shd; wc; chem disp; mv service pnt; serviced pitches; baby facs; shwrs inc; el pts (4-10A) inc; gas; lndtte; ice; shop; snacks; playgrnd; 2 htd pools, (1 covrd); waterslide; jacuzzi; sand beach 150m; tennis; games area; fitness rm; entmnt; child entmnt; 40% statics; dogs €4; adv bkg; Eng spkn; quiet; red low ssn; cc acc; red low ssn/CCI. "Interesting coast line nr La Baule; caves & rocky headlands; salt flats at ent to Le Croisic; pleasant walk to walled city of Guerande adj; excel pools complex." ♦ 2 Apr-30 Sep. € 33.00 (3 persons)   2005*

See advertisement on page 474

CROIX EN TERNOIS see St Pol sur Ternoise *3B3*

CROIXILLE, LA see Ernee *2E4*

CROMARY see Rioz *6G2*

CROTOY, LE *3B2* **Camping La Ferme du Tarteron, 80550 Le Crotoy [03 22 27 06 75; fax 03 22 27 02 49]** Fr N1 head exit junc 24 onto D32, then D940 twd Le Crotoy. Site on R. Med, some hdg pitch, pt shd; wc; chem disp; shwrs inc; el pts €2.70; gas; shop; tradsmn (bread); snacks; playgrnd; sand beach 4km; pool; many statics. "Conv Marquenterre & steam train fr Le Crotoy; dep req for barrier key; ltd facs low ssn." 1 Mar-31 Oct. € 14.95   2003*

CROTOY, LE *3B2* (Urban/Coastal) **Camping La Prairie, 2 Rue de Mayocq, 80550 Le Crotoy [tel/fax 03 22 27 02 65]** Fr S exit A16 at Abbeville onto D86/D940 to Le Crotoy to rndabt at ent to town. Cont strt for 1.5km then 2nd L, site on L in 500m. Fr N exit A16 for Rue onto D32, then D940, then as above. Lge, hdg pitch, pt shd; wc (some cont); chem disp (wc); shwrs; el pts (3-6A) €2.70-5.40; tradsmn; playgrnd; sand beach 400m; 90% statics; dogs €1; phone; poss cr; quiet. "Ltd pitches for tourers but conv beach & town; excel cycle paths in area." ♦ 1 Apr-30 Sep. € 12.60   2005*

CROTOY, LE *3B2* (3km N) **Camping du Ridin, Mayocq, 80550 Le Crotoy [03 22 27 03 22; contact@campingleridin.com; www.campingleridin.com]** Fr Abbeville, take D904A & in approx 8km turn R at T-junc onto D260. In approx 4km turn R, foll sps to site. Med, unshd; htd wc; chem disp; mv service pnt; shwrs; el pts (6-10A) €1.80-5.50; gas; lndtte; ice; shop; supmkt 1km; rest; snacks; bar; playgrnd; htd pool; paddling pool; sand beach 1.5km; cycle hire; weights rm; child entmnt; TV rm; 20% statics; dogs €1.20; poss cr; adv bkg; quiet. "Le Crotoy beautiful town; bird sanctuary at Marquenterre." ♦ 1 Apr-31 Oct. € 17.00 (CChq acc)   2004*

CROUY SUR COSSON see Muides sur Loire *4G2*

†**CROZON** *2E2* (5km E Coastal) **Camping L'Aber, Tal-ar-Groas, 29160 Crozon [02 98 27 02 96; fax 02 98 27 28 48; camping.aber.plage@presquile-crozon.com]** On Chateaulin-Crozon rd turn S in Tal-ar-Groas foll camp sp to site in 1km on R. Med, mkd pitch, pt sl, terr, pt shd; wc; shwrs inc; el pts (5A) inc; gas; lndtte; snacks; bar; sand beach 1km; sailing; fishing; windsurfing; adv bkg; quiet. € 11.50   2003*

CROZON *2E2* (3km SW) **Camping Les Bruyeres, Le Bouis, 29160 Crozon [tel/fax 02 98 26 14 87; camping.les.bruyeres@presquile-crozon.com]** Take D887 then D255 SW fr Crozon (sp Cap de la Chevre). In 1.5km turn R & site on R in 700m. Lge, mkd pitch, pt shd; wc (mainly cont); shwrs €1; gas; ice; shop in ssn; el pts (5A) €2.80; playgrnd; sand beach 1.8km; dogs €0.90; Eng spkn; adv bkg; quiet; red 2+ days. 1 Jun-15 Sep. € 12.30   2003*

CUBJAC *7C3* (1.5km E Rural) **Camping L'Ilot, 24640 Cubjac [05 53 05 53 05; fax 05 53 05 37 82; musitelli@wanadoo.fr]** Take D5 E fr Perigueux to Cubjac (21km). Fork R off D5 into vill. At x-rds in vill E & site on R in 1.5km. Sm, mkd pitch, pt shd; wc (some cont); baby facs; shwrs inc; el pts (5A) €2.50; ice; lndtte; shop adj; rest; snacks; bar; BBQ; playgrnd; pool 4km; rv sw; fishing; canoes; tennis adj; games area; entmnt; adv bkg. ♦ 1 Apr-30 Sep. € 13.00   2004*

CUCURON see Cadenet *10E3*

CUERS *10F3* (7km SE Rural) **Camping de Deffends, 109 Route de Collobrieres, 83390 Pierrefeu-du-Var [04 94 28 20 62; fax 04 94 48 26 75]** Fr Cuers A57 N exit 10 R onto D14 thro Pierrefeu-du-Var; foll sp E to Collobrieres site on L 1km. Med, mkd pitch, terr, pt shd; wc; chem disp; shwrs inc; el pts (6-10A); gas 1km; lndtte; ice; tradsmn; rest; snacks; bar in ssn; playgrnd; pool (no shorts); sand beach 20km; 10% statics; dogs; phone; Eng spkn; adv bkg; quiet; CCI. "Some pitches diff for lge o'fits; gates clsd 2200-0800; scenic views in wine-growing area." 15 Apr-15 Sep. € 15.10   2002*

CUERS *10F3* (6km W Rural) **Camping Les Tomasses, 83210 Belgentier [04 94 48 92 70; fax 04 94 48 94 73]** Exit A8 junc 34 St Maximin onto N7. After Tourves take D205 then D5/D554 sp Sollies-Pont. After Belgentier in 1.5km turn R at yellow sp, site in 200m on L. Or N fr Toulon onto D554. Well sp on R in vill. Med, hdg/mkd pitch, pt shd; wc (mainly cont); chem disp (wc); shwrs inc; el pts (6A) inc; gas; lndtte; ice; shop; snacks; bar; BBQ; playgrnd; pool; tennis; entmnt; 10% statics; dogs €2; phone; bus 300m; adv bkg (dep req); quiet; red low ssn; CCI. "Pretty site & area; easy access, friendly management; twin-axles welcome; CL-type environment." ♦ ltd. 1 Apr-30 Sep. € 16.80   2005*

CUISEAUX *9A2* (5km S Rural) **Camping Domaine de Louvarel, 71480 Champagnat [tel/fax 03 85 76 62 71; contact@domainedelouvarel.com; www.domainedelouvarel.com]** Exit A39 junc 9 dir Cuiseaux, then onto N83 dir Louhans, site sp. Med, pt shd; wc; chem disp; mv service pnt; baby facs; shwrs inc; el pts (10A) €3; lndtte; rest; snacks; bar; BBQ; playgrnd; lake adj; fishing; games area; cycle hire; some statics; dogs €1.50; phone; o'night area for m;vans; adv bkg; quiet; CCI. 1 Jun-30 Oct. € 13.00 (CChq acc)   2005*

CULAN *7A4* (1km N) **Camp Municipal La Guinguette, 18270 Culan [02 48 56 64 41; fax 02 48 56 67 08]** On D65 1km N of Culan. Sm, hdg pitch, shd; wc; chem disp; 50% serviced pitches; shwrs inc; el pts €1.60; shops 2km; lake sw & fishing 500m; quiet. "Old-fashioned san facs, but clean; pleasant area; chateau worth visit." 15 Jun-20 Sep. € 5.60   2003*

CULAN *7A4* (7km E) **Camp Municipal Les Bergerolles**, 18360 Vesdun [02 48 63 03 07 (Mairie); fax 02 48 63 12 62; mairie.vesdun. cher@wanadoo.fr] Exit Culan S on D943 twd Montlucon; 200m turn L D4 to Vesdun. Site sp in vill adj stadium. Sm, pt shd; wc; shwrs inc; el pts €3.05; shops 1km; quiet. "Vill has monument 'Centre of France'; pay site fees at Mairie 300m." Whitsun-30 Sep. € 3.04   2003*

CULAN *7A4* (12km W Rural) **Camp Municipal L'Etang Merlin**, 18370 Chateaumeillant [02 48 61 31 38; fax 02 48 61 39 89; camping. chateaumeillant.chalets@wanadoo.fr] Rec app fr W to avoid narr town rds. Site sp fr rndabt at W end of town on D80 N of Chateaumeillant on lakeside. Fr Culan by pass town on D943, then as above. Sm, hdg/mkd pitch, pt shd; wc; serviced pitches; chem disp; shwrs inc; el pts (5A) €2; lndry rm; shop 3km; playgrnd; lake adj (no sw); fishing; dogs €1; Eng spkn; adv bkg; quiet; no cc acc; CCI. "Superb quality; v clean; v friendly, caring owners; chalets for hire in winter to anglers; rec arr early high ssn to secure pitch; easy walk to town." ♦ 1 May-30 Sep. € 8.00   2005*

CULOZ see Ruffieux *9B3*

CUVILLY *3C3* (1.5km N) **Camping de Sorel**, 24 Rue de St Claude, 60490 Orvillers-Sorel [03 44 85 02 74; fax 03 44 42 11 65; contact@ aestiva.fr] Exit a'route A1/E15 at junc 12 (Roye) S'bound or 11 (Ressons) N'bound. Site on E of N17. Med, mkd pitch, pt sl, pt shd; htd wc; chem disp; shwrs inc; el pts (6A) inc; lndry rm; shop; tradsmn; rest 2km; snacks; playgrnd; games area; TV; 50% statics; poss cr; quiet. "Conv NH nr a'route; 30 mins Parc Asterix; rec early arr in ssn; quiet & pleasant situation; ltd hot water & san facs not well looked after; v busy at w/e." 1 Feb-15 Dec. € 18.00 (CChq acc)   2005*

DABO see Saverne *6E3*

DAGLAN *7D3* (3km Rural) **Camping Le Moulin de Paulhiac**, 24250 Daglan [05 53 28 20 88; fax 05 53 29 33 45; francis.armagnac@wanadoo.fr; www.moulin-de-paulhiac.com] D57 SW fr Sarlat, across rv into St Cybranet & site in 2km. Fr Souillac W on D703 alongside Rv Dordogne; x-ing rv onto D46 (nr Domme) & D50, to site. Med, hdg/mkd pitch, shd; wc (some cont); chem disp; mv service pnt; shwrs; el pts (6A) inc; gas; lndtte; ice; shop; rest; snacks; bar; playgrnd; 4 htd pools; waterslide; TV rm; entmnt; shgl beach/rv adj with canoeing/fishing; 20% statics; Eng spkn; adv bkg; quiet with some rd noise; cc acc; CCI. "Vg; vg fruit/vegetable mkt Sun in vill; helpful staff; excel long stay." ♦ ltd. 18 May-15 Sep. € 22.00   2004*

DAMAZAN *7D2* (6km E) **Camp Municipal du Vieux Moulin**, Route de Villeneuve, 47190 Aiguillon [05 53 79 61 43] On ent town on N113, turn E onto D666 to site on bank of Rv Lot. Clearly sp. Or exit junc 6 dir Damazan fr A62 onto D8 to Aiguillon. Med, shd; wc (cont); shwrs; el pts (2-6A); ice; shops adj; tradsmn; rv sw; playgrnd; quiet. "Site adj old mill house." 15 Jun-15 Sep.   2002*

DAMAZAN *7D2* (2km S Rural) **Camp Municipal du Lac/Camping Gabaston**, Route de Buzet-sur-Baise, 47160 Damazan [05 53 79 44 14; fax 05 53 79 26 92] Fr A62 take junc 6, turn R at rndabt. Almost immed take slip rd sp Damazan/Buzet. At top turn R sp Buzet. Site 1km on R (2nd turning goes to lake only). Med, some hdg/mkd pitch, pt sl, pt shd; wc (some cont); chem disp (wc); shwrs inc; el pts (4A) €1.83; gas 2km; lndtte; shops, rest, snacks, bar 2km; BBQ; playgrnd adj; lake sw adj; 2% statics; dogs; phone adj; poss cr; adv bkg; quiet but nr a'route; CCI. "Excel NH as 2km fr a'route; next to cricket club!; by pretty lake; v helpful management."♦ ltd. 15 Jun-15 Sep. € 8.00   2004*

DAMBACH *5D3* (Rural) **Aire Naturelle Municipal du Hohenfels**, 67110 Dambach [03 88 09 24 08; fax 03 88 09 21 81] Fr N on D35 turn S onto D853, site sp. Med, pt sl, terr, pt shd; wc; chem disp; shwrs inc; el pts inc; quiet. "Lovely area; walk fr site to Maginot Line relics." 1 Apr-31 Oct. € 10.00   2005*

DAMBACH LA VILLE see Selestat *6E4*

DAMGAN see Muzillac *2G3*

DAMPIERRE *6G2* (2km SE) **Camp Municipal**, Rue de Gard, 39700 Fraisans [03 84 71 10 88] Exit A36 junc 2.1 to Dampierre. Fr Dampierre take D73, site sp on R at school bef rv bdge. Sm, mkd pitch, pt shd; wc (some cont); shwrs; el pts (4A) inc; shops adj; supmkt nr; dir access Rv Doubs; fishing; quiet. "Basic, clean, quiet site; lge pitches; pleasant little town; conv Besancon." 1 May-30 Sep. € 15.00   2005*

DAMPIERRE *6G2* (7km W) **Camp Municipal**, 39700 Orchamps [03 84 81 24 63] N73 Besancon-Dole rd. Turn S at sp in vill. Sm, mkd pitch, pt shd; wc; shwrs inc; el pts €2 (poss long lead req); lndry rm; shops 500m; rv fishing adj; dogs; quiet. "Excel CL-type site bet Rv Doubs & canal; warden calls each eve; old but v clean facs; vg NH." € 8.00   2004*

DAMPIERRE SUR BOUTONNE *7A2* (Rural) **Camp Municipal**, 17470 Dampierre-sur-Boutonne [05 46 24 02 36 (Mairie); fax 05 46 33 95 49; dampierre-sur-boutonne@mairie17.com] S fr Niort on N150 twds St Jean d'Angely; in vill of Tout-y-Faut turn E on D115 sp Dampierre; turn N in vill on D127 twds Rv Boutonne, site behind vill hall; well sp. Sm, hdg pitch, shd; wc; shwrs inc; el pts (6A) inc; shop 500m; fishing; dogs €0.76. "Clean site; san facs outside camp boundary & open to public; poss noisy, local youths congregate nrby; rec sh stay/NH only." 30 Apr-30 Sep. € 6.10   2003*

DAMVIX see Maillezais *7A2*

DANGE ST ROMAIN *4H2* (4km N Rural) **Camp Municipal, 8 Rue des Buxieres, 86220 Les Ormes [05 49 85 61 30 (Mairie); fax 05 49 85 66 17]**
Turn W off N10 in cent Les Ormes onto D1a sp Velleches & Marigny-Marmande, foll site sp. Sm, pt sl, pt shd; wc; chem disp; shwrs inc; el pts (10A) inc; shop 1km; lndry rm; playgrnd; tennis 100m; quiet, but some rlwy noise; adv bkg; Eng spkn; dogs; CCI. "Friendly warden; gd sh stay." 1 Apr-30 Sep. € 6.10
2003*

DANGE ST ROMAIN *4H2* (6km SW) **LES CASTELS Le Petit Trianon de St Ustre, 86220 Ingrandes-sur-Vienne [05 49 02 61 47; fax 05 49 02 68 81; chateau@petit-trianon.fr; www. petit-trianon.fr or www.les-castels.com]**
Leave a'route A10/E5 at Chatellerault Nord foll sp Tours. Cross rv heading N on N10 (not numbered on early sp) twd Tours & Dange-St Romain. At 2nd traff lts in Ingrandes by church, turn R. Cross rlwy line & turn L at site sp in 300m. After 1.5km turn R at site sp, site at top of hill. Med, pt sl, pt shd; wc; chem disp; mv service pnt; baby facs; shwrs inc; el pts (10A) inc; gas; lndtte; shop; tradsmn (to order); rest & bar 50m; snacks; BBQ; playgrnd; htd pools; games area; cycle hire; minigolf; tennis 1.5km; rv fishing 3km; games rm; TV; dogs €2; some rlwy noise at night; recep 0900-1300 & 1500-2000; Eng spkn; adv bkg; cc acc; CCI. "Excel, friendly, helpful." ♦ 20 May-20 Sep. € 26.50 ABS - L07 2005*

DAON see Chateau Gontier *4F1*

DARBRES *9D2* **Camping Les Lavandes, 07170 Darbres [tel/fax 04 75 94 20 65; sarl. leslavandes@online.fr]** SE fr Aubenas on N102 twds Montelimar. Turn L after 10km in vill Lavilledieu onto D224 sp Lussas. Cont 5km to Darbres, site sp. Med, terr, unshd; wc; chem disp; baby facs; shwrs inc; el pts (6A) €3.40; lndtte; ice; shop; rest; snacks; bar; playgrnd; pool; waterslide; games area; cycle hire; entmnt; TV; dogs €2.30; poss cr; Eng spkn; quiet; cc acc. "Attractive site; gd san facs." Easter-15 Sep. € 15.20 2003*

DARDILLY see Lyon *9B2*

DAX *8E1* (3.5km NE) **Camping Le St Vincent de Paul, 40990 St Vincent-de-Paul [tel/fax 05 58 89 99 60; camping.stvincentdepaul@ clubinternet.fr]** NE on N124 fr Dax twd Mont-de-Marsan on dual c'way, take exit to St Vincent-de-Paul at rndabt; sp on rd; site in 200m on L. Med, hdg/mkd pitch, pt shd; wc; chem disp; shwrs inc; el pts (6A) €3; gas; lndtte; shop 1km & 5km; rest; snacks; pool; sand beach 30km; 50% statics; dogs €1; phone; barrier clsd 2230-0730; Eng spkn; adv bkg; CCI. "Pretty, well-kept, clean site; friendly; well shd; v clean san facs; excel." ♦ 1 Apr-31 Oct. € 12.30 2005*

DAX *8E1* (1.5km W Rural) **Camping Les Chenes, Allee du Bois de Boulogne, 40100 Dax [05 58 90 05 53; fax 05 58 90 42 43; camping-chenes@wanadoo.fr; www.camping-les-chenes.fr]** Fr N124 to Dax, foll sp Bois de Boulogne, cross rlwy bdge & rv bdge & foll camp sp on rv bank. Well sp. Lge, mkd pitch, shd; htd wc (cont); chem disp; some serviced pitches; shwrs inc; el pts (6A) inc; gas; lndtte; ice; shop; tradsmn; rest; snacks; bar; playgrnd; pool; beach 20km; TV rm; cycle hire; 40% statics; dogs €1; poss cr; Eng spkn; adv bkg; quiet; cc acc; CCI. "Excel position; conv thermal baths at Dax; easy walk along rv into town; excel." ♦ 27 Mar-30 Nov. € 17.50 2005*

†DAX *8E1* (9km W Rural) **Camping a la Ferme Bertranborde (Lafitte), 40180 Riviere-Saas-et-Gourby [05 58 97 58 39]** Turn S off N124 5km W of Dax onto D113, sp Angoume; at x-rd in 2km turn R (by water tower); then immed L; site on R in 100m. Sm, pt shd, pt sl; wc; chem disp; mv service pnt; shwrs inc; el pts (4-6A) €2-3; lndtte; shops 1km; rv sw 7km; quiet; adv bkg; CCI. "Peaceful CL-type site; friendly owners; meals on request; excel long/sh stay." € 6.00 2003*

DAX *8E1* (9km W Rural) **Camping Lou Bascou, 40180 Riviere-Saas-et-Gourby [05 58 97 57 29; fax 05 58 97 59 52; loubascou@wanadoo.fr; http://perso.wanadoo.fr/loubascou/]** Leave N10 at junc 8 for N124 twd Dax. In 3.5km turn R onto D113 sp Riviere-Saas-et-Gourby. Well sp fr N124. Med, hdg/mkd pitch, pt shd; wc; chem disp; shwrs inc; el pts (6-10A) €3-5; lndtte; shop 300m; tradsmn; snacks; bar; BBQ; playgrnd; pool 9km; sand beach 25km; tennis; entmnt; 50% statics; dogs €1; Eng spkn; adv bkg; quiet; red long stay/low ssn. "Excel facs; quiet, friendly site; thermal facs in Dax; 60km fr Spanish border; nrby wetlands wildlife inc storks worth seeing." ♦ 1 Mar-10 Nov. € 14.00 2005*

DAX *8E1* (3km NW Rural) **Camping Les Pins du Soleil, La Pince, 40990 St Paul-les-Dax [05 58 91 37 91; fax 05 58 91 00 24; pinsoleil@ aol.com; www.pinsoleil.com]** Exit N10 sp Dax onto D459. At traff lts turn R sp Bayonne & 3 Campings. In 1.5km turn L sp Dax/La Pince. Site sp in pine forest. Med, hdg/mkd pitch, pt sl, pt shd; htd wc, chem disp; mv service pnt; serviced pitches; baby facs; shwrs inc; el pts (5A) inc; gas; lndtte; ice; shop; tradsmn; rest 1km; snacks; bar; playgrnd; pool; tennis 2km; cycle hire; entmnt; TV rm; 25% statics; dogs €2; phone; Eng spkn; some rd noise; red low ssn; cc acc. "Various pitch sizes, some spacious; soft, sandy soil poss problem when wet; spa 2km; v helpful & friendly." ♦ 1 Apr-30 Oct. € 23.00 (CChq acc) 2005*

DEAUVILLE *3D1* (6km NE Coastal) **Camping La Bruyere**, 14113 Villerville [02 31 98 24 39; fax 02 31 98 42 85] Fr Villerville S. Situated on rd bet D513 & D62. Site sp both dir in town. (App not suitable for all o'fits) Lge, hdg pitch, pt sl, pt shd; wc; chem disp; baby facs; shwrs inc; el pts (6A) €5; lndtte; shop; rest; playgrnd; pool; sand beach 3km; 75% statics; adv bkg; quiet; CCI. "Sm pitches, adequate facs; sh stay only." 1 Mar-31 Oct. € 16.50
2003*

DEAUVILLE *3D1* (2km S Urban) **Camping des Haras**, Chemin du Calvaire, 14800 Touques [02 31 88 44 84; fax 02 31 88 97 08; les.haras@wanadoo.fr] N on N177 Pont l'Eveque-Deauville rd, ignore 1st slip rd sp Touques (too narr, vans prohibited); stay on by-pass & turn R at traff lts by g'ge sp Trouville. Turn R again at next rndabt sp Touques then L on D62; fork L to site after church. Also sp fr D513 Deauville-Caen rd. Lge, hdg pitch, pt sl, pt shd; wc; own san; chem disp; shwrs; el pts (10A) €4.12; gas; lndtte; shop; rest; snacks; bar; playgrnd; pool 2km; sand beach 2km; entmnt; 60% statics; poss cr; adv bkg; red low ssn. "Some pitches poss diff lge o'fits; in winter phone ahead; conv Honfleur & WW2 sites; office clsd fr 1830 low ssn & Sun; san facs run down; c'vans sited nr playgrnd." ♦ 1 Feb-30 Nov. € 16.35
2005*

DEAUVILLE *3D1* (3km S Urban) **Camping La Vallee de Deauville**, Route de Beaumont, 14800 St Arnoult [02 31 88 58 17; fax 02 31 88 11 57; campinglavalleededeauville@wanadoo.fr; www.camping-deauville.com] Fr Deauville take D27 dir Caen, turn R onto D278 to St Armoult, foll site sp. Lge, hdg/mkd pitch, hdstg, pt shd; htd wc (some cont); baby facs; shwrs inc; el pts (10A) €5.50; gas; lndtte; shop; tradsmn; rest; snacks; bar; playgrnd; htd pool; waterslide; sand beach 4km; fishing lake; games rm; entmnt; child entmnt; 80% statics; dogs €3; phone; Eng spkn; some rlwy noise; red low ssn; cc acc; CCI. "Easy access to beaches & resorts; conv Le Havre using Pont de Normandie; lake walks & activities on site; excel san facs." ♦ 1 Apr-31 Oct. € 26.40
2004*

DEAUVILLE *3D1* (6km S Rural) **Camping Le Lieu Roti**, 14800 Vauville [tel/fax 02 31 87 96 22; info@deauville-camping.com; www.deauville-camping.com] Fr Deauville, take D27 S twd Caen. Site on R 200m after Tourgeville church. Well sp. Med, mkd pitch, pt shd; htd wc; chem disp; shwrs inc; el pts (5A) inc; lndtte; ice; shop 3km; tradmn; rest; snacks; bar; playgrnd; htd pool; sand beach 3km; 50% statics; dogs €2; phone; Eng spkn; adv bkg; quiet; cc acc; CCI. "Pleasant countryside location; helpful reception; excel long stay." ♦ 15 Apr-15 Oct. € 25.00
2003*

DECAZEVILLE *7D4* (5km NW Rural) **Camping Le Roquelongue**, 12300 Boisset-Penchot [tel/fax 05 65 63 39 67; www.camping-aveyron.com] Fr D963 in Decazeville turn W onto D140 & D42 to Boisset-Penchot. Rte via D21 not rec (steep hill & acute turn). Site mid-way bet Boisset-Penchot & Livinhac-la-Haute on D42. Med, hdg/mkd pitch, pt shd; wc; chem disp; shwrs inc; el pts (10A) inc; gas; lndtte; shop; tradsmn; supmkt 5km; snacks; bar; playgrnd; rv sw; fishing; boat launching ramp; tennis; 10% statics; dogs; phone; adv bkg; quiet; CCI. "Direct access rv; pitches gd size; san facs clean; site run down & untidy low ssn; no twin-axles; mkd walks fr site with stunning views." ♦ ltd. 1 Mar-31 Dec. € 13.50
2004*

DECIZE *4H4* (6km N Rural) **Camping L'Etang Grenetier**, Route du Pre Charpin, 58260 La Machine [03 86 50 49 00; fax 03 86 50 46 13] Fr Nevers take N81 twds Decize; in Decize turn L(N) onto D34 twds La Machine; at town ent foll sp to site (dir E). Sm, mkd pitch, hdstg, pt shd; wc; chem disp; shwrs; el pts inc; shop 3km; rest; snacks; bar; playgrnd; lake sw & beach adj; poss cr; poss noise fr adj bar; CCI. "V sm site - 10 pitches; own key to all locked facs; lakeside walks; excel sh stay; conv NH." ♦ 1 May-30 Sep. € 8.90
2004*

DECIZE *4H4* (12km SE) **Camping La Varenne a la Ferme**, 58300 Charrin [03 86 50 30 14] Fr Decize take D979 twd Digoin & foll sp Camping la Ferme; site off to R thro vill of Charrin. In vill foll sp for Chambres d'Hote. Sm, pt shd; wc; chem disp; shwrs inc; el pts inc (long lead req); shops 500m; fishing 2km; quiet. "A lovely, quiet CL-type site; friendly proprietors; breakfast & some farm produce avail; poss entmnt fr piglets!; chambres d'hote; gd sh stay/NH." Jun-Sep. € 8.00
2005*

DECIZE *4H4* (NW Urban) **Camp Municipal Les Halles**, Allee Marcel Melle, 58300 Decize [03 86 25 14 05 or 03 86 25 03 23 (Mairie); fax 03 86 77 11 48; camping@ville-decize.fr; www.ville-decize.fr] Fr Nevers take N81 to Decize, look for sp for 'Stade Nautique Camping'. Lge, mkd pitch, pt shd; wc (some cont); snacks; shwrs inc; el pts (10A) inc; gas; ice; shop; sand beach adj; sat TV; dogs; poss cr; some Eng spkn; quiet; cc acc; CCI. "V helpful staff; €11.30 extra for twin-axles; poss diff access pitches due trees." ♦ 1 May-30 Sep. € 11.28
2005*

DELLE *6G3* (5km N Rural) **Camp Municipal du Passe Loup**, Rue des Chenes, 90100 Joncherey [03 84 56 32 63 or 03 84 56 26 07; fax 03 84 56 27 66] Exit A75 junc 11 Sevenans onto N19 S dir Delle. Turn L onto D3 N dir Boron, site on R in approx 3km. Med, sl, pt shd; wc; chem disp; shwrs inc; el pts (6A) inc; playgrnd; lake fishing adj; 45% statics; quiet; CCI. "Pleasant, spacious site; basic san facs." 1 Apr-31 Oct. € 13.90
2005*

DENNEVILLE PLAGE see Barneville Carteret *1C4*

DESAIGNES see Lamastre *9C2*

DESCARTES *4H2* (5km SE) **Camp Municipal Ile de la Claise, 37169 Abilly [02 47 59 78 01 (Mairie); fax 02 47 59 89 93]** Fr Descartes take D750 S for 3km; SE on D42 to Abilly. Site on island in Rv Claise. Sm, shd; wc; shwrs €1.12; el pts €1.30; playgrnd; pool 6km; dogs; fishing; tennis; quiet. ♦ 1 May-15 Sep. € 3.20   2003*

DESCARTES *4H2* (S Urban) **Camp Municipal La Grosse Motte, 37160 Descartes [02 47 59 85 90 or 02 47 92 42 20; fax 02 47 59 72 20; otm-descartes@wanadoo.fr]** 500m W of D750 on S side of town. Sm, hdg pitch, pt sl, shd; wc (some cont); baby facs; shwrs inc; shops in town; el pts (rev pol) €1.65; pool adj; playgrnd, tennis, mini-golf nr; boating on rv; activities; barrier key dep €15; dogs €0.80; adv bkg; quiet; cc not acc; CCI. "Beautiful site by rv in historic birth place of Descartes; delightful public gardens adj; spacious pitches; v clean facs; friendly staff; excel value, a real find; pop for school parties; gd NH." 1 May-15 Oct. € 5.25   2005*

DEUX CHAISES see Montmarault *9A1*

DEVILLAC see Villereal *7D3*

†**DEYME** *8F3* (Urban) **Camping Les Violettes, 31450 Deyme [05 61 81 72 07; fax 05 61 27 17 31]** SE fr Toulouse to Carcassonne on N113, sp on L. Med, pt shd; wc (cont); shwrs inc; el pts (4-6A) €2.40-3.50; lndtte; shop; rest; snacks; playgrnd; TV; 60% statics; dogs €1; poss cr; quiet but rd noise; CCI. "Helpful, friendly staff; poss v muddy in wet weather; sh stay/NH only." € 10.00   2003*

DIE *9D2* (N Urban) **Camp Municipal Le Justin (formally de la Piscine), Rue de Chabestar, 26150 Die [04 75 22 14 77; fax 04 75 22 20 42]** Ent town fr W on D93, fork R D751, sp Gap & 'rugby stade' (not football stade); foll sps for Camp Municipal & piscine; site on S of rlwy line bef sw pool 'piscine'. Poss diff bdge for long o'fits. Med, pt sl, pt shd; wc (some cont); chem disp; mv service pnt; shwrs inc; el pts (10A) €2.75; ice; lndtte; shops, rest 500m; tradsmn; snacks; playgrnd; rv sw adj; entmnts; dogs €1.60; Eng spkn; adv bkg; cc acc; CCI. "Gd facs; site in beautiful setting in Drome valley; poor security - vehicles use track thro site as short cut; easy walk to Die - interesting town." 1 May-15 Sep. € 10.00   2005*

DIE *9D2* (400m N Urban) **Camping La Riou-Merle, Route de Romeyer, 26150 Die [tel/fax 04 75 22 21 31]** Fr Gap on D93 heading twd Valence. Cont on D93 twd town cent; R on D742 to Romeyer. Site on L in 200m. On D93 fr Crest foll sp round town cent onto D742. Sharp turn at ent. Med, pt sl, pt shd; wc (some cont); shwrs inc; el pts (5A) €2.80; lndry rm; shops in town; playgrnd; pool; fishing; 30% statics; dogs €1; quiet; red low ssn. "Site clean but unattractive in wet weather; guardian calls am & pm; gd, renovated san facs." Easter-31 Oct. € 10.60   2005*

DIE *9D2* (1km SE Urban) **Camping La Glandasse, Route de Gap, Quartier de la Maladrerie, 26150 Die [04 75 22 02 50; fax 04 75 22 04 91; camping-glandasse@wanadoo.fr; www.camping-glandasse.com]** Take D93 S twds Gap; site on R 1km outside of Die, under rlwy bdge (3m wide, 2.8m high). Med, hdg pitch, pt sl, pt shd; wc; chem disp; baby facs; shwrs inc; el pts (10A) inc; gas; lndtte; ice; shop; rest; snacks; bar; playgrnd; pool; paddling pool; shgl rv beach; cycle hire; some statics; dogs €2; poss cr; adv bkg; quiet; CCI. "Gd cent for touring mountains & Parc de Vercours; some noise fr rd, rlwy & air." ♦ 1 Apr-30 Sep. € 19.30   2005*

DIE *9D2* (2km W Rural) **Camping La Pinede, Quartier du Pont Neuf, 26150 Die [04 75 22 17 77; fax 04 75 22 22 73; info@camping-pinede.com]** On ent Die fr W on D93, take 1st rd on R 200m after 1st site on rd D93. Access diff for lge vans - narr rv bdge 2.75m wide. Med, pt shd; wc; shwrs inc; el pts (10A) inc; gas; lndtte; ice; rest; shop; playgrnd; pool; shgl beach, rv sw adj; tennis; mini-golf; fishing; canoeing; entmnt; TV; dogs €2; adv bkg ess; noisy; red low ssn. Easter-15 Sep. € 30.00   2003*

DIE *9D2* (1km NW) **Camp de Chamarges, 26150 Die [04 75 22 14 13 or 04 75 22 06 77]** Foll D93 twd Valence, site on L of rd in 1.5km by Rv Eygues. Med; wc; shwrs; el pts (3-6A) €2.25-2.60; gas; shops 1km; playgrnd; pool; rv sw, fishing & canoeing adj; entmnts; TV; dogs €2; rec adv bkg high ssn; quiet. "Beautiful mountainous area; gd long/sh stay." 1 Apr-24 Sep. € 8.60   2003*

DIE *9D2* (12km NW Urban) **Aire Naturelle Le Moulin du Rivet (Szarvas), 26150 St Julien-en-Quint [tel/fax 04 75 21 20 43; le.moulin.du.rivet@wanadoo.fr; www.moulindurivet.com]** On D93 E fr Crest twd Die, turn L onto D129 dir St Croix/St Julien. Foll sp St Julien. Site on L in 9km. Sm, hdstg, terr, pt shd; wc; chem disp (wc only); shwrs inc; el pts (6A) €2.50; shop 9km; tradsmn; rest; playgrnd; rv sw adj; dogs; poss cr; Eng spkn; adv bkg; quiet; CCI. "Atrractive, CL-type site on Rv Sure; gd views; v peaceful; friendly owners; fair sh stay." 1 May-31 Oct. € 10.00   2003*

DIENVILLE see Brienne Le Chateau *6E1*

DIEPPE *3C2* (4km SW Rural) **Camping La Source, Le Plessis, Petit-Appeville, 76550 Hautot-sur-Mer [02 35 84 27 04; fax 02 35 82 25 02]** Fr Dieppe ferry terminal foll sp Paris, take D925 W dir Fecamp. In 2km at Petit Appeville turn L, site in 800m on rvside. Med, mkd pitch, hdstg; pt shd; wc (some cont); chem disp; mv service pnt; shwrs inc; el pts (6A) €3; lndtte; ice; shop 2km; tradsmn; snacks; bar; playgrnd; sand beach 3km; rv sw, fishing & boating adj; games area; games rm; cycle hire; golf 4km; entmnt; TV; 30% statics; dogs €1.50; Eng spkn; adv bkg; quiet; cc acc; CCI. "Friendly owner; excel sh stay/NH bef or after ferry; price reduced if pool not ready for 2005 ssn." ♦ 15 Mar-15 Oct. € 16.00 (CChq acc)   2005*

FRANCE

DIEPPE *3C2* (6km SW Urban) **Camp Municipal du Colombier, 76550 Offranville** [02 35 85 21 14; fax 02 35 04 52 67] W fr Dieppe on D925, take L turn on D55 to Offranville, site clearly sp in vill to Parc du Colombier. Med, hdg/mkd pitch; pt shd; wc; chem disp; shwrs inc; el pts (6A) €2; gas; lndtte; shop & supmkt 500m; rest; shgl beach 5km; ltd Eng spkn; CCI. "Vg clean site; helpful staff; set in ornamental gardens with equestrian cent; security gates clsd 2200-0700; m'van ask warden how to operate barrier in his absence; conv ferries." ♦
1 Apr-15 Oct. € 15.90   2004*

DIEPPE *3C2* (10km W) **Camping a la Ferme Aire Naturelle (Halfon), 76119 Ste Marguerite-sur-Mer** [02 35 85 15 59] Take D925 fr Dieppe twd St Valery. Turn R after 6km on D55 to Pourville. Cont 1km & turn L onto D75 thro Varengeville; cont for 3km almost into Ste Marguerite. Sm, pt shd; wc; shwrs; shops 3km; shgl beach 3km; quiet. "No elec; pleasant CL-type site but with some perm tourers; lovely walks on beach. " 15 Mar-15 Nov.   2004*

DIGNE LES BAINS *10E3* (1km NE) **Camp du Bourg, Route de Barcelonnette, 04000 Digne-les-Bains** [04 92 31 04 87; fax 04 92 34 59 80] Fr rndabt by rv bdge take main st (Boulevard Gassendi) thro cent town, sp D900 La Javie, Barcelonnette. Camp sp on R. Med, pt shd; wc; shwrs inc; el pts (4A) €2.50; shops 1.5km; pool 1.5km; games area; 95% statics; dogs €1. "Pleasant town with fine scenery; thermal baths; beautiful & fascinating area; poss diff access to some pitches on terraced areas for lge o'fits; pitches not mkd; recep manned few hrs only." ♦
15 May-30 Oct. € 11.50   2004*

DIGNE LES BAINS *10E3* (1.5km SE) **Camping Les Eaux Chaudes, Route des Thermes, 04000 Digne-les-Bains** [04 92 32 31 04; fax 04 92 34 59 80; info@campingleseauxchaudes.com] Fr S foll N85 sp 'Centre Ville' over bdge keeping L to rndabt, turn 1st R sp Les Thermes (D20). Past Intermarche, site on R 1.6km after leaving town. Med, mkd pitch, pt shd; htd wc; chem disp; shwrs inc; el pts (4A) inc (poss rev pol); gas; lndtte; ice; shops 1.5km; snacks; pool 1.5km; lake sw 3km; games area; 30% statics; dogs €1; poss cr; adv bkg; quiet; CCI. "Pleasant, British-owned site; new san facs 2004; gd for touring Haute Provence; 500m fr thermal baths; Digne beautiful; National Geological Reserve in town cent; phone ahead low ssn to check open." ♦ ltd.
1 Apr-31 Oct. € 15.70   2004*

DIGOIN *9A1* (Urban) **Camp Municipal La Chevrette, Rue de la Chevrette, 71160 Digoin** [03 85 53 11 49; fax 03 85 88 59 70; lachevrette@wanadoo.fr] Exit new N79 at junc 24 sp Digoin-la-Greve D994, then on (old) N79 cross bdge over Rd Loire. Take 1st L, sp campng/piscine. Sm, some hdg pitch, terr, pt shd; htd wc (some cont); chem disp; shwrs inc; el pts (10A) €3.20; tradsmn; lndry rm; shops 500m; rest 500m; snacks; playgrnd; htd pool adj; fishing; some statics; dogs €1; sep car park; adv bkg; some rd noise; CCI. "Vg; well-run; gd sized pitches; friendly warden resident on site; barrier clsd 2200-0800; ltd facs low ssn."
1 Mar-31 Oct. € 16.10   2004*

DIJON *6G1* (2km W Urban) **Camp Municipal du Lac, Blvd Chanoine Kir, 21000 Dijon** [tel/fax 03 80 43 54 72; infotourisme@ot-dijon.fr; www.ville-dijon.fr] Site situated nr N5, Lac Kir. Fr Dijon ring rd take N5 exit (W) sp A38 twd Paris. At traff lts L sp A31, site immed on R under 3m high bdge. Do not tow thro town cent. Med, mkd pitch, hdstg, shd; htd wc (mainly cont); chem disp; shwrs inc; el pts (6A) inc; (poss rev pol); gas; lndtte; ice; shop; supmkt nr; tradsmn; rest; snacks; sw lake 1km; fishing, sw & boating; dogs; bus; poss cr; Eng spkn; quiet but some rd noise; cc acc; CCI. "Gd security; attractive, orderly, busy site on edge of town beside lake; v friendly & relaxed; 30 min walk to town; poss flooding; lge pitches; excel." 1 Apr-15 Oct. € 11.45   2005*

DINAN *2E3* (Urban) **Camp Municipal Chateaubriand, 103 Rue Chateaubriand, 22100 Dinan** [02 96 39 11 96 or 02 96 39 22 43 (LS); fax 02 96 85 06 97; mairie@dinan.fr] Fr N176 (E or W) take slip rd for Dinan cent; at lge rndbt in cent take 2nd R; down hill to site on L (500m). Sm, mkd pitch, pt sl, pt shd; wc; chem disp; mv service pnt; shwrs inc; el pts (6A) €2.60; gas 500m; lndry rm; shop, rest, snacks 500m; bar adj; BBQ; sand beach 18km; games area; dogs; phone; poss cr; Eng spkn; adv bkg; daytime rd noise; cc not acc; CCI. "Gd cent for Rance valley, St Malo & coast; sh walk to charming town; basic/dated facs poss unclean; pleasant, helpful staff; high kerb onto pitches; opening dates vary each year." 15 Jun-30 Sep. € 9.30   2005*

DINAN *2E3* (3km NE Rural) **Camp International de la Hallerais, 22100 Taden** [02 96 39 15 93 or 02 96 87 63 50 (Mairie); fax 02 96 39 94 64; camping.la.hallerais@wanadoo.fr; www.wdirect.fr /hallerais.htm] Fr Dinan take D766 N twd Dinard. In 3km turn R onto D12 to Taden. Foll Le Hallerais & Taden sp to site. Fr N176 take unmarked exit onto D12A for Taden but do not ent Dinan. Site adj Rv Rance. Lge, mkd pitch, terr, pt shd; wc; chem disp; mv service pnt; serviced pitches; shwrs inc; el pts (6A) inc (rev pol); gas; lndtte; shop adj; tradsmn; rest; bar; BBQ; playgrnd; htd pool; shgl beach 10km; tennis; games rm; fishing; horseriding 1km; recep 0900-1200 & 1500-1900; statics; dogs; storage facs; Eng spkn; adv bkg; quiet; cc acc. "Excel, clean, spacious san facs; some facs clsd low ssn; mkt Thu am; rv trips; rvside walk to Dinan medieval town; oyster beds at Cancale; phone ahead if arr late at night low ssn." ♦
11 Mar-5 Nov. € 19.50 ABS - B01   2005*

DINAN *2E3* (10km NE) **Camping Ville Ger, 22690 Pleudihen-sur-Rance [02 96 83 33 88]** Fr Dinan take D676 in dir Dol de Bretagne; turn L on D29 after 6km; site sp after 4km on L. Sm, mkd pitch; pt shd; wc (cont); rec own san high ssn; shwrs €1; el pts (3-10A) €1.75-4.30; lndtte; shops 1.5km; rest; bar; playgrnd; dogs; poss cr; adv bkg ess high ssn; quiet; CCI. "Lovely area; close to rv; farm 1km for milk & eggs; local fish; gd for dog-walking."
1 Apr-15 Oct. € 6.80   2004*

DINAN *2E3* (3km E Rural) **Camp Municipal Beausejour, La Hisse, 22100 St Samson-sur-Rance [02 96 39 53 27 or 02 96 39 16 05 (Mairie); fax 02 96 87 94 12; stsamson.mairie@wanadoo. fr]** Fr N176 W, after 7.5km past junc with N137 turn S onto D366 then onto D12 dir Taden thro Plouer-sur-Rance to La Hisse; site in 2km sp. Med, hdg/mkd pitch, hdstg, pt sl, pt shd; wc; chem disp; mv service pnt; shwrs inc; el pts (10A) €2.85; lndtte; ice; sm shop; supmkt 5km; tradsmn; rest; snacks; bar; playgrnd; htd pool; tennis; games area; sailing; mini-golf; 5% statics; dogs €2.30; phone; poss cr; Eng spkn; adv bkg; quiet; 1 free night in 5 low ssn; CCI. "No twin-axles; v pleasant, friendly site; helpful owners; v well kept; clean; quiet & spacious Jun/Sep; site yourself & report to office; pitches grouped in 3s & 4s; Dinan worth a visit; excel rv walks; vg long/sh stay. " ♦ ltd. 1 Jun-30 Sep.
€ 10.30   2005*

DINARD *2E3* (3km S) **Camp Municipal Bellevue, Rue de Bellevue, 35780 La Richardais [02 99 88 50 80 (Mairie); fax 02 99 88 52 12; info@ ville-larichardais.fr; www.ville-larichardais.fr]** S of Dinard on D114; on ent vill of La Richardais, turn R at traff lts, 1st L into Rue de Bellevue, site on L in 50m. Med, mkd pitch, pt sl, pt shd; wc; chem disp (wc only); shwrs inc; el pts (16A) inc; lndtte; shops, gas adj; BBQ; playgrnd; sand beach 3km; lake/rv sw 1km; dogs; phone; poss cr; quiet. "Ltd o'fit access low ssn due locked height barriers; recep clsd 1200-1400; park in layby bef booking in."
1 Apr-15 Sep. € 10.20   2005*

†**DINARD** *2E3* (6km S) **Camp Municipal L'Estuaire, Rue Jean Boyer, 35730 Pleurtuit [tel/fax 02 99 88 44 06]** Fr N on D266 or S on D766 in cent of vill, sp fr each dir. Med, hdg pitch, pt shd; wc (cont); baby facs; shwrs inc; el pts (6A) €3; lndtte; shops adj; quiet; tradsmn; playgrnd; sand beach 4km; 50% statics; €20 dep for barrier key. "Friendly site." € 10.00   2003*

DINARD *2E3* (1.5m W Coastal) **Camping La Touesse, La Fourberie, 35800 St Lunaire [02 99 46 61 13; fax 02 99 16 02 58; camping.la. touesse@wanadoo.fr]** Exit Dinard on St Lunaire coast rd D786, site sp. Med, mkd pitch, pt shd; wc; mv service pnt; baby facs; shwrs inc; el pts (5-10A) €3-3.20; lndtte; shop; snacks; bar; playgrnd; 2 pools (1 htd, covrd); sand beach 300m; tennis 1.5km; golf 2km; entmnt; TV rm; adv bkg (dep); quiet, some late night noise; 25% low ssn red; CCI. "Gd beach & rocks nr; friendly recep; clean; ltd facs low ssn." ♦
1 Apr-30 Sep. € 17.90   2004*

DINARD *2E3* (1km W Coastal) **Camp Municipal Le Port Blanc, Rue de Sergent Boulanger, 35800 Dinard [02 99 46 10 74; fax 02 99 16 90 91; camping@free.fr]** Fr Dinard foll sp to St Lunaire on D786 for 1.5km. Turn R at traff lts by football ground to site. Lge, mkd pitch, pt sl, terr, pt shd; wc (some cont); chem disp; child/baby facs; shwrs inc; el pts (5-10A) €3.30-4.20; lndtte; ice; sm shop; supmkt 800m; rest 500m; snacks; bar; playgrnd; pool; sand beach adj; 40% statics; dogs; phone; bus; poss cr; adv bkg; quiet at night; cc acc; CCI. "Overlooks sand beach; bus fr ent; cr in late May & French holiday ssn." ♦ Easter-Sep. € 16.80
                                                                       2004*

DINARD *2E3* (4km W Coastal) **Camping Longchamp, Blvd St Cast, 35800 St Lunaire [02 99 46 33 98; fax 02 99 46 02 71; camping_langchap@yahoo.fr]** Fr St Malo on D168 turn R sp St Lunaire, ln 1km turn R at g'ge into St Lunaire, site sp to W of vill on D786 dir St Briac. Lge, hdg/mkd pitch, pt shd; wc; chem disp; mv service pnt; baby facs; shwrs inc; el pts (4-10A) €2.60-3.80; gas; lndtte; ice; shop; tradsmn; snacks; bar; playgrnd; sand beach 300m; 30% statics; dogs €1.30; bus 500m; Eng spkn; adv bkg; CCI. "V clean beach for all ages 300m; v helpful staff; conv Brittany Ferries at St Malo; excel." ♦ ltd.
10 May-10 Sep. € 19.00   2005*

DIOU see Dompierre sur Besbre *9A1*

DISSAY see Jaunay Clan *4H1*

DIVONNE LES BAINS *9A3* (3km N Rural) **Camping Le Fleutron, Quartier Villard, 01220 Divonne-les-Bains [04 50 20 01 95 or 04 42 20 47 25 (LS); fax 04 50 20 00 35; info@homair-vacances.fr; www. homair-vacances.fr]** Exit E62 dir Divonne-les-Bains approx 12km N of Geneva. Fr town on D984, foll sp to site. Lge, hdg/mkd pitch, pt sl, terr, shd; htd wc; shwrs inc; chem disp; el pts (4A) €4.20; gas; lndtte; shop, snacks & rest in ssn; bar; supmkts 3km; lake sw 3km; htd pool; paddling pool; lake sw 3km; tennis; games area; entmnt in ssn; TV rm; 50% statics; dogs €3.70; Eng spkn; adv bkg; quiet; red low ssn; cc acc; CCI. "Helpful owner; Lake Geneva 8km." 26 Mar-23 Oct. € 25.80   2005*

DOL DE BRETAGNE *2E4* (6km N Coastal) **Camp Municipal, 35960 Le Vivier-sur-Mer [02 99 48 91 92 (Mairie) or 02 99 48 91 57; fax 02 99 48 80 93]** On sea front in Le Vivier-sur-Mer at E end of town; sp. Med, mkd pitches, pt shd; wc; mv service pnt; shwrs €1.35; el pts (6A) €2.10; lndtte; shop in vill; dogs €1.36; poss cr; quiet; no adv bkg; Eng spkn; CCI. "Ask at Mairie to have barrier raised; muddy beach not suitable for sw; basic site; gd NH to see mussel/oyster beds; tours fr museum nrby."
Easter-30 Sep. € 7.66   2005*

FRANCE

DOL DE BRETAGNE *2E4* (7km NE Coastal) **Camping de l'Aumone, 35120 Cherrueix** [02 99 48 95 11 or 02 99 80 87 37] On L of D797 Pontorson-Cancale rd, opp rd leading into vill of Cherrueix. Med, unshd; wc; shwrs inc; el pts (10A) €2.30; gas; lndtte; shops 300m; snacks; sand beach 500m (not suitable for bathing); TV; dogs €0.50; adv bkg rec high ssn. "Friendly, sm farm with modern san facs; sand yachting nrby; gd sh stay/NH." 1 Apr-15 Sep. € 9.00   2003*

DOL DE BRETAGNE *2E4* (8km NE Coastal) **Camping Le Tenzor de la Baie (former Municipal), 35120 Cherrueix** [02 99 48 98 13] Fr Dol-de-Bretagne, take D155 N to Le Vivier-sur-Mer; turn R onto D797, L onto D82 to Cherrueix; site in vill 150m E of church, just beyond 'Mairie', sp. Sm, pt shd; wc; shwrs; el pts inc; shop adj; playgrnd; beach 150m; rv fishing & sw 14km; 75% statics; poss cr; adv bkg; quiet; cc not acc. "V pleasant, clean, flat site in interesting bay of Mont St Michel; sand yachting, mussel & oyster beds nr; basic facs." 15 Jun-15 Sep. € 11.80   2005*

DOL DE BRETAGNE *2E4* (4km E) **Camping du Vieux Chene, 35120 Baguer-Pican** [02 99 48 09 55; fax 02 99 48 13 37; vieux.chene@wanadoo.fr; www.camping-vieuxchene.fr] Leave N176 E of Dol on slip rd sp Baguer-Pican. At traff lts turn L thro vill, site on R of D576 at far end vill adj lake. Lge, hdg pitch, pt sl, pt shd; wc; chem disp; baby facs; shwrs inc; el pts (10A) inc (poss rev pol & poss long cable req); gas; lndtte; shop; supmkt nr; rest; bar; BBQ; playgrnd; 2 htd pools; lake fishing; tennis; mini-golf; games area; games rm; entmnt; internet; TV rm; dogs; phone; Eng spkn; adv bkg; quiet; red long stay; cc acc; CCI. "Friendly & helpful site; fruit trees on pitches; conv Mont St Michel; basic facs stretched in high ssn; nice clean site; shop & rest ltd low ssn; poss sm pitches; gates & recep clsd 2200-0830; mkt in Dol Sat." ◆
1 Apr-17 Sep. € 31.50 ABS - B10   2005*

DOL DE BRETAGNE *2E4* (7km SE Rural) **LES CASTELS Le Domaine des Ormes, Epiniac, 35120 Dol-de-Bretagne** [02 99 73 53 00 or 02 99 73 53 01 (LS); fax 02 99 73 53 55; info@lesormes.com; www.lesormes.com or www.les-castels.com] S fr Dol on D795 twd Combourg & Rennes, site on E of rd, clearly sp. V lge, hdg/mkd pitch, pt sl, pt shd; wc; chem disp; shwrs inc; el pts (6A) inc (poss long lead req); gas; lndtte; ice; shop; tradsmn; snacks; bar; BBQ; playgrnd; htd pool complex; waterslide; lake fishing, canoeing; sand beach 25km; tennis; horseriding; archery; golf course adj (discount to campers); cycle hire; entmnt (child & adult); internet; TV rm; 80% statics; dogs €2; poss cr; adv bkg; Eng spkn; poss noisy (disco); cc acc; CCI. "Conv Mont St Michel, St Malo & Dinan; helpful staff; expensive but worth it; few bins or water taps; mkt Sat; disco at night." ◆
20 May-10 Sep. € 40.30 ABS - B08   2005*

DOLE *6H2* (6km NE Rural) **Camping Les Marronniers, 39700 Rochefort-sur-Nenon** [03 84 70 50 37; fax 03 84 70 55 05] NE fr Dole on N73 twds Besancon. Turn R on D76 & pass thro vill of Rochefort-sur-Nenon. Site in 2km, well sp. Med, hdg pitch, pt shd; wc; mv service pnt; serviced pitches; shwrs inc; el pts (5A) €2.50; lndtte; tradsmn; snacks; bar; playgrnd; pool; cycle hire; mini-golf; entmnt; 10% statics; dogs €1; adv bkg; noisy; Eng spkn; red low ssn; CCI. "Poss noisy disco; fair sh stay/NH." ◆ 1 Apr-31 Oct. € 17.00
                                                    2003*

DOLE *6H2* (8km SE Rural) **Camping Les Bords de Loue, 39100 Parcey** [03 84 71 03 82; fax 03 84 71 03 42; contact@jura-camping.com; www.bords-de-loue.com] Leave A39 at junc 6 onto N5 dir Chalon-sur-Saone. Turn L (SE) at rndabt after going under A39 & in 6km turn R into vill of Parcey at 'Camping' sp. Lge, pt shd; wc; chem disp; 10% serviced pitches; shwrs inc; el pts (5A) €2.20; lndtte; tradsmn; rest; snacks; bar; BBQ; playgrnd; pool; paddling pool; beach adj; fishing; boating; 20% statics; dogs €1.20; phone; poss cr; Eng spkn; adv bkg; poss some noise when busy; cc acc; CCI. "Pleasant site; able to find a pitch even in high ssn; poss no hot water for clothes/dishwashing; gd long/sh stay." ◆ 15 Apr-11 Sep. € 12.30   2005*

DOLE *6H2* (S Urban) **Camping Le Pasquier, 18 Chemin Thevenot, 39100 Dole** [03 84 72 02 61; fax 03 84 79 23 44; lola@camping-le-pasquier.com; www.camping-du-pasquier.com] Fr A39 foll sp dir Dole & Le Pasquier. Fr all dir foll sp 'Centre ville' then foll site name sp & 'stade camping' in town; well sp. Site on rvside private rd. Narr app. Med, hdg/mkd pitch, pt shd; wc (some cont); chem disp; mv service pnt; shwrs inc; el pts (6-10A) €2.80-4.60 (rev pol); lndry rm; ice; shop & 1km; tradsmn; snacks; bar; playgrnd; pool; aqua park; dir access rv 500m; rv sw; fishing; entmnt; 10% statics; dogs €1.60; poss cr; Eng spkn; quiet; 5% red 7+ days; cc not acc; CCI. "Friendly recep; quiet early ssn; Dole worth visit; modern clean san facs; facs ltd low ssn; poss mosquito problem due to rv; gd rests within walking dist." 15 Mar-15 Oct. € 12.70   2005*

DOLLON see Connerre *4F1*

DOMAZAN see Avignon *10E2*

DOMFRONT *4E1* (6km N Rural) **Camping La Nocherie, 61700 St Bomer-les-Forges** [02 33 37 60 36; fax 02 33 38 16 08] S fr Flers 1km after Les Forges turn L. Site sp Camping a la Ferme, narr rd with long hill. Sm, pt shd; wc; shwrs inc; el pts (6A) €1.50; shop 4km; rest; playgrnd; tennis 3km; fishing; quiet. "Farm site in apple orchard; gd." 15 Mar-15 Dec. € 10.00   2003*

DOMFRONT *4E1* (S Urban) **Camp Municipal, 4 Rue du Champ Passais, 61700 Domfront** [02 33 37 37 66 or 02 33 38 92 24 (LS); mairie@ domfront.com] Turn L on ent town when app fr Vire onto N176, well sp bet old quarter & town cent, dir Mont St Michel. Sm, hdg/mkd pitch, hdstg, terr, pt shd; wc; chem disp (wc); shwrs inc; el pts (5-10A) €1.80-3; lndtte; shops, rest, snacks, bar 1km; playgrnd; rv fishing nr; TV rm; dogs €0.60; phone; Eng spkn; some rd noise; red low ssn; CCI. "V pleasant location with extensive views; helpful, charming staff; site & facs immac; gd security; sh walk to interesting, medieval town; no twin-axles; superb." ♦ 1 Apr-30 Sep. € 8.30   2005*

DOMFRONT *4E1* (12km SW Rural) **Camp Municipal des Chauvieres, 61350 St Fraimbault** [02 33 30 69 60 or 02 33 38 32 22 (Mairie); st. fraimbault@wanadoo.fr] S fr Domfront on D962 sp Mayenne. At Ceauce turn R on D24 sp St Fraimbault, site on R past lake on ent to vill. Sm, mkd pitch, unshd; wc; shwrs; el pts (3A) €2; shop adj; rest, snacks, bar in vill; playgrnd; lake adj; sw 8km; tennis; cycle hire; games area; some statics; quiet. "Warden calls; site in lge park with excel floral displays." 20 Mar-30 Oct. € 3.00   2004*

DOMME see Sarlat la Caneda *7C3*

DOMPIERRE LES ORMES *9A2* (Rural) **Camp Municipal Le Village des Meuniers, 71520 Dompierre-les-Ormes** [03 85 50 36 60; fax 03 85 50 36 61; levillagedesmeuniers@wanadoo. fr; www.villagedesmeuniers.com] Fr A6 exit Macon Sud onto N79 dir Charolles. After approx 35km take slip rd onto D41 for Dompierre-les-Ormes. Well sp nr stadium. Med, hdg/mkd pitch, terr, pt shd; wc; chem disp; mv service pnt; 50% serviced pitch; shwrs inc; el pts (16A) €4; gas; lndtte; shops 2km; tradsmn; rest; snacks; bar; playgrnd; htd pools; waterslide; cycle hire; mini-golf; tennis; entmnt; child entmnt; dogs €1.50; adv bkg (ess high ssn); quiet; cc acc; red low ssn; CCI. "Excel; elevated position with beautiful views; pitches enormous; scrupulously clean; additional flat field at cheaper rates but with full facs high ssn; facs stretched high ssn; excel site for children; gd sp walks in area; pools, rest, bar etc used by public; free m'van hdstg outside site ent; gd shops, etc in adj vill." ♦ 1 May-30 Sep. € 25.50
2005*

DOMPIERRE SUR BESBRE *9A1* (Urban) **Camp Municipal, 03290 Dompierre-sur-Besbre** [04 70 34 55 57 or 04 70 48 11 30 (Mairie)] At E end of town nr rv behind stadium; sp. Med, hdg pitch, pt shd, pt sl; wc (some cont); chem disp; mv service pnt; shwrs inc; el pts (10A) inc; lndtte; shop 500m; BBQ; pool; full sports facs adj; dogs; phone; poss cr; Eng spkn; adv bkg; quiet; CCI. "Well-run site with spotless san facs; vg value; state of the art sports complex; poss stretched high ssn; beautifully maintained; highly rec low ssn; gd for Loire Valley, vineyards & chateaux; vg long stay." ♦
15 May-15 Sep. € 6.90   2005*

DOMPIERRE SUR BESBRE *9A1* (5km E Rural) **Camp Municipal du Gue de Loire, 03290 Diou** [04 70 42 90 44 (Mairie)] Sp in cent of town in both dirs, off N79. Sm, hdg/mkd pitch, pt sl, shd; wc; mv service pnt; shwrs inc; el pts €1.55; lndry rm; shop 500m; traff noise; no cc acc; CCI. "Gd touring base." 1 Jul-15 Sep. € 8.10   2004*

DOMPIERRE SUR VEYLE see Bourg en Bresse *9A2*

DONJON, LE *9A1* (N Urban) **Camp Municipal, Route de Monteray-sur-Loire, 03130 Le Donjon** [04 70 99 56 35 or 04 70 99 50 25; fax 04 74 99 58 02] Sp fr town cent on D166 Rte de Monteray-sur-Loire. Sm, pt sl, pt shd; wc (some cont); shwrs inc; el pts (10A) €2; shop 250m; playgrnd; fishing, sailing & windsurfing 900m; quiet; CCI. ♦ May-Oct. € 5.50   2003*

DONJON, LE *9A1* (7km SW) **Camp Municipal, 03130 Bert** [04 70 99 60 90; fax 04 70 99 64 28] Exit Le Donjon on D989 to NW, after 1km turn L onto D23, after 7km turn L to Bert in 3km. Site on E edge of vill alongside sm lake. sp. Sm, pt shd; wc (cont); shwrs inc; el pts (3-5A) €1.60; ice; shops adj; pool adj; tennis; cycle hire; mini-golf adj; lake (not rec) & fishing adj; dogs; quiet. " Clean facs." 13 May-10 Sep. € 6.50   2004*

DONZENAC *7C3* (10km N Rural) **Camp Municipal Les Escures, 19270 St Pardoux-l'Ortigier** [05 55 84 51 06 (Mairie)] Fr A20 take D9 dir Tulle for 2km. Med, pt sl, pt shd; wc; own san rec; shwrs inc; el pts inc; gas 1km; shop; rest; playgrnd; adj lake; adv bkg; CCI. 15 Jun-15 Sep. € 6.35   2002*

DONZENAC *7C3* (2km S Rural) **Camping La Riviere, Route d'Ussac, 19270 Donzenac** [05 55 85 63 95; fax 05 55 98 16 47; lariviere@ sud-villages.com] Exit A20 at junc 47. Take 1st exit at rndabt dir Donzenac. Site on L in 3km. Avoid app thro Donzenac as narr & diff for lge o'fits. Med, mkd pitch, pt shd; wc; chem disp; shwrs inc; el pts (5A) €2.55 (rev pol); lndtte; shops 1km; snacks; bar; pool Jul/Aug; rv adj; fishing 5km; cycle hire; dogs €1.20; adv bkg rec high ssn. "No warden, site yourself; excel facs; gd sh stay." ♦ 1 Apr-30 Sep. € 14.80   2004*

DORMANS *3D4* (Urban) **Camping Sous Le Clocher/Essi Plage, 02850 Trelou-sur-Marne** [03 26 58 21 79; fax 03 26 53 35 87] On N3 E fr Chateau Thierry; in Dormans foll sp, over Rv Marne; camp site 50m fr end of bdge. Med, hdg pitch, pt shd; wc (some cont); shwrs; el pts (3-6A) inc (rev pol); ice; shop 200m; playgrnd; pool adj high ssn; dogs €1.52; poss cr; rlwy noise & noisy at w/e; no cc acc. "Ideal for Champagne area; vg long/sh stay; facs poss stretched high ssn." Easter-15 Sep. € 11.00   2002*

FRANCE

DORMANS *3D4* (7km NE Rural) **Camping Rural** (Nowack), 10 Rue Bailly, 51700 Vandieres [03 26 58 02 69 or 03 26 58 08 79; fax 03 26 58 39 62; champagne.nowack@wanadoo.fr] Fr N3, turn N at Port Binson, over Rv Marne, then turn W onto D1 for 3km, then N into Vandieres. Site on R about 50m fr start of Rue Bailly, sp 'Champagne Nowack' or 'Camping Nowack.' Sm, pt sl, pt shd; wc; chem disp; shwrs inc; el pts inc; lndtte; BBQ; playgrnd; pool 8km; fishing 1km; rv sw & boating 6km; tennis 2km; TV; quiet; adv bkg. "Charming CL-type site in champagne producer's orchard; facs excel; bread van in vill mornings; excel value." 1 Mar-31 Oct. € 12.00   2005*

DORTAN *9A3* (3km N Rural) **Camp Municipal Les Cyclamens**, La Presqu'ile, 01590 Chancia [tel/fax 04 74 75 82 14; campinglescyclamens@wandadoo.fr] Fr N on D436 to Dortan; R at traff lts sp Bourg-en-Bresse; in 1.5km R (furniture shop) onto D60 sp Chancia; foll sp. NB go past Camping du Lac. Lge, pt shd; wc; chem disp; mv service pnt; shwrs inc; el pts (6-10A) €2.40; gas; lndtte; shop 6km; tradsmn; rest 1km; sm bar; playgrnd; lake sw & shgl beach 100m; fishing, tennis, walking & water sports near; 50% statics; dogs; phone; poss cr; adv bkg; quiet; CCI. "Beautiful area; clean, friendly; few tourists; excel." 1 Apr-30 Sep. € 9.60   2005*

DOSCHES see Troyes *4E4*

DOUAI *3B4* (11km SW) **Camp Municipal Les Etangs**, Chemin du Marais, 62118 Biache-St Vaast [03 21 50 15 02 or 03 21 50 07 27 (Mairie); fax 03 21 50 46 89] Fr N50 Douai-Arras turn L in Fresnes to Biache-St Vaast. Site thro vill on R. Sm, hdg pitch, shd; wc (own san rec); shwrs inc; el pts (6A) €3.05; shops 2km; tradsmn; fishing adj; playgrnd; poss cr; noisy. 1 Apr-30 Sep.   2005*

> Will you fill in the site report forms at the back of the guide, or shall I?

DOUARNENEZ *2E2* (8km NE Urban) **Camp Municipal de Placerhorn**, Rue de la Tromenie, 29180 Locronan [02 98 91 87 76; fax 02 98 51 80 80] Fr Quimper/Douarnenez foll sp D7 Chateaulin; ignore town sp, take 1st R after 3rd rndabt. Fr Chateaulin, turn L at 1st town sp & foll site sp at sharp L turn. Lge, hdg pitch - mainly sm, steeply terr, pt shd; wc; shwrs; el pts (3-6A) €3.05; shops 1km; sand beach 8km; phone; quiet; CCI. "Elec hook-up avail fr 1930 on day of arr." 1 Jun-30 Sep. € 10.60   2005*

DOUARNENEZ *2E2* (8km NE Coastal) **Camping de Treguer Plage, Ste Anne-la-Palud, 29550 Plonevez-Porzay** [02 98 92 53 52; fax 02 98 92 54 89; camping-treguer-plage@wanadoo.fr; www.camping-treguer-plage.com] Fr Douarnenez take D107 twd Chateaulin. After 8km turn L to Ste Anne-la-Palud & foll sp. Lge, hdg/mkd pitch, hdstg, pt shd; wc (some cont); chem disp; mv service pnt; shwrs inc; el pts (6A) €2.70; gas; lndtte; ice; shop; tradsmn; snacks; bar; BBQ; playgrnd; sand beach adj; games area; entmnt; child entmnt; some statics; dogs €1.60; Eng spkn; adv bkg; cc acc; rec CCI. "Well-situated touring base; vg, friendly site." 15 Jun-15 Sep. € 14.40   2005*

See advertisement opposite (top)

DOUARNENEZ *2E2* (8km NE Coastal) **Camping International de Kervel, 29550 Plonevez-Porzay** [02 98 92 51 54; fax 02 98 92 54 96; camping.kervel@wanadoo.fr; www.kervel.com] Fr Douarnenez take D107 twd Chateaulin. After 8km turn L to Plage de Kervel & foll sp. Med, hdg/mkd pitch, pt shd; htd wc; mv service pnt; chem disp; baby facs; shwrs inc; el pts (10A) €3.10; gas; lndtte; ice; shop; rest; snacks; bar; playgrnd; 3 htd pools; waterslide; sand beach 800m; games rm; tennis; mini-golf; cycle hire; entmnt (Jul & Aug); child entmnt; TV; 30% statics; dogs €2.30; poss cr; Eng spkn; adv bkg (rec in high ssn); quiet; cc acc; 5% red CCI. "Gd touring base for lovely area; helpful staff; excel, clean san facs." ♦ 15 May-10 Sep. € 22.50   2005*

See advertisement opposite (bottom)

DOUARNENEZ *2E2* (8km NE Coastal) **Camping Trezmalaouen, 20 Route de la Baie, 29550 Plonevez-Porzay** [tel/fax 02 98 92 54 24; contact@campingtrezmalaouen.com; www.camping-trezmalaouen.com] Fr Douarnenez take D107 N dir Plonevez-Porzay, site sp. Med, hdg/mkd pitch; pt shd; wc; chem displ mv service pnt; shwrs inc; el pts; lndtte; BBQ; playgrnd; sand beach adj; 75% statics; 2 mobile homes for disabled; dogs; adv bkg; cc acc; red long stay/low ssn/CCI. "Sea views; vg touring base." 15 Mar-15 Oct. € 13.00   2005*

See advertisement below

DOUARNENEZ *2E2* (10km E) **Camp Municipal de La Motte, 29136 Plogonnec** [02 98 91 70 09 or 02 98 91 72 06 (Mairie); fax 02 98 91 83 43] Fr Locronan take D7 twd Chateaulin. By side of church, foll sp. La Motte at top of hill by Chapelle-Ar-Zonj. Med, mkd pitch, pt sl, terr, unshd; wc; shwrs inc; el pts; ice; shop 2km; sand beach 10km; poss cr; adv bkg; quiet. 1 Jul-31 Aug.   2004*

DOUARNENEZ *2E2* (2km W Urban) **Camping de Trezulien, 29100 Douarnenez** [02 98 74 12 30 or 02 98 92 81 40; fax 02 98 74 01 16; contact@camping-trezulien.com] Ent Douarnenez fr E on D7; foll sp 'Centre Ville'; turn L at traff lts sp to Trebool. Cross rv bdge into Ave de la Gare, at post office turn L, then 1st L. Turn R at island, foll site sp. Lge, pt terr, pt shd; wc; baby facs; shwrs inc; el pts (6-10A) €2.50-3.10; gas; lndtte; ice; shops 1km; playgrnd; sand beach 1.5km; dogs €1; quiet. "Pleasant, modernised site; vg sh/long stay." 9 Apr-24 Sep. € 10.50   2005*

DOUARNENEZ *2E2* (6km W Rural) **Camping Pil Koad, Poullan-sur-Mer, 29100 Douarnenez** [02 98 74 26 39; fax 02 98 74 55 97; info@pil-koad.com; www.pil-koad.com] Fr E take circular rd around Douarnenez on D7/D765 to Audierne. After x-ing rv estuary, turn R at traff lts (D7) sp Poullan-sur-Mer. After 7km, foll site sp on L of rd; site approx 500m bef Poullan-sur-Mer. Med, hdg/mkd pitch, pt shd; htd wc (some cont); chem disp; shwrs inc; el pts (10A) inc; gas; lndtte; ice; shop; snacks; bar; BBQ; playgrnd; htd pool; paddling pool; sand beach 5km; watersports 4km; lake fishing; tennis; mini-golf; games area; archery; entmnt; internet; games/TV rm; dogs €3; recep 0830-2030; card op barrier (€20 dep req); Eng spkn; adv bkg; quiet; cc acc; red long stay; CCI. "UK tour ops use site; ltd facs low ssn; guided walks high ssn; typical Breton ports nr; mkt Mon & Fri." ♦ 20 May-30 Sep. € 27.50 (CChq acc) ABS - B04   2005*

See advertisement on next page (top)

DOUARNENEZ *2E2* (11km W Coastal) **Camping Pors Peron, 29790 Beuzec-Cap-Sizun** [02 98 70 40 24; fax 02 98 70 54 46] W fr Douarnenez take D7 sp Poullan-sur-Mer. Thro Poullan & in approx 4km turn R sp Pors Peron, foll site & beach sp. Site bef Beuzec-Cap-Sizun vill. Med, hdg/mkd pitch, pt shd; wc; chem disp; mv service pnt; baby facs; shwrs inc; el pts (6A) inc; gas; lndtte; ice; shop & 3km; snacks; BBQ; playgrnd; sand beach 200m; games area; cycle hire; 5% statics; dogs €1.20; phone 200m; adv bkg; quiet; CCI. "British owners; refurbed san facs; nr beautiful; sandy cove; gd coastal walks; excel." ♦ ltd. 1 May-30 Sep. € 12.00   2005*

DOUCIER *6H2* (3km N Rural) **Camping Sunelia La Pergola, Lac de Chalain, 39130 Marigny** [03 84 25 70 03; fax 03 84 25 75 96; contact@ lapergola.com; www.lapergola.com] Fr D471 Lons-le-Saunier to Champagnole rd, turn S on D27 twd Marigny, site on L in 6km on N shore of Lac de Chalain. Lge, hdg pitch, pt sl, terr, pt shd; wc (some cont); chem disp; baby facs; some serviced pitches; shwrs inc; baby facs; el pts (10A) inc; gas; lndtte; ice; shop; rest; snacks; bar; BBQ; playgrnd; htd pool; paddling pool; lake sand beach 500m; fishing; games rm; games area; entmnt; internet; TV; 50% statics; dogs €4; phone; poss cr; Eng spkn; adv bkg; red long stay; cc acc; CCI. "Beautiful gorges in surrounding area; naturist beach on lake 500m; some sm pitches; busy, popular site." ♦ 13 May-18 Sep. € 36.00 (CChq acc)   2005*

See advertisement below

DOUCIER *6H2* (6km N Rural) **Camping Le Git, 39300 Montigny-sur-l'Ain** [03 84 51 21 17 or 03 84 52 20 81] W fr Champagnole on D471 foll sp Monnet-la-Ville & onwards to Montigny-sur-l'Ain, foll camp sp thro vill, turn L at x-rds to church; site immed afterwards on R. Med, mkd pitch, pt sl, pt shd; wc; chem disp; shwrs inc; el pts (5A) inc; ice; lndtte; lndry rm; supmkt 800m; rest; snacks; bar; playgrnd; lake sw 4km; rv sw 2km; sports area; fishing, kayaking 1.5km; dogs; adv bkg; quiet; CCI. "Tranquil site; beautiful views; excel facs."♦ 15 May-15 Sep. € 12.90   2004*

Mustn't forget to post our site report forms to The Club, otherwise sites might be deleted.

DOUCIER *6H2* (7km N Rural) **Camping Sous Doriat, 39300 Monnet-la-Ville** [03 84 51 21 43 or 03 84 51 25 39; fax 03 84 51 21 43; camping. sous-doriat@wanadoo.fr] Take D471 fr Champagnole toPont-du-Navoy. After 10km fork L to Monnet-la-Ville. Site on L. Sm, unshd; wc; shwrs inc; el pts (10A) €2.15; shops adj; lake sw 6km; adv bkg; quiet. 1 May-20 Sep. € 10.00   2003*

As we're travelling out of season, we'd better phone ahead to check that the site is actually open.

†DOUCIER *6H2* (8km N Rural) **Camping Le Bivouac, Route du Lac de Chalain, 39300 Pont-du-Navoy** [03 84 51 26 95; fax 03 84 51 29 70; gillesferreux@voila.fr] D471 to Pont-du-Navoy, S over bdge & immed fork R onto D27; 2nd site on R. Med, mkd pitch, pt shd; htd wc; chem disp; shwrs inc; el pts (8A) €2.85 (poss rev pol/no earth); lndtte; shops 1km; tradsmn; rest; snacks; bar; playgrnd; rv adj; lake sw 6km; TV; 20% statics; dogs €1.05; adv bkg; quiet; cc not acc; CCI. "In beautiful countryside, friendly owners; poss unreliable opening dates." 1 May-15 Sep. € 12.55   2005*

DOUCIER *6H2* (3km NE Rural) **Domaine de Chalain, 39130 Doucier** [03 84 25 78 78; fax 03 84 25 70 06; chalain@chalain.com; www. chalain.com] Fr Lons-le-Saunier take D39 E. In Doucier, site sp to L. Fr Champagnole take D471 for 11km, L onto D27 at Pont-du-Navoy to Doucier & foll sp to site. V lge, pt shd; wc (some cont); mv service pnt; chem disp; sauna; shwrs inc; el pts (6A) €2.60; gas; lndtte; ice; shops; rest; snacks; bar; htd, covrd pools; waterslide & aquatic cent; lake sw adj; boating; fishing; watersports; cycle hire; tennis; horseriding; games area; mini-golf; entmnt; internet; statics; dogs €2.55; poss cr; adv bkg ess. "Extra for lakeside pitches; famous caves Grottes des Beaume adj; vg sh/long stay." 1 May-19 Sep. € 28.00 (3 persons)   2005*

See advertisement on next page

DOUCIER *6H2* (6km SE Rural) **Camping Le Relais de l'Eventail, Route de la Vallée du Hérisson, 39130 Menetrux-en-Joux** [03 84 25 71 59; fax 03 84 25 76 66; relais-de-leventail@club-internet. fr] Fr Doucier take D326 E (site not accessable fr D39). Med, mkd pitch, pt shd; wc; chem disp; mv service pnt; shwrs inc; el pts (6A) €2.50 lndtte; rest; bar; tradsmn; poss cr; dogs €1; quiet. "Site in limestone gorge nr 'Herisson Cascades'; gd walks; lovely, peaceful site; helpful staff." 15 May-15 Sep. € 13.00   2005*

DOUCIER *6H2* (1.5km S Rural) **Camping Domaine de l'Epinette, 15 Rue de l'Epinette, 39130 Chatillon-sur-Ain** [03 84 25 71 44; fax 03 84 25 71 25; info@ domaine-epinette.com; www.domaine-epinette. com] Exit A39 junc 7 to Poligny, then N5 to Champagnole & D471 W. Turn S onto D27 to Lac de Chalain then D39 to Chatillon. Lge, pt sl, terr, pt shd; wc; baby facs; shwrs; el pts (6A) inc; lndtte; shop; rest; snacks; bar; playgrnd; pool; paddling pool; rv sw & fishing; canoeing; horseriding 3km; child entmnt; 20% statics; dogs €2; adv bkg; quiet. ♦ 5 Jun-17 Sep. € 26.50 (CChq acc)   2005*

See advertisement opposite (bottom)

DOUE LA FONTAINE *4G1* (N Urban) **Camp Municipal Les Rives de Douet, Route d'Angers, 49700 Doue-la-Fontaine** [02 41 59 14 47] Fr Doue N on D761 twd Angers; site in sports ground on o'skts of town; sp. Med, mkd pitch, pt shd; wc; chem disp; shwrs inc; el pts (6A) inc; lndtte; shop 1km; rests nr; htd pool high ssn adj; tennis; few statics; poss cr; quiet; no cc acc; 5% red CCI. "Some noise at E end fr factory; lovely park & museum; helpful warden; clean & well-organised site but poss itinerant workers in old c'vans low ssn; gd san facs; gate clsd lunchtime; dep req for key to gate; vg value; gd, flat pitches; conv Cadre Noir Equestrian Cent." ♦ ltd. 1 Apr-30 Sep. € 11.00   2005*

DOUE LA FONTAINE *4G1* (2km SW Rural) **Camping La Vallee des Vignes, 49700 Concourson-sur-Layon** [02 41 59 86 35; fax 02 41 59 09 83; campingvdv@aol.com] D960 fr Doue-la-Fontaine, site 1st R after bdge on leaving vill. Med, mkd pitch, pt shd; htd wc; chem disp; mv service pnt; serviced pitches; baby facs & fam bthrm; shwrs inc; el pts (10A) €3; gas; lndtte; ice; shop 200m; tradsmn; rest; snacks; bar; BBQ; playgrnd; pool; paddling pool; lake sw 10km; mini-golf; cycle hire; entmnt; 20% statics; dogs €3; phone; Eng spkn; adv bkg; some rd noise; cc acc; red long stay & 10% red low ssn; CCI. "Site only open all year weather-conditions permitting - phone ahead to check; v friendly, helpful Eng owners; vg, clean facs; excel rest; conv for Loire chateaux & vineyards, Futuroscope; excel long/sh stay." ♦ 19 Mar-15 Oct. € 20.00   2005*

†**DOUE LA FONTAINE** *4G1* (15km W Rural) **Camping-KathyDave, Les Beauliers, 49540 La Fosse-de-Tigne** [02 41 67 92 10 or 06 14 60 81 63 (mob); bookings@camping-kathydave.co.uk; www.camping-kathy dave.co. uk] Fr Doue-la-Fontaine on D84 to Tigne, turn S to La Fosse-de-Tigne. Pass chateau, site sp on R. Sm, pt shd; htd wc; chem disp; shwrs inc; el pts (8A) inc; ice; tradsmn; rest nr; BBQ; adv bkg; quiet; CCI. "Picturesque area; British owners; excel welcome." € 7.60   2005*

CHALAIN ★★★★

DOUHET, LE *7B2* (2km S Rural) **Camping La Roulerie**, 17100 Le Douhet [05 46 97 74 83; fax 05 46 59 01 06; guysiddons@aol.com] Fr Niort to Saintes, site on W side of N150 in vill of La Roulerie. Sm, some hdstdg, pt shd; 1 wc; chem disp; shwrs inc; el pts (10A) inc; shops 5km; playgrnd; pool 8km; adv bkg; quiet but some rd noise; cc not acc. "Sm pitches; full by early eve; site yourself; bureau open late eve; helpful British owners; friendly; fair sh stay." 1 May-31 Oct. € 12.00   2005*

DOULLENS *3B3* (6km NE) **Camp Municipal La Foret**, 80600 Lucheux [03 22 77 07 03 or 03 22 32 44 94] To L of Doullens-Arras rd (N25), sp at each x-rd. Med, pt shd; wc (cont); shwrs; el pts; shops 2km; playgrnd; 75% statics; adv bkg; v quiet; CCI. "Isolated site; fair NH only." Easter-15 Sep. € 11.50   2003*

DOURDAN *4E3* (Urban) **Camping Les Petits Pres**, 11 Rue Pierre Mendes France, 91410 Dourdan [01 64 59 64 83 or 01 60 81 14 17; fax 01 60 81 14 29] Exit A10 dir. Fr Dourdan take D116 sp Arpajon. After 1-way system turn R immed bef Renault g'ge. On for approx 1km & camp sp nr pool. Med, pt sl, pt shd; wc; shwrs; el pts; gas & supmkt 500m; rest; playgrnd; pool 500m; poss cr; 75% statics; noisy; Eng spkn; adv bkg rec high ssn & w/e in winter. "Gd sh stay; town worth visit." 1 Apr-30 Sep. € 11.89   2002*

DOUSSARD see Faverges *9B3*

DOUVAINE *9A3* (4km NW) **Camp Municipal Le Lemania**, Rue du Port, 74140 Chens-sur-Leman [04 50 94 22 43 or 04 76 80 74 71 (LS); fax 04 50 94 22 43] Fr Geneva to Thonon rd N5 turn L on to D20 dir Touges at Douvaine. Site sp. Med, pt shd; wc (some cont); chem disp; shwrs; el pts (5A) €2.20; shops 1km; shgl beach 200m on lake; dogs €1; red low ssn. "Gd NH." 1 May-30 Sep. € 13.60   2005*

DOUVILLE *7C3* (2km S Rural) **Camping Lestaubiere**, Pont-St Mamet, 24140 Douville [05 53 82 98 15; fax 05 53 82 90 17; lestaubiere@cs.com; www.lestaubiere.com] Foll sp for 'Pont St Mamet' fr the N21; then watch for camping sp. Med, mkd pitch, pt sl, shd; wc; chem disp (wc); fam bthrm; shwrs inc; el pts (4-10A) €2.70-4; gas; lndtte; ice; shop in ssn; tradsmn; rest 5km; bar; playgrnd; pool & lake; fishing; tennis 5km; games area; TV; dogs €0.75; Eng spkn; adv bkg; quiet; CCI. "Run by friendly Dutch couple; superb out of ssn; v lge pitches." ♦ 1 May-30 Sep. € 19.00   2004*

DOUZE, LA *7C3* (3km E Rural) **Camping Laulurie en Perigord (Naturist)**, 24330 La Douze [05 53 06 74 00; fax 05 53 06 77 55; toutain@laulurie.com; www.laulurie.com] Fr Perigueux take N89; in 8km turn S on D710 twd Le Bugue. Turn E 150 past church in La Douze sp Laulurie. (Turn bet buildings - care needed). Sm, hdg/mkd pitch, pt sl, pt shd; wc (some cont); chem disp; shwrs inc; el pts (10A) €5; gas; ice; shop; rest; snacks; bar; playgrnd; pool; dogs €2.50; sep car park; adv bkg; quiet; red low ssn/long stay. "Excel; friendly owners; gd touring base for Dordogne & Perigueux; INF card req." ♦ ltd. 15 May-15 Sep. € 19.00   2005*

DOUZE, LA *7C3* (4km SW Rural) **Camping La Prade**, 24330 La Douze [tel/fax 05 53 06 73 59] Site sp on N710 adj sm lake. Med, pt sl, pt shd; wc; chem disp; shwrs; el pts (6A) inc; rest; bar; BBQ; playgrnd; lake fishing; dogs; some statics; phone; quiet. "V friendly, helpful owners; facs basic but clean." 1 Apr-15 Sep. € 12.40   2003*

DOUZY see Sedan *5C1*

DRAGUIGNAN *10F3* (7km NE Rural) **Domaine de la Haute Garduere (Naturist), Route de Thoronet**, 83830 Callas [tel/fax 04 94 67 95 20] Fr Draguignan D562 NE twd Grasse. After 9km turn R (see sp); site in woodland at end of 3km gravel rd. If poss avoid Draguignan when towing. Lge, hdg pitch, sl, terr, shd; wc; chem disp; shwrs; el pts (6A) €3; gas; lndtte; shop 10km; tradsmn; rest; snacks; bar; playgrnd; pool; sand beach 30km; golf; archery; 25% statics; dogs €3; phone; Eng spkn; adv bkg quiet "Excel; INF card req; helpful owners; woodland walks." 1 Apr-31 Oct. € 16.00   2004*

DRAGUIGNAN *10F3* (2km S) **Camping La Foux, Quartier La Foux**, 83300 Draguignan [tel/fax 04 94 68 18 27] Fr a'route A8, take Le Muy intersection onto N555 N to Draguignan. Site ent on R at ent to town sp Sport Centre Foux. Fr Draguignan, take N555 S; just after 'End of Draguignan' sp, double back at rndabt & turn R. Lge, pt sl, unshd; wc; shwrs inc; el pts (4-10A) €2.50-5; lndtte; shop; rest; playgrnd; sand beach 20km; rv adj; fishing; entmnt; TV rm; dogs €2; poss cr; quiet. "V clean san facs; care needed long vehicles on ent site; easy access to Riviera coast; gd sh stay." 20 Jun-30 Sep. € 18.00   2005*

†DREUX *4E2* (6km W) **Camping Les Etangs de Marsalin**, 3 Place du General de Gaulle, 28500 Vert-en-Drouais [02 37 82 92 23; fax 02 37 82 85 47; camping.etangs.de.marsalin@wanadoo.fr] Take N12 sp Alencon fr Dreux W & turn R on D152 to Vert-en-Drouais; on ent turn R to church, site on L. Med, hdg/mkd pitch, hdstg, pt sl, pt shd; htd wc (some cont); chem disp; shwrs inc; el pts (16-20A) €3.70 (poss rev pol, long leads poss req, avail at recep); tradsmn; rest 1km; snacks; bar 100m; lake fishing 2km; 90% statics; dogs; poss cr; quiet; CCI. "Sm pitches - poss diff for lge vans; peaceful location; v helpful staff; refurbished san facs; conv NH en rte Spain." € 9.20   2005*

*Last year of report

DUN SUR MEUSE *5C1* (10km SE Rural) **Camping Le Brouzel, 55110 Sivry-sur-Meuse [03 29 85 86 45]** On D964 11km S of Dun twd Verdun, site sp in vill of Sivry. Sm, unshd; wc (cont); chem disp; shwrs €0.80; gas; el pts (4-6A) €2.60-3.10; shop adj; rest; snacks; bar; playgrnd; games area; dir access to rv; fishing; sailing 2km; 80% statics; adv bkg; quiet. "V clean site." 1 Apr-1 Oct. € 7.50   2004*

DUN SUR MEUSE *5C1* (10km SW Rural) **Camping La Gabrielle, 55110 Romagne-sous-Montfaucon [03 29 85 11 79; La-Gabrielle@wanadoo.fr]** Sit is on D998 10km SW of Dun, 800m beyond end of Romagne. Well sp. Sm, pt sl, pt shd; wc; shwrs inc; el pts (6A) €2 (rev pol); ice; playgrnd; 10% statics; Eng spkn; quiet; CCI. "Meals avail by arrangement; v friendly Dutch owners; parts of site uneven; close to WW1 historic monuments." ♦ 1 Apr-30 Sep. € 10.00   2004*

DUNKERQUE *3A3* (2km N Coastal) **Camping Mer & Vacances (formerly Les Argousiers), Rue J Baptiste Charcot, 59495 Leffrinckoucke [tel/fax 03 28 20 17 32]** Leave A16 at junc 34; foll sp to Leffrinckoucke (cent); go over canal & bear L to cent. Foll sp 'information' & tourist office. Site behind local tourist office & sports facs. Med, mkd pitch, terr; htd wc; chem disp; shwrs inc; el pts (6A) €3; ice; lndtte; shop & supmkt 1km; rest & bar 500m; playgrnd; beach, fishing & watersports 100m; tennis; entmnt; 50% statics; dogs €1.20; adv bkg rec high ssn; some noise at w/e. "Gd site." ♦ 1 Apr-31 Oct. € 14.50   2005*

DUNKERQUE *3A3* (3km NE Coastal) **Camp Municipal La Licorne, 1005 Blvd de l'Europe, 59240 Dunkerque [03 28 69 26 68]** Leave A16 sp 'Malo'. At end of slip rd traff lts turn L sp Malo-les-Bains. In 2km (at 5th traff lts) turn R at camping sp. At 2nd traff lts past BP g'ge turn L. Site on L (cont strt to rndabt & return on opp side of dual c'way to ent). Lge, mkd pitch, pt sl, unshd; wc; chem disp; shwrs; el pts (10A) €4.10 (poss long lead); gas; lndtte; ice; sm shop; supmkt 1km; rest; snacks; bar; playgrnd; pool in high ssn; sand beach adj; 80% statics; dogs €0.85; bus fr site ent; poss cr; adv bkg (dep & bkg fee req); quiet; CCI. "Gd NH for Calais to/fr Belgium; pitches uneven; promenade to town cent; lge supmkts nr with petrol; obliging owners; dogs roaming site." ♦ ltd. 1 Apr-30 Nov. € 13.35   2005*

†**DUNKERQUE** *3A3* (11km NE Coastal) **Camp Municipal des Dunes, 222 Rue de l'Eglise, 59123 Bray-Dunes [03 28 26 61 54 or 03 28 26 57 63]** Dunkerque-Ostend on N1, take R slip rd sp Bray-Dunes (approx 100m bef Belgian border), foll rd over N1 for 3km into Bray-Dunes. Foll Camping Municipal sp in town. V lge, mkd pitch, pt sl, unshd; wc; chem disp (wc); shwrs €1; el pts (5A) inc; shop 200m; playgrnd; sand beach 300m; 90% statics; dogs €0.50. "Friendly staff; clean facs; ltd space for tourers; conv for ferry." € 19.45   2005*

DUNKERQUE *3A3* (12km NE Coastal) **Camping Perroquet Plage Frontiere, 59123 Bray-Dunes [03 28 58 37 37; fax 03 28 58 37 01; camping-perroquet@wanadoo.fr]** On Dunkerque-Ostend rd N1/E5, about 100m fr Belgian frontier, thro vill on D947; cont 1km to traff lts, R on D60 thro vill, past rlwy stn to site on L. V lge, pt shd; wc; chem disp; shwrs inc; el pts (4-10A) €3.80-4.60; lndtte; shop; rest; snacks; bar; playgrnd; sand beach adj; watersports; tennis; 85% statics; dogs €0.45; poss cr; adv bkg; Eng spkn; quiet; CCI. "Gd; many local attractions." ♦ 1 Apr-30 Sep. € 14.00   2003*

†**DURAS** *7D2* (500m N Rural) **Camping Le Cabri, Malherbe, Route de Savignac, 47120 Duras [05 53 83 81 03; fax 05 53 83 08 91; holidays@lacabri.eu.com; www.lecabri.eu.com]** On ent Duras fr N turn R onto D203. Site well sp fr D708. Sm, pt shd; wc (cont); chem disp (wc); baby facs; fam bthrm; shwrs inc; el pts (4-10A) €3-4; gas 500m; lndtte; shop 500m; rest; bar; playgrnd; pool; tennis 1km; 50% statics; dogs €1; bus 500m; Eng spkn; adv bkg (dep req); quiet; cc acc; red long stay; CCI. "Excel, clean, spacious site; gd facs." ♦ € 12.00   2005*

DURAVEL see Puy l'Eveque *7D3*

DURTAL *4G1* (Urban) **Camp Municipal L'Internationale, 9 Rue de Camping, 49430 Durtal [02 41 76 31 80 or 02 41 76 30 24 (Mairie); fax 04 21 76 32 67; mairie@ville-durtal.fr]** Exit A11 junc 11 dir La Fleche, by-passing Durtal. At N23 turn R for Durtal, site on L at ent to town. Med, hdg pitch, pt shd; wc (mainly cont); chem disp; shwrs inc; el pts (6-10A) inc; gas; lndtte; ice; shops 500m; tradsmn; playgrnd; pool adj; entmnt; TV rm; 5% statics; dogs €1.45; Eng spkn; adv bkg; red long stay; ltd facs low ssn; quiet. "Pleasant position on Rv Loir; interesting vill; v helpful warden; PA system intrusive." ♦ Easter-30 Sep. € 10.00   2005*

EAUX BONNES see Laruns *8G2*

†**EAUX PUISEAUX** *4F4* (1km S Rural) **Camping a la Ferme des Haut Frenes (Lambert), 10130 Eaux-Puiseaux [03 25 42 15 04; fax 03 25 42 02 95; les.hauts.frenes@wanadoo.fr]** N fr St Florentin or S fr Troyes on N77. Ignore D374 but take next turning D111 in NW dir. Site in 2km; well sp. Med, pt shd; htd wc; chem disp; shwrs inc; el pts (10A) €2 (some rev pol); lndtte; shop 2km; tradsmn; rest; BBQ; playgrnd; tennis 3km; TV & games rm; dogs €1.50; poss cr; Eng spkn; adv bkg; quiet; red 10+ days; CCI. "Beautiful, quiet setting; excel farm site with vg san facs; helpful owners; cider museum in vill; v high standard site; meals on request; poss v muddy winter." ♦ € 8.00   2005*

EAUZE *8E2* (Urban) **Camp Municipal Le Moulin du Pouy**, 32800 Eauze [05 62 09 86 00; fax 05 62 09 79 20; eauze.mairie@wanadoo.fr] On D931 on N o'skts, sp. Site in 2 parts, connected by bdge. Sm, pt shd; wc (some cont); shwrs inc; el pts; rest; snacks; bar; supmkt 500m; pool; TV rm; library; quiet; red CCI. "Noise fr pool during day; gd rest & pool; friendly staff; gd NH/sh stay." 1 Jun-30 Sep. € 11.20   2003*

EBREUIL see Gannat *9A1*

ECHELLES, LES *9B3* (6km NE) **Camping La Bruyere**, Hameau Cote Barrier, 73160 St Jean-de-Couz [tel/fax 04 79 65 74 27 or 04 79 65 79 11; bearob@libertysurf.fr] Heading S on N6 Chambery-Lyon rd, 15km S of Chambery take D45 to St Jean-de-Couz; site sp. Med, pt sl, pt shd; wc (cont); chem disp; shwrs inc; el pts (6A); gas; shop; tradsmn; rest, snacks high ssn; bar; BBQ; playgrnd; TV; 30% statics; dogs €1; adv bkg; quiet. "Chartreuse caves open to public adj; gd walking area." 20 Apr-10 Oct. € 7.80   2004*

ECHELLES, LES *9B3* (6km S) **Camp Municipal Les Berges du Guiers**, 38380 St Laurent-du-Pont [04 76 55 20 63 or 04 76 06 22 55 (LS); fax 04 76 06 22 55] On D520 Chambery-Voiron S fr Les Echelles. On ent St Laurent-du-Pont. R just bef petrol stn on L. Sm, pt shd; wc; chem disp; shwrs; el pts (5A) €2.40; shops 400m; rv adj; dogs €0.80; cc not acc; CCI. "V clean & well-kept; nice area; gates clsd 1100-1530." 15 Jun-15 Sep. € 9.40   2003*

ECLASSAN see St Vallier *9C2*

ECOMMOY *4F1* (1km NE Urban) **Camp Municipal Les Vaugeons**, Rue de la Charite, 72220 Ecommoy [02 43 42 14 14 or 02 43 42 10 14 (Mairie); fax 02 43 42 62 80; mairieecommoy@wanadoo.fr] Heading S on N138 foll sp. Turn E at 2nd traff lts in vill; sp Stade & Camping. Also just off A28. Med, pt sl, pt shd; wc (some cont); chem disp; shwrs €1.30; el pts (6A) inc; lndtte; shops 1km; playgrnd; tennis; poss cr; Eng spkn; adv bkg; quiet; cc not acc; red low ssn; CCI. "Site v full during Le Mans week; close to circuit; friendly; gd ltd facs; recep open early am/eve; pitch yourself; coarse sand/grass surface." ♦ ltd. 1 May-30 Sep. € 9.05   2005*

ECOMMOY *4F1* (4km SE Rural) **Camp Municipal Le Chesnaie**, 72220 Marigne-Laille [02 43 42 12 12 (Mairie); fax 02 43 42 61 23; mairie.marigne-laille@wanadoo.fr] S on N138 Le Mans-Tours, turn E 3km after Ecommoy twds Marigne-Laille. Site in 1.5km. Sm, pt shd, mkd pitch; wc; shwrs; el pts (10A) €1.20; shops 300m; playgrnd; pool 5km; lake & fishing adj; tennis; poss cr; v quiet; CCI. "If height barrier down, go to recreation office adj on road in." 1 Apr-30 Sep. € 7.00   2005*

ECOMMOY *4F1* (8km S Rural) **Camp Municipal Plan d'Eau du Fort des Salles**, 72360 Mayet [02 43 46 68 72; fax 02 43 46 07 61] On N138 Le Mans-Tours rd turn W at St Hubert onto D13 to Mayet & site. Sp 'Camping Plan d'Eau' Med, mkd pitch, pt shd; wc, chem disp (wc); shwrs inc; el pts (10A) €2.30; gas; lndtte; ice; shops 500m; playgrnd; lake sw & fishing; cycle hire; statics; quiet; CCI. "Well-maintained, clean site; mkd walks nrby; card operated barrier; recep open 0830-1130 & 1600-1900; arr only between these times as nowhere to wait if arr earlier." ♦ ltd. Easter-15 Oct. € 8.90   2005*

†EGLETONS *7C4* (2km NE) **Camping Egletons-Lac**, 19300 Egletons [tel/fax 05 55 93 14 75] Site off N89 Clermont-Ferrand-Tulle rd to NE of Egletons; 2km bef Egletons twd Ussel; 300m after Hotel Ibis on L. Med, mkd pitch, terr, pt shd; wc; chem disp; baby facs; fam bthrm; shwrs inc; el pts (4-8A); gas; lndtte; shops 2km; tradsmn; rest; snacks; bar; lake sw, fishing & watersports 500m; playgrnd; entmnts; TV; 30% statics; dogs; phone; Eng spkn; quiet; CCI. "Fair sh stay; pitches further away fr rest quieter."   2004*

EGUISHEIM see Colmar *6F3*

†EGUZON CHANTOME *7A3* (3km SE Rural) **Camp Municipal du Lac Les Nugiras**, Route de Messant, 36270 Eguzon [02 54 47 45 22; fax 02 54 47 47 22] Fr Argenton-sur-Creuse D913 to Eguzon; at x-rds R twds cent; fr vill cent D36 & foll site sp. Fr A20 exit junc 20, E on D36 to Eguzon; foll site sp. Lge, hdg/mkd pitch, pt sl, terr, pt shd; htd wc; shwrs inc; el pts (10A) €3.30 (rev pol); lndtte; shop; tradsmn; rest; snacks; bar; playgrnd; sand beach 300m; watersports; waterski school; games rm; some statics; security barrier; quiet but poss noise fr statics; red low ssn; CCI. "Scenic site & region; ample, clean facs but ltd low ssn; site yourself on arr; warden avail early evening." ♦ € 6.90   2005*

ELNE *10G1* (1.8km NE) **Camp Municipal El Moli** (Al Mouly), Rue Gustave Eiffel, 66200 Elne [04 68 22 08 46; fax 04 68 37 95 05; contact@ot-elne.fr] Exit A9 at Perpignan Sud dir Argeles. Site well sp fr Elne cent in dir St Cyprien on D40. Lge, pt shd; wc; chem disp; baby facs; shwrs inc; el pts (10A) inc; lndte; shop; rest & snacks high ssn; playgrnd; pool; sand beach 5km; tennis; horseriding; games area; entmnt; TV; poss cr; quiet; adv bkg; CCI. ♦ 1 Jun-30 Sep. € 19.90   2005*

FRANCE

[amping Municipal d'Epernay

Allée de Cumières - 51200 • EPERNAY - FRANCE
Phone : 00 33 (0)3 26 55 32 14 • Fax : 00 33 (0)3 26 52 36 09
E-mail : camping.epernay@free.fr

Situated in the heart of the Champagne vineyards on the banks of
a river, in a green, peaceful and pleasant environment.

Be sure to visit the prestigious mansions of the Champagne and
its winemakers. Let the serenity seduce you, and the beautiful
facades in « Belle Epoque » style, the cosy, small and hospitable
corners charm you and receive you with open arms.

ELNE *10G1* (4km S Rural) **Camping Le Haras**, Domaine St Galdric, 66900 Palau-del-Vidre [04 68 22 14 50; fax 04 68 37 98 93; haras8@wanadoo.fr; www.camping-le-haras.com] Fr A9 N or S, exit 42 Perpignan S dir Argeles-sur-Mer. Foll sp for Argeles until exit 9 onto N114 for Palau-del-Vidre. Site on L at ent to vill immed after low & narr rlwy bdge. Med, mkd pitch, shd; wc; chem disp; shwrs inc; el pts (6A) inc; lndtte; ice; shop; tradsmn; rest, snacks, bar in ssn; BBQ (gas/elec only); pool; sand beach 6km; entmnt; internet; TV; some statics; dogs €3; no c'vans over 6.50m acc high ssn; poss cr; Eng spkn; adv bkg; some rlwy noise; 20-30% red low ssn; CCI. "Lovely, well-run, family site in wooded parkland; helpful & friendly; excel facs; Roman remains; music festival; conv Spanish border; rds around site poss liable to flood in winter; some corners on site rds narr for lge o'fits; staff can tow lge o'fits to pitch; 5 mins walk to vill with gd rest; excel." ♦ 20 Mar-20 Oct. € 27.50 (CChq acc) ABS - C26   2005*

> We're having a great holiday - must fill in some site report forms and send them to The Club as soon as possible.

EMBRUN *9D3* (6km N Rural) **Camping Les Cariamas**, 05380 Chateauroux-les-Alpes [04 92 43 22 63 or 06 65 00 32 88; patricktim@9online.fr] Fr Embrun on N94 in 3km turn L to Chateauroux & foll sp to site. Site in 1km. Med, mkd pitch, pt sl, terr, pt shd; wc; own san adv; chem disp; mv service pnt (water only); shwrs inc; el pts (6A) €3; lndtte; ice; shop 1km; rest; snacks; bar; BBQ; playgrnd; htd pool; lake sw adj; beach 6km; sailing; rafting; canoeing; tennis 500m; no statics; dogs €2; phone; Eng spkn; adv bkg; some rd noise; red low ssn; CCI. "Excel for watersports & walking; mountain views; National Park 3km." 1 Apr-31 Oct. € 13.00   2003*

EMBRUN *9D3* (4km S Rural) **Camping Le Verger**, 05200 Baratier [04 92 43 15 87; fax 04 92 43 49 81; bresgilbert@minitel.net; www.campingleverger.fr] Fr Embrun N94 twd Gap. L at rndabt onto D40. Ignore 1st sp to Baratier & take 2nd after 1km, thro vill & fork L by monument. Site on R next to trout farm. Med, hdg pitch, hdstg, terr, pt shd; htd wc; chem disp; shwrs; el pts (10A) €4.60; ice; lndtte; snacks; BBQ; pool; playgrnd; entmnts; lake 3km; TV; 30% statics; poss cr; adv bkg; red low ssn; CCI. "Lge pitches; gd views; ltd maintenance/facs low ssn." 1 Jun-15 Sep & 15 Dec-30 Apr. € 13.00   2003*

EMBRUN *9D3* (4km S Rural) **Camping Les Grillons**, Route de la Madeleine, 05200 Embrun [tel/fax 04 92 43 32 75; info@lesgrillons.com; www.lesgrillons.com] Fr Embrun take the N94 twds Gap; over the bdge; L at rndabt onto D40. Turn L at 1st sharp bend; site on L in 400m. Med, mkd pitch, pt sl, pt shd; wc; chem disp; shwrs inc; el pts (6-10A) €3.05-3.96; ice; lndtte; tradsmn; snacks high ssn; playgrnd; 2 pools (caps ess); tennis; lake sw & fishing 2km; 5% statics; dogs €1.52; Eng spkn; adv bkg (bkg fee & dep req); CCI. "Helpful, pleasant owners; vg long stay." 26 May-15 Sep. € 13.20   2004*

ENTRAIGUES see Mure, La *9C3*

ENTRAYGUES SUR TRUYERE *7D4* (Urban) **Camp Municipal du Val de Saures**, 12140 Entraygues-sur-Truyere [05 65 44 56 92; fax 05 65 44 27 21; sogeval@wanadoo.fr; www.camping-massif central.com] Fr town cent take Rodez rd & in 200m turn R over narr bdge, foll site sp. Med, mkd pitch, pt shd; wc (some cont); shwrs; el pts (5A) €3; lndtte; shops in town; playgrnd; pool adj; entmnt; dogs €1.05; quiet. "Direct access to town via footbdge over rd; new san facs 2003; gd touring base." ♦ 1 May-30 Sep. € 10.00   2003*

ENTRAYGUES SUR TRUYERE *7D4* (5km NE Rural) **Camp Municipal du Lauradiol**, 12460 Campouriez [05 65 44 53 95; fax 05 65 44 81 37] On D34 5km NE of Entraygues; sp. Sm, hdg/mkd pitch, pt shd; wc; el pts (6A) inc; shop 5km; htd pool; rv adj; quiet; CCI. "Beautiful setting & walks; excel long stay." 20 Jun-10 Sep. € 14.50 (4 persons)   2002*

ENTRECHAUX see Vaison la Romaine *9D2*

ENVEITG see Bourg Madame *8H4*

EPERLECQUES see St Omer *3A3*

EPERNAY *3D4* (1km NW Urban) **Camp Municipal d'Epernay, Allee de Cumieres, 51200 Epernay** [03 26 55 32 14; fax 03 26 52 36 09; camping. epernay@free.fr] Fr Reims take the N51 twd Epernay, cross rv & turn R at rndabt onto D301 sp Cumieres (look for sp 'Stade Paul Chandon'), site sp. Site adj Stadium. Avoid town at early evening rush hour. Med, hdg/mkd pitch, hdstg, pt shd; htd wc (mainly cont); chem disp; mv service pnt; shwrs inc; el pts (5A) €3; lndtte; tradsmn; supmkt 300m; rest; snacks; bar; BBQ; playgrnd; htd, covrd pool & waterslide 2km; fishing; canoeing; tennis; cycle hire; games area; 3% statics; dogs; phone; poss cr; Eng spkn; adv bkg; quiet - some rlwy/rd noise; cc acc; red long stay/CCI. "Friendly, helpful staff; san facs stretched high ssn; conv Champagne area; Mercier train tour with wine-tasting; gd walks; NB no twin-axle vans or vans over 6m acc; site open to public; excel site." ♦ End Apr-1 Oct. € 15.00   2005*

See advertisement opposite

EPESSES, LES *2H4* (Rural) **Camping La Breteche, Zone de Loisirs de la Breteche, 85590 Les Epesses** [02 51 57 33 34; fax 02 51 57 41 98; contact@ camping-la-bretache.com; www.camping-la-bretache.com] Fr Les Herbiers foll sp to Les Epesses. Turn N on D752, site sp on R by lake. Site sp fr cent Les Epesses. Med, hdg/mkd pitch, pt shd; wc, chem disp; shwrs inc; el pts (15A) €2.60; lndtte; shop 1km; tradsmn; rest; snacks; bar; playgrnd; htd pool adj; tennis; fishing; horseriding; entmnt; TV; dogs €1.50; adv bkg (fee €8); poss cr; cc acc; red low ssn; CCI. "Clean, well-run site; helpful staff; plenty of attractions nr; conv for Puy du Fou." ♦ 15 Apr-15 Sep. € 14.00   2004*

EPINAC *6H1* (Urban) **Camp Municipal Le Pont Vert, 71360 Epinac** [03 85 82 00 26 or 03 85 82 10 12 (LS(; fax 03 85 82 13 67; mairie-epinac@wanadoo.fr] D973 Autun to Beaune 16km. L on D43 to Epinac, site on drive to public sports facs, sp in town. Med, pt shd; wc; chem disp; shwrs inc; el pts (10A) €2.65; lndtte; shops in vill; snacks; rv sw; dogs €0.60; quiet. 15 Jun-15 Sep. € 10.00   2005*

EPINAL *6F2* (1km E) **Camping Parc du Chateau, 37 Rue du Chaperon Rouge, 88000 Epinal** [03 29 34 43 65; fax 03 29 31 05 12; camping.parc. du.chateau@wanadoo.fr; www.parcduchateau. com] Sp fr town cent. Or fr N57 by-pass take exit sp Razimont, site sp in 1km. Med, hdg/mkd pitch, some hdstg, terr, pt shd; htd wc (some cont); chem disp; mv service pnt; shwrs inc; el pts (6A) €4; gas; lndtte; ice; shop; snacks; BBQ; playgrnd; pool; lake sw 8km; tennis; TV; dogs €1.50; Eng spkn; adv bkg; quiet but stadium adj; cc acc; red low ssn/long stay; CCI. "Vg; lge pitches; ltd facs low ssn." ♦ 1 Apr-30 Sep. € 15.00   2005*

†**EPINAL** *6F2* (8km W Rural) **Club du Lac de Bouzey, 19 Rue du Lac, 88390 Sanchey** [03 29 82 49 41; fax 03 29 64 28 03; camping.lac. de.bouzey@wanadoo.fr; www.camping-lac-de-bouzey.com] Fr Epinal take D460 sp Darney. In vill of Bouzey turn L at camp sp. Site in few metres, by reservoir. Lge, hdg/mkd pitch, hdstg, pt sl, terr, pt shd; htd wc (some cont); chem disp; mv service pnt; baby facs; shwrs inc; el pts (6A) €4; gas; lndtte; shop; tradsmn; rest; snacks; bar; playgrnd; htd pool; sand beach & lake 500m; fishing; games area; cycle hire; horseriding; child/teenager entmnt; internet; TV rm; 15% statics; dogs €3; phone; adv bkg; Eng spkn; quiet; cc acc; red low ssn/long stay; CCI. "Attractive site; modern san facs; gd shop & excel pool; excel touring base." ♦ € 23.00 (CChq acc)   2005*

See advertisement below

EPINIAC see Dol de Bretagne *2E4*

ERDEVEN see Carnac *2G3*

FRANCE

ERNEE *2E4* (E Urban) **Camp Municipal d'Ernee,** 53500 Ernee [02 43 05 19 90] Site sp on app to town, off Fougeres-Mayenne rd on E side of town. Head for Centre Ville, turn L for Fougeres, round rndabt & site on R. Med, pt sl, pt shd; hdg pitch; serviced pitch; wc; shwrs inc; el pts (6A) inc; shops 300m; pool adj; quiet. 15 May-15 Sep. € 11.20   2004*

ERNEE *2E4* (10km SW Rural) **Camping-Caravaning a la Ferme (Jarry), La Lande, 53380 La Croixille** [02 43 68 57 00] SW fr Ernee on D29 to La Croixille. In vill L onto D30 twds Laval. In 2.5km L onto D158, dir Juvigne, then R at next x-rds, sp Le Bourgneuf-le-Foret. Site in 2km. Fr A81 exit junc 4 onto D30. Sm, pt shd; wc; shwrs €1.20; el pts €1.80 (rev pol); lndtte; supmkt 4km; playgrnd. "Excel CL-type farm site with orchard; friendly owners, farm produce for sale; quiet & beautiful." 1 May-1 Oct. € 7.40   2005*

ERQUY *2E3* (1km N Coastal) **Yelloh! Village Les Pins, Le Guen, Route des Hopitaux, 22430 Erquy** [02 96 72 31 12; fax 02 96 63 67 94; camping.des. pins@wanadoo.fr; www.yellohvillage-les-pins.com] Site sp on all app rds to Erquy. Lge, pt shd, pt sl, terr; wc (some cont); chem disp; sauna; shwrs inc; el pts (6A) €2; gas; lndtte; ice; shop; tradsmn; rest; snacks; bar; htd pool; sand beach 800m; tennis; fitness rm; jacuzzi; entmnt & child entmnt; some statics; dogs €2; Eng spkn; adv bkg; cc acc; CCI. "Gd family holiday site." ♦ 1 May-9 Sep. € 27.00   2005*

ERQUY *2E3* (3km NE Coastal) **Camping Les Hautes Grees, 123 Rue St Michel, Les Hopitaux, 22430 Erquy** [02 96 72 34 78; fax 02 96 72 30 15; hautesgrees@wanadoo.fr; www.camping-hautes -grees.com] Fr Erquy NE D786 dir Cap Frehel & Les Hopitaux so to site. Med, hdg/mkd pitch, hdstg, pt shd; wc (some cont); chem disp; mv service pnt; shwrs inc; el pts (10A) €3.20 (rec long lead); gas; lndtte; ice; shop; tradsmn; rest, snacks 2km; bar; BBQ; playgrnd; pool; sand beach 400m; fishing; tennis; horseriding; mini-golf; some statics; dogs €1.10; adv bkg; red low ssn; cc acc; CCI. "Pleasant, well-run site; helpful staff." ♦ 15 Apr-30 Sep. € 17.20   2005*

See advertisement above

ERQUY *2E3* (1km E Coastal) **Camping Le Vieux Moulin, Route de Tues-Roc, Hopitaux, 22430 Erquy** [02 96 72 34 23; fax 02 96 72 36 63; camp. vieux.moulin@wanadoo.fr; www.campingvieux moulin.com] Sp fr all dirs on D786. Lge, sl, pt shd; wc; shwrs inc; el pts (6-9A) €4-4.50; gas; lndtte; shop; rest; snacks; htd pool; sand beach 1km; games rm; entmnt; TV; poss cr; quiet. "Site set in pine woods; plenty of beaches in 20 mins drive; ideal for family holiday; poss diff access lge o'fits; lower pitches subject to flooding." ♦ 11 May-14 Sep. € 23.00   2002*

ERQUY *2E3* (5km S Rural) **Camping Bellevue, Route de Pleneuf-Val-Andre, La Couture, 22430 Erquy** [02 96 72 33 04; fax 02 96 72 48 03; campingbellevue@yahoo.fr; www.camping bellevue.fr] Fr Erquy, take D786 twd Le Val-Andre, site sp. Med, hdg/mkd pitch, hdstg, pt shd; wc; chem disp; mv service pnt; baby facs; shwrs inc; el pts (6A) €3.20; gas; lndtte; ice; shop; tradsmn; snacks; bar; BBQ; 3 playgrnds; htd pool; paddling pool; sand beach 2km; watersports; tennis 2km; games area; games rm; mini-golf; library; entmnt; child entmnt high ssn; TV rm; 20% statics; dogs €1.60; phone; Eng spkn; adv bkg; quiet; red low ssn/long stay; CCI. "Gd for families." ♦ 15 Apr-15 Sep. € 18.00   2005*

See advertisement opposite (top)

ERQUY *2E3* (700m SW Coastal) **Aire Communale Erquy, Ave de Caroual, 22430 Erquy** [02 96 63 52 42; fax 02 96 63 50 41] Take D786 fr Erquy dir Pleneuf-Val-Andre. Site on R at Plage de Carouel, sp. Med, chem disp; mv service pnt; el pts €2; water fill €2 for 100 litres; rest; beach 100m; poss cr; m'vans only. "Rec arr early as full by 1700." Apr-Oct. € 2.00   2003*

ERQUY *2E3* (2km SW) **Camping Les Roches, Caroual, 22430 Erquy** [02 96 72 32 90; fax 02 96 63 57 84; camping.les.roches@wanadoo.fr] Sp fr D786 fr Erquy or Le Val-Andre. Med, hdg pitch, pt sl, unshd; wc; baby facs; shwrs inc; el pts (6A) €2.50; lndtte; sm shop; bar; playgrnd; sand beach 2km; games rm; adv bkg; quiet. "New trees planted; pleasant." 1 Apr-30 Sep. € 12.60   2003*

FRANCE

ERQUY *2E3* (4km SW Rural/Coastal) **Camping de la Plage de St Pabu**, 22430 Erquy [02 96 72 24 65; fax 02 96 72 87 17; camping@saintpabu.com; www.saintpabu.com] Sp on D786 bet Erquy & Le Val-Andre at St Pabu. Narr rd, restricted passing places. Lge, hdg/mkd pitch, hdstg, terr, pt shd; wc; chem disp; mv service pnt; serviced pitches; baby facs; shwrs inc; el pts (6A) €3.30; gas; lndtte; ice; shop; tradsmn; snacks; bar; BBQ; playgrnd; sand beach adj; entmnt; child entmnt; TV; some statics; dogs €1.20; Eng spkn; adv bkg; quiet; cc acc; red long stay/low ssn; CCI. "Marvellous beach adj; beautifully situated with hills around; vg touring base; conv St Malo, Dinan, Granit Rose coast; san facs gd." ♦ 1 Apr-10 Oct. € 17.80   2005*

See advertisement below

ERR see Bourg Madame *8H4*

ERVY LE CHATEL *4F4* (2km E Rural) **Camp Municipal Les Mottes**, 10130 Ervy-le-Chatel [03 25 70 07 96; mairie-ervy-le-chatel@wanadoo.fr] Exit N77 sp Auxon (int'l camping sp Ervy-le-Chatel) onto D374, then D92; site clearly sp. Med, pt shd; wc; shwrs inc; el pts (5A) €1.85; shops adj; playgrnd; rv fishing 300m; tennis; adv bkg; quiet. "Pleasant, well kept, grassy site; v clean facs; lge pitches; friendly warden; no twin-axle c'vans; rec." ♦ 15 May-15 Sep. € 9.00   2002*

ESCALLES see Wissant *3A2*

ESNANDES see Rochelle, La *7A1*

ESPALION *7D4* (300m E Urban) **Camp Municipal Le Roc de l'Arche**, 12500 Espalion [tel/fax 05 65 44 06 79; rocher.benoit@wanadoo.fr] Sp in town off D920 & D921. Site on S banks of Rv Lot 300m fr bdge in town. Med, hdg/mkd pitch, pt shd; wc; mv service pnt; baby facs; shwrs inc; el pts (6-10A) inc; lndtte; shops 250m; snacks; BBQ; playgrnd; pool adj; tennis; fishing; canoeing; poss cr; Eng spkn; adv bkg; quiet; red low ssn. "Med pitches; service rds narr; friendly manager; well kept; clean, modern san facs; gd sh stay." 1 Apr-30 Sep. € 15.00   2005*

ESPALION *7D4* (4km E Rural) **Camping Belle Rive, Rue de Terral**, 12500 St Come d'Olt [05 65 44 05 85; www.ot.espalion.fr] Fr Espalion take D987 E to St Come. Site on N bank of Rv Lot, sp fr vill cent. Med, pt shd; wc; shwrs inc; el pts (6A) €1.76 (poss rev pol & long lead may be req); lndtte; shop, rest in vill; 10% statics; poss cr; Eng spkn; quiet. "Pleasant rvside site; delightful medieval vill; v friendly, helpful warden; excel long/sh stay." 15 May-30 Sep. € 11.50   2004*

ESPERAZA see Quillan *8G4*

ESSARTS, LES *2H4* (800m W) **Camp Municipal du Patis**, 85140 Les Essarts [02 51 62 95 83 or 02 51 62 83 26 (Mairie); fax 02 51 62 81 24] Exit A83 junc 5 onto N160. On ent Les Essarts, foll sp to site. Site on L just off rd fr Les Essarts to Chauche. Sm, pt shd; wc; shwrs inc; el pts €2; supmkt, rests in town; tradsmn; snacks; playgrnd; 2 pools, paddling pool tennis & sports cent adj; dogs; no statics; v quiet. "Gd NH off A83; superb, clean san facs; warden calls pm." ♦ 15 Jun-15 Sep. € 8.80   2004*

ESTAGEL *8G4* (6km NE) **Camping Le Priourat**, Rue d'Estagel, 66720 Tautavel [tel/fax 04 68 29 41 45; j. ponsaille@libertysurf.fr] W fr Estagel on D117. In 2km turn R onto D611 & keep R onto D9 to Tautavel. Site on R bef cent of vill. NB Steep exit fr site onto narr lane. Sm, hdg/mkd pitch, pt sl, pt shd; wc; shwrs inc; el pts (6A) €3 (rev pol) ; lndry rm; ice; shop in vill; rest; bar; BBQ; playgrnd; pool high ssn; lake 3km; beach 40km; no statics; Eng spkn; adv bkg ess high ssn; quiet; cc acc; red low ssn; CCI. "Lovely, friendly, sm site; sm pitches." 1 Apr-30 Sep. € 15.00   2004*

ESTAING (AVEYRON) *7D4* (2km N Rural) **Camp Municipal La Chantellerie**, 12190 Estaing (Aveyron) [05 65 44 72 77 or 05 65 44 70 32; fax 05 65 44 03 20] Fr D920 in Estaing nr rv bdge take D167; fork R onto D97; site on L. Well sp fr Estaing cent adj stadium. Med, hdg/mkd pitch; pt shd; wc (some cont); shwrs inc; el pts €2; shop 2km; rest, snacks & bar 2km; pool 2km; rv sw 2km; phone; quiet; CCI. "Gd walking country; vg rest in Logis Hotel in Estaing; warden calls am & pm; fair sh stay/NH." 22 May-30 Sep. € 9.10   2005*

ESTAING (HAUTES PYRENEES) see Argeles Gazost *8G2*

ESTAVAR see Bourg Madame *8H4*

ETABLES SUR MER *2E3* (1km S Coastal) **Camping L'Abri Cotier**, Rue de la Ville-es-Rouxel, 22680 Etables-sur-Mer [02 96 70 61 57 or 06 07 36 01 91 (LS); fax 02 96 70 65 23; camping. abricotier@wanadoo.fr; www.camping-abricotier. fr] N on N12 around St Brieuc, exit on D786 sp Binic & St Quay-Portrieux. Foll sp Etables-sur-Mer, site sp on far side of vill after turn for Plage du Moulin. Med, mkd pitch, pt sl, pt shd; htd wc; chem disp; mv service pnt; 15% serviced pitch; baby facs; shwrs inc; el pts (6A) inc; gas; lndry; shop; tradsmn; snacks; bar; BBQ; playgrnd; htd pool & paddling pool; jacuzzi; sand beach 500m; watersports 2km; tennis in vill; golf 4km; games rm; internet; TV; 10% statics; dogs; Brit owned; c'vans over 7.50m not acc high ssn; adv bkg; quiet; cc acc; CCI. "Vg, immac site; excel beach; 80% Eng occupied; trips organised; mkt Tue & Sun; entry narr & steep, narr corners on site rds diff lge o'fits; friendly & helpful." ♦ 30 Apr-11 Sep. € 19.40 ABS - B09   2005*

†**ETAMPES** *4E3* (3km S Rural) **Caravanning Le Vauvert**, 91150 Ormoy-la-Riviere [01 64 94 21 39; fax 01 69 92 72 59] Fr Etampes S on N20 take D49 sp Saclas. Site on L in approx 3km. Med, hdg pitch, shd; wc (cont); shwrs inc; el pts (10A) €2.50; gas; shop 3km; bar; pool 3km; tennis; fishing; rv adj; games area; many statics; quiet; site clsd 15 Dec-14 Jan; cc not acc; CCI. "Wcs in touring area clsd winter; facs in statics block excel, touring area below standard; if travelling in winter phone to check site open; vg." € 13.00   2003*

> This site entry hasn't been updated for a while; we'd better fill in a site report form and send it to The Club.

ETAPLES *3B2* (2km N) **Camp Municipal La Pinede**, Rue de Boulogne, 62630 Etaples [tel/fax 03 21 94 34 51] Take the D940 S fr Boulogne-sur-Mer for 25km, site on R after war cemetary & bef Atac supmkt. Or N fr Etaples for 2km on D940. Med, hdg pitch, terr, pt sl, pt shd; wc; chem disp; mv service pnt; shwrs inc; el pts (5A) €3.80; gas 500m; lndtte; rest high ssn; snacks; bar; shop high ssn 500m & 1km; playgrnd; beach 4km; rv 500m; dogs; phone; 15% statics; adv bkg red high ssn; CCI. "Vg long/sh stay; some rd/rlwy noise; no twin-axles." ♦ 15 Feb-15 Dec. € 10.40   2005*

ETEL see Plouhinec *2F2*

ETIVAL see Clairvaux les Lacs *6H2*

ETREAUPONT see Vervins *3C4*

ETREHAM see Bayeux *3D1*

ETRETAT *3C1* (4km E Rural) **Hameau Epivent**, 76790 Bordeaux-St Clair [02 35 27 12 60] Sp fr vill on D940 E of Etretat. Med, pt shd; wc; shwrs; el pts; shop 2km; beach 4km; quiet; adv bkg. "Lovely rural site with pleasant owner." 15 Apr-15 Oct.   2004*

ETRETAT *3C1* (6km E Rural) **Camping de l'Aiguille Creuse**, 24 Rue de l'Aiguille, 76790 Les Loges [02 35 29 52 10; fax 02 35 10 86 64; camping@aiguillecreuse.com] On S side of D940 in Le Loges; sp. Med, unshd; wc (some cont); chem disp; shwrs inc; el pts (10A) €4.50; lndtte; shops 500m; bar; BBQ; playgrnd; dogs €2.50; adv bkg; quiet. ♦ Easter-30 Sep. (CChq acc)   2005*

ETRETAT *3C1* (1km SE Urban/Coastal) **Camp Municipal, Rue Guy de Maupassant, 76790 Etretat [02 35 27 07 67]** Fr Fecamp SW on D940 thro town cent of Etretat & site on L. Or fr Le Havre R at 2nd traff lts; site on L in 1km on D39. Med, mkd pitch, some hdstg, pt sl, pt shd; htd wc (some cont); chem disp; mv service pnt; shwrs inc; el pts (6A) €4.80; gas; lndtte; shop 1km; BBQ; playgrnd; shgl beach 1km; no statics; phone; poss cr; no adv bkg; quiet; cc acc; CCI. "Busy site; pleasant seaside resort, attractive beach nr; clsd 2200-0730; site v well-maintained; lge pitches; immac san facs; friendly staff; conv for Le Havre ferry; gd clifftop walks nr; level walk to town; excel." ♦ Easter-10 Oct. € 9.20   2005*

ETRETAT *3C1* (4km S) **Camping Les Tilleuls, Hameau de Grosse Mare, 76790 Le Tilleul [tel/fax 02 35 27 11 61]** Fr Le Havre N on D940 18km to vill of Le Tilleul. Turn R after filling stn. Med, shd; wc (some cont); chem disp; shwrs inc; el pts €1.70; lndtte; shop; snacks; BBQ; playgrnd; beach 3km; adv bkg; quiet. 1 Apr-30 Sep. € 9.00   2002*

ETRETAT *3C1* (7km SW) **Camping du Grand Hameau, 76280 St Jouin-Bruneval [tel/fax 02 35 55 88 41; richard.lecoq@m6net.fr]** Take rd D940 fr Le Havre. Site sp after 18km on D111 on L. Med, hdg pitch, pt shd; wc; shwrs; el pts (5A) €2.30; lndtte; shop; rest; snacks; playgrnd; beach 2km; 80% statics; poss cr; quiet. 1 Apr-31 Oct. € 8.40
                                                                    2002*

ETRETAT *3C1* (10km SW Rural) **Camping Le Beau Soleil, 76280 Criquetot-l'Esneval [02 35 20 24 22; fax 02 35 20 82 09; le.beau.soleil@wanadoo.fr; www.lebeausoleil.online.fr]** S fr Etretat on D39 to Criquetot-l'Esneval. Site is 3km SW of Criquetot-l'Esneval on D79 twd Turretot. Med, pt shd; wc; chem disp; shwrs €1; el pts (6A) €3.30; bar; beach 8km; playgrnd; Eng spkn; 70% statics; dogs €0.60; CCI. "Pleasant site, v friendly owners; conv Le Havre ferry." 13 Mar-15 Nov. € 7.00   2003*

ETRIGNY see Tournus *9A2*

EU *3B2* (Urban) **Camp Municipal du Parc Chateau, 76260 Eu [02 35 86 20 04]** App fr Blangy on D1015 turn L at junc with D925 & foll camp sp to site in grounds of Hotel de Ville (chateau). Fr Abbeville on D925 fork R at 1st rndabt in town S of rlwy then immed strt on over cobbled rd right up to chateau walls. Turn R at chateau walls. Ignore sp to Stade. Med, some hdg pitch, mainly terr, pt shd; wc; chem disp; shwrs inc; el pts (6A) inc; gas; lndtte; shops 250m; shgl beach 3km; 10% statics; poss cr. "Louis-Philippe museum in chateau; poss itinerants; vg Fri mkt." 1 Apr-31 Oct. € 12.00   2005*

EVAUX LES BAINS *7A4* (N Urban) **Camp Municipal, 23110 Evaux-les-Bains [05 55 65 55 82 or 05 55 65 55 38]** Fr N on D993/D996 sp 'International'. Also site sp fr other dirs. Sm, pt sl, pt shd; wc (some cont); chem disp (wc); shwrs inc; el pts (3A) €2.30; shops 500m; playgrnd; pool 500m; 10% statics; dogs €0.45; quiet. "Evaux attractive health spa." ♦ ltd. 1 Apr-31 Oct. € 5.80   2004*

EVIAN LES BAINS *9A3* (3km E) **Camping Clos Savoyard, 74500 Maxilly-sur-Leman [04 50 75 25 84 or 04 50 75 30 19 (LS); fax 04 50 75 30 19]** Heading E on N5 in Evian, turn R at traff lts sp Thollon. At mini rndabt, take 2nd exit, then foll sp. Med, mkd pitch, pt sl, terr, pt shd; wc (some cont); shwrs inc; el pts (2-6A) €1.70-3.70; lndtte; ice; sm shop; playgrnd; lake sw 1.5km; 10% statics; dogs €1; adv bkg; quiet; CCI. "Site several hundred metres up overlooking lake; steep access upper pitches." 1 Apr-30 Sep. € 10.70   2003*

EVIAN LES BAINS *9A3* (4km E) **Camping de Vieille Eglise, 21 Ave de Grande Rive, 74500 Lugrin [04 50 76 01 95; fax 04 50 76 13 12; camping vieilleeglise@wanadoo.fr; www.camping-vieille-eglise.com]** D21 fr Evian via Maxilly, or turn S off N5 at Tourronde, sp. Med, some mkd pitches, pt terr, pt sl, pt shd; wc; chem disp; shwrs inc; el pts (4-10A) €2.60-3.70; gas; lndtte; supmkt 1km; rest 1km; playgrnd; htd pool; shgl beach 1km; lake 1km; 3% statics; dogs; adv bkg; quiet; 5% red for 15 days; CCI. "Gd sh stay; modern toilet block; view of Lac Leman; poss mkt traders on site." ♦ 1 Apr-15 Oct. € 15.00   2004*

EVIAN LES BAINS *9A3* (3km W) **Camping Les Huttins, 74500 Publier [04 50 70 03 09]** Fr Thonon on N5 twds Evian, at start of Amphion turn L onto Rte du Plaine sp; ent 200m on R after rndabt. Fr Evian on N5 twds Thonon, at end of Amphion turn R & foll sp. Med, mkd pitch, shd; wc (mainly cont); chem disp; shwrs inc; el pts (6A) €4; gas; ice; lndtte; shop; hypermkt 500m; snacks; BBQ; lake sw 400m; playgrnd; pool & sports complex 200m; tennis adj; TV; 5% statics; adv bkg; Eng spkn. "Quiet; simple site with enthusiastic & helpful owners; gd base for Lake Leman area; conv day trips to Mont Blanc." 1 May-15 Oct. € 11.00
                                                                    2002*

†EVIAN LES BAINS *9A3* (3.5km W) **Camping de La Plage, Rue de la Garenne, 74500 Publier [04 50 70 00 46; fax 04 50 70 84 45; info@ camping-dela-plage.com; www.camping-dela-plage.com]** Site sp at rndabt on main lakeside rd (N5) at Amphion-les-Bains. Sm, mkd pitch, pt shd; wc (some cont); chem disp; mv service pnt; baby facs; shwrs inc; el pts (3-6A) €3-4; gas; lndtte; ice; shop adj; hypmkt 1km; tradsmn; snacks; bar; BBQ; playgrnd; covrd pool; sports complex, waterslide; jacuzzi; shgl beach 150m; lake sw; tennis; TV; 20% statics; dogs; phone; poss cr; Eng spkn; adv bkg; site clsd 1 Nov-24 Dec; quiet; CCI. "Helpful owner; overspill field cheaper; vg long stay; excel." ♦ € 21.00   2005*

FRANCE

EVRON *4F1* (7km SW Rural) **Camp Municipal la Croix Couverte**, La Croix Couverte, 53270 Ste-Suzanne [02 43 01 41 61 or 02 43 01 40 10 (Mairie); fax 02 43 01 44 09] Take D7 SW fr Evron sp Ste Suzanne. Site 800m S (downhill) after this sm fortified town. Sm, some hdg/mkd pitch, pt shd; wc; shwrs inc; el pts (3-5A) €2; shops 800m; playgrnd; htd pool; walking & horseriding adj; quiet. "V helpful warden; clean, simple site in lovely area; sm pitches; castle with historic Eng connections; perfect, unspoilt town; high ssn site facs used by coaches of tourists to vill; excel NH. " ♦
1 May-30 Sep. € 6.00   2005*

†**EVRON** *4F1* (W Urban) **Camp Municipal de la Zone Verte** (formerly du Parc des Loisirs), Blvd du Marechal Juin, 53600 Evron [02 43 01 65 36; fax 02 43 37 46 20; camping@evron.fr]
On ring rd, W of town, nr Super-U supmkt; clearly sp fr all rds into town. Med, some hdg pitch, pt shd; wc (some cont); chem disp; shwrs inc; el pts (6-10A) €1.54-2.36; lndtte; ice; shops 1km; playgrnd; htd pool nrby; mini-golf; full sports complex adj; 50% statics; dogs €0.75; adv bkg; quiet. "Sm triangular hdg pitches diff for c'vans - enter tow bar 1st & manhandle; v well-kept; friendly & pleasant with lots of flowers; v restricted recep hrs in winter - warden on site lunchtime & early eve only; no twin-axle vans; vg." ♦ ltd. € 7.87   2005*

EXCENEVEX see Thonon les Bains *9A3*

EYGLIERS see Guillestre *9D4*

EYGURANDE *7B4* (Rural) **Camping de l'Abeille**, 19200 Eygurande [05 55 94 31 39 or 04 73 43 00 43; fax 05 55 94 41 98] NE fr Ussel on N89, in Eygurande, turn L at sp 'Village de Vacances et Camping'. In 100m turn L into private rd. Med, pt sl, shd; wc; chem disp; shwrs inc; el pts; lndtte; ice; shop 1km; snacks; pool; lake adj; fishing; entmnt; quiet.   2003*

EYMET *7D2* (Urban) **Camping du Chateau**, Rue de la Sole, 24500 Eymet [05 53 23 80 28; fax 05 53 22 22 19; jeanjacques@eymetcamping.com] Go thro Miramont onto D933 to Eymet. Turn opp Casino supmkt & foll sp to site. Sp on ent to Eymet fr all dirs. Med, hdg pitch, pt shd, wc; chem disp; mv service pnt; shwrs inc; el pts (5-10A) inc (poss rev pol); gas; lndtte; ice; shops adj; rest, snacks, bar 850m; playgrnd; pool 1.5km; lake & rv sw nrby; dogs; poss cr; Eng spkn; adv bkg; quiet; red long stay; CCI. "V pleasant, clean, well-run site behind ruined medieval chateau by rv; lovely Bastide town but rec not to take car; shops within easy walk; Thurs mkt; don't be deterred by chicane & fire gate at site ent - gate opened on request." ♦
1 May-30 Sep. € 12.60   2005*

EYMET *7D2* (6.5km N Rural) **Camping Lou Tuquet**, Le Mayne, 24500 Fonroque [05 53 74 38 32; fax 05 53 27 35 65; olivierbagard@hotmail.com]
Take D933 SW of Bergerac dir Eymet. In vill of Fonroque turn R & foll sp. Site well sp. Sm, mkd pitch, pt sl, pt shd: wc; chem disp (wc); shwrs; el pts (5A) €2.30; lndry rm; ice; shop, rest, snacks, bar 2km; playgrnd; 15% statics; Eng spkn; quiet; red long stay. "Ideal for walking & cycling on deserted rds; produce avail; basic but peaceful CL-type site; vg all stays." ♦ ltd. 1 May-1 Nov. € 7.80   2004*

EYMOUTHIERS see Montbron *7B3*

EYMOUTIERS *7B4* (8km N) **Camp Municipal Les Peyrades**, Auphelle, Lac de Vassiviere, 87470 Peyrat-le-Chateau [05 55 69 41 32 or 05 55 69 40 23 (Mairie); fax 05 55 69 49 24] Fr Peyrat E on D13, at 5km sharp R onto D222 & foll sp for Lac de Vassiviere. At wide junc turn L, site on R. Med, pt sl, pt shd; wc cont; shwrs €0.38; el pts (5A) €2.29; shop, rest, snacks, bar adj; BBQ; lake sw adj; sand beach adj; dogs; phone; poss v cr; adv bkg; quiet. "Helpful warden; some pitches overlook lake."
2 May-30 Sep. € 7.62   2003*

EYMOUTIERS *7B4* (8km N Rural) **Camp Municipal Moulin de l'Eau**, 87470 Peyrat-le-Chateau [05 55 69 41 01 or 05 55 69 40 23]
1.5km N of Peyrat on D940 to Bourganeuf, site on L immed bef bdge. Med, pt sl, pt terr, pt shd; wc; shwrs; el pts €2.29; shops 2km; fishing; no adv bkg; quiet; CCI. "Pleasant NH; beautiful area; pay at Mairie in town."1 Jul-15 Sep. € 6.00   2003*

EYMOUTIERS *7B4* (2km S) **Camp Municipal, St-Pierre-Chateau**, 87120 Eymoutiers [05 55 69 27 81; fax 05 55 69 14 24; OT. eymoutiers@wanadoo.fr]   On E of D940 S fr Eymoutiers site sp on R. Diff sharp bend bef ent. Sm, pt sl, terr, pt shd; wc; shwrs; el pts (16A) €2 (long lead poss req); shops 2km; adv bkg; quiet. "Gd views; clean site; attractive town & area."
1 Jun-30 Sep. € 6.50   2005*

EYMOUTIERS *7B4* (13km SW Rural) **Camp Municipal Beausejour, Plan d'Eau**, 87130 Sussac [05 55 69 62 41; fax 05 55 69 36 80] Fr Eymoutiers take D30 dir Chamberet & turn R onto D43 at Chouviat for Sussac. Cont for approx 9 km & foll sp. Site adj lake Sm, mkd pitch, terr, pt shd; wc (cont); chem disp; shwrs inc; el pts €2.30; lndtte; shops 500m; snacks; bar; playgrnd; sw lake adj; Eng spkn; adv bkg; quiet. "Gd site; gd walks, fishing." Jul-Aug.
€ 8.00   2004*

EYMOUTIERS *7B4* (10km W Rural) **Camp Municipal du Lac**, Ave Michel Sinibaldi, 87130 Chateauneuf-la-Foret [05 55 69 63 69; fax 05 55 69 70 02; otsi.chateauneuflaforet@wanadoo.fr] Fr Limoges E on D979 for 33km. Turn R at Lattee D15 & in 4km foll sp to site fr vill of Chateauneuf. Med, mkd pitch, pt shd; wc; shwrs inc; el pts (6A) €4.20; tradsmn; bar/rest; lake sw adj. "Excel site, rec; gd size pitches; pristine facs; pretty rural area; factory on 24hr shift gives cont background hum; gd walks; excel long stay."
1 Jun-15 Sep. € 8.50   2005*

BEG ER ROCH ★★★ OPEN FROM MARCH TILL END OF SEPTEMBER

**LE FAOUËT
SOUTH BRITTANY**

Pat will welcome you in English
Discounts for CCI holders. Very large marked pitches. Free leisure activities:
mini-golf, halfcourt, table tennis, children's playground, games room available.

IN LUSH COUNTRYSIDE, 25 MIN FROM BRITTANY'S BEACHES, 90 MIN DRIVE FROM ROSCOFF FERRY
IDEAL FOR FISHING (TROUT AND SALMON), HIKING (MANY MARKED TRAILS) OR RELAXING ON THE BANKS OF
THE BEAUTIFUL RIVER ELLE.
MANY SITES OF NATURAL AND HISTORICAL INTEREST TO VISIT LOCALLY.

Rental of mobile homes and Canvas bungalows
Phone: +33 (0)2 97 23 15 11 – Fax: +33 (0)2 97 23 11 66 – Route de Lorient, F-56320 LE FAOUËT

†EYZIES DE TAYAC, LES *7C3* (4km NE Rural)
Camping Auberge Veyret, Bardenat-Marquay,
24620 Les Eyzies-de-Tayac [05 53 29 68 44; fax
05 53 31 58 00] Leave Les Eyzies dir Sarlat on
D47; in 4km go L onto D48 (dir Tamnies); in 3.5km
turn L & foll sp for Auberge Veyret. Sm, sl, pt shd;
wc; chem disp (wc); shwrs inc; el pts (16A) €2.30;
tradsmn; rest; snacks; playgrnd; pool; adv bkg low
ssn ess; quiet; CCI. "Excel rest (regional cuisine);
views; simple CL-type site with sl grass pitches;
conv Sarlat (15km); sells foie gras etc." € 9.15
2003*

EYZIES DE TAYAC, LES *7C3* (4km NE Rural)
Camping La Ferme du Pelou, 24620 Tursac
[05 53 06 98 17] Fr Les Eyzies-de-Tayac take
D706 dir Tursac. In 3km turn R, site sp. 1km up hill
on L. Sm, hdg pitch, pt shd; wc; chem disp; mv
service pnt; shwrs inc; el pts (6A) inc; lndtte; shop,
rest & bar 4km; BBQ; playgrnd; pool nrby; 10%
statics; dogs; phone; adv bkg; quiet; CCI. "Friendly
owners; gd views across valley, nr prehistoric sites;
vg san facs & pool; farm produce; excel long/sh
stay." ♦ 15 Mar-15 Nov. € 11.80   2003*

EYZIES DE TAYAC, LES *7C3* (5km NE Rural)
Camping Le Pigeonnier, 24620 Tursac [tel/fax
05 53 06 96 90; le-pigeonnier-tursac@wanadoo.
fr; www.campinglepigeonnier.com] NE fr Les
Eyzies for 5km on D706 to Tursac; site is 200m
fr Mairie in vill cent; ent tight but manageable. Sm,
hdg/mkd pitch, pt sl, terr, shd; wc; chem disp in vill;
shwrs inc; el pts (10A) €3; gas; lndtte; ice; shop
5km; tradsmn; snacks; bar; playgrnd; sm pool; shgl
beach 1km; rv sw, fishing & canoeing 1km;
horseriding; cycle hire; dogs €1; adv bkg (dep req);
quiet; no cc acc; CCI. "Excel welcome; British
owners; helpful with local knowledge; close to
prehistoric sites; freshwater pool on site (v cold);
grass pitches; facs poss stretched high ssn; v quiet
hideaway site in busy area." 1 Jun-30 Sep. € 13.50
2005*

EYZIES DE TAYAC, LES *7C3* (2km S Rural)
Camping Le Pech Charmant, 24620 Les Eyzies-de-
Tayac [05 53 35 97 08; fax 05 53 35 97 09; info@
lepech.com; www.lepech.com] Fr D47 Les Eyzies
take D706, site sp on L. Med, mkd pitch, terr, pt shd;
wc; chem disp; shwrs; el pts (10A) €3; gas; lndtte;
shop; tradsmn; snacks; bar; playgrnd; pool; rv sw
2km; 5% statics; dogs €1; Eng spkn; adv bkg; quiet;
cc acc; CCI. "Pre-history cent of the world." ♦
1 Apr-1 Oct. € 17.30   2002*

Some of these sites have changed
their opening dates - we'd better
fill in some site report forms and
let the editor of
the guide know.

EYZIES DE TAYAC, LES *7C3* (2km SW Rural)
Camping Le Queylou, 24620 Les Eyzies-de-
Tayac [05 53 06 94 71; henri.appels@wanadoo.
fr] Take D706 fr Les Eyzies dir Le Bugue; after
2km turn L (after sharp L hand bend) up hill on narr
rd to Le Queylou in 1km sp on app. Sm, pt sl, pt
shd; wc; shwrs inc; el pts (16A) inc; ice; shops 3km;
BBQ; dogs; poss cr; Eng spkn; adv bkg; quiet; CCI.
"Helpful owner; pleasant CL-type site; woodland
walks; red for C'van Club members staying 7+
days." 15 Apr-1 Oct. € 11.25   2005*

EYZIES DE TAYAC, LES *7C3* (1km NW Rural)
Camping La Riviere, 24620 Les Eyzies-de-Tayac
[05 53 06 97 14; fax 05 53 35 20 85; la-riviere@
wanadoo.fr] Site off D47 Rte de Perigueux. Lge
o'fits use 2nd ent by sw pool & walk to recep. Med,
hdg/mkd pitch, pt shd; wc; chem disp; mv service pnt;
shwrs; el pts (6A) €3; lndtte; shop; rest; snacks; bar;
playgrnd; pool; paddling pool; canoe hire 500m;
tennis; internet; TV rm; 5% statics; dogs €1; phone;
Eng spkn; adv bkg; quiet; cc acc; CCI. "Pleasant site;
facs clean but simple; walking dist many prehistoric
caves." ♦ 3 Apr-31 Oct. € 17.20   2004*

FALAISE *3D1* (500m W Urban) **Camp Municipal du Chateau, Rue du Val d'Ante, 14700 Falaise** [02 31 90 16 55 or 02 31 90 30 90 (Mairie); fax 02 31 90 53 38; camping@failaise.fr] Fr N on N158, at rndabt on o'skirts of town, turn L into vill; at next rndabt by Super U go strt on. Sp after 200m. In 2km sp on L to site. Or fr S on N158, at 1st rndabt foll sp town cent & site. Cont down hill thro town then turn L (avoid 1st site sp as v narr bdge) foll site sp as rd starts to climb poss diff for lge o'fits. Cont approx 1km then as above fr castle. Med, hdg/mkd pitch, pt sl, terr, pt shd; wc (some cont); chem disp; shwrs inc; el pts (5A) €2.50; gas 500m; lndry rm; ice; shops, rest, snacks, bar 500m; BBQ; playgrnd; htd pool adj; tennis; TV rm; sat TV some pitches; dogs €1; poss cr; some Eng spkn; adv bkg; quiet; cc acc; red long stay; CCI. "Access to pitches diff for lge o'fits; interesting old town; pleasant surroundings; birthplace of William the Conqueror; impressive ruined castle; vet in Falaise; site attractive & clean; v well tended; facs poss stretched high ssn & clsd 2200-0800; arr before 1900, office closes." ♦ ltd. 1 May-30 Sep. € 9.00   2005*

FANJEAUX *8F4* (2.5km S Rural) **Camping Aire Naturelle Les Brugues, 11270 Fanjeaux** [04 68 24 77 37; fax 04 68 24 60 21; lesbrugues@free.fr; http://lesbrugues.free.fr] Exit A61 junc 22 onto D4 to Fanjeaux, then take D119 dir Mirepoix. At top of hill turn L onto D102 sp La Cortete & turn R in 100m to site in 2.5km. Site well sp fr Fanjeaux. Sm, hdg pitch, pt sl, terr, pt shd; wc; chem disp; shwrs; el pts (15A) inc (rev pol); lndtte; tradsmn; rest, bar 2.5km; playgrnd; htd pool 10km; few statics; dogs; Eng spkn; adv bkg; quiet; CCI. "Delightful, under-used, clean site adj sm lake; v lge pitches; excel touring base; friendly, helpful owners." ♦ 1 Jun-30 Sep. € 13.00   2005*

FAOUET, LE *2F2* (2km SE Rural) **Camp Municipal Beg er Roch, Route de Lorient, 56320 Le Faouet** [02 97 23 15 11 or 06 89 33 75 70; fax 02 97 23 11 66] SE fr Le Faouet on D769 site sp on L. Med, hdg/mkd pitch, pt shd; wc; mv service pnt; chem disp; shwrs inc; el pts (3-5A) €1.60-2.90; gas 2km; lndtte; ice; shops, rest, bar 2km; BBQ; tradsmn; playgrnd; htd pool, lake sw 2km; fishing; tennis; games area; golf; games/TV rm; 25% statics; dogs €0.92; Eng spkn; adv bkg; no cc acc; red long stay; 10% red CCI. "Pleasant, clean, quiet rvside site with many mkd walks; lovely, historic area; helpful warden." ♦ 15 Mar-30 Sep. € 12.50   2005*

See advertisement on previous page

FARAMANS see Beaurepaire *9C2*

FAUTE SUR MER, LA see Tranche sur Mer, La *7A1*

FAVERGES *9B3* (2km N Rural) **Camp Municipal Les Pins, 74210 St Ferreol** [04 50 32 47 71 or 04 50 44 56 36 (Mairie); fax 04 50 44 49 76] Fr N508 nr Faverges go N on D12 for 2km to site. Med, mkd pitch, pt sl, pt shd; wc (some cont); chem disp; shwrs inc; el pts (10A) €1.83; gas; lndtte; shop 2km; tradsmn; rest; snacks; bar; playgrnd; rv adj; dogs; phone; poss cr; Eng spkn; adv bkg; quiet; cc not acc; CCI. "Excel; gd for walking; twin-axle vans or 4 x 4s not allowed." ♦ 15 Jun-15 Sep. € 11.75   2002*

FAVERGES *9B3* (6km NW Rural) **Campeole La Nubliere, 74210 Doussard** [04 50 44 33 44; fax 04 50 44 84 35; nubliere@wanadoo.fr] Fr Annecy take N508 twd Albertville, site on L in 20km, 300m after Camp du Lac Bleu. Fr Faverges NW on N508. Lge, mkd pitch, pt shd, wc (some cont); chem disp; mv service pnt; shwrs inc; el pts (6A) inc; gas; lndtte; ice; shop; rest; snacks; playgrnd; lake sw adj; boating; golf; entmnt; poss cr; adv bkg; poss noisy; cc acc. "Helpful staff; gd san facs." ♦ 1 May-30 Sep. € 17.60   2005*

FAVERGES *9B3* (6km NW Urban) **Camping International de Lac Bleu, 74210 Doussard** [04 50 44 30 18 or 04 50 44 38 47; fax 04 50 44 84 35; camping-lac-bleu@nwc.fr; www.camping-lac-bleu.com] S fr Annecy on N508 twd Albertville. Site on L in 20km just past Bout-du-Lac & bef Camp La Nubliere. Lge, hdg/mkd pitch, pt sl, pt shd; wc; chem disp; mv service pnt; some serviced pitches; shwrs inc; el pts (6A) €3.50; gas adj; lndtte; shop 250m; hypmkt 4km; rest & snacks in high ssn; bar; playgrnd; pool; lake beach adj; watersports; dogs €3.50; poss cr; Eng spkn; rd noise some pitches; cc acc; CCI. "Excel location; rest & shop clsd after 1st week Sep; some lge pitches; gd shops in Doussard 1.5km; gd watersport facs; easy walk for boat trip to Annecy; cycle path into Annecy; ltd facs low ssn; beautiful location beside lake." ♦ 6 Apr-25 Sep. € 23.50   2005*

FAVERGES *9B3* (6km NW Rural) **Camping La Ravoire, Route de la Ravoire, Bout-du-Lac, 74210 Doussard** [04 50 44 37 80; fax 04 50 32 90 60; info@camping-la-ravoire.fr; www.camping-la-ravoire.fr] On N508 S fr Annecy twd Doussard, keep lake to your L. Fr Faverges N on N508. Turn at traff lts at Bredannaz then immed L. Site on L in 1km, sp. Med, mkd/hdg pitch, pt shd; wc; chem disp; mv service pnt (poss diff access); serviced pitches; shwrs inc; el pts (10-15A) inc (poss rev pol); gas; lndtte; sm shop; tradsmn; supmkt 5km; rest 800m; snacks; bar; playgrnd; htd pool; waterslide; lake sw 1km; TV; cycle hire; fishing, golf, horseriding, sailing & windsurfing adj; statics; phone; poss cr; Eng spkn; adv bkg rec Jul/Aug (dep req); quiet; 20% red low ssn; cc acc; CCI. "Immac facs; mountain views; lake ferry fr Doussard; excel, well cared for site; cycle paths adj; excel long stay." ♦ 15 May-15 Sep. € 31.00 (CChq acc)   2004*

FAVERGES *9B3* (8km NW Rural) Camping Le Taillefer, 1530 Route de Chaparon, 74210 Doussard [tel/fax 04 50 44 30 30; info@camping letaillefer.com; www.campingletaillefer.com]
Fr Annecy take N508 twd Faverges & Albertville. At traff lts in Bredannaz turn R, then immed L for 1.5km; site immed on L by vill sp 'Chaparon'. Do NOT turn into ent by Bureau but stop on rd & ask for instructions as no access to pitches fr Bureau ent. Or, to avoid Annecy, fr Faverges, along N508, turn L (sp Lathuile) after Complex Sportif at Bout du Lac. Turn R at rndabt (sp Chaparon), site is on R after 1.5km. Sm, mkd pitch, pt sl, terr, pt shd; wc; chem disp; mv service pnt; shwrs inc; el pts (6A) inc (check rev pol); lndtte; sm shop & 3km; tradsmn; rest, snacks, bar (high ssn); BBQ (gas/charcoal only); playgrnd; lake sw 1km; shgl beach 3km; tennis 100m; watersports 2km; cycle hire; TV; dogs €1; Eng spkn; adv bkg (€30.49 dep req); some rd noise; 10% red 1 month; cc not acc. "Lovely area; mains water & waste disp only avail fr wc block at recep; helpful, friendly owners; spotless facs, highly rec; recep 0730-2000; vg rest within easy walking dist; excursions organised; mkt Mon." ♦
1 May-30 Sep. € 17.40 ABS - M06   2005*

FAVERGES *9B3* (8km NW Rural) Camping Les Fontaines, Bredennaz, 74210 Lathuile [04 50 44 31 22; fax 04 50 44 87 80; info@ campinglesfontaines.com] N508 fr Annecy twd Albertville. In Bredannaz turn R at traff lts. Then immed L. Site in 1.5km on R. Lge, pt shd, mkd pitch; wc; chem disp; baby facs; shwrs inc; el pts (6A) inc; ice; gas; lndtte; shop; tradsmn; rest in ssn; snacks; bar; pool; no dogs; poss cr; quiet; adv bkg ess in ssn; 10% statics; Eng spkn; cc acc. ♦
18 May-15 Sep. € 21.00   2002*

FAVERGES *9B3* (8km NW Rural) Camping L'Ideal, 715 Route de Chaparon, 74210 Lathuile [04 50 44 32 97; fax 04 50 44 36 59; info@ camping-ideal.com; www.camping-ideal.com]
Take Annecy Sud exit fr A41, foll Albertville sp on N508 on W side of lake. In vill of Bredannaz R at traff lts, immed L on narr rd for 100m; site on R after 2km. Lge, mkd pitch, pt sl, pt shd; wc; chem disp; shwrs inc; el pts (6A) €3.40; gas; lndtte; shop; rest; snacks; bar; BBQ: playgrnd; htd pool; waterslide; lake sw 2km; games area; entmnt; TV; 15% statics; dogs €2; phone; poss cr high ssn; adv bkg (dep & bkg fee); quiet; red long stay; CCI. "Pleasant, family-run site; less cr than lakeside sites; panoramic views of mountains & lake."
1 May-15 Sep. € 20.00   2005*

FAVEROLLES *9C1* (S Rural) Camp Municipal, 15320 Faverolles [04 71 23 49 91 or 04 71 23 40 48 (Mairie); fax 04 71 23 49 65; faverolles.mairie@wanadoo.fr] Fr A75 exit junc 30 & take D909 S, turn L onto D13 at Viaduct de Garabit & foll sp for Faverolles for 5km, then sp to site dir St Chely-d'Apcher. Sm, mkd pitch, pt sl, pt shd; htd wc (some); chem disp; shwrs inc; el pts (6A) inc (rev pol); shops 500m; lndtte; playgrnd; some statics; phone; cc not acc; quiet. "Nr pretty lake; vg rest in vill." ♦ 1 Jun-30 Sep. € 10.40   2005*

FAVEROLLES SUR CHER see Montrichard *4G2*

FAYENCE *10E4* (10km S Rural) Parc Camping, 83440 St Paul-en-Foret [04 94 76 15 35; fax 04 94 84 71 84; campingleparc@wanadoo.fr]
Fr D562 midway bet Draguinan & Grasse turn S onto D4. Site sp on L. Exit A8 junc 39, N on D37 for 11km, at junc with D562 turn L for 10km, L onto D4 for 4km. Med, mkd pitch, terr, shd; htd wc; chem disp; shwrs inc; el pts (10A) inc; gas; lndtte; shop; tradsmn; snacks, bar high ssn; playgrnd; pool (caps ess); beach 30km; tennis; fishing; lake sw 15km; 10% statics; poss cr; adv bkg; quiet; red low ssn; CCI. "Conv hill vills of Provence; gd rests in St Paul; vg long/sh stay." 1 Apr-30 Sep. € 21.50   2002*

FAYENCE *10E4* (3km W Rural) Camping des Prairies, 83440 Callian [04 94 76 48 36]
Fr D562 Grasse-Draguignan foll sp Callian; site on L next to Renault g'ge. Fr A8 take D37 fr junc 39; gd rd to D562. Med, mkd pitch, hdstg, pt shd; wc; chem disp; mv service pnt; shwrs inc; el pts (4A) inc; ice; lndtte; shops 400m; playgrnd; pool; shgl beach 30km; lake 6km; 50% statics; dogs €1.50; poss noisy; adv bkg; no cc acc; Eng spkn; CCI.
1 Apr-31 Oct. € 13.50   2002*

FAYENCE *10E4* (6km W Rural) Camping La Tuquette (Naturist), 83440 Fayence [04 94 76 21 78; fax 04 94 76 23 95; robert@tuquette.com; www. tuquette.com] Fr Fayence take N562. At km 64.2 sp turn R, site ent 100m. Sm, mkd pitch, terr, pt shd; wc; chem disp; shwrs ind; el pts (6-10A) €4; lndtte; shop 6km; tradsmn; snacks; bar; BBQ; playgrnd; 2 htd pools; some statics; dogs €1.50; poss cr; Eng spkn; adv bkg; quiet; INF card. "Vg site; friendly owners." ♦ 1 Apr-31 Oct. € 24.00   2004*

FECAMP *3C1* (6km SE Rural) Camp Municipal du Canada, 76400 Toussaint [02 35 29 78 34; fax 02 35 27 48 82; mairie-toussaint@wanadoo.fr]
On D926 N of Toussaint (sharp turn at side of golf course). Med, hdg pitch, pt sl, shd; wc (some cont); shwrs inc; el pts (10A) €2.43; lndtte; shop 2km; playgrnd; 70% statics; quiet; CCI. "Gd warden; gd value." ♦ 15 Mar-15 Oct. € 7.35   2005*

FECAMP *3C1* (SW) Camping Le Domaine de Reneville, Chemin de Nesmond, 76400 Fecamp [02 35 28 20 97 or 02 35 10 60 00; fax 02 35 29 57 68; camping-de-reneville@tiscali.fr]
Site off Etretat rd (D940) on o'skts of Fecamp; sp. Lge, hdg/mkd pitch, terr, pt sl, pt shd; htd wc; chem disp; shwrs inc; el pts (6A) €2 (poss long cable req); ice; lndtte; shop 1km; tradsmn; rest, snacks & bar in town; playgrnd; pool adj; shgl beach 500m; 15% statics; phone; Eng spkn; CCI. "Fine sea & harbour views; interesting town with excel rests; Benedictine distillery tours; v nice site - can be windy." 15 Mar-30 Nov. € 11.50   2005*

FENOUILLER, LE see St Gilles Croix de Vie *2H3*

FERE, LA *3C4* (Urban) **Camp Municipal de la Fere** (formerly Marais de la Fontaine), Rue Vauban, 02800 La Fere [03 23 56 82 94; fax 03 23 56 40 04] S on N44 (St Quentin to Laon); R onto D338; turn E at rndabt; ignore 1st camping sp; turn N at next rndabt; site sp. Sm, hdg/mkd pitch, pt shd; wc; chem disp (wc); mv service pnt; shwrs inc; el pts (6A) €2.70; shop; tradsmn; rest, snacks & bar 1km; BBQ; htd, covrd pool adj; dogs €1; adv bkg rec; quiet; red long stay; CCI. "Canals & museums nrby; gates shut 2200-0800 when no vehicle/person access; adj recreation cent; warden calls morn & eve; clean san facs." ♦ ltd. 1 Apr-30 Sep. € 6.60
2005*

FERMANVILLE see Cherbourg *1C4*

FERRIERE AUX ETANGS, LA see Flers *4E1*

FERRIERE D'ALLEVARD, LA see Allevard *9B3*

FERRIERES EN GATINAIS see Montargis *4F3*

FERTE BERNARD, LA *4F2* (1.5km S Rural) **Camp Municipal Le Valmer**, Espace du Lac, 72400 La Ferte-Bernard [tel/fax 02 43 71 70 03; camping@la-ferte-bernard.com] Fr A11/E50 junc 5, take D1 to La Ferte-Bernard. At 1st rndabt in town cent, take 3rd exit. Join N23 & at next rndabt, take 3rd exit. Foll sp Le Valmer. Site off N23 by Rv L'Huisne & lake. Med, hdg/mkd pitch, pt sl, shd; wc; chem disp; mv service pnt; shwrs inc; el pts (6A) €2.10; lndry rm; ice; shop 1km; playgrnd; sand beach 500m; watersports; child entmnt Jul/Aug; 10% statics; dogs €1.30; Eng spkn; quiet; CCI. "Vg, friendly, clean site; local mkt Mon am; excel facs; rural but v close to shops & all facs; well lit at night; pitches v soft, wet & muddy after rain; some pitches diff for lge o'fits; vg sh stay." ♦ 1 May-15 Sep. € 11.40
2004*

FERTE MACE, LA *4E1* (Urban) **Camping Municipal La Saulaie**, Blvd Hamonic, 61600 La Ferte-Mace [02 33 37 44 15] Fr town cent foll rd to Flers & turn R onto dual c'way in 500m. Site on L next to stadium. Sp. Sm, pt shd; wc; shwrs inc; el pts (10A) €1.59; shops 1km; BBQ (gas); dogs; phone; rv 2km; quiet but little rd noise. "Excel little site; gd sh stay/NH; key operated gates; call to house adj when recep clsd." ♦ 15 Apr-15 Oct. € 4.42
2002*

FERTE ST AUBIN, LA *4G3* (N Urban) **Camp Municipal Le Cosson**, Ave Lowendal, 45240 La Ferte-St Aubin [02 38 76 55 90] S fr Orleans on N20; ent on R on N o'skts twd Municipal pool. NB Access fr S poss diff for lge o'fits thro narr high st in business hrs. Sm, pt shd; wc (cont); chem disp; shwrs €1.15; el pts (2-10A) inc (poss rev pol); shops 1km; tradsmn; rest 100m; pool adj; fishing adj; dogs; some train noise; cc not acc; CCI. "Friendly recep; easy walk to towns & gd rests; conv A71; gd value; fair sh stay." 1 May-30 Sep. € 10.00
2005*

FEUILLERES see Peronne *3C3*

FEURS *9B2* (N Urban) **Camp Municipal Le Palais**, Route de Civens, 42110 Feurs [tel/fax 04 77 26 43 41] Sp fr N82 St Etienne-Roanne. Turn R fr N82 sp on N o'skts on town. Lge, pt shd; htd wc; chem disp (wc); mv service pnt; shwrs inc; el pts (6A) €2.50; gas; ice; sm shop; tradsmn; snacks; playgrnd; pool adj; 40% statics; dogs €0.50; phone; quiet; CCI. "Busy site; several san facs, all clean." ♦ 1 Mar-31 Oct. € 7.50
2005*

FIGEAC *7D4* (1.5km E) **Camping Les Rives du Célé**, Domaine du Surgié, 46100 Figeac [05 65 34 59 00; fax 05 65 34 83 83; surgiecamp. lois@wanadoo.fr; www.domainedesurgie.com] Site by Rv Célé clearly sp on D140 when app Figeac fr all dir. Narr ent, light controlled. Med, hdg/mkd pitch, pt shd, wc; chem disp; mv service pnt; chem disp; shwrs inc; el pts (10A) inc; gas 1km; lndte; ice; shop; rest; snacks; bar; playgrnd; htd pool & waterslide adj; boating; rv sw adj; tennis; cycle hire; entmnt; 30% statics; dogs €1; Eng spkn; adv bkg; quiet; red low ssn/long stay. "Excel pool with water chute & wave machine at leisure cent adj; modern san facs; vg." ♦ 1 Apr-30 Sep. € 17.50
2005*

See advertisement

FIGEAC *7D4* (7km SW Rural) **Camping de Pech-Ibert, Route de Cajarc, 46100 Beduer [05 65 40 05 85; fax 05 65 40 08 33; camping.pech. ibert@wanadoo.fr; www.camping-pech-ibert.com]** SW fr Figeac on D19 twds Cajarc. Site well sp on R after Beduer. Sm, pt sl, pt shd; wc; chem disp; mv service pnt; baby facs; shwrs inc; el pts (16A) €2.90; lndtte; ice; snacks high ssn; BBQ; playgrnd; pool; tennis; cycle hire; fishing & sw 1km; dogs €1.70; Eng spkn; adv bkg ess high ssn; quiet; 5% red 17+ days/low ssn; CCI. "Excel CL-type site; pleasant owners; facs poss ltd low ssn; gd walking fr vill (mkd trails)." ♦ 1 Mar-31 Dec. € 9.80   2005*

FIGEAC *7D4* (7km W Rural) **Camping La Belle Epoque, Vallee du Cele, 46100 Camboulit [tel/fax 05 65 40 04 42; julieetpierre@worldonline.fr; www.restaurantlabelleepoque.com]** Take D802 W fr Figeac for 6km, then turn L onto D41 opp viaduct. Site on R in 3km at junc with D211. Sm, mkd pitch, terr, shd; wc (cont); chem disp (wc only); shwrs inc; el pts (10A) inc (long lead poss req); gas 5km; ice; shops 5km; rest; bar; BBQ; pool; some statics; dogs; Eng spkn; adv bkg; quiet; cc acc (long stay only); CCI. "Helpful owners; essentials avail fr rest; acc rd steep with loose surface, help given if req; gd sh stay." 15 Jun-15 Sep. € 11.50   2005*

FIQUEFLEUR EQUAINVILLE see Honfleur *3C1*

FISMES *3D4* (800m W Urban) **Camp Municipal de Fismes, Allee des Missions, 51170 Fismes [03 26 48 05 50; fax 03 26 48 82 25; mairie-fismes@wanadoo.fr; www.fismes.fr]** Fr Reims N on N31. At Fismes do not ent town, but stay on N31 past Champion supmkt on L, under bdge & at rndabt strt on N31 sp Soissons. Site on L in 100m down little lane at end of sports stadium wall. Sm, hdstg, unshd; wc (some cont); chem disp; baby facs; shwrs inc; el pts (12A) inc (poss rev pol); shop 250m; supmkt 1km; BBQ (gas & el); playgrnd; games rm; horseriding 5km; TV rm; dogs; recep 0700-1000 & 1600-1900; no twin-axle vans; Eng spkn; adv bkg; cc not acc; CCI. "Conv for Laon, Epernay, Reims; noisy due to busy rd & position on indus est; san facs usually immac but old; gates locked 2200-0730; warden on site ltd hrs; mkt Sat am; delightful site; vg NH." ♦ 2 May-15 Sep. € 11.50 ABS - P02   2005*

FLAVIGNY SUR MOSELLE see Nancy *6E2*

FLECHE, LA *4G1* (10km E Rural) **Camp Municipal La Chabotiere, Place des Tilleuls, 72800 Luche-Pringe [02 43 45 10 00 or 02 43 45 44 50 (Mairie); fax 02 43 45 10 00; lachabotiere.ville-luche-pringe.fr; www.ville-luche-pringe.fr]** SW fr Le Mans on N23 twd La Fleche. At Clermont-Creans turn L on D13 to Luche-Pringe. Site sp. Med, hdg/mkd pitch, pt sl, pt shd; wc (some cont); chem disp; baby facs; shwrs; el pts (10A) inc; lndtte; shops 100m; playgrnd; pool adj high ssn; cycle hire; TV; 10% statics; dogs €1.50; phone; sep car park high ssn; Eng spkn; adv bkg; quiet; red low ssn; CCI. "Lovely site; gd position by Rv Loir; helpful, friendly warden; v clean, modern facs; san facs v clean but no heating; helpful staff; gd site for children; conv chateaux; excel; highly rec." ♦ 1 Apr-15 Oct. € 10.00   2005*

FLECHE, LA *4G1* (500m S Urban) **Camp Municipal La Route d'Or, Allee de la Providence, 72200 La Fleche [02 43 94 55 90 or 02 43 48 53 53 (Mairie); fax 02 43 94 33 78; camping@ville-lafleche.fr]** Fr NW dir Laval D306, keep to W of town, leave S on D306 twd Bauge; site on L after x-ing rv; sp. Fr S take dir for A11 & Laval, site clearly sp on R. Lge, some hdg pitch, some hdstg, pt shd; htd wc; chem disp; mv service pnt; shwrs inc; el pts (10A) €3.60 (rec long lead); gas; lndtte; ice; shop 500m; supmkt nr; tradsmn; rest nr; snacks; playgrnd; pool; sand beach 1km; canoeing adj; tennis; games area; cycle hire; dogs; phone; Eng spkn; poss noisy; cc acc; CCI. "Excel facs; warm welcome; well-managed site, v family high ssn; office hrs 0800-2030, barrier clsd 2200-0800; helpful staff; facs poss ltd low ssn; conv ferries: on rv bank; sh walk to interesting town; mkt Wed; scenic surroundings; lge pitches." ♦ 1 Mar-31 Oct. € 8.25   2005*

FLECHE, LA *4G1* (7km W Rural) **Camp Municipal Le Vieux Pont, 72200 Bazouges-sur-Le Loir [02 43 45 03 91 or 02 43 45 32 20 (Mairie); fax 02 43 45 38 26]** Off N23 fr Le Mans to Angers turn L over rv at 2nd traff lts in cent Bazouges. Sp to site on R after x-ing rv. Sm, hdg pitch, pt shd; wc (some cont); shwrs inc; el pts (6A) inc; lndtte; playgrnd; pool 7km; fishing, horseriding adj. "Pleasant on bank of rv; gd sh stay." 15 May-15 Oct. € 6.75   2005*

FLERS *4E1* (9km SE) **Camp Municipal Auberge du Lac, Rue de l'Etang, 61450 La Ferriere-aux-Etangs [02 33 96 00 22]** Sp on D18 Flers to La-Ferte-Mace rd on S side of vill adj lake. Foll camping & Auberge du Lac rest sp. Look for sm pond on S side of D18 & E end of vill La Ferriere. Rd on either side of pond goes to site. Sm, pt shd; pt sl; wc; shwrs inc; el pts (3-6A) €2; tradsmn; snacks & creperie adj; lake sw adj; adv bkg; quiet but some rd noise. "Pleasant owners; vg small site in attractive setting; v peaceful; area for m'vans just outside main site; recep open v early & after 1700; rec phone bef arr as height bar at ent must be removed." 1 Apr-30 Sep. € 7.90   2003*

FLEURANCE *8E3* (500m E Urban) **Camp Municipal, 32500 Fleurance [05 62 06 10 01 (Mairie); fax 05 62 06 29 97; ville.fleurance@ mipnet.fr]** On D654 Fleurance-Mauvezin rd at ent to town. Sm, pt shd; wc; shwrs inc; el pts (5A); shop 500m; pool, waterslide adj; entmnt; adv bkg; quiet. "By rv; footbdge to park with lake, tennis, gardens." 15 Jun-15 Sep. 2004*

FLEURANCE *8E3* (11km E Rural) **Camping Les Roches (Naturist), 32380 Mauroux [tel/fax 05 62 66 30 18]** Fr Fleurance take D953 to St Claire then D167 for 3km to site on L. Sm, hdg pitch, pt sl, pt shd; wc; chem disp; shwrs; el pts (6A) inc; lndtte; shops; tradsmn; rest; snacks; bar; pool; TV rm; some statics; dogs; adv bkg; Eng spkn; cc acc; INF card. "Pleasant owners; fishing in lake; gd sized pitches; excel long stay." ♦ ltd. 1 Apr-30 Sep. € 20.00 2004*

†**FLEURANCE** *8E3* (12km E Rural) **Centre Naturiste de Deveze (Naturist), 32380 Gaudonville [05 62 66 43 86; fax 05 62 66 42 02; camping.deveze@wanadoo.fr]** Fr Fleurance to St Clar on D953, then D167 to site 4km on L. Lge, hdg pitch, pt sl, terr, pt shd; wc; chem disp; 80% serviced pitches; shwrs inc; el pts (5A) €3.65; ice; gas; lndtte; shop; tradsmn; rest, snack high ssn; bar; pool; lge lake; playgrnd; TV rm; entmnt; fishing; tennis; 15% statics; phone; Eng spkn; adv bkg; quiet; cc acc; CCI. "Excel long stay; excursions arranged. "♦ € 16.00 2002*

FLEURANCE *8E3* (7km SW) **Camping en Ferme d'Accueil (Daguzan), Route de Ceran, Saubis, 32390 Montestruc-sur-Gers [05 62 62 26 12]** N fr Auch take N21 twd Fleurance, exit at Montestruc-sur-Gers nr level x-ing. Foll D251 1.5km, take R fork. Farm ent on L in 500m with conifer drive, site on L 50m. Sm, shd; wc; chem disp (wc); shwrs inc; el pts (6A) (long cable poss req); shops 2km; playgrnd; golf 4km; poss cr; quiet. "Gd CL-type site with gd facs; peaceful farm with pleasant walks; farmer v friendly." 15 Jun-30 Sep. € 6.25 2002*

FLEURIE *9A2* (500m SE Rural) **Camp Municipal La Grappe Fleurie, 69820 Fleurie [04 74 69 80 07 or 04 74 04 10 44 (Mairie); fax 04 74 69 85 71; info@fleurie.org; www.fleurie.org]** S dir Lyon on N6 turn R (W) at S end of Romaneche onto D32; 4km to vill of Fleurie (beware sharp turn in vill & narr rds) & foll site sp. Med, hdg/mkd pitch, terr, pt shd; wc (some cont); chem disp; mv service pnt; serviced pitches; shwrs inc; baby facs; el pts (10A) inc; gas; lndtte; shop 500m; tradsmn; rest; snacks; bar; playgrnd; pool; tennis; internet; some statics; poss cr; Eng spkn; adv bkg rec Jul/Aug; quiet; cc acc; red CCI. "Gates & wash rms clsd 2200-0700; vg value; excel for touring Beaujolais vills; footpath to town thro vineyards; site v clean; gd entmnt & wine-tasting Tues & Fri eves (May-Aug); excel free, escorted visits to local producers; facs 1st class; turn L when leaving site; highly rec." ♦ 25 Mar-23 Oct. € 13.00 2005*

FLORAC *9D1* (1km N) **Camp Municipal Le Pont du Tarn, Route de Pont de Montvert, 48400 Florac [04 66 45 18 26 or 04 66 45 17 96 (LS); fax 04 66 45 26 43; pontdutarn@aol.com]** Exit Florac N on N106 & turn R in 500m by by-pass on D998; site on L in 300m. Lge, pt shd, mkd pitch; htd wc (some cont); chem disp; mv service pnt; shwrs inc; el pts (6A) inc; lndtte; ice; sm shop 2km; tradsmn; rest, snacks, bar 2km; BBQ; playgrnd; pool; rv fishing adj; 60% statics; dogs €0.80; phone; poss cr; some Eng spkn; adv bkg rec; quiet; red low ssn; CCI. "In high ssn vans & tents v close; c'van storage facs; no twin-axle vans allowed; gd base for area; mv service pnt poss diff to use; 20 min walk to town, gd shops & lge mkt Thurs; vg long/sh stay." ♦ 1 Apr-15 Oct. € 12.80 2004*

FLORAC *9D1* (4km NE) **Camping Chon du Tarn, 48400 Bedoues [04 66 45 09 14; fax 04 66 45 22 91]** Exit Florac N on N106, turn R in 500m onto D998 (sp Pont de Monvert), site on L in 3km in vill. Med, mkd pitch, pt sl, terr, pt shd; wc; chem disp; mv service pnt; shwrs inc; el pts (6A) inc; gas; lndtte; ice; shop & 4km; rest, bar adj; playgrnd; rv sw & sand beach; games area; dogs €1; adv bkg (dep req); quiet; cc not acc; CCI. "Gd views; conv Tarn Gorges, Causses & Cevennes National Park; beautiful location; helpful staff; clean san facs, ltd low ssn." 1 Apr-20 Oct. € 11.70 2005*

FLORAC *9D1* (1km S Urban) **Camping Velay 'Le Pont Neuf', 48400 Florac [04 66 45 19 23 or 04 66 45 12 19]** Site on Rv Tarnon adj to bdge connecting D907 & N106; ent fr N106. Sm, pt sl, pt shd; wc; shwrs inc; el pts (6A) €2.20; gas; lndtte; shop 300m; tradsmn; rests nr; rv sw & shgl beach adj; 10% statics; dogs €1; some rd noise. "Gd walks; conv Gorges du Tarn & National Park de Cevennes." 1 Jul-30 Sep. € 8.70 2004*

†**FLUMET** *9B3* (1.5km NE Rural) **Camping Le Vieux Moulin, 73590 Flumet [tel/fax 04 79 31 70 06]** Fr Albertville go N on N212 strt to Flumet & cont past Flumet for 1km. Turn R watch for sp. Med, mkd pitch, hdstg, pt shd; htd wc; chem disp; shwrs inc; el pts (3-10A) €4.20-7.30; lndtte; tradsmn; rest nr; playgrnd; rv sw; ski lifts 100m; 20% statics; dogs; phone; poss cr; Eng spkn; some rd noise; CCI. "Superb san block but ltd; friendly staff; gd touring cent for Mont Blanc, Geneva, Annecy etc; highly rec; clsd 15 Apr-30 May; excel all stays." ♦ € 11.25 2003*

†FOIX *8G3* (2km N Rural) **Camping du Lac, Quartier Labarre, 09000 Foix [05 61 65 11 58; fax 05 61 05 32 62; camping-du-lac@wanadoo.fr; www.campingdulac.com]** On N20 Toulouse-Andorra pass thro Varilhes, St Jean & St Jean-de-Verges, site on R in 2km opp Peugeot dealer in Labarre hamlet. Lge, mkd pitch, pt shd; wc (some cont); chem disp; mv service pnt; shwrs inc; baby facs; el pts (6A) inc; lndtte; ice; supmkt adj; tradsmn; rest; snacks; bar; BBQ; playgrnd; pool; paddling pool; lake fishing adj; boating; windsurfing; entmnts; TV; some statics; dogs €1.50; Eng spkn; poss cr; adv bkg rec high ssn; quiet but some rd (N20) noise; CCI. "Quiet, spacious pitches on L of camp; facs poss stretched high ssn; gd disabled facs; gates clsd 2300-0700." ♦ € 19.00 (CChq acc) 2005*

FOIX *8G3* (4km S Urban) **Camping Roucateille, 15 Rue du Pradal, 09330 Montgaillard [tel/fax 05 61 65 22 50; info@roucateille.com]** S on N20 turn L in vill of Montgaillard at Camping-en-Ferme sp; site in 200m. Med, pt shd; wc; chem disp; shwrs; el pts (4-10A) €2-4; lndtte; shop 500m, supmkt 2km; playgrnd; pool 3km; some statics; adv bkg; quiet; 10% red 3+ days; CCI. "Excel facs; charming, helpful owners; picturesque site; garden produce in ssn; gd base for touring; excel long stay." ♦ 1 Apr-30 Sep. € 11.00 2005*

†FOIX *8G3* (5km NW Rural) **Camp Municipal de Rieutort, 09000 Cos [tel/fax 05 61 65 39 79]** Fr Foix take D117 dir Tarbes. Foll sp Cos onto D617, site on L in 3km. Sm, pt sl, pt shd; wc (some cont); chem disp; 25% serviced pitches; baby facs; fam bthrm; shwrs inc; el pts (10A) inc; lndtte; ice; shop 5km; rest, snacks, bar 5km; playgrnd; pool; tennis; dogs; quiet; CCI. "Site amongst trees with gd views; no c'vans over 6m; sm step into disabled facs; vg long/sh stay." ♦ € 12.40 2003*

FONTAINE DE VAUCLUSE see Isle sur la Sorgue, L' *10E2*

FONTAINEBLEAU *4E3* (5km NE Rural) **Camp Municipal Grange aux Dimes, 77210 Samoreau [01 64 23 72 25; fax 01 64 23 98 31]** Fr cent of Fontainebleau take D210 (dir Provins); in approx 4km at rndabt cross bdge over Rv Seine; take R at rndabt; sp; site at end of rd thro Samoreau vill. Med, hdg/mkd pitch, pt sl, pt shd; wc; chem disp; mv service pnt; shwrs inc; el pts (10A) inc; lndtte; shop 250m; snacks & bar 100m; rest 500m; 10% statics; poss v cr; Eng spkn; adv bkg; CCI. "Attractive location by Rv Seine; peaceful; v helpful managers; gd sized pitches; v clean; gd, clean san facs; conv palace, Paris (gd train service) & Disneyland; 24hr access for cars, but 2m high barrier for c'vans, can be opened anytime by warden, give notice of early starts; no parking area outside camp." ♦ ltd. 1 Mar-31 Oct. € 13.50 2005*

FONTAINEBLEAU *4E3* (10km S Rural) **Camping-Caravaning Le Parc du Gue, Route de Montigny-la-Genevraye, 77690 Montigny-sur-Loing [01 64 45 87 79; fax 01 64 78 31 46; contact@camping-parcdugue.com; www.camping-parcdugue.com]** Exit A6 junc 15 ont N7 & foll sp Montigny-sur-Loing, site sp. Lge, hdg/mkd pitch, pt shd; htd wc (some cont); chem disp; shwrs inc; el pts (6A) €3.20; lndtte; ice; tradsmn; BBQ; playgrnd; rv sw adj; watersports; kayaks; fishing; 10% statics; dogs €4.50; mkt Sat 2km; Eng spkn; adv bkg; quiet; red CCI. "Beautiful, wooded country; excel walking & cycling; rec pay in cash." ♦ 15 Mar-30 Nov. € 14.00 2005*

Will you fill in the site report forms at the back of the guide, or shall I?

FONTENAY LE COMTE *7A2* (7km NE) **Camping La Joletiere, 85200 Mervent [02 51 00 26 87 or 06 14 23 71 31 (LS); fax 02 51 00 27 55; camping.la.joletiere@wanadoo.fr; www.campinglajoletiere.fr.st]** Fr Fontenay-le-Comte N on D938; after 6.5km, turn R onto D99; in 3km enter vill of Mervent; site on R. Med, hdg/mkd pitch, some hdstg, pt sl, pt shd; wc; shwrs inc; el pts (5A) €3.35 (rev pol); gas; lndtte; ice; shop 1km; rest; snacks; bar; playgrnd; htd pool high ssn; sw 2km; fishing; boating/windsurfing 2km; forest walks 500m; 25% statics; dogs €1.70; poss cr; adv bkg; cc acc. "Gd lge pitches; quiet & pleasant; poss ltd & poss scruffy facs low ssn." ♦ Easter-1 Nov. € 12.50 2005*

FONTENAY LE COMTE *7A2* (7km NE Rural) **FFCC Camping Le Chene Tord, Route du Chene-Tord, 85200 Mervent [02 51 00 20 63; fax 02 51 00 27 94]** Exit A83 junc 8 & foll D938 N fr Fontenay-Le-Comte twd La Chataigneraie for 6km to vill of Fourchaud. Turn E to Mervent on D99 & foll camp sps, sharp L turn immed bef vill at stone cross. Med, mkd pitch, pt sl, pt shd; wc; chem disp; shwrs inc; el pts (6-10A) €2.70-3.30; gas; lndtte; shop 1km; rest, snacks, bar 1km; BBQ (gas only); rv/lake sw & fishing 2km; games area; 25% statics; dogs €1.10; phone; Eng spkn; adv bkg rec high ssn; v quiet; red low ssn; CCI. "Nice area; welcoming & friendly; forest location; 30% site forest adventure park - poss noisy high ssn; poss scruffy low ssn; €50 dep req." Easter-31 Oct. € 12.20 2005*

FRANCE

FONTENAY TRESIGNY *4E3* (6km NE Rural) Camping des Quatre Vents, 77610 Crevecoeur-en-Brie [01 64 07 41 11; fax 01 64 07 45 07; f. george@free.fr; www.caravaning-4vents.fr] At Calais take A26/E15 dir Arras, then A1/E15 dir Paris. Just after airport Charles de Gaulle, take A104 dir A4 Metz/Nancy/Marne-la-Vallée, then A4 dir Metz/Nancy, exit junc 13 dir Provins. At junc with D231 (lge monument) turn L dir Provins, then in 3km turn R dir Crevecoeur-en-Brie & foll site sp. Lge, hdg/mkd pitch, pt shd; htd wc; chem disp; serviced pitches; baby facs; shwrs inc; el pts (6A) inc; lndtte; shops 2km; tradsmn; snacks; BBQ; playgrnd; pool; horseriding; games rm; games area; TV rm; 50% statics sep area; dogs €2; poss cr; Eng spkn; adv bkg ess in ssn; quiet; CCI. "Immac site & facs; lge pitches; excel pool; v helpful, welcoming staff; recep 0830-2300; conv Disneyland & Paris by metro; late access to site poss." ♦ 1 Mar-15 Nov. € 22.00 ABS - P09   2004*

FONTES see Pezenas *10F1*

FONTVIEILLE see Arles *10E2*

FORCALQUIER *10E3* (500m E Urban) Camping Indigo Forcalquier, St Promasse, Route de Sigonce, 04300 Forcalquier [04 92 75 27 94; fax 04 92 75 18 10; forcalquier@camping-indigo.com] Fr town cent foll sp Digne/Sisteron. After 400m turn L at petrol stn, then 1st R. Site on R in 200m. Med, hdg/mkd pitch, terr, pt sl, pt shd; wc; chem disp; shwrs inc; el pts (6-10A) €3.60-5.50; lndtte; shop 500m; rest; snacks; bar; htd pool; playgrnd; internet; dogs €2; Eng spkn; adv bkg; quiet; CCI. ♦ 8 Apr-30 Sep. € 17.00   2005*

FOREST MONTIERS see Rue *3B2*

FORET FOUESNANT, LA *2F2* Camping Manoir de Pen Ar Steir, 29940 La Foret-Fouesnant [02 98 56 97 75; fax 02 98 56 80 49; info@camping-penarsteir.com; www.camping-penarsteir.com] Fr Concarneau take D783 twd Quimper. In 8km after sp Kerlevan L to La Foret- Fouesnant. After 1km R at bottom of hill opp car pk to site in 100m. Med, hdg pitch, pt sl, terr, unshd; wc (some cont); chem disp; mv service pnt; shwrs inc; el pts (3-10A) €2.30-3.20; ice; lndtte; shop adj; rest 500m; playgrnd; sand beach 2km; entmnt; 60% statics; dogs; adv bkg; fairly quiet; CCI. "Close to gd beaches; golf course adj; statics in sep area; security barrier; nice welcome; excel site." ♦ 1 Feb-15 Nov. € 17.40   2002*

Mustn't forget to post our site report forms to The Club, otherwise sites might be deleted.

FORET FOUESNANT, LA *2F2* (2.5km SE Coastal) Camping Club du St Laurent, Kerleven, 29940 La Foret-Fouesnant [02 98 56 97 65; fax 02 98 56 92 51; info@campingsaintlaurent.com; www.camping-du-saint-laurent.fr] Fr Quimper take the D783 SE. Turn R onto the D44 twds La Foret-Fouesnant; in the vill cent foll sp for Beg Menez for 200m, then take the 1st R twds Kerleven; turn L at Kerleven seafront rndabt, cont for 500m & at next rndabt foll site sp. (NB: Camping St Laurent shares the same ent with Keranterec.) Lge, hdg/mkd pitch, pt shd; wc; mv service pnt; chem disp; shwrs inc; el pts (6A) inc (long lead req); gas; lndtte; ice; shop; tradsmn; snacks; bar; playgrnd; htd pool; waterslide; jacuzzi; sauna; sand beach adj; tennis; gym; entmnt; TV; 50% statics; poss cr; adv bkg; phone; Eng spkn; cc acc; red low ssn; CCI. "V friendly; well-run site with excel facs; lge pitches; many excel, quiet beaches within 10km; beautiful coast, sea views; highly rec. " ♦ 2 May-10 Sep. € 33.00   2004*

FORET FOUESNANT, LA *2F2* (2.5km SE Coastal) **Camping de Keranterec, Route de Port la Foret, Kerleven, 29940 La Foret-Fouesnant** [02 98 56 98 11; fax 02 98 56 81 73; info@camping-keranterec.com; www.camping-keranterec.com] Fr Quimper take the D783 SE. Turn R onto the D44 twds La Foret-Fouesnant; in the vill cent foll sp for Beg Menez for 200m, then take the 1st R twds Kerleven; turn L at the Kerleven seafront rndabt, cont for 500m & at next rndabt foll site sp. (NB: Keranterec shares the same ent with Camping St Laurent.) Lge, hdg/mkd pitch, terr, pt shd; wc; serviced pitches; chem disp; baby facs; shwrs inc; el pts (6A) €3.50; gas; lndtte; ice; shop; tradsmn; snacks; bar; playgrnd; htd pool; waterslide; sand beach 400m; tennis; games area; fishing & watersports adj; entmnt; TV; 30% statics; dogs €2.30; adv bkg (ess high ssn); Eng spkn; cc acc; red low ssn/CCI. "Modern san facs; gd long stay." ♦ 10 Apr-19 Sep. € 23.00   2004*

FORGES LES EAUX *3C2* (1km S) **Aire de Service** (M'vans only), 76440 Forges-les-Eaux Fr Forges-les-Eaux cent, take D921 S sp Lyons-la-Foret. In 500m turn R foll sp, camp on L in 250m opp municipal site. Med, hdstg, unshd; mv service pnt; water points. "Free 1st night, 2nd night €5; warden visits; town cent easy walk; views of open countryside; m'vans only."   2004*

FORGES LES EAUX *3C2* (1km S Urban) **Camp Municipal La Miniere, 76440 Forges-les-Eaux** [02 35 90 53 91] Fr Forges-les-Eaux cent, take D921 S sp Lyons-la-Foret. In 750m turn R foll sp, camp on R in 150m. Med, hdg pitch, pt sl, pt shd; wc; mv service pnt opp; shwrs inc; el pts (4-8A) inc (rev pol); lndry rm; shops nr; htd pool in town; 85% statics (sep area); poss cr; quiet; CCI. "Site well-presented; friendly warden; poss run-down san facs in low ssn; useful NH." 1 Apr-30 Oct. € 9.55   2005*

FORT MAHON PLAGE *3B2* (1km E Urban) **Airotel Camping Le Royon, 1271 Route de Quend, 80120 Fort-Mahon Plage** [03 22 23 40 30; fax 03 22 23 65 15; info@campingleroyon.com; www.camping leroyon.com] Exit A16 at junc 24 Forest-Monstier onto D32 to Rue, then dir Quend & Fort-Mahon-Plage, site sp. Lge, hdg/mkd pitch, pt shd; wc (some cont); mv service pnt; chem disp; shwrs inc; el pts (6A) inc; gas; lndtte; shop; tradsmn; snacks; bar; playgrnd; htd indoor pool; sand beach 2km; games area; sailing, fishing, golf nr; cycle hire; entmnt; child entmnt; 50% statics; dogs €2.50; phone; Eng spkn; adv bkg; cc acc; red low ssn/long stay/CCI. "Conv Marcanterra nature reserve; discount voucher given on departure for next visit. ♦ 5 Mar-1 Nov. € 27.00   2005*

See advertisement opposite

FOUESNANT *2F2* (1km S Coastal) **Camping Les Mimosas, Descente du Cap-Coz, 29170 Fouesnant** [02 98 56 55 81; fax 02 98 51 62 56; yjuhel@club-internet.fr] Fr Fouesnant take rte 2 (rd by church) to Cap-Coz. Site on R in 800m. Med, terr, pt shd; wc; chem disp; shwrs; el pts (6A) inc; ice; lndtte; shop; beach 800m; entmnt; playgrnd; golf, tennis, pool & horseriding nrby; adv bkg; quiet. 1 May-15 Sep. € 13.00   2002*

FOUESNANT *2F2* (3km S) **Camping La Grande Allee - Les Hortensias, Route de Mousterlin, 29170 Fouesnant** [02 98 56 52 95; fax 02 98 71 55 07; jean-bernard.toulemonde@wanadoo.fr] Fr Quimper on D34 dir Fouesnant, then S twds Mousterlin, site sp. Med, hdg pitch, pt shd; wc; chem disp; shwrs; el pts (6A) €2.52; gas; lndtte; snacks; BBQ; playgrnd; TV; games rm; entmnt; phone. Easter-30 Sep. € 11.50   2002*

FOUESNANT *2F2* (4km S Coastal) **Camping Le Kervastard, Hent-Kervastard, Beg-Meil, 29170 Fouesnant** [02 98 94 91 52; fax 02 98 94 99 83; camping.le.kervastard@wanadoo.fr; www.camping lekervastard.com] Foll rd fr Quimper thro Beg-Meil. Site sp on R immed after rd bends sharply to L. Med, hdg/mkd pitch, pt shd; wc; chem disp; mv service pnt; baby facs; serviced pitches; shwrs; el pts (6-10A) €3.20; gas; lndtte; ice; shops adj; playgrnd; htd pool; paddling pool; sand beach 300m; sailing, watersports nr; entmnt; TV; 30% statics; dogs €2; phone; adv bkg (fee); Eng spkn; quiet; cc acc; red low ssn/CCI. "Quiet part of Brittany with several sheltered coves; boat trips to adj towns & islands; excel site; vg long/sh stay." ♦ 25 May-15 Sep. € 20.60   2005*

FOUESNANT *2F2* (5km S Coastal/Rural) **Camping Le Vorlen, Plage de Kerambigorn, Beg-Meil, 29170 Fouesnant** [02 98 94 97 36; fax 02 98 94 97 23; vorlen@club-internet.fr; www.vorlen.com] Fr Fouesnant on D45 to Beg-Meil. Fr cent of Beg-Meil turn R at hotel Bon Acceuil & foll sp Kerambigorn; site 300m W of this beach & sp at most rd juncs. V lge, hdg/mkd pitch, pt shd; wc (some cont); mv service pnt; chem disp; baby facs; shwrs inc; el pts (5-10A) €3; gas; lndtte; ice; shop; tradsmn; snacks; playgrnd; htd pool & paddling pool; waterslide; sand beach 200m; games area; fishing; watersports; golf nr; TV; 10% statics; dogs €1.80; phone; Eng spkn; adv bkg (dep & fee req) red low ssn; cc acc; CCI. "Friendly; Beg-Meil excel resort." ♦ 20 Mar-15 Sep. € 22.80   2005*

See advertisement on next page

FRANCE

FOUESNANT *2F2* (3km SW Rural) **Camping La Piscine**, 51 Hent Kerleya, 29170 Fouesnant [02 98 56 56 06; fax 02 98 56 57 64; contact@campingdelapiscine.com; www.campingdelapiscine.com] Turn R off Quimper-Beg Meil rd D45 on exit Fouesnant onto D145 sp Mousterlin; In 1km L at site sp. Lge, hdg/mkd pitch, pt shd; wc (some cont); chem disp; mv service pnt; baby facs; shwrs inc; el pts (3-10A) €3-4.40; gas; lndtte; ice; shop; tradsmn; snacks; BBQ; playgrnd; htd pool; paddling pool; waterslide; sand beach 1.5km; lake adj; golf, tennis, mini-golf nrby; games rm; 15% statics; dogs €1.80; Eng spkn; adv bkg; quiet; cc acc; red low ssn; CCI. "Highly rec family-run site; gd walking, cycling." ♦ 15 May-15 Sep. € 22.00   2005*

FOUESNANT *2F2* (3km SW Coastal) **Camping La Roche Percee**, Chemin de Kerveltrec, 29170 Fouesnant [02 98 94 94 15; fax 02 98 94 48 05] S fr Quimper on D34 then D45 to Fouesnant; 3km after exit Fouesnant-Benodet site on L. Med, hdg/mkd pitch, pt shd; wc; chem disp; mv service pnt; shwrs inc; el pts (10A) inc; lndtte; shop, rest 3km; tradsmn; snacks adj; bar; sm playgrnd; 2 htd pools; sand beach 300m; cycle hire; entmnt high ssn; 28% statics; dogs €2; adv bkg; quiet; CCI. "Excel sh/long stay; British owners; well-maintained site." Easter-30 Sep. € 23.50   2004*

FOUESNANT *2F2* (4.5km SW Coastal) **Camping Sunelia L'Atlantique**, Route de Mousterlin, 29170 Fouesnant [02 98 56 14 44; fax 02 98 56 18 67; information@camping-atlantique.fr; www.camping-atlantique.fr] Exit Quimper on D34 sp Fouesnant, take D45 L to Fouesnant & after lge int'section with D44 look for next R to Mousterlin, site sp. Lge, pt shd; wc (some cont); chem disp; mv service pnt; baby facs; shwrs inc; el pts (6-10A) inc; gas; lndtte; ice; shop; rest; snacks; bar; playgrnd; htd pool; paddling pool; waterslide; sand beach 400m; watersports; lake fishing 200m; tennis; cycle hire; games rm; games area; golf 12km; internet; entmnt; TV rm; 90% statics; no dogs; phone; poss cr; adv bkg rec; cc acc. "Site now mostly statics; san facs poss stretched in high ssn." ♦ 30 Apr-11 Sep. € 38.00 (CChq acc)   2004*

FOUESNANT *2F2* (5km SW Coastal) **Camping Kost-Ar-Moor**, Pointe de Mousterlin, 29170 Mousterlin [02 98 56 04 16; fax 02 98 56 65 02; kost-ar-moor@wanadoo.fr; www.camping-kost-ar-moor.com] S fr Fouesnant on D145, site sp. Lge, pt shd; wc (some cont); chem disp; shwrs inc; el pts (5-10A) €2.50-3.50; lndtte; shop; bar; playgrnd; sand beach 300m; lake adj; games area; entmnt; TV; golf, horseriding nr; 10% statics; phone; adv bkg; quiet. ♦ 27 Mar-30 Sep. € 16.80   2004*

FOUESNANT *2F2* (6km SW Coastal) **Camping Le Grand Large**, Mousterlin, 29170 Fouesnant [02 98 56 04 06 or 04 66 73 97 39; fax 02 98 56 58 26; info@campingbretagnesud.com; www.campingsbretagnesud.com or www.yellohvillage.com] Site sp fr D145 Fouesnant- Mousterlin rd. Lge, hdg/mkd pitch, pt shd; wc; serviced pitch; shwrs inc; el pts (5A) inc; gas; lndtte; ice; shop; tradsmn; creperie; bar; playgrnd; htd pool; sand beach adj; tennis; TV; watersports; cycle hire; entmnt; cinema high ssn; 15% statics; dogs €3; poss cr; quiet; adv bkg ess Jul & Aug; red low ssn; CCI. "Excel long stay." ♦ 28 Apr-8 Sep. € 31.00   2002*

FOUGERES *2E4* (1.5km E Urban) **Camp Municipal de Paron**, Route de la Chapelle-Janson, 35300 Fougeres [02 99 99 40 81; fax 02 99 94 27 94; fougeres.mda@wanadoo.fr] Fr A84/E3 take junc 30 then ring rd E twd N12.Turn L at N12 & foll sp. Site on D17 sp R after Carrefour. Well sp on ring rd. Med, hdg pitch, hdstg, pt sl, pt shd; wc; serviced pitches; chem disp; shwrs inc; el pts (5-10A) €2.50-3 (poss rev pol); lndtte; ice; shops 1.5km; hypmkt 800m; tradsmn high ssn; rest 600m; playgrnd; pool 1km; tennis; horseriding adj; dogs; adv bkg; quiet; red low ssn; cc acc; CCI. "Gd facs; gates clsd to cars 2200-0700; tours of 12thC castle; pleasant area; conv town cent; superb Sat mkt; clean; well-tended, gd value site but; poss poor security; poss itinerants." 1 Apr-30 Sep. € 8.00   2004*

†FOURAS *7A1* (Coastal) **Camp Municipal du Cadoret, Blvd de Chaterny, 17450 Fouras** [05 46 82 19 19 or 05 46 84 67 31; fax 05 46 84 51 59; campinglecadoret@mairie17.com] Fr Rochefort take N137, L onto D937 at Fouras, fork R at sp to site in 1km. Lge, mkd pitch, pt sl, pt shd; wc (some cont); chem disp; baby facs; shwrs inc; el pts (6-10A) €2.80-4.60; gas; lndtte; shop, snacks 800m; htd pool; paddling pool; sand beach adj; pool; fishing; boating; tennis 1km; golf 5km; 50% statics; dogs €2.20; bus to La Rochelle, Rochefort, ferry to Ile d'Aix; poss cr; Eng spkn; adv bkg; CCI. "Vg site & v clean; poorly lit except for wc block; ltd facs low ssn." ♦ € 18.50   2005*

FOURAS *7A1* (1km E Rural) **Camping Les Charmilles, Fouras, 17450 St Laurent-de-la-Pree** [05 46 80 00 05 or 02 51 33 05 05 (LS); fax 02 51 33 94 04; chadotel@wanadoo.fr; www.camping-chadotel.fr] N fr Rochefort on N137, after 2km L onto D937. Site on L in 2km bef ent Fouras. Lge, hdg/mkd pitch, pt shd; htd wc; chem disp; mv service pnt; shwrs inc; el pts (6-10A) inc; gas; lndtte; ice; shop 1km; snacks; bar; BBQ (gas); playgrnd; htd pool; waterslide; cycle hire; entmnt; sand beach 2km; bus to beach high ssn; 20% statics; dogs; poss cr; adv bkg; cc acc; CCI. "Gd; some pitches tight for sm o'fits." ♦ 3 Apr-26 Sep. € 26.50   2003*

FOURAS *7A1* (3km NW Coastal) **Camp Municipal de la Fumee, Pointe de la Fumee, 17450 Fouras** [05 46 84 26 77 or 05 46 84 60 11 (Mairie); fax 05 46 84 51 59] Fr N137, take D214E twd Fouras. Foll sps La Fumee/Ile d'Aix to end of peninsula. Ent on L immed in front of car park ent for ferry. Med, mkd pitch, pt shd; wc; chem disp; shwrs inc; el pts (3-10A) €1.40-3.70; gas 3km; lndtte; shop & 3km; rest, bar 100m; snacks; pool 2km; sand beach; tennis 2km; boat excursions; fishing; 10% statics; dogs €1.40; phone; poss cr; Eng spkn; quiet; red long stay; CCI. "Clean, friendly site; vg facs; friendly staff; water on 3 sides; excel beaches; conv La Rochelle, Rochefort; ferry to Ile d'Aix; gd sh stay." ♦ 15 Mar-15 Oct. € 7.70   2005*

FOURCHAMBAULT see Nevers *4H4*

FOURMIES see Hirson *3C4*

FRAISSE SUR AGOUT see Salvetat sur Agout, La *8F4*

FRANGY *9A3* (4km E Rural) **Camping Le Chamaloup, 74270 Contamine-Sarzin** [04 50 77 88 28 or 06 72 80 09 84; fax 04 50 77 99 79; camping@chamaloup.com] Exit A40 junc 11 onto N508 dir Annecy, thro Frangy. Site sp on L in 10km. Med, hdg/mkd pitch, pt shd; wc; chem disp; serviced pitches; mv service pnt; baby facs; shwrs inc; el pts (10A) €3.50; gas; lndtte; shop; tradsmn; snacks; bar; BBQ; htd pool; 20% statics; dogs €1.50; poss cr; Eng spkn; some noise fr bar music; adv bkg; cc acc; CCI. "V friendly owners; chalets on site to hire; rv & fish pond (fenced-off) on site; vg all stays." ♦ 1 Jun-15 Sep. € 16.00   2005*

★★★★ Route de Bagnols - 83600 FREJUS
Tel.: 00 33 494 40 88 43 - Fax: 00 33 494 40 81 99
www.lespinsparasols.com • lespinsparasols@wanadoo.fr

FREJUS *10F4* (2.5km N Urban) **Aire Naturelle La Bravet, Route de Bagnols, 83600 Frejus** [04 94 40 85 92; fax 04 94 44 41 24] Fr Frejus N onto D4 dir Bagnols-en-Foret, site on R in 2.5km. Sm, pt sl, pt shd; wc; chem disp (wc); shwrs €1.60; el pts €3.50; shops; rest, bar 500m; snacks; htd pool; sand beach 5km; 20% statics; dogs; Eng spkn; quiet; CCI. "Cold shwrs free; san facs poss stretched; gd sh stay." ♦ ltd 15 Apr-15 Oct. € 13.50   2003*

FREJUS *10F4* (2.5km N Urban) **Camping Les Pins Parasols, Route des Bagnols, 83600 Frejus** [04 94 40 88 43; fax 04 94 40 81 99; lespinsparasols@wanadoo.fr; www.lespinsparasols.com] Fr a'route A8 exit junc 38 sp Frejus cent. Fr E'bound dir foll Bagnols sp at 2 rndabts & Frejus cent/Cais at 3rd. Fr W'bound dir foll Bagnols at 3 rndabts & Frejus cent/Cais at 4th. Site on L in 500m. Lge, mkd pitch, terr, pt sl, pt shd, htd wc; chem disp; san facs on individual pitches; baby facs; shwrs inc; el pts (5-6A) inc; gas; lndtte; shop; tradsmn; rest; snacks; bar; playgrnd; pool; paddling pool; waterslide; sand beach 6km; tennis; entmnt; TV rm; 30% statics; phone; adv bkg; quiet; Eng spkn; cc no acc; CCI. "Tractor to terr pitches; pleasant, family-run site; excel." ♦ 8 Apr-30 Sep. € 25.50   2005*

See advertisement above

FRANCE

FREJUS *10F4* (4km N) **Camping Caravanning de Montourey, Route des Bagnols, Chemin du Reyran, 83600 Frejus [04 94 53 26 41; fax 04 94 53 26 75; montouray@wanadoo.fr; www. campingmontouray.com]** Fr A8 take exit sp Puget-sur-Argens to N7 twd Frejus. Turn onto D4 twd Bagnols. Site on R. Lge, mkd pitch, shd; wc; chem disp; shwrs inc; el pts (3A) €3; gas; lndtte; shop; rest; snacks; bar; playgrnd; 2 pools; sand beach 5km; tennis; games area; games rm; entmnt; 80% statics; dogs €3; quiet. "Helpful staff." ♦ 1 Apr-30 Sep. € 18.00 (3 persons)   2005*

FREJUS *10F4* (4km NE Coastal) **Domaine du Colombier, 1052 Rue des Combattants d'AFN, 83600 Frejus [04 94 51 56 01 or 04 94 51 52 38 (LS); fax 04 94 51 55 57; info@domaine-du-colombier.com; www.domaine-du-colombier.com]** Fr E (Nice) on A8 exit junc 38 sp Frejus. Go strt over 3 rndabts, turn R at 4th rndabt, then R again at next rndabt, site on R. Fr W (Aix-en-Provence) exit A8 junc 38 & turn R at 1st rndabt, then L at intersection. Site on L. Lge, hdg/mkd pitch, hdstg, terr, pt shd; htd wc (some cont); chem disp; 30% serviced pitches; baby facs; shwrs inc; el pts (16A) inc; gas; lndtte; ice; supmkt; tradsmn; rest; snacks; bar; BBQ (elec); playgrnd; htd pool & waterslides; sand beach 4km; tennis; sports area; games rm; excursions; entmnt high ssn; internet; TV rm; 80% statics/tour ops; dogs €4; poss cr; Eng spkn; adv bkg (dep req + bkg fee); quiet; red low ssn; cc acc; CCI. "In pine forest with exotic trees; excel." ♦ 8 Apr-30 Sep. € 43.00 (3 persons) (CChq acc)   2005*

FREJUS *10F4* (5km W) **Domaine de la Bergerie, Quartier du Fournel, 83520 Roquebrune-sur-Argens [04 98 11 45 45; fax 04 98 11 45 46; info@ domainelebergerie.com; www.domainelebergerie. com]** On N7 twd Frejus, turn R onto D7 sp St Aygulf & Roquebrune; after passing Roquebrune, site sp in approx 6km on R. Lge, hdg/mkd pitch, pt sl, pt shd; wc; chem disp; baby facs; shwrs inc; el pts (6A) inc; gas; lndtte; ice; supmkt; rest; snacks; bar; BBQ (gas); playgrnd; 2 pools; paddling pool; waterslide; sand beach 10 mins drive; tennis; sauna; jacuzzi; creche; child entmnt; archery; disco; statics in sep area; poss cr; Eng spkn; adv bkg (bkg fee); CCI. "Open air cinema twice weekly; ltd facs up to mid Jun; v well organised site; masses of entmnt/activities for all ages; early bkg ess for summer; excel site; vg long stay." ♦ 1 Apr-30 Sep. € 30.00 (3 persons)   2002*

†FREJUS *10F4* (8km W) **Camping Domaine J Bousquet (Camping Club de France), Route de la Bouverie, 83520 Roquebrune-sur-Argens [04 94 45 42 51; fax 04 94 81 61 06]** Exit A8 at Puget-sur-Argens, turn R onto N7, R onto minor rd at rndabt in about 2km. Site on R after about 300m. Lge, pt sl, v shd; wc (cont); chem disp; baby facs; shwrs inc; el pts (10A) €3.19; gas; shop; rest; bar; sand beach 10km; pool; entmnt; playgrnd; dogs €0.78; poss cr; adv bkg; quiet but some rd & rlwy noise; 95% statics; CCI ess. "Poss untidy & ltd facs off ssn." € 15.62   2004*

FREJUS *10F4* (8km W) **Camping Le Moulin des Iscles, 83520 Roquebrune-sur-Argens [04 94 45 70 74; fax 04 94 45 46 09; moulin. iscles@wanadoo.fr]** Twd Frejus on N7, turn R onto D7 to St Aygulf sp Roquebrune. Site on L after passing thro Roquebrune vill. Med, shd; wc (some cont); baby facs; shwrs inc; el pts (6A) €2.70; lndtte; ice; shop; rest; snacks; bar; playgrnd; sand beach 12km; games rm; internet; entmnt; TV; 10% statics; dogs €1; adv bkg; quiet; red low ssn/long stay; cc acc. "Gd security; helpful owners; excel family site; clean, well-managed." ♦ 1 Apr-30 Sep. € 18.50 (3 persons) (CChq acc)   2004*

FREJUS *10F4* (8km W Rural) **Camping Lei Suves, Quartier du Blavet, 83520 Roquebrune-sur-Argens [04 94 45 43 95; fax 04 94 81 63 13; camping.lei.suves@wanadoo.fr; www.lei-suves. com]** Exit a'route at Le Muy, thro Le Muy twd Frejus on N7. After 5km turn L (under a'route not into Roquebrune-sur-Argens) at sp. Foll sp to camp. Lge, mkd pitch, terr, shd; wc; chem disp; mv service pnt; baby facs; shwrs inc; el pts (6A) €4.20; gas; lndtte; ice; shop; rest; snacks; bar; playgrnd; htd pool; paddling pool; sand beach 14km; lake sw & fishing 3km; tennis; games rm; entmnt; child entmnt; excursions; internet; 50% statics; dogs €3; phone; Eng spkn; adv bkg; quiet; cc acc; red low ssn; CCI. "Well-maintained, family-run site; facs v clean; gd sw pool; v nice location in pine forest; conv Cote d'Azur." ♦ 1 Apr-15 Oct. € 31.00 (3 persons) (CChq acc)   2005*

See advertisement opposite (top)

FREJUS *10F4* (10km W Rural) **Camping Les Pecheurs, Quartier Verseil, 83520 Roquebrune-sur-Argens [04 94 45 71 25; fax 04 94 81 65 13; info@camping-les-pecheurs.com; www.camping-les-pecheurs.com]** Exit A8 dir Le Muy, onto N7 then D7 sp Roquebrune; camp 2km on L (bef bdge over Rv Argens) at ent to vill. Lge, hdg/mkd pitch, hdstg, pt shd; htd wc; chem disp; mv service pnt; baby facs; sauna; shwrs inc; el pts (6-10A) €4.20-5.20; gas; lndtte; ice; shop; tradsmn; rest; snacks; bar; BBQ (gas or elec); playgrnd; htd pool; sand beach 12km; lake sw, fishing, canoeing adj; spa & jacuzzi; tennis 2km; mini-golf; horseriding; cycle hire 1km; entmnt; child entmnt; TV rm; internet; 10% statics; dogs €3; phone; Eng spkn; adv bkg; quiet; cc acc; red low ssn/CCI. "Historic vill 1km; helpful staff; lovely site; pleasant views; organised excursions high ssn; conv St Tropez, St Raphael; gd walking, cycling." ♦ 1 Apr-30 Sep. € 32.50 (CChq acc)   2005*

See advertisement opposite (middle)

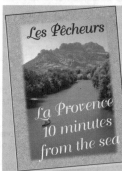

As we're travelling out of season, we'd better phone ahead to check that the site is actually open.

†FREJUS *10F4* (3km NW Rural) **Camping Le Frejus, Route de Bagnols, 83600 Frejus** [04 94 19 94 60; fax 04 94 19 94 69; contact@lefrejus. com; www.lefrejus.com] Exit A8 junc 38, at 1st rndabt turn L, then L at 2nd rndabt & L again at 3rd rndabt, Site on R in 200m. Lge, mkd pitch, pt sl, pt terr, pt shd; wc (some cont); chem disp; mv service pnt; baby facs; shwrs inc; el pts (6A) inc; gas high ssn; lndtte; ice; shop high ssn & 500m; tradsmn, rest & snacks high ssn; bar; playgrnd; pool; waterslide; sand beach 6km; tennis; games rm; entmnt; internet; 10% statics; dogs; site closed 16 Dec-14 Jan; Eng spkn; adv bkg; quiet; cc acc; red low ssn; CCI. "Ideal position for coast bet Cannes & St Tropez; lge pitches." ♦ € 28.00   2005*

See advertisement on previous page (bottom)

FREJUS *10F4* (4km NW) **Camping La Baume, Route de Bagnoles, 83600 Frejus** [04 94 19 88 88; fax 04 94 19 83 50; reception@labaume-lapal meraie.com; www.labaume-lapalmeraie.com] Fr a'route A8 exit junc 38 sp Frejus cent. Fr E'bound dir foll Bagnols sp at 2 rndabts & Frejus cent/Cais at 3rd. Fr W'bound dir foll Bagnols at 3 rndabts & Frejus cent/Cais at 4th. Site on L in 300m. V lge, pt sl, pt shd; htd wc; shwrs; el pts (6A) inc; gas; lndtte; ice; shop; snacks; rest; bar; 3 sw pools + paddling pool; sand beach 5km; waterslide; tennis; horseriding; entmnt; many tour ops statics; dogs €3.40; adv bkg ess Jul/Aug; quiet (except N part of site adj to m'way); 15% red low ssn. ♦ 23 Mar-29 Sep. € 37.00 (3 persons)   2002*

FREJUS *10F4* (5km NW Rural) **Camping Caravaning des Aubredes, 408 Chemin des Aubredes, 83480 Puget-sur-Argens** [04 94 45 51 46; fax 04 94 45 28 92; Campingaubredes@wanadoo.fr; www.camping aubredes.com] Sp on R of N7 W fr Frejus. Fr A8 exit junc 37 dir Frejus/Puget-sur- Argens. Lge, mkd pitch, pt sl, pt shd; wc (some cont); chem disp; mv service pnt; shwrs inc; el pts (8A) €4.30; gas; lndtte; ice; shop; tradsmn; rest, snacks, bar high ssn; playgrnd; pool; sand beach 5km; tennis; games rm; entmnt; 30% statics; dogs €1.60; poss cr; Eng spkn; adv bkg rec high ssn; quiet; cc acc; red long stay/low ssn; CCI. "Excel esp low ssn; conv m'way." 1 May-15 Sep. € 21.50   2005*

FREJUS *10F4* (6km NW Rural) **Camping La Bastiane, Chemin de Suivieres, 83480 Puget-sur-Argens** [04 94 55 55 94; fax 04 94 55 55 93; info@labastiane.com; www.labastiane.com] Exit A8 at junc 37 Puget/Frejus. At N7 turn R dir Le Muy & in 1km turn R immed after 2nd bdge. Foll sp to site. Fr N7 turn L at traff lts in Puget, site is 2km N of Puget. Lge, hdg/mkd pitch, terr, shd; wc; chem disp; baby facs; fam bthrm; shwrs inc; el pts (3A) inc; lndtte; ice; shop; tradsmn; rest; snacks; bar; BBQ (elec); playgrnd; htd pool; sand beach 7km; watersports; tennis; cycle hire; games rm; cinema; disco; child entmnt; TV; car wash area; 40% statics; dogs €4; phone; poss cr; Eng spkn; adv bkg; quiet; cc acc; red long stay/low ssn/CCI. "Excel; family-run, friendly." ♦ ltd. 25 Mar-21 Oct. € 34.00   2005*

See advertisement opposite

FREJUS *10F4* (6km NW Rural) **Parc Saint James Oasis, Route de la Bouverie, 83480 Puget-sur-Argens** [04 94 45 44 64; fax 04 94 45 44 99; info@camping-parcsaintjames.com; www.camping-parcsaintjames.com] Exit A8 at junc 37 for Puget-sur-Argens onto N7 dir Le Muy, in 2.5km turn R into Rte de la Bouverie, site in 1km on R. Lge, pt shd; wc; shwrs; el pts; gas; lndtte; shop; tradsmn; rest; snacks; bar; htd pool; tennis; games area; entmnt; child entmnt; all statics; phone; dogs; adv bkg. 8 Apr-30 Sep.   2005*

See advertisement on page 562

FREJUS *10F4* (7km NW Rural) **Camping La Pierre Verte, Route de Bagnols-en-Foret, 83600 Frejus** [04 94 40 88 30; fax 04 94 40 75 41; info@campinglapierreverte.com; www.campinglapierreverte.com] Exit A8 junc 38 onto D4 dir Bagnols-en-Foret. Site N of military camp. Lge, mkd pitch, hdstg, pt sl, terr, pt shd; wc; chem disp; baby facs; fam bthrm; shwrs inc; el pts (6A) €4; gas; lndtte; ice; shop; tradsmn; rest; bar; snacks; no BBQ; htd pool; waterslide; sand beach 8km; tennis; games area; cycle hire; mini-golf; games rm; entmnt; child entmnt; internet; TV rm; 50% statics; dogs €3; phone; adv bkg; quiet; Eng spkn; cc acc; red long stay/low ssn; CCI. "Well situated for local attractions; vg long/sh stay." ♦ 8 Apr-30 Sep. € 27.00   2005*

See advertisement above

FRELAND see Kaysersberg *6F3*

FRENEUSE see Mantes *3D2*

FRESNAY SUR SARTHE *4E1* (Rural) **Camp Municipal Le Sans Souci, Ave Victor Hugo, 72130 Fresnay-sur-Sarthe** [02 43 97 32 87; fax 02 43 33 75 72; camping-fresney@wanadoo.fr] Fr Alencon S on N138; in 14km at La Hutte turn R on D310 to Fresnay; sp in town on traff lts bef bdge; fr Beaumont-sur-Sarthe NW on D39 to Fresnay. Med, hdg/mkd pitch, pt sl, terr, pt shd; wc; chem disp; shwrs; el pts (6A) €2.60 (poss rev pol); lndtte; shops high ssn & 500m; htd pool adj; rv adj; fishing; canoe hire; cycle hire; mini-golf; entmnt; dogs €1.05; Eng spkn; adv bkg; quiet; CCI. "V pleasant, clean site; adj to Rv Sarthe; gd rvside pitches; interesting site; facs poss stretched high ssn; excel value; vg." 1 Apr-30 Sep. € 8.80   2005*

FREVENT *3B3* (Rural) **Les Domaine Le Val du Ternois, 75 Rue du General de Gaulle, 62270 Frevent** [03 21 03 78 79; fax 03 21 04 92 41; levalduternois@wanadoo.fr] Fr Doullens, take D916 to Frevent, site sp fr town cent. Med, hdg/mkd pitch, hdstg, pt shd; wc; chem disp; shwrs inc; el pts (10A) inc; gas; lndtte; shop 800m; tradsmn; pool; tennis 500m; many statics; dogs; adv bkg; quiet; cc ac, CCI. "Pleasant town cent for shops & rests; pleasant, improved site; conv NH." ♦ 31 Mar-31 Oct. € 15.00   2004*

FRONCLES BUXIERES *6E1* **Camp Municipal Les Deux Ponts, 52320 Froncles-Buxieres** [03 25 02 38 35 or 03 25 02 31 20 (Mairie); fax 03 25 02 09 80] Fr Chaumont take N67 twd Joinville, ignore sp to Vovecourt but take R turn E on D253 sp Froncles. Site sp fr main rd. Sm, hdg pitch, pt shd; wc; chem disp; shwrs; el pts (6A) inc; shops in vill; fishing; adv bkg; quiet. "Facs clean; pleasant situation; gd NH." 15 Mar-15 Oct. € 10.75   2005*

†**FRONTIGNAN** *10F1* (6km NE) **Camping Le Clos Fleuri, 34110 Vic-la-Gardiole** [04 67 78 15 68; fax 04 67 78 77 62; www.camping-clos-fleuri.fr] Fr N9 dir Montpellier take exit 33 for N300 twd Sete. At Sete take N112 for 13 km then R into D114 sp Vic-la-Gardiole. Ignore 1st turn & go round vill & foll sp. Med, hdg/mkd pitch, shd; wc; chem disp; mv service pnt; shwrs inc; el pts (3-6A) €2.90-3.50; lndtte; shops in ssn or 1km; rest; snacks; bar; pool; shgl beach 2km; 30% statics; dogs €2.20; phone adj; poss cr; adv bkg; quiet but noise fr bar; cc not acc; CCI. "Friendly but not suitable for small children or lge o'fits; cycle hire avail; sheltered fr Mistral; gd long/sh stays." € 15.50 (3 persons)   2004*

FRONTIGNAN *10F1* (1km S Coastal) **Camping Mediterranee, 11 Ave des Vacances, 34110 Frontignan-Plage** [04 67 48 12 32 or 04 42 58 11 19 (LS)] 3km fr Sete on N112 to Montpellier, turn R at rlwy bdge, in approx 1km L at x-rds to site. Or on D129 fr Frontignan to Frontignan-Plage site on R 100m past reclamation area. Med, unshd; wc; shwrs inc; el pts (5-6A) €2.60; lndtte; ice; shop; rest; snacks; playgrnd; pool; sand beach 200m; tennis; lake 500m; games area; entmnt; quiet but some rlwy & rd noise; adv bkg rec high ssn. 5 Apr-20 Sep. € 12.00   2003*

FRONTIGNAN *10F1* (6km S Coastal) **Camping Les Tamaris, 140 Ave d'Ingril, 34110 Frontignan-Plage** [04 67 43 44 77 or 04 78 04 67 92 (LS); fax 04 67 18 97 90; les-tamaris@wanadoo.fr; www.les-tamaris.fr] Fr A9/E15 take exit Montpellier (St Jean-de-Vedas) & foll sp Sete. At the next rndbt foll sp Sete N112. After approx 8km turn L sp Vic-la-Gardiole onto D114. Cross rlwy & Canal du Rhone. Pass Les Aresquiers-Plages & turn L in 500m, site sp on L in 500m. Fr N on N113, take N300 to Sete; then N112 to Frontignan-Plage. Lge, hdg pitch, pt shd; wc; chem disp; mv service pnt; baby facs; shwrs inc; el pts (10A) inc; lndtte; ice; shop; tradsmn; rest; snacks; bar; BBQ (gas/charcoal only); playgrnd; pool; sand beach adj; watersports; lake fishing; cycle hire; horseriding nrby; games rm; weights rm; entmnt; internet; many statics; dogs €3; phone; poss cr; adv bkg (dep req); quiet; red long stay/low ssn; cc acc; CCI. "Excel, friendly, family-run site; gd san facs; recep 0800-2000; pitches poss tight for lge o'fits; mkt Thu & Sat am; gd family seaside site." ♦ 1 Apr-17 Sep. € 35.00 (CChq acc) ABS - C11   2005*

FUILLA see Vernet les Bains *8H4*

FUMEL *7D3* (10km NE Rural) **Camping Le Moulin de Laborde, 46700 Montcabrier** [05 65 24 62 06; fax 05 65 36 51 33; moulindelaborde@wanadoo.fr; www.moulindelaborde.com] Fr Fumel take D673 NE & site 1km past Montcabrier on L. Med, hdg pitch, pt shd; wc; chem disp; baby facs; shwrs inc; el pts (6A) €2.25; gas; ice; lndtte; shop; tradsmn; rest; snacks; bar; playgrnd; pool; sm lake; games area; cycle hire; entmnt high ssn; TV rm; no dogs; Eng spkn; phone; poss cr; adv bkg (dep req); quiet; 20-30% red low ssn. "Many attractions & activities nrby; excel all stays." ♦ 1 May-15 Sep. € 18.00   2003*

FUMEL *7D3* (2km E Rural) **Camping de Condat - Les Catalpas, Route de Cahors, 47500 Fumel** [05 53 71 11 99; fax 05 53 71 36 69] Take D811 fr Fumel E twd Cahors. Clearly sp after Condat. Med, mkd pitch, hdstg, pt sl, pt shd; htd wc; chem disp (wc); mv service pnt; shwrs inc; el pts (10A) inc; lndtte; ice; shops 1km; rest in vill; snacks; BBQ; playgrnd; pool; rv sw & fishing adj; 15% statics; dogs; Eng spkn; adv bkg; CCI. "V helpful, friendly owner; poss security probs; vg long stay." ♦ ltd. 1 Apr-31 Oct. € 15.00   2003*

†**FUMEL** *7D3* (4km E Rural) **Aire Naturelle Le Valenty, 46700 Soturac** [tel/fax 05 06 36 59 50; campingdevalenty@tiscali.fr] Fr Fumel take D811 dir Cahors. Thro Soturac, site immed on L outside vill. Sm, terr, pt shd; wc; shwrs inc; el pts (4-10A) inc; gas 3km; ice; lndtte; shops, snacks, bar 2.5km; tradsmn; rest 1km; playgrnd; pool; minigolf; pony rides; 20% statics; dogs; bus 200m; Eng spkn; adv bkg; quiet; CCI. "Delightful CL-type site; helpful owners; tranquil but secure; organic produce for sale; excel long/sh stays." € 13.50   2004*

FUMEL *7D3* (8km E) **Camping Le Ch'Timi, 46700 Touzac** [05 65 36 52 36; fax 05 65 36 53 23; info@campinglechtimi.com; www.campinglechtimi.com] Fr N20-E9 at Cahors, turn R at rndabt onto D811 sp Bergerac. In Duravel, take 3rd exit at rndabt, sp Vire-sur-Lot & foll rd to L. After about 3km, cross bdge & turn R at rndabt, sp Touzac. Site on R on rvside, on hill, in about 2km, well sp. Med, mkd pitch, pt sl, pt shd; wc; baby facs; shwrs inc, chem disp; el pts (6A) inc; gas; lndtte; shop & 700m; tradsmn; rest; snacks; bar; BBQ; playgrnd; pool; canoeing; fishing 100m; cycle hire; archery; games rm; games area; entmnt; 20% statics; dogs €1.50; Eng spkn; adv bkg; quiet but poss noisy teenagers high ssn; cc acc; CCI. "Gd position; gd local rests; wine-tasting tours; gd savings on wine; day trips; mkt Puy l'Eveque Tue; ltd facs low ssn." 1 Apr-30 Sep. € 19.20 ABS - D05   2005*

†**FUMEL** *7D3* (9km S Rural) **Camping Le Pouchou, 47370 Courbiac [tel/fax 05 53 40 72 68 or 06 80 25 15 13 (mob); camping-le-pouchou@ cario; www.camping-le-pouchou.com]** S fr Fumel on D102 thro Tournon-d'Agenais; Courbiac sp to L on S side of town. Sm, pt sl, shd; wc; chem disp; mv service pnt; shwrs inc; el pts (10A) €3 (poss rev pol); lndry rm; ice; shop; snacks; bar; playgrnd; pool & paddling pool; cycle hire; fishing; horseriding; archery; internet; sat TV; some statics; dogs €1.10; site clsd 21 Dec-9 Jan; Eng spkn; adv bkg ess high ssn; quiet; CCI. "Lge pitches each with picnic table; many sl pitches poss diff; gd views; always a pleasure to visit; hospitable owners; gd cycling; vg long/sh stay." ♦ ltd. € 12.00   2005*

FUMEL *7D3* (10km NW) **Camping des Bastides, 47150 Salles [05 53 40 83 09; fax 05 53 40 81 76; bastides@wanadoo.fr]** Fr Fumel take D162 for 4km to join the D710. N for 3km on D710. Turn W on D162. Site at junc of D162 & D150 to Gavaudum Valley. Med, terr, pt shd; htd wc; chem disp; shwrs inc; el pts (4A inc); lndtte; shop; rest; snacks; pool; waterslides; entmnt; cycle hire; Eng spkn; adv bkg; quiet. "Lovely views." ♦ 1 Apr-30 Sep. € 20.00   2002*

FUTEAU see Clermont en Argonne *5D1*

GABARRET *8E2* (E Rural) **Camp Municipal La Cheneraie, 40310 Gabarret [05 58 44 92 62; fax 05 58 44 35 38]** N on D656 fr Barbotan-les-Thermes, or D35 to Gabarret & thro vill, site sp on leaving vill. Look for bright orange site sp. Sm, hdg pitch, pt sl, pt shd; wc; chem disp; shwrs inc; el pts (10A) inc; lndtte; shops 1km; playgrnd; htd pool; adv bkg ess Jul/Aug; quiet; CCI. "Vg long stay." 1 Mar-31 Oct. € 8.50   2003*

GABARRET *8E2* (6km SE Rural) **Camp Municipal de l'Uby, 32150 Barbotan-les-Thermes [05 62 69 50 01 or 05 62 09 53 91 (Mairie); fax 05 62 09 56 97]** Fr Eauze take D626 sp Cazaubon, immed bef Intermarche in town, turn R on D656 sp Barbotan. Site on R in 2km. Lge, pt shd; wc; chem disp; el pts (5A) inc; lndtte; ice; shop & 2km; cooking facs; playgrnd; pool; beach 300m; tennis; games area; entmnt; fishing; sailing; windsurfing; lake sw adj; adv bkg rec; red low ssn; cc acc; CCI. "Gd food & interesting Bastide towns nrby." ♦ 15 Mar-30 Nov. € 12.20   2002*

†**GACE** *4E1* (2km N) **Camping Les Petits Champs, 61230 St Evroult-de-Montfort [tel/fax 02 33 35 67 39; johannes.bouma@wanadoo.fr]** Fr Gace turn L in vill halfway down hill (no L turn but turn R & cross over). Site 500m on L, sp. Sm, mkd pitch, terr, unshd; wc; shwrs; el pts (6A) inc; tradsmn; playgrnd; Eng spkn; quiet but some rd noise. "Lovely little site; v boggy in wet/winter; poss diff acc for long o'fits; peaceful farm site with views; welcoming; gd NH." € 13.00   2005*

GACE *4E1* (1km E Rural) **Camp Municipal Le Pressoir, 61230 Gace [02 33 35 50 24 or 02 33 35 50 18; fax 02 33 35 92 82; ville.gace@wanadoo. fr]** Turn off N138 E opp Intermarche; foll sp. Sm, hdg/mkd pitch, sl, pt shd; wc (cont); chem disp; mv service pnt in vill; shwrs inc; el pts €2; lndry rm; supmkt & rest 100m; playgrnd; rv 500m; poss cr; quiet. "Clean, neatly managed site; warden calls am & pm; rec early arrival; sm pitches poss diff for lge vans; gd sh stay/NH." 1 Jun-1 Sep. € 5.00   2005*

GACILLY, LA *2F3* (200m E Rural) **Camp Municipal de l'Aff, Le Bout du Pont, 35550 Sixt sur Aff [02 99 08 10 59 or 02 99 08 10 18 (Mairie)]** On ent La Gacilly exit rv bdge onto D777 dir Sixt-sur-Aff. Site on L outside town sp. Well sp fr town cent. Sm, mkd pitch, pt shd; wc; shwrs inc; el pts (6A) €1.50; shops 500m; tradsmn; rests 200m; playgrnd; rv; dogs €0.50; quiet; Eng spkn. "V pretty town with local artisans; visits to cosmetics factory nrby; vg facs; area for m'vans; easy walk to town; vg sh stay." ♦ ltd. 1 Jun-30 Sep. € 7.50   2005*

GAILLAC *8E4* (8km N) **Camp Municipal au Village, Route de Cordes, 81140 Cahuzac-sur-Vere [05 63 33 91 94 or 05 63 33 90 18 (Mairie); fax 05 63 33 94 03]** Fr Gaillac, take D922 N twd Cordes. Site on L of rd, clearly sp thro vill of Cahuzac. Sm, pt sl, pt shd; wc; shwrs; el pts (3A) €2.30 (rev pol); shops 500m; rest, snacks, bar nr; playgrnd; pool; tennis; games area; cycle hire; phone; adv bkg; quiet. "Vg rest opp site; gd, clean site." 1 Jun-30 Sep. € 8.00   2002*

GAILLAC *8E4* (2km W Urban) **Camping La Source, 9 Rue Guynemer, 81600 Gaillac [05 63 57 18 30; fax 05 49 52 28 58]** Exit A68 junc 9 onto D999 then in 3.5km at rndabt turn onto D968 dir Gaillac. In 100m turn R immed past Le Clerc petrol stn, then L by Aldi. Site 200m on R, well sp fr town cent.. Med, hdg/mkd pitch, hdstg, terr, unshd; htd wc (some cont); chem disp (wc); baby facs; shwrs inc; el pts (10A) €2.50; lndtte; shop 500m; tradsmn; snacks; bar; playgrnd; pool; entmnt; TV; 20% statics; dogs €1; quiet; CCI. "New site 2004; helpful staff; peaceful site; purpose-made dog-walk area; steep walk to recep & bar but san facs at pitch level; gd touring base Tarn & Albi region." 1 Apr-30 Oct. € 12.00   2005*

GALLARGUES LE MONTUEUX see Lunel *10E2*

GAMACHES *3B2* (Rural) **Camping Les Marguerites, Rue Antonin Gombert, 80220 Gamaches [tel/fax 03 22 30 89 51]** A28 exit 5 onto D1015 dir Eu & Le Treport to Gamaches in 8km. Site sp fr town, 200m fr stadium, Lge, mkd pitch, hdstg, pt shd; wc; chem disp; shwrs inc; el pts (4-10A) €3.86-10; lndtte; ice; tradsmn; rest; snacks; bar; BBQ; playgrnd; pool; paddling pool; rv adj; games area; 25% statics; dogs; poss cr; quiet; adv bkg; red long stay/CCI. "Nr forest of Eu & Somme coast; gd fishing, riding." ♦ ltd. 15 Mar-15 Oct. € 15.00   2004*

Camping Filature de la Sioule

F-03450 Ebreuil • Phone: +33 (0)4 70 90 72 01 • www.campingfilature.com

Four star campsite in orchard setting beside one of the finest trout rivers in France. Level grassy pitches with good shade. Clean facilities, quiet location. 6 km from exit 12 of A 71 (Paris – Clermond-Ferrand). Shop. Excellent bar and take-away from June onwards. Ideal country for walking and cycling. Fishing, canoeing and swimming in the river. 1 km from Ebreuil town centre (easy walk). Sioule gorges at 5 km. Reduced low season prices, up to 50% after 6 nights. Special rates for daily meals over 4 nights. Good starting point to visit Vichy, the volcano park and Vulcania, and to explore the Auvergne. Good for long or short stay. Open from 31/03 till 01/10.

GANNAT *9A1* (7km N Rural) Camp Municipal, 03800 Jenzat [04 70 56 86 35 or 04 70 56 81 77 (Mairie); fax 04 70 56 85 38; mairie-jenzat@ pays-allier.com] N9 N fr Gannat for 4.5km, turn L onto D42, site in 3km in Jenzat on R just bef rv bdge, sp as Champs de la Sioule. Med, pt shd; wc; shwrs inc; el pts (6-10) €1.80-2.80; ice; lndtte; shops 250m; playgrnd; rv sw adj; Eng spkn; spotless facs; quiet; CCI. "Clean facs; helpful warden; pleasant site on rv bank." ♦ ltd.
16 Apr-18 Sep. € 7.90   2005*

> This site entry hasn't been updated for a while; we'd better fill in a site report form and send it to The Club.

GANNAT *9A1* (1km SW) Camp Municipal Le Mont Libre, Route de la Batisse, 03800 Gannat [04 70 90 12 16 or 06 73 86 04 95; fax 04 70 90 12 16; camping.gannat@wanadoo.fr; www.ville-gannat. fr] App Gannat fr S on N9, L 2km bef town, 1st R behind Stade, foll sp to L 1st R uphill. Med, terr, pt shd; wc; chem disp; mv service pnt; el pts (10A) €2.20; ice; lndtte; shop & 500m, supmkt 1km; playgrnd; small pool; rv 5km; TV; poss cr; adv bkg; quiet. "Excel; helpful warden; delightful situation; spotless facs; walking dist to town facs & excel rest; barrier clsd at night; gd sh stay." 1 Apr-30 Oct.
€ 9.50   2005*

GANNAT *9A1* (10km W) Camp Municipal Les Nieres, 03450 Ebreuil [04 70 90 70 60 or 04 70 90 71 33 (Mairie); mairie-ebreuil@wanadoo.fr] Site 1km SW of Ebreuil, sp fr D915. Sm, shd; wc (cont); chem disp; shwrs; el pts (4-12A) €1.75-4.15; lndtte; shops 1km; snacks; playgrnd; fishing; access to rv; quiet. "NH only; barrier at ent to site locked until 0900; warden calls pm; sh walk into vill."
1 May-30 Sep. € 7.80   2005*

GANNAT *9A1* (10km W Rural) Camping La Filature de la Sioule, Route de Chouvigny, 03450 Ebreuil [04 70 90 72 01; fax 04 70 90 79 48; camping. filature@libertysurf.fr; www.campingfilature.com] Fr A71 exit 12 (avoid 12.1); foll sp to Ebreuil N 500m, then W for 5km thro vill. Turn W onto D915 dir Chouvigny, site in 1km. Med, hdg/mkd pitch, pt shd; wc (some cont); chem disp; mv service pnt 800m; baby facs; shwrs inc; el pts (3-6A) €2-3; gas; lndtte; ice; shop; tradsmn high ssn; bar; snacks; BBQ; playgrnd; rv sw; tennis 500m; canoes; cycle hire; table tennis; trout-fishing; horseriding; TV; dogs; Eng spkn; adv bkg (€30 dep req); v quiet; cc acc; red long stay/low ssn; CCI. "Resident peacocks; v gd value take-away; v clean facs recently refitted; lge pitches; peaceful site." ♦ ltd.
31 Mar-1 Oct. € 16.00   2005*

See advertisement above

GAP *9D3* (1.5km N Rural) Camping Alpes-Dauphine, Route Napoleon, 05000 Gap [04 92 51 29 95; fax 04 92 53 58 42; alpes.dauph@ wanadoo.fr; www.alpesdauphine.com] On N85 1.5km N of Gap. Med, mkd pitch, some hdstg, pt sl, terr, pt shd; htd wc; chem disp; mv service pnt; baby facs; shwrs inc; el pts (6A) €3; gas; lndtte; ice; shop; tradsmn; vg rest; snacks; bar; playgrnd; htd pool; paddling pool; games area; sat TV; 20% statics; dogs €2.10; phone; poss cr; Eng spkn; adv bkg rec high ssn; quiet; red low ssn; cc acc; CCI. "M'vans need levellers; excel cent for touring area; gd mountain views." ♦ 1 Apr-12 Nov.
€ 17.50 (CChq acc)   2005*

†GAP *9D3* (2km N) Camping Napoleon, 05000 Gap [tel/fax 04 92 52 12 41; chabre.bernard@ wanadoo.fr] On E of Gap-Grenoble rd (N85), sp. Ent on bend, but easy access. Med, sl, terr, pt shd; wc (some cont); shwrs €0.50; el pts (2-6A) €2.60-3.35; shops 1km; pool 3km; 50% statics; some rd noise. "Steep gravel track to higher (best) terraces; excel views of mountains & town." € 8.25
                                                        2003*

GAP *9D3* (10km S Rural) **Camp Municipal Le Chene, Route de Marsailles, 05130 Tallard** [04 92 54 10 14 (Mairie)] Fr S take the N85 twds Gap; turn R at traff lts onto the D942; site on R after 3km. Fr Gap take the N85 S; turn L at traff lts, D942; site on R 3km. Med, hdstg, sl, terr, pt shd; wc (some cont); shwrs inc; el pts (6A) €4; lndtte; shop 2km; playgrnd; htd pool; tennis; BBQ; entmnts; phone; dogs; adv bkg; CCI. "Gd long/sh stay; poss unsuitable for lgs o'fits, sm pitches." 15 Jun-31 Aug. € 10.00   2005*

GAP *9D3* (8km SW Rural) **Camping Les Bonnets, Le Haut-du-Village, 05000 Neffes** [04 92 57 93 89; fax 04 92 57 94 61; www.alpes-campings.com] N85 SW fr Gap, turn R onto D46, site sp 1km fr vill. Med, mkd pitch, pt shd; htd wc; baby facs; shwrs; el pts (10A) €3.70; lndtte; shop; supmkt 5km; rest, bar 1km; playgrnd; pool; fishing 3km; games area; entmnt; TV rm; quiet. "Well-maintained farm site in beautiful area; excel pool; friendly owner." 1 May-30 Sep. € 11.00   2004*

GARDONNE see Bergerac *7C3*

GASSIN see St Tropez *10F4*

†GASTES *7D1* (Rural) **Camping Les Pres Verts, Ave du Lac, 40160 Gastes** [tel/fax 05 58 09 74 11; camping@presverts.net] S fr Bordeaux on N10 exit junc 17 & turn W on D43 to Parentis-en-Born & foll D652 to Gastes; site sp in vill. Med, shd; wc; shwrs inc; el pts (10A) €2.95; gas; lndtte; ice; shop; rest; snacks; bar; playgrnd; htd pool; lake sw; watersports; fishing; cycle hire; tennis; statics; dogs €2; adv bkg; quiet; CCI. "Gd walking; important ecological site." € 14.30   2005*

GASTES *7D1* (3km SW Rural) **Camping La Reserve, 1229 Ave Felix Ducourneau, 40160 Gastes** [05 58 09 74 79 or 05 58 09 79 23; fax 05 58 09 78 71; lareserve@siblu.fr; www.siblu.com] At traff lts in cent Parentis-en-Born, turn L sp Pontenx & Gastes on D652. After 3km turn R dir Gastes, Ste Eulalie & Mimizan-Plage. Cont onto rndabt & take 2nd exit D652, then turn immed R sp La Reserve. Site sp. V lge, pt shd; wc; chem disp; shwrs inc; el pts (6A) inc; gas; lndtte; rest; snacks; bar; ice; shop; BBQ (gas only); playgrnd; pools (l htd, covrd); waterslide; lake sw & private beach adj; watersports high ssn; windsurfing; sand beach 25km; cycle hire; tennis; games area; archery; mini-golf; entmnt; child entmnt; 70% statics; no dogs; Eng spkn; adv bkg ess high ssn; cc acc; red low ssn; CCI. "Situated in pine forest & by lakeside; lge pitches; watersports & sailing school avail; children's club inc in site fee." ♦ 29 Apr-23 Sep. € 39.00   2005*

See advertisement

GAUGEAC see Monpazier *7D3*

GAVARNIE *8G2* (2km N Rural) **Camping Le Pain de Sucre, 65120 Gavarnie** [tel/fax 05 62 92 47 55; claude.trescazes@wanadoo.fr; www.camping-gavarnie.com] N of Gavarnie, across rv by sm bdge; clearly visible & sp fr rd. Med, pt shd; wc; mv service pnt; shwrs inc; el pts (2-10A) €1.75-5.95; ice; lndtte; shops, rest, snacks, bar 3km; BBQ; playgrnd; no dogs; quiet; cc acc. "Gd facs; gd location; vg long stay." 1 Jun-30 Sep & 15 Dec-15 Apr. € 10.40   2004*

GEMAINGOUTTE see St Die *6E3*

GEMOZAC *7B2* (400m W) **Camp Municipal, Place de Champ de Foire, 17260 Gemozac.** [05 46 94 50 16; fax 05 46 94 16 25] Exit A10 junc 36 (or turn W off off N137) onto D732 sp Gemozac. In 7km foll site sp. Turn L immed after Elan/Renault garage at end of vill. Sm, mkd pitch, pt shd; wc; chem disp; mv service pnt adj; baby facs; shwrs inc; el pts (10A) inc (poss rev pol); ice; lndtte; shop, pizzaria & snacks 500m; tradsmn; rest & bar 100m; BBQ; htd pool adj; dogs; adv bkg; Eng spkn; phone in vill; cc not acc; quiet; CCI. "Excel long/sh stay; pool free to campers; pleasant sm town; gate clsd 1300-1600; no twin-axles." 15 Jun-15 Sep. € 12.15   2004*

GENETS see Avranches *2E4*

FRANCE

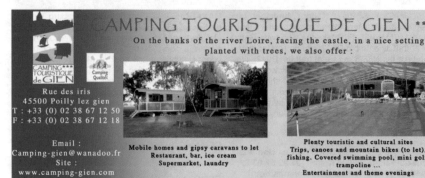

CAMPING TOURISTIQUE DE GIEN ★★★

On the banks of the river Loire, facing the castle, in a nice setting planted with trees, we also offer :

Rue des iris
45500 Poilly lez gien
T : +33 (0) 02 38 67 12 50
F : +33 (0) 02 38 67 12 18

Email :
Camping-gien@wanadoo.fr
Site :
www.camping-gien.com

Mobile homes and gipsy caravans to let
Restaurant, bar, ice cream
Supermarket, laundry

Plenty touristic and cultural sites
Trips, canoes and mountain bikes (to let),
fishing. Covered swimming pool, mini golf,
trampoline ...
Entertainment and theme evenings

GENOUILLE *7A2* (Rural) **Camp Municipal L'Etang des Rosees, 17430 Genouille [05 46 27 70 01 or 05 46 27 72 13 (Mairie); fax 05 46 27 89 03]** Fr Surgeres SW on D911 for 11km. At rndabt turn sharp L D112, site sp on R after 3km. Sm, mkd pitch, pt sl, pt shd; wc; own san; shwrs inc; el pts (15A) €2.10; lndtte; shops 700m; tradsmn; rest, snacks, bar 1km; playgrnd; lake fishing adj; adv bkg; quiet; CCI. "Rural site away fr main tourist area; facs clean but ltd in number." 21 Jun-11 Sep. € 8.00
2004*

GERARDMER *6F3.* **See also sites listed under Corcieux, Granges-sur-Vologne, La Bresse and Le Tholy.**

†GERARDMER *6F3* (3km E) **Camp Municipal de Domaine de Longemer, 88400 Xonrupt-Longemer [03 29 63 07 30; fax 03 29 63 27 10; camping.dudomaine@wanadoo.fr]** Fr W thro Gerardmer on D417. immed after sp Xonrupt-Longemer turn R & cont thro vill. Site 1st one; turn L over bdge. App fr E (Colmar), turn L opp Hotel du Lac de Longemer. Site on both sides of rd. Lge, unshd; htd wc; mv service pnt; shwrs inc; el pts (6A) €3.81; shop; snacks; playgrnd; lake sw; fishing; x-country skiing; phone; poss cr; quiet; 5% red for long stays; CCI. "Pleasant lakeside in Vosges; gd walking, attractive, clean site." € 10.00   2002*

†GERARDMER *6F3* (4km E Rural) **Camping La Verte-Vallee, 4092 Route du Lac, Retournemer, 88400 Xonrupt-Longemer [tel/fax 03 29 63 21 77]** Exit Gerardmer on D417 for Colmar/St Die. After 3km at junc turn R. Cont on D417 for Colmar. After 3km turn R opp Hotel du Lac on D67 for Retournemer. Keep to N side of lake & site 300m past lake at junc on R. Med, mkd pitch, pt sl, shd; htd wc (some cont); baby facs; shwrs inc; el pts (2-6A) €3-6.10; gas; lndtte; shops 2km; tradsmn; rest, bar 1km; htd pool; playgrnd; TV; lake sw 300m; fishing; games rm; 50% statics; dogs €1; poss cr; adv bkg; quiet. "Beautiful scenery, many walks." ♦
€ 11.00   2004*

GERARDMER *6F3* (6km E) **Camping Belle Rive, 88400 Xonrupt-Longemer [03 29 63 31 12]** W fr Gerardmer on D417 (sp Colmar) in approx 1km over bdge, turn R at T-junc (still on D417). After 2km turn R opp Hotel du Lac de Longemer & immed R round W side of lake to S bank where site located. Med, mkd pitch, pt sl, terr, pt shd; wc; chem disp; shwrs €0.70; el pts (1-3A) €1-2; lndry rm; shops adj & 2km; snacks; bar adj; playgrnd; pool 8km; lake sw adj; 10% statics; dogs €0.80; phone adj; quiet. "New san block, ltd but clean; lakeside beautiful area; lovely position in heart of Vosges; next to camping Les Jonquilles." 15 May-15 Sep. € 8.00
2004*

GERARDMER *6F3* (6km E) **Camping Les Jonquilles, Route du Lac, 88400 Xonrupt-Longemer [03 29 63 34 01; fax 03 29 60 09 28]** Sp off D417 SE of Xonrupt-Longemer. Fr W thro Gerardmer on D417 (sp Colmar) in approx 1km over bdge & turn R at T-junc (still on D417). After 3km turn R opp Hotel du Lac de Longemer & almost immed R round W end of lake for 500m to T-junc, turn L, site on S bank 1000m. Lge, mkd pitch, pt sl, unshd; wc (some cont); chem disp; mv service pnt; baby facs; shwrs inc; el pts (6-10A) €2.50-4.50; gas; lndtte; shop; rest; snacks; bar; playgrnd; lake beach & sw adj; fishing; sailing; entmnt; TV; few statics; dogs €1.10; phone; bus 1km; Eng spkn; adv bkg (dep req); quiet but some noise fr entmnt at night; cc acc; CCI. "Friendly, well-maintained, family-run site; gd views; poss uneven pitches; excel for Alsace wine region/Colmar." ♦ 15 Apr-10 Oct.
€ 14.80   2005*

GERARDMER *6F3* (1.5km SW) **Camping Les Sapins, 18 Chemin de Sapois, 88400 Gerardmer [03 29 63 15 01; fax 03 29 60 03 30]** Nr lakeside site Camping Ramberchamp, 150m up C17. Rd sp Col de Sapois. On S side of lake. Med, pt shd; wc; shwrs inc; el pts (4-6A) €2.80-4.70; ice; sm shop; rest; snacks; bar; playgrnd; games area; TV rm; lake with beach 200m; fishing & watersports adj; quiet; red low ssn; adv bkg rec. "Nice, comfortable site; san facs poss in need of modernisation; lge pitches but overlooked by sport stadium; no lake views." 1 Apr-30 Sep. € 11.50   2004*

Les Bois du Bardelet ★★★★

Loire Valley
Poilly - 45500 GIEN
Tel. 00 33/238 67 47 39 - Fax. 00 33/238 38 27 16
Internet: www.bardelet.com
E-mail: contact@bardelet.com

2 lakes, 3 swimming pools, relaxing area with indoor pool, jacuzzi, fitness room. Children aquatic play area with paddling indoor pool.
Other activities : fishing, canoe, tennis, crazy golf, ping pong.

Sunelia

Weekly and weekend-renting. Chalets and mobile-homes.

FRANCE

GERAUDOT *6E1* (1km E) **Camp Departmental l'Epine aux Moines**, 10220 Geraudot [tel/fax 03 25 41 24 36] Exit A26 at junc 23 onto N19 to Lusigny-sur-Barse; foll sp Parc de la Foret d'Orient. Turn N along lake to site. Or fr Troyes D960 E. At Rouilly head S on D43 sp Geraudot. Site 1km E of vill. Lge, mkd pitch, pt sl, pt shd; htd wc (some cont); chem disp; mv service pnt; shwrs inc; el pts (4-6A) €3.10 (poss rev pol); lndtte; ice; shop 200m; tradsmn; rest; snacks; bar; playgrnd; lake sw adj; boat hire; poss cr; adv bkg; cc acc; CCI. "Friendly warden; well-maintained site; attractive area; ltd facs low ssn; poss mosquitoes; nr bird observatory." 15 Mar-15 Oct. € 11.80   2005*

GERE BELESTEN see Laruns *8G2*

GERSTHEIM *6E3* (1km NE) **Camp Municipal au Clair Ruisseau**, Rue de Ried, 67150 Gerstheim [03 88 98 30 04 or 03 88 98 30 20; fax 03 88 98 43 26] Site 1km fr Gerstheim sp on D924. Med, unshd; wc; shwrs inc; el pts (6A) inc; gas; shop; playgrnd; 60% statics; dogs €0.50; quiet. 15 Apr-30 Sep. € 9.80   2003*

GETS, LES see Morzine *9A3*

GEX *9A3* (Urban) **Camp Municipal Les Genets**, 400 Ave des Alpes, 01170 Gex [04 50 41 61 46 or 04 50 42 63 00 (Mairie); fax 04 50 41 68 77; camp-gex-@cc-pas-de-gex.fr] Fr all dir head for 'Centre Ville'; at rndabt take D984 twd Divonne/ Lausanne. Site sp to R (tight turn) after rlwy sheds (poor sp in town). Site on R after Musee Sapeurs Pompiers. Med, hdg pitch, hdstg, pt sl, pt shd; wc (some cont); chem disp; shwrs inc; el pts (16A) €2.50; gas 500m; lndtte; shops 500m; tradsmn; snacks; bar; playgrnd; htd pool; games area; TV rm; dogs €0.80; phone; gates clsd 2200-0800; dep req for barrier key; Eng spkn; adv bkg; quiet; cc acc; CCI. "Excel site; excel games facs/playgrnd; v friendly, helpful staff; v clean facs; quiet with lots of privacy; vg long or sh stay." ♦ 1 Jun-16 Sep. € 12.00   2005*

GIBLES see Clayette, La *9A2*

GICQ, LE see Matha *7B2*

GIEN *4G3* (1km SW Urban) **Camping Touristique de Gien**, 1 Rue des Iris, 45500 Poilly-lez-Gien [02 38 67 12 50; fax 02 38 67 12 18; camping-gien@ wanadoo.fr; www.camping-gien.com] Off D952 Orleans-Nevers rd; turn R over old rv bdge in Gien & then R again; site on R on Rv Loire. Lge, hdg/mkd pitch, hdstg, terr, pt shd; htd wc (some cont); chem disp; mv service pnt; baby facs; shwrs inc; el pts (4-10A) €3-4.50; gas adj; lndtte; shop; rest; snacks; bar adj; BBQ; playgrnd; covrd pool; canoeing; tennis; cycle hire; mini-golf; entmnt; internet; TV rm; 2% statics; dogs €1; phone; dep req for barrier card; Eng spkn; adv bkg; quiet; cc acc; red low ssn/long stay/CCI. "Lovely rvside site but no sw allowed; porcelain factory 'seconds' in town; gd san facs." ♦ 4 Mar-12 Nov. € 17.00   2005*

See advertisement opposite

GIEN *4G3* (5km SW Rural) **Sunelia Les Bois du Bardelet**, Route de Bourges, 45500 Poilly-lez-Gien [02 38 67 47 39; fax 02 38 38 27 16; contact@ bardelet.com; www.bardelet.com] Fr Gien take D940 dir Bourges; site is on D53 to L, but no L turn allowed. Cont to x-rds & turn R, then R again onto unclassified rd to go back across D940; foll sp to site on L side of this rd. Site well sp fr D940. Lge, hdg/mkd pitch, some hdstg, pt shd; wc; chem disp; mv service pnt; 50% serviced pitches; baby facs; shwrs inc; el pts (6A) inc (some rev pol); gas; lndtte; shop 5km; rest; snacks; bar; BBQ; playgrnd; 3 pools (2 htd/covrd); paddling pool; jacuzzi; lake fishing; canoeing; tennis; games rm; mini-golf; cycle hire; archery; fitness rm; internet; entmnt; 17% statics; dogs €4; phone; adv bkg (dep req + bkg fee); quiet; cc acc; red snr citizen/low ssn; cc acc; red long stay; CCI. "Friendly welcome; site poss noisy late eves - live music in bar area; trips arranged; modern facs but ltd low ssn; purchase leisure passport to use sports facs; o'door pools beautiful; v pleasant site." ♦ 1 Apr-30 Sep. € 30.00 (CChq acc) ABS - L05   2005*

See advertisement above

GIGNAC *10F1* (1km NE Rural) **Camp Municipal La Meuse**, Route d'Aniane, 34150 Gignac [04 67 57 92 97; infos-gignac@wanadoo.fr] Turn NE off N109 in Gignac to D32. Site on L in 1km; sp fr town cent dir Aniane Med, hdg pitch, pt shd; wc; chem disp; mv service pnt; shwrs inc; el pts (6A) €2.20; gas 1km; lndtte; shop 1km; bar; rv sw; tennis; dogs €1.50; Eng spkn; adv bkg (dep req); quiet; no cc acc; red long stay; CCI. "Easy access; lge pitches; friendly, clean, v pleasant; gd rest in town; excel supmkt in town; vg long/sh stay." ♦ ltd. Jun-Sep. € 14.60   2005*

GIGNAC *10F1* (1.5km W) **Camping du Pont**, 730 Blvd Moulin, 34150 Gignac [tel/fax 04 67 57 52 40] Foll sp fr town cent. Sm, pt shd; wc; chem disp; shwrs inc; el pts (6A) €2.44; ice; lndtte; shop; rest; snacks; tradsmn; entmnt; sm pool; playgrnd; fishing; tennis adj; adv bkg; quiet; some Eng spkn. "Friendly welcome." ♦ 1 Apr-15 Oct. € 14.48   2002*

GIGNAC *10F1* (5km W Rural) **Camping Le Septimanien**, Route de Cambous, 34725 St Andre-de-Sangonis [04 67 57 84 23; fax 04 67 57 54 78; leseptimanien@aol.com; www.camping-leseptimanien.com] Exit A75 junc 57. At rndabt on E site of A'route take D128 to Brignac. In Brignac turn L at T-junc, then fork R on D4 twd St Andre-de-Sangonis. Site on R in 3km. Med, hdg pitch, pt shd; wc; chem disp; shwrs inc; el pts (6A) inc; gas; lndtte; ice; shop & 1km; tradsmn; rest; snacks; bar; playgrnd; pool; paddling pool; entmnt; 15% statics; dogs €1.70; phone; adv bkg; quiet; cc acc; CCI. "Well-organised site; vg sh stay/NH." ♦ ltd. 1 Apr-15 Oct. € 18.00   2005*

GIGNY SUR SAONE see Sennecey le Grand *6H1*

†**GISAY LA COUDRE** *3D2* (500m S Rural) **Aire Communale**, 27330 Gisay-la-Coudre [02 32 44 38 86] Turn S of N138 at Bernay onto D833 to La Barre-en-Ouche. In town turn R onto D49 dir Broglie & in 200m turn L onto D35, site on R in 3km, sp. M'vans only. Sm, hdstg, unshd; own san; chem disp; mv service pnt; el pts €2 for 2 hrs; water €2 for 100 litres; shop, rest, snacks, bar 200m; quiet. "Payment for services with jeton obtainable fr Bar-Rest La Tortue 500m further on fr site; car/c'vans probably acc; vg NH."   2003*

GISORS *3D3* (7km SW Rural) **Camping de l'Aulnaie** (formerly Municipal), Etang de l'Aulnaie, 27720 Dangu [02 32 55 43 42] On ent Gisors fr all dirs, take ring rd & exit dir Vernon D10, then L onto D181 dir Dangu. Site on L bef Dangu. Site sp fr D10. NB speed humps. Lge, mkd pitch, pt shd; htd wc; chem disp; mv service pnt; shwrs inc; el pts (10A) inc; gas; lndry rm; tradsmn; rest, bar 200m; snacks; playgrnd; lake sw; fishing; 75% statics; office clsd 1200-1500; dogs €1.70; poss cr; adv bkg; some rd noise; CCI. "Conv Giverny & Gisors local attractions; Gisors attractive town; many permanent statics & poss intinerants; poss unkempt; barrier & office erratic opening hours; san facs gd & clean but ltd & poss stretched at w/e; avoid pitches nr recep as owners' dogs foul area; friendly owner, tourers welcome." ♦ ltd. 24 Mar-24 Oct. € 13.10   2005*

GIVET *5B1* (500m N Urban) **Caravaning Municipal La Ballastiere**, Rue Berthelot, 08600 Givet [03 24 42 30 20] Site at N end of town on Foll 'caravaning' sp fr W end of rv bdge or Dinant rd. Med, some hdg pitch, hdstg, pt shd; wc; chem disp; shwrs inc; shops 500m; lndtte; el pts (10A); lndtte; shop 500m; 95% statics; quiet. "Mainly residential site adj sports & watersports complex; gd NH." 1 Apr-15 Sep. € 5.30   2004*

GIVET *5B1* (2km SW Rural) **Camping Le Sanglier**, Givet-la-Meuse, 08600 Rancennes [03 24 42 72 61] Off D949 Givet to Beauvrang rd. Immed after x-ing rv bdge turn R. Turn R again foll sp to site at end narr access rd on rvside. Sm, pt sl, pt shd; wc; chem disp; shwrs €1.50; el pts (4A) inc; shop 2km; snacks; rv sw; fishing; watersports; 60% statics; phone; Eng spkn; adv bkg; quiet; CCI. "Gd touring base; clean, basic facs; gd NH." 1 May-30 Sep. € 7.90   2004*

GIVORS *9B2* (7km NW) **Camp Municipal de la Trillonniere**, 69440 Mornant [04 78 44 16 47 or 04 78 44 00 46 (Mairie); fax 04 78 44 91 70; mairiemornant@wanadoo.fr] Exit A7 at Givors & foll sp for St Etienne via D488, thro Givors onto D2 till sp seen for Mornant via D34, cont on D34 up hill for 7km, cross D42 & cont 1km to o'skts of Mornant, L at junc island & site on L. Med, pt sl, pt shd; wc; chem disp; shwrs; el pts (10A) €3.50; shops, rest, snacks bar 500m; pool 250m; dogs; adv bkg; some rd noise; access for vans 0815-1015 & 1700-2200. 1 May-30 Sep. € 12.00   2005*

GIVRAND see St Gilles Croix de Vie *2H3*

GIVRE, LE *7A1* (Rural) **Camping La Grisse** (formerly Camping Aire Naturelle), 85540 Le Givre [02 51 30 83 03] Fr Lucon take D949 & turn L at junc with D747 (La Tranche rd). Turn L in 3km & foll sps. Sm, pt shd; wc; chem disp; shwrs inc; el pts; lndry rm; sand beach 10km; dogs €1; Eng spkn; adv bkg; cc not acc; CCI. "Peaceful, friendly, farm site; beautiful area/beach; gd for dogs." ♦ ltd. 15 Apr-15 Oct. € 11.00   2004*

GIVRY EN ARGONNE *5D1* (N Rural) **Camp Municipal Val d'Ante,** 51330 Givry-en-Argonne [03 26 60 04 15 or 03 26 60 01 59 (Mairie); fax 03 26 60 18 22; mairie.givryenargonne@wanadoo. fr] Exit a'route A4 at Ste Menehould; S on D382 to Givry-en-Argonne; site sp on R. Sm, pt sl, pt shd; wc (some cont); chem disp; shwrs inc; el pts (3A) €1.41; shops 200m; playgrnd; shgl lake beach sw; boats for hire adj; dogs €0.77; poss cr; quiet; no cc acc. "Attractive site adj to lake; basic but pleasant; san facs old but clean; warden calls am & pm; gd bird-watching; not suitable lge m'vans."
1 May-15 Sep. € 4.95   2005*

GLUIRAS see St Sauveur de Montagut *9D2*

GONDREXANGE see Heming *6E3*

GONDRIN *8E2* (Rural) **Camping Le Pardaillan,** 32330 Gondrin-en-Armagnac [05 62 29 16 69; fax 05 62 29 11 82; Camplepardaillan@wanadoo.fr; www.camping-le-pardaillan.com] Fr Condom take D931 S for 12km to Gondrin. Site clearly sp. Med, hdg/mkd pitch, hdstg, pt shd; wc; chem disp; baby facs; shwrs inc; el pts (6A) inc; gas; ice; lndtte; shop; tradsmn; rest; snacks; bar; playgrnd; entmnt; lake sw adj; TV rm; games rm; archery; table tennis; pool nrby; 10% statics; dogs €1.50; phone; poss cr; Eng spkn; adv bkg; dep req; CCI. "Excel site, lovely region, highly rec." ♦
30 Mar-15 Sep. € 18.00   2002*

GORDES *10E2* (2km N Rural) **Camping Les Sources, Route de Murs,** 84220 Gordes [04 90 71 12 48; fax 04 90 72 09 43] Fr A7 junc 24, E on D973; then D22; then N100 twds Apt. After 18km at Coustellet turn N onto D2 then L on D15 twds Murs; site on L in 2km beyond Gordes. Med, mkd pitch, hdstg, terr, pt shd; wc (some cont); chem disp; mv service pnt; baby facs; shwrs inc; el pts (6A) €4 (long lead poss req); lndtte; shop & 2km; rest; snacks; bar; playgrnd; pool; child entmnt; 25% statics; dogs €3; Eng spkn; adv bkg; quiet; red long stay; cc acc; CCI. "Lovely location & views; access rd narr & rough (200m); security barriers with 24 hr supervision; sm pitches v diff lge o'fits; ask for easy pitch & inspect on foot; gd walking; friendly staff." 18 Mar-18 Sep. € 18.90   2005*

GORDES *10E2* (10km NE Rural) **Camp Municipal Les Chalottes,** 84220 Murs [04 90 72 60 84 or 04 90 72 60 00 (Mairie); fax 04 90 72 61 73] W on N100 fr Avignon, L onto D2 at Coustellet. Do not turn L sp Gordes but cont 3.5km & turn L D102 sp Joucas/Mura. Or fr Apt twd Avignon N100, R to D4 after 4km site sp to Murs. Do not app site thro Gordes. Sm, mkd pitch, pt sl, pt shd; wc (some cont); chem disp; shwrs inc; el pts (16A) €2; tradsmn; playgrnd; dogs; phone; quiet; CCI. "Peaceful, pretty site among pines, vill 1.8km."
Easter-15 Sep. € 11.00   2005*

GOUAREC *2E3* **Camping Tost Aven,** 22570 Gouarec [02 96 24 85 42; baxter.david@ wanadoo.fr] Sp fr town cent on D5 S. Med, mkd pitch, pt shd; wc (some cont); chem disp; mv service pnt; baby facs; shwrs inc; el pts (10A); gas adj; lndtte; lndry rm; ice; shops adj; supmkt nr; rest, snacks, bar 200m; BBQ; sm playgrnd; lake sw 10km; cycle, canoe hire; entmnt; dogs; bus 200m; poss cr; Eng spkn; quiet. "Helpful British owners; clean, tidy site; excel san facs; Nantes-Brest canal adj; excel towpath for cycling; a gem of a site between canal & rv on edge of lovely vill cent for touring; gd all stays/NH." ♦ ltd. 1 Apr-30 Sep.
€ 11.70   2005*

†GOUAREC *2E3* (7km NE Rural) **Camping Chaumiere du Sapin, Kerveller,** 22570 St Igeaux [tel/fax 02 96 24 04 38; kerveller@yahoo.co.uk] W on D790 Corlay-Rostrenen for 8km; at St Nicolas-de-Pelem x-rd turn L into sm rd C1 sp Kerledec. In 100m cross stone bdge & immed R onto C4 sp St Igeaux. Foll rd for 3.5km over galvanised bdge. In 100m at Kerveller turn L. Site ent 50m on R at end of houses. Sm, shd; wc; chem disp; shwrs inc; el pts (10A) inc; shops, rest, snacks, bar 4km; sand beach 10km; no dogs; Eng spkn; adv bkg; red 5+ nights; cc not acc; CCI. "Upmarket & pretty CL-type site; v clean facs; fishing nr; lndry on request; worth finding; poss diff ent/exit for lge o'fits; new owners making improvements 2004; conv Lac de Guerledan (watersports, sand beach)." € 12.50   2004*

GOUDARGUES *10E2* (1km NE Rural) **Camping Les Amarines, La Verune Cornillon,** 30630 Goudargues [04 66 82 24 92; fax 04 66 82 38 64] Fr D928 foll sp onto D23 & site between Cornillon & Goudarugues. Med, hdg/mkd pitch, shd; wc; baby facs; shwrs inc; el pts (6A) €3.20; lndtte; ice; snacks; bar; playgrnd; pool; rv fishing; entmnt; statics; dogs €1.25; adv bkg; quiet; red low ssn. "Lge pitches; site liable to flood after heavy rain; excel long/sh stay." ♦ 1 Apr-15 Oct. € 15.05   2002*

GOUEX see Lussac Les Chateaux *7A3*

GOURDON *7D3* (4km E Rural) **Camping Le Reve,** 46300 Le Vigan [05 65 41 25 20; fax 05 65 41 68 52; info@campinglereve.com] On N20, Souillac to Cahors, 3km S of Payrac. R onto D673, sp Le Vigan & Gourdon. After 2km turn R onto sm lane, foll camp sp for 2.5km. Med, pt sl, pt terr, pt shd; wc; chem disp; baby facs; shwrs inc; el pts (6A) €2.60; gas; lndtte; sm shop & 4km; playgrnd; pool & paddling pool; games area; TV rm; entmnt; cycle hire; dogs €0.75; Eng spkn; adv bkg ess Jun-mid Aug (dep req); v quiet; red long stay/low ssn; cc not acc; CCI. "Welcoming, helpful Dutch owners; excel long/sh stay." ♦ 25 Apr-15 Sep. € 14.00   2005*

FRANCE

GOURDON *7D3* (11km S Urban) **Camp Municipal Le Moulin Vieux, 46310 St Germain-du-Bel Air** [05 65 31 00 71 or 05 65 31 02 12] W fr N20 Cahors-Souillac rd on D23 sp St Germain-du-Bel Air. On ent vill turn R at camping sp. After 150m turn R & foll narr rd, over sm bdge then imm turn L for site. Lge, shd; wc; chem disp; shwrs; el pts (10A) €2.13; gas; lndtte; rest; shops 1km; pool adj; playgrnd; lake sw & fishing; entmnt; some statics; quiet. "Excel, clean site; vg walks in lovely valley; friendly recep; v helpful warden; pool free for campers; excel value; highly rec." 1 Jun-15 Sep. € 13.00   2005*

GOURDON *7D3* (1km SW Rural) **Aire Naturelle Le Paradis (Jardin), La Peyrugue, 46300 Gourdon** [tel/fax 05 65 41 65 01; contact@leparadis.com] S on D673 Gourdon/Fumel rd, after supmkt on L, turn L onto track sp site. Track shares ent to supmkt. Sm, pt sl, pt shd; wc; shwrs inc; el pts (6A) €2.29; rest; supmkt adj; pool; quiet; adv bkg; gd. "Gd welcome; farm produce; facs poss stretched if full." 15 Jun-30 Sep. € 7.62   2003*

GOURDON *7D3* (5km W Rural) **Camping Le Marcassin de St Aubin (Naturist), 24250 St Aubin-de-Nabirat** [tel/fax 05 53 28 57 30; le. marcassi@freesurf.fr; www.best-of-perigord.tm. fr] Fr Gourdon foll sp for hospital. At hospital take R fork sp Nabirat (D1) & in about 8km turn L at Renault tractor g'ge & foll sp for site in 1.5km. Site on R immed past speed limit sp. Sm, hdg pitch, pt shd; wc; chem disp; shwrs inc; el pts (6A) €2.50; ice; lndry rm; tradsmn; BBQ gas; pool; TV rm; dogs €2.75/week; Eng spkn; adv bkg (dep req); no cc acc; INF card. "Beautiful area with lots to see; owned by helpful, friendly Dutch couple; excel long/sh stay." ♦ ltd. 10 Apr-28 Sep. € 18.00   2004*

GOURDON *7D3* (10km W Rural) **Camping Calmesympa, La Greze, 24250 St Martial-de-Nabirat** [05 53 28 43 15; fax 05 53 30 23 65] SW fr Gourdon take D673 twd Salviac; at Pont Carat turn R onto D46 sp Sarlat. Site 1.5km N of St Martial on L. Sm, hdg pitch, pt sl, pt shd; wc; chem disp; baby facs; shwrs inc; el pts (8A) €2.50; lndtte; ice; sm shop; playgrnd; pool; entmnt; games area; adv bkg; quiet; CCI. "Off the tourist track." ♦ Easter-1 Nov. € 10.50   2002*

GOURDON *7D3* (10km W Rural) **Camping Le Carbonnier, 24250 St Martial-de-Nabirat** [05 53 28 42 53; fax 05 53 28 51 31] On D46, sp in St Martial-de-Nabirat. Lge, pt sl, pt shd; wc; chem disp; shwrs inc; el pts (6A) inc; lndtte; shop; rest; snacks; bar; playgrnd; htd pool; waterslide; lake adj; tennis; mini golf; horseriding adj; canoeing 8km; child entmnt; 50% statics; dogs €3.15; poss cr; little Eng spkn; adv bkg; quiet. "Domme worth a visit; excel all stays." ♦ 5 Apr-25 Oct. € 22.95   2003*

GOURDON *7D3* (1.5km NW) **Camp Municipal Ecoute s'il Pleut, 46300 Gourdon** [05 65 41 06 19; fax 05 65 41 09 88] On R of Sarlat-Gourdon rd D704 1.5km bef Gourdon. Lge, pt sl, shd; wc; shwrs inc; el pts (6A) €2.30; shop & 4km; lndtte; ice; cooking facs; playgrnd; pool; lake beach; fishing; sailing, watersports 200m; tennis; games area; 50% statics; adv bkg rec high ssn; quiet; red low ssn. "50% tented vill; recep clsd 0800-0930, rec pay eve bef departure to avoid waiting; Gourdon attractive town; NH only." 1 Jun-30 Sep. € 9.70   2003*

GOUZON *7A4* (Urban) **Camp Municipal de la Voueize, 23230 Gouzon** [05 55 81 73 22] On E62/N145 Gueret/Montlucon exit at sp for Gouzon. In cent of vill bear R past church & site is sp on edge of Rv Voueize. Sm, pt shd; wc; chem disp; shwrs inc; el pts (10A) inc; gas adj; lndry rm; shop, rest, bar in vill; playgrnd; fishing; golf 2km; birdwatching on lake 8km; adv bkg; quiet. "Friendly recep; clean site & facs; lovely aspect; gd walking & cycling rtes avail fr tourist office in vill; excel touring cent." 1 May-31 Oct. € 12.00   2004*

GRACAY see Vatan *4H3*

GRAMAT *7D4* (8km NE Rural) **Camping de la Cascade, Le Boutel, 46500 Mayrinhac-Lentour** [tel/fax 05 65 38 20 91; campinglacascade@ wanadoo.fr; http://campinglacascade.monsite. wanadoo.fr] E fr Gramat on D807 (formerly D677) for 10km. Turn L on D38 sp Autoire. Site on R in 100m. Or fr St Cere leave D673 to W, then SW at rndabt sp Gramat. In 7km at Le Boutel turn R (still on D673) foll site sp & site approx 350m on L. Sm, hdg pitch, pt sl, pt shd; wc; chem disp; shwrs inc; el pts (5A) inc; gas 10km; ice; shop 6km; tradsmn; snacks; breakfast avail; BBQ; pool; rv sw 8km; games area; dogs €1.15; adv bkg; quiet; cc not acc; CCI. "Peaceful, pleasant, welcoming CL-type site; new British owners (2004) v friendly & helpful; bread & croissants baked on site; excel meal service avail; many activities avail in area eg walking, horseriding, potholing, canoe hire; pool immac; new facs block planned for 2005." 1 Apr-31 Oct. € 16.90   2005*

†**GRAMAT** *7D4* (7km SE) **Camping Le Teuliere, 46500 Issendolus** [05 65 40 86 71; fax 05 65 33 40 89; laparro.mcv@free.fr; http://laparro.mcv.free. fr] Site on R on N140 at l'Hopital, clearly sp. Access fr ent narr & tight corners, not for underpowered. Sm, pt sl, pt shd; wc; shwrs inc; el pts (20A) €1.90 (poss rev pol); lndtte; shop; rest; snacks; bar; BBQ; playgrnd; pool; tennis; fishing; TV; some statics; poss cr; adv bkg; quiet. "Conv Rocamadour; basic san facs; ltd facs low ssn; site rds unmade, steep & narr - gd traction req; pitches muddy when wet." € 7.50   2005*

---

† Site open all year   334   *Help update this Guide*

CAMPING LA STENIOLE ★★★
F88640 GRANGES SUR VOLOGNE • TEL 03 29 51 43 75
EMAIL: steniole@wanadoo.fr • www.steniole.fr

Natacha and Rudi welcome you from 15/4 till 31/10. The campsite is situated in a wooded and peaceful environment.

You can swim in the small lake and make a campfire close to your tent or caravan in the evening. You can taste regional dishes in our restaurant or pick up take away meals. We have a playing ground, a tennis court and the campsite is an ideal starting point for hiking and cycling. Rental of studios all year long. In winter you can go cross-country skiing from the campsite. Trout fishing.

GRAMAT 7D4 (2km S Rural) **Camp Municipal Les Segalieres**, Route de Cajarc, 46500 Gramat [05 65 38 76 92 or 05 65 38 70 41 (Mairie); fax 05 65 33 16 48] Fr N140 take D14 dir Livernon. Site well sp fr town cent, opp zoo. Med, mkd pitch, pt shd; wc; own san rec; chem disp; shwrs inc; el pts (6A) €2; lndtte; shop 2km; playgrnd; pool; tennis; mini-golf; games area; TV rm; 40% statics; adv bkg; v quiet; CCI. "Ideal for families; lge pitches." ◆ 1 Jun-15 Sep. € 10.00   2004*

GRAND BORNAND, LE see Clusaz, La 9B3

GRAND LANDES see Lege 2H4

GRAND PRESSIGNY, LE 4H2 (Urban) **Camp Municipal**, 37350 Le Grand-Pressigny [02 47 94 06 55 or 02 47 94 90 37 (Mairie); fax 02 47 91 04 77] Fr Descartes take D750 S for 3km, L onto D42 to Le Grand-Plessigny. Site at SE end of vill by rv. Sm, pt shd; wc; chem disp; shwrs inc; el pts; shops adj; pool adj; quiet. "Pleasant location with lots of places to visit."   2003*

GRANDCAMP MAISY 1C4 (W Coastal) **Camping Le Joncal**, 14450 Grandcamp-Maisy [02 31 22 61 44 or 02 31 22 50 82 (LS)] Ent on Grandcamp port dock area; visible fr vill. Fr N13 take D199 sp Grandcamp-Maisy & foll Le Port & Camping sps. Lge, unshd; wc; shops, rest adj; gas; el pts (3-6A) €2.50-3.50; many statics; dogs €1; bus. ◆ 1 Apr-30 Sep. € 11.40   2003*

GRANDE MOTTE, LA 10F1 (Coastal) **FFCC/ATC Camping de la Grande Motte**, 195 Allee des Peupliers, 34280 La Grande-Motte [04 67 56 54 75; fax 04 67 29 92 58; info@ffcc.fr; www.ffcc.fr] Exit A9 for Lunel or Montpellier to La Grande Motte, site sp on D59 coast rd. Lge, shd, wc; shwrs; el pts (3A); shop; rest; snacks; bar; playgrnd; sand beach 700m; entmnt; statics; no dogs; poss cr; adv bkg; CCI. 1 Apr-30 Sep. € 15.00   2004*

GRANDE MOTTE, LA 10F1 (2km W Coastal) **Camp Intercommunal Les Cigales**, 34280 La Grande-Motte [tel/fax 04 67 56 50 85] Ent La Grande-Motte fr D62. Turn R at 1st traff lts; 1st on R to site. Lge, mkd pitch, pt shd; htd wc (cont); shwrs inc; el pts (10A) inc; lndry rm; shop 200m; snacks; bar; playgrnd; paddling pool; sand beach 900m; quiet. "One of several sites grouped together in well-planned seaside town; quiet low ssn & ltd facs." Easter-30 Nov. € 18.00   2004*

Some of these sites have changed their opening dates - we'd better fill in some site report forms and let the editor of the guide know.

GRANDPRE 5D1 (Rural) **Camp Municipal**, 08250 Grandpre [03 24 30 50 71 or 03 24 30 52 18 (Mairie)] Fr D946 in Grandpre turn at vill sq by church twd rv, site in 200m on rvside. Med; wc; shwrs; el pts (6-10A) €2.90; lndtte; shops 200m; playgrnd; rv sw; fishing; poss cr; quiet. "Gd sh stay." 1 Apr-30 Sep. € 4.55   2003*

GRANE see Crest 9D2

GRANGES SUR VOLOGNE 6F3 (5km S Rural) **Camping La Steniole**, 1 Le Haut Rain, 88640 Granges-sur-Vologne [03 29 51 43 75; steniole@wanadoo.fr; www.steniole.fr] D423 fr Gerardmer NW to Granges-sur-Vologne & foll sp. Well sp. Med, hdg pitch, terr, pt shd; wc (some cont); chem disp; shwrs inc; el pts (4-10A) €2.90-4; gas; lndtte; shop; supmkt 3km; tradsmn; rest; snacks; bar; BBQ; playgrnd; lake sw & shgl beach adj; fishing; tennis; walking rte; horseriding 4km; games rm; TV rm; 10% statics; dogs €1; Eng spkn; adv bkg rec high ssn; quiet; CCI. "Pleasant, wooded, relaxing site; vg rest;." 15 Apr-31 Oct. € 9.00   2005*

See advertisement

FRANCE

Camping "La Route Blanche" ★★★ 273 pitches
Phone: +33 (0)2.33.50.23.31 / Fax: +33 (0)2.33.50.26.47 • F-50290 BREVILLE-SUR-MER
http://www.camping-breville.com • E-mail: larouteblanche@camping-breville.com

Campsite situated in the Bay of Mont Saint Michel, facing the Channel Islands, at approx. 500 yards from the beach. You only have to cross one road to get to one of the most beautiful 18 and 9 holes golf courses of France.

GRANGES SUR VOLOGNE *6F3* (200m W) Camping Les Peupliers, 12 Rue de Pre Dixi, 88640 Granges-sur-Vologne [03 29 57 51 04 or 03 29 51 43 36; fax 03 29 57 51 04] D423 fr Gerardmer NW to Granges-sur-Vologne. Turn L into sm rd just bef rv bdge into town. Well sp. 200m fr D423 & town cent. Sm, mkd pitch, pt shd; wc; chem disp; shwrs €1; el pts (6A) €2.80 shop adj; rv; dogs €0.70; phone; poss cr high ssn; no Eng spkn; adv bkg; quiet; no cc acc; CCI. "V friendly owner; modern, clean san facs, poss ltd high ssn; site attractively landscaped; gd walking area inc farm; v peaceful area; excel long/sh stay."
1 May-30 Sep. € 7.40   2003*

GRANVILLE *1D4* (2km NE Coastal) Camping L'Ermitage Intercommunal Granville-Donville, Rue de l'Ermitage, 50350 Donville-les-Bains [02 33 50 09 01; fax 02 33 50 88 19; camping-ermitage@wanadoo.fr] Turn off D971E in Donville at sm rndabt, site sp. Fr Brehal turn R immed after post office on R. Lge, pt sl, pt shd; wc; chem disp; shwrs; el pts (3A) inc, (10A) €3.75; lndtte; shop 1km; rest, snacks, bar adj; sand beach; tennis adj; 10% statics; phone; poss cr; adv bkg; quiet; CCI. ♦
15 Apr-15 Oct. € 16.00   2004*

GRANVILLE *1D4* (6km NE Coastal) Camping La Route Blanche, 6 La Route Blanche, 50290 Breville- sur-Mer [02 33 50 23 31; fax 02 33 50 26 47; larouteblanche@ camping-breville.com; www.camping-breville.com] Exit A84 junc 37 onto D924 dir Granville. Bef Granville turn L onto D971, then L onto D114 which joins D971e. Site on R bef golf club. Lge, hdg/mkd pitch, hdstg, pt shd; wc (some male cont); chem disp; mv service pnt; baby facs; shwrs inc; el pts (6-10A) €2.60-3.60; gas; lndtte; shop; tradsmn; playgrnd; pools; waterpark; waterslide; sand beach 500m; sailing school; golf & tennis nr; games area; entmnt; 40% statics; dogs €1.70; poss cr; Eng spkn; quiet; cc acc; red long stay; CCI. "Pleasant old walled town & harbour; pleasant site with vg facs." ♦
1 Apr-31 Oct. € 24.00 (CChq acc)   2005*

See advertisement above

GRANVILLE *1D4* (2.5km SE Coastal) Camping La Vague, St Nicholas, 50400 Granville [02 33 50 29 97] On D911 coast rd S fr Granville, or on D973 dir Avranches, site sp. Med, pt shd, hdg/mkd pitch; wc; chem disp; mv service pnt; some serviced pitches; shwrs inc; el pts (4A) inc; gas; lndtte; ice; shop 1km; tradsmn; snacks; playgrnd; sand beach adj; TV; fishing; mini-golf; dogs; poss cr; adv bkg; quiet; CCI. ♦ Easter-30 Sep. € 23.80   2004*

> Will you fill in the site report forms at the back of the guide, or shall I?

GRANVILLE *1D4* (3km SE) Camping de l'Ecutot, Route de l'Ecutot, 50380 St Pair-sur-Mer [02 33 50 26 29; fax 02 33 50 64 94; camping. ecutot@wanadoo.fr] Fr Avranches NW on D973 twds Granville. 5km S of Granville turn onto D309 sp St Pair-sur-Mer; site on R (wide rear ent). Lge, hdg pitch, indiv san facs some pitches; wc; chem disp; shwrs inc; el pts (2-10A) €1.60-4; lndtte; ice; sm shop; snacks; bar; playgrnd; htd pool; beach 1.2km; games area; entmnt; TV rm; 20% statics; dogs €1; eng spkn; adv bkg; quiet; cc acc. "Conv ferry to Channel Is, Bayeux Tapestry, Mont St Michel; beware soft ground early ssn." 1 Jun-15 Sep.
€ 17.60   2004*

GRANVILLE *1D4* (3.5km SE) Camping Angomesnil, 50380 St Pair-sur-Mer [02 33 50 61 41] Take D973 SE fr Granville twd Avranches. At D154 exit to R sp Kairon-Bourg & site in 1km. Sm, pt sl, pt shd; wc; chem disp; mv service pnt; shwrs inc; el pts (3A) inc; shops 4km; tradsmn; playgrnd; pool high ssn; sand beach 3.5km; tennis. "Helpful warden; roomy pitches." ♦ 20 Jun-10 Sep. € 12.65   2003*

GRANVILLE *1D4* (6km SE) **LES CASTELS Chateau Lez Eaux, 50380 St Pair-sur-Mer** [02 33 51 66 09; fax 02 33 51 92 02; lez.eaux@ wanadoo.fr; www.lez-eaux.com or www.les-castels.com] App site on D973 Granville dir Avranches rd (not via St Pair). At rndabt at Intermarche cont for 2km, site sp on R. Take care not to miss site turning 2km past Intermarche. Med, mkd pitch, pt sl, pt shd; wc (some cont); chem disp; serviced pitches; baby facs; shwrs inc; el pts (5A) inc, 10A extra; gas; lndtte; ice; shops; snacks; bar; BBQ; playgrnd; htd pool; waterslide; jacuzzi; beach 3km; lake fishing; tennis; cycle hire; boat hire 7km; horseriding 4km; entmnt; games rm; 80% statics; dogs; poss cr; poss noise fr bar; cc acc; CCI. "Extra charge for bkg by phone; conv Mont St Michel & Dol; gd for children; gd cycling; clean facs & spacious pitches; facs stretched high ssn; mkt Thu St Pair." ♦ 1 Apr-15 Sep. € 38.00 ABS - N02
2005*

GRANVILLE *1D4* (5km S Coastal) **Camping La Chaussee, 1 Ave de la Liberation, 50610 Jullouville** [02 33 61 80 18; fax 02 33 61 45 26; jmb@camping-lachaussee.com; www.camping-lachaussee.com] On coast rd D911 fr Granville to Jullouville. Site on L heading S, sp. Lge, mkd pitch, hdstg, pt shd; wc (some cont); chem disp; mv service pnt; shwrs inc; el pts (6-10A) €3.60-4; gas; lndtte; ice; shop; snacks; bar; BBQ; playgrnd; htd pool; sand beach 100m; tennis 500m; games area; games rm 400m; archery; games rm; entmnt; internet; TV rm; dogs €1.50; bus; office open 0800-1230 & 1400-2000; Eng spkn; adv bkg; quiet; cc acc; red low ssn; CCI. "On attractive coast; lovely promenade walk; lge pitches; lovely pool; conv Mont St Michel; v pleasant site." 8 Apr-17 Sep. € 23.00
2005*

See advertisement above

GRASSE *10E4* (7km E) **Caravan Inn, 06860 Opio** [04 93 77 32 00; fax 04 93 77 71 89] Exit a'route A8 at Cannes/Grasse, foll sp for Grasse & to Valbonne, D3. (Can also exit A8 at Antibes, foll D103 to D3 & Valbonne). On D9 thro Valbonne, R at N end of vill sq. Cont D3 sp Opio. After 3km site on L. Med, sl (terr vineyard), shd; wc; chem disp; shwrs inc; el pts (2-4A) inc; shops 1km; gas; lndtte; rest; snacks; bar; playgrnd; pool; sand beach 14km; tennis, horseriding; golf 1km; 90% statics; dogs €2.14; poss cr; Eng spkn; adv bkg; quiet but some rd noise; cc not acc; CCI. "Beautiful location conv Cote d'Azur & Provence Alps; helpful staff; dep for gate key." 1 Jun-1 Sep. € 26.26
2002*

†**GRASSE** *10E4* (8km NW Rural) **Camping Parc des Arboins, 755 Route Napoléon, 06460 St Vallier-de-Thiey** [04 93 42 63 89; fax 04 93 09 61 54] N fr Cannes on N85 foll sp thro Grasse for Digne; approx 1.5km bef vill of St Vallier-de-Thiey, site located on R of rd. Med, mkd pitch, hdstg, shd; htd wc; mv service pnt; shwrs; el pts (3A) €2.40; gas; ice; lndtte; shop; supmkt 1.5km; rest; snacks; bar; playgrnd; htd pool; paddling pool; sand beach 30km; tennis 1.5km; golf 10km; games area; entmnt; TV rm; 95% statics; dogs €1.20; adv bkg; quiet but poss rd noise; CCI. "Lovely position on hillside; ltd touring pitches; vg rest adj." € 17.40
2004*

GRAU DU ROI, LE *10F2* (1km N Coastal) **Camping Le Boucanet, Route de Carnon, 30240 Le Grau-du-Roi** [04 66 51 41 48; fax 04 66 51 41 87; contact@campingboucanet.fr; www.camping boucanet.fr] Fr A9 fr N exit junc 26, fr S exit junc 29 Montpellier Airport dir Aigues-Mortes. Fr Aigues-Mortes take D62/D62A to Le Grau-du-Roi, twd La Grande-Motte. Site clearly sp off rndabt after area called Le Boucanet (on L). Lge, hdg/mkd pitch, some hdstg, pt shd; wc (some cont); chem disp; mv service pnt; shwrs inc; el pts (6A) €3.50; gas; lndtte; ice; shop; tradsmn; rest; snacks; bar; no BBQs; playgrnd; htd pool & paddling pool; dir access to sand beach adj; surf school; tennis; horseriding; golf 2km; creche; entmnt; no dogs; Eng spkn; adv bkg; quiet; cc acc; CCI. "Excel, popular site; some sm pitches poss diff lge o'fits; some pitches sandy; m'van parking on rd opp site." ♦ 16 Apr-25 Sep. € 31.00 (CChq acc)
2005*

FRANCE

GRAU DU ROI, LE *10F2* (4km S Rural) **Camping Les Petits Camarguais**, Route du Phare de l'Espiguette, 30240 Le Grau-du-Roi [04 66 51 16 16 or 04 66 53 98 98 (LS); fax 04 66 51 16 17; petitscamarguais@yellohvillage.com; www.yelloh village.com & www.homair-vacances.fr] Leave A9 junc 26, foll D979 dir L'Espiguette. Bef seafront turn L twd Espiguette & foll site sp. Site is 4km fr cent of Le Grau-du-Roi. Lge, pt shd; wc (some cont); chem disp; serviced pitches; baby facs; shwrs inc; el pts (6A) inc; gas; lndtte; ice; shop; tradsmn; rest; snacks; bar; BBQ; playgrnd; htd pool + paddling pool; waterslide; sand beach 2km; tennis; games rm; jacuzzi; fitness cent; entmnt; cycle hire; archery; watersports 2km; horseriding 5km; free shuttle to beaches in ssn; 50% statics; free spkn; quiet; red low ssn; cc acc; CCI. "Excel for families; gd base for Camargue & Arles; local mkts Tue, Thu & Sat am." ♦ 3 Apr-18 Sep. € 35.00   2003*

GRAU DU ROI, LE *10F2* (4km SW Coastal) **Camping L'Espiguette**, 30240 Le Grau-du-Roi [04 66 51 43 92; fax 04 66 53 25 71; reception@ campingespiguette.fr] Fr A9 exit junc 26 onto D979 S to Aigues-Mortes & La Grande-Motte. Foll sps to Port Camargue & L'Espiguette & site sp on R fr rndabt; access via L bank of Le Grau-du-Roi; 3km fr Port Camargue & lighthouse. V lge, pt shd; wc; baby facs; shwrs inc; el pts (6A) €3.50; gas; lndtte; shop; rest; snacks; bar; sand beach adj & access to naturist beach; adv bkg; 10% statics; dogs €2.50; quiet; cc acc; red long stay/low ssn; CCI. "Some pitches on sand poss diff in wet; caution on app due to height barrier; v ltd facs low ssn; poss mosquitoes; naturist beach 3km; helpful staff; gd security; vg long stay." ♦ Whitsun-1 Nov. € 24.00
                                                                                       2005*

GRAVE, LA *9C3* (1km E Rural) **Camping de la Meije**, 05320 La Grave [tel/fax 04 76 79 93 34 or 06 08 54 30 84; nathalie-romagne@wanadoo.fr; www.camping-delameije.com] On N91 travelling W to E site ent end of vill immed after last building. Site sp easily missed, by stream below vill. Awkward app fr Briancon (sharp L-hand turn) cont & turn in parking area 150m. NB Rec app fr W. Sm, mkd pitch, pt sl, pt shd; wc (cont); chem disp (wc); baby facs; fam bthrm; shwrs €1; el pts (4A) €2.50; lndtte; shop 500m; tradsmn; rest, snacks, bar 500m; playgrnd; htd pool high ssn; bus; poss cr; Eng spkn; adv bkg (dep req); quiet; red 5 days+; CCI. "Mountain views, walks & excursions; immac kept, beautiful site; poss cr mid-July Tour de France." ♦ 15 May-20 Sep. € 10.00   2005*

GRAVE, LA *9C3* (1km W Rural) **Camping Le Gravelotte, La Meije**, 05320 La Grave [04 76 79 93 14 or 04 76 79 91 34] On N91, 1km W of La Grave. Med, pt sl, pt shd; wc; chem disp; shwrs inc; el pts (5A) inc; gas 1km; lndtte; shop; tradsmn; bar; htd pool; rv rafting/sw; dogs; poss cr; quiet; CCI. "Vg long stay; friendly welcome; spacious & open situation." 15 Jun-15 Sep. € 13.60   2004*

GRAVELINES *3A3* (1km N Coastal) **Camping Les Dunes**, Rue Victor-Hugo, Petit-Fort-Philippe, 59820 Gravelines [03 28 23 09 80 or 03 28 23 29 10; fax 03 28 65 35 99; vpa@club-internet.fr; www.camping-des-dunes.com] On N1 foll sp to Gravelines. Heading W fr Dunkirk exit N1 E of Gravelines foll sp for Petit-Fort-Philippe & foll rd to sp for camping. Site on both sides of rd. Lge, pt shd; wc; shwrs inc; el pts (10A) €2.45; lndtte; shop; snacks; playgrnd; sand beach nr; entmnt dogs; bus; noisy; many statics; adv bkg; red low ssn. "Gates locked at night; NH only." 1 Apr-30 Oct. € 9.90
                                                                                       2004*

GRAVELINES *3A3* (3km W Coastal) **Camping de la Plage**, Rue du Maréchal-Foch, 59153 Grand-Fort-Philippe [03 28 65 31 95 or 03 28 23 09 80; fax 03 28 65 47 40] Fr Calais turn N off A16/E40 or D940 at sp Grand-Fort-Philippe, site at far end town. Tricky to find. Med, mkd pitch, pt shd; htd wc; chem disp; shwrs inc; el pts inc; lndtte; shops 1km; sand beach adj; pool 3km; playgrnd; entmnt; adv bkg; quiet. "Lge pitches; nice walk to sea front; poss itinerants & circus vans; conv ferry; pleasant sh stay; improving." 1 Apr-31 Oct. € 15.55   2005*

GRAVESON see St Remy de Provence *10E2*

GRAY *6G2* (NE) **Camp Municipal Longue Rive**, Route de la Plage, 70100 Gray [03 84 64 90 44; fax 03 84 65 22 29] S on D67 Chalons-sur-Marne to Besancon rd, ent town, cross bdge over rv, L at rndabt, after 300m L at sp for La Plage. Well sp fr all rtes. Med, hdg/mkd pitch, pt shd; wc (mainly cont); mv service pnt; shwrs inc; el pts (10A) inc; gas; lndtte; ice; shop 1.5km; rest, bar, & pool opp; playgrnd; boating & fishing; tennis; mini-golf; dogs €0.80; poss cr; Eng spkn; quiet; cc not acc; CCI. "Friendly recep; 3 supmkts in town; "De la Plage" rest opp site rec; several Bastide vills within cycling dist; many pitches waterlogged early in ssn; facs poss dirty; noisy." 1 Apr-30 Sep. € 11.40   2003*

GRAYAN ET L'HOPITAL see Soulac sur Mer *7B1*

GRENOBLE *9C3* (12km SE) **Camping de Luiset**, 38410 St Martin-d'Uriage [04 76 89 77 98; fax 04 76 59 70 91; camping@leluiset.com] Take D524 SE fr Grenoble to Uriage-les-Bains; turn L on D280 to St Martin-d'Uriage; site behind church in vill; steep climb fr Uriage-les-Bains. Med, pt terr, pt shd; wc (cont); shwrs; el pts (2-6A) €2-2.60; ice; lndtte; BBQ; playgrnd; sports area; rv fishing 100m. "Beautiful setting; basic facs." ♦ 1 May-30 Sep. € 8.50   2005*

GRENOBLE *9C3* (8km S Rural) **Camping a la Ferme Le Moulin de Tulette (Gaudin), Route du Moulin de Tulette, 38760 Varces-Allieres-et-Risset [04 76 72 55 98; tulette@wanadoo.fr]** Fr A51, exit junc 12 to join N75 N, Varces in approx 2km. Turn R at traff lts & foll sp to site, (approx 2km fr N75). If driving thro Grenoble look for sp Gap - N75 diff to find. Sm, mkd pitch, pt sl, pt shd; wc; chem disp; baby facs; shwrs inc; el pts (5-10A) €2.30-3.80; shop 1km; tradsmn; poss cr; Eng spkn; adv bkg; quiet; CCI. "Friendly owners; stunning views; marvellous site; facs ltd but v clean - stretched high ssn; same hose used for disposal point & m'van water top-up; gd base for touring/x-ing Alps." ♦ 1 May-31 Oct. € 13.50   2005*

†GRENOBLE *9C3* (7km SW Urban) **Camping Caravaning Les 3 Pucelles, Rue des Allobroges, 38180 Seyssins [04 76 96 45 73; fax 04 76 21 43 73; contact@camping-trois-pucelles.com; www.camping-trois-pucelles.com]** On A480 in dir of rocade (by-pass) S exit 5B, on R after supmkt then foll sp to R then L. Clearly sp. Well sp fr m'way. Med, hdg pitch, hdstg, pt shd; htd wc (some cont); chem disp; shwrs inc; el pts (10A) €2.30; lndtte; ice shop; tradsmn; rest; snacks; bar; playgrnd; pool; 70% statics; phone; bus nr; poss cr; Eng spkn; noise fr indus area; CCI. "Site part of hotel campus; run by friendly family; san facs gd; NH only to explore interesting city; conv Grenoble by bus/tram." € 12.00   2005*

GREOUX LES BAINS *10E3* (600m S Rural) **Yelloh! Village Verdon Parc, La Paludette, 04800 Greoux-les-Bains [04 92 78 08 08; fax 04 92 77 00 17]** Take D907 over rv R on D4 to Les Hameaux. Turn L on D952. At Greoux turn R on D8 rd to St Pierre. Cross bdge over Rv Verdon (v narr) take immed rd to L. Site 500m. Lge, mkd pitch, hdstg, terr, pt shd; wc; chem disp; baby facs; fam bthrm; shwrs inc; el pts (10A) €4; gas 1km; lndtte; shop & 1km; rest; snacks; bar; playgrnd; pool; paddling pool; lake sw & fishing 3km; tennis; star golf; games area; entmnts; TV rm; 50% statics; dogs €1.52 (low ssn only); phone; bus 1km; adv bkg; quiet; CCI. "V helpful new manager; v clean facs; interesting & pleasant spa town; excel long stay." ♦ 1 Apr-20 Oct. € 24.00   2003*

GREOUX LES BAINS *10E3* (1.2km S Rural) **Camping Le Verseau, Route de St Pierre, 04800 Greoux-les-Bains [tel/fax 04 92 77 67 10]** Fr W on D952 go thro town to rndabt & take D8 1st exit but no R turn so go completely round rndabt. Foll D 8 to Narr bdge & turn R after bdge. Campsite in 1km. Med, hdg pitch, pt sl, pt shd; wc; chem disp; shwrs inc; el pts (10A) inc; lndtte; shop 1km; rest; snacks; bar; el/gas BBQ; playgrnd; pool; tennis 1km; entmnt; phone; adv bkg; quiet; CCI. "Friendly owners; interesting spa town; great views; excel long stay." 1 Apr-31 Oct. € 17.92   2004*

GREOUX LES BAINS *10E3* (8km SW Rural) **Camp Municipal du Verdon, 83560 Vinon-sur-Verdon [04 92 78 81 51]** D973 fr Cavaillon. S on N96 at Mirabeau, E in 1.5km onto D952. Cross rv bdge in vill, site on R. Med, shd; wc (some cont); shwrs inc; el pts (6A) €2.03; shop 500m; playgrnd; rv fishing & sw adj; dogs €0.80; quiet. ♦ 1 May-30 Sep. € 9.15   2002*

Mustn't forget to post our site report forms to The Club, otherwise sites might be deleted.

GRESSE EN VERCORS see Monestier de Clermont *9C3*

GRIGNAN see Valreas *9D2*

GRIMAUD *10F4* (2km E) **Aire Naturelle (Gerard), Les Cagnignons, 83310 Grimaud [04 94 56 34 51; fax 04 94 56 51 26; lyons.cagnignons@wanadoo.fr]** Leave A8 at junc 36 onto D25 at Le Muy sp Ste Maxime then onto N98 dir St Tropez. Take R onto D14 spf Grimaud & 2nd rd on R to site. Sm, terr, shd; wc; chem disp; shwrs inc; el pts (3-6A) €2.80-3.40; lndtte; basic playgrnd; pool adj, tennis 500m; sand beach 2km; horseriding 2km; phone; 30% statics; dogs; adv bkg; quiet; no cc acc; CCI. "V clean; away fr bustle of St Tropez; not rec teenagers; some pitches ltd for long o'fits; vg long/sh stay." ♦ Easter-30 Sep. € 17.50   2004*

GRIMAUD *10F4* (2km E Rural) **Camping Domaine du Golfe de St Tropez, Chemin des Vignaux, 83310 Grimaud [04 94 43 26 95; fax 04 94 43 21 06; info@golfe-st-tropez.com; www.golfe-st-tropez.com]** Sp down lane nr junc of D14 & D61. Med, hdg/mkd pitch, pt shd; wc; chem disp; shwrs inc; el pts (4-10A) €3-5; rest; snacks; bar; playgrnd; pool; beach 3km; 30% statics; dogs €1.50; phone; cc acc. "Conv for Port Grimaud & beaches; fair." 31 May-28 Aug. € 18.00   2005*

GRIMAUD *10F4* (3km E Coastal) **Domaine des Naiades ACF, St Pons-les-Mures, 83310 Grimaud [04 94 55 67 80; fax 04 94 55 67 81; naiades@lesnaiades.com; www.lesnaiades.com]** Fr St Maxime take N98 twd Toulon. After 6km turn R at rndabt in St Pons-les-Mures; site sp & ent 500m on L. Lge, terr, shd, mkd pitch; wc (some cont); shwrs inc; el pts (10A) inc (poss rev pol); lndtte; ice; shops; rest; snacks; bar; BBQ (el only); playgrnd; htd pool + paddling pool in ssn; waterslides; sand beach 900m; watersports; games area; entmnt; internet; some statics; dogs €3; poss cr; adv bkg ess; quiet except noisy disco & dog kennels adj; cc acc; CCI. "Gd views; vg, clean san facs; 24hr security; gd recep; 7 nights for 6 in low ssn; rec." ♦ 8 Apr-29 Oct. € 46.00 (3 persons) ABS - C27   2005*

FRANCE

GRIMAUD *10F4* (4km E Coastal) **Camping Club Holiday Marina, Le Ginestel, 83310 Grimaud** [04 94 56 08 43; fax 04 94 56 23 88; info@ holiday-marina.com; www.holiday-marina.com] Leave A8/E20 a'route at sp Le Muy & foll dir Ste Maxime to coast rd N98. Turn R & foll sp St Tropez. After approx 6km pass under sm flyover at Port Grimaud. Site on R in approx 500m just after Rocchieta garden cent. Lge, hdg/mkd pitch, pt shd; htd wc; chem disp; mv service pnt; serviced pitches; pitches have private bthrms; shwrs inc; el pts (20A) inc; gas; lndtte; shop; tradsmn; rest; snacks; bar; BBQ (el only); playgrnd; 2 pools; jacuzzi; sand beach 950m; fishing; cycle & scooter hire; games rm; entmnt; child entmnt; internet; sat TV; 70% statics; dogs €3; €50 dep for barrier card & bathrm; recep 0800-2000 high ssn; sep car park; British owners; poss cr; adv bkg ess high ssn; some rd noise; red low ssn/long stay; cc acc; CCI. "Helpful staff; lovely pool area with htd jacuzzi; excel sports facs; v conv for all Cote d'Azur; touring pitches poss diff manoeuvring for lge o'fits." ◆ 1 Mar-10 Nov. € 45.00 ABS - C23   2005*

See advertisement opposite

GRIMAUD *10F4* (4km E Coastal) **Camping de la Plage, 83310 Grimaud** [04 94 56 31 15; fax 04 94 56 49 61; www.camping-de-la-plage.net] Fr St Maxime turn onto N98 sp to St Tropez; camp 3km on L, sited both sides of rd (subway links both parts of site). Lge, pt shd; wc; chem disp; mv service pnt; shwrs inc; el pts (4-10A) €4.20-8.50; gas; lndtte; ice; shop; rest; snacks; bar; playgrnd; sand beach adj; tennis; dogs €1.60; poss cr; some rd noise; adv bkg ess high ssn, rec bkg in Jan (non-rtnable bkg fee €35); cc acc; CCI. "Conv for Ste Maxime & Port Grimaud; ferry to St Tropez, Monte Carlo; beautiful mountains; pitches nr beach or inshd woodland; some noise fr disco; some sm pitches; little pitch maintanence low ssn & poss problems with hot water; excel situation, but site appears to be going downhill." ◆ 4 Apr-26 Oct. € 24.00   2005*

GRIMAUD *10F4* (4km E Coastal) **Camping Les Mures, St Pons-les-Mures, 83310 Grimaud** [04 94 56 16 17; fax 04 94 56 37 91; info@camping-des-mures.com; www.camping-des- mures.com] Exit Ste Maxime by N98 twd St Tropez, site in 5km visible on both sides of rd midway bet Ste Maxime & Grimaud. V lge, mkd pitch, pt sl, pt shd; wc (some cont); chem disp; shwrs inc; el pts (6A) inc; gas; lndtte; ice; shop; rest; snacks; bar; playgrnd; sand beach adj; boat hire; water-skiing; games area; entmnt; some statics; dogs €2; poss cr; quiet but rd noise & disco (high ssn); CCI. "Beach pitches avail; well-run, clean site; position justifies charge; v ltd facs low ssn." Easter-1 Oct. € 29.00   2005*

GRIMAUD *10F4* (4km E Coastal) **Camping Les Prairies de la Mer, St Pons-les-Murs, 83360 Grimaud** [04 94 79 09 09; fax 04 94 79 09 10; prairies@campazur.com; www.campazur.com & www.homair-vacances.fr] Leave A8/E80 at Ste Maxime/Draguignan exit. Take D25 twd Ste Maxime. The site is on L of N98 heading SW, 400m bef St Pons-les-Mures with rndabt at ent. V lge, mkd pitch, pt shd, sm pitch; wc; chem disp; mv service pnt; shwrs inc; el pts (10A) €5; gas; lndtte; ice; shop; supmkt; rest; snacks; bar; playgrnd; sand beach adj; fishing; watersports; entmnt; 60% statics; dogs; adv bkg ess high ssn; CCI. "Port Grimaud sh walk; gd security; well organised site; gd recep; poss tatty low ssn; vg long stay." ◆ 3 Apr-16 Oct. € 35.00   2004*

GRIMAUD *10F4* (6km S) **Camping a la Ferme Les Caramagnols (Fontanini), 83310 Cogolin** [04 94 54 40 06; fax 04 94 54 19 02; accueil@ lescaramagnols.com] Take N98 Cogolin-Le Mole & site on L in 2.5km. Med, pt shd; wc; shwrs; el pts (2A); shops 2km; sand beach 8km; some statics; adv bkg; quiet. "Vg." 15 Jun-15 Sep.   2004*

†**GRISOLLES** *8E3* (1km NE) **Camping Aquitaine, Route de Montauban, 82170 Grisolles** [05 63 67 33 22; campingaquitaine@aol.com] S on N20, site on L just bef junc N20/N113. Watch for flags at ent. Steep app. Sm, sl, terr, pt shd; wc; shwrs inc; el pts (10A) €2.50; gas; ice; lndry rm; sm shop; BBQ; playgrnd; rv fishing 1km; lake sw 5km; dogs €1; no twin-axle vans acc; adv bkg; quiet but some rd & rlwy noise; CCI. "Overlooks valley of Garonne; v steep site; poss itinerants; fair NH only." € 10.00   2003*

GRISOLLES *8E3* (4km NW Rural) **Camping Le Grand Gravier, 82600 Verdun-sur-Garonne** [05 63 64 32 44 or 05 63 26 30 64; camping@ garonne-gascogne.com] Exit A20/E09 at junc 68 onto A72 & exit junc 10 onto N20 S to Grisolles. At rndabt turn R onto N113 NW for 3km, then L at rndabt onto D6 W sp Verdun-sur-Garonne. Cross rv bdge; site sharp R in 500m. Med, hdg pitch, pt shd; wc (mainly cont); shwrs inc; el pts (6A) €2.80; shop 1km; BBQ; playgrnd; rv fishing; tennis; games rm; dogs €0.80; adv bkg; quiet; red long stay; CCI. "Pleasant, interesting site; next to fast flowing river, poss floods wet weather; boating poss but not sw; gd modern facs; 1k fr town; no access 1400-1600; walled town." 28 May-4 Sep. € 9.40   2005*

GROLEJAC see Sarlat la Caneda *7C3*

†**GROS THEIL, LE** *3D2* (3km SW Rural) **Camp de Salverte, Route de Brionne, 27370 Le Gros-Theil** [02 32 35 51 34; fax 02 32 35 92 79]   Fr Brionne take D26 E twd Le Gros-Thiel. After 10km turn R at Salverte, site sp. Lge, hdg pitch, terr, pt shd; htd wc; shwrs inc; el pts (3A) inc (poss rev pol); lndry rm; shop; snacks; bar; playgrnd; covrd pool; tennis; mini-golf; entmnt; many statics; quiet; CCI. "Conv NH Le Havre/Caen ferries; attractive site but ltd facs low ssn; sm area for tourers diff when wet." € 13.00   2005*

Camping Club Holiday Marina

bay of ST. TROPEZ

Holiday Marina is a friendly, safe site ideal for families. Situated at 600 from the centre of Port Grimaud and just 950 from the beach, we are perfectly situated for visiting this famous area of France. Our touring pitches come with their own fully equipped private bathroom, heated in low season with a water and 20 amp electrical hook up. Facilities onsite include pool, Jacuzzi, bar, take-away restaurant, shop, rental store, kids club, playing area. TV & games room, car wash, diving club, WIFI, moorings with access to the Mediterranean & more.
Opening dates 1/3/06 – 10/11/06.

RN98 Le Ginestrel, 83310 Grimaud, France. Tel. + 33 494 56 08 43 Fax + 33 494 56 23 88
Web site: www.holiday-marina.com **Email:** info@holiday-marina.com

GROSBREUIL *2H4* (2km SE) **Camping La Vertonne, Route du Poiroux, 85440 Grosbreuil** [tel/fax 02 51 22 65 74; lavertonne.camping@ wanadoo.fr] Fr La Roche-sur-Yon take N160 to La Mothe-Achard, D21 S to Grosbreuil. Fr Sables-d'Olonne 12km on D36. Med, mkd pitch, pt shd; wc; shwrs inc; chem disp; el pts (4A) €2.50; lndtte; ice; shop; snacks; 2 playgrnd; pool; mini-golf; few statics; quiet. "Lge indiv pitches; helpful owners; conv for local resorts; well shaded with gd facs."
1 Apr-30 Sep. € 12.00   2002*

GRUISSAN *10F1* (5km NE Coastal) **Camping Les Ayguades, 11430 Gruissan** [04 68 49 81 59; fax 04 68 49 05 64; loisirs-vacances-languedoc@ wanadoo.fr] Exit A9 junc 37 onto D168/D32 sp Gruissan. In 10km turn L at island sp Les Ayguades, foll site sp. Lge, hdg/mkd pitch, unshd; htd wc; chem disp; mv service pnt; baby facs; shwrs inc; el pts (6A) inc; lndtte; shop; rest; bar; playgrnd; sand beach adj; entmnt; TV; 25% statics; dogs €2.20; Eng spkn; adv bkg; quiet; cc acc; CCI. ♦
Easter-6 Nov. € 20.00   2004*

GUEBWILLER *6F3* (2km E) **Camping Le Florival, Route de Soultz, 68500 Issenheim** [tel/fax 03 89 74 20 47; contact@camping-leflorival.com]   Fr Mulhouse take D430 N. Then take D5 twd Issenhiem. Site well sp. Med, hdg/mkd pitch, pt shd; wc; chem disp; shwrs inc; baby facs; el pts (6A) €3; lndtte, shop & 200m; tradsmn; playgrnd; pool, waterslide 100m; TV rm; 30% statics; dogs €1.50; phone; Eng spkn; quiet; red 7 days; cc acc; CCI. "Gd long/sh stay." 1 Apr-31 Oct. € 12.62   2005*

GUEGON see Josselin *2F3*

GUEMENE PENFAO *2G4* (1km SE Rural) **Camping L'Hermitage, 36 Ave du Paradis, 44290 Guemene-Penfao** [02 40 79 23 48; fax 02 40 51 11 87; contact@campinglhermitage.com; www.camping lhermitage.com] On D775 fr cent of Guemene-Penfao, dir Chateaubriant for 500m, turn R, site sp. Med, mkd pitch, hdstg, pt shd; wc; chem disp; mv service pnt; baby facs; shwrs inc; el pts (6A) €2.50; gas; lndtte; ice; shop 1.5km; tradsmn; rest; snacks; bar; BBQ; playgrnd; htd, covrd pool adj; paddling pool; waterslide; jacuzzi; rv sw & fishing 300m; canoeing; tennis; games area; games rm; cycle hire; entmnt; child entmnt; TV; 20% statics; dogs €1; phone; some Eng spkn; adv bkg; quiet; red low ssn; CCI. "Gd walking in area; excel." ♦ 1 Apr-31 Oct. € 10.30   2005*

See advertisement on next page

GUENROUET *2G3* (E Rural) **Camp Municipal St Clair, 44530 Guenrouet** [02 40 87 61 52; fax 02 40 87 60 88; www.campingsaintclair.com] S fr Redon take D164 dir Blain, turn R onto D2 to Guenrouet, over bdge & site directly on L after bdge. Med, hdg/mkd pitch, pt sl, pt shd; wc; chem disp; mv service pnt; 50% serviced pitches; shwrs inc; el pts (10A) €2.80; gas 1km; ice; shop & 1km; tradsmn; rest 100m; playgrnd; htd pool adj; waterslide; fishing; canoe hire; dogs €1.50; Eng spkn; quiet; CCI. "On banks of canal; special area for late arrivals; excel." ♦ 16 Apr-30 Sep. € 13.00   2005*

GUERANDE *2G3* (2km NE Rural) **Camping de Brehadour, 44350 Guerande** [02 40 24 93 12 or 04 42 20 47 25 (LS); fax 04 20 24 92 77; info@homair-vacances.com; www.homair-vacances.fr] Exit N165 onto D774 to Guerande. In Guerande take D61 dir St Lyphard, site in 2km. Lge, hdg pitch, pt shd; wc; shwrs inc; el pts (6-10A) €3-4; gas; ice; BBQ; lndtte; shop; rest; snacks; bar; playgrnd; htd pool; sand beach 3km; entmnt; tennis; golf; 40% statics; dogs €1.83; adv bkg; quiet; Eng spkn; red low ssn; cc acc; CCI. 29 May-18 Sep. € 26.00   2002*

GUERANDE *2G3* (2km E) **Domaine de Leveno, Route de Sandun, 44350 Guerande** [02 40 24 79 30; fax 02 40 62 01 23; info@camping-leveno.com; www.camping-leveno.com] Fr Guerande foll sps to l'Etang de Sandun. Med, pt shd; wc; serviced pitches; shwrs; el pts (6A) inc; gas; lndtte; ice; shop; rest; snacks; bar; BBQ; playgrnd; htd, covrd pool; paddling pool; waterslide; sand beach 5km; tennis; mini-golf; games area; entmnt; TV rm; 60% statics; dogs €3; adv bkg; quiet; red low ssn. "Conv La Baule; vg in lovely park." 9 Apr-2 Oct. € 25.00   2005*

See advertisement on page 474

GUERANDE *2G3* (7km E) **Camping de l'Etang en Kerjacob, 47 Rue des Chenes, Sandun, 44350 Guerande** [02 40 61 93 51; fax 02 40 61 96 21; camping-etang@wanadoo.fr; www.camping-etang.com] Fr Guerande take D51 NE for approx 5km, turn R onto D48 for 3km. Turn L to site on lakeside. Sp fr each junc on Guerande by-pass. Med, hdg/mkd pitch, pt shd; wc; chem disp; baby facs; shwrs inc; el pts (10A) inc; gas; lndtte; shop; snacks, bar high ssn; BBQ; playgrnd; htd pool & paddling pool; sand beach 9km; watersports 9km; lake fishing; tennis; cycle hire; TV; 40% statics; dogs €1.45; poss cr; Eng spkn; adv bkg; cc acc; CCI. "Pleasant, peaceful site; friendly staff; ltd facs low ssn; noisy pool & playgrnd; mkt Wed & Sat." ♦ 15 May-15 Sep. € 17.50 ABS - B19   2005*

GUERANDE *2G3* (1km S Urban/Rural) **Camping Tremondec, 48 Rue du Chateau de Careil, 44350 Guerande** [02 40 60 00 07; fax 02 40 60 91 10; info@camping-tremondec.com; www.camping-tremondec.com] Fr Nantes on N171 dir La Baule. Take D192 dir La Baule cent, turn W in 800m dir Brenave, Careil. Site sp. Med, hdg/mkd pitch, hdstg, pt sl, pt shd; wc; chem disp; baby facs; shwrs inc; el pts (6A) €3.30; gas 1km; lndtte; ice; tradsmn; supmkt 900m; rest, snacks, bar high ssn; BBQ; playgrnd; htd pool; sand beach 2km; games area; entmnt; child entmnt; 30% statics; dogs; adv bkg; Eng spkn; quiet; cc acc; red low ssn/long stay/CCI. "Friendly, helpful owner; Chateau de Careil 200m; Guerande medieval city; lovely beaches & coast; pleasant walks thro salt marshes; cycle rtes; excel sh/long stay." ♦ 2 Apr-25 Sep. € 18.20   2005*

GUERANDE *2G3* (6km S) **Camping Le Pre du Chateau de Careil, 44350 Guerande** [tel/fax 02 40 60 22 99; chateau.careil@free.fr; www.careil.com] 2km N of La Baule on E of D92 on L side S past supmkt on L. Turn L at x-rds. Camp on L. Sm, pt shd; wc; shwrs; el pts inc; lndtte; supmkt 1km; rest; bar; pool; beach 2.5km; tennis; mini-golf; fishing; sailing; horseriding; entmnt; dogs €1; poss cr; adv bkg ess. "Conducted tours of chateau." ♦ 8 May-21 Sep. € 21.00   2003*

FRANCE

GUERANDE *2G3* (7km W Coastal) **Camp Municipal Les Chardons Bleus, Blvd de la Grande Falaise, 44420 La Turballe** [02 40 62 80 60; fax 02 40 62 85 40; camping.les.chardons.bleus@wanadoo.fr] Foll D99 to La Turballe. Site well sp fr town cent along D92. Lge, hdg/mkd pitch, unshd; wc; chem disp; mv service pnt adj; shwrs inc; el pts (6-10A) €2.70-3.65 (poss rev pol)(long lead poss req); lndtte; shop; tradsmn; rest in ssn; snacks; bar; playgrnd; htd pool; sand beach adj (part naturist) & 2km; entmnt; dogs €2.05; phone; Eng spkn; cc acc; CCI. "Nature reserve adj with bird life; becoming a little shabby but beach superb; ltd el pts when full; san facs stretched high ssn; variable opening dates - phone ahead to check early ssn; vg long/sh stay." ♦ 30 Apr-30 Sep. € 14.50   2005*

As we're travelling out of season, we'd better phone ahead to check that the site is actually open.

GUERANDE *2G3* (7km NW Coastal) **Camping-Caravaning La Falaise, 1 Blvd de Belmont, 44220 La Turballe** [02 40 23 32 53; fax 02 40 62 87 07; info@camping-de-la-falaise.com; www.camping-de-la-falaise.com] Fr Guerande exit on D99 sp La Turballe/Pirac-sur-Mer; pass La Turballe; site easily seen on L 200m after Intermarche. Med, hdg/mkd pitch, pt shd; htd wc (some cont); chem disp; some serviced pitches; shwrs inc; el pts (4-10A) inc; lndtte; ice; shop 200m; tradsmn; rest 100m; bar; BBQ; playgrnd; sand beach adj; watersports; naturist beach 2km; horseriding & mini-golf 3km; entmnts; TV; 5% statics; dogs €2; Eng spkn; adv bkg; quiet (some rd noise); CCI. "V pleasant site." ♦ 25 Mar-31 Oct. € 28.30   2004*

See advertisement above

GUERANDE *2G3* (7km NW Rural) **LES CASTELS Le Parc Ste Brigitte, Manoir de Brehet, 44420 La Turballe** [02 40 24 88 91; fax 02 40 15 65 72; saintebrigette@wanadoo.fr; www.campingsainte brigitte.com or www.les-castels.com] Take D99 NW fr Guerande twd La Turballe thro vill of Clis. Sp on R in 900m. Lge, mkd pitch, shd; wc; chem disp; mv service pnt; serviced pitch; shwrs inc; baby facs; el pts (6-10A) inc; gas; lndtte; ice; shop; rest; snacks; bar; playgrnd; htd, covrd pool; sand beach 2km; fishing; cycle hire; entmnt; TV rm; some statics; dogs €1.50; phone; poss cr; adv bkg (dep req); poss noisy; cc not acc; CCI. "V peaceful; excel rest & bar; some sm pitches; gd sh/long stay." ♦ 1 Apr-1 Oct. € 26.00   2004*

GUERCHE DE BRETAGNE, LA *2F4* (6km E Rural) **Camp Municipal, 35130 La Selle-Guerchaise** [02 99 96 26 81; fax 02 99 96 46 72] Fr N on D178 Vitre to Chateaubriant rd 3km N of of La Guerche de Bretagne; turn L onto D106 to Availles-sur-Seiche, then foll sp La Selle-Guerchaise; site behind Mairie in vill. Sm, hdg/mkd pitch, pt sl, pt shd; htd wc; chem disp (wc only); shwrs inc; el pts (4A) €2; (rev pol, poss long cable req); lndtte; playgrnd adj; mini-golf; fishing adj; 50% statics; dogs; adv bkg; poss noisy; CCI. "Welcoming; excel san facs; site poss untidy low ssn; poss noisy church bells & barking dogs; locked barrier poles OK for cars but too low 4x4s or similar; fair NH." ♦ € 6.80   2003*

GUERCHE SUR L'AUBOIS, LA *4H3* (2km SE Rural) **Camp Municipal Robinson, 18150 La Guerche-sur-l'Aubois** [02 48 74 18 86 or 02 48 77 53 53; fax 02 48 77 53 59] Site sp fr D976 opp church in vill cent. Sm, hdg/mkd pitch, pt shd; wc; mv service pnt; shwrs inc; el pts (6A) €2.20; ice; shops 2km; tradsmn; bar; playgrnd; lake sw adj; fishing; pedalo boating; entmnt; poss cr; poss noisy; CCI. "Pleasant situation in country area; poss problems with youths at night; some noise fr rlwy; mv service pnt fee for non-campers; fair sh stay/NH." ♦ ltd. 15 Apr-15 Oct. € 9.00   2003*

GUERET *7A4* (10km S Rural) **Camp Municipal, 23000 La Chapelle-Taillefert** [05 55 52 36 17 (Mairie)] Take junc 48 from N145 sp Tulle/ Bourganeuf (D33 thro Gueret); S on D940 fr Gueret, turn off at site sp. Foll sp thro vill, well sp. Sm, hdstg, pt sl, terr, shd; wc; shwrs €1; el pts (16A) €2; shops, rest, snacks, tradsmn; playgrnd; no dogs; fishing in Rv Gartempe; quiet; cc not acc; CCI. "Attractive, peaceful, well-kept site hidden away; trout stream runs thro site; gd walking; ltd facs low ssn; warden calls 1900; gd auberge in vill; site poss clsd bef end of Sep, phone ahead to check open." 1 Apr-30 Sep. € 7.00   2005*

GUERET *7A4* (3km W Rural) **Camp Municipal du Plan d'Eau de Courtille, Route de Courtille, 23000 Gueret** [05 55 81 92 24 or 05 55 52 99 50 (LS)] Fr W N145 take D942 to town cent, Route de Benevent. Site sp 'L'Aire de Loisirs de Courtille'. Med, hdg/mkd pitch, pt sl, pt shd; wc (some cont); chem disp; mv service pnt; baby facs; shwrs inc; el pts (10A) inc; shops 2km; rest, bar 500m; playgrnd; pool 1.5km; sand beach & lake sw; dogs; phone; poss cr; no adv bkg; quiet; CCI; "Well-managed site; pleasant scenery; watersports on lake; vg mkd walks nrby; poss noisy w/e." ♦ 1 Jun-30 Sep. € 10.85   2005*

GUERNO, LE see Muzillac *2G3*

GUICHEN *2F4* (8km SE) **Camp Municipal La Courbe, 11 Rue du Camping, 35580 Bourg-des-Comptes** [06 77 04 37 47 or 02 99 05 62 62 (Mairie); fax 02 99 05 62 69; bourg-des-comptes@wanadoo.fr] Fr Rennes take N137 S dir Nantes. At Crevin take rd W dir Guichen. Site sp on L bef rv bdge. Sm, pt shd; wc; chem disp; shwrs €0.91; el pts (10A) €2.20-3.40; shops 1km; playgrnd; lake & rv 100m; fishing; some long-stay statics; dogs €0.53; adv bkg; quiet. "Rough field." 1 Apr-31 Oct. € 5.60   2005*

GUIDEL see Pouldu, Le *2F2*

GUIGNICOURT *3C4* (Urban) **Camp Municipal Bord de l'Aisne, Rue des Godins, 02190 Guignicourt** [03 23 79 74 58 or 03 23 25 36 60; fax 03 23 79 74 55; camping.guignicourt@free.fr] Exit a'route A26 at junc 14 Guignicourt/Neufchatel & foll sp for Guignicourt (3km). Site sp in vill on rv bank. Turn R at g'ge down narr rd to site (12% descent at ent). Med, pt shd; htd wc (some cont); chem disp; shwrs; el pts (6-A) €2.75 (rev pol, poss long cable req); shops 500m; snacks; BBQ; playgrnd; tennis; fishing; 50% statics (sep area); dogs €1; poss cr; adv bkg; CCI. "Well-organised, well-kept, tranquil, rvside site; v friendly staff; well-guarded; wine for sale on site; v popular NH; unisex san facs low ssn; pleasant town; gd for Reims, Epernay; gd cycle tracks; easy access." 1 Apr-30 Sep. € 10.00   2005*

GUILLESTRE *9D4* (SW) **Camp Municipal de la Rochette, 05600 Guillestre** [tel/fax 04 92 45 02 15; guillestre@aol.com] On N94 Briancon-Embrun rd take D902 to Guillestre. Fr town on by-pass (D902) turn S at rndabt onto D86 sp Risoul, cross bdge, immed turn W along rv, site in 1km. Lge, shd; wc (cont); shwrs inc; el pts (10A) €3; gas; lndtte; ice; shop; snacks; BBQ; playgrnd; sports area; pool; fishing; dir access to rv; entmnt; poss cr; adv bkg; quiet. ♦ 15 May-22 Sep. € 12.70   2004*

†GUILLESTRE *9D4* (3km W) **Camping Le Villard, 05600 Guillestre** [04 92 45 06 54; fax 04 92 45 00 52; camping-le-villard@wanadoo.fr] Exit N94 onto D902A twd Guillestre. Site on R in 1km. Ent few metres down side rd with site sp at corner. Med, shd; wc (some cont); chem disp; shwrs inc; el pts (6-10A) €2.40-2.80; gas; lndry rm; shop 500m; tradsmn; rest; snacks; bar; playgrnd; sports area; pool; rv adj; fishing; lake 2km; tennis; mini-golf; wintersports; TV rm; entmnt; 10% statics; adv bkg; red low ssn; CCI. "Vg long stay." ♦ € 16.50   2004*

GUILLESTRE *9D4* (6km W) **Camp Municipal Les Iscles, 05600 Eygliers** [04 92 45 14 18; fax 04 92 45 40 71] Site clearly sp on N94 on ent to Mont-Dauphin-Gare fr S. Take rd by Hotel du Durance. Site on W edge of Eygliers on Rv Durance. Lge, pt shd; wc; chem disp; shwrs inc; el pts; gas; shop; lndtte; rest; snacks; playgrnd; entmnt; sw, canoeing & pedaloes in sm lake adj; fishing; sailing; cycle hire; tennis; mini-golf; horseriding; poss cr; adv bkg; quiet.   2003*

GUILVINEC *2F2* (2.5km W Coastal) **Yelloh! Village de la Plage, 29730 Guilvinec** [02 98 58 61 90 or 02 98 82 23 89 (LS); fax 02 98 58 89 06; info@ campingsbretagnesud.com;   www.campings bretagnesud.com or www.yellohvillage.com] Fr Pont l'Abbe on D785 SW to Plomeur; cont S on D57 sp Guilvinec. Bear R on app to town, W along coast rd twd Penmarch. Site on L in approx 1.5km. Lge, pt shd; wc; chem disp; baby facs; sauna; shwrs inc; el pts (5A) inc; gas; lndtte; rest; snacks; bar; BBQ; playgrnd; htd pool & paddling pool; waterslide; sand beach adj; tennis; games rm; entmnt (child & adult); mini-golf; cycle hire; entmnt; 70% statics; dogs €3.50; c'vans over 8m not acc; poss cr; adv bkg; quiet; cc acc. "Spacious pitches; mkt Tue & Sun; excursions booked; ideal for families; site rds poss diff lge o'fits." ♦ 5 May-9 Sep. € 33.30 ABS - B15   2005*

GUINES *3A3* (2km W Rural) **LES CASTELS de la Bien Assise**, 62340 Guines [03 21 35 20 77; fax 03 21 36 79 20; www.camping-bien-assise.fr or www.les-castels.com] Exit A16 at junc 40 dir Frethun Gare TGV onto D215. At 1st rndabt take 3rd exit sp Guines, then D246 thro St Tricat & Hames-Boucres (NB this is 30 km/h zone & you must give way to the R). In Guines turn R sp Marquise, site on L. Lge, hdg/mkd pitch, pt sl, pt shd; htd wc (some cont); chem disp; mv service pnt; baby facs; shwrs inc; el pts (6A) inc (poss rev pol); gas; lndtte; ice; shop; tradsmn; rest (clsd Mon); snacks; bar; BBQ; playgrnd; htd, covrd pool; paddling pool; waterslide; beach 15km; tennis; entmnt; cycle hire; library; horseriding 3km; TV/games rm; many statics; dogs €1; v cr high ssn; Eng spkn; adv bkg; red long stay & low ssn; cc acc; CCI. "V busy site high ssn; beware-soft ground on some pitches low ssn; ask for pitch away fr v busy rd; 2* gourmet rest on site; vg san facs; own wine sold; lge pitches; Guines vill worth a visit; vet in Ardres 9km; mkt Fri am; late arrivals area - much night movement high ssn." ♦ 15 Apr-24 Sep. € 28.00 ABS - P05 2005*

GUIPRY see Bain de Bretagne *2F4*

GUISE *3C4* (SE Urban) **Camp de la Vallee de l'Oise**, Rue du Camping, 02120 Guise [03 23 61 14 86; fax 03 23 61 21 07] Foll Vervin sp in town & camp clearly sp fr all dir in town. Med, pt shd; wc (some cont); shwrs inc; el pts (3-6A) €2.30-3.40 (rev pol); lndry rm; ice; shops 500m; tradsmn; playgrnd; rv fishing & canoe hire adj; cycle hire; games rm; TV; entmnt; 50% statics; dogs; some Eng spkn; adv bkg; v quiet; red low ssn; CCI. "Calm, spacious with mature trees; friendly on outskirts of town; supervised fishing; san facs in need of updating & more frequent cleaning; interesting old town with gd rests; if arr late, pitch & pay next morning." 1 Apr-31 Oct. € 10.00 2005*

GUISSENY see Plouguerneau *2E2*

GUJAN MESTRAS see Arcachon *7D1*

GURMENCON see Oloron Ste Marie *8F2*

HAGETMAU *8E2* (200m E Urban) **Camp Muncipal**, 40700 Hagetmau [05 58 79 79 79; fax 05 58 79 79 98] On D933 S fr Mont-de-Marsan, go thro St Sever & cont on D933 to Hagetmau. Take ring rd & ent town fr S, sp 'Cite Verte'. Heading N fr Orthez on D933, also foll sp 'Cite Verte'. Sm, hdg pitch, pt shd; wc; chem disp (wc only); mv service pnt; serviced pitch; fam bthrm; sauna; shwrs inc; el pts (16A) inc; shops 500m; rest, snacks, bar 1km; BBQ; htd, covrd pool; jacuzzi; gym; dogs; phone; little Eng spkn; adv bkg ess (dep req); quiet. "A unique site associated with sports cent inc Olympic-sized pool; 24 pitches with personal facs; gd base for touring area; v attractive town; excel long stay, (minimum 6 days)." 1 Jun-30 Sep. € 18.00 (5 persons) 2003*

HAGUENAU *5D3* (2km S Urban) **Camp Municipal Les Pins**, Rue de Strasbourg, 67500 Haguenau [03 88 73 91 43 or 03 88 93 70 00; fax 03 88 93 69 89; tourisme@ville-haguenau.fr] N fr Strasbourg; after passing township sp turn L at 1st set of traff lts; foll camping sp. Med, mkd pitch, terr, pt shd; wc; chem disp; shwrs inc; el pts (6A) €2.60; gas; lndry rm; shop, rest 2km; bar adj; playgrnd; dogs €0.90; phone; adv bkg; quiet; CCI. 1 May-30 Sep. € 7.10 2005*

HANNONVILLE SOUS LES COTES *5D2* (Rural) **Camping Le Longeau**, 55210 Hannonville-sous-les-Cotes [03 29 87 30 54; fax 03 29 88 84 40] Fr Hannonville on D908. Foll sp 'Etang du Longeau.' Narr, steep forest tracks to site not rec trailer c'vans. Med, pt shd; wc; chem disp; shwrs inc; el pts (3-6A) €2.50-4; rest; snacks; bar; fishing; no Eng spkn; quiet. "Gd long stay." Easter-15 Sep. € 8.00 2004*

HAULME see Charleville Mezieres *5C1*

HAUTECOURT ROMANECHE see Bourg en Bresse *9A2*

HAUTEFORT *7C3* (2km S) **Camping Le Moulin des Loisirs**, Nailhac, 24390 Hautefort [05 53 50 46 55; moulin.des.loisirs@wanadoo.fr; www.moulin-des-loisirs.fr] S on D704 fr Lanouaille & after 17km turn L on D71. Site sp to R at side of lake in 2km. Sm, pt sl, pt shd; wc; chem disp; shwrs inc; el pts (6A) €2.80; lndtte; sm shop; rest; snacks; pool; fishing; canoeing; horseriding; dogs €1.20; quiet. "Excel setting; gd local walks; new san facs block 2004." ♦ Easter-30 Sep. € 12.00 2004*

HAUTEFORT *7C3* (8km W Rural) **Camping Les Tourterelles**, 24390 Tourtoirac [05 53 51 11 17; fax 05 53 50 53 44] Fr N or S on D704 turn W at Hautefort on D62/D5 to Tourtoirac. In Tourtoirac turn R over rv then L. Site in 1km. Med, hdg/mkd pitch, terr, pt shd; wc; chem disp; mv service pnt; baby facs; shwrs; el pts (6A) inc; gas; lndtte; shop 2km; rest; snacks; bar; playgrnd; pool; tennis; horseriding; mini-golf; TV rm; 20% statics; dogs €3.50; bus 1km; phone; poss cr; Eng spkn; adv bkg (dep req); quiet; low ssn/snr citizens red; cc acc; CCI. "Beautiful Auvezere valley; rallies welcome; owners v helpful." ♦ Easter-15 Oct. € 20.00 2004*

HAUTERIVES see Beaurepaire *9C2*

HAUTOT SUR MER see Dieppe *3C2*

FRANCE

SITES

†HAVRE, LE *3C1* (300m N Urban) **Camping de la Foret de Montgeon**, 76620 Le Havre [tel/fax 02 35 46 52 39; chlorophile1@wanadoo.fr] Fr ferry foll Paris sp at rndabt, over x-ing of dock, strt on at traff lts & foll sp 'Haut Ville'. Turn R at next traff lts & almost immed L at 'Cours de la Republique' thro tunnel (max 2.8m). L at rndabt & foll sp to site. NB Two tunnels on this rte - 1st max height vehicles 2.8m (but there is rd parallel), 2nd max height 3.8m. Site poorly sp. Lge, mkd pitch, hdstg, mainly shd; htd wc (some cont); chem disp (wc); baby facs; shwrs inc; el pts (5A) inc (poss rev pol); gas; lndtte; shop, rest, snacks high ssn; playgrnd; pool 3km; TV; 60% statics; dogs €1.22; phone; poss cr; Eng spkn; adv bkg; noise fr adj car park; 10% red long stay; CCI. "Woodland site, ltd touring pitches; poss unkempt; restricted office hrs low ssn - pitch yourself if clsd; gates clsd 2230-0700 low ssn; ltd facs; most wc blocks refurbished; mostly permanent workers on site; phone fr ferry & site will poss stay open for you high ssn (if not, then ltd parking at ferry port) but will not open for departure for early morning ferries; diff to find pitch if arr in dark; lge boating lake 5 mins; major security probs on site & carpark at nrby Auchan supmkt reported Apr 05; NH only." € 16.72
2005*

HAYE DU PUITS, LA *1D4* (1km N Rural) **Camping L'Etang des Haizes**, 50250 St Symphorien-le-Valois [02 33 46 01 16; fax 02 33 47 23 80; etang.des.haizes@wanadoo.fr; www.campingetangdeshaizes.com] Heading N fr La Haye-du-Puits on D900 under rlwy bdge & site L, well sp. Med, hdg pitch, some hdstg, pt sl, pt shd; wc; chem disp; mv service pnt; baby facs; shwrs inc; el pts (6-10A) inc; gas; lndtte; supmkt 1km; shop; tradsmn; rest; snacks; bar; playgrnd; pool; waterslide; beach 15km; archery; fishing; cycle hire; games area; entmnt; TV; 50% statics (sep area); dogs €2; bus; phone; poss cr; Eng spkn; adv bkg rec (dep req); quiet; red low ssn; CCI. "Clean, pretty site; barrier clsd 2300-0700; pool area v clean; grounds v well-tended; helpful & pleasant owners; conv vill & Cherbourg ferry (1hr); elec pts poss insuff - cables across rd; ltd facs low ssn." 15 Apr-15 Oct. € 30.00 (CChq acc)
2005*

HAYE DU PUITS, LA *1D4* (6km N Urban) **Camp Municipal du Vieux Chateau**, Ave Division Leclerc, 50390 St Sauveur-le-Vicomte [02 33 41 72 04 or 02 33 21 50 44; fax 02 33 95 88 85; ot.ssv@wanadoo.fr] Fr Cherbourg site on R after x-ing bdge at St Saveur. Med, mkd pitch, pt shd; wc; chem disp; shwrs inc; el pts (4-6A) €1.70 (rev pol); lndtte; ice; shop 500m; tradsmn; rest at auberge adj; BBQ; playgrnd adj; games area; games rm; TV; dogs €1; phone; adv bkg; quiet; cc acc; CCI. "Excel site; ideal 1st stop fr Cherbourg; in grounds of old chateau; office open until 2200 & barrier clsd 2200-0800." 1 Jun-15 Sep. € 8.70
2004*

HEIMSBRUNN see Mulhouse *6F3*

HEMING *6E3* (5km SW) **Camping Les Mouettes**, 57142 Gondrexange [03 87 25 06 01; fax 03 87 25 01 13] Exit Heming on N4 Strasbourg- Nancy. Foll sp Gondrexange & site sp. App fr W on D955 turn to site sp on L about 1km bef Heming. Lge, pt sl, unshd; wc; chem disp; shwrs inc; el pts (6A) €4 (rev pol) adapter req; lndtte; shop, snacks & rest 1km; bar; playgrnd; lake beach, sw, fishing & sailing adj; cycle hire; tennis; mini-golf; 40% statics; phone; poss cr; quiet; CCI. "Pleasant site by lake; poss noisy w/e; friendly warden; basic facs but immac; gd sh stay." 1 Apr-30 Sep. € 11.10
2004*

HENDAYE *8F1* (1km N Coastal) **Camping Alturan**, 64700 Hendaye-Plage [05 59 20 04 55] Foll sps to Hendaye-Plage. Site 100m fr prom rd at N end of town but steep app. Best way to drive N thro Hendaye-Plage rlwy stn yard & take cent of 3 rds sp to site. Lge, terr, shd; wc (cont); chem disp; shwrs inc; el pts (4A); gas; lndtte; shop; rest; snacks in ssn; bar; playgrnd; sand beach 100m; poss cr; some rlwy noise; no adv bkg. 1 Jun-30 Sep. € 20.20
2002*

HENDAYE *8F1* (2km N) **Camping Les Acacias**, Route de la Glaciere, 64700 Hendaye-Plage [tel/fax 05 59 20 78 76; info@les-acacias.com; www.les-acacias.com] Exit Hendaye by N10 Rte de la Corniche for St Jean-de-Luz. In 1km turn R on D658. Site sp on R. Caution under rlwy bdge. Lge, sl, shd; wc; shwrs; el pts (6A) €4.20 (rev pol); gas; lndtte; shop; rest; snacks; bar in high ssn; playgrnd; sand beach 1.4km (free shuttle); lake sw & waterslide 1.5km; poss cr; adv bkg; quiet but some rlwy noise. "Helpful management; 5km to Spanish frontier; many tours in mountains; easy access shops & beaches; own lake for trout fishing." 1 Apr-1 Oct. € 18.00
2004*

HENDAYE *8F1* (2km W Urban/Coastal) **Camping Ametza**, Bvld de l'Empereur, 64700 Hendaye-Plage [05 59 20 07 05; fax 05 59 20 32 16; contact@camping-ametza.com; www.camping-ametza.com] Exit A63 junc 2 St Jean-de-Luz S onto D192. Foll sp to site. Turn L on hill down to seafront, cross rlwy, site immed on L. Lge, sl, shd; wc; chem disp; baby facs; shwrs inc; el pts (6A) €3.80; lndry rm; shop; snacks; bar; playgrnd; pool; sand; beach 900m; games area; entmnt; 30% statics; dogs €1.90; poss cr; Eng spkn; quiet; CCI. "Henday pleasant resort with excel beach." 1 Jun-30 Sep. € 19.80
2005*

HENNEBONT see Lorient *2F2*

HENRIDORFF see Phalsbourg *5D3*

HENVIC see St Pol de Leon *1D2*

HERBIGNAC *2G3* (E) **Camp Municipal de Ranrouet**, Rue Cadou, 44410 Herbignac [02 40 88 96 23 or 02 40 91 36 52] Site at intersection D774 & D33 on E edge of vill. Med, pt shd; wc; chem disp; shwrs; el pts (6A) inc; lndtte; shop; supmkt adj; playgrnd; beach 10km; entmnt; TV; CCI. "Immac san facs; gd cent for Guerande." Easter-30 Oct. € 12.55
2005*

† Site open all year   346   *Help update this Guide*

†HERIC *2G4* (2km W Rural) **Camping La Pindiere, La Denais, Route de la Fay-de-Bretagne, 44810 Heric [tel/fax 02 40 57 65 41; patrick-ara@ wanadoo.fr; www.camping-la-pindiere.com]** Exit N137 twd Heric at traff lts in town, leave town & turn W onto D16 (sp Camping). Site on L after rndabt supmkt, turn at sp Notre Dames-des-Landes. Med, hdg pitch, hdstg, pt shd; wc; chem disp; mv service pnt; baby facs; shwrs inc; el pts (6-10A) €2.80-4; gas; lndtte; ice; shop; tradsmn; rest; bar; playgrnd; htd pool (caps ess); paddling pool; sports facs; tennis; horseriding 200m; TV; many statics; dogs €1.30; phone; Eng spkn; adv bkg rec, site poss clsd w/e low ssn; some noise fr rd on N side; CCI. "Excel NH; lge, grass pitches, soft in wet weather." ♦ € 11.10 2005*

HERICOURT EN CAUX see Yvetot *3C2*

HERISSON *7A4* **Camp Municipal de l'Aumance, Crochepot, 03190 Herisson [04 70 06 87 86 or 04 70 06 80 45 (LS)]** Exit A71 junc 9 onto N144 N. Turn R onto D11 to Herisson. Bef vill turn L at blue sp (high on L), site on R down hill. Fr S exit A71 junc 10 onto D94 to Cosne, then D11 to Herisson. Foll lorry rte to avoid town cent; site on D157 on rv. Med, mkd pitch, pt shd; wc; shwrs inc; el pts (10A) inc; ice; playgrnd; games area; rv adj; phone. "Idyllic setting; delightful rvside site; warden calls eves." 1 Apr-30 Oct. € 5.90 2005*

HERPELMONT see Bruyeres *6E2*

HESDIN *3B3* (6km SE Rural) **Camping de la Route des Villages Fleuris, Rue de Poissonniers, 62770 St Georges [03 21 03 11 01 or 03 21 41 97 45]** Fr Hesdin, SE on D340 for 5.5km. Site on L in vill, in same rd as Camping St Ladre. Look for correct sp. Med, p sl, pt shd; wc (some cont); chem disp; shwrs €1; el pts (4A) €2.30; gas; shops 6km; tradsmn; BBQ; playgrnd; 90% statics; adv bkg; quiet; CCI. "Space for approx 7 tourers at rear of site; friendly warden; security barrier; can find warden in bungalow to L of site ent; gd sh stay/NH." 1 Apr-30 Sep. € 5.90 2003*

HESDIN *3B3* (6km SE Rural) **Camping St Ladre, Rue de Poissonniers, 62770 St Georges [03 21 04 83 34]** Fr Hesdin SE on D340 for 5.5km. Site on L after St Georges, ent narr lane next cottage on bend. Fr W on N39 or D349 foll sp Frevent, then St Georges. This is 2nd site you will come across so do not confuse. Sm, hdg/mkd pitch, pt shd; wc; chem disp; shwrs inc; el pts (5A) €2.50; lndtte; tradsmn; no statics; adv bkg; quiet; cc not acc; CCI. "Sm family-run & peaceful; basic facs but clean; conv Channel ports, Agincourt & Crecy; pleasant orchard site; usual agricultural noises." 1 Apr-30 Sep. € 6.80 2005*

†HESDIN *3B3* (12km NW) **Camp Municipal La Source, Rue des Etangs, 62990 Beaurainville [03 21 81 40 71 or 06 80 32 17 25; fax 03 21 90 02 88]** Fr Hesdin take D349 NW to Beaurainville. Site on R bef cent of town, 1.5km E of town cent; sp. Med, mkd pitch, pt shd; htd wc; shwrs inc; el pts (10A) inc; lndtte; shop 1km; bar; playgrnd; fishing; boating; games area; horseriding; 90% statics; 10% red long stay; CCI. "Ltd touring pitches; site poss clsd in winter - phone ahead; pleasant area with plenty wildlife; poss cold shwrs low ssn; gd NH." ♦ € 12.40 2005*

We're having a great holiday - must fill in some site report forms and send them to The Club as soon as possible.

HEUDICOURT see St Mihiel *5D2*

HILLION see St Brieuc *2E3*

HIRSON *3C4* (3km N Rural) **Camp Municipal de la Cascade de Blangy, 02500 Hirson [03 23 58 18 97 or 03 23 58 03 91 (LS); fax 03 23 58 25 39; tourisme.info.hirson@wanadoo.fr]** Site off N43; on exit Hirson twd La Capelle turn R on D963; at rndabt (site sp) fork R imm; foll site sp. Long, narr access rd. Med, hdg/mkd pitch, pt sl, pt shd; wc; chem disp; mv service pnt; shwrs inc; el pts (6-13A) €3-4; lndtte; shop; tradsmn; rest, snacks 2km; bar; BBQ; playgrnd; pool; 25% statics; dogs €0.50; Eng spkn; adv bkg ess high ssn; quiet but some rlwy noise; CCI. "V clean site, 2500kg weight limit; rec arr bet 1000-1200 & 1700-1900; immac san facs; pop with youth groups; v helpful owners." ♦ ltd. 15 Apr-15 Sep. € 9.00 2005*

HIRSON *3C4* (10km N) **Camp Municipal des Etangs des Moines, 59610 Fourmies [03 27 60 04 32 or 03 72 60 03 15]** Fr Hirson head N on D964 to Anor 4km. Turn L to Fourmies 3km. Sp on R on ent town. Med, hdg pitch, hdstg, pt shd; wc; chem disp; shwrs €1; el pts inc; lndtte; shop 1km; tradsmn; playgrnd; htd pool; 80% statics; dogs; no twin-axles; poss cr; Eng spkn; some rlwy noise; CCI. "Textile & eco museum in town; vg long stay." 1 Apr-31 Oct. € 13.00 2004*

†HOHWALD, LE *6E3* (1km W Urban) **Camp Municipal Le Hohwald, 28 Rue du Herrenhaus, 67140 Le Hohwald [tel/fax 03 88 08 30 90]** Site on W o'skts of town on D425 300m fr cent. Med, pt sl, terr, shd; wc; shwrs inc; lndtte; shops adj; el pts (10A) €5.10; snacks; playgrnd; tennis 300m; many statics; adv bkg; quiet. "Set in woodland park; tired, dated facs." € 10.25 2005*

HONFLEUR *3C1* (5km S Rural) **Camping Domaine Catiniere**, Route d' Honfleur, 27210 Fiquefleur-Equainville [02 32 57 63 51; fax 02 32 42 12 57; info@camping-catiniere.com; www.camping-catiniere.com] Fr A29/Pont de Normandie (toll) bdge exit junc 3 sp Le Mans, pass under m'way onto D580/D180. In 3km go strt on at rndabt & in 100m bear R onto D22 dir Beuzeville; site sp on R in 500m. Med, hdg/mkd pitch, pt shd; wc (some cont); chem disp; mv service pnt; shwrs inc; baby facs; el pts (4A) inc (long lead poss req), extra charge for 8-13A; gas 5km; lndtte; shop & 5km; tradsmn; snacks & bar in high ssn; BBQ; snacks; playgrnd; htd pool; games rm; entmnt; TV rm; 25% statics; dogs €2; phone; poss cr; Eng spkn; adv bkg rec high ssn & w/e; (dep req); quiet; cc acc only over €70; CCI. "Lge & sm pitches; tidy & clean; excel san facs; v friendly/helpful owner; gate clsd 2200-0800 (2300 high ssn); dep €20 req for barrier; 20 mins to Le Havre ferry via Normandy bdge; Honfleur lovely & interesting; poss school groups; vg." ♦ 7 Apr-24 Sep. € 20.00   2005*

See advertisement above

HONFLEUR *3C1* (2.5km SW Rural) **Camping La Briquerie**, 14600 Equemauville [02 31 89 28 32; fax 02 31 89 08 52; campinglabriquerie@ regionnormande.com; www.region-normande.com/labriquerie] Fr E ent town cent keeping harbour on R. Turn L onto D279 then in 2km turn R at rndabt at Intermarche. Site on R, N of water tower, E of Equemauville. Site well sp fr town cent. Fr S take D579 dir Honfleur Centre. At water tower on R turn L at Intermarche rndabt, site on R in 300m. Lge, hdg pitch, pt shd; wc; chem disp; mv service pnt; baby facs; fam bthrm; shwrs inc; el pts (5A) €4.50; gas; ice; lndtte; supmkt adj; rest, snacks, bar high ssn; BBQ; playgrnd; 3 htd pools; waterslide; sand beach 3km; games rm; fitness rm; tennis 500m; TV rm; entmnt; 50% statics; dogs €1.50; poss cr; Eng spkn; adv bkg (fee for Jul/Aug); quiet; red low ssn; cc not acc; CCI. "Gd pitches; clean facs; v helpful late/early ferry arrivals; local vets geared up for dog inspections, etc; rather impersonal." ♦ 1 Apr-30 Sep. € 17.00   2005*

HONFLEUR *3C1* (800m NW Coastal) **Camp Le Phare**, Blvd Charles V, 14600 Honfleur [02 31 89 10 26 or 02 31 91 05 75 (LS); fax 02 31 24 71 47] Fr E on D580. Foll sp 'Centre Ville' then Vieux Bassin dir Trouville. At rectangular rndabt with fountain turn R sp Deauville & Trouville; foll rd round over bdge. Turn 1st R, site in 500m to L of lighthouse. Med, hdg pitch; pt shd; wc (some cont); chem disp; mv service pnt; shwrs €1.20; el pts (2-10A) €4.04-5.72; gas; lndtte; shop 800m; tradsmn; rest 1km; snacks; bar; BBQ; playgrnd; htd, covrd pool nr; sand beach 100m; fishing; 10% statics; dogs €2.50; phone; poss cr; Eng spkn; rd noise; no cc acc; CCI. "Conv NH Le Havre ferry; some ill-maintained elecs; easy walk to delightful town & harbour/beach; m'van pitches narr & adj to busy rd (€20), el pts (6A) inc; some surface water after rain; some soft, sandy pitches; facs ltd low ssn; barrier clsd 2200-0700." 1 Apr-30 Sep. € 16.60   2005*

HONNECOURT SUR ESCAUT *3B4* (Rural) **Camp Municipal de l'Escaut**, 59226 Honnecourt-sur-Escaut [03 27 78 50 88; fax 03 27 74 31 52]   Fr Cambrai on N44 S twd St Quentin. Turn R onto D16. Or fr A26 exit junc 9 onto D917 then N44. In Honnecourt-sur-Escaut turn R over canal; site behind church. Med, hdg/mkd pitch, pt shd; wc; chem disp (wc); shwrs €1; mv service pnt; el pts (6A) inc (poss rev pol); lndtte; snacks; BBQ; playgrnd; fishing; 80% statics; dogs; little Eng spkn; adv bkg; noise fr church bells; CCI. "Peaceful, rural site on banks of St Quentin Canal & stream; warden v friendly; san facs spartan & in need of renovation; lge pitches; if barrier clsd seek help fr nrby statics; fair NH." 1 Apr-30 Sep. € 13.00   2002*

HOSPITALET, L' *8G4* (600m N Rural) **Camp Municipal**, 09390 L'Hospitalet [05 61 05 20 04; fax 05 61 05 23 08] Site clearly sp on N20 fr Ax-les-Thermes to Andorra. Med, terr, unshd; wc; shwrs inc; el pts (5A) €2.30; lndtte; shops 200m; adv bkg; quiet but some rd noise. "Mainly tents, ltd space for tourers; vg walking; immac facs; conv day trips to Andorra & Spain; friendly warden; excel views; gd sh stay." 1 Jun-31 Oct. € 8.80   2003*

HOSSEGOR *8E1* (6km N Rural) **Camping Aire Naturelle Loustalet (Bellante), Quartier Lamontagne, Blvd Maritime, 40510 Seignosse** [05 58 43 20 20 or 05 58 43 32 19] Exit N10 at St Vincent; turn R onto D33. In Hossegor turn R onto D152/D79. Site on L in approx 6km, after x-rds sp 'Plage de Casernes'. (Ignore no ent sp at site ent.) Sm, pt shd; wc (some cont); chem disp; shwrs inc; el pts; BBQ; ice; lndry rm; shops 1km; sand beach 1km by foot only (patrolled beach 6km); playgrnd; horseriding; golf; adv bkg; CCI. "Vg long stay; site in Landes forest; v peaceful; family-run; basic facs; helpful, friendly owner." 1 Apr-30 Sep. 2004*

HOSSEGOR *8E1* (6km N Coastal) **Camping Loisirs Houorn-Naou (formerly Municipal), Ave des Lucs, 40510 Seignosse** [05 58 43 30 30; fax 05 58 41 64 21; infos@hourn-naou.com] Take D79 N fr Hossegor. After 6km turn L at rndabt. Site lge. Lge, mkd pitch, pt sl, shd; wc; shwrs inc; el pts (6A) €3; lndtte; ice; shop; rest; snacks; bar; playgrnd; pool 500m; sand beach 600m; lake 2km; adv bkg; quiet, "Min stay Jul/Aug 7 days; pleasant staff; in pine forest." ♦ 1 Apr-30 Sep. € 21.20 2004*

HOSSEGOR *8E1* (2km S Coastal) **Camp Municipal La Civelle, Rue des Biches, 40130 Capbreton** [05 58 72 15 11 or 05 58 72 10 09 (Mairie)] Fr N on A63, take exit 8 & foll sps to Capbreton; cont twds cent. At 1st rndabt, turn L past Intermarche. Strt on at 2nd rndabtat. At 3rd rndabt take 3rd exit & foll sp for site. Lge, mkd pitch, shd; wc (some cont); chem disp; 10% serviced pitches; el pts €3.20; gas; lndtte; ice; shop 1.5km; snacks; rest; pool; phone; cc acc; CCI. "Vg sh stay." 1 Jun-30 Sep. € 13.00 2004*

†HOSSEGOR *8E1* (3km S Coastal) **Camp Municipal Bel Air, Ave de Bourret, 40130 Capbreton** [05 58 72 12 04] Fr N10 or A63, take D28 sp Hossegor/Capbreton. After town sp strt over rndabt, then R at next rndabt turn R (sp Hossegor) onto D652. Turn L at 5th rndabt, site on L in 200m. Med, hdg pitch, pt sl, pt shd; wc; chem disp; shwrs; el pts (10A) inc; ice; gas; lndry rm; shops 500m; tradsmn; playgrnd; sand beach 1km; cycle hire adj; dogs €2.05; quiet; 10% red low ssn; CCI. "No arr bef 1500; site office clsd 1200-1500 (1600 in winter); card-op barrier; marina nrby, gd fishing; excel network of cycle paths; excel surfing; conv Biarritz; arr bef 2000 unless late arr agreed in advance; vg winter NH/sh stay." ♦ € 20.00 2005*

HOSSEGOR *8E1* (4km S Coastal) **Camping de la Pointe, Ave Jean Lartigau, 40130 Capbreton** [05 58 72 14 98 or 05 58 72 35 34; www.homair-vacances.fr] Fr N10 at Labenne, take D652 twd Capbreton. In 5km turn L at camp sp. Site in 1km on R. Lge, shd; wc; chem disp; shwrs inc; el pts; gas; lndtte; ice; shop; rest; snacks; playgrnd; htd pool; paddling pool; sand beach 800m; entmnt; TV; mini-golf; some statics; dogs; quiet. 3 Apr-25 Sep. 2002*

HOULGATE *3D1* (3.5km NE Coastal) **Camping Les Falaises, Route de la Corniche, 14510 Gonneville-sur-Mer** [02 31 24 81 09; fax 02 31 28 04 11] Fr D513 take D163; site clearly sp close to Auberville. Lge, pt sl, pt shd; wc; chem disp (wc); shwrs inc; el pts inc; snacks; shop; gas; ice; htd pool; playgrnd; beach reached by cliffs (230 steps); 30% statics; poss cr. "Nice site, diff areas sep by trees; towns of interest, Honfleur, Caen, Deauville; gd, clean facs; red facs low ssn; pleasant, helpful staff." 1 Apr-31 Oct. € 18.30 (3 persons) 2005*

This site entry hasn't been updated for a while; we'd better fill in a site report form and send it to The Club.

HOULGATE *3D1* (1km E Urban) **Camp Municipal des Chevaliers, Chemin des Chevaliers, 14510 Houlgate** [02 31 24 37 93; fax 02 31 28 37 13] Fr Deauville take the D513 SW twds Houlgate. Before 'Houlgate' sp, turn L & foll camping sps to site, 250m after Camping de la Vallee. Lge, mkd pitch, pt sl, unshd; wc; shwrs inc; el pts (10A) €3.90; tradsmn; sand beach 800m; fishing & boating 800m; dogs €0.70; adv bkg (rec high ssn); v quiet. ♦ 1 Apr-30 Sep. € 7.80 2005*

HOULGATE *3D1* (2km E Coastal) **Camping La Vallee, 88 Rue de la Vallee, 14510 Houlgate** [02 31 24 40 69; fax 02 31 24 42 42; camping.lavallee@wanadoo.fr; www.campinglavallee.com] Exit junc 29 or 29a fr A13 onto D45 to Houlgate. Or fr Deauville take D513 W. Before Houlgate sp, turn L & foll sp to site. Lge, hdg/mkd pitch, pt sl, terr, pt shd; wc; chem disp; some serviced pitches; shwrs inc; el pts (6A) inc; gas; lndtte; ice; supmkt; tradsmn; rest; snacks; bar; playgrnd; htd pool; paddling pool; sand beach 900m; lake fishing 2km; tennis; cycle hire; golf 1km; games rm; entmnt; internet; TV rm; 30% statics; dogs €4; Eng spkn; adv bkg (fee); cc acc; red low ssn; CCI. "Superb site; v clean san facs; friendly recep; v busy; some pitches sm for lge o'fits; conv town cent." ♦ ltd. 1 Apr-15 Oct. € 28.00 (CChq acc) 2005*

See advertisement on next page

HOUMEAU, L' see Rochelle, La *7A1*

HOUPLINES see Armentieres *3A3*

NORMANDY BETWEEN CABOURG AND DEAUVILLE, 900 M. FROM THE BEACH
CAMPING - CARAVANING ★★★★
88, rue de la Vallée – 14510 HOULGATE
Tel: 00 33 (0)2 31 24 40 69 Fax: 00 33 (0)2 31 24 42 42
www.campinglavallee.com • camping.lavallee@wanadoo.fr
LA VALLÉE
FRANCE
• Grocery • Bar • Children's playground • Heated swimming pool • Paddling pool • Organized leisure • Internet terminal • Bikes and cross bikes for hire • Ponies • Mobile homes to let • Golf course at 1 km. 10% discount.

HOURTIN *7C1* (1.5km N) **Camping L'Oree du Bois, Route des Lacs, 33990 Hourtin [tel/fax 05 56 09 15 88 or 06 09 65 48 96; loree-du-bois@ wanadoo.fr]** Fr Hourtin, take D101E twd beach, site in 1.5km. Med, shd; wc; shwrs inc; el pts (3-6A) inc; gas; lndtte; ice; shop; bar; snacks; playgrnd; pool; sand beach 8km; entmnt; dogs €1.50; adv bkg; quiet; red low ssn. "In Medoc area with its chateaux & wines." May-Sep. € 19.00   2003*

HOURTIN *7C1* (1.5km W) **Camping La Rotonde, Chemin de Becassine, 33990 Hourtin [05 56 09 10 60; fax 05 56 73 81 37; la-rotonde@ wanadoo.fr]** In Hourtin, foll sp Hourtin Port; in 1.5km L at sp; site on L 200m. Lge, pt shd; wc; shwrs inc; el pts (6A) inc; gas; ice; lndtte; shop & 2km; rest/snacks/bar Jul-Aug; playgrnd; pool in ssn; lake/beach 1km; tennis & watersports nr; entmnt; 30% statics; adv bkg; quiet; CCI. "In pine forest nr largest lake in France; gate shut 2100-0900." ♦ 1 Apr-30 Sep. € 17.40   2002*

HOURTIN *7C1* (10km W Coastal) **Airotel Camping Caravaning de la Cote d'Argent, 33990 Hourtin-Plage [05 56 09 10 25; fax 05 56 09 24 96; info@ camping-cote-dargent.com; www.cca33.com]** Fr a'route exit 7 to Le Verdon & Soulac. At Lesparre-Medoc take D3 Hourtin, D101 to Hourtin-Plage, site sp. V lge, mkd pitch, pt sl, terr, shd; wc (some cont); mv service pnt; chem disp; baby fac; fam bthrm; shwrs inc; el pts (6A) €5; gas; lndtte; ice; shop; tradsmn; rest; snacks; bar; BBQ playgrnd; 3 htd, covrd pools; waterslide; jacuzzi; sand beach 300m; watersports; lake sw & fishing 4km; tennis; cycle hire; games rm; horseriding; entmnt; internet; TV in bar; 25% statics; dogs €4; Eng spkn; adv bkg; quiet; red low ssn; cc acc; CCI. "Peaceful site in pine forest & dunes; conv Medoc region chateaux & vineyards." ♦ 13 May-18 Sep. € 32.00 (CChq acc)   2004*

HOURTIN PLAGE see Hourtin *7C1*

HUANNE MONTMARTIN see Baume les Dames *6G2*

HUELGOAT *2E2* (3km E Rural) **Camping La Riviere d'Argent, La Coudraie, 29690 Huelgoat [02 98 99 72 50; fax 02 98 99 90 61; campriviere@ aol.com]** Sp fr town cent 3km on D769A sp Poullaouen & Carhaix. Med, some hdg/mkd pitch, shd; wc; chem disp; shwrs inc; el pts (6A) €2.50; lndtte; shops 3km; rest, snacks, pool & tennis high ssn; playgrnd; dogs €0.80; adv bkg; quiet; red long stay/low ssn. "Lovely wooded site on rv bank; some pitch by rv side or in field or hdgd; helpful owner; gd walks with maps provided; ltd facs low ssn." 20 Apr-30 Sep. € 11.40   2005*

HUELGOAT *2E2* (1km W Rural) **Camp Municipal du Lac, 29690 Huelgoat [02 98 99 78 80 or 02 98 99 72 32 (Mairie)]** Fr cent of Huelgoat foll unnumbered rd W sp La Feuillee/Brest; foll site sp. Med, hdg pitch, pt shd; wc (cont); chem disp; shwrs inc; el pts (10A) inc; lndry rm; shops 2km; htd pool adj; playgrnd; quiet; no cc acc; CCI. "At end of lake (no sw); gd walking; gd san facs; gd size pitches; v peaceful." 15 Jun-15 Sep. € 10.70   2002*

HUELGOAT *2E2* (10km W Rural) **Camp Municipal Nestavel-Bras, 29218 Brennilis [02 98 99 66 57 or 02 98 99 61 07 (Mairie)]** Fr Huelgoat take D764 W for 8km & turn S onto D36. Site sp in Brennilis. Sm, hdg pitch, terr, pt shd; wc (cont); chem disp; shwrs inc; el pts (13A) €0.76; ice; shop; playgrnd; TV rm; entmnt; lake sw nrby; fishing; quiet; CCI. "Lge pitches, rec sh stay." 15 Jun-15 Sep. € 6.08   2002*

HUISSEAU SUR COSSON see Blois *4G2*

HUMES JORQUENAY see Langres *6F1*

†**HYERES** *10F3* (6km N) **Camping Vert Gapeau, Vallee de Sauvebonne, 83400 Hyeres [tel/fax 04 94 65 68 55]** On D12 bet Pierrefeu & Hyeres on L, approx 7km fr junc with N98. Lge, shd; wc; shwrs inc; el pts (5A) inc; gas; lndtte; sm shop; rest; snacks; playgrnd; pool; sand beach 7km; entmnt; fishing; dogs; adv bkg (ess Jul/Aug); quiet; red low ssn. "Narr access rd; red facs low ssn; conv Cinque Terre vills." € 22.00   2002*

HYERES *10F3* (4km E Coastal) **Camping Port Pothuau**, 83400 Hyeres [04 94 66 41 17; fax 04 94 66 33 09; pothuau@free.fr; www.homair-vacances.fr] About 4km fr Hyeres E twds Nice on N98, turn R on D12 sp Salins d'Hyeres. Site 2nd on R. Lge, shd; wc; shwrs; el pts (6-10A) €5.50-6; gas; lndtte; ice; shop; rest; snacks; bar; playgrnd; pool; sand beach 1km; tennis; games area; cycle hire; mini-golf; child entmnt; TV; 60% statics; dogs €2.50; red low ssn. "Nr interesting town of Hyeres; excursions to Iles d'Hyeres & peninsula of Giens."
3 Apr-2 Oct. € 20.50   2002*

HYERES *10F3* (8km E) **Camping La Pascalinette**, 83250 La Londe-les-Maures [04 94 66 82 72 or 04 94 87 46 62; fax 04 94 87 55 75] Site sp on N98 E of Hyeres. Lge, mkd pitch, shd; wc; shwrs inc; el pts (6A) inc; gas; lndtte; ice; shop; snacks; playgrnd; sand/shgl beach 3km; games rm; TV; adv bkg; CCI.
♦ 1 Jun-15 Sep. € 18.40   2003*

HYERES *10F3* (8km E Coastal) **Camping Les Moulieres, Route de Port-de-Miramar**, 83250 La Londe-les-Maures [04 94 01 53 21; fax 04 94 01 53 22; camping.les.moulieres@wanadoo.fr] On N98, in cent La Londe-les-Maures turn S at traff lts. After 1km turn R over white bdge & foll rd for 1km. Camping sp on R. Lge, pt shd; wc; baby facs; shwrs inc; el pts (6A) inc; lndtte; shop; rest; snacks; bar; playgrnd; sand beach 800m; entmnt; TV; poss cr; adv bkg rec high ssn; quiet. ♦ 14 Jun-6 Sep.
€ 25.00 (3 persons)   2003*

HYERES *10F3* (10km E Rural) **Camping Le Val Rose**, 83250 La Londe-les-Maures [04 94 66 81 36; fax 04 94 66 52 67; camping-valrose@wanadoo.fr] Take N98 E to La Londe, thro town cent, strt over traff lts & foll D559 to site 4km on R. No access to site fr N98. Lge, mkd pitch, some hdstg, pt sl, pt shd; wc; chem disp; shwrs inc; el pts (3-10A) €3-5; gas; lndtte; shop & 4km; tradsmn; rest; snacks; bar; BBQ; playgrnd; htd pool; sand beach 5km; 75% statics; adv bkg ess; rd noise; cc acc; CCI. "In foothills of Maures mountains."
1 Mar-31 Oct. € 16.00 (3 persons)   2003*

HYERES *10F3* (4km SE Coastal) **Campeole Eurosurf, Plage de la Capte**, 83400 Hyeres [04 94 58 00 20; fax 04 94 58 03 18] Foll sp for Hyeres Airport & Giens & after airport sp for Giens on D97. Site 1st on E after passing thro sm vill of La Capte. V lge, mkd pitch, pt sl, pt shd; wc; chem disp; mv service pnt; baby facs; shwrs inc; el pts (10A) inc; gas; lndry rm; shop; tradsmn; rest; snacks; bar; no BBQ; playgrnd; sand beach adj; watersports; diving cent; 50% statics; dogs; phone; poss cr; adv bkg; some rd noise; cc acc. "Some areas of soft sand & pitches not mkd; excel for watersports." ♦ ltd.
1 Mar-31 Oct. € 20.00   2002*

HYERES *10F3* (5km SE Coastal) **Camping La Bergerie, 4231 Route de Giens**, 83400 Hyeres [04 94 58 91 75; fax 04 94 58 14 28; camping.bergerie@tiscali.fr] On L of D97 fr Hyeres to Giens on Presqu'ile de Giens. Med, pt shd; wc; shwrs; el pts (5-10A) €2.60-4.10; tradsmn; snacks (high ssn); bar; beach; 50% static. "Fair sh stay low ssn." 10 Feb-10 Jan. € 22.50   2004*

HYERES *10F3* (5km SE Coastal) **Domaine du Ceinturon III, Rue du Ceinturon, L'Ayguade**, 83400 Hyeres [04 94 66 32 65; fax 04 94 66 43 43; ceinturon3@securmail.net; www.provence-campings.com/azur/ceinturon3.htm] Fr Hyeres take L'Ayguade rd sp airport. At T-junc in L'Ayguade turn R. Site 400m twd Hyeres harbour & adj airport adj D42. Fr NE on D42 drive thro L'Ayguade, turn R at traff lts just after end of vill sp. Lge, mkd pitch, shd; htd wc (some cont); chem disp; serviced pitch; shwrs inc; el pts (2-10A) €2-3.50; gas; lndtte; ice; shop high ssn; tradsmn; rest; snacks; bar; playgrnd; beach adj, tennis; TV rm; excursions; TV; 15% statics; dogs €3.45; poss cr; Eng spkn; adv bkg ess Jul/Aug; quiet but some daytime noise fr adj airport; no cc acc; CCI. "Excel, popular site; v busy high ssn; sm pitches; smart shwrs; excel cycle paths in area; gd long/sh stay. ♦ 1 Apr-30 Sep. € 16.00
2005*

HYERES *10F3* (10km S Coastal) **Camping La Presqu'lle de Giens, 153 Route de la Madrague, Giens**, 83400 Hyeres [04 94 58 22 86 or 04 94 57 20 18; fax 04 94 58 11 63; camping- giens@wanadoo.fr; www.camping-giens.com] Fr Toulon A 570 dir Hyeres. Thro palm-lined main street in Hyeres dir Giens-les-Iles & foll sp to La Capte & Giens past airport on L, thro La Capte, turn R at rndabt to site on L, sp. Lge, pt sl, terr, pt shd; htd wc; mv service pnt; baby facs; shwrs inc; el pts (6A) €4.20; gas; lndtte; ice; shop; tradsmn; snacks; playgrnd; TV; games rm; entmnt; sand beach 600m; fishing & boat excursions; 25% statics; dogs €2.30; poss cr; adv bkg; quiet. "Access to pitches awkward lge o'fits." ♦ 1 Apr-30 Sep. € 17.60 (CChq acc)
2005*

HYERES *10F3* (13km S Coastal) **Camping International La Reserve, 1737 Route de la Madrague, Presq'ile de Giens**, 83400 Hyeres [04 94 58 90 16; fax 04 94 58 90 50; Thierry.Coulomb@wanadoo.fr; www.international-giens.com] S fr Hyeres on D97 dir Giens, once past La Capte foll sp La Bergerie & La Madrague, site sp. Lge, mkd pitch, hdstg, terr, pt shd; wc; chem disp; mv service pnt; shwrs inc; el pts (6A) €5; gas; lndtte; ice; shop; rest; snacks; bar; no BBQ; playgrnd; sand beach 300m; tennis adj; watersports; windsurfing; skin-diving; solarium; horseriding; internet; entmnt; some statics; no dogs; Eng spkn; adv bkg; quiet. "Excel family site; many activities."
20 Mar-31 Oct. € 18.00   2003*

FRANCE

HYERES *10F3* (6km W) **Camping Le Beau Veze,** Route de la Moutonne, 83320 Carqueiranne [tel/fax 04 94 57 65 30; info@camping-beauveze. com; www.camping-beauveze.com] Fr Toulon take D559 E dir Carqueiranne. Approx 2km after Le Pradet turn L onto D76 twd La Moutonne. Site on R in 1.5km. Med, terr, pt shd; wc (some cont); chem disp; baby facs; shwrs inc; el pts (6A) €4; gas; Indtte; ice; shop; rest; snacks; bar; BBQ (gas only); playgrnd; 2 pools & paddling pool; beach 4km; tennis; mini-golf; cycle hire; entmnt; 75% statics; dogs €2.30; poss cr; adv bkg; quiet but some rd noise; red low ssn; cc not acc. "Poss diff access some pitches for lge o'fits; no twin-axle c'vans; recep clsd 1300-1500 & after 1600; mkt Thu." 15 May-15 Sep. € 28.00 (CChq acc)   2004*

IGOVILLE see Pont de l'Arche *3D2*

ILE BOUCHARD, L' *4H1* (Rural) **Camp Municipal Les Bords de Vienne,** La Fougetterie, 37220 L'Ile Bouchard [02 47 95 23 59; fax 02 47 58 67 35] On N bank of Rv Vienne 100m E of rd bdge nr junc of D757 & D760. Med, mkd pitch, pt sl, pt shd; wc; chem disp; shwrs €1; el pts (6-10A) €2.80; gas; Indtte; supmkt adj; playgrnd; pool, tennis 500m; rv sw adj; dogs €0.80; phone adj; adv bkg (Mairie); CCI. "Clean site; helpful warden; v attractive location; conv Loire chateaux." ♦ ltd. 14 Jun-10 Sep. € 6.50   2004*

ILLIERS COMBRAY *4E2* (2km SW Rural) **Camp Municipal de Mont Jouvin,** Route de Brou, 28120 Illiers-Combray [02 37 24 03 04; fax 02 37 24 16 21] S on D921 fr Illiers for 2km twd Brou. Site on L. Med, hdg pitch, pt shd; htd wc; chem disp; some serviced pitches; shwrs inc; el pts (5A) €2.65; gas; Indry rm; shop 2km; htd pool 500m; fishing adj; 20% statics; poss cr; adv bkg; quiet; CCI. "Excel san facs; gd security; many pitches wooded & with flowers; excel cycle path to vill; helpful warden; barrier clsd 1200-1500; 2100-0800 low ssn, 2200-0700 high ssn; office clsd 1800." ♦ 1 Apr-31 Oct. € 7.50   2005*

INGRANDES SUR VIENNE see Dange St Romain *4H2*

Some of these sites have changed their opening dates - we'd better fill in some site report forms and let the editor of the guide know.

ISIGNY SUR MER *1D4* (N Rural) **Escapades Terre Oceane Camping Le Fanal,** Rue du Fanal, 14230 Isigny-sur-Mer [02 31 21 33 20 or 05 46 55 10 01; fax 02 31 22 12 00; info@campingterreoceane. com; www.campingterreoceane.com] Fr N13 Bayeux Carentan rd exit into Isigny, site immed N of town. Foll sp to 'Stade' in town, (just after sq & church on narr street just bef R turn). Med, hdg/mkd pitch, pt shd; wc; chem disp; mv service pnt; shwrs inc; el pts (10A) inc (long cable poss req) €3; Indtte; ice; shop; snacks; bar; playgrnd; pool; aquapark; sand beach 10km; lake fishing adj; horseriding; tennis; games area; games rm; entmnt; TV; 50% statics; dogs €2; phone; adv bkg; quiet; cc acc; CCI. "Friendly staff; poss boggy in wet weather; vg site." ♦ 13 May-16 Sep. € 29.00   2005*

See advertisement

ISLE ET BARDAIS see Cerilly *4H3*

ISLE JOURDAIN, L' *7A3* (500m N) **Camp Municipal du Lac de Chardes,** Rue de Chardes, 86150 L'Isle-Jourdain [05 49 48 72 46 or 05 49 48 70 54 (Mairie); fax 05 49 48 84 19; mairieisle@europost.org] Fr N147 in Lussac take D11 S to L'Isle-Jourdain. Site sp on R. Sm, mkd pitch, terr, pt shd; wc (some cont); shwrs inc; el pts €1.95; shops, rest, snacks, bar 500m; htd pool 100m; boating; fishing; adv bkg; quiet. "Peaceful; excel san facs; sh walk to Rv Vienne; site yourself; warden calls am & pm." ♦ 15 May-15 Oct. € 5.65   2003*

ISLE SUR LA SORGUE L' *10E2* (2km E) **Camping La Sorguette, Route d'Apt, 84800 L'Isle-sur-la-Sorgue [04 90 38 05 71; fax 04 90 20 84 61; sorguette@wanadoo.fr; www.camping-sorguette. com]** Fr Isle-sur-la-Sorgue take N100 twd Apt, on L site in 1.5km, sp. Med, hdg/mkd pitch, pt shd; wc (male cont); chem disp; mv service pnt; shwrs inc; el pts (4-6A) €4.10-4.60; gas; lndtte; shop; tradsmn; rest adj; BBQ; playgrnd; beach adj; trout fishing adj; canoeing; tennis; games area; internet access; adv bkg (dep & booking fee req); 10% statics; dogs €2.60; poss cr; Eng spkn; quiet; cc acc; CCI. "Lovely site, gd facs; poss some pitches bare & muddy; attractive town surrounded by water; excel Sun mkt (free shuttle fr site); plenty of rests (rest adj site excel); rvside walk into town (1.5km); conv Luberon, Gordes & Fountain de Vaucluse; v helpful, friendly staff; high m'vans beware low trees." ♦ ltd. 15 Mar-15 Oct. € 19.50   2005*

ISLE SUR LA SORGUE L' *10E2* (3km E Rural) **Aire Naturelle de Sorgiack, Route de Lagnes, 84800 L'Isle-sur-la-Sorgue [04 90 38 13 95]** 2.5km E of L'Isle-sur-la-Sorgue on N100; take D99 N twd Lagnes; site sp 500m on L. Sm, mkd pitch, hdstg, pt shd; htd wc; chem disp; shwrs inc; el pts (6A) inc; lndtte; ice; shop, rest, snacks, bar 2.5km; paddling pool; sw 3km; rv & fishing 500m; games rm; phone; adv bkg; quiet; cc not acc; CCI. "V friendly hosts; delightful site in cherry orchard; excel facs; gd mkts in area esp antiques; excel touring base." ♦ ltd. 1 Apr-15 Oct. € 15.30   2005*

†ISLE **SUR LA SORGUE L'** *10E2* (5km E Rural) **Aire Communale, Parking Vergnes, 84800 Fontaine-de-Vaucluse [04 90 20 31 79]** D25 fr Isle-sur-la-Sorgue; site on R after vill boundary; or on D 24 fr Cavaillon then join D25. Sm, hdstg, unshd; wc; own san; chem disp; shops, rest, snacks & bar 500m; dogs; poss cr; cc acc. "Pleasant location next to rv; mainly for m'vans but spaces for c'vans; gd NH." € 3.00   2005*

ISLE **SUR LA SORGUE L'** *10E2* (5km NW) **Camping Le Jantou, 84250 Le Thor [04 90 33 90 07; fax 04 90 33 79 84; lejantou@avignon. pacwan.net]** Exit A7 at Avignon Nord onto D942 sp Carpentras. Turn S onto D6; in 8km join N100 E sp Le Thor. Site sp bef vill. App fr E fork R at sharp bend, thro town gate take L turn after passing church & L. Med, pt shd, hdg pitch; wc; chem disp; shwrs inc; el pts (10A) inc; lndtte; snacks; shops nr; playgrnd; pool 5km; cycle hire; adv bkg; quiet. "By Rv Sorgue; sm pitches, ltd access; san facs poss not v clean." ♦ ltd. Apr-Oct. € 17.30   2002*

ISLE SUR LA SORGUE, **L'** *10E2* (5km E Rural) **Camping La Couteliere, 84800 Lagnes [04 90 20 33 97; fax 04 90 20 27 22]** Leave L'Isle-sur-la-Sorgue by N100 dir Apt, fork L after 2km sp Fontaine-de-Vaucluse. Site on L on D24 bef ent Fontaine. Med, hdg pitch, shd; wc; shwrs inc; el pts (10A) €4; lndtte; ice; snacks; bar; playgrnd; pool; tennis, canoeing nr; entmnt; 40% statics; dogs €2.60; phone; Eng spkn; adv bkg; quiet; CCI. "Gd but ltd snacks menu; 2km easy cycle ride to Fontaine; gd sh stay." 1 Apr-15 Oct. € 12.90   2003*

ISLE **SUR LE DOUBS, L'** *6G2* (400m Rural) **Camping Les Lumes, Rue des Lumes, 25250 L'Isle-sur-le-Doubs [tel/fax 03 81 92 73 05]** Well sp fr town edge on N83 bef rv bdge. Med, pt shd; wc; chem disp; shwrs; el pts (10A) inc (long lead req & poss rev pol); shop; tradsmn; playgrnd; rv sw; dogs; poss cr; Eng spkn; adv bkg; CCI. "Sh walk to town; gd long/sh stay." 1 May-30 Sep. € 11.50   2003*

ISLE **SUR SEREIN, L'** *4G4* (Rural) **Camp Municipal Le Parc de Chateau, 89440 L'Isle-sur-Serein [03 86 33 93 50 or 03 86 33 80 74 (Mairie); fax 03 86 33 91 81]** Exit A6 junc 21 or 22 & foll sp Noyers or Montreal & L'Isle-sur-Serein on D117. Or fr Avallon, take D957 twd Sauvigny-le-Bois; then D86 to L'Isle-sur-Serein; site on L on ent to vill. Sm, hdg pitch, pt shd; wc; chem disp; shwrs inc; el pts (10A) 2.29; lndry rm; ice; shop 1km; rest; bar; BBQ; playgrnd; tennis & boating adj; adv bkg; some rd noise; CCI. "Basic site & facs, water taps at el pts; reported chem disp adj dish washing area; some rd noise; few lorries; attractive area; helpful warden on site; vg long/sh stay." 1 May-30 Sep. € 6.08   2003*

†ISOLA *9D4* (1km NW) **Camping Lac des Neiges, 06420 Isola [04 93 02 18 16; fax 04 93 02 19 40]** SE fr St Etienne-de-Tinee on D2205. site on R after approx 13km, site sp. Med, hdg/mkd pitch, hdstg, pt shd; wc; chem disp; shwrs inc; el pts (10A) €3.81; lndtte; ice; shops 1km; tradsmn; playgrnd; sw pool 1km; lake adj; ski stn 20 mins; fishing; kayaking; tennis; TV rm; 25% statics; phone; Eng spkn; adv bkg; quiet; cc not acc; CCI. ♦   2003*

ISPAGNAC *9D1* (1km W Rural) **Camp Municipal Le Pre Morjal, 48320 Ispagnac [04 66 44 23 77 or 04 66 44 20 50 (Mairie); fax 04 66 44 23 84]** 500km W of town, turn L off D907 & then 200m on R. Med, hdg pitch, pt shd; htd wc; chem disp; baby facs; shwrs inc; el pts (10-16A) €2.50; lndtte; shops 200m; rest; playgrnd; pool 50m; paddling pool; rv sw 200m; games area; dogs €1; quiet. "Vg base for Tarn & Joute Gorges; gd size pitches on rocky base; lovely family site; friendly staff; gd rvside walks." ♦ 1 Apr-15 Oct. € 12.30   2005*

ISPAGNAC *9D1* (10km W) **Camp Municipal, 48210 La Malene** [04 66 48 58 55 or 04 66 48 51 16; fax 04 66 48 58 51] Site on L of D907 W of Ispagnac in vill of La Malene. Site well sp. Sm, pt sl, pt shd; wc (some cont); chem disp; mv service pnt; shwrs; el pts (10A) inc; shops, rest, snacks, bar 200m; BBQ; rv sw & fishing; dogs; poss cr; adv bkg; quiet; CCI. "Kayak hire; boat trips fr vill." Easter-30 Oct.
€ 10.00   2004*

ISQUES see Boulogne sur Mer *3A2*

ISSAMBRES, LES see St Aygulf *10F4*

ISSENDOLUS see Gramat *7D4*

ISSIGEAC *7D3* (4km NW Rural) **Camping a la Ferme (Versanne), 24560 Monsaguel** [05 53 58 26 18] On N21 Bergerac-Villeneuve, 3km S of Bouniagues at crest of incline. Farm sp; ensure taking farm ent not public rd adj. Could be diff in wet. Sm, pt sl, pt shd; wc; shwrs inc; el pts; lndtte; playgrnd; quiet. 1 Mar-15 Sep.   2003*

ISSOIRE *9B1* (10km N) **Camp Municipal, La Croix de Vent, 63270 Vic-le-Comte** [04 73 69 22 63 or 04 73 69 02 12 (Mairie)] Fr N exit A75 junc 5 onto D213/D225 to Vic-le-Comte & foll sp for camping or sw pool, 'piscine'. Fr S exit A75 junc 8 onto D229 to Vic Sm, pt shd; wc; shwrs; el pts €2; lndry rm; shops 500m; pool adj; tennis; adv bkg; quiet. "Friendly helpful staff; gd san facs." 15 Jun-Sep.
€ 9.00   2004*

ISSOIRE *9B1* (2.5km E Rural) **Camp Municipal du Mas, Ave du Dr Bienfait, 63500 Issoire** [04 73 89 03 59 or 04 73 89 03 54 (LS); fax 04 73 89 41 05; camping-mas@wanadoo.fr] Fr Clermont-Ferrand S on A75/E11 take exit 12 sp Issoire; turn L over a'route sp Orbeil; at rndabt, take 1st exit & foll site sp. Med, hdg/mkd pitch, pt shd; htd wc (most cont); chem disp; shwrs inc; el pts (10-13A) €2.40 (long lead poss req); gas; lndtte; shops & supmkt 2km; tradsmn; snacks; playgrnd; rv sw; fishing in adj lake; TV rm; 5% statics; dogs; phone; poss cr; adv bkg (rec high ssn); quiet but some rd noise; red long stay; cc acc; CCI. "Well-run site but san facs just adequate; v helpful warden; pitches mkd/hdg in pairs; poss boggy after rain; code for barrier; office clsd 1200-1415; supmkt opp exit A75." ♦ 1 Apr-31 Oct. € 11.60   2005*

ISSOIRE *9B1* (10km E) **Camp Sauxillanges, 63490 Sauxillanges** [04 73 96 86 26 or 04 73 71 02 43 (HS); fax 04 73 71 07 69; chateau@grangefort.com] Exit A75 (E11) at junc 13 to D996, head E twd Sauxillanges. Turn R 100m after Gendarmerie in vill. Sp. Med, mkd pitch, shd; wc; chem disp; some serviced pitches; shwrs inc; el pts (4A) €2.25 (rev pol); lndtte; ice; playgrnd; pool adj (Jul/Aug); tennis; archery; fishing 50m; no statics; dogs €2.30; Eng spkn; adv bkg ess high ssn; quiet; cc acc. "Adj leisure cent with pool (free to campers); sh walk to charming, interesting town with 3 rests; excel." ♦ 15 Jun-15 Sep. € 13.00   2005*

ISSOIRE *9B1* (6km SE) **Camping Chateau La Grange Fort, 63500 Les Pradeaux** [04 73 71 05 93 or 04 73 71 02 43; fax 04 73 71 07 69; chateau@ grangefort.com] S fr Clermont Ferrand on A75, exit junc 13 onto D996 to Parentignat rd changes to D999 for 50m. In Parentignat turn R onto D34 dir Nonette & foll sp to site on hill-top. Narr app rd & steep ent. Med, hdg/mkd pitch, shd; htd wc; chem disp; mv service pnt; baby facs; sauna; shwrs inc; el pts (6A) €3; lndtte; gas; ice; shop in vill; tradsmn; rest; snacks; bar; playgrnd; htd pool; paddling pool; rv fishing; tennis; canoe & mountain bike facs; internet; TV rm; some statics; dogs €1.75; phone; office clsd 1200-1400; Eng spkn; adv bkg (fee); quiet; cc acc; CCI. "Pleasant, peaceful Dutch-run site in chateau grounds; site on hilltop so excel views; some sm pitches; long walk to facs fr some pitches & ltd low ssn; pitches muddy after rain; mosquito problem on shadiest pitches; ltd parking at recep; gd rest in chateau, adv bkg ess; vg." 1 Apr-15 Oct. € 20.25 (CChq acc)   2005*

ISSOIRE *9B1* (11km S) **Camping Les Loges, 63340 Nonette** [04 73 71 65 82; fax 04 73 71 67 23; camping.les.loges.nonette@wanadoo.fr; www. lesloges.com] Exit 17 fr A75 onto D214 sp Le Breuil, dir Nonette. Turn L in 2km, cross rv & turn L to site. Site perched on conical hill. Steep app. Med, mkd pitch, pt shd; wc; chem disp; child/baby facs; shwrs inc; el pts (10A) €3.35; gas; lndtte; shop; tradsmn; rest; snacks; bar; playgrnd; htd pool; rv sw & fishing adj; TV; entmnt; 30% statics; dogs €1.50; quiet; red low ssn; CCI. "Friendly site; conv Massif Central & A75; san facs poss unclean high ssn." Easter-10 Sep. € 15.60   2004*

ISSOUDUN *4H3* (2km N Urban) **Camp Municipal Les Tapeaux, 36100 Issoudun** [02 54 03 13 46 or 02 54 21 74 02; tourisme@ville-issoudun.fr; www.ville-issoudun.fr] Fr Bourges SW on N151, site sp fr Issoudun. Sm, hdg pitch, pt shd; wc; shwrs inc; el pts inc; rd noise. "Poor security - intinerants on site; warden calls am & pm." Jun-Sep. € 8.00
                                                 2003*

ISSY L'EVEQUE *4H4* (S Rural) **Camping L'Etang Neuf, 71760 Issy-l'Eveque** [03 85 24 96 05; info@ camping-etang-neuf.com; www.camping-etang-neuf.com] Fr Luzy take D973 S for 2km. Then take D25 to Issy-l'Eveque. Site off D42 well sp in town cent. Sm, mkd/mkd pitch, terr, pt shd; wc (some cont); chem disp; mv service pnt; shwrs inc; el pts (6A) €3; gas; lndtte; shop 800m; tradsmn; rest; bar; playgrnd; pool; paddling pool; lake sw, fishing adj; tennis; TV rm; dogs €2; phone; Eng spkn; adv bkg; quiet; cc acc; CCI. "Peaceful, unspoilt area; helpful warden." ♦ 1 May-15 Sep. € 17.00 (CChq acc)
                                                 2005*

ISTRES *10F2* (2km Coastal) **Camping Le Vitou, 13 Route de St Chamas, 13800 Istres** [04 42 56 51 57; fax 04 12 10 64 98] Fr Martigues take D5 N. Foll sp to Istres (D16). Site sp. Med, pt shd; wc; chem disp; shwrs; el pts; gas; shop; snacks; playgrnd; pool; sand/shgl beach 1km; adv bkg; poss aircraft noise; red CCI.   2003*

ISTRES *10F2* (6km S Coastal) **Camping Felix de la Bastide, Massane Plage, 13920 St Mitre-les-Ramparts** [04 42 80 99 35; fax 04 42 49 96 85; campingfelix@aol.com; www.campingfelix.com] S fr Istres on D5 to end of built up area. At 2nd rndabt turn L (foll sp); approx 2km on L. Med, mkd pitch, pt shd; wc; chem disp; shwrs inc; el pts (6A) €2.30; gas 2km; shop; tradsmn; rest; bar; playgrnd; pool; shgl beach; phone; poss cr; Eng spkn; adv bkg. "Spacious pitches; poss strong winds; algae on lake - no sw; v friendly Dutch owners; beautiful scenery; vg long stay." 1 Apr-1 Nov. € 15.50
2003*

JABLINES see Meaux *3D3*

JARD SUR MER *7A1* (Coastal) **Camping La Ventouse, Rue Pierre Curie, 85520 Jard-sur-Mer** [02 51 33 58 65 or 02 51 33 40 17 (Mairie); fax 02 51 33 91 00; campings-parfums-ete@wanadoo.fr] Fr Talmont St-Hilaire take D21 to Jard turn R on app & foll sps. Look for blue sp Port de Plaisance; pass Camping Les Ecureuils, site shortly after. Lge, pt sl, pt shd; wc; baby facs; shwrs inc; el pts (10A) €3 (poss rev pol); gas; lndtte; ice; shops, rest, snacks, bar 500m; playgrnd; sand beach 500m; dogs €1.50; poss cr; quiet. "Gd site with plenty of pine trees, adj vill & harbour."
1 Jun-15 Sep. € 10.00
2004*

JARD SUR MER *7A1* (Coastal) **Camping Le Bosquet, Rue de l'Ocean, 85520 Jard-sur-Mer** [02 51 33 56 57 or 02 51 33 06 72; fax 02 51 33 04 07; campings-parfums-ete@wanadoo.fr; www.campings-parfums-ete.com] Exit D949 at Talmont St Hilaire onto D21 to Jard-sur-Mer. In town look for sp Port de Plaisance, pass Camping Les Ecureuils & La Ventouse on L & take 2nd rd, Rue de l'Ocean, to the R. Med, pt sl, shd; wc; baby facs; shwrs inc; el pts (10A) €3; lndry rm; shops adj; pool 1.5km; sand beach; tennis adj; entmnt; dogs €1.50; adv bkg; quiet. "Picturesque boating cent, with man-made harbour." 1 Apr-Oct. € 10.00
2002*

JARD SUR MER *7A1* (Coastal) **Camping Les Ecureuils, Route des Goffineaux, 85520 Jard-sur-Mer** [02 51 33 42 74; fax 02 51 33 91 14; camping-ecureuils@wanadoo.fr; www.camping-ecureuils.com] Fr Talmont St Hilaire take D21 to Jard-sur-Mer. Turn R app vill, site sp. Lge, mkd pitch, shd; wc; serviced pitches; baby facs; shwrs inc; el pts (10A) inc (rev pol); gas; lndtte; ice; sm shop 1km; rest; snacks; BBQ (gas); playgrnd; htd indoor pool, outdoor pool; rocky beach 400m, sand beach 300m; TV rm; tennis adj; 33% statics; no dogs; poss cr; Eng spkn; adv bkg (dep €45 & bkg fee €16); quiet; cc acc. "Gd rds & lighting; boating cent & man-made tidal harbour; facs clean but dated; no traffic allowed on site at night; security guard patrols at night." ♦ 15 May-15 Sep. € 28.50
2004*

JARD SUR MER *7A1* (Coastal) **CHADOTEL Camping L'Oceano d'Or, Rue Georges Clemenceau, 85520 Jard-sur-Mer** [02 51 33 65 08 or 02 51 33 05 05 (LS); fax 02 51 33 94 04; chadotel@wanadoo.fr; www.camping-chadotel.fr] D21 & D19 to Jard-sur-Mer. Site sp. Lge, hdg/mkd pitch, pt shd; wc; chem disp; baby facs; shwrs inc; el pts (6A) inc; gas; lndtte; ice; shop; snacks; bar; playgrnd; htd pool; waterslide; sand beach 900m; tennis; mini-golf; cycle hire; entmnt; dogs €2.90; adv bkg; quiet; red long stay/low ssn; CCI. "Vg; gd walking." ♦ 1 Apr-24 Sep. € 28.00
2005*

JARD SUR MER *7A1* (2km NE) **Camping La Mouette Cendree, Les Malecots, 85520 St Vincent-sur-Jard** [02 51 33 59 04; fax 02 51 20 31 39; camping.mc@free.fr; www.mouette cendree.com] Fr Les Sables d'Olonne take D949 SE to Talmont-St-Hilaire; then take D21 dir Jard-sur-Mer. Bef ent Jard-sur-Mer turn L onto D19 in NE dir to site in about 1km on L. Or on D949 fr Lucon turn L onto D19 at Avrille sp Jard-sur-Mer. Site on R in 6km. Med, hdg/mkd pitch, pt shd; wc; chem disp; baby facs; shwrs inc; el pts (10A) inc; lndtte; supmkt nr; tradsmn; BBQ (gas/elec); playgrnd; pool; waterslide; sand beach 2km; fishing; windsurfing 2km; table tennis; horseriding 500m; golf 10km; 30% statics; dogs €2.40; recep 0800-1230 & 1330-2000; c'van max 7.50m high ssn; Eng spkn; adv bkg; quiet; cc acc; CCI. "Friendly, peaceful site; v welcoming & helpful owners; gd woodland walks & cycle routes nr; mkt Sun in vill." ♦ Easter-15 Sep. € 21.40 ABS - A20
2005*

JARD SUR MER *7A1* (SE Coastal) **CHADOTEL Camping La Pomme de Pin, Rue Vincent Auriol, 85520 Jard-sur-Mer** [02 51 33 43 85 or 02 51 33 05 05 (LS); fax 02 51 33 94 04; chadotel@wanadoo.fr; www.camping-chadotel.fr] Foll sp fr town. Lge, hdg/mkd pitch, shd; htd wc; serviced pitches; baby facs; shwrs inc; el pts (6A) inc; gas; lndtte; ice; shop; snacks; bar; BBQ (gas); playgrnd; pool; waterslide; sand beach 150m; games rm; TV rm; entmnt; mainly statics; dogs €2.90; Eng spkn; adv bkg; quiet; cc acc; CCI. "Well-maintained; early arrival rec; vg." ♦ Easter-26 Sep. € 28.00 2005*

JARD SUR MER *7A1* (2km SE Rural) **Camping L'R Pur (Ferret), 85520 St Vincent-sur-Jard** [tel/fax 02 51 33 94 32 or 06 15 21 56 17] Fr Talmont-St Hilaire take D21 to Jard-sur-Mer & St Vincent-sur-Jard. Site sp. Sm, hdg pitch, pt shd; wc; chem disp; shwrs; el pts (10A); playgrnd; sand beach 3km, tennis, fishing, boating 3km; 10% statics; quiet; adv bkg. "CL-type site; friendly owner, lge pitches."
1 Apr-1 Oct.
2004*

FRANCE

JARD SUR MER *7A1* (2km SE Coastal) **CHADOTEL Camping La Bolee d'Air, Le Bouil, Route de Longeville, 85520 St Vincent-sur-Jard** [02 51 90 36 05 or 02 51 33 05 05 (LS); fax 02 51 33 94 04; chadotel@wanadoo.fr; www.camping-chadotel.fr] Fr A11 junc 14 dir Angers. Take N160 to La Roche-sur-Yon & then D747 dir La Tranche-sur-Mer to Moutier-les-Mauxfaits. At Moutiers take D19 to St Hilaire-la-Foret & then L to St Vincent-sur-Jard. In St Vincent turn L by church sp Longeville-sur-Mer, site on R in 1km. Lge, hdg/mkd pitch, pt shd; htd wc; chem disp (wc); serviced pitches; shwrs inc; el pts (6A) inc; gas; ice; lndtte; shop; snacks; bar; BBQ (gas); playgrnd; pt htd/covrd pool; waterslide; sand beach 900m; tennis; cycle hire; entmnt; games rm; TV rm; 25% statics; dogs €2.90; recep 0800-2000; no c'vans over 8m high ssn; Eng spkn; adv bkg; quiet; red long stay/low ssn; cc acc; CCI. "Ltd facs fr end Aug; popular, busy site; excel." ♦ 1 Apr-23 Sep. € 27.50 ABS - A31   2005*

JARGEAU see Chateauneuf sur Loire *4F3*

JARNAC see Cognac *7B2*

JAULNY *5D2* (500m S Rural) **Camping La Pelouse, 54470 Jaulny** [tel/fax 03 83 81 91 67; lapelouse@aol.com] SW fr Metz on N57, cross rv at Corny-sur-Moselle & turn W onto D28 dir Thiaucourt-Regnieville. Site sp, easy to find off D28. Med, sl, pt shd; wc; chem disp; shwrs inc; el pts (6A) €2.60; lndtte; ice; tradsmn; rest; bar; BBQ; playgrnd; 25% statics; rv sw 100m; fishing; quiet; CCI. "No fresh or waste water facs for m'vans; gd site." 1 Apr-30 Sep. € 8.60   2005*

JAUNAY CLAN *4H1* (1km N Rural) **Camping La Croix du Sud, Route de Neuville, 86130 Jaunay-Clan** [05 49 62 58 14 or 05 49 62 57 20; fax 05 49 62 57 20; camping@la-croix-du-sud.fr; www.la-croix-du-sud.fr/] On A10 fr N or S, take Futuroscope exit. Take last exit at rndabt sp Neuville & after 1.5km turn L onto D20/D62. Site on L immed after x-ing m'way. Also clearly sp fr N10 at traff lts in Jaunay Clan. Lge, hdg/mkd pitch, pt shd, 20% serviced pitches; wc; chem disp; mv service pnt; shwrs inc; el pts (10A) €2.30; gas; lndtte; shop & hypmkt 1km; tradsmn; rest, snacks high ssn; bar; playgrnd; pool; entmnt; 15% statics; dogs; Eng spkn; adv bkg; quiet but some rd noise; cc acc; red low ssn/CCI. "Clean, tidy site; 3km to Futuroscope - mini-bus fr site high ssn; 10km to Poitiers; poss itinerants." ♦ 24 Mar-14 Sep. € 13.10   2005*

JAUNAY CLAN *4H1* (6km NE Rural) **Camp Municipal du Parc, 86130 Dissay** [05 49 62 84 29 or 05 49 52 34 56 (Mairie); fax 05 49 62 58 72] N on N10 Poitiers dir Chatellerault. At rndabt turn R on D15 sp Dissay. Turn R ent Dissay & site on R 50m. Med, mkd pitch, pt shd; wc; chem disp; shwrs inc; el pts (10A) inc; lndtte; shop 100m; quiet; CCI. "Friendly warden; clean modern facs; conv Futuroscope; 15thC chateau adj; gate locked 2200 but can request key to unlock if later; gd sh stay." ♦ 23 May-3 Sep. € 11.60   2004*

JAUNAY CLAN *4H1* (7km NE Rural) **Parc de Loisirs de St Cyr, 86130 St Cyr** [05 49 62 57 22; fax 05 49 52 28 58; contact@parcdesaintcyr. com; www.parcdesaintcyr.com] Fr A10 a'route take Chatellerault Sud exit & take N10 dir Poitiers; at Beaumont turn L at traff lts for St Cyr, foll camp sp in leisure complex by lakeside. Or fr S take Futuroscope exit to N10. Lge, hdg/mkd pitch, pt sl, pt shd; wc; chem disp; mv service pnt; serviced pitches; shwrs inc; el pts (10A) inc; gas; lndtte; shop; rest; snacks; bar; BBQ; playgrnd; sand beach & lake sw; watersports; tennis; mini-golf; boat & cycle hire; fitness rm; games area; golf course adj; entmnt; child entmnt; TV rm; 15% statics; dogs €1.50; poss cr; some Eng spkn; adv bkg (dep req); quiet but some train noise; red long stay; cc acc; CCI. "Excel, well-maintained site; modern, clean san facs but poss stretched high ssn; rec long o'fits unhitch at barrier due R-angle turn; perfect for families; poss school & club groups w/ high ssn; gd golf nr; gd rest; beautiful lake; if late return to site check barrier closing time; public access to site fr lakeside beach; Futuroscope approx 13km; superb site; highly rec." ♦ 1 Apr-30 Sep. € 22.70 ABS - L09   2005*

†**JAUNAY CLAN** *4H1* (2km SE Urban) **Camping Le Futuriste, Rue du Chateau, 86130 St Georges-les-Baillargeaux** [tel/fax 05 49 52 47 52; camping-le-futuriste@wanadoo.fr; www.camping-le-futuriste. fr] On A10 fr N or S, take Futuroscope exit 28; fr toll booth foll site sp through tech park twd St Georges. At rndabt under N10 take slip rd N onto N10. After 150m exit N10 onto D20, foll sp. Cross sm rv & up hill, site on R. Med, hdg/mkd pitch, pt shd; htd wc; chem disp; mv service pnt; some serviced pitches; shwrs inc; el pts (6A) €3.40 (poss rev pol); gas; lndtte; ice; shop; hypmkt 2km; tradsmn; rest; snacks; bar; BBQ; playgrnd; 2 htd pools; waterslide; lake fishing; games area; games rm; entmnt; excursions; TV rm; no statics; dogs €1.70; poss cr; Eng spkn; adv bkg; quiet; red low ssn/long stay; cc acc; CCI. "Ideal touring base; gd for Poitiers & Futuroscope; conv fr a'route; do not arr bef 1200; excel winter site - clean, htd san facs; well-drained pitches; gd value; friendly, helpful, family-owned; tickets for Futuroscope (2km) avail fr site." ♦ € 18.80 (3 persons) (CChq acc)   2005*

See advertisement

JAUNAY CLAN *4H1* (4km SE Rural) **Camp Municipal Parc des Ecluzelles, 86360 Chasseneuil-du-Poitou** [05 49 62 58 85; fax 05 49 52 52 23; chasseneuil-du-poitou@cg86.fr] Fr A10 or N10 N or Poitiers take Futuroscope exit 28/18. Take Chasseneuil rd, sp in town to site. Sm, mkd pitch, some hdstg, pt shd; wc; chem disp; mv service pnt; shwrs inc; el pts (8A) inc; shop 1km; tradsmn; playgrnd; pool; poss cr; no adv bkg; quiet. 5 Apr-15 Oct. € 12.50   2004*

CAMPING LE FUTURISTE ★★★

F-86130 St. Georges les Baillargeaux
Tel./ Fax: 05 49 52 47 52
www.camping-le-futuriste.fr

Open from 1.1 till 31.12.
Reservations recommended from June till August.
2 km from FUTUROSCOPE.
At the river CLAIN, beautiful panorama on the park and the CLAIN-valley. Heated sanitary installations. 2 heated swimming pools with free waterslide. Quiet site with ample entertainment and excursions programme. Fishing on site.
Motorway A 10, exit FUTUROSCOPE, follow signs to park entrance, then follow St. Georges.

JAVIE, LA *10E3* (Rural) **Camp Municipal, 04420 La Javie** [04 92 34 91 76] Sp in vill on D900. Sm, pt shd; wc; shwrs inc; el pts; quiet. "Basic, unattended site; clean facs; NH." € 6.00   2002*

JOIGNY *4F4* (8km E Rural) **Camping Les Confluents, Allee Leo Lagrange, 89400 Migennes** [tel/fax 03 86 80 94 55; planethome2003@yahoo. fr; www.les-confluents.com] A6 exit at junc 19 Auxerre Nord onto N6 & foll sp to Migennes & site. Med, hdg/mkd pitch, hdstg, pt shd; htd wc (some cont); chem disp; mv service pnt; baby facs; fam bthrm; shwrs inc; el pts (6-10A) €2.40-3.40; gas; lndry rm; shop; rest; snacks; BBQ; playgrnd; htd pool; water sports 300m; lake sand beach; entmnt; sports area; cycle, canoe hire; TV rm; 8% statics; phone; bus; quiet; cc not acc; red long stay; CCI. "Friendly, family-run., clean site; lge pitches; medieval castle, wine cellars, Puisaye potteries nrby; walking dist to Migennes; mkt Thurs." ♦ ltd. 1 Apr-2 Nov. € 10.00   2004*

JOIGNY *4F4* (10km E) **Camping A Tou Vert, Allee Leo Lagrange, 89400 Migennes** [03 86 80 17 63; fax 04 71 59 65 56; a.tou.vert@net-up.com] Exit A6 junc 18 onto N943 to Joigny & Migennes. Or exit junc 19 Auxerre Nord onto N6 N, then D43 to Migennes. Site sp. Med, shd; shwrs inc; el pts (6A) €2.30; lndtte; ice; shop; snacks; bar; playgrnd; pool in town; tennis; games area; entmnt; rv 300m. 1 Mar-31 Oct. € 8.40   2002*

JOIGNY *4F4* (3.5km NW Rural) **Camping L'Ile de L'Antonnoir, Route de St Aubin-sur-Yonne, 89410 Cezy** [03 86 63 17 87 or 03 86 63 12 58 (LS); fax 03 86 63 02 84] Site sp off N6 N & S-bound (Joigny by-pass). Thro St Aubin vill, cross bdge over Rv Yonne. Site on L bank of rv. Or exit N6 Joigny by-pass at N of rndabt onto N2006 twd St Aubin. After St Aubin turn R to Cezy & site in 1km. Rec app via St Aubin - narr bdge 3.5t weight restriction. Sm, mkd pitch, pt shd; wc; shwrs inc; chem disp; shops 1km; el pts (6-10A) €2.20; lndtte; shop 1km; rest, snacks, bar, BBQ; playgrnd; rv sw & beach 100m; dogs €1; Eng spkn; adv bkg; quiet; CCI. "Helpful owners; v pleasant, quiet site; conv Chablis area; barrier clsd 2200." Easter-1 Oct. € 10.00   2005*

JOINVILLE *6E1* (6km E Rural) **Camp Municipal Poissons, 52230 Poissons** Fr N67 to Joinville 'Centre Ville'. At end slip rd R onto D60, then 1st R onto D427 to Poissons. Site sp in vill. Sm, pt sl, pt shd; htd wc (cont); chem disp (wc); shwrs inc; el pts inc; shop 1km; rest, snacks, bar 1km; BBQ; 20% statics; dogs; quiet; CCI. "V basic, peaceful CL-type site; warden calls in evenings or call at No 7 same rd to pay; uneven pitches; facs poor; easy to find; NH." € 6.70   2005*

JOINVILLE *6E1* (6km NW) **Camp Municipal Le Jardinot, 52300 Chatonrupt-Sommermont** [03 25 94 80 30 or 03 25 94 80 07] Leave N67 at sp Joinville Centre & cont N on old N67 (now D335) to Chatonrupt. Site on R on ent vill. Sm, pt shd; wc (cont); shwrs; el pts (6-10A) €1.50; shops 4km; rv sw adj; fishing in rv & canal adj; rd & rlwy noise. "NH only; run down & poss itinerants." 1 May-30 Sep. € 4.00   2004*

JONQUIERES see Orange *10E2*

JONZAC *7B2* **Camp Municipal, Parc des Expositions, 17500 Jonzac** [05 46 48 51 20 or 05 46 48 49 29; fax 05 46 48 51 07; Tourisme. Jonzac@wanadoo.fr] Fr A10/N137 to Bordeaux exit D699 to Jonzac, site well sp in all dirs in town past school & sports complex, adj Rv Seugne. Sm, mkd pitch, hdstg, pt shd; wc; mv service pnt; shwrs; el pts (6-16A) €3.45-5.15; lndtte; shop 2km; tradsmn; pool adj; dogs €1.10; lake fishing 1km; poss cr; adv bkg. "Excel situation; pleasant warden; plenty of hot water; facs clean but basic; pitches well-drained in wet at end ssn; well worn; gd sh stay; public footpath thro site." ♦ 1 Apr-31 Oct. € 8.50   2005*

JONZAC *7B2* (2km SW Rural) **Camping des Castors, St Simon de Bordes, 17500 Jonzac** [05 46 48 25 65; fax 05 46 04 56 76] Fr Jonzac take the D19 S twds Montendre, after approx 2km, immed after ring rd rndabt, turn R into minor rd. Site ent adj. Med, hdg pitch, hdstg, pt shd; wc; chem disp; shwrs inc; el pts (4-10A) €3-4.50; lndtte; tradsmn; snacks; bar; playgrnd; pool; rv sw 2km; entmnts; TV; 5% statics; dogs €1.55; some Eng spkn; quiet; CCI. "Peaceful & well-supervised; vg long/sh stay." ♦ 4 Mar-Oct. € 12.00   2004*

JOSSELIN *2F3* (2km SW) **Camping Bas de la Lande, 56120 Guegon [02 97 22 22 20 or 02 97 22 20 64; fax 02 97 73 93 85; camping basdelalande@wanadoo.fr]** Exit N24 by-pass W of town sp Guegon; foll sp 1km; do not attempt to cross Josselin cent fr E to W. Site on D724 just S of Rv Oust (canal). Med, hdg pitch, terr, pt shd; wc; chem disp; baby facs; shwrs inc; el pts (6A) €3.10; lndtte; shops 2km; bar high ssn; playgrnd; mini-golf; quiet but some rd noise; red low ssn; CCI. "Barrier clsd 1200-1400; well-positioned site for walk to Josselin, chateau & old houses; facs poss unclean low ssn; vg." ♦ 1 Apr-31 Oct. € 11.00   2003*

> Will you fill in the site report forms at the back of the guide, or shall I?

JUGON LES LACS *2E3* (Rural) **Camp Municipal au Bocage du Lac, 22270 Jugon-les-Lacs [02 96 31 60 16 or 02 96 31 70 75; fax 02 96 31 69 08; camping-le-bocage@wanadoo.fr]** Bet Dinan & Lamballe by N176. Foll 'Camping Jeux' sp on D52 fr Jugon-les-Lacs. Situated by lakes, sp fr cent of Jugon. Lge, pt sl, pt shd; wc; shwrs inc; el pts (5A) €2.80; lndtte; ice; shops adj; tradsmn; bar; playgrnd; pool; fishing & watersports in lake/rv adj; entmnts; TV; dogs €1.50; adv bkg; 20% red low ssn. "Resident warden Jul/Aug only; water pts in wc only; poss stretched san facs high ssn; many sports & activities offered; excel rests in vill." 1 May-30 Sep. € 14.30   2005*

JULLOUVILLE see Granville *1D4*

JUMIEGES *3C2* (1km E Rural) **Camping de la Foret, Rue Mainberthe, 76480 Jumieges [02 35 37 93 43; fax 02 35 37 76 48; info@campinglaforet.com; www.campinglaforet.com]** Exit A13 junc 25 onto D313 N dir Pont de Brotonne. Cross bdge & immed turn R onto D982 sp Yainville & Jumieges onto D143. Turn L in Jumieges & foll site sp. Turn L at x-rds after cemetary & church, site on R in 1km. Med, hdg/mkd pitch, pt shd; wc; chem disp; mv service pnt; baby facs; shwrs; el pts (10A) inc; gas; lndtte; shop; supmkt, rest, bar nr; BBQ; playgrnd; htd pool; lake beach 2.5km; watersports; fishing; golf; TV rm; 40% statics; dogs; phone; €15 dep for barrier key; poss cr; adv bkg; quiet. "Well-kept site but poss unkempt low ssn; san facs poss stretched high ssn; adj Abbey of Jumieges; conv Paris & Giverny; gd walking, cycling; some sm pitches." ♦ 1 Apr-29 Oct. € 20.60 (CChq acc) ABS - N15   2005*

JUMIEGES *3C2* (S Rural) **Camping Boucles de la Seine Normande, Base de Plein Air du Parc de Brotonne, 76480 Jumieges [02 35 37 31 72; fax 02 35 37 99 97]** E fr Le Havre on N15; foll D131 S fr Yvetot by-pass twd Pont de Brotonne (toll). Bef bdge turn SE on D982, thro Le Trait. Turn S on D143 at Yainville for Jumieges. Site on lake S side of D65 3km beyond vill. Fr S fr Bourg-Achard take D313 twd Pont de Brotonne; turn off after bdge on D982 as above. Med, hdg pitch, pt sl, pt shd; wc; chem disp; shwrs inc; el pts (6A) €1.80 (check pol); lndry rm; shops 3km; tradsmn; rest, snacks, bar 3km; playgrnd; lake sw adj; watersports; tennis; games area; archery; golf, 30% statics; dogs €1.05; barrier clsd 2200-0800; poss cr; adv bkg; quiet; red long stay; CCI. "Lovely area; helpful warden; poss itinerants low ssn; poss youth camps; san facs stretched high ssn; gd sh stay." ♦ ltd. 1 Mar-31 Oct. € 11.70   2005*

JUNIVILLE *5C1* (2km E Rural) **Camping Le Moulin de la Chut, Route de Bignicourt, 08310 Juniville [03 24 72 72 22]** Fr Juniville on D925 dir Bignicourt. Foll lane on R after Moulin de la Chut rest. Sm, mkd pitch, pt sl, terr, pt shd; wc (some cont); chem disp (wc); shwrs inc; el pts (4A) €2; shops 2km; tradsmn; rest, snacks, bar adj; BBQ; pool; fishing adj; 20% statics; dogs €1; adv bkg rec; CCI. "Conv Reims; vg sh stay/NH." ♦ ltd. 15 Apr-30 Sep. € 12.00   2004*

JUSSAC *7C4* (W Rural) **Camp Municipal du Moulin, Impasse du Moulin, 15250 Jussac [tel/fax 04 71 46 69 85]** On D922 8km N of Aurillac; on L immed after bdge. Med, mkd pitch, pt shd; wc; chem disp; shwrs inc; el pts (10A) €2; lndry rm; shop & rest 150m; pool 150m; fishing nr; quiet. "Quiet, country-style site nr lge vill; clean, well-kept, grassy; interesting countryside; pleasant, helpful owners; extremely gd value." ♦ 15 Jun-15 Sep. € 11.00   2004*

KAYSERSBERG *6F3* (Urban) **Aire Communale, Rue Rocade, 68240 Kaysersberg [03 89 47 30 60 or 03 89 78 11 12 (Mairie)]** Fr N415 site adj junc with D28. Foll sp, clearly visible. Med, hdstg, unshd; wc; chem disp; mv service pnt; shop, rest, snacks, bar 200m; poss cr; some rd noise. "Gd NH; m'vans only; pay at machine." 15 Mar-31 Dec. € 6.00   2005*

KAYSERSBERG *6F3* (1km NW) **Camp Municipal, Rue des Acacias, 68240 Kaysersberg [tel/fax 03 89 47 14 47 or 03 89 78 11 11 (Mairie); camping@ville-kaysersberg.fr; www.kaysersberg.com]** Fr Kaysersberg, take N415 NW twd St Die, site sp at NW of town at junc of N415 by-pass & D28 to town. Med, pt shd; wc; chem disp; shwrs; el pts (8-13A) €3.35-4.25; gas; lndtte; shops adj; supmkt 700m; tradsmn; pool 500m; playgrnd; TV; fishing, tennis adj; dogs €1.60 (no dogs Jul/Aug); poss cr; quiet. "Many attractions in lovely area; many sm pitches; vg, busy site; rec arr early high ssn; recep clsd for new arr 1200-1400 & 2000-0700; wine-tasting on site; barrier locked 2200; vill is birth place Albert Schweitzer." 1 Apr-30 Sep. € 11.70   2005*

KAYSERSBERG *6F3* (7km NW) **Camping Les Verts Bois, 3 Rue de la Fonderie, 68240 Freland [tel/fax 03 89 47 57 25; marcel.florence@ wanadoo.fr; www.camping-lesvertsbois.com]** Sp off N415 Colmar/St Die rd bet Lapoutroie & Kaysersberg. Site approx 5km after turn fr main rd on D11 at far end of vill. D11 steep & rd to site has sharp L turn when main rd doubles back on itself. Sm, pt sl, terr, pt shd; htd wc; chem disp; shwrs inc; el pts (10A) inc; gas; lndtte; ice; shop & bank in vill; rest; snacks, bar; dogs €0.50; poss cr; Eng spkn; poss cr; adv bkg; quiet; cc acc; CCI. "Attractive setting adj fast-flowing rv; lovely site; sm pitches; clsd 1200-1400 & 2230-0700; friendly welcome; eve meals avail - rest open all year." 1 May-31 Oct.
€ 11.30   2005*

†**KESKASTEL** *5D3* (700m NE Rural) **Camp Municipal Les Sapins, Centre des Loisirs, 67260 Keskastel [03 88 00 19 25 (Mairie); fax 03 88 00 34 66]** Exit A4 junc 42 fr N or junc 43 fr S dir Sarralbe/Keskastel. In Keskastel cent turn onto D338 twds Herbitzheim. Cont for approx 1km; turn R for approx 400m; site on L, well sp on lakeside. Med, hdg/mkd pitch, pt shd; htd wc (some cont); chem disp; shwrs inc; el pts (10A) inc (poss rev pol:; lndtte; shop 1km; tradsmn; rest & snacks (high ssn); bar; BBQ; playgrnd; sand beach adj; lake sw & fishing; tennis nr; 60% statics; dogs; phone; poss cr; some Eng spkn; quiet; adv bkg; cc acc; CCI. "Relaxing location; ltd san facs low ssn; office poss clsd Sun morn; barrier closes 2300; conv m'way; helpful warden; excel." ♦ € 16.15   2005*

†**LABENNE** *8E1* (4km S Rural) **Camping du Lac, 518 Rue de Janin, 40440 Ondres [05 59 45 28 45 or 06 80 26 91 51; fax 05 59 45 29 45; contact@ camping-du-lac.fr; www.camping-du-lac.fr]** Fr N exit A63 junc 8 onto N10 S. Turn R just N of Ondres sp Ondres-Plage, at rndabt turn L & foll site sp. Fr S exit A63 junc 7 onto N10 to Ondres. Cont thro town cent & turn L at town boundary, then as above; tight turns thro housing est. Med, hdg/mkd pitch, terr, pt shd; wc; chem disp; baby facs; shwrs inc; el pts (10A) €4; gas; lndtte; ice; shop 500m; rest in ssn; snacks; bar; playgrnd; pool in ssn; sand beach 4km; lake sw adj; fishing; boating; games area; entmnt; cycle hire; 60% statics; dogs €3; phone; Eng spkn; adv bkg (dep); quiet; red long stay/low ssn; CCI. "Gd welcome; peaceful, lakeside site; ltd facs low ssn; excel." ♦ € 20.00   2005*

LABENNE *8E1* (4km S Coastal) **Camping Lou Pignada, Ave de la Plage, 40440 Ondres [05 59 45 30 65; fax 05 59 45 25 79; www. loupignada.com]** Turn R off N10 at N end of Ondres vill, sp Ondres-Plage, site immed after rlwy level x-ing on L. Med, shd; wc; baby facs; shwrs; el pts (6-8A) €6; gas; ice; lndtte; shop; rest; snacks; BBQ; playgrnd; cvrd/htd pools & paddling pool; waterslide; spa/jacuzzi; sand beach 500m; games area; tennis; cycle hire; horseriding, golf nrby; entmnts; TV; 50% statics; no dogs; adv bkg; red low ssn; v quiet; cc acc. "Sea bathing unsuitable young children but poss supervised in ssn; tight manoeuvring amongst trees." 30 Mar-30 Sep.
€ 29.00   2004*

LABENNE *8E1* (2km W Coastal) **Camping La Cote d'Argent, Ave de l'Ocean, 40530 Labenne [05 59 45 42 02; fax 05 59 45 73 31; info@ camping-cotedargent.com; www.camping-cote dargent.com]** Fr N10 take D126 W fr Labenne to Labenne-Plage & site. Lge, hdg/mkd pitch; shd; wc; 10% serviced pitches; mv service pnt; chem disp; baby facs; shwrs inc; el pts (6A) €3.60; gas 300m; lndtte; ice; shop 200m; tradsmn, rest, snacks, bar high ssn; BBQ; playgrnd; pool; sand beach 900m; fishing 300m; games rm; mini-golf; archery; tennis nr; entmnt high ssn; TV rm; cycle hire; 25% statics; dogs €2.50; poss cr; Eng spkn; adv bkg rec; quiet; cc acc; CCI. "Excel; conv Biarritz." ♦ ltd.
Easter-31 Oct. € 22.50 (CChq acc)   2005*

LABENNE *8E1* (2km W Coastal) **Camping La Mer, 40530 Labenne [05 59 45 42 09; fax 05 59 45 43 07; campinglamer@wanadoo.fr]** Turn W off N10 in Labenne at traff lts in town cent onto D126 to Labenne-Plage. Site 2km on L. Lge, shd; wc; shwrs inc; el pts (6A) €3.40; gas; lndtte; shop; snacks; playgrnd; pool; sand/shgl beach 1km; few statics; dogs €2.20; adv bkg; quiet. Easter-30 Sep. € 18.30   2003*

LAC D'ISSARLES, LE *9C1* (Rural) **Camp Municipal Les Bords du Lac, 07470 Le Lac-d'Issarles [04 66 46 20 70 or 04 66 46 20 06 (Mairie)]** On N88 S fr Le Puy-en-Velay, take D16 N sp Coucouron. Foll sp for Lac-d'Issarles. Site on L well sp. Lge, mkd pitch, pt sl, terr, pt shd; wc; chem disp (wc); shwrs inc; el pts inc; lndtte; lndry rm; shop, rest, snacks, bar 500m; playgrnd; sand beach; lake sw, fishing, boating; dogs; Eng spkn; quiet. "Pleasant views with dir access to lake; poss diff for long o'fits; gd long/sh stay." ♦ 1 May-15 Sep.
€ 12.10   2004*

LAC D'ISSARLES, LE *9C1* (2km Rural) **Camping La Plaine de la Loire, Pont de Laborie, 07470 Le Lac-d'Issarles [04 66 46 25 77 or 04 66 46 21 64; fax 04 66 46 21 55]** Fr N102 Aubenas-Le Puy-en-Velay rd going N take D16 sp Le Lac-d'Issarles. After Coucouron (5km) site on R. Med, mkd pitch, pt shd; wc (cont); chem disp; shwrs inc; el pts (6A) inc; gas; shop; tradsmn; lndtte; playgrnd; rv sw adj; 5% statics; adv bkg; quiet; CCI. "Lovely, tranquil site - a real gem." ♦ 1 Jun-15 Sep. € 12.00   2004*

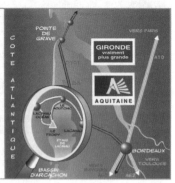
LACANAU OCEAN *7C1* (1km N Coastal) **Airotel de l'Ocean, Rue du Repos, 33680 Lacanau-Ocean** [05 56 03 24 45; fax 05 57 70 01 87; www. airotel-ocean.com] On ent town at end of sq in front of bus stn turn R, fork R & foll sp to site (next to Camping Grand Pins). Lge, pt sl, pt shd; wc; chem disp; shwrs inc; el pts (15A) inc; gas; lndtte; ice; shop; rest; snacks; bar; pool; sand beach 600m; tennis; entmnt; fishing; watersports; cycle hire; TV; poss cr; adv bkg; quiet; red low ssn. "Attractive site/holiday vill in pine woods behind sand dunes & enormous sand beach; care in choosing pitch owing to soft sand." Easter-24 Sep. € 23.63   2002*

LACANAU OCEAN *7C1* (1km N Coastal) **Camping Les Grand Pins, Rue des Pins, 33680 Lacanau-Ocean** [05 56 03 20 77; fax 05 57 70 03 89; reception@lesgrandspins.com; www.lesgrands pins.com] On ent town, by bus stn at sq turn R, fork R & foll sp. V lge, hdg/mkd pitch; terr; pt shd; wc; serviced pitches; chem disp; shwrs inc; el pts (10A) inc; gas; lndtte; ice; shop; rest; snacks; bar; playgrnd; htd pool; sand beach 500m; TV; cycle hire; entmnt; 20% statics; dogs €4; poss cr; adv bkg red high ssn; quiet; red low ssn. "Excel well organised site; lge pitches; doesn't feel overcr - even when full." 23 Apr-24 Sep. € 33.00   2004*

LACANAU OCEAN *7C1* (7km E Rural) **Camping Talaris Vacances, Route de L'Ocean, 33680 Lacanau** [05 56 03 04 15; fax 05 56 26 21 56; talarisvacances@free.fr; www.talaris-vacances. fr] Fr Lacanau-Ocean towards Lake Lacanau, site on R. Lge, mkd pitch, hdstg, shd; wc (some cont); chem disp; mv service pnt; baby facs; shwrs inc; el pts (6A) €3; gas; lndtte; ice; shop; rest; snacks; bar; BBQ area; playgrnd; pool; waterslide; lake sw 2km; tennis; mini-golf; 50% statics; dogs €3; bus adj; Eng spkn; adv bkg (dep req); some rd noise; CCI. "Nr Lake Lacanau, sw & watersports; ideal for cycling, excel network cycle tracks." ♦ 1 Apr-17 Sep. € 26.50   2005*

LACANAU OCEAN *7C1* (5km SE Rural) **Camping Le Tedey, Par Le Moutchic; Route de Longarisse, 33680 Lacanau-Ocean** [05 56 03 00 15; fax 05 56 03 01 90; camping@le-tedey.com; www.le-tedey. com] Fr Bordeaux take D6 to Lacanau & on twd Lacanau-Ocean. On exit Moutchic take L fork twd Longarisse. Ent in 2km well sp on L. V lge, mkd pitch, shd; wc (some cont); chem disp; mv service pnt; baby facs; shwrs inc; el pts (10A) €4; gas; lndtte; ice; shop; snacks; bar; playgrnd; lake sw & sand beach adj; boating; cycle hire; golf 5km; entmnt; internet; TV rm; no dogs; poss cr; Eng spkn; adv bkg (ess Jul/Aug); quiet, but poss live music Sat night high ssn; red low ssn; cc acc; CCI. "Set in pine woods - avoid tree sap; friendly, family-run site; golf nr; gd cycle tracks; no el pts for pitches adj to beach; access diff to some pitches; excel long stay." ♦ 29 Apr-20 Sep. € 19.80   2005*

See advertisement

LACAPELLE MARIVAL *7D4* (1km NW Rural) **Camp Municipal Bois de Sophie, Route d'Aynac, 46120 Lacapelle-Marival** [05 65 40 82 59] On W side of D940 dir St Cere, visible fr rd. Med, pt sl, pt shd; wc; chem disp; shwrs inc; el pts (10A) inc; shops 1km; playgrnd; pool adj; tennis; some statics; quiet; CCI. "Gd sh stay/NH." ♦ 15 May-15 Sep. € 12.50   2004*

†LACAUNE *8E4* (5km E Rural) **Camping Le Clot, Les Vidals, 81230 Lacaune** [tel/fax 05 63 37 03 59; le-clot@worldoline.fr] Fr Castres to Lacaune on D622. Cont on D622 past Lacaune then turn R on D62 for Les Vidals. Site sp 500m on L after Les Vidals. Sm, terr, pt shd; htd wc; chem disp; shwrs inc; el pts (10A) €2.50; lndtte; shop 5km; rest; snacks; playgrnd; lake sw, fishing, sailing, windsurfing 12km; dogs €1.50; Eng spkn; quiet; CCI. "Gd views; gd walking in Monts de Lacaune; friendly Dutch owner; excel long stay." ♦ € 13.00   2004*

LACAUNE *8E4* (10km SE Rural) **Camping Indigo Rieu-Montagne**, 81320 Nages [05 63 37 24 71; fax 05 63 37 15 42; rieumontagne@camping-indigo. com] E fr Lacaune on D622 for 8km. R on D62 twds Nages. 2km after Nages turn E on shore of Lac de Laouzas. Sp fr junc D662/D62. Lge, hdg/mkd pitch, terr, pt shd; wc (mainly cont); serviced pitches; baby facs; shwrs inc; el pts (10A) inc; gas; lndtte; shop; rest; snacks; bar; pool; playgrnd, cycle hire, archery, tennis & mini-golf nr; lake sw adj; adv bkg; cc acc; CCI. "Vg rest 100m W of beach; bread made daily on site." 15 Jun-15 Sep. € 25.00   2003*

LACELLE *7B4* (Rural) **Camp Municipal**, 19170 Lacelle [05 55 95 51 47 or 05 55 46 38 84 (Mairie); fax 05 55 46 03 86] Fr Bugeat on D979 to Lacelle. Or on D940 15km SE of Eymoutiers. Sm, shd; wc; shwrs; el pts (6A) €1.50; shop adj; rest; bar; playgrnd; paddling pool; games area; v quiet; adv bkg; phone. "In sm vill with communal fishing pond; v restful; warm welcome fr warden; v cheap!" 15 Jun-15 Sep. € 3.20   2005*

LADIGNAC LE LONG see St Yrieix la Perche *7B3*

LAFFREY see Vizille *9C3*

LAGRASSE *8G4* (1km NE Urban) **Camp Municipal de Boucocers**, 11220 Lagrasse [04 68 43 10 05 or 04 68 43 15 18; fax 04 68 43 10 41; mairiela grasse@wanadoo.fr; www.ecamp.com] 1km on D212 fr Lagrasse to Fabrizan (N). Sm, hdstg, pt sl, pt shd; wc; chem disp; shwrs inc; el pts (15A) €2.50; shops, rest 500m; rv sw 1km; dogs €1.50; phone; adv bkg; CCI. "Helpful warden; gd walking; o'lookng superb medieval town; 8thC abbey; beautiful area; rec arrive early." ♦ ltd. 1 Mar-31 Oct. € 10.00   2005*

LAGUENNE see Tulle *7C4*

LAGUEPIE *8E4* (E Rural) **Camp Municipal Les Tilleuls**, 82250 Laguepie [05 63 30 22 32 or 05 63 30 20 81 (Mairie)] Exit Cordes on D922 N to Laguepie; turn R at bdge, still on D922 sp Villefranche; site sp to R in 500m; tight turn into narr lane. NB App thro Laguepie poss diff lge o'fits. Med, pt shd; wc (some cont); shwrs inc; el pts (10A) €2; shops 1km; playgrnd; pool; 4% statics; dogs; phone; quiet. "V attractive setting on rv bank; Aveyron gorges; pleasant rvside walk to shops; gd sh stay." Easter-30 Sep. € 6.70   2002*

LAIGNES *6F1* (1km N) **Aire de Service (M'vans only), 21300 Laignes** Fr Chatillon-sur-Seine take D965 16km W to Laignes. Site clearly sp 1km before town. Sm (3 m'vans), pt shd; wc; mv service pnt; water points; el pts; picnic tables; shops & rest 15 min walk. "Free of charge, delightful site by mill-pond."   2002*

LAISSAC *7D4* (4km N Urban) **Camping Aire de Service Camping Car**, 12310 Laissac [05 65 69 60 45; fax 05 65 70 75 14; mairie-de-Laissac@wanadoo.fr] Exit N88 sp Laissac. Foll sp to site. N of Laissac 4km & site adj live stock mkt. Sm, mkd pitch, hdstg, unshd; wc (some cont); chem disp; mv service pnt; shop, bar 200m; rest, snacks 500m; phone 500m; rd noise. "Gd NH only; clean san facs & washing up facs; room for 6 m'vans only." ♦ ltd. 1 Mar-30 Nov. Free   2004*

LAISSAC *7D4* (3km SE) **Camping La Grange de Monteillac**, 12310 Severac-l'Eglise [05 65 70 21 00; fax 05 65 70 21 01; info@le-grange-de-monteillac. com; www.la-grange-de-monteillac.com] Fr A75, at junc 42, go W on the N88 twds Rodez; after approx 22km; bef Laissac; turn L twds Severac-l'Eglise; site sp. Med, hdg/mkd pitch, pt sl, terr, unshd; wc; chem disp (wc); mv service pnt; shwrs inc; el pts (6A) inc (long lead poss req); ice; lndtte; rest, bar & shops high ssn; playgrnd; 2 pools; archery; horseriding; cycle hire; walking; tennis; entmnts; TV; dogs €1.30; phone; Eng spkn; adv bkg rec high ssn; quiet; CCI. "Beautiful site; excel long stay." ♦ 1 May-15 Sep. € 21.50   2005*

LAIVES see Sennecey le Grand *6H1*

LALINDE *7C3* (1.5km E) **Camping Moulin de la Guillou, Route de Sauveboeuf**, 24150 Lalinde [05 53 61 02 91 or 05 53 73 44 60 (Mairie); fax 05 53 73 44 69; laguillou@wanadoo.fr] Take D703 E fr Lalinde (Rv Dordogne on R) & keep strt where rd turns L over canal bdge. Site in 300m; sp. Med, shd; wc; shwrs inc; el pts (5A) €1.60; ice; shops 1km; tradsmn; pool; playgrnd; rv sw & fishing adj; entmnt; tennis adj; dogs €1.10; adv bkg. "Basic, clean facs." 1 May-30 Sep. € 9.40   2005*

LALINDE *7C3* (4km E) **Camping Les Bo-Bains**, 24150 Badefols-sur-Dordogne [05 53 22 51 89; fax 05 53 22 46 70; info@bo-bains.com; www. bo-bains.com] Take D29 E fr Lalinde, site sp on L immed after vill sp for Badefols. Med, shd, hdg pitch; wc; chem disp; shwrs inc; el pts (6A) inc; lndtte; shop & 4km; rest; snacks; bar; entmnt; playgrnd; pool; waterslide; rv sw; tennis; games area; canoe hire; mini-golf; archery; boules; entmnt; child entmnt; quiet; adv bkg; cc acc. "Delightful site on banks of Rv Dordogne." ♦ 1 Apr-30 Sep. € 28.00   2003*

LALINDE *7C3* (8km SE) **Camping La Grande Veyiere**, 24480 Molieres [05 53 63 25 84; fax 05 53 63 18 25; la-grande-veyiere@wanadoo.fr] Fr Bergerac take D660 E for 19km to Port de Couze. Turn SW still on D660 sp Beaumont. In 6km turn L on D27. Site sp fr here. In approx 6km, ent on R. Med, hdg/mkd pitch, pt sl, terr, pt shd; wc (some cont); chem disp; shwrs inc; el pts (6A) inc; gas; shop; tradsmn; snacks; bar; playgrnd; pool; games/TV rm; some statics; Eng spkn; adv bkg (rec Jul/Aug); phone; CCI. "Vg long stay; off beaten track, worth finding; owners friendly & helpful; staff will help you pitch with tractor in wet weather." ♦ 1 Apr-2 Nov. € 16.48   2004*

FRANCE

Camping – Caravaning DOMAINE DE GATINIE ★★★

gatinie@wanadoo.fr • www.domainedegatinie.com

F-34600 Les Aires
Phone (summer): +33 (0)4 67 95 71 95
Phone (winter): +33 (0)4 67 28 41 69
Fax: +33 (0)4 67 95 65 73
2 km from LAMALOU LES BAINS. A 3 ha site situated in the heart of the 50 ha nature reserve of the Haut-Languedoc.
NEW: swimming pool
Right on the riverbanks – canoes – kayaks – fishing.
Large pitches – quiet – shade – Oak trees – Chestnuts.
At the foot of the CAROUX-mountains: hiking trails, climbing, mountain biking. At 2 km: golf course, horse riding, tennis.
Mobile homes and cottages to let.
Reception, snack-bar, bar-restaurant.

LALINDE *7C3* (10km S) **Centre Naturiste de Vacances Le Couderc (Naturist)**, 24440 Naussannes [05 53 22 40 40; fax 05 53 23 90 98; le.couderc@perigord.com; www.lecouderc.com] S on D660 to Beaumont fr Couze; take D25 thro Naussannes & hamlet of Leydou. Just beyond Leydou turn R into site, well sp. Lge, mkd pitch, pt sl, pt shd; wc; chem disp; shwrs inc; el pts (3A) €3.65; sm shop; rest; snacks; bar; playgrnd; htd pool; sm lake; cycle hire; quiet; INF card req (can be purchased at site); adv bkg; dep req (€10 per nt); bkg fee €17; cc acc; red long stay/low ssn. "Gd san facs, spread over 5 camping areas; beautiful Dutch-run site; v friendly & helpful staff; Bastide towns nrby; excel long stay." 1 Apr-30 Sep. € 20.55
2003*

LALINDE *7C3* (4km W Urban) **Camping Des Moulins, Route de Cahors**, 24150 Couze-et-St Front [05 53 61 18 36; fax 05 53 24 99 72; camping-des-moulins@wanadoo.fr; www.campingdesmoulins.com] Fr Lalinde take D703 to Bergerac. In 2km turn L on D660 sp Port de Couze; over bdge (Dordogne Rv) into Couze. Turn R on D37 sp Lanquais, turn immed L, site sp. (NB Do not take D37E) Sm, hdg pitch, pt sl, pt shd; wc; chem disp; mv service pnt; shwrs inc; el pts (10A) inc; gas; lndtte; ice; snacks; bar; playgrnd; 3 pools; lake sw 3km; 20% statics; dogs €2; phone adj; poss cr; Eng spkn; adv bkg; quiet; CCI. "Generous pitches; v friendly & helpful owner; poss unruly youth groups; ltd facs low ssn & poss unclean; vg." 1 Apr-31 Oct. € 24.00 4 persons
2004*

LALLEY *9D3* (S Rural) **Camp Municipal Belle-Roche**, 38930 Lalley [04 76 34 75 33 or 06 86 36 71 48; fax 04 76 34 75 33; gildapatt@aol.com] Off N75 at D66 for Mens; down long hill into Lalley. Site on R thro vill. Med, some hdg pitch, hdstg, pt sl, pt shd; wc; chem disp; mv service pnt; baby facs; shwrs inc; el pts (10A) €3.40 (poss rev pol); gas; lndtte; ice; shop 500m; tradsmn Jul-Aug; rest; snacks; bar; playgrnd; htd pool; TV; entmnt; dogs €1; poss cr; Eng spkn; adv bkg; quiet; no cc acc; CCI. "Spacious pitches; friendly staff; vg facs for disabled; v clean san facs; gd for alpine flowers, walking; nr Vercors National Park; well worth a visit." ♦ 1 May-30 Sep. € 14.00 (CChq acc)   2004*

LAMALOU LES BAINS *10F1* (NE Urban) **Camp Municipal Le Verdale**, 34240 Lamalou-les-Bains [04 67 95 86 89; fax 04 67 95 87 70; omt. lamalou@wanadoo,fr] S fr Bedarieux on D908 twds Lamalou. Turn N off D908 at traff lts into Lamalou. At 2nd rndbt turn E foll sp to site on NE side of town. Med, mkd pitch, pt shd; htd wc; shwrs; el pts (6A) €2.30; shop, pool, tennis & golf in town; 30% statics; phone; poss cr; adv bkg rec. "San facs clean; helpful, friendly warden; sm pitches; nr thermal baths; easy walk to town & shops."
15 Mar-31 Oct. € 11.20   2005*

LAMALOU LES BAINS *10F1* (2km SE Rural) **Camping Domaine de Gatinie, Route de Gatinie**, 34600 Les Aires [04 67 95 71 95 or 04 67 28 41 69 (LS); fax 04 67 95 65 73; gatinie@wanadoo.fr; www.domainedegatinie.com] Fr D908 fr Lamalou-les- Bains or Herpian dir Poujol-sur-Orb, site sp. Fr D160 cross rv to D908 then as above. Med, hdg/mkd pitch, pt sl, pt shd; wc (some cont); chem disp; baby facs; shwrs inc; el pts (6A) inc; lndtte; ice; tradsmn; rest; snacks; bar; BBQ; playgrnd; pool; paddling pool; rv sw 100m; canoeing; fishing; games area; golf, horseriding, tennis 2km; entmnt; some statics; dogs €2.30; Eng spkn; adv bkg; quiet; red low ssn/long stay/CCI. "Beautiful situation; many leisure activities; vg." ♦ 1 Mar-30 Nov. € 17.00   2005*

See advertisement above

LAMASTRE *9C2* (5km NE Rural) **Camping Les Roches, Les Roches**, 07270 Le Crestet [04 75 06 20 20; fax 04 75 06 26 23; camproches@ club-internet.fr; www.campinglesroches.com] Take D534 fr Tournon-sur Rhone dir Lamastre. Turn R at Le Crestet & foll sp for site, 3km fr vill. Sm, mkd pitch, hdstg, terr, pt shd; wc (some cont); chem disp; mv service pnt; baby facs; shwrs inc; el pts (4-6A) €2.80-3.50; lndtte; ice; shop; tradsmn; rest; snacks; bar; BBQ; playgrnd; htd pool; rv sw adj; sports area; fishing; TV rm; 30% statics; bus 1km; adv bkg dep req; quiet; cc acc; 5% red CCI. "Family-run site; v clean facs; lovely views; gd base for touring medieval vills; gd walking; excel all stays." ♦ 15 Apr-30 Sep. € 15.00   2004*

LAMASTRE *9C2* (5km W) **Camp Municipal, 07570 Desaignes** [04 75 06 61 49 or 04 75 06 63 53] Fr Lamastre take D533 twd St Agreve, thro Desaignes, site on R at exit of vill (8km by rd fr Lamastre). Sm, terr, pt shd; wc (cont); shwrs inc; el pts; ice; shops 500m; bar; lake sw; playgrnd; poss cr; no adv bkg; quiet. "Overlooking mountain valley." Jul-Aug. 2002*

> Mustn't forget to post our site report forms to The Club, otherwise sites might be deleted.

LAMASTRE *9C2* (2km NW Rural) **Camping Le Retourtour, 1, Rue de Retourtour, 07270 Lamastre.** [tel/fax 04 75 06 40 71; campingde retourtour@wanadoo.fr] Fr Lamastre take D533 W. Site well sp. Med, mkd pitch, pt shd; wc (some cont); chem disp; mv service pnt; baby facs; shwrs inc; el pts (4-13A) €2.50-€4.60; gas; ice; lndtte; shop; tradsmn; rest; snacks; bar; BBQ; playgrnd; entmnt; rv sw 500m; 8% statics; dogs; phone; quiet; adv bkg (25% dep req); Eng spkn; cc not acc; CCI. "V friendly, helpful owners; vg long/sh stay." ♦ Easter-30 Sep. € 11.50 2002*

LAMBALLE *2E3* (700m NE Urban) **Camp Municipal, Rue St Sauveur, 22400 Lamballe** [tel/fax 02 96 34 74 33 or 02 96 50 13 50 (LS)] NE side of town beyond church; nr water tower. Clearly sp. Sm, terr, pt shd; wc; shwrs inc; el pts (5A) €2.74; shops 700m; htd pool 700m; quiet. "Interesting town, historical 17thC church." 19 Jun-10 Sep. € 8.80 2004*

LAMONTELARIE see Brassac *8F4*

LANDEBIA see Plancoet *2E3*

LANDEDA *2E1* (2km NW Coastal) **Camping Les Abers, Plage de Ste Marguerite, 29870 Landeda** [02 98 04 93 35; fax 02 98 04 84 35; camping-des-abers@wanadoo.fr; www.camping-des-abers.com] NW fr Brest on D13/D10 to Landeda via Bourg-Blanc & Lannilis; foll sp to Dunes de Ste Marguerite & site. Lge, hdg/mkd pitch, hdstg, terr, pt shd; wc; mv service pnt; chem disp; baby facs; fam bthrm; shwrs €0.80; el pts (5A) €2.50; gas; lndtte; ice; shop & snacks in ssn; rest 200m; bar 100m; BBQ; playgrnd; sand beach; games rm; cycle hire; entmnt; 10% statics; dogs €1.60; Eng spkn; adv bkg (rec high ssn); quiet; 20% red low ssn; cc acc; CCI. "Attractive site adj spectacular, wild coast; unspoilt area; gd sized pitches - highest have views; pitches by play area not rec; site well landscaped with flowers; facs clean & well-maintained; gd walks, cycling; friendly, helpful manager; excel." ♦ 1 May-30 Sep. € 13.80 (CChq acc) 2005*

See advertisement below

LANDEDA *2E1* (3km NW Coastal) **Camp Municipal de Penn-Enez, 29870 Landeda** [02 98 04 99 82; info@camping-penn-enez.com; www.camping-penn-enez.com] Proceed NW thro Landeda, turn R in 1km sp Penn-Enez then L in 600m. Site sp. Med, pt hdg pitch, pt sl, unshd; wc; chem disp (wc); shwrs inc; el pts (16A) €2.70; playgrnd; sand beach 500m; 2% statics; dogs €1.30; Eng spkn; quiet. "Friendly, helpful management; grassy headland site; beach views fr some pitches; san facs poss stretched high ssn; site self, warden calls 1100-1200 & 1800-1900; gd walks; gd sh stay." ♦ ltd. 25 Apr-30 Sep. € 9.10 2004*

LANDERNEAU *2E2* (SW Urban) **Camp Municipal Les Berges de l'Elorn, Route de Calvaire, 29800 Landerneau** [02 98 85 44 94 or 02 98 85 00 66 (Mairie); fax 02 98 85 43 35] Fr main town bdge foll sp to pool, sports stadium & site (200m). Sm, hdg pitch, hdstg, pt shd; wc; chem disp; mv service pnt; shwrs inc; el pts (7A) €3.05; shops, rest, snacks bar 250m; BBQ; playgrnd adj; pool 500m; tennis; dogs €1.05; phone adj; Eng spkn; adv bkg; quiet, some rd noise; CCI. "Pretty town on rv; pitches all have el pts & some have water tap; poss itinerants." ♦ 15 May-15 Oct. € 8.85 2005*

CAMPING DES ABERS ★★★

Outstandingly positioned in Brittany, 45 min. West from ROSCOFF - Direct access to a remarkable sandy beach with little islands accessible at low tide. Splendid ocean views. Ideal for families with younger children and nature-lovers. English spoken.

Plage de Sainte-Marguerite 29870 LANDEDA
FINISTERE - BRETAGNE - FRANCE
Phone: 00 33 298 04 93 35 ● fax: 00 33 298 04 84 35
camping-des-abers@wanadoo.fr
www.camping-des-abers.com

LANDEVIEILLE see Bretignolles sur Mer *2H3*

LANDIVISIAU *2E2* (7km NE) **Camp Municipal Lanorgent, 29420 Plouvorn [02 98 61 32 40 (Mairie); fax 02 98 61 38 87]** Fr Landivisiau, take D69 N twd Roscoff. In 8km turn R onto D19 twd Morlaix. Site sp, in 700m turn R. Sm, hdg/mkd pitch, pt shd; wc (cont for men); mv service pnt; shwrs; el pts (3A) €2; ice; lndtte; shops 500m; BBQ; playgrnd; sand beach; lake sw; sailboards & canoes for hire; tennis; fishing; adv bkg; quiet. "Ideal NH for ferries; v diff lge o'fits." 15 Jun-15 Sep. € 6.10
2002*

LANDUDEC *2F2* (2km W Rural) **Domaine de Bel-Air, Route de Quimper-Audierne, Keridreuff, 29710 Landudec [02 98 91 50 27; fax 02 98 91 55 82; camping-dubelair@wanadoo.fr; www. belaircamping.com]** Fr N165 exit dir Quimper Cent. On ring rd foll sp Douarnenez & Audierne & exit ring rd onto D765 immed after Carrefour supmkt sp Douarnenez. Turn L at rndabt onto D784 dir Audierne/Landudec. Strt on at traff lts in Landudec, site on L in 750m. Lge, hdg/mkd pitch, terr, pt shd; wc; chem disp; shwrs inc; el pts (10A) inc; gas; lndtte; ice; shop; tradsmn; rest; snacks; playgrnd; htd pool; paddling pool; beach 10km; lake adj; waterslide; watersports; tennis; games rm; entmnt; child entmnt; TV; dogs €3; poss cr; Eng spkn; adv bkg; quiet; cc acc; red low ssn; CCI. "Well situated site; excel." ♦ 1 May-30 Sep. € 22.00   2005*

LANGEAC *9C1* (1km N Rural) **Camping Les Gorges de l'Allier, Domaine du Pradeau, 43300 Langeac [04 71 77 05 01; fax 04 71 77 27 34; infos@campinglangeac.com; www.camping langeac.com]** Site sp on Clermont-Ferrand to Le Puy rd (N102) at D56. Take D56 to Langeac. Site at junc of D590 & D585. Lge, pt shd; wc (some cont); chem disp; mv service pnt; shwrs inc; el pts (10A) €2.50; gas 500m; lndtte; ice; shop 500m; tradsmn; snacks; playgrnd; pool; rv sw, fishing, canoeing & walking rtes adj; child entmnt; cycle hire; entmnt; TV rm; some statics; dogs €1; Eng spkn; quiet; red low ssn; CCI. "Tourist train thro Gorges d'Allier Fr Langeac to Langogne." 1 Apr-31 Oct. € 10.50
2005*

LANGEAIS *4G1* (1km E) **Camp Municipal du Lac, 37130 Langeais [02 47 96 85 80 or 02 47 96 12 50 (Mairie); fax 02 47 96 69 23; ville.langeais@ wanadoo.fr]** Fr Langeais take N152 twd Tours, site on R in 500m. Med, shd; wc; mv service pnt; shwrs inc; el pts (6A) €2; ice; shops 500m; pool adj; playgrnd; poss cr; adv bkg. "Gd value; vg sh stay." 1 Jun-15 Sep. € 6.10   2002*

LANGOGNE *9D1* (1km S Urban) **Camp Municipal de l'Allier, 9 Route de St Alban-en-Montagne, 48300 Langogne [04 66 69 28 98]** Fr Le Puy take N88 dir Mende. At Langogne over rv bdge & 1st L. Foll sp, site in 1km. Med, mkd pitch, pt sl, pt shd; wc (some cont); chem disp (wc); shwrs inc; el pts (6A) €2.40; ice; lndtte; shops 500m; rest; snacks; bar; pool 500m; phone; poss cr; quiet; adv bkg; CCI. "Gd walking area; lake for sailing 2km; close to walking routes; gd all stays." ♦ 1 May-30 Sep. € 6.60
2004*

LANGOGNE *9D1* (2km W Rural) **Camping Les Terrasses du Lac de Naussac, 48300 Naussac [04 66 69 29 62; fax 04 66 69 24 78; naussac@ club-internet.fr; www.naussac.com]** S fr Le Puy-en-Velay on N88. At Langogne take D26 to lakeside, site sp. Lge, terr, pt shd; wc; chem disp; baby facs; shwrs; el pts (6A) €2.50; lndtte; lndry rm; shop 2km; rest; snacks; bar; BBQ; playgrnd; pool; lake sw & sand beach adj; watersports adj; sailing school; games area; cycle hire; golf 1km; horseriding 3km; entmnt; excursions; TV rm; 10% statics; dogs €1; phone; Eng spkn; adv bkg (dep req); quiet; CCI. "Vg views; vg cycling & walking." ♦ 1 Apr-30 Sep. € 14.10 (CChq acc)   2005*

LANGON *7D2* (4km NE) **Camp Municipal Les Bords de Garonne, 33490 St Pierre-d'Aurillac [05 56 63 39 00 or 05 56 63 30 27 (Mairie); fax 05 56 63 17 39]** Fr Langon E on N113 thro St Macaire. Site to R in cent of vill of St Pierre- d'Aurillac. Fr E on N113 approx 15km after La Reole site sp L. Easy access. Sm, pt shd; wc (some cont); chem disp; shwrs inc; el pts 6A) inc; lndtte; shops 500m; quiet; CCI. "Site attended by warden but poss no access 1200-1700; gd fruit & wine region; poor san facs & lndtte low ssn; when leaving with m'van not poss to turn L twd Bordeaux, take alt lanes or turn round in g'ge twd La Reole; poss many itinerants." 15 Jun-15 Sep. € 10.70   2004*

†LANGRES *6F1* (6km NE) **Camping Hautoreille, 52360 Bannes [tel/fax 03 25 84 83 40; camping hautoreille@free.fr; www.campinghautoreille. com]** N fr Dijon on N74 to Langres; foll rd around Langres to E; onto D74 NE to Bannes; site on R on ent vill. Or exit A31 junc 7 Langres Nord onto N19, then D74 NE to Bannes. Med, mkd pitch, some hdstg, pt sl, pt shd; htd wc; chem disp; shwrs inc; el pts (6A) €3.50 (rev pol); lndtte; ice; shops 5km; tradsmn; rest; snacks; bar; playgrnd; lake sw 2.5km; horseriding & tennis 5km; dogs €1; phone; poss cr; Eng spkn; adv bkg; quiet; CCI. "Peaceful site; gd facs being improved; pleasant owners; gd site rest; v busy NH at w/e; site muddy when wet - parking on hdstg or owner will use tractor; ltd facs low ssn." ♦ € 13.40   2005*

LANGRES *6F1* (5km E Rural) **Camping du Lac de la Liez, Rue du Camping, 52200 Peigney [03 25 90 27 79; fax 03 25 90 66 79; camping liez@free. fr; www.campingliez.com]** Exit A5/A31 at Langres Nord or Sud & head twd Vesoul, then foll sp for Lac de la Liez, site sp fr N19. Lge, hdg pitch, terr, pt sl, pt shd; htd wc; chem disp; mv service pnt; sauna; baby facs; shwrs inc; el pts (10A) inc; ice; lndtte; shop; tradsmn; rest; snacks; bar; BBQ; playgrnd; 2 pools (1 htd covrd); spa; lake sw & sand beach adj; fishing, windsurfing, sailing & pedaloes; tennis; cycle hire; horseriding, golf 10km; games rm; internet; TV rm; 15% statics; dogs €1.50; phone; Eng spkn; cc acc; CCI. "Excel site; sm pitches; modern, clean facs but poss stretched high ssn; v cr high ssn; well-run site; office clsd 1230-1500 - instruction about barrier on office door; lake views; pleasant rvside walk; lovely pool; gd walking; Langres interesting walled Roman town." ♦1 Apr-1 Nov. € 20.00 (CChq acc) ABS - J05   2005*

LANGRES *6F1* (5km S Rural) **Camp Municipal La Croix d'Arles, 52200 Bourg [tel/fax 03 25 88 24 02; croix.arles@wanadoo.fr; www.croixdarles.com]** Site is 4km S of Langres on W side of N74 S of junc of N74 with D428. Med, hdg/mkd pitch, hdstg, pt sl, pt shd; wc; chem disp; mv service pnt; shwrs inc; el pts (10A) €3.50 (poss rev pol) (long cable req); lndtte; shop; tradsmn; rest; snacks; bar; playgrnd; pool; mini-golf; statics; dogs; phone; poss cr; Eng spkn; red low ssn; cc acc; CCI. "Popular site, fills up quickly after 1600; some lovely hidden pitches in woodland; friendly staff; v conv NH; conv Langres historic town." ♦ 15 Mar-1 Nov. € 14.50   2005*

As we're travelling out of season, we'd better phone ahead to check that the site is actually open.

LANGRES *6F1* (1km SW Urban) **Camp Municipal Navarre, Blvd de Lattre de Tassigny, 52200 Langres [03 25 87 37 92]** Fr N19 L at sp in town; foll sp to 'Centre Ville'. Site well sp fr town cent; inside old town walls. NB Travelling S ignore 1st sp to town centre, continue to top of hill to rndabt. Med, pt sl, pt shd; wc (some cont); chem disp; shwrs inc; el pts (6A) inc (long cable req); lndry rm; playgrnd nr; dogs; phone; poss cr in high ssn & w/e; Eng spkn; quiet, some rd noise; cc not acc; CCI. "Sh walk into Langres, interesting Roman walled town; excel Little Train; tour of town & walls 1km fr site; gd shops, rests etc in town; recep open 1800-2200; on arr site self & see warden at recep; gd security; no twin-axle vans; site pleasantly situated but poss scruffy low ssn; san facs clean but old & used by visitors to adj museum; excel basic site." ♦ ltd. 15 Mar-31 Oct. € 10.65   2005*

LANGRES *6F1* (8km NW Rural) **Camp Municipal La Mouche, Rue de la Mouche, 52200 Humes-Jorquenay [03 25 87 50 65 (Mairie)]** Leave A31 at junc 7, foll N74 S for 7km. Site sp in vill cent or S fr Chaumont on N19, into vill of Humes. Sm, unshd; wc; shwrs inc; el pts (8A) €1.80 (poss long cable rec); shop in vill; tradsmn; rest 2km; snacks; playgrnd; poss cr; quiet. "Pretty, basic, busy site; early arr rec; fees collected each pm; interesting area; gd sh stay/ NH." 1 May-30 Sep. € 8.80   2004*

†**LANGUIDIC** *2F3* (5km NW Rural) **Camping a la Ferme (Le Fur), Stang-Er-Huerne, Poulic, 56440 Languidic [02 97 65 84 29]** Site sp fr Languidic exit on N24 Rennes-Lorient. Sm, pt shd, wc; shwrs inc; el pts (10A) inc (poss rev pol); shop & gas 3km; playgrnd; sand beach 15km; fishing 500m; horseriding nrby; adv bkg; quiet. "Gd site but diff to find." € 12.50   2003*

LANLOUP *2E3* (W Rural) **Camping Le Neptune, Kerguistin, 22580 Lanloup [02 96 22 33 35 or 06 75 44 39 69 (mob); fax 02 96 22 68 45; contact@ leneptune.com; www.leneptune.com]**   Take D786 fr St Brieuc or Paimpol to Lanloup, site sp. Med, hdg/mkd pitch, pt shd; wc; chem disp; mv service pnt; baby facs; shwrs inc; el pts (6-16A) €3; gas; lndtte; ice; shop; tradsmn; rest; snacks; bar; BBQ; playgrnd; htd, covrd pool; sand beach 1km; tennis 300m; horseriding 4km; cycle hire; mini-golf; TV rm; 10% statics; dogs €1.70; phone; poss cr; Eng spkn; adv bkg; quiet; CCI. "Well-maintained; gd sized pitches; spotless san facs; friendly owner." ♦ 1 Apr-30 Sep. € 20.25 (CChq acc)   2005*

LANNEMEZAN *8F2* (6km W) **Camping Les Craoues, 65130 Capvern-les-Bains [05 62 39 02 54]** Fr Lannemezan N117 to rndabt, take 2nd turn sp Bagneres, ent immed on R. Med, pt sl, shd; wc; shwrs inc; el pts (6A) inc; gas; lndtte; ice; shops 500m; playgrnd; games rm; dogs €1; poss cr; adv bkg; red low ssn. 1 May-15 Oct. € 15.00   2003*

LANNION *1D2* (2km SE) **Camp Municipal Les Deux Rives, Rue du Moulin du Duc, 22300 Lannion [02 96 46 31 40 or 02 96 46 64 22; fax 02 96 46 53 35; infos@ville.lannion.fr]** SW fr Perros-Guirec on D788 to Lannion; fr Lannion town cent; foll dir Guincamp on D767; site well sp approx 1.5km just bef Leclerc supmkt (do not confuse with hypmkt). Med, mkd pitch, unshd; wc; chem disp; shwrs inc; el pts (6A) €2; lndtte; shop high ssn & 1km; bar high ssn; playgrnd; security barrier; dogs €1; adv bkg; CCI. "Excel site; easy rvside walk to old town; helpful warden; gd san facs; phone ahead low ssn to check open." ♦ 1 Apr-30 Sep. € 12.50   2005*

LANOBRE see Bort les Orgues *7C4*

LANSARGUES see Lunel *10E2*

LANSLEBOURG MONT CENIS *9C4* **Camp Municipal Les Balmasses, 73480 Lanslebourg [04 79 05 82 83; fax 04 79 05 91 56; burdin61@ club-internet.fr]** Fr Modane, site on R on ent to town; cross car park; site on rv over wooden bdge. Med, mkd pitch, pt shd; wc (some cont); shwrs inc; el pts (6-10A) €4-4.60; lndtte; ice; shop 500m; rest; snacks; bar; BBQ; playgrnd; dogs; phone; Eng spkn; quiet; CCI. "Pleasant site; v clean facs; lovely mountain views." ♦ ltd. 1 Jun-20 Sep. € 12.00   2005*

LANVEOC *2E2* (1km N Coastal) **Camping La Cale, 29160 Lanveoc [tel/fax 02 98 27 58 91]** N fr Crozon dir Roscanvel. After approx 5.5km turn R onto D55 for Lanveoc. Site sp. Med, terr, unshd; shwrs inc; el pts (10A) €2.40; lndtte; rest; snacks; bar; dir access to coast; fishing; no statics; quiet; CCI. "Sea views; low ssn unisex san facs." 1 May-15 Sep. € 8.00   2005*

LAON *3C4* (1km SW Rural) **Camp Municipal La Chenaie, Allee de la Chenaie, 02000 Laon [tel/fax 03 23 20 25 56; aaussel@ville-laon.fr]** Fr N44 junc with N2 rndabt turn N sp Laon/Semilly, then L at next rndabt. Site well sp. Med, hdg/mkd pitches, pt shd; wc; chem disp; shwrs inc; el pts (10A) inc (rev pol); lndtte; shop 3km; tradsmn; bar; playgrnd; fishing lake 500m (no sw); watersports at nrby Parc de l'Ailette; dogs €1.10; phone; poss cr; Eng spkn; adv bkg; quiet; cc not acc; CCI. "Gd site; excel, clean san facs; if travelling Sep phone to check if site still open; steep access; lgest pitches at end of site rd; twin-axles not allowed; gates close 2200." ♦ 1 May-30 Sep. € 12.80   2005*

LAPALISSE *9A1* (250m S Urban) **Camp Municipal, Rue des Vignes, 03120 Lapalisse [04 70 99 26 31; fax 04 70 99 33 53; contact@paysdelapalisse.fr; www.ville-lapalisse.fr]** N7 fr Moulins, site on R 50m bef Lapalisse cancellation sp. Med, mkd pitch, pt shd; htd wc (some cont); shwrs inc; el pts (6A) €2.10; lndtte; shops 300m; tradsman; playgrnd; dogs €1; quiet; Eng spkn; cc acc; CCI. "Pop NH; no twin-axle vans." ♦ 1 Apr-30 Sep. € 8.00   2005*

LAPALME see Sigean *10G1*

LAPALUD *9D2* (Urban) **Camping Caravaning Le Village, 84840 Lapalud [tel/fax 04 90 40 31 03]** Fr Montelimar N7 S dir Pont-St Esprit; L into Lapalud, foll sp to site. Med, hdg/mkd pitch, hdstg, pt shd; wc (some cont); chem disp; shwrs inc; el pts (3-16A) €2-8.50; shop, rest, snacks, bar in vill; BBQ; playgrnd; dogs; phone; Eng spkn; quiet but poss noise fr rd/rlwy. "Nr gorges of Ardeche/Rhone; poss open all yr phone ahead to check; gd long stay." € 9.10   2002*

LAPEYROUSE *7A4* (Rural) **Camp Municipal Les Marins, La Loge, 63700 Lapeyrouse [04 73 52 02 73 or 04 73 52 00 79 (Mairie); fax 04 73 52 03 89]** Fr Montlucon S on N144 sp Montaigut. In 24km turn L on D13 sp Lapeyrouse. In 7km turn R onto D998, site on R at end of vill, well sp. Med, mkd pitch, pt shd; wc; chem disp; baby facs; shwrs inc; el pts inc; lndtte; bar nr; lake sw; windsurfing; fishing; playgrnd; cycle hire; TV; quiet; adv bkg; CCI. "Delightful countryside; barrier access." 15 Jun-1 Sep. € 13.00 (3 persons)   2002*

LARGENTIERE *9D2* (4km SE Rural) **Camping Les Chataigniers, Le Mas-de-Peyrot, 07110 Laurac-en-Vivarais [04 75 36 86 26; chataigniers@hotmail.com; www.chataigniers-laurac.com]** Fr N on A7, at junc Loriol take N104 via Privas or Aubenas dir Ales. Site sp fr La Chapelle. Sm, mkd pitch, pt sl, pt shd; wc, chem disp (wc); baby facs; shwrs; el pts (10A) €2.30; lndtte; ice; playgrnd; pool; 10% statics; dogs €1; poss cr; adv bkg; quiet. "Attractive site in S Ardeche, sh walk to vill shops, supmkt & auberge; vg long stay." ♦ 1 Apr-30 Sep. € 18.00   2004*

LARGENTIERE *9D2* (1.6km NW Rural) **Camping Les Ranchisses, Route de Valgorge, Chassiers, 07110 Largentiere [04 75 88 31 97; fax 04 75 88 32 73; reception@lesranchisses.fr; www.lesranchisses.fr]** Fr Aubenas S on D104. 1km after vill of Uzer turn R onto D5 to Largentiere. Go thro Largentiere on D5 in dir Rocher/Valgorge. DO NOT use D103 bet Lachapelle-Aubenas & Largentiere - this rd is too steep & narr for lge vehicles & c'vans. Med, mkd pitch, pt shd; wc; shwrs inc; el pts (10A) inc; lndtte; ice; shop; rest; snacks; bar; BBQ (gas/elec only) playgrnd; 2 htd pools; paddling pool; rv sw, fishing; canoeing; tennis; mini-golf; games area; entmnt; internet; TV rm; 30% statics; dogs; poss cr; adv bkg ess; red low ssn. "Excel rest; noisy rd adj to S end of site, also noisy when site full; lovely, well-managed site adj vineyard; vg rest & pool; helpful, hard-working staff; close to museums." ♦ 14 Apr-24 Sep. € 32.50 (CChq acc) ABS - C32   2005*

LARGENTIERE *9D2* (8km NW Rural) **Camping La Marette, Route de Valgorge, 07110 Joannas [04 75 88 38 88; fax 04 75 88 36 33; www.lamarette.com]** Fr Aubenas D104 SW to Largentiere. Foll D5 3km N of Largentiere then W on D24 to Valgorge. Site 3km past vill of Joannas. Med, mkd pitch; pt sl, terr, pt shd; wc; chem disp; mv service pnt; shwrs; el pts (10A) €3.10; lndtte; shop; tradsmn; snacks; bar; playgrnd; pool; 5% statics; dogs €1.30; quiet; adv bkg; Eng spkn; CCI. "Friendly family-run site; excel for children; organised tours, canoe hire, walking; new san facs 2004; not rec for lge trailer o'fits." ♦ Easter-15 Sep. € 18.00   2004*

LAROQUE DES ALBERES see Argeles sur Mer *10G1*

†**LARUNS** *8G2* (5km N) **Camp Municipal de Monplaisir, 64260 Gere-Belesten [05 59 82 61 18; fax 05 59 82 60 71]** Bet rte D934 & Rue Gave d'Ossau, on E side of rd, sp. Med, pt shd; wc; serviced pitches; shwrs €0.70; el pts (3-16A) €3.64-6; tradsmn; shops 5km; playgrnd; fishing; TV; 50% statics; adv bkg; quiet. € 8.50   2003*

LARUNS *8G2* (2km E) **Camping Le Valentin, 64440 Laruns [05 59 05 39 33 or 05 59 05 32 80 (LS); fax 05 59 05 65 84; camping duvalentin@wanadoo.fr]** Fr Laruns take D934 dir Col de Pourtalet. Site well sp on L app RH bend. If app fr Col d'Aubisque another site ent is well sp on R at sharp LH bend just bef D934. Med, hdg/mkd pitch, terr, pt shd; wc; shwrs inc; el pts (3-5A) €2.35-3.20; lndtte; shop; tradsmn; rest, snacks high ssn; bar; playgrnd; pool 3km; 20% statics; dogs €1.10; adv bkg; quiet at night but some rd noise; red low ssn/long stay; CCI. "Extremely pleasant, well-managed site, friendly, helpful management; some pitches cramped if using awning; facs ltd low ssn; conv Spanish border, cable car & mountain train; surrounded by 5 mountain peaks; thermal baths in nrby vill of Eaux-Chaudes; gd sh stay/NH." ♦ 25 Apr-1 Nov. € 14.00   2005*

LARUNS *8G2* (6km SE Rural) **Camping d'Iscoo, 64440 Eaux-Bonnes [05 59 05 36 81; http://iscoo. free.fr]** Site is on R 1.4km fr Eaux-Bonnes on climb to Col d'Aubisque (site sp says Camping * *, no name). Site ent in middle of S-bend so advise cont 500m & turn on open ground on L. Sm, mkd pitch, pt sl, pt shd; wc (some cont); shwrs €0.76; el pts (2-5A) inc; shops 1.5km; playgrnd; pool 3km; dogs; quiet; cc not acc; CCI. "V pleasant location; site not well maintained low ssn." 1 Jun-30 Sep. € 11.00
2004*

†**LARUNS** *8G2* (1km S Urban) **Camping du Pont Lauguere, 64440 Laruns [tel/fax 05 59 05 35 99]** Site on S side of Elf petrol stn, same side of rd, on corner of side turning for several camp sites. Sm, unshd; wc; shwrs €0.80; el pts (2-4A) €1.90-3.50; lndtte; shop 1km; dogs €1; poss cr; red low ssn. € 10.80
2003*

†**LARUNS** *8G2* (1km S) **Camping Les Gaves, Pon, 64440 Laruns [05 59 05 32 37; fax 05 59 05 47 14; campingdesgaves@wanadoo.fr]** Site on S edge of town, N of Hotel Le Lorry & bdge. Fr town sq cont on Rte d'Espagne (narr exit fr sq) to end of 1-way system. After Elf & Total stns turn L at site sp immed bef bdge (high fir tree each side of bdge ent). Ignore 1st site on L. At v constricted 'T' junc at ent to quartier 'Pon', turn R & foll rd into site. Med, mkd pitch, pt shd; htd wc; chem disp; serviced pitch; shwrs inc; el pts (10A) €3.20; lndtte; shops 1.5km; bar; playgrnd; pool 1km; fishing; TV; dogs €1.68; rv fishing adj; games area; 75% statics; quiet; CCI. "Beautiful site; excel facs; level walk to vill." € 17.00
2004*

LARUSCADE *7C2* (4km SW Rural) **Aire Naturelle Le Lac Vert (Saumon), 33620 Laruscade [tel/fax 05 57 68 64 43]** N on N10 fr Bordeaux for 28km, about 1km S of Cavignac, sp off to R. Access over narr bdge. Sm, pt shd; wc; chem disp; shwrs inc; ltd el pts inc (long cable req); shops 1km; rest; snacks; bar; lake sw; playgrnd; dogs; Eng spkn; CCI. "V pretty site by lake; v quiet but some rlwy noise; Auberge rest on site; fair NH." 1 May-30 Sep.
2004*

LARUSCADE *7C2* (5km NW) **Camping Le Relais du Chavan, 33620 Laruscade [05 57 68 63 05]** Exit A10 junc 39a or 39b sp St Andre-de-Cubzac & take N10 N dir Angouleme. Site sp on L in approx 15km. Med, pt shd; wc (some cont); chem disp; shwrs inc; el pts (5A) €2.30; gas; lndtte; ice; shop & 8km; snacks; playgrnd; pool; adv bkg; quiet. 15 May-15 Sep. € 8.50
2002*

LATHUILE see Faverges *9B3*

LATTES see Montpellier *10F1*

†**LAUBERT** *9D1* (Rural) **Camp Municipal La Pontiere, 48170 Laubert [04 66 47 71 37 or 04 66 47 72 09; fax 04 66 47 73 08; pms.laubert@ wanadoo.fr]** Site on R in hamlet of Laubert on N88. 7% hill descent fr Laubert to Mende. Sm, sl, pt shd; wc; shwrs inc; el pts inc; lndtte; bar; snacks; quiet. "Peaceful; site at 1000m - can be chilly." ♦
€ 9.50
2005*

†**LAURENS** *10F1* (1km S Rural) **Camping L'Oliveraie, Chemin de Bedarieux, 34480 Laurens [04 67 90 24 36; fax 04 67 90 11 20; oliveraie@free.fr; www.oliveraie.com]** Clearly sp on D909 Beziers to Bedarieux rd. Sp reads Loisirs de L'Oliveraie. Med, mkd pitch, terr, pt shd; htd wc; chem disp; baby facs; sauna; shwrs inc; el pts (6-10A) €3.20-6.60; lndtte; ice; shop; tradsmn; rest; snacks; bar; playgrnd; pool; games rm; beach 30km; leisure cent adj (avail high ssn); TV rm; 30% statics; dogs €2; phone; adv bkg; quiet; cc acc; CCI. "Site in wine-growing area nr Haut Languedoc regional park; gd san facs; gd winter NH." ♦ € 23.60
2005*

> We're having a great holiday - must fill in some site report forms and send them to The Club as soon as possible.

LAURIERE *7A3* (2km N Rural) **Camping du Lac de Pont a l'Age (formerly Intercommunal du Lac), 87370 Lauriere [05 55 71 42 62; fax 05 55 71 49 29]** Fr N on A20 turn E at Bessines onto D27; at Bersac-sur-Rivalier turn L on D28 to Lauriere. At o'skts of Lauriere turn L on D63 (N) sp Folles, in 2km R sp Camping du Lac (17km by rd). Fr S turn E at Chanteloube on D28 to Bersac-sur-Rivalier & Lauriere. Med, pt sl, terr, pt shd; wc; shwrs; el pts inc; ice; lndtte; shop 2km; playgrnd; mini-golf; sand beach; lake sw, fishing & boating adj; poss cr; quiet; adv bkg. 15 Apr-15 Oct. € 11.60
2004*

LAVAL *2F4* (10km N) **Camp Municipal Le Pont, Allee de Isles, 53240 Andouille [02 43 69 72 72 (Mairie); fax 02 43 68 77 77; mairie.and53@ wanadoo.fr]** N on N162 at rndabt in Louverne foll rd to St Jean & then Andouille; camp sp fr vill cent. Sm, hdg pitch, pt shd; wc; chem disp; shwrs inc; el pts (3A) inc; lndtte; shops 300m; playgrnd; pool 10km; 50% statics; poss cr; quiet but some minor rd noise; no cc acc. "Liable to flooding; pretty site, excel value; v busy; excel rest in hotel; superb, spotless shwrs; warden on site 0900-1000 & 1600-1800; code operated barrier - if warden not on site, visit Mairie for access code." 1 Apr-31 Oct.
€ 4.90
2004*

LAVAL *2F4* (4km S) **Camping du Potier, Route d'Angers, 53000 Laval [02 43 53 68 86; office. tourisme@mairie-laval.fr]** Fr Laval take N162 S to Thevalles, & on S o'skts of Thevalles turn R onto C35 & foll sps, camp on R. Sm, pt sl, terr, shd; wc (some cont); shwrs; el pts (6A) €1.20; lndtte; ice; shop & 1km; bar; playgrnd; entmnt; TV; dogs €0.80; Eng spkn; adv bkg rec high ssn; quiet; cc not acc; CCI ess. "Excel welcome; helpful staff, local advice given; well-kept facs; elevated pitches overlooking rv; lovely town; poss some rd noise." ♦
1 May-30 Sep. € 8.40
2005*

FRANCE

LAVAL *2F4* (3km W) **Camp Municipal de Coupeau, 53940 St Berthevin [02 43 68 30 70 or 02 43 69 28 27; fax 02 43 69 20 88; mairie.saint. berthevin@wanadoo.fr]** Fr Laval W on N157 twd Rennes. Site sp at St Berthevin. Sm, hdg/mkd pitch, terr, pt shd; wc; shwrs inc; el pts (10A) €2.05; shops 2km; rest in ssn; bar adj; BBQ; pool adj; adv bkg; quiet; phone adj; no cc acc; CCI. "Vg long/sh stay; attractive setting on hillside by rv; gd pool; well-maintained site; gd walks by rv & in woods; poss diff access lge o'fits; poor security, no barrier." 1 May-30 Sep. € 7.30   2002*

LAVANDOU, LE *10F3* (Urban/Coastal) **Camping St Pons, Ave Marechal Juin, 83960 Le Lavandou [04 94 71 03 93; campingsaintpons@wanadoo.fr]** App fr W on N98 via La Londe. At Bormes keep R onto D559. At 1st rndabt turn R sp La Faviere, at 2nd rndabt turn R, then 1st L. Site on L in 200m. Med, shd; wc (some cont); shwrs inc; el pts (6-10A) €3.80-4.40; lndtte; ice; shop; adj; rest, snacks, bar high ssn; sand beach 800m; playgrnd; entmnt; 10% statics; phone; dogs €2.13; poss cr; some rd noise; Eng spkn; red low ssn; CCI. "Much improved site; helpful owner." Easter-10 Oct. € 16.00   2005*

LAVANDOU, LE *10F3* (5km E Coastal) **Parc-Camping, Ave Ducourneau, Pramousquier, 83980 Le Lavandou [04 94 05 83 95; fax 04 94 05 75 04; camping-lavandou@wanadoo.fr]** At Pramousquier; ent clearly mkd on main rd; awkward bend. Lge, terr on steep hillside, pt shd; wc; shwrs inc; el pts (6A) €3; gas; lndtte; shop; snacks; bar; playgrnd; sand beach 400m; Eng spkn. "Poss cr but pleasant aspects; camp lighting poor; gd cycle track to Le Lavandou; not rec for disabled." May-Sep. € 18.00   2005*

LAVANDOU, LE *10F3* (2km S Coastal) **Camping du Domaine, La Faviere, 83230 Port de Bormes-les-Mimosas [04 94 71 03 12; fax 04 94 15 18 67; mail@campdudomaine.com; www.campdu domaine.com]** App Le Lavandou fr Hyeres turn R on o'skts of town clearly sp La Faviere. Site on L in 1.5km about 200m after ent to Domaine La Faviere (wine sales). V lge, sl, shd, 50% serviced pitch; rec long leads; wc; chem disp; shwrs inc; el pts (10A) inc; (long lead req some pitches) gas; lndtte; ice; shop; supmkt; tradsmn; rest; snacks; bar; playgrnd; sand beach adj; dogs, but not in Jul & Aug; phone; poss cr; Eng spkn; adv bkg ess; noisy (music fr bar all day) but quiet areas; cc acc; red low ssn. "Gas BBQs only; lge pitches, some v uneven with many trees - siting poss diff, pitches also muddy & dusty; 20% pitches only suitable sm vans/tents; well-organised; excel facs but ltd low ssn; gd walking & attractions in area; arr after 1400, leave bef 1000." ♦ ltd. Easter-31 Oct. € 29.00   2005*

LAVANDOU, LE *10F3* (2km S Coastal) **Caravaning St Clair, 83980 Le Lavandou [04 94 01 30 20; fax 04 94 71 43 64]** N559 thro Le Lavandou twd St Raphael; after 2km at sp St Clair turn R immed after bend 50m after blue 'caravaning' sp (easy to overshoot). Med, shd; wc (cont); mv service pnt; shwrs inc; el pts (10A) €3.35 (rev pol); lndtte; shops 100m; rest nrby; sand beach adj; fishing; boat hire; TV rm; dogs €1; poss cr; adv bkg ess Jul-Aug; some noise fr rd; no cc acc. "Popular with Eng; pitch & ent screened by trees; conv beach & rests." ♦ 15 Mar-20 Oct. € 22.70 (3 persons)   2002*

LAVANDOU, LE *10F3* (3km SW Coastal) **Camping Beau Sejour, Quartier St Pons, 83980 Le Lavandou [04 94 71 25 30]** Take Cap Benat rd on W o'skts of Le Lavandou. Site on L approx 500m. Lge, mkd pitch, pt shd; wc; shwrs inc; el pts (6A) inc; ice; shop; rest; snacks; beach adj; poss cr; adv bkg; rd noise on W side. "Fixed height barrier 2.60m at ent to site; sm pitches." ♦ Easter-30 Sep. € 15.10   2003*

†**LAVANDOU, LE** *10F3* (9km W) **Camping Manjastre, 150 Chemin des Girolles, 83230 Bormes-les-Mimosas [04 94 71 03 28; fax 04 94 71 63 62]** App fr N98 W about 3km NE of where N559 branches off SE to Le Lavandou. Fr E site is 2km beyond Bormes/Collobrieres x-rds; sp. Lge, hdg/mkd pitch, v sl, terr, pt shd; wc; chem disp; shwrs inc; el pts (10A) inc; rest; snacks; bar; shop; gas; ice; lndtte; pool; playgrnd; sand beach 8km; 8% statics; poss cr; adv bkg; quiet; Eng spkn; fair long/sh stay; CCI. "Helpful, friendly staff; winter storage; facs poss stretched in ssn; site on v steep hillside - vans taken in & out by tractor; hardwork even walking - not for unfit or disabled; beautiful location in vineyard; excel long stay." € 20.80 (3 persons)   2004*

LAVELANET *8G4* (1km SW Urban) **Camping de Lavelanet, Rue Jacquard, 09300 Lavelanet [tel/fax 05 61 01 55 54; camping.avelana@ wanadoo.fr]** Fr Lavelanet, take D117 twd Foix & foll sp. Adj 'piscine'. Med, mkd pitch, pt shd; wc (mainly cont); chem disp; shwrs; el pts (16A) inc; lndtte; ice; shops 1km; BBQ; playgrnd; pool adj; sports area; rv 4km; entmnt; TV rm; some statics; adv bkg; quiet; CCI. "Gd sized pitches, some with mountain views; poss open in winter with adv bkg; gates locked 2200; quiet town; vg." ♦ 1 Jun-15 Oct. € 15.00   2005*

†**LAVELANET** *8G4* (6km SW) **Camp Municipal Fount-de-Sicre, 09300 Montferrier [05 61 01 20 97 or 05 61 01 10 08; fax 05 61 01 93 14]** Fr Lavelanet S on D109/D9 twd Montsegur. Sm, sl, unshd; htd wc; shwrs; el pts (6A); shop adj; rest, bar adj; poss cr; adv bkg; quiet. "A bit scruffy; long-stay residents; NH only." € 6.00   2004*

LAVOUTE SUR LOIRE see Puy en Velay, Le *9C1*

LECTOURE *8E3* (6km NE Rural) **Camping La Ferme de Barrachin (Esparbes), Route de Miradoux, 32700 Lectoure** [05 62 68 84 57; fax 05 62 68 97 32] Fr Lectoure take N21 NE twds Agen; turn R onto D23 sp Miradoux; site in 3.5km on L; at farm ent stop bef farm yd; narr site ent poss diff lge o'fits. Sm, mkd pitch, shd; wc; shwrs inc; el pts (6A) €1.52; snacks; shops 6km; lake sw 6km; playgrnd; fishing; sep car park area; dogs; quiet; CCI. "V friendly owners; meals by arrangement; excel farm produce & wine; farm on Chemin Historique de Compostella; ltd facs." 1 Apr-30 Oct.
€ 8.00   2004*

LECTOURE *8E3* (2.5km SE) **Camping Le Lac des Trois Vallees, 32700 Lectoure** [05 62 68 82 33; fax 05 62 68 88 82; lac.des.trois.vallees@wanadoo.fr; www.lac-des-3-vallees.com or www.homair-vacances.fr] Site sp fr N21, on lake between Lectour & Fleurance. Narr app rd with steep gradient. Lge, hdg/mkd pitch, pt sl, pt shd; wc; chem disp; baby facs; shwrs inc; el pts (10A) inc; gas; lndtte; ice; shop; bar; rest; snacks; BBQ (gas/charcoal only); playgrnd; lake sw; waterslides; fishing; watersports; tennis; mini-golf; cycle hire; skateboard course; entmnt; games/TV rm; dogs €2.50; recep 0800-2100; poss cr; adv bkg; quiet (some disco noise); cc acc. "Excel lake pool; excursions to Pau, Lourdes, Andorra; mkt Tue Fleurance." ♦ 20 May-10 Sep. € 42.00 ABS - D18
                                          2004*

LEGE *2H4* (7km S Rural) **Camp Municipal de la Petite Boulogne, Rue du Stade, 85670 St Etienne-du-Bois** [02 51 34 52 11 or 02 51 34 54 51; fax 02 51 34 54 10; la.petite.boulogne@wanadoo.fr] S fr Lege on D978 dir Aizenay. Turn E onto D 94 twd St Etienne-du-Bois. Foll sp to site. Sm, mkd pitch, pt sl, terr, pt shd; wc; chem disp (wc); shwrs inc; el pts (10A) €2.50; gas 7km; lndtte; shops 500m; tradsmn; rest in vill; pool; sand beach 30km; TV rm; dogs €2; Eng spkn; adv bkg (dep req); quiet; CCI. "Excel site; helpful warden; v clean; vg long/sh stay." ♦ 1 May-15 Sep.
€ 12.00   2004*

†LEGE *2H4* (8km SW Rural) **Camping Les Bles d'Or, 85670 Grand-Landes** [02 51 98 51 86; fax 02 51 98 53 24] Take D753 fr Lege twd St Jean-de-Monts. In 4km turn S on D81 & foll sp. Fr S on D978, turn W sp Grand-Landes. 3km N of Palluau. Sm, pt sl, pt shd; wc; chem disp; shwrs inc; el pts (5A) €2; gas, shops 3km; playgrnd adj; 30% statics; Eng spkn; adv bkg; quiet; cc not acc. "V pleasant site in tiny vill with helpful staff; gd value; ent barrier clsd 2000 (poss earlier), rec arr early but helpful warden lives in c'van at site ent & will open up; height barrier only, cars 24hr access." € 6.30
                                          2005*

LEGE CAP FERRET see Andernos les Bains *7D1*

LELIN LAPUJOLLE see Aire sur l'Adour *8E2*

LEMPDES SUR ALLAGNON *9C1* (N) **Camping A Tou Vert, Route de Chambezon, 43410 Lempdes-sur-Allagnon** [04 71 76 53 69; fax 04 71 59 65 56; a.tou.vert@net-up.com] Going S on A75 exit junc 19 (ltd access) onto D909; turn R on D654 bef vill, site sp at junc. Or fr junc 20 going N; foll sp. Site just outside vill. Med, hdg pitch, pt shd; wc (some cont); chem disp (wc); mv service pnt; shwrs inc; baby facs; el pts (10A) €2.50; lndtte; shops 500m; bar; playgrnd; pool 100m; phone; dogs €1; adv bkg; quiet; cc acc. "Pleasant site; poss a bit scruffy in early ssn; v beautiful area; gd sh stay." ♦
1 Apr-31 Oct. € 11.00   2005*

LEON *8E1* (6km N Rural) **Camping Sunelia Le Col Vert, Lac de Leon, 40560 Vielle-St Girons** [05 58 42 94 06; fax 05 58 42 91 88; contact@colvert.com; www.colvert.com] S fr Bordeaux on N10; at Castets-des-Landes turn R onto D42 to Vielle-St Girons. In vill turn L onto D652 twd Leon sp Soustons. In 4km, bef Vielle, take 2nd of 2 RH turns twd Lac de Leon. Site on R at end of rd. V lge, shd; wc (some cont); chem disp; baby facs; serviced pitches; shwrs inc; el pts (3A) inc; gas; lndtte; ice; shop; tradsmn; rest; snacks; bar; BBQ; playgrnd; htd, covrd pool; paddling pool; sand beach 6km; lake sw, fishing, sailing nrby; tennis; fitness rm; mini-golf; archery; horseriding; cycle hire; games rm; entmnt; child entmnt; internet; TV; 60% statics; dogs €2.80; recep 0900-2100; max 6m c'van length high ssn; poss cr; adv bkg; poss noisy (nightclub); red for 15+ days; cc acc; CCI. "Lakeside site in pine forest with sailing school; organised tours to Lourdes & Spain; lge site so some pitches 800m fr facs; daily mkt in Leon in ssn; ideal site for children & teenagers." ♦ 8 Apr-24 Sep. € 36.70 (CChq acc) ABS - A08   2005*

LEON *8E1* (5km NE Rural) **Camping Aire Naturelle du Cayre (Capdupuy), 40550 St Michel-Escalus** [05 58 48 78 15] Fr N10 exit Castets & St Girons onto D42 sp St Girons/Linxe. In Linxe turn L onto D374 sp Escalus & camping. In 1km R sp Leon, site on L in 1km. Sm, pt shd; wc; shwrs inc; el pts inc; gas; lndtte; shops 4km; snacks; rest; playgrnd; sand beach 11km; some statics; poss cr; cc not acc. "In pine forest; friendly & helpful owner; ltd facs low ssn, rec NH only." ♦ 1 Apr-30 Sep.
€ 9.15   2002*

LEON *8E1* (1.5km NW Rural) **Camping Lou Puntaou, 40550 Leon** [05 58 48 74 30; fax 05 58 48 70 42; reception@loupuntaou.com; www.loupuntaou.com] Site sp fr D142 on Etang de Leon. V lge, mkd pitch, pt shd; wc; chem disp; mv service pnt; shwrs inc; el pts (15A) inc; lndtte; supmkt; rest 100m; snacks; bar; playgrnd; 3 pools (1 htd, covrd); waterslide; jacuzzi; lake sw 100m; sand beach 5km; tennis; watersports; games area; cycle hire; fitness rm; cash machine; entmnt; child entmnt; 20% statics; dogs €2; adv bkg; quiet. "Excel sports facs; lovely location; vg long/sh stay." ♦
1 Apr-1 Oct. € 39.00   2005*

LEON *8E1* (10km NW Coastal) **Camping Eurosol,** 40560 Vielle-St Girons [05 58 47 90 14 or 05 58 56 54 90; fax 05 58 47 76 74; contact@ camping-eurosol.com; www.camping-eurosol.com & www.homair-vacances.fr] Turn W off D652 at St Girons on D42. Site on L in 4km. Lge, pt sl, pt shd; wc; chem disp; baby facs; shwrs inc; el pts (6-10A) inc; gas; lndtte; ice; shop; rest; snacks; playgrnd; 2 pools; sand beach 700m; games rm; adj horseriding; lake trips; cycle hire; tennis; entmnt; TV; no dogs; poss cr; red low ssn; quiet. "Pitches poss tight for long vans; new san facs 2003." ♦ 8 May-18 Sep. € 24.00   2003*

LEON *8E1* (10km NW Coastal) **Centre Naturiste Arna (Naturist),** Arnaoutchot, 40560 Vielle-St Girons [05 58 49 11 11; fax 05 58 48 57 12; contact@arna.com; www.arna.com] Fr St Girons turn R onto D328 at Vielle sp Pichelebe. Site in 5km on R. Lge, pt sl, shd; wc (some cont); chem disp; baby facs; shwrs inc; el pts (3A) inc; gas; lndtte; ice; shop; rest; snacks; bar; BBQ (gas/elec); playgrnd; htd pool & paddling pool; sand beach adj; lake adj; fishing; watersports 5km; tennis; cycle hire; golf nr; archery; horseriding; games area; games rm; entmnt; internet; TV; many statics (sep area); dogs €2.90; recep 0900-2000; adv bkg; quiet; red long stay/low ssn; cc acc; CCI. "In pine forest; organised excursions; fantastic beach; some pitches sandy; INF card req; facs ltd low ssn; daily mkt in Leon in ssn; c'vans over 6m not acc high ssn; excel naturist site." ♦ 8 Apr-24 Sep. € 41.00 (CChq acc) ABS - A07   2005*

LEPIN LE LAC see Chambery *9B3*

LERAN *8G4* (2km E Rural) **Camping La Regate,** 09600 Leran [tel/fax 05 61 01 92 69; contact@ montbel.com.fr; www.montbel.com.fr] Fr Lavelanet go N on D625, turn R onto D28 & cont to Leran. Site sp fr vill. Ent easily missed - rd past it is dead end. Med, hdg/mkd pitch, terr, shd; wc; chem disp; baby facs; shwrs; el pts (8A) inc; lndtte; ice; shop 2km; tradsmn; rest; bar; BBQ; playgrnd; pool; leisure cent nr; lake adj; watersports; entmnt; 10% statics; dogs; phone; quiet; adv bkg; cc acc; CCI. "Conv chateau Montsegur; v clean san facs; gd long stay." 1 Apr-30 Sep. € 14.00   2004*

LESCAR see Pau *8F2*

LESCHERAINES *9B3* (1km S) **Camp Municipal de l'Ile,** Base de Loisirs, 73340 Lescheraines [tel/fax 04 79 63 80 00; contact@iles-du-cheran.com; www.iles-du-cheran.com] Fr Lescheraines foll sp for Base de Loisirs. Lge, mkd pitch, pt shd; wc; chem disp; mv service pnt; baby facs; shwrs inc; el pts (10A) inc; ice; gas 1km; lndtte; shop; snacks; bar; BBQ; rest 500m; playgrnd; lake sw; canoe & boat hire; fishing; entmnt; 6% statics; dogs €1.22; phone; Eng spkn; quiet; CCI. ♦ 26 Apr-29 Sep. € 13.40   2002*

LESCONIL see Pont l'Abbe *2F2*

LESCUN *8G2* (1.5km SW Rural) **Camp Municipal** Le Lauzart, 64490 Lescun [05 59 34 51 77; campinglauzart@wanadoo.fr] Turn L (W) off N134 8km N of Urdos on D239 sp Lescun & foll camping sp for 5km; app rd gd but steep with hairpins; avoid Lescun cent by taking L fork. Sm, mkd pitch, sl, pt shd; htd wc; chem disp; shwrs inc; el pts (10A) €2.75; gas; lndtte; ice; shop; rest & bar nr; no dogs; adv bkg; quiet. "Gd walks; stunning views; poss many flies." ♦ 1 May-30 Sep. € 9.40   2003*

LESPERON *8E1* (4km SW Rural) **Parc de Couchoy, Route de Linxe,** 40260 Lesperon [tel/fax 05 58 89 60 15] Exit N10 junc 13 to D41 sp Lesperon; in 1km turn L, thro vill of Lesperon; L at junc onto D331; bottom of hill turn R & immed L; site on R in 3km dir Linxe. Med, mkd pitch, pt shd; wc; chem disp; child/baby facs; shwrs inc; el pts (6A) inc; gas; lndtte; shops 3km; tradsmn; snacks; bar; playgrnd; pool; sand beach 8km; lake sw 5km; 75% statics; phone; poss cr; adv bkg; quiet; cc acc high ssn; 10% red long stay; CCI. "Edge of wine country; gd facs on lakes for sailing, windsurfing; British owners; san facs poss neglected; v isolated." 1 Apr-30 Sep. € 20.00   2004*

LESSAY *1D4* (6km SW Coastal) **Camp Municipal des Dunes,** 832 Blvd de la Mer, 50710 Creances [02 33 46 31 86 or 02 33 07 40 42; fax 02 33 07 40 42] Turn W onto D72/D652 in Lessay, after 3km turn L on D650 at T-junc. After 1.5km turn R at rndabt on D394 sp 'Creances Plage' & site office opp seafront car pk. Med, mkd pitch, pt shd; wc; shwrs inc; el pts (10A) €2.30; gas; lndtte; shop 3km; tradsmn; rest; snacks; bar; playgrnd; paddling pool; sand beach adj; games area; poss cr; adv bkg; quiet; CCI. ♦ ltd. 19 Jun-5 Sep. € 9.00   2004*

LEUCATE PLAGE *10G1* (200m S Coastal) **Camp Municipal du Cap Leucate,** Chemin de Mouret, 11370 Leucate-Plage [04 68 40 01 37; fax 04 68 40 18 34; cap.leucate@wanadoo.fr] Exit A9 junc 40 onto D627 thro Leucate vill to Leucate-Plage approx 9km fr a'route. Site sp. Lge, hdg pitch, shd; wc (some cont); chem disp; mv service pnt; baby facs; fam bthrm; shwrs inc; el pts (6A) inc; lndtte; ice; shop 200m; tradsmn; rest, snacks, bar 500m; BBQ; playgrnd; htd pool; sand beach 100m; games area; entmnt; TV; 60% statics; dogs €2; phone; adv bkg; quiet; CCI. "Sandy site in gd position; popular with surfers; spacious in low ssn." € 13.00   2004*

LEVIER *6H2* (1km NE Rural) **Camping La Foret, Route de Septfontaine,** 25270 Levier [03 81 89 53 46; fax 03 81 49 54 11; camping@ camping-dela-foret.com; www.camping-dela-foret.com] Fr D72 turn L at rndabt by supmkt onto D41, site on L in 700m. Med, mkd pitch, pt sl, terr, shd; wc; baby facs; shwrs inc; el pts (6A) €2.30; gas; lndtte; ice; supmkt 500m; snacks; playgrnd; htd pool; poss cr; adv bkg; quiet. ♦ 15 May-15 Sep. € 13.00   2004*

LEVIGNAC DE GUYENNE see Miramont de Guyenne *7D2*

POMMIERS DES TROIS PAYS ★★★

253, le Breuil
F-62850 Licques
Phone: +33 (0)3 21 35 02 02
Fax: +33 (0)3 21 35 02 02

Open from 1.4 till 31.10.

Small family campsite with 38 pitches, situated in the heart of the "Parc naturel des Caps et Marais d'Opale".
The camping/caravanning part has a modern sanitary block and large pitches. To rent: 35m2 chalets with all modern conveniences. Swimming pool, playground, games room, bar, take-away meals.
Label "Tourisme et Handicap" in process. Label "Camping Qualité" in process.

FRANCE

LEVROUX *4H2* (500m N Rural) **Camp Municipal La Piscine, 36110 Levroux** [02 54 35 70 54 (Mairie); fax 02 54 35 35 50] Site on N o'skts of town on W of D956 bet Chateauroux & Valencay. Sm, pt shd; wc; shwrs inc; el pts (5A); shops 500m; pool; playgrnd; quiet. "Site yourself, warden calls gates open 0800-1100 & 1600-2100 (Mon-Fri), 0800-1100 & 1800-2100 (Sat & Sun); no twin-axle c'vans." ♦ 2004*

LEZIGNAN CORBIERES *8F4* (10km S) **Camping Le Pinada, 11200 Fabrezan** [04 68 43 61 82; fax 04 68 43 68 61; lepinada@libertysurf.fr] Fr Lezignan-Corbieres foll sp to aerodrome & a'route. After airfield, fork L thro Ferrals-les-Corbieres on D106 site sp & on L after 4km. Med, hdg/mkd pitch, pt sl; terr; shd; wc; chem disp (wc); baby facs; shwrs inc; el pts (6A) €4; ice; lndtte; shop; tradsmn; snacks; bar; playgrnd; pool; rv sw & fishing 3km; tennis; mini-golf; entmnt; TV rm; 25% statics; dogs; poss cr; Eng spkn; adv bkg, bkg fee; quiet; cc not acc; CCI. "Friendly owners; gd base for Carcassonne & the Med coast; well-run site; excel long/sh stay." ♦ 1 May-10 Oct. € 13.00 2004*

LEZIGNAN CORBIERES *8F4* (500m NW Urban) **Camp Municipal de la Pinede, Ave Gaston Bonheur, 11200 Lezignan-Corbieres** [tel/fax 04 68 27 05 08; campinglapinede@wanadoo.fr] On N113 fr Carcassonne to Narbonne on N of rd; foll 'Piscine' & 'Restaurant Le Patio' sp. Med, hdg/hdstg pitch, pt sl, terr, pt shd; wc; chem disp; mv service pnt; shwrs inc; el pts (6A) inc; gas; lndtte; ice; shop 1km; rest; snacks; bar; htd pool adj; tennis; 5% statics; dogs €1.50; adv bkg (dep req); quiet; no cc acc; CCI. "Well-run, clean site; gd san facs & m'van facs; superb pool; v pleasant, friendly staff; red low ssn; excel snack bar; gd sh/long stay."♦ 1 Mar-30 Oct. € 15.70 2005*

LICQUES *3A3* (1km E Rural) **Camping Les Pommiers des Trois Pays, 253 Rue de Breuil, 62850 Licques** [tel/fax 03 21 35 02 02; denis. lamce@wanadoo.fr; www.pommiers-3pays.com] Fr Calais to Guines on D127 then on D215 to Licques. Take D191 fr vill foll sp. Site on L in 1km. NB If joining A26 at junc 2 need €3 in coins (car & c'van) for automatic toll machine. NB Ent slopes, longer o'fits beware grounding. Sm, hdg/mkd pitch, sl, pt shd; wc; chem disp; mv service pnt; baby facs; shwrs inc; el pts (16A) €4; lndtte; ice; shops 1km; rest; snacks; bar; BBQ; playgrnd; htd, covrd pool; sand beach, golf, sailing 25km; fishing 2km; games area; games rm; TV rm; 35% statics; adv bkg; quiet; cc acc; red long stay/low ssn. "New site 2004; pleasant wooded countryside; high quality facs & lge pitches; friendly & helpful owners; gd walking; well worth drive to wonderful beaches; conv Calais ferries." ♦ 1 Apr-31 Oct. € 14.00 2005*

See advertisement

LICQUES *3A3* (2.5km E Rural) **Camping-Caravaning Le Canchy, Rue de Canchy, 62850 Licques** [tel/fax 03 21 82 63 41] Fr Calais D127 to Guines, then D215 sp Licques; site sp in vill on D191; site on L in 1km with narr app rd. Or fr Ardres take D224 to Liques then as above. Or A26 fr Calais exit junc 2 onto D217 dir Zouafques/Tournehem/Licques. Foll site sp in vill. Med, hdg/mkd pitch, pt shd; wc (some cont); chem disp; shwrs inc; el pts (3-5A) €1.80-3.20; lndtte; shops 2km; snacks; bar; BBQ; playgrnd; entmnt; 30% statics; Eng spkn; adv bkg; quiet; CCI. "Friendly, helpful staff; poorly-maintained el pts, adaptor req; gd walking/cycling; conv Calais; busy site; vg sh/long stay." 15 Mar-31 Oct. € 10.60 2005*

LIEPVRE see Selestat *6E4*

LIGNIERES *4H3* (Urban) **Camp Municipal de L'Ange Blanc, Rue de l'Ange Blanc, 18160 Lignieres** [02 48 60 00 18 (Mairie)] Site sp in vill at junc of D940 & D925. Sm, pt shd; wc (some cont); shwrs; el pts inc; shops adj; quiet. "NH only; facs not clean." Apr-Sep. € 9.60 2002*

LIGNY EN BARROIS *6E1* (500m W) **Camp Municipal, Rue des Etats-Unis, 55500 Ligny-en-Barrois [03 29 78 41 33 or 03 29 78 02 22 (Mairie)]** On N4 for Paris sp fr town cent. Leave N4 at Ligny-en-Barrois N exit, turn S twd town. In approx 500m turn R at junc (before rd narr). Foll sm sp, site 500m on L. Sm, hdstg, terr, pt shd; wc (some cont), own san facs; chem disp (wc); shwrs; el pts inc; ice; shop 500m; pool 1km; rv sw & fishing 500m; dogs; rd noise; Eng spkn; CCI. "Poss diff lge o'fits; gd NH." 1 Jun-15 Sep. € 9.40   2005*

LIGNY LE CHATEL *4F4* (2km W Rural) **Camp Municipal La Noue Marrou, 89144 Ligny-le-Chatel [03 86 47 56 99 or 03 86 47 41 20 (Mairie); fax 03 86 47 44 02]** Exit A6 at junc 20 Auxerre S onto D965 to Chablis. In Chablis cross rv & turn L onto D91 dir Ligny. On ent Ligny turn L onto D8 at junc after Maximart. Cross sm rv, foll sp to site on L in 200m. Sm, mkd pitch, pt shd; wc; chem disp; mv service pnt; shwrs inc; el pts (7A) €2.40; lndtte; ice; shop; rest; snacks; bar; playgrnd; rv sw adj; tennis; dogs; phone; bus 200m; quiet; CCI. "Lge pitches; long mains lead poss req; no twin-axle vans; pleasant vill; gd rests." ♦ 1 Apr-30 Sep. € 8.45   2005*

†**LIGUEIL** *4H2* (2km N) **Camping de la Touche, Ferme de la Touche, 37240 Ligueil [02 47 91 94 61 or 06 33 97 02 00 (mob); stuart. may@theloirevalley.com; www.theloirevalley. com]** Fr Loches SW on D31; turn L at x-rds with cross on R 2km after Ciran. In 500m turn R, site on R bef hotel. Fr a'route A10 take exit St Maure. Sm, mkd pitch, pt shd; wc; chem disp (wc); shwrs inc; el pts (5A) €4; ice; shop; playgrnd; pool; cycle hire; adv bkg (dep req); cc acc; quiet; CCI. "Excel CL-type site; helpful British owners; castles, rvs & wines in area; site ent & surface uneven; c'van storage, B&B & gite avail; nightingales in trees around site; well-maintained; conv Loire chateaux & m'way." € 15.00   2005*

LIGUGE see Poitiers *7A2*

†**LILLE** *3A4* (15km S Rural) **Le Parc de Tourmignies, 17 Rue du Chateau, 59551 Tourmignies [03 20 61 41 58; fax 03 20 59 58 30; camping.de.tourmignies@wanadoo.fr]** Leave A1 exit 19 onto D549E, foll sp Pont-a-Marcq at 1st rndabt, then sp Tourmignies at next. Site on L in 4km. Lge, hdg pitch, some hdstg, pt shd; wc (some cont); own san facs; chem disp; shwrs; el pts (3-6A) €1.40-2.70; gas; lndtte; ice; shop; bar; BBQ; playgrnd; fishing; 80% statics; CCI. "Ltd facs but gd for WWI sites in area; noisy in school hols; half day's drive fr Channel ports; under new management 2005; offices, bar etc in spectacular but crumbling chateau; san facs shabby; phone ahead low ssn to check open." € 7.60   2005*

†**LILLEBONNE** *3C2* (4km W Rural) **Camping Hameau des Forges, 76170 St Antoine-la-Foret [02 35 39 80 28 or 02 35 91 48 30]** Fr Le Havre take rd twds Tancarville bdge, D982 into Lillebonne, D81 W to site on R in 4km, sp. Fr S over Tancarville bdge onto D910 sp Bolbec. At 2nd rndabt turn R onto D81, site 5km on L. Med, pt shd; wc; chem disp; shwrs €1.15; el pts (5A) inc; tradsmn; 90% statics; dogs; poss cr; adv bkg; quiet; no cc acc; CCI. "Basic site but v clean; conv for Le Havre ferries late arr & early depart; staff welcoming & helpful; facs ltd low ssn; Roman amphitheatre in town worth visit; conv NH." € 6.80   2005*

This site entry hasn't been updated for a while; we'd better fill in a site report form and send it to The Club.

LIMERAY see Amboise *4G2*

LIMEUIL see Bugue, Le *7C3*

†**LIMOGES** *7B3* (10km N) **Camp Municipal d'Uzurat, Allee d'Uzurat, 87280 Limoges [05 55 38 49 43; fax 05 55 37 32 78; lemaire@ ville-limoges.fr]** S twd Limoges on A20 take exit 30 sp Limoges Nord Zone Industrielle, Lac d'Uzurat; foll sp to Lac d'Uzarat & site. N fr Limoges on A20 exit junc 31 & foll sp as above. Lge, pt shd; htd wc (some cont); chem disp; serviced pitches; shwrs inc; el pts (6A) €3.20; lndtte; hypmkt 500m; playgrnd adj; lake fishing; bus; phone; quiet but some rd noise; red low ssn; cc acc. "Excel site; pleasant, helpful staff; clean facs; pitch on chippings; awnings diff; site popular with British; conv memorial vill Oradour-sur-Glane." ♦ € 13.00   2005*

LIMOGNE EN QUERCY *7D4* (1km W) **Camp Municipal Bel-Air, 46260 Limogne-en-Quercy [05 65 31 51 27 or 06 15 62 71 78; fax 05 65 24 73 59; alainbach@minitel.net]** E fr Cahors on D911 just bef Limogne vill. W fr Villefranche on D911 just past vill; 3 ents about 50m apart. Sm, mkd pitch, sl, shd; wc; shwrs inc; el pts (6A) inc; shops 1km; pool; quiet; adv bkg rec high ssn. "V friendly welcome; if warden absent, site yourself." 1 Apr-1 Oct. € 10.90   2003*

LIMOUX *8G4* (SE Urban) **Camp Municipal du Breil, Ave Salvador Allende, 11300 Limoux [04 68 31 13 63; fax 04 68 31 18 43]** Site off D118 heading S fr Limoux. Sm, pt sl; wc; shwrs; el pts (inc); shops adj; pool adj; rv sw; fishing; boating; quiet but some rd noise. "Basic rvside site, walking dist town; clean facs." 1 Jun-30 Sep. € 10.40   2004*

LINDOIS, LE see Montbron *7B3*

LION D'ANGERS, LE *2G4* (500m N Urban) **Camp Municipal Les Frenes, Route de Laval, 49220 Le Lion-d'Angers [02 41 95 31 56]** On N162 Laval-Angers rd, site on R bef bdge over Rv Oudon app Le Lion-d'Angers, easily missed. Med, pt shd, mkd pitch; wc; chem disp; shwrs inc; el pts (10A) €2.20; lndry rm; ice; shops adj; rest; BBQ; playgrnd; rv fishing adj; phone; recep open 1000-1200 & 1400-1900 low ssn; card operated barrier (€40 dep); no twin-axle vans; poss cr; Eng spkn; adv bkg; quiet but some rd noise; CCI. "Excel site; friendly staff; gd location; wc followed up 2 flights concrete steps; no m'vans; unreliable opening dates - phone ahead." ♦ 15 May-15 Sep. € 5.05   2005*

LION D'ANGERS, LE *2G4* (4km S Rural) **Camp Municipal, 49220 Grez-Neuville [02 41 95 61 19 or 02 41 95 35 13 (Mairie); fax 02 41 95 67 93]** S on N162 fr Le Lion-d'Angers to Angers take 2nd sp to Grez-Neuville D291 on L; into vill, over bdge & site on R immed after bdge. Med, mkd pitch, pt sl, pt shd; wc; mv service pnt; shwrs inc; el pts (8A) inc; shop 200m; BBQ; playgrnd; rv sw & fishing; barrier card (dep req); quiet; CCI. "Pretty site by rv; no twin-axles; unreliable opening dates - phone ahead." 15 May-14 Sep. € 7.70   2004*

LISIEUX *3D1* (2km N) **Camp Municipal de La Vallee, 9 Rue de la Vallee, 14100 Lisieux [02 31 62 00 40; fax 02 31 48 18 11; tourisme@cclisieuxpaysdauge.fr]** N on D579 to Lisieux twd Pont l'Eveque. Approx 500m N of Lisieux take L to Coquainvilliers onto D48 & foll sp for Camping (turn L back in Lisieux dir). Site on D48 parallel to main rd. Med, hdstg, pt shd; wc (some cont); shwrs inc; el pts (15A) €1.85; gas; shop 1km, rest, snacks, bar 2km; htd pool, waterslide nrby; 50% statics; poss cr; quiet; cc not acc; CCI. "Interesting town, childhood home of St Therese; gates locked 2200-0700; NH only." 1 Apr-30 Sep. € 7.85   2004*

LISIEUX *3D1* (1km NE Urban) **La Ferme sous les Pommiers, Ave Jean XXIII, 14100 Lisieux [02 31 61 15 16 or 02 31 62 37 69; fax 02 31 61 15 16]** Fr cent of Lisieux, take Ave Ste Therese past basilica in dir of Paris-Evreux. Ent on R of Ave Jean XXIII just behind basilica. Sm, terr, pt shd; own san; el pts inc; tradsmn; shop adj; no statics; quiet. "V friendly; wine-tasting; san facs planned; m'vans only." € 7.00   2003*

LISLE *7C3* **Camp Municipal du Pont, 24350 Lisle [05 53 04 50 02 or 05 53 04 51 76]** W fr Riberac on D78, site 6km NE of junc with D710 at Tocane-St Apre, on rvside. Sm, mkd pitch, pt shd; wc; shwrs inc; el pts; lndry rm; shops 500m; rest, bar 800m; playgrnd; tennis; fishing. "Pleasant site." 1 Jun-15 Sep. € 5.00   2004*

LISLE *7C3* (6km SW) **Camp Municipal Le Pre Sec, 24350 Tocane-St Apre [05 53 90 40 60 or 05 53 90 70 29; fax 05 53 90 25 03]** Fr Riberac E on D710 sp Brantome. At rndabt to Tocane cont on D710 until trees in boxes in middle of rd. Turn L at yellow sp by sports cent. Med, pt shd; wc; chem disp; mv service pnt; most serviced pitch; shwrs inc; el pts (6-10A) inc; mv service pnt; shops in vill; cycling; boating; rv sw; tennis; rv sw; quiet; adv bkg; CCI. "Excel; poss noisy fr eve entmnt." 1 May-30 Sep. € 8.84   2003*

LIT ET MIXE *8E1* (2km N) **Camping Airotel Les Vignes, Route de la Plage du Cap de l'Homy, 40170 Lit-et-Mixe [05 58 42 85 60; fax 05 58 42 74 36; contact@les-vignes.com; www.les-vignes.com]** N10 S to exit 13 onto D41 twd Lit-et-Mixe. S on D652 dir St Girons. W on D88 twd Cap de l'Homy Plage. Lge, pt shd; wc; chem disp; serviced pitches; shwrs inc; el pts (10A) inc; gas; lndtte; ice; supmkt; rest; snacks; bar; playgrnd; pool; waterslide; jacuzzi; beach 3km; tennis; mini-golf; cycle hire; games rm; fitness rm; entmnt; internet; dogs €3; quiet; adv bkg; red low ssn/CCI. "Wonderful site - everything you need; immac san facs." ♦ 1 Jun-17 Sep. € 35.00   2005*

LIT ET MIXE *8E1* (8km W Coastal) **Camp Municipal de la Plage du Cap de l'Horny, Ave de l'Ocean, 40170 Lit-et-Mixe [05 58 42 83 47; fax 05 58 42 49 79; camplage@wanadoo.fr]** S fr Mimizan on D652. In Lit-et-Mixe R on D88 to Cap de l'Homy Plage. Site on R when rd becomes 1-way. Lge, hdg/mkd pitch, pt sl, shd; wc (some cont); chem disp; mv service pnt; 5% serviced pitches; shwrs inc; el pts (10A) inc (poss rev pol); lndtte; shop high ssn; rest high; playgrnd; beach 300m; surfing; dogs €1.57; poss cr; quiet. "Site in pine woods on sandy soil; gd walks; interesting flora & fauna; excel long/sh stay." 1 May-30 Sep. € 18.45   2002*

LITTEAU see Balleroy *1D4*

LIVAROT *3D1* (Urban) **Camp Municipal, Place de la Gendarmerie, 14140 Livarot [02 31 63 53 19 (Mairie)]** On D579 Lisieux to Vimoutiers turn R into car park in Livarot 200m after traff lts. Sp fr by-pass & in Livarot. Med, terr, pt shd; wc; chem disp; shwrs; el pts (6A) inc; shops, rest, bar nr; playgrnd adj; no statics; quiet; CCI. "Delightful site; feels rural tho in town cent; public footpath thro site; facs basic but clean; security barrier clsd at night." 15 Apr-10 Sep. € 5.50   2003*

LIVERDUN see Nancy *6E2*

LLAURO see Boulou, Le *8G4*

FRANCE

LOCHES *4H2* (800m S Urban) **Camping de la Citadelle, Ave Aristide Briand, 37600 Loches [02 47 59 05 91 or 06 21 37 93 06; fax 02 47 59 00 35; camping@lacitadelle.com; www. lacitadelle.com]** Easiest app fr S. Fr any dir take by-pass to S end & leave at Leclerc rndabt; site well sp on R in 800m. Med, hdg/mkd pitch, pt shd; htd wc (some cont); chem disp; mv service pnt; serviced pitches extra charge; shwrs inc; el pts (10A) €3.40 (poss rev pol); gas; lndtte; ice; shop & 2km; tradsmn; rests, snacks; bar; BBQ; playgrnd; pool on site & 2 htd pools adj; fishing; boating; games area; tennis nr; cycle hire; entmnt; internet; TV; 80% statics; dogs €1.50; poss cr; Eng spkn; adv bkg rec (bkg fee); poss night noise fr entmnts; red 7+ days/low ssn; cc acc; CCI. "Attractive site; sh walk to beautiful town, chateau & medieval quarter worth visit; gd sized pitches; gd facs but poss stretched high ssn; barrier clsd 2200-0800; ltd facs low ssn." ♦ 19 Mar-14 Oct. € 18.90 (CChq acc)
2005*

LOCMARIAQUER *2G3* (1km N Rural) **Camping La Ferme Fleurie, Kerlogonan, 56740 Locmariaquer [02 97 57 34 06]** Sp off D781. Sm, mkd pitch, pt shd; wc; shwrs inc; el pts (10A) €2.50; shop; lndtte; playgrnd; beach 1.5km; fishing; sailing; entmnt; dogs €1; adv bkg ess high ssn; quiet. "Lovely, friendly, CL-type site; coastal path nr; excel, clean facs but poss stretched when site full; midge repellent rec." 1 Feb-31 Dec. € 11.00
2004*

LOCMARIAQUER *2G3* (2km S Coastal) **Camp Municipal de la Falaise, Route de Kerpenhir, 56740 Locmariaquer [02 97 57 31 59 or 02 97 57 32 32 (LS); fax 02 97 57 32 85]** Site sp fr Locmariaquer. On ent vill, site sp R avoiding narr cent (also sp fr vill cent). Lge, mkd pitch, pt sl; wc; shwrs; chem disp; mv service pnt; el pts (5A) inc; gas; lndtte; shop 300m; playgrnd; sand beach adj; entmnt (high ssn); dogs €0.70; poss cr. "Gd, quiet site in pleasant countryside; archaeological remains; gd fishing, boating,& cycling, coastal walking; long, sandy beach adj; san facs need updating & poss unclean low ssn." ♦ 1 Apr-30 Sep. € 12.00
2005*

LOCRONAN see Douarnenez *2E2*

LOCUNOLE see Quimperle *2F2*

LODEVE *10E1* (5km NE Rural) **Camping des Sources, 34700 Soubes [tel/fax 04 67 44 32 02; jlsources@wanadoo.fr]** Fr Montpellier take N109 & N9 to Lodeve. Take R turn to Soubes; ent Soubes take 1st R in dir Fozieres; foll sp. Sm, terr, pt shd; wc; chem disp; shwrs inc; el pts (6A) inc; ice; lndtte; tradsmn; shop 1km; snacks; playgrnd; children pool; rv sw, sailing & fishing adj; no dogs; adv bkg rec high ssn; quiet; cc acc; CCI. "Helpful, pleasant owner; excel, peaceful site; relaxed atmosphere; surrounded by beautiful countryside; not suitable lge o'fits as app rd v narr & some pitches sm; immac facs." ♦ 15 May-15 Sep. € 17.00   2005*

†LODEVE *10E1* (6km SE Rural) **Camping Les Peupliers, Les Casseaux, 34700 Le Bosc [tel/fax 04 67 44 38 08]** Take exit 54 on A75; sp Le Bosc. Med, mkd pitch, pt sl, terr, pt shd; wc (cont); shwrs inc; el pts (5A) €3 (rev pol); gas; ice; shop 4km; tradsmn Jul-Aug; snacks; bar; playgrnd; pool; sand beach 40km; lake 5km; 50% statics; dogs €0.80; Eng spkn; adv bkg; dep req; quiet; CCI. "Friendly staff; ltd facs low ssn; gd cent for Herault region; windsurfing Lac du Salagou; winter NH." ♦ ltd. € 11.60   2005*

LODEVE *10E1* (2km S Urban) **Camping Les Vals, Route de Puech, 34700 Lodeve [tel/fax 04 67 44 36 57; info@campinglesvals.com; www. campinglesvals.com]** Fr Lodeve take D148 along W bank of Rv Lergue, twd Puech; site in 2km on W of rd. Med, pt sl, pt terr, pt shd; wc; chem disp; shwrs; el pts inc; lndtte; ice; shop; rest; playgrnd; pool; rv fishing, watersports & sw adj; cycle hire; tennis; mini-golf; TV; entmnt; v ltd facs low ssn; quiet. ♦ 29 Apr-29 Oct. € 16.00   2004*

LODEVE *10E1* (7km S Rural) **Camp Municipal Les Vailhes, Lac du Salagou, 34702 Lodeve [04 67 44 25 98]** Fr N exit N9 S of Lodeve dir Octon & Lac du Salagou. Foll site sp. Lge, hdg pitch, terr, pt shd; wc; chem disp; shwrs inc; el pts inc; lndtte; tradsmn; playgrnd; beach by lake; water sports; poss cr; quiet; CCI. "Site by lake, excel get-away; walks by lake & up hills; dark red rocks; gd." 1 Apr-30 Sep. € 13.00   2005*

LODEVE *10E1* (4km W Rural) **Domaine de Lambeyran (Naturist), 34700 Lodeve [04 67 44 13 99; fax 04 67 44 09 91; lambeyran@ wanadoo.fr]** Fr N or S on N9 take sliprd to Lodeve. Leave town on D35 W twd Bedarieux. In 2km take 2nd R, sp L'Ambeyran & St Martin. Foll sp 3.7km up winding hill to site. Lge, hdg/mkd pitch, terr, pt shd; wc; chem disp; 60% serviced pitches; shwrs inc; el pts (6A) inc €3.20; gas; lndtte; shop & supmkt 4km, rest, snacks, bar high ssn; BBQ; playgrnd; pool; sailing, windsurfing 10km; 5% statics; dogs; phone; adv bkg (dep req); cc acc; INF card req. "Lge pitches, superb views; gd walking; excel long/sh stay." 15 May-15 Sep. € 17.90   2003*

LODS see Ornans *6G2*

LONG see Abbeville *3B3*

LONGCHAUMOIS see Morez *9A3*

LONGEAU PERCEY *6F1* (3km S Rural) **Camp Municipal du Lac, 52190 Villegusien-le-Lac [03 25 88 47 25 or 03 25 88 45 24]** Exit A31 junc 6 dir Longeau. Site sp fr both D67 & N74 S of Longeau. Visible fr N74. Med, pt shd; wc (some cont); chem disp; shwrs inc; el pts (6A) €2.60; ice; shop; tradsmn; snacks; playgrnd; tennis; fishing; boating & sw in lake; poss cr; adv bkg; rd & rlwy noise; "Conv NH." ♦ 15 Apr-30 Sep. € 10.10
2005*

LONGEVILLE SUR MER *7A1* (1.5km SE) **Camping La Michenotiere, Route d'Angles, 85560 Longeville-sur-Mer [02 51 33 38 85; fax 02 51 33 28 09]** Fr D949 or D747 to Longeville, then D70 dir Angles, site sp in vill. Med, pt shd; wc; chem disp; shwrs inc; el pts (10A); lndtte; shop 1km; snacks; playgrnd; sm pool; cycle hire; sand beach 4km; playgrnd; rv sw 6km; canoeing; fishing; horseriding; quiet; adv bkg; CCI. ♦ 1 Apr-30 Oct. € 16.50   2002*

LONGEVILLE SUR MER *7A1* (1.5km S Coastal) **Camp Municipal Le Rocher, 85560 Longeville-sur-Mer [02 51 90 31 57]** Fr La Tranche-sur-Mer take D105 N. In 8km site clearly sp 'Le Rocher' at 3rd exit fr rndabt (Ave du Dr Mathevet. Site on R in 1km at beginning of beach rd. Lge, hdg/mkd pitches, pt sl, shd; wc; chem disp; shwrs inc; el pts (6A) €3; gas; ice; shops adj; rest & snacks nrby; sand beach 300m; adv bkg; quiet; CCI. "Gd beach holiday; gd facs." 15 May-15 Sep. € 12.00   2005*

LONGEVILLE SUR MER *7A1* (2km S Coastal) **Camping Le Sous-Bois, La Haute Saligotiere, 85560 Longeville-sur-Mer [02 51 33 36 90; fax 02 51 33 32 73]** Sp fr D105. Med, hdg pitch, pt shd; wc; chem disp; shwrs; el pts (5A) inc (poss rev pol); shop 3km; tradsmn; lndtte; playgrnd; sand beach 1km; tennis; 25% statics; phone; dogs; quiet; cc not acc.. "Well-managed, family site; pleasant woodland walk to beach; excel long/sh stay." ♦ 1 Jun-15 Sep. € 17.00   2004*

LONGEVILLE SUR MER *7A1* (3km S Coastal) **Camping Les Clos des Pins, Les Conches, 85560 Longeville-sur-Mer [02 51 90 31 69; fax 02 51 90 30 68; philip.jones@freesbee.fr; www. efrancevacances.com]** Fr La Tranche-sur-Mer take D105 coast rd N, turn L in Les Conches into Ave de la Plage, site on R in 1km. Med, mkd pitch, pt sl, shd; wc; chem disp; shwrs inc; el pts (6A) inc; gas; ice; lndtte; shop; rest; snacks; bar; BBQ (gas/elec only); playgrnd; htd pool; waterslide; sand beach 200m; activities inc silk painting, jogging, canoeing, aerobics; entmnt; 60% statics; dogs €2.50; phone; bus; Eng spkn; adv bkg (dep req); quiet except for disco; 20% red low ssn. "Set among pine trees; v helpful owners; some pitches unsuitable for c'vans due to soft sand & diff access - adv bkg rec to ensure a suitable pitch; vg." ♦ ltd. Easter-10 Oct. € 24.00   2004*

LONGEVILLE SUR MER *7A1* (3km SW Coastal) **Camping Les Brunelles, Le Bouil, 85560 Longeville-sur-Mer [02 51 33 50 75; fax 02 51 33 98 21; camping@les-brunelles.com; www.les-brunelles.com]** Site bet Longeville-sur-Mer & Jard-sur-Mer, foll D21. Lge, mkd pitch, pt sl, pt shd; wc; shwrs inc; el pts (6A) inc; lndtte; shop; rest 500m; snacks; bar; playgrnd; 2 htd pools (1 covrd) & paddling pool; waterslide; sand beach 700m; watersports; tennis; cycle hire; games area; mini-golf; horseriding 2km; golf 15km; internet; entmnt; TV rm; 75% statics; dogs €3; adv bkg; cc acc. ♦ 1 May-18 Sep. € 25.00 (CChq acc)
                                                                     2004*

LONS LE SAUNIER *6H2* (1km NE) **Camping La Marjorie, Blvd de l'Europe, 39000 Lons-le-Saunier [03 84 24 26 94; fax 03 84 24 08 40; info@camping-marjorie.com; www.camping-marjorie.com]** Site clearly sp in town on N83 twd Besancon. Lge, hdg pitch, some hdstg, pt sl, pt shd; wc (some cont); baby facs; shwrs inc; el pts (6A) inc; gas; lndtte; shop; tradsmn; playgrnd; 2 htd pools (1 covrd) adj; games area; mini-golf; golf 8km; entmnt; dogs €1; phone; Eng spkn; some rd noise; red low ssn; cc acc; CCI. "Beautiful area; gorges, lakes & limestone escarpments nr; walk to pleasant town; friendly staff; excel long stay; NB overflow site Les Pommiers adj."♦ 1 Apr-15 Oct. € 16.50   2005*

LONS LE SAUNIER *6H2* (8km NE) **Camp Municipal de la Toupe, 39210 Baume-les-Messieurs [03 84 44 63 16; fax 03 84 44 95 40]** On D471 Lons-le-Saunier to Champagnole rd, take L onto D4 then D70 to Baume-les-Messieurs. Site 500m thro vill on D70 - narr, steep app rd not suitable lge o'fits. Or, fr N83 turn E onto D120 at St Germain-les-Aux to Voitear then onto D70. Sm, pt shd; wc (cont); shwrs inc; el pts (9A) inc; shops 500m; playgrnd; direct access to lake; dogs; quiet. 1 Apr-30 Sep. € 9.50   2004*

LONS LE SAUNIER *6H2* (8km SW Rural) **Camp Municipal, Grande Rue, 39570 Chilly-le-Vignoble [03 84 43 09 34 or 03 84 43 09 32 (Mairie); fax 03 84 47 34 09]** Fr A39 exit junc 8 onto N78. After approx 5km turn R to Courlans & Chilly-le-Vignoble. Site sp 2km. Med, pt shd; wc (most cont); shwrs inc; el pts (5A) inc; ice; supmkt 3km; tradsmn; rest; snacks; playgrnd; games rm; golf nrby; quiet; CCI. "V pleasant in quiet vill; ent for c'vans fr 1530 only; gd." 1 Jun-15 Sep. € 11.20   2005*

LORIENT *2F2* (8km N) **Camp Municipal St Caradec, 56700 Hennebont [02 97 36 21 73]** Fr Port Louis D781 to Hennebont. L in cent cross bdge, then sharp R along Rv Blavet for 1km. On R on rv bank. Sm, pt shd; wc; chem disp; shwrs inc; el pts inc; shop 1km; sand beach 12km; rv; sw; quiet; adv bkg; CCI. "Pretty site." 15 Jun-15 Sep. € 7.50
                                                                     2003*

†**LORIENT** *2F2* (9km N Rural) **Camping Ty Nenez, 56620 Pont-Scorff [02 97 32 51 16; fax 02 97 32 43 77; camping-ty-nenez@wanadoo.fr]** N fr N165 on D6, look for sp Quevin in approx 5km on R. If missed, cont for 1km & turn around at rndabt. Site sp fr Pont-Scorff. Med, hdg pitch, pt shd; wc; chem disp; shwrs inc; el pts (16A) inc; supmkt 1km; bar; dogs €0.50. "Site barrier locked 2200-0800; zoo 1km." € 9.65   2003*

LORIENT *2F2* (3km SW Coastal) **Camp Municipal des Algues, 21 Blvd de Port Maria, 56260 Larmor Plage [02 97 65 55 47; fax 02 97 84 26 27; camping@larmor-plage.com]** Fr N165, take Lorient exit, foll D29 for Larmor Plage. Site adjoins beach, turn R after Tourist Info office. Lge, pt shd; wc; chem disp; shwrs inc; el pts (10A) €2.60; lndtte; shop adj; rest, playgrnd; sand beach; fishing, sailing; dogs €1.05; poss cr; quiet. ♦ 15 Jun-15 Sep. € 11.00   2003*

FRANCE

†LORIENT *2F2* (4km SW Coastal) **Camping La Fontaine, Kerderff, 56260 Larmor Plage** [02 97 33 71 28 or 02 97 65 11 11; fax 02 97 33 70 32; camping-la-fontaine@sellor.com] At Larmor Plage 300m fr D152. Well sp. Med, pt sl; htd wc; mv service pnt; chem disp; shwrs inc; el pts (10A) (rev pol); lndtte; shop adj; snacks; bar; playgrnd; beach 800m; child entmnt; horseriding; tennis adj; sailing; sports; dogs €1.54; Eng spkn. "Excel site; gd facs." ♦ € 13.50   2005*

†LORIENT *2F2* (8km W Coastal) **Camping L'Atlantys, Route du Couregant, Fort Bloque, 56270 Ploemeur** [02 97 05 99 81; fax 02 97 05 95 78] Fr cent Lorient take rd D162 in dir of Ploemeur then coast rd D152 dir Guidel-Plage. Site ent on R adj to sp Fort Bloque. Or D29 fr Lorient then onto D152 & site on R at ent Fort Bloque. Lge, mkd pitch, terr, pt sl, unshd; wc; shwrs inc; el pts (6-10A) inc (rev pol); ice; lndry rm; shop; bar; snacks; playgrnd; pool, sand beach, golf adj; fishing; horseriding 2km; 85% statics; poss cr; Eng spkn; adv bkg; quiet; CCI. "Ltd facs low ssn; poss no access to site on Sun; vg long stay." € 13.50
                                                        2003*

LORMES *4G4* (500m S) **Camp Municipal L'Etang du Goulot, 2 Rue des Campeurs, 58140 Lormes** [03 86 22 82 37; fax 03 86 85 19 28] On D944, Chateau Chinon to Avallon, site on R 250m after junc with D17 fr Montsauche, 500m bef town cent. Med, hdg pitch, pt shd, pt sl; wc (some cont); chem disp; shwrs inc; el pts (4A) €2; shop 500m; snacks; 5% statics; dogs; quiet; red low ssn; CCI. "Overlooking lake with gd walks." 15 Jun-15 Sep. € 15.00   2004*

LOUBRESSAC *7C4* (250m Rural) **Camping La Garrigue, 46130 Loubressac** [tel/fax 05 65 38 34 88; pelled@wanadoo.fr] Fr D 940 S to Bretenoux, then D14 to Loubressac. Fr cent vill foll sp 200m. Sm, hdg/mkd pitch, pt sl, terr, pt shd; wc; chem disp; shwrs inc; el pts (6A) €2.60; gas; lndtte; ice; shop; tradsmn high ssn; snacks; bar; BBQ; playgrnd; pool; TV rm; 20% statics; dogs €1.25; phone; quiet; Eng spkn; adv bkg; CCI. "Access poss diff for lge vans; walks in pretty vill; vg long stay." ♦ 1 Apr-30 Sep. € 14.00   2003*

LOUDEAC *2E3* (1km E) **Camp Municipal Pont es Bigots, 22600 Loudeac** [02 96 28 14 92 or 02 96 66 85 00 (Mairie); fax 02 96 66 08 93; mairie.loudeac@wanadoo.fr] Fr Loudeac, take N164 twd Rennes, site on L by lake in 1km, sp. Height barrier into site 1.8m. Med, hdg pitch, pt shd; wc; shwrs; el pts €1.80; ice; shops 1km; playgrnd; entmnt; lake sw; fishing; horseriding; quiet. "V pleasant; site clsd 1100-1700." 15 Jun-15 Sep. € 6.10   2005*

LOUDENVIELLE see Arreau *8G2*

LOUDUN *4H1* (1km W Rural) **Camp Municipal de Beausoleil, Chemin de l'Etang, 86200 Loudun** [05 49 98 14 22; fax 05 49 98 12 88] On main rte fr Poitiers to Saumur/Le Mans; N on N147 around Loudun, foll rdside sp; site turn L just N of level x-ing, then on R approx 250m. Sm, hdg/mkd pitch, terr, pt shd; wc, chem disp; shwrs inc; el pts €2.75; lndry rm; shop 1km; playgrnd; lake adj for fishing; bus adj; Eng spkn; quiet; CCI. "V well-kept; excel; low ssn site yourself." ♦ 15 May-31 Aug. € 12.30
                                                        2005*

LOUHANS *6H1* (2km W Urban) **Camp Municipal de Louhans, 10, Chemin de la Chapellerie, 71500 Louhans** [03 85 75 19 02 or 03 85 76 75 10 (Mairie); fax 03 85 76 75 11] In Louhans foll sp fr Romenay on D971. Go under rlwy & over rv. Site on L just after stadium. Med, hdg/mkd pitch, hdstg, shd; wc (some cont); chem disp (wc); mv service pnt; shwrs inc; el pts; ice; snacks; playgrnd; pool & tennis courts adj; sw rv adj; poss cr; adv bkg; some rlwy noise; CCI. "Lge town mkt Mon am; sports complex adj; rv location; clean & well appointed; vg sh stay/NH." ♦ ltd. 1 Apr-1 Oct. € 10.45   2004*

LOUPIAC see Payrac *7D3*

LOURDES *8F2* (1km N Urban) **Caravaning Plein-Soleil, Route de Tarbes, 65100 Lourdes** [05 62 94 40 93; fax 05 62 94 51 20; camping. plein.soleil@wanadoo.fr; www.camping-plein-soleil.com] Fr N site sp on N21. Sm, terr, pt shd; htd wc; chem disp; shwrs inc; el pts (6A) inc; lndtte; snacks; playgrnd; poss cr; Eng spkn; adv bkg; quiet; CCI. "Gd facs; guarded; helpful staff; ltd access for lge o'fits." Easter-15 Oct. € 21.50
                                                        2004*

LOURDES *8F2* (2km N) **Camping Le Moulin du Monge, Ave Jean Moulin, 65100 Lourdes** [05 62 94 28 15; fax 05 62 42 20 54; camping. moulin.monge@wanadoo.fr] S on N21 fr Tarbes, site on L of rd 2km bef Lourdes, visible fr rd. Med, pt shd; htd wc; sauna; shwrs inc; el pts (2-6A) €2-4; ice; lndtte; shops & farm produce; playgrnd; htd, covrd pool; some rd & rlwy noise. "Pleasant site but not well lit at night; c'vans broken into summer 2004." 15 Mar-15 Oct. € 12.40   2004*

LOURDES *8F2* (1km S) **Camping du Ruisseau Blanc, Route de Bagneres, 65100 Lourdes** [05 62 42 94 83; fax 05 62 42 94 62] Exit Lourdes on D937 twd Bagneres & foll sp. Site has 2 entrances. C'vans ignore 1st sp for site on R & cont on D937 foll next sp. Med, pt shd; wc (most cont); mv service pnt; shwrs; el pts (2-4A) inc; lndry rm; shop (local produce); playgrnd; TV rm; no dogs; "Gd views; beautiful site but facs poss stretched high ssn." 1 Apr-10 Oct. € 11.10   2004*

LOURDES *8F2* (2.5km W Urban) **Camp du Loup, Route de la Foret, 65100 Lourdes** [05 62 94 23 60] Fr town take rd along N side of rv twd D937 sp Betharram. L at junc over rv. Site on R in 300m. Sm, pt shd; wc; chem disp; mv service pnt; shwrs €1; el pts (6A) €2.50; lndtte; shop 1km; tradsmn; playgrnd; dogs; poss cr; adv bkg ess; quiet; CCI. "Excel CL-type, friendly host; conv site to walk to shrine, 1km easy walk by rv; site v cr with pilgrims, gd atmosphere; itinerant camp adj Aug 05; gd site security." ♦ 1 Apr-31 Oct. € 11.00　　　2005*

†**LOURDES** *8F2* (4km W) **Camping d'Arrouach, 9 Rue des Trois Archanges, Biscaye, 65100 Lourdes** [05 62 42 11 43; fax 05 62 42 05 27; camping.arrouach@wanadoo.fr] Fr Lourdes take D940 twd Pau. As you leave Lourdes take L fork D937 (sp) Betharram. Site on R 200m. Med, hdg/mkd pitch, hdstg, pt sl, pt shd; wc; chem disp; mv service pnt; shwrs inc; el pts (3-6A) €2.45-3.60; gas; lndtte; shop 2km; bar 2km; BBQ; playgrnd; 10% statics; phone; poss cr; quiet; adv bkg; Eng spkn; CCI; red 15 days. "Elevated site with mountain views; poss flooding in v wet weather; clean san facs; easy access parking for Lourdes via Rue de Pau; excel long/sh stay." ♦ € 11.00　　　2003*

LOURDES *8F2* (4km W Rural) **Camping La Foret, Route de la Foret, 65100 Lourdes** [05 62 94 04 38 or 05 62 45 04 57 LS; fax 05 62 42 14 86] Fr Lourdes take D937 twd Pau; turn L on level x-ing; foll sp to site. Med, pt shd; wc; mv service pnt; shwrs €1.37; el pts (6-10A) €4.60; gas; lndtte; ice; shop; rest; snacks; bar; playgrnd; few statics; dogs €1.30; poss cr; Eng spkn; adv bkg; quiet; CCI. "Pleasant countryside; lovely site near Pyrenees; helpful owners; conv town cent; 15 mins walk to Grotto." 1 Apr-31 Oct. € 13.30　　　2005*

LOURDES *8F2* (6km W Rural) **Camping Le Prat dou Rey (formerly Arc en Ciel), 31 Route de Pau, 65270 Peyrouse** [05 62 41 81 54; fax 05 62 41 89 76; pradourey@wanadoo.fr; www.pradourey.fr] Take D940 fr Lourdes then in 2km take D937 E sp Betharram. Cont thro Peyrouse vill & site on L in 500m. Med, pt shd; wc; shwrs inc; el pts (6A) inc; lndry rm; shop in ssn & 6km; snacks; BBQ; playgrnd; pool; rv 100m; fishing; 10% statics; CCI. "Immac san facs; various sports activities; friendly warden." 1 Apr-30 Sep. € 11.50　　　2005*

LOURDES *8F2* (4km NW) **Camp Relais Ocean Pyrenees, Poueyferre, 65100 Lourdes** [05 62 94 57 22 or 05 62 94 95 23] Fr Pau on D940, site on R at S junc with rd to Poueyferre. Do not take 1st sp for Poueyferre & camp site as app fr vill not rec. Med, hdg pitch, sl, terr, pt shd; wc; chem disp; serviced pitches; shwrs; el pts (4A) inc; gas; lndtte; tradsmn, snacks, bar, shop in ssn; playgrnd; free pool; adv bkg; 10% dep req; no cc acc; quiet; CCI. ♦ 1 Apr-30 Sep. € 16.00　　　2002*

LOURES BAROUSSE see Montrejeau *8F3*

LOUROUX, LE *4G2* (N Rural) **Camping a la Ferme de La Chaumine (Baudoin), 37240 Le Louroux** [06 85 45 68 10; fax 02 47 92 29 24; lachaumine@free.fr] Fr Tours, take D50 S for 30km. Site immed on R bef Le Leroux. Sm, hdg pitch, shd; wc; chem disp; shwrs inc; el pts (10A) €2.30; BBQ; playgrnd; dogs; phone nrby; bus 200m; Eng spkn; adv bkg; quiet. "Superb CL-type site nr quaint vill; excel tourist office in vill; helpful owners; gd walks fr site.." 1 May-15 Oct. € 6.90　　　2004*

Some of these sites have changed their opening dates - we'd better fill in some site report forms and let the editor of the guide know.

†**LOUVIE JUZON** *8F2* (1km E) **Camping Le Rey, Quartier Listo, Route de Lourdes, 64260 Louvie-Juzon** [05 59 05 78 52; fax 05 59 05 78 97; campinglerey@club-internet.fr; www.camping-pyrenees-ossau.com] Site on L at top of hill E fr Louvie; v steep app. Sm, mkd pitch, pt sl, pt shd; htd wc; chem disp; shwrs inc; el pts (6-1A) €3.30-4.20; lndtte; ice; shops 1km; tradsmn; rest 1km; snacks; bar; playgrnd; sm pool; watersports, fishing nr; games area; entmnt; 50% statics; dogs €2; phone; site clsd mid-Oct to mid-Nov; adv bkg; quiet; CCI. "Fascinating area; chateau nr." ♦ € 12.10　　　2005*

LOUVIE JUZON *8F2* (4km E Rural) **Camping a la Ferme, Quartier Pedestarres, 64260 Louvie-Juzon** [05 59 05 70 37 or 06 88 63 32 52; fax 05 59 05 70 37; www.vallee-ossau.com] On the D934 S fr Pau twd Louvie-Juzon. In vill, turn L onto D35. Site on R in 4km. Sm, terr, pt shd; wc; chem disp; shwrs inc; el pts (4A) €2; lndtte; playgrnd; adv bkg; quiet. "Excel site; friendly, helpful owner; excel all stays." 1 Mar-30 Oct. € 7.00　　　2003*

LOUVIE JUZON *8F2* (4km E Rural) **Camping a la Ferme, Quartier Pedestarres, 64260 Louvie-Juzon** [05 59 05 70 37 or 06 88 63 32 52; fax 05 59 05 70 37; www.vallee-ossau.com] On the D934 S fr Pau to Louvie-Juzon. In vill, turn L onto D35. Site on R in 4km. Sm, terr, pt shd; wc; chem disp; shwrs inc; el pts (4A) €2; lndtte; playgrnd; adv bkg; quiet. "Excel site; 1 Mar-30 Oct. € 7.00　　　2003*

LOUVIE JUZON *8F2* (3km S Rural) **Camping L'Ayguelade, 64260 Bielle** [05 59 82 66 50; ayguelade@aol.com] S fr Louvie-Juzon on L of main rd clearly sp. Med, mkd pitch, pt shd; wc; shwrs inc; el pts (6A); lndtte; shop 4km; tradsmn; rest adj; snacks; bar; 25% statics; Eng spkn; adv bkg; quiet; CCI. "Rv runs thro site, pleasant setting." ♦ ltd. 1 Mar-15 Oct.　　　2004*

LOUVIERS *3D2* (2km W Rural) **Camping Le Bel Air**, Route de la Haye-Malherbe, Hameau de St-Lubin, 27400 Louviers [tel/fax 02 32 40 10 77; le.belair@wanadoo.fr; www.cyber-normandie.com/belair.htm] Leave A13 junc 18 sp Louviers; join A154 fr Evreux to Louviers; in cent foll D81 W for 4km in dir La Haye-Malherbe; twisting rd uphill; site on R. If travelling S leave a'route at junc 19 (as junc 18 has no S'bound exit) & foll dirs as bef. NB In town cent look for sm green sp after Ecole Communale (on L) and bef Jardin Public - a v narr rd (one-way) & easy to miss. Med, hdg/mkd/hdstg pitch, pt shd; wc (chem clos); chem disp; mv service pnt; shwrs inc; el pts (6A) €2.80; gas; lndtte; shop; tradsmn; playgrnd; pool; 40% statics; dogs €1.20; poss cr; Eng spkn; adv bkg (dep req); quiet; red low ssn; 10% red CCI. "Pretty site; friendly staff & v helpful owners; will open out of ssn if you phone ahead; barrier clsd at 2200; some pitches sm for van & awning; conv for Le Havre." 1 Mar-1 Nov. € 12.60   2005*

LOYAT see Ploermel *2F3*

LUBERSAC *7B3* (Urban) **Camp Municipal La Vezenie**, 19210 Lubersac [05 55 73 50 14 (Mairie); fax 05 55 73 67 99; mairie.lubersac@wanadoo.fr] Fr N20 4km N of Uzerche turn W onto D902 to Lubersac. At far end of mkt sq take rd L of Hotel de Commerce; turn immed L; then 1st L; at T-junc turn R; then L at mini rndabt onto site. Sm, mkd pitch, pt sl, terr, pt shd; wc (some cont); shwrs inc; el pts; lndry rm; shop adj; rest, snacks; playgrnd; paddling pool; sand beach & lake sw, fishing 400m; tennis; horseriding; poss cr; quiet. "Modern, clean site overlkg lake." 1 Jun-15 Sep. € 8.00   2004*

LUC EN DIOIS *9D3* (Rural) **Camp Municipal Les Foulons**, 26310 Luc-en-Diois [04 75 21 36 14 or 04 75 21 31 01 (Mairie); fax 04 75 21 35 70; camping.luc@wanadoo.fr] Sp in vill off D93. Med, pt shd; wc; shwrs; el pts (6A) €2.50; lndtte; shops & rest 500m; playgrnd; pool; rv adj; games area adj; tennis; Eng spkn; adv bkg; quiet; CCI. "Excel site; modern & well-maintained; gd walking/cycling; 5 mins walk fr attractive sm town; gates clsd 2200-0700; outstanding scenery; Fri mkt; canoeing, horseriding, hang-gliding avail in area." ♦ 1 Apr-15 Oct. € 8.50   2004*

LUC EN DIOIS *9D3* (6km N Rural) **Camping L'Hirondelle de St Ferreol**, Bois de St Ferreol, 26410 Menglon [tel/fax 04 75 21 82 08; contact@campinghirondelle.com; www.campinghirondelle.com] Foll D93 S twd Luc-en-Dois, in 6km at Pont-de-Quart turn L on D539 sp Chatillon, in 5km turn R on D140 sp Menglon, Recoubeau, site on R in 150m over rv. Med, shd; wc (some cont); baby facs; shwrs inc; el pts (3-6A) €3-4; lndtte; shop; rest; snacks; bar; playgrnd; htd pool complex; waterslide; rv sw; archery; entmnt; TV rm; 10% statics; dogs €3.15; adv bkg; quiet. "Lovely area." ♦ 1 Apr-15 Sep. € 21.90 (CChq acc)   2005*

LUC EN DIOIS *9D2* (5km NW Rural) **Camping Le Couriou**, 26310 Recoubeau-Jansac [04 75 21 33 23; fax 04 75 21 38 42] Fr Die on D93 twds Luc-en-Diois for 13 km. Turn R at D140 & foll sp. Med, mkd pitch, some hdstg, terr, pt shd; wc; chem disp; shwrs inc; baby facs; el pts (6A) €3; gas; lndtte; shop high ssn; rest; snacks; bar; playgrnd; htd pool; 5% statics; dogs; phone; poss cr; adv bkg ess high ssn; quiet; CCI. "Panoramic mountain views; vg long/sh stay." ♦ ltd. 1 May-31 Aug. € 19.00
                          2004*

LUC SUR MER see Ouistreham *3D1*

†**LUC, LE** *10F3* (6km SE) **Camping Les Bruyeres**, Route de Mayons, 83340 Le Luc [04 94 73 47 07; fax 04 94 60 99 26] Fr N97 at sports stadium in Le Luc turn L on D33. Site in 3.5km. Med, mkd pitch, pt shd; htd wc; shwrs inc; el pts (6A) €2.75; gas; lndtte; shop 4km; snacks; bar; playgrnd; pool; games area; TV; some statics; quiet. € 13.05
                          2005*

LUCAY LE MALE *4H2* (4km SW Rural) **Camp Municipal La Foulquetiere**, 36360 Lucay-le-Male [02 54 40 52 88 or 02 54 40 43 31 (Mairie); fax 02 54 40 42 47; mairie@ville-lucaylemale.fr] SW fr Valencay & thro Lucay, on D960, then fork L onto D13, site on R in 1km. Sm, hdg/mkd pitch, pt sl, pt shd; htd wc; chem disp; 60% serviced pitch; shwrs inc; el pts (6A) €1.50; lndtte; shop 3km; rest; snacks; bar; playgrnd; watersports; canoeing; fishing; tennis; mini-golf; games area; Eng spkn; adv bkg; v quiet; CCI. "Excel site but isolated; gd sized pitches; basic facs; gd walking country; by lake in pretty setting; if no one at recep, pay at Mairie or rest." 1 Apr-15 Oct. € 6.50   2005*

LUCENAY L'EVEQUE *6H1* (S Rural) **Aire Naturelle Municipal**, 71540 Lucenay-l'Eveque [03 85 82 65 41 (Mairie); fax 03 85 82 65 37; mairie.lucenay.l.eveque@wanadoo.fr] On D980 Autun to Saulieu rd, 300m S of vill site ent immed bef vill sp. Ent narr; easier when warden opens 2nd gate. Sm, pt shd; wc (some cont); shwrs inc; el pts; playgrnd; shops 300m; quiet; tennis; cc acc; CCI. "Nice neat site with brook running thro; gd walking country situated in Morvan regional park; v quiet low ssn; warden visits 1730 & 0930; narr ent to pitches with el pts; site yourself." 1 May-1 Sep.   2004*

LUCHE PRINGE see Fleche, La *4G1*

LUCON *7A1* (11km E) **Camp Municipal Le Vieux Chene**, 85370 Nalliers [02 51 30 91 98 or 02 51 30 90 71; fax 02 51 30 94 06; nalliers.mairie@wanadoo.fr] Turn R & foll site sp off D949 Lucon-Fountenay rd at Nalliers; site sp easy to miss. Sm, hdg/mkd pitch, pt shd; wc; chem disp; shwrs inc; el pts (8A) €2.70; shop 500m; tradsmn; playgrnd; adv bkg; quiet; site yourself on lge pitch; CCI. "Excel site; v clean; plenty hot water; in low ssn contact Mairie for ent to site; lots of interest in area; vg rest nrby; vg NH." 15 May-15 Sep. € 6.60
                          2005*

†LUCON *7A1* (10km SW Rural) **Camping La Fraignaye, Rue de Beau Laurier, 85580 St Denis-du-Payre [02 51 27 21 36 or 02 51 27 20 28 (Mairie); fax 02 51 27 27 74; camping.fraignaye@wanadoo.fr; www.camping-fraignaye.com]** Fr A8 exit junc 7 onto N137 dir La Rochelle. Turn L after Gemme onto D949 to Lucon, then take D746 to Triaize. Take D25 to St Denis-du-Payre, in vill turn L bef church & foll sp. Sm, mkd pitch, pt shd; wc; chem disp; shwrs inc; el pts (6-10A) €2.50-4; gas; lndry rm; ice; shop & 7km; rest; snacks; bar; playgrnd; sand beach 12km; games rm; cycle hire; TV; 20% statics; dogs €1.50; phone; poss cr; Eng spkn; adv bkg; quiet; cc acc; red long stay/low ssn. "Pleasant owner; nr nature reserve." ♦ € 11.40
2003*

LUDE, LE *4G1* (1km NE) **Camp Municipal au Bord du Loir, Route du Mans, 72800 Le Lude [02 43 94 67 70; fax 02 43 94 93 82; camping-lelude@wanadoo.fr]** Fr town cent take D305 (E); in 1km take the D307 (N) sp 'Le Mans'; site immed on L. Well sp. Med, hdg/mkd pitch, pt shd; wc (some cont); chem disp; mv service pnt; shwrs inc; el pts (5A); lndtte; shops 300m; tradsmn; rests 100m; snacks adj (high ssn); playgrnd; free pool adj; waterslide; tennis; beach 6km; canoeing; fishing; entmnt; TV; 10% statics; phone; poss cr; Eng spkn; adv bkg; poss traff noise far end of site; cc acc; CCI. "V clean, gd value site; helpful staff; excel rests adj; easy walk to town; Chateau du Lude worth visit; highly rec; excel long/sh stay." ♦ 1 Apr-30 Sep. € 9.30
2005*

LUGNY see Pont de Vaux *9A2*

LUNE, LA *4F1* (5km W) **Camp Municipal de la Charnie, 72350 St Denis-d'Orques [02 43 88 43 14 (Mairie); fax 02 43 88 21 08]** On N137 Le Mans-Laval rd in St Denis-d'Orgues turn R at traff lts & foll sp to site. Sm, pt shd; wc; shwrs; el pts; shops 1km; quiet.
2003*

LUNEL *10E2* (5km NE Rural) **Camping Les Amandiers, Clos de Manset, 30660 Gallargues-le-Montueux [tel/fax 04 66 35 28 02; camp amandiers@wanadoo.fr; www.camping-les-amandiers.com]** Exit A9 at junc 26 Gallargues/ Les Plages. Turn R after pool, site in 2km. Med, pt shd; wc; chem disp; mv service pnt; shwrs inc; el pts (10A) inc; gas; lndtte; ice; shops adj; snacks; bar; playgrnd; pool; sand beach 15km; fishing 800m; tennis; games area; entmnt; TV; 20% statics; dogs €1.50; adv bkg; quiet; cc acc; CCI. "Nr m'way en rte to Spain; gd touring area." ♦ 28 Apr-10 Sep. € 19.10
2005*

LUNEL *10E2* (9km E) **Club International, 30121 Mus [tel/fax 04 66 35 07 06]** 8km NE of Lunel on N113 turn N at canal x-ing sp Mus & Calvisson & foll sp. Fr m'way exit Gallargues. Sm, pt shd; wc; chem disp; shwrs inc; el pts (6A) €3; gas; lndtte; shop & 2km; rest; snacks; playgrnd; pool; entmnt; TV; quiet; red low ssn. 15 Feb-15 Nov. € 15.00 (3 persons)
2003*

LUNEL *10E2* (1km SE Rural) **Camping Le Mas de L'Isle, 85 Chemin du Clapas, 34400 Lunel [04 67 83 26 52; fax 04 67 71 13 88]** Foll D34 twd Marsillargues, site sp on R. Lge, hdg pitch, pt shd; wc; shwrs inc; el pts (3A) €2.15; lndtte; snacks; playgrnd; pool; entmnt; 10% statics; dogs €1.50; adv bkg; quiet; red long stay; CCI. "Conv a'route & Camargue; close to supmkts." 1 Apr-31 Aug. € 13.00
2003*

LUNEL *10E2* (6km SW) **Camping Le Fou du Roi, Chemin des Cotonniers, 34130 Lansargues [04 67 86 78 08; fax 04 67 86 78 06; lefouduroi@aol.com]** SW fr Lunel on D24 to Lansargues, 100m past vill turn N. Site 50m on R. Med, hdg pitch, pt shd; wc; chem disp; mv service pnt; shwrs inc; el pts (5A); lndtte; shop; supmkt 4km; snacks; bar; playgrnd; pool; tennis; horseriding; 75% statics; dogs €2.50; poss cr; adv bkg rec high ssn; quiet; CCI. ♦ ltd. 15 Mar-31 Oct. € 13.00
2004*

LUNEVILLE *6E2* (1km NE Urban) **Camp Municipal Les Bosquets, 65 Quai des Petits Bosquets, 54300 Luneville [03 83 73 37 58]** Exit N4 Luneville by-pass sp 'Luneville-Chateau' & foll sp to Luneville. Fr traff lts in sq in front of chateau, take rd that passes to L of chateau (Quai des Bosquest). At sm rndabt do not ent site on R but cont round rndabt to L to yard opp warden's house. Warden will open barrier. Sm, mkd pitch, terr, pt shd; wc; chem disp; shwrs inc; el pts (16A) inc; lndtte; shops 500m; pool 200m; playgrnd nrby; some statics; some rd noise; "Pay at house opp; cycle & motorcycle museum opp chateau; tourist office by chateau ent in sq; if travelling end of ssn, phone ahead to check site open." ♦ 1 Apr-31 Oct. € 12.00
2004*

LURE *6F2* (1.5km SE Urban) **Camp Intercommunal Les Ecuyers, Route de la Saline, 70200 Lure [03 84 30 43 40 or 03 84 89 00 30; fax 03 84 89 00 31; magalie-sarre@pays-delure.fr]** Well sp fr town cent. Med, hdg pitch, unshd; wc; chem disp; shwrs inc; el pts (6A) inc; lndtte; ice; supmkt 500m; playgrnd; htd, covrd pool 3km; archery; adv bkg; quiet; no cc acc; CCI. "Le Corbusier church worth visit 8km in Ronchamp; vg clean, well kept site; rec." ♦ 1 Jun-30 Sep. € 10.00
2005*

LUS LA CROIS HAUTE see St Julien en Beauchene *9D3*

LUSIGNAN *7A2* (Urban) **Camp Municipal de Vauchiron, 86600 Lusignan [05 49 43 30 08; fax 05 49 43 61 19; lusignan@cg86.fr]** Site sp fr N11, 22km SW of Poitiers; foll camp sp in Lusignan. Med, pt shd; wc (some cont); own san adv; shwrs inc; el pts (16A) €1.70 (poss rev pol); lndry rm; lndtte; ice; shops 1km; tradsmn; snacks; bar adj; playgrnd; rv adj; fishing; boat hire; entmnt; some statics; CCI. 15 Apr-15 Oct. € 5.80
2003*

FRANCE

LUSSAC LES CHATEAUX *7A3* (6km SW) **Camp Municipal du Moulin Beau, 86320 Gouex** [05 49 48 46 14; fax 05 48 84 50 01] Fr Lussac on N147-E62 dir Poitiers, cross rv bdge sp Poitiers & immed turn L on D25; foll sp to Gouex; site on L. Sm, pt shd; wc (some cont); chem disp; shwrs inc; el pts (15A) €1.90 (check pol); shop 500m in vill; pool 50m; v quiet; no cc acc; CCI. "Excel site on bank of Rv Vienne; facs v clean but ltd; friendly; new bollards at site ent, care needed if van over 7m or twin-axle; highly rec." 15 Jun-15 Sep. € 5.80
2004*

LUSSAC LES CHATEAUX *7A3* (11km SW Rural) **Camp Municipal du Renard, 86150 Queaux** [05 49 48 48 32 or 05 49 48 48 08 (Mairie)] Fr Lussac cross rv bdge sp Poitiers & immed turn L. Foll sp to Gouex & Queaux. Site on D25 S of vill. Med, pt sl, pt shd; wc; shwrs inc; el pts (6A) inc; shops 500m; paddling pool; quiet. "Lovely rvside site nr pleasant vill; manned high ssn or apply to Mairie." Jun-Sep. € 6.80
2003*

LUSSAC LES CHATEAUX *7A3* (3km W Rural) **Camp Municipal Mauvillant, 86320 Lussac-les-Chateaux.** [tel/fax 05 49 48 03 32] Fr Lussac on N147/E62 dir Les Poitiers, bef bdge turn L at Municipal sp & foll to site approx 1.5km on L. Site parallel to Rv Vienne. Exit L turn onto N147 can be diff for lge o'fits Med, hdg/mkd pitch, hdstg, pt shd; wc (mainly cont); chem disp; baby facs; shwrs inc; el pts (12A) inc; lndtte; BBQ; playgrnd; pool nr; rv 200m; no dogs; Eng spkn; adv bkg; quiet; CCI. "Warden calls 0800-1000 & 1800-2000, if office clsd site yourself & register later; v clean san facs; vg sh stay/NH." 1 May-15 Oct. € 10.00
2004*

LUYNES see Tours *4G2*

LUZ ST SAUVEUR *8G2* (1km N) **Airotel Pyrenees, 46 Ave du Barege, La Ferme Theil, 65120 Esquieze-Sere** [05 62 92 89 18; fax 05 62 92 96 50; airotel.pyrenees@wanadoo.fr; www.airotel-pyrenees.com] On main rd fr Lourdes to Luz on L past International Campsite. L U-turn into ent archway needs care - use full width of main rd & forecourt. Med, mkd pitch, pt sl, pt shd; htd wc (some cont); mv service pnt; chem disp (wc only); sauna; shwrs inc; fam bthrm; el pts (3-10A) €3-6.20 (rev pol); gas; ice; lndtte; shop; supmkt 800m; tradsmn, rest & snacks in high ssn; bar; playgrnd; indoor & o'door pools; ski in winter; fishing; walking; horseriding; rafting; TV; entmnts; dogs €1.22; 30% statics; poss cr; quiet but some rd noise; Eng spkn; adv bkg (dep req); cc acc; CCI. "Excel site; helpful manager; facs poss stretched high ssn; beautiful area; excel walking & wildlife; vg long stay. " ♦ ltd. 1 Dec-30 Sep. € 21.00
2005*

LUZ ST SAUVEUR *8G2* (500m E Rural) **Camping Le Bergons, Route de Baregas, 65120 Esterre** [05 62 92 90 77; abordenave@club-internet.fr] On D918 to Col du Tourmalet, site on R. Med, pt sl, pt shd; htd wc; shwrs inc; chem disp; el pts (3A) €3.50; gas; lndtte; ice; shops adj; BBQ; playgrnd; pool 500m; dogs €0.70; rd noise; 10% red long stay/low ssn; CCI. "Excel site; gd facs; helpful owner; conv for Cirque de Garvanie mountain area; ski at Bareges & walking in Pyrenees National Park with cable cars to peaks; excel long stay." ♦ 15 Dec-15 Oct. € 9.15
2004*

Will you fill in the site report forms at the back of the guide, or shall I?

LUZ ST SAUVEUR *8G2* (8km E Rural) **Camping La Ribere, 65120 Bareges** [tel/fax 05 62 92 69 01; fourtine.denis@wanadoo.fr] On N side of rd N618 on edge of Bareges, site sp as 'Camping Caraveneige'. Phone kiosk at ent. Sm, pt sl, pt shd; htd wc ltd; chem disp; shwrs inc; el pts (6A) inc; lndtte; shops, tradsmn; rest adj; some statics; poss cr; quiet. "Very friendly staff; gd facs; magnificent views." 15 May-15 Oct & 25 Dec-1 May. € 12.80
2004*

LUZECH see Castelfranc *7D3*

LUZENAC see Ax les Thermes *8G4*

LUZERET see Argenton sur Creuse *7A3*

LUZY *4H4* (1km N) **Camp Municipal La Bedure, 58170 Luzy** [03 86 30 02 34 (Mairie)] Foll camping sps on N81 Luzy-Autun rd to site. Med, pt sl, pt shd; wc; shwrs; shops 1km; el pts €1.50 (rev pol); pool; quiet. "Pleasant, gd walking; municipal pool adj; poss itinerants; gd touring base." 15 Jun-15 Sep. € 6.00
2004*

LUZY *4H4* (7km NE Rural) **Camping Domaine de la Gagere (Naturist), 58170 Luzy** [03 86 30 48 11; fax 03 86 30 45 57; info@la-gagere.com; www.la-gagere.com] Fr Luzy take N81 dir Autun. In 6.5km over rlwy, turn R onto unclassified rd sp 'La Gagere'. Site at end of rd in 3.5km on L. Med, mkd pitch, pt sl, terr, pt shd; wc; chem disp; mv service pnt; child/baby facs; fam bthrm; sauna; shwrs inc; el pts (6A) €5; gas 10km; lndtte; ice; sm shop & shops 10km; tradsmn; rest; snacks; bar; BBQ; playgrnd; 2 htd pools; lake, shgle beach 12km; TV rm; entmnt; 20% statics; dogs €3.50; bus 10km; phone; poss cr; Eng spkn; adv bkg (dep req); quiet; cc acc; INF card req. "Excel site; gd touring base; excel san facs; v friendly, helpful owners; set in woodlands overlooking beautiful valley on edge of National Park." ♦ 1 Apr-30 Sep. € 16.00
2005*

LUZY *4H4* (4km SW Rural) **Camping Chateau de Chigy,** 58170 Tazilly [03 86 30 10 80; fax 03 86 30 09 22; reception@chateaudechigy.com. fr; www.chateaudechigy.com.fr] Fr Luzy take D973 S twd Bourbon-Lancy, in 4km turn L on minor rd sp Chigy, site sp. Fr S turn R onto rd to Chigy. Site is E of D973 - do not take sp rd to Tazilly vill. Med, pt sl, pt shd; wc; chem disp; baby facs; shwrs inc; el pts (6A) €3.50; gas; lndtte; rest; snacks; bar; playgrnd; pool; paddling pool; fishing; games area; entmnt; TV; some statics; dogs €1.50; adv bkg; quiet; red long stay/snr citizens. ♦ 15 Apr-30 Sep. € 22.35   2005*

†**LYON** *9B2* (12km E) **Camping Le Grand Large, Rue Victor Hugo,** 69330 Meyzieu [04 78 31 42 16; fax 04 72 45 91 78; camping.grand.large@ wanadoo.fr] Exit N346 junc 6, E onto D6 dir Jonage. In approx turn L twd Le Grand Large (lake), site in 1km. Lge, pt shd; wc (most cont); chem disp; mv service pnt; shwrs inc; el pts (5A) inc; gas; lndtte; shop 2km; snacks; pool 2km; lake sw adj; boating, fishing in lake; games area; entmnt; TV; 75% statics; bus 1km; poss cr; quiet; adv bkg; cc acc; CCI. "Direct access big lake with sm beach; scruffy san facs; stn 2km for trains to Lyon; fair." € 16.00 (3 persons)   2005*

†**LYON** *9B2* (10km SW Urban) **Camping Les Barolles,** 88 Ave Foch, 69230 St Genis-Laval [04 78 56 05 56; fax 04 72 67 95 01] Exit A7 at Piierre-Benite cent onto A450 & exit at Basses Barolles. Foll sp. Or fr D42 to St Genis-Laval cent main sq (Place Joffre) then take Ave Foch SW to site. Sm, hdstg, terr, pt shd; wc; own san rec; shwrs; el pts (3-13A) €1.70-6.70; gas; lndtte; lndry rm; ice; snacks; bar; playgrnd; dogs; quiet. "Ungated; fair NH only."   2004*

†**LYON** *9B2* (8km NW) **Camp Municipal International, La Porte de Lyon,** 69570 Dardilly [04 78 35 64 55; fax 04 72 17 04 26; camping. lyon@mairie-lyon.com; www.camping-lyon.com] Fr N6 Paris rd, take Limonest-Dardilly-Porte de Lyon exit at Auchan supmkt. Fr A6 exit junc 33 Porte de Lyon. Site on W side of A6, foll sp (poss obscured by trees) for 'Complexe Touristique'. Fr E take N ring rd dir Roanne, Paris, then as above. Lge, hdg/mkd pitch, hdstg, pt shd; htd wc; chem disp; mv service pnt; serviced pitches; mv service pnt; baby facs; shwrs inc; el pts (10A) €3; gas 100m; lndtte; hypmkt 200m; rest 100m; snacks high ssn; playgrnd; pool; games rm; TV rm; dogs €1.50; phone; bus/train to city nr; extra for twin-axle c'vans; Eng spkn; adv bkg; quiet but some rd noise; cc acc; CCI. "Quiet insisted after 2200; gates clsd 2200-0630 but allow arr up to 2400; v helpful staff; excel san facs; ltd facs low ssn when gates clsd 2000; max stay 7 days; Lyon easily accessible by bus & metro; gd touring base for interesting area; pitches basic; excel NH." ♦ € 14.60   2005*

LYONS LA FORET *3D2* (500m NE Rural) **Camp Municipal St Paul,** 27480 Lyons-la-Foret [02 32 49 42 02] Fr Rouen E on N31/E46 for 33km; at La Feuillie, S on D921/321 for 8km; site on L at ent to town adj Rv Lieure. Med, hdg pitch, pt shd; htd wc; chem disp; shwrs inc; el pts (6A) inc; lndtte; shops, tradsmn; rest, snacks, bar 1km; playgrnd; pool adj; fishing; tennis; horseriding; poss cr; 55% statics; dogs; adv bkg; quiet; 15% red 7+ days; CCI. "Walking & cycling in forested area, gd tour base; Lyons-la-Foret lovely half-timbered town, conv Dieppe ferry; site prone to flood after heavy rain; lge pitches; facs poss inadequate for site size; vg." 1 Apr-31 Oct. € 16.50   2005*

MACHECOUL *2H4* (500m SE Urban) **Camp Municipal La Rabine, Route de Challans,** 44270 Machecoul [tel/fax 02 40 02 30 48] Sp fr all dirs. Med, pt shd; wc; chem disp; shwrs €0.80; el pts (13A) inc; lndtte; shops 500m; tradsmn; BBQ (gas only) playgrnd; pool adj; sand beach 14km; entmnt; dogs; adv bkg; quiet. "Vg long/sh stay." 15 Apr-15 Sep. € 9.55   2004*

MACHINE, LA see Decize *4H4*

MACON *9A2* (3km N Urban) **Camp Municipal, Rue des Varennes,** 71000 Macon [03 85 38 16 22 or 03 85 38 54 08; fax 03 85 39 39 18] A6 fr S exit Macon Sud, thro town on main rd. Pass Auchan hypmkt on L, turn R immed after petrol stn, opp fire stn. Site sp. Fr A40, exit junc 1 & foll sp. Fr N on A6 exit junc 28 & cont S on N6 twd Macon. Site on L in approx 3km, sp. Lge, mkd pitch, pt sl, pt shd; htd wc (some cont); chem disp; mv service pnt; shwrs inc; el pts (5A) inc (rev pol) extra for 10A; gas; lndtte; ice; shop; supmkt nr; hypmkt 1km; rest; snacks; bar; playgrnd; 2 pools; tennis 1km; golf 6km; TV; dogs €0.75; phone; poss cr; Eng spkn; adv bkg; quiet but some noise fr rds & rlwy; cc acc; red 6+ days; CCI. "Well-maintained facs; friendly staff; excel rest; superb facs; busy cosmopolitan NH nr A6; rec arr early as poss full after 1800; gates clsd 2200-0630; poss flooding bottom end of site; excel sh stay/NH; rec." ♦ 15 Mar-31 Oct. € 14.10   2005*

MACON *9A2* (8km S) **Camp Municipal du Port d'Arciat, Route du Port d'Arciat,** 71680 Creches-sur-Saone [03 85 36 57 91 or 03 85 37 48 32 (LS); fax 03 85 36 51 57; camping-creches.sur. saone@wanadoo.fr] S fr Macon on N6 to Creches-sur-Saone. Site well sp at 3rd set of traff lts in cent vill on N6, turn E, cross m'way bdge; site on R by rv, sp on rndabt. NB Adj rv bdge has 2.6m height limit. Lge, mkd pitch, pt sl, shd; wc (some cont); chem disp; mv service pnt; shwrs inc; el pts (6A) inc; gas; lndtte; ice; shop; supmkt 1km; rest; snacks; bar; playgrnd; pool 1km; lake sw, fishing & boating; entmnt; dogs €1.15; poss cr; gates clsd 2200-0700; adv bkg; some noise fr a'route; cc acc; 20% red 7+ days; CCI. "Gd long stay." ♦ 15 May-15 Sep. € 13.00   2005*

Les îlots de St Val
Caravaning de loisir ★★★ NN
28130 Villiers le Morhier
Tel.: 02 37 82 71 30 - Fax: 02 37 82 77 67

5 km. NW of Maintenon. This calm family site lies on a flat area of 10 ha., with 150 shady and level touring pitches of 120 sq. m., with interesting touristy sites in the surroundings. Within 4 km.: shops, golf course, swimming pool, tennis, fishing in the river (1 km) and pond, pony club, visits to the Castles, the historic city of Chartres and the famous Cathedral, the Royal Chapel in Dreux at 20 km.

open all year

www.campinglesilotsdestval.com • e-mail : lesilots@campinglesilotsdestval.com

---

MADIRAN *8F2* (Urban) **Camp Municipal Le Madiran**, Route de Vignoble, 65700 Madiran [tel/fax 05 62 31 92 83 or 06 84 67 26 13; irma. hofstede@wanadoo.fr] S fr Riscle on D935 after approx 12km turn R onto D58 to Madiran. Site in middle of town. Sm, mkd pitch, pt sl, unshd; wc; chem disp; shwrs inc; el pts €2.30; gas, shop, snacks, bar 50m; playgrnd; pool; dogs; Eng spkn; quiet; cc acc; CCI. "Excel site; friendly Dutch warden with gd Eng & extensive knowledge of local wine area." ♦ 15 Jun-30 Aug. € 9.00   2005*

MAGNAC BOURG see Pierre Buffiere *7B3*

MAGNIERES *6E2* (Rural) **Camping du Pre Fleury**, 54219 Magnieres [06 20 87 17 43] Fr N333 exit junc 4 S onto D914 to Magnieres. Site sp. Or on D22 fr Bayon or Baccarat go to Magnieres. Site sp. Sm, mkd pitch, hdstg, pt sl, pt shd; wc; chem disp; mv service pnt; shwrs inc; el pts (10A) €2.50; lndtte; shops 1km; rest, bar adj; playgrnd; fishing; quiet. "Gd site for touring Vosges; gd cycling, birdwatching, walks; excel sh stay." ♦ € 7.00   2004*

†**MAICHE** *6G3* (1km S) **Camp Municipal St Michel**, 25120 Maiche [03 81 64 12 56 or 03 81 64 03 01 (Mairie); fax 03 81 64 12 56; camping.maiche@wanadoo.fr] Fr S turn R off D437 onto D442. App on D464 L on o'skts of town. Sp fr both dir. Med, hdstg, sl, terr, pt shd; htd wc; chem disp; shwrs inc; el pts (6A) €2.30; lndtte; shops 1km; playgrnd; pool adj; 10% statics; phone; site clsd 3rd week Nov & Dec; adv bkg; rd noise. "Attractive with gd views & walks in woods; clean, well-run site; phone ahead low ssn to check open; gd sh stay." ♦ € 9.30   2004*

†**MAICHE** *6G3* (10km SW) **Camp Municipal Les Sorbiers**, Rue Foch, 25210 Le Russey [03 81 43 75 86] On D437 Maiche-Morteau, 1st R after vill church, site sp on L in 250m. Sm, hdstg, pt shd; wc (men cont); chem disp; shwrs inc; el pts (10A) €2.10; gas; lndtte; ice; shop 300m; playgrnd; tennis; games rm; 20% statics; adv bkg; quiet; cc not acc. "Excel cent for superb Doubs scenery; high altitude, poss cold nights; slightly scruffy & run down; clsd at 1200 for lunch; gd sh stay." € 4.00   2003*

MAILLE see Maillezais *7A2*

MAILLEZAIS *7A2* (Rural) **Camp Municipal de l'Autize**, Route de Maille, 85420 Maillezais [02 51 00 70 79 or 02 51 00 70 25] Fr Fontenay take N148 twd Niort; after 9km, turn R onto D15 to Maillezais; at church in vill on L, site on R after 200m. Sm, hdg pitch, pt shd; wc (some cont); chem disp; shwrs inc; el pts (5A) inc; lndtte; shop 1km; playgrnd; games area; 30% statics; adv bkg; quiet; cc not acc; CCI. "V clean site; spacious pitches; €23 supplement charge for twin-axles; warden calls am & pm." ♦ 1 Apr-30 Sep. € 13.10   2004*

MAILLEZAIS *7A2* (6km S Rural) **Camping Les Conches**, 85420 Damvix [tel/fax 02 51 87 17 06] Fr Fontenay-le-Comte exit N148 at Benet then W on D25 thro Le Mazeau to sp on L for Damvix. Or exit A83 junc 8 then S on D938 & E on D25 dir Benet. Site 1km thro vill on R over bdge (sp). Med, shd; wc; chem disp; shwrs; el pts (6A) €2.50; lndry rm; shops adj; rest adj; playgrnd; pool; tennis; golf; horseriding; rv fishing & boating adj; pedaloes & canoes for hire; dogs €1; adv bkg rec; quiet but some noise fr disco opp; CCI. "Gd rest." 1 Jun-15 Sep. € 9.00   2004*

MAILLEZAIS *7A2* (5km SW Rural) **Camp Municipal La Petite Cabane**, 85420 Maille [02 51 87 05 78 (Mairie); fax 02 51 87 02 48; mairiedemaille@wanadoo.fr] 500m W of Maille, clearly sp. Sm, pt shd; wc; shwrs inc; el pts (6-15A) inc; gas 500m; lndry rm; shops 500m; playgrnd; paddling pool; boat & canoe hire; adv bkg; quiet; CCI. "Site by canal in cent of Marais Poitevin National Park; gd cycle rtes; gd sh/long stay." 1 Apr-30 Sep. € 11.00   2005*

MAILLY LE CHATEAU *4G4* **Camp Municipal Le Pre du Roi**, Pertuis des Bouchets, 89660 Mailly-le-Chateau [03 86 81 44 85 or 03 86 81 40 37 (Mairie); fax 03 86 81 40 37] NW on N6 fr Avallon twd Auxerre, turn W in Voutenay-sur-Cure on D950 to Mailly-la-Ville. Cross bdge twd Mailly-le-Chateau, site sp. Heading S fr Auxerre, turn R off N6 SE of Vincelles on D100 to Bazarnes & Mailly-le-Chateau. Med, mkd pitch, pt shd; wc; shwrs; el pts (20A) €2.50; shops 2km; fishing; quiet. "Pleasant situation by Rv Yonne." 1 Jun-3 Sep. € 7.80   2003*

MAILLY LE CHATEAU *4G4* (5km S Rural) **Camp Municipal Escale, Base de Plein Air, 89660 Merry-sur-Yonne** [03 86 81 01 60; fax 03 86 81 00 28] Fr Auxerre, take N151. Turn E onto D21 at Coulanges. Thro Chatel-Censoir turn L over rv into Merry-sur-Yonne. Site sp. Med, mkd pitch, pt shd; wc; mv service pnt (some cont); el pts (10A) €3.20; gas; sw in rv adj; tennis, canoe hire, fishing; dogs €1; quiet; phone; CCI. "Gd for all length of stays; poss children's groups in adj gite; some level hdstg pitches." ♦ ltd. 15 Mar-15 Nov. € 9.30   2003*

†**MAINTENON** *4E2* (5km NW Rural) **Camping Les Ilots de St Val, 28130 Villiers-le-Morhier** [02 37 82 71 30; fax 02 37 82 77 67; lesilots@campinglesilotsdestval.com; www.campingles ilotsdestval.com] Take D983 N fr Maintenon twd Nogent-le-Roi, in 5km 2nd L onto D101 sp Neron/Vacheresses-les-Basses/Camping to site in 1km on L at top of hill. Lge, some hdg/mkd pitch, hdstg, pt shd; htd wc; chem disp; baby facs; shwrs inc; el pts (6-10A) €3-6; gas 4km; lndtte; shops 4km; tradsmn; BBQ; playgrnd; pool 4km; rv sw 1km; tennis; 70% statics; dogs €1.50; train 4km; little Eng spkn; adv bkg; quiet; CCI. "Conv Chartres, Versailles, Maintenon chateau & train to Paris; v pleasant, peaceful site in open countryside; excel facs; immac san facs; lge private pitches; helpful staff; highly rec." ♦ € 14.40   2005*

See advertisement

MAISONS LAFFITTE see Paris *3D3*

MALAUCENE *10E2* (Rural) **Camping Le Bosquit, Route de Suzette, 84340 Malaucene** [04 90 65 24 89 or 04 90 65 29 09; fax 04 90 65 12 52] Fr D938 N dir Vaison-la-Romaine turn L onto D90 at Malaucene dir Suzette. Site on R in 300m. Sm, hdg pitch, all hdstg, terr, pt shd; wc; shwrs inc; el pts (10A) €2.50 (rev pol); gas; lndtte; ice; shop 600m; tradsmn; snacks; bar; playgrnd; pool; 2% statics; dogs; phone; adv bkg; quiet; cc not acc; CCI. "Modern site; v clean san facs; friendly owner; gd base for touring area & climbing Mt Ventoux; excel long/sh stay." ♦ Easter-30 Sep. € 13.90   2003*

MALAUCENE *10E2* (4km N Rural) **Camping La Saousse, La Madelaine, 84340 Malaucene** [04 90 65 14 02] Fr Malaucene take D938 N & after 3km turn R onto D13 where site sp. After 1km turn R & site is 1st on R. Sm, hdg pitch, terr, shd; wc; chem disp; shwrs inc; el pts (5A) inc; tradsmn in high ssn; snacks, rest, bar, shop, pool 4km; dogs; quiet; cc not acc. "Site overlooks vineyards with views to Mt Ventoux; some pitches in woods with steep incline to reach; cash only; excel." Easter-30 Oct. € 13.20   2005*

MALAUCENE *10E2* (6km SE) **Camp Municipal de la Pinede, Collet de Florans, 84410 Bedoin** [04 90 65 61 03] Take D938 S fr Malaucene for 3km, L onto D19 for 9km to Bedoin. Site adj to vill & sp. Med, sl, terr, shd; wc; shwrs inc; el pts (10A) €2.13; shops in vill; snacks; pool (high ssn); quiet; cc not acc; CCI. "Pool clsd Mon; office open 0900-1800; 5 min walk to vill & gd mkt on Mon; excel long stay." 1 Apr-30 Sep. € 13.50   2004*

MALAUCENE *10E2* (6km SE) **Domaine de Belezy** (Naturist), **84410 Bedoin** [04 90 65 60 18; fax 04 90 65 94 45; info@belezy.com; www.belezy. com] Fr Carpentras D974 to Bedoin, to top of vill rd; turn R on D974, turn L in 100m sp Domaine de Belezy, foll site sp in Bedoin; site on L in approx 1km. Lge, pt sl, shd; htd wc (some cont); chem disp; mv service pnt; sauna; steam rm; shwrs inc; el pts (12A) €4.20; gas; lndtte; shop; rest; snacks; bar; playgrnd; 2 htd pools; paddling pool; games area; horseriding 2km; golf 20km; internet; entmnt; child entmnt; 20% statics; no dogs; poss cr; quiet; adv bkg (dep req); Eng spkn; phone; red long stay; cc acc; CCI. "Delightful site; lovely location; extensive amenities; welcoming & peaceful; gd base for Mont Ventoux, Cotes du Rhone; INF card req; some sm & awkward pitches; excel." 20 Mar-2 Oct. € 32.50 (3 persons) (CChq acc)   2005*

MALAUCENE *10E2* (8km S Rural) **Camping Le Bouquier, Route de Malaucene, 84330 Caromb** [tel/fax 04 90 62 30 13; lebouquier@wanadoo.fr] NE fr Carpentras on D974 then D13; site on R 1.5km after Caromb cent. Fr Malaucene S on D938 for 8km; turn L D13 sp Caromb. Site 800m on L just bef vill. Med, hdg/mkd pitch, terr, pt shd, htd wc; chem disp; shwrs inc; el pts (10A) inc; lndtte; ice; shops 1.5km; tradsmn; snacks; playgrnd; pool; lake sw 1km; gd walking/cycling; 5% statics; dogs; phone; poss cr; adv bkg; some rd noise; CCI. "Well-kept site; attractive scenery; gd touring base; spotless san facs; steps to disabled facs; no twin-axle vans." ♦ 4 Apr-15 Oct. € 18.20   2005*

MALBUISSON *6H2* (S Urban) **Camping Les Fuvettes, 25160 Malbuisson** [03 81 69 31 50; fax 03 81 69 70 46; les-fuvettes@wanadoo.fr; www. camping-fuvettes.com] Site 19km S of Pontarlier on N57 & D437 to Malbuisson, thro town, R down rd to Plage. Lge, pt shd; htd wc (some cont); shwrs inc; el pts (4A) €3; gas; lndtte; ice; shop; rest; snacks; bar; playgrnd; shgl beach for lake sw; fishing; boating; 30% statics; poss cr; quiet; CCI. "Mkd walks/cycle paths in adj woods." 1 Apr-1 Oct. € 17.00   2005*

FRANCE

MALBUISSON *6H2* (2km S Rural) **Camping du Lac, 10 Rue du Lac, 25160 Labergement-Ste Marie** [03 81 69 31 24; camping.lac.remoray@wanadoo.fr; www.camping-lac-remoray.com] Exit N57/E23 junc 2 onto D437 thro vill & turn L onto D9 then R to site, sp. Site 300m fr Lake Remoray. Med, pt shd; wc; chem disp; mv service pnt; baby facs; shwrs inc; el pts (6A) €3; gas; lndtte; lndry rm; ice; rest; snacks; bar; playgrnd; beach adj; fishing; walking; cycling; sports area; internet; phone; adv bkg; Eng spkn; cc acc; CCI. "V kind & helpful owner; excel, roomy site; v clean san facs; vill 500m with gd shops; castles, museums nrby." ♦ 1 May-30 Sep. € 20.00   2004*

Mustn't forget to post our site report forms to The Club, otherwise sites might be deleted.

MALEMORT DU COMTAT see Carpentras *10E2*

†**MALESHERBES** *4E3* (5km S Rural) **Camping Ile de Boulancourt, 6 Allee des Marronniers, 77760 Boulancourt** [01 64 24 13 38; camping-ile-de-boulancourt@wanadoo.fr; www.camping-paris.com] Exit a'route A6 at junc 14 Ury & Fontainebleau. SW on N152 to Malesherbes; S on D410 for 5km into Boulancourt. Site sp fr D410 & in vill. Med, pt shd; htd wc (some cont); chem disp; shwrs €1; el pts (3-6A) €1.80; lndtte; ice; shop 3km; rest; BBQ; playgrnd; pool nr; tennis; rv adj; fishing 3km; waterslide 5km; 80% statics; dogs €1; sep field for tourers; Eng spkn; quiet; red low ssn; CCI. "V friendly, helpful staff; attractive rv thro site; golf course in vill; excel." € 11.60   2004*

MALESTROIT *2F3* (Urban) **Camp Municipal de la Daufresne, 56140 Malestroit** [02 97 75 13 33 or 02 97 75 11 75 (Mairie); fax 02 97 75 06 68] S fr Ploermel to Malestroit; site on N bank of Oust canal in town. Sm, hdg pitch, pt shd; wc; chem disp; shwrs; el pts (6A) €2.35; lndry rm; playgrnd; tennis; adv bkg; rv & fishing adj; CCI. "Vg; pleasant, peaceful site; spotless facs; v helpful warden; no twin-axle vans; facs stretched high ssn." 1 May-15 Sep. € 6.30   2005*

MALESTROIT *2F3* (8km S) **Camp Municipal de Halage, 56140 St Congard** [tel/fax 02 97 43 50 13] Exit N177 onto D10 dir Malestroit then St Congard on D764, site sp in vill. Sm, hdg pitch, pt shd; wc; chem disp; shwrs €1.70; el pts (6A) €1.40; gas; shop; playgrnd; fishing; boat hire; Eng spkn. "Adj Brest-Nantes canal; Parc de Prehistoire nrby." 15 Jun-15 Sep. € 4.00   2002*

MALICORNE SUR SARTHE *4F1* **Camp Municipal Porte Ste Marie, 72270 Malicorne-sur-Sarthe** [02 43 94 80 14; fax 02 43 94 57 26; mairie. malicorne@wanadoo.fr; www.ville-malicorne.fr] Fr A11/E501 take D306 exit twds la Fleche. Turn E onto D23 twds Malicorne. Site across rv on W of town adj stadium. Med, pt shd; wc; chem disp; mv service pnt, shwrs inc; el pts (4-12A) inc; lndtte; ice; shops 500m; rest 500m; bar; BBQ; playgrnd; pool; tennis adj; dogs €0.50; poss cr; quiet; red low ssn; "Quiet position by rv; gd san facs & lndry facs; no access when recep clsd 1230-1430 & after 1930; poss noise (church bell); no waiting area; diff turning; gd long/sh stay." 1 Apr-31 Oct. € 10.15
                                                        2004*

MALLEMORT see Salon de Provence *10E2*

MALLEYRAND see Rochefoucauld, La *7B2*

†**MAMERS** *4E1* (500m N Rural) **Camp Municipal La Grille, Route de Contilly, 72600 Mamers** [02 43 97 68 30; fax 02 43 97 38 65; camping. mamers@free.fr] Sp fr D311 (Alencon rd). Best app fr turn to N on N o'skts of town. Foll sp fr E app thro town bit tricky. Sm, hdg pitch, pt sl, terr, pt shd; htd wc; mv service pnt; shwrs inc; el pts (10A) €2.50 (long lead poss req); lndtte; shop & 500m; snacks; pool 200m; lakeside beach; games area; TV rm; 30% statics; dogs €0.50; poss cr; adv bkg; quiet; CCI. "Well-kept, secure site; admittance low ssn 1700-1900 only; Mamers pretty; poss itinerants." ♦ € 7.80   2005*

MANDEURE *6G3* (500m W Urban) **Camping Les Grands Ansanges, Rue de l'Eglise, 25350 Mandeure** [03 81 35 23 79; fax 03 81 30 09 26] Exit A36 sp Exincourt, site sp fr cent Mandeure. Med, mkd pitch, pt shd; wc; chem disp; shwrs inc; el pts (4-10A) €2.50-3.30; lndry rm; sm shop; tradsmn; rest; bar; playgrnd; games rm; archery & golf nrby; rv; 10% statics; poss cr; CCI. "Gd sh stay; faces open farmland; site barrier operated by token; helpful staff; not suitable disabled as san facs up step." 1 Apr-31 Oct. € 8.00   2002*

MANDRES AUX QUATRE TOURS *5D2* (1.5km) **Camp Municipal, Route Foret de la Reine, 54470 Mandres-aux-Quatre-Tours** [03 83 23 17 31] On D958 Commercy to Pont-a-Mousson, sp as Camping Mandres. Turn R at sp in Beaumont & foll sp to vill Mandres-aux-Quatre-Tours. Sm, mkd pitch, pt shd; wc; shwrs inc; el pts (10A) €1.30; ice; tradsmn; playgrnd; tennis; mini-golf; watersports; sailing 500m; horseriding adj; quiet; some statics; CCI. "Gd NH; lovely scenery nr Lac de Madine; warden 0800-1000 & 1800-2000; clean facs but need update; peaceful site; gd birdwatching, walking, cycling; site poss muddy in wet weather." 1 Apr-31 Oct. € 6.02   2004*

MANOSQUE *10E3* (1.5km) **FFCC Camping Les Ubacs, Ave de la Repasse, 04100 Manosque** [04 92 72 28 08; fax 04 92 87 75 29] Sp fr D207 dir Apt. Med, pt shd; wc; serviced pitches; shwrs; el pts (3-9A) inc; lndtte; shop; rest in ssn; playgrnd; pool; tennis; lake sw 5km; entmnt; dogs €1; cc acc; red long stay/CCI. 1 Apr-30 Sep. € 14.00   2002*

MANOSQUE *10E3* (8.5km NE) **Camp Municipal de la Vandelle, Chemin de Pietramal, 04130 Volx** [04 92 79 35 85 or 04 92 70 18 00; fax 04 92 79 32 27] Fr N96 (Aix-Sisteron) turn W at traff lts in Volx, foll sp to site in 1km. Sm, pt sl, terr, pt shd; wc; shwrs inc; el pts (3A) inc; lndtte; shops 1.3km; sm pool; adv bkg; quiet. ♦ 1 Jun-30 Sep. € 14.50   2003*

As we're travelling out of season, we'd better phone ahead to check that the site is actually open.

MANS, LE *4F1* (9km N Rural) **Camping Le Vieux Moulin, 72190 Neuville-sur-Sarthe** [02 43 25 31 82; fax 02 43 25 38 11; vieux.moulin@wanadoo.fr] Leave N138 6km N of Le Mans at St Saturin; turn E onto D197 to Neuville & foll sp for 3km to site. Med, pt shd, hdg/mkd pitch, serviced pitch; wc (some cont); chem disp; mv service pnt; baby facs; shwrs inc; el pts (10A) €3 (poss rev pol); gas; lndtte; sm shop (high ssn) & 500m; tradsmn; rest adj; playgrnd; sm htd pool; tennis; mini-golf; 5% statics; dogs €1; Eng spkn; adv bkg; quiet; 20% red low ssn; cc acc; 5-10% red CCI. "Lge, well-grassed pitches; friendly, helpful owner; sm lake & water-mill adj; 5 mins walk to Rv Sarthe; peaceful setting; gd simple hotel rest in vill; highly rec; san facs clean but need updating ; gates clsd 2200-0730; new British owner in 2004 - phone to check opening dates, prices etc; gd sh stay/NH." 1 Jul-31 Aug. € 11.00   2004*

MANSIGNE *4F1* **Camp Municipal de la Plage, 72510 Mansigne** [02 43 46 14 17 or 02 43 46 10 33 (Mairie); fax 02 43 46 16 65; campingmansigne@wanadoo.fr] N fr Le Lude on D307 to Pontvallain. Take D13 E for 5km to Mansigne, thro vill & foll site sp. Lge, pt shd; wc; chem disp; shwrs inc; el pts (10A) inc; lndtte; shop 200m; rest; pool; sand beach adj; lake sw adj; dogs €1.22; adv bkg; quiet; red long stay; CCI. "Conv for Loir Valley & Le Mans 24-hour race; v ltd facs & office hrs low ssn." ♦ Easter-1 Oct. € 11.70
                    2004*

MANSIGNE *4F1* (5km W) **Camp Municipal du Moulin de St Jean, 72510 St Jean-de-la-Motte** [02 43 45 45 66 (Mairie); fax 02 43 45 78 17] Fr N23 Le Mans to La Fleche rd foll sps to St Jean-de-la-Motte, & camping sps to site on D54 SW of vill. Sm, pt shd; wc; shwrs inc; el pts (4A) €1.20; shop 800m; pool 5km; lake sw, fishing, watersports 7km; quiet; CCI. "Site yourself." ♦ 1 Jun-1 Sep. € 5.15   2003*

MANSLE *7B2* (NE Urban) **Camp Municipal Le Champion, 16230 Mansle** [05 45 20 31 41 or 05 45 22 20 43; fax 05 45 22 86 30; mairie. mansle@wanadoo.fr] N on N10 fr Angouleme, foll sp Mansle Ville. Leave N10 at exit to N of town. Rec ent/leave fr N as rte thro town now diff due to parked cars on main rd making access fr S v hazardous, then site rd on L, well sp. Med, hdg pitch, pt shd; wc; chem disp; mv service pnt; shwrs inc; el pts (16A) inc; gas in town; lndtte; shops 200m; shop 800m; rest; snacks, bar adj; BBQ; playgrnd; rv sw & boating adj; fishing; mini-golf; entmnt; 5% statics; phone; poss cr; quiet but some rd noise; adv bkg; phone 1km; Eng spkn; cc not acc; CCI. "Beside Rv Charente; well-maintained; immac san facs; excel for quiet, restful hols; choose own pitch; gd rest & bar adj; sm provision mkt Tues, Fri am; popular NH nr N10; excel long stay." ♦ 15 May-15 Sep. € 13.00
                    2004*

MANSLE *7B2* (8km NE Rural) **Camp Municipal Le Magnerit, Les Maisons Rouges, 16460 Aunac** [05 45 22 24 38; fax 05 45 22 23 17] N on N10 fr Mansle, exit onto D27 to Bayers & Aunac. Site 1km SE vill, well sp. Sm, pt shd; wc; chem disp; shwrs; el pts (8A) €1.50; shop 1km; playgrnd; rv sw adj; fishing; quiet; CCI. "Warden visits; peaceful CL-type site beside Rv Charente; facs ltd but v clean & well-kept; quiet, simple, rural site; vg NH." 15 Jun-15 Sep. € 6.50   2005*

MANSLE *7B2* (10km SE Rural) **Camping Devezeau, 16230 St Angeau** [tel/fax 05 45 39 21 29; bookings@campingdevezeau. com; www.devezeaucamping.com] N or S on N10 exit Mansle; in cent vill at traff lts foll sp twd La Rochefoucauld (D6); past Champion supmkt; over bdge; 1st R onto D6. In approx 9km at T-junc turn R, site sp. App down narr rd. Sm, hdstg, pt sl, pt shd; wc; chem disp; 20% serviced pitches; shwrs inc; el pts (10A) inc; ice; gas; lndtte; shop 1.5km; tradsmn; supmkt in Mansle; rest 5km; snacks & bar 1.5km; BBQ; playgrnd; htd pool; cycling; walking; canoeing; golf 20 mins; fishing; horseriding; 10% statics; no dogs; phone 1km; Eng spkn; adv bkg (dep req); quiet; CCI. "Excel CL-type site; facs exceptionally clean; poss electrics probs; v friendly British owners; traction diff in wet (4WD avail); gd cycling country." ♦ ltd. 1 Feb-30 Nov. € 15.00   2005*

MANTENAY MONTLIN *9A2* (400m W Rural) **Camp Municipal du Coq, 01560 Mantenay-Montlin** [04 74 52 66 91or 04 74 52 61 72 (Mairie)] Exit A40 junc 5 Bourg-en-Bresse Nord onto D975 to Mantenay-Montlin; site sp in vill on D46. Or exit A39 junc 10 to St Thivier-de-Courtes, then S to Mantenay. Sm, hdg/mkd pitch, pt shd; wc; chem disp; shwrs inc; el pts (6A) €1.70; shop, rest & bar 400m; playgrnd; tennis; bus 400m; quiet; red long stay; cc acc. "Vg site in pretty area; quiet rvside site; san facs old but clean; warden calls pm; lge pitches." 1 Jun-15 Sep. € 7.50   2005*

Camping ★★★ Loisirs des Groux

78270 Mousseaux sur Seine
Phone: 00 33 (0)1 34 79 33 86

45 minutes from Paris by A13 : visit of the capital and the Palace of Versailles.

45 minutes from Rouen by A13 : visit of "the town of 100 bell-towers".

15 minutes from Giverny : the road of the impressionists — Monet museum.

At 500 meters : leisure park close to pool and golf 18 holes.

E-mail: infos@loisirsdesgroux.com

MANTES *3D2* (12km NW Rural) **Camping Loisirs des Groux, Chemin de Vetheuil, 78270 Mousseaux-sur-Seine** [01 34 79 33 86; infos@loisirsdesgroux.com; www.loisirsdesgroux.com] Fr Rouen exit A13 junc 15 onto N13 dir Bonnieres. At x-rds with N15 (offset junc) turn R, then L dir Bonnieres. Cont thro Bonnieres & past commercial cent dir Rolleboise. Turn L at next traff lts onto D37 sp Parc de Loisirs & strt at rndabt onto D124/D125 dir Mousseaux. Strt at x-rds, site sp at next R. Fr Paris exit A13 junc 13 onto N13 dir Bonnieres, N fr Rolleboise on N13 dir Mousseaux, turn R at traff lts onto D37, then as above. Med, hdg/mkd pitch, pt shd; wc (some cont); shwrs inc; mv service pnt; chem disp; el pts (6A) €1.90; lndtte; BBQ; pool, leisure cent 500m; dir access to Rv Seine; lake sw & beach 500m; games area; entmnt; 90% statics; dogs; Eng spkn; adv bkg rec; v quiet; CCI. "Conv Paris (65km), Versailles, Rouen, Monet's garden at Giverny; basic, well-maintained san facs; gates locked at 2130 - given key for late entry; friendly, helpful staff; poss noisy youth groups; excel walks or cycling along the Seine; adv bkg rec high ssn; ltd touring pitches." ♦ 1 Apr-30 Nov. € 14.20   2005*

See advertisement above

---

†**MANTES** *3D2* (14km NW) **Camping Le Criquet, 78840 Freneuse** [tel/fax 01 30 93 07 95] Fr N15 at Bonnieres to Freneuse on D37. Thro vill, site sp at end of vill past cemetary. Lge, pt shd; wc; chem disp; shwrs €1.90; el pts (10A) €2.70; BBQ; playgrnd; games area; mainly statics; adv bkg; quiet. "Monet's garden 12km; pitches poss unkempt low ssn." € 11.00   2005*

MARANS *7A1* (Urban) **Camp Municipal Le Bois Dinot, Route de Nantes, 17230 Marans** [tel/fax 05 46 01 10 51; campingboisdinot.marans@wanadoo.fr] Heading S, site on L of N137 on ent Marans. Heading N, site is well sp on R 300m after supmkt on L. Lge, shd; wc; shwrs inc; el pts (10A) €2.70; shops adj; rest, snacks, bar 200m; pool adj; fishing; dogs €0.85; Eng spkn; poss cr; some rd noise; red 10% low ssn; CCI. "V clean well-kept site; quieter pitches at back of site; gd cycling area; helpful warden; recep open 1000-1300 & 1500-2000; gd sh stay/NH." 1 May-30 Sep. € 9.40   2005*

MARANS *7A1* (10km W Rural) **Camp Municipal Les Pres de Charron, 17230 Charron** [05 46 01 50 22] Fr N137 take D105 E, cross D9 & foll camp sp to site. Sm, mkd pitch, unshd; wc; shwrs inc; el pts (10A) €1.50; lndry rm; shops, rest, bar 1km; playgrnd; quiet. "Vg NH." ♦ 15 Jun-15 Sep. € 6.90   2004*

> We're having a great holiday - must fill in some site report forms and send them to The Club as soon as possible.

MARCENAY *6F1* (Rural) **Camping Les Grebes, 21300 Marcenay** [03 80 81 61 72 or 03 80 81 43 03 (Mairie); fax 03 80 81 61 99] On D965 bet Laignes & Chatillon-sur-Seine. Fr Chatillon sp on R 8km after vill of Cerilly. Foll sp to lake & camp. Med, pt shd; wc; chem disp; shwrs inc; el pts (10A) €2.75; lndtte; shop; snacks; playgrnd; fishing; golf; horseriding; watersports; TV rm; adv bkg rec; quiet; CCI. "Well-run, pleasant site in Burgundy area; excel value; recep clsd 1200-1500; well worth finding; Chatillon museum & Abbey de Fontenay outstanding." 1 Apr-15 Sep. € 8.90   2005*

MARCHAINVILLE *4E2* (N Rural) **Camp Municipal Les Fosses, 61290 Marchainville** [02 33 73 69 65 or 02 33 73 65 80 (Mairie); fax 02 33 73 65 80] Fr Verneuil-sur-Avre take D941 S to La Ferte-Vidame & at start of town turn R onto D4/D11 SW to Marchainville; site sp at x-rds in vill on D243. Sm, hdg/mkd pitch, pt sl, pt shd; wc; shwrs; el pts (10A) €2.20; shop, rest, snacks, bar 8km; tennis; no statics; phone; adv bkg; quiet; CCI. "Warden visits." ♦ ltd. 1 Apr-30 Oct. € 9.70   2005*

MARCIAC *8F2* (1.5km NW Rural) **Camping du Lac, 32230 Marciac [tel/fax 05 62 08 21 19; camping.marciac@wanadoo.fr; www.camping-marciac.com]** E fr Maubourguet take D943 to Marciac. Take D3 to lake dir Plaisance. At lake turn R & R again at sp. Site on L in 200m. Fr N exit A62 at junc 3 & foll D932 sp Pau to Aire-sur- Adour then E on D935 & D3 & foll sp. Med, mkd pitch, some hdstg, pt shd; wc chem disp; mv service pnt (also avail to m'vans not staying on site); baby facs; shwrs inc; el pts (6A) inc; gas; lndtte; ice; shop & 800m; rest 300m; snacks; bar; BBQ; playgrnd; pool; lake adj; internet; 8% statics; dogs €1.50; phone; adv bkg (dep req); red long stay/low ssn; cc acc; CCI. "Friendly British owners improving the site; lge pitches with easy access; interesting old town; picturesque area; busy for jazz festival 1st 2 weeks in Aug." ♦ 15 Mar-30 Oct. € 20.50   2005*

MARCIGNY *9A1* (7km W) **Camping La Motte aux Merles, 71110 Artaix-par-Marcigny [03 85 25 19 84]** Leave D982 (Digoin-Roanne) at Marcigny by-pass. Take D989 twd Lapalisse. In 2km at Chambilly cont on D990, site sp in 5km on L 200m down side rd. Sm, pt sl, pt shd; wc; shwrs; el pts €2.40; lndry rm; snacks; pool (high ssn); playgrnd; fishing; tennis; golf nrby; rec. "Peaceful area; v friendly owners; gd sightseeing in area; excel." ♦ 1 Apr-15 Oct. € 10.00   2004*

MARCILLAC LA CROISSILLE *7C4* (2km SW Rural) **Camp Municipal Le Lac, Route du Viaduc, 19320 Marcillac-la-Croisille [tel/fax 05 55 27 81 38 or 05 55 27 82 05 (Mairie)]** S fr Egletons on D16 & D18. Site sp at S end of vill at intersection with D978. Lge, pt sl, shd, wc; shwrs; el pts (6A) inc; lndtte; ice; shops 2km; snacks; playgrnd; lake & sand beach adj; tennis adj; entmnt; TV; dogs €0.80; adv bkg; quiet; red low ssn. 1 Jun-1 Oct. € 12.30   2003*

MARCILLAC ST QUENTIN see Sarlat la Caneda *7C3*

MARCON see Chateau du Loir *4G1*

MARENNES *7B1* (5km SE Rural) **LES CASTELS Sequoia Parc, La Josephtrie, 17320 St Just-Luzac [05 46 85 55 55; fax 05 46 85 55 56; sequoia.parc@wanadoo.fr; www.sequoiaparc.com or www. les-castels.com]** Fr A10/E05 m'way exit at Saintes foll sp Royan (N150) turning off onto D728 twd Marennes. Take 2nd sp to site after St Just-Luzac; sp on L. Or fr Rochefort take D733 & D123 S; just bef Marennes turn L on D241 sp St Just-Luzac. Lge, hdg/mkd pitch, sl, unshd; wc; chem disp; mv service pnt; baby facs; shwrs inc; el pts (6A) inc; gas; lndtte; shop; rest; snacks; bar; BBQ; playgrnd; pool complex; paddling pool; waterslide; sand beach 5km; fishing; watersports 5km; tennis; cycle hire; games area; games rm; entmnt; child entmnt; internet; TV rm; internet; 60% statics (tour ops); dogs €5; recep 0830-2000 high ssn; card op barrier, dep €10 req, clsd 2230; exchange bureau; adv bkg (dep req + bkg fee); poss noisy; cc acc; red long stay/low ssn; CCI. "Excel free club for children; nice, lge pitches; clean san facs; superb pools; wonderful flowers; excursions to Cognac." ♦ 13 May-10 Sep. € 37.00 (CChq acc) ABS - A28   2005*

See advertisement above

MARENNES *7B1* (2km NW Coastal) **Camp Municipal La Giroflee, 17560 Bourcefranc-le-Chapus [05 46 85 06 43 or 05 46 85 02 02 (Mairie); fax 05 46 85 48 58; camping-lagiroflee-bourcefranc@mairie17.com]** Fr S on D26, 2km after junc with rd marked 'Royan par La Cote', turn N at traff lts. Site on L after 1km (after sailing school) opp beach. Med, pt shd; wc (few cont); shwrs €0.80; el pts (8A) €2.65; lndry rm; shops 2km; snacks; playgrnd; beach adj; poss cr; quiet. 1 May-30 Sep. € 6.65   2005*

MAREUIL *7B2* (5km N Rural) **Camping Les Graulges**, Le Bourg, 24340 Les Graulges [tel/fax 05 53 60 74 73; info@lesgraulges.com] Fr D939 at Mareuil turn L onto D708 & foll sp to Les Graulges in 5km. Sm, mkd pitch, pt sl, terr, pt shd; wc; chem disp (wc); baby facs; shwrs inc; el pts (6A) €3; lndtte; ice; tradsmn; rest; snacks; bar; BBQ; playgrnd; pool; fishing; dogs €2; phone 300m; poss cr; Eng spkn; adv bkg (dep req); quiet; red 7+ days. "Tranquil site in forested area; superb fishing in lge lake on site; ideal touring base; friendly Dutch owners; excel rest; excel." ♦ 1 Apr-15 Sep. € 13.75 2005*

MAREUIL *7B2* (5km NE) **Camping Corneuil**, 24340 St Sulpice-de-Mareuil [05 53 60 79 48; fax 05 53 60 79 47; campingcorneuil@wanadoo.fr; www.corneuil.com] Fr Brantome on D939 to Mareuil, turn R onto D708, site in L. Or S fr Nontron on D675/708, thro St Sulpice, site 3km on R, site sp on D708. Med, mkd pitch, terr, pt shd; wc; chem disp; shwrs inc; el pts (8A) €3; lndtte; shop; rest; snacks; bar; playgrnd; pool; dogs €2; poss cr; adv bkg rec; quiet; red low ssn/red CCI. "Vg san facs; vg NH/sh stay." 14 May-11 Sep. € 22.00 2004*

MAREUIL *7B2* (4km SE) **Camping L'Etang Bleu**, 24340 Vieux-Mareuil [05 53 60 92 70; fax 05 53 56 66 66; marc@letangbleu.com; www. letangbleu.com] On D939 Angouleme-Perigueux rd, after 5km turn L cent of Vieux-Mareuil onto D93, foll camping sp to site in 2km. Narr app thro vill. Lge, hdg/mkd pitch, pt shd; wc; chem disp; mv service pnt; baby facs; fam bthrm; shwrs inc; el pts (10A) inc; gas; lndtte; ice; shop; tradsmn; rest; snacks; bar; BBQ; playgrnd; pool; paddling pool; lake fishing 500m; TV; entmnt; 10% statics; dogs €3; phone; adv bkg €25 dep reqd; 30% red low ssn; cc acc; CCI. "Lovely site in beautiful, unspoilt countryside; v pleasant; gd for lge o'fits; friendly British owners; gd san facs; excel." ♦ 1 Apr-10 Oct. € 22.50 2005*

†**MAREUIL** *7B2* (6km SE Rural) **Camping La Charrue**, Les Chambarrieres, 24340 Vieux- Mareuil [tel/fax 05 53 56 65 59; info@la-charruefrance.com; www.la-charruefrance.com] SE fr Angouleme on D939 sp Perigueux to Mareuil. Fr Mareuil stay on D939 twds Brantome, thro Vieux-Mareuil then in 2km site immed on L after passing a lge lay-by on R with white stone chippings. Awkward turn. Sm, mkd pitch, pt shd; wc; chem disp; shwrs inc; el pts (4A) €3.40; gas 3km; lndtte; shop 2km; tradsmn; rest & bar 500m; snacks; BBQ; playgrnd; pool; sand beach, lakes & watersports nr; fishing 3km; cycle hire; bowls; table-tennis; dogs (low ssn); adv bkg (full payment req); some rd noise; 10% red +14 days; CCI. "CL-type site; nr many chateaux; v friendly British owners; vg rest; golf, walking nr; B&B & gites avail; excel." € 13.30 2005*

MAREUIL *7B2* (500m SW) **Camp Municipal Vieux Moulin**, 24340 Mareuil [05 53 60 91 20 (Mairie) or 05 53 60 99 80; fax 05 53 60 51 72] Fr town cent take D708 (sp Riberac); after 300m turn L on D99 (sp 'La Tour Blanche'); after 100m turn L opp lge school, site 100m ahead. Sm, mkd pitch, shd; wc; shwrs; el pts (5A) €1.50; shops, rest, snacks, bar 500m; playgrnd; rv 1km; adv bkg; quiet. "Friendly warden; interesting chateau in vill; vg." ♦ 1 Jun-30 Sep. € 8.00 2004*

MARIGNY see Doucier *6H2*

MARNAVES see Cordes *8E4*

MARNAY (HAUTE SAONE) *6G2* (500m SE Urban) **Camp Municipal, Route de Besancon**, 70150 Marnay [03 84 31 71 41 or 03 84 31 73 16; sidmarnay@wanadoo.fr] Fr N stay on D67 Marnay by-pass; ignore old camping sp into town. Proceed to S of town on by-pass then turn L at junc. Bef bdge in 1km take gravel rd on S side, round under bdge to site (app thro town fr N v narr). After heavy rain access to site under rd bdge imposs due rv flooding. Use slip rd at vill end of bdge but fr dir of vill only (turn fr opp dir too acute & nr dangerous corner). Med, pt shd; wc (some cont); shwrs inc; el pts (3-5A) inc; shops 500m; snacks; BBQ; fishing; canoeing; 20% statics; adv bkg; quiet. "Tree-top walks." 1 May-30 Sep. € 11.50 2005*

MARNAY (SAONE ET LOIRE) see Chalon sur Saone *6H1*

MARQUISE *3A3* (4km S) **Camping L'Escale**, 62250 Wacquinghen [tel/fax 03 21 32 00 69] Fr A15 S fr Calais exit junc 34. Fr A15 N fr Boulogne exit junc 33. Foll sp. Lge, shd; wc (cont); shwrs €1; el pts (10A) €3.20; gas; lndtte; shop; supmkt 3km; rest; snacks; bar; playgrnd; 90% statics; dogs; poss cr; quiet; cc acc. "Open 24 hrs; conv WW2 coastal defences; conv NH; o'fits staying 1 night pitch in front of site for ease of exit; card barrier; vg." ♦ 15 Mar-15 Oct. € 14.80 2005*

MARSAC EN LIVRADOIS see Ambert *9B1*

MARSEILLAN PLAGE *10F1* (Coastal/Urban) **Camping Beauregard-Est, Chemin de l'Airette**, 34340 Marseillan-Plage [04 67 77 15 45; fax 04 67 01 21 78; campingbeauregardest@ wanadoo.fr] On N112 Agde-Sete rd, turn S at rndabt to Marseillan-Plage onto D51 & foll camping sp thro town. Site immed on leaving town cent. Lge, hdg pitch, pt shd; wc; chem disp; mv service pnt; baby facs; shwrs inc; el pts (6A) inc; lndtte; shop, rest, snacks, bar adj; playgrnd; sand beach adj; entmnt; TV; 5% statics; no dogs; Eng spkn; adv bkg; poss cr; quiet. "Superb sand beach sheltered by dunes." ♦ Easter-30 Sep. € 27.50 2005*

MARSEILLAN PLAGE *10F1* (Coastal) **Camping La Nouvelle Floride, 34340 Marseillan Plage** [04 67 21 94 49; fax 04 67 21 81 05; nouvelle-floride@wanadoo.fr; www.nouvelle-floride.com & www.homair-vacances.fr] Exit a'route A9 sp Agde & Bessan foll sps to site. Turn R at traff lts in Marseillan-Plage, site 1.5km. Lge, shd; wc; mv service pnt; shwrs inc; baby facs; el pts (6A) inc; gas; lndtte; ice; supmkt; rest; snacks; bar; playgrnd; htd pool; waterslide; sand beach adj; games area; horseriding; entmnt; child entmnt; 10% statics; dogs €3.50; adv bkg; quiet; red long stay/low ssn; cc acc; CCI. "Excel family site." ♦
3 Apr-25 Sep. € 38.00 (3 persons)   2003*

MARSEILLAN PLAGE *10F1* (Coastal) **Camping Le Charlemagne, Ave des Campings, 34340 Marseillan-Plage** [04 67 21 92 49; fax 04 67 21 86 11; charlemagnecamping@wanadoo.fr; www.charlemagne-camping.com] In Marseillan-Plage, off N112 Sete-Agde rd, take D51e SW to site. Lge, hdg/mkd pitch, shd; wc; chem disp; mv service pnt; baby facs; shwrs inc; el pts (6A) inc; shop; lndtte; rest; snacks; bar; playgrnd; 3 htd pools; waterslide; sand beach 200m; games area; golf 5km; entmnt; 50% statics; dogs €3.50; phone; poss cr; Eng spkn; adv bkg (dep & bkg fee); red low ssn for 14+ days; quiet. "Site also owns Nouvelle Floride opp on beach of similar standard; lge pitches; lots of shops, rests nrby; many tour operators; poss mosquitoes; excel." ♦
Easter-23 Sep. € 41.00 (3 persons) (CChq acc)
                                          2004*

MARSEILLAN PLAGE *10F1* (500m) **Camping La Plage, 69 Chemin du Pairollet, 34340 Marseillan Plage** [04 67 21 92 54; fax 04 67 01 63 57; contact@laplage-camping.com; www.laplage-camping.com] On N112 Agde to Sete, turn S at rndabt dir Marseillan Plage onto D51. Foll sp for site. At 2nd rndabt, take 3rd exit. Site on L in 150m. Med, hdg pitch, pt shd; wc; chem disp; shwrs inc; child/baby facs; el pts (10A) €2; gas; lndtte; ice; rest; snacks; bar; BBQ; playgrnd; sand beach adj; watersports; games area; entmnt; TV in bar; 1% statics; dogs €3; phone; poss cr; Eng spkn; adv bkg (dep req+bkg fee); quiet; cc acc, CCI. "Excel family-run site; superb beach; v popular with gd, friendly atmosphere." ♦ 15 Mar-31 Oct. € 24.00
                                          2003*

MARSEILLAN PLAGE *10F1* (1km NE Coastal) **Camping Le Paradou, 2 Impasse Ronsard, 34340 Marseillan-Plage** [04 67 21 90 10; info.paradou@wanadoo.fr; www.paradou.com] Fr Beziers on N12 dir Agde & Sete, 3.5km after Agde turn R 300m after bdge, then L to site. Site well sp on N12. Med, hdg pitch, pt shd; wc; chem disp; shwrs inc; el pts (10A) €2.80; lndtte; ice; shop 1km; tradsmn; rest, bar 1km; snacks; playgrnd; dir access sand beach adj; 5% statics; dogs; phone; bus 500m; poss cr; CCI. "Gd area for cycling; vg long/sh stay/NH." ♦ ltd.
1 Apr-15 Nov. € 18.00   2003*

MARSEILLAN PLAGE *10F1* (SW Coastal) **Camping La Creole, 74 Ave des Campings, 34340 Marseillan-Plage** [04 67 21 92 69; fax 04 67 26 58 16; campinglacreole@wanadoo.fr; www.campinglacreole.com] Fr Agde-Sete rd N112, turn S at rndabt onto D51 & foll sp thro town. Narr ent easily missed among lger sites. Med, hdg/mkd pitch, hdstg, pt shd; wc; chem disp; mv service pnt; baby facs; shwrs inc; el pts (6A) €2.60; lndtte; shop; rest, snacks, bar adj; playgrnd; sand beach adj; tennis 1km; games area; entmnt; 10% statics; dogs €2; phone; adv bkg; quiet; red long stay; CCI. "Dir access to excel beach; naturist beach 600m; well-maintained, quiet site." ♦ 4 Apr-10 Oct.
€ 24.00   2004*

MARSEILLAN PLAGE *10F1* (SW Coastal) **Languedoc Camping, 117 Chemin du Pairollet, 34340 Marseillan-Plage** [04 67 21 92 55; fax 04 67 01 63 75; languedoc.camping.fr@wanadoo.fr] On N112 Agde-Sete rd, turn S at rndabt to Marseillan-Plage onto D51 & foll Camping sp thro town. At 2nd rndabt take 3rd exit & site 100m on L. Med, hdg/mkd pitch, .pt shd; wc; chem disp; mv service pnt; baby facs; shwrs inc; el pts (10A) inc; lndtte; shop; rest; snacks; bar; playgrnd; sand beach adj; dogs €3.50; poss cr; Eng spkn; adv bkg ess; quiet; CCI; "V helpful staff; dir access to excel sandy beach." ♦
1 Mar-31 Oct. € 34.00 (3 persons)   2005*

MARSEILLAN PLAGE *10F1* (500m SW Coastal) **Camping Europ 2000, 960 Ave des Campings, 34340 Marseillan-Plage** [tel/fax 04 67 21 92 85; contact@camping-europ2000.com; www.camping-europ2000.com] Fr cent of Marseillan-Plage S on coast rd, site on L. Med, hdg/mkd pitch, hdstg, pt shd; wc; chem disp; mv service pnt; shwrs inc; el pts (10A) €3.50; gas; lndtte; shop & 500m; tradsmn; snacks; BBQ; playgrnd; sand beach adj; games area; 10% statics; dogs €2; phone; poss cr; Eng spkn; adv bkg; quiet; red low ssn CCI. "Easy access to beach; v friendly, helpful owner; gd value, family-run site." ♦ 1 Apr-20 Oct. € 20.50   2005*

MARTEL *7C3* (5km SE) **Camping du Port, 46600 Creysse** [05 65 32 20 82 or 05 65 32 27 59; fax 05 65 38 78 21; circal@wanadoo.fr] To Martel take D703 to Martel. On ent Martel turn R on D23 on rd to Creysee. Alt app via N140 fr Cressensac to Martel. Site sp. Narr, twisty rd fr Gluges. Med, pt sl, pt shd by rv; wc (some cont); shwrs inc; el pts (5A); ice; lndtte; shops in Martel; rest in Creysse; pool; playgrnd; canoe hire; adv bkg; quiet. 1 May-30 Sep.
                                          2002*

MARTEL *7C3* (500m NW) **Camp Municipal de la Callopie, Ave de Turenne, 46600 Martel** [05 65 37 30 03 (Mairie); fax 05 65 37 37 27] On NW o'skts of vill of Martel on D23, 100m fr rndabt on L, ent opp Auberge des 7 Tours. Sm, shd; wc; shwrs inc; el pts (10A) €1.60; shops, rest, bar 200m; rv 5km; no statics; poss cr; no adv bkg; rd noise. "Attractive site in beautiful medieval vill; facs ltd & tired; site unattended, warden calls or pay at Mairie; gd meals at auberge." 15 Jun-15 Sep.
€ 6.80   2005*

FRANCE

MARTIEL see Villefranche de Rouergue *7D4*

MARTIGNE FERCHAUD *2F4* (NE Rural) **Camp Municipal Le Bois Feuillet, 35640 Martigne-Ferchaud [02 99 47 84 38; fax 02 99 47 84 65]** After ent Martigne-Ferchaud on E of D178; fr N cross level x-ing, site on L in 400m; fr S, thro vill, site on R after bend at bottom of hill. Site sp fr town cent. Med, terr, unshd; wc; chem disp; shwrs inc; el pts (16A) €2; lndtte; ice; shop adj; rest, snacks, bar 1km; BBQ; playgrnd; lake sw with sm shgl beach; fishing & boating; sports area; tennis; quiet; CCI. "Attractive site beside picturesque lake; lovely position; in June & Sep barrier opened at 0900 & 1900 - foll instructions in Eng on office door or report to town hall to gain ent (parking diff); lge pitches; gd san facs; 2nd week Aug excel water spectacular; vg sh stay." ♦ 1 Jun-30 Sep. € 8.50   2004*

MARTIGUES *10F2* (8km S Coastal) **Camping L'Arquet, Chemin de la Batterie, 13500 Martigues [04 42 42 81 00 or 04 42 44 34 00 (LS); fax 04 42 42 34 50; arquet@semovim-martigues. com; www.semovim-martigues.com]** Exit A55 at Martigues Sud exit for D5 dir Sausset & Carro. In 4km turn R onto rd to La Couronne. Pass under dual c'way. On main rd turn L at church & foll camp sp. Lge, pt shd; wc (cont); chem disp; shwrs; el pts inc; lndtte; shops 1km; lndtte; playgrnd; sand beach 300m; tennis nr; fishing; boating; diving; cycling; dogs €2.50; adv bkg; quiet. ♦ 6 Mar-30 Sep. € 21.65   2004*

MARTRAGNY see Bayeux *3D1*

MARTRES DE VEYRE, LES see Clermont Ferrand *9B1*

MARTRES TOLOSANE *8F3* (2km E) **Camp Intercommunal Le Plantaurel, 31220 Palaminy [05 61 97 03 71; fax 05 61 90 62 04]** Exit a'route A64 at junc 23 onto D6 to Cazares, cross rv bdge. Turn W (R) on D62, foll rv for 1.5km. Site well sp, Lge, shd; wc; chem disp; shwrs inc; el pts (10A) inc; gas; ice; BBQ; lndry rm; shop & 2km; snacks; pool; playgrnd; TV; entmnt; many statics; phone; dir access to rv; dogs €0.91; adv bkg; red long stay; CCI. "Poss itinerants; poss noisy; could be better maintained." € 16.77 (4 persons)   2005*

MARTRES TOLOSANE *8F3* (1.5km S Rural) **Camping Le Moulin, 31220 Martres-Tolosane [05 61 98 86 40; fax 05 61 98 66 90; info@ campinglemoulin.com; www.campinglemoulin. com]** Exit A64 junc 21 or 22, site sp adj Rv Garonne. Med, pt sl, pt shd; htd wc (some cont); baby facs; shwrs inc; el pts (6-10A) inc; lndtte; shops 1.5km; snacks; bar; playgrnd; pool; paddling pool; tennis; cycle hire; rv fishing adj; games area; games rm; entmnt; TV; 20% statics; dogs €1.50; adv bkg rec high ssn; quiet; red long stay; 20% red low ssn; cc acc; CCI. "Excel new san facs; well maintained site." 15 Apr-30 Sep. € 21.00   2005*

MARTRES TOLOSANE *8F3* (7km SW Rural) **Camp Municipal, 31360 St Martory [05 61 90 44 93 or 05 61 90 22 24]** Leave A64 at junc 20. Turn R onto D117 twd St Martory. In 1km turn L (sp) soon after Gendarmerie. Sm, hdg pitch, pt shd; htd wc (some cont); chem disp (wc); shwrs inc; el pts inc; no dogs; quiet; CCI. ♦ 15 Jun-15 Sep. € 9.00   2003*

MARVAL *7B3* (3.5km N Rural) **Camping La Nozilliere, L'Age Milhaguet, 87440 Marval [05 55 57 82 56; adriaan-von-bekkum@wanadoo. fr]** Fr Marval N D67 sp Milhaguet; take D73 to St Barhelemy, turn L in 500m, site sp. Sm, pt sl, pt shd; wc; chem disp; shwrs inc; el pts (6A) inc; gas 3.5km; ice; BBQ; tradsmn; rest, snacks, bar, shops 3.5km; playgrnd; htd pool 7km; sw lake 3km; dogs; quiet; adv bkg (dep req); Eng spkn; cc acc; CCI. "Excel all stays; table d'hote meals avail." ♦ 1 May-31 Oct. € 15.00   2002*

MARVEJOLS *9D1* (1km NE) **Camp Municipal L'Europe, 48100 Marvejols [04 66 32 03 69 or 04 66 32 00 45 (Mairie); fax 04 66 32 43 56]** Exit A75 junc 38 onto D900 & N9. Foll E ring rd onto D999, cont over rv & foll sp to site; no R turn into site, cont 500m to Aire de Retournement, & turn L into site. Med, hdg pitch, pt shd; wc (mainly cont); shwrs inc; el pts (5A) €3.50 (poss rev pol); lndtte; shop & 1km; playgrnd; pool 1km; TV rm; phone; poss cr; adv bkg; quiet. "Interesting walled town; vg sh stay." ♦ 15 May-15 Sep. € 14.20   2003*

MARVEJOLS *9D1* (6km SW) **Camping au Soleil Levant, 48100 Chirac [04 66 32 71 92]** Fr S on N9 fr Marvejols, ent on L at sp Auberge Camping immed after passing Chirac sp N9. Diff access for long units due to R angle bend. Sm, terr, pt shd; wc (some cont); shwrs inc; el pts (10A) €1.80; gas; shops 300m; snacks; pool 4km; fishing; walking; horseriding; quiet. "Shops & g'ge in vill can supply all reqs; slippery after rain but tractor tow avail; run down but handy NH." 1 May-15 Sep. € 9.00   2003*

MARVILLE *5C1* (Rural) **Camp Syndicat Mixte d'Amenagement de la Vallee de l'Othain, 55600 Marville [03 29 88 19 06 or 03 29 88 15 15; fax 03 29 88 14 60]** Sp on N43 app Marville fr both dirs. Med, hdg pitch, pt shd; wc (cont); shwrs; el pts (3A); lndtte; sm shop; snacks; rest; playgrnd; covrd pool; entmnt; 20% statics; CCI. 1 Feb-30 Nov.   2002*

MASEVAUX *6F3* (Urban) **Camp Municipal, Rue du Stade, 68290 Masevaux [tel/fax 03 89 82 42 29; camping@masevaux.fr]** Fr N66 in Thann take D14 to Masevaux. This rd narr & steep & requires plenty of power. Fr N83 Colmar-Belfort rd take N466 W to Masevaux. Med, mkd pitch, pt shd; htd wc; chem disp; baby facs; shwrs inc; el pts (4-6A) inc; lndtte; ice; shop 1km; tradsmn; playgrnd; htd pool & sports complex adj; entmnt; TV rm; 40% statics; dogs €0.80; no twin-axles; poss cr; Eng spkn; adv bkg; quiet; some rd noise; cc acc; CCI. "Pleasant walks; interesting town - annual staging of Passion Play; helpful staff; excel facs; excel long/sh stay." ♦ Easter-30 Sep. € 12.90   2004*

MASSAT *8G3* (4km W Rural) **Aire Naturelle L'Azaigouat, Route du Col de Saraille, 09320 Biert** [tel/fax 05 61 96 95 03; camping.azaigouat@club-internet.fr] Take D618 S fr St Girons dir Massat. At Biert turn R onto D118 dir Oust & Col de Saraille, site sp. Sm, pt sl, pt shd; wc; shwrs inc; el pts (6-10A) €2.50; lndry rm; ice; shop, rest, snacks 800m; BBQ; games area; games rm; horseriding 3km; fishing nr; dogs; adv bkg; quiet; CCI. "Excel CL-type site beside stream; v friendly owners; gd wildlife walks." 1 Apr-30 Oct. € 9.00   2003*

MASSERET *7B3* (9km N Rural) **Camp Municipal Montreal, 87380 St Germain-les-Belles** [05 55 71 86 20 or 05 55 71 80 09 (LS); fax 05 55 71 82 25] S on N20/A20 fr Limoges, turn L onto D7, junc 42. Vill is 4.5km. Site sp in vill. Care needed due to narr rds. Med, terr, unshd, hdg pitch; wc; shwrs inc; el pts (5A) inc; ice; rest, snacks, bar 250m; sm shop 800m; playgrnd; lake sw adj; fishing; watersports; walks; dogs; phone; poss cr; quiet; adv bkg; CCI. "Peaceful site in attractive setting; excel san facs; warden calls every pm low ssn; vg sh stay." ♦ ltd. 1 Jun-15 Sep. € 10.00   2004*

MASSERET *7B3* (5km E Rural) **Camping de l'Eau** (formerly Camp du Syndicat Intercommunal), **19510 Lamongerie** [05 55 73 44 57; fax 05 55 73 49 69] Exit A20 at junc 43 sp Masseret. At Masseret foll sp Camp Plan d'Eau twd Lamongerie. Site ent bet 2 lge stone pillars. Med, sl, shd; wc; chem disp; shwrs; el pts (12A) €1.90 (poss rev pol); lndtte; sm shop; snacks; playgrnd; lake beach & sw; fishing; tennis; golf nrby; fitness course thro woods & round lake; TV; poss cr; quiet. "V pleasant situation; NH." ♦ 1 Apr-30 Sep. € 9.30   2004*

MASSEUBE *8F3* (12km NE Rural) **Camping Domaine Naturiste du Moulin de Faget (Naturist), Au Grange, 32450 Faget-Abbatial** [05 62 65 49 09; fax 05 62 66 29 21; info@moulin-faget.com] Fr Masseube D929 for 7 km; in Seissan R on D104 sp Faget-Abbatial; in 8.5km R at T-junc onto D40; site sp on L in 300m; at top of track after 500m. Sm, pt sl, unshd; wc; chem disp (wc); shwrs inc; el pts (6A) £3.25; lndry rm; tradsmn; rest; bar ltd; 10% statics; Eng spkn; adv bkg; quiet; CCI. "V quiet; place to get away fr it all; rather isolated; gd walks; friendly Dutch owners; gd sh stay." ♦ ltd. 1 May-1 Oct. € 18.00   2005*

MASSEUBE *8F3* (400m E Rural) **Camping Les Cledelles, Route de Simorre, 32140 Masseube** [05 62 66 01 75 or 01 40 33 93 33 (LS); fax 01 40 33 94 74; cledelles@aol.com; www.lescledelles.com.fr] Fr Auch take D229 dir Lannemezan, site sp on E o'skts of Masseube. Med, pt shd; wc; chem disp; shwrs inc; el pts (6A) €5; gas; lndtte; shop 250m; tradsmn; snacks; bar; BBQ; playgrnd; htd pool adj; access to rv; tennis; cycle hire; entmnt; TV; 40% statics; dogs €2.30; Eng spkn; adv bkg; quiet; red long stay/low ssn; CCI. "V pleasant setting; security barrier." ♦ 15 Jun-15 Sep. € 17.00   2003*

MASSIAC *9C1* (7km N Rural) **Camp Municipal La Bessiere, 43450 Blesle** [04 71 76 25 82; fax 04 71 76 25 42] Fr Massiac take D909 N. In 5km at Babory turn L & in 2km L again, site sp. Sm, some hdg/mkd pitch; terr, pt shd; wc (some cont); chem disp (wc); mv service pnt; shwrs inc; el pts (10A) €1.50; lndry rm; BBQ; playgrnd; tennis; 30% statics; dogs €0.80; phone 200m; poss cr; CCI. "Blesle one of most beautiful vills in France; attractive site; helpful, friendly warden; gd touring base; vg site." ♦ ltd. Easter-5 Oct. € 6.00   2005*

MASSIAC *9C1* (800m SW Rural) **Camp Municipal de l'Allagnon, Ave de Courcelles, 15500 Massiac** [tel/fax 04 71 23 03 93 or 04 71 23 02 61 (Mairie)] Take N122 off N9 in Massiac, rte to Murat, site sp on rvside. Med, mkd pitch, shd; wc; shwrs; el pts (6-10A) €2; gas; lndtte; shops adj; playgrnd; pool adj; fishing; tennis; poss cr; CCI. "Popular site; sh walk to town cent; vg." ♦ 1 May-30 Sep. € 9.30   2005*

MASSIAC *9C1* (6km SW Rural) **Camp Municipal, Pre Mongeal, 15500 Molompize** [04 71 73 62 90 or 04 71 73 60 06; fax 04 71 73 60 24] Exit junc 23 fr A75, take N122 twd Aurillac. Site on L just bef Molompize. Med, pt shd; wc; chem disp; mv service pnt; shwrs inc; el pts (10A) €1.52; lndry rm; shops 500m; playgrnd; 6% statics; quiet; CCI. "Rvside site behind stadium; tennis courts; friendly warden." ♦ ltd. 15 Jun-15 Sep. € 4.40   2005*

†**MATAMALE** *8G4* (1.7km SW Rural) **Camping Le Lac, Foret de la Matte, 66210 Matamale** [04 68 30 94 49; fax 04 68 04 35 16] N on D118 fr Mont Louis, site sp in vill. App rd narr & poss diff lge o'fits. Sm, pt sl, pt shd; wc; baby facs; shwrs; el pts (6A) €4; lndtte; tradsmn; snacks; bar; BBQ; lake 200m; fishing; watersports; dogs €1. "Friendly site amid pine trees." ♦ € 10.50   2003*

MATHA *7B2* (9km NE Rural) **Camping La Forge, 10B Rue de la Forge, 17160 Le Gicq** [tel/fax 05 46 32 48 42; mail@la-forge-holidays.com; www.la-forge-holidays.com] Fr Matha take D131 thro Les Touches-de-Perigny. In 5km turn R at x-rds sp Le Gicq & foll sp to site. Sm, hdg pitch, pt shd; wc; chem disp; mv service pnt; shwrs inc; el pts (10A) inc; gas 5km; lndtte; tradsmn; shop, rest, snacks, bar 5km; htd pool; lake sw 10km; no dogs; phone; adv bkg; quiet. "British owners; peaceful CL-type site with added extras; vg touring base Cognac, La Rochelle & coast; gd cycling area." ♦ ltd. 1 May-30 Sep. € 22.00   2005*

MATHA *7B2* (5km S Rural) **Camping Le Relais de l'Etang, Route de Matha, 17160 Thors** [05 46 58 26 81 or 05 46 58 75 36; fax 05 46 58 62 21] Fr Matha take D121 S twd Cognac. Site on L in 5km. Sm, hdg/mkd pitch, pt shd; wc (some cont); chem disp; shwrs inc; el pts (10A) inc; rest; snacks; bar; playgrnd; lake sw; mini-golf; adv bkg; quiet; CCI. "Gd for visiting Cognac." 15 May-30 Sep. € 8.30   2003*

Swimming pool - Entertainment - Mobile homes to let
1188 route de la Fouasse - 17570 Les Mathes
Phone : +33 5 46 22 40 53
fax : +33 5 46 22 56 96
www.la-cledeschamps.com
E-mail : contact@la-cledeschamps.com

MATHES, LES *7B1* (3.5km N Rural) Camping L'Oree du Bois, 225 Route de la Bouverie, La Fouasse, 17570 Les Mathes [05 46 22 42 43; fax 05 46 22 54 76; info@camping-oree-du-bois.fr; www.camping-oree-du-bois.fr] Fr A10 to Saintes, then dir Royan. Fr Royan take D25 thro St Palais & La Palmyre twd Phare de la Coubre. Cont 4km past Phare & turn R on D268 to La Fouasse. Site on R in 4km. Lge, hdg/mkd pitch, hdstg, pt shd; wc (some cont); 40 pitches with own san; chem disp; baby facs; shwrs inc; el pts (6A) inc; gas; lndtte; ice; shop; rest; snacks; bar; BBQ; playgrnd; 3 htd pools; waterslide; sand beach 4km; tennis; cycle hire; golf 20km; games area; games rm; entmnt/child ent 1 Jul & Aug; internet; sat TV rm; 50% statics; dogs €3.50; Eng spkn; adv bkg rec high ssn; quiet; cc acc; red low ssn/CCI. "Site in pinewood; local beaches ideal for sw & surfing; zoo in La Palmyre worth visit; min stay 7 days high ssn; excel." ♦ 29 Apr-16 Sep. € 32.00 (CChq acc)   2005*

MATHES, LES *7B1* (500m SW Rural) Camping au Joyeux Faune, Ave de la Palmyre, 17570 Les Mathes [05 46 22 42 29 or 05 46 85 06 17; fax 05 46 85 65 80] Fr St Palais-sur-Mer foll sp 'Phare de la Coubre' to Palmyre. Turn R in Palmyre twd La Tremblade/Les Mathes. Site in 3.5km on R. Lge, pt shd; wc; shwrs inc; el pts (6A) €2.44; gas; lndtte; ice; shop; snacks; playgrnd; pool; sand beach 3km; fishing & watersports 3km; TV rm; games rm; some statics; dogs; poss cr. "Poss clsd low ssn - phone to check." 1 Apr-30 Sep. € 10.98 (3 persons)   2002*

MATHES, LES *7B1* (4km SW Coastal) Camping Bonne Anse Plage, 17570 La Palmyre [05 46 22 40 90; fax 05 46 22 42 30; contact@ campingbonneanseplage.com; www.camping bonneanseplage.com] N fr Royan on D25 thro St Palais-sur-Mer to La Palmyre, after zoo at rndbt site sp; site on L after x-rds D25 & D141 in 600m. Lge, mkd pitch, terr, pt sl, shd; wc; chem disp; mv service pnt; shwrs inc; el pts (6A) €5.80; gas; lndtte; ice; shops; rest; playgrnd; pool; waterslide; sand beach 600m; games area; many tour ops statics; no dogs; poss cr; Eng spkn; no adv bkg more than 2 days ahead; some rd noise; cc acc; CCI. "Superb pool complex, friendly, family site; dated but clean san facs; cycle path." ♦ 21 May-5 Sep. € 34.00 (3 persons)   2005*

MATHES, LES *7B1* (6km SW Coastal) Camping Parc de la Cote Sauvage, Phare de la Coubre, 17570 Les Mathes [05 46 22 40 18 or 05 49 35 83 60; contact@ parc-cote-sauvage.com; www.parc-cote-sauvage. com] D25 fr Royan, thro La Palmyre, at rndabt foll sp 'Phare de la Coubre'. Turn L at junc sp as bef, turn L on R-hand bend. Lge, mkd pitch, pt terr, pt shd; wc (some cont); chem disp; mv service pnt; shwrs inc; el pts (6-10A) €4.50-5.50; gas; lndtte; shop; rest/bar adj; snacks; playgrnd; pool complex; sand beach 500m - can be v windy; tennis; cycle hire adj; boating; surf school; entmnt; internet; TV; 25% statics; dogs €2.60 (not 1 Jul-31Aug); poss cr (NH area); Eng spkn; v cr Jul/Aug; no adv bkg; cc acc; red low ssn; CCI. "Lge pitches; wc facs poss grubby; low ssn expensive for facs provided; fair sh stay." ♦ 1 May-15 Sep. € 25.50   2005*

MATHES, LES *7B1* (2km W Rural) Camping La Pinede, La Palmyre, 17570 Les Mathes [05 46 22 45 13; fax 05 46 22 50 21; contact@ campinglapinede.com; www.campinglapinede. com] Fr La Tremblade, take D141 twd Les Mathes. Turn W after vill onto D141 E twd La Fouasse, foll sp. Site in 2km. Lge, mkd pitch, pt shd; wc; chem disp; shwrs inc; el pts (5A) €6.50; lndtte; ice; shop; rest; snacks; bar; playgrnd; 2 pools (1 htd, covrd); waterslide; sand beach 4km; tennis; cycle hire; archery; mini-golf; games area; games rm; entmnt; child entmnt; mini-farm; many statics; dogs €4.80; private san facs avail for extra charge; adv bkg; quiet. "Dir access to rv; excel for children." 1 May-4 Sep. € 36.80   2005*

MATHES, LES *7B1* (2km NW) Camping Atlantique Foret (formerly Le Moulin Rouge), La Fouasse, 17570 Les Mathes [05 46 22 40 46 or 05 46 36 82 77 (LS)] Fr La Tremblade by-pass, foll sp Diree (D268). Drive thro vill & cont for 2km. Site on L. Or fr La Palmyre on D141 twd Les Mathes; at rndabt take dir La Fouasse. Last site on R. Med, pt shd; wc (some cont); chem disp; baby facs; shwrs inc; el pts (6A) €3.30; gas; lndtte; ice; shop 100m; BBQ (gas only); playgrnd; pool; tennis 300m; sand beach 6km; dogs; phone; Eng spkn; adv bkg; quiet; CCI. "Roomy, clean & peaceful; gd alt to nrby lge sites; friendly, family-run; excel for young children; cycle paths thro forest; farm produce avail; gd long/sh stay." 16 Jun-15 Sep. € 16.00   2004*

MATHES, LES *7B1* (2.5km NW) **Camping La Cle des Champs, 1188 Route de la Fouasse, 17570 Les Mathes** [05 46 22 40 53; fax 05 46 22 56 96; contact@la-cledeschamps.com; www.la-cledes champs.com] S of La Tremblade, take D141 twd La Palmyre, site sp. Lge, mkd pitch, pt shd; wc (some cont); chem disp; baby facs; shwrs inc; el pts (6-10A) €3.70-4.50; gas; lndtte; shop; rest; snacks; bar; BBQ; playgrnd; htd, covrd pool; sand beach 3.5km; cycle hire; fishing & watersports 3km; cycle hire; games rm; TV rm; entmnt; 30% statics; dogs €2.50; Eng spkn; adv bkg; cc acc; quiet; CCI. "Well-equipped, busy site; many excel beaches in area; local oysters avail; Cognac region; Luna Park nrby - poss noise at night." ♦ 1 Apr-30 Sep. € 17.50
2005*

See advertisement opposite

MATHES, LES *7B1* (3km NW Rural) **Camping L'Estanquet, 2596 Route de la Fouasse, 17570 Les Mathes** [05 46 22 47 32 or 05 46 93 93 51 (LS); fax 05 46 22 51 46; contact@campinglestanquet. com; www.campinglestanquet.com] Fr Royan take D141 by-pass onto D25 twd La Palmyre. Turn R in town cent dir Les Mathes. Cont on D141 passing racecourse; turn L bef Les Mathes along La Fouasse. Site in 2.5km on L. Lge, hdg/mkd pitch, pt shd; wc; chem disp; baby facs; shwrs inc; el pts (10A) inc; gas; lndtte; ice; shop; rest; snacks; bar; BBQ; playgrnd; pool; paddling pool; waterslide; sand beach 5km; fishing, windsurfing 5km; tennis; mini-golf; cycle hire; horseriding 1km; golf 9km; entmnt; games/TV rm; 85% statics; dogs €3; recep 0900-1930; poss cr; adv bkg; quiet ♦ 1 May-30 Sep. € 28.50 ABS - A10   2005*

MATIGNON see St Cast le Guildo *2E3*

MATOUR *9A2* (1km W) **Camp Municipal Matour, 71520 Matour** [03 85 59 70 58; fax 03 85 59 74 54; mairie.matour@wanadoo.fr; www.matour.com] On W o'skts of Matour off Rte de la Clayette. Med, hdg/mkd pitch, pt shd; wc; chem disp; shwrs inc; el pts (10A) inc; ice; lndtte; shop 500m; bar; snacks; BBQ; playgrnd; pool (Jun-Aug); tennis; TV; entmnt; lake adj; quiet; adv bkg; CCI. "Conv touring vineyards; highly rec; facs poss inadequate high ssn." ♦ 1 May-30 Sep. € 13.85   2002*

MAUBEC see Cavaillon *10E2*

†MAUBEUGE *3B4* (1km N Urban) **Camp Municipal du Clair de Lune, 212 Route de Mons, 59600 Maubeuge** [tel/fax 03 27 62 25 48; camping-municipal-clair-de-lune@wanadoo.fr; www.ville-maubeuge.fr] Fr Mons head S on N2 twd Maubeuge, site on L about 1.5km bef town cent, sp. Med, hdg/mkd pitch, some hdstg, pt shd; wc; chem disp; baby facs; shwrs inc; el pts (6A) inc (rev pol); lndtte; shops 500m; hypmkt nr; tradsmn; rest, snacks, bar 2km; BBQ; playgrnd; watersports 25km; internet; few statics; dogs; site clsd Xmas to early Feb; Eng spkn; adv bkg; quiet; cc not acc. "Attractive, busy transit site in high ssn; well-kept; facs poss stretched high ssn; pitches spacious; recep 0900-1200 & 1400-2000; some rd noise; mkt Sat am; barrier clsd 2200 Apr-Sep & 2000 Oct-Mar; friendly staff; gd NH." ♦ ltd. € 14.05 ABS - P07
2005*

See advertisement below

MAUBOURGUET *8F2* (Urban) **Camp Municipal de l'Echez, Rue Jean Clos Pucheu, 65700 Maubourguet** [05 62 96 37 44 or 06 12 90 14 55] On D935 (NW of Tarbes), sp in Maubourguet, on S bank of Rv Adour. Sm, pt shd; wc; shwrs inc; el pts; ice; shops 200m; lndtte; playgrnd; TV; rv fishing 300m; quiet. "Pleasantly situated; nice country town." 15 Jun-15 Sep. € 10.40   2003*

MAULEON LICHARRE *8F1* (1km S Rural) **Camping Uhaitza Le Saison, Route de Libarrenx, 64130 Mauleon-Licharre** [05 59 28 18 79; fax 05 59 28 00 78; camping.uhaitza@wanadoo.fr; www.camping-uhaitza.com] Fr Sauveterre take D936 twd Oloron. In 500m turn R onto D23 to Mauleon, then take D918 dir Tardets, site on R. Sm, hdg/mkd pitch, pt sl, pt shd; wc; chem disp; baby facs; shwrs inc; baby facs; el pts (4-6A) €2.50-3.20; lndtte; shops 1.5km; bar high ssn; BBQ; playgrnd; pool 4km; rv fishing adj; some statics; dogs €1; adv bkg; quiet; CCI. "Lovely quiet site beside rv - steep access; friendly owners." ♦ Easter-30 Oct. € 12.10
2005*

MAUPERTUS SUR MER see Cherbourg *1C4*

FRANCE

MAURIAC *7C4* (1km SW Rural) **Camping Le Val St Jean**, 15200 Mauriac [04 71 67 31 13 or 04 73 34 75 53 (Res); fax 04 71 68 17 34; info@ camping-massifcentral.com] Site in town adj to lake; well sp. Med, hdg/mkd pitch, terr, unshd; wc; chem disp; shwrs inc; el pts €3.50; lndry rm; ice; shop; tradsmn; playgrnd; pool; sand beach adj; lake sw, golf adj; fishing; dogs €1.50; adv bkg; quiet; red low ssn; CCI. "Excel site; exceptionally clean & tidy; gd cent for touring." ♦ 30 Apr-1 Oct. € 17.00
2005*

MAURIAC *7C4* (1.5km SW) **Camp Municipal La Roussilhe**, 15200 Mauriac [04 71 68 06 99] Foll sp for Ally & Pleux (D681); downhill, past supmkt, sp to R, 1st L. Med, pt shd; wc; 50% serviced pitches; shwrs; el pts (3A) inc; quiet. "Site situated around perimeter of a football grnd; plenty of shade; gd sh stay." 15 Jun-15 Sep. € 6.00
2005*

MAUROUX see Fleurance *8E3*

MAURS *7D4* (Urban) **Camp Municipal du Vert, Route de Decazeville, 15600 Maurs** [04 71 49 04 15; fax 04 71 49 00 81] Fr Maurs take D663 dir Decazeville. Site on L 400m after level x-ing thro sports complex. Narr ent. Med, mkd pitch, shd; wc; chem disp; baby facs; shwrs inc; el pts (3-5A) inc; lndtte; shops 1km; playgrnd; pool; tennis; rv fishing; poss cr; adv bkg; quiet. "V pleasant on side of rv; sports complex adj." ♦ 1 May-30 Sep. € 9.60
2004*

MAURS *7D4* (6km SE) **Camping Moulin de Chaules, Route de Calvinet, 15600 St Constant** [04 71 49 11 02; fax 04 71 49 13 63] Fr N122 in Maurs, foll sp to St Constant on D663. Take by-pass round St Constant & turn L to Calvinot, well sp fr Maurs. Med, mkd pitch, terr, pt shd; wc (some cont); chem disp; shwrs inc; el pts (4A); lndtte; shop; tradsmn; rest; snacks; bar; playgrnd; pool; poss cr; some statics; adv bkg; quiet; red low ssn/long stay; CCI. "Friendly owner; excel for young children; terr access steep - care needed." 2003*

MAURY see St Paul de Fenouillet *8G4*

MAUSSANE LES ALPILLES see Mouries *10E2*

MAUVEZIN DE PRAT see Salies du Salat *8F3*

MAUZE SUR LE MIGNON *7A2* (1km NW Urban) **Camp Municipal Le Gue de La Riviere, 79210 Mauze-sur-le-Mignon** [05 49 26 76 28 or 05 49 26 30 35 (Mairie); fax 05 49 26 71 13; tourisme@ville-mauze-mignon.fr; www.ville-mauze-mignon.fr] Site clearly sp. Sm, hdg pitch, shd; wc; chem disp; shwrs inc; el pts (5-10A) €1.40-€2.81; ice; lndtte; shop 1km; playgrnd; rv fishing; quiet; adv bkg; Eng spkn; CCI. "Vg long/sh stay; pleasant site; v clean facs; warden calls to office am & pm." 1 Jun-30 Sep. € 4.86
2002*

MAXONCHAMP see Remiremont *6F2*

MAYENNE *4E1* (1km N Rural) **Camp Municipal du Gue St Leonard, Route de Brives, 53100 Mayenne** [02 43 04 57 14; fax 02 43 30 21 10] Fr N, sp to E of D23, 1km bef Mayenne. Well sp fr cent of Mayenne 'Municipal Camping'. Med, hdg/mkd pitch, pt shd; wc; chem disp; some serviced pitches; shwrs inc; el pts (10A) €1.85; gas 1km; lndtte; BBQ; shop (high ssn) & 1km; tradsman high ssn; snacks; rest 1km; playgrnd; htd, covrd pool high ssn; rv fishing adj; 20% statics; phone; adv bkg; some noise fr adj factory; red low ssn; CCI. "Pleasant location adj parkland walks; peaceful; well maintained; clean facs; boules park. " ♦ 1 Apr-30 Sep. € 9.70 (3 persons) 2005*

MAYENNE *4E1* (12km N) **Camp Municipal de Vaux, Rue des Cloverts, 53300 Ambrieres-les-Vallees** [02 43 04 00 67 or 02 43 04 90 25; fax 02 43 08 93 28; otsiambrieres@wanadoo.fr] Sp 'Parc de Loisirs de Vaux'. D23 N of Mayenne. At rv brdge take D33 dir Lassay in 200m site on R on rv bank. Med, hdg pitch, some hdstg, pt sl, pt shd; wc; shwrs inc; el pts (10A) €2.40; lndtte; ice; shops 2km; tradsmn; bar; BBQ; playgrnd; htd pool; canoe hire; fishing; crazy golf inc; tennis; TV rm; adv bkg; quiet; red long stay; CCI. "Excel site; facs ltd low ssn; san facs v clean; beautiful surroundings; overlkg rv. " 1 Apr-30 Sep. € 9.80 2005*

MAYET see Ecommoy *4F1*

MAYRES *9D1* (500m S Rural) **Camping La Chataigneraie, Hameau de Cautet, 07330 Mayres** [04 75 87 20 40 or 04 75 87 20 97] Fr Aubenas on N102; L after Mayres vill, over Ardeche bdge, up hill in 500m. Sm, mkd pitch, terr, pt shd; wc (cont); shwrs inc; el pts (3-6A) €2.50-4; tradsmn; rv sw 2km; dogs €1; quiet; cc acc. "Vg CL-type site; secluded by tributary of Rv Ardeche; helpful owners. ♦ ltd. Easter-30 Sep. € 11.50   2005*

MAYRINHAC LENTOUR see Gramat *7D4*

MAZAMET *8F4* (1km E) **Camp Municipal de la Lauze, Stade de la Chevaliere, 81200 Mazamet** [tel/fax 05 63 61 24 69] Exit Mazamet on St Pons rd N112, site on R past rugby grnd. Med, hdstg, pt sl, pt shd; wc (mainly cont); chem disp; shwrs inc; el pts (6-10A) €2.50-3.50; lndry rm; supmkt 300m; BBQ; htd pool adj; tennis; dogs; poss cr; adv bkg; poss some rd noise; 10% red CCI. "San facs excel; gd touring base 'Black Mountain' region." 1 Jun-30 Sep. € 11.00   2003*

MAZAN see Carpentras *10E2*

MAZIERES see Chasseneuil sur Bonnieure *7B3*

MAZURES, LES see Rocroi *5C1*

MEAUDRE see Villard de Lans *9C3*

MEAULNE *7A4* (W Rural) **Camp Municipal Le Cheval Blanc, Rue de Dr Conquet, 03360 Meaulne** [04 70 06 91 13 or 04 70 06 95 34; fax 04 70 06 91 29; mairie.meaulne@wanadoo.fr] Site off main N144 rd in Mealne on bank Rv Aumance. Sm, mkd pitch, pt shd; wc; chem disp (wc); shwrs inc; el pts (6A) €2; lndtte; shop, rest, bar 300m; BBQ; playgrnd; rv fishing; canoeing; dogs; phone; quiet; CCI. "Basic, pleasant rvside site; warden calls 1300 & 1900 or put money in letterbox; site yourself; poss flooding in high rainfall." ♦ ltd. 1 May-30 Sep. € 8.00   2005*

†**MEAUX** *3D3* (4km NE Rural) **Camping Village Parisien (formerly L'Ile du Bac), Route de Congis, 77910 Varreddes** [01 64 34 80 80; fax 01 60 22 89 84; leslie@villageparisien.com; www.villageparisien.com] Fr Meaux foll sp on D405 dir Soissons then Varreddes, site sp on D121 dir Congis. Med, hdg pitch, pt shd; htd wc; serviced pitches; shwrs inc; el pts (6A) €2; gas; lndtte; sm shop & 1km; tradsmn; snacks; bar; BBQ; playgrnd; pool; paddling pool; waterslide; fishing; tennis; games area; cycle hire; golf 5km; games rm; entmnt; TV rm; 50% statics; dogs free; site clsd mid-Dec to mid-Jan; Eng spkn; adv bkg; quiet; red low ssn/CCI. "Conv Paris cent (drive to metro), Parc Asterix & Disneyland - tickets avail fr site; lge pitches; friendly, helpful staff." 1 Apr-1 Sep. € 25.00   2005*

See advertisement opposite

†**MEAUX** *3D3* (11km NE Urban) **Camping de l'Ile, Ave des Trois Valets, 77440 Mary-sur-Marne** [01 60 01 67 07; caillaud.benoit@wanadoo.fr] Fr Meaux on D405 twd Soissons. In approx 10km turn R onto D401 sp Lizy-sur-Ourcq thro to Mary-sur-Marne. Site sp on L in vill. Sm, hdg pitch, shd; wc; chem disp; shwrs; el pts (3A) inc; lndtte; shop; rv sw 3km; adv bkg rec; red long stay; TCI. "Conv Paris & Disneyland; friendly, Eng-spkg owner; only 6 pitches for tourers, otherwise permanent residents; san facs poss poor; not gd value; sh stay only." € 15.00   2003*

MEAUX *3D3* (10km SW Rural) **Camping International de Jablines, 77450 Jablines** [01 60 26 09 37; fax 01 60 26 43 33; welcome@ camping-jablines.com; www.camping-jablines. com] Fr N A1 then A104 exit Claye-Souilly. Fr E A4 then A104 exit Meaux. Fr S A6, A86, A4, A104 exit Meaux. Site well sp 'Base de Loisirs de Jablines'. Lge, mkd pitch, pt sl, pt shd; htd wc; chem disp; mv service pnt; shwrs inc; el pts (10A) inc; gas 10km; lndtte; ice; shop; tradsmn; rest; snacks; bar; playgrnd; sand beach & lake sw 500m; fishing; sailing; windsurfing; tennis 500m; horseriding; mini-golf; cycle hire; dogs; bus to Eurodisney; Eng spkn; adv bkg; quiet; red low ssn; cc acc; CCI. "V clean, well-run site; ideal for Disneyland (tickets for sale on site), Paris & Versailles; well-guarded; pleasant staff." ♦ 31 Mar-29 Oct. € 22.00 (CChq acc)   2005*

See advertisement on next page

MEAUX *3D3* (14km W Rural) **Camping L'Ile Demoiselle, Chemin du Port, 77410 Annet-sur-Marne** [01 60 26 03 07 or 01 60 26 18 15; ile. demoiselle@wanadoo.fr] Fr Meaux take N3 W, then turn L onto D404 twd Annet. Foll sp to 'Base de Loisirs de Jablines'. Fr Annet take D45 twd Jablines. Site on R immed bef bdge over rv. Med, some hdg pitch, pt shd; wc; chem disp (wc); shwrs €1; el pts (4-6A) €2.50-4; gas 4km; lndry rm; shops 1km; BBQ; lake sw, sand beach 1km; 25% statics; dogs; some Eng spkn; adv bkg; rd noise; cc acc; CCI. "Conv Paris & Disneyland Paris; many other attractions in area; gd sh stay/NH." Apr-Oct. € 11.00   2003*

MEGEVE *9B3* (2km SW) **Camping-Caravaning Gai Sejour, 332 Route de Cassioz, 74120 Megeve** [tel/fax 04 50 21 22 58] On N212 Numet-Megeve rd, site on R 1.5km after Praz-sur-Arly, well sp. Med, mkd pitch, sl (blocks needed), pt shd; wc; chem disp; shwrs inc; el pts (4A) €2.20; lndry rm; ice; shops 1.5km; dogs €0.80; Eng spkn; adv bkg; quiet; CCI. "Pleasant site with gd views, lge pitches; gd walks; 40km fr Mont Blanc; helpful owners; vg long/sh stay." 20 May-15 Sep. € 9.80   2005*

CAMPING INTERNATIONAL DE JABLINES ★★★

ANWB · Camping cheque · Alan Rogers

BASE DE PLEIN AIR
F-77450 JABLINES

Tel. +33.(0)1.60.26.09.37 • Fax +33.(0)1.60.26.43.33
welcome@camping-jablines.com
www.camping-jablines.com

9 km from DISNEYLAND PARIS, away from the noise, you will find a 450 ha green terrain with the longest beach of the ILE DE FRANCE. Restaurant, tennis, mini golf, playground, fishing, sailing, mountain bikes to rent, horseback riding, waterskilift and all comfort a campsite could possibly offer. Open since 1997.

Tickets for Disneyland Paris for sale on site.

Reservation recommended • Open from 26.3 till 31.10 • 150 pitches

---

MEHUN SUR YEVRE *4H3* (500m N Urban) **Camp Municipal**, Ave Chatelet, 18500 Mehun-sur-Yevre [02 48 57 13 32 or 02 48 57 30 25 (Mairie); fax 02 48 57 34 16] Leave A71 junc 6 onto N76 dir Bourges. App Mehun turn L into site at 2nd traff lts. Sm, mkd pitch, pt shd; wc; shwrs inc; el pts (4A) inc; shop, rest, bar 600m; playgrnd; free pool & tennis adj; quiet with some rd noise; cc not acc. "Excel value; v clean san facs; 5 min walk to interesting town with gd rests; no twin-axles; relaxed atmosphere with friendly warden; site v quiet when pool clsd. " ♦ 1 Jun-31 Aug. € 9.00   2005*

MEILHAN SUR GARONNE see Reole, La *7D2*

MEIX ST EPOING, LE see Sezanne *4E4*

MELE SUR SARTHE, LE *4E1* (500m SE Rural) **Camp Intercommunal de la Prairie, La Breteche, St Julien-Sarthe**, 61170 Le Mele-sur-Sarthe [02 33 27 18 74] Turn off N12 onto D4 S, site sp. Med, mkd pitch, pt shd; wc; chem disp; mv service pnt; shwrs; el pts (6A) €2; lndtte; supmkt 300m; playgrnd; sand beach/lake 300m; sailing; tennis; mini-golf; adv bkg; CCI. "Site part of excel municipal sports complex; vg." 1 May-30 Sep. € 8.60   2005*

MELISEY *6F2* (7km E Rural) **Camping La Broche, Route du Mont de Vanne**, 70270 Fresse [tel/fax 03 84 63 31 40] Fr Lure head NE on D486 twd Melisey. Fr Melisey stay on D486 twd Le Thillot, in 2.5km turn R onto D97 dir Plancher-les-Mines. In approx 5.5km site sp on R in Fresse. Sm, pt sl, terr, pt shd; wc; shwrs; el pts (10A) €2; shop 1km; playgrnd; fishing adj; quiet apart fr double-chiming church bells; adv bkg; CCI. "In regional park, v secluded; friendly owner; great site." ♦ 1 Apr-15 Oct. € 8.00   2005*

MELISEY *6F2* (SE) **Camping Le Bergereine, Route de Thillot**, 70270 Melisey [tel/fax 03 84 20 01 57; christiane.caritey@tele2.fr] Fr Lure (or by-pass) take D486 dir Le Thillot; site sp. Sm, pt shd; wc; chem disp; shwrs; el pts €2; gas; leisure cent & pool 500m; adv bkg; v quiet; fishing in adj rv; CCI. "Gd NH; simple farm site, friendly owner; attractive scenery, gd rest adj; gd family site." 1 Apr-30 Sep. € 8.00   2005*

MELLE *7A2* (2km N Urban) **Camp Municipal La Fontaine de Villiers, Route de Villiers**, 79500 Melle [05 49 29 18 04 or 05 49 27 00 23 (Mairie); fax 05 49 27 01 51] Fr N on D950 to ent Melle turn R at 1st rndabt, site is 1km fr Super U, well sp. Sm, hdg/mkd pitch, pt sl, pt shd; wc (some cont); chem disp; mv service pnt; shwrs inc; el pts (4-10A) €2.40-3.80; shop, rest; snacks, bar 1km; BBQ; playgrnd; htd pool 500m; tennis 1km; phone; adv bkg; quiet; CCI. "Gd sh stay/NH." Easter-30 Sep. € 7.65   2004*

†**MELLE** *7A2* (8km S Rural) **Camping La Maison de Puits, 14 Rue de Beauchamp**, 79110 Tillou [05 49 29 38 24; juneandtrevor@aol.com] Fr Niort on D948. At Melle foll sp Angouleme, R turn (to ring rd & avoids Melle cent). At Total stn rndabt turn R onto D948 dir Chef-Boutonne. In 3.5km turn R onto D737 sp Chef-Boutonne. After approx 5km at x-rds of D111 & D737, strt over & take 2nd turn R in 1km (sm sp to Tillou) along narr rd sp Tillou. In 1.6km site on L. Sm, sl, unshd; own san; chem disp; el pts (16A) €3; BBQ; splash pool; adv bkg; quiet. "CL-type site in orchard (6 vans only); friendly, helpful British owners; quiet & peaceful; ring ahead to book; B&B avail; interesting area; a real gem; vg long/sh stay." € 10.00   2004*

MELLE *7A2* (10km SW Urban) **Camp Municipal, Rue des Merlonges**, 79170 Brioux-sur-Boutonne [05 49 07 50 46; fax 05 49 07 27 27] On ent Brioux fr Melle on D950 turn R immed over bdge; site on R in 100m. Sm, pt shd; wc; shwrs inc; el pts (6A) €1.60; lndry rm; shops 300m; playgrnd; Eng spkn; quiet. "Pleasant rural setting; tidy, well cared for site; spotless ltd facs; choose own pitch & pay at Mairie on departure if no warden; vg sh stay/NH." 1 Apr-31 Oct. € 6.00   2004*

†**MELLE** *7A2* (6km NW Rural) **Camp Municipal La Boissiere, Deux Sevres**, 79370 Celles-sur-Belle [05 49 32 95 57 or 05 49 79 80 17 (Mairie); fax 05 49 32 95 10] Fr Melle or Niort on D948. Exit by-pass into Celles & in town foll sp to Sports Complex & camping. Sm, pt sl, pt shd; htd wc (some cont); shwrs inc; el pts (6A) inc; gas, shop 500km; BBQ; playgrnd; pool adj; rv 200m; lake 400m; tennis; dogs; 20% statics; adv bkg rec high ssn. "Warden calls 0930 & 1800; quiet apart fr football ground adj; gd NH."♦ € 8.35   2004*

MELUN *4E3* (3km S Rural) **Camping La Belle Etoile, Quai Joffre, 77000 La Rochette** [01 64 39 48 12; fax 01 64 37 25 55; info@campinglabelleetoile.com; www.campinglabelleetoile.com] On ent La Rochette on N6 fr Fontainbleu pass Total stn on L; turn immed R into Ave de la Seine & foll site sp; turn L at Rv Seine & site on L in 500m. Lge, hdg/mkd pitch, pt shd; wc; chem disp; mv service pnt; shwrs; el pts (6A) €3.20; gas; lndtte; shop 1km; snacks (high ssn); bar; playgrnd; htd pool; rv fishing; tennis 500m; golf 8km; internet; 10% statics; phone; dogs €1.30; Eng spkn; adv bkg; cc acc; red low ssn; CCI. "Helpful owners; conv Paris, Fontainbleau & Disneylnd (ticket fr recep); gates locked 2300; indus area; sports complex nrby; gd walking & cycling in forest; rlwy noise thro night." ♦ ltd. 1 Apr-31 Oct. € 15.30 (CChq acc) 2005*

> This site entry hasn't been updated for a while; we'd better fill in a site report form and send it to The Club.

MEMBROLLE SUR CHOISILLE, LA *4G2* (Urban) **Camp Municipal, Route de Fondettes, 37390 La Membrolle-sur-Choisille** [02 47 41 20 40] On N138 Tours to Le Mans rd. Site on L on ent La Membrolle, sp. Med, pt shd; wc (some cont); chem disp; mv service pnt; shwrs incl; el pts (6A) inc; lndtte; shop 5mins; hypmkt 3km; playgrnd; fishing; tennis, rv walks; dogs; bus 5min; phone; adv bkg; some rd noise; CCI. "Clean, well-maintained; gd san facs; wardens friendly/helpful; office/ent clsd 1300-1500." ♦ 1 May-30 Sep. € 9.30 2005*

MENAT *7A4* (2km E Rural) **Camp Municipal des Tarteaux, 63560 Menat** [04 73 85 52 47 or 04 73 85 50 29 (Mairie); fax 04 73 85 50 22] Heading SE on N144 foll sp Camping Pont de Menat. Exit N144 at Menat opp Hotel Pinal. Site alongside Rv Sioule. Med, terr, pt sl, shd; wc (cont); shwrs incl; el pts (5A) €2.40; ice; lndtte; tradsmn; shop & 2km; playgrnd; rv adj; fishing & boating 2km; adv bkg; quiet; CCI. "Beautiful position." 1 Apr-30 Sep. € 7.70 2003*

†MENDE *9D1* (2km S Rural) **Camping Tivoli, Route des Gorges du Tarn, 48000 Mende** [tel/fax 04 66 65 00 38; tivoli.camping@libertysurf.fr] Sp fr N88, turn R 300m downhill (narr but easy rd). App diff fr S owing to sharp bend off rd. Site adj Rv Lot Med, pt shd; htd wc (some cont); mv service pnt; shwrs; el pts (3-6A) inc; lndry rm; bar; shops 1km; playgrnd; pool; fishing; TV rm; some statics; dogs €0.90; quiet; adv bkg. € 15.40 2002*

MENDE *9D1* (8km SW Rural) **Camping Le Clos des Peupliers, 48000 Barjac** [04 66 47 01 16] On N88 in dir of Mende turn N on D142 sp Barjac & Camping. Site ent almost immed on R thro sh narr but not diff tunnel (max height 3.4m), adj Rv Lot. Lge, pt shd; wc; chem disp; shwrs inc; el pts (6-10A) €2.50-3; lndtte; rest 500m; snacks; shops 500m; rv fishing adj; TV; dogs €1.30; quiet. "Facs clean, ltd low ssn; pleasant rvside site; poss unkempt low ssn; gd walks; helpful warden." 1 May-15 Sep. € 9.00 2005*

MENESPLET see Montpon Menesterol *7C2*

MENETRUX EN JOUX see Doucier *6H2*

MENGLON see Luc en Diois *9D3*

MENIL see Chateau Gontier *4F1*

MENITRE, LA see Rosiers sur Loire, Les *4G1*

MENNETOU SUR CHER see Villefranche sur Cher *4G3*

MENTON *10E4* (1km N Urban/Coastal) **Camp Municipal du Plateau St Michel, Route de Mont Gros, 06500 Menton** [04 93 35 81 23; fax 04 93 57 12 35] Fr A8 Menton exit foll sp to town cent. After 2km with bus stn on L & rlwy bdge ahead turn L at rndabt, then R at T-junc. L at next T-junc, foll sp to site & Auberge Jeunesse. Rd is v steep & narr with hairpins - not rec trailer c'vans. Med, mkd pitch, terr, pt shd; wc (some cont); shwrs; el pts (6A) €2.75; ice; shop; rest; snacks; bar; sand beach 1km; poss v cr with tents; noisy; cc acc; CCI. "V steep walk into town; some new san facs." 1 Apr-31 Oct. € 16.50 2005*

†MEOUNES LES MONTRIEUX *10F3* (Rural) **Camping aux Tonneaux, Les Ferrages, 83136 Meounes-les-Montrieux** [04 94 33 98 34] D554 fr Brignoles to Toulon. Site sp off D554 at exit to vill - busy, narr rd. Sm, mkd pitch, shd; wc; chem disp; shwrs incl; el pts (3-6A); gas; ice; lndtte; shop; rest; bar; playgrnd; pool; tennis; 20% statics; dogs; Eng spkn; no adv bkg; quiet; 25% red low ssn; CCI. € 15.00 2004*

MERDRIGNAC *2E3* (800m N) **Camping Le Val de Androuet, 22230 Merdrignac** [02 96 28 47 98; fax 02 96 26 55 44] Sp fr town cent, 500m fr town on D793 twd Broons, site on L. Med, pt sl, pt shd; wc; baby facs; shwrs incl; el pts (4A) inc; lndtte; shops adj; bar; playgrnd; pool adj; tennis; lake sw 3km; fishing; no dogs; quiet. 1 Jun-14 Sep. € 11.05 2003*

†MERENS LES VALS *8G4* (1km W Rural) **Camp Municipal Ville de Bau, 09110 Merens-les-Vals** [05 61 02 85 40; fax 05 61 64 03 83; camping.merens@wanadoo.fr] Fr Ax-les-Thermes on N20 sp Andorra past Merens-les-Vals turn R nr start of dual c'way sp Camp Municipal. Site on R in 800m. Sm, hdg pitch; wc (some cont); shwrs; el pts (6A) €2.30 (poss rev pol); shop; playgrnd; pool 8km; dogs €0.50; poss cr; quiet; CCI. "Conv Andorra, Tunnel de Puymorens; excel facs & walks fr site." € 8.70 2005*

MERIBEL *9B3* (2km N Rural) **Camping Le Martagon, Le Raffort, Route de Meribel, 73550 Les Allues** [04 79 00 56 29; fax 04 79 00 44 92] Fr Moutiers on D915 S to Brides-les-Bains then D90 S dir Meribel. Site on L at Le Raffort. Park in public car park & go to rest. Sm, hdstg, terr, unshd; htd wc; chem disp; shwrs inc; el pts (13A) €4.50; gas 200m; lndtte; shop 2km; tradsmn; rest; bar; no statics; dogs; adv bkg; rd noise; cc acc. "Ski bus every 20 mins at site ent; skilift 100m; htd boot room; mountain-biking in summer." ♦ 15 Dec-25 Apr & 1 Jul-31 Aug. € 25.00   2005*

MERINCHAL *7B4* (Rural) **Camp Municipal du Chateau de la Mothe, 23420 Merinchal** [05 55 67 25 56; fax 05 55 67 23 71; tourisme. merinchal@wanadoo.fr] E fr Pontaumur on N141 twds Aubusson. R onto D27 to Merinchal. Site in vill. Sm, pt sl, pt shd; wc; shwrs inc; el pts inc; lndtte; shop, rest, bar nr; playgrnd; TV; fishing; quiet. ♦ 1 Apr-30 Oct. € 9.35   2003*

MERVANS *6H1* (Rural) **Camp Municipal du Plan d'Eau, 71310 Mervans** [03 85 76 11 70 (Mairie); fax 03 85 76 16 93; mairie-de-mervans@ wanadoo.fr] E on N78 fr Chalon-sur-Saone. At Thurey fork L onto D24; at x-rds turn L onto D996 to Mervans. Site sp in vill by lake. Sm, pt shd; wc (some cont); shwrs inc; el pts (6A) inc; rest & shops adj; quiet; CCI. "Lovely countryside; v attractive vill; ltd amount wc but well-kept & clean; excel long/sh stay." ♦ 1 Jun-15 Sep. € 5.60   2003*

MERVENT see Fontenay le Comte *7A2*

MERVILLE FRANCEVILLE PLAGE see Cabourg *3D1*

MERY SUR SEINE *4E4* (1km N Rural) **Camp Municipal, 10170 Mery-sur-Seine** [03 25 21 23 72 or 03 25 21 20 42 (Mairie); fax 03 25 21 13 19] Turn N off N19 Troyes to Romilly onto D373 sp Mery-sur-Seine; in vill turn 1st L after x-ing Rv Seine; site on L in 1km on rv bank. Med, hdg/mkd pitch, hdstg, pt sl, pt shd; wc (some cont); chem disp; shwrs inc; el pts (3-10A) €1.40-2.70; lndtte; shops 50m; BBQ; playgrnd; rv sw adj; fishing; 75% statics; poss cr; Eng spkn; adv bkg; quiet; CCI. "Gd san facs but no tap for attaching hose - poss diff for m'vans to fill tank; v clean; friendly warden on site for initial access (0900-1200 & 1700-1900 & 0900-1200); €15 dep for barrier card; pleasant town with mkt & bank; excel long stay." ♦ ltd. 1 Apr-30 Sep. € 7.00   2005*

MESCHERS SUR GIRONDE see Royan *7B1*

MESLAND see Onzain *4G2*

MESLAY DU MAINE *4F1* (2.5km NE Rural) **Camp Municipal La Chesnaie, 53170 Meslay-du-Maine** [02 43 98 48 08 or 02 43 64 10 45 (Mairie); fax 02 43 98 75 52; cc-meslaydumaine@wanadoo.fr] Take D21 SE fr Laval to Meslay. Turn L in cent of vill onto D152. Site on R in 2.5km. Med, hdg/mkd pitch, pt shd; wc (cont); shwrs; el pts (6-12A) €2.10; lndtte; shop 2.5km; tradsmn; snacks; bar; playgrnd; lake adj; watersports, leisure cent adj; 10% statics; poss cr; adv bkg; cc acc; CCI. "Excel, clean & quiet." ♦ Easter-30 Sep. € 6.90   2005*

MESNIL ST PERE see Vendeuvre sur Barse *6F1*

MESNOIS see Clairvaux les Lacs *6H2*

MESSANGES see Vieux Boucau les Bains *8E1*

METZ *5D2* (12km SW) **Camping Le Paquis, 57680 Corny-sur-Moselle** [03 87 52 03 59 or 03 87 60 68 67; fax 03 87 60 71 96] SW fr Metz on N57; site sp on ent to vill. Or S on A31 take junc 29 Fey & turn R onto D66 into Corny-sur-Moselle. At T-junc in vill turn R. Site is 300m on L. Lge, shd; wc (mainly cont); chem disp; shwrs inc; el pts (6A) €2.50 (long cable poss req); lndry rm; gas; ice; snacks; bar; shops 1km; tradsmn; lndtte; playgrnd; rv sw adj; TV; entmnt; dogs €0.90; poss cr; adv bkg; cc acc; CCI. "Gd, well-run site on banks of Moselle; friendly owners; poss rlwy noise; rec arr early for quieter pitch at far end site." 1 May-30 Sep. € 9.00   2005*

METZ *5D2* (NW Urban) **Camp Municipal Metz-Plage, Allee de Metz Plage, 57000 Metz** [03 87 68 26 48; fax 03 87 38 03 89; jmwingerter@ mairie-metz.fr] Exit A31 at Metz-Nord/Pontiffroy exit. Foll 'Autres Directions' sp back over a'route & Rv Moselle; site sp. Fr S turn R over Rv Moselle & as above. Med, mkd pitch, pt sl, pt shd; wc; chem disp; shwrs inc; el pts (10A) inc (poss rev pol); lndtte; shop, snacks 500m; playgrnd; pool adj; rv fishing adj; dogs €0.75; Eng spkn; adv bkg; traff noise fr rv bdge; cc acc; CCI. "Lovely site; views over rv; gd sized pitches but tightly packed high ssn; early arr ess high ssn; recep open 0700-2030; flood warning area; easy walk to attractive town with cathedral; gd san facs for disabled." ♦ 5 May-26 Sep. € 11.20   2005*

MEURSAULT see Beaune *6H1*

MEYRAS see Thueyts *9D2*

MEYRIEU LES ETANGS *9B2* (800m SE Rural) **Base de Loisirs du Moulin, Route de Chatonnoy, 38440 Meyrieu-les-Etangs** [04 74 59 30 34; fax 04 74 58 36 12; basedeloisirs.du-moulin@ wanadoo.fr; www.camping-meyrieu.com] Exit A43 at junc 8. Enter Bourgoin & foll sp for La Gare to pick up D522 SW twd St Jean-de-Bournay. Site next to lake 1km fr D522, sp. Med, mkd pitch, hdstg, terr, pt shd; wc; shwrs; el pts (6-10A) €3.40-4.60; lndry rm; ice; shop; rest; lake sw; pedaloes; fishing; canoeing; archery; mini-golf; games rm; entmnt in ssn; TV; dogs €1; phone; adv bkg; quiet. "Lovely views across lake; hdstg on all pitches for car parking; v clean san facs & site; vg." ♦ 15 Apr-30 Sep. € 14.80   2005*

MEYRUEIS *10E1* (1km NE Rural) **Camping Le Pre de Charlet, Route de Florac, 48150 Meyrueis** [04 66 45 63 65; fax 04 66 45 63 24] Exit Meyrueis on rd to Florac (D996). Site on R on bank of Rv Jonte. Med, mkd pitch, pt sl, terr, pt shd, pt sl; wc (some cont); chem disp; mv service pnt; baby facs; shwrs inc; el pts (10A) €2.30; gas; lndtte; shop & 11km; tradsmn; bar; BBQ; playgrnd; pool 400m; rv fishing; phone; adv bkg; phone; quiet; cc acc; CCI. "Friendly owner; excel long stay." ♦ ltd. Easter-15 Oct. € 10.50   2003*

MEYRUEIS *10E1* (500m E Rural) **Camping Le Champ d'Ayres, Route de la Breze, 48150 Meyrueis** [tel/fax 04 66 45 60 51; campingle champdayres@wanadoo.fr; www.campingle champdayres.com] Fr W on D907 dir Gorges de la Jonte into Meyrueis. Foll sp Chateau d'Ayres & site. Med, hdg/mkd pitch, pt sl, pt shd; wc (some cont); chem disp; mv service pnt; baby facs; fam bthrm; shwrs inc; el pts (6-10A) €2.50; lndtte; shop; tradsmn; snacks; bar; playgrnd; htd pool; 15% statics; dogs free; phone; poss cr; Eng spkn; adv bkg; red low ssn; cc not acc; CCI. ♦ 9 Apr-25 Sep. € 17.00   2005*

MEYRUEIS *10E1* (800m NW Rural) **Camping Le Capelan, Route de Jonte, 48150 Meyrueis** [tel/fax 04 66 45 60 50 or 04 90 53 34 45 (LS); camping. le.capelan@wanadoo.fr; www.campingcapelan. com] Site sp on D996 on banks of Rv Jonte. Med, mkd pitch, shd; wc; chem disp; mv service pnt; baby facs; fam bthrm; shwrs inc; el pts (4-10A) inc; gas; lndtte; ice; shop; tradsmn; supmkt 500m; BBQ; rest 1km; snacks; bar; playgrnd; 2 htd pools (no shorts); rv sw; fishing; tennis 1km; games rm; games area; rockclimbing; internet; entmnt; sat TV; 70% statics; private bthrms avail; Eng spkn; adv bkg; quiet; red low ssn; cc acc; CCI. "Gd rvside site; conv touring Gorges du Tarn & Cevennes National Park; beautiful scenery." ♦ 30 Apr-17 Sep. € 20.50 (CChq acc)   2005*

MEYSSAC *7C3* (2km NE Rural) **Intercommunal Moulin de Valance, Route de Collonges-la-Rouge, 19500 Meyssac** [05 55 25 41 59; fax 05 55 84 07 28; mairiedemeymac@i.france.com] Well sp on D38 bet Meyssac & Collonges-la-Rouge. Med, mkd pitch, pt sl, pt shd; wc; chem disp; shwrs; el pts (10A) €2.40; lndtte; shop; rest; snacks; bar; playgrnd; pool; tennis; many statics; adv bkg; CCI. "Within walking dist of attractive vill; fair only." ♦ 1 May-30 Sep. € 12.50   2005*

MEZE *10F1* (1km N Coastal) **Camping Beau Rivage, 34140 Meze** [04 67 43 81 48; fax 04 67 43 66 70; reception@camping-beaurivage. fr; www.camping-beaurivage.fr] Fr Meze cent foll N113 dir Montpellier, site on R 100m past rndabt on leaving town; well sp. Lge, mkd pitch, pt shd; wc; chem disp; mv service pnt; shwrs inc; el pts (3-6A) inc; lndtte; shop; supmkt 200m; rest; snacks; bar; BBQ; playgrnd; htd pool & paddling pool; sand beach 700m; fishing; sailing; tennis 900m; entmnt; TV rm; 50% statics; phone; dogs €4; poss cr; Eng spkn; adv bkg; quiet; cc acc; CCI. "Gd rests nr harbour; excel local oysters; conv Sete & Noilly Prat distillery; san facs need updating." ♦ 1 Apr-30 Sep. € 29.00 (CChq acc)   2004*

MEZE *10F1* (3km N Rural) **Camp Municipal Loupian, Ave de la Gare, 34140 Loupian** [04 67 43 57 67] Fr Meze tak N113 & turn l at 1st Loupian sp then foll sp for site. Med, hdg/mkd pitch, pt shd; wc; shwrs; el pts (5A) €2; lndtte; snacks; bar; playgrnd; sand beach 3km; poss cr; Eng spkn; adv bkg; quiet; CCI. "Pleasant site in popular area; gd rests near Meze; vg all stays." ♦ ltd. 1 May-15 Sep. € 10.00   2004*

MEZEL *10E3* (W Rural) **Camp Municipal Le Claus, 04270 Mezel** [04 92 35 53 87 (Mairie); fax 04 92 35 52 86] Sp fr N85 fr both dir. Heading S fr Digne onto D907; turn R to site on L. Sm, pt sl, pt shd; wc (cont); shwrs; el pts (3-6A); shops adj; snacks nr; poss cr; quiet. "Private rlwy to Nice v nr." 1 Jul-31 Aug.   2004*

MEZIERES EN BRENNE *4H2* (500m E Rural) **Camp Municipal La Cailauderie, 36290 Mezieres-en-Brenne** [02 54 38 12 24 or 02 54 38 09 23] On D925 to Chateauroux, sp Stade. Sm, mkd pitch, pt shd; wc; chem disp; shwrs inc; el pts (6A) inc; shop, rest, bar 500m; playgrnd; rv adj; dogs; quiet; CCI. "Bird-watching; site yourself, warden calls am & pm; rv fishing on site; poss itnerants; poss vicious mosquitoes; gd sh stay." 1 May-30 Sep. € 9.00   2004*

MEZIERES EN BRENNE *4H2* (6km E Rural) **Camping Bellebouche, 36290 Mezieres-en-Brenne** [02 54 38 32 36; fax 02 54 38 32 96; v.v. n@wanadoo.fr] Sp on D925. Med, mkd pitch, pt sl, pt shd; wc (cont); chem disp (wc); baby facs; shwrs inc; el pts €3; lndtte; shop 6km; rest high ssn; bar 6km; playgrnd; lake sw adj; watersports; fishing; no statics; no dogs high ssn; phone; quiet; cc acc; CCI. "In country park; gd walking, cycling, bird-watching; vg long/sh stay." 1 Jul-31 Aug. € 11.00   2003*

MEYZIEU see Lyon *9B2*   **MEZOS see St Julien en Born** *8E1*

FRANCE

MIELAN *8F2* (2km N) **Camping Les Reflets du Lac**, 32170 Mielan [05 62 67 51 59; fax 05 62 67 64 12; lac.mielan@wanadoo.fr] Site E of N21. Exit N21 at camping sps & site at lakeside in 500m. Lane may be restricted at w/e by parked cars visiting leisure cent. Med, pt sl, unshd; wc; baby facs; shwrs inc; el pts (10A) €2.60; gas; lndtte; ice; shop; rest; snacks; bar; BBQ; playgrnd; pool; sand beach & lake sw; tennis; watersports; sailing; entmnt; TV; dogs €1; red low ssn. 1 Apr-1 Nov. € 15.50   2003*

Some of these sites have changed their opening dates - we'd better fill in some site report forms and let the editor of the guide know.

MIGENNES see Joigny *4F4*

†MILLAS *8G4* (3km W Rural) **Camping La Garenne**, 66170 Nefiach [tel/fax 04 68 57 15 76] Fr Millas on R of N916, sp. Med, shd; htd wc (some cont); chem disp; shwrs inc; el pts (6-10A) €3.50; gas; lndtte; shop; snacks; bar; BBQ; playgrnd; pool high ssn; tennis 500m; 20% statics; dogs €1.80; adv bkg rec high ssn; quiet; red low ssn. "New, friendly owners 2005; site being upgraded, inc enhanced bar/rest area." ♦ € 12.60   2005*

MILLAU *10E1* (NE Urban) **Camping Larribal**, Ave de Millau Plage, 12100 Millau [05 65 59 08 04; camping.larribal@wanadoo.fr; www.camping larribal.com] Exit Millau on D991 (sp Nant), cross rv & at rndabt take 3rd exit, site on L. Med, mkd pitch, shd; htd wc; chem disp; mv service pnt; shwrs inc; el pts (6A) inc; gas; lndtte; ice; shop; tradsmn; playgrnd; rv sw adj; shgl beach; TV; 5% statics; phone; adv bkg; quiet; red 30+ days; CCI. "Excel, well kept site; wc old but spotless." ♦ 1 May-30 Sep. € 12.00   2005*

MILLAU *10E1* (1km NE Urban) **Camping du Viaduc, Millau-Cureplat**, 121 Ave du Millau-Plage, 12100 Millau [05 65 60 15 75; fax 05 65 61 36 51; info@ camping-du-viaduc.com; www.camping-du-viaduc.com] Exit Millau on N991 (sp Nant) over Rv Tarn via Cureplat bdge. At rndabt take D187 dir Paulhe, 1st campsite on L. Lge, hdg/mkd pitch, hdstg, shd; wc (some cont); chem disp; some serviced pitches; baby facs; shwrs inc; el pts (6A) €3; gas; lndtte; ice; shop & 1km; rest; snacks; bar; BBQ; playgrnd; pool; paddling pool; rv sw & private sand beach; entmnt; child entmnt; Eng spkn; cc acc; red long stay; CCI. "Easy walk to Millau cent; many sports & activities in area; conv for gorges & viaduct." ♦ 14 Apr-25 Sep. € 21.00   2005*

See advertisement

MILLAU *10E1* (1km NE Urban) **Camping Les Erables, Route de Millau-Plage**, 12100 Millau [05 65 59 15 13; fax 05 65 59 06 59; chrismartin2@wanadoo.fr] Exit Millau on D991 (sp Nant) over Rv Tarn bdge; take L at island sp to Millau-Plage & site on L immed after Camping du Viaduc & bef Camping Larribal. Med, hdg/mkd pitch, pt shd; wc; chem disp; baby facs; shwrs inc; el pts (6A) inc (poss rev pol); lndtte; ice; shop; snacks high ssn; bar; BBQ; playgrnd; direct acc to rv - sw & canoeing; entmnt; TV; dogs €1.20; phone; Eng spkn; adv bkg; some rd noise; cc acc; CCI. "Excel; v clean; friendly, helpful owners." ♦ 1 Apr-30 Sep. € 15.80   2005*

MILLAU *10E1* (2km NE Urban) **Camping Cote-Sud, Ave de l'Aigoual**, 12100 Millau [tel/fax 05 65 61 18 83] Fr N turn L at 2nd traff island sp 'Camping'. Site on R over bdge in 200m. Fr S on N9 cross rv on by-pass, turn R at 1st traff island sp Nant on D991, cross bdge, site on R in 200m, sp. Med, mkd pitch, pt sl, shd; wc; chem disp; shwrs inc; el pts (5A) €2.76; gas; lndtte; ice; shop; snacks; playgrnd; pool; rv sw adj; games, fishing, canoe hire; Eng spkn; adv bkg; CCI. "Lge mkt Fri; conv Tarn Gorges; pleasant, friendly staff; gd long stay." 1 Apr-30 Sep. € 11.00   2002*

MILLAU *10E1* (9km NE Rural) **Camping d'Aguessac, 12520 Aguessac** [05 65 59 84 67; fax 05 65 59 08 72; camping.aguessac@ wanadoo.fr; www.camping-aguessac.com] Site on N9 in vill, ent on R immed past level x-ing when app fr Millau. Med, pt shd; wc; chem disp; shwrs inc; el pts (6-10A) €2.50; gas; lndtte; shops adj; rest; rv adj; fishing; canoeing; games area; sports grnd adj; entmnt; 10% statics; dogs €1; Eng spkn; quiet; red long stay/low ssn; CCI. "V pleasant & helpful owners; rvside site with mountain views; gd sized pitches; new san facs (2004); pleasant open-air rest; picturesque vill & viaduct; excel touring base; excel long stay." ♦ 1 May-30 Sep. € 11.00   2005*

MILLAU *10E1* (E Rural) **Camping Club Le Millau-Plage, Route de Millau-Plage, 12100 Millau** [05 65 60 10 97; fax 05 65 60 16 88; info@ campingmillauplage.com; www.campingmillau plage.com] Exit Millau on D991 (sp Nant) over Rv Tarn & take 1st L (unclassed rd). Site in 1km (4th site) on L. Lge, mkd pitch, pt shd; wc (some cont); chem disp; shwrs inc; el pts (5A) inc; gas; lndtte; shop; rest; snacks; bar; playgrnd; pool; multi-sports area; child entmnt; TV; play rm; 10% statics; dogs €2.50; poss cr; Eng spkn; adv bkg; quiet; red low ssn; cc acc; CCI. "Magnificent scenery." ♦ 1 Apr-30 Sep. € 22.00   2004*

MILLAU *10E1* (1km E Urban) **Camping Les Deux Rivieres, 61 Ave de l'Aigoual, 12100 Millau** [tel/fax 05 65 60 00 27] Fr N on D911 foll sp for Montpellier down to rv. At rndabt by bdge turn L over bdge, site immed on L well sp. Fr S D992 3rd bdge, sp camping. Med, mkd pitch, shd; htd wc (50% cont); shwrs inc; el pts (8A) €2.40; gas; lndry rm; shops adj; tradsmn; snacks; playgrnd; fishing; phone; poss cr; quiet; CCI. "Gd base for touring gorges; facs aged & in need of refurb." 1 Apr-31 Oct. € 13.50   2005*

MILLAU *10E1* (1km E Urban) **Camping Les Rivages, Ave de l'Aigoual, 12100 Millau** [05 65 61 01 07; fax 05 65 59 03 56; campinglesrivages@wanadoo.fr; www.campingles rivages.com] Fr Millau take D991 dir Nant (sp Gorges du Dourbie & Campings). Cross Rv Tarn & cont on this rd, site is 500m after bdge on R. Lge, pt shd; htd wc (some cont); chem disp (wc); serviced pitches (additional charge); baby facs; shwrs inc; el pts (6A) inc (poss rev pol); gas; lndtte; ice; sm shop; supmkt 2km; tradsmn; rest; snacks; bar; BBQ (gas or electric); playgrnd; 2 pools; tennis; rv sw; fishing; canoeing; games rm; mini-golf; cycle hire; archery; handgliding; entmnt; TV rm; 10% statics; dogs €3; phone; poss cr; Eng spkn; adv bkg; quiet; red low ssn; CCI. "V scenic, pleasant site, esp rv/side pitches, in o'standing area; gd security; excursions; v busy high ssn; Gorge du Tarn nr for family canoeing; staff v helpful & friendly; mkt Wed & Fri am; vg rest & bar; san facs clean but need update." ♦ 1 May-30 Sep. € 24.50 ABS - D20   2005*

MILLAU *10E1* (2.5km E) **Camping St Lambert, Ave de l'Aigoual, 12100 Millau** [05 65 60 00 48; fax 05 65 61 12 12] Fr N on either N9 or D11 foll dir D992 St Affrique/Albi. Turn L at rndabt over bdge onto D991 dir Nant. Site on R, sp. Fr S on D992 turn R at rndabt & dir as above. Med, shd; wc (some cont); chem disp; mv service pnt; shwrs inc; el pts (6A) €2.50; gas; lndtte; ice; shop; bar; playgrnd; sand/shgl beach & rv sw adj; dogs €1; poss cr; adv bkg; quiet; CCI. "Particularly gd low ssn; owners helpful; twin-axles not acc; gd long/sh stay." 1 May-30 Sep. € 12.00   2005*

MILLY LA FORET *4E3* (4km SE Rural) **Camping La Musardiere, Route des Grandes Vallees, 91490 Milly-la-Foret** [tel/fax 01 64 98 91 91; lamusardiere@infonie.fr] Fr S exit A6 junc 14 onto N152 then D16 dir Milly. Fr N exit A6 junc 13 onto D372 to Milly. Site on sm rd joining D16 & D837/D409. Lge, mkd pitch, hdstg, pt sl, pt shd; htd wc (some cont); chem disp; mv service pnt; shwrs inc; el pts (6A) inc; lndtte; ice; shop 4km; tradsmn (w/e only low ssn); playgrnd; htd pool high ssn; 60% statics; dogs; Eng spkn; adv bkg; quiet; cc acc; CCI. "Excel wooded site; excel pool closes 1200-1400 every day (proper sw trunks only); gd walks in nrby forest; €20 dep for barrier key; helpful, friendly staff; some unmade pitches & app rds; vg site." ♦ 16 Feb-1 Dec. € 20.50   2005*

See advertisement on next page (top)

MIMIZAN *7D1* (2km N Rural) **Camp Municipal du Lac, Ave de Woolsack, 40200 Mimizan** [05 58 09 01 21; fax 05 58 09 43 06] Fr Mimizan N on D87, site on L. Lge, mkd pitch; pt shd; wc; chem disp; baby facs; shwrs inc; el pts (3A) inc; gas; lndtte; ice; shop; playgrnd; sand beach 6km; lake adj - no sw; boating; fishing; entmnt; dogs €1; poss cr; adv bkg; quiet; red low ssn. "Rec; gd site." ♦ ltd. 1 Apr-11 Sep. € 11.10   2003*

MIMIZAN *7D1* (10km N Rural) **Camp Municipal du Lac, 1590 Route du Lac, 40200 Ste Eulalie-en-Born** [05 58 09 70 10; camping@sainte eulalieenborn.fr; www.sainteeulalieenborn.fr] N fr Mimizan on D87/D652. Pass Ste Eulalie & turn W at water tower, site sp. Med, mkd pitch, pt shd; wc; chem disp; mv service pnt; shwrs inc; el pts (6A) inc; gas; lndtte; snacks; bar; pool; lake sw & beach adj; boat hire; games area; some statics; dogs €2; phone; poss cr; Eng spkn; adv bkg; quiet; cc acc; CCI. "Friendly site on Lake Biscarrosse; vg for familes; do not confuse with site of same name on Lac Aureilhan, 2km N of Mimizan." Apr-Sep. € 15.00   2005*

FRANCE

MIMIZAN *7D1* (3km E Rural) **Camping de la Route des Lacs**, 40200 Aureilhan [05 58 09 01 42; fax 05 58 09 20 83] 100m off D626 on E side of Aureilhan. Clearly sp on D626. Med, mkd pitch, shd; wc; chem disp; mv service pnt; shwrs inc; el pts (6A) €2.80; gas; lndtte; ice; shop; tradsmn; snacks; bar; playgrnd; pool; sand beach, lake sw & watersports 2km; ocean beach 8km; TV rm; 20% statics; dogs; phone; Eng spkn; adv bkg; quiet; CCI. "Unspoilt site ideal for long, restful stay; gd for families." 1 Apr-30 Sep. € 11.80   2002*

MIMIZAN *7D1* (3km E Rural) **Escapades Terre Oceane Camping Aurilandes**, 1001 Promenade de l'Etang, 40200 Aureilhan [05 58 09 10 88 or 05 46 55 10 01; fax 05 46 55 10 00; info@campingterreoceane.com; www.campingterre oceane.com] Fr N10 S of Bordeaux take D626 W fr Aureilhan twrds Mimizan. Site 1km fr D626 by Lake Aureilhan. V lge, mkd pitch, pt shd; wc; mv service pnt; sauna; shwrs inc; el pts (6-10A) €3; lndtte; shop; tradsmn; rest; playgrnd; htd pool complex; paddling pool; spa; sand beach 10km; dir access to lake; watersports; tennis; games rm; entmnt; child entmnt; statics; Eng spkn; adv bkg; cc acc; quiet; cc acc. ♦ 13 May-16 Sep. € 29.00   2005*

See advertisement below

MIMIZAN *7D1* (3km E Rural) **Parc Saint James Eurolac**, 1001 Promenade de l'Etang, 40200 Aureilhan [05 58 09 02 87; fax 05 58 09 41 89; info@camping-parcsaintjames.com; www.camping-parcsaintjames.com] Fr Bordeaux take N10 S to Labouheyre & cont on D626 W twd Mimizan. Turn R 3km bef Mimizan onto D329 twd Etang d'Aureilhan. Site beside lake. V lge, hdg/mkd pitch, pt sl, pt shd; wc; chem disp; mv service pnt; baby facs; sauna; shwrs inc; el pts (6-10A) €3; gas; lndtte; ice; shop; supmkt; rest; snacks; bar; BBQ area; playgrnd; htd pool & waterpark; paddling pool; sand beach 10km; lake sw adj; fishing; sailing; canoe hire; windsurfing; tennis; cycle hire; games area; horseriding nr; archery; mini-golf; games rm; golf 2km; entmnt; TV rm; 90% statics; dogs €5; Eng spkn; adv bkg; quiet; cc acc; red low ssn; CCI. ♦ 8 Apr-30 Sep. € 26.00   2005*

See advertisement opposite (top)

MIMIZAN PLAGE *7D1* (1km E Coastal) **Camp Municipal La Plage**, Blvd d'Atlantique, 40200 Mimizan-Plage [05 58 09 00 32; fax 05 58 09 44 94; contact@mimizan-camping.com] Turn off N10 at Labouheyre on D626 to Mimizan (28km). Approx 5km after Mimizan turn R. Site in approx 500m. V lge, pt sl, shd; wc; mv service pnt; shwrs; el pts (6A) inc; ice; shops 500m; playgrnd; sand beach 850m; entmnt; poss cr; noisy. Easter-30 Sep. € 17.10   2002*

MIMIZAN PLAGE *7D1* (3km E Coastal) **Club Marina-Landes, Rue Marina, 40202 Mimizan-Plage-Sud [05 58 09 12 66; fax 05 58 09 16 40; contact@clubmarina.com; www.marinalandes. com]** Turn R off N10 at Labouheyre onto D626 to Mimizan (28km). Approx 5km fr Mimizan-Plage turn L at Camping Marina sp on dual c'way. Site sp on S bank of rv. V lge, hdg pitch, hdstg, pt shd; wc; chem disp; mv service pnt; baby facs; shwrs inc; el pts (10A) €3; gas; lndtte; lndry rm; shop; rest; snacks; bar; BBQ; playgrnd; 2 pools (1 htd, covrd); paddling pool; sand beach 500m; tennis; horseriding; games area; mini-golf; cycle hire; games rm; fitness rm; golf 7km; entmnt; child entmnt; internet; TV rm; some statics; dogs €4; poss cr; Eng spkn; adv bkg; cc acc; quiet; CCI. "Excursions to Dax, Biarritz & Bordeaux areas; excel leisure facs; vg long/sh stay." ♦ 12 May-18 Sep. € 36.65 (3 persons)   2005*

See advertisement below

MIOS see Audenge *7D1*

†**MIRAMBEAU** *7C2* (8km S Rural) **Camping Chez Gendron, 33820 St Palais [tel/fax 05 57 32 96 47; chezgendron@wanadoo.fr]** N fr Blaye on N137; turn to St Palais, past church 1km; turn L twd St Ciers. Site sp R down narr lane. Or N fr Bordeaux on A10 exit juncs 37 or 38 onto N137 to St Palais & as above. Sm, mkd pitch, terr, pt sl, pt shd; htd wc; chem disp; shwrs; fam bthrm; el pts (6A) €1.70; lndtte; shops 3km; tradsmn; rest; snacks; bar; BBQ; playgrnd; pool; paddling pool; games area; tennis 3km; TV rm; dogs; phone; Eng spkn; adv bkg; quiet; red low ssn; CCI. "Friendly Dutch owners re-developing site (2004/05) inc new san facs; conv NH fr m'way; peaceful, relaxed atmosphere." ♦ € 16.00   2005*

MIRAMONT DE GUYENNE *7D2* (6km NE Rural) **Camp Municipal Le Dropt, Rue du Pont, 47800 Allemans-du-Dropt [05 53 20 68 61 or 05 53 20 23 37 (Mairie); fax 05 53 20 68 91]** Fr D668 site well sp in vill. Sm, shd; wc (some cont); chem disp (wc); shwrs inc; el pts (20A) €2; shop 400m; rest, snacks & bar 400m; playgrnd; quiet; CCI. "V attractive, grassed site on opp side of Rv Dropt to vill; v quiet; v friendly warden; excel." 1 May-31 Oct. € 7.00   2005*

FRANCE

CAMPING ★★★
L'ILE DU BIDOUNET
82200-MOISSAC
TEL : 00 33 (0)5 63 32 52 52

Rental of tent bungalows.
Swimming pool from June till September.

Please visit our website to make your reservation:
www.moissac.fr (Choose "tourisme" and then "hébergements")

Situated in the heart of the South-West region Mossaïc is a charming city full of history with its Roman Quarter which is classified by Unesco as World Heritage. Recognized as "Qualité Tourisme" and member of "Camping Qualité" Camping l'Ile du Bidounet offers you all the comfort of a three star camping and invites you to come and spend your holidays in the tranquillity of the riverside in a green environment at only 2 km of the town centre. Ideal for fishing.
More than just a stop this is a holiday destination from which you can discover great places to visit like Cahors, Rocamadour, Toulouse, Albi and Lourdes.
Access: Route A62, exit Castelsarrasin and then follow direction Moissac by route RN113.
Open from 01/04 till 30/09.

MIRAMONT DE GUYENNE *7D2* (1.5km SE Rural) Camping Lac du Saut du Loup, 47800 Miramont-de-Guyenne [05 53 93 22 35; fax 05 53 93 55 33; saut.du.loup@wanadoo.fr] Sp fr D933 in Miramont, site on S side of D227 sp Lavergne. Med, hdg pitch, pt sl, pt shd; wc; chem disp; shwrs inc; el pts (6-10A) €2.92-4.15; lndtte; ice; shops 1.5km; rest; pool; lake sw (supervised); boating; fishing; horseriding; tennis; entmnt; phone; adv bkg; quiet; red 7+ days; 5% red CCI. "Beautifully maintained site; pleasant & secluded setting; lakeside rest open all year; gd touring base for Bastide towns; excel long/sh stay." 15 Mar-15 Nov. € 12.75 2004*

†**MIRAMONT DE GUYENNE** *7D2* (13km W Rural) Parc St Vincent, 47120 Levignac-de-Guyenne [05 53 83 75 17] Fr Miramont take D668 to Allemans-du-Dropt, then D211. At junc D708 turn S to Levignac, site sp. Fr Marmande N on D708 sp St Foy & Duras. Turn E at Levignac church to further green site sp on D228. Sm, pt shd; wc; chem disp; mv service pnt; shwrs inc; el pts (5A); gas; lndtte; ice; shops 2.5km; tradsmn; rest; BBQ; playgrnd; pool; lake sw 6km; entmnt; TV rm; 90% statics; adv bkg; quiet; Eng spkn; dogs; phone; 10% red 7+ days; CCI. ♦ 2003*

MIRANDE *8F2* (500m E) Camp Municipal L'Ile du Pont, 32300 Mirande [05 62 66 64 11 or 05 62 66 52 87 (Mairie); fax 05 62 66 69 86; www. chalet-iledupont.com] On N21 Auch-Tarbes, foll camping sp as rd ent Mirande fr either dir. Med, pt shd; wc (cont); chem disp; shwrs inc; el pts (10A) inc; lndtte; tradsmn; lndtte; pool; canoeing; sailing; windsurfing; tennis; fishing; archery; dogs €1; quiet (poss rd noise); red low ssn; adv bkg rec; cc not acc; CCI. "Excel site; gd long stay; helpful staff; €15.24 dep ent gate key; recep/barrier clsd 1200-1500; many sports free; bread order/pay previous night." 1 Apr-15 Sep. € 14.00 2002*

†**MIRANDE** *8F2* (4km S Rural) Aire Naturelle La Hourguette, 32300 Berdoues [tel/fax 05 62 66 58 47] Exit Mirande on N21 S dir Tarbes. 1st L after 'Intermarche' onto D524 to Berdoues, sp 'Camping Le Ferme'. After 600m, turn R at fork in rd. Site in 2km. Sm, pt sl, pt shd; wc; chem disp; shwrs inc; el pts (10A) €2; lndtte; rest, snacks, bar 3km; playgrnd; pool 3km; 25% statics; dogs; Eng spkn; quiet. "Friendly Dutch owners; adequate san facs; CL-style site." ♦ ltd € 10.00 2005*

MIRANDOL BOURGNOUNAC see Carmaux *8E4*

MIREPOIX (ARIEGE) *8F4* (1km E) Camp Municipal Dynam'eau, Route de Limoux 09500 Mirepoix [05 61 68 28 63 or 05 61 68 10 47 (Mairie); fax 05 61 68 89 48] E fr Pamiers on D119 to Mirepoix. Site well sp on D626. Med, mkd pitch, shd; wc (some cont); shwrs; el pts €3; shops 1km; pool; fishing 1km; tennis; dogs €2; quiet. "If warden not present pay at Mairie in town; interesting medieval town; gd mkt Mon; facs being updated 2004/05." ♦ 1 Jul-1 Sep. € 11.00 2004*

†**MIREPOIX (ARIEGE)** *8F4* (10km SE) Camp Municipal La Pibola, 09500 Camon [05 61 68 12 14; fax 05 61 68 10 59] E fr Pamier to Mirepoix. S on D625 twds Lavelanet. L after 4km sp Lagarde. Foll D7 for 4km sp on R, 1km to site. App is steep & narr. Sm, terr, pt shd, mkd pitch; wc; chem disp; shwrs inc; el pts (10A) €2.30; rest; snacks; shop; playgrnd; pool; adv bkg; quiet. "Gd sh stay." € 9.50 2002*

†**MIREPOIX (ARIEGE)** *8F4* (10km SE Rural) Camping La Besse, 09500 Camon [05 61 68 84 63; fax 05 61 68 80 29] Fr Mirepoix take D625 S. In 3km turn L onto D7 & foll to Camon. Site sp fr vill 1km on L. Sm, pt sl, pt shd; wc (some cont); shwrs inc; el pts (10A) €2.10; gas 7km; lndtte; ice; BBQ; playgrnd; pool; lake sw 10km; entmnt; adv bkg; quiet. "Site situated on working farm; splendid views; friendly farmer & family; facs poss stretched high ssn; gd long stay." ♦ ltd € 11.00 2003*

---

† Site open all year   *Tell us about the sites you visit*

MIRMANDE *9D2* (3km SE Rural) **Camping La Poche, 26270 Mirmande [04 75 63 02 88; fax 04 75 63 14 94; camping@la-poche.com]** Fr N on N7, 3km after Loriol turn L onto D57 sp Mirmande. Site sp in 7km on L. Fr S on N7 turn R onto D204 in Saulce & foll sp. Med, hdg/mkd pitch, some hdstg, terr, shd; wc; chem disp; baby facs; shwrs inc; el pts (6A) €4; lndtte; shop; snacks; rest & bar high ssn; playgrnd; pool; paddling pool; games area; entmnt; TV; poss cr; 90% statics; adv bkg; quiet; red low ssn; CCI. "Set in wooded valley; excel scenery; gd walking/cycling area; friendly owner." 15 Apr-15 Oct.
€ 15.70   2005*

Will you fill in the site report forms at the back of the guide, or shall I?

MITTLACH see Munster *6F3*

†MODANE *9C4* (7km NE Rural) **Camp Municipal La Buidonniere, 73500 Aussois [04 79 20 35 58 or 04 79 20 30 80; fax 04 79 20 35 58; info@aussois.com]** Fr cent of Aussois take D215 to Modane. In 400m turn L & foll sp. Fr Modane take 2nd R after ent Aussois & foll sp. Lge, mkd pitch, hdstg, pt sl, terr, unshd; htd wc (cont); chem disp; shwrs inc; el pts (10A) inc; lndtte; shops 500m; playgrnd; 50% statics; adv bkg; CCI. "Mountain views; skiing resort." ♦ € 14.80   2004*

MODANE *9C4* (10km NE) **Camp Municipal Val d'Ambin, 73500 Bramans-le-Verney [04 79 05 22 88 or 06 16 51 90 91 (mob); fax 04 79 05 23 16; campingdambin@aol.com]** 10km after Modane on N6 twd Lanslebourg, take 2nd turning R twd vill of Bramans, & foll camping sp, site by church. App fr Lanslebourg, after 12km turn L at camping sp on N6 at end of vill. Med, unshd; wc; shwrs; el pts (8-12A) €3.20; shops 5km; playgrnd; pool 10km; dogs €1.50; no adv bkg; v quiet. "Away-from-it-all site worth the climb; beautiful area." 15 May-15 Sep.
€ 9.50   2005*

MOELAN SUR MER see Pont Aven *2F2*

MOIRANS EN MONTAGNE see St Claude *9A3*

MOISSAC *8E3* (9km SE Urban) **Camping Intercommunal du Plan d'Eau, Base de Loisirs, 82210 St Nicholas-de-la-Grave [05 63 95 50 02; fax 05 63 95 50 01]** Fr Moissac on N113 turn S on D15 to St Nicolas-de-la-Grave; foll Int'l camp sps to x-rds; site 500m on R; app by narr suspension bdge 2.5m bet pillars. Med, pt shd; wc; shwrs; el pts (6A) €2.29; lndry rm; shop 1km; pizzaria nr; playgrnd; pool; cycle hire; archery; quiet; adv bkg; CCI. "Gd sports complex adj." 15 Jun-15 Sep. € 9.00
                                           2002*

MOISSAC *8E3* (1km S Rural) **Camp Municipal L'Ile de Bidounet, St Benoit, 82200 Moissac [tel/fax 05 63 32 52 52; camping-bidounet@moissac.fr; www.moissac.fr]** Exit A62 at junc 9 at Castelsarrasin onto N113 dir Moissac, site sp. Or fr N on N113 cross Rv Tarn, turn L at 1st rndabt & foll camp sp, site on L by rv. Med, hdg/mkd pitch, pt shd; wc (some cont); chem disp; mv service pnt; baby facs; shwrs inc; el pts (6A) inc; gas 2km; lndtte; ice; shop, rest & snacks 2km; tradsmn; bar; BBQ; playgrnd; pool; fishing; watersports; boat & canoe hire; cycle hire; entmnt; 10% statics; dogs €1.10; phone; Eng spkn; adv bkg; quiet; red long stay; cc acc; CCI. "Excel rvside site; height restriction 3.05m for tunnel at ent & tight turn lge o'fits; surcharge €30.50 for twin-axle vans; recep & barrier clsd 1230-1500; helpful staff; clean san facs; highly rec; Moissac lovely, historic area." ♦ 1 Apr-30 Sep.
€ 14.60   2005*

See advertisement

MOLIERES (DORDOGNE) see Lalinde *7C3*

MOLIERES (TARN ET GARONNE) *8E3* (Rural) **Domaine des Merlanes, 82220 Molieres [05 63 67 64 05; fax 05 63 24 28 96; simone@domaine-de-merlanes.com]** Fr N on N20, exit on D20 to Montpezat-de-Quercy & Molieres; sp in vill. Sm, terr, pt shd; wc; chem disp; baby facs; shwrs; el pts (6A) inc; tradsmn; rest; bar; playgrnd; htd pool; 10% statics; poss cr; Eng spkn; quiet; red low ssn; cc acc; CCI. "Pleasant, Dutch owned; clean & well-kept; excel child facs; adv bkg ess high ssn; excel." 1 May-3 Sep. € 16.50   2005*

MOLIETS ET MAA *8E1* (2km W Coastal) **Airotel Camping St Martin, Ave de l'Ocean 40660 Moliets-Plage [05 58 48 52 30; fax 05 58 48 50 73; contact@camping-saint-martin.fr; www.camping-saint-martin.fr]** On N10 exit for Leon, Moliets-et-Maa. At Moliets foll sp to Moliets-Plage. Camp site after Les Cigales, by beach. V lge, hdg/mkd pitches, pt sl, terr, pt shd; htd wc (some cont); chem disp; some serviced pitches (surcharge); baby facs; sauna; shwrs inc; el pts (10A) inc; gas; lndtte; ice; shops; supmkt; rests; snacks; bar; playgrnd; 3 pools (1 htd, covrd); paddling pool; jacuzzi; dir access to sand beach 300m; rv 250m; watersports; tennis; golf 3km; games area; cycle paths; entmnt high ssn; TV rm; dogs €3 (free low ssn); Eng spkn; adv bkg rec high ssn (fee); quiet; cc acc; red low ssn; CCI. "Excel family site; vg san facs." Easter-30 Oct.
€ 32.50   2005*

FRANCE

AN OASIS SITUATED ON THE ILE DE FRANCE AND CLOSE TO BEAUCE

www.camping-boislajustice.com

LE BOIS DE LA JUSTICE ★★★

91930 MONNERVILLE

Bookings: tel.: 00 33 (0)1 64 95 05 34
Fax: 00 33 (0)1 64 95 17 31

Just off Beauce, in a forest with pine trees and leaf trees. Heated swimming pool – bar – children's games – table tennis – French boules – volleyball.
Many hiking paths and bicycle routes. 50 km from Paris, Versailles and Orléans. Close to Fontainebleau and the Loire Castles. The campsite is ideally situated to visit these cities with their rich history and to return at night to the peace and quiet of the countryside.

Open from 4/02 till 26/11

MOLIETS ET MAA *8E1* (2km W Coastal) **Camping Les Cigales,** Ave de l'Ocean, 40660 Moliets-et- Maa [05 58 48 51 18; fax 05 58 48 53 27; reception@ camping-les-cigales.fr; www.camping- les-cigales. fr] In Moliets-et-Maa, turn W for Moliets-Plage, site on R in vill. Lge, pt sl, shd; wc; chem disp; mv service pnt; shwrs inc; el pts (5A) €2.80; lndtte; shop; tradsmn; rest; snacks; bar; BBQ; playgrnd; sand beach 300m; games area; TV; many statics; adv bkg; quiet; cc acc; CCI. "Site in pine wood - sandy soil; narr access tracks; poorly lit at night; excel beach & surfing; many shops, rests 100m." Easter-30 Sep. € 16.00   2005*

MOLOMPIZE see Massiac *9C1*

MOLSHEIM see Obernai *6E3*

MONCEAUX SUR DORDOGNE see Argentat *7C4*

MONDRAGON see Bollene *9D2*

MONESTIER DE CLERMONT *9C3* (700m W Rural) **Camp Municipal Les Portes du Trieves,** Chemin de Chambons, 38650 Monestier-de-Clermont [04 76 34 01 24; fax 04 76 34 19 75; campingles portesdubrieves@libertysurf.fr] On N75, sp in vill. Turn W at traff lts, foll sp to site, 700m up steep hill behind pool. Sm, hdg/mkd pitch, hdstg, pt terr, pt shd; wc; chem disp; shwrs inc; el pts (6A) €2.29; lndry rm; rest & shop in vill; playgrnd; htd pool 50m; tennis adj; lake 12km; quiet; adv bkg; CCI. "Watersports at lake; spectacular countryside." ♦ 1 May-30 Sep. € 9.15   2002*

MONESTIER DE CLERMONT *9C3* (6km W Rural) **Camping Les 4 Saisons,** 38650 Gresse-en-Vercors [04 74 34 30 27; fax 04 76 34 39 52; becquetjacques@aol.com] Fr Sisteron take N75 twd Grenoble. At N end of Monestier-de-Clermont, take D8 for 13km. Med, pt sl, unshd; wc; chem disp; shwrs inc; el pts (2-10A) €2.30-4; lndtte; rest 200m; snacks; playgrnd; htd pool; ski stn; TV; dogs €1.30; Eng spkn; adv bkg (rec in summer & ess in winter). "Friendly; at high altitude & poss cold even in Aug." ♦ 21 Dec-9 Mar & 24 May-1 Sep. € 12.20   2003*

MONFORT *8E3* (Urban) **Camp Municipal de Monfort,** 32120 Monfort [tel/fax 05 62 06 83 26 (Mairie)] SE fr Fleurance on D654 to Monfort, then foll sp to 'Centre Ville' & then camping sp. Town has narr rds so foll sp. Sm, hdg pitch, pt sl, pt shd; wc; chem disp (wc); shwrs inc, el pts (6A) €1.50; shop, rest & bar 200m; BBQ; playgrnd; pool 19km; dogs €0.50; phone; quiet; cc not acc; CCI. "Excel CL-type site on ramparts of Bastide town; marvellous views; pitch yourself, warden calls am & pm."
1 May-15 Oct. € 8.00   2005*

MONISTROL D'ALLIER *9C1* (Urban) **Camp Municipal du Vivier,** 43580 Monistrol-d'Allier [04 71 57 24 24 or 04 71 57 21 21 (Mairie); fax 04 71 57 25 03] Fr Le Puy-en-Velay W on D589 to Monistrol d'Allier. Turn L in vill immed after rlwy stn & cont down steep entry rd bef x-ing bdge. Site sp in town cent. Sm, mkd pitch, pt shd; wc; chem disp; shwrs inc; el pts (5-10A) €2.80; shops, rest, snacks; bar 200m; BBQ; rv sw; no statics; dogs; phone; train 500m; quiet; CCI. "Vg site situated in steep sided rv valley; rv activities avail; vg long/sh stays." ♦ ltd.
15 Apr-15 Sep. € 8.30   2004*

MONISTROL D'ALLIER *9C1* (4km N Rural) **Camp Municipal Le Marchat,** 43580 St Privat-d'Allier [tel/fax 04 71 57 22 13] Fr Le Puy-en-Velay W on D589. Turn R in cent of vill at petrol stn, site on R in 200m. Sm, hdg pitch, terr, shd; wc; chem disp; shwrs inc; el pts (10A) inc; shops, bar in vill; quiet. "Beautifully kept site; not suitable lge o'fits; excel long/sh stay." ♦ ltd. 1 May-30 Oct. € 6.75   2003*

MONISTROL SUR LOIRE *9C1* **Camp Municipal Beau Sejour,** Route de Chaponas, 43120 Monistrol-sur-Loire [04 71 66 53 90] Site on N88, on W edge of town, sp. Exit by-pass at 1 of exits to Monistrol - head for casino, then Intermarche. Med, hdg pitch, pt sl, shd; htd wc; shwrs inc; el pts (6A) €2.44; lndtte; supmkt adj; playgrnd; pool, tennis adj; 90% statics; adv bkg; quiet. "Gd NH." ♦
1 Apr-31 Oct. € 10.00   2004*

---

† Site open all year   406   *Help update this Guide*

MONISTROL SUR LOIRE *9C1* (7km SE Rural) Camping Le Vaubarlet, 43600 Ste Sigolene [04 71 66 64 95; fax 04 71 66 11 98; camping@vaubarlet.com; www.vaubarlet.com] Fr Monistrol take D44 SE twd Ste Sigolene & turn R into vill. In vill take D43 dir Grazac for 6km. Site by Rv Duniere, ent L bef bdge. Site well sp fr vill. Med, mkd pitch, pt shd; wc; chem disp; mv service pnt; shwrs inc; el pts (6A) €3 (poss rev pol); Indtte; shop & 6km; tradsmn; rest; snacks; bar; playgrnd; htd pool; paddling pool; rv sw adj; fishing; cycle hire; games area; entmnt; TV rm; 15% statics; phone; dogs €1; Eng spkn; adv bkg; quiet; red low ssn; cc acc; CCI. "V friendly & helpful staff; trout rv; snail museum nrby; gd weaving museum in Ste Sigolene; well-run site; excel san facs." ♦ 1 May-30 Sep. € 16.00 (CChq acc)   2005*

Mustn't forget to post our site report forms to The Club, otherwise sites might be deleted.

MONNERVILLE *4E3* (Rural) Camping Le Bois de la Justice, Mereville, 91930 Monnerville [01 64 95 05 34; fax 01 64 95 17 31; www.camping-boislajustice.com] Fr N20 S of Etampes, turn onto D18 at Monnerville, site well sp. Long narr app rd. Med, hdg/mkd pitch, pt sl, pt shd; wc; chem disp (wc); mv service pnt; shwrs inc; el pts (6A) €2.50; Indtte; ice; shop; tradsmn; snacks high ssn; bar; BBQ; cooking facs; playgrnd; htd pool high ssn; tennis; games area; 50% statics; dogs €1; phone; Eng spkn; adv bkg; quiet; red low ssn; cc acc. "Delightful woodland oasis in open countryside; v pleasant welcome; ideal for Chartres, Fontainebleau, Orleans, Paris." ♦ 4 Feb-26 Nov. € 19.50   2005*

See advertisement opposite

MONPAZIER *7D3* (3km SW) Camping Moulin de David, Route de Villereal, 24540 Gaugeac-Monpazier [05 53 22 65 25; fax 05 53 23 99 76; info@moulin-de-david.com; www.moulin-de-david.com] Fr Monpazier, take D2 SW twd Villereal, site sp on L after 3km. Narr app rds. Lge, hdg/mkd pitch, unshd; htd wc; chem disp; mv service pnt; serviced pitch; baby facs; shwrs inc; el pts (5A) inc; gas; Indtte; ice; shop; tradsmn; rest; snacks; bar; BBQ; playgrnd; pool; paddling pool; lake sw & waterslide high ssn; fishing adj; tennis; games area; games rm; cycle hire; archery; internet; entmnt; 40% statics; dogs €2.90; poss cr; Eng spkn; adv bkg; quiet; cc acc; see ad for UK address for site info; CCI. "Charming, highly rec site nr lovely town; excel facs; helpful owners; recep 0830-1200 & 1400-1900; mkt Thu Monpazier." ♦ 20 May-9 Sep. € 27.55 (CChq acc) ABS - D14   2005*

See advertisement below

MONPLAISANT see Belves *7D3*

MONSAGUEL see Issigeac *7D3*

MONT DORE, LE *7B4* (Urban) Camp Municipal des Crouzets, 4 Ave des Crouzets, 63240 Le Mont-Dore [tel/fax 04 73 65 21 60 or 04 73 65 22 00 (Mairie); camping.crouzets@wanadoo.fr] Ent on D130 at N end of town on rd to La Bourboule opp rlwy stn. Lge, mkd pitch, hdstg, pt sl, unshd; htd wc; chem disp; mv service pnt adj; shwrs inc; el pts (6-10A) €2.60-5.15; Indtte; ice; tradsmn; shops & rests adj; BBQ; playgrnd; pool 4km; sports area; dogs €1.30; poss cr; Eng spkn; cc acc. "Cent position in town but quiet; gd sized pitches; well run; excel san facs; helpful warden; cable car to Puy de Sancy, for walks to mountain tracks." ♦ 15 Dec-20 Oct. € 9.00   2005*

MONT DORE, LE *7B4* (12km N Rural) Camp Municipal La Buge, 63210 Rochefort-Montagne [04 73 65 84 98 or 04 73 65 82 51; fax 04 73 65 93 69; mairie.rochefort@rochefort-montagne.com] Fr NE on N89. Thro vill L after x-ing bdge. Sp 200m R. Med, pt shd; wc; chem disp; shwrs inc; el pts (15A) €2.55; Indtte; shop adj; playgrnd; rv 500m; tennis; dogs €0.82; adv bkg. 1 Jun-15 Sep. € 8.40 (3 persons)   2003*

MONT DORE, LE *7B4* (1.5km NW Urban) **Camp Municipal L'Esquiladou, Le Queureuilh, Route des Cascades, 63240 Le Mont-Dore [04 73 65 23 74 or 04 73 65 20 00 (Mairie); fax 04 73 65 23 74; camping.esquiladou@wanadoo. fr]** Fr Mont Dore cent, take D996 dir La Bourboule (not D130). Pass 'La Poste' on L & at rlwy stn app turn R, then L at T-junc onto D996. In Queureuilh fork R at 'Route Cascades' sp, then foll camping sp. Med, hdg/mkd pitch, hdstg, terr, pt shd; htd wc; chem disp; mv service pnt; shwrs inc; el pts (6-10A) €2.50-5.15; gas; lndtte; shops 1km; tradsmn; BBQ; playgrnd; dogs €1.30; phone; Eng spkn; adv bkg; quiet; cc acc; CCI. "Gd views; gd mountain walks; well-run site; excel facs." ♦ ltd. 1 May-15 Oct. € 8.70   2005*

MONT LOUIS *8G4* (3km N Rural) **Camp Municipal, Place de Barres, 66210 La Llagonne [04 68 04 26 04 or 04 68 04 21 18 (Mairie)]** Leave Mont-Louis on D118 dir Formigueres rd; site sp on L at top of hill; cont for 1km. Lge, pt shd; wc (cont); shwrs; el pts (10A) €3; playgrnd; paddling pool; rv sw; fishing; quiet. "Most of site in pine forest; ground poss boggy." 15 Jun-30 Sep. € 7.90   2004*

MONT ST MICHEL, LE *2E4* (8km E Rural) **Camping de la Baie & Camping Le Courtils, Rue de St Michel, 50220 Courtils [02 33 70 96 90; fax 02 33 70 99 09; infos@campingsaintmichel.com]** Fr E exit A84 junc 33 to N175. Take D43 coast rd fr Pontaubault twds Le Mont St Michel. Site in vill of Courtils on R. Sm, hdg/mkd pitch, some hdstg, unshd; wc; chem disp; shwrs; el pts (6A) €2.60; tradsmn; rest; bar; dogs €1; Eng spkn; adv bkg; quiet but rd noise; CCI. "Excel facs; clean adj sites with same helpful owner; cycle paths adj; turn up & owner will open gate to Le Courtils for low ssn visitors; no privacy in shwrs/wcs; gd NH for St Malo; excel long/sh stay." ♦ ltd. 15 Mar-15 Oct. € 14.50   2005*

MONT ST MICHEL, LE *2E4* (8km E) **Camping Le St Michel, Route du Mont St Michel, 50220 Courtils [02 33 70 96 90; fax 02 33 70 99 09; infos@campingsaintmichel.com; www. campingsaint michel.com]** Site on R on main rte D75 fr Mont St Michel to Courtils. Med, pt shd; wc; chem disp; mv service pnt; baby facs; shwrs inc; el pts (6A) €2.60; lndtte; shop; rest; bar; playgrnd; htd pool; sand beach 8km; cycle hire; dogs €1; poss cr; noisy (farm adj); Eng spkn; CCI. "Excel, flat site; v clean facs." 15 Mar-15 Oct. € 14.50   2004*

MONT ST MICHEL, LE *2E4* (2km S) **Camping du Mont St Michel, 50150 Le Mont St Michel [02 33 60 22 10; fax 02 33 60 20 02; stmichel@ le-mont-saint-michel.com]** Located at junc of D976 (Pontorson/Le Mont St Michel) with D275; on L behind Hotel Vert. Lge, hdg/mkd pitch, pt shd; wc; chem disp; mv service pnt €2.60; shwrs inc; baby facs; el pts (5A) €2.60 (poss rev pol); gas; lndtte; supmkt, rest adj; snacks; bar; playgrnd; mini-golf; sand beach 2km; fishing; TV; dogs; phone; adv bkg; Eng spkn; cc acc; CCI. "Excel san facs, inc for disabled; vg shady pitches behind hotel; poss noisy, annexe on opp side D275 quieter, closes end Sep; beach at 2km reported unsafe for sw (quicksand); Abbey nrby; pitches poss muddy after heavy rain; diff to get onto some pitches due trees; well- maintained, well-located site." ♦ 15 Feb-31 Oct. € 13.90   2004*

MONT ST MICHEL, LE *2E4* (4km S Rural) **Camping aux Pommiers, 28 Route du Mont St Michel, 50170 Beauvoir [tel/fax 02 33 60 11 36; pommiers@aol. com; www.camping-auxpommiers.com]** N fr Pontorson foll D976 sp Le Mont St Michel. Site 5km on R on ent vill of Beauvoir. Med, hdg/mkd pitch, hdstg, pt shd; htd wc (some cont); chem disp; mv service pnt; shwrs inc; el pts (6A) €2.60; lndtte; ice; shop; supmkt 4km; tradsmn; rest; snacks; bar; BBQ; playgrnd; htd pool; waterslide; sand/shgl beach 2km; tennis 900m; games area; games rm; entmnt; TV; 20% statics; dogs €1.20; Eng spkn; adv bkg; quiet; red long stay/low ssn; CCI. "Friendly, helpful staff & owner; clean facs; gd touring base; easy cycle ride to Mont St Michel." 20 Mar-14 Nov. € 13.40   2005*

See advertisement

MONTAGNAC MONTPEZAT see Riez *10E3*

MONTAGNY LES LANCHES see Annecy *9B3*

†MONTAIGU *2H4* (10km SE) **Camping L'Eden, 85600 La Boissiere-de-Montaigu [02 51 41 62 32; fax 02 51 41 56 07; domaine.eden@free.fr]**
Fr Montaigu S N137, in 8km turn E on D62, thro Le Pont-Lege. Site sp on L off D62. Med, mkd pitch, pt shd; wc (some cont); shwrs inc; el pts (10A) €3; gas; lndtte; shop & 4km; rest; snacks; bar; playgrnd; htd pool; tennis; mini-golf; entmnt; TV; 40% statics; dogs €2; poss cr; adv bkg; quiet; red low ssn; CCI. "Gd NH/sh stay." ♦ ltd. € 15.00   2004*

MONTARGIS *4F3* (12km N Rural) **Camp Municipal, Rue du Perray, 45210 Ferrieres-en-Gatinais [02 38 96 64 68 or 02 38 96 52 96 (Mairie); fax 02 38 96 62 76]** N fr Mantargis on N7. R onto D32 sp Ferrieres & foll camp sp. Med, mkd pitch, pt shd; wc; chem disp; shwrs inc; el pts (4-6A) inc (rev pol); ice; playgrnd; rv fishing adj; entmnt; 5% statics; quiet. "Vg sh stay." 1 Apr-30 Sep. € 10.00
2003*

MONTARGIS *4F3* (2km NE Urban) **Camp Municipal de la Foret, 38 Ave Chautemps, 45200 Montargis [02 38 98 00 20]** Heading N on N7 at town boundary take R fork sp Paucourt/camping symbol. Or head E on N60, take 2nd L to site in 1km. Med, mkd pitch, hdstg, shd; htd wc (some cont); shwrs inc; el pts (6A) €2.60; shop 200m; playgrnd; pool adj; 50% statics; quiet. "Conv for train to Paris; pleasant views; lovely old vill, abbey & church; nice walks; no vans over 6m; poss muddy in wet weather; facs dated but clean; gate/recep closes 1900; NH only." 1 Feb-30 Nov. € 10.80
2004*

MONTARGIS *4F3* (10km W) **Camping du Huillard, 45700 St Maurice-sur-Fessard [02 38 97 85 32 or 02 38 97 81 99 (LS); flora.tony@wanadoo.fr]**
On N side of N60 by-pass bet Ladon & Montargis Well sp twd St Maurice-sur-Fessard. Sm, pt shd; wc; chem disp (wc); mv service pnt; shwrs inc; el pts (6-10A) €2-2.50 (poss rev pol); gas; ice; shop; playgrnd; fishing; dogs €1; some rd noise; adv bkg. "Delightful site; poss resident workers; gd long/sh stay." 1 May-15 Oct. € 5.60   2003*

MONTAUBAN *8E3* (10km NE) **Camping La Forge, 82350 Albias [05 63 31 00 44 or 06 76 38 81 22; contact@camping-laforge.com]** Fr S turn R at traff lts on N20 in Albias onto D65 sp Negrepelisse. Site clearly sp 1km on L adj cemetary extension. Sm, pt shd; wc; chem disp; shwrs inc; el pts (3-6A) €1.85-3.65; lndtte; shops 500m; tradsmn; sm pool; 10% statics; dogs €0.75; adv bkg; quiet; red low ssn; CCI. "Quiet, unpretentious woodland site; helpful & friendly owner; facs dated; poss unsuitable for sm children due to v steep bank to fast flowing rv; excel rest in vill; gd sh stay/NH." 1 Apr-10 Oct.
€ 11.00   2005*

MONTAUBAN DE BRETAGNE *2E3* (500m Urban) **Camp Municipal de la Vallee St Eloi, 35360 Montauban-de-Bretagne [02 99 06 42 55; fax 02 99 06 59 89]** 25km NW of Rennes on N12. Fr N12 foll sp to Montauben cent. Site in 500m on R at ent to town by sm lake. Sm, mkd pitch, pt shd; wc; shwrs inc; el pts (6A) €1.90; shop 500m; quiet; no statics; CCI. "Conv for Brittany Ferries; basic but clean san facs; picturesque location; rest in town Logis de France; unreliable opening dates, phone ahead." 1 Jul-31 Aug. € 8.25   2004*

MONTBALEN *7D3* **Ferme Equestre Criniere au Vent, 47340 Montbalen [05 53 95 18 61; SLX47@wanadoo.fr]** Site 15km N Agen & 13km S Villeneuve-sur-Lot. Fr Agen, take N21 N dir Villeneuve-sur-Lot. In approx 15km turn R onto D110 sp Laroque-Timbaut & foll 'Camping' sp. Fr Villeneuve-sur-Lot, take N21 S dir Agen. In approx 10km turn L onto D110 sp Laroque-Timbaut & foll 'Camping' sp. Sm, pt sl, shd; wc (some cont); chem disp; shwrs inc; el pts (10A) €2; lndry rm; ice; tradsmn; bar (soft drinks only); horseriding; no statics; little Eng spkn; no cc acc; CCI. "Owner v pleasant; horseriding for all ages on site; playgrnd 2004; vg." ♦ May-Oct. € 9.95   2003*

MONTBARD *6G1* (1km W Urban) **Camp Municipal, Rue Michel Servet, 21500 Montbard [tel/fax 03 80 92 21 60; mairie.montbard@wanadoo.fr]**
Lies off N side D980. Camping sp clearly indicated on all app including by-pass. Turn onto by-pass at traff lts at rndabt at junc of D905 & D980. Site nr pool. Med, hdg pitch, pt shd, wc; chem disp; shwrs inc; el pts (16A) €3; lndry rm; shop 1km; supmkt 300m; tradsmn; BBQ; snacks; playgrnd; cycle hire; rv sw 100m; dogs €1; phone; poss cr; quiet but rd/rlwy noise at far end; CCI. "V clean, well-kept but poss shabby low ssn; v quiet low ssn; smart lge san facs; excel." ♦ 1 Mar-28 Oct. € 13.40   2005*

MONTBAZON *4G2* (300m N Rural) **Camping de la Grange Rouge, 37250 Montbazon [02 47 26 06 43; fax 02 47 26 03 13; Ma.Widd@wanadoo.fr; www.camping-montbazon.com]** On N10 site clearly visible & clearly sp on W side of rd at N end of town. Med, mkd pitch, shd; wc (some cont for men); chem disp; shwrs inc; el pts (6A) €3.20; lndtte; shops 300m; tradsmn; rest & bar adj; playgrnd; htd pool; fishing; tennis; dogs €0.70; adv bkg; quiet; cc acc; CCI. "Vg site; helpful, friendly owner; conv Tours; vg long/sh stay." ♦ 1 May-15 Sep. € 10.20   2004*

See advertisement on next page

FRANCE

MONTBAZON 4G2 (2km E Rural) **Camping de la Plage**, 37250 Veigne [02 47 26 23 00; fax 02 47 73 11 47; camping.veigne@wanadoo.fr; www.touraine-vacance.com] Exit A10 junc 23 dir Montbazon onto N10. N of Montbazon after 'Les Gues' turn SE onto D50 to Veigne & site. Site in 2km on R at rvside. Med, mkd pitch, pt shd; htd wc; chem disp; baby facs; shwrs, el pts (6-10A) €3.60-3.90; gas 200m; lndtte; ice; shop 200m; rest; snacks; BBQ; playgrnd; htd pool high ssn; canoeing; fishing; mini-golf; games area; entmnt; child entmnt; 13% statics; dogs €1.50; Eng spkn; adv bkg; quiet; red long stay; cc acc; CCI. "Lovely rvside site; friendly, helpful owners; ideal for Loire chateaux & Tours; gd walking & cycling; excel long/sh stay." ♦ 10 Apr-3 Oct. € 15.20   2005*

MONTBERT 2H4 (500m Rural) **Camping Le Relais des Garennes**, La Bauche Coiffee, 44140 Montbert [tel/fax 02 40 04 78 73; phgendron@wanadoo.fr; www.relais-garennes.fr.st] Fr Nantes on N937 dir La Roche, at Geneston turn L dir Montbert & foll site sp. Or fr Nantes on N137 dir La Rochelle turn R at Aigrefeuille-sur-Maine for Montbert. Sm, mkd pitch, pt shd; htd wc; serviced pitches; baby facs; fam bthrm; shwrs inc; el pts (10A) €2; lndry rm; ice; htd pool 1km; tennis, sports facs nrby; sm lake; fishing; dogs; Eng spkn; adv bkg; quiet; CCI. "V peaceful & picturesque; immac facs; friendly owners; rabbits & hens on site; toys for children; many attractions nrby; nice walk to town; excel." ♦ 1 Jun-30 Sep. € 7.50   2004*

MONTBLANC see Beziers 10F1

MONTBRISON 9B1 (2km S) **Camp Municipal Le Surizet**, Route de St Etienne, Moingt, 42600 Montbrison [04 77 58 08 30; fax 04 77 58 00 16] Fr St Etienne on D8, at rndabt junc with D204 turn L sp St Antheme & Ambert. Cross rlwy & turn R in 400m, site sp. Med, pt shd; wc; shwrs; el pts (5-10A) €2.60-4.65; shop 1km; playgrnd; pool; fishing; pool, tennis 2km; 60% statics; dogs €0.85; quiet; adv bkg. "No twin-axles vans." 15 Apr-15 Oct. € 8.30
2005*

MONTBRISON 9B1 (2km W Rural) **Camping Le Bigi**, Vinols, 42600 Bard [tel/fax 04 77 58 06 39] Fr Montbrison cent take D113 twd Bard, site sp. Sm, hdg/mkd pitch, sl, terr, pt shd; wc; chem disp; mv service pnt; shwrs inc; el pts (5A) €2.80; lndtte; tradsmn; playgrnd; pool; tennis; 60% statics; dogs €1; poss cr; CCI. "Charming family, v helpful; v well-run; delightful site in landscaped former nursery garden nr medieval town; no twin-axle c'vans." ♦ 15 Apr-30 Sep. € 10.40   2005*

MONTBRON 7B3 (11km NE Rural) **Camping de l'Etang**, Les Geloux, 16310 Le Lindois [05 45 65 02 67; fax 05 45 65 08 96] Fr S take D16 N fr Montbron, in 9km turn R onto D13, in 3km turn R onto D27. Site sp in vill opp lake. Sm, hdg/mkd pitch, pt sl, pt shd; htd wc; chem disp; baby facs; shwrs inc; el pts (16A) €3.35; lndtte; ice; small shop; rest; snacks; bar; playgrnd; lake sw adj; fishing; sand beach adj; dogs €1.55; Eng spkn; adv bkg rec high ssn; cc acc; quiet; CCI. "Beautiful, peaceful, wooded site by sm lake; lge pitches in indiv clearings in trees; friendly Dutch owners; excel." 1 Apr-1 Nov. € 14.20   2005*

MONTBRON 7B3 (6km SE Rural) **LES CASTELS Les Gorges du Chambon**, Le Chambon, 16220 Eymouthiers [05 45 70 71 70; fax 05 45 70 80 02; gorges.chambon@wanadoo.fr; www.gorgesdu chambon.fr or www.les-castels.com] Fr N141 turn onto D6 at Rochefoucauld. Take D6 out of Montbron; after 5km turn L at La Tricherie on D163; foll camp sp to site in approx 3km. Med, mkd pitch, pt sl, pt shd; htd wc; chem disp; mv service pnt; baby facs; shwrs inc; el pts (6A) inc; gas; lndtte; ice; shop; tradsmn; rest; snacks; bar; BBQ (gas/charcoal only); playgrnd; pool; sand/shgl beach 15km; rv sw; fishing, canoe hire; tennis; cycle hire; mini-golf; walking; horseriding, golf nrby; entmnts; games rm; TV rm; 25% statics; no dogs; Eng spkn; adv bkg; quiet; red long stay/low ssn; cc acc; CCI. "Beautiful site; helpful staff; gd walks & bird-watching; gd views; excel." ♦ 15 Apr-16 Sep. € 24.70 (CChq acc) ABS - D11   2005*

See advertisement opposite

MONTBRUN LES BAINS *10E3* (500m Rural) **Camp Municipal Le Pre des Arbres, 26570 Montbrun-les-Bains [04 75 28 85 41 or 04 75 28 82 49; fax 04 75 28 81 16]** Site well sp in Montbrun. Sm, mkd pitch, terr, pt shd; wc; shwrs; el pts; pool adj; quiet. "Gd, clean site in pleasant town; walking dist to town; warden visits." 1 Apr-31 Oct. € 7.40   2002*

MONTCLAR (ALPES DE HAUTE PROVENCE) *9D3* (2km N Rural) **Camping Etoile des Neiges, St Jean, 04140 Montclar [04 92 35 01 29 or 04 92 35 07 08; fax 04 92 35 12 55; contact@ etoile-des-neiges.com; www.etoile-des-neiges. com]** On D900 turn S at St Vincent-les-Forts twd Col St Jean & Digne, site sp at the Col. Med, terr, shd; htd wc; some serviced pitches; shwrs; el pts (6A) inc; lndtte; rest; bar; snacks; playgrnd; htd pool; tennis; rv fishing; games area; entmnt; TV; dogs €2; adv bkg rec winter & summer. "Ski stn in winter; steep access rds to pitches poss diff; site 1300m above sea level; excel." ♦ 21 May-30 Sep. € 25.00 (CChq acc)   2004*

MONTCLAR (AUDE) see Carcassonne *8F4*

MONTCUQ *7D3* (Rural) **Camp Municipal St Jean, 46800 Montcuq [05 65 22 93 73 or 05 65 31 80 05 (Mairie)]** Fr Cahors on N20 twd Montauban. 3km S take D653 sp to vill. Site sp on R in vill. Sm, mkd pitch, shd; wc; shwrs inc; el pts (10-15A); lndtte; supmkt, rest 300m; bar 200m; playgrnd; pool; tennis adj; lake fishing, lake sw & watersports 800m; tennis; horseriding; adv bkg rec high ssn; quiet. ♦ 15 Jun-15 Sep. € 6.00   2004*

MONTCUQ *7D3* (7km NE Rural) **Camping des Arcades, 46800 St Pantaleon [05 65 22 92 27 or 06 80 43 19 82; fax 05 65 31 98 89; info@ des-arcades.com; www.des-arcades.com]** Foll sp to Montauban on N20, 3km S of Cahors take D653 sp Montcuq, after 17km site in hamlet of St Martial on L. Med, mkd pitch, pt sl, pt shd; wc; chem disp; shwrs inc; el pts (6A) 3.10; lndtte; sm shop; tradsmn; rest; snacks; bar; BBQ; playgrnd; pool; child entmnt; 5% statics; Eng spkn; adv bkg; quiet; red low ssn; cc acc; CCI. "Vg Dutch-owned site with restored 13thC windmill; sm lake; lovely countryside; vg rest; clean facs." ♦ 25 Apr-20 Sep. € 19.20   2003*

MONTDIDIER *3C3* (1km W Urban) **Camp Le Pre Fleuri, 46 Route d'Ailly-sur-Noye, 80500 Montdidier [03 22 78 93 22 or 06 60 08 11 03]** App Montdidier fr Breteuil (W) on D930; on W o'skts, foll site sp & turn L onto D26. Site 1km on R. Or leave A1 at junc 11 foll sp for D935 Montdidier. In town foll sp for Breteuil until rlwy x-ing & turn R onto D26; then as above. Sm, hdg/mkd pitch, pt sl, pt shd; wc (some cont); mv service pnt; chem disp; shwrs inc; el pts (6-10A) inc (poss rev pol); gas; lndtte; shop 1km; tradsmn; rest, snacks, bar 1km; playgrnd; pool 1km; fishing, tennis nr; horseriding; 15% statics; adv bkg; noise fr adj rd; red long stay; CCI. "V helpful owners; guided walks; insufficient san facs; diff to level m'van; excel sh stay." ♦ Easter-15 Oct. € 15.00   2003*

†MONTELIMAR *9D2* (12km N Rural) **Camping Floral, 26740 La Coucourde-Derbieres [04 75 90 06 69; info@campingfloral.com; www. campingfloral.com]** Exit A7 at junc 17 Montelimar Nord, S on N7 for 4km. Site sp S of vill. Sm, mkd pitch, hdstg, pt sl, pt shd; wc; mv service pnt; shwrs inc; el pts (6A) inc; gas; lndtte; sm shop; rest; snacks; bar; playgrnd; pool; entmnt; dogs €0.50; Eng spkn; quiet but some rlwy & rd noise; red low ssn; CCI. "Welcome drink on arr; v friendly owners; gd home cooked rest food; facs poss stretched high ssn; clean site; vg sh/long stay." € 12.50   2004*

MONTELIMAR *9D2* (11km S Urban) **Camping Rochecondrie, 07220 Viviers [tel/fax 04 75 52 74 66; campingrochecondrie@wanadoo.fr]** Fr site 1km N of Viviers (dir Le Teil); ent on E side of N86. Fr N ent for S'bound traff tricky; best option to cont past site to junc with D107, turn W (dir Aubenas) & turn around; app fr S as bef. Med, mkd pitch, pt shd; wc (some cont); chem disp; el pts (6A) €3; gas; lndtte; BBQ; rest & bar high ssn; playgrnd; pool high ssn; fishing; 30% statics; dogs €1; phone; Eng spkn; noise fr food on cont in site & rlwy; red low ssn; cc acc; CCI. "Nr rlwy; nr to Ardeche gorges, canoe & raft excursions; Viviers interesting medieval vill with Roman bdge; resident llamas; sm shwr cubicles." ♦ ltd. 1 Apr-15 Oct. € 17.30   2005*

FRANCE

MONTENDRE *7C2* (2km S) **Camping Escapade La Foret, Route de Onda, 17130 Montendre** [04 79 70 09 09; fax 04 79 70 04 04; relaisoleil. recontres@wanadoo.fr] 2km S of Montendre on rd to St Savin (D145). Montendre app via D730 fr either A10 or N10. Med, shd; wc; shwrs; el pts; lndtte; shops 2km; playgrnd; pool; watersports on lake adj; tennis; TV; adv bkg; quiet. 15 Jun-15 Sep. 2003*

MONTERBLANC see Vannes *2F3*

MONTESTRUC SUR GERS see Fleurance *8E3*

MONTEUX see Carpentras *10E2*

MONTFAUCON *7D3* (2km N Rural) **Domaine de la Faurie, Seniergues, 46240 Montfaucon** [05 65 21 14 36; fax 05 65 31 11 17; contact@ camping-lafaurie.com; www.camping-lafaurie. com] Fr N20 turn E onto D2 sp Montfaucon, or fr A20 exit junc 56. In 5km site sp. Med, pt sl, pt shd; wc; chem disp; shwrs inc; el pts (6A) €3; lndtte; ice; shop; rest; playgrnd; pool; cycle hire; entmnt; some statics; dogs €1; Eng spkn; adv bkg; quiet. "Superb, pretty site in lovely location; v welcoming owners; gd touring base." ♦ 1 Apr-30 Sep. € 15.00 (CChq acc) 2005*

MONTFERRAND *8F4* **Domaine St Laurent (Naturist), Les Touzets, 11320 Montferrand** [tel/fax 04 68 60 15 80; naturisme-st-laurent@ wanadoo.fr] S fr Toulouse on N113 past Villefranche de Lauragais. L at Avignonet, foll sps to St Laurent. Sps fr vill, site in 4km. Sm, some hdg pitch, pt shd; wc; chem disp; shwrs inc; el pts (3A) inc; lndtte; shop; rest; snacks; bar; playgrnd; pool; tennis; archery; cycle hire; entmnt; TV rm; dogs €2; Eng spkn; adv bkg; quiet; cc not acc; red low ssn; INF card req. "Clean san facs; well kept site; friendly owners; ideal for those new to naturist lifestyle; gd views." 1 May-30 Sep. € 20.50 2003*

MONTFERRAND *8F4* (6km SE) **Camping Le Cathare, Chateau de la Barthe, 11410 Belflou** [04 68 60 32 49; fax 04 68 60 37 90] Fr Villefranche-de-Lauragais on N113, foll D622 sp Toulouse/Carcassonne over rlwy, a'route, canal, then immed L on D625 for 7km. Thro St Michel-de-Lanes then take D33 to Belflou; foll sp to Le Cathare. Sm, mkd pitch, pt shd; wc (some cont); chem disp; shwrs inc; el pts (3A) €2.20; shops 12km; tradsmn; rest in ferme auberge; snacks, bar 4km; lake sw 3km; sand/shgl beach; v quiet; CCI. "Poss long walk to san facs & poss sh timer for lts at san facs; Centre Nautique on lake." 1 May-30 Oct. € 7.50 2004*

MONTFERRAT see Abrets, Les *9B3*

MONTFERRIER see Lavelanet *8G4*

MONTGAILLARD see Foix *8G3*

MONTGEARD see Villefranche de Lauragais *8F3*

MONTGENEVRE see Briancon *9C4*

MONTHERME see Charleville Mezieres *5C1*

MONTIGNAC *7C3* (7km SE) **Camp La Fage, 24290 La Chapelle-Aubareil** [05 53 50 76 50; fax 05 53 50 79 19] Fr Montignac take D704 twd Sarlat. In approx 7km R to La Chapelle-Aubareil & foll camp sp to site ent 1km bef La Chapelle. Long winding drive thro woods to site. Med, pt sl, pt shd; wc; baby facs; shwrs inc; el pts (6A) inc; lndtte; shop; snacks; bar; playgrnd; pool; sports organised; entmnt; TV; 30% statics; adv bkg; red CCI. "Owner & facs v gd; excel site; red facs low ssn." 1 May-27 Sep. € 19.00 2003*

MONTIGNAC *7C3* (500m S Urban) **Camping Le Moulin du Bleufond, Ave Aristide Briand, 24290 Montignac** [05 53 51 83 95; fax 05 53 51 19 92; le. moulin.du.bleufond@wanadoo.fr; www.bleufond. com] S on D704, cross bdge in town & turn R immed of rv on D65; site sp in 500m nr stadium. Med, hdg pitch, pt shd; wc (some cont); shwrs inc; el pts (10A) €3; ice; shops 500m; rest; snacks; bar; BBQ; htd pool high ssn; paddling pool; tennis adj; fishing; entmnt; dogs €1.52; poss cr; quiet; cc acc. "V pleasant site; poss diff lge o'fits due trees; pleasant, helpful owners; conv Lascaux caves & town; gd walking area; helpful staff, facs excel." Easter-15 Oct. € 14.80 2005*

MONTIGNAC *7C3* (8km SW Rural) **Camping La Castillonderie, 24290 Thonac** [05 53 50 76 79; fax 05 53 51 59 13; castillonderie@wanadoo.fr; www.castillonderie.nl] Take D706 dir Les Eyzies. At Thonac take D65 sp Fanlac in 1km after x-rd take R, site is sp 2km. Med, mkd pitch, pt shd; wc; chem disp; mv service pnt; shwrs inc; el pts (16A) €3; gas 5km; lndtte; lndry rm; ice; sm shop & 2km; tradsmn; rest; snacks; bar; BBQ; playgrnd; pool; paddling pool; canoeing 3km; TV rm; some statics; dogs; Eng spkn; adv bkg (dep req); quiet; 20% red low ssn; CCI. "Dutch owners v friendly & helpful; excel for relaxation; gd cent for historic visits; designated pitches with water & elec avail low ssn; vg long/sh stay." ♦ Easter-30 Sep. € 15.00 2004*

MONTIGNAC *7C3* (9km SW Rural) **Camping Le Paradis, 24290 St Leon-sur-Vezere** [05 53 50 72 64; fax 05 53 50 75 90; le-paradis@perigord.com; www.le-paradis.com] On W bank of Rv Vezere on D706 Montignac-Les Eyzies rd, 1km fr Le Moustier. D706 poss rough rd. Med, hdg pitch, pt shd; htd wc; chem disp; mv service pnt; baby facs; shwrs inc; el pts (10A) €3; lndtte; ice; shop; tradsmn; rest; snacks; bar; BBQ; playgrnd; htd pools; beach adj; boat hire; fishing; tennis; cycle hire; entmnt; TV rm; 10% statics; dogs €1; phone; poss cr; Eng spkn; adv bkg; poss rd noise; red low ssn; cc acc; CCI. "Gd for families; immac san facs & gd pool; rest & take-away vg; excel, esp low ssn." ♦ 1 Apr-25 Oct. € 27.70 (CChq acc) 2005*

MONTIGNAC CHARENTE see Angouleme *7B2*

MONTIGNY EN MORVAN *4H4* (2km E Rural) **Camp Municipal Plat du Lac**, Bonin, 58120 Montigny-en-Morvan [tel/fax 03 86 84 73 05 or 03 86 84 71 77; montignyenmorvan@free] N fr Chateau-Chinon on D944. At Montigny take D303 on R sp Barrage de Panneciere. Foll sp Bonin & site. Access fr D303 narr & not rec lge o'fits. Med, pt sl, shd; wc; chem disp; shwrs; el pts (10A) inc (poss rev pol); tradsmn; lake sw; fishing; CCI. "Pitches poss soft after rain; helpful, friendly warden." 1 May-30 Sep. € 11.30   2005*

MONTIGNY LE BRETONNEUX see Versailles *4E3*

MONTIGNY LE ROI *6F2* (1km N Rural) **Camping du Chateau**, Rue Hubert Collot, Val-de-Meuse, 52140 Montigny-le-Roi [tel/fax 03 25 87 38 93] Fr A31 junc 8 for Montigny-le-Roi. Site well sp in cent vill on D74. Med, terr, pt shd; htd wc; chem disp; baby facs; shwrs inc; el pts (5A) €2; ice; shop; snacks; playgrnd; tennis; cycle hire; fishing 5km; entmnt. "Modern facs; steep ent; rests & shops in vill." ♦ 15 Apr-15 Oct. € 11.00   2005*

MONTIGNY SUR LOING see Fontainebleau *4E3*

MONTJEAN SUR LOIRE see Chalonnes sur Loire *2G4*

MONTLIEU LA GARDE *7C2* (8km N Rural) **Camp Municipal Bellevue**, 17210 Chevanceaux [05 46 04 60 03 or 05 46 04 60 09 (Mairie)] N fr Montlieu on N10, site by church in vill of Chevanceaux. Sm, mkd pitch, pt sl, pt shd; wc; chem disp (wc); mv service pnt; shwrs inc; el pts €2.20; shops, rest, bar in vill; playgrnd; pool adj; tennis; quiet; CCI. "Excel, peaceful site in pleasant vill, highly rec." 1 Apr-30 Oct. € 6.00   2005*

†**MONTLIEU LA GARDE** *7C2* (9km N Rural) **Camping Chez Frapier**, 16360 Chantillac [05 45 79 00 53; momorley@hotmail.com] Fr N10 ent Chevanceaux & leave vill on D156 dir Chatenet. Turn R at x-rds sp La Ferme Auberge. Site in 1km on L. Narr, single track app rd. Sm, pt shd; own san req; chem disp (septic tank); el pts (10A) €3; rest nrby; BBQ; sm splash pool; riding school, sw lakes picnic area 1.5km; Eng spkn; adv bkg rec; quiet. "British-owned, basic, CL-type site in secluded countryside; gd base for Cognac, Bordeaux & the Medoc wine country, Atlantic coast, La Rochelle." € 12.00   2005*

MONTLIEU LA GARDE *7C2* (1km NE Rural) **Camp Municipal des Lilas**, 17210 Montlieu-la-Garde [05 46 04 44 12 (Mairie); fax 05 46 04 50 91; montlieulagarde@mairie17.com] On L N10 sp Montlieu-la-Garde; take D730 into vill. Turn L at multiple sp on corner (diff to see) & in 1km turn R & foll site sp. Site along vill lane. Sm, pt sl, pt shd; wc; shwrs; el pts €2.10; tradsmn; shop in vill; pool 1km; quiet. "Vg NH; clean san facs; some rd noise." 1 May-30 Sep. € 5.70   2005*

MONTLUCON *7A4* (12km NW) **Camp Municipal Le Moulin de Lyon**, 03380 Huriel [06 75 55 52 55 or 04 70 28 60 08 (Mairie); fax 04 70 28 94 90; mairie.huriel@wanadoo.fr] Exit A71 junc 10 & foll sp Domerat, then D916 to Huriel. Site well sp. Or fr N D943 turn SW at La Chapelaude to Huriel on D40, foll sp to site. Last km narr with steep incline to site ent. Med, hdg pitch, pt sl, pt shd; wc; chem disp; mv service pnt; shwrs; el pts (10A) inc (poss rev pol); gas; lndry rm; shops, tradsmn; snacks, bar 1km; BBQ; playgrnd; lake/rv fishing; tennis; TV; Eng spkn; quiet. "Wonderful, v peaceful & clean; amongst trees; friendly; site yourself; 10 mins walk to vill; excel value; gd sh stay." 15 Apr-15 Oct. € 6.80   2005*

†**MONTMARAULT** *9A1* (5km N Rural) **Camping La Ferme La Charviere**, 03390 St Priest-en-Murat [04 70 07 38 24; fax 04 70 02 91 27; robert. engels@wanadoo.fr] Exit A71 junc 11 at Montmarault onto D68 dir Sazaret/Chappes. Site 4km beyond Sazaret. Site sp. Sm, pt shd; wc; shwrs inc; el pts (10A) €2.50; lndtte; ice; rest; playgrnd; pool; adv bkg; quiet; red low ssn; CCI. "Helpful Dutch owner; v peaceful & quiet at night; ltd facs low ssn; gd, clean san facs, stretched if busy; poss clsd winter - phone ahead; easy access to m'way; vg NH." € 15.00   2005*

MONTMARAULT *9A1* (4.5km NE Urban) **Camping La Petite Valette**, La Vallette, 03390 Sazeret [04 70 07 64 57 or 06 80 23 15 54; fax 04 70 07 25 48; la.petite.valette@wanadoo.fr; www.valette.nl] Leave A71 at junc 11 & take 3rd exit at 1st rndabt onto D46; after 400m turn L at next rndabt, site sp on L in 3km. Or N of Monmarault in vill of Suzaret site well sp. Med, hdg/mkd pitch, pt shd; htd wc; chem disp; shwrs inc; el pts (6A) €2.85; gas; lndtte; lndry rm; ice; tradsmn; rest (high ssn); bar; playgrnd; htd pool (caps ess) & paddling pool; cycle hire; fishing; entmnt; dogs €1.70; Eng spkn; adv bkg, bkg fee req; quiet. "Well-maintained, clean, pretty site; excel shwrs; grass on all pitches; Dutch owners; ltd capacity in rest & takeaway, bkg req; narr rd to site; pleasant walks sp fr site." ♦ 1 Apr-31 Oct. € 17.40   2005*

MONTMARAULT *9A1* (9km NE) **Camp Municipal**, 03240 Deux-Chaises [04 70 47 12 33] Fr A71 in Montmarault take 2nd rndabt to Deux-Chaises; site on R in vill; well sp. Sm, hdg pitch, pt sl, unshd; wc; shwrs; el pts (16A) €2; shop; rest & bar 200m; playgrnd; tennis; lake fishing adj. "Warden calls for fees pm; phone to check opening bef arr, esp low ssn; gd NH." 25 Mar-15 Oct. € 6.50   2005*

MONTMARAULT *9A1* (9km E Rural) **Camp Municipal Les Brosses**, 03140 Voussac [04 70 42 30 47] A71 exit junc 11 at rndabt, take 3rd exit onto D46 dir Voussac; after 7km sp to site on L bef Voussac vill. Sm, hdg pitch, pt sl, pt shd; wc; chem disp; shwrs inc; el pts €2; quiet. "Ideal NH/sh stay when travelling A71." ♦ ltd. € 8.00   2002*

FRANCE

MONTMARAULT *9A1* (500m W) **Camp Municipal, 03390 Montmarault [04 70 07 60 50 (Mairie)]** E fr Montlucon site on N145 on ent Montmarault by stadium. Sm, pt shd; wc (cont); own san rec; shwrs; el pts inc; shops 500m; quiet but some rd noise. "San facs poss stretched high ssn; fair NH." 1 Apr-15 Sep. € 8.00   2004*

MONTMARTIN SUR MER see Agon Coutainville *1D4*

MONTMAUR see Veynes *9D3*

MONTMEDY *5C1* (N Urban) **Camp Municipal La Citadelle, Rue Vauban, 55600 Montmedy [03 29 80 10 40 (Mairie); fax 03 29 80 12 98]** On L of N43 (Montmedy-Sedan rd). Do not foll sp in Montmedy town, as rds narr & steep, keep to N43 & at top of hill at sharp R-hand bend turn L sp Montmedy Haut. Site in 100m clearly sp if app fr Sedan on N43. Sm, hdg pitch, pt sl, pt shd; wc; chem disp; mv service pnt; shwrs inc; el pts (5-10A) €2.80-3.97; lndry rm; shops 1km; tradsmn; playgrnd; dogs €1.82; phone; Eng spkn; quiet; 25% red 4+ days; CCI. "Warden calls am & pm; nr Montmedy Haut, old fortified town with ramparts & dry moat, excel views all round; 10A hook-up not avail in high ssn; facs v clean; office open 0730-0800 & 1930-2000 but not accurate; vg sh stay/NH." 1 May-30 Sep. € 8.00   2005*

MONTMEYAN *10E3* (500m S Rural) **Camping Le Chateau de L'Eouviere, 83670 Montmeyan [tel/fax 04 94 80 75 54; leouviere@wanadoo.fr; www.leouviere.com]** Fr Montmeyan take D13 dir Fox-Amphoux; site 500m on R out of Montmeyan. Med, mkd pitch, terr, pt shd; wc; chem disp; shwrs inc; el pts (10A) inc; lndtte; ice; shop; tradsmn; rest; snacks; bar; BBQ (el only on pitch); pool; tennis; games rm; TV rm; no statics; Eng spkn; adv bkg (dep req); quiet; red low ssn; Eng spkn. "Diff access; badly managed; poor san facs; peaceful site in lovely area." ♦ 15 Apr-15 Oct. € 28.10   2003*

MONTMIRAIL *3D4* (1km E) **Camp Municipal Les Chataigniers, Rue du Petit St Lazare, 51210 Montmirail [03 26 42 25 61; fax 03 26 81 14 27]** Site opp junc of D933 & D373 at E o'skts of town. Med, mkd pitch, pt shd; wc (cont); own san rec; shwrs inc; el pts (20A) €4; shops 500m; pool 500m; playgrnd; tennis; golf; cc not acc; CCI. "NH only; fees collected each pm; approx 1 hr drive fr Paris; call at warden's house L of ent for removal of barrier." 1 Apr-31 Oct. € 4.20   2002*

MONTMORILLON *7A3* (500m E Urban) **Camp Municipal de l'Allochon, Ave Tribot, 86500 Montmorillon [05 49 91 02 33 or 05 49 91 13 99 (Mairie); fax 05 49 91 58 26; montlorillon@cg86. fr]** On D54 to Le Dorat, approx 400m SE fr main rd bdge over rv at S of town. Site on L. Fr S v sharp RH turn into site. Med, mkd pitch, terr, pt shd; htd wc (some cont); mv service pnt; shwrs inc; el pts (6-10A) inc; lndtte; shop 1km; rest, snacks, bar 500m; BBQ; playgrnd; htd, covrd pool 300m; fishing; games area; TV; poss cr; adv bkg; some rd noise; CCI. "Delightful, clean, friendly & peaceful site; barrier card; gd touring base." ♦ 1 Mar-31 Oct. € 8.40   2004*

MONTOIRE SUR LE LOIR *4F2* (500m S Urban) **Camp Municipal Les Reclusages, Ave des Reclusages, 41800 Montoire-sur-le Loir [tel/fax 02 54 85 02 53]** Foll site sp, out of town sq, over rv bdge & 1st L on blind corner at foot of old castle. Med, some mkd pitch, pt shd; wc (some cont); chem disp; mv service pnt; shwrs inc; el pts (10A) €3.23; lndtte; ice; shops 500m; bar; snacks (morning only); playgrnd; htd pool adj; playgrnd; canoeing; fishing; mini-golf; 20% statics; adv bkg; no cc acc; CCI. "Delightfully situated bet high wooded hill & Rv Loir; friendly & helpful; v clean san facs & v secure site; wc facs ltd low ssn; conv troglodyte vills; pleasant walk over bdge to town cent; excel." ♦ 15 May-15 Sep. € 6.40   2005*

MONTOLIEU see Carcassonne *8F4*

†**MONTPELLIER** *10F1* (5km N) **Camping Sunelia Le Plein Air des Chenes, Route de Castelnau, 34830 Clapiers [04 67 02 02 53; fax 04 67 59 42 19; pleinairdeschenes@free.fr; pleinairdeschenes.net]** Exit A9 junc 28 onto N113 twd Montpellier. Foll D21 twd Castelnau Centre & Jacou, 5km after Castelnau foll sp to site on D112E. Med, pt sl, terr, pt shd; wc (cont); shwrs inc; el pts (10A); gas; lndtte; shops 800m; rest; snacks; bar; playgrnd; pool; paddling pool; waterslides; sand beach 16km; tennis; games area; horseriding; 60% statics; dogs €6; private htd washrms avail; quiet; red long stay/low ssn. ♦ € 37.00 (CChq acc)   2005*

MONTPELLIER *10F1* (6km SE) **Camping Le Parc, Route de Mauguio, 34970 Lattes [04 67 65 85 67; fax 04 67 20 20 58; camping-le-parc@wanadoo. fr; www.leparccamping.com]** Exit A9 junc 29 for airport onto D66. In about 4km turn R onto D172 sp Lattes & campings, cross over D21. Site ent in 200m on R. NB Hard to find - few sp. Med, hdg pitch, shd; wc; chem disp; some serviced pitches; shwrs inc; el pts (10A) inc; gas; lndtte; ice; sm shop; huge shopping cent 1km; tradsmn; snacks high ssn; playgrnd; pool; sand beach 4km; 15% statics; dogs €2.80; Eng spkn; adv bkg (dep); quiet; CCI. "V friendly, helpful owners; lge pitches but dusty; gd facs, excel pool & snack bar; conv Cevennes mountains; Montpellier & Mediterranean beaches; sporting activities organised, eg hiking & mountain biking; barrier locked 2200." ♦ 1 Apr-31 Oct. € 23.40   2005*

MONTPELLIER *10F1* (4km S Rural) **Camping L'Oasis Palavasienne, Route de Palavas, 34970 Lattes [04 67 15 11 61; fax 04 67 15 10 62; oasis. palavasienne@wanadoo.fr; http://oasis-palavasienne.com]** Leave A9 at exit Montpellier Sud. Take D986 sp Palavas. About 1.5km after Lattes take slip rd sp Camping; turn under dual c'way. Site opp. Lge, hdg pitch, pt shd; wc; gym & sauna; shwrs inc; el pts inc; lndtte; ice; shop; rest; snacks; bar; playgrnd; pool; rv adj; sand beach, water sports 4km; cycle hire; horseriding 2km; entmnt; disco; TV; free bus to beach; Eng spkn; adv bkg ess; some traff noise; CCI. "Fair long/sh stay; bus to Palavas & Montpellier."
1 May-31 Aug. € 26.00   2004*

MONTPEZAT DE QUERCY see Caussade *8E3*

MONTPON MENESTEROL *7C2* (300m N Urban) Escapades Terre Oceane Camping Port Vieux, Route de Riberac, 24700 Montpon-Menesterol [05 53 05 75 24 or 05 46 55 10 01; fax 05 46 55 10 00; info@campingterreoceane.com; www.campingterreoceane.com] Fr Montpon town cent traff lts take D730 N to Menestrol. Site on L bef bdge beside rv L'Isle. Med, hdg/mkd pitch, pt shd; wc; chem disp; shwrs inc; el pts (10A) €3; lndtte; shop 100m; tradsmn; rest; snacks; bar; playgrnd; leisure park nrby; rv sw; boat hire; fishing; child entmnt; TV rm; dogs; adv bkg (30% dep); quiet; cc acc; CCI. "Gd touring base for St Emilion region; gd walking, cycling." ♦ 17 Jun-16 Sep.
€ 12.00   2005*

MONTPON MENESTEROL *7C2* (10km SE) Domaine de Chaudeau (Naturist), 24700 St Geraud-de-Corps [05 53 82 49 64; fax 05 53 81 18 94; chadeau.naturiste@wanadoo.fr; www.domainedechaudeau.com] Fr Montpon take D708 S; after 8km turn E on D33 for St Geraud-de-Corps; foll black & white sp Chaudeau. Fr St Foy-la-Grande take D708 N; after 11km on exit St Meard-du-Gurcon turn E & foll sp as above. Med, hdg/mkd pitch, shd; wc; chem disp; shwrs inc; el pts (5A) €3.20; lndtte; ice; shop; snacks; bar; pool; fishing; entmnt; child entmnt; some statics; dogs €2.30; phone; quiet; red low ssn. "An excel naturist site; INF card req but holiday membership avail; v lge pitches." 1 Apr-30 Sep.
€ 18.00   2005*

MONTPON MENESTEROL *7C2* (4km S Rural) Caravaning La Tuiliere, 24700 St Remy-sur-Lidoire [tel/fax 05 53 82 47 29 or 06 87 26 28 04 (mob); la-tuiliere@wanadoo.fr; www.camping latuiliere.com] On W side of D708 4km S of Montpon-Menesterol. Med, hdg/mkd pitch, shd; wc; chem disp; shwrs inc; el pts (5-10A) €2.50-3.20; gas; lndtte; ice; sm shop 3km; tradsmn; rest; snacks; bar; playgrnd; pool; tennis; crazy golf; boating; lake on site; 20% statics; dogs €1.20; poss cr; Eng spkn; adv bkg; quiet; red long stay; cc acc; CCI. "Family-run site, v friendly welcome; excel rest." ♦
1 May-15 Sep. € 12.00   2005*

MONTPON MENESTEROL *7C2* (9km W Rural) Camping Les Loges, 24700 Menesplet [05 53 81 84 39; fax 05 53 81 62 74] At Menesplet turn S of N89 onto D10 sp Minzac. Turn L after level x-ing, foll sp. Sm, hdg pitch, pt shd; wc; mv service pnt; shwrs inc; el pts (16A) €4-6; gas 7km; lndtte; shops 2.5km; playgrnd; rv sw 5km; games area; 5% statics; adv bkg; quiet; CCI. "V quiet site in pleasant countryside." ♦ 1 May-30 Sep. € 13.00   2003*

As we're travelling out of season, we'd better phone ahead to check that the site is actually open.

MONTREAL *8E2* (2km NW Rural) **Camping Rose d'Armagnac, 32250 Montreal [tel/fax 05 62 29 47 70; campingrosedarmagnac@free.fr]** Exit Montreal in dir of Fources; L turn to Sos; after sm bdge 1st L, uphill 1km. Sm, some mkd pitch, pt terr, pt shd; wc; chem disp; shwrs inc; el pts (6A) €2.25; gas; lndtte; ice; shop high ssn; tradsmn; rest, snacks, bar 2km; BBQ; sm playgrnd; unhtd paddling pool; waterslide; sand beach 2km; dogs; British owners; poss cr; quiet; adv bkg; cc not acc; CCI. "V quiet relaxing site; picturesque area; Roman villa nr; Bastide vill; choice of pitches in woods or on open terr; clean; san facs poss overstretched high ssn; vg long stay." ♦ ltd. 1 May-31 Oct. € 10.00   2004*

†**MONTREJEAU** *8F3* (1.5km N Rural) **Camping Midi-Pyrenees, Route de Cuguron, Quartier Loubet, 31210 Montrejeau [05 61 95 86 79; fax 05 61 95 90 67; marcel.perez@wanadoo.fr]** N fr Montrejeau on D34 on terr hillside, well sp. Med, hdstg, pt sl, some terr, pt shd; htd wc; shwrs inc; el pts (6-10A) inc; ice; rest; snacks; bar; playgrnd; pool; rv & lake 2km; mini-golf; entmnts; 30% statics; Eng spkn; quiet; CCI. "Excel views Pyrenees; gd welcome; gd san facs." € 14.00   2005*

MONTREJEAU *8F3* (7km S) **Camping Es Pibous, Chemin de St-Just, 31510 St Bertrand-de-Comminges [05 61 94 98 20 or 05 61 88 31 42; fax 05 61 95 63 83]** Turn S fr N117 or exit A64 junc 17 at Montrejeau onto N125 sp Bagneres-de-Luchon & Espagne. Foll past 'Super U' to lge rndabt & turn R sp St Bertrand-de-Comminges/Valcabrere then at 1st traff lts turn R & foll sp for St Bertrand & site. Med, hdg/mkd; pt shd; wc; shwrs inc; el pts (6A) €3; gas; lndtte; shop; rest, bar 300m; playgrnd; pool; fishing, tennis 3km; TV; 5% statics; dogs; adv bkg; quiet; cc acc. "Excel, friendly, peaceful site; lge pitches among cherry trees; gd touring area nr mountains, prehistoric caves & picturesque town with cathedral; cultural activities in area; ltd facs low ssn." ♦ 1 Mar-31 Oct. € 11.00   2005*

FRANCE

La Plaine Tonique is a holiday and sports resort, situated at the banks of a lake of 130 ha, in the heart of an area known worldwide for its gastronomy: La Bresse. Along this 4 stars campsite with 560 pitches lays a beach of 500 m. and on the campsite one can enjoy the pleasures of a water park with 5 swimming pools (of which 1 covered) with natural warm water, two giant slides, a big children's pool and a fun pool. Almost all of the sanitary blocks have been recently constructed. During summer we offer animation and activities: mountain biking, roller-skating, archery, tennis, waterskiing, catamaran, sailing, motorboat trips, canoeing, water cycling. Rental of chalets and apartments (2-7 persons)

plaine.tonique@wanadoo.fr
www.laplainetonique.com
Phone : 33 (0)4 74 30 80 52
Fax : 33 (0)4 74 30 80 77
01340 MONTREVEL-EN-BRESSE

Water, nature, sports

MONTREJEAU 8F3 (8km S Rural) **Camp Municipal Bords de Garonne**, Chemin du Camping, 65370 Loures-Barousse [05 62 99 29 29] Exit A64 junc 17 onto A645 by-passing Montrejeau.. Or fr Montrejeau take N125 to Luchon & 'Espagne'. In 5km cont onto D33. Site on R in 3km, visible fr rd. Access fr D122 sp Loures-Barousse across rv bdge. Med, shd; htd wc (some cont); chem disp (wc only); shwrs; el pts (4A) €2.50; rest & snacks in adj hotel; shops 500m; 80% statics; adv bkg; some Eng spkn; quiet but some rd noise; CCI. "Touring pitches on rvside; clean san facs but site looking run down; friendly, helpful staff; ideal for exploring Pyrenees or as NH to/fr Spain; pleasant site; easy walk to vill." ♦ 1 Mar-31 Oct. € 6.35   2005*

MONTREJEAU 8F3 (6km W Rural) **Camping La Neste**, 65150 St Laurent-de-Neste [05 62 39 73 38 or 05 62 99 01 49] S fr Toulouse on N117 at W end of Montrejeau keep L on D938 sp La Barthe-de-Neste; in 6km turn S in vill of St Laurent-de-Neste & immed W on N bank of rv at camp sp; site on L in 1km. Sm, pt shd, mkd pitch; wc; chem disp; shwrs inc; el pts (3-6A) €3; lndry rm; shop 1km; playgrnd; rv sw & beach; phone; quiet; adv bkg; CCI.
1 May-30 Sep. € 10.00   2004*

MONTREUIL 3B3 (N Urban) **Camping La Fontaine des Clercs**, 1 Rue de l'Eglise, 62170 Montreuil [tel/fax 03 21 06 07 28; freddy.monchaux@ wanadoo.fr] Fr N or S turn W off N1 at traff lts. Take 2nd R after rlwy x-ing, site sp on Rv Canche. Med, mkd pitch, pt sl, terr, pt shd, terr; wc; chem disp; shwrs inc; el pts (6A) inc; lndtte; shops 500m; tradsmn; pool 1.5km; rv adj; fishing; games rm; dogs €1; adv bkg rec high ssn; quiet; red 4+ days; CCI. "V useful NH fr ferry; some pitches on steep terr; interesting, historic town; conv Le Touquet & beaches " 1 Mar-31 Oct. € 14.80   2005*

MONTREUIL 3B3 (7km SW Rural) **Camping a la Ferme**, 14 Rue Verte, 62170 Wailly-Beaucamp [03 21 81 26 29] Fr Montreuil take N1 S to Wailly-Beaucamp. In Wailly turn L along side of lge car park. Site within 500m at fork in rd. Sm, pt shd; wc; shwrs; el pts (4A); shop 800m; playgrnd; sand beach 12km; poss cr; adv bkg; quiet. "Beautiful CL-type site; friendly owners; gd facs."   2005*

†MONTREUIL BELLAY 4H1 (4km E Rural) **Camping Le Thouet**, Les Coteaux-du-Chalet, 49260 Montreuil-Bellay [02 41 38 74 17; fax 02 41 50 92 83; Brian.Senior@wanadoo.fr; www. camping-le-thouet.co.uk] Fr N147 N of Montreuil-Bellay take dir 'Centre Ville'; turn L immed bef rv bdge & foll sp to Les Coteaux-du-Chalet. Access via narr, rough rd for 1km. Sm, mkd pitch, pt shd; wc; chem disp (wc); shwrs inc; el pts (10A) inc; gas; lndtte; shop 4km; tradsmn; bar; playgrnd; pool; fishing; boating; dogs; phone; quiet but some rlwy noise; adv bkg (dep req); cc acc; red long stay; CCI. "Gd, spacious site; British owners; lge area grass & woods; pitches in open grass field; surrounded by vineyards; gd walks; vill not easily accessed by foot." ♦ ltd. € 18.50   2005*

We're having a great holiday - must fill in some site report forms and send them to The Club as soon as possible.

MONTREUIL BELLAY 4H1 (1km W Urban) **Camping Les Nobis**, Rue Georges Girouy, 49260 Montreuil-Bellay [02 41 52 33 66; fax 02 41 38 72 88; campinglesnobis@wanadoo.fr; www.campingles nobis.com] Fr S on D938 turn L immed on ent town boundary & foll rd for 1km to site; sp fr all dir. Fr N on N147 ignore 1st camping sp & cont on N147 to 2nd rndabt & foll sp. Fr NW on D761 turn R onto N147 sp Thouars to next rndabt, foll site sp. Lge, hdg/mkd pitch, pt shd; wc (some cont); chem disp; mv service pnt; shwrs inc; el pts (10A) €2.50 (poss long cable req); gas; lndtte; ice; shop; tradsmn; rest; snacks; bar; playgrnd; pool; cycle hire; TV rm; 7% statics; dogs; phone; poss cr; Eng spkn; adv bkg (dep req) quiet; 10% red 15+ days/low ssn; cc acc; CCI. "Spacious, improved site between castle & rv; vg rest; local chateaux & town worth exploring; aire de service for m'vans adj." ♦ 1 Apr-2 Oct. € 15.00   2005*

MONTREVEL EN BRESSE *9A2* (500m E Rural) Camping La Plaine Tonique, Base de Plein Air, 01340 Montrevel-en-Bresse [04 74 30 80 52; fax 04 74 30 80 77; plaine.tonique@wanadoo.fr; www.laplainetonique.com] Exit A40 junc 5 Bourg-en-Bresse N onto D975 N dir Montrevel-en-Bresse; foll sp Marboz. Or exit A6 junc 27 Tournus S onto D975. V lge, hdg pitch, shd; wc; chem disp; mv service pnt; baby facs; shwrs inc; el pts (10A) inc; lndtte; ice; shop; rest; snacks; bar; BBQ; playgrnd; 3 htd, covrd pools; 2 paddling pools; 2 waterslides; lake beach & sw adj; watersports; fishing; tennis; cycle hire; games area; archery; mountain biking; entmnt; child entmnt; TV; statics; dogs €1.90; adv bkg; quiet; cc acc; red CCI. "Superb leisure facs & excursions; vg san facs; excel family site." ♦ 15 Apr-22 Sep. € 21.10   2005*

See advertisement

MONTRICHARD *4G2* (3km S) Camping Touraine Vacances, 41400 Faverolles-sur-Cher [02 54 32 06 08; fax 02 54 32 61 35; touraine-vacances@wanadoo.fr; www.touraine-vacances.com] E fr Tours on N76 thro Blere; at Montrichard turn S on D764 twd Faverolles-sur-Cher, site 200m fr junc, adj to supmkt. Med, pt shd; wc; chem disp; mv service pnt; shwrs inc; el pts (6A) €3-3.50 (rev pol); gas 1km; lndtte; rest; snacks; bar; playgrnd; pool; sailing; 5% statics; dogs €1.50; Eng spkn; adv bkg; quiet, but some rd noise; gate clsd 2200-0800; cc acc. "Gd site; well-run; Belgian owners." ♦ 1 Mar-1 Nov. € 15.60   2003*

MONTRICHARD *4G2* (1km W Urban) Camp Municipal L'Etourneau, 41400 Montrichard [02 54 32 10 16 or 02 54 32 00 46 (Mairie); fax 02 54 32 05 87] Fr D150 site sp twd rv. Med, mkd pitch, pt shd; wc; chem disp; mv service pnt; shwrs inc; el pts (13A) inc (poss long leads req); supmkt & shops, rest, snacks 1km; bar; playgrnd; pool 2km; rv sw 2km; poss cr; Eng spkn; CCI. "Well-run site; helpful staff; card operated barrier; excel long/sh stay." 1 Jun-15 Sep. € 12.00   2004*

MONTRIGAUD *9C2* (3km E) Camping La Griveliere, 26350 Montrigaud [tel/fax 04 75 71 70 71; courrier@lagriveliere.com; www.lagriveliere.com] Fr Romans-sur-Isere take D538 N 13km to La-Cabaret-Neuf, then NE on D67 to Montrigaud. Nr vill take D228 & foll sp to site. Med, hdg pitch, pt shd; wc (some cont); shwrs inc; el pts (4A) inc; lndtte; ice; sm shop; tradsmn; rest; snacks; bar; BBQ; playgrnd; pool; sports area; lake sw, fishing 2km; entmnt; 50% statics; dogs €1.40; phone; adv bkg 25% dep + booking fee; quiet, but some noise fr disco; CCI. "Many activities avail; key operated barrier, dep req; gd sh stay." ♦ ltd. 1 Apr-15 Sep. € 14.50   2004*

MONTSALVY *7D4* (4km NE Rural) Camp Municipal de la Riviere, Route de Entraygues-sur-Truyere, 12140 Pons [05 65 66 18 16; fax 05 65 66 22 71] Site is 1km SE of vill on D526. Sm, pt shd; shwrs; el pts inc; lndtte; pool; tennis; rv adj; adv bkg; quiet. ♦ 15 Jun-15 Sep. € 7.85   2002*

MONTSALVY *7D4* (800m S) Camp Municipal de la Grangeotte, Route d'Entraygues, 15120 Montsalvy [04 71 49 26 00 or 04 71 49 20 10 (Mairie); fax 04 71 49 26 93; mairie-montsalvy@wanadoo.fr] On W of D920 behind sports complex. Sm, pt sl, pt shd; wc; shwrs; el pts (3-6A) €2.50-3.70; lndtte; shops in vill; rest; snacks; bar; playgrnd; sports area; htd pool adj (Jun-Aug) free to campers; fishing 2km; adv bkg; quiet but some rd noise. "Pleasant vill; entmnt; panoramic views fr some pitches; friendly warden." 4 Jun-15 Sep. € 12.10   2004*

MONTSAUCHE LES SETTONS *4G4* (4km SE) Camping Plage des Settons, Rive Gauche, Lac des Settons, 58230 Montsauche-les-Settons [03 86 84 51 99; fax 03 86 84 54 81; jpbosset@aol.com] Fr Montsauche foll sp Chateau-Chinon. In 500m fork L to Les Settons. After 2km foll sp for Rive Gauche, after 1km L at bend for site. Med, hdg/mkd pitch, terr, pt shd; wc; chem disp; shwrs inc; el pts (3-10A) €2.29-4.12; lndtte; ice; shops 500m; tradsmn; playgrnd; pool nrby; sand/shgl lake beach adj; fishing; pedaloes; lake sw; cycle hire; Eng spkn; poss noisy; cc acc; CCI. "In cent of Parc du Morvan; direct access to Lac des Settons; long elec cable rec; access rd busy pm." ♦ ltd. 1 May-17 Sep. € 11.00   2002*

MONTSAUCHE LES SETTONS *4G4* (5km SE Rural) Camping Les Mesanges, 58230 Montsauche-les-Settons [03 86 84 55 77 or 03 86 84 53 92] Fr Montsauche S foll sp Chateau-Chinon. In 500m L fork to Les Settons. Foll sp to Rive Gauche on W side of lake. Med, terr, pt shd; wc (some cont); chem disp; shwrs inc; el pts (4A); gas; ice; shop; snacks; playgrnd; lake sw; fishing; table tennis; poss cr; quiet; adv bkg; CCI. "Excel." 1 May-15 Sep. € 13.00   2002*

MONTSAUCHE LES SETTONS *4G4* (5km SE) Camping L'Hermitage de Chevigny, 58230 Moux-en-Morvan [03 86 84 50 97] Fr Montsauche take D520 S & after approx 5km turn L on D290; at T-junc in 3km turn L & in further 800m turn L into Chevigny & foll sp to L'Hermitage. App rds narr & twisting. Med, pt shd; wc (mainly cont); chem disp; shwrs inc; el pts (3A) inc; gas; lndtte; sm shop; tradsmn; snacks; bar; playgrnd; lake sw; watersports; fishing; games area; dogs €1.50; adv bkg; Eng spkn; cc not acc; CCI. "Excel; secluded site; facs poss stretched high ssn." 1 Apr-30 Sep. € 14.50   2005*

MONTSAUCHE LES SETTONS *4G4* (7km SE) Camping Plage du Midi, Lac des Settons, 58230 Montsauche-les-Settons [03 86 84 51 97; fax 03 86 84 57 31; PlageDuMidi@aol.com] Fr Salieu take D977 bis to Montsauche, then D193 'Rive Droite' to Les Settons for 5km. Cont a further 3km & take R fork sp 'Les Branlasses' Centre du Sport. Site on L after 500m at lakeside. Med, mkd pitch, terr, pt shd; wc (cont); chem disp; baby facs; shwrs inc; el pts (10A) €3.35; gas; shop; rest; snacks; bar; playgrnd; lake sw; sand beach adj; watersports; horseriding 2km; dogs €0.91; phone; poss cr; Eng spkn; adv bkg; poss noisy; red low ssn; CCI. ♦ Easter-15 Oct. € 13.08   2003*

FRANCE

MONTSOREAU *4G1* (Rural) **Airotel L'Isle Verte (formerly Municipal), Ave de la Loire, 49730 Montsoreau [02 41 51 76 60 or 02 41 67 37 81; fax 02 41 51 08 83; isleverte@wanadoo.fr]** Fr S at Saumur turn R immed bef bdge over Rv Loire; foll sp to Chinon. Fr N foll sp for Fontevraud & Chinon fr Rv Loire bdge; site on D947 in vill on banks of Loire opp Traiteur. Med, mkd pitch, pt shd; wc; chem disp; mv service pnt; shwrs inc; el pts (16A) €3.10 (poss long lead req); gas; lndry rm; shops 200m; tradsmn; ice; rest 100m; snacks; bar; playgrnd; pool; paddling pool; rv fishing/watersports; tennis; games area; golf 13km; entmnt high ssn; TV: poss cr; Eng spkn; adv bkg rec high ssn; rd noise; red low ssn; cc acc; CCI. "Simple rvside site - no frills; v clean san facs; chem disp diff to access; gd wine caves + chateaux; ltd power pts; barrier clsd 2100-0700; 10 min rvside walk to vill." ♦ 1 Apr-30 Sep. € 16.30 (CChq acc)   2005*

MONTSURS *4F1* (500m Urban) **Camp Municipal de la Jouanne, Rue de la Jouanne, 53150 Montsurs [02 43 01 00 31 (Mairie); fax 02 43 02 21 42]** Well sp fr town cent. Med, pt shd; wc; chem disp (wc); shwrs inc; el pts (2-10A); lndry rm; shop, rest, snacks, bar 500m; playgrnd; rv fishing adj; phone; adv bkg rec; quiet; no cc acc; CCI. "Pretty, well-kept rvside site, extremely gd value; conv many medieval vills; barrier (dep req) open approx 0930-1030 & 1630-1730, ask at house opp if clsd." 1 Jun-30 Sep.   2004*

MONTVIRON see Avranches *2E4*

MOOSCH see Thann *6F3*

†MORCENX *8E1* (3km SE Rural) **Camping Le Clave, 40110 Morcenx [58 07 83 11]** Exit junc 14 fr N10 onto D38 thro Morcenx. Site on o'skts of vill on D27 bordering rv in chateau grounds. Med, pt sl, pt shd; wc; shwrs; el pts; ice; shops 500m; site clsd 16-31 Dec; quiet. "Poss unkempt. NH ony." € 15.50   2004*

MORCENX *8E1* (2km S Rural) **Camping Fortanier, 40110 Morcenx [05 58 07 82 59]** Fr N10 turn E at junc 14 onto D38 dir Mont-de-Marsan. At Morcenx turn R on D27. Site on R 1km past Camping le Clave. Well sp. Sm, mkd pitch, shd; wc; chem disp (wc); shwrs inc; el pts (6A) €2.50-3.50; gas; lndtte; shop, rest, bar 1km; playgrnd; pool, lake 3km; BBQ; 5% statics; dogs; phone 500m; dv bkg; quiet; cc not acc; CCI. "Friendly owners; well kept site, clean & tidy; peaceful & relaxing; flat, excel all stays." May-Oct. € 8.00   2004*

MOREE *4F2* (S Rural) **Aire Naturelle Municipale du Plan d'Eau, 41160 Moree [02 54 82 06 16 or 02 54 89 15 15; fax 02 54 89 15 10]** W fr Orleans on N157 or N fr Vendome on N10 & foll sp in vill onto D19 to site. Sm, pt shd; wc; chem disp; mv service pnt; shwrs inc; el pts (8A) inc; ice; gas; shops 400m; snacks; bar; playgrnd; lake sw & beach adj; fishing; canoeing; tennis 500m; golf 5km; adv bkg (dep req); red long stay; CCI. "Lovely, lakeside site; ltd san facs stretched if site full; pop school parties high ssn." 15 Jun-10 Sep. € 14.50   2005*

MOREE *4F2* (3km W Rural) **Camp Municipal, Rue de l'Etang, 41160 Freteval [02 54 82 63 5 (Mairie)]** Site on N157, sp fr junc with N10. By rv in vill cent. Med, pt shd; wc; shwrs inc; el pts €2.40; shops 500m; fishing; quiet. "San facs old but adequate; lovely location; diff ent/exit esp med/lge o'fits; vg sh stay." 15 Mar-15 Oct. € 5.00   2003*

MOREE *4F2* (3km NW Rural) **Camping La Maladrerie, 41160 Freteval [tel/fax 02 54 82 62 75]** Fr Le Mans on N157, turn L in vill. Fr N10 site nr Le Plessis. Foll sp. Med, pt shd; wc; chem disp; shwrs inc; el pts (4-6A) €1.55-2.30; gas; lndtte; shops 1km; bar; playgrnd; pool; 75% statics; cc acc; CCI. "V ltd facs low ssn; site was a medieval leper colony!!" ♦ 15 Mar-31 Oct. € 8.45   2005*

†MORESTEL *9B3* (8km S Urban) **Camping Les Epinettes, 6 Rue du Stade, 38630 Les Avenieres [tel/fax 04 74 33 92 92; infos@camping-les-avenieres.com; www.camping-les-avenieres.com]** S fr Morestel on N74, turn onto D40 to Les Avenieres, site well sp. Med, hdg/mkd pitch, hdstg, pt shd; wc; chem disp; mv service pnt; baby facs; shwrs inc; el pts (10A) inc; lndtte; ice; shop; tradsmn; rest; snacks; bar; BBQ; playgrnd; pool; rv sw 2km; entmnt; TV rm; 35% statics; dogs €1.95; phone; adv bkg; noise fr adj stadium; red low ssn; cc acc; CCI. "Phone ahead low ssn to check open." ♦ € 17.10   2005*

MORESTEL *9B3* (W Urban) **Camp Municipal, Route de Cremieu, 38510 Morestel [04 74 80 14 97]** Foll camping sps in town. Site by pool on N517. (NB No ent sps do not apply to campers). Med, pt shd; wc; shwrs inc; el pts (6A) inc; supmkt 1km; pool & sports complex adj; quiet. "Sm, poss awkward pitches; ent barrier operated by adj sw pool staff; pleasant NH." 1 May-30 Sep. € 9.30   2003*

MORET SUR LOING *4E3* (2km NW Urban) **Camping Les Courtilles du Lido, Chemin du Passeur, 77250 Veneux-les-Sablons [01 60 70 46 05; fax 01 64 70 62 65; jack.richard@wanadoo.fr]** Use app fr N6 sp Veneux-les-Sablons & foll sp. 1km fr N6. Or fr Moret foll sp; long, tortuous rte; narr streets; 35m, 1-width tunnel. NB sp say 'Du Lido' only. Lge, mkd pitch, pt shd; wc; chem disp; shwrs; el pts (6-10A) €3; gas; lndtte; ice; shops 1km; tradsmn; rest; snacks; bar; playgrnd; sm pool; tennis; table tennis; mini-golf; 75% statics; dogs €1; poss cr; Eng spkn; adv bkg; rlwy noise at night; CCI. "Early arr advised; conv Fontainebleau; lge pitches; v clean facs but poss insufficient high ssn; friendly owners; vg for children; lovely old town; conv for train to Paris; excel." 3 Apr-20 Sep. € 13.75   2005*

SITES

†MOREZ *9A3* (3km N) **Camp Municipal La Bucle,** **39400 Morbier [tel/fax 03 84 33 48 55; info.bucle@** **wanadoo.fr; www.euro-tourisme.com/ pub/bucle]** Fr N on N5 look for sps 10km after St Laurent. Pass supmkt & lge car pk on R, take sharp L turn after L bend in rd. Fr S turn R 50m past bdge. Med, some hdstg, pt sl, pt terr, unshd; wc; shwrs inc; el pts (10A) €2.30; shops 1km; pool; dogs €0.60; quiet; red low ssn; gd NH. "Lovely site & town but poss slightly unkempt." € 14.50   2005*

MOREZ *9A3* (9km S) **Camping Caravaneige Le** **Baptaillard, 39400 Longchaumois [03 84 60 62 34]** Foll D69 S, site sp on R. Med, pt sl, pt shd; htd wc; chem disp; shwrs inc; el pts (6A) €2.35; lndtte; playgrnd; paddling pool; fishing 3km; tennis; mini-golf; skiing; games rm; adv bkg essential winter; quiet. "Beautiful CL-type site; lovely views; lge pitches." 1 Jan-30 Sep & Dec. € 12.30   2003*

MORHANGE *5D2* (6.5km N Rural) **Centre de** **Loisirs de la Mutche, Harprich, 57340 Morhange** **[03 87 86 21 58; fax 03 87 86 24 88; mutche@** **wanadoo.fr]** Fr N74 turn N onto D78 sp Harprich, site sp on shore of Etang de la Mutche. Med, mkd pitch, hdstg, pt shd; wc; chem disp; shwrs €0.70; el pts €2.80; lndtte; shop 2km; tradsmn; rest 2km; playgrnd; pool; sand beach; tennis; lake sw; watersports; games area; entmnt; 20% statics; Eng spkn; adv bkg; quiet; red long stay. "Gd long/sh stay." ♦ ltd. 1 Apr-31 Oct. € 11.00   2002*

MORLAIX *2E2* (6km N Rural) **Camping La Ferme** **de Keroyal, Le Bois de la Roche, 29610 Garlan** **[02 98 79 12 54]** Fr Morlaix take D786 dir Lannion. Foll blue & white camping sps. At app 6km turn R, farm on L. Sm, some hdg pitch, pt shd; wc; chem disp (wc); shwrs inc; el pts inc; beach 20km; dogs; quiet. "Gd sh stay; CL-type site." ♦ Easter-31 Oct. € 11.00   2005*

MORLAIX *2E2* (11km E Rural) **Camping Aire** **Naturelle la Ferme de Croas Men (Cotty), Garlan,** **29610 Plouigneau [tel/fax 02 98 79 11 50;** **croasmen@wanadoo.fr; http://perso.wanadoo.fr/** **camping.croamen]** Fr D712 rndabt W of Plouigneau twd Morlaix (exit from N12) 2km R sp Garlan; thro Garlan site 1km on L. Sm, hdg pitch, pt shd; wc; 50% serviced pitches; chem disp; baby facs; shwrs; el pts (10A) €2.50; playgrnd; horseriding 1km; farm museum; donkey/tractor rides; dogs; quiet; CCI. "Lovely site; ideal for children; welcome to visit farm & see animals; gd facs; produce avail inc cider & crepes." ♦ 1 Apr-31 Oct. € 9.60   2004*

MORLAIX *2E2* (15km S Rural) **Aire Naturelle Les** **Bruyeres, 29410 Le Cloitre-St Thegonnec** **[02 98 79 71 76 or 01736 362512 (England)]** Fr Morlaix take D769 S twd Huelgoat/Carhaix & Le Cloitre-St Thegonnec. At Le Plessis after 14.5km turn L for Le Cloitre-St Thegonnec. When ent vill, take L fork at Musee des Loups, 1st L, 500m then R to camp. Sm, mkd pitch, pt sl, pt shd; wc; chem disp; shwrs inc; lndry rm; shop 500m; rest; bar; BBQ; playgrnd; dogs €2; quiet; adv bkg; CCI. "Helpful British owners; NB no electricity/el pts; water htd by gas; oil lamps in san block; camp fires; for stays outside of Jul/Aug tel to request." 1 Jul-31 Aug. € 13.00   2004*

MORMOIRON *10E2* (4km E Rural) **Camp** **Municipal, Route de la Nesque, 84570 Villes-sur-** **Auzon [04 90 61 82 05]** E on D942 fr Carpentras; at T-junc in Villes-sur Auzon turn R; foll sp Gorge de la Nesque & sports complex 400m. R into site. Med, pt shd; wc; shwrs inc; el pts (5A) €2.30; shop nrby pool 500m; playgrnd; quiet. "Friendly, helpful owners; spotles facs; gd walking & choice of local wines." 1 Apr-30 Sep. € 9.70   2004*

MORMOIRON *10E2* (4km E Rural) **Camping Les** **Verguettes, Route de Carpentras, 84570 Villes-** **sur-Auzon [04 90 61 88 18; fax 0490 61 97 87;** **info@provence-camping.com; www.provence-** **camping.com]** E on D942 fr Carpentras dir Sault. Site nxt to Villes-sur-Auzon beyond wine cave. Or at Veulle-les-Roses turn E onto D68. Cont thro Sottenville-sur-Mer. Site on L in 2km. Lge, hdg/mkd pitch, pt sl, pt shd; wc; chem disp; shwrs inc; el pts (6A) €2.80; lndry rm; shops 1km; rest; pool; tennis; games rm; mini-golf; fishing 300m; internet; dogs €2.30; adv bkg rec all times; quiet. "View of Mont Ventoux; gd walking; friendly & helpful owner; families with children sited nr pool, others at end of camp away fr noise; poss muddy when it rains; sm pitches & poor access, not suitable lge o'fits; gd facs; poss unkept low ssn." ♦ 25 Mar-15 Oct. € 17.10 (CChq acc)   2005*

MORMOIRON *10E2* (2km SE Rural) **Camping de** **l'Auzon, 84570, Mormoiron [tel/fax 04 90 61 80 42]** Fr Carpentras or Sault on D942, turn S of D942 onto D14. Foll sp. Sm, terr, shd; wc; chem disp (wc); shwrs inc; el pts (6A) €2.50; lndtte; shop, rest, snacks, bar 1km; playgrnd; 50% statics; dogs €1.20; quiet "Asparagus fair last w/e in Apr; m'vans could be charged extra; fair sh stay." ♦ Easter-15 Oct. € 7.80   2004*

MORNAS *10E2* (2km E Rural) **Camping Beauregard, Route d'Uchaux, 84550 Mornas** [04 90 37 02 08; fax 04 90 37 07 23; beauga@wanadoo.fr; www.camping-beauregard.com] Exit A7 a'route at Bollene, then N7 twd Orange. On N end of Mornas turn L on D74 to Uchaux, site after 1.7km, sp. Lge, pt sl, shd; htd wc (some cont); chem disp; mv service pnt; shwrs inc; el pts (6-10A) €3.30-4.30; gas; lndtte; shop; rest; snacks; bar; playgrnd; 3 htd pools; games rm; tennis; golf; horseriding; cycle hire; entmnt; dogs €4.10; statics; adv bkg rec high ssn; quiet; Eng spkn; cc acc; red CCI. "Open until 2230; phone ahead to check open low ssn; many derelict vans; poorly maintained low ssn; renovated san facs." ♦
15 Mar-23 Oct. € 27.50 (3 persons)   2005*

MORNAY SUR ALLIER see St Pierre le Moutier *4H4*

†**MORTAGNE SUR GIRONDE** *7B2* (1km SW Coastal) **Aire Communale, Le Port, 17120 Mortagne-sur-Gironde** [05 46 90 63 15; fax 05 46 90 61 25; mairie-mortagne@smic17.fr] Fr Royan take D730 dir Mirambeau for approx 28km. Turn R in Boutenac-Touvent onto D6 to Mortagne, then foll sp Le Port & Aire de Camping-Car. M'vans only. Sm, unshd; chem disp; mv service pnt; shwrs €1; el pts (10A) inc; shop 500m; rest, snacks, bar 600m; dogs; poss cr; quiet. "Car/c'vans may be acc; shwrs & mv service pnt are 800m fr site; fees collected 0900; gd sh stay."
€ 5.00   2003*

†**MORTAGNE SUR SEVRE** *2H4* (5km SE Rural) **Camping Le Rouge Gorge, Les Gautres, Route de la Verrie, 85290 St Laurent-sur-Sevre** [02 51 67 86 39; fax 02 51 67 73 40; camping lerougegorge@wanadoo.fr; http://perso.wanadoo. fr/ campinglerougegorge] Fr Cholet on N160 dir La Roche-sur-Yon; at Mortagne-sur-Sevre take N149 to St Laurent-sur-Sevre. In St Laurent foll sp La Verrie. Med, pt shd; htd wc; mv service pnt; baby facs; shwrs inc; el pts (4-13A) €1.80-3.80; lndtte; shop; snacks; bar; playgrnd; pool; paddling pool; rv & lake fishing 500m; games area; golf 15km; 30% statics; dogs €1.50; adv bkg; quiet. "Peaceful family site." ♦
€ 14.20 (CChq acc)   2005*

MORTAGNE SUR SEVRE *2H4* (10km SE Rural) **Camp Municipal La Vallee de Poupet, 85590 St Malo-du-Bois** [02 51 92 31 45; fax 02 51 92 38 65; camping@valleedepoupet.com; www.valleede poupet.com] Fr N on N149 turn S onto D752 at La Trique. At St Malo-du-Bois (4km) foll sp for 4.5km. Fr S fr Mauleon on N149 turn L onto D11 twd Mallievre. 4km after Mallievre turn R onto D752. After 2.5km turn R & foll sp. Steep app to site. Med, mkd pitch, pt shd; wc; chem disp; shwrs; el pts (6A) €2.50; lndtte; shops 2km; rest, snacks, bar 500m; playgrnd; covered pool; rv sw; entmnt inc theatre; 15% statics; dogs; phone adj; Eng spkn; adv bkg (dep req); quiet; CCI. "Rvside site in depths of country; nr Puy du Fou Grand Parc; rds poss busy on Wed & Sat evening for theatre entmnt; gd all stays." ♦ 31 May-15 Sep. € 10.50   2004*

†**MORTAIN** *2E4* (8km S Rural) **Camping Les Taupinieres, La Raisnais, 50140 Notre-Dame-du-Touchet** [tel/fax 02 33 69 49 36; kevin.gimbert@wanadoo.fr; http://lestaupinieres.mysite.wanadoo-members.co.uk] Fr Mortain S on D977 sp St Hilaire-du-Harcouet; shortly after rndabt take 2nd L at auberge to Notre-Dame-deTouchet. In vill turn L at post office, sp Le Teilleul D184, then 2nd R sp La Raisnais. Site at end of lane on R (haycart on front lawn). Sm, pt sl, pt shd; wc; chem disp; shwrs inc; el pts (10A) inc; shop 1km; htd pool 8km; dogs; adv bkg; quiet. "Friendly, helpful British owners; tranquil, luxurious CL-type site; excel." € 12.00
2005*

MORTAIN *2E4* (500m W) **Camp Municipal Les Cascades, Place du Chateau, 50140 Mortain** [06 23 90 42 65] On D977 S fr Ville twd St Hilaire-du-Harcouet; site in cent of Mortain, sp to R. Sm, pt shd; wc; chem disp; mv service pnt; shwrs inc; el pts €1.50; shop 200m; sm playgrnd; no statics; dogs. "Vg sh stay, 48 hrs max allowed." ♦ € 7.00   2003*

MORTEAU *6H3* (Urban) **Camping Le Cul de la Lune, Cul de la Lune, 25500 Morteau** [03 81 67 17 52 or 03 81 67 18 53; fax 03 81 67 62 34; otsi.morteau@wanadoo.fr] Fr Besancon take N57 E then D461. In Morteau foll sps to Pontarlier then 'Toutes Directions'. Site on R over rlwy/rv bdge. Clearly sp on brown sps thro'out town. Across rv bdge. Sm, pt shd; wc (some cont); shwrs inc; el pts (10A) €2.30; ice; shops 300m; tradsmn; rv sw, fishing & boating; cycling; dogs €0.80; poss v cr; adv bkg; noise fr rd & rlwy; "In beautiful countryside; helpful local tourist office; poss cold at nights (altitude)." 1 Jun-15 Sep.
€ 12.30   2005*

MORZINE *9A3* (7km SW Rural) **Camping La Grange au Frene, 74260 Les Gets** [04 50 75 80 60 or 04 50 75 80 55; fax 04 50 75 84 39] Fr Morzine go S on D902 to Les Gets. Site sp at end of vill. Sm, hdg/mkd pitch, terr, pt shd; htd wc; 50% serviced pitches; baby facs; shwrs inc; el pts (6A) €3.20; lndtte; shop 3km; tradsmn; rest, snacks & bar 3km; playgrnd; lake sw nr; TV rm; dogs; phone; Eng spkn; quiet; adv bkg (dep req). "Vg; golf, climbing, fishing, tennis, bowling, walking, adventure park & watersports nrby." 1 Jun-30 Sep. € 14.50   2002*

MORZINE *9A3* (3km NW Rural) **Camping Les Marmottes, 74110 Essert-Romand** [tel/fax 04 50 75 74 44 or 06 12 95 00 48; camping.les. marm ottes@wanadoo.fr] Exit A40 junc 18 or 19 onto D902 twd Morzine, then turn L onto D328 to Essert-Romand. Fr A40 take junc 18 to Morzine. Sm, hdstg, unshd; wc; chem disp; serviced pitches; shwrs inc; el pts (3-10A) €3.50-6.50; lndtte; ice; shop 2km; tradsmn; playgrnd; lake sw 3km; TV; dogs €1; Eng spkn; adv bkg (dep req); quiet; red long stay; CCI. "Specialises in winter c'vanning for skiers; tractor to tow to pitch in snow." ♦ 22 Jun-15 Sep & 15 Dec-15 Apr.
€ 14.50   2005*

MOSNAC *7B2* (Rural) **Camp Municipal Les Bords de la Seugne, 17240 Mosnac [05 46 70 48 45; fax 05 46 70 49 13]** Fr Pons, S on N137 for 4.5km; L on D134 to Mosnac; foll sp to site behind church. Sm, pt shd; wc; shwrs inc; el pts (3A) €2; gas; shop 100m; 10% statics; dogs; Eng spkn; adv bkg; no cc acc; poss noisy; red long stay; CCI. "Excel facs; charming, clean, neat site in sm hamlet; helpful staff; site yourself, warden calls; conv Saintes, Cognac & Royan; bakery nr." 1 Apr-31 Oct. € 6.00   2005*

MOSTUEJOULS see Peyreleau *10E1*

MOTHE ACHARD, LA *2H4* (1km S) **Camping Le Pavillon, Rue des Sables, 85150 La Mothe-Archard [02 51 05 63 46; fax 02 51 09 45 58; campinglepavillon@wanadoo.fr]** Foll N160 by-pass twd Les Sables d'Olonne. Site on R on S app. Med, pt shd; wc; shwrs inc; el pts (10A) inc; lndtte; ice; shops 1km; tradsmn; snacks; bar; playgrnd; 2 pools; waterslide; sand beach 15km; lake fishing; games area; entmnt; quiet; cc acc; CCI. "Gd facs for children." ◆ 31 Mar-30 Sep. € 16.70   2005*

MOTHE ACHARD, LA *2H4* (5km NW Rural) **Camping La Guyonniere, 85150 St Julien-des-Landes [02 51 46 62 59; fax 02 51 46 62 89; info@ laguyonniere.com; www.laguyonniere.com]** Leave A83 junc 5 onto N160 W twd La Roche-sur-Yon. Foll ring rd N & cont on N160 twd Les Sables-d'Olonne. Leave dual c'way foll sp La Mothe-Achard, then take D12 thro St Julien-des-Landes twd La Chaize-Giraud. Site sp on R. Lge, hdg pitch, pt sl, pt shd; wc; chem disp; shwrs inc; el pts (6A) inc (long lead rec); gas; lndtte; shop; tradsmn; rest; snacks; bar; BBQ; playgrnd; htd, covrd pool; outdoor pool; waterslide; sand beach 10km; lake fishing, canoe hire, windsurfing 400m; cycle hire; internet; cab/sat TV rm; some statics; dogs; phone; Eng spkn; adv bkg, dep req; cc acc; red low ssn. "V lge pitches; gd walking area; friendly owners." ◆ 23 Apr-24 Sep. € 28.00   2004*

MOTHE ACHARD, LA *2H4* (5km NW) **Terrain de Camping Domaine de la Foret, Rue de la Foret, 85150 St Julien-des-Landes [02 51 46 62 11; fax 02 51 46 60 87; domaine.de.la.foret@wanadoo.fr; www.domaine-de-la-foret.com]** Take D12 fr La Mothe-Achard to St Julien. Turn R onto D55 at x-rds & site sp on L. Med, hdg/mkd pitch, pt shd; wc; all serviced pitches; shwrs inc; el pts (6A) €3.80; gas; ice; lndtte; shop & in vill; rest; snacks; bar; BBQ; 2 htd pools (no shorts); gd playgrnd; games rm; sand beach 12km; cycle hire; tennis; mini-golf; lake fishing adj; entmnt; dogs; 60% statics; poss cr; adv bkg rec high ssn; quiet; cc not acc; CCI. "Part of private chateau estate, pop with British visitors; gd for families; excel facs; gates clsd 2200-0800." 15 May-15 Sep. € 27.20 (3 persons)   2002*

MOTHE ACHARD, LA *2H4* (6km NW Rural) **Camping La Bretonniere, 85150 St Julien-des-Landes [02 51 46 62 44 or 06 14 18 26 42; fax 02 51 46 61 36]** Fr La Roche-sur-Yon take N160 to La Mothe-Achard, then D12 dir St Gilles-Croix-de-Vie. Site on R 2km after St Julien. Med, mkd pitch, pt sl, pt shd; wc; chem disp (wc); baby facs; shwrs inc; el pts (6-10A) €1.50-3; lndtte; ice; shops, bar 1km; BBQ; playgrnd; pool; sand beach 14km; fishing, sailing, lake sw 3km; dogs €1; Eng spkn; adv bkg; quiet; CCI. "Excel friendly site; adj working dairy farm, elec extension cables avail; 10 mins fr Bretignolles-sur-Mer sand dunes; vg long/sh stay." ◆ ltd. 1 Jun-15 Oct. € 14.50   2004*

MOTHE ACHARD, LA *2H4* (7km NW) **LES CASTELS La Garangeoire, 85150 St Julien-des-Landes [02 51 46 65 39; fax 02 51 46 69 85; garangeoire@ wanadoo.fr; www.camping-la-garangeoire.com or www.les-castels.com]** Site sp fr La Mothe- Achard. At La Mothe-Achard take D12 for 5km to St Julien, D21 for 2km to site. Or fr Aizenay W on D6 turn L dir La Chapelle-Hermier. Site on L, well sp. Lge, hdg/mkd pitch, pt sl, shd; serviced pitch; wc; chem disp; mv service pnt; shwrs inc; el pts (6A) inc; gas; lndtte; ice; shop; rest; snacks; bar; playgrnd; htd pool complex; waterslide; lake fishing; sand beach 12km; horseriding; tennis; 50% statics; dogs €3; phone; poss cr; adv bkg (ess Aug); cc acc; red low ssn; CCI. "Busy site; lge pitches; many tour ops' static tents & vans; vg, clean facs; gd for families; pleasant helpful owners; super site." ◆ 2 Apr-24 Sep. € 34.50 (CChq acc)   2005*

See advertisement on next page

MOUCHARD *6H2* (8km N Rural) **Camp Municipal La Louve, Rue du Pont, 39600 Champagne-sur- Loue [tel/fax 03 84 37 69 12; camping.champagne@ valdamour.com]** Fr Mouchard NW on D121 to Cramans then NE on D274. Sm, shd; wc (some cont); mv service pnt; shwrs inc; el pts (6A) €2.50; shops 2km; tradsmn; rest 1km; BBQ; playgrnd; fishing; dogs €0.80; adv bkg; quiet; CCI. "Beautiful situation on rv; nr historic Salines at Arc-et-Senans; gd." ◆ 1 May-13 Sep. € 6.30   2005*

MOULIHERNE see Vernantes *4G1*

MOULINS *9A1* (500m SW) **Camping de la Plage, 03000 Moulins [04 70 44 19 29]** Fr Moulins turn W across Rv Allier at town bdge sp Clermont-Ferrand. Turn L on N9 & in 100m turn L & foll sp to site. Med, some hdstg, pt shd; wc; own san facs rec high ssn; shwrs inc; el pts (10A) inc (poss rev pol); gas; lndtte; ice; shop 500m; snacks; bar; playgrnd; pool 1km; rv fishing & boat hire; entmnt; TV; phone; poss cr; Eng spkn; poss noisy high ssn; cc acc; CCI. "Lovely site; lots of space; san facs need refurb; poss tepid water only & poss unclean; 10 min stroll to medieval town; gates clsd 2200-0700; NH only." 1 May-15 Sep. € 11.50   2005*

FRANCE

MOURIES *10E2* (2km E Rural) Camping a la Ferme Les Amandaies (Crouau), 13890 Mouries [04 90 47 50 59; fax 04 90 47 61 79] Fr Mouries take D17 E sp Salon-de-Provence. Site sp 200m past D5 rd to R. Foll site sp to farm in 2km. Sm, pt shd; wc; shwrs inc; el pts €2 (rec long lead); tradsmn; dogs; quiet. "Simple CL-type site with super facs; some lge pitches; friendly owners; conv coast & Avignon; book in using intercom on LH wall at ent to shwr block." 15 Mar-10 Oct. € 11.00   2005*

MOURIES *10E2* (2km NW Rural) Camping Le Devenson, Route des Farigoulas,13890 Mouries [04 90 47 52 01; fax 04 90 47 63 09; deveson@ libertysurf.fr] Exit St Remy by D5 for Maussane-les-Alpilles, turn L on app to vill onto D17 (sps), after 5km (NW edge of vill) bef g'ge on o'skts of Mouries, sharp L to D5, site on R, approach narr. Med, hdstg, pt sl, terr, pt shd; wc; chem disp; shwrs inc; el pts (5A) €3 (rec long cable); lndtte; ice; shop; no BBQ; pool; playgrnd; TV; dogs €1.60; adv bkg; quiet; red low ssn; CCI. "Tractor tow to pitch if necessary; simple, spotless facs; min 1 week stay high ssn; attractive situation in pine & olive trees; simple but v special site." 19 Mar-15 Sep. € 14.20   2005*

MOURIES *10E2* (7km NW) Camp Municipal Les Romarins, Route de St Remy-de-Provence, 13520 Maussane-les-Alpilles [04 90 54 33 60; fax 04 90 54 41 22; camping-municipal-maussane@ wanadoo.fr; www.maussane.com] Fr Mouries on D17 NW, turn onto D5 on o'skts of vill dir St Remy-de-Provence, turn immed L site on R adj municipal pool. Med, hdg pitch, pt shd; wc (some cont); chem disp; baby facs; shwrs inc; el pts (4A) €3.20; gas 200m; lndtte; shops 200m; BBQ; playgrnd; pool adj; tennis free; cycle hire; dogs €2.10; adv bkg rec (dep req); quiet but some rd noise; 10% red for 8+ days; cc acc; CCI. "Office clsd 1200-1500 & 2200-0700; well managed, clean site; lovely area; vg shops & rests within 5 min walk; Eng library; excel long stay." ♦ 15 Mar-15 Oct. € 14.00   2005*

MOUSSEAUX SUR SEINE see Mantes *3D2*

MOUSTERLIN see Fouesnant *2F2*

MOUSTIERS STE MARIE *10E3* (6km N) Camping a la Ferme, 04410 St Jurs [04 92 74 72 24; fax 04 92 74 44 18; contact@ferme-de-vauvenieres. fr; www.ferme-de-vauvenieres.fr] Fr Riez take D953 N to 1km beyond Puimoisson then fork R onto D108 sp St Jurs & site sp. Sm, pt shd; wc; chem disp; shwrs; el pts €2.70; shops 2km; lake sw 2.5km; sports area; Eng spkn; adv bkg; quiet; CCI. "Peaceful; off beaten track; gd for mountain walking; lavender production area; gd Sunday mkt in Riez." 1 Apr-1 Oct. € 8.10   2004*

MOUSTIERS STE MARIE *10E3* (300m S Rural) Camping Le Vieux Colombier, Quartier St Michel, 04360 Moustiers-Ste Marie [04 92 74 61 89 or 04 92 74 61 82 (LS); fax 04 92 74 61 89; camping. vieux.colombier@wanadoo.fr] Fr Moustiers go E on D952 dir Castellane. Site on R in 300m opp garage. Med, mkd pitch, sl, terr, pt shd; htd wc; 80% serviced pitches; chem disp; baby facs; shwrs inc; el pts (3-6A) €2.50-3 (rev pol); gas; lndtte; shop 600m; snacks; bar; BBQ; playgrnd; lake sw 5km; dogs €1.60; Eng spkn; adv bkg ess high ssn; quiet; cc acc; CCI. "V helpful staff; well situated for Gorge du Verdon & conv for town/shops; gd walking; canoing; windsurfing; Moustiers v attractive; steep terrs, park at top & walk down; vg long/sh stay;" ♦ ltd. 1 Apr-30 Sep. € 13.11   2004*

MOUSTIERS STE MARIE *10E3* (1km SW Rural) Camping St Jean, Route de Riez, 04360 Moustiers-Ste Marie [tel/fax 04 92 74 66 85; camping-saint-jean@wanadoo.fr] On D952 opp Elf petrol stn. Med, some hdg pitch, pt sl, pt shd; wc (some cont); shwrs inc; el pts (6A) inc; gas; lndtte; ice; shop 700m; tradsmn; sand beach & lake sw 4km; 3% statics; poss cr; Eng spkn; adv bkg (dep req for 7+ days); quiet; cc acc; CCI. "Excel long/sh stay; conv Gorges du Verdon." ♦ ltd. 1 May-22 Sep. € 15.00   2003*

MOUSTIERS STE MARIE *10E3* (500m W Rural) Camping-Caravaning Manaysse, 04360 Moustiers-Ste Marie [04 92 74 66 71; fax 04 92 74 62 28; camping-manaysse@aol.com] Fr Riez take D952 E, pass g'ge on L & turn L at 1st rndabt for Moustiers; site on L off RH bend; strongly advised not to app Moustiers fr E (fr Castellane, D952 or fr Comps, D71) as these rds are diff for lge vehicles/c'vans - not for the faint-hearted. Med, mkd pitch, pt sl, pt shd; wc (some cont); chem disp; shwrs inc; el pts (5-10A) inc; shops 500m; tradsmn; playgrnd; sand/shgl beach; rv or lake sw; dogs €0.50; adv bkg; quiet; CCI. "Welcoming, family-run site; super views; gd san facs; cherry trees on site - avoid parking under during early Jun; steep walk into vill; lge o'fits do not attempt 1-way system thro vill, park & walk." ♦ ltd.
1 Apr-30 Oct. € 13.00   2004*

MOUTHIER HAUTE PIERRE see Ornans *6G2*

MOUTIERS *9B3* (3km N Rural) Camping Eliana, 205 Ave de Savoie, 73260 Aigueblanche [tel/fax 04 79 24 11 58] Fr Albertville take N90 S & exit 38 for Aigueblanche. Foll sp in vill for 'Camping' on D97 dir La Lechere. Site on L 700m after supmkt; well sp. NB Final L turn from D97 is through a NO ENTRY sign. Sm, mkd pitch, terr, shd; htd wc; chem disp; mv service pnt; shwrs inc; el pts (4-10A) €1.90-3.50; gas 1km; lndtte; ice; shop 1km; tradsmn; rest; snacks; bar; BBQ; htd pool 500m; phone; dogs €0.30; quiet; CCI. "Well-managed site; friendly warden; facs vg & v clean; warden calls 1800 - lives nr; excel centre for Alps, walking & cycling; beautiful location in orchard." ♦ ltd.
1 Apr-30 Sep. € 8.50   2005*

MOUTIERS *9B3* (4km S Urban) Camping La Piat, Ave du Comte Greyfie de Brides-les-Bains, 73570 Brides-les-Bains [04 79 55 22 74; fax 04 79 55 28 55] Fr Moutiers on D90 fr dual c'way foll sp for 'Vallee du Bozel' then take D915 to Brides-les-Bains into town cent. Turn R onto Ave du Comte Greyfie de Brides-les-Bains & foll sp to site. Med, mkd pitch, some hdstg, pt sl, terr, pt shd; wc (some cont); chem disp; mv service pnt; baby facs; shwrs inc; el pts (30-16A) €1.50-3.60; gas; lndtte; lndry rm; shops, rest, snacks, bar 500m; tradsmn; playgrnd; pool adj; 10% statics; dogs €0.70; phone adj; bus 500m; poss cr; Eng spkn; adv bkg; quiet but some rd noise; cc acc; CCI. "Gd base for valleys, mountain biking, walking; ski lift 500m; Brides-les-Bains is thermal spa town specialising in obesity treatments; some pitches v muddy in wet weather; vg sh stay." ♦ 21 Apr-27 Oct. € 9.50   2004*

MOUTIERS EN RETZ, LES see Pornic *2G3*

MOUZON *5C1* (SE Rural) Camp Municipal La Tour St Jerome, 08210 Mouzon [03 24 26 28 02 or 03 24 26 10 63; fax 03 24 26 27 73; mairie-mouzon@wanadoo.fr] Fr SE on N43, turn L onto D19 at Carignan; foll site sp on ent Mouzon; twisting rd to site fr main rd. Sm, some hdg/mkd pitch, pt shd; wc; shwrs inc; el pts (4A) inc; gas, shops 200m; snacks; pool adj; adv bkg; CCI. "V interesting town with gd shops; sports ground opp; 5 mins walk into vill; vg sh stay." ♦ 15 May-15 Sep. € 9.70   2003*

MOYAUX *3D1* (3km NE Rural) LES CASTELS Chateau Le Colombier, Manoir du Val Sery, 14590 Moyaux [02 31 63 63 08; fax 02 31 63 15 97; mail@camping-lecolombier.com; www.camping-lecolombier.com or www.les-castels.com] Fr Pont de Normandie (toll) on A29, at junc with A13 branch R sp Caen. At junc with A132 branch R & foll sp Lisieux to join A132, then D579. Turn L onto D51 sp Blangy-le-Chateau. Immed on leaving Moyaux turn L onto D143 & foll sp to site on R in 3km. Lge, mkd pitch, pt shd; wc; mv service pnt; chem disp; baby facs; shwrs inc; el pts (10A) inc (poss rev pol); gas; lndtte; shop; tradsmn; rest; snacks; bar; BBQ; playgrnd; pool; tennis; games rm; internet; child entmnt; mini-golf; cycle hire; games area; horseriding 8km; golf & watersports 20km; entmnt; excursions; internet; static tents/tour ops; dogs; phone; recep open 0800-2230; no c'vans or m'vans over 9m; Eng spkn; adv bkg (€15 non-refundable fee if bkd direct); quiet; 10% red long stay; cc acc; CCI. "Excel, spacious, well-kept, family-run site; vg for children; helpful staff; gd shop & creperie; excel rest in chateau; shgl paths poss diff some wheelchairs etc; mkt Sun; barrier closes at 2230." ♦ 29 Apr-11 Sep. € 30.00
ABS - N04   2005*

MOYENNEVILLE see Abbeville *3B3*

MUIDES SUR LOIRE *4G2* (6km E Rural) Camp Municipal du Cosson, 41220 Crouy-sur-Cosson [02 54 87 08 81 or 02 54 87 50 10; fax 02 54 87 59 44] Fr Muides-sur-Loire, take D103 E dir Crouy-sur-Cosson. In vill, turn R onto D33 dir Chambord. Site 200m fr village, well sp. Med, mkd pitch, pt shd; wc; shwrs inc; el pts (5A) (poss rev pol); lndry rm; shops 500m; tradsmn; rest 300m; snacks; bar 300m; BBQ; playgrnd; rv fishing nr; few statics; dogs; adv bkg; quiet; CCI. "Pleasant, gd value site; woodland setting; nr Rv Loire; 10km to Chambord, 26km to Blois; poss long-stay workers."
1 Apr-15 Sep.   2005*

MUIDES SUR LOIRE *4G2* (1km SE Rural) Camping Le Chateau des Marais, 27 Rue de Chambord, 41500 Muides-sur-Loire [02 54 87 05 42; fax 02 54 87 05 43; chateau.des.marais@wanadoo.fr; www.camping-des-marais.com] Exit A10 at junc 16 sp Chambord & take N152 sp Mer, Chambord, Blois. At Mer take D112 & cross the Rv Loire. After 300m site on L on edge of vill. Well sp. Lge, mkd pitch, pt sl, shd, wc; chem disp; all serviced pitches; baby facs; shwrs inc; el pts (6A) inc (poss rev pol); gas; lndtte; ice; shop adj; supmkt 7km; rest; snacks; bar, BBQ; playgrnd; htd, covrd pool; waterslide; tennis; cycle hire; games area; entmnt; TV; 35% statics (tour ops); dogs €4; poss cr; Eng spkn; adv bkg fee & deposit; cc acc; CCI. "Excel facs; v well-run site; friendly recep staff; plenty of gd quality children's play equipment; gd for visiting chateaux & Loire; mkt Sat am Blois." ♦
13 May-15 Sep. € 36.00 ABS - L10   2005*

FRANCE

MUIDES SUR LOIRE *4G2* (W Rural) **Camp Municipal Belle Vue**, Ave de la Loire, 41500 Muides-sur-Loire [02 54 87 01 56 or 02 54 87 50 08 (Mairie); fax 02 54 87 01 25; mairie.muides@wanadoo.fr] Fr A10/E5/E60 exit junc 16 S onto D205. Turn R onto N152 then D112 over rv. Site on S bank of rv on D112 W of bdge. Tight U-turn into site. Med, mkd pitch, pt shd; wc; chem disp; shwrs inc; el pts (5A) inc; gas in vill; lndtte; ice; shops 100m; rest, snacks adj; playgrnd; rv fishing/sw adj; cycling; 5% statics; dogs €1.20; vehicle barrier; quiet; CCI. "Gd views over rv; pitches by rv; lovely neat & clean site; low ssn office hrs 0800-0930 & 1800-1930; excel for cycing." ♦ 1 May-15 Sep. € 8.90   2005*

MULHOUSE *6F3* (6km NE Urban) **Camping Le Safary**, Rue de la Foret-Noire, 68390 Sausheim [03 89 46 18 15 or 03 89 61 99 29] W fr Germany on A36/E54, 1st exit to Mulhouse, Ile Napoleon. Foll site sp for 2.8km, site on E of N422 Mulhouse-Colmar rd. Med, mkd pitch, pt shd; wc; chem disp; shwrs inc; el pts (6-10A) €1-2; shops 2km; bar; lndtte; 25% statics; CCI. "Barrier clsd 2200-0800; few facs for size of site, poss inadequate if site full; not rec if itinerants in residence; scruffy."   2002*

MULHOUSE *6F3* (2km SW) **Camping de l'Ill**, 1 Rue de Pierre Coubertin, 68100 Mulhouse [03 89 06 20 66; fax 03 89 61 18 34; camping delill@aol.com] Fr A36 take Mulhouse/Dornach exit & foll sp Brunstatt at 1st traff lts. At 2nd traff lts turn R, foll University/Brunstaff/Camping sps, site approx 2.5km. Lge, mkd pitch, pt sl, pt shd; wc; chem disp; mv service pnt; shwrs inc; el pts (5A) inc; gas; supmkt & rest 1km; tradsmn; snacks; pool adj; dogs €1; quiet but some rlwy noise; 10% red CCI. "Poss unkempt low ssn; welcoming recep; day pass for bus to gd museums in town; superb sw complex & park adj." 1 Apr-31 Oct. € 14.50   2005*

†**MULHOUSE** *6F3* (10km SW Rural) **Camping Parc La Chaumiere**, 62 Rue de Galfingue, 68990 Heimsbrunn [tel/fax 03 89 81 93 43 or 03 89 81 93 21; accueil@camping-lachaumiere.com; www.camping-lachaumiere.com] Leave A36 junc 16 (new flyover) dir Dornach. At rndabt take Morschwiller exit on N466 & cont to Heimsbrunn for approx 4km. Turn L in vill into D19 sp Altkirch. Site on R in 800m. Med, hdg pitch, hdstg, pt sl, shd; htd wc; chem disp; mv service pnt; shwrs inc; el pts (10A) €2.50 (rev pol); lndry rm; ice; shop 1km; tradsmn; snacks; playgrnd; pool; 50% statics; dogs €1; quiet; cc acc; CCI. "Sm pitches not suitable long o'fits." € 9.50   2004*

†**MUNSTER** *6F3* (8km N) **Camping Les Moraines**, 68370 Orbey [03 89 71 25 19] Fr Kaysersberg take N415 E. At Lapoutroie L onto D48 sp Orbey. Cont thro Orbey & on to Pairis to site. Pass 'Ferme Auberge du Chevremont' & further 1km, site 200m after Hotel du Bon Repos: ent on R. Med, hdg/mkd pitch, pt sl, terr, pt shd; wc; shwrs; el pts (6A) inc; lndtte; shops 3km; tradsmn; rest; snacks; bar; 30% statics; poss cr; adv bkg (dep req + bkg fee); quiet. "Attractive rural area with sp walks." € 15.95   2003*

MUNSTER *6F3* (10km N Rural) **Camp Municipal Lefebure**, 68370 Orbey [03 89 71 37 42] Fr Colmar take N415 to St Die. At rndabt just beyond Hachimette, turn L onto D48 to Orbey. Turn R after supmkt at site sp. Site on L after 2km climb. Med, mkd pitch, terr, pt shd; wc; chem disp (wc only); shwrs inc; el pts (5A) €2.50 (long cable req some pitches); lndtte; shops 1km; tradsmn; snacks; playgrnd; 5% statics; dogs €1; phone; quiet; cc not acc; CCI. "Peaceful site 300m above Rhine valley; helpful staff; gd value." Easter-15 Oct. € 9.40   2004*

MUNSTER *6F3* (1km E Rural) **Escapades Terre Oceane Camping Le Parc de la Fecht**, 68140 Munster [03 89 77 31 68 or 05 46 55 10 01; fax 05 46 55 10 10; info@campingterreoceane.com; www.campingterreoceane.com] Clear site sp on all app to Munster & in town. Site on D10. Lge, hdg/mkd pitch, pt shd; wc; chem disp; shwrs inc; el pts (6A) inc; lndtte; shops adj; rest; snacks; bar; BBQ; playgrnd; htd pool, waterslide adj; entmnt; child entmnt; TV; some statics; dogs; Eng spkn; quiet; CCI. "Gd sightseeing area with mountains & lakes; o/night waiting area; pleasant site within sh walk of town; gd area for walking & cycling." ♦ 13 May-16 Sep. € 16.00   2005*

MUNSTER *6F3* (3km E) **Camping Beau Rivage**, 8 Rue des Champs, 68140 Gunsbach [03 89 77 44 62; fax 03 89 77 13 98] Site on rv off D417 Colmar to Munster rd. Med, pt shd; htd wc; chem disp; shwrs inc; el pts (6A) €3.10; gas; lndtte; ice; shop (high ssn); supmkt 2.5km; snacks; bar; playgrnd; rv adj; fishing; sports area; 50% statics; dogs €0.65; adv bkg; quiet; CCI. "Excel for visiting Albert Schweitzer house & memorial." 1 Apr-20 Oct. € 11.30   2004*

MUNSTER *6F3* (4km E Rural) **Camping La Route Verte**, Rue de la Gare, 68230 Wihr-au-Val [0389 71 10 10; info@camping-routeverte.com; www.camping-routeverte.com] Take D417 out of Colmar twd Munster & turn R int Wihr-au-Val. Site on L 800m. Well sp. Med, mkd pitch, pt sl, shd; wc; chem disp; mv service pnt; shwrs (4A) €2.60-3.75; ice; lndtte; shops, rest, bar 50m; pool 4km; games rm; dogs €1.10; phone; poss cr; adv bkg; quiet; 10% red long stay; CCI. "Owner v helpful & friendly; not suitable for lge c'vans (6m max); site surrounded by vineyards; excel san facs; gd base for exploring Alsace region; forest walks." ♦ 1 May-30 Sep. € 8.90   2005*

MUNSTER *6F3* (2km SW) **FFCC Camping Les Amis de la Nature**, 68140 Luttenbach [03 89 77 38 60; fax 03 89 77 25 72; camping.an@wanadoo.fr] Fr Munster take D27 sp Luttenbach, site sp. Lge, pt shd; wc; shwrs inc; el pts (2-6A) €3.05; lndtte; ice; shop; rest; snacks; playgrnd; golf; entmnt; TV; dir access to rv; 50% statics; poss cr; quiet. 15 Feb-30 Nov. € 8.85   2002*

MUNSTER *6F3* (9km SW Rural) **Camp Municipal de Mittlach Langenwasen, 68380 Mittlach** [03 89 77 63 77; fax 03 89 77 74 36; mairiemittlach@wanadoo.fr] Fr Munster on D10 to Metzeral then R onto D10. Site at end rd in 6km. Med, hdg/mkd pitch, pt sl, pt shd, serviced pitch; wc; chem disp; shwrs inc; el pts (4A) €1.15: gas; lndtte; ice; sm shop & 6km; tradsmn; playgrnd; 10% statics; dogs €0.75; adv bkg; quiet; CCI. "Peaceful location in mountains; wooded site at bottom of valley; local walks; helpful staff; san facs gd & v clean." ♦ ltd. 1 May-30 Sep. € 8.90   2005*

†**MUR DE BRETAGNE** *2E3* (6km N Rural) **Camping Le Boterff d'en Haut, 22320 St Mayeux** [02 96 24 02 80; victor.turner@wanadoo.fr; www.holidayinbrittany.net] N fr Mur-de-Bretagne on D767 to St Mayeux. Turn R into vill & R after vill hall (Salle Municipal); to T-junc, turn R & site on L. Sm, unshd; wc; chem disp; shwrs inc; el pts (6-10A) inc; gas 8km; shops, rest, bar 2km; lake sw & watersports 8km; adv bkg; v quiet; cc not acc; red low ssn. "Excel site; gd touring cent; gd walks & cycling; excel san facs; v friendly British owners (C'van Club members) will cook eve meal." € 15.00   2005*

MUR DE BRETAGNE *2E3* (6km SE Rural) **Camping Le Cosquer, 22530 St Connec** [tel/fax 02 96 28 55 88; lecosquer@compuserve.com] Fr N164 turn S onto D81 sp St Connec, then L at Quatre rtes, 1st L Lamrivaux, then R at cross in rd, 1st house on R at rdside. Sm, pt sl, pt shd; wc; chem disp; shwrs inc; el pts (10A) inc; lndtte; shop 2km; rest nr; playgrnd; pool; sand beach 5km; lake sw 6km; quiet; adv bkg; red low ssn; CCI. "In remote, pleasant countryside; friendly British owner, v helpful; watersports & horseriding nrby; gd long stay." 1 Apr-31 Oct. € 16.25   2002*

MUR DE BRETAGNE *2E3* (2km SW Rural) **Camp Municipal, Au Rond-Point du Lac de Guerledan, 22530 Mur-de-Bretagne** [02 96 26 01 90 or 02 96 28 51 32 (LS); fax 02 96 26 09 12] Fr Mur-de-Bretagne take D18 & foll site sp; ent opp view point of Lake Guerledan. Med, pt sl, pt shd; wc (mainly cont); chem disp; shwrs inc; el pts €2.20; 50m; shops 3km; lndry rm; playgrnd; sand beach/lake 500m; poss cr; quiet; CCI. "Gd walking & watersports." ♦ 15 Jun-15 Sep. € 7.10   2004*

MUR DE BRETAGNE *2E3* (4km NW) **Camping Beau Rivage Les Pins, 22530 Caurel** [02 96 28 52 22] Fr Mur-de-Bretagne foll Caurel sp W on N164. Turn L off Caurel by-pass onto D111. Fork L after church in Caurel & foll sp to site. Med, pt sl, pt shd; wc; chem disp; shwrs inc; el pts (6A) €2.20; lndtte; ice; shop; playgrnd; lake sw; boating; watersports; dogs €1; adv bkg; quiet. "Attractive countryside; friendly owners; san facs dated & poss unclean low ssn; site unkempt low ssn; poss noise fr adj campsite." 1 Apr-30 Sep. € 11.90   2005*

MUR DE BRETAGNE *2E3* (4km NW Rural) **Camping Le Guerledan, 22530 Caurel** [02 96 26 08 24; fax 02 96 26 08 24] Fr Mur-de-Bretagne head W on D164 & foll sp to Caurel. L off new Caurel by-pass onto D111. L after church in town & foll sp to site on lakeside. Med, mkd pitch, pt sl, pt shd; wc; shwrs inc; el pts (poss rev pol); gas; playgrnd; lake sw adj; quiet; CCI. "Vg; attractive lakeside setting; friendly, helpful owners." 1 Jul-31 Aug. € 10.80   2003*

MUR DE BRETAGNE *2E3* (4km NW) **Camping Nautic International, Route de Beau Rivage, 22530 Caurel** [02 96 28 57 94; fax 02 96 26 02 00; contact@campingnautic.fr.st; www.camping nautic.fr.st] App Caurel fr Loudeac on N164, turn L off new Caurel by-pass onto D111, fork L 100m past church, site is 1st on L, beside Lac de Guerledan. NB App fr Pontivy on D767 via Mur-de-Bretagne v steep in places & not rec when towing. Med, mkd pitch, terr, pt shd; wc (some cont); chem disp; baby facs; shwrs inc; el pts (10A) inc; lndtte; shop; snacks; BBQ; playgrnd; htd pool; lake fishing; watersports nr; tennis; games rm; dogs €1.50; recep 1000-2100; adv bkg; quiet; cc acc; CCI. "Excel position in attractive countryside; facs poss stretched when site full; dated san facs; poss diff lge o'fits; peaceful site & set up; nice pitches; wonderful pool & lake." ♦ 15 May-25 Sep. € 23.90 ABS - B22   2005*

MURAT *7C4* (1km S Urban) **Camp Municipal de Stalapos, 8 Rue de Stalle, 15300 Murat** [04 71 20 01 83 or 04 71 20 03 80; fax 04 71 20 20 63; ville.murat@wanadoo.fr] On N122, Aurillac-Murat to turning sp on L over rlwy bdge, sp fr cent of Murat. Lge, some hdstg, pt sl, pt shd; wc (cont); chem disp; shwrs inc; el pts (6-10A) €2.45-3.80; lndry rm; ice; shops 1km; playgrnd; rv fishing adj; poss cr; Eng spkn; quiet; CCI. "Gd views medieval Murat; walk to town; steep in places; excel touring base; gd sh/long stay." ♦ 1 May-30 Sep. € 5.50   2005*

MURAT *7C4* (5km SW Rural) **Camping Les Trois Pierres, Le Bourg, 15300 Albepierre-Bredons** [04 71 20 12 23; pascale.martres@libertysurf.fr] Fr Murat take D39 sp Prat de Bouc. Site sp fr cent of vill of Albepierre-Bredons. Sm, pt sl, pt shd; wc; chem disp (wc); shwrs inc; el pts inc; shop, rest, bar 500m; dogs; Eng spkn; adv bkg; quiet; CCI. "Excel, peaceful location for Cantal mountains, touring or walking; v helpful owner." ♦ ltd. 1 May-30 Sep. € 9.00   2005*

MURE ARGENS, LA see St Andre les Alpes *10E3*

MURE, LA *9C3* (9km E Rural) **Camp Municipal du Plan d'Eau, 38740 Valbonnais** [04 76 30 21 28; fax 04 76 30 21 19] S fr Grenoble using lorry rte (Drac), N85 too steep for average o'fit; go thro La Mure turn L at Its sp Valbonnais, Entraigues & Bourg d'Oisans; site well sp in Valbonnais. Lge, pt shd; wc (cont); 80% serviced pitches; shwrs inc; el pts (10A); shops in vill; rest adj; playgrnd; lake sw; poss cr; 15% statics; quiet; adv bkg. 1 May-30 Sep.   2002*

FRANCE

MURE, LA 9C3 (13km E Rural) **Camp Municipal Les Vigneaux, 38740 Entraigues** [tel/fax 04 76 30 27 06 or 04 76 30 20 18 (Mairie)] S on N85 fr La Mure, turn L on D114, fork R on D26 to Valbonnais. This rd becomes D526. Site on L on ent Entraigues, 4km beyond Valbonnais. Ent on bend in rd, more diff if ent fr Bourg d'Oisans. Sm, pt shd; wc; shwrs inc; el pts (5A) inc (poss rev pol); shops 100m; rv 100m; lake 3km; fishing; 15% statics; adv bkg; quiet; red long stay; CCI. "Clean facs; mountainous National Park adj; warden resident; vg long stay." ♦ 1 May-30 Sep. € 12.00   2003*

MURE, LA 9C3 (7km SE Rural) **Camping Belvedere de l'Obiou, Les Egats, 38350 St Laurent-en-Beaumont** [tel/fax 04 76 30 40 80; info@camping-obiou.com; www.camping-obiou.com] Clearly sp fr N85. Sm, pt sl, pt terr, pt shd; htd wc; chem disp; mv service pnt; shwrs; el pts (4-6A) €3-3.50 (poss rev pol); lndtte; ice; tradsmn; rest; snacks; playgrnd; htd, covrd pool; cycle hire; internet; TV; English library; 5% statics; dogs €2.50; poss cr; Eng spkn; quiet; 10% red long stay/low ssn; CCI. "Superb, immac, family-run site; excel facs; v helpful owners; picturesque & interesting area of lakes, mountains, monasteries; guide given for local walks." 1 Apr-15 Oct. € 16.50 (CChq acc)   2005*

MUROL 7B4 (1km S) **Camp Le Repos du Baladin, 63790 Murol** [04 73 88 61 93; fax 04 73 88 66 41; reposbaladin@free.fr] Fr D996 at Murol foll sp 'Groire' to E, site on R in 1.5km just after vill. Med, hdg/mkd pitch, pt sl, shd; wc (some cont); chem disp; shwrs inc; el pts (5A) €3; lndtte; shop 1.5km; tradsmn; snacks; playgrnd; lake sw 5km; poss cr; quiet; Eng spkn; CCI. "Lovely quiet site with immac san facs; friendly & helpful owners; gd sh/long stay." 1 Jun-15 Sep. € 12.00   2003*

MUROL 7B4 (1km S Rural) **Camping La Ribeyre, Route de Jassat, 63790 Murol** [04 73 88 64 29; fax 04 73 88 68 41; laribeyre@free.fr; www.camping-laribeyre.com] Exit 6 fr A75 onto D978 S sp Champeix/St Nectaire, then D996 to Murol. In Murol take D5 S sp Besse-et-St Anastaise. In approx 500m take D618 twd Jassat & site in 500m on rvside. Sp fr Murol. Lge, mkd pitch, pt shd; wc (some cont); chem disp; serviced pitches; baby facs; shwrs inc; el pts (6A) €4.30-4.90 (poss rev pol); gas; lndtte; ice; shop 1km; tradsmn; rest; snacks & creperie; bar; BBQ; playgrnd; pools (1 htd, covrd) & aqua park; waterslides; lake sw & sand beach adj; fishing; boat hire; tennis; horseriding; hiking; games area; games rm; entmnt; TV rm; 25% statics; dogs €1.95; Eng spkn; adv bkg (dep req + bkg fee); quiet; red low ssn; CCI. "Ideal touring base; spacious pitches; excel scenery & mountains nr; activities on site for all ages; new pool/aquapark 2006; lge open spaces for games, etc; barrier operated 2300-0700; groups welcome low ssn." ♦ 1 May-15 Sep. € 20.70 (CChq acc)   2005*

See advertisement

MUROL 7B4 (4km S Rural) **Camp Municipal de Bellevue, 63790 St Victor-la-Riviere** [04 73 88 52 77 or 04 73 88 66 72 (Mairie); fax 04 73 88 80 40] Fr A75 take D996 to Murol. At Murol turn S onto D5 (sp Besse-en-Chandesse) to St Victor-la-Riviere in 5km. At junc of D5 & D635, turn W, sp Camping Bellevue. Ent to site 150m on R behind church. Sm, mkd pitch, pt sl, terr, unshd; wc (some cont); chem disp; shwrs inc; el pts (3-6A) €3-3.50; tradsmn; shops, rest, snacks, bar 2km; Eng spkn; adv bkg; quiet; cc not acc; CCI. "Excel views; facs old & basic but clean; Murol has gd shops & rests; gd sh/long stay." 1 Jul-31 Aug. € 9.60   2003*

MUROL *7B4* (2km W Rural) **Camping La Plage du Lac Chambon, 63790 Murol [04 73 88 60 27; fax 04 73 88 80 08]** Exit A75 junc 6 sp Champeix/St Nectaire; cont for 34km thro St Nectaire to Murol on D996; 1km past Murol turn L sp Lac Chambon /Centre Touristique; bear L past lge car park to site ent. Lge, hdg/mkd pitch, terr, pt shd; htd wc; chem disp; shwrs inc; baby facs; el pts (6-10A) €2.44-3.35; gas & 2km; lndtte; ice; shop & 2km; playgrnd; lake sw & fishing adj; tennis; mini-golf; archery; cycle hire; entmnts; TV; dogs; phone; Eng spkn; adv bkg; quiet; cc acc; CCI. "Gd birdwatching & walking." ♦ ltd. 1 May-31 Aug. € 18.00   2002*

MUROL *7B4* (2km W Rural) **Camping Le Pre Bas, 63790 Chambon-sur-Lac [04 73 88 63 04; fax 04 73 88 65 93; prebas@lac-chambon.com; www.campingauvergne.com]** Take D996 W fr Murol twd Mont-Dore. Site 1.5km on L, immed after lake. Lge, hdg/mkd pitch, pt sl, pt shd; wc; chem disp; mv service pnt; serviced pitches; baby facs; shwrs inc; el pts (6A) €4; gas 1km; lndtte; ice/freezer; shop & 1km; tradsmn; snacks; 2 pools (l htd, covrd); waterslide; lake sw; entmnt; 40% statics; dogs €1.70; phone; poss cr; Eng spkn; adv bkg; quiet; CCI. "Excel, friendly, family-run site; v helpful recep; superb views; v clean san facs; excel walking area; highly rec; access to sm pitches poss diff lge o'fits." ♦ 1 May-30 Sep. € 17.50   2003*

MUROL *7B4* (5km W Rural) **Camp Municipal Les Bombes, 63790 Chambon-sur-Lac [04 73 88 64 03 or 04 73 88 61 21 (Mairie); fax 04 73 88 62 59]** Site is on D996. Nr exit fr vill Chambon. Med, mkd pitch, pt shd; wc (cont); chem disp; mv service pnt; shwrs; el pts (3-6A); lndtte; lake sw 1km; shops, rest 500m; TV rm; dogs; quiet; Eng spkn; phone; cc acc; CCI. "Gd, clean, well-maintained facs; gd for touring volcanic park; v lge pitches; v clean facs; helpful warden; open views of countryside." ♦ 15 Jun-15 Sep.   2005*

MUS see Lunel *10E2*

MUY, LE *10F4* (3km W Rural) **Camping Les Cigales, 721 Chemin du Jas de la Paro, 83490 Le Muy [04 94 45 12 08; fax 04 94 45 92 80; contact@ les-cigales.com; www.les-cigales.com]** Exit A8 at Le Muy, keep in L hand lane & take 1st L across dual c'way after Peage, foll lge sp at sm lane ent to site. Fr N7 W of Le Muy take A8 access rd, turn R into lane 250m bef toll booth & foll lane past toll to site in 1km. Lge, hdg/mkd pitch, pt sl, terr, shd; wc (some cont); chem disp; shwrs inc; el pts (6-10A) €3-5; gas; lndtte; ice; sm shop & 3km; rest; snacks; bar; playgrnd; pool; sand beach 20km; tennis; rv sw 2km; entmnt; 7% statics; dogs; Eng spkn; adv bkg (rec); quiet; red long stay; cc acc; CCI. "Conv for St Raphael & a'route to Nice; beautiful facs blocks." ♦ 1 Apr-30 Oct. € 22.00   2004*

MUZILLAC *2G3* (12km N) **Camp Municipal de l'Etang de Celac, Place du General de Gaulle, 56230 Questembert [02 97 26 11 24 or 02 97 26 11 38 (LS)]** Site on D7 W of Questembert on o'skts of town. Med, mkd pitch, pt shd; wc (some cont); chem disp; mv service pnt; shwrs; el pts (12A) inc; shop; rest; tradsmn; lndry rm; playgrnd; TV; beach 25km; fishing; CCI. "V clean facs, attractive location by lake; Monday mkt sp fr vill." 15 Jun-15 Sep. € 10.00   2004*

This site entry hasn't been updated for a while; we'd better fill in a site report form and send it to The Club.

MUZILLAC *2G3* (5km NE) **Camping Le Moulin de Cadillac, Route de Beric, 56190 Noyal-Muzillac [02 97 67 03 47; fax 02 97 67 00 02; infos@ moulin-cadillac.com; www.moulin-cadillac.com]** Fr N165 take D140 N to Lauzach, turn R at x-rds, site well sp; care on LH hairpin at rd junc 100m fr site. Sh app rd but steep & sharp bends. Med, hdg pitch, terr, shd; wc; chem disp; mv service pnt; baby facs; shwrs inc; el pts (4A) inc; gas; lndtte; ice; shop; tradsmn; rest; bar; playgrnd; htd pool; waterslide; beach 15km; fishing lake; tennis; games area; pets corner; golf 15km; TV rm; 30% statics; dogs €1; phone; adv bkg rec high ssn; quiet; "In pleasant wooded valley away fr cr coastal sites; relaxing site." ♦ 1 May-30 Sep. € 13.60   2004*

MUZILLAC *2G3* (7km NE Rural) **Camp Municipal Borg-Nehue, 56190 Le Guerno [02 97 42 80 35 or 02 97 42 94 76 (Mairie); fax 02 97 42 84 36; mairie-leguerno@wanadoo.fr]** N165 Nantes-Vannes rd; exit Muzillac; D20 E for 7km; N on D139A to Le Guerno (1km); site sp on ent vill. Med, hdg/mkd pitch, pt sl, pt shd; wc; chem disp; mv service pnt; shwrs inc; el pts (10A) €1.65; lndry rm; ice; shop 400m & 7km; playgrnd; shgl beach 15km; 5% statics; dogs; Eng spkn; adv bkg; cc not acc; CCI. "Quiet site in sm vill; beautiful facs; zoo & botanical gardens 2km; book/pay at Mairie low ssn." ♦ 1 Mar-30 Nov. € 6.50   2003*

MUZILLAC *2G3* (E Urban) **Camp Municipal, 56190 Muzillac [02 97 41 67 01 or 06 08 03 33 36; fax 02 97 45 67 06; daniel.tatard@wanadoo.fr]** N165 Nantes-Vannes rd, site sp in Muzillac cent. Med, level, pt shd, hdg pitch; wc (some cont); chem disp; mv service pnt; shwrs inc; el pts (10A); lndtte; rest, snacks, bar & shop 500m; playgrnd; TV; dogs; poss cr; adv bkg (dep req); Eng spkn; CCI. "Delightful, quiet site in early ssn; school coaches drive thro site daily; gd sh stay/NH." ♦ Easter-30 Sep. € 8.85   2003*

MUZILLAC *2G3* (8km SW Coastal) **Camping Ty Breiz, 15 Grande Rue, 56750 Damgan [tel/fax 02 97 41 13 47; marielebayon@libertysurf.fr]** Turn S off Muzillac-Damgan rd for Kervoyal; site on L opp church. Med, pt shd; wc; shwrs inc; el pts (10A) €3.20; lndtte; shop adj; playgrnd; sand beach 300m; dogs €1.40; Eng spkn; adv bkg rec; quiet; cc acc; CCI. "Gd welcome; v happy, family-run site; excel shellfish in Damgan; mkt on Wed (high ssn only); book early for Jul/Aug." 26 Apr-5 Oct. € 13.30
                                                        2003*

MUZILLAC *2G3* (8km SW Coastal) **Oasis Camping, Rue du Port, Kervoyal, 56750 Damgan [tel/fax 02 97 41 10 52]** Turn S off Muzillac- Damgan rd (D153). Turn L at x-rds on ent vill (sp). Site in 400m on R. Lge, mkd pitch, pt shd; wc (some cont) shwrs inc; el pts (6A) inc; gas 1km; lndtte; shops 1km; snacks; playgrnd; beach adj; 80% statics; CCI. 1 Apr-20 Oct. € 15.70   2003*

MUZILLAC *2G3* (4km W Coastal) **Camping du Bedume, Betahon-Plage, 56190 Ambon-Plages [02 97 41 68 13; fax 02 97 41 56 79; camping dubedume@free.fr; www.bedume.com]** Fr N165 take D20 W dir Ambon, foll to Betahon, site sp. Lge, hdg pitch, pt shd; wc; chem disp; baby facs; shwrs inc; el pts (5A) inc; lndtte; ice; shop; tradsmn; snacks; bar; BBQ; playgrnd; htd pools; waterslide; sand beach adj; games area; games rm; TV rm; 75% statics; dogs €4.20; Eng spkn; adv bkg req; quiet; cc acc; red low ssn. "Gd long/sh stay." ♦ 1 Apr-30 Sep. € 34.10
                                                        2005*

See advertisement

MUZILLAC *2G3* (10km NW) **Camp Municipal de Lann Floren, Rue des Sports, 56450 Surzur [02 97 42 10 74; fax 02 97 42 03 54; mairie-surzur@wanadoo.fr]** Sp fr vill cent. Med, hdg/mkd pitch, pt shd; htd wc; chem disp; baby facs; shwrs inc; el pts (10A); lndtte; shop, rest, bar 500m; playgrnd; sand beach 4km; bus 1km; adv bkg; quiet; CCI. "Attractive site." ♦ ltd. 25 Jun-31 Aug. € 4.42
                                                        2005*

NAGES see Lacaune *8E4*

NAJAC *8E4* **Camping Le Paisserou, 12270 Najac [05 65 29 73 96; fax 05 65 29 72 29]** Take D922 fr Villefranche-de-Rouergue. Turn R on D39 at La Fouillade to Najac. Site by rv, sp in vill. Or fr A20 exit junc 59 onto D926. At Caylus take D84 to Najac. Med, hdg pitch, shd; wc; chem disp; shwrs inc; el pts €3; ice; lndtte; shops & rest in vill; tradsmn; snacks; bar; pool adj (free); rv sw; tennis adj; some statics; dogs €1.50; phone; poss cr; Eng spkn; adv bkg (dep req, bkg fee); quiet; red low ssn; CCI. "Conv for Aveyron gorges; bungalows avail; friendly owners; lovely vill." 29 Apr-30 Sep. € 13.00   2002*

NALLIERS see Lucon *7A1*

†NAMPONT ST MARTIN *3B3* (2km NE) **Camping Auberge des Etangs, 91 Rue Vallee de l'Authie, 62870 Roussent [03 21 81 20 10; www.auberge-des-etangs.fr]** 11km S of Montreuil on N1, take D119 E to Roussent, site on R in vill. Med, mkd pitch, pt sl, pt shd; wc; chem disp; shwrs inc; el pts (6A) inc; gas; lndtte; ice; shop; rest; snacks; playgrnd; entmnt; rv fishing 2km; TV; many statics; site clsd Jan; quiet but noise fr hotel (disco); red long stays. € 14.20   2004*

NAMPONT ST MARTIN *3B3* (3km W Rural) **Camping La Ferme des Aulnes, 1 Rue du Marais, Fresnes-sur-Authie, 80120 Nampont-St Martin [03 22 29 22 69 or 06 22 41 86 54 (LS); fax 03 22 29 39 43; contact@fermedesaulnes.com; www.fermedesaulnes.com]** N1-E402 S fr Montreuil 13km thro Nampont-St Firmin to Nampont-St Martin; turn R in vill onto D485; site in 3km; sp fr N1. Med, some hdg pitch, pt sl, pt shd; htd wc; chem disp; shwrs inc; el pts (6A) €5; lndry rm; shop 5km; tradsmn, snacks, bar high ssn; el BBQ only; playgrnd; htd pool; beach 15km; TV & cinema rm; 75% statics; dogs €4; poss cr; adv bkg; quiet but noisy cockerels; CCI. "Nice, well-organised site; clean facs, stretched high ssn; clsd 2200-0800; bkg rec low ssn - overflow site in field not gd." ♦ ltd. 26 Mar-1 Nov. € 20.00 (3 persons) (CChq acc)
                                                        2005*

NANCAY *4G3* (Rural) **Camp Municipal des Pins, Route de Salbris, La Chaux, 18330 Nancay [02 48 51 81 80 or 02 48 51 81 35 (Mairie); fax 02 48 51 80 60]** Site on N944 fr Salbris twd Bourges clearly sp on L immed bef ent Nancay. Med, mkd pitch, shd, hdstg; htd wc; chem disp; shwrs inc; el pts (6-12A) €3.80-€6.90; gas; lndtte; shops 1km; playgrnd; tennis; sw 12km; fishing; 50% statics; adv bkg; quiet; CCI. "No twin-axle vans; friendly recep; lovely setting in pine woods but many scruffy statics & old facs; poor site lighting; beautiful vill; gd walking." 1 Apr-2 Nov. € 6.10   2004*

NANCY *6E2* (12km S Rural) **Camping du Chaubourot, 54630 Flavigny-sur-Moselle [03 83 26 75 64; fax 03 83 26 74 76]** Take A33 then A330 S fr Nancy sp Flavigny-sur-Moselle; on N570 in vill on bank of Rv Moselle; sm sp in main st. Sm, mkd pitch, pt shd; wc; chem disp; shwrs €1; el pts (4-6A) €2.50-3.10; shops adj; playgrnd; sand/shgl beach 250m; fishing; pedalo hire; mini-golf; 65% statics; adv bkg; some rd noise; CCI. "Fair NH only." 1 May-30 Sep. € 10.00   2003*

NANCY *6E2* (6km SW Urban) **Campeole Le Brabois, Ave Paul Muller, 54600 Villers- les-Nancy [03 83 27 18 28; fax 03 83 40 06 43; campeoles. brabois@wanadoo.fr; www.campeoles.fr]** Fr A33 exit junc 2b sp Brabois onto D974 dir Nancy; after 400m turn L at 2nd traff lts; at 2nd further traff lts turn R on slip rd & site on R; site well sp. Lge, mkd pitch, pt shd; wc (some cont); chem disp; mv service pnt; shwrs inc; el pts (5-A) €3.95; gas; lndtte; ice; shop; supmkt & petrol 2km; rest; snacks; bar; BBQ; playgrnd; games area; TV; dogs €2.60; bus; poss cr; Eng spkn; adv bkg; quiet; red low ssn; cc acc; CCI. "Nice setting; v helpful staff; well run site with lge pitches; comfortable club rm; no twin-axle c'vans over 5.50m (m'vans OK); interesting town; arr early - site v popular NH; bus tickets to town fr recep." ♦ 1 Apr-15 Oct. € 12.90   2005*

NANCY *6E2* (10km NW Rural) **Camping de Liverdun (formerly Municipal Defranoux), 54460 Liverdun [tel/fax 03 83 24 43 78]** Fr A31 take Frouard exit. In Frouard bear L onto D90 to Liverdun; cross rv bdge (sp Liverdun); under rlwy bdge L at traff lts, thro town, fork L & foll sp to site by sports area. Do not turn L at site exit when towing. Lge, pt shd; htd wc; own san; shwrs (0730-1000) inc; el pts (6A) €2.90; lndtte; shop & 1.5km; rest; snacks; bar Aug; playgrnd; paddling pool; entmnt; 80% statics; dogs; quiet except rlwy noise; cc not acc; CCI. "Lovely site & area; helpful staff; beautiful city of Nancy worth visit; situated in Lorraine National Park; basic facs; fair sh stay/NH." May-Sep. € 10.20   2005*

NANS LES PINS *10F3* (Rural) **Camping International La Ste Baume, 83860 Nans-les-Pins [04 94 78 92 68; fax 04 94 78 67 37; ste.baume@ wanadoo.fr; www.saintebaume.com]** Exit A8 junc 34 dir St Maximin onto D560. Cross N7 & at next lge junc turn R onto D560 then immed L onto D80. Site 600m after sp Nans-les-Pins, then up private rd to site. Lge, pt sl, shd; wc; chem disp; baby facs; shwrs inc; el pts (6A) inc; gas; lndtte; ice; shop; rest; bar; playgrnd; 3 pools; jacuzzi; sand beach 35km; horseriding; 90% statics; dogs €1.80; adv bkg; red low ssn. "Friendly owners; path into pleasant vill; noise fr pool till late; modern facs; excel long stay." ♦ 3 May-7 Sep. € 30.00   2003*

†**NANS LES PINS** *10F3* (1.5km S Rural) **Camp Municipal La Petite Colle, 83860 Nans-les-Pins [04 94 78 65 98 or 06 62 58 83 76; fax 0494 78 95 39; camping.denis@club-internet.fr; www.sudinfo7. com]** Exit A8/E80 at junc 34 onto N560 dir St Maximin. Foll sp St Zacharie, then in approx 8km fr leaving m'way, turn L onto D80 sp Nans-les-Pins. Foll sp to site thro village into woods. Rough rd on L to site. Med, hdstg, terr, shd; wc; chem disp; serviced pitch; baby facs; shwrs inc; el pts (6A) €3.50; lndtte; tradsmn; snacks; bar; many statics; dogs €1.50; phone; Eng spkn; adv bkg; quiet; red long stay/low ssn; CCI. "Mkd woodland walks & to vill; san facs poss stretched if busy; helpful owner; NH only." € 14.00   2005*

NANT *10E1* (2km N Rural) **Camping Le Roc Qui Parle, Les Cuns, 12230 Nant [tel/fax 05 65 62 22 05]** Fr Millau take D991E to site passing Val de Cantobre. Fr La Cavalerie take D999E to Nant & at T-junc on o'skts of Nant turn N; Millau & Les Cuns approx 2km; site on R. Med, hdg/mkd pitch, pt sl, pt shd; wc; serviced pitches; chem disp; mv service pnt; shwrs inc; el pts (6A) €2.80; lndtte; ice; shop; BBQ; playgrnd; rv sw & fishing on site; adv bkg; quiet; no cc acc; CCI. "Excel site; v lge pitches with views; friendly & helpful; v warm welcome; pool in Nant opens 1 Jul; rv walk; shop sells farm produce; vg long/sh stay." ♦ ltd. 1 Apr-30 Sep. € 12.50   2005*

NANT *10E1* (4km N Rural) **LES CASTELS Le Val de Cantobre, Domaine de Vellas, 12230 Nant [05 65 58 43 00 or 06 80 44 40 63 (mob); fax 05 65 62 10 36; info@valdecantobre.com; www. valdecantobre.com or www.les-castels.com]** Exit A75 junc 47; foll sp D999 E to Nant for 12 km. At Nant at T-junc turn L onto D991 sp Val de Cantobre. Site on R in 4km - steep access rd, care req. Lge, mkd pitch, terr, pt shd; wc (some cont); chem disp; mv service pnt; baby facs; shwrs inc; el pts (6A) inc; gas; lndtte; shop; tradsmn; rest; snacks; bar; BBQ; playgrnd; htd pool; paddling pool; tennis; games rm; rv sw; mini-golf; organised walks; entmnt; many tour op statics & tents; dogs €2 (free low ssn); poss cr; Eng spkn; adv bkg ess; quiet; red low ssn; cc acc. "Excel; friendly, family-owned, busy & popular site; v helpful staff; 1st class amenities; san facs immac; gd disabled facs; outstanding scenery; lovely views most pitches; some steep site rds poss diff; mkt Tue." ♦ 13 May-10 Sep. € 31.50 (CChq acc) ABS - C19   2005*

FRANCE

NANT *10E1* (7km E) **Camping La Claparede, 12230 St Jean-du-Bruel** [05 65 62 23 41 or 05 65 62 26 45; fax 05 65 62 17 23] S on N9 turn L & E on D999 for 21km via Nant, to St Jean-du-Bruel, site on L on ent town. Sp. Med, shd; wc (some cont); chem disp; shwrs inc; el pts (3-6A) €1.52; ice; lndry rm; lndtte; tradsmn; shop; pool 5km; tennis; rv sw & fishing adj; entmnts; 50% statics; adv bkg ess; cc not acc. "V scenic area; sm pitches; poss unkempt low ssn." ♦ 1 Mar-31 Oct. € 11.00   2002*

NANT *10E1* (1km S Rural) **Camping Les Deux Vallees, 12230 Nant** [05 65 62 26 89 or 05 65 62 10 40; fax 05 65 62 17 23] Take the A75 twds Millau; then N9 twds Montpellier/Beziers for 19km; at La Cavalerie turn L onto D999 for 14km to Nant; site sp. Med, mkd pitch, pt shd; wc (some cont); own san; chem disp; mv service pnt; some serviced pitches; shwrs inc; el pts (6A) €2; lndtte; tradsmn; rest; snacks; bar; shop 1km; pool 500m; playgrnd; entmnts; rv fishing; TV; dogs €1; phone; quiet; adv bkg; CCI. "Stunning scenery; well-kept, friendly site; peaceful; ltd facs low ssn; 15 mins walk fr vill cent; outstanding scenery; gd walking." ♦ 1 Apr-31 Oct. € 11.00   2005*

NANT *10E1* (2.5km S Rural) **Camping Castelnau (Gely), 12230 Nant** [05 65 62 25 15] Fr Nant take D999 E twds Le Vigan; site is sp on L in 2.5km. Sm, pt shd; wc; chem disp (wc only); shwrs inc; el pts (7A) €1.50; lndtte; shop, rest, snacks, bar 2.5km; playgrnd; pool 3km; sw & fishing nr; poss cr; adv bkg; quiet; cc not acc; CCI. "Nice CL-type site with plenty of space; lovely location; conv Roquefort." 1 Apr-15 Nov. € 9.00   2005*

NANT *10E1* (500m SW Rural) **Camping Les Vernedes, Route de Durzon, 12230 Nant** [05 65 62 15 19] Fr vill cent 500m, sp. Sm, shd; wc (some cont); chem disp; shwrs inc; el pts (10A) €2; gas 500m; lndtte; ice; rest adj; BBQ; playgrnd; dogs; Eng spkn adv bkg; quiet; CCI. "Pleasant stroll to Nant cent; gd trout rest adj; gd touring base; gd long stay; helpful owners." 1 Mar-31 Oct. € 10.00   2004*

†**NANTES** *2G4* (3km N Urban) **Camping Le Petit Port, 21 Blvd de Petit Port, 44300 Nantes** [02 40 74 47 94 or 02 51 84 94 51; fax 02 40 74 23 06; camping-petit-port@nge-nantes. fr; www.nge- nantes.fr] Fr N137 ring rd exit Porte de la Chapelle & foll sp Centre Ville, Camping Petit Port or University when ent o'skts of Nantes; site ent opp Hippodrome. Site nr racecourse & university; well sp. Fr S keep on ring rd & exit Porte de la Chapelle, then as before. Lge, hdg/mkd pitch, hdstg, shd, wc; serviced pitches; chem disp; mv service pnt; shwrs inc; el pts (10A) inc; gas; lndtte; ice; shop; tradsmn; snacks, rest & bar 100m; BBQ; playgrnd; htd, covrd pool adj; waterslide; cycle hire; TV; 30% statics; dogs €0.90; tram; twin-axles acc (extra charge); poss cr; Eng spkn; adv bkg (groups); quiet; red long stay; cc acc; CCI. "Trams fr site ent to town; ice skating adj; well-appointed site but poss unkempt low ssn; access to san facs by security code; poss youth groups." ♦ € 16.80   2005*

†**NANTES** *2G4* (6km E) **Camping Belle Riviere, Rue des Rivieres, 44980 Ste Luce-sur-Loire** [tel/fax 02 40 25 85 81; belleriviere@wanadoo.fr] Fr 'Nantes Peripherique Est' take exit 42 thro St Luce on D68 twds Thouare; at traff lights turn S & foll sp over rlwy bdge. Fr E via D68, thro Thouare twd Ste Luce. At traff lts nr g'ge, S over rlwy bdge twd rv (sp). Med, hdg/mkd pitch, hdstg, pt shd; wc (50% cont); chem disp; shwrs inc; el pts (3-10A) €2.45-3.50; gas; lndry rm; shops 3km; rest; snacks; bar; BBQ; playgrnd; 50% statics; poss cr; Eng spkn; adv bkg; quiet; red low ssn/CCI. "Pleasant rv walks; elec barrier (€20 dep) & office clsd 1230-1630 (1530 Jul/Aug); spotless, modern san facs; v helpful owners; conv for Nantes peripherique & city cent; highly rec; excel." ♦ € 12.50   2004*

NANTES *2G4* (13km E) **Camping Le Chene, 44450 St Julien-de-Concelles** [02 40 54 12 00; fax 02 40 36 54 79; campingduchene@free.fr] Fr Nantes, cross Rv Loire dir Poitiers; immed turn E sp St Sebastien; thro town onto D751 to Le Bout-des-Pont; turn S onto D57 sp Camping. Site on L immed after lake. Med, shd; wc; mv service pnt; shwrs €1; el pts (10A) €2.60; shops 1.2km; rest; bar; BBQ; playgrnd; tennis; child entmnt; cycle hire; golf; lake adj; fishing; sailing; windsurfing; dogs €1; adv bkg rec high ssn; rd noise. 1 Apr-31 Oct. € 9.05   2002*

NANTES *2G4* (7km S Urban/Rural) **Camp Municipal du Loiry, Blvd Guiche-Serex, 44120 Vertou** [tel/ fax 02 40 80 07 10] Exit Nantes junc 47 sp Porte de Vertou. Strt at 1st rndabt & cont along rd, which becomes Blvd Guiche-Serex. Site on L, well sp. Med, hdg/mkd pitch, pt shd; wc; chem disp; shwrs inc; el pts (6-10A) €2.25-3.60; lndtte; rest, snacks, bar, fishing, entmnt adj; no statics; dogs €1; phone; Eng spkn; adv bkg; quiet; CCI. "No twin-axles; site adj parkland, rvside walks." ♦ 1 Apr-30 Sep. € 8.75   2005*

NANTIAT *7B3* (Rural) **Camp Municipal Les Haches, 87140 Nantiat** [05 55 53 42 43 (Mairie); fax 05 55 53 56 28] Turn E off N147 at x-rds in Chamboret, site 1km on L, sp fr N147. Sm, pt sl, pt shd; wc; chem disp; shwrs inc; el pts €1.40; shops 1km; fishing; train noise & kennels opp; CCI. "Gd facs; poss lukewarm water when site busy; v clean; lovely setting o'looking lake; conv 'Martyr Vill' at Oradour-sur-Glane; gd rest at hotel in vill; phone ahead as opening dates not reliable; height barrier 2.50m; gd sh stay/NH." 15 Jun-15 Sep. € 10.24   2005*

NANTUA *9A3* (1km W Urban) **Camping Le Signal, 01130 Nantua** [04 74 75 02 09] E on N84 Pont d'Ain/Nantua, rd passes alongside Nantua lake on R. At end of lake bef ent town turn R & foll sps. Med, shd; wc; shwrs inc; el pts; ice; shops 200m; rest; snacks; playgrnd; lake sw 300m; poss cr; sports cent nr; quiet. "V attractive site." Jun-Aug.   2002*

NANTUA *9A3* (4km NW) **Camping du Lac, 5 Route de Lyon, 01460 Montreal-la-Cluse [04 74 76 01 63]** Fr Nantua foll N84 round lake. In La Cluse turn L at traff lts at sp 'Port'. Site ent on L at 'Restaurant du Lac'. Ent easily missed. Med, pt shd; wc (some cont); shwrs inc; el pts (4A) €2.30 (rev pol); supmkt adj; rest; snacks; playgrnd; shgl beach for lake sw; poss v cr; some rd noise. "Wonderful location but v poor san facs; boggy grnd; lovely views of lake." 1 May-30 Sep. € 10.00   2003*

†**NAPOULE, LA** *10F4* (2km N Coastal) **Camping Les Cigales, 505 Ave de la Mer, Quartier d'Etang, 06210 Mandelieu-la-Napoule [04 93 49 23 53; fax 04 93 49 30 45; campingcigales@wanadoo.fr; www.lescigales.com]** Take Mandelieu exit fr A8 & turn R twice in Mandelieu cent into Ave des Ecureulis, sp Campings. Pass under a'route & in 1km turn L at T-junc into Ave de la Mer. Site in 50m on L. Or on N7 fr Frejus turn R at rndabt with fountains app Mandelieu. Or fr coast rd turn inland at bdge over Rv La Siagne into Blvd de la Mer & site in 1km on R. Med, mkd pitch, shd; htd wc; baby facs; shwrs inc; el pts (6A) €4; lndtte; ice; shop 1.5km; rest; snacks; bar; playgrnd; pool; sand beach 800m; solarium; dir access to rv; fishing, sailing & other waterports 800m; entmnt; dogs €1; poss cr; Eng spkn; quiet; red low ssn/long stay. "High quality site in excel location; gd san facs; ltd facs low ssn; excel site." ♦ € 38.00   2005*

NAPOULE, LA *10F4* (2km N Urban) **Camping Les Pruniers, 18 Rue de la Pinea, 06210 Mandelieu-la-Napoule [04 92 97 00 44 or 04 93 49 99 23; fax 04 93 49 37 45; contact@bungalow-camping.com; www.bungalow-camping.com]** Fr A8 turn R twice in Mandelieu cent into Blvd des Ecureuils sp 'Sofitel Royal Casino'. Pass under a'route & in 1km turn L at T-junc into Ave de la Mer. At rndabt bear R & next R sp Pierre-Vacances. Turn R in 50m, site at end of rd. On N7 fr Frejus, turn R at rndabt with fountains app Mandelieu. Fr coast rd take slip rd for Mandelieu. Sm, mkd pitch, hdstg; shd; wc; chem disp (in cont wc); shwrs inc; el pts (5-20A) €4; lndtte; shop & 300m; rests, snacks, bar in vill; playgrnd; htd pool; sand beach 500m; sea & rv fishing; entmnt; 60% statics (sep area); dogs €5; no twin-axle c'vans & max length c'van 6m, m'van 7m; poss cr; Eng spkn; adv bkg; quiet; red low ssn; cc acc; CCI. "Delightful, peaceful site on rv & facing marina; v clean facs; friendly recep; excel base for area; easy cycling to beach & Cannes." 1 Apr-15 Oct. € 31.00   2005*

NAPOULE, LA *10F4* (3km N Urban) **Camping de La Ferme, 06210 Mandelieu-la-Napoule [04 93 49 94 19; fax 04 93 49 18 52]** Fr A8 turn L in Mandelieu cent sp Frejus; 200m after rndabt with palm tree centre, fork R into Ave Marchal Juin & strt into Bvd du Bon Puits. Avoid La Napoule vill when towing. Med, shd; wc; shwrs €0.50; el pts (6-10A) €2.50-€3.00; gas; ice; lndtte; shops; snacks; sand beach 650m; dogs; adv bkg; quiet. "Helpful staff; nice atmosphere; mobile bank; facs looking old & tired; some pitches v sm; cr high ssn." ♦ 25 Mar-3 Oct. € 13.80   2004*

†**NAPOULE, LA** *10F4* (5km N Urban/Coastal) **Camping L'Argentiere, Blvd du Bon-Puits, 06210 Mandelieu-la-Napoule [tel/fax 04 93 49 95 04]** Fr A8 turn L in Mandelieu cent (sp Frejus). At rndabt with fountains take 2nd exit, at next rndabt take 2nd exit to L of BP stn, at next rndabt take 2nd exit, site on R in 150m. Avoid La Napoule vill when towing. Med, hdg/mkd pitch, hdstg, pt shd; wc; chem disp; mv service pnt; shwrs inc; el pts (6A) €3; ice; lndtte; shop; hypmkt 1km; rest; snacks; bar; sand beach 1km; fishing; entmnt; TV rm; 80% statics; bus; Eng spkn; adv bkg ess in ssn; poss cr; quiet; CCI. "Tired, basic san facs, but clean; endless hot water; lovely local beaches." € 18.20   2003*

NAPOULE, LA *10F4* (10km W Rural) **Camping Les Philippons, 83600 Les Adrets-de-l'Esterel [04 94 40 90 67; fax 04 94 19 35 92; info@philipp onscamp.com]** Exit A8 at junc Les Adrets (14km fr Cannes). Foll sp Les Adrets on D387 S. In 2km turn L on D237 thro vill, site on L; sm ent. Sm, pt sl, terr, shd; wc; shwrs; el pts (6A) inc; shop; snacks; bar; playgrnd; pool; sand beach 9km; poss cr; 90% statics; adv bkg; quiet. "V diff access for towed c'van with steep, narr & twisty rd, v ltd turning space; not rec for c'vans, adequate for m'vans & tents only." Apr-Sep. € 19.50   2003*

NARBONNE *10F1* (10km N Rural) **Camp Municipal, Rue de la Cave Cooperative, 11590 Salleles-d'Aude [04 68 46 68 46 (Mairie); fax 04 68 46 91 00; ot. sallelesdaude@wanadoo.fr; www.salleles-daude. com]** Fr A9/E15 S to Perpignan, exit at junc 36 onto D64 & in approx 4km turn L to join D11 W. Cont on this rd for approx 18km, then turn L onto D13 S to Ouveillan. In vill, turn R onto D418 SW to Salleles-d'Aude. Site in vill. NB Nr Canal du Midi some narr app rds. Sm, hdg/mkd pitch, pt shd; wc; chem disp; el pts inc; shops 1km; BBQ; no statics; dogs; adv bkg; quiet. "V clean site; 16 pitches; adj canal; gd long/sh stay."1 May-30 Sep. € 12.30   2005*

NARBONNE *10F1* (6km S Rural) **Camping Les Mimosas, Chaussee de Mandirac, 11100 Narbonne [04 68 49 03 72; fax 04 68 49 39 45; info@ lesmimosas.com; www.lesmimosas.com]** Leave A9 junc 38 at Narbonne Sud foll sp Narbonne. Keep to R-hand lane past Macdonalds, turn R at traff lts, then R at 3rd rndabt (Rue des Lunes), to level x-ing then L & site on R in 4km. Lge, hdg/mkd pitch, pt shd; wc; chem disp; some serviced pitches (extra); baby facs; sauna; shwrs inc; el pts (6A) inc; gas; lndtte; ice; shop; rest; snacks; bar; no BBQ; playgrnd; 3 pools (1 htd); waterslide; sand beach 6km; jacuzzi; watersports; tennis; fishing; cycle hire; table tennis; mini-golf; horseriding nrby; entmnt high ssn; TV; some statics; dogs €2.30; Eng spkn; adv bkg; red low ssn/long stay; cc acc; CCI. "Excel touring base; gd for birdwatching; cycle path into Narbonne; noise fr entmnt most eves; facs poss need upgrading but clean; vg for children; gd pitches; recep clsd 1200-1400; poss mosquito/insect problem fr nrby lagoon; helpful staff." ♦ 24 Mar-31 Oct. € 24.80 (CChq acc)   2005*

FRANCE

NARBONNE *10F1* (4km SW Urban) **Camping La Nautique, 11100 Narbonne [04 68 90 48 19; fax 04 68 90 73 39; info@campinglanautique.com; www.campinglanautique.com]** Take exit 38 fr A9 at Narbonne Sud. After toll take last rndabt exit & foll sp La Nautique. Site on R 2.5km fr A9 exit. Lge, hdg/mkd pitch, some hdstg, pt shd; chem disp; mv service pnt; all serviced pitches; individ wash cubicles (wc, shwr) on each pitch inc; el pts (10A) inc; gas; lndtte; ice; shop high ssn & 3km; tradsmn; rest, snacks & bar high ssn; BBQ; playgrnd; htd pool; waterslide; paddling pool; sand beach 10km; lake sw adj; tennis; 30% statics; dogs €3.50; Eng spkn; adv bkg; quiet with some rd noise; cc acc; red low ssn/long stay; CCI. "Spotless facs; caution - hot water v hot; some pitches lge but v narr; special pitches for disabled; excel rest; helpful, friendly Dutch owners; many sports activities avail; recep clsd 1200-1400 low ssn." ♦ 15 Feb-15 Nov. € 32.60   2005*

See advertisement

Some of these sites have changed their opening dates - we'd better fill in some site report forms and let the editor of the guide know.

†NARBONNE *10F1* (12km SW Rural) **Camping La Figurotta, Route de Narbonne, 11200 Bizanet [tel/fax 04 68 45 16 26 or 06 88 16 12 30; camping.figurotta@wanadoo.fr]** Exit A9 at Narbonne Sud onto slip rd N9/N113 twd Lezignan-Corbieres; in 3km at new rndabt head L twd D613 & then D224 sp Bizanet & site. App fr W not rec due narr D rds. Sm, mkd pitch, hdstg, pt sl, pt terr, shd; htd wc; chem disp; shwrs €0.50; el pts (4-5A) €3; gas; lndtte; sm shop & 2km; tradsmn; rest; snacks; bar; playgrnd; sm pool; sand beach 20km; games area; no dogs; phone; Eng spkn; adv bkg; rd noise; up to 50% red low ssn; 10% red 7+ days; red low ssn; CCI. "Well-managed site; ltd facs low ssn; helpful & friendly Dutch owners; a gusty & stony site in beautiful location - steel pegs req; conv Corbieres & Minervois wine areas; gd NH en rte Spain." ♦ ltd. € 13.00   2005*

NARBONNE PLAGE *10F1* (Coastal) **Camp Municipal La Falaise, 11000 Narbonne-Plage [04 68 49 80 77; fax 04 68 49 40 44; pronaplage@ mairie-narbonne.fr]** Exit A9 at Narbonne Est junc 37 onto D168 for 10km to Narbonne-Plage. Site on L at ent to vill. Lge, hdg pitch, shd; wc; shwrs; el pts 5A) inc; gas; lndtte; ice; shop; rest; snacks; playgrnd; beach 300m; waterslide 1.5km; games area; cycle hire; TV; some statics; dogs €2; poss cr; adv bkg; poss noise fr open air theatre; red low ssn. "Gd for beach holiday." 1 Apr-22 Sep. € 19.00   2003*

NARBONNE PLAGE *10F1* (8km NE Coastal) **Camping La Grande Cosse (Naturist), St Pierre-sur-Mer, 11560 Fleury-d'Aude [04 68 33 61 87; fax 04 68 33 32 23; contact@grandecosse.com; www.grandecosse.com]** Exit A9 junc 36 onto D64 to Vendres. R on D37 to Lespignan. L on D14 to Fleury. L on D718 sp 'Les Cabanes de Fleury' to site. Care needed lge o'fits. Lge, hdg/mkd pitch, pt shd; wc; chem disp; serviced pitches; chem disp; mv service pnt; shwrs inc; el pts (10A) €3.50; gas; lndtte; ice; shop; rest, snacks; bar high ssn; playgrnd; htd pool; sand beach 300m; tennis; games area; games rm; gym; entmnt; boat hire; fishing; TV rm; 20% statics; dogs €3; phone; poss cr Aug; Eng spkn; adv bkg (dep req); red long stay/low ssn; cc acc; INF card req. "Excel site; helpful, friendly staff; gd san facs; naturist walk to beach thro lagoons & dunes; mosquitoes poss problem June; gd long stay." ♦ 26 Mar-9 Oct. € 27.00   2005*

NASBINALS *9D1* (1km N Rural) **Camp Municipal, Route de St Urcize, 48260 Nasbinals [02 46 32 51 87 or 04 66 32 50 17]** Fr A75 exit 36 to Aumont-Aubrac, then W on D987 to Nasbinals. Turn R onto D12, site sp. Med, pt sl, pt shd; htd wc; chem disp; mv service pnt; shwrs inc; el pts (16A) inc; shop, rest in vill; BBQ; dogs; quiet; red CCI. "Excel long/sh stay." ♦ ltd 25 May-30 Sep. € 8.30   2004*

NAUCELLE *8E4* (Rural) **Camp Municipal du Lac, L'Etang de Bonnefon, 12800 Naucelle [05 65 69 33 20; fax 05 65 69 33 20; camping-du-lac-de-bonnefon@wanadoo.fr]** N fr Carmaux turn L off N88 Albi-Rodez rd at Naucelle Gare onto D997, sp Naucelle Centre. Site sp in 2km. Med, mkd pitch, pt sl, pt shd; wc; chem disp; mv service pnt; shwrs inc; el pts (6A) inc; lndry rm; shop 1.5km; rest; snacks; bar; playgrnd; pool; TV; 25% statics; dogs €2.50; quiet; CCI. "Pleasant, clean site adj lge fishing lake; gd san facs; conv Sauveterre-de- Rouergue; gd sh stay." 1 Apr-31 Oct. € 18.00   2005*

NAUSSANNES see Lalinde *7C3*

NAVARRENX *8F1* (200m S Rural) **Camping Beau Rivage, Allee des Marronniers, 64190 Navarrenx [05 59 66 10 00; curtisrw@free.fr; www.beau camping.com]** Fr E exit A64 junc 9 at Artix onto D281 dir Mourenx, then Navarrenx. Fr N exit junc 7 Salies-de-Bearn onto D933 to Sauveterre-de-Bearn, then D936 to Navarrenx. Med, hdg/mkd pitch, terr, pt shd; htd wc; chem disp; shwrs inc; el pts (8-10A) €3.50; gas; lndtte; ice; shop, rest, snacks & bar 300m; BBQ; playgrnd; htd pool & paddling pool adj; tennis; 13% statics; dogs €2; phone; Eng spkn; adv bkg; quiet; CCI. "Peaceful site bet town & rv; gd area for walking, fishing, cycling; lovely town; helpful, friendly, British owners; excel, well run site; clean san facs; pool planned 2007; conv for Biarritz & Spain." ♦ ltd. 15 Mar-15 Oct. € 11.50   2005*

NEBOUZAT *9B1* (1km W Rural) **Camping Les Domes, 4 Route de Nebouzat, 63210 Nebouzat [04 73 87 14 06 or 04 73 93 21 02 (LS); fax 04 73 87 18 81; camping-les-domes@wanadoo. fr; www.les-domes.com]** Exit 5 fr a'route A75 twd Col de la Ventouse; turn L on N89 sp Tulle. Do not ent vill of Nebouzat but cont for 1km. Take L onto D216 sp Orcival then immed L. Site on L in 100m. Med, mkd pitch, hdstg, pt shd; wc (mainly cont); chem disp; baby facs; shwrs inc; el pts (10A) €4 (poss long lead req); gas; lndtte; ice; shop; tradsmn; snacks; playgrnd; htd covrd pool; boules areas; walking; sailing; windsurfing; entmnt; TV rm; phone; dogs; Eng spkn; adv bkg; quiet; cc not acc; 10% red CCI C'van Club members. "V friendly, helpful staff; gd welcome; sm pitches; basic san facs - dep req for key; max 6m height; in volcanic region, conv Volcania." 9 May-16 Sep. € 15.50   2005*

NEMOURS *4F3* (5km N Urban) **Camp Municipal Les Pres, 77880 Grez-sur-Loing [tel/fax 01 64 45 72 75; camping-grez@wanadoo.fr]** Fr Fontainebleau on N7 twd Nemours (S) for 8km; look for camping sps. At traff island turn L onto D40D, in 1km immed after x-ing bdge turn R; site on L. Do not tow into Grez-sur-Loing Med, pt shd; wc; chem disp; shwrs inc; el pts (5A) €2.60; gas; lndtte; ice; shops 500m; playgrnd; fishing; cycle hire; adv bkg; 60% statics; poss cr; Eng spkn; CCI. "In v attractive area; conv Fontainebleau; facs dated but v clean; helpful warden." ♦ 15 Mar-15 Nov. € 9.50   2005*

NEMOURS *4F3* (5km S Urban) **Camping de Pierre Le Sault, Chemin des Greves, 77167 Bagneaux-sur-Loing [01 64 29 24 44]** Well sp bef town fr both dir off N7. Med, hdg/mkd pitch, pt shd; wc; shwrs inc; el pts (3-6A) €1.85-2.90; gas 2km; lndtte; shop 2km; tradsmn; playgrnd; tennis; rv sw; 90% statics; poss cr; some Eng spkn; ent barrier clsd 2200-0700; no adv bkg; some rd noise; red low ssn; no cc acc; CCI. "Lovely site by canal & rv; excel clean facs." ♦ 1 Apr-31 Oct. € 6.90   2005*

NERIS LES BAINS *7A4* (1km N Urban) **Camping du Lac (formerly Municipal), Ave Marx Dormoy, 03310 Neris-les-Bains [04 70 03 17 59 or 04 70 03 24 70 (recep); fax 04 70 03 79 99; neris-les-bains@wanadoo.fr]** Site on N side of Neris off N144. Fr at rndabt by blue tourist office, opp park, & foll sp round 1 way system to site in 500m. Med, hdg/mkd pitch, pt sl, terr, pt shd; wc (some cont); chem disp; shwrs inc; el pts (10A) inc; gas; shops 1km; tradsmn; snacks; bar; playgrnd; covrd pool 500m; quiet; red long stay. "6 free pitches for m'vans at ent to site, charge for el pts (10A) & water; some chalets on site; spa town - thermal baths, theatre & parks etc; vg long stay." Easter-28 Oct. € 13.30   2005*

NESLES LA VALLEE see Beaumont sur Oise *3D3*

NESMY see Roche sur Yon, La *2H4*

NEUF BRISACH *6F3* (6km NE) **Camping de L'Ile du Rhin, Zone Touristique 68, 68600 Biesheim [03 89 72 57 95; fax 03 89 72 14 21; camping@shn. fr; www.campingiledurhin.com]** On rte Colmar to Freiburg (Germany). Site on island in Rv Rhine, on R after French Customs Point off N415. Lge, hdstg, pt shd; wc; shwrs inc; el pts (4-10A) €4-5.75; lndtte; ice, snacks & shop (high ssn); htd, covrd pool adj; tennis; rv fishing 100m; 50% statics ssp area; poss cr Jul-Aug; Eng spkn; cc acc. "Excel facs; gates clsd 1200-1400 & 2000-0700; €10 dep barrier card; vg." ♦ 18 Mar-1 Oct. € 13.36   2005*

NEUF BRISACH *6F3* (1.2km E Urban) **Camp Municipal Vauban, 68600 Neuf-Brisach [tel/fax 03 89 72 54 25 or 03 89 72 51 68 (Mairie)]** Fr N415 (Colmar-Freiburg) at E of Neuf-Brisach turn NE on D1 bis (sp Neuf-Brisach & Camping Vauban). At next junc turn L & immed R into site rd. Med, pt shd; wc; mv service pnt; shwrs €1.27; el pts (6A) €2.45; ice; shops in town; playgrnd; pool 3km; adv bkg; quiet; CCI. "Dep for barrier token, no new arr 1200-1400." 1 Apr-1 Oct. € 8.75   2003*

NEUFCHATEAU *6E2* (Urban) **Camp Municipal, Rue de Moulinot, 88300 Neufchateau [03 29 94 19 03 or 03 29 94 14 75 (Mairie); fax 03 29 94 33 77]** Clear sp on ent town next to sports stadium. Sm, pt shd; wc; chem disp; shwrs inc; el pts (10A) inc; lndry rm; shops 500m; htd pool nr; poss cr; some rlwy noise. "No twin-axles; excel." ♦ 15 Apr-30 Sep. € 12.70   2005*

NEUFCHATEAU *6E2* (10km N) **Camp Municipal, 88630 Domremy-la-Pucelle** [03 29 06 90 70; fax 03 29 94 33 77] Take D164 fr Neufchateau, site in cent of Domremy vill, clear sp by stadium. Sm, pt shd; wc (cont); chem disp; shwrs; el pts (16A) inc; shops adj; tennis; pool nrby; quiet; some rlwy noise. "Site yourself, warden calls (not Sun); nr birthplace of Joan of Arc; excel rest La Marmite adj."
15 Apr-30 Sep. € 7.50   2002*

NEUFCHATEL EN BRAY *3C2* (1km W Urban) **Camping de Ste Claire, Route de Dieppe, 76270 Neufchatel-en-Bray** [02 35 93 03 93 or 02 35 94 56 94] Fr S exit A28 at junc 9 sp Neufchatel. Immed after rv bdge turn L into Rue de la Grande Flandre, strt on into Rue Ste Claire. Site visible after Leclerc supmkt on L. Or Fr N exit A28 junc 8 dir Neufchatel. In approx 5km turn R onto D1 for Dieppe & in approx 1km turn L at site sp. Med, pt sl, pt shd; wc (some cont); chem disp; shwrs inc; el pts (3-10A) €2.30-6; sm shop; supmkt 1km; tradsmn; bar/rest; snacks; playgrnd; few statics; dogs; phone adj; bus 1km; adv bkg; quiet; no cc acc; red long stay; CCI. "V pleasant, well-kept, family site by rv in parkland setting; friendly, helpful owner; cycle route adj; Sat mkt; conv Le Havre/Dieppe ferries & a'route; site much improved but strong smell fr sewage works!"
1 Apr-31 Oct. € 9.45   2005*

NEUFGRANGE see Sarreguemines *5D3*

NEUILLY SUR MARNE see Paris *3D3*

NEUNG SUR BEUVRON *4G3* (1km NE Rural) **Camp Municipal de la Varenne, 41210 Neung-sur-Beuvron** [tel/fax 02 54 83 68 52; mairie-neungsurbeuvron@wanadoo.fr] On A10 heading S take Orleans Sud exit & join N20 S. At end of La Ferte-St Aubin take D922 SW twd Romorantin-Lanthenay. In 20km R onto D925 to Neung. Turn R at church pedestrian x-ing in cent of vill ('stade' sp), R at fork (white, iron cross) & site on R in 1km. Site by rvside. Sm, hdg/mkd pitch, pt sl, pt shd; wc; chem disp; shwrs inc; el pts (10A) €2.30 inc; gas; lndtte; ice; shops 1km; tradsmn; rest, playgrnd; tennis; few statics; dogs; poss cr (Aug); adv bkg; v quiet; cc acc. "Friendly warden; vg cent for hiking, cycling, birdwatching; immac facs; lge pitches, levelling boards poss req; Sat mkt."
Easter-30 Sep. € 5.60   2005*

NEUVE LYRE, LA *3D2* (Rural) **Camp Municipal La Salle des Fetes, Rue de l'Union, 27330 La Neuve-Lyre** [02 32 60 14 98 or 02 32 30 50 01(Mairie); fax 02 32 30 22 37] Fr NE on D830 into vill turn R at church (sp not visible), fr S (Rugles) foll sp. Med, mkd pitch, pt shd; wc (some cont) ltd; chem disp (wc); shwrs €0.75; el pts (5A) €1.70; shops 500m; fishing; dogs; quiet; CCI. "Delightful quiet & clean site, friendly, helpful warden; excel sh stay/NH." ♦ 15 Mar-15 Oct.
€ 4.90   2003*

NEUVEGLISE see Chaudes Aigues *9C1*

NEUVIC (CORREZE) *7C4* (4km) **LES CASTELS Domaine de Mialaret, Route d'Egletons, 19160 Neuvic** [05 55 46 02 50; fax 05 55 46 02 65; info@ lemialaret.com; www.lemialaret.com or www. les-castels.com] Fr N on A89 exit 23 twds St Angel then D171 to Neuvic or foll sp fr Neuvic on D991 (v narr). Med, some hdg pitch, pt sl, pt shd; htd wc; chem disp; mv service pnt; baby facs; shwrs inc; el pts (6A) €4.50; ice; lndtte; shop; tradsmn; rest in chateau fr May; snacks; bar; playgrnd; pool; 2 carp fishing pools; watersports nrby; mini-farm; mountain bike routes; walking tours; games rm; entmnt; child entmnt; internet; 30% statics (sep area); dogs; phone; bus 4km; poss cr; quiet; adv bkg; Eng spkn; red 7 days/low ssn; CCI. "Excel site in grounds of chateau; excel welcome pack; children's mini-zoo & rare sheep breeds nrby; friendly staff; facs ltd low ssn." 1 Apr-31 Oct.
€ 17.00 (CChq acc)   2005*

NEUVIC (CORREZE) *7C4* (4km N Rural) **Camping du President Queuille, Antiges, 19160 Neuvic** [05 55 95 81 18; fax 05 55 46 02 50] Fr Neuvic, D982 N twd Ussel. In 3km turn R onto D20 sp Antiges. Site in 1km. Or fr N/S A89 exit 23 then foll St Angel & take D171. Foll sp. Med, pt sl, pt shd; wc; shwrs; el pts (10A) €1.49; lndtte; snacks; rest; sand beach; lake sw adj; adv bkg; red low ssn; quiet. "Gd site but basic; pleasant views on lake." 1 May-30 Sep. € 10.82   2004*

NEUVIC (CORREZE) *7C4* (7km NW Rural) **Camping Le Vianon, Les Plaines, 19160 Palisse** [05 55 95 87 22; fax 05 55 95 98 45; camping. vianon@wanadoo.fr; www.levianon.com] Fr Neuvic take D47 twd Pallisse. Site well sp. Med, mkd pitch, pt sl, pt shd; htd wc; chem disp; mv service pnt; baby facs; shwrs inc; el pts (6A) €3.80; lndtte; ice; shops; tradsmn; rest; snacks; bar; BBQ; playgrnd; pool; sports activities; tennis; child entmnt; watersports; TV rm; 15% statics; dogs €2; poss cr; Eng spkn; adv bkg (dep req); quiet; red 7+ days; CCI. "Woodland walks & great scenery; v friendly Dutch owners; vg rest & bar; spotless facs; fully equipped chalets avail." ♦ ltd. 10 Apr-16 Oct.
€ 19.10   2005*

NEUVIC (DORDOGNE) *7C3* **Camping Le Plein Air Neuvicois, 24190 Neuvic** [05 53 81 50 77; fax 05 53 80 46 58; camp.le.plein.air.neuvicois@ libertysurf.fr] On N89, 26km SW fr Perigueux (Mussidan-Bordeaux rd). After 24km, turn R (D44) at Neuvic. Site clearly sp thro vill, by rv bef bdge, on both sides of rv. Med, pt shd; wc; baby facs; shwrs inc; el pts (5A) €2.50; lndtte; ice; shop; tradsmn; snacks; bar; pool; tennis; games rm; fishing; some statics; dogs €0.50; phone; adv bkg; quiet. "Formerly municipal & pool still run by municipality; charming owners; beautiful location; vg long/sh stay." 1 Jun-15 Sep. € 11.00   2003*

NEUVILLE DE POITOU see Poitiers *7A2*

NEUVILLE SUR SARTHE see Mans, Le *4F1*

NEVACHE *9C3* **Camp Municipal de Foncouverte, 05100 Nevache [04 92 21 38 21 or 04 92 21 31 01]** Fr Briancon take N94 NE twd Turin, then turn L onto D994 sp Nevache. Rd is narr with passing places. Site is 2nd in vill. Med, pt sl, pt shd; wc; chem disp; shwrs €1.20; lndry rm; shop; tradsmn; Eng spkn; quiet. "V gd for walkers; lovely alpine flowers." 15 Jun-15 Sep. € 7.55   2003*

NEVERS *4H4* (Urban) **Camping de Nevers, Rue de la Jonction, 58000 Nevers [06 84 98 69 79; info@ campingnevers.com; www.campingnevers.com]** Exit A77 junc 37 dir Centre Ville. Site on R immed bef bdge over Rv Loire. Med, mkd pitch, hdstg; pt shd; htd wc; chem disp; mv service pnt; baby facs; shwrs inc; el pts (4-10A) €2.50-4.70; lndtte; ice; shop 70m; tradsmn; rest 40m; snacks; bar; playgrnd; pool 100m; sand beach 100m; TV; dogs €2; bus 20m; phone; poss cr; Eng spkn; adv bkg; quiet, subdued traff noise; CCI. "Re-opened 2005; site on Rv Loire, magical views of Nevers with cathedral; sh walk to town cent; immac facs; excel." ♦ € 13.00   2005*

†NEVERS *4H4* (10km SE Rural) **Camp Municipal Plan d'Eau Bagnade, Route de Magny-Cours, 58160 Chevenon [03 86 68 71 71 or 03 86 68 72 75; fax 03 86 38 30 33]** Fr N7 site sp at Magny-Cours turn R fr S (L fr N) onto D200, site ent on R just bef Chevenon. Or fr opp dir, site is thro Chevenon past end of town sp. Med, hdg pitch, terr, pt sl, pt shd; htd wc; shwrs inc; el pts (1-16A) €1-€9; lndry rm; shops 14m; playgrnd; lake sw adj; fishing; mini golf; many statics; quiet; no cc acc; CCI. "Pleasant, peaceful site nr lakes & close to French Grand Prix circuit; site yourself if warden not present; san facs & pitches unkempt low ssn." ♦ ltd. € 8.00   2005*

NEVERS *4H4* (7km NW Urban) **Camping La Loire, 2 Rue de la Folie, 58600 Fourchambault [03 86 60 81 59; fax 03 86 60 96 24]** Fr Nevers on D40 thro town, site on L bef rv bdge. Med, pt shd; wc; chem disp; mv service pnt; shwrs inc; el pts (6-20A) €3-7; lndtte; shop 500m; rest 100m; snacks; bar; BBQ; htd, covrd pool; rv adj; dogs €1; bus; red long stay/CCI. "New owners (2005); friendly, helpful." ♦ ltd. 1 Apr-30 Sep. € 9.00 2005*

NEVEZ see Pont Aven *2F2*

NEXON *7B3* (3km S) **Camp Municipal de l'Etang de la Lande, 87800 Nexon [05 55 58 35 44 or 05 55 58 10 19 (Mairie); fax 05 55 58 33 50]** Exit Nexon by D11 spf Ladignac & Camping, site 3km S at junc with D17. Fr W on D15 take D15A nr Nexon & foll sp. Sm, sl, pt shd; wc; shwrs; el pts (5-10A) inc; ice; lndtte; shops 3km; lake sw adj; playgrnd; cycle hire; entmnts; TV rm; Eng spkn; quiet. "Excel base for Limoges; site open to adj leisure pk; warden visits 3-4 times day; arrive & site self." 1 Apr-30 Sep. € 10.00   2004*

NEYDENS see St Julien en Genevois *9A3*

NIBELLE *4F3* (2km E Rural) **Caravaning de Nibelle, Route de Boiscommun, 45340 Nibelle [02 38 32 23 55; fax 02 38 32 03 87; contact@ caravaningnibelle.com]** Fr N60 turn N onto D114 dir Nibelle. Turn R onto D6, site sp. Med, pt shd; wc; shwrs inc; el pts inc; lndtte; shop; tradsmn; rest; bar; BBQ; playgrnd; htd, covrd pool; tennis; games area; cycle hire; entmnt; Eng spkn; adv bkg; quiet. "Excel site." ♦ 1 Mar-30 Nov. € 25.00   2002*

NICE *10E4* (14km NE Rural) **Camping Caravaning La Laune, Moulin de Peillon, 06440 Peillon [04 93 79 91 61]** Leave A8 a'route junc 55 (Nice Est); foll D2204 twds Sospel; cont until R turn at rndbt sp D21 Peillon/Peille; site on R in vill of Le Moulin approx 4km. Sm, mkd pitch, pt shd; wc; chem disp; shwrs inc; el pts (10A) inc (rev pol); lndtte; shop 4km; tradsmn; shgl beach 14km; dogs €2; phone adj; adv bkg; quiet; no cc acc; CCI. "Sm family-run site; v helpful owner; conv for Monaco, Monte Carlo, Nice; sm pitches; some rd/rlwy noise; ltd facs low ssn." 1 Jun-30 Sep. € 18.50   2003*

NIEDERBRONN LES BAINS *5D3* (3.5km N Rural) **Camping Heidenkopf, Route de la Lisiere, 67110 Niederbronn-les-Bains [tel/fax 03 88 09 08 46; heidenkopf@tiscali.fr]** Fr Niederbronn NW on N62 & foll sp rd R into forest fr mineral spring. Med, pt sl, terr, pt shd; htd wc (some cont); chem disp; mv service pnt; baby facs; shwrs inc; el pts (6A) €2.90; gas; lndtte; shops 3km; tradsmn; BBQ; playgrnd; pool 1km; dogs €1.25; adv bkg; quiet. "Forest walks; 20 mins walk to town." ♦ 1 Apr-31 Oct. € 10.50   2005*

†NIMES *10E2* (7km NE) **Camping Les Cypres, 5 Rue de la Bastide, 30320 Bezouce [04 66 75 24 30; fax 04 66 75 64 78]** Sp on N86 Nimes-Avignon rd. Site not well sp in Bezouce - sign high on wall. Narr site access. Sm, pt shd; wc; chem disp; shwrs; el pts (4-6A) €3.70; shop, rest, bar in vill; sm pool; mostly statics; dogs; poss cr; adv bkg; rd noise & cockerels. "Facs rustic & v basic but clean; v friendly & helpful owners; basic meals in hotel adj; conv Pont-du-Gard, Nimes, Arles; not rec lge o'fits; closes early evening low ssn; NH only." € 12.00   2005*

†NIMES *10E2* (7km S Rural) **Domaine de la Bastide, Route de Generac, 30900 Nimes [tel/fax 04 66 38 09 21]** Site well sp fr town cent. Lge, hdg/mkd pitch, pt shd; wc; chem disp; mv service pnt; serviced pitches; shwrs inc; el pts (15A); gas; lndtte; shop; tradsmn; hypmkt nr; rest; bar; TV rm; 10% statics; dogs €2; bus; phone; Eng spkn; adv bkg; some rd noise; CCI. "Lge pitches; friendly recep; gd base to explore Nimes, 20 mins by bus fr site; site poss unkempt; poss no lighting after dark; poss itinerants; fair sh stay." ♦ ltd. € 22.40 (4 persons)   2005*

NIORT *7A2* (13km NE Rural) **Camp du Plan d'Eau de St Christophe, 79410 Cherveux [05 49 05 21 38 or 05 49 75 01 77 (Mairie); fax 05 49 75 86 60]** Exit A83 junc 10 onto D743. Turn E onto D6 sp Auge. Turn R at x-rds, site on R in 1km on lake, 2km fr Cherveux. Med, mkd pitch, pt sl, unshd; wc; shwrs inc; el pts (16A); lndry rm; ice; shop 3km; tradsmn; rest; bar; playgrnd; lake sw; sand beach; boating; fishing; mini-golf; quiet; CCI. "Gd rest & bar; friendly; fair." 1 Apr-31 Oct. € 9.50   2004*

NIORT *7A2* (1km SW Urban) **Camp Municipal de Niort Noron, Blvd Salvador Allende, 79000 Niort [tel/fax 05 49 79 05 06]** Well sp fr all dirs. Foll sp for Parc des Expositions & des Loisirs. Med, hdg/mkd pitch, pt shd; wc; chem disp; shwrs inc; el pts (3-13A) €2.50-5.85; lndtte; ice; shop 1km; tradsmn; snacks; playgrnd; pool 1km; rv fishing adj; dogs €0.85; Eng spkn; adv bkg; quiet but some rd noise; CCI. "Pleasant town; conv 'Green Venice' area; friendly, helpful staff; poss itinerants on site; gd sh stay." ♦ 1 Apr-30 Sep. € 11.90   2005*

NOAILLES see Brive la Gaillarde *7C3*

NOCLE MAULAIX, LA *4H4* (W Rural) **Camp Municipal du l'Etang Marnant, Route de Decize, 58250 La Nocle-Maulaix [tel/fax 03 86 30 84 13]** Fr Luzy twd Fours on N81, turn L on D3 & foll sp. Site in 5km at La Nocle-Maulaix by junc with D30. Sm, mkd pitch, pt sl, pt shd; wc; shwrs; el pts; shops 400m; lndtte; playgrnd; sports area; fishing; adv bkg; quiet. "Take 2nd ent to site; site yourself & warden calls; watersports on lake." 15 May-15 Sep. € 9.90   2004*

NOGENT L'ARTAUD *3D4* (1km S Rural) **Camp Municipal des Monts, 56237 Nogent-l'Artaud [03 23 70 01 18]** Site sp W of D222/D11, 1km S fr Nogent-l'Artaud. Sm, hdg/mkd pitch, terr, pt shd; wc; chem disp (wc); shwrs inc; el pts (6A) inc; shop 1.5km; playgrnd; table tennis; games area adj; 25% statics; dogs €0.60; phone; quiet; CCI. "Helpful; gd views fr site; wc old but clean; beautiful garden-type site; gd long/sh stay." 30 Mar-29 Sep. € 9.20   2004*

NOGENT SUR SEINE *4E4* (10km NE Rural) **Camp Municipal, 10400 Pont-sur-Seine [tel/fax 03 25 39 76 67 or 03 25 39 42 00 (Mairie)]** Fr Nogent-sur-Seine take D19 twd Romilly-sur-Seine. In 10km turn L on D52 to Pont-sur-Seine. Site on L thro vill. Med, unshd; wc; chem disp (wc); el pts (6A) €1.50; rest, shop 750m; quiet; adv bkg; phone. "Excel value; gd facs; gd sh stay." ♦ 1 May-17 Sep. € 7.20   2004*

NOIRETABLE *9B1* **Camp Municipal de la Roche, Route de la Roche, 42440 Noiretable [04 77 24 72 68]** Leave A72/E70 junc 4 sp Noiretable; thro toll & turn SW onto D53. Ignore narr tourist rte sp to W; cont downhill to T-junc & turn R onto N89. Take next L & site on R in 750m. Sm, hdstg, sl, pt shd; wc (cont); shwrs; el pts (10A) €2; lake adj; cc not acc. "V friendly warden." 1 Apr-Oct. € 5.30   2002*

NOIRMOUTIER EN L'ILE *2H3* (2km E Coastal) **Camp Municipal Le Clair Matin, Les Sableaux, 85330 Noirmoutier-en-l'Ile [02 51 39 05 56; fax 02 51 39 74 36]** Ent Noirmoutier on D948 & foll sp to Les Sableaux. Site well sp. Med, mkd pitch, terr, pt shd; wc; shwrs €1; el pts (10A) €3.30; lndtte; shop; playgrnd; pool 2.5km; sand beach adj; fishing; dogs €1.20; adv bkg rec; quiet. "Gd; clean facs; excel cycle paths & beach fishing." ♦ Easter-30 Oct. € 13.00 (3 persons)   2005*

NOIRMOUTIER EN L'ILE *2H3* (2km E Coastal) **Camping de la Vendette, 23 Allée des Sableaux, 85330 Noirmoutier-en-l'Ile [02 51 39 06 24; fax 02 51 35 97 63; vendette@huttopia.com; www.camping-vendette.com]** Ent Noirmoutier on D948, turn R at Quay bdge, E on dyke for 2km to site on R. Lge, shd; wc; mv service pnt; shwrs inc; el pts (10A) €0.90; lndtte; ice; shops adj; tradsmn; rest; snacks; bar; playgrnd; sand beach adj; fishing; boat-launching; dogs €2; phone; poss cr; adv bkg; quiet; red low ssn; CCI ess. "Gd for children; shellfish at low tide; set in pine forest & nr salt water marshes." Easter-30 Sep. € 15.80   2005*

NOIRMOUTIER EN L'ILE *2H3* (10km SE Coastal) **Camp Municipal du Midi, 85630 Barbatre [02 51 39 63 74; fax 02 51 39 58 63; camping-du-midi@wanadoo.fr]** Cross to island by passage du Gois (low tide - 2.5 hrs per day) or bdge. Turn L after 2.5km off dual c'way to Barbatre. Site sp N thro vill. Lge, pt sl, shd; wc; shwrs; el pts (5A) inc; gas; lndtte; ice; shop; rest; bar; 3 pools; sand beach adj; tennis; mini-golf; entmnt; poss cr; no adv bkg; quiet; cc acc. ♦ 1 Apr-22 Sep. € 23.00 (3 persons) 2002*

NOIRMOUTIER EN L'ILE *2H3* (3.5km SW Coastal) **Camp Municipal La Bosse, 85740 L'Epine [02 51 39 01 07]** Fr bdge take D38 to La Gueriniere: turn W along D38 to L'Epine & foll camp sp to La Bosse. Lge, pt sl, pt shd; wc; chem disp; shwrs; el pts (5A) €2.50; ice; lndtte; BBQ; sand beach, boat hire, sw & fishing 100m; playgrnd; entmnt; quiet; adv bkg. ♦ 1 Apr-30 Sep. € 11.16   2002*

NOIRMOUTIER EN L'ILE *2H3* (8km W Coastal) **Camp Municipal La Pointe de l'Herbaudiere, 85330 Noirmoutier-en-l'Ile [02 51 39 16 70; fax 02 51 39 74 15]** Fr bdge to island foll sp to Noirmoutier town, then to L'Herbaudiere & port. At port turn L, 500m to site. Med, mkd pitch, unshd; wc (cont); chem disp; mv service pnt; shwrs €1; el pts (10A) €3.25 (long elec leads poss req); gas; lndry rm; shop; rest, snacks & bar in town; beach adj; adv bkg; noisy; CCI. "Gd, open, sometimes windy site with sea on 2 sides; gd rests nr; clean facs; gd cycle rtes on island." 1 Apr-6 Oct. € 11.90 (3 persons)   2003*

NOLAY *6H1* (500m S) **Camp Municipal Les Chaumes de Mont**, Route de Couches, 21340 Nolay [03 80 21 79 61; fax 03 85 91 14 13; contact@campingnolay.com] Exit m'way A6 at junc 24.1 at Beaune & foll N74. Turn R on D973 sp Nolay, Autun. Vill in 20km. Turn by Hotel de Ville onto D33a dir Couches, site sp. Med, pt sl, terr; pt shd; wc; chem disp (wc); shwrs inc; el pts (6A) inc; lndtte; shops 500m; snacks; BBQ (gas); playgrnd; lake sw; fishing; tennis; dogs €0.60; phone; quiet; cc not acc; CCI. "Lovely site; ideal stop en rte S; gates clsd 2200-0730; sm, interesting town; lake is meeting point for local youngsters - poss noisy."
1 May-15 Sep. € 12.80   2005*

NOLAY *6H1* (9km SW Rural) **Camp Municipal La Gabrelle**, La Varenne, 71490 Couches [03 85 45 59 49 or 03 85 98 19 20 (Mairie); fax 03 85 98 19 29; danielemaire@aol.com] Exit a'route A6 at Chalon Nord onto D978 sp Autun. In 26km at Couches, site W of vill. Sm, hdg pitch, terr, pt shd; wc; shwrs inc; el pts (6A) inc; lndtte; supmkt 5km; snacks; bar; playgrnd; lake adj; some daytime rd noise. "Attractive countryside nr wine area." ♦ 1 Jun-15 Sep. € 7.60   2005*

†**NOLAY** *6H1* (1km NW Rural) **Camping La Bruyere**, Rue du Moulin Larche, 21340 Nolay [tel/fax 03 80 21 87 59; camping.labruyere@nolay.com] Fr Beaune take D973 W dir Autun. In approx 20km, arr in vill of Nolay & cont on D973 thro vill. Site on L in 1km after vill, opp supmkt. Sm, hdg pitch, terr, pt shd; wc; chem disp; mv service pnt; shwrs inc; el pts (10-16A) €3.15; lndry rm; dogs; no Eng spkn; quiet; cc acc. "Lovely little site in quiet, hidden valley; v friendly owner; gd, clean san facs; wine area." ♦
€ 13.10   2005*

NONANCOURT *4E2* (4km E Urban/Rural) **Camp Municipal du Pre de l'Eglise**, Ensemble Sportif, 28380 St Remy-sur-Avre [02 37 48 93 87 or 02 37 62 52 00; fax 02 37 48 80 15] Fr Dreux take N12 W to St Remy, site on N of rd clearly sp in cent of vill on Rv Avre. Turn R at traff lts, then L fr Nonancourt on N12. Site on rvside. Or S fr Evreux on N154 turn L (E) onto N12. Sm, hdg/mkd pitch (some grouped x 4), pt shd; wc; chem disp; shwrs inc; el pts (10A) €2.56 (rev pol); lndtte; ice; shop, tradsmn; rest 500m; playgrnd; tennis & trout fishing adj; sat TV; dogs; phone; poss cr; Eng spkn; adv bkg rec high ssn; quiet; CCI. "Pleasant, well-maintained, popular NH; spotless, modern facs but ltd low ssn; friendly warden; local youth groups poss congregate eves; barrier clsd 2100-0730; no twin-axles (but negotiable); poss itinerants/long stay workers; rec lge o'fits arr early - poss diff access." ♦1 Apr-30 Sep.
€ 8.53   2005*

NONETTE see Issoire *9B1*

†**NONTRON** *7B3* (7km NE Rural) **Camping Manzac Ferme**, 24300 Augignac [05 53 56 02 62; manzac-ferme@wanadoo.fr] Fr Nontron take D675 N dir Rochechouart & after 7km on ent Augignac turn R sp Abjat-sur-Bandiat then immed R sp Manzac. Site on R 3.5km Sm, mkd pitch, pt hdstg, sl, pt shd; htd wc; chem disp; shwrs inc; el pts (6A) inc; gas 6km; ice; lndtte; shops, rest, bar 5km; BBQ; dogs by arrangement; adv bkg; quiet. "Adults only, relaxing site; ideal for birdwatching & wildlife; v helpful British owners; excel." ♦ ltd. € 18.00   2005*

NONTRON *7B3* (11km NE) **LES CASTELS Chateau Le Verdoyer**, 24470 Champs-Romain [05 53 56 94 64; fax 05 53 56 38 70; chateau@verdoyer.fr; www.verdoyer.fr or www.les-castels.com] Fr Limoges on N21 twd Perigeux. At Chalus turn R sp Nontron (D6 bis-D85). After approx 18km turn L twd Champs Romain on D96 to site on L in 2km. Med, terr, pt shd; wc; chem disp; baby facs; shwrs inc; el pts (5A) inc; gas; lndtte; ice; shop; rest, B&B in chateau; bistro Jul/Aug; bar; BBQ (charcoal/gas); playgrnd; 2 pools (1 covrd); paddling pool; waterslide; lake fishing; tennis; mini-golf; cycle hire; games rm; golf 25km; child entmnt (5-13yrs) high ssn; creche (0-4yrs); internet; TV rm; 20% statics; dogs €3; phone; recep 0830-2000; poss cr; adv bkg; quiet; cc acc; CCI. "Friendly, Dutch family owners; excel, peaceful site; gd, clean facs; poss steep access some pitches; excursions booked in high ssn." ♦ 15 Apr-14 Oct. € 29.00
(CChq acc) ABS - D21   2005*

NONTRON *7B3* (1km S) **Camping de Nontron** (formerly **Camp Municipal Masviconteaux**), 24300 Nontron [05 53 56 02 04; fax 06 30 66 25 74; terry.homain@club-internet.fr; www.campingdenontron.com] Thro Nontron S twd Brantome on D675. Site on o'skts of town on L nr stadium. Sp. Med, hdg/mkd pitch, pt shd; wc; mv service pnt; shwrs; el pts (10A) €2; gas; ice; lndtte; shops adj; tradsmn; rest, snacks, bar 600m; playgrnd; pool adj; paddling pool; games area; games rm; entmnt; TV rm; statics; dogs; poss cr; Eng spkn; quiet; CCI. "V helpful staff; gd touring base." 1 Jun-15 Sep. € 10.00   2004*

NORDAUSQUES see Ardres *3A3*

NORT SUR ERDRE *2G4* (1.5km S) **Camp Municipal du Port Mulon**, 44390 Nort-sur-Erdre [02 40 72 23 57; fax 02 40 72 16 09; acceuil@mairie-nort-sur-erdre.fr; www.nort-sur-erdre.fr] Sp fr all ents to town; foll 'Camping' & 'Hippodrome' sp. NB: C'vans banned fr town cent, look for diversion sp. Med, shd; wc; chem disp; shwrs inc; el pts (6A) €2; lndtte; ice; supmkt 1.5km; playgrnd; tennis; fishing; boating; dogs €0.65; adv bkg; quiet; CCI. "Delightful site but area not v interesting."
1 Mar-31 Oct. € 8.00   2005

NOTRE DAME DE MONTS *2H3* (600m N Coastal) **Camping Le Grand Jardin, Route de la Barre-de-Monts, 85690 Notre-Dame-de-Monts [tel/fax 02 28 11 21 75]** Fr Notre-Dame-de-Monts heading N on D38 site on R. Med, pt shd; wc; shwrs inc; el pts (10A) inc; ice; lndtte; shops 500m; snacks; playgrnd; sand beach 1km; pool 1km; dogs; adv bkg; quiet. 1 Apr-31 Oct. € 18.30   2002*

> Will you fill in the site report forms at the back of the guide, or shall I?

NOTRE DAME DE MONTS *2H3* (2km N) **Camping Le Bois Soret, 85690 Notre-Dame-de-Monts [02 51 58 84 01; fax 02 51 59 70 16]** Fr St Jean-de-Monts take D38 NW thro Notre-Dame-de-Monts. Site sp 2km on main rd. Lge, pt shd; wc; serviced pitches; shwrs inc; el pts; gas; ice; shop in ssn; snacks; playgrnd; htd pool; sand beach 2km; fishing 500m; TV; some static tents; adv bkg; quiet.   2003*

NOTRE DAME DE RIEZ *2H3* (1km N) **Domaine des Renardieres, Route des Garateries, 85270 Notre-Dame-de-Riez [02 51 55 14 17 or 06 20 98 37 46 (mob); fax 02 51 54 96 13; caroline.raffin@free.fr; www.camping-renardieres.com]** On D38 to Notre-Dame-de-Riez. Thro vill, over rv & 1st L over rlwy to site in 1km. Med, pt shd; wc; chem disp; baby facs; shwrs inc; el pts (6A) €3; gas; ice; lndtte lndry rm; tradsmn; rest; bar; snacks; BBQ; pool; playgrnd; sand beach 5km; TV rm; 20% statics; dogs €3; Eng spkn; adv bkg; quiet phone; 15% red low ssn; cc not acc; CCI. "Gd site; helpful owner; picturesque; poss cash only; rec." ♦ ltd. Easter-4 Sep. € 14.00   2005*

NOTRE DAME DE RIEZ *2H3* (2km SW) **Camping Fonteclose,   85270   Notre-Dame-de-Riez [02 51 55 22 22; fax 02 51 55 91 98; www.fonteclose.com]** Sp fr D83 & D32. Med, pt shd, wc; baby facs; shwrs inc; el pts (6A) inc; lndtte; ice; shop; rest; bar; BBQ; playgrnd; htd pool; tennis; entmnt; fishing; dogs €1.52; adv bkg. "Friendly site." 1 Jun-30 Sep. € 16.01   2002*

NOTRE DAME DU TOUCHET see Mortain *2E4*

NOUAN LE FUZELIER *4G3* (Urban) **Camping La Grande Sologne, 1 Ave Cauchoix, 41600 Nouan-le-Fuzelier [02 54 88 70 22; fax 02 54 88 41 74]** On E side of N20, at S end of Nouan opp rlwy stn. Sp fr town cent. NB Lge site sp on W side of N20 opp main ent. Lge, mkd pitch, pt shd; wc (some cont); chem disp; mv service pnt; baby facs; shwrs inc; el pts (6-10A) €3.20; gas; lndtte; shops 800m; tradsmn; rest; snacks; bar; playgrnd; htd pool adj; tennis; games area; fishing; mini-golf; golf 15km; dogs €1; poss cr; Eng spkn; adv bkg; quiet; red long stay; CCI. "Lge lake on site but no sw allowed; some pitches boggy in wet weather; spotless san block; excel rest in vill; nr chateaux country; pretty site; rec arr early; excel NH." Apr-2 Oct. € 10.00   2005*

NOUANS LES FONTAINES *4H2* (N Urban) **Camp Municipal, Rue des Dames de Touraine, 37460 Nouans-les-Fontaines [02 47 92 62 09; fax 02 47 92 70 93]** On N675 Blois-Limoges rd, site clearly visible fr rd. Sm, unshd; wc; shwrs inc; el pts €0.90; shops adj; pool adj; quiet. "Conv Loire chateaux." 1 Jun-30 Sep. € 4.15   2003*

NOUATRE MARCILLY see Ste Maure de Touraine *4H2*

NOUVION EN THIERACHE, LE *3B4* (7km N Rural) **Camp Municipal du Chemin du Friset, 59550 Prisches [03 27 77 59 00 (Mairie); fax 03 27 77 97 01; prisches-mairie@wanadoo.fr]** Fr Cambrai SE on N43 to Le Cateau & Catillon; D934 & D116 to Prisches. Sp in vill cent. Sm, mkd pitch, pt shd; wc; shwrs inc; el pts (10A); shops adj; rv 3km; quiet. "Only 6 pitches for tourers; peaceful in sleepy vill; modern, clean san facs; ideal NH." 1 Apr-31 Oct. € 8.00   2005*

NOUVION EN THIERACHE, LE *3B4* (1km S Urban) **Camp Municipal du Lac de Conde (formerly L'Astree), Promenade Henri d'Orleans, Rue de Guise (Le Lac), 02170 Le Nouvion-en-Thierache [03 23 98 98 58; fax 03 23 98 94 90; mairie. nouvion@wanadoo.fr; www.lenouvion.com]** Sp fr cent of Le Nouvion fr N43 on D26, dir Guise opp chateau. Med, hdg/mkd pitch, some hdstg, pt sl, pt shd; wc; chem disp (wc); shwrs inc; el pts (4-8A) €2.80-3.50; ice; shop 1km; tradsmn; rest, snacks, bar 1km; BBQ; playgrnd; htd pool adj; tennis, mini-golf, canoe hire, horseriding nrby; dogs €0.70; phone; 10% red 15 days; quiet; cc acc; CCI. "Attractive site; gd cent for Picardy area; gd value; pleasant site adj lake; friendly & helpful; excel shwrs; gd for sm families - lots of space/play areas; vg all stays." ♦ 15 Apr-15 Oct. € 8.00   2005*

NOYERS *4G4* (200m S Rural) **Camping Rurale, 89310 Noyers [03 86 82 83 72; fax 03 86 82 63 41; mairie-de-noyers@wanadoo.fr]** Exit A6 at Nitry & turn R onto D944. In 2km at N edge of Nitry, turn R onto D49 sp Noyers. In 10km in Noyers, turn L onto D86 sp Centre Ville/Camping. Immed after crossing rv & bef gate, turn L bet 2 obelisks. Site at end of track. Sm, mkd pitch, terr, shd; wc; own san; chem disp; shwrs inc; el pts €1.05; shop, rest, snacks, bar 200m; BBQ; playgrnd; dogs; quiet. "Only 6 pitches; v attractive, secluded site nr Rv Serein; ent key obtained fr Mairie on R after going thro town gate, on 1st floor (€15 dep req); ltd san facs; gd sh stay."
€ 4.30   2004*

†**NOYON** *3C3* (4km E Rural) **Camping L'Etang du Moulin, 54 Rue du Moulin, 60400 Salency [tel/fax 03 44 09 99 81 or 03 44 43 06 78]** Take N32 fr Noyon dir Chauny. On ent Salency turn L & foll site sp. Site in 1km. Sm, pt sl, shd; htd wc; chem disp; mv service pnt; shwrs €1.80; el pts (10A) €1.55; gas; shop, rest 4km; tradsmn; bar; BBQ; playgrnd; fishing; tennis; mini-golf; 60% statics; dogs €0.90; quiet; CCI." ♦ € 10.00   2004*

†**NOYON** *3C3* (8km S Rural) **Camping Les Araucarias, 870 Rue du General Leclerc, 60170 Carlepont [03 44 75 27 39; fax 03 44 75 26 00; camping-les-araucarias@wanadoo.fr; www.les-araucarias.com]** Fr S, fr A1 exit junc 9 or 10 for Compiegne. There take D130 sp Tracy-le-Val & Carlepont. Site on L 100m fr Carlepont vill sp. Or fr N on D934 Noyon-Soissons rd take D130 dir Carlepont & Tracy-le-Val. Site on R after vill on SW twd Compiegne. Sm, mkd pitch, pt sl, pt shd; wc; chem disp; mv service pnt; baby facs; shwrs inc; el pts (6-10A) €2.90; gas; lndtte; ice; shop, rest, bar 1km; BBQ; playgrnd; 75% statics; dogs; poss cr; Eng spkn; adv bkg; quiet; cc acc; CCI. "V secluded site, previously an arboretum; close Parc Asterix & La Mer de Sable (theme park); 85km Disneyland; ltd facs; site being extended; poss diff when wet; new owner 2005; fair NH." ♦ ltd. € 9.70   2005*

NOZAY *2G4* (500m Urban) **Camp Municipal Henri Dubourg, Route de Chateaubriant, 44170 Nozay [02 40 87 94 33 or 02 40 79 79 79 (Mairie); fax 02 40 79 35 64; mairie@nozay44.fr]** N on N137 twd Rennes fr Nantes, (on by-pass) exit onto N171 sp Chateaubriant, immed R onto D121 sp Nozay; pass lake, site on R in 1km. Well sp. Sm, hdg pitch, pt shd; wc; chem disp; mv service pnt; shwrs inc; el pts (6A) €1.80 (poss rev pol); lndry rm; ice; supmkt/shops 500m; BBQ; pool adj; lake 300m; lake sw, beach, windsurfing, canoeing, sailing & fishing; tennis; miniature golf; cinema; dogs €1; quiet but some rd noise; adv bkg; Eng spkn; cc acc; CCI. "Well-kept, basic site; ideal NH to/fr Cherbourg; extremely pretty setting; easy walking dist to town & lake; vg." ♦ ltd.
15 May-15 Sep. € 7.50   2005*

NUITS ST GEORGES *6G1* (3km SW Urban) **Camping Le Moulin de Prissey, 21700 Premeaux-Prissey [03 80 62 31 15; fax 03 80 61 37 29]** Exit Beaune on N74 twd Nuits-St Georges & Dijon; app Premeaux-Prissey turn R soon after vill sp, under rlwy bdge & foll site sp. Fr A31 exit at Nuits-St George & foll camp sp for Saule-Guillaume, thro Premeaux-Prissey & foll site sp. Sm, mkd pitch, pt sl, pt shd; wc (some cont); chem disp (wc); mv service pnt; shwrs inc; el pts (6A) inc; gas; lndtte; ice; shops 3km; tradsmn; snacks; rest, bar 4km; BBQ; playgrnd; dogs €0.90; poss cr; adv bkg; noisy rlwy adj; cc not acc; CCI. "Arr early; popular NH; sm pitches; access poss diff for lge o'fits; gd cent Beaune wine area; lots of quiet minor rds for cycling."
♦ ltd. 1 Apr-15 Oct. € 13.50   2005*

NUITS ST GEORGES *6G1* (6km SW Rural) **Camp Intercommunal Saule Guillaume, 21700 Premeaux-Prissey [03 80 62 30 78 or 03 80 61 27 99 (LS); fax 03 80 61 35 19]** Fr N on N74 foll sps in Nuits-St George for A31 to rndabt bef a'route. Fr A31 to 1st rndabt & foll sp for camping via Quincey. Med, hdg pitch, pt shd; wc (some cont); shwrs inc; el pts (6-12A) €2.80-4.30; ice; shop & 7km; tradsmn; playgrnd; lake beach, fishing, boating & sw adj; dogs €2; poss cr; Eng spkn; adv bkg; quiet but some rd & rlwy noise; CCI. "Facs poss unclean; helpful staff; gd rest; fair sh stay."
14 Jun-1 Sep. € 9.10   2004*

NYOISEAU see Segre *2F4*

NYONS *9D2* (1km NE Rural) **Camping Les Clos, Route de Gap, 26110 Nyons [04 75 26 29 90; fax 04 75 26 49 44; camping-les-clos@clario.fr; www.campinglesclos.com]** Fr rndabt in town cent take D94 sp Gap & site on R in 1km. Med, hdg/mkd pitch, hdstg, pt shd; wc; chem disp; shwrs inc; baby facs; el pts (6A) inc; gas; lndtte; ice; shop; rest 1km; snacks; bar; BBQ (gas/elec only); playgrnd; pool; shgl rv beach & fishing; entmnt (ltd); 20% statics; dogs €2; phone; Eng spkn; adv bkg (dep & fee req) red low ssn; quiet; cc acc; CCI. "Beautiful scenery; excel touring cent for Drome Provencale; v clean & well kept; friendly staff." ♦
1 Mar-22 Oct. € 17.00 (3 persons)   2005*

NYONS *9D2* (3km NE) **Camping L'Or Vert, 26110 Aubres [tel/fax 04 75 26 24 85]** Fr Nyons take D94 twd Serre, site on R of rd. Med, hdstg, pt sl, pt shd; wc (cont); chem disp; shwrs inc; el pts (6A) €3.05; gas; lndtte; shops 3km; snacks; playgrnd; pool 3km; rv adj; fishing; entmnt; some statics; quiet; cc not acc. "Vg long stay; interesting scenic countryside; min stay 10 days Jul-Aug; nice rv site; ltd facs low ssn; phone ahead to check opening dates low ssn; v clean facs." 1 Apr-1 Oct. € 11.00   2002*

NYONS *9D2* (10km NE Rural) **Camping Le Chambron, Route de St Pons, 26110 Condorcet [tel/fax 04 75 27 70 54]** Fr Nyons on D94 dir Serres. In 7km turn L onto D227 to Condorcet & foll site sp. Med, shd; wc; shwrs inc; el pts (6A) €3; lndry rm; tradsmn; bar; playgrnd; pool; tennis; 10% statics; quiet. 1 Apr-30 Sep. € 11.50   2002*

FRANCE

CAMPING MUNICIPAL ★★★
1, rue de Berlin - 67210 Obernai
Tel.: 03 88 95 38 48
Fax: 03 88 48 31 47
E-mail: camping@obernai.fr
Internet: www.obernai.fr

OPEN ALL YEAR

NYONS *9D2* (12km NE Rural) **Camping de Trente Pas**, 26110 St Ferreol-Trente-Pas [04 75 27 70 69] NE fr Nyons on D94. L on D70 to St Ferreol-Trente-Pas. Site 100m fr vill on banks of stream. Med, shd; wc; shwrs; el pts (6A) inc; Indry rm; shop; snacks; playgrnd; pool; games rm; tennis; cycle hire; horseriding 4km; entmnt; TV; many statics. "Excel value; v clean san facs; gd views & pool; lovely area; rec." 1 May-15 Sep. € 13.30   2005*

NYONS *9D2* (12km NE Rural) **Camping Le Pilat**, 26110 St Ferreol-Trente-Pas [04 75 27 72 09; fax 04 75 27 72 34; info@campinglepilat.com] Fr D94 N or Nyons turn N at La Bonte onto D70 to St Ferreol, site sp 1km N of vill. Med, hdg pitch, shd; wc (some cont); chem disp; shwrs inc; el pts (6A) €2.90; Indtte; shop high ssn & 3km; tradsmn; snacks; playgrnd; covrd pool; lake sw adj; games area; entmnt; TV; 25% statics; dogs €1.50; phone; Eng spkn; quiet; CCI. "Site among lavender fields; beautiful area; Thurs mkt Nyons; v pleasant, helpful owners; clean facs; gd walking & off-rd cycling." ♦ 1 Apr-30 Sep. € 13.10   2003*

†NYONS *9D2* (6km SW Rural) **Camping Le Sagittaire**, 26110 Vinsobres [04 75 27 00 00; fax 04 75 27 00 39; camping.sagittaire@wanadoo.fr; www.le-sagittaire.com] Fr Nyons on D94, sp Orange, site on L just after junc with D4, well sp. Lge, hdg pitch, pt shd; htd wc; chem disp; shwrs inc; el pts (6-10A) €3.40-4,40; gas; Indtte; shop; tradsmn; rest, snacks, bar in ssn; playgrnd; htd, covrd pool; waterslide; cycle hire; entmnt; TV; 25% statics; dogs €4.10; poss cr; adv bkg (bkg fee & dep req) quiet but some rd noise on edge of site; red long stay/low ssn; cc acc; CCI. "Part of holiday complex in attractive, uncommercialised area." € 25.50   2005*

NYONS *9D2* (7km SW Rural) **Camp Municipal, Champessier**, 26110 Vinsobres [04 75 27 61 65 or 04 75 27 64 49 (Mairie); fax 04 75 27 59 20] Fr Nyons on D94 sp Orange. Turn R 500m after junc with D4 twd Vinsobres vill. Site 500m on L bef vill. Sm, mkd pitch, pt shd; wc; chem disp; shwrs inc; el pts (6A) €2.20; Indry rm; BBQ; playgrnd; adv bkg; quiet; cc acc; CCI. "Peaceful site; excel touring area." ♦ 1 Apr-30 Sep. € 7.40   2004*

NYONS *9D2* (4km NW Urban) **Camping Les Terrasses Provencales**, 26110 Venterol [tel/fax 04 75 27 92 36; novezan@lesterrasses provencales. com; www.lesterrasses provencales.com] Exit A7/E15 at junc 18 sp Nyons. Join D541 E twd Nyons. Site in Venterol, sp bet Valreas & Nyons. Med, hdg/mkd pitch, hdstg; terr, pt shd; wc; chem disp; shwrs inc; baby facs; fam bthrm; el pts (10A) inc (poss rev pol); gas; Indtte; shop 6km; tradsmn; rest, bar 2km; playgrnd; pool; dogs low ssn only; poss cr; some Eng spkn; quiet; cc acc; CCI. "Owner will tow c'van onto terr pitch; pizza delivery twice weekly; excel." ♦ 1 Apr-31 Oct. € 18.00   2003*

OBERBRONN *5D3* (1.5km S Rural) **Camp Municipal L'Oasis, 3 Rue de Frohret**, 67110 Oberbronn [03 88 09 71 96; fax 03 88 09 97 87; oasis.oberbronn@laregie.fr] Fr N62 turn S on D28 away fr Niederbronn; thro Oberbronn, site sp. Lge, mkd pitch, pt sl, pt shd; wc; chem disp; mv service pnt; sauna; shwrs inc; el pts (6A) €3.90; Indtte; shop & 1.5km; tradsmn; rest; snacks; bar; BBQ; playgrnd; htd, covrd pool high ssn; paddling pool; tennis; fitness rm; walking, cycling, horseriding rtes; golf, games rm; fishing 2km; 20% statics; dogs €1.80; clsd 1200-1300; poss cr; adv bkg rec high ssn; quiet; red long stay/low ssn; cc acc; CCI. "Vg site with lovely views; part of leisure complex; v quiet low ssn; sm area for tourers poss sl; some san facs tired; site gravel paths not suitable wheelchair users." ♦ ltd. 13 Mar-12 Nov. € 12.00   2005*

OBERNAI *6E3* (10km N Urban) **Camp Municipal, 9 Rue des Sports**, 67120 Molsheim [03 88 49 82 45 or 03 88 49 58 58 (LS); fax 03 8 49 58 59] On ent town fr Obernai on N422 site sp on R immed after x-ing sm rv bdge. Med, mkd pitch, pt shd; wc; chem disp; mv service pnt; shwrs inc; el pts €2.50; Indtte; tradsmn; BBQ; pool adj; dogs €1; train to Strasbourg 700m; poss cr; Eng spkn; adv bkg; quiet; CCI. ♦ 8 May-30 Sep. € 9.40   2005*

†OBERNAI *6E3* (1km W Urban) **Camp Municipal Le Vallon de l'Ehn, 1 Rue de Berlin, 67210 Obernai [03 88 95 38 48; fax 03 88 48 31 47; camping@obernai.fr; www.obernai.fr]** Fr Strasbourg SW on N422/E35; leave at junc 11 sp Obernai; on ent town, turn L at 2nd rndabt (McDonalds) sp D426 Ottrott; in 3km after 3rd rndabt turn R at T-junc sp Obernai then almost immed L at camping sp; site on L in 200m, sp but obscure. Look for sp Camping VVF. Fr S on A35, exit at junc 12 sp Obernai. Foll sp Obernai, then Centre Ville, then site. Lge, mkd pitch, some hdstg, pt sl, unshd; wc; chem disp; mv service pnt; 75% serviced pitches; baby facs; shwrs inc; el pts (16A) €3.50; gas 1km; ice; lndtte; sm shop & 1km; tradsmn; BBQ; playgrnd; pool 200m, tennis, horseriding adj; cab TV; internet; dogs; train; poss cr; Eng spkn; adv bkg; quiet; cc acc; 5% red C'van Club members. "Well-maintained; superb clean facs; sm pitches; card operated barrier - CCI as dep for card; friendly & helpful recep, clsd 1230-1400; Obernai v attractive old town on N part of Rte du Vin; easy walk to cent; highly rec; arr early high ssn." ♦ € 12.00   2005*

See advertisement

OCTON *10F1* (Rural) **Camping Le Village du Bosc (Naturist), Ricazouls, 34800 Octon [04 67 96 07 37; fax 04 67 96 35 75]** Exit 54 or 55 fr N9/A75 dir Octon onto D148, foll sp to Ricazouls/site. Med, terr, pt shd; wc; chem disp; shwrs; el pts (4-10A) €2.44-4.60 rest; snacks; bar; shop; lndtte; playgrnd; htd pool; lake sw; watersports; 20% statics; dogs €1.50; Eng spkn; adv bkg; CCI. "Tight turns on terr access for lge o'fits; v pleasant naturist site (INF card reqd) with wooded walks on site; Octon vill pretty." ♦ ltd. 1 Apr-30 Sep. € 14.02   2004*

OCTON *10F1* (4km E Rural) **Aire Naturelle Les Arcades, Lac-de-Salagou, 34800 Octon [04 67 96 99 13]** Sp fr Octon. Sm, pt shd; wc; chem disp (wc); shwrs inc; el pts; BBQ; fishing nrby; quiet. "Excel clean & tidy; lge pitches under acacia trees; gd views; vg long/sh stays." 15 May-30 Sep. € 13.50   2004*

OCTON *10F1* (600m SE Rural) **Camping Le Mas des Carles, 34800 Octon [04 67 96 32 33]** Leave A75 at junc 54, foll sp for Octon, 100m after vill sp turn L & foll white site sp keeping L. Ent on L opp tel kiosk (sharp turn). Sm, some hdg/mkd pitch, pt sl, terr, pt shd, pt shd; wc; chem disp; shwrs inc; el pts (3-6A) inc; lndtte; lndry rm; ice; shop 500m; rest adj; playgrnd; pool; boating/watersports in lake 800m; 30% statics; dogs; phone; poss cr; adv bkg; quiet; cc not acc; CCI. "Lovely views, v pleasant site; facs a little tired; helpful owner; Lac de Salagou with abandoned vill of Celles 1km." 1 Apr-15 Oct. € 20.40   2005*

ODOMEZ see St Amand les Eaux *3B4*

OFFRANVILLE see Dieppe *3C2*

OISY LE VERGER see Cambrai *3B4*

OLARGUES *8F4* **Camp Municipal Le Baous, 34390 Olargues [04 67 97 71 50 or 04 67 97 70 79 (Mairie)]** Take D908 W fr Bedarieux, site immed bef ent Olargues. Site sp over sm bdge on L. At end of bdge turn R to site. Last 50m rough track but looks worse than it is. Sm, pt shd; wc (cont); chem disp; shwrs inc; el pts (6A) €2.20; shop 300m; playgrnd; adv bkg Jul/Aug; quiet. "Lovely mountain area; helpful warden; site poss flooded by Rv Jaur in spring; hill climb to services block; water hot in name only; cherries in ssn; narr turn into site." € 7.00
2003*

OLLIERES SUR EYRIEUX, LES see St Sauveur de Montagut *9D2*

OLONNE SUR MER see Sables d'Olonne, Les *7A1*

OLONZAC *8F4* (6km N Rural) **Camping Bastibarres, Route de Fauzan, 34210 Cesseras [04 68 91 11 66; fax 04 68 91 32 43; frans.vangeldorp@worldonline.fr]** Fr D610/D11 turn N to Olonzac & Cesseras. In Cesseras foll dir Fauzan, site on D182 500m N of Cesseras, sp. Sm, hdg/mkd pitch, terr, pt shd; wc; chem disp; shwrs inc; el pts (6A) €2.50; lndtte; shop; rest; snacks; bar; playgrnd; pool; 50% statics; dogs €2; Eng spkn: adv bkg; quiet; cc not acc; CCI. "Beautiful area; gd local rests." 1 Mar-1 Nov. € 16.00   2005*

OLONZAC *8F4* (6km N Rural) **Camping Le Mas de Lignieres (Naturist), 34210 Cesseras-en-Minervois [tel/fax 04 68 91 24 86; lemas1@tiscali.fr]** Fr Olonzac go N on D182 thro Cesseras & cont N dir Fauzan. Site sp. Accss narr last 4km after Olonzac, care needed thro Cesseras. Sm, hdg/mkd pitch, hdstg, pt sl, pt shd; wc (some cont); chem disp; baby facs; fam bthrm; shwrs inc; el pts (6-10A) €3-4.50; gas; lndtte; sm shop & 2km; tradsmn; covrd pool; tennis; library; TV rm; 5% statics; dogs €1.50; phone; poss cr; adv bkg; red 10 days; quiet; cc acc; INF card ess & avail at site. "Magnificent scenery, gorges; well-run site; lge pitches; gd san facs; wonderful walks." ♦ ltd 1 Apr-15 Oct. € 23.00   2005*

†OLONZAC *8F4* (9km E Rural) **Camping Les Auberges, 11120 Pouzols-Minervois [tel/fax 04 68 46 26 50; pradalveronique@net-up.com]** Fr D5 site 500m S of vill of Pouzols. Sm, mkd pitch, pt shd; wc; chem disp (wc); shwrs inc; el pts (6A) inc; gas adj; lndtte; ice; shop adj; playgrnd; pool; 30% statics; poss cr; Eng spkn; adv bkg rec; quiet; CCI. "Friendly owners; sm Sat mkt at 'cave' opp." € 11.00   2005*

†OLORON STE MARIE *8F2* (6km S Rural) Camping Val du Gave d'Aspe, 64400 Gurmencon [05 59 36 05 07; fax 05 59 36 00 52; chalet.aspe@wanadoo.fr] Fr Oloron on N134 sp in 10km vill of Gurmencon. L past church then immed R (to avoid diff ent). Site in 100m. Sm, hdg pitch, terr, pt shd; wc; shwrs inc; el pts (6-10A) €2.60-4.90; lndtte; tradsmn; shop & rest 100m; bar; playgrnd; pool; cycle hire; mostly statics; dogs; phone 100m; site clsd 22 Oct-5 Dec; poss cr; adv bkg (dep req); quiet; CCI. "Excel winter site on Col du Somport rte to Spain; gd clean facs; helpful & friendly warden; only 6 touring pitches; low hanging trees; poss diff access." ♦ € 9.00   2002*

> **Mustn't forget to post our site report forms to The Club, otherwise sites might be deleted.**

OLORON STE MARIE *8F2* (2km W Urban) Camping-Gites du Stade, Chemin de Lagravette, 64400 Oloron-Ste Marie [05 59 39 11 26; fax 05 59 36 12 01; camping-du-stade@wanadoo.fr] Fr N on ring rd foll sp to Sarragosse (Spain); at rndabt take 2nd exit onto D6 still sp Sarragosse, site sp on R just after sports field. Med, hdg/mkd pitch, pt shd; wc; chem disp; shwrs inc; el pts (6-10A) €3-5.50 (some rev pol); lndry rm; ice; tradsmn; supmkt 1km; rest; snacks; playgrnd; pool adj; rv fishing & sw 1km; tennis; cycle hire; entmnts; TV; dogs €1.20; adv bkg; CCI. "Excel base for Pyrenees; spotless facs but stretched in ssn; well-maintained; lge pitches; v quiet; open for wintersports; gd walking; barrier clsd 1200-1500." 1 May-30 Sep. € 14.00   2005*

OMONVILLE LA ROGUE see Beaumont Hague *1C4*

ONESSE ET LAHARIE *8E1* Camp Municipal Le Bienvenue Bourg, Route de Mimizan, 40110 Onesse-et-Laharie [05 58 07 30 49; fax 05 58 07 30 78] On N10 Bordeaux-Bayonne rd, turn W onto D38 at Laharie. Site in 5km. Med, mkd pitch, pt shd; wc (some cont); chem disp; shwrs inc; el pts (6A) €2.60; lndry rm; shops & bar adj; playgrnd; beach 23km; quiet; adv bkg; red long stay; CCI. "Well-run, family site." 15 Jun-15 Sep. € 12.55   2004*

†ONZAIN *4G2* (2km N Rural) Camping Domaine de Dugny, 45 Route de Chambon-sur-Cisse, 41150 Onzain [02 54 20 70 66; fax 02 54 33 71 69; info@dugny.fr; www.camping-de-dugny.fr] Exit A10 junc 17 Blois onto N152 dir Tours. After 16km at rndabt at bdge to Chaumont, turn N dir Onzain. Take D45 N to Chambon-sur-Cisse. Site sp on a minor rd to L, beside sm lake. Site well sp fr Onzain cent. Lge, hdg/mkd pitch, hdstg, pt sl, pt shd; htd wc; chem disp; mv service pnt; serviced pitches; baby facs; fam bthrm; shwrs inc; el pts (6A) €5; gas; lndtte; ice; shop; tradsmn; rest; snacks; bar; BBQ; playgrnd; htd pool & paddling pool; waterslide; lake sw & 10km; fishing; cycle hire; games rm; games area; golf 8km; boules; boat hire; entmnt high ssn; poss ultra-light flying lessons; TV rm; internet; 10% statics; dogs €5; train 4km; Eng spkn; adv bkg; quiet; cc acc; red low ssn; CCI. "Peaceful, lakeside site; v welcoming; clean san facs but ltd low ssn; chateaux close by - World Heritage site; supmkt with petrol in Onzain; gd facs for children; ltd facs low ssn; ideal NH." ♦ € 32.00 (CChq acc)   2005*

ONZAIN *4G2* (1.5km SE) Camp Municipal, Ave General de Gaulle, 41150 Onzain [02 54 20 85 15 or 02 54 51 20 40 (Mairie); fax 02 54 20 74 34; marie@ville-onzain.fr] Fr N of Chaumont-sur-Loire, at rndabt at junc N152 & D1 take D1 N twds Onzain then take 1st turn on R. Foll sp. Sm, hdg pitch, pt sl, pt shd; wc (some cont); chem disp; shwrs inc; el pts (10A) inc; gas; lndtte; ice; shops 500m; playgrnd; dogs €1.40; no twin-axle vans; gates locked 2000-0800; poss cr; some rd & rlwy noise; cc not acc; CCI. "Excel; friendly guardienne; rlwy service to Paris; central for Loire chateaux." ♦ 1 May-30 Aug. € 7.90   2004*

ONZAIN *4G2* (6km W Rural) Camping Le Parc du Val de Loire, Route de Fleuray, 41150 Mesland [02 54 70 27 18; fax 02 54 70 21 71; parc.du.val.de.loire@wanadoo.fr; www.parcduvaldeloire.com] Fr Blois take N152 twd Amboise. In 16km turn R to Onzain, foll sp Mesland, thro vill, turn L sp Fleuray, site on R after 2km. Lge, hdg/mkd pitch, pt sl, shd; wc; chem disp; mv service pnt; serviced pitches; baby facs; shwrs inc; el pts (6A) inc gas; lndtte; ice; shop; snacks; bar; BBQ; playgrnd; 2 htd pools; paddling pool; waterslide; tennis; games area; mini-golf; cycle hire; wine-tasting; entmnt; internet; TV rm; 20% statics; dogs €1.80; Eng spkn; adv bkg; red low ssn; cc acc; CCI. "Secluded site; conv Loire chateaux; visits arranged to vineyards; mkt Thu Onzain; excel." ♦ 15 Apr-30 Sep. € 24.90 ABS - L02   2005*

OPIO see Grasse *10E4*

OPPEDE see Cavaillon *10E2*

ORANGE *10E2* (6km N Rural) **Camping La Ferme de Rameyron, Chemin de Roard, Route de Camaret-sur-Aigues, 84830 Serignan-du-Comtat** [04 90 70 06 48] Fr Orange on N7 dir Bollene turn R sp Serignan-du-Comtat. In town cent turn R at x-rds sp Camaret. At 3rd R turn R into Chemin de Roard. Site on L in 100m. Sm, mkd pitch, pt shd; wc (some cont); chem disp; mv service pnt; shwrs inc; el pts (10A) inc; gas, shops, rest, bar 800m; playgrnd; pool; dogs; poss cr; quiet; cc acc. "Friendly owners; CL-type; san facs old but clean; close to historic vill; 5km fr m'way; gd all stays." 1 Jun-31 Aug. € 11.00   2004*

ORANGE *10E2* (10km NE Rural) **Aire Naturelle Domaine des Favards, Route d'Orange, 84150 Violes** [04 90 70 90 93; fax 04 90 70 97 28] Fr N exit A7 junc 19 Bollene. Foll D8 dir Carpentras & Violes. In Violes foll dir Orange & look for camp sp. Fr S exit A7 junc 22 sp Carpentras, take dir Avignon, then dir Vaison-la-Romaine to Violes. Avoid cent of Orange when towing. Sm, hdg/mkd pitch, unshd; htd wc (some cont); baby facs; shwrs inc; el pts (6-10A) €3 (poss rev pol); lndry rm; tradsmn; snacks; bar; playgrnd; pool; child entmnt; dogs €1; poss cr; Eng spkn; adv bkg; quiet; no cc acc; red low ssn; CCI. "Well-maintained site; superb shwr block & laundry; some pitches diff due low trees; wine-tasting on site high ssn; facs poss stretched; dust clouds fr Mistral wind." ♦ 1 May-30 Sep. € 13.00   2005*

ORANGE *10E2* (8km SE Urban) **Camp Municipal Les Peupliers, Ave Pierre-de-Coubertin, 84150 Jonquieres** [04 90 70 67 09; fax 04 90 70 59 01] Exit junc 22 fr A7 onto N7 S. In 2km turn L (E) onto D950. In 5km at rndabt turn L onto D977. In 500m turn L sp Jonquieres, site on L in 2km, sp in vill. Site behind sports complex. Med, mkd pitch, pt shd; wc; chem disp; shwrs inc; el pts (10A) inc; gas 500m; lndtte; ice; shop, rest, snacks, bar 500m; playgrnd; pool, tennis adj; dogs €2.50; phone; poss cr; Eng spkn; adv bkg; noise fr airfield (week days); cc not acc; CCI. "Excel site; friendly & welcoming new owners; v well-run site; v clean san facs; shwrs excel; arrive bef 1600; gates close 2200; extensive Roman ruins nrby; gd long/sh stay." 15 May-30 Sep. € 10.20   2005*

ORANGE *10E2* (1.5km NW Urban) **Camping Le Jonquier, 1321 Rue Alexis Carrel, 84100 Orange** [04 90 34 49 48; fax 04 90 51 16 97; info@campinglejonquier.com; www.campinglejonquier.com] Site N of Arc de Triomphe off N7; turn W at traff lts to site in 500m & foll site sp across rndabt, R at next rndabt. Med, hdg/mkd pitch, mostly unshd; wc (some cont); chem disp; mv service pnt; baby facs; shwrs inc; el pts (3A) inc; lndtte; ice; supmkt 500m; bar; playgrnd; htd pool; tennis; mini-golf; pony rides; some statics; dogs €3; poss cr; Eng spkn; quiet; cc acc; CCI. "1.5km walk into historic town; lge mkt Thurs; helpful staff; unkempt low ssn; san facs poss stretched high ssn." ♦ 1 Apr-30 Sep. € 25.70   2005*

ORBEC *3D1* (Urban) **Camp Municipal les Capucins, 14290 Orbec** [02 31 32 76 22] Sp fr N819 & thro town & 1-way system. Sm, pt shd; wc; chem disp; shwrs inc; el pts inc; shops adj; playgrnd; quiet. "Sm immac site; san facs old but clean; delightful countryside; steep drag up to site & care req down to town." 25 May-8 Sep. € 8.40   2004*

ORBEY see Munster *6F3*

ORCET see Clermont Ferrand *9B1*

ORCHAMPS see Dampierre *6G2*

ORCIVAL *7B4* (6km NE Rural) **Camping La Haute Sioule, 63210 St Bonnet-Pres-Orcival** [04 73 65 83 32; fax 04 73 65 85 19; hautesioule@wanadoo.fr; www.camping-hautesioule.com] Fr Clermont-Ferrand take N89 S then W twds La Bourboule for approx 20km. At junc with D216 turn L twds Orcival. Site in 4km. Foll site sp. Med, sl, pt shd; wc; shwrs inc; el pts (4-13A) €2.30-5.50; gas; lndtte; shops 250m; snacks; playgrnd; rv sw adj; golf; fishing adj; games rm; entmnt; 50% statics; poss cr; Eng spkn; CCI. "Owners friendly; v pleasant late ssn but poss untidy; poss diff for lge o'fits; ltd facs low ssn & no recep, site self; fair NH." 15 Mar-31 Oct. € 11.50   2004*

†ORGEVAL *3D3* (2km N Rural) **Caravaning Club des Renardieres, Route Vermouillet, 78670 Villennes-sur-Seine** [01 39 75 88 97] E on A13 twd Paris take exit sp Poissy. Foll Orgeval & Centre Commercial sp at rndabt. In approx 2km turn R immed after lge green Habitat warehouse. Site 1km on L after 2nd x-rds. No site sp so look for title on wall of white building on L. Or W on A13, foll sp to Poissy & Villennes, & immed after a'route turn L (over dual c'way), as above. Steep access, narr gate; check on foot bef ent site. Lge, mkd pitch, pt sl, terr, shd; wc (some cont); shwrs inc; el pts (6A) inc (rev pol); gas; shops 4km; 90% statics; dogs; adv bkg (dep req); quiet; CCI. "Conv Paris by RER fr Poissy; friendly recep open Mon-Fri 1000-1800 & clsd for lunch 1200-1400; do not rec arr/depart Sat/Sun; simple, spacious site; basic but clean htd facs; twin-axle vans over 8m not acc." ♦ ltd. € 13.45   2002*

ORLEANS *4F3* (10km E) **Camp Municipal Les Patures, 55 Chemin du Port, 45430 Checy** [02 38 91 13 27] Take D960 E twd Chateauneuf. In Checy, foll site sp. Access thro town v narr streets. Med, hdg pitch, pt shd; wc; chem disp; mv service pnt; shwrs €0.30/3 mins; el pts (16A) inc; lndtte; ice; shop 1km; BBQ; tennis; fishing; golf 5km; no statics; dogs; Eng spkn; adv bkg; some noice fr adj site; CCI. "Superb site on banks of Rv Loire; helpful warden; gd clean san facs; gd walking; conv Orleans; excel." ♦ 28 May-3 Sep. € 11.70   2005*

FRANCE

ORLEANS *4F3* (4km S Urban) **Camp Municipal d'Olivet, Rue de Pont-Bouchet, 45160 Olivet [02 38 63 53 94 or 02 38 63 82 82 (Mairie); fax 02 38 63 58 96]** N on N20 bef Orleans sp on RH side turn R opp Auchan supmkt foll sp; at 1km turn R at rndabt over rv bdge (3,500 kg weight limit/3.1m height restriction) over rv bdge & L at traff lts on D14 & L down Rue de Pont-Bouchet; narr app rd. To avoid height restriction, fr A71 exit junc 2 onto N271 dir Orleans-La Source. Cont on N271 until rd crosses N20 keeping L at all forks until Rue de Bourges. Turn L at 2nd traff lts into Rue de Chateauroux, turn L at traff lts onto D14, Rue de la Source then in 500m R into Rue to Pont-Bouchet (narr rd). Sp from Olivet but sps diff to pick out (sm, green). Med, hdg pitch, pt sl, pt shd; htd wc (some cont); chem disp; mv service pnt; shwrs inc; el pts (16A) inc; lndtte; ice; shop 500m; tradsmn; snacks; playgrnd; dogs; bus/tram 200m (secure car park); poss cr; Eng spkn; adv bkg rec, confirm by tel bef 1800 (booking fee & dep); quiet; red long stay; CCI. "Well-run, busy, friendly site by Rv Loiret; vg san facs; poss noisy at w/e; excel tram service into town; vineyards nr; gd walking." ♦ 1 Apr-15 Oct. € 14.80   2005*

ORLEANS *4F3* (10km SW Urban) **Camping Fontaine de Rabelais, Chemin de la Plage, 45130 St Ay [02 38 88 94 35 or 02 38 88 65 56; fax 02 38 88 82 14]** Exit A10/E60 at junc 15 Meung-sur-Loire onto N152 dir Orleans; site sp on app to St Ay on N bank Rv Loire. Fr A71 exit junc 1 dir Blois & Beaugency onto N152. Lge, pt sl, pt shd; wc; chem disp; mv service pnt; shwrs inc; el pts (6A) €2.30-3.10 (poss rev pol); gas; shops 500m; tradsmn; rest 500m; BBQ; playgrnd; rv fishing & boating adj; dogs €1.80; phone; bus 500m; no twin-axles; dep for ent barrier; adv bkg; quiet; cc not acc; CCI. "Friendly, helpful staff; pleasant site; excel modern facs for sm site but poss stretched high ssn; clean & tidy; pleasant surroundings, on bank of Loire; conv Orleans; gd base for chateaux." ♦ 15 Apr-31 Oct. € 9.00   2005*

ORLEANS *4F3* (3km W Urban) **Camping Gaston Marchand, Rue de la Roche, 45140 St Jean-de-la-Ruelle [02 38 88 39 39; fax 02 38 79 33 62; sports@ville-saintjeandelaruelle.fr]** On ent Orleans fr S take N152 to Blois W. Site sp on L after 2nd set of traff lts on N bank of rv. On N152 fr Blois turn R immed at Gaston Marchand sp. Med, mkd pitch, pt sl, pt shd; wc (some cont); chem disp; shwrs inc; el pts (6A) €2.75; gas; shops 2km; pool 1.5km; dogs €1; bus; poss cr; adv bkg; some rd noise. "On bank of Rv Loire; ltd facs; conv Orleans; gd NH." 1 Jul-31 Aug. € 9.30   2003*

ORLEAT see Thiers *9B1*

ORNANS *6G2* (6km SE Rural) **Camp Municipal Le Pre Bailly, 25840 Vuillafans [03 81 60 91 52; fax 03 81 60 95 68]** Site sp fr D67 adj rv. Sm, terr, pt shd; wc; shwrs inc; el pts (4-6A) €1.50-2.30; shop 50m; playgrnd; phone adj; quiet. "Simple site; pleasant situation in pretty vill; gd walks; site yourself, warden calls; vg sh stay." 15 Mar-30 Sep. € 7.20   2003*

ORNANS *6G2* (10km SE Rural) **Camping Les Oyes, 25920 Mouthier-Haute-Pierre [03 81 60 91 39]** SE fr Ornans on D67. Site 1.5km on R past Lods. Site sp & easily visible fr rd. Sm, pt shd; wc (some cont); shwrs; el pts; shops 1.5km; playgrnd; rv sw, fishing, canoeing & shgl beach; quiet; CCI. "Fair NH; warden collects fees each pm; magnificent views; area of interest to archaeologists & geologists; dangerous exit; no water point." Apr-Oct.   2002*

ORNANS *6G2* (11km SE Rural) **Camp Municipal, Champaloux, 25930 Lods [03 81 60 9011 (Mairie); fax 03 81 60 93 86]** Fr Ornans SE on D67. In Lods turn R across Rv Loue. Site in 150m beside rv. Or N fr Pontarlier on N57/E23 to St Gorgon then W on D67 to Lods. Med, pt shd, hdstg; wc; shwrs inc; el pts (5A) €2.50; shop 1.5km; playgrnd; fishing; quiet. "Site on disused rlwy stn in attractive area; woodland walk; office open 1800; excel shwrs; site yourself; lovely views by rv." 15 Jun-15 Sep. € 10.60   2005*

ORNANS *6G2* (1km S Rural) **Domaine Le Chanet, 25290 Ornans [03 81 62 23 44; fax 03 81 62 13 97; chanet@netcourrier.com; www.lechanet.com]** Fr Besancon take D67 25km to Ornans. In Ornans at rndabt cont to town cent. Take 1st R, cross Rv Loue then turn R. Foll sp to site in 1km. Look for R turn after school. Med, hdg pitch, steep sl & terr, pt shd; wc; 25% serviced pitches; chem disp; mv service pnt; baby facs; shwrs inc; el pts (6-10A) €2.75; ice; lndry rm; shop; tradsmn; BBQ; sm playgrnd; htd pool 500m; rv 1km; many statics; dogs €1.20; phone; poss cr; quiet low ssn; adv bkg; 5% red low ssn. "Gd long/sh stay; sm pitches; facs poss stretched in ssn; picturesque site; but becoming shabby." 1 Mar-15 Nov. € 12.50   2002*

ORPIERRE *9D3* (S Rural) **Camping Les Princes d'Orange, 05700 Orpierre [04 92 66 22 53; fax 04 92 66 31 08; campingorpierre@wanadoo.fr; www.campingorpierre.com]** N75 S fr Serres for 11km to Eyguians. Turn R in Eyguians onto D30, 8km to Orpierre, turn L in vill to site (sp). Med, hdstg, pt sl, terr, pt shd; wc; chem disp; mv service pnt; baby facs; shwrs inc; el pts (4A) €2.50; gas; lndtte; ice; shop; snacks; bar; playgrnd; pool; waterslide; tennis; games area; entmnt; TV; fishing; some statics; adv bkg; red low ssn. "Rock-climbing area; gd walking; beautiful vill; site being developed." ♦ 1 Apr-30 Oct. € 19.00 (3 persons)   2003*

ORTHEZ *8F1* (2km SE) **Camp Municipal de la Source, Blvd Charles de Gaulle, 64300 Orthez [05 59 67 04 81; fax 05 59 69 12 00; tourisme.orthez@wanadoo.fr]** Leave Orthez on N117 twd Pau, turn L at sp Mont-de-Marsan & site on R in 300m. Sm, pt sl, some hdstg, pt shd; wc; shwrs inc; chem disp; el pts (10A) €1.25; shops 1km; pool 2km; fishing; phone; v quiet; CCI. "Walking dist fr interesting town; some pitches soft in wet weather; helpful staff; poss itinerants; NH only." 1 Apr-30 Sep. € 7.80   2002*

OUISTREHAM *3D1* (1km S Urban) **Camp Municipal Les Pommiers, Rue de la Haie Breton, 14150 Riva-Bella [tel/fax 02 31 97 12 66]** Fr ferry terminal foll sp Caen; in approx 1.5km site sp at rndabt; take 3rd exit. Lge, hdg pitch, pt shd; htd wc; chem disp; mv service pnt; shwrs inc; el pts (10A) €4.50 (poss no earth); gas; lndry rm; ice; shop 500m; tradsmn; playgrnd; pool 1km; sand beach 1.8km; tennis; rv 200m; 80% statics; poss cr; no adv bkg; some rd noise; cc acc; CCI. "Conv for late or early ferry (5 mins to ferry terminal); separate section for 'Brittany Ferries' tourers; gates open 0700-2300, (open automatic outgoing at other times); v nice walk/cycle ride along Caen canal to Ouistreham; rests by harbour; twin-axle vans not permitted; mkt Thu; friendly recep; site water poor, rec bottled water; excel NH." 15 Feb-15 Dec.
€ 11.00   2005*

†**OUISTREHAM** *3D1* (6km S Rural) **Camping des Capucines, 14860 Ranville [02 31 78 69 82; fax 02 31 78 16 94]** App Caen fr E or W, take Blvd Peripherique Nord, then exit 3a sp Ouistreham car ferry (D515). In approx 8.5km turn R onto D514 sp Cabourg, cross Pegasus Bdge & cont to sp rndabt. Take exit Ranville, at x-rds in 500m turn L, site 300m on L. Fr Ouistreham foll D514 dir Caborg to Pegasus Bdge, then as above. Med, hdg/mkd pitch, hdstg, terr, pt shd; htd wc; chem disp; mv service pnt; 2 shwrs inc; el pts (10A) €3.25 (poss rev pol); gas; lndtte; sm shop; supmkt 2km; rest, bar 1km; playgrnd; sand beach 3km; 60% statics; dogs €1.60 (not German Shepherds or other 'dangerous' breeds); phone; poss cr; some Eng spkn; adv bkg if late arr; quiet; cc acc; red low ssn/CCI. "Pleasant position; take care overhanging trees; smallish pitches for lge o'fits; gd san facs; helpful, friendly owner but recep clsd at times; barrier open 0600-2400; late arr use intercom at recep; conv ferries (if arr late fr ferry, phone in advance for pitch number & barrier code); conv Pegasus Bdge, museum, War Cemetery; excel."
€ 14.00   2005*

OUISTREHAM *3D1* (3km SW Urban) **Camping Les Hautes Coutures, Route de Ouistreham, 14970 Benouville [02 31 44 73 08 or 06 07 25 26 90 (LS); fax 02 31 95 30 80; camping-hautes-coutures@wanadoo.fr]** Leave Ouistreham ferry & foll sp Caen & A13 over 2 rndabts. After 2nd rndabt join dual c'way. Leave at 2nd exit (close after 1st) sp St Aubin d'Arquenay (D35) & ZA de Benouville. Foll slip rd to Benouville. Turn L at new rndabt, thro vill. Site uphill on R. Or fr Caen twd port on dual c'way, site has own exit after Pegasus Memorial exit; site clearly visible on R of dual c'way. Med, hdg pitch, pt sl & uneven, pt shd; wc; chem disp; baby facs; shwrs inc; el pts (6A) inc (rev pol); gas; lndtte; sm shop; hypmkt at Heroubille; tradsmn; rest, snacks; bar; BBQ; playgrnd; htd pool; beach 2km; fishing; tennis; mini-golf; horseriding, windsurfing 1km; golf 4km; games rm; 40% statics; dogs; recep 0900-2000; poss cr; Eng spkn; adv bkg; cc acc; CCI. "Friendly staff; v clean san facs; conv for ferry; tourist info at recep; access code req for fishing (fr recep); gates clsd 2200-0630 but staff will open gate for late ferry arrivals; busy, poss noisy site; overlooks Caen Canal; daily mkt in Ouistreham." ♦ 1 Apr-30 Sep. € 30.90
ABS - N05   2005*

As we're travelling out of season, we'd better phone ahead to check that the site is actually open.

OUISTREHAM *3D1* (7km W Coastal) **Camping des Hautes Sentes, Chemin des Hautes Sentes, 14880 Hermanville [02 31 96 39 12; fax 02 3196 92 98; leshautessentes@yahoo.fr; www.campingdes hautessentes.fr]** Well sp on D514 fr Ouistreham. Med, mkd pitch, pt shd; wc; chem disp; shwrs inc; el pts (6A) €5.50; lndtte; tradsmn; rest; snacks; bar; playgrnd; beach 700m; games area; TV rm; 30% statics; bus 400m; quiet; Eng spkn. "Extremely friendly; rec sh stay." 1 Apr-30 Sep. € 17.10   2004*

FRANCE

OUISTREHAM *3D1* (12km NW Coastal) **Camping Capricieuse, 2 Rue Brummel, 14530 Luc-sur-Mer [02 31 97 34 43; fax 02 31 97 43 64; info@ campinglacapricieuse.com; www.campingla capricieuse.com]** Fr ferry terminal turn R at 3rd traff lts (D514) into Ave du G. Leclerc. Cont to Luc-sur-Mer; 1st turn L after casino; site on R in 300m. Ave Lecuyer is sp & Rue Brummel is off that rd. Lge, hdg/mkd pitch, terr, pt shd; wc; mv service pnt; chem disp; shwrs inc; el pts (6-10A) €3.80-5.20; gas; lndtte; shop 300m; tradsmn; playgrnd; sand beach adj; tennis; games rm; entmnt; child entmnt; excursions; TV rm; dogs €2.10; Eng spkn; adv bkg; quiet; cc acc; red low ssn; CCI. "Some lge pitches with easy access; gd position - conv WW2 beaches; v clean; excel site." ♦ 1 Apr-15 Nov. € 13.40   2005*

See advertisement on previous page

OUNANS *6H2* (1km N Rural) **Camping de la Plage Blanche, 3 Rue de la Plage, 39380 Ounans [03 84 37 69 63; fax 03 84 37 60 21; reservation@ la-plage-blanche.com; www.la-plage-blanche.com]** Exit A39 junc 6 sp Dole Centre. Foll N5 SE for 18km dir Pontarlier. After passing Souvans, turn L on D472 sp Mont-sous-Vaudrey. Foll sp to Ounans. Site well sp in vill. Lge, mkd pitch, hdstg, pt shd; wc; chem disp; mv service pnt; shwrs inc; el pts (6A) €3.20 (poss rev pol); gas 1km; lndtte; ice; shop 1km; supmkt 4km; tradsmn; rest; snacks; bar; playgrnd; pool; paddling pool; shgl rv beach & sw 500m; trout & carp fishing lake; canoeing; horseriding; entmnt; TV rm; 1% statics; dogs €1; Eng spkn; adv bkg rec (bkg fee) quiet; red low ssn; cc acc; CCI. "Excel san facs; superb rvside pitches; rest v gd." ♦ 1 Apr-15 Oct. € 16.70 (CChq acc)   2005*

See advertisement below

OURSEL MAISON see Crevecoeur le Grand *3C3*

OUSSE see Pau *8F2*

†**OUST** *8G3* (Rural) **Camping Les Quatre Saisons, Route d'Aulus-les-Bains, 09140 Oust [05 61 96 55 55; fax 05 61 04 48 62; www.ariege.com/ les4saisons]** Take the D618 S fr St Girons; then D3 to Oust; on N o'skts of town turn L (sp Aulus) onto D32; site 150m on R. Med, hdg pitch, pt shd; htd wc; chem disp; shwrs inc; el pts (5-10A) €2.30-4.60; lndtte; shop 200m; bar; playgrnd; pool; TV; 25% statics; dogs €1; phone; Eng spkn; adv bkg rec; quiet; CCI. "In beautiful, comparatively unspoilt area; friendly site; footpath to vill; vg long stay." € 18.50   2003*

OUST *8G3* (2km N Rural) **Camp Municipal La Claire, Rue La Palere, 09140 Soueix-Rogalle [05 61 66 84 88; campinglaclaire@aol.com]** S fr St Girons take D3/D618; in 13km just bef rndabt turn R onto D32 sp Soueix. Turn L at vill sq & site in 200m. Sm, pt shd; wc (cont); shwrs inc; el pts (10A) €3.15; lndtte; shop 1.5km; rest 200m; playgrnd; paddling pool; fishing; 10% statics; dogs €1; phone; quiet; CCI. "Pleasant, well-maintained rvside site; gd hiking & touring cent." 1 Apr-31 Oct. € 7.00   2005*

OUST *8G3* (1km S Rural) **Camp Municipal La Cote, 09140 Oust [05 61 95 50 53 or 05 61 66 81 12 (Mairie); fax 05 61 66 86 95]** Take D618 fr St Girons; after 13km cross rv; turn R onto D3 sp Aulus-les-Bains; site in 4km on R after passing Oust on L. Med, hdg/mkd pitch, pt shd; wc; chem disp; shwrs inc; el pts (6-10A) €1.55-€3.05 (rev pol); ice; lndtte; shop 1km; playgrnd; BBQ; tennis; fishing; dogs €1; 25% statics; adv bkg; quiet. "Gd long stay; easy access to site & pitches; hot water poss unreliable early am & eves; by Rv Salat." ♦ 1 Mar-31 Oct. € 10.60   2002*

†**OUST** *8G3* (2.5km S Rural) **Camping Le Haut Salat, La Campagne, 09140 Seix [05 61 66 81 78; fax 05 61 66 94 17; camping.le-haut-salat@wanadoo.fr]** Take D618 S fr St Girons, at Oust take D3 twds Seix. Site well sp just N of vill. Med, hdg/mkd pitch, pt shd; htd wc (some cont); chem disp; shwrs inc; el pts (6A) inc; lndtte; bar; BBQ; shops 500m; pool; rv sw; games rm; 60% statics; dogs; adv bkg; quiet; CCI. "Gd facs but tourers squeezed in with statics; gd walking area." € 15.00   2003*

OYE PLAGE see Calais *3A3*

FRANCE

PACAUDIERE, LA 9A1 (200m E Rural) Camp Municipal Beausoleil, 42310 La Pacaudiere [04 77 64 11 50 or 04 77 64 30 18 (Mairie); fax 04 77 64 14 40] NW on N7 Roanne to Lapalisse; turn R in La Pacaudiere, D35; site well sp; fork R in 50m; site ent in 400m. Sm, hdg pitch, hdstg, sl, unshd; wc; chem disp; shwrs inc; el pts (10A) inc; gas; lndtte; shop; playgrnd; public pool; crazy golf; TV rm; quiet. "Pleasant site; gd base for interesting area; ideal NH & gd sh stay; ltd facs low ssn; Sat mkt in town." 15 May-30 Sep. € 10.30   2005*

†PAIMBOEUF 2G3 (Urban) Camp Municipal de l'Estuaire, 44560 Paimbeouf [02 40 27 52 12; fax 02 40 27 61 14; info@camping-lestuaire.com; www. camping-lestuaire.com] Site on N23. Med, unshd; wc; shwrs inc; el pts (10A) €3.20; lndtte; shop; playgrnd; pool; rv adj; cycle hire; entmnt; dogs €1.15; adv bkg; red low ssn. € 12.30   2003*

PAIMPOL 1D3 (2km SE Coastal) Camp Municipal Crukin, Ave Crukin, Kerity, 22500 Paimpol [02 96 20 78 47 or 02 96 55 31 70 (Mairie); fax 02 96 20 75 00; camping.cruckin@wanadoo.fr] On D786 fr St Brieuc/Paimpol, site sp in vill of Kerity 80m off main rd. Med, hdg pitch, pt shd; htd wc; chem disp; mv service pnt; shwrs inc; el pts (6-12A) €2.40-2.69; lndtte; shops 1km; playgrnd; shgl beach 250m; rv sw; fishing; watersports; TV rm; 10% statics; dogs €1.12; bus 100m; poss cr; quiet; CCI. "Clean & tidy; friendly warden; excel sh stay/NH." ♦ 1 Apr-30 Sep. € 12.20   2005*

PAIMPOL 1D3 (5km SE Coastal) Camping Le Cap Horn, Port-Lazo, 22470 Plouezec [02 96 20 64 28; fax 02 96 20 63 88; lecaphorn@hotmail.com; www.lecaphorn.com] Foll D786 fr Paimpol or Plouezec. Site sp 3km NE of Plouezec dir Port-Lazo. Med, hdg/mkd pitch, pt sl, terr, pt shd; wc; chem disp; baby facs; shwrs inc; el pts (6A) €3.50 (poss rev pol); gas; lndtte; ice; shop; rest 1km; snacks; bar; playgrnd; htd pool; paddling pool; direct access to shgl beach 500m; boating; games rm; entmnt; 5% statics; dogs €1.80; adv bkg; quiet; cc acc; red low ssn/long stay; CCI. "On 2 levels in valley & hillside with beautiful views; steep path to beach; gd facs." ♦ 1 Apr-30 Sep. € 18.00   2005*

See advertisement above

PAIMPONT see Plelan le Grand 2F3

PALAU DEL VIDRE see Elne 10G1

†PALAVAS LES FLOTS 10F1 (1km Urban) Aire Communale/Camping-Car Halte, 34250 Palavas-les-Flots [04 67 07 73 48; fax 04 67 50 61 04] Fr Montpellier on D986 to Palavas. At rndabt 'Europe' strt on to 2nd rndabt in 100m. Turn sharp L & foll sp site in 100m. Med, hdstg, pt shd; wc; chem disp; mv service pnt; shwrs inc; el pts (6A) €2; lndtte; shop, rest, snacks, bar adj; sand beach 1km; phone; bus 500m; poss cr; some rd noise; cc acc; CCI. "M'vans only; some pitches along marina quayside; conv Montpellier, Camargue; 3 night max stay." € 10.00   2004*

PALAVAS LES FLOTS 10F1 (2km E Urban/Coastal) Camping Les Roquilles, 34250 Palavas-les-Flots [04 67 68 03 47; fax 04 67 68 54 98; roquilles@wanadoo.fr] Site on D21 E of Palavas-les-Flots town cent. V lge, mkd pitch, hdstg, pt shd; wc (mainly cont); chem disp; mv service pnt; serviced pitches; shwrs inc; el pts (6A) €3.20; gas 100m; lndtte; ice; rest; snacks; bar; playgrnd; 3 pools (1 htd); sand beach 100m; entmnt; 30% statics; no dogs; phone; bus; poss cr; Eng spkn; adv bkg (dep req + bkg fee); poss noisy high ssn; cc acc; CCI. 15 Apr-15 Sep. € 20.50   2003*

PALINGES 9A2 (1km N Rural) Camp Municipal du Lac, 71430 Palinges [03 85 88 14 49] N70 Montceau-les-Mines dir Paray, turn L onto D92 into Palings cent (4km). By church turn L church onto D128. Site in 1km. Sm, hdg/mkd pitch, pt sl, pt shd; htd wc; chem disp; baby facs; shwrs inc; el pts (10A) inc; lndtte; ice; shop 1km; rest 1km; snacks; bar; playgrnd; child club; lake fishing adj; cycle hire; tennis; dogs; quiet; adv bkg; Eng spkn; no cc acc; CCI. "Excel long/sh stay; friendly; kept immac." ♦ Apr-Sep. € 14.50   2004*

PALMYRE, LA see Mathes, Les 7B1

SITES

PALUD SUR VERDON, LA *10E3* (100m W) **Camp Municipal Le Grand Canyon, 04120 La Palud-sur-Verdon** [tel/fax 04 92 77 38 13 or 02 92 77 38 02 (Mairie)] W on D952 fr Castellane, site on L (S) of rd just bef vill La Palud (30km W of Castellane, max gradient 1-in-8). Or on D952 fr Moustiers-Ste-Marie site on R (S) after leaving vill La Palud (also with steep & narr sections). App fr Moustiers easier. Med, mkd pitch, pt sl, pt shd; wc (some cont); chem disp (wc); baby facs; shwrs inc; el pts (6A) €2 (poss rev pol); gas 800m; lndtte; shops, rest, snacks, bar 500m; dogs; phone; poss cr; quiet; cc not acc. "Basic facs but well-kept; helpful staff; interesting area; many activities nrby; conv Gorge du Verdon." ♦ ltd. 1 May-30 Sep.
€ 8.00   2005*

PAMPELONNE *8E4* (2km NE Rural) **Camping Thuries, 81190 Pampelonne** [05 63 76 44 01; fax 05 63 76 92 78; campthuries@wanadoo.fr] N fr Carmaux on N88 turn L onto D78 sp Pampelonne. Site sp & 2km fr town over narr bdge; steep, winding rd. Or S fr Rodez on N88 turn R onto D17 sp Pampelonne. Site bef rv bdge on L. Sm, mkd pitch, shd; htd wc; chem disp; mv service pnt; shwrs inc; el pts (6A) €2.60; lndtte; ice; shop & 3km; tradsmn; rest, snacks 3km; dogs €1; phone; poss cr; Eng spkn; quiet; CCI. "Pleasant site; conv Albi & Rodez." 15 Jun-1 Sep. € 11.60   2005*

PARAY LE MONIAL *9A1* (1km NW Urban) **Camping de Mambre, Route du Gue-Leger, 71600 Paray-le-Monial** [03 85 88 89 20; fax 03 85 88 87 81] Fr N79 Moulin to Macon; site at W end of town; just after level x-ing turn NE into Rte du Gue-Leger. Turn R into site after x-ing rv; well sp. Lge, hgd/mkd pitch, pt shd; wc; chem disp; shwrs inc; el pts (10A) €2.30; lndtte; sm shop & 500m; rest; snacks in high ssn; bar; playgrnd; pool 200m high ssn; dogs; quiet, but some rd noise; CCI. "Paray is pilgrimage cent; walking dist town; ltd facs low ssn & poss poorly maintained." 15 Apr-31 Oct.
€ 13.00   2003*

PARAY SOUS BRIAILLES see St Pourcain sur Sioule *9A1*

PARENTIS EN BORN *7D1* (2km W Rural) **Camp Municipal Pipiou, Route du Lac, 40160 Parentis-en-Born** [05 58 78 57 25; fax 05 58 78 93 17; pipiou@parentis.com] Site on D43 rd twds lake beach. In vill foll sp 'Lac'. After 2km where rest on R, turn R. Site is 150m on R. Lge, hdg/mkd pitch, pt shd; wc; chem disp; 100% serviced pitches; baby facs; shwrs inc; el pts (10A) €2.60 (poss rev pol); gas high ssn; lndtte; ice; shop; rest; snacks; bar; playgrnd; lake sw & sand beach adj, fishing & watersports adj; entmnts; TV; 25% statics; dogs €1.10; phone; poss cr; adv bkg; quiet but pitches adj rd noisy; cc acc; red long stay; CCI. "Swipe card barrier (refundable dep €20); phone to check open in low ssn; lovely location on lakeside; some pitches tight; smart shwr facs stretched high ssn; cycle tracks thro vill & woods; dogs beware lge, hairy caterpillars (cause acid burns); excel." 15 Feb-15 Nov. € 15.65   2005*

PARENTIS EN BORN *7D1* (3km W Rural) **Camping La Foret Lahitte, Route des Plages, 40160 Parentis-en-Born** [05 58 78 47 17 or 06 81 25 74 26; fax 05 58 78 43 64; contact@camping-lahitte.com; www.camping-lahitte.com] Fr Biscarrosse on D652, site sp adj lake. Fr N10 turn N onto D43 at Liposthey (junc 17), thro Parentis-en-Born, site sp. Med, pt shd; wc; shwrs; el pts (6-10A) €3; lndtte; shop; snacks; bar; playgrnd; child club; pool; jacuzzi; lake sw; sailing; fishing; entmnt; games/TV rm; statics; dogs €2;adv bkg; red low ssn; quiet.
14 Apr-28 Aug. € 24.00   2004*

PARIS *3D3* (12km E) **Camp Municipal La Haute Ile, Rue de l'Ecluse, 93330 Neuilly-sur-Marne** [01 43 08 21 21; fax 01 43 08 22 03; camping municipal.nsm@wandadoo.fr] Fr Peripherique (Porte de Vincennes) foll N34 sp Vincennes. Shortly after passing Chateau de Vincennes on R, L at fork, sp Lagny. At next major x-rds sharp L (still N34) sp Chelles. Thro Neuilly-Plaisance to Neuilly-sur- Marne. In cent lge x-rds turn R sp N370 Marne-la-Vallee & A4 Paris. In 200m, bef rv bdge, foll Camping Municipal sp (no tent or c'van symbols on this or previous sp) turn L. Site at junc of rv & canal. Lge, mkd pitch, pt shd; wc (some cont); shwrs inc; el pts (10A) inc (check rev pol); gas; lndtte adj; ice; shop; rest adj; BBQ; playgrnd; rv fishing; 25% statics; dogs €2.45; bus/train; poss cr; adv bkg (rec high ssn); quiet. "Lovely location; wooden posts on pitches poss diff manoeuvring lge o'fits; some sm pitches; gd base & transport for Paris; lovely location; soft after rain; card barrier; gd NH." 1 Apr-30 Sep. € 15.00   2005*

†**PARIS** *3D3* (15km SE Urban) **Camping Paris Est Le Tremblay, Blvd des Allies, 94507 Champigny-sur-Marne** [01 43 97 43 97; fax 01 48 89 07 94; receptcc@stereau.fr or champigny@camping paris. fr; www.campingparis.fr] Rec rte for c'vans. Fr A4 (Paris-Reims) exit 5 sp Nogent/Champigny-sur -Marne. D45 dir Champigny to end of dual c'way at traff lts go R on N303 dir St Maur. Join N4 after 1km (traff lts) & take 2nd R (200m). Site sp. NB site also known as 'Camping de Champigny' or 'Camping International/IDF'. Med, hdg/mkd pitch, pt shd; htd wc (some cont); chem disp; mv service pnt; shwrs inc; el pts (10A) inc; gas; lndtte; shop; rest; snacks; bar; games rm; TV; playgrnd; 20% statics; dogs €2.50; adv bkg; some rd noise; red low ssn; cc acc; CCI. "Vg site conv for Paris, easy parking nr metro or bus fr camp to rlwy stn direct to city & Disneyland; take care to avoid grounding on kerb to pitches; clsd to cars 0200-0600." ♦ € 25.80   2005*

See advertisement opposite

†PARIS 3D3 (10km W Urban) **Camping Bois de Boulogne, 2 Allee du Bord de l'Eau, 75016 Paris** [01 45 24 30 81; fax 01 42 24 42 95; camping-boulogne@stereau.fr; www.camping paris.fr or www.hotelparispleinair.com] Site bet bdge of Puteaux & bdge of Suresnes. App fr A1: take Blvd Peripherique W to Bois de Boulogne exit at Porte Maillot; foll camp sp. App fr A6: Blvd Peripherique W to Porte Dauphine exit at Porte Maillot; foll camp sp. App fr Pont de Sevres (A10, A11): on bdge take R lane & take 2nd rd R mkd Neuilly-sur-Seine; rd runs parallel to Seine; cont to site ent. App fr A13: after St Cloud Tunnel, foll sp twd Paris; immed after x-ing Rv Seine, 1st turn on R sp Bois de Boulogne; foll camp sps; traff lts at site ent. NB Sharp turn to site, poorly sp fr N - watch for lge 'Parking Born de l'Eau 200m'. V lge, hdg/mkd pitch, hdstg, pt sl, pt shd; htd wc (some cont); chem disp; mv service pnt; baby facs; shwrs inc; el pts (10A) inc; gas; lndtte; shop in ssn; rest, bar, pool 1km; TV; Metro Porte Maillot 4km; shuttle bus (Apr-Sep) to & fr site morn/eve to 2300; some statics; dogs; phone; poss cr; Eng spkn; adv bkg rec high ssn; rd noise; red low ssn; cc acc; CCI. "Excel location, easy access A13; conv cent Paris; site open 0600-0200; some sm pitches; walk over Suresne bdge for shops, food mkt etc; some v sm pitches; some commercial units on site; excel." € 31.70   2005*

PARIS 3D3 (20km NW Urban) **Camping International de Maisons Laffitte, Ile de la Commune, 1 Rue Johnson, 78600 Maisons-Laffitte** [01 39 12 21 91; fax 01 39 12 70 50; ci.mlaffitte@wanadoo.fr; www. campint.com] Easy access fr A13 sp Poissy; take N308 to Maisons-Laffitte; foll site sp bef town cent. Fr A15 take N184 S fr Poissy, foll sp St Germain; approx 6km after x-ing Rv Seine & approx 300m after x-ing lge steel bdge, take L lane ready for L turn onto D308 to Maison-Laffitte; foll camp sp. Or A1 to St Denis, then A86 exit Bezons, then dir Poissy, Noailles, Sartrouville & Maisons-Laffitte. NB Narr app rd diff due parked cars. Lge, hdg/mkd pitch, pt shd; htd wc; chem disp; mv service pnt; shwrs inc; el pts (6A) €3 (poss rev pol); gas; lndtte; sm shop; tradsmn; hypmkt 5km; rest; snacks; bar; BBQ; playgrnd; games area; games area; TV rm; 50% statics; dogs €2.50; metro 1km; poss cr; Eng spkn; adv bkg (dep req & bkg fee); quiet but some noise fr rlwy & rv traff; cc acc; CCI. "Mobilis ticket covers rlwy, metro & bus for day in Paris; site on island in Rv Seine; ideal for visiting Paris - 20 min by metro - & Disneyland, Versailles; friendly & v helpful staff; ltd facs low ssn; busy tourist site - pressure on san facs & facilities; gd." ♦ 1 Apr-31 Oct. € 23.00   2005*

See advertisement on next page

PARRANQUET see Villereal 7D3

See advertisement above

PARTHENAY 4H1 (1km SW Urban) Camping Le Bois Vert, 14 Rue de Boisseau, 79200 Parthenay [tel/fax 05 49 65 78 43; bois-vert@wanadoo.fr] Site on D743 to Niort. Sp fr N & S. Fr S 1km bef town turn L at sp La Roche-sur-Yon immed after rv bdge turn R; site on R in 500m. Med, hdg/mkd pitch, some hdstg, pt sl, pt shd; htd wc (some cont); chem disp; baby facs; shwrs inc; el pts (10A) €3.80; lndtte; shops 1km; tradsmn; rest; snacks; bar; playgrnd; pool adj; boating; fishing; 10% statics; dogs €0.80; phone; poss cr; adv bkg; noisy nr main rd & bar; cc not acc; red low ssn; CCI. "Excel pitches; conv Futuroscope; m'van o'night area adj; friendly & helpful wardens; interesting old town; ltd facs low ssn; gd sh stay/NH to Spain." ♦ 1 May-1 Sep. € 18.00 (CChq acc) 2005*

PARTHENAY 4H1 (9km W Urban) Camp Municipal Les Peupliers, 79130 Azay-sur-Thouet [05 49 95 37 13 (Mairie); fax 05 49 70 07 07] Fr Parthenay take D949 dir Secondigny to Azay-sur-Thouet. Sm, mkd pitch, pt shd; wc; shwrs inc; el pts (10A) inc; shop 500m; BBQ; playgrnd; dogs; quiet. "Barrier clsd to exclude itinerants, key fr Mairie 200m; site adj stadium; gd long stay." 1 Jun-30 Sep. € 9.50 2002*

PARTHENAY 4H1 (10km W Rural) Camping a la Ferme (Baudoin), La Chagnee, 79450 St Aubin-le-Cloud [05 49 95 31 44; fax 06 71 10 09 66; baudoinge@ccparthenay.fr] Fr Parthenay on D949 bis dir Secondigny. Turn R in Azay-sur-Thouet onto D139 dir St Aubin, site on R in 1km, sp. Sm, pt shd; wc; shwr; el pts inc; lndtte; shops 1km; pool 1km; fishing; dogs; Eng spkn; quiet. "CL-type site; v friendly owners; farmhouse meals avail; beautiful setting o'looking lake; spotless facs; unltd hot water; excel." ♦ Easter-31 Oct. € 12.80 2005*

PASSY see Sallanches 9A3

PATORNAY see Clairvaux les Lacs 6H2

†PAU 8F2 (8km E) Camping Les Sapins, Route de Tarbes, 64320 Ousse [05 59 81 74 21] Site alongside Hotel des Sapins on S side of N117 (Pau-Tarbes rd) at Ousse. Sm, pt shd; wc; mv service pnt; shwrs inc; el pts (4-6A) €2-3; ice; shop adj; rest in hotel adj; fishing; poss cr; noisy; some rd noise. "Red facs low ssn; hot water in shwrs but no heating; pleasant site; helpful owners." € 10.30 2005*

†PAU 8F2 (6km W Urban) Camping Le Terrier, Ave du Vert-Galant, 64230 Lescar [05 59 81 01 82; fax 05 59 81 26 83; camping.terrier@wanadoo.fr] Fr N117 at Lescar foll sp S dir Artiguelouve, site at rv bdge. Access via narr lane - no parking or turning space. Med, hdg/mkd pitch, pt shd; wc; chem disp; baby facs; shwrs inc; el pts (6A) €3.10; gas; lndtte; shop 500m; tradsmn; hypmkt 2km; rest, snacks, bar high ssn; playgrnd; htd pool high ssn; rv fishing adj; tennis; car wash; 10% statics; dogs €1.50; poss cr; Eng spkn; adv bkg; quiet; 30% red 30+ days; CCI. "Gd base for Pau & district, also for Tour de France; some permanent residents; 2 gd golf courses nr; gd value; fair NH." € 12.60 2005*

PAUILLAC 7C2 (1km S Urban) Camp Municipal Les Gabarreys, Route de la Riviere, 33250 Pauillac [05 56 59 10 03 or 05 56 73 30 50; fax 05 56 73 30 68; camping.les.gabarreys@wanadoo. fr] On ent Pauillac on D206, turn R at rndabt, sp site. On app Quays, turn R bef 'Maison du Vin'. Site on L in 1km. Med, hdg/mkd pitch, hdstg, pt shd; wc; chem disp; mv service pnt; serviced pitch; shwrs inc; el pts (5-10A) €3.50-4.80; lndtte; ice; shop 1km; tradsmn; BBQ; playgrnd; htd, covrd pool 1km; mini-golf; games rm; TV; 6% statics; dogs €1.60; Eng spkn; adv bkg; quiet; red low ssn; cc acc; CCI. "Excel, well-kept, well-equipped site; helpful manager; immac san facs; peaceful situation; 20 min walk to town with rests etc; conv major wine chateaux - cycle rtes." ♦ 25 Mar-8 Oct. € 12.50 2005*

PAULHAGUET 9C1 (500m SE Urban) Camping La Fridiere, 6 Route d'Esfacy, 43230 Paulhaguet [04 71 76 65 54; campingpaulhaguet@wanadoo.fr] On SE side of town on D4. Sm, hdg pitch, pt shd; wc; shwrs inc; el pts (16A) €3.05; lndtte; tradsmn; playgrnd; rv fishing; internet; Eng spkn; quiet. "Useful NH; immac san facs; lge pitches; friendly owners; popular with young Dutch families; Chateau Lafayette nr." 1 Apr-15 Oct. 2005*

PAULHIAC see Biron *7D3*

†PAYRAC *7D3* (1km N Rural) **Camping Panoramic, Route de Loupiac, 46350 Payrac-en-Quercy** [05 65 37 98 45; fax 05 65 37 91 65; camping. panoramic@wanadoo.fr; www.campingpanoramic. com] N fr Payrac, site W of N20 at start of dual c'way, foll sp Loupiac, then site. Med, pt sl, pt shd; htd wc; chem disp; baby facs; shwrs inc; el pts (4A) €2.40; gas; lndtte; ice; shop 1km; tradsmn; rest high ssn; snacks; bar; BBQ; playgrnd; pool 400m; rv sw 5km; canoe hire; walking; table tennis; TV rm; cycle hire; 10% statics; phone; poss cr; Eng spkn; adv bkg; v quiet; cc acc; CCI. "Well-run, busy site with excel san facs; v clean; poss v muddy in bad weather; friendly Dutch owner; organised canoe trips & entmnt; excel winter NH." ♦ € 9.60   2005*

PAYRAC *7D3* (6km N) **Camping a la Ferme Le Treil, 46350 Loupiac** [05 65 37 64 87; francis. gatignol@wanadoo.fr] Fr N or S on N20, sp 'A la Ferme'. Sm, sl, pt shd; wc; chem disp (wc); shwrs inc; el pts (6A) €2 (long lead poss req); lndtte; shops 2km; tradsmn; bar; playgrnd; pool; fishing; boating; tennis; golf 3km; TV; BBQ; poss cr; Eng spkn; adv bkg; quiet; 10% red low ssn. "Pleasant site; mkd ent for c'vans poss diff long o'fits - rec use ent for tents if gd power/weight ratio; v friendly owner; gd long/sh stay." 1 May-30 Oct. € 11.00   2003*

PAYRAC *7D3* (6km N Rural) **Camping Les Hirondelles, Al Pech, 46350 Loupiac** [05 65 37 66 25; fax 05 65 37 66 65; camp.les-hirondelles@ wanadoo.fr; www.les-hirondelles.com] Fr Souillac foll N20 for about 12km. Site on R bef dual c'way. Sm, hdg/mkd pitch, pt sl, shd; htd wc; chem disp; baby facs; shwrs inc; el pts (6A) inc (poss rev pol); gas; lndtte; ice; shop; tradsmn; rest; snacks; bar; playgrnd; htd pool; cycle hire; entmnt; TV; 40% statics; dogs €1.20; phone; poss cr w/e; Eng spkn; adv bkg (dep req); quiet; CCI. "Vg friendly, & extremely helpful owners; clean site; gd views fr some pitches; excel." ♦ 1 Apr-15 Sep. € 15.00   2005*

PAYRAC *7D3* (500m S Rural) **Camping Les Pins, 46350 Payrac-en-Quercy** [05 65 37 96 32; fax 05 65 37 91 08; info@les-pins-camping.com; www. les-pins-camping.com] Exit A20 junc 55 dir Souillac onto N20 dir Cahors. Foll sp Payrac 12km S of Souillac on N20, site sp & clearly visible as climb hill. Med, hdg/mkd pitch, hdstg, terr, pt shd; wc; mv service pnt; chem disp; serviced pitches; shwrs inc; el pts (10A) inc; gas 1km; lndtte; ice; shop 1km; rest; snacks; bar; playgrnd; 2 htd pools; waterslide; tennis; TV; entmnt; some statics; dogs; some rd & disco noise; adv bkg; Eng spkn; cc acc; red low ssn; CCI. "V interesting area; Rocamadour & Lacave worth visit." ♦ 8 Apr-15 Sep. € 24.60 ABS - D25
                    2005*

PAYRAC *7D3* (5km NW Rural) **Camping Les Grands Chenes (Naturist), Le Peyronnet, 46350 Lamothe-Fenelon (Postal address 46300 Fajoles)** [tel/fax 05 65 41 68 79; camping@les-grands-chenes.com; www.les-grands-chenes.com] Leave A20/E9 at junc 55 onto N20 S Cahors to Payrac. Turn R onto minor rd to Lamothe-Fenelon. Site on D12, sp in vill. Fr S exit junc 56 onto D80, then turn R onto N20 Sm, mkd pitch, pt sl, pt shd; wc; chem disp; baby facs; shwrs inc; el pts (6A) €3 (long lead poss req); lndtte; shop; tradsmn; rest 6km; snacks; bar; playgrnd; pool; games area; canoe hire, golf, horseriding nrby; 2% statics; dogs €1.50; poss cr; little Eng spkn; adv bkg (dep req); quiet; INF card req. "Beautiful situation, charming & peaceful site; stunningly attractive & unusual architecture on site; excel san facs; green toilet chem only; v beautiful & historic area; v friendly staff; close to Rv Dordogne & attractions; excel." ♦ ltd. 1 May-25 Sep. € 19.00   2005*

PEGOMAS see Cannes *10F4*

PEIGNEY see Langres *6F1*

PEILLAC *2F3* (2km N) **Camp Municipal du Pont d'Oust, 56220 Peillac** [02 99 91 31 83 or 02 99 91 26 76 (Mairie); fax 02 99 91 31 83] Fr La Gacilly on D777, turn L onto D14 sp Les Fougerets. Thro vill, site on R opp canal. Med, pt shd; wc; shwrs €1; el pts €2.10; shops 1km; pool adj; rv adj. "Vg site; within walking dist of pretty vill of Pont d'Oust; gd shops; v flat, ideal for cycling." 1 May-30 Sep. € 5.10   2003*

PEILLON see Nice *10E4*

PEISEY NANCROIX see Bourg St Maurice *9B4*

PENESTIN *2G3* (1.5km N Coastal) **Camping Les Pins, Route de La Roche-Bernard, 56760 Penestin** [tel/fax 02 99 90 33 13; camping.lespins@wanadoo. fr] Fr Roche-Bernard take D34 to Penestin. 2km bef Penestin take L turn sp Camping Les Pins. Site on R in 1km. Med, pt sl, pt shd; wc (some cont); chem disp; shwrs inc; el pts (5A) €2.40; gas; lndtte; shop & 2km; tradsmn; bar; BBQ; htd pool; paddling pool; waterslide; playgrnd; sand beach 1km; games area; entmnt; TV; statics; dogs €1; adv bkg; red long stay/CCI. "Sunday mkt at Penestin." ♦ 1 Apr-23 Oct. € 14.70   2005*

PENESTIN *2G3* (1.5km E Rural) **Camping Le Cenic, 56760 Penestin-sur-Mer** [02 99 90 45 65; fax 02 99 90 45 05; info@lecenic.com; www. lecenic.com] Fr La Roche-Bernard take N774 sp La Baule. In 1.5km turn R onto D34. At Penestin turn L opp Intermarche & foll sp to site in 800m. Lge, mkd pitch, pt sl, pt shd; wc; chem disp; mv service pnt; shwrs inc; el pts (4-6A) €4; lndtte; shop adj; snacks; bar; playgrnd; htd, covrd pool/aquatic park; waterslides; beach 3km; lake fishing; tennis; sports cent; games rm; few statics; dogs €2.50; Eng spkn; adv bkg rec high ssn; poss noisy high ssn; red low ssn; CCI. "Vg rural site nr unspoilt coastline; pleasant staff; take care when pitching due trees." ♦ 9 Apr-18 Sep. € 22.00 (CChq acc)   2005*

FRANCE

PENESTIN *2G3* (2km S) **Camping Domaine d'Inly, Route de Couarne, 56760 Penestin [02 99 90 35 09; fax 02 99 90 40 93; inly-info@wanadoo. fr; www.camping-inly.com]** Fr Vannes or Nantes on N165, exit junc 15 W onto D34 fr La Roche-Bernard to Penestin, then onto D201, site sp on L. Lge, hdg pitch, hdstg, pt shd; wc; chem disp; shwrs inc; el pts (10A) €3.30; lndtte; shop; rest; snacks; bar; playgrnd; htd pool; paddling pool; waterslide; sand beach 1.5km; tennis; TV; entmnt; child entmnt; horseriding; 20% statics; dogs €2.10; Eng spkn; adv bkg; cc acc; red long stay/low ssn; cc acc; CCI. "V pleasant site." ♦ 14 Apr-24 Sep. € 30.80   2005*

PENESTIN *2G3* (2km S Coastal) **Camping Le Kerfalher, Allee de Bihen, 56760 Penestin [02 99 90 33 45; fax 02 23 10 03 71]** Fr La Roche Bernard, take D34 to Penestin, then D201 for 2.5km & foll sp to site. Med, hdg pitch, pt shd; wc; chem disp; mv service pnt; serviced pitches; shwrs inc; el pts (6A) €2.75; gas at supkt 1km; lndtte; shops 300m; tradsmn; rest adj; snacks; playgrnd; sand beach 500m; 10% statics; dogs; adv bkg (ess high ssn); quiet; CCI. "Quaint vill; gd walking, cycling." ♦ 15 Apr-30 Sep. € 11.50   2002*

PENESTIN *2G3* (3km S Coastal) **Camping des Iles, La Pointe du Bile, 56760 Penestin [02 99 90 30 24; fax 02 99 90 44 55; contact@camping-des-iles.fr; www.camping-des-iles.fr]** Fr La Roche Bernard take D34 to Penestin; cont on D201 for 2.5km & foll site sp. Lge, hdg/mkd pitch, pt shd; wc (some cont); chem disp; some serviced pitches; baby facs; shwrs inc; el pts (6A) inc; gas; lndtte; shop; tradsmn; rest; snacks; bar; BBQ (gas/charcoal); playgrnd; htd pool & paddling pool; waterslide; sand beach adj; fishing adj; tennis; cycle hire; games rm; entmnt; some tour op statics; no c'vans over 7m high ssn; dogs €2.50; poss cr; Eng spkn; adv bkg; quiet but noisy nr rd; cc acc; CCI. "Gd clean, quiet site; v helpful staff; lovely cliff top walks; lovely clean beach; boat trips fr Vannes; mkt Sun (also Wed in Jul/Aug)." ♦ 1 Apr-1 Oct. € 37.20 ABS - B06   2005*

PENNAUTIER see Carcassonne *8F4*

PENVINS see Sarzeau *2G3*

PERASSAY see Ste Severe sur Indre *7A4*

PERIERS *1D4* (5km SE Rural) **Aire Naturelle Municipale, 50190 St Martin-d'Aubigny [02 33 46 57 03 or 02 33 07 73 92 (Mairie); fax 023 3 07 73 92; mairie-st-martin-daubigny@wanadoo.fr]** E fr Periers on D900 twd St Lo; site sp 14km on R; behind church in vill. Sm, pt shd; wc; shwrs inc; el pts €1.52; shop 1km; playgrnd; fishing, tennis & golf 2km; quiet; red low ssn; cc not acc. "Easy 70km run to Cherbourg." ♦   2003*

†**PERIGUEUX** *7C3* (12km NE Rural) **Camping Le Bois du Coderc, Route Les Gaunies, 24220 Antonne-et-Trigonant [05 53 05 99 83; fax 05 53 05 15 93; coderc-camping@wanadoo.fr]** NE fr Perigueux on N21 twd Limoges, thro Antonne approx 500m turn R at x-rds bet car park & Routiers cafe. Site in 500m. Sm, hdg pitch, hdstg, pt shd; wc; chem disp; baby facs; shwrs inc; el pts (6-10A) €4; gas 5km; ice; lndtte; shop 4km; tradsmn; rest 1km; snacks; bar; BBQ; playgrnd; htd, covrd pool 12km; rv sw & shgl beach adj; cycle & canoe hire; some statics; dogs; Eng spkn; adv bkg (dep req); red 14 days low ssn; quiet; cc not acc; red long stay/CCI. "British/Dutch owners; quiet, secluded site; excel san facs; rallies welcome; ent for o'fits over 11m poss diff - suggest inspect pitch 1st." ♦ ltd. € 14.00   2005*

†**PERIGUEUX** *7C3* (1.5km E Rural) **Camping de Barnabe Plage, Rue des Bains, Boulazac, 24000 Perigueux [05 53 53 41 45; fax 05 53 54 16 62; contact@barnabe-perigord.com]** Fr Perigueux on rd to Brive, sp to L. Well sp. Med, hdg pitch, pt shd; htd wc; chem disp; shwrs inc; el pts (4-6A) €2.55-2.95; ice; shops 500m; supmkt 1km; rest; snacks; bar; rv fishing; no statics; dogs €1.10; poss cr; Eng spkn; adv bkg; quiet; red long stay/low ssn; cc acc. "Pleasant site adj to rv; facs dated but clean; pitches cramped for lge o'fits; poss noisy at times due to busy café/bar; pleasant walk to town cent." € 12.40   2005*

PERIGUEUX *7C3* (10km E Rural) **Camping au Fil de l'Eau, 6 Allee des Platanes, 24420 Antonne-et-Trigonant [05 53 06 17 88; fax 05 53 08 97 76; campingaufildeleau@wanadoo.fr; http://camping-aufildeleau.monsite.wanadoo.fr]** E fr Perigueux on N21 twd Limoges; sp on R at end of vill; camp 350m along rd to Escoire. Sm, pt shd; wc; chem disp; shwrs inc; el pts (5A) inc; lndtte; shops 1km; tradsmn; snacks; playgrnd; lake sw; canoe hire; fishing; cycle hire; some statics; adv bkg (dep req); quiet; CCI. "Helpful staff; woods, birds & wildlife around; gd base for area; v clean facs; red facs low ssn; excel." € 15 Jun-15 Sep. € 13.50   2005*

PERIGUEUX *7C3* (7km S) **Camping Le Grand Dague, 24750 Atur [05 53 04 21 01; fax 05 53 04 22 01; info@legranddague.fr; www.legranddague. fr]** Fr cent Perigueux, take N21 & N89 twd Brive. Fork L onto D2 to Atur (main rd bears R). In Atur turn L after bar/tabac; foll site sp for 2.5km. Med, pt sl, shd; wc; chem disp; baby facs; shwrs inc; el pts (6A) €3.75; lndtte; ice; ltd shop; tradsmn; rest; snacks; bar; playgrnd; pool; games rm; entmnt; mini-golf; TV; dogs €1.75; phone; Eng spkn; adv bkg; quiet; cc acc; CCI. "Ltd clean facs; badly placed water points; gd family site; friendly owners; lots to do; gd long/sh stay."♦ Easter-30 Sep. € 18.75
2004*

PERNES LEZ BOULOGNE see Boulogne sur Mer *3A2*

PERONNE *3C3* (Urban) **Camp Municipal du Brochet, Rue Georges Clemenceau, 80200 Peronne [03 22 84 02 35 or 03 22 73 31 00; fax 03 22 73 31 01]** Fr N on N17 turn R into town. L at lights & L immed after footbdge. 1st R & site on L. Well sp fr all dirs. Go to town cent then foll 'Intn't Camping Site' sps. Sm, hdstg, pt sl, terr, pt shd; wc; mv service pnt; shwrs €1; el pts (5A) inc; lndtte; shops 500m; tradsmn; playgrnd; bus 500m; phone; poss cr; Eng spkn; adv bkg; quiet; CCI. "Basic but clean & inexpensive site; san facs need refurb; arr early high ssn; conv WWI museum & tour; lots of tourist info avail; poss itinerants." ♦ ltd.
1 May-15 Sep. € 8.90   2005*

PERONNE *3C3* (Urban) **Camping Port de Plaisance, Route de Paris, 80200 Peronne [03 22 84 19 31; fax 03 22 73 36 37; contact@camping-plaisance.com; www.camping-plaisance.com]** Site on L when ent town fr S on N17, sp 500m after 1st traff lts. Med, mkd pitch, pt shd; htd wc; chem disp; mv service pnt; shwrs inc; el pts (6-10A) €3.50-6.00 (some rev pol & long lead poss req); lndtte; ice; sm shop; tradsmn; bar; playgrnd; htd pool high ssn; jacuzzi; 20% statics; dogs €1.10; poss cr; Eng spkn; poss some rd noise; red low ssn; cc acc. "Overlooks canal; gd play park & pool; gates locked 2200-0800; when clsd - park outside; gd rest nr; rec visit to war museum in Peronne castle; popular with Dutch ralliers; helpful owners; vg facs; supmkt walking dist; highly rec." ♦ 1 Mar-31 Oct. € 20.00   2005*

†PERONNE *3C3* (11km SE Rural) **Camping Les Hortensias (formerly G.A.E.C. de l'Avenir), 22 Rue Basse, 80240 Vraignes-en-Vermandois [03 22 85 64 68; fax 03 22 85 63 20; www. camping hortensias.com]** Fr N A1/E15 a'route take exit 13 onto N29 sp St Quentin; strt rd 16km until rndabt, take D15 (Vraignes) exit; site sp 1st on R in vill. Or fr S & A26, take junc 10 onto N29 sp Peronne; after 15km at rndabt take D15 as bef. Sm, hdg pitch, pt shd; htd wc; chem disp; shwrs €1.10; el pts (4A) inc; lndtte; ice; shop 1km; tradsmn; red 5km; snack, bar 1.5km; BBQ; 50% statics; dogs €1.10; quiet; red long stay; CCI. "Excel site; v quiet; v gd clean san facs; v helpful & friendly couple; conv for Somme battlefields; 4WD needed if wet." € 11.50   2005*

PERONNE *3C3* (10km SW Rural) **Camping Chateau de l'Oseraie, 10 Rue du Chateau, 80200 Feuilleres [03 22 83 17 59 or 03 22 84 10 45 (LS); fax 03 22 83 04 14; jsg-bred@wanadoo.fr]** Fr A1/E15 exit 13.1 Maurepas, R onto D938 & then L onto D146; R at x-rds in Feuilleres & site on R in 500m. Med, hdg/mkd pitch, pt shd; wc; chem disp; shwrs €1; el pts (6A) €2.90; gas; lndtte; ice; tradsmn; supmkt 10km; snacks; bar; BBQ; playgrnd; htd pool 10km; fishing; tennis; games rm; entmnt high ssn; 50% statics; dogs €1; Eng spkn; adv bkg rec high ssn; quiet; red long stay/CCI. "Excel site; immac san facs; in Valley de la Haute Somme; conv WW1 battlefields & Disneyland Paris." ♦ 1 Apr-31 Oct. € 12.80   2005*

PERPIGNAN *8G4* (5km NE) **Roussillon Camping Catalan, Route de Bompas, 66000 Perpignan [04 68 63 16 92; fax 04 68 63 34 57]** Fr Perpignan N on D1, Bompas rd. Site on R bef rndabt. Med, shd; wc; serviced pitches; shwrs; el pts (4-10A) €2.45-€3.05; ice; lndtte; shop 500m; rest; snacks; bar; pool; playgrnd; beach 10km; TV; entmnt; poss cr; adv bkg; 60% statics; dogs €1.50; CCI. "Pool deep, no shallow end." 1 Apr-30 Sep. € 15.00   2004*

PERPIGNAN *8G4* (6km S Rural) **Camping Les Rives du Lac, Chemin de la Serre, 66180 Villeneuve-de-la-Raho [04 68 55 83 51; fax 04 68 55 86 37; campingvilleneuve@worldonline. fr]** Fr a'route A9 exit Perpignan Sud, dir Porte d'Espagne. In 3km turn R onto N9 dir Le Boulou. In 1km after Auchan supmkt take slip rd to N91 dir Villeneuve-de-la-Raho. In 2km rd becomes D39, turn R to site, site on L in 1km. Beware ford on D39 in v wet weather (usually dry). Lge, mkd pitch, pt sl, hdstg, unshd; htd wc; chem disp; mv service pnt; shwrs inc; el pts (6A) €3; lndtte; shop; supmkt 10 mins; rest; snacks; bar; BBQ (elec/gas); playgrnd; lake sw, beach, fishing & watersports 1.5km; tennis; some statics; dogs €1.50; Eng spkn; adv bkg; quiet; red low ssn; cc acc; CCI. "Conv trips to Spain; busy public beach nr; gd for families." ♦ 1 Mar-30 Nov. € 13.30   2005*

See advertisement opposite   *See advertisement on next page*

FRANCE

CAMPING★★
"LES RIVES DU LAC"
Chemin de la Serre F-66180 VILLENEUVE DE LA RAHO

- Peaceful
- Family atmosphere
- Fishing (carp, whitebait)
- Windsurfing

- Swimming
- Rowing
- 15 km from the sea

MOBILE HOMES AND CANVAS BUNGALOWS TO LET

Open from 1st March till 30th November
Phone: +33 (0)4.68.55.83.51 / Fax: +33 (0)4.68.55.86.37

PERROS GUIREC *1D2* (10km E Coastal/Rural) **Camping de Port l'Epine, 10 Venelle de Pors-Garo, 22660 Trelevern** [02 96 23 71 94; fax 02 96 23 77 83; camping-de-port-lepine@wanadoo.fr; www.camping-port-lepine.com] Fr Guingamp take D8 N twd La Roche-Derrien then D6. Cont twd Perros-Guirec & after 7km turn R on D73 twd Trelevern. Strt over x-rds in Trelevern, foll sp Camp Municipal & beach. Site on L at bottom of hill opp municipal site. Med, hdg/mkd pitch, pt sl, pt shd; wc; chem disp; serviced piches; shwrs inc; el pts (16A) inc (poss rev pol); gas; lndtte; shop; tradsmn; rest; snacks; bar; BBQ; playgrnd; htd pool; paddling pool; dir access shgl beach; cycle hire; games rm; entmnt; 30% statics; dogs €2.50; c'vans over 8m not acc high ssn; poss cr; Eng spkn; adv bkg; quiet; cc acc; red long stay/low ssn; CCI. "Quiet, pleasant site; friendly, family-run; facs poss stretched in high ssn; narr site rds; gd touring base; recep 0930-1800; mkt Perros-Guirec Fri; deluxe pitches avail at extra cost; NB site clsd/locked up 2230-0730." ♦ 8 Apr-23 Sep.
€ 27.00 (CChq acc) ABS - B18   2005*

PERROS GUIREC *1D2* (1km SE Coastal) **Camp Municipal Ernest Renan, Louannec, 22700 Perros-Guirec** [02 96 23 11 78; fax 02 96 49 04 47; mairie-louannec@wanadoo.fr] 1km W of Louannec on D6. Lge, unshd; wc; chem disp; shwrs inc; el pts (6A) inc; gas; ice; shop high ssn; rest; bar; playgrnd; htd pool; sand beach adj; fishing & watersports adj; TV rm; dogs €1; poss cr; adv bkg; Eng spkn; traff noise early am (minimal away fr rd). ♦
1 Jun-30 Sep. € 13.85   2004*

PERROS GUIREC *1D2* (1km W Urban) **Camping La Claire Fontaine, Tour ar Lann, 22700 Perros-Guirec** [02 96 23 03 55; fax 02 96 49 06 19] Fr Lannion N on D788 twd Perros-Guirec. At 2nd rndabt W on D11, then N on D6, L fork sp. Med, pt sl, pt shd; wc (some cont); chem disp; shwrs inc; baby facs; el pts (4-6A) inc; ice; lndry rm; tradsmn; shops 800m; sand beach 800m; playgrnd; TV rm; dogs €0.95; quiet; adv bkg rec high ssn; Eng spkn. "Helpful staff."
1 May-15 Sep. € 21.96   2004*

PERROS GUIREC *1D2* (3km NW Coastal) **Camping Le Ranolien, Ploumanac'h, 22700 Perros-Guirec** [02 96 91 43 58 or 02 96 91 43 56; fax 02 96 91 41 90; leranolien@wanadoo.fr; www.yellohvillage.com] At Perros-Guirec harbour turn R at Marina foll sp Tregastel. Up hill above coast into Perros Guirec town. Cont strt thro traff lts & into La Clarte vill; strt at traff lts & sharp R at Camping & Le Ranolien sp. Ent shortly on L. Foll Tregastel sp all way. Lge, pt sl, pt shd; wc; mv service pnt; shwrs inc; el pts (4-6A) inc; shop; rest; snacks; bar; 2 pools; waterslide; sand & rock beach; tennis; golf; fishing; horseriding; entmnt; many static tents; dogs; poss cr; Eng spkn; adv bkg; cc acc. "Excel for Corniche Bretonne beaches; wonderful coastal walks within 250m." ♦ 1 Apr-22 Sep. € 29.00   2002*

PERTRE, LE *2F4* (1km W Rural) **Camp Municipal Le Chardonneret, Route des Martyres, 35370 Le Pertre** [02 99 96 99 27; fax 02 99 96 98 92; marieleperte@wandadoo.fr] 25km W of Laval on N157 or A81; sp Le Pertre. Sm, hdg pitch, pt sl, pt shd; wc; shwrs; el pt (16A) inc; lndry rm; BBQ; 20% statics; dogs; phone; quiet. "Warden calls am/pm; o'night area for m'vans outside site; vg sh stay/NH." ♦ ltd. € 8.00   2005*

†PERTUIS *10E3* (8km N Rural) **Camping Etang de la Bonde, 84730 Cabrieres-d'Aigues** [04 90 77 63 64 or 04 90 77 77 15 (HS); fax 04 90 07 73 04; camping@la-bonde.com; www.la-bonde.com] NE fr Pertuis on D956, fork L onto D9 (sp Cabrieres & Etang de la Bonde). At x-rds in 8km turn R onto D27. Site on L in 200m. Med, pt shd; wc (some cont); shwrs; el pts (6A) €3; gas; ice; shop; rest; snacks; playgrnd; pool 8km; games area; lake sw, watersports & fishing; tennis; many statics; dogs €1.60; poss cr; adv bkg; quiet; cc acc; CCI. "Lovely lakeside & beach; ltd facs low ssn - phone ahead to check open." € 10.50   2004*

PERTUIS *10E3* (2km E) **Camp Municipal Les Pinedes, Quartier St Sepulcre, 84120 Pertuis [04 90 79 10 98; fax 04 90 09 03 99; camping lespinedes@free.fr]** Exit Pertuis on D973 twd Manosque. After 1km fr cent of Pertuis turn R foll sp Camping & Piscine. In 2km pass pool to site 100m on brow of hill. Lge, hdg pitch, pt sl, terr, pt shd; wc (some cont); chem disp; mv service pnt; baby facs; shwrs inc; el pts (6A) inc; gas; lndry rm; ice; shop & 2km; playgrnd; pool 200m; entmnt; 5% statics; dogs €1; phone; quiet; red long stay; CCI. "Spacious, attractive site; gates clsd 2200-0700; no twin-axle c'vans; vg." 15 Mar-15 Oct. € 13.00   2005*

PERTUIS *10E3* (6km SW Rural) **Camping Messidor (Naturist), Route de St Canadet, 13610 Le Puy-Ste Reparade [04 42 61 90 28; fax 04 42 50 07 08; messidor@online.fr]** S fr Pertuis on D956/D556 twds Aix-en-Provence; after 5km turn R onto D561 twds Le Puy-Ste Reparade & Silvacane; in vill take 1st sharp L onto D13; site after 2km, sp. Med, pt sl, pt shd; wc; shwrs inc; el pts (4A) €2.30; lndtte; ice; shop 3km; tradsmn; rest; snacks; bar; pool; tennis; rv fishing & watersports; dogs; Eng spkn; adv bkg; quiet; INF card req. "Gd sh stay; gd facs & pool; site untidy." 1 Apr-30 Sep. € 14.00   2002*

PESMES *6G2* (500m S Rural) **Camp Municipal La Colombiere, Route de Dole, 70140 Pesmes [03 84 31 20 15; fax 03 84 31 20 54; camp colombiere@aol.com]** On D475 halfway bet Gray & Dole. S fr Pesmes immed on L after x-ing rv bdge. N fr Dole, site sp on R immed bef rest at rv bdge. Med, some hdg pitch, pt shd; wc; own san rec high ssn; chem disp (wc); shwrs; el pts (6-10A) €2.30-3.60; lndtte; shop 500m; rest; snacks; bar; cycle hire; dogs €1; phone; Eng spkn; adv bkg rec high ssn; quiet. "Picturesque vill; rest pleasant low ssn; helpful, friendly management." 1 Apr-30 Sep. € 6.80   2005*

PETIT PALAIS *7C2* (1.5km NW Rural) **Camping Le Pressoir, Queyrai, 33570 Petit-Palais-et-Cornemps [05 57 69 73 25; fax 05 57 69 77 36; camping. lepressoir@wanadoo.fr; www.campinglepressoir. com]** Leave A9/E70 junc 11, then N89 Bordeaux-Perigueux rd to St Medard-de-Guizieres onto D21 & foll sp, site bef Petit-Palais. Fr Castillon-la-Bataille on D936 Bergerac-Bordeaux rd take D17/D21 sp St Medard & foll site sp. Take care on access & exit. Med, hdg/mkd pitch, pt sl, pt shd; wc; chem disp; shwrs inc; el pts (6A) inc; lndtte; shop 1.5km; tradsmn; rest; snacks; bar; BBQ; playgrnd; pool; dogs €1.70; phone; Eng spkn; quiet; cc acc; red CCI. "Barrier card ent, close to vineyards; helpful Belgian owners; sw pool terr with sunbeds & parasols; basic san facs; site poss unkempt." ♦ 1 Apr-30 Sep. € 21.50 (CChq acc)   2004*

PEUPLINGUES see Calais *3A3*

PEYNIER see Trets *10F3*

PEYRAT LE CHATEAU see Eymoutiers *7B4*

PEYREHORADE *8F1* (Urban) **Camping Les Gaves, 40300 Peyrehorade [05 58 73 60 20]** On ent town fr Pau, site clearly visible across rv. Cross rv to site ent on L. Sm, shd; wc; shwrs; el pts; shops 500m; pool 200m; playgrnd; rv & fishing adj; poss cr; quiet. Jul-Aug.   2002*

PEYRELEAU *10E1* (1km N Rural) **Camp Municipal de Brouillet, 48150 Le Rozier [05 65 62 63 98; fax 05 65 62 60 83; contact@camping-lerozier.com]** Fr Millau take N9 N to Aguessac, onto D907; in Le Rozier, x bdge over Rv Tarn onto D996 & in 200m (opp church); take rd on R to site; sp. Lge, mkd pitch, pt shd; wc; chem disp (wc); baby facs; shwrs inc; el pts (3-6A) €2.60-3.10; lndtte; ice; shop 200m; playgrnd; htd pool; poss cr; adv bkg rec high ssn; quiet; red low ssn; CCI. "V pleasant, busy site; friendly recep; vg base for Tarn Gorges; gd area walking & birdwatching; conv, spacious site adj to rv; vg for m'vans; facs stretched when site full & poss poor cleaning." ♦ ltd. 15 Apr-15 Sep. € 13.00   2005*

PEYRELEAU *10E1* (1km W Rural) **Camping Saint Pal, Route des Gorges du Tarn, 12720 Mostuejouls [tel/fax 05 65 62 64 46 or 05 65 59 88 08 (LS); saintpal@wanadoo.fr; www.campingsaintpal.com]** Exit A75 exit junc 44.1 onto D29 to Aguessac then L onto D907 to Mostuejouls. Or fr Millau take N9 N to Aguessac, turn R onto D907 to Mostuejouls. Site in 10km 500m fr Rozier bdge. Med, hdg/mkd pitch, pt shd; wc (some cont); chem disp; mv service pnt; baby facs; fam bthrm; shwrs; el pts (6A) €3; gas; lndtte; shop & 1km; tradsmn; snacks, bar high ssn; BBQ; playgrnd; pool; rv sw adj; games rm; TV; 10% statics; dogs €2; phone; poss cr; Eng spkn; adv bkg; quiet; cc acc; red low ssn/long stay/CCI. "Gd walks, canoeing, fishing & bird watching; v helpful owner; vg info rm; excel facs; poss diff for lge o'fits." ♦ 1 May-30 Sep. € 18.00   2005*

See advertisement on next page

†**PEYRIGNAC** *7C3* (1km W Rural) **Camping La Garenne, 24210 Peyrignac [tel/fax 05 53 50 73; campinglagarenne@aol.com; http://membres. lycos.fr/campinglagarenne]** E fr Perigueux, N89 twd Terrasson. At Peyrignac foll site sp. Narr, steep rd poss diff lge o'fits. Med, mkd pitch, pt sl, shd; wc; chem disp; mv service pnt; shwrs inc; el pts (3-5A) €3.30-€5 (poss rev pol); gas; lndtte; ice; shops; tradsmn; rest; bar; playgrnd; pool; cycle hire; 50% statics; dogs €1.50; poss cr; adv bkg (dep req); quiet; CCI. "Gd touring base; gd size pitches; v clean san facs." ♦ ltd. € 11.00   2004*

PEYRILLAC ET MILLAC see Souillac *7C3*

PEYRUIS see Chateau Arnoux *10E3*

FRANCE

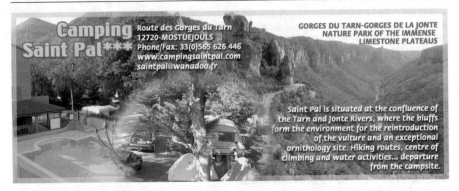

Camping Saint Pal ★★★
Route des Gorges du Tarn
12720-MOSTUEJOULS
Phone/Fax: 33(0)565 626 446
www.campingsaintpal.com
saintpal@wanadoo.fr

GORGES DU TARN-GORGES DE LA JONTE
NATURE PARK OF THE IMMENSE
LIMESTONE PLATEAUS

Saint Pal is situated at the confluence of the Tarn and Jonte Rivers, where the bluffs form the environment for the reintroduction of the vulture and an exceptional ornithology site. Hiking routes, centre of climbing and water activities... departure from the campsite.

PEZENAS *10F1* (1km NE Urban) **Camping St Christol**, Chemin de St Christol, 34120 Pezenas [04 67 98 09 00 or 06 11 39 59 17 (mob); fax 04 67 98 89 61; saintchristol@worldonline.fr; www.campingsaintchristol.com] Exit A75 junc 59 Pezenas N onto N9 by-pass for town cent; turn R immed bef bdge; sp on R in 200m. NB app rds narr. Med, hdg/mkd pitch, hdstg, shd; wc (some cont); chem disp (wc); baby facs; shwrs inc; el pts (10A) €2.50; gas; lndtte; shop; tradsmn; rest; snacks; BBQ area; playgrnd; pool; fishing; entmnt; games rm; TV; some statics; dogs €1.25; poss cr; adv bkg rec Jul/Aug; quiet; cc acc; CCI. "V friendly; easy walk to historic town; rest rec; lots of lge poplar trees on site - diff to manoeuvre; excel shwrs; lively site; vg." ♦ 15 Apr-15 Sep. € 14.10   2005*

PEZENAS *10F1* (5km NE Urban) **Camp Municipal La Piboule**, 34530 Montagnac [04 67 24 01 31] Fr Pezenas on N9 dir Clermont l'Herault, in approx 1km turn R onto N113 sp Montagnac. Site sp. Narr app unsuitable lge o'fits. Med, hdg/mkd pitch, pt sl, pt shd; wc (cont); chem disp; shwrs inc; el pts (10A) €3.20; lndry; shop, rest, snacks, bar 800m; playgrnd; phone; CCI. 15 Mar-15 Dec. € 8.00 2004*

PEZENAS *10F1* (5km NE Rural) **Domaine St Martin-du-Pin**, 34530 Montagnac [04 67 24 00 37; fax 04 67 24 47 50; http://saint-martin-du-pin.st] Exit A75 junc 59 onto D113 to Montagnac. 2km past Montagnac turn R immed past picnic site at end of dual c'way, site sp. Sm, hdg pitch, pt sl, pt shd; wc; chem disp; baby facs; shwrs inc; el pts €2.50; lndtte; ice; shop 2.5km; tradsmn; playgrnd; pool; sand beach 9km; few statics; Eng spkn; adv bkg (dep req); quiet; red low ssn; CCI. "Friendly owners; delightful site; spotless facs; rec." 15 May-30 Sep. € 16.50   2004*

PEZENAS *10F1* (8km S) **Camping Le Pin Parasol**, 34630 St Thibery [tel/fax 04 67 77 84 29] Fr A9 exit junc 34 onto D13 & foll Pezenas sps; in 2.5km turn R to St Thibery & site 150m on R. Med, mkd pitch, pt shd; wc; shwrs inc; el pts (10A) €3.40; snacks; supmkt 2km; tradsmn; playgrnd; pool; sand beach 10km; tennis 1km; games rm; rv sw 1km; fishing; entmnt; TV; 30% statics; adv bkg (dep req); quiet but some rd noise; cc not acc; CCI. "Gd san facs but could be cleaner; interesting vill; lovely pool but site run down low ssn." ♦ 1 May-30 Sep. € 14.40   2005*

PEZENAS *10F1* (1km SW Urban) **Campotel Municipal de Castelsec**, Chemin de Castelsec, 34120 Pezenas [04 67 98 04 02; fax 04 67 90 72 47] Fr Beziers take N9 to Pezenas. At rndabt turn L towards Centre Ville; in 300m turn L at ent Champion supmkt & foll Campotel sp. Sm, mkd pitch, pt sl, pt terr, pt shd; wc; shwrs inc; el pts (10A) €2.35; lndtte; shops 500m; playgrnd; pool 1km; tennis adj; TV; 30% statics; dogs; adv bkg; quiet; red low ssn; cc acc; CCI. "V friendly staff; pleasant, functional site; clean facs; sh walk into lovely vill." ♦ 1 Apr-10 Oct. € 13.00   2005*

†**PEZENAS** *10F1* (10km NW) **Camping Les Clairettes**, 34320 Fontes [04 67 25 01 31; fax 04 67 25 38 64; camping-clairettes@wanadoo.fr; www.campinglesclairettes.com] Sp both ways on N9. Turn onto D128 sp Adissan, Fontes. Fr A75 exit junc 58. Foll sp for Fontes. Med, hdg/mkd pitch, pt shd; wc; chem disp; serviced pitches; shwrs inc; el pts (6A) inc; gas; lndtte; sm shop, rest, snacks, bar in ssn; BBQ; playgrnd; pool; entmnt; TV; 50% statics; adv bkg; red low ssn. "V quiet; friendly owners; ltd facs low ssn." ♦ ltd. € 20.50   2004*

PEZENAS *10F1* (10km NW Rural) **Camping L'Evasion**, 34320 Fontes [04 67 25 32 00; fax 04 67 25 31 96; campingevasion34@yahoo.fr] Fr A75 exit junc 59 (Pezenas). At rndabt take D124 to Lezignan-la-Cebe then fork L, cont on D124 to Fontes. In vill foll sp to site. Sm, hdg/mkd pitch, pt sl, pt shd; wc; chem disp; baby facs; shwrs inc; el pts (6A) inc; gas; lndtte; rest; snacks; bar; BBQ; playgrnd; pool; beach 30km; 20% statics; dogs €2.60; phone; adv bkg; quiet; CCI. "Excel san facs; gd value." ♦ ltd. 1 Apr-30 Oct. € 13.30   2005*

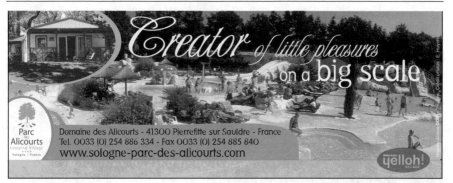

PEZOU see Vendome *4F2*

PEZULS see Bugue, Le *7C3*

PHALSBOURG *5D3* (2km N Rural) **Camping de Bouleaux, Route des Trois Journeaux, 57370 Vilsberg** [tel/fax 03 87 24 18 72; secretariat@ campingclub.asso.fr] Fr A4 exit Phalsbourg junc 44, twd town, site sp R on N61, about 2km fr town. Med, pt shd; wc; chem disp; shwrs inc; el pts (6A) inc; lndry rm; shop; tradsmn; playgrnd; 80% statics; red low ssn; CCI. "Gd facs; clean; gd long/sh stay." 1 Jan-31 Oct. € 16.25   2003*

> We're having a great holiday - must fill in some site report forms and send them to The Club as soon as possible.

PHALSBOURG *5D3* (6km SW Rural) **Camping du Plan Incline, 57820 Henridorff** [tel/fax 03 87 25 30 13 or 06 71 21 86 91; campingplan incline@ wanadoo.fr] Exit A4 at junc 44. In Phalsbourg take D38 twds Lutzelbourg; turn R onto D98 dir Arzviller & foll sp to Henridorff & site on R in 3km, (narr ent). Med, some hdg/hdstg pitches, pt shd; wc; chem disp; shwrs inc; el pts (6A) €2.50; gas; lndtte; ice; shop 2km; tradsmn; rest; snacks; bar; playgrnd; pool high ssn; rv sw, fishing & boating adj; entmnts; 30% statics; dogs €1; phone; Eng spkn; adv bkg; rlwy noise & some rd & boat noise; red low ssn; cc not acc; CCI. "By canal in wooded valley; friendly warden; facs a little run-down; gd lndry rm; cycle path to Strasbourg; many local attractions; gd sh stay." ♦ 1 Apr-30 Oct. € 11.10
                                    2003*

PICQUIGNY *3C3* (Urban) **Camp Municipal, 66 Rue du Marais, 80310 Picquigny** [03 22 51 25 83 or 03 22 51 40 31 (Mairie); fax 03 22 51 30 98] Site sp fr town cent. Med, unshd; wc; chem disp; shwrs inc; el pts (10A) €4; lndry rm; shop nr; rv & fishing; mainly statics; dogs €1.35; quiet; occasional noise fr rlwy line; adv bkg rec high ssn. "Very nice site; modern san facs; British cemetery nr town; shops nrby." 1 Apr-1 Oct. € 10.00   2005*

PIERRE BUFFIERE *7B3* (11km SE) **Camp Municipal Les Ecureuils, 87380 Magnac-Bourg** [05 55 00 80 28 (Mairie); fax 05 55 00 49 09; mairie.magnac-bourg@wanadoo.fr] Leave A20 at junc sp Magnac-Bourg; foll sps to site in vill. Site behind town hall. Sm, pt sl, pt shd, some hdg pitch; wc; shwrs inc; el pts (5A) €3; supmkt, petrol & rest nr; playgrnd; fishing 2km; quiet; CCI. "Coded barrier access if arr at lunchtime; warden calls at 1600; mkt Sat am; gd NH/ sh stay." Easter-30 Sep. € 10.00
                                    2005*

PIERRE BUFFIERE *7B3* (1.5km S Rural) **Camp Intercommunal Chabanas, 87260 Pierre-Buffiere** [tel/fax 05 55 00 96 43] Approx 20km S of Limoges on A20, take exit 40 on D420; foll sps for 'Stade-Chabanas' for 1km. Med, hdg/mkd pitch, pt sl, pt shd; htd wc; chemp disp (wc); shwrs inc; el pts €2.30 (poss rev pol); lndtte; ice; shop & snacks 2 km; playgrnd; fishing; dogs €0.76; phone; adv bkg; quiet; red low ssn; CCI. "V helpful staff; excel facs; v clean; v quiet; some pitches diff for lge o'fits; no twin-axle vans; warden site 1600-2200, but gate poss locked all day low ssn (code issued); phone ahead; conv Limoges; excel NH fr A20." ♦ 15 May-30 Sep. € 10.00   2005*

PIERREFITTE SUR SAULDRE *4G3* (6km NE Rural) **Yelloh! Village Parc des Alicourts, Domaine des Alicourts, 41300 Pierrefitte-sur-Sauldre** [02 54 88 63 34; fax 02 54 88 58 40; info@yellohvillage-parc-des-alicourts.com; www.sologne-parc-des-alicourts.com] Fr S of Lamotte-Beuvron, turn L on D923. After 14km turn R on D24E sp Pierrefitte. After 750m turn L, foll sp to site approx 750m on R. Med, pt shd; wc; mv service pnt; chem disp; baby facs; shwrs inc; el pts (6A) inc; gas; lndtte; shop; rest; snacks; bar; BBQ; playgrnd; 3 pools; waterslide; tennis; lake sw; kayak/pedalo hire; skating rink; mini-golf; cycle hire; games rm; entmnt; child entmnt; some statics; dogs €7; extra for lakeside pitches; poss cr (but roomy); Eng spkn; adv bkg (bkg fee); quiet; red low ssn; cc acc; CCI. "Excel site; v peaceful; gd, clean facs; v lge pitches." ♦ 19 May-9 Sep. € 40.00   2005*

See advertisement above

FRANCE

PIERREFONDS *3D3* Camp Municipal de Batigny, Rue de l'Armistice, 60350 Pierrefonds [03 44 42 80 83] Take D973 fr Compiegne; after 14km site on L adj sp for Pierrefonds at ent to vill. Med, hdg pitch, pt shd; htd wc; chem disp; mv service pnt; 90% serviced pitches; shwrs inc; el pts (8A) inc; lndtte; shops 800m; rest in vill; 80% statics; dogs €1; poss cr; adv bkg; quiet; cc not acc; CCI. "Attractive site; well-maintained; facs stretched high ssn; much bird song; nr Armistice train & museum; Chateau Pierrefonds nr; red price 2nd night onwards; gd all stays." 1 Apr-13 Oct. € 7.45   2003*

PIERREFORT *7C4* (7km SW Rural) Camping La Source, 12600 Therondels [05 65 66 05 62; fax 05 65 66 21 00; campinglasource@wanadoo.fr; www.camping-la-source.com] Fr A75 at St Flour, take D921 to Les Ternes, then D990 thro Pierrefort. Approx 2km after Pierrefort, turn L onto D34. Go thro Paulhenc, site on L after approx 7km. Med, hdg pitch, terr, pt shd; wc; chem disp; mv service pnt; baby facs; shwrs inc; el pts (6-10A) €3-5; gas; lndtte; ice; shop; tradsmn; rest; snacks; bar; playgrnd; htd pool; paddling pool; waterslide; lake sw adj; fishing; water sports; games area; entmnt; TV; dogs €1.50; 20% statics; quiet; adv bkg (dep req) rec high ssn; CCI. "Excel lakeside site; boats for hire etc; poss diff lge o'fit due many lge trees." ♦ 24 Jun-2 Sep. € 19.00   2005*

†PIEUX, LES *1C4* (6km SE Rural) Camp Municipal, 2 Route du Rozel, 50340 St Germain-le-Gaillard [02 33 52 55 64] Take 904 fr Cherbourg. 3km beyond Les Pieux turn R sp Le Rozel. Site on R 100m. Sm, hdg pitch, some hdstg, unshd; wc; chem disp; shwrs inc; el pts (15A) €2.50; 4 water stand pts; lndry rm; shop; playgrnd; pool & sand beach 3km; 85% statics (sep area); dogs €1.05; poss cr; adv bkg. "Modern, clean, well-kept san facs; rec arr early high ssn - ltd touring pitches; poss diff in wet." ♦ € 6.10   2004*

PIEUX, LES *1C4* (3km SW Coastal) Camping Village Le Grand Large, 50340 Les Pieux [02 33 52 40 75; fax 02 33 52 58 20; le-grand-large@wanadoo.fr; www.legrandlarge.com] Fr ferry at 1st rndabt take 1st exit sp Centre Ville. Closer to town cent foll old N13 sp Caen. In about 1.5km branch R onto D900 then L onto D650 (formerly D904) sp Carteret. Foll this rd past Les Pieux, continue on D650 to sp Super U. Turn R & foll site sp onto D517, then D117 for 3km until reaching beach rd to site, site on L in 2km. Lge, mkd pitch, unshd; htd wc; chem disp; mv service pnt; baby facs; shwrs inc; el pts (6A) inc; gas; lndtte; ice; shop; tradsmn; rest, snacks high ssn; bar; BBQ; playgrnd; htd pool & paddling pool; sand beach adj; tennis; games rm; entmnt; horseriding 4km; games/TV rm; 50% statics; dogs; phone; recep 0900-2200; poss cr; Eng spkn; adv bkg; quiet; cc acc; CCI. "V clean facs; friendly staff; great sunsets; barrier clsd 2100-0900; exterior pitches avail for early departure for ferries; dir access to excel beach; mkt Fri." ♦ 8 Apr-17 Sep. € 32.00 (CChq acc) ABS - N07   2005*

PIEUX, LES *1C4* (4km SW Coastal) Camping Le Ranch, 50340 Le Rozel [02 33 10 07 10; fax 02 33 10 07 11; contact@camping-leranch.fr; www.camping-leranch.fr] Fr Les Pieux take D117 to Le Rozel. Turn L thro Rozel, foll sps to site. Site is on R at end rd. Med, pt sl, unshd; wc; chem disp; shwrs inc; el pts (3A); lndtte; ice; shop; rest; snacks; bar; playgrnd; pool; sand beach adj; fishing; watersports; 10% statics; dogs €2; quiet; CCI. "Vg long/sh stay." 1 Apr-31 Oct. € 18.00   2003*

PIEUX, LES *1C4* (6km NW Coastal) Camp Municipal Clairefontaine, 50340 Siouville-Hague [02 33 52 42 73] Take D3/904 fr Cherbourg onto D23 fr Les Pieux to Siouville, site sp fr beach rd. Lge, pt shd; wc; shwrs; el pts (6A) €2.19; ice; lndtte; shops 500m; playgrnd; sand beach 300m; rv adj; mini-golf; quiet.   2004*

PINSAC see Souillac *7C3*

PIRIAC SUR MER *2G3* **Camping Le Pouldroit, Route de Mesquer, 44420 Piriac-sur-Mer [02 40 23 50 91; fax 02 40 23 69 12]** Foll coast rd fr La Baule to Guerande D99, NW to La Turballe & Piriac; on ent Piriac turn R & site 1km on L, on D52; sp. Lge, pt shd; wc; shwrs inc; el pts (10A) €1.98; gas; lndtte; shop; snacks; rest; BBQ; playgrnd; htd pool; sand beach 300m; tennis & archery; adv bkg; no cc acc; phone; CCI. "Gd long stay; nr walled town of Guerande, La Baule, St Nazaire; bus stop 100m." ♦ ltd 1 May-6 Sep. 2002*

PIRIAC SUR MER *2G3* (3.5km E Coastal/Rural) **Parc du Guibel, Route de Kerdrien, 44420 Piriac- sur-Mer [02 40 23 52 67; fax 02 40 15 50 24; camping@parcduguibel.com; www.parcduguibel.com]** Fr Guerande take D99 to La Turballe, D333 to St Sebastien. In St Sebastien turn R to Kerdrien over x-rds & site on R in approx 500m. Lge, mkd pitch, hdstg, pt sl, pt shd; wc (some cont); chem disp; mv service pnt; serviced pitches; shwrs inc; el pts (3-10A) €2.70-3.80 (poss rev pol); gas; lndtte; shop; rest; snacks; bar; BBQ; playgrnd; htd pool high ssn; paddling pools; mini-waterslide; sand beach 1km; tennis; games area; cycle hire; entmnt; TV rm; 5% statics; dogs €1.60; phone; adv bkg; cc acc; CCI. "Helpful owner; lovely, quiet location in woods; gd touring base." ♦ 27 Mar-30 Sep. € 16.60 2005*

See advertisement

PITGAM see Bergues *3A3*

†**PITHIVIERS** *4F3* (8km S) **Camping Le Close des Tourterelles, Rue des Rendillons, 45300 Bouzonville-aux-Bois [02 38 33 01 00]** S fr Pithiviers on D921 twds Jargeau; enter Bouzonville. Turn R immed bef cafe; site 500m on R sp in vill. Med, pt shd; htd wc; chem disp; shwrs inc; el pts (6A) inc; lndtte; shop 8km; playgrnd; 90% statics; adv bkg; quiet; CCI. "Ltd space for tourers; modern facs; gd NH." ♦ € 13.50 2005*

†**PITHIVIERS** *4F3* (1km SW Urban) **Camping Les Peupliers, Rue de Laas, 45300 Pithiviers [tel/fax 02 38 30 76 96; lespeupliers45@aol.com]** On N152 to Orleans, site on bend on L 400m past Gendarmerie. Sm, pt shd; wc (some cont); chem disp; shwrs inc; el pts (10A) inc; gas; lndtte; shops 800m; snacks; bar; playgrnd; pool 500m; rv fishing adj; dogs €1; adv bkg; quiet but some rd noise; 10% red long stay. "Picturesque setting; welcoming owner; tourist steam rlwy (Suns) & museum nr; gd rest in vill." € 16.00 2004*

PLAINE SUR MER, LA see Pornic *2G3*

PLAISANCE *8F2* (500m Urban) **Camping de l'Arros, Allee de Ormeaux, 32160 Plaisance [05 62 69 30 28]** N from Tarbes on D935, approx 25 km N of Maubourget turn R onto D946 to Plaisance. Foll sp to site on o'skts of town. Sm, mkd pitch; pt sl, pt shd; wc; chem disp; shwrs inc; el pts (3-5A) inc; lndtte; shops 500m; rest; snacks; bar; gas BBQ only; playgrnd; pool; 20% statics; no dogs; phone; adv bkg ess high ssn; cc acc; CCI. "Close to rv; canoes avail; gd all stays." ♦ ltd. 1 Apr-30 Sep. € 11.43 2004*

PLANCOET *2E3* (1km Urban) **Camp Municipal du Verger, 22130 Plancoet [02 96 84 03 42 or 02 96 84 39 70 (Mairie); fax 02 96 84 19 49]** On D974 fr Dinan descend to bdge over rlwy lines & site well sp. Med, mkd pitch, pt shd; wc; chem disp; shwrs inc; el pts (5A) inc; lndtte; shops 50m; sand beach 13km; cycle hire; rv fishing; TV; adv bkg rec high ssn; quiet; CCI. "Excel sand beach at Pen Guen; adj pleasant park & rv with canoeing & close to rests/bars; poss itinerants/mkt traders." 1 Jun-15 Sep. € 6.50 2002*

PLANCOET *2E3* (4km SW Rural) **Camping Pallieter (Naturist), Parc de Loisirs Naturistes 22130 Plancoet [02 96 83 05 15]** NW fr Dinan on D794 to Plancoet. S fr Plancoet on D792 sp Bourseul. Well sp fr rd tho sp are small. Med, unshd, mkd pitch; wc; chem disp; shwrs inc; el pts (6A) €3; lndtte; shop 4km; tradsmn; snacks; bar; playgrnd; pool; Eng spkn; adv bkg; quiet. "Gd naturist site; min stay 3 nights high ssn; INF card req." € 20.00 2003*

PLANCOET *2E3* (8km W Rural) **Camping a la Ferme (Robert), Le Pont-a-l'Ane, 22130 Landebia [tel/fax 02 96 84 47 52]** Fr Plancoet, take D768 twd Lamballe; in 8km turn L at 1st sp to Landebia, farm in 800m on R, sp fr Plancoet. Sm, pt shd; wc; own san; shwrs inc; el pts (10A) €2.70; shops 1km; tradsmn; playgrnd; dogs €0.50; some Eng spkn; quiet; cc not acc. "CL-type in old orchard; nice rural site but facs v basic/primitive; owners v helpful & friendly; gd base for N coast beaches; poss mosquitoes." 1 Apr-31 Oct. € 8.40 2005*

PLELAN LE GRAND *2F3* (400m S Urban) **Camp Municipal, Rue de l'Hermine, 35380 Plelan-le-Grand [02 99 06 81 41 (Mairie)]** Fr Rennes on N24. Leave N24 at town sp. Site sp on L at W end of town. Sm, shd; wc (some cont); chem disp (wc); mv service pnt; shwrs inc; el pts €2.35; lndtte; shops 400m; playgrnd; htd pool; rv 2km; tennis; dogs; quiet but some traff noise. "Well-organised, gd facs for municipal site; warden calls am & pm, site yourself; gd NH." 15 Apr-15 Sep. € 8.40 2004*

PLELAN LE GRAND *2F3* (7km SW Rural) **Camp Municipal L'Etang d'Aleth, 56380 St Malo-de-Beignon [02 97 75 83 70 or 06 81 76 97 06]** Fr N24 twds Rennes exit N onto D773 to St Malo-de-Beignon in 5km, site L by church. Sm, pt sl, pt shd; wc; chem disp; 50% serviced pitches; mv service pnt; shwrs; el pts (10A) €1.11; lndtte; rest; bar; BBQ; playgrnd; dogs; quiet. "Gd all stays; by lake with boats for children." 1 Apr-15 Sep. € 10.15 2002*

PLELAN LE GRAND *2F3* (7km NW Rural) **Camping a la Ferme (Grosset), Trudeau, 35380 Paimpont [02 99 07 81 40; www.stpi.com]** Leave N24 for Plelan. L at end of slip rd, 1st R thro Plelan. Turn R at W end of town onto D38 (sp to Paimpont); after approx 4km turn R onto D40; site sp 2km on R. Sm, pt shd; wc; shwrs inc; el pts (10A) €3; rest in high ssn; playgrnd; no statics; dogs; phone; poss cr; quiet. "Peaceful basic site; rest gd value; ltd san facs; m'van water €2; poss noisy dogs; gd NH." 1 Jun-30 Sep. € 12.40 2003*

FRANCE

PLELAN LE GRAND *2F3* (8km NW) **Camp Municipal Broceliande**, Route de Gael, 35380 Paimpont [02 99 07 89 16 or 02 99 07 81 18 (Mairie); fax 02 99 07 88 18] Sp on N edge of vill. Med, mkd pitch, pt shd; wc; mv service pnt; shwrs; el pts (5A) €2.30; lndtte; playgrnd; rv & lake sw & fishing adj; cycle hire; tennis; entmnts; quiet. "V pleasant site; attractive vill." ♦ 1 May-30 Sep. € 7.80   2003*

PLESSIS FEU AUSSOUS, LE see Touquin *4E4*

PLESTIN LES GREVES *2E2* (2km NE Coastal) **Camp Municipal St Efflam**, Rue Lan-Carre, 22310 Plestin-les-Greves [02 96 35 62 15; fax 02 96 35 09 75; campingmunicipal@plestingreves.com] Fr Morlaix D786 thro Plestin, on R at foot of hill, well sp. Lge, mkd pitch, pt sl, terr, pt shd; wc; chem disp; mv service pnt; shwrs inc; el pts (7A) €2.30; gas; lndry rm; lndtte; shop 150m; tradsmn; rest; bar; BBQ; playgrnd; sand beach 150m; sw, fishing, boating adj; dogs €1.08; Eng spkn; adv bkg ess high ssn; red low ssn; cc acc; CCI. "Excel; v helpful recep; gd long stay." ♦ ltd. 1 Apr-30 Sep. € 10.60   2004*

PLEUBIAN see Treguier *1D3*

PLEUMEUR BODOU see Tregastel *1D2*

PLEYBEN *2E2* (5km S Rural) **Camp Municipal de Pont-Coblant**, 29190 Pleyben [02 98 73 31 22 or 02 98 26 68 11 (Mairie); fax 02 98 26 38 99; communedepleyben@wanadoo.fr] On D785 Quimper rd. Turn L immed by phone box on ent Pont-Coblant. Med, mkd pitch, pt shd; wc; shwrs inc; el pts (4-10A) €2; shop 4km; rest, bar adj; rv sw; canoe & cycle hire; poss cr; some rd noise. "Beautiful, quiet site; v clean facs; pleasant with tow-path walks; warden visits twice daily; nr 400 yr old vill church calvaries." 15 Jun-15 Sep. € 6.00   2004*

PLOBANNALEC see Pont l'Abbe *2F2*

PLOEMEL see Auray *2F3*

PLOEMEUR see Lorient *2F2*

PLOERMEL *2F3* (3km N Rural) **Camping du Lac, Les Belles Rives**, 56800 Taupont-Ploermel [tel/fax 02 97 74 01 22; direction1@camping-du-lac-ploermel.com; www.camping-du-lac-ploermel.com] Fr Ploermel cent, take D8 twds Taupont; under narr bdge; foll sp to Lac-au- Duc 3km. Site clearly sp on R on edge of lake. Med, hdg/mkd/hdstg pitch, terr, pt shd; htd wc; mv service pnt; chem disp; shwrs inc; el pts (5A) €2; gas; lndtte; ice; shop; tradsmn; snacks; bar; BBQ; playgrnd; pool & waterslide nrby; sand beach & lake sw adj; watersports; cycle hire nrby; tennis; 10% statics; dogs €0.60; Eng spkn; adv bkg; quiet; cc acc high ssn; red low ssn; CCI. "Golf & horseriding 1km; watersports adj; interesting area; vg." ♦ 1 Apr-30 Oct. € 8.90   2005*

See advertisement

PLOERMEL *2F3* (6km N Rural) **Camping Parc Merlin l'Enchanteur, Vallee de l'Yvel**, 56800 Loyat [02 97 93 05 52/06 03 23 01 42; fax 02 97 60 41 92; qualitypark1@aol.com] Fr Ploermel take D766 N sp St Malo. In 5km turn L to Loyat. Site immed on L on ent vill opp garage. Med, hdg/mkd pitch, pt shd; htd wc; chem disp; mv service pnt; shwrs inc; el pts (6-10A) €2.60-3.60 (poss rev pol); gas; lndtte; ice; sm shop & other shops 600m; tradsmn high ssn; rest & bar 200m; BBQ; sand beach/lake sw adj; tennis; games area; fishing; cycle hire; 10% statics; dogs €1; phone 1km; Eng spkn; adv bkg; v quiet; 10% red 21+ days; cc not acc; red CCI. "Peaceful site, spacious pitches 120 sq m, v soggy in winter; new welcoming British owners (2004); excel rest in vill; v clean facs but poss stretched when site full; Chateau Josselin, Lizio & Broceliande worth visiting; Broceliande forest with legend of King Arthur & his knights; pool planned for 2005." ♦ 27 Mar-10 Sep. € 12.00   2004*

PLOERMEL *2F3* (10km S Urban) **Camp Municipal du Pont Salmon, Rue General de Gaulle,** 56460 Serent [02 97 75 91 98; fax 02 97 75 98 35] Fr N166 Vannes-Rennes take D10 W 5km to Serent. At N end of vill turn L at Pont Salmon, site on R. Med, hdg pitch, pt sl, pt shd; htd wc (male all cont); chem disp; mv service pnt; shwrs inc; el pts (10A) €2.15 (poss rev pol); lndtte; shops 300m; playgrnd; htd pool; 5% statics; adv bkg; quiet. "Excel site, well kept; Resistance Museum at St Marcel-Malestroit; gd san facs." ♦ ltd. 1 May-15 Sep. € 6.60   2004*

PLOERMEL *2F3* (7km NW Rural) **Camping La Vallee du Ninian, Route du Lac,** 56800 Taupont [02 97 93 53 01; fax 02 97 93 57 27; infos@ camping-ninian.com; www.camping-ninian.com] Fr Ploermel cent foll sp to Taupont or Lac au Duc; N on D8. Thro vill Taupont take L hand turn sp La Vallee du Ninian; site on L 1km fr Hellean. Sm, hdg pitch (lge), pt shd; wc; chem disp; shwrs inc; baby facs; el pts (3-6A) €1.60-3.10; ice; lndtte; shop; bar; playgrnd; htd pool; lake sw & watersports 4km; sand beach 4km; entmnt; dogs €0.70; quiet; adv bkg. "Farm produce; helpful owners; v peaceful; singing rd campfire some nights; vg." ♦ 1 May-30 Sep. € 14.30   2004*

PLOMBIERES LES BAINS *6F2* (10km S Rural) **Camp Municipal Le Val d'Ajol, Chemin des Oeuvres,** 88340 Le Val-d'Ajol [03 29 66 55 17] Fr N on N57 after Plombieres-les-Bains turn onto D20 sp Le Val-d'Ajol. Site sps in vill. Sm, hdg pitch, pt shd; wc; chem disp; shwrs inc; el pts (3A) €2.20; shop 1km; pool adj; TV; dogs; phone; adv bkg; quiet; CCI. "Clean facs; gd for touring Vosges & walking; one of best municipal sites seen." ♦ 15 Apr-30 Sep. € 8.10   2005*

PLOMBIERES LES BAINS *6F2* (3km W) **Camp Municipal du Fraiteux, 81 Rue du Camping, Ruaux,** 88370 Plombieres-les-Bains [03 29 66 00 71 or 03 29 66 00 24 (Mairie); fax 03 29 30 06 64] Turn W fr N57 in cent of Plombieres-les-Bains onto D20, foll sp to Epinal for 2km L onto D20B to Ruaux, site on L. Sm, pt sl; wc; shwrs inc; el pts (6A) inc; gas; lndtte; ice; shops adj; playgrnd; pool 3km; poss cr; quiet; 20% red CCI. 15 Mar-31 Oct. € 13.05   2003*

PLONEOUR LANVERN see Pont l'Abbe *2F2*

PLONEVEZ PORZAY see Douarnenez *2E2*

PLOUAY *2F2* (4km NW Rural) **Camping Bois des Ecureuils,** 29300 Guilligomarc'h [tel/fax 02 98 71 70 98; bois-des-ecureuils@tiscali.fr; www.bois-des-ecureuils.fr] N fr Plouay on D769 dir Faouet, for 5km; turn L to Guilligomarc'h; site sp. Sm, mkd pitch, pt sl, shd; wc (some cont); chem disp; shwrs inc; el pts (5A) €2.40; gas; lndtte; ice; shop 3km; tradsmn; playgrnd; rv sw 3km; lake 6km; sand beach 25km; cycle hire; dogs €1; poss cr; Eng spkn; adv bkg; quiet; no cc acc; CCI. "Friendly British owners; conv touring Brittany; gd walking; excel peaceful site; lge pitches." ♦ ltd. 15 May-15 Sep. € 10.00   2005*

PLOUESCAT *2E2* (W Coastal) **Escapades Terre Oceane Camping La Baie de Kernic, Rue de Pen-an-Theven,** 29430 Plouescat [02 98 69 86 60 or 05 46 55 10 01; fax 05 46 55 10 00; info@ campingterreoceane.com; www.campingterre oceane.com] Site sp W of Plouescat fr D10. Lge, mkd pitch, hdstg, pt shd; wc; sauna; shwrs inc; el pts (6A) inc; lndtte; shop; rest; snacks; bar; BBQ; pool; paddling pool; sand beach adj; watersports; tennis; games area; cycle hire; entmnt; child entmnt; some statics; dogs €2; Eng spkn; adv bkg; red low ssn. "Pleasant resort; well-run site." ♦ 8 Apr-16 Sep. € 29.00   2005*

PLOUEZEC see Paimpol *1D3*

PLOUGASNOU *1D2* (1.5km SE Rural) **Camping Le Tregor, Rue de Cosquero,** 29228 Kerjean [02 98 67 37 64; bookings@campingdutregor.com; www. campingdutregor.com] At junc of D46 to Plougasnou. Site is on L just bef town sp. Sm, hdg/mkd pitch, pt shd; wc; chem disp (wc); shwrs inc; el pts (6-10A) inc; gas; ice; lndtte; shop 1km; BBQ; playgrnd; sand beach 1.2km; lake sw & watersports 3km; 10% statics; dogs €0.80; poss cr; adv bkg; quiet; CCI. "British owners planning to rebuild san facs 2005; ideal for walking, cycling & fishing; beautiful countryside & beaches nrby; convenient for Roscoff ferries & Morlaix town; phone if req NH after end Oct." Easter-31 Oct. € 13.00   2005*

PLOUGASNOU *1D2* (3km NW Coastal/Urban) **Camp Municipal de la Mer,** 29630 Primel-Tregastel [tel/fax 02 98 72 37 06 or 02 98 67 30 06; primel-tregastel.camping-de-la-mer@wanadoo.fr] Fr Morlaix take D46 to Plougastel on to Primel-Tregastel. Bear R in vill & 1st L opp cafe to site on R in 100 m. Med, unshd, wc; chem disp; mv service pnt; shwrs (with token); el pts (10A) inc; gas 1.5km; lndtte; shops 1.5km; tradsmn high ssn; playgrnd; sand beach 500m; dogs; phone; poss cr; no cc acc; CCI. "Fine coastal views; gd walking & cycling; ltd facs low ssn; vg long/sh stay." ♦ ltd. 1 Jun-30 Sep. € 15.30   2005*

†**PLOUGASTEL DAOULAS** *2E2* (4.5km NW Coastal) **Camping St Jean,** 29470 Plougastel-Daoulas [02 98 40 32 90; fax 02 98 04 23 11; campingstjean@wanadoo.fr; www.campingsaint jean.com] Fr Brest, take N165 E for approx 12km then leave m'way after Plougsatel exit & foll sp. Site in 2km at end of rd by rv. Med, pt sl, terr, pt shd; wc; mv service pnt; shwrs; el pts (6-10A) €2.50-€3 (poss rev pol); lndtte; ice; shop & 5km; snacks; playgrnd; htd, covrd pool; TV; dogs €1; poss cr; quiet; red low ssn. "€20 dep for security barrier." € 15.00   2004*

PLOUGOULM see Roscoff *1D2*

PLOUGRESCANT see Treguier *1D3*

FRANCE

PLOUGUERNEAU *2E2* (2km N Coastal) **Camping La Greve Blanche, St Michel, 29880 Plouguerneau** [02 98 04 70 35 or 02 98 04 63 97 (LS); fax 02 98 04 63 97; lroudaut@free.fr] Fr Lannilis D13 to Plouguerneau, D32 sp La Greve, St Michel (look out for lorry rte sp). Avoid Plouguerneau vill when towing - tight RH bend. Med, pt sl, terr, unshd; wc; shwrs €1; el pts (9A) €2.20; bar; shops 3km; playgrnd; sand beach; dogs €1.80; Eng spkn; adv bkg; 10% red low ssn; CCI. "Gd views over sea & islands; in fog lighthouse sounds all night otherwise quiet; facs clean & well-kept; low ssn recep open eves only; helpful staff." ♦ ltd.
1 Jun-30 Sep. € 9.30   2004*

PLOUGUERNEAU *2E2* (6km N Coastal) **Camping Le Vougot, Route de Prat Leden, 29880 Plouguerneau** [02 98 25 61 51]
D10 fr Plouguerneau or Guisseny turn N onto D52 dir Greve du Vougot, site sp. Med, hdg/mkd pitch, pt shd; wc; mv service pnt; chem disp; shwrs €1; el pts (10A) €2.30; gas; ice; shop; tradsmn; snacks; playgrnd; sand beach 250m; watersports, horseriding nr; 17% statics; dogs €1.07; adv bkg; Eng spkn; cc acc; red long stay; CCI. "Gd walking; interesting area." ♦ Easter-30 Sep. € 11.60   2004*

PLOUGUERNEAU *2E2* (5km NE Coastal) **Aire Naturalle de Keralloret (Yvinec), 29880 Guisseny** [02 98 25 60 37; fax 02 98 25 69 88; auberge@keralloret.com; www.keralloret.com] On N10 dir Plouguerneau, site 2.5km after Guisseny. Sp on L. Sm, pt shd; wc; chem disp (wc); shwrs inc; el pts (6A) inc; tradsmn; rest; snacks; beach 5km; Eng spkn; adv bkg; quiet; cc acc; CCI. "Delightful CL-type site with pitches around a sm lake; excel all stays." ♦ ltd
1 May-21 Oct. € 11.35   2004*

PLOUHA *2E3* (Rural/Coastal) **Camping Domaine de Kerjean, 22580 Plouha** [05 46 22 38 22; fax 05 46 23 65 10; kerjean@yukadivillages.com; www.yukadivillages.com] Exit N12 at Les Rampes onto D786 N to Plouha. Site sp fr town cent. Lge, mkd pitch, hdstg, pt shd; wc; shwrs inc; el pts €4; ice; shop 3km; snacks; bar; BBQ (gas/elec); playgrnd; htd, covrd pool nr; sand beach 1km; fishing, sailing 10km; tennis 4km; horseriding 2km; dogs; adv bkg; Eng spkn; quiet. "Well-situated for beautiful local beaches; gd walking area; vg." ♦ 13 May-9 Sep. € 18.00   2005*

See advertisement below

PLOUHA *2E3* (5km NE Coastal) **Camping Le Varquez-sur-Mer, 5 Route de la Corniche, Brehec-Plage,** 22580 Plouha [02 96 22 34 43; fax 02 96 22 68 87; campinglevarquez@wanadoo.fr; www.camping-le-varquez.com] Sp bet St Quay-Portrieux & Paimpol fr D786. Med, hdg/mkd pitch, hdstg, pt sl, pt shd; wc; chem disp; shwrs; el pts (6-10A) €3; gas; lndtte; shop 4km; tradsmn; snacks; bar; BBQ; playgrnd; htd pool; paddling pool; sand beach 600m; cycle hire; entmnt; TV; 30% statics; dogs €1.60; Eng spkn; quiet cc acc; CCI. "Lovely coast; peaceful, family-run site; adj walking rte G34." ♦ 1 Apr-1 Nov. € 15.90   2005*

See advertisement opposite

PLOUHARNEL see Carnac *2G3*

PLOUHINEC *2F2* (1km SE Coastal) **Camping Le Moteno, Route du Magouer,** 56680 Plouhinec [02 97 36 76 63; fax 02 97 85 81 84; campingmoteno@wanadoo.fr; www.camping-le-moteno.com] App Auray on D22, take 2nd turn L after Pont Lerois & foll sps. Lge, hdg/mkd pitch, pt shd; wc; chem disp; shwrs; el pts (6-10A) €2.50-3; gas; lndtte; ice; shop; rest; snacks; bar; playgrnd; pool; waterslide; rv sw, beach 600m; fishing & watersports 100m; cycle hire; games rm; entmnt; TV; dogs €2; Eng spkn; adv bkg; quiet; red low ssn. "Gd base for visiting Carnac & Quiberon Peninsula." ♦ 26 Apr-13 Sep. € 16.60   2003*

PLOUHINEC *2F2* (5km S Coastal) **Camp Municipal de la Falaise, Rue de la Barre,** 56410 Etel [02 97 55 33 79; fax 02 97 55 34 14] Fr L'Orient, take D781 twd Carnac, turn R to Etel (sp) after x-ing bdge over Etel rv. Foll sp for La Plage or Camping. Or fr Carnac, exit D781 at Erdeven on D105 to Etel. Med, pt sl, pt shd; wc; shwrs inc; el pts (poss rev pol); lndtte; ice; shop 500m; sand beach; lake sw; quiet; boat trips; walks; windsurfing & canoes; CCI. 15 May-15 Sep. € 10.21   2002*

PLOUVORN see Landivisiau *2E2*

PLOZEVET *2F2* (500m W) **Camping de la Corniche,** 29710 Plozevet [02 98 91 33 94 or 02 98 91 32 93; fax 02 98 91 41 53] Fr N165 foll sp Audierne onto D784 to Plozevet & foll sps to site. Med, hdg pitch, pt shd; wc; chem disp; mv service pnt; baby facs; shwrs inc; el pts (6A) inc; lndtte; shop; tradsmn; playgrnd; pool; beach 2km; 10% statics; CCI. "Lge pitches; helpful owner; excel facs; gd long stay." ♦ 1 Apr-30 Sep. € 20.50 2003*

POILLY LEZ GIEN see Gien *4G3*

POITIERS *7A2*. **For sites convenient for Futuroscope, also see listings under Chatellerault and Jaunay Clan.**

POITIERS *7A2* (10km N Rural) **Camping du Futur, 1, Rue des Bois,** 86170 Avanton [05 49 54 09 67; fax 05 49 54 09 59; campingdufutur@wanadoo.fr; www.camping-du-futur.com] Exit A10 junc 28. After toll take 1st exit at rndabt sp Avanton. Site well sp fr Avanton. Med, hdg/mkd pitch, pt shd; wc; chem disp (wc); mv service pnt; shwrs inc; el pts (10A) €2.30; lndtte; tradsmn; rest; bar; playgrnd; pool high ssn; mini-golf; TV; dogs €1.50; Eng spkn; adv bkg; quiet; red low ssn; CCI. "Lovely site & well-managed; v helpful Brit owners; modern, clean, excel facs (unisex in winter); 5 mins Futuroscope (tickets avail fr office high ssn); conv A10; excel site." ♦ 1 Apr-30 Sep. € 12.60   2005*

POITIERS *7A2* (8km S) **Camp Municipal, Ave de la Plage,** 86240 Liguge [05 49 55 29 50; fax 05 49 55 38 45; liguge@cg86.fr] E of N10 site sp & off D4 Poitiers-Vivonne rd (not N10) in Liguge. Sm, mkd pitch, pt shd; wc; chem disp; shwrs; el pts (8A) inc; ice; tradsmn; shops 2km; playgrnd; rv fishing 200m; football stadium adj; TV; Eng spkn; quiet; CCI. "V pleasant & helpful young resident wardens; ample san facs; barrier unlocked for each ent/exit; some rd & rlwy noise; public access to stadium thro site; twin-axle €45.73 extra." 15 Jun-15 Sep. € 7.30   2003*

POITIERS *7A2* (1.5km NW Urban) **Camp Municipal du Porteau, Rue du Porteau,** 86000 Poitiers [05 49 41 44 88] Sp off N10. Sm, mkd pitch, unshd; wc; chem disp; shwrs; CCI.   2002*

POITIERS *7A2* (12km NW Rural) **Camp Municipal de La Drouille, Ave de l'Europe,** 86170 Neuville-de-Poitou [05 49 51 20 44; fax 05 49 54 85 09; neuville-de-poitou@cg86.fr] NW fr Poitiers on N147 to Neuville-de-Poitou; site on L just after ent to vill; well sp. Sm, hdg/mkd pitch, some hdstg, pt shd; wc; chem disp; shwrs inc; el pts (12A) €2; supmkt in vill 1km; quiet; no cc acc; CCI. "Conv for Futuroscope (8km); v clean & well-maintained; spacious; choose a pitch & owner comes to collect bet 0730-0830 & 1800-1900; poss itinerants; excel sh stay." ♦ ltd. 1 Jun-31 Aug. € 7.00   2005*

POIX DE PICARDIE *3C3* (300m SW Rural) **Camp Municipal Le Bois des Pecheurs, Route de Forges-les-Eaux,** 80290 Poix-de-Picardie [03 22 90 11 71 or 03 22 90 32 90 (Mairie); fax 03 22 90 32 91; camping@ville-poix-de-picardie.fr; www.ville-poix-de-picardie.fr] Fr town cent by D901 dir Beauvais, turn R onto D919 sp Camping. Fr Beauvais, turn L at bottom of steep hill opp Citroen agent, site 500m on R. Med, hdg/mkd pitch, hdstg, pt shd; wc; chem disp; shwrs inc; el pts (10A) €3.80; gas 300m; lndtte; ice; shops, supmkt adj; rest, bar 500m; BBQ; playgrnd; htd, covrd pool 800m; rv & fishing adj; tennis 800m; games rm; cycle hire; TV; dogs €1.30; tourist info; poss cr; Eng spkn; adv bkg; quiet; red long stay; CCI. "Pleasant, peaceful site in delightful area; friendly; clean facs; gd touring base area &/or NH; vg walking & cycling; mkt Sun." ♦ 1 Apr-30 Sep. € 11.00   2005*

See advertisement on next page

FRANCE

POLGASTEL ST GERMAIN see Quimper *2F2*

POLIGNY *6H2* (1km SW Rural) **Camp Communautaire de la Croix du Dan**, 39800 Poligny [03 84 37 01 35; fax 03 84 37 10 30; villedepoligny.jura@wanadoo.fr] Fr W on N83 site on R immed bef town sp Poligny. Med, mkd pitch, pt wc (mainly cont); chem disp; shwrs inc; el pts (10A) inc; lndtte; shops 1km; tradsmn; playgrnd; no statics; dogs; phone; poss cr; Eng spkn; quiet; CCI. "Excel site; spotlessly clean & tidy; helpful warden; welcome aperitif every Sat in Jul/Aug; twin-axle c'vans €27 per night; v pretty, friendly town." ♦ ltd. 15 Jun-15 Sep. € 11.80   2005*

POLMINHAC see Vic sur Cere *7C4*

POMMEROL see Remuzat *9D2*

POMMEUSE *4E4* (1km SW Rural) **Camping Le Chene Gris**, 24 Place de la Gare de Faremoutiers, 77515 Pommeuse [01 64 04 21 80; fax 01 64 20 05 89; campinglechenegris@wanadoo.fr; www.lechene gris.com] Fr A4, take N34 SE dir Coulommiers, turn R onto D25 sp Pommeuse & Faremoutiers. Site on R after stn at Faremoutiers. Well sp. Lge, hdg pitch, hdstg, pt sl, terr, pt shd; htd wc; chem disp; mv service pnt; baby facs; shwrs inc; el pts (10A) inc; lndtte; shop; supmkt 3km; tradsmn; rest; snacks; bar; playgrnd; 2 pools (1 htd, covrd); paddling pool; games rm; 30% statics; dogs €2.50; phone; adv bkg; quiet; red low ssn; CCI. "Conv Paris cent, Disneyland & Parc Asterix; walking dist to trains - direct line to Paris; excel new san facs; vg." 31 Mar-27 Oct. € 35.00   2005*

See advertisement opposite (bottom)

PONCIN see Pont d'Ain *9A2*

PONS (AVEYRON) see Montsalvy *7D4*

PONS (CHARENTE MARITIME) *7B2* (W Urban) **Camp Municipal Le Paradis, Ave de Poitou,** 17800 Pons [05 46 91 36 72; fax 05 46 96 14 15; ville.pons@smic17.fr] Well sp fr town o'skts. Med, mkd pitch, pt shd; wc; shwrs inc; el pts (6-10A) inc; shops adj; tradsmn; pool, waterslide 100m; fishing; TV; dogs €1.76. "Excel; attractive grounds; interesting town; conv for Saintes, Cognac, Royan; helpful warden." ♦ 1 May-30 Sep. € 15.00   2004*

†**PONS (CHARENTE MARITIME)** *7B2* (1km N Rural) **Camping Les Moulins de la Vergne, 9 Route de Colombiers,** 17800 Pons [tel/fax 05 46 94 11 49; moulinsdelavergne@wanadoo.fr; www.moulins delavergne.nl] Exit A10 junc 36 onto D732 sp Pons. Take N137 N in 3km then turn R in 4km onto D125 (E2). Site sp in 1.5km on L on D234. Fr town cent foll yellow sps in Pons - do not confuse with municipal site Le Paradis. NB c'vans not allowed thro Pons & should stay on by-pass. Med, mkd pitch, pt shd; wc; chem disp; shwrs inc; el pts (10A) inc; lndtte; shops 1km; tradsmn; rest; snacks; bar; BBQ; playgrnd; pool; adv bkg; Eng spkn; quiet; cc acc; CCI. "Conv touring base or NH en rte Spain; v friendly, helpful Dutch owners; vg clean facs; worth stay for restaurant alone (high ssn); grass patches soft in wet weather - park on site roads off ssn; gates locked overnight; conv A10; vg." ♦ € 17.00   2005*

†**PONS (CHARENTE MARITIME)** *7B2* (2km W Rural) **Camping Chardon,** 17800 Pons [50 46 95 01 25] Fr N or S on A10, exit junc 36 onto D732 (take care as heavy, fast traff). Site sp on R in 1km. Narr ent to rd. Or fr N or S on N137 take D732 twd Gemozac, site on L 2km fr Pons. Site lies to S of D732, bet N137 & A10. Foll yellow Camping Chardon sp (easily missed). Sm, hdg pitch, pt shd; wc; chem disp; serviced pitch; shwrs; el pts (10A) inc; gas 2km; lndtte; shops 1km; tradsmn; rest; pizzeria; bar; playgrnd; pool 1km; 25% statics; dogs; adv bkg (20% dep req); quiet; no cc acc. "Basic, open-air san facs, not well-maintained; poss not clean; drinking water not easy to find; poor facs for disabled; quaint, rustic site; ltd low ssn facs; vg rest; v friendly owners; accomm at farm; conv Cognac, Saintes & Royan; resident llama in paddock; low ssn phone ahead to check if open; conv NH if using A10 or N137." ♦ ltd. € 15.00   2005*

FRANCE

PONT AUDEMER *3D2* (2km NW Rural) **Camp Municipal Risle-Seine Les Etangs, Route des Etangs, 27500 Toutainville** [tel/fax 02 32 42 46 65; camping@ville-pont-audemer.fr; www.ville-pont-audemer.fr] Fr Le Havre on A131/E05 cross rv at Pont de Normandie (toll). Take D580 & at junc 3 branch R & take 2nd exit sp Beuzeville. At edge of Fiquefleur take D180, then N175 to Pont-Audemer. In Toutainville foll site sp, turn L just bef A13 underpass, then immed R. Site approx 2km on R. Med, hdg/mkd pitch, pt shd; wc; chem disp; mv service pnt; serviced pitches; shwrs inc; el pts (10A) inc; lndtte; ice; shop 1.5km; tradsmn (pre-order); snacks; bar; BBQ; playgrnd; paddling pool; htd pool & tennis 2km; fishing; canoeing, watersports; cycle hire; games area; games rm; TV rm; internet; dogs; Eng spkn; adv bkg; quiet; red long stay/low ssn; cc acc. "Lovely, well run, immac site; poss school groups at w/e; helpful warden; bread avail fr recep; barrier clsd 2200-0830 but flexible for ferry; many leisure activities; 1hr Le Havre ferry; excel." ♦ ltd.
15 Mar-15 Nov. € 15.60 ABS - N13   2005*

See advertisement above

PONT AUTHOU see Brionne *3D2*

PONT AVEN *2F2* (10km N Rural) **Camping Les Genets d'Or, Kermerour, Pont Kereon, 29380 Bannalec** [tel/fax 02 98 39 54 35; info@holidaybrittany.com; www.holidaybrittany.com] Fr Pont Aven/Bannalec exit on N165 N to Bannalec on D4; after rlwy x-ing turn R sp Quimperle. In 1km turn R, sp Le Trevoux; site on L 500m. Sm, hdg/mkd pitch, pt sl, pt shd; wc; chem disp; shwrs inc; el pts (6A) €3; lndtte; sm shop; supmkt 1km; tradsmn; rest; snacks; bar; playgrnd; pool 10km; sand beach 15km; games rm; cycle hire; some statics; dogs €1; Eng spkn; adv bkg; quiet; 10% red 7 days; CCI. "Well-kept, peaceful site in orchard; lge pitches; friendly, helpful, welcoming British owners; excel touring base." ♦ ltd.
1 Apr-30 Sep. € 11.50   2005*

PONT AVEN *2F2* (6km SE Coastal) **Camping de l'Ile Percee, Plage de Trenez, 29350 Moelan-sur-Mer** [02 98 71 16 25 or 02 35 84 89 35 (LS)] App thro Moelan-sur-Mer, 6km SE of Pont-Aven or 6km SW of Quimperle - watch for R turn after Moelan. Take D116 sp to Kerfany. Keep strt at Kergroes, turn L after 500m sp L'Ile Percee. Med, pt sl, unshd; wc (cont); shwrs; el pts (4-6A) inc; ice; lndtte; bar; playgrnd; sandy/rocky beach adj; sw; fishing & watersports 50m; TV; dogs €1; poss cr; adv bkg; v quiet. "Well-run site; superb sea views some pitches; ent narr & winding; sm pitches; san facs poss stretched high ssn." Easter-23 Sep.
€ 16.00   2003*

PONT AVEN *2F2* (7km SE) **Camping La Grande Lande, 7 Rue de Grande Lande, Kergroes, 29116 Moelan-sur-Mer** [02 98 71 00 39; fax 02 98 71 00 19; camping.grande.lande@wanadoo.fr]
Exit N165/E60 dir Pont Aven. Then D783 & D24 to Moelan. Fr Quimperle S on D16 to Clohars-Carnoel, W on D24 to Moelan-sur-Mer; thro town on rd to Kerfany Plage site on R in vill of Kergroes. Med, mkd pitch, pt sl, pt shd; wc (mainly cont); chem disp (wc); baby facs; shwrs inc; el pts (3-10A) €2.80-3.80; lndtte; ice; shop in vill; tradsmn; rest; snacks; bar; BBQ; playgrnd; pool; sand beach 2km; tennis; games area; mini-golf; cycle hire; horseriding; archery; entmnt; TV rm; 6% statics; dogs €1; phone; some Eng spkn; adv bkg; quiet. "Gd touring base; Port-du-Belon (2km) boat trips; scuba diving; fishing." ♦ Easter-30 Sep. € 16.00   2005*

PONT AVEN *2F2* (10km SE Rural) **Camping Tal Ar Moor, Kerfany Plage, 29350 Moelan-sur-Mer** [02 98 71 11 98] Exit N165/E60 dir Pont Aven. Then D783 & D24 to Moelan. Fr Quimperle take D116 thro Moelan-sur-Mer (watch for R turn 1km after Moelan) site behind beach. Med, hdg/mkd pitch, pt shd; wc; chem disp; shwrs; el pts (6-10A); lndtte; playgrnd. "Beautiful, quiet area; beach, cliff & inland walks."
Easter-15 Sep.   2002*

PONT AVEN *2F2* (8km S Coastal) **Camping Les Chaumieres, Kerascoet, 29920 Nevez** [02 98 06 73 06; fax 02 98 06 78 34; campingdes chaumieres@wanadoo.fr] S fr Pont-Aven thro Nevez to Kerascoet. Med, hdg/mkd pitch, pt shd; wc; chem disp; mv service pnt; serviced pitches; shwrs inc; el pts (4-6A) €2.29-2.74; gas 3km; lndtte; ice; shop 3km; tradsmn high ssn; rest, snacks, bar adj; playgrnd; sand beach 800m; dogs €0.80; Eng spkn; adv bkg ess; quiet; red low ssn; CCI. "Excel site; well-organised recep; lovely sandy bay; cliff walks." ♦ 15 May-15 Sep. € 11.74   2003*

PONT AVEN *2F2* (10km S Coastal) **Camping Le St Nicolas, Port Manech, 29920 Nevez** [02 98 06 89 75; fax 02 98 06 74 61; info@campingsaint nicolas.com; www.campingsaintnicolas.com] Take D783 W fr Pont-Aven for 2km, turn L onto D77 S thro Nevez to Port Manech. Site well sp. Narr app to site. Lge, hdg pitch; pt sl, pt shd; wc; shwrs inc; el pts (6-10A) inc; gas; lndtte; ice; tradsmn high ssn; playgrnd; pool; sand beach 200m; watersports; games area; tennis; horseriding nrby; TV rm; dogs €1.10; poss cr; adv bkg; quiet; red low ssn; cc acc; CCI. "Friendly owners; cliff walks; gd touring base.".
May-Sep. € 20.00   2003*

PONT AVEN *2F2* (3km SW Rural) **Domaine de Kerlann, Land Rosted, 29930 Pont Aven** [02 98 06 01 77; fax 02 98 06 18 50; kerlann@siblu. fr; www.siblu.com] Fr Pont Aven foll sp twd Concarneau. After 1.5km, turn L onto D77 twd Nevez. Site approx 1.5km on R. V lge, hdg/mkd pitch, hdstg, pt sl, pt shd; htd wc; chem disp; baby facs; shwrs inc; el pts (8A) inc; gas; lndtte; shop; rest; snacks; bar; playgrnd; htd pools (1 covrd); waterslide; sand beach 3km; tennis; cycle hire; entmnt; child entmtn; TV rm; 85% statics; Eng spkn; adv bkg ess high ssn; cc acc; red low ssn/low ssn; CCI. "Wooded site & areas poss muddy after rain; children's club all ssn; teenagers' club Jul/Aug; sports pitch; all facs open all ssn." ♦ ltd.
1 Apr-29 Oct. € 144.00 (7 nights)   2005*

See advertisement

PONT AVEN *2F2* (5km SW Rural) **Camping Les Genets, Route St Philibert, 29920 Nevez** [02 98 06 86 13 or 02 98 06 72 31; camping lesgenets@aol.com] Turn S off D783 onto D77 to Nevez. At church in town, bear R & turn immed R to exit Nevez with post office on R. Site on L, clearly sp. Med, hdg/mkd pitch, pt shd; wc (some cont); shwrs inc; el pts (3-10A) €2.10-4.40; gas 500m; lndtte; ice; shops 500m; playgrnd; sand beach 5km; 10% statics; dogs €1; some Eng spkn; adv bkg; quiet; CCI. "Choice of excel beaches adj; vg."
1 Jun-15 Sep. € 10.00   2005*

PONT AVEN *2F2* (6km SW Coastal) **Camping Les Deux Fontaines, 29920 Raguenes [02 98 06 81 91; fax 02 98 06 71 80; www.les2fontaines.fr]** Leave N165/E60 at Kerampaou foll sp D24 twds Pont Aven. In approx 4.5km turn R (S) foll sp Nevez then Raguenes. Site 3km fr Nevez. Lge, mkd pitch, pt shd; wc (some cont); shwrs inc; baby facs; el pts (6A) €3.40; lndtte; shop; rest; bar; sand beach 800m; htd pool; tennis; 80% statics; dogs €2.40. "Holiday camp atmosphere high ssn; many tour operator statics, pop with British families." ♦ ltd. 15 May-15 Sep. € 18.70   2005*

PONT AVEN *2F2* (8km SW Coastal) **Camping de l'Ocean, Ker Oren, 29920 Raguenes [02 98 06 87 13; fax 02 98 06 78 26]** Leave a'route N165 at Kerampaou; foll sp D24 twds Pont Aven; in approx 4.5km turn R; foll sp Nevez then Raguenes; site 3km fr Nevez. Med, hdg/mkd pitch, unshd; serviced pitches; wc; chem disp; shwrs inc; baby facs; el pts (3A) inc; ice; lndtte; shops adj; tradsmn; playgrnd; pool; sand beach 300m; sailing; fishing; adv bkg rec high ssn; quiet; CCI. "Dir access to beach." ♦ 15 May-15 Sep. € 19.06   2002*

PONT AVEN *2F2* (8km SW Coastal) **Camping Raguenes-Plage, 19 Rue des Iles, 29920 Raguenes [02 98 06 80 69; fax 02 98 06 89 05]** Fr Pont-Aven take D783 dir Tregunc; in 2.5km turn L for Nevez, foll sps to Raguenes fr Nevez. Or fr N165 take D24 at Kerampaou exit; in 3km turn R to Nizon; at church in vill turn R onto D77 to Nevez; site on L 3km after Nevez. Lge, mkd pitch, shd; wc (some cont); chem disp; mv service pnt; baby facs; sauna; shwrs inc; el pts (6A) inc; gas; lndtte; ice; shop; rest; snacks adj; bar; BBQ; playgrnd; htd pool & paddling pool; waterslide; sand beach adj; watersports school adj; tennis nr; games rm; trampoline; games area; horseriding; entmnt; 20% statics (sep area); dogs €1.50; adv bkg rec (dep req); quiet; red low ssn; cc acc; CCI. "Pretty, wooded site; private path to lge, sandy beach; excel family-run site; v clean facs; 1st class site." ♦ 26 Apr-30 Sep. € 24.40   2005*

PONT D'AIN *9A2* (6km NE Rural) **Camping Vallee d'Ain (formerly Camp Municipal Poncin), 01450 Poncin [tel/fax 04 74 37 20 78; camping-vallee-de-lain@laposte.net; www.chez.com/campingponcin]** Fr Pont d'Ain cent foll N75 S & when exit Pont d'Ain turn L on N84 (sp 300m fr vill); site on D81 off D91. Med, pt shd; wc; chem disp; shwrs inc; el pts (5A) €2.40; gas; ice; lndtte; shops adj; snacks; BBQ; playgrnd; entmnt; rv adj; canoe, cycle hire; quiet; some m'way noise; CCI. "New san facs 2004; walks by rv, helpful staff" 1 Apr-3 Oct. € 13.80   2004*

PONT D'AIN *9A2* (3km E Urban) **Camping de l'Oiselon, 01160 Pont d'Ain [tel/fax 04 74 39 05 23; campingoiselon@libertysurf.fr]** Fr A42 exit Pont d'Ain foll D90 to vill. In vill cent turn R on N75. Turn L immed after x-ing Rv L'Ain. Foll rd passing tennis club on L. Site on L. Lge, pt shd; wc; chem disp; shwrs inc; el pts (6-10A) €2.20-3.05; shops; rest; snacks; BBQ; playgrnd; pool; rv sw & beach; fishing; canoeing; tennis adj; horseriding 5km; cycle loan; poss cr; adv bkg; quiet (some noise fr disco). "Fair NH; v helpful staff." 19 Mar-9 Oct. € 11.10   2005*

PONT DE L'ARCHE *3D2* (Urban) **Camp Municipal Eure et Seine, Quai du Maréchal-Foch, 27340 Pont-de-l'Arche [02 35 23 06 71 or 02 32 98 90 70 (Mairie); fax 02 35 23 90 88]** N15 fr Rouen, foll sp for Vernon then Evereux & Pont-de-l'Arche; after x-ing Rv Seine at rndabt turn R sp Centre Ville & turn R at War Memorial. Restricted width on app. Med, mkd pitch, pt sl, unshd; wc; chem disp; shwrs inc; el pts (6A) inc; lndtte; shop 200m; playgrnd; rv fishing adj; some statics; dogs; phone; poss v cr; some Eng spkn; rd noise; CCI. "Rvside site; sm pitches; v helpful warden; clean, peaceful but facs poss stretched high ssn; poss itinerants." ♦ 1 Apr-30 Oct. € 9.10   2005*

†PONT DE L'ARCHE *3D2* (3km N) **Camping Les Terrasses, 2 Rue de Rouen, 27460 Igoville [tel/fax 02 35 23 08 15]** Site sp fr N15 in both dirs. Fr A13 take exit sp Pont-de-l'Arche D321, pass thro town & at intersection of D321 & N15 turn L. Cross Seine to Igoville & cont up N15 & foll site sp. App hill may cause problems heavy/lge vans. Sm, mkd pitch, hdstg, sl, terr, pt shd; wc; chem disp, shwrs €1; el pts (6-10A) €1.68; lndtte; supmkt 1km; playgrnd; 80% statics; dogs €1; adv bkg; quiet; red low ssn; CCI. "Suitable m'van or sm van & 4WD only - steep, bumpy access rd poss diff towed vehicles; not rec as NH; bus to Rouen; site clsd Xmas & New Year; excel views Seine valley; warm welcome; v sm shwr cubicles." € 14.50   2003*

†PONT DE L'ARCHE *3D2* (10km S) **Camping Le St Pierre, 1 Rue du Chateau, 27430 St Pierre-du-Vauvray [tel/fax 02 32 61 01 55]** Fr S exit N154 junc 3 or A13 junc 18 (Louviers) onto N155 E until junc with N15. Turn L & in 4km turn R to St Pierre. Fr N on N15 after x-ing Rv Seine at Pont-de-l'Arche cont for approx 6km & turn L to St Pierre. Do not ent St Pierre fr E on D313 due low bdge under rlwy line. Med, hdg/mkd pitch, pt shd; wc; chem disp; shwrs inc; el pts (6-10A) €2.30; lndry rm; shop 1km; BBQ; playgrnd; 25% statics; dogs €1.10; site clsd 2 weeks at Xmas; adv bkg rec; noise fr rlwy adj; CCI. "Main Paris/Le Havre TGV rlwy line adj site; rlwy noise; in grnds sm chateau; conv Giverny; walks by Seine; friendly staff; ltd facs; NH only." € 11.40   2005*

FRANCE

PONT DE SALARS *7D4* (1.5km N Rural) **Parc Camping du Lac,** 12290 Pont-de-Salars [05 65 46 84 86; fax 05 65 46 60 39; camping.du.lac@wanadoo.fr] Fr Rodez on D911 La Primaube-Millau rd, turn L bef ent Pont-de-Salars. Site sp. Lge, mkd pitch, pt sl, terr, pt shd; wc (some cont); chem disp; shwrs inc; el pts (3-6A) €2-3.50; gas; lndtte; ice; shop & 1km; tradsmn; rest; snacks; bar; BBQ; playgrnd; pool; lake sw; sailing; fishing; entmnt; TV; 5% statics; no dogs; phone; poss cr; Eng spkn; adv bkg (dep req + bkg fee); noisy nr entmnt area; red low ssn. "Site has own slipway & landing stage; beautiful situation; poss unkempt & ltd facs low ssn; san facs clean & well kept but poss stretched high ssn; fair sh stay/NH." ♦ ltd. 15 Jun-15 Sep. € 15.50   2005*

PONT DE SALARS *7D4* (4km N Rural) **Camping Les Terrasses du Lac, Route du Vibal,** 12290 Pont-de-Salars [05 65 46 88 18 or 06 72 89 84 34; fax 05 65 46 85 38; campinglesterrasses@wanadoo.fr; www.campinglesterrasses.com] Dir Albi fr Rodez N88 to La Primaube. Turn L in La Primaube on D911 for Pont-de-Salars. Turn L on D523 by timberyard to Le Vibal & foll sp to site approx 4km fr vill cent. Lge, terr, pt shd; wc; chem disp; shwrs inc; el pts (10A) €3.75; gas; lndtte; ice; shop; rest; snacks; bar; BBQ; playgrnd; htd pool; sand beach & lake sw; boating; fishing; entmnt; TV; dogs €1.35; Eng spkn; adv bkg; quiet; cc acc; CCI. "Well laid-out site overlooking lake; gd touring area; vg long/sh stay." ♦ 1 Apr-30 Sep. € 19.95   2005*

PONT DE SALARS *7D4* (7km SE Rural) **Camping Sunelia Le Caussanel, Lac de Pareloup,** 12290 Canet-de-Salars [05 65 46 85 19; fax 05 65 46 89 85; info@lecaussanel.com; www.lecaussanel.com] Exit A75 junc 44.1 onto D911 dir Pont-de-Salars, then D993 Salles-Curan & D538 Canet-de-Salars, dir Lac de Pareloup. In 6km fork R to Le Caussanel: in 100m fork L to site. Fr N88 exit at La Primaube then D911 to Pont-de-Salars, then as above. Lge, mkd pitch, hdstg, pt sl, terr, pt shd; wc; mv service pnt; chem disp; shwrs inc; el pts (5A) inc; shop; tradsmn; rest; snacks; bar; playgrnd; htd pools; waterslide; fishing; windsurfing & sailing; boat & cycle hire; games rm; entmnt; internet; 20% statics; dogs €2; Eng spkn; adv bkg; quiet; CCI. "Beautiful situation; friendly owner; vg." ♦ 30 Apr-24 Sep. € 29.00 (CChq acc)   2005*

PONT DE SALARS *7D4* (8km S Rural) **Camping Le Soleil Levant, Lac de Pareloup,** 12290 Canet-de-Salars [05 65 46 03 65; fax 05 65 46 03 62; contact@camping-soleil-levant.com; www.camping-soleil-levant.com] S fr Pont-de-Salars on D993 dir Salles-Curan. Site in 8km bef bdge on L. Lge, mkd pitch, terr, pt sl, pt shd; htd wc (some cont); chem disp; baby facs; shwrs inc; el pts (6A) €2; gas; lndtte; ice; shop 4km; tradsmn; snacks; bar; BBQ; playgrnd; lake sw & sand beach adj; fishing; watersports; games area; games rm; entmnt; internet; TV rm; 10% statics; dogs €1.80; Eng spkn; adv bkg; quiet; cc acc; red low ssn; CCI. "Beautiful location on lakeside; excel san facs." ♦ 1 Apr-30 Sep. € 18.50   2005*

See advertisement

PONT DE VAUX *9A2* (4km NE Rural) **Camping Les Ripettes,** 01190 St Benigne [03 85 30 66 58; info@camping-les-ripettes.com; www.camping-les-ripettes.com] Take D2 fr Pont de Vaux sp St Trivier-des-Courtes for 3km. Immed after water tower on R turn L onto D58 sp Romenay, then immed L. Site well sp on L in 100m. Med, hdg/mkd pitch, pt sl, pt shd; wc; chem disp; shwrs inc; el pts (10A) €2.50; lndtte; shop & 4km; tradsmn; snacks; playgrnd; 2 pools; games area; cycle hire; 2 statics; dogs €2.50; phone; Eng spkn; adv bkg; quiet; cc acc; CCI. "Beautiful location & excel touring base; pitches diff when wet; spacious pitches, some v lge; immac facs but stretched high ssn; elec supply variable; if planning to stay in Oct, make an adv bkg or phone ahead bef arr; gd NH en rte S France; friendly, helpful British owners." ♦ ltd. Easter-30 Sep. € 13.00   2005*

PONT DE VAUX *9A2* (5km W) **Camping aux Rives du Soleil (formerly Les Peupliers),** 01190 Pont-de-Vaux [tel/fax 03 85 30 33 65; info@rives dusoleil.com] N on N6 fr Macon to Tournus. Cross Rv Saone on D933A at Fleurville. Lge, pt shd; wc; mv service pnt; baby facs; shwrs inc; el pts (6A) €2.75; gas; lndtte; ice; shop; rest adj; snacks; bar; BBQ; playgrnd; paddling pool; rv beach adj; fishing; boating; entmnts; TV; dogs €2; poss cr; Eng spkn; adv bkg; some rlwy noise; red long stay. "Beautiful site; new management 2005; gd facs being improved." Easter-30 Sep. € 19.00   2005*

SITES

PONT DE VAUX 9A2 (15km W Rural) **Camp Municipal St Pierre, 71260 Lugny [03 85 33 20 25 or 03 85 33 21 96 (Mairie); fax 03 85 33 00 58]** W of A6/N6; take C7 off D56 N out of Lugny; foll sp for Rest St Pierre; site adj & sp fr town. Diff app for lge o'fits. Sm, mkd pitch, pt shd; wc; shwrs inc; el pts inc; lndry rm; shop 1.5km in Lugny; rest & 1.5km; v quiet; cc not acc. "Beautiful panoramic views of vineyards; simple site poss run down low ssn; warden calls am & pm; facs v clean; v steep ascent to site fr town; excel cent for touring vineyards; gd local walks."
1 May-30 Sep. € 6.90   2005*

This site entry hasn't been updated for a while; we'd better fill in a site report form and send it to The Club.

PONT D'OUILLY see Conde sur Noireau 3D1

PONT DU CHATEAU 9B1 (3km SW) **Camping Les Ombrages, 63111 Dallet [tel/fax 04 73 83 10 97; lesombrages@hotmail.com]** Vill & site sp off N89 bet Clermont-Ferrand & Pont du Chateau on D81 E. Sm, shd; wc; shwrs inc; el pts (6A) €3.50; lndtte; shop; rest; snacks; playgrnd; rv sw adj; fishing; TV; quiet; red low ssn. "Gd for fishing & canoeing."
1 Jun-15 Sep. € 17.50   2003*

PONT DU NAVOY see Doucier 6H2

PONT EN ROYANS see St Marcellin 9C2

PONT FARCY 1D4 (Rural) **Camp Municipal Pont-Farcy, Quai de la Vire, 14380 Pont-Farcy [02 31 68 32 06; fax 02 31 67 94 01; pontfarcy@free.fr]** Leave A84 junc 39 to Pont-Farcy vill cent; site on L 50m. Med, mkd pitch, terr, pt shd; wc; chem disp; mv service pnt; shwrs inc; baby facs; el pts (15A) €1.85; shop, rest & bar 500m; playgrnd; rv fishing & boating adj; cycle hire; 30% statics; dogs; phone; adv bkg; quiet; CCI. "Gates poss locked periods during day but plenty of parking space; spotless facs; excel sh stay; " ♦ 1 Apr-30 Sep. € 9.00   2005*

PONT L'ABBE 2F2 (2km NE) **Camping Le Bois Soleil, Route de Kerguz, 29120 Pont l'Abbe [tel/fax 02 98 87 03 39; www.camping-finistere.com]** Fr Quimper on 785 dir Pont l'Abbe, then D44 dir Benodet. Turn R in 1km, site on L, sp. Med, mkd pitch, pt sl, pt shd; wc (some cont); chem disp; shwrs inc; el pts (6A) €3; gas; lndtte; ice; shop; supmkt 2km; bar; BBQ; playgrnd; htd pool; sand beach 5km; tennis; games area; games rm; entmnt; child entmnt; mini-golf; TV; 15% statics; dogs €0.90; phone; adv bkg; Eng spkn; quiet; red CCI. "Spacious pitches; much improved site in lovely situation."
29 Apr-30 Sep. € 13.20   2005*

PONT L'ABBE 2F2 (6km S Rural/Coastal) **Camping des Dunes, 67 Rue Paul Langevin, 29740 Lesconil [02 98 87 81 78; fax 02 98 82 27 05]** Fr Pont l'Abbe, S on D102 for 5km to Plobannelec; over x-rds; in 1km turn R, 100m after sports field; green sp to site in 1km. Med, hdg/mkd pitch, pt shd; wc (few cont); chem disp; mv service pnt; baby facs; shwrs inc; el pts (6-10A) €3.15; gas 1km; lndtte; ice; shop 1km; tradsmn; snacks; bar; playgrnd; sand beach 200m; trampolines; games rm; games area; dogs €3.15; poss cr high ssn; adv bkg (dep req); cc acc; CCI. "Helpful owner; 800m fr fishing port; ltd rests & bars etc; dune & heathland conservation area; gd walking, cycling & birdwatching; san facs modern & clean; site ideal for children." ♦
1 Jun-15 Sep. € 17.60   2003*

PONT L'ABBE 2F2 (7km S) **Yelloh! Village Le Manoir de Kerlut, 29740 Plobannalec [02 98 82 23 89 or 04 66 73 97 39; fax 02 98 82 26 49; info@campingsbretagnesud.com; www.campings bretagnesud.com or www.yellohvillage.com]** Fr Pont l'Abbe S on D102 to Plobannalec & head for Lesconil; site on L after supmkt. Lge, hdg/mkd pitch, pt shd; wc; serviced pitches; mv service pnt; chem disp; sauna; shwrs inc; el pts (5A) €3; gas; lndtte; ice; shop; tradsmn; rest; snacks; bar; playgrnd; htd pool; waterslide; sand beach 2km; fitness rm; tennis; games area; 30% statics; dogs €3.50; phone; Eng spkn; adv bkg; quiet; red long stay; cc acc; CCI. ♦
29 Apr-10 Sep. € 37.00   2005*

PONT L'ABBE 2F2 (5km NW) **Camp Municipal, 29720 Ploneour-Lanvern [02 98 87 74 80 or 02 98 82 66 00; fax 02 98 82 66 09]** Fr Pont l'Abbe, take D2 to Ploneour-Lanvern, site sp fr cent town; fr cent L of church & strt to T-junc, turn R 2nd on L. Med, pt shd, hdg pitch; wc; shwrs inc; shops 400m; el pts (5A) €3; lndtte; sand beach 13km; pool 6km; playgrnd; tennis adj; adv bkg; quiet. ♦
15 Jun-15 Sep. € 9.00   2002*

PONT L'ABBE 2F2 (10km NW Rural) **Camping Kerlaz, Route de la Mer, 29670 Treguennec [tel/fax 02 98 87 76 79; contact@kerlaz.com; www.kerlaz.com]** Fr Ploneour-Lanvern take D156 SW to Treguennec. Med, pt shd; wc; chem disp; mv service pnt; shwrs inc; el pts (3-10A) €2.40-3.20; lndry rm; shop 300m; tradsmn; snacks; playgrnd; htd, covrd pool; sand beach 2km; tennis; 10% statics; dogs €1.20; adv bkg; quiet; cc acc. "Nice, friendly site."
1 Apr-30 Sep. € 12.00   2005*

PONT L'ABBE D'ARNOULT see Cadeuil 7B1

PONT LES MOULINS see Baume les Dames 6G2

PONT L'EVEQUE 3D1 (500m NW Urban) **Camping du Stade, Rue de Beaumont, 14130 Pont l'Eveque [02 31 64 15 03]** Fr town cent take N175 W twd Caen, turn R at traff lts bef town o'skts to site in 300m. Site sp on R in 300m on D118. Med, mkd pitch, pt shd; wc; chem disp; shwrs inc; el pts (6A) €2.50 (poss rev pol); lndry rm; shops in town; tradsmn; playgrnd; beach 12km; rv fishing; tennis; 2% statics; quiet; cc not acc; CCI. "Staff v friendly & helpful; site poss waterlogged after heavy rain." ♦ ltd. 1 Apr-30 Sep. € 9.80   2005*

Deadline September   469   *Last year of report*

PONT ST ESPRIT *9D2* (5km W Rural) **Camping Les Oliviers, Chemin de Tete Grosse, 30130 St Paulet-de-Caisson** [04 66 82 14 13] Exit A7 at Bollene-Pont-St Esprit. Foll D994 to Pont-St Esprit, then sp to St Paulet-de-Caisson. Turn R into vill & foll sp to St Julien-de-Payroles on D343, site sp 1.5km off narr rd - unsuitable lge o'fits. Sm, hdg/mkd pitch, terr, pt shd; wc; chem disp; shwrs inc; el pts (4A) inc; lndtte; ice; shops 2km; tradsmn; rest; snacks; bar; pool; playgrnd; rv sw 5km; Eng spkn; adv bkg; quiet; CCI. "Ardeche, Rhone Valley, Roman sites nr; v helpful Dutch owners; gd rest; guided walks; painting tuition; ltd water points & long way fr lower levels."
1 Mar-24 Oct. € 21.00   2004*

PONT ST ESPRIT *9D2* (6km NW Rural) **Camping Le Pontet, 07700 St Martin-d'Ardeche** [04 75 04 63 07 or 04 75 98 76 24; fax 04 75 98 76 59; contact @campinglepontet.com] N86 N of Pont-St Esprit; turn L onto D290 at sp Gorges de l'Ardeche & St Martin-d'Ardeche, site on R after 3km, lge sp. Med, kd, pt shd; wc; chem disp; mv service pnt; shwrs inc; el pts (6A) €3.50 (rev pol); gas; lndry rm; ice; tradsmn; shop, rest high ssn; snacks; bar; playgrnd; pool; rv sw 1km; 5% statics; dogs €1; phone; Eng spkn; adv bkg; quiet (poss noisy w/e); cc not acc; CCI. "Vg; helpful owners; entmnts some evenings; beware low tree branches; mainly cherry trees, falling fruit can make mess of roof; access disabled facs thro passage bet shwrs; peaceful & gd value out of ssn." ♦ 2 Apr-30 Sep.
€ 17.80   2005*

PONT ST ESPRIT *9D2* (7km NW) **Camping Les Cigales, 30760 Aigueze** [04 66 82 18 52; fax 04 66 82 25 20; striducette@aol.com] N fr Pont-St Esprit on N86 take D901 NW twd Barjac & D141 to St Martin-d'Ardeche. Site on L bef rv bdge. Avoid app fr St Martin-d'Ardeche over narr suspension bdge. Care at ent. Sm, shd; wc; mv service pnt; shwrs inc; el pts (4-6A) €2.30-2.75; gas; lndtte; ice; shops, rest 500m; tradsmn; BBQ; htd pool, caps ess; rv sw 500m; 25% statics; dogs €1.25; poss cr; adv bkg; rd noise; cc not acc; CCI. "Helpful owner; easy walk to rest in St Martin-d'Ardeche."
15 Mar-15 Oct. € 13.00   2004*

PONT ST ESPRIT *9D2* (7.5km NW Urban) **Camp Municipal Le Village, Rue du Nord, 07700 St Martin-d'Ardeche** [04 75 04 65 25 or 04 75 04 66 33; fax 04 75 98 71 38] N on N86 fr Pont-St Esprit, turn L onto D290 at St Just. Foll D290 around St Martin-d'Ardeche, turn L at sp Le Castelas & immed L into Chemin La Joyeusse, site on L in 300m. Med, mkd pitch, pt shd; wc; chem disp; shwrs inc; el pts (4-13A) €1.70-2.80; lndtte; shop, rest, snacks, bar 200m; playgrnd; rv beach adj; fishing; tennis; adv bkg; quiet. "Excel facs; quiet, lovely vill; gd sh/long stay."
Easter-30 Sep. € 11.50   2005*

PONT ST ESPRIT *9D2* (7.5km NW Urban) **Camping Le Castelas, Chemin de Tabion, 07700 St Martin-d'Ardeche** [tel/fax 04 75 04 66 55; camping-le-castelas@wanadoo.fr] N fr Pont-St Esprit on N86. At St Just turn W onto D290 sp Ardeche Gorges, St Martin. In 4km take 2nd L sp St Martin-de l'Ardeche & site. In 50m turn R at site sp; site on R in 150m. Med, hdg/mkd pitch, sl, shd; wc; chem disp; shwrs inc; el pts (3-4A) €1.80-1.90; lndtte; ice; shops 300m; tradsmn; rest, bar 500m; snacks; BBQ; playgrnd; rv sw; canoeing; fishing; poss cr; Eng spkn; adv bkg (ess Jul/Aug - bkg fee); noisy; red low ssn. "V shd pitches; position van with door to S or E in case Mistral blows; helpful, friendly owner; delightful site with beautiful views over gorge; gd NH."
20 Mar-3 Oct. € 10.30   2005*

PONT ST ESPRIT *9D2* (8km NW) **Camp Municipal Le Moulin, 07700 St Martin-d'Ardeche** [04 75 04 66 20; fax 04 75 04 60 12; contact@camping-lemoulin.com] Exit A7 junc 19 to Bollene, then D994 to Pont-St Esprit & N86 to St Just. Turn L onto D290 to St Martin in 4km. Site on L on rvside. Med, pt sl, pt shd; htd wc; chem disp; mv service pnt; shwrs inc; el pts (6-16A) €3; lndtte; ice; shop; rest 5km; snacks; bar; playgrnd; rv sw adj; fishing; canoeing; tennis 500m; 5% statics; dogs €1.50; phone; Eng spkn; no adv bkg; cc acc; quiet. "Footpath to vill; vg site." ♦ 15 Apr-30 Sep. € 15.00   2004*

PONT ST ESPRIT *9D2* (8km NW) **Camping Le Peyrolais, Route de Barjac, 30760 St Julien-de-Peyrolas** [04 66 82 14 94; fax 04 66 82 31 70; www.camping-lepeyrolais.com] N fr Pont-St. Esprit on N86 take L turn on D901 sp Barjac. Site on R on bank of Rv Ardeche. Med, pt shd; wc (some cont); shwrs inc; el pts (3-10A) €2.30-3.80; lndtte; ice; tradsmn; rest; snacks; bar; playgrnd; rv sw; sports area; fishing; kayaking; cycling; hiking; entmnt; disco; TV rm; dogs €1.60; phone; adv bkg; quiet; cc acc. 3 Apr-26 Sep. € 22.70   2004*

†**PONT ST ESPRIT** *9D2* (8km NW Rural) **Camping Les Truffieres, Route de St Rameze, 07700 St Marcel-d'Ardeche** [04 75 04 68 35 or 06 82 01 28 30; fax 04 75 98 75 86] S fr Bourg-St Andeol, turn W on D201; in vill foll sp to site located approx 3km W of vill. Med, mkd pitch, terr, pt shd; htd wc; shwrs inc; el pts (2-6A) €2.20-6.20 (poss rev pol); gas; lndtte; ice; shops 3km; rest; snacks; bar; playgrnd; pool; entmnt; 70% statics; dogs €1.25; adv bkg; quiet; red low ssn; CCI. "Friendly owners; glorious views; gd location for Ardeche, away fr crowds along gorge; gd NH nr A7." ♦ € 10.00   2005*

†**PONT STE MAXENCE** *3D3* (1km N Urban) **Camping au Bon Accueil, 638 Ave d'Auvelais, 60700 Pont-Ste Maxence** [03 44 72 20 07; fax 03 44 70 16 20] Take N17 N fr Pont-Ste Maxence, site on R opp Leclerc Centre Distributeur. Lge, mkd pitch, unshd; wc; chem disp; shwrs €0.80; el pts (5A) €3; lndry rm; shops adj; pool 2km; dogs €1; adv bkg; quiet, but some rlwy noise. "Poor san facs."
€ 13.40   2004*

PONT SUR SEINE see Nogent sur Seine *4E4*

PONTARLIER *6H2* (1km SE Rural) **FFCC Camping Le Larmont, Rue du Toulombief, 25300 Pontarlier** [03 81 46 23 33; fax 03 81 46 23 34; lelarmont. pontarlier@ffcc.fr; www.ffcc.fr] Leave N57 at Pontarlier Gare & foll site sp. Site uphill, turning nr Nestle factory. Med, some hdstg, terr, unshd; htd wc; chem disp; mv service pnt; shwrs inc; el pts (10A) €3.05; gas; lndtte; sm shop; tradsmn; snacks; bar; playgrnd; pool 2km; horseriding adj; skiing winter; 10-20% statics; dogs; Eng spkn; adv bkg; no cc acc; red CCI. "Friendly; easy access; immac san facs; ltd pitches for awnings; battery-charging; excel long stay." ♦ ltd. 1 Apr-1 Nov. € 14.80   2004*

PONTARLIER *6H2* (12km S Rural) **Camp Municipal, 8 Rue du Port, 25160 St Point-Lac** [03 81 69 61 64 or 03 81 69 62 08 (Mairie); fax 03 81 69 65 74; camping-saintpointlac@wanadoo .fr] Exit Pontarlier on N57 dir Lausanne, turn R on D437, after further 6km turn R on D129. Site on L in 2nd vill St Point-Lac. Med, mkd pitch, unshd; wc; mv service pnt; chem disp; shwrs inc; el pts (16A) inc; lndtte; shops 100m; BBQ; adv bkg rec high ssn; quiet; 30% statics; dogs €1; cc acc; CCI. "Vg meals at hotel at ent; pleasantly situated base for birdwatching, local nature reserves; on edge of lake, shgl landing for boats; beautiful views; excel local cheesemaker; rec adv bkg for lakeside pitches; sm pitches; o'night parking area across rd fr site for m'vans with waste, water, wcs etc." ♦ 1 May-30 Sep. € 13.80   2005*

PONTAUBAULT *2E4* (Urban) **Camping La Vallee de la Selune, 7 Rue Marechal Leclerc, 50220 Pontaubault** [tel/fax 02 33 60 39 00; campselune @wanadoo.fr] Foll sp to Pontaubault (well sp fr all dirs). In vill head twd Avranches. Turn L immed bef bdge over Rv Salune. In 100m turn L, site strt in 100m, well sp. Med, mkd pitch, pt sl, pt shd; wc; chem disp; mv service pnt; shwrs inc; el pts (8-10A) inc; lndtte; ice; shops 100m; tradsmn; supmkt 6km; rest 100m; snacks; bar high ssn; playgrnd; pool 7km; sand beach 10km; tennis adj; fishing adj; horseriding, cycling & golf nrby; 10% statics; dogs €1.30; poss cr; British owners; adv bkg rec; rd/rlwy noise; 10% red CCI 4+ days. "Conv Mont St Michel, Avranches, St Malo & Cherbourg ferries." 1 Apr-20 Oct. € 12.80   2005*

PONTAUBAULT *2E4* (4km E Rural) **Camp Municipal La Selune, Rue de Boishue, 50220 Ducey** [02 33 48 46 49 or 02 33 48 50 52; fax 02 33 48 87 59] Exit A84 junc 33 onto N176 E fr Pontaubault. In Ducey turn R onto D178 twd St Aubin-de-Terregatte. Ent to site at Municipal sports ground in 200m. Sm, hdg pitch, pt sl, shd; wc; chem disp; shwrs inc; el pts (10A) (rev pol) inc; gas; lndtte; shop; rest, snacks, bar in vill; playgrnd; sand beach 25km; tennis adj; 10% statics; dogs €1.30; phone; bus; poss cr; Eng spkn; adv bkg; quiet; CCI. "Poss diff to manoeuvre onto pitches due sl, soft ground & ruts." 1 Apr-30 Sep. € 7.00   2003*

PONTAUBAULT *2E4* (6km SW Coastal) **Camping St Gregoire, Le Haut Bourg, 50170 Servon** [02 33 60 26 03; fax 02 33 60 68 65] Foll N175 fr Pontaubault twd Pontorson. After 6km site sp on R twd Servon vill. Med, pt shd; wc; shwrs; el pts (6A) €2.50; lndtte; sm shop; playgrnd; pool; TV; 30% statics; dogs €2; adv bkg; quiet but some rd noise on S side of site; cc acc; CCI. "Gd NH; conv ferries." Easter-31 Oct. € 11.80   2003*

PONTCHATEAU *2G3* (4km W Rural) **Camping Le Chateau du Deffay, Ste Reine-de-Bretagne, 44160 Pontchateau** [02 40 88 00 57; fax 02 40 01 66 55; camping-le-deffay.com] Leave N165 Vannes-Nantes rd at Pontchateau to join D33 twd Herbignac. Site on R approx 2km after Le Calvaire de la Madeleine x-rds. Site sp fr by-pass. Med, mkd pitch, pt terr, pt shd; wc; chem disp; mv service pnt; serviced pitches; baby facs; shwrs inc; el pts (6A) inc; BBQ; lndtte; shop; rest; snacks; bar; playgrnd; covrd pool; paddling pool; lake fishing; tennis & pedaloes; mini-golf; cycle hire; woodland walks; horseriding; games rm; golf 10km; entmnt; internet; TV rm; dogs; recep 0830-2000; adv bkg (dep req); red low ssn; cc acc (not in rest); CCI. "Friendly owners; lovely site, well worth 4-star designation; lakeside pitches not fenced; staff v welcoming & helpful; weekly chateau dinners high ssn; rest gd value; mkt Mon." ♦ 1 May-30 Sep. € 24.70 (CChq acc) ABS - B25   2005*

PONTCHATEAU *2G3* (2km NW Rural) **Camping Le Bois Beaumard, 1 Rue de la Beaumard, 44160 Pontchateau** [tel/fax 02 40 88 03 36; obocamp@ aol.com; www.campingbeaumard.com] Fr Nantes on N165 by-pass; ignore sp Pontchateau Est, take 2nd sp & foll site sp. Fr Vannes NW of town exit sp Beaulieu; foll site sp. Site also sp bef Pontchateau on D773 S fr Redon. Sm, hdg/mkd pitch, pt shd; wc; chem disp; shwrs inc; el pts (10-12A) €3; lndtte; ice; shops 2km; tradsmn; BBQ; playgrnd; TV rm; dogs €1; Eng spkn; adv bkg; some rd noise; CCI. "Delightful, immac site in orchard; friendly, helpful owners; on edge of Briere regional nature park." 1 Mar-1 Oct. € 9.00   2004*

PONTENX LES FORGES *7D1* (1km S Rural) **Camp Municipal Le Guilleman, 40200 Pontenx-les-Forges** [05 58 07 40 48; MLHH@wanadoo.fr] Exit N10 at Labouheyre onto D626 W for 16km. Ent vill, sp to L, foll sm lane for 1km, clearly sp. Med, mkd pitch, pt shd; wc (some cont); chem disp; shwrs inc; el pts inc; lndtte; shop; snacks; pool 1km; sand beach 15km; 10% statics; dogs €1; poss cr; adv bkg; poss noisy at times; CCI. "Friendly management; relaxed, spacious site away fr cr coastal sites; esp gd for children." ♦ 1 Jun-30 Sep. € 15.00   2005*

PONTET, LE see Avignon *10E2*

FRANCE

CAMPING MUNICIPAL DE LA PALLE ★★

Open from 15.04 till 15.10
Phone : 00 33 (0)4.73.88.96.99
Out of season:
00 33 (0)4.73.88.70.42
Fax : 00 33 (0)4.73.88.77.77

Along the riverside, in the middle of the natural volcanic park. 5 mins. away from Vulcania, the European park for volcanism.

All shops within walking distance.

PONTGIBAUD *7B4* (3km NE) **Camping Bel-Air,** 63230 St Ours [04 73 88 72 14; fax 01 73 72 22 40; camping.belair@free.fr; http://camping.belair.free. fr] Fr Riom SW on D986, then D941 dir Le Cratere, St Ours, Pontgibaud. After passing Col de la Nugere, thro Le Vauriat to St Ours. Site on R 800m after vill. Med, mkd pitch, pt sl, shd; wc; chem disp; mv service pnt; baby facs; shwrs inc; el pts (6A) €2.60; gas; lndry rm; ice; shop 1.5km; tradsmn; rest; snacks; bar; BBQ; playgmd; golf; dogs €1.50; Eng spkn; adv bkg; quiet, but some rd noise; CCI. "Beautiful area with panoramic views of Puy-de-Dome volcanic mountains fr site ent; peaceful site; spotless facs; gd walking; v helpful owners; ltd facs low ssn." 1 May-2 Oct. € 11.00   2005*

PONTGIBAUD *7B4* (200m S Rural) **Camp Municipal La Palle, Route de la Miouze, 63230 Pontgibaud** [04 73 88 96 99 or 04 73 88 70 42 (LS); fax 04 73 88 77 77] At W end of Pontgibaud turn S over bdge on D986 & site in 500m on L. Med, hdg/mkd pitch, hdstg, pt shd; htd wc (some cont); chem disp; mv service pnt; shwrs inc; el pts (6-10A) €2.50-2.90; gas 400m; lndtte; ice; shops 400m; tradsmn; rest; BBQ; playgrnd; lake sw & beach 4km; games area; tennis, cycle hire 400m; entmnt; 5% statics; dogs; Eng spkn; adv bkg; quiet; red long stay/low ssn; CCI. "Pleasant site; helpful staff; gd touring base; conv Vulcania; gd sh stay/NH." ♦ 13 May-15 Oct. € 11.40   2005*

See advertisement above

PONTORSON *2E4* (400m Urban) **Camping Haliotis, Chemin des Soupirs, 50170 Pontorson** [02 33 68 11 59; fax 02 33 58 95 36; info@ camping-haliotis-mont-saint-michel.com; www. camping-haliotis-mont-saint-michel.com] Turn N off N176 at W end of town cent (well sp); take L turn to site. Med, hdg pitch, pt sl, pt shd; wc (cont); chem disp; mv service pnt; baby facs; sauna; shwrs inc; el pts (6A) €3; gas; lndtte; ice; shop; supmkt 400m; tradsmn; rest; snacks; bar; BBQ; playgrnd; htd pool; spa; fishing; boating; tennis; cycle hire; games rm; child entmnt; internet; 5% statics; dogs €0.50; phone; bus 400m; poss cr; Eng spkn; adv bkg; quiet; red low ssn; cc not acc; CCI. "Modern & well maintained; immac; gd, clean san facs; close to Mont St Michel - bus nrby & cycle rte; gd rv walk fr site; friendly, helpful staff; locked at night till 0730; highly rec." ♦ ltd. 25 Mar-11 Nov. € 19.00 (CChq acc)   2005*

PONTRIEUX *2E3* (4km E Rural) **Camp Municipal du Bois d'Amour, 22260 Quemper-Guezennec** [02 96 95 13 40 or 02 96 95 62 62; fax 02 96 95 36 07] Exit N12 at Guincamp; D787 twds Pontrieux. At rndabt ent to Pontrieux, turn R & foll rd to indus est over level x-ing. Turn R along rv front, site in approx 200 yrds. Sm, pt shd, mkd pitch; wc; shwrs; el pts (15A) inc; lndry rm; ice; sm shop; tradsmn; playgrnd; fishing; cc not acc; quiet; CCI. "Pay at Marie in Quemper-Guezennec low ssn, as site office not open; gd touring base; best pitches overlook Rv Trieux; clean & roomy san facs; excel long stay." ♦ 15 Jun-15 Sep. € 12.00   2005*

†PONTRIEUX *2E3* (1km W Urban) **Camping de Traou Meledern (Thomas), 22260 Pontrieux** [02 96 95 68 72 or 02 96 95 69 27; http://camping pontrieux.free.fr] N on D787 fr Guingamp; on ent town square turn sharp L sp Traou Meledern, cross rv bdge & turn R alongside church. Site in 400m. Access poss diff for lge o'fits; steep exit on 1-way system. Med, hdg/mkd pitch, pt sl, pt shd; wc; chem disp; shwrs inc; el pts (8A) €2.70; lndtte; shops, supmkt 1km; tradsmn; playgrnd; BBQ; dogs; €0.80; poss cr; Eng spkn; adv bkg; quiet but some daytime factory noise; CCI. "Among apple trees; gd for touring pink granite coast; Pontrieux attractive sm town; conv Brehat & train to Brest, WW2 museum Fort Montbarey, Allee Bir Hakiem; friendly owner; steep junc nr site poss problem for lge o'fits; gd long/sh stay." € 7.80   2003*

PONTS DE CE, LES see Angers *4G1*

PORDIC see Binic *2E3*

PORGE, LE *7C1* (9km W Coastal) **Camp Municipal La Grigne, Ave de l'Ocean, 33680 Le Porge** [05 56 26 54 88; fax 05 56 26 52 07; camping duporge@wanadoo.fr] Fr Bordeaux ring rd take N215 twd Lacaneau. In 22km at Ste Helene D5 to Saumos & onto Le Porge. Site on L of rd to Porge-Ocean in approx 9km. V lge, pt sl, shd; wc; chem disp; shwrs; el pts (10A) €3.50; gas; shop; lndtte; ice; bar; snacks; playgrnd; beach 1km; tennis; games area; TV; poss cr; adv bkg; quiet. ♦ 1 Apr-30 Sep. € 17.00   2005*

PORNIC *2G3*. **Caravans are prohibited in Pornic. If approaching from E on D751 or from SE on D13, remain on bypass to N of Pornic and take D286/D13 exit.**

PORNIC *2G3* (10km N Urban) **Camp Municipal Le Grand Fay, Rue du Grand Fay, 44320 St Pere-en-Retz** [02 40 21 77 57; fax 02 40 21 72 03] Fr Mairie in cent St Pere-en-Retz take D78 E twds Frossay. After 400m turn R into Rue des Sports, after 200m turn L into Rue du Grand Fay. Site on L in 200m adj Sports Cent. Med, mkd pitch, pt sl, pt shd; wc (some cont); shwrs inc; el pts (6A) €3; lndry rm; ice; tradsmn; supmkt nrby; playgrnd; htd pool; beach 8km; quiet; CCI. "Pleasant site nr sandy beaches." ♦ 1 May-15 Sep. € 11.20   2003*

PORNIC *2G3* (9km NE) **Camping La Renaudiere, 44770 La Plaine-sur-Mer** [02 40 21 50 03; fax 02 40 21 09 41; camping.la.renaudiere@wanadoo. fr; www.campinglarenaudiere.com] S fr St Nazaire on D213 twd Pornic, turn onto D96 twd Prefailles. Fr Nantes D751 W to Pornic then D13, dir La Plaine-sur-Mer, then Rte de la Pree. Med, pt shd; wc; chem disp; baby facs; shwrs; el pts (10A) €3.10; gas; ice; lndtte; shop adj; rest; snacks; bar; BBQ; playgrnd; htd pool; beach & watersports 2km; entmnts; TV; some statics; dogs €2; adv bkg; CCI. ♦ 1 Apr-30 Sep. € 14.50   2004*

PORNIC *2G3* (3km E Rural) **Camping La Chenaie, 36 Rue du Patisseau, 44210 Pornic** [02 40 82 07 31; fax 02 40 82 62 62; la.chenaie@free.fr; www.campinglachenaie.com] Fr Nantes on D751 to Pornic, at 1st rndabt turn R. Fr St Nazaire on D213, foll sp Nantes & Le Clion-sur-Mer to avoid Pornic cent. Med, hdg/mkd pitch, hdstg, pt sl, terr, pt shd; wc; chem disp; mv service pnt; serviced pitch; child/baby facs; shwrs inc; el pts (6A) €3.50; lndtte; ice; shop; tradsmn; snacks; bar; BBQ; playgrnd; 3 pools; sand beach 2.5km; horseriding; golf; cycle hire; entmnt; child entmnt; 37% statics; dogs €2; Eng spkn; adv bkg; quiet; cc acc; red low ssn; CCI. "Nice, lge pitches; friendly site; gd walking." ♦ 8 Apr-30 Sep. € 18.00   2005*

PORNIC *2G3* (4km E Rural) **Camping Sunelia Le Patisseau, 29 Rue de Patisseau, 44210 Pornic** [02 40 82 10 39; fax 02 40 82 22 81; contact@lepatisseau. com; www.lepatisseau.com] Fr N or S on D213, take slip rd D751 Nantes. At rndabt take exit sp to Le Patisseau, foll sp. Lge, hdg/mkd pitch, hdstg, pt sl, pt shd; htd wc; chem disp; mv service pnt; sauna; shwrs inc; el pts (6A) inc; gas; lndtte; ice; shop; tradsmn; rest; snacks; bar; BBQ; playgrnd; 2 htd pools (1covrd); 2 htd paddling pools (1 covrd); 2 waterslides; sand beach 2.5km; jacuzzi; fitness rm; tennis 1km; games area; games rm; golf 2km; entmnt; child entmnt; TV; 30% statics; dogs €5; Eng spkn; adv bkg rec high ssn; quiet; red low ssn; cc acc. "Excel, modern, family site; modern htd san facs block." ♦ 8 Apr-6 Nov. € 34.50 (CChq acc)   2005*

See advertisement opposite (bottom)

PORNIC *2G3* (5km E Coastal) **Camping La Boutinardiere, Rue de la Plage, Le Clion-sur-Mer, 44210 Pornic** [02 40 82 05 68; fax 02 40 82 49 01; info@laboutinardiere.com; www.camping-boutinardiere.com] SW fr Nantes on D723; turn L on D751 twd Pornic. Foll sp La Berniere & site sp. Lge, hdg pitch, pt sl, pt shd; wc (some cont); chem disp; mv service pnt; serviced pitches; baby facs; shwrs inc; el pts (6-10A) €3.50-4 (poss rev pol); gas; lndtte; ice; shop; supmkt; rest; snacks; bar; BBQ; playgrnd; 3 pools (1 htd, covrd); waterslide; sand beach 200m; lake sw 3km; tennis; jacuzzi; golf 5km; cycle hire; entmnt & activities; TV rm; 15% statics; dogs €3; poss cr; Eng spkn; adv bkg; quiet; red low ssn; cc acc; CCI. "Excel family site; v busy high ssn; Pornic interesting town." ♦ 1 Apr-30 Sep. € 30.00   2005*

See advertisement on next page

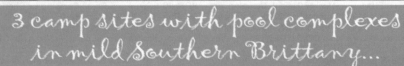

PORNIC *2G3* (6km SE Rural/Coastal) **Camping Les Ecureuils, 24 Ave Gilbert Burlot, 44760 La Bernerie-en-Retz** [02 40 82 76 95; fax 02 40 64 79 52; contact@camping-les-ecureuils.com; www. camping-les-ecureuils.com] Fr Pornic take D13 S for 5km, then D66 for 1km; site sp. Lge, hdg pitch, pt sl, pt shd; wc; chem disp; baby facs; shwrs inc; el pts (10A) €4; lndtte; shops 500m; snacks; bar; BBQ area; playgrnd; htd pool; paddling pool; waterslide; sand beach 400m; tennis; golf 5km; entmnt; children's club; 30% statics; dogs (up to 10kg only) €3; Eng spkn; adv bkg; quiet; cc acc; red low ssn/CCI. "Excel." ♦ 1 May-19 Sep. € 26.00   2005*

See advertisement above

PORNIC *2G3* (7km SE Coastal) **Camping de la Plage, 53 Route de la Bernerie, 44580 Les Moutiers-en-Retz** [02 40 82 71 43; fax 02 40 82 72 46; bernard.beaujean@wanadoo.fr; www. camp ing-la-plage.com] SE fr Pornic dir Bourgneuf, in 5km turn R for La Bernerie. 1st L after church. Site on R in 2km. Foll sps fr cent Les Moutiers. Lge, hdg/mkd pitch, pt sl, pt shd; wc; chem disp; shwrs inc; el pts (10-16A) €3.05; lndtte; rest; shop; BBQ; playgrnd; htd pool; beach; TV; adv bkg; dogs €0.76; Eng spkn; red low ssn; cc acc; CCI. "Vg long stay, diff access to some pitches - manhandling poss req." 1 Apr-30 Sep. € 16.46
                                                          2002*

PORNIC *2G3* (9km SE Coastal) **Camping Le Village de la Mer, 18 Rue de Prigny, 44760 Les Moutiers-en-Retz** [02 40 64 65 90; fax 02 51 74 63 17; info@village-mer.fr; www.village-mer.fr] Site sp on D97 dir Bourgneuf, site is 100m to SE of Les Moutiers-en-Retz. Lge, hdg/mkd pitch, pt shd; mv service pnt; chem disp; baby facs; shwrs inc; el pts (8A) inc; gas; lndtte; shop adj; snacks; bar; BBQ; playgrnd; htd pool; waterpark; sand beach 300m; watersports; tennis; games rm; entmnt; internet; excursions; 50% statics; dogs €3; Eng spkn; adv bkg; red low ssn; cc acc; CCI. "Quiet; ideal for families." ♦ 15 Jun-15 Sep. € 26.00   2005*

PORNIC *2G3* (600m W Coastal/Urban) **Camping du Golf, 40 Rue de la Renaissance, 44210 Pornic** [02 40 82 41 18 or 06 09 71 23 92 (LS); fax 02 51 74 06 62; campingdugolf@yahoo.fr or cledelles@aol.com; www.camping-du-golf.com or www.lescledelles.com.fr] Fr Nantes, take D751 W dir Ste Marie. App Pornic, take D213 dir St Nazaire & foll sp Ste Marie & site; well sp. Med, mkd pitch, hdstg, pt shd; wc; chem disp (wc); baby facs; fam bthrm; shwrs inc; el pts (6-10A) €5-6; gas; lndtte; ice; shop 600m; tradsmn; rest, snacks, bar high ssn; BBQ; htd pool high ssn; playgrnd; sand beach 600m; lake sw 200m; tennis; games rm; golf 1km; cycle hire; entmnt; child entmnt; TV; 90% statics; dogs €2.20; Eng spkn; adv bkg; quiet; red low ssn/long stay; cc acc; CCI. "Conv coastal path; 40 mins walk to Pornic; twin-axles not acc; gd san facs poss unclean; ltd space for tourers." ♦ 1 Apr-30 Sep. € 22.00   2005*

Some of these sites have changed their opening dates - we'd better fill in some site report forms and let the editor of the guide know.

PORNIC *2G3* (1km W Coastal) **Camping La Madrague, Chemin de la Madrague, Ste Marie-sur-Mer, 44210 Pornic** [02 40 82 06 73; fax 02 51 74 11 93; info@madrague.net; www.madrague.net] Fr Pornic on D213 foll sp Ste Marie-sur-Mer. Foll D286 then R on D13. Turn L into Rue du Moulin Neuf, then R into Rue des Bougrenets. Cont on Rue Yves Ponceau, then Chemin de la Madrague to site. Lge, hdg/mkd pitch, pt sl, pt shd; htd wc; chem disp; mv waste; baby facs; fam bthrm; shwrs inc; el pts (3-6A) €3-3.50; gas; lndtte; ice; shop; tradsmn; rest; snacks; bar; playgrnd; dir access to sand beach 500m; games area; entmnt; 60% statics; dogs €2; phone; bus; poss cr; adv bkg; quiet. "V clean, well-organised site; helpful staff; excel coastal path walks; gd for dog owners; sea views." ♦ 1 Apr-15 Oct.   2005*

FRANCE

PORNIC *2G3* (5km W Rural) **Camping La Tabardiere,** 44770 La Plaine-sur-Mer [02 40 21 58 83; fax 02 40 21 02 68; info@camping-la-tabardiere.com; www.camping-la-tabardiere.com] Take D13 out of Pornic sp Prefailles & La Plaine-sur-Mer. In about 5.5km turn R (nr water tower) & site sp on D213. Foll sps to site, about 1km fr main rd. Lge, mkd pitch, hdstg, pt sl, terr, pt shd; wc (some cont); chem disp; shwrs inc; el pts (3-8A) €2.80-4.20; gas; lndtte; shop & 3km; snacks; bar; playgrnd; pool & paddling pool; waterslides; sand beach 3km; tennis; mini-golf; fishing 3km; horseriding 5km; entmnt; games rm; TV; 40% statics; dogs €2.70; Eng spkn; adv bkg; quiet; cc acc; red low ssn. "Excel, peaceful site; gates clsd 1200-1500; children's club Mon-Fri mornings." ♦ 1 May-30 Sep. € 21.00   2005*

See advertisement above

Will you fill in the site report forms at the back of the guide, or shall I?

PORNIC *2G3* (5km W Coastal) **Camping Le Ranch,** Les Hautes Railleres, 44770 La Plaine-sur-Mer [02 40 21 52 62; fax 02 51 74 81 31; ranch@free.fr; www.camping-le-ranch.com] S fr St Nazaire on D213 twd Pornic, turn onto D96 twd Prefailles. Site between Tharon-Plage & La Plaine-sur-Mer on D96. Lge, hdg/mkd pitch, pt shd; wc; chem disp; baby facs; shwrs; el pts (6A) €3.50; gas; lndtte; shop; tradsmn; snacks; bar; BBQ; playgrnd; htd pool; paddling pool; waterslide; sand beach 800m; tennis; games rm; games area; entmnt; dogs €1.80; adv bkg; quiet; red low ssn; CCI. "Excel, family site." ♦ 1 Apr-30 Sep. € 19.80   2005*

See advertisement opposite

PORNIC *2G3* (8km W Coastal) **Camping Eleovic,** Route de la Pointe St Gildas, 44770 Prefailles [02 40 21 61 60; fax 02 40 64 51 95; contact@ camping-eleovic.com; www.camping-eleovic.com] W fr Pornic on D13 to La Plaine-sur-Mer, turn S to Prefailles, cont twds Pointe-St Gildas 1km, L site sp. Med, hdg pitch, terr, pt shd; htd wc; chem disp; mv service pnt; serviced pitches; baby facs; shwrs inc; el pts (6A) €4.10; lndtte; tradsmn; rest; snacks; bar; BBQ; htd, covrd pool; waterslide; playgrnd; sand beach adj; fishing; sailing; TV; entmnt; child entmnt; 20% statics; dogs €3-4.50; phone; Eng spkn; adv bkg; red low ssn/long stay/CCI; cc acc. "Dir access to coast path; vg long stay." ♦ 8 Apr-31 Oct.
€ 26.40   2005*

PORNIC *2G3* (6km NW Coastal) **Camping Thar-Cor,** 43 Ave du Cormier, Tharon-Plage, 44730 St Michel-Chef-Chef [02 40 27 82 81; fax 02 40 27 81 51; le.thar.cor.com; www.camping-le-thar-cor.com] Take D77 fr Pornic to Mindin. After 5km turn L. sp Tharon-Plage. Site on L in 2km. Med, mkd pitch, pt shd; wc (cont); shwrs inc; el pts (6A); gas; ice; lndtte; tradsmn; rest; shop adj; playgrnd; pool; sand beach 200m; dogs €1.53; poss cr; quiet; adv bkg rec Jul-Aug; red low ssn. "Good town site, mkt at Tharon-Plage high ssn; 200m to promenade & sandy beach." 1 Apr-15 Sep. € 20.12   2002*

PORNIC *2G3* (7km NW Coastal) **Camping Bel Essor,** Rue de Bel Essor, 44730 St Michel-Chef-Chef [02 40 27 85 40 or 02 47 38 89 07 (LS); www.campingbelessor.com] Take D123 fr Pornic sp St Nazaire. After 8.5km for R onto D78 sp St Michel-Chef-Chef. At rndabt turn L, at next rndabt turn L. Strt on at traff lts, then fork R. Site on R in 300m, sp. Lge, mkd pitch, pt sl, pt shd; wc (some cont); chem disp (wc); shwrs inc; el pts (6A) €3.20; lndtte; supmkt opp; tradsmn; snacks; bar; playgrnd; sand beach 400m; some statics; dogs €1.30; phone adj; poss cr in high ssn; Eng spkn; adv bkg; CCI. "10 min walk to beach fr rear ent of site; vg & clean facs; helpful owners; vg long stay." ♦ 1 May-15 Sep. € 12.50   2005*

PORNIC *2G3* (8km NW Coastal) **Camping Le Vieux Chateau, 44730 Tharon-Plage [02 40 27 83 47 or 02 33 65 02 93 (LS)]** Fr Pornic dir St Nazaire, turn W twd Tharon-Plage, site sp. Med, hdg/mkd pitch, terr, pt shd; wc; chem disp; shwrs inc; el pts; lndtte; ice; shop; tradsmn; snacks; bar; htd pool; paddling pool; sand beach 500m; playgrnd; games rm; 10% statics; quiet; adv bkg; Eng spkn; cc acc; red long stay; CCI. "Excel san facs; vg long/sh stay." ♦ 1 May-30 Sep. € 14.50   2002*

PORNICHET *2G3* (2km E Coastal) **Camping Bel Air, 150 Ave de Bonne Source, Ste Marguerite, 44380 Pornichet [02 40 61 10 78; fax 02 40 61 26 18; reception@bel-air-pornichet.com; www.belair pornichet.com]** Foll coast rd fr La Baule to Pornichet. Site visible on L of main rd, sp. Lge, hdg/mkd pitch, pt sl, pt shd; htd wc; chem disp; mv service pnt; baby facs; fam bthrm; shwrs inc; el pts some (10A) €4; gas; lndtte; ice; shop; tradsmn; snacks; rest; snacks; bar; BBQ; playgrnd; htd pool; sand beach 50m; multi-sport area; tennis; fishing; sailing; cycle hire; internet; TV rm; 50% statics; dogs €1.50; no twin-axles; Eng spkn; adv bkg; quiet; cc acc; red long stay/low ssn. "Easy access to lge sand beach 50m; close to shopping area; pleasant town; St Nazaire shipyards worth visit." ♦ 24 Mar-1 Oct. € 28.00   2005*

PORNICHET *2G3* (2km E Urban/Coastal) **Camping du Bugeau, 33 Ave des Loriettes, 44380 Pornichet [02 40 61 02 02 or 02 40 61 15 44 (LS); fax 02 40 61 22 75; campingdubugeau@wanadoo.fr; http://campingdubugeau.free.fr]** W fr St Nazaire on D92 then L at rndabt at St Marguerite by car showrm; site sp 2nd L, site 500m on L. Med, hdg/mkd pitch, pt shd; htd wc; chem disp; mv service pnt; shwrs inc; el pts (4-10A) €2.90-3.80; lndtte; ice; shop & 500m; tradsmn; snacks; BBQ; playgrnd; covrd pool; sand beach & watersports 500m; tennis 500m; cycle hire 1km; child entmnt; TV; 30% statics; dogs; Eng spkn; adv bkg; cc acc. "Gd long/sh stay." ♦ 1 Jun-15 Sep. € 18.00   2003*

†**PORNICHET** *2G3* (4km E) **Camping au Repos des Forges, 44380 Pornichet [02 40 61 18 84; fax 02 40 60 11 84]** To N of D92 halfway bet St Nazaire & Pornichet. Accessible also fr N171; sp. Med, pt sl, pt shd; wc; chem disp; shwrs inc; el pts (3-10A) inc; gas; lndry rm; ice; shop in ssn; snacks; playgrnd; pool; beach 3km; games rm; 70% statics; Eng spkn; adv bkg; quiet; CCI. "Friendly reception; barrier clsd 2300-0700; excel san facs." ♦ € 17.00   2004*

PORT EN BESSIN HUPPAIN *3D1* (500m W Coastal) **Camping Port'land, Chemin de Castel, 14520 Port-en-Bessin [02 31 51 07 06; fax 02 31 51 76 49; campingportland@wanadoo.fr; www.camping-portland.com]** Site sp fr D514 W of Port-en-Bessin. Lge, hdg/mkd pitch, pt shd; wc; mv service pnt; chem disp; shwrs inc; el pts (15A) €5; gas 1km; lndtte; shop; tradsmn; rest; snacks; bar; BBQ; playgrnd; htd, covrd pool; sand beach 4km; tennis 500m; games area; entmnt; child entmnt; games rm; TV; 20% statics; dogs €2.50; Eng spkn; adv bkg; red long stay/low ssn; cc acc; red CCI. "Conv D-Day landing beaches & US cemetery, Bayeux; many activities; extra charge for lger pitches; excel touring base." ♦ 1 Apr-3 Nov. € 20.50   2003*

PORT LA NOUVELLE see Sigean *10G1*

PORT SUR SAONE *6F2* (800m Rural) **Camp Municipal Parc de la Maladiere, 70170 Port-sur-Saone [03 84 91 51 32 or 03 84 78 18 00 (Mairie); fax 03 84 78 18 09; tourisme.portsursaone@wanadoo.fr]** Take N19 SE fr Langres or N19 NW fr Vesoul. Site sp in vill bet rv & canal off D6 at municipal bathing area. Med, hdg pitch, shd; wc (poss cont); own san facs; chem disp; shwrs inc; el pts (6A) €2.50 (poss rev pol); lndry rm; shops 1km; tradsmn high ssn; rest, bar; in vill; playgrnd; pool adj; tennis; fishing; adv bkg; no cc acc; quiet; CCI. "Gd walks; 48km rvside cycle path; peaceful site on isle bet canal & Rv Saone; sports facs, sm pool & deer park adj; conv touring Franche Compte; golf 40km at Cubrial; gd sh stay/NH." ♦ ltd. 15 May-15 Sep. € 8.50   2005*

FRANCE

†PORT VENDRES *10G1* (500m W Urban) **Aire Communale des Tamarins, Route de la Jetee, 66660 Port-Vendres [04 68 82 01 03; fax 04 68 82 22 33]** Fr N114 at Port-Vendres at Banyuls side of town turn N on D86B sp Port de Commerce & Aire de Camping-Cars. Foll sp to site on R in 700m. Sm, hdstg, pt shd; chem disp; mv service pnt; wc (part cont); own san; gas 1km; shop 1km; rest 500m; snacks, bar 1km; playgrnd adj; shgl beach 100m. "Vg NH m'vans only; walking dist rlwy stn; poss cr even low ssn." € 7.50   2005*

PORT VENDRES *10G1* (2km NW Coastal) **Camping Les Amandiers, Plage de l'Ouile, 66190 Collioure [04 68 81 14 69; fax 04 68 81 09 95]** On N114 SE fr Perpignan, leave at junc 13 sp Collioure. After rndabt foll rd to Collioure. Climb coastal rd; site on L, steep descent, not rec lge o'fits. Med, mkd pitch, terr, pt shd; wc; shwrs inc; el pts (10A) €3.50; lndtte; gas; sm shop; rest, bar high ssn; playgrnd; beach 150m; dogs €2.90; poss cr; Eng spkn; cc not acc; CCI. "Site access v diff, esp for lge/med o'fits, probably manhandling req - rec investigation bef ent; facs stretched high ssn; many trees - dusty site; sm pitches; v friendly & helpful owners." ♦ 1 Apr-30 Sep. € 19.50   2005*

PORTIRAGNES PLAGE *10F1* (2km NE) **Camping Les Mimosas, Port Cassafières, 34420 Portiragnes [04 67 90 92 92; fax 04 67 90 85 39; info@mimosas.fr or les.mimosas.portiragnes@wanadoo.fr; www.mimosas.com]** Exit A9 junc 35 Beziers Est & take N112 sp Vias, Agde. After 3km at rndabt foll sp Portiragnes & cont along side of Canal du Midi. Cross canal, site sp. Lge, mkd pitch, hdstg, pt shd; wc; sauna; shwrs inc; el pts (6-10A) €4; gas; lndtte; ice; shop; supmkt; rest; snacks; bar; BBQ area; playgrnd; pools; paddling pool; waterslide; jacuzzi; sand beach 1km; cycle hire; games area; fitness rm; entmnt; 50% statics; dogs €5.50; Eng spkn; adv bkg; quiet; cc acc. "Excel touring base in interesting area; friendly welcome; gd for families." ♦ 20 May-2 Sep. € 30.00   2005*

See advertisement above

POUANCE *2F4* (1.5km NW Urban) **Camp Muncipal La Roche Martin, 23 Rue des Etangs, 49420 Pouance [02 41 92 43 97; fax 02 41 92 62 30]** Take D6 (sp St Aignan) N fr town. After level x-ing turn L onto D72 (sp La Guerche-de-Bretagne). In 300m, site on L. Sm, pt terr, pt sl; wc; shwrs; el pts (10A) €1.65; gas; ice; shops 1km; playgrnd; sports area; tennis; direct access to lake; watersports; poss cr; adv bkg. "Well-kept, friendly site overlooking lge lake; noise fr rd & sailing school; low ssn facs inadequate & in need or refurb." 1 May-30 Sep. € 6.20   2004*

POUGUES LES EAUX *4H4* (N Urban) **Camp Municipal Les Chanternes, 58320 Pougues-les-Eaux [03 86 68 86 18]** On NE side of N7 in Pougues-les-Eaux at rear of open-air pool & thro same ent. Med, mkd pitch, pt shd; wc (some cont); shwrs inc; el pts; shops, rest & snacks in vill; pool adj; adv bkg; N7 rd & rlwy noise; CCI. Easter-1 Nov.   2003*

POUILLY EN AUXOIS *6G1* **Camp Municipal Le Vert Auxois, 21320 Pouilly-en-Auxois [03 80 90 71 89; fax 03 80 90 77 58; vert. auxois@wanadoo.fr]** Exit A6 at Dijon/Pouilly-en-Auxois onto A38. Exit A38 at junc 24. Thro vill & turn L after church on R, site sp. Med, hdg pitch, pt shd; wc; mv service pnt; shwrs inc; el pts (6-10A) €2.50-3.50; gas; lndtte; ice; shop 400m; tradsmn; rest 400m; snacks, bar high ssn; playgrnd; rv fishing adj; lake 5km; quiet; bus 300m; cc not acc; CCI; "Helpful warden; gd facs; gd cycling; boat trips on Burgundy canal avail; conv NH; gd sh/long stay." Easter-30 Sep. € 9.10   2005*

POUILLY SUR LOIRE *4G3* (1km N Urban) Camping Le Malaga, 58150 Pouilly-sur-Loire [tel/fax 03 86 39 14 54 or 03 86 58 74 38 (LS)] Fr N7 go to town cent & take D59/D4289 W. Bef rv bdge turn R along rv, site in 1km on rv. Med, pt sl, pt shd; wc; chem disp; shwrs inc; el pts (10A) €2.40 (poss long lead rec); lndry rm; ice; shop & 1km; tradsmn; snacks; bar; playgrnd; rv sw; dogs €1; phone; Eng spkn; quiet. "Excel; spacious; lge pitches; new mod san facs; wildlife reserve adj." ♦ 1 Jun-1 Sep. € 9.80   2005*

POULDU, LE *2F2* (Urban/Coastal) Camping Les Grands Sables, Rue du Philosophe Alain, Le Pouldu, 29360 Clohars-Carnoet [02 98 39 94 43; fax 02 98 39 97 47; camping.grands-sables@libertysurf.fr] Sp in town, adj to chapel of Notre Dame. Med, pt sl, terr, pt shd; wc; shwrs; el pts (6A); lndtte; shops 500m; snacks; playgrnd; sand beach 500m; sailing, fishing, horseriding, tennis nrby; quiet. 30 Mar-15 Sep. € 14.40   2002*

POULDU, LE *2F2* (N Urban/Coastal) Camping Les Embruns, Rue du Philosophe Alain, Clohars-Carnoet, 29360 Le Pouldu [02 98 39 91 07; fax 02 98 39 97 87; camping-les-embruns@wanadoo.fr; www.camping-les-embruns.com] Exit N165 dir Quimperle Cent, onto D16/D24 to Clohars-Carnoet. Foll sp Le Pouldu & site on R on ent 1-way traff system. Lge, hdg/mkd pitch, hdstg, terr, pt shd; wc; chem disp; mv service pnt; all serviced pitches; baby facs; fam bthrm; shwrs inc; el pts (10A) inc; gas; lndtte; ice; shop; rest; snacks; bar; BBQ; playgrnd; 2 pools (1 htd, covrd); sand beach 200m; watersports; tennis 200m; fishing; cycle hire; horseriding nr; games area; games rm; TV rm; 50% statics; dogs €1; adv bkg (dep req + bkg fee); quiet; cc acc; red low ssn; CCI. "Gd location - town was home of Paul Gauguin; luxury pitches extra charge; well-appointed & spotless san facs; card-op barrier; gd walking along coastal paths." ♦ 8 Apr-16 Sep. € 27.00   2005*

See advertisement above

POUILLY SOUS CHARLIEU *9A1* (1km N Urban) Camp Municipal Les Ilots, 42720 Pouilly-sous-Charlieu [04 77 60 80 67; fax 04 77 69 96 15] Site sp on ring rd 1km N of town, turn E into stadium. Med, pt shd; wc (cont); shwrs €1; el pts (6A) €1.90; gas; lndtte; shops 1km; playgrnd; pool; fishing; poss cr; Eng spkn; quiet; cc not acc. "Lge pitches grouped in circles with lge common area in cent." 1 May-15 Sep. € 5.10   2002*

POUILLY SOUS CHARLIEU *9A1* (4km E Urban) Camp Municipal de Charlieu, Rue Roittier, 42190 Charlieu [04 77 69 01 70; fax 04 77 69 07 28; camp-charlieu@voila.fr] N fr Roanne on D482. E on D487 to Charlieu town cent & site clearly sp. Do not confuse with Camp Municipal Pouilly-sous-Charlieu which is sp fr main rd. Med, hdg/mkd pitch, pt shd; wc; chem disp; mv service pnt; shwrs inc; el pts (6-10A) €2.50-4.60; gas; lndtte; ice; shops 1km; snacks; bar; playgrnd; pool adj; sports area; fishing, boating adj; entmnt; 40% statics; poss cr; Eng spkn; adv bkg; CCI. "Gd sh stay/NH; modern, clean san facs block; ent to adj pool & tennis site; facs poss stretched high ssn, excel low ssn; vg value." ♦ 1 May-30 Sep. € 8.40   2004*

POULDU, LE *2F2* (2km N) Camping du Quinquis, 29360 Clohars-Carnoet [02 98 39 92 40; fax 02 98 39 96 56; andrew.munro@clara.co.uk; www.campingquinquis.com] On D16 fr Quimperle, 2km S of x-rds with D224. Or fr N165 exit Guidel junc 45; foll sps to Le Pouldu & zoo adj to site. Med, hdg pitch, pt sl, pt shd; wc; shwrs; el pts (10A) inc; gas; lndtte; ice; sm shop; snacks; bar; playgrnd; pool & paddling pool; sand beach 2km; games rm; entmnt; child entmnt; TV; 80% statics; dogs; phone; poss cr; Eng spkn; quiet. "Vg site; new owner working hard upgrading; excel takeaway with French chef." ♦ 1 Apr-30 Sep. € 23.00   2005*

Camping KERANQUERNAT ★★★

29360 LE POULDU • CLOHARS CARNOËT
Tel: 00 33 (0) 298 399 232 • Fax: 00 33 (0) 298 399 984
A campsite with many flowers, 700 m from the beaches and
the harbour. Rental of mobile homes
www.camping-keranquernat.com
camping.keranquernat@wanadoo.fr

POULDU, LE *2F2* (500m NE Urban) **Camping Keranquernat, Le Pouldu, 29360 Clohars-Carnoet** [02 98 39 92 32; fax 02 98 39 99 84; camping.keranquernat@wanadoo.fr; www.camping-keranquernat.com] Fr Quimperle D16 to Clohars-Carnoet D24 to Le Pouldu - twd port. Turn R at x-rds nr Ar Men Hotel. Site ent immed on R. Med, hdg/mkd pitch, pt shd; wc (some cont); chem disp; baby facs; shwrs; el pts (3-5A) €3-3.50; gas; lndtte; ice; shops 300m; tradsmn; playgrnd; htd pool; paddling pool; sand beach 500m; fishing; sailing; tennis; games rm; TV; Eng spkn; adv bkg; quiet. "Beautifully-kept site; lots to do in area; excel." 1 Jun-5 Sep. € 14.50   2005*

See advertisement

POULDU, LE *2F2* (2km E Rural/Coastal) **Camping Les Jardins de Kergal, 56520 Guidel** [tel/fax 02 97 05 98 18; jardins.kergal@wanadoo.fr] Fr N165 Brest-Nantes take Guidel exit; thro Guidel & onto Guidel-Plages; camp sp in 1km. Lge, hdg/mkd pitch, pt sl, pt shd; wc; chem disp; baby facs; shwrs inc; el pts (10A) inc; gas; lndtte; gas; ice; shops 2km; tradsmn high ssn; snacks, bar high ssn; BBQ; playgrnd; pool; sand beach 1.5km; tennis; entmnt; cycle hire; games area; 75% statics; dogs €2; adv bkg; quiet but poss noisy youth groups high ssn; red low ssn; CCI. "Friendly, helpful, welcoming wardens; well-run peaceful site; conv beaches & touring; facs being upgraded; most pitches triangular - poss diff; excel long stay." ♦ 19 Apr-14 Sep. € 26.80   2004*

POULIGUEN, LE *2G3* (Urban/Coastal) **Camp Municipal du Clein, Ave de Kerdun, 44510 Le Pouliguen** [02 40 42 43 99 or 02 40 15 08 08 (Mairie); fax 02 40 15 14 60; leclein@mairie-lepouliguen.fr] Fr La Baule (W end) take coast rd to Le Pouliguen & foll sps. Lge, pt shd; wc; shwrs; el pts (6-10A) €1.82-2.13; ice; playgrnd; sand beach, fishing, sailing 500m; windsurfing 1.50m; dogs €1.52; poss cr; red low ssn. Easter-15 Sep. € 11.59   2002*

POULIGUEN, LE *2G3* (Urban/Coastal) **Camp Municipal Les Mouettes, 45 Blvd de l'Atlantique, 44510 Le Pouliguen** [02 40 42 43 98 or 02 40 15 08 08 (Mairie); fax 02 40 15 08 03; lesmouettes@mairie-lepouliguen.fr] Fr La Boule (W end) take coast rd to Le Pouliguen & foll sps. Lge, unshd; wc; baby facs; shwrs; el pts (6A) €2; shop, supmkt 200m; rest; snacks; bar; playgrnd; sports area; & beach 1km; fishing; sailing; cycle hire 200m; entmnt; TV; dogs €1.50 "Poss workers residing on site." 1 Apr-15 Oct. € 12.80   2005*

†**POUZAUGES** *2H4* (1.5km W Rural) **Camping du Lac, L'Esperance, 85700 Pouzauges** [02 51 91 37 55; fax 02 51 57 07 69; camplac@aol.com; www.campingpouzauges.com] W fr Pouzauges on D960, turn R in 1km onto unclass rd, site in 1km. Sp fr all dir. Sm, hdg/mkd pitch, pt sl, shd; wc; shwrs; el pts (6A) inc (poss rev pol); lndtte; shops 1.5km; tradsmn; rest, snacks, bar 1.5km; lake sw & fishing adj; boat hire; play & picnic area adj; dogs; poss cr; Eng spkn; adv bkg; quiet; CCI. "Excel site; idyllic setting; gd local walks; friendly, helpful British owners; new san facs 2004." ♦ € 13.75   2004*

PRADEAUX, LES see Issoire *9B1*

PRADES *8G4* (500m N Urban) **Camp Municipal Plaine St Martin, 66500 Prades** [04 68 96 29 83 or 04 68 05 41 00 (Mairie)] Site sp on ent town on N116 fr both dirs. Med, hdg/mkd pitch, pt sl, shd; wc (some cont); chem disp; 50% serviced pitches; shwrs inc; el pts (6-10A) €2.40; gas 500m; lndtte; ice; shop rest, snacks & bar 500m; playgrnd; htd, covrd pool; fishing; 30% statics; dogs €1.10; phone; poss cr; adv bkg; quiet; no cc acc; CCI. "Lge pitches; facs old but clean; poss unkempt low ssn; excel area for walking & sightseeing; conv Pyrenees & Perpignan; music festival in Jul; mkt Tues; NH sh stay only." 1 Apr-30 Sep. € 8.40   2004*

PRADES *8G4* (10km NE) **Camp Municipal des Escoumes, 66320 Vinca [04 68 05 84 78; fax 04 68 05 94 69; mairievinca@wanadoo.fr]** Fr Perpignan take N116 W twd Andorra. 10km E of Prades in vill of Vinca take 1st L foll camp sps to site (400m). Vinca 32km W of Perpignan. Med, mkd pitch, pt sl, pt shd; wc; chem disp; shwrs inc; el pts (6-10A) inc; gas; lndtte; shops adj; supmkt at Prades; sand beach, lake sw; fishing; 20% statics; dogs €1; poss cr; Eng spkn; quiet. "Beautiful quiet site; helpful staff." ♦ ltd. 1 Jun-30 Oct. € 12.10
2004*

PRADES *8G4* (7km E Rural) **Camping Le Canigou, 66320 Espira-de-Conflent [04 68 05 85 40; fax 04 68 05 86 20; canigou@yahoo.com]** On N116 Andorra-Perpignan, 2km after Marquixanes, R at sm site sp also sp 'Espira-de-Conflent'. Or, fr Perpignan on N116, turn L 7km bef Prades onto D25 & foll sp for 3.5km. Med, hdg/mkd pitch, pl sl, terr, shd; wc; chem disp; shwrs inc; el pts (6A) inc; lndry rm; shop; tradsmn; rest; snacks; bar; playgrnd; rv pool; sand beach 30km; rv sw adj; 5% statics; quiet; adv bkg; cc acc; Eng spkn; 20% red 14+ days low ssn; cc acc; CCI. "Beautiful rvside site in foothills of Pyrenees; youth groups in summer; some noise; narr site rds - not rec for lge o'fits; excel long stay." ♦ ltd. 1 Mar-31 Oct. € 18.80
2002*

PRADES *8G4* (3km W) **Camping Bellevue, Rue de St Jean, 66500 Ria Sirach [04 68 96 48 96]** W on N116 fr Perpignan, thro Prades. In 1km at far edge of vill of Ria, turn L on D26A & foll sps to site. Access steep. Med, pt sl, terr, shd; wc; shwrs inc; el pts (6A) €2.52; shops 3km; quiet; adv bkg. "Site formerly cherry orchard; vg long stay; peaceful with gd valley outlook." 1 Apr-30 Sep. € 8.05
2002*

PRADES *8G4* (5km W Rural) **Camping Mas de Lastourg, 66500 Villefranche-de-Conflent [04 68 05 35 25; maslastourg@aol.com; www.camping-lastourg.com]** W fr Prades on N116. Site on L of main rd 2km after Villefranche. U-turn at end of dual c'way to rtn. Med, hdg/mkd pitch, pt shd; wc; chem disp (wc only); shwrs inc; el pts (10-6A) €3; lndtte; shops 2km; tradsmn; snacks; bar; pool; few statics; dogs €1; phone; poss cr; quiet but some rd/rlwy noise; Eng spkn; CCI. "Nice pitches; conv 'Little Yellow Train'; gd long stay." 1 Apr-30 Sep.
€ 17.30
2005*

PRALOGNAN LA VANOISE *9B4* (8km N Rural) **Camp Municipal Le Chevelu, 73350 Bozel [04 79 22 04 80 or 04 79 55 03 06 (LS); fax 04 79 22 01 47; otbozel@wanadoo.fr]** Foll D915 thro Bozel dir Pralognan. Site on R immed beyond vill. Lge, mkd pitch, terr, shd; wc; shwrs inc; el pts (6-10A) €2.60-4.40; lndtte; ice; shops 1km; playgrnd; lake fishing & sw 300m; adv bkg (dep req); quiet; CCI. "In wood by rv; excel walking & climbing; vg." 11 Jun-4 Sep. € 9.60
2004*

PRALOGNAN LA VANOISE *9B4* (500m SE Rural) **Camping Le Parc Isertan, 73710 Pralognan-la-Vanoise [04 79 08 75 24; fax 04 79 08 76 73; isertan@pralo.com]** Fr Moutier, take D915 E to Pralognan. Pass under concrete bdge & foll camping sp. Site behind pool adj Municipal site. Lge, terr, pt shd; wc; chem disp; mv service pnt; shwrs inc; el pts (2-10A) €3-5; gas 500m; tradsmn; shop 500m; rest; snacks; bar; BBQ; playgrnd; htd, covrd pool, sports cent adj; horseriding 500m; dogs €1; phone; poss cr; Eng spkn; adv bkg; quiet; cc acc; red low ssn/CCI. "Superb scenery; wonderful walking; cable car in vill; v peaceful; excel long/sh stay." ♦ 15 Dec-30 Apr & 24 May-13 Sep. € 15.00
2003*

PRALOGNAN LA VANOISE *9B4* (S Rural) **Camp Municipal Le Chamois, 73710 Pralognan-la-Vanoise [04 79 08 71 54; fax 04 79 08 78 77]** Fr Moutiers take D915 to Pralognan. Pass under concrete bdge, turn SW & foll camping sp; keep L past recep of bigger Iseran site. Lge, pt sl, unshd; terr; wc (some cont); chem disp (wc); shwrs inc; el pts (2-10A) €2.30-3.90; lndtte; shops 500m; pool 500m; rv fishing; poss cr; quiet. "Marvellous scenery; v peaceful; wonderful walks; v friendly staff; lots of free hot water; cable car up mountain." 1 Jun-15 Sep. € 9.85
2003*

PRATS DE CARLUX see Sarlat la Caneda *7C3*

PRATS DE MOLLO LA PRESTE *8H4* (11km E Rural) **Camp Municipal Le Verte Rive, 66260 St Laurent-de-Cerdans [04 68 39 54 64 or 04 68 39 55 75; fax 04 68 39 59 59]** Fr Le Boulou, take D115 twd Prats-de-Mollo, turn L on D3 twd St Laurent. Site 4km fr Spanish border. Med, pt sl, pt shd; wc; shwrs inc; el pts (5A) €2.60; lndtte; shop 1.5km; playgrnd; pool adj; poss cr; adv bkg; CCI. "Poss itinerants; NH only." 1 May-30 Sep. € 7.00
2003*

PRATS DE MOLLO LA PRESTE *8H4* (12km E Rural) **Caming Domain Le Clols, 66260 St Laurent-de-Cerdans [tel/fax 04 68 39 51 68; info@leclols.com; www.leclols.com]** Fr A9 at Le Boulou take D115 dir Prats-de-Mollo; 6km past Arles-sur-Tech take D3 on L sp St Laurent-de-Cerdans; at La Forge-del-Mitg turn sharp L sp Le Clols; site on R in 3km. Sm, pt sl, pt shd; wc (some cont); chem disp (wc); shwrs inc; el pts (4A) €3; gas; lndtte; ice; shop; snacks; playgrnd; pool; TV; dogs €1.50; Eng spkn; adv bkg; quiet; red 10+ days; CCI. "Spectacular views; friendly British owners; narr winding rd fr La Forge-del-Mitg, but easily navigable; walks fr site." ♦ ltd. 1 May-30 Sep. € 19.00
2005*

FRANCE

PRE EN PAIL *4E1* (200m N Urban) **Camp Municipal Alain Gerbault, Rue des Troenes, 53140 Pre-en-Pail [02 43 03 04 28]** Fr E on N12, take R fork at major traff lts (N176 Domfront). Turn R twd sports cent & well sp fr there. Sm, mkd pitch, pt shd; wc (some cont); chem disp; shwrs inc; el pts (16A) €2.65; shop 250m; rest; snacks; bar; playgrnd; htd pool adj; dogs €1; phone; CCI. "Pleasant wooded region; places of historical interest; poss mkt traders on site on mkt day; OK as touring base." Easter-30 Sep. € 9.00   2005*

As we're travelling out of season, we'd better phone ahead to check that the site is actually open.

PRECIGNE see Sable sur Sarthe *4F1*

PRECY SOUS THIL *6G1* (Rural) **Camp Municipal, Rue de l'Hotel de Ville, 21390 Precy-sous-Thil [03 80 64 43 32 or 03 80 64 57 18 (Mairie); fax 03 80 64 43 37]** Exit A6 a'route at Bierre-les-Saumur exit, turn R at camping sp. Sp in vill, 6km fr a'route. Sm, pt sl, pt shd; wc; shwrs inc; el pts (4A) €2.40; lndtte; ice; shops adj; playgrnd; rv adj; horseriding; entmnt; TV; dogs €1.30; quiet. 19 Apr-2 Nov. € 9.00   2004*

PREFAILLES see Pornic *2G3*

PREIXAN see Carcassonne *8F4*

PREMEAUX PRISSEY see Nuits St Georges *6G1*

PREMERY *4G4* (500m NW) **Camp Municipal Les Pres de la Ville, 58700 Premery [03 86 37 99 42 or 03 86 68 12 40 (Mairie); fax 03 86 37 98 72; mairie-premery@wanadoo.fr]** N fr Nevers L off D977, turn R approx 500m after 2nd rndabt at Premery. Med, pt shd; wc (some cont); chem disp (wc); shwrs inc; el pts (8-16A) €0.90-1.50; shops 500m; lake & rv adj with sand beach, sw, fishing & boating; tennis adj; adv bkg; quiet; 10% red 10+ days. "Lovely site; a well-run & popular NH; poss market traders; excel value." ◆ 1 May-30 Sep. € 6.90   2005*

PREMIAN see St Pons de Thomieres *8F4*

PRESILLY LA TUILIERE see St Julien en Genevois *9A3*

PRESSAC *7A3* (7km E Urban) **Camp Municipal Le Parc, 86460 Availles-Limouzine [05 49 48 51 22; fax 05 49 48 66 76]** Fr Confolens N on D948 & turn R on D34 to Availles-Limouzine. Site on rv by town bdge. Med, pt shd; wc; chem disp; mv service pnt; shwrs inc; el pts (16A) inc; gas; shops 750m; playgrnd; paddling pool; rv sw; dogs €2.65; poss cr; Eng spkn; adv bkg; quiet; CCI. "Attractive site on Rv Vienne; barrier opp ent, clsd 2200-0800; excel san facs; warden lives on site; vg sh stay." ◆ 1 May-30 Sep. € 10.50   2004*

PREUILLY SUR CLAISE *4H2* (SW Urban) **Camp Municipal, 37290 Preuilly-sur-Claise [02 47 94 50 04; fax 02 47 94 63 26]** Fr E on D725 descend hill into vill. At T-junc opp town hall turn R & in 30m take 2nd L sp Camping & Piscine - poss diff turn long o'fits due narr rd. Site adj pool in 300m. Sm, hdg pitch, pt shd; wc; chem disp (wc); shwrs inc; el pts (5A) inc; lndry rm; shop, rest in vill; BBQ; htd pool adj; rv fishing adj; poss cr; quiet. "No twin-axles allowed." 1 May-15 Sep. € 10.20   2005*

PRISCHES see Nouvion en Thierache, Le *3B4*

PRIVAS *9D2* (8km NE Rural) **Camping L'Albanou (formerly Pampelonne), Quartier Pampelonne, 07000 St Julien-en-St Alban [04 75 66 00 97; camping.albanou@wanadoo.fr; http://camping. albanou.free.fr]** Fr A7 (junc 16), exit at Loriol dir Le Pouzin, go thro Le Pouzin on N104 dir Aubenas. Site in 6km on L just bef vill of St Julien-en-St Alban. Med, hdg/mkd pitch, pt sl, pt shd; wc; chem disp; mv service pnt; baby facs; shwrs inc; el pts (6A) €3.50; lndtte; ice; shops 1km; tradsmn; snacks; playgrnd; pool; rv fishing adj; some statics; dogs €2; Eng spkn; adv bkg; quiet; CCI. "Friendly welcome; helpful owners; v clean, well-run site by rv; gd size pitches; gd all stays." 28 Apr-22 Sep. € 15.00   2005*

PRIVAS *9D2* (3km E) **Camping Le Moulin d'Onclaire, 07000 Coux [04 75 64 51 98; michelelampe@voila.fr]** Fr Privas take N304 E twds Le Pouzin, sp Valence. Site on R after passing narr bdge to Coux. Sm, pt shd; wc; shwrs inc; el pts (5A) €2.60; ice; shop; snacks; rest & bar adj; BBQ; pool 3km; tennis; Eng spkn; adv bkg; CCI. "Somewhat run-down; site rds not suitable for disabled; poss itinerants; owner's dog roaming site; helpful staff; NH only." 1 Apr-15 Oct. € 11.50   2004*

PRIVAS *9D2* (8km SE) **Camp Municipal Les Civelles d'Ozon, 07210 St Lager-Bressac [04 75 65 01 86; fax 04 75 65 13 02; camping@ saintlagerbressac.fr; www.saintlagerbressac. com]** On N86, turn W 3km S of St Pauzin. Site well sp; sm narr rd leading to site easily missed on RH bend. Sm, pt shd, mkd pitch; serviced pitches; wc; chem disp; shwrs inc; el pts (6-10A) inc; ice; lndtte; tradsmn; shops 3km; playgrnd; pool; tennis; dogs €2; adv bkg; quiet. ◆ 1 May-30 Sep. € 11.00   2002*

PRIVAS *9D2* (1km S Urban) **Ardeche Camping, Blvd de Paste, Quartier Ouveze, 07000 Privas** [04 75 64 05 80; fax 04 75 64 59 68; jcray@ wanadoo.fr; www.ardechecamping.fr] Exit A7 junc 16 dir Privas. Fr Privas take D22 twd Montelimar on Rte de Chomerac. Site sp. Lge, mkd pitch, pt sl, pt shd; wc (some cont); chem disp; mv service pnt; baby facs; shwrs inc; el pts (5-10A) €3.50; lndtte; ice; shops adj; supmkt 100m; rest; snacks; bar; BBQ; playgrnd; htd pool; rv fishing; tennis adj; entmnt; TV rm; 80% statics; dogs €2; Eng spkn; adv bkg; some rd noise fr D2; red low ssn; cc acc; CCI. "Excel management; conv fr town; gd touring base; m'vans beware low canopy on service stn at Intermarche opp." ♦ 1 Apr-30 Sep. € 18.00 (CChq acc) 2005*

PRIVEZAC *7D4* (1km W Rural) **Aire Naturelle Les Malenies, 12350 Privezac** [05 65 81 92 80; fax 05 65 81 96 77] N fr Villefranche-de-Rouergue on D1 dir Rodez, at Lanuejouls turn onto D614 & D48 to Privezac. In vill foll sp 'Plan d'Eau', site sp in 1km by lake. Sm, hdg pitch, pt shd; wc; shwrs inc; el pts €1.50; playgrnd; sand beach & lake sw adj; 10% statics; dogs; quiet. "Fair sh stay." ♦ 1 Jun-30 Sep. € 6.00 2003*

PROISSANS see Sarlat la Caneda *7C3*

PROVINS *4E4* (1km NE Urban) **Camping Fontaine Riante, Maison des Jeunes, 9 Ave Mal D Lattre de Tassigny, 77483 Provins** [01 64 00 53 62; fax 01 64 00 57 55; mjc.provins@wanadoo.fr] App Provins fr N D403, foll sp at rndabt NE of town. After 200m turn R for site. Sm, pt sl, terr, pt shd; wc; shwrs inc; el pts (4-6A) €2.75-€3.50; gas, lndtte, shop, rest etc 1km; dogs €1.60; poss cr; quiet. "Nice view of medieval town, mkt Sat, facs old but clean; avoid town cent narr rds; sh, steep gravel slopes bet terr levels." 1 Apr-31 Oct. € 9.40 2005*

PRUNIERES see Chorges *9D3*

PUGET SUR ARGENS see Frejus *10F4*

PUGET THENIERS *10E4* (9km E Rural) **Camping L'Amitie, 06710 Touet-sur-Var** [tel/fax 04 93 05 74 32] Site sp at both end of vill on N202. Fr Nice turn L off N202, site in 800m immed after x-ing rv & sp fr town cent. App v difficult - rv bdge v narr & site ent req tight turn; imposs for vans +6m long. Sm, mkd pitch, pt shd; wc; chem disp; shwrs; el pts (3-16A) inc; gas; lndtte; shop; tradsmn; snacks; bar; BBQ; playgrnd; rv sw & fishing adj; horseriding; cycle hire; games area; entmnts; TV; dogs €2; 30% statics; adv bkg (ess high ssn); CCI. "Fair NH; steam train ride down valley to coast." ♦ 1 Apr-30 Sep. € 14.65 2004*

PUGET THENIERS *10E4* (500m S) **Camp Municipal Lou Gourdan, Quartier de la Condamine, 06260 Puget-Theniers** [04 93 05 18 17; fax 04 93 05 18 63; lou-gourdan@wanadoo.fr] Fr N202 Nice-Digne rd, turn S in Puget-Theniers over rlwy x-ing & rv bdge. Foll sp, sharp L after bdge. Site sp, beside Rv Var. Sm, mkd pitch, pt shd; wc; chem disp; shwrs inc; el pts inc; gas 500m; lndtte; shops 500m; tradsmn high ssn; snacks; bar; playgrnd; tennis; 10% statics; dogs; phone adj; adv bkg; quiet; red 7 days; CCI. "Attentive warden; warm welcome; facs dated; plenty hot water; interesting medieval town; v peaceful; gd walking; gd long/sh stay." ♦ 1 Apr-31 Oct. € 15.00 2005*

†PUGET THENIERS *10E4* (8km W Rural) **Camping Le Brec, 04320 Entrevaux** [tel/fax 04 93 05 42 45; camping.dubrec@wanadoo.fr] Site sp on R just after bdge 3km W of Entrevaux on N202. Rd (2km) to site narr with poor surface, passing places & occasional lge lorries. Med, mkd pitch, pt shd; htd wc; chem disp; baby facs; shwrs inc; el pts (10A) €3; lndtte; ice; tradsmn; snacks; BBQ; lake/rv sw, fishing & boating adj; TV; 10% statics; dogs €1; phone; Eng spkn; adv bkg; quiet; cc acc; 10% red CCI. "Situated in beautiful Alpes-Maritimes area." € 13.00 2004*

PUGET THENIERS *10E4* (2km NW Rural) **Camping L'Origan (Naturist), 06260 Puget-Theniers** [04 93 05 06 00; fax 04 93 05 09 34; origin@wanadoo.fr; www.origan-village.com] On N202 fr Entrevaux (dir Nice) at Puget-Theniers, immed turn L at rlwy x-ing (sp), site approx 1km up track. Med, hdg/mkd pitch, hdstg, pt sl, terr, pt shd; htd wc; sauna; shwrs inc; el pts (6A) €4; gas 2km; lndtte; ice; shop; tradsmn; rest; snacks; bar; BBQ; playgrnd; htd pool; white water rafting adj; fishing; tennis; archery; internet; TV rm; 50% statics; dogs €2.30; phone; adv bkg (dep req); Eng spkn; cc acc. "INF Card req; gd position; hilly site but pitches level; tourist train to Nice fr Puget-Theniers; interesting area." ♦ 2 Apr-2 Oct. € 31.50 (CChq acc) 2005*

PUIVERT *8G4* **Camp Municipal de Fontclaire, 11230 Puivert** [04 68 20 00 58; fax 04 68 20 82 29] Take D117 W fr Quillan twd Lavelanet for 16km. Site by lake well sp. Med, hdg pitch, pt sl, pt shd; wc; chem disp (wc); mv service pnt; shwrs; el pts inc; lndtte; shops in vill 500m; lake adj; fishing; quiet. "Attractive scenery & lake sw, poss diff lge c'vans; gd long/sh stay." 1 May-30 Sep. € 11.00 2004*

PUTANGES PONT ECREPIN *4E1* (1km Rural) **Camp Municipal Le Val d'Orne, 61210 Putanges-Pont-Ecrepin** [02 33 35 00 25 (Mairie)] S fr Falaise on D909 to Putanges. Ent Putanges cross rv bdge & ignore camping sp immed on L (Grand Rue). Go thro vill for approx 1km, turn L sp camping 200m. Site on R. Sm, hdg/mkd pitch, pt shd; wc; shwrs inc; el pts (6A) inc; shops & rest 5 mins walk via rv bank; rv fishing; playgrnd; dogs; adv bkg. "Site yourself, warden visits am & pm; excel rvbank site; ltd facs but clean & well-run." 1 Apr-30 Sep. € 7.70 2003*

FRANCE

SITES

PUY EN VELAY, LE *9C1* (500m N Urban) **Camping du Puy en Velay (formerly Camp Municipal Bourthezard), Avenue d'Aiguilhe, 43000 Le Puy-en-Velay [04 71 09 55 09 or 06 15 08 23 59 (mob)]** Fr Le Puy heading NW on N102 turn R at traff lts & foll site sp; blue sp showing mv with 'Site de Service' at ent rd to site. Site ent immed opp Chapel St Michel. Med, some hdg pitches, pt shd; wc; chem disp; mv service pnt; shwrs inc; el pts (6A) €3 (rev pol); lndtte; shop 200m & supmkt 500m; snacks; playgrnd adj; pool & tennis adj; dogs; poss cr; Eng spkn; adv bkg; noise of church bells (not night-time); cc not acc; CCI. "V popular site; efficient & helpful staff; gates clsd 2200-0700; recep clsd 1200-1430; mv area with adj disp point; may flood in v heavy rain; excursions to extinct volcanoes; conv town cent; sh walk to Cathedral & old Le Puy; interesting area to explore; on pilgrim route to Santiago de Compostela; poss diff access thro cr mv service area; busy site, rec arr early." ♦ ltd 30 Mar-30 Sep. € 9.35   2005*

PUY EN VELAY, LE *9C1* (9km N) **Camp Municipal Les Longues, Route des Rosieres, 43800 Lavoute-sur-Loire [04 71 08 18 79; fax 04 71 08 16 96; mairie.lavoutesurloire@ wanadoo.fr]** Fr Le Puy take N on D103 sp Lavoute & Retournac. In Lavoute turn R onto D7 bef rv bdge, site on L in 1km. Med, mkd pitch, pt shd; wc; shwrs; el pts (6A) inc; lndtte; shops 9km; bread 1km; playgrnd; pool 1km; rv sw 50m; dogs; quiet. "On banks of Loire; fishing; walking; scenic views; supplement for m'vans." ♦ 1 May-15 Sep. € 9.85   2005*

PUY EN VELAY, LE *9C1* (4km E Urban) **Camp Municipal Audinet, Route de Valence, 43700 Brives-Charensac [tel/fax 04 71 09 10 18 or 04 71 02 12 55 (LS)]** Fr Le Puy foll green sp E twd Valence. Fr S on N88 at bottom of hill in Le Puy bear R & foll white sp. Lge, pt shd; wc; chem disp; shwrs inc; el pts (6A) €2.50; lndtte; sm shop & shops 500m; supmkt 1.5km; snacks; rest; playgrnd; rv & lake sw/fishing; quiet. "Nice site on rvside; friendly, helpful staff; plenty of space; poss itinerants - but not a prob; poss shabby; conv Le Puy-en-Velay; reg bus into town; vg long/sh stay." ♦ 12 Apr-15 Sep. € 10.70   2005*

PUY EN VELAY, LE *9C1* (9km E) **Camping Le Moulin de Barette, Le Pont de Sumene, 43540 Blavozy [04 71 03 00 88; fax 04 71 03 00 51; hotel@lemoulindebarette.com]** Take N88 dir St Etienne. Exit after 7km at D156 Blavozy. At rndabt foll sp for Rosiers & 1st L to Moulin-de-Barette. Med, mkd pitch, pt sl, pt shd; wc; chem disp; shwrs inc; el pts €3; lndtte; shop; rest; pool; playgrnd; tennis; cycle hire; TV rm; few statics; dogs €1; quiet; 10% red low ssn/long stay; cc acc. "Part of hotel complex; san facs block old but gd; facs poss stretched in high ssn; poss elect probs." ♦ Easter-15 Oct. € 13.60   2004*

PUY EN VELAY, LE *9C1* (7km S Rural) **Camping Comme au Soleil, Le Cours de l'Eau, 43700 Coubon [tel/fax 04 71 08 32 55; comme.au. soleil@wanadoo.fr]** S fr Puy-en-Velay on N88, turn E onto D38 to Coubon, site sp. Sm, pt shd; wc; baby facs; shwrs; el pts €3; lndtte; ice; tradsmn; rest; snacks; bar; playgrnd; pool; rv sw; games area; cycle hire; 5% statics; dogs €1; bus; Eng spkn; adv bkg; red long stay; CCI. ♦ 15 Apr-15 Oct. € 13.00   2004*

PUY EN VELAY, LE *9C1* (11km S Rural) **Camp Municipal, 43370 Solignac-sur-Loire [04 71 03 11 46 (Mairie); fax 04 71 03 12 77]** Fr Le Puy S on N88 twd Mende; after about 7km at Les Baraques turn L on D27 dir Solignac & foll camping sp. Sm, hdg/mkd pitch, pt shd, pt sl; wc; shwrs inc; el pts (6-10A) €1.60; lndry rm; shops 1km; playgrnd; quiet; CCI. "Site yourself; warden calls am & pm; open site, no barriers; gd views Valley of Volcanoes; excel facs; clean & tidy; no twin-axle c'vans, but mkt traders sometimes tolerated." ♦ 15 Jun-15 Sep. € 7.80   2003*

†PUY GUILLAUME *9B1* (6km SW Rural) **Camping a la Ferme (Lehalper), Les Marodons, 63290 Noalhat [04 73 94 11 68; fax 04 73 94 10 30]** Fr D906 turn W at La Croix-St Bonnet onto D44 to Noalhat, site sp. Sm, shd; wc; shwrs; lndry rm; games area; fishing; rv sw nr; dogs; quiet. "San facs gd; c'vans phone ahead to ensure access."   2003*

PUY GUILLAUME *9B1* (1km W Rural) **Camp Municipal de la Dore, Rue Joseph Claussat, 63290 Puy-Guillaume [04 73 94 78 51 or 04 73 94 70 49 (Mairie); fax 04 73 94 78 51; mairie.puyguillaume@wanadoo.fr]** N fr Thiers by D906A join D906 as far as Puy-Guillaume. Ent vill, turn L at rndabt onto D343 which joins D63, then L again at 3rd rndabt. Site on R by rv. Med, pt shd; wc (some cont); chem disp; some serviced pitches; shwrs inc; el pts (6A) €2.50; lndtte; shops 500m; playgrnd; pool (high ssn) adj; rv fishing adj; dogs; adv bkg rec high ssn. "Neat, tidy site; v clean san facs; pleasant location by Rv Dore; facs poss used by locals; helpful wardens; excel long stay." ♦ ltd. 1 May-30 Sep. € 10.50   2005*

PUY L'EVEQUE *7D3* (3km E) **Village-Camping Les Vignes, Le Meoure, 46700 Puy-l'Eveque [tel/fax 05 65 30 81 72; lesvignes@puy-leveque. fr; www.campinglesvignes.com]** On D811 dir Villeneuve-sur-Lot, just bef ent Puy-l'Eveque turn L, foll sp for 3km. Site adj Rv Lot. Avoid town cent while towing. Med, shd; wc; baby facs; shwrs; el pts; (6A) €2.30; gas; lndtte; shops 3km; tradsmn; snacks; bar; playgrnd; pool; tennis; rv sw; games area; fishing; entmnt high ssn; cycle hire; TV; quiet; red over 55s. "Adj rv in beautiful countryside; gd san facs; friendly owners." 1 Apr-30 Sep. € 12.35   2003*

PUY L'EVEQUE *7D3* (10km S Rural) **Camping Le Clos Barrat (Naturist), 46700 Serignac** [05 65 31 97 93; fax 05 65 31 91 17; le.clos. barrat@wanadoo.fr] Fr Fumel by-pass turn S on D139 to Montayral, rd cont but becomes D4. Site sp fr Mauroux. Fr Puy-l'Eveque take D44 S to Floressas & Serignac. Med, pt shd, mkd pitch; wc; chem disp; shwrs inc; el pts (6A) €2.60; gas; lndtte; rest; snacks; shop; tradsmn; ice; pool; playgrnd; entmnt; dogs €0.80; quiet. "Nr Rv Lot, INF card req - can be bought on site." Easter-31 Oct. € 15.40
2002*

PUY L'EVEQUE *7D3* (6km W Urban) **Club de Vacances Duravel, Route de Vire, 46700 Duravel** [05 65 24 65 06 or 0031 74 2666499 (LS-N'lands); fax 05 65 24 64 96 or 0031 74 2668205 (LS-N'lands); clubduravel@aol.com; www. clubdevacances.net] Fr D811 Puy-l'Eveque to Fumel rd at Duravel town cent, opp Mairie turn S onto D58 sp Vire-sur-Lot. Site in 2.5km. Lge, hdg/mkd pitch, pt sl, pt shd; wc (some cont); chem disp; mv service pnt; shwrs inc; el pts (10A) €3.15; gas; lndtte; ice; shop; tradsmn; rest; snacks; bar; playgrnd; 2 pools (1 htd); waterslide; beach nr; tennis; games area; guided walks; canoeing; fishing; cycle hire; entmnt; 12% statics; poss cr; Eng spkn; adv bkg (dep req); quiet; 10% red low ssn; cc acc; CCI. "Vg site; v friendly staff; lovely situation; conv Cahors; all signs & notices on site in Dutch - enquire at recep for info in Eng on excursions/activities etc; excel long stay." ♦ ltd. Apr-30 Sep. € 22.05 2003*

PUYCELI *8E3* (4km W Rural) **Centre Naturiste Le Fiscalou (Naturist), 1 Route de Montclar, 81140 Puyceli** [05 63 30 45 95; fax 05 62 30 32 88; fiscalou@wanadoo.fr; www.fiscalou.com] Fr Bruniquel D964 S twd Castelnau. Take D1 sp Monclar-de-Quercy. Site on L after 4km. Sm, pt sl, pt shd; wc; chem disp; shwrs inc; el pts (6A) inc (poss long lead req); tradsmn; rest; bar; playgrnd; pool; Eng spkn; adv bkg; quiet. "A pleasant, rustic site; excel cent for touring area." 1 May-30 Sep.
€ 17.00 2004*

PYLA SUR MER *7D1* (7km S Coastal) **Camping La Dune, Route de Biscarosse, 33115 Pyla-sur-Mer** [tel/fax 05 56 22 72 17; campingdeladune@ wanadoo.fr; www.campingdeladune.fr] Fr Bordeaux app Arcachon; at rndabt foll sp Dune du Pilat & 'campings'; at T-junc turn L & foll 'plage' & camping sp on D218; site on R. Lge, pt sl, pt shd; wc (some cont for men); shwrs inc; el pts inc; gas; lndtte; ice; shop; rest; snacks; bar; playgrnd; pool; sand beach 500m; tennis; cycle hire; entmnt; TV rm; poss cr; adv bkg (ess Jul/Aug); quiet; "Diff pitches for c'vans; sm, unlevel, narr access; dominated by Europe's largest sand dunes." 1 May-30 Sep. 2002*

PYLA SUR MER *7D1* (7km S Coastal) **Camping La Foret, Route de Biscarosse, 33115 Pyla-sur-Mer** [05 56 22 73 28; fax 05 56 22 70 50; camping. foret@wanadoo.fr; www.campinglaforet.fr] Fr Bordeaux app Arcachon on A660 by-pass rd; at La Teste-de-Buch at rndabt foll sp for Dune du Pilat & 'campings'. At T-junc turn L; foll sp 'plage' & camping sp on D218. Site on R. Lge, hdg/mkd pitch, pt sl, shd; wc; chem disp; mv service pnt; shwrs inc; el pts (6A) inc; lndtte; shop; rest; snacks; bar; BBQ; playgrnd; pool; sand beach 600m; solarium; tennis; cycle hire; child entmnt; some statics; dogs €2.50; adv bkg; red low ssn; cc acc; CCI."Forest setting at foot of lgest sand dune in Europe; well organised; many facs; hang-gliding, surfing, sailing nrby." ♦ 4 Apr-31 Oct. € 31.00 2005*

PYLA SUR MER *7D1* (7km S Coastal/Rural) **Camping Panorama, Route de Biscarosse, 33115 Pyla-sur-Mer** [05 56 22 10 44; fax 05 56 22 10 12; mail@ camping-panorama.com; www.yellohvillage.com or www.camping-panorama.com] App Arcachon fr Bordeaux on A63/660, at rndabt foll sp for Dune-du-Pilat & 'campings'. Foll sp for 'plage' & 'campings' on D218. Site on R next to Camping Le Petit Nice. Lge, mkd pitch, pt sl, terr, pt shd; wc (some cont); chem disp; mv service pnt; sauna; shwrs inc; el pts (3-10A) €3.05-4.57; gas; rest; snacks; bar; shop; playgrnd; htd pool; sand beach adj; tennis; mini-golf; TV; entmnt; dogs €4.57; adv bkg; quiet; Eng spkn; CCI." Pleasant site on wooded dune, direct access to beach down steps, sm pitches poss diff lge o'fits; gd facs." ♦ 1 May-30 Sep. € 26.06 2004*

PYLA SUR MER *7D1* (9km S Coastal) **Camping Le Petit Nice, Route de Biscarosse, 33115 Pyla-sur-Mer** [05 56 22 74 03; fax 05 56 22 14 31; camping. petit.nice@wanadoo.fr; www.petitnice.com] Fr Bordeaux on app Arcachon foll sp for Dune-du-Pilat & 'campings'. At T-junc turn L; foll 'plage' & camping sp on D218. Site on R. Lge, pt sl, shd; wc; chem disp; mv service pnt; baby facs; shwrs inc; el pts (5A) inc; gas; lndtte; ice; shop; rest; snacks; bar; playgrnd; htd pool; paddling pool; sand beach adj tennis; TV rm; entmnt; TV rm; 50% statics; dogs €3; poss cr; adv bkg; quiet but poss noisy disco; red low ssn. "Open beach with steep wooden steps." 1 Apr-30 Sep. € 32.00 (CChq acc)
2005*

QUEAUX see Lussac les Chateaux *7A3*

QUESTEMBERT see Muzillac *2G3*

QUETTEHOU *1C4* (8km NE Coastal) **Camping Municipal le Jonville, Reville, 50760 Reville** [02 33 54 48 41; www.camping-joinville@saint-vaast-reville.com] S fr Barfleur on D1 twd St Vaast-la-Hougue & turn L in Reville. Foll sp. Med, hdg pitch, pt sl, pt shd; wc; shwrs inc; el pts (6A) €3.50; lndry rm; shops 1km; snacks; beach adj; phone; poss cr; adv bkg; quiet; CCI "Gd sh stay; gd boating & sw." 1 Apr-30 Sep. € 10.00 2004*

FRANCE

QUETTEHOU *1C4* (2km S Coastal) **Camping Le Rivage, Route de Morsalines, 50630 Quettehou** [02 33 54 13 76] Fr Quettehou on D14, sp on L. Med, unshd; wc; shwrs inc; el pts (6A) €3.50; lndtte; shop; snacks; bar; BBQ; playgrnd; htd pool; paddling pool; sand beach 400m; 50% statics; dogs €1.52; Eng spkn; adv bkg rec high ssn; quiet. "Gd base for Normandy beaches, boating, shrimping & seafood; gd clean site." 1 Apr-30 Sep. € 15.50
2003*

QUIBERON *2G3* (1.5km N Coastal) **Camp Municipal de Rohu, Rue des Men-Du, 56510 St Pierre-Quiberon** [02 97 50 27 85 or 02 97 30 92 00 (Mairie)] On D768 Auray to Quiberon, 1km past exit of St Pierre turn L at camp sp. Turn R in 200m & L after 250m at T-junc sp Le Petit Rohu. Site on R in 50m on beach. Well sp. Med, mkd pitch, (grass/gravel), pt sl, unshd; wc; shwrs; el pts (10A) inc; gas; lndtte; ice; shop; snacks adj; playgrnd; sand beach adj; boating; fishing; sports area; some statics; dogs €0.82; poss cr; quiet. "Vg site; featureless but beautiful location on beach; gd, clean facs; boat ramp nr; gd cycling country; recep open 1000-1200 & 1700-1900; button on wall to open barrier." ♦ 26 Mar-9 Oct. € 13.91
2005*

QUIBERON *2G3* (1.5km N Coastal) **Camping Do Mi Si La Mi, St Julien-Plage, 56170 Quiberon** [02 97 50 22 52; fax 02 97 50 26 69; camping@domisilami.com; www.domisilami.com] Take D768 down Quiberon Peninsular, 3km after St Pierre-Quiberon & shortly after sp for rlwy level x-ing turn L into Rue de la Vierge, site on R in 400m. Lge, hdg/mkd pitch, pt sl, pt shd; wc (some cont); chem disp; mv service pnt; shwrs inc; el pts (3-10A) €2.60-4; gas; lndtte; shop, snacks, bar adj; BBQ; playgrnd; sand/shgl beach 100m; games area; cycle hire; sailing, horseriding, tennis nr; 40% statics; dogs €2.10; poss cr; Eng spkn; quiet; red low ssn; cc acc; CCI. "Gd touring base; vg." ♦ 1 Apr-4 Nov. € 19.80
2005*

See advertisement above

QUIBERON *2G3* (2km N Coastal) **Camp Municipal de Kerhostin, 56510 St Pierre-Quiberon** [02 97 30 95 25 or 02 97 30 92 00 (Mairie)] Off D768 turn SE onto Rue des Foelettes by rail x-ing (no thro rd sp), turn L at 1st sm island, turn L at end, site 300m on R. Med, pt shd; wc; shwrs inc; el pts (3A) inc; lndtte; shops adj; pool 2km; sand beach adj; dogs €0.80; poss cr. 1 Jun-31 Aug. € 17.20
2003*

QUIBERON *2G3* (2.5km N Coastal) **Camping Beausejour, St Julien-Plage, 56170 Quiberon** [tel/fax 02 97 30 44 93; nfo@campingbeausejour.com; www.campingbeausejour.com] On D768 S, turn L at camping sp & L onto coast rd. Site on L facing sea. Lge, hdg/mkd pitch, pt sl, pt shd; wc (mainly cont); chem disp; shwrs inc; el pts (3-6A) €3-4.20; gas; lndtte; shop; snack bar; playgrnd; sand beach adj; 5% statics; dogs €2; Eng quiet; spkn; red low ssn; CCI. 15 May-15 Sep. € 18.20
2004*

QUIBERON *2G3* (8km N Coastal) **Camping de l'Ocean, 16 Ave de Croix, Kerhostin, 56510 St Pierre-Quiberon** [02 97 30 91 29; fax 02 97 30 80 18; stjo56@free.fr; www.relaisdelocean.com] S fr Carnac at traff lts in Kerhostin, turn R dir Route de la Cote Sauvage, site sp. Lge, hdg/mkd pitch, pt shd; wc; chem disp; baby facs; shwrs inc; el pts (10A) €3.80; gas; lndtte; shop 1km; tradsmn; rest; snacks; bar; BBQ; playgrnd; sand beach adj; games area; games rm; cycle hire; golf 15km; thelassotherapy 8km; entmnt; TV; 20% statics; dogs €2.15; Eng spkn; adv bkg; quiet; cc acc; red low ssn/CCI. "Pleasant site; gd for families." ♦ 1 Apr-1 Nov. € 15.00
2004*

QUIBERON *2G3* (SE Urban) **Camping Les Joncs du Roch, Rue de l'Aerodrome, 56170 Quiberon** [02 97 50 24 37 or 02 97 50 11 36 (LS)] Foll sp to aerodrome. Site ent opp. Lge, pt shd; wc (some cont); chem disp; shwrs inc; el pts (4-10A) €2.50-3.50; gas; ice; shops 1km; sand beach 1km; dogs; poss cr; quiet, but minimal aircraft noise; 15% red Sep. "Vg clean site, good facs; well looked after." Easter-25 Sep. € 18.60
2004*

Camping ★★★★ "Le Ty Nadan"
from the 19th of March
the only campsite where you can do this...
www.camping-ty-nadan.fr

FRANCE

QUIBERON 2G3 (1.5km SE Coastal/Rural) **Camping Le Bois d'Amour, Rue St Clement, 56170 Quiberon [02 97 50 13 52 or 04 42 20 47 25 (LS); fax 02 97 50 42 67; info@homair-vacances.fr; www.homair-vacances.fr]** Exit N165 at Auray onto D768. In Quiberon foll sp 'Thalassotherapie', site sp. Lge, hdg/mkd pitch, pt shd; wc; mv service pnt; chem disp; shwrs inc; baby facs; el pts (10A) €4; gas; lndtte; ice; shop; rest; snacks; bar; BBQ; playgrnd; pool; beach 200m; games area; tennis; horseriding; cycle hire; entmnt; dogs €4; adv bkg; quiet; Eng spkn; red low ssn; cc acc; CCI. ♦ 3 Apr-2 Oct. € 35.00   2003*

QUIBERON 2G3 (1km S Coastal) **Camp Municipal Le Goviro, Blvd du Goviro, 56170 Quiberon [02 97 50 13 54]** Fr D768 at Quiberon foll sp Port Maria & 'Centre Thalassotherapie'. Site 1km on L. Lge, hdg/mkd pitch, terr, pt shd; wc; chem disp; mv service pnt; shwrs; el pts (13A) €3; gas; ice; lndtte; rest adj; playgrnd; sand beach, fishing & watersports adj; dogs €1.60; poss cr. "Gd sea views & coastal path; gd san facs; quiet; clean; vg sh stay." ♦ ltd. 4 Apr-9 Oct. € 12.60   2005*

QUIBERVILLE SUR MER see Veules les Roses 3C2

QUILLAN 8G4 (6km N) **Camp Municipal, 11260 Esperaza [04 68 74 08 60]** Exit D118 over bdge fr Couiza (app thro Esperaza v narr) site clearly sp. Sm, pt shd; wc; shwrs inc; el pts (6A) €2; shops 500m; rv sw; quiet; CCI. "NH or fair sh stay; rec own san facs." 1 May-30 Sep. € 8.40   2002*

QUILLAN 8G4 (1km W Urban) **Camp Municipal La Sapinette, 11500 Quillan [04 68 20 13 52; fax 04 68 20 27 80]** Foll D118 fr Carcassonne to Quillan; turn R at 2nd traff lts in town cent; site sp in town. Med, sl, terr, pt shd; wc; shwrs inc; el pts (6A) €2.80; shops 400m; playgrnd; pool & leisure cent 500m in town; dogs €1; poss cr; adv bkg; quiet; cc acc; red CCI. "Excel site; gd touring base; sm pitches; low tree branches; basic san facs; early arr rec; helpful staff; town nr, gd mkt Wed; vet adj; rec." 1 Apr-31 Oct. € 13.20   2005*

QUILLAN 8G4 (8km NW) **Camping Le Fontaulie-Sud, 11500 Nebias [tel/fax 04 68 20 17 62; lefontauliesud@free.fr; www.fontauliesud.com]** In Quillan take D117 twd Foix. Turn L at sp immed after leaving Nebias vill. Site in 1km. NB Steep rd to site. Med, pt sl, pt shd; wc; chem disp; shwrs inc; el pts (4A) inc; lndtte; ice; shop; snacks; bar; playgrnd; pool; paddling pool; tennis, horseriding, watersports nr; TV rm; some statics; adv bkg; quiet; CCI. "Beautiful scenery & many mkd walks; owners friendly, helpful; ltd facs low ssn; gd touring base." 1 May-15 Sep. € 16.00   2005*

QUIMPER 2F2 (9km SE Rural) **Aire Naturelle (Hemidy), Creach Lann, 29170 St Evarzec [02 98 56 29 88 or 06 68 46 97 25; jean-claude.hemidy@wanadoo.fr]** On D783 on St Everzec to Concarneau rd. Sm, hdg pitch, pt sl, pt shd; wc; chem disp; shwrs; el pts (10-13A) €2; lndry rm; shop 3km; playgrnd; sand beach 5km; adv bkg; quiet. "V friendly, helpful owner; poss to stay after end Sep by arrangement; lovely old town; gd shopping & daily covrd mkt." 1 May-30 Sep. € 9.00   2003*

QUIMPER 2F2 (2km S Rural) **LES CASTELS L'Orangerie de Lanniron, Chateau de Lanniron, 29336 Quimper [02 98 90 62 02; fax 02 98 52 15 56; camping@lanniron.com; www.lanniron.com or www.les-castels.com]** Fr Brest or Lorient on N165/E60 join Quimper ring rd S. At rndabt for D34 Benodet cont on ringrd & shortly take slip rd R, sp Lanniron. Site on R in 50m, sp. Fr other dirs foll sp to Lanniron fr ring rd S. Lge, pt shd; wc; chem disp; baby facs; some serviced pitches; shwrs inc; el pts (10A) inc; gas; lndtte; shop; supmkt adj; rest; snacks; bar; BBQ; playgrnd; htd pool & paddling pool; fishing; beach 12km; tennis; mini-golf; entmnt; internet; TV/games rm; 25% statics; dogs €3.50; bus; phone; recep 0800-2100; poss cr; Eng spkn; adv bkg; 10% red low ssn due ltd facs; cc acc; CCI. "Well-spaced pitches; vg san facs; excursions booked; 30 mins walk town cent; excel." ♦ 15 May-15 Sep. € 36.20 (CChq acc) ABS - B21   2005*

QUIMPER *2F2* (12km W Rural) **Camping La Rocaille, Kerandoare, 29710 Polgastel-St Germain [02 98 54 58 13]** Fr N165 exit Quimper Sud & foll sp dir Audierne onto D784. Turn R at Kerandore; site sp 100m. Avoid Quimper town cent. Sm, hdg/mkd pitch, terr, pt shd; wc (some cont); 50% serviced pitch; shwrs inc; el pts inc; lndtte; shop 500m; tradsmn; beach 10km; Eng spkn; quiet. "Excel facs; immac san facs; v friendly & helpful owner; lovely touring area; poss diff m'vans if wet; vg long/sh stay." 1 Jun-15 Sep. € 10.00   2003*

QUIMPERLE *2F2* (7km NE Rural) **LES CASTELS Le Ty-Nadan, Route d'Arzano, 29310 Locunole [02 98 71 75 47; fax 02 98 71 77 31; infos@camping-ty-nadan.fr; www.camping-ty-nadan.fr]** Fr N165 take exit to Quimperle Est & Kerfleury then D22 to Arzano 9km. At Arzano turn L on un-numbered rd W sp Locunole & site on L after x-ing Rv Elle. Or fr Roscoff on D69 S join N165/E60 but take care at uneven level x-ing at Pen-ar-Hoat 11km after Sizun. Lge, hdg/mkd pitch, shd; wc; chem disp; mv service pnt; sauna; serviced pitches; baby facs; shwrs inc; el pts (10A) inc (long lead poss req); gas; lndtte; ice; shop; rest; snacks; bar; BBQ; playgrnd; htd pools (1 covrd); waterslides; sand beach 18km; rv fishing, canoeing adj; tennis; cycle hire; horseriding; archery; rock-climbing; excursions; adventure park nrby; games area; entmnt; sat TV/games rm; internet; 40% statics; dogs €4; c'vans over 8.50m not acc high ssn; Eng spkn; adv bkg; cc acc; red CCI. "Excel touring base; peaceful site; excel." ◆ 1 Apr-7 Sep. € 44.10 (CChq acc) ABS - B20   2005*

See advertisement on previous page

QUIMPERLE *2F2* (1.5km SW Urban) **Camp Municipal de Kerbertrand, 29300 Quimperle [02 98 39 31 30 or 02 98 96 01 41 (Mairie); fax 02 98 96 37 39]** Exit N165 at Kervidanou junc SW of town. Foll sp Centre Ville along Rue de Pont Aven. In 1km turn L opp supmkt, sp v sm. Sm, hdg pitch, pt shd; wc; shwrs; el pts €1.50; ice; playgrnd; TV. "Delightful site; helpful warden; conv for old town." 1 Jun-15 Sep. € 8.00   2004*

QUINGEY *6H2* (Urban) **Camp Municipal Les Promenades, 25440 Quingey [03 81 63 74 01 or 03 81 63 63 25 (Mairie); fax 03 81 63 63 25; mairie-quingey@wanadoo.fr]** Site sp off N83 by-pass, then in Quingey. Thro vill, immed on L after bdge over Rv Loue. Sm, pt shd; wc (some cont); chem disp; shwrs inc; el pts (6A) €2.60; lndtte; ice; shop; snacks; rest; playgrnd; rv sw; fishing, sailing, tennis; canoeing, tennis, cycle hire & archery adj; quiet but some daytime rd noise. ◆ May-Sep. € 10.50   2004*

QUINSON *10E3* (Rural) **Escapades Terre Oceane Camping Les Pres du Verdon, 04500 Quinson [04 92 74 58 80 or 05 46 55 10 01; fax 05 46 55 10 00; info@campingterreoceane.com; www.camping terreoceane.com]** Lge, mkd pitch, pt shd; wc; shwrs inc; el pts €3; lndtte; shop; snacks; bar; playgrnd; pool; lake fishing adj; entmnt; child entmnt; statics; dogs; Eng spkn; adv bkg; cc acc. "Beautiful area; vg site." ◆ 13 May-16 Sep. € 16.00   2005*

See advertisement above

QUINTIN *2E3* (NE Urban) **Camp Municipal, 22800 Quintin [02 96 74 92 54 or 02 96 74 84 01 (Mairie); fax 02 96 74 06 53]** Site on D790, N (100m) of town gardens & boating lake, on R of D790 N. Or 3rd L after Quintin sp (as Le Lac). Sm, pt sl, pt shd; wc (some cont); shwrs; el pts (6A) €2.60; BBQ; shops, rest, snacks, bar 500m; playgrnd; fishing; quiet. "Fair sh stay; interesting town with gd tourist office." ◆ Easter-31 Oct. € 7.80   2003*

RABASTENS *8E3* (2km NW Rural) **Camp Municipal des Auzerals**, Route de Grazac, 81800 Rabastens [05 63 33 70 36 or 06 12 90 14 55 (mob); fax 05 63 33 64 05; mairie.rabastens@libertysurf.fr] Exit A68 junc 7 onto D12. In Rabastens town cent foll sp dir Grazac, site sp. Sm, hdg/mkd pitch, pt sl, terr, pt shd; wc (mainly cont); chem disp; shwrs inc; el pts (10-12A); lndtte; ice; shop 2km; rest 2km; playgrnd; pool adj high ssn; quiet; adv bkg ess high ssn; CCI. "V attractive lakeside site; facs old but spotless; highly rec; friendly warden on site 0800-1100 & 1700-2000 otherwise height barrier in operation; conv m'way NH." 1 May-15 Sep. € 8.40   2005*

RAGUENES see Pont Aven *2F2*

RAMATUELLE see St Tropez *10F4*

RAMBOUILLET *4E3* (3km E Rural) **Camping L'Etang d'Or**, Route du Chateau d'Eau, 78120 Rambouillet [01 30 41 07 34; fax 01 30 41 00 17; rambouillet.tourisme@wanadoo.fr; www.ot-rambouillet.fr] Fr S on N10 (sp Camping) twd Paris, turn onto D906 dir Cheveuse & foll sm white sp to site. Fr N on N10 go past D906 junc, take next slip rd, stay in inside lane & foll sp Rambouillet, Les Eveuses. Avoid Rambouillet town cent. Lge, hdg/mkd pitch, pt shd; htd wc (some cont); mv service pnt; chem disp; baby facs; shwrs inc; el pts (6-10A) €3-3.80 (poss rev pol); lndtte; shop & 2km; tradsmn, rest, snacks & bar high ssn; BBQ (gas/elec); playgrnd; htd, covrd pool & waterslide 3km; fishing adj; bowling; 10% statics; dogs €1.50; phone; Eng spkn; adv bkg (rec high ssn); quiet; red low ssn; cc acc; CCI. "Helpful, friendly warden; san facs clean but ageing; conv Paris by train - stn 3km, parking €2.50; gd cycling routes; interesting town & gd tourist office." ♦ 30 Jan-17 Dec. € 13.50 (CChq acc)   2005*

See advertisement above

RANG DU FLIERS see Berck *3B2*

RANVILLE see Ouistreham *3D1*

RAON L'ETAPE *6E3* (10km NE Rural) **Camping des Lacs**, 88110 Celles-sur-Plaine [03 29 41 28 00; fax 03 29 41 18 69; camping@sma-lacs-pierre-percee.fr; www.sma-lacs-pierre-percee.fr] Fr Raon L'Etape turn onto D392A to Celles-sur-Plaine, site sp. Med, hdg/mkd pitch, hdstg, pt sl, pt shd; wc (some cont); solarium; chem disp; shwrs inc; el pts (4-10A) €2.60-4; lndtte; shop; tradsmn; snacks; bar; playgrnd; htd pool; sand beach (lake) 400m; tennis; fishing; sports; windsurfing; 10% statics; dogs €1.30; Eng spkn; adv bkg (dep req); quiet; red low ssn/long stay; cc acc; CCI. "Beautiful location; vg site." ♦ 1 Apr-30 Sep. € 15.45   2005*

RAON L'ETAPE *6E3* (10km E Rural) **Camping des 7 Hameaux, Chez Fade, Ban-de-Sapt**, 88210 Senones [03 29 58 95 75] Fr St Die NE on D49 to St Jean D'Ormont (turn R after cathedral in St Die). Then D32 sp 'Saales' to Ban-de-Sapt. Turn L onto D49 to La Fontenelle. Site on R 1km past sp to military cemetery. Or fr N59 take D424 sp Senones. In 3.3km in Moyenmoutiers turn R onto D37 sp Ban-de-Sapt. In 6.1km join D49. site on L in 1.3km. Sm, pt sl; wc; chem disp; shwrs €1; el pts (6A) €2; rest, bar & shop 1km; tradsmn; pool 7km; quiet; adv bkg; cc not acc; CCI. "Walks, cycle rtes; farm prod; friendly; tourist info on site; vg." 15 Mar-15 Nov. € 5.20   2004*

†RAON L'ETAPE *6E3* (4km SE) **Camping Beaulieu-sur-l'Eau, Rue de Trieuche**, 88480 Etival-Clairefontaine [tel/fax 03 29 41 53 51] SE fr Baccarat on N59 turn R in vill of Etival-Clairefontaine on D424 sp Rambervillers & Epinal & foll sp for 3km. Ent on L in front of Epicurie. Med, terr, pt shd; wc; shwrs inc; el pts (6A) €2.90; ice; shop; playgrnd; rv sw & beach 400m; 10% statics; adv bkg rec high ssn; quiet; CCI. "Vg sh stay/NH." € 10.00   2004*

FRANCE

†RAON L'ETAPE *6E3* (5km SE) **Camping Vosgina, 1 Rue la Cheville, St Blaise, 88420 Moyenmoutier** [tel/fax 03 29 41 47 63; camping-vosgina@wanadoo.fr; www.vosges-camping.com] On N59 St Die-Luneville rd, take exit mkd Senones, Moyenmoutier. At rndabt take rd twd St Blaise & foll camping sp. Site is on minor rd parallel with N59 bet Moyenmoutier & Raon. Med, hdg pitch, terr, shd; wc; shwrs inc; el pts (4-10A) €2.20-5.50; gas; lndtte; sm shop & 3km; tradsmn; snacks; bar; 20% statics; dogs €1.50; Eng spkn; quiet; CCI. "Vg all stays; gd site for quiet holiday in a non-touristy area of Alsace; friendly recep; lovely countryside; many cycle/walking routes in area; barrier clsd 2200-0700." € 12.30   2004*

RAUZAN *7D2* (200m N Rural) **Camping du Vieux Chateau, 33420 Rauzan** [05 57 84 15 38; fax 05 57 84 18 34; hoekstra.camping@wanadoo.fr; www.vieux-chateau.com] Fr Libourne S on D670, site is on D123 about 1.5km, off D670, sp. Sm, mkd pitch, pt shd; wc; chem disp; baby facs; shwrs inc; el pts (6-10A) €2.70-3.60; gas; lndtte; ice; shop, tradsmn; rest 200m; snacks; sm bar & in 200m; playgrnd; pool; tennis; rv/lake 5km; cycle hire; horseriding; wine-tasting; entmnt; TV; 10% statics; dogs €1.20; poss cr; Eng spkn; adv bkg; quiet; red low ssn; cc acc; CCI. "Conv vineyards; helpful owners; view of ruined chateau fr site; lovely site but care as some pitches badly pitted due lge tree roots; poss ltd facs low ssn." ♦ 1 Apr-30 Oct. € 15.00
2004*

RAVENOVILLE PLAGE see Ste Mere Eglise *1C4*

REALMONT *8E4* (2km SW) **Camp Municipal de la Batisse, 81120 Realmont** [05 63 55 50 41 or 05 63 45 50 68; fax 05 63 55 65 62]   On   N112 fr Albi heading S thro Realmont. On exit turn R on N631 where site sp. Site 1.5km on L. Sm, pt shd; wc; shwrs; el pts (3A) inc; gas; shops 2km; rv adj; fishing; quiet. "Pleasant, well-kept site; friendly warden; gd NH/sh stay." 1 May-30 Sep. € 7.50
2003*

RECOUBEAU JANSAC see Luc en Diois *9D3*

REDON *2F3* Camp Municipal de la Goule d'Eau, Rue de la Goule d'Eau, 35600 Redon [02 99 72 14 39 or 02 99 71 05 27 (Mairie)] Foll sp in town. Sm, shd; wc; shwrs inc; el pts; ice; shop; playgrnd; fishing; sailing; quiet; CCI. 15 Jun-15 Sep.
2004*

REGUINY *2F3* (1km S Urban) Camp Municipal de l'Etang, 56500 Reguiny [02 97 38 61 43 or 02 97 38 66 11; fax 02 97 38 63 44]   On   D764 fr Pontivy to Ploermel, turn R into D11 to Reguiny then foll sp. Med, pt shd; wc; chem disp; mv service pnt; baby facs; shwrs inc; el pts (10A) €2; lndtte; shop 2km; rest, bar 1km; playgrnd; htd pool 500m; no statics; dogs; phone; Eng spkn; quiet; cc acc. "New facs, site refurb 2004; gd touring base; fishing; excel long stay." 1 Jun-15 Sep. € 10.60   2004*

REGUSSE *10E3* (1.5km NW Rural) Village-Camping Les Lacs du Verdon, Domaine de Roquelande, 83630 Regusse [04 94 70 17 95; fax 04 94 70 51 79; info@leslacsduverdon.com; www.lacs-verdon.com] Fr W exit A8 junc 34 at St Maximin onto D560 Barjols, Tavernes, Montmeyan then D30 to Regusse. At rndabt in Regusse turn L twd St Jean & foll sp. Fr E exit A8 junc 36 Le Muy then Draguignan then D557 to Villecroze, Aups & Régusse. At rndabt turn R twd St Jean & foll sp. Lge, mkd pitch, pt shd; wc; chem disp; mv service pnt; shwrs inc; el pts (6A) €4; gas; lndtte; ice; shop; rest; snacks; bar; BBQ; playgrnd; pool; tennis; mini-golf; entmnt; internet; TV rm; 10% statics; dogs €3; poss cr; Eng spkn; adv bkg ess high ssn; quiet; cc acc; CCI. "Beautiful area; mainly gravel pitches under pine trees; recep closes 1800." ♦ 23 Apr-24 Sep. € 27.00 (CChq acc)   2004*

REHAUPAL see Tholy, Le *6F3*

REILLANNE *10E3* (2km W Rural) Camping le Vallon des Oiseaux (Naturist), 04110 Reillanne [04 92 76 47 33; fax 04 92 76 44 64]   Fr Apt take N100 twd Cereste. Approx 2km after Cereste sharp turn L onto minor rd. Site sp. Med, pt sl, pt shd; wc; chem disp; shwrs inc; el pts (4A) €3; lndtte; shop 2km; tradsmn; rest; snacks; bar; playgrnd; pool; TV rm; 5% statics; no dogs; phone; poss cr; Eng spkn; adv bkg; quiet; INF acc. "V friendly & helpful staff; office closed 1300-1600." ♦ 1 Apr-1 Nov. € 23.00
2004*

REIMS *3D4* (16km SE Rural) **Camp Municipal, 8 Rue de Routoir Courmelois, 51360 Val-de-Vesle** [03 26 03 91 79; fax 03 26 03 28 22] Fr Reims twd Chalons-en-Champagne on N44, turn L by camp sp on D326 to Val-de-Vesle, foll camp sp; look for tall grain silos by canal. Sm, shd; wc; chem disp; shwrs inc; el pts (6-10A) €2.50 (long lead poss req); gas; shop & bar 50m; rest; BBQ; playgrnd; rv fishing; 30% statics; dogs €0.60; poss cr; adv bkg; quiet; no cc acc; CCI. "V popular, rvside location; friendly staff; san facs high standard & spotless; vineyards nr; Champagne caves at Reims; chilled Champagne at recep; pitching haphazard; gd off-lead dog-walking adj; poss mosquito problem; poss grapepickers; excel for visitng Reims." 1 Apr-15 Oct. € 6.90   2005*

REMIREMONT *6F2* (8km SE Rural) **Camping de Maxonchamp, Rue du Camping, 88360 Maxonchamp** [03 29 24 30 65] Fr Remiremont on N66 twrds Maxonchamp; site clearly sp to L; also visible 300m down lane. Sm, pt shd; wc; chem disp; shwrs €1; el pts (6A) €2; shop 3km; playgrnd; rv sw adj; 20% statics; dogs €0.50; poss cr; quiet; CCI. "Vg, attractive site on rv; conv S Vosges area" ♦ 1 Apr-31 Oct. € 6.00   2005*

REMIREMONT *6F2* (3.5km W Rural) **Camping de Ste Anne, Fallieres, 88200 Remiremont** [03 29 62 20 98] Fr Epinal on N57 foll sp for Remiremont. After turning for N66/D3 foll sp for Fallieres & Camping Ste Anne. Sm, pt sl, pt shd; wc; shwrs inc; el pts (6A) inc; no dogs; quiet; no cc acc; CCI. "10 pitches only; spotless, attractive site with modern facs; peaceful." € 10.00   2004*

REMOULINS *10E2* (1.5km S Rural) **Camping La Soubeyranne, Route de Beaucaire, 30210 Remoulins** [04 66 37 03 21; fax 04 66 37 14 65; soubeyranne@wanadoo.fr; www.soubeyranne. com] Exit A9 a'route for Remoulins onto D986. On N86 Remoulins to Nimes rd turn L on D986 after x-ing bdge fr Remoulins. Site on L in 1km. Lge, hdg pitch, shd; wc; chem disp; baby facs; shwrs inc; el pts (6A) €3; gas; ice; lndtte; shop; rest; snacks; bar; BBQ; playgrnd; pool; fishing; tennis; TV rm; some statics; dogs €2; some rd & rlwy noise; adv bkg; CCI. "Gd site; plenty hot water." 3 Apr-13 Sep. € 22.00   2005*

REMOULINS *10E2* (2km NW Rural) **Camping La Sousta, Ave du Pont de Gard, 30210 Remoulins** [04 66 37 12 80; fax 04 66 37 23 69; info@lasousta. fr; www.lasousta.fr] Fr A9 exit Remoulins, foll sp for Nimes, then sp 'Pont du Gard par Rive Droite' thro town. Immed over rv bdge turn R sp 'Pont du Gard etc'; site on R 800m fr Pont du Gard. Lge, mkd pitch, shd; wc (some cont); chem disp; mv service pnt; baby facs; shwrs inc; el pts (6A) €3.20; gas; lndtte; shop; tradsmn; rest; snacks; bar; BBQ in sep area; playgrnd; pool; tennis; rv sw adj; watersports; fishing; cycle hire; mini-golf; entmnt; child entmnt; TV; 20% statics; dogs €2; poss cr; Eng spkn; adv bkg; quiet; red low ssn; cc acc; CCI. "Walking dist of Pont-du-Gard; friendly, helpful staff; poss diff for lge o'fits due trees; interesting area; excel cent for excursions." ♦ 1 Mar-31 Oct. € 19.00   2005*

See advertisement opposite

REMOULINS *10E2* (4km NW Rural) **Camping International Les Gorges du Gardon, Chemin de la Barque Vieille, Route d'Uzes, 30210 Vers-Pont-du-Gard** [04 66 22 81 81; fax 04 66 22 90 12; camping.international@wanadoo.fr; www.le-camping-international.com] Exit A9 junc 23 Remoulins & head N twd Uzes on D981. Pass turn for Pont-du-Gard & site on L in 1.5km. Or fr E on N100 turn N onto N86 then D19A to Pont-du-Gard (avoiding Remoulins cent). Lge, hdg/mkd pitch, pt shd; wc; chem disp; mv service pnt; baby facs; shwrs inc; el pts (6-15A) €3; gas; lndtte; ice; shop; tradsmn; rest; snacks; bar; BBQ; playgrnd; htd pool; rv sw & private beach adj; boating; fishing; tennis; games area; games rm; entmnt; internet; TV rm; 10% statics; dogs €2; twin-axles not allowed; Eng spkn; adv bkg; quiet; cc acc; red low ssn/long stay; CCI. "Friendly, cheerful owners; gd san facs; beautiful location; cycle track to Roman aquaduct at Pont-du-Gard 2km down stream; conv Avignon, Nimes; site poss subject to flooding & evacuation; excel." ♦ 15 Mar-31 Oct. € 16.50   2005*

See advertisement below

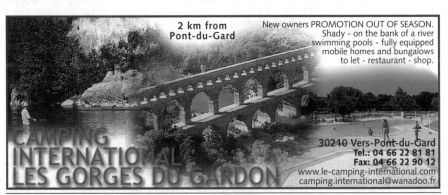
FRANCE

REMOULINS *10E2* (7km NW) **Camping Le Barralet, 30210 Collias [04 66 22 84 52 or 04 66 22 80 40 (LS); fax 04 66 22 89 17; camping@barralet.fr; www.barralet.fr]** W off A9 on D981 to Uzes; thro Remoulins; foll camp sp; turn S on D112 D3 to Collias; sp in 4km on L past quarry on bend; turn L up narr rd & site in 50m on R. Med, pt shd; wc; shwrs inc; el pts €3.50 (adaptors supplied free); lndtte; shop; rest; snacks; bar; pool; playgrnd; volleyball; fishing & canoe/kayak hire adj; tennis & horseriding in vill; dogs €2; phone; quiet; cc acc; CCI. "Excel site; gd rvside walks; sm pitches; lge youth groups use this activity cent." ♦ 1 Apr-30 Sep. € 16.00   2005*

REMUZAT *9D2* (8km N Rural) **Camp Municipal Le Village, Chemin du Piscine, 26470 La Motte-Chalancon [04 75 27 22 95 or 04 75 27 20 41 (Mairie); fax 04 75 27 20 38; mairie@lamotte chalancon.com; www.lamottechalancon.com]** Take D93 dir Luc/Aspres fr Die for 18km, then turn R onto D61 S twd La Motte fr 19km. In La Motte, just bef rv bdge & Citroen garage on L, turn sharp L. Site sp in 500m on L. Med, pt shd; wc (cont); mv service pnt; shwrs inc; el pts (5-10A) €1.83-3.05; lndtte; shops, rest 500m; snacks; bar; playgrnd; pool; lake sw, beach 2km; dogs €0.76; phone; poss noisy; cc acc; CCI. "Beautiful views fr site; attractive vill; usually v quiet but no resident warden on site so can be noisy, esp at w/e; fair sh stay." 15 May-15 Sep. € 7.86   2003*

REMUZAT *9D2* (9km NE Rural) **Aire Naturelle de Camping, Quartier Lemoulin, 26470 Pommerol [04 75 27 25 83 or 04 75 98 26 25 (LS); fax 04 75 27 25 63; camping.pommerol@wanadoo.fr]** Fr Remuzat, take D61 N dir La Motte-Chalancon. In vill, turn R & cont on D61 for 6km dir La Charce, then turn R onto D138 sp Montmorin/Pommerol. In 1km bear R onto D338 to Pommerol. Site sp in 2km on R. Sm, terr, pt shd; htd wc; chem disp; shwrs inc; el pts €2 (long lead req); gas 10km; lndtte; shops 10km; rest, snacks, bar, (high ssn only or 10km); BBQ; playgrnd; htd pool 10km; lake sw, beach 12km; dogs €2; Eng spkn; adv bkg (dep req); quiet; CCI. "Superb views fr site; situated in Pommerol Gorge adj to stream; access poss diff for lge o'fits; adv bkg essential high ssn; vg sh stay." 1 Apr-30 Oct. € 8.00   2003*

REMUZAT *9D2* (2km S) **Camp Municipal Les Aires, 26510 Remuzat [04 75 27 81 43 or 04 75 25 85 78 (Mairie)]** Fr Rosans take D994 W for approx 10km & then R on D61 to Remuzat. Sm, hdg/mkd pitch, pt shd; wc; baby facs; shwrs inc; el pts (4-10A) €1.50-2.50; lndtte; shop nr; BBQ; dogs €1; quiet; CCI. "V helpful warden; beautiful site, vill & area; excel long/sh stay." ♦ 30 May-15 Sep. € 7.30   2003*

REMUZAT *9D2* (10km W Rural) **Camp Municipal Les Oliviers, 26510 Sahune [04 75 27 40 40; fax 04 75 27 44 48]** Take N94 fr Nyons dir Serres. In 16km at Sahune turn R over bdge & foll sp to site. Sm, pt shd; wc; chem disp (wc); shwrs inc; el pts (4-10A) €1.70-2.70; gas 500m; lndtte; shop, rest, snacks, bar 500m; rv sw; Eng spkn; quiet; CCI. "Vg all stays." 50 May-15 Sep. € 8.90   2004*

REMUZAT *9D2* (10km W Rural) **Camping La Vallee Bleue, La Plaine-du-Pont, 26510 Sahune [tel/fax 04 75 27 44 42; www.lavalleebleue.com]** On D94 well sp. Med, pt shd; wc; chem disp; shwrs; el pts (6A) €3; lndtte; shop 500m; tradsmn; rest; snacks; bar; playgrnd; pool; 5% statics; dogs €1.50; phone; poss cr; adv bkg; quiet; CCI. "Vg long stay; golf & fishing nrby." ♦ 1 Apr-30 Sep. € 16.00   2004*

†RENNES *2F4* (2km NE Urban) **Camp Municipal des Gayeulles, Rue du Professeur Maurice Audin, 35700 Rennes [02 99 36 91 22 or 02 99 65 01 11; fax 02 23 20 06 34]** Fr Fougeres, exit A84 at junc 25 sp dir Thorigny Fouillard. Join N12 for approx 10km to city ring rd. At rndabt La Gayeulles (Elf g'ge), turn R to 'Centre Loisirs' & university campus. Site sp on R. Med, mkd pitch, hdstg, pt sl, pt shd; wc; chem disp; mv service pnt; baby facs; shwrs; el pts (10A) €2.60; lndtte; shops 500m; tradsmn; snacks; BBQ; playgrnd; pool 500m; tennis, archery & mini-golf nrby; internet; dogs €0.90; phone; bus; Eng spkn; adv bkg; quiet; red low ssn; cc acc; CCI. "Excel, clean, well-kept site; friendly staff; lge pitches; slight sl for m'vans; 1st class facs; magnificient park adj; v narr app to site; arr low ssn bet 0800-0900 & 1800-2000 only when office open; Rennes well worth a visit." ♦ € 17.10   2005*

RENNES LES BAINS *8G4* (Rural) **Camping La Bernede, 11190 Rennes-les-Bains [04 68 69 86 49; fax 04 68 74 09 31]** S fr Carcassonne or N fr Quillan on D118, turn E at Couiza on D613. In 5km turn R onto D14 to Rennes-les-Bains in 3km. Site at far end of vill on L. Sm, mkd pitch, pt shd; wc; chem disp (wc); shwrs inc; el pts (5A) €2.20; lndtte; ice; shop; tradsmn; rest in vill; bar; playgrnd; rv adj; fishing; 10% statics; dogs; adv bkg; quiet; CCI. "Vg long/sh stay." ♦ 14 Apr-9 Nov. € 9.50   2002*

REOLE, LA *7D2* (10km SE) **Camp Municipal au Jardin,   47200   Meilhan-sur-Garonne [06 08 03 54 77 (Mob) or 05 53 94 30 04 (Mairie); fax 05 53 94 31 27; communedemeilhan.47@ wanadoo.fr]** On N side of Canal Lateral, below Meilhan; exit A62 at junc 4 onto D9; or turn off N113 at Ste Bazeille; foll sp. Med, pt shd; wc; shwrs €0.80; el pts (10A) €1.20; lndtte; shops 500m; playgrnd; pool 500m; rv sw, fishing 100m; quiet; CCI. "If barrier down & no warden, key is in elect cupboard." 1 Jun-30 Sep. € 7.00   2003*

REOLE, LA *7D2* (S Urban) **Camping La Rouergue,** 33190 La Reole [05 56 61 04 03 or 05 56 61 82 73; fax 05 56 61 89 13; entredeuxmers@wanadoo.fr] On N113 bet Bordeaux & Agen or exit A62 at junc 4. In La Reole foll sps S on D9 to site on L immed after x-ing suspension bdge. Med, pt shd; wc; shwrs inc; el pts €2; gas; shop; tradsmn; snacks; pool 500m; fishing, boating; dogs €0.80; some rd noise. "Resident Eng warden; 2m barrier clsd 1200-1700, phone ahead to arr outside these hrs; v clean site & facs; Sat morning mkt on rv bank; conv for historical, cultural & gastronomic Entre-Deux-Mers area." 15 May-15 Oct. € 8.60   2004*

This site entry hasn't been updated for a while; we'd better fill in a site report form and send it to The Club.

RETHEL *5C1* (14km E Urban) **Camp Municipal Le Vallage,** 38, Chemin de l'Assaut, 08130 Attigny [03 24 71 23 06 or 03 24 71 20 68; fax 03 24 71 94 00] E on D983 fr Rethel to Attigny; fr town cent take D987 twd Charleville; over rv bdge; 2nd turn on L; sp. Med, hdg/mkd pitch, unshd; wc; chem disp; shwrs inc; el pts (10A) inc; lndry rm; shop 1km; tradsmn; sw adj; playgrnd; fishing; tennis; 50% statics; dogs; phone; quiet; CCI. "Park & sports stadium adj with sw pool, tennis etc." Easter-30 Sep. € 8.10   2005*

REVEL *8F4* (500m E Urban) **Camp Municipal Le Moulin du Roy, Rue de Soreze,** 31250 Revel [05 61 83 32 47 or 05 62 18 71 40 (Mairie)] Fr Revel ring rd take D85 dir Soreze, site sp. Med, hdg pitch, pt shd; shwrs inc; el pts €2.30; shop 500m; supmkt nr; playgrnd; pool adj; lake sw & beach 2.5km; tennis adj; dogs €0.50; phone; bus; Eng spkn; quiet. "Pleasant, helpful staff; Sat mkt in Revel; vg site." 18 Jun-2 Sep. € 6.80   2004*

REVEL *8F4* (8km SE Rural) **Camping La Rigole, 81540 Les Cammazes [tel/fax 05 63 73 28 99; mary@campingbr.com]** Fr Revel take D629 E to Les Cammazes. Thro vill 300m take 1st L. Site well sp, 1km fr vill. Med, mkd pitch, pt sl, terr, pt shd; wc; chem disp; shwrs inc; el pts (4-13A) €3.10-6; lndtte; ice; shop &1km; rest 1km; playgrnd; pool; lake sw 400m; TV rm; dogs €1; phone; poss cr; Eng spkn; adv bkg; quiet; 20% red low ssn; CCI. "Pleasant site; help req to access some pitches; gd disabled facs but wheelchair movement on site impossible unaided & diff at best; gd walks adj; phone ahead to check open low ssn." ♦ 15 Apr-15 Oct. € 14.00   2005*

REVEL *8F4* (4km S Rural) **Camping En Salvan,** 31350 St Ferreol [05 61 83 55 95; lvt-en-salvan@wanadoo.fr] Fr Revel head S on D629 up long hill. At lake at top turn R for 2km, site on R. Sm, mkd pitch, hdstg, shd; shwrs; el pts; quiet. "V pleasant." 1 Apr-31 Oct. € 12.00   2002*

REVIGNY SUR ORNAIN *5D1* (Urban) **Camp Municipal du Moulin des Gravieres, Stade Louis Boyer,** 55800 Revigny-sur-Ornain [tel/fax 03 29 78 73 34 or 03 29 70 50 55 (Mairie); contact@ot-revigny-ornain.fr] N fr Bar-le-Duc on D994 to Revigny-sur-Ornain; fr town cent take D995 twd Vitry-le-Francois. Site on R, sp. Sm, hdg/mkd pitch, pt shd; wc; chem disp; shwrs inc; el pts (5-16A) inc; ice; lndry rm; supmkt 500m; snacks; playgrnd; TV rm; 40% statics; Eng spkn; adv bkg; v quiet; cc not acc; CCI. "V pleasant, clean, beautifully maintained site; excel value; v lge pitches but poss mkt traders/itinerants spread over lgest pitches; superb facs; weekly mkt (Wed am) at sports complex adj; trout stream running thro site; v highly rec." ♦ 1 May-30 Sep. € 11.85   2004*

REVIN *5C1* (500m Urban) **Camp Municipal Les Bateaux, Quai Edgar Quinet,** 08500 Revin [03 24 40 15 65 or 03 24 40 19 59 (LS); fax 03 24 40 21 98; camping.les.bateaux-revin@wanadoo.fr] Fr Fumay take D988 to Revin, or fr Charleville take D989/988 (23km). Take rte D1 E fr Rocroi. On ent Revin turn L after narr bdge (1-way) over Rv Meuse. Site sp fr cent of Revin. Easy to miss sp in hedge nr site - ent on L at rv. Med, hdg/mkd pitch, pt shd; htd wc; chem disp; baby facs; shwrs; el pts (6-10A) 2.60; ice; lndtte; shop; tradsmn; playgrnd; rv fishing; games rm; TV rm; 5% statics; dogs €0.90; Eng spkn; adv bkg; quiet; CCI. "Peaceful, beautiful, rvside site; gd cent for Ardennes region; lge pitches; if office clsd find own pitch & book in later; clean, modern site; excel." ♦ Easter-30 Oct. € 10.70   2005*

RHINAU *6E3* **Camping Ferme des Tuileries,** 67230 Rhinau [03 88 74 60 45] S on D468 at Boofzheim, turn L at sp Rhinau, D5. Site 2.4km after L turn. Ent Rhinau site 3rd turn R. Med, some hdstg; shd; wc; chem disp; shwrs inc; el pts (2-6A) €1.40-3.20; lndtte; gas; ice; shops 500m; tradsmn; sm htd pool; tennis; 50% statics; dogs; poss cr; quiet. "Extended site; spacious with excel facs; regimented; barrier key req; free ferry adj for x-ing Rhine." 1 Apr-30 Sep. € 9.60   2004*

RHINAU *6E3* (2.5km NW Rural) **Camping du Ried, 1 Rue du Camping, 67860 Boofzheim [03 88 74 68 27; fax 03 88 74 62 89; info@camping-ried.com; www.camping-du-ried.com]** Site sp fr D5 1km E of Boofzheim. Lge, hdg/mkd pitch, pt shd; htd wc; chem disp; mv service pnt; shwrs; el pts (5A) €4; lndtte; shop 200m; snacks; bar; BBQ; playgrnd; 2 htd pools (1 htd, covrd); paddling pool; lake sw; watersports; fishing; games area; mini-golf; cycle hire; entmnt; TV rm; 20% statics; dogs €3; phone; adv bkg; quiet; red low ssn; cc acc. "Conv Strasbourg, Colmar; vg long/sh stay." ♦ 1 Apr-31 Oct. € 17.50   2005*

See advertisement on next page

RIBEAUVILLE *6E3* (2km E Urban) **Camp Municipal Pierre-de-Coubertin, Rue de Landau, 68150 Ribeauville [tel/fax 03 89 73 66 71; camping.ribeauville@wanadoo.fr]** Exit N83 at Ribeauville, turn R on D106 & foll rd to o'skts, at traff lts turn R & then immed R again. Site on R in 750m. Camp at sports ground nr Ribeauville Lycee. Lge, mkd pitch, pt sl, pt shd; wc; chem disp; baby facs; shwrs inc; el pts (2-6A) €2.50-4 (rev pol & poss long lead req); gas; lndtte; sm shop; pool adj; dogs €1; poss cr; quiet; CCI. "Easy walk to town cent; friendly, helpful managers; o'skts of attractive, historical town on Rte des Vins; recep clsd 1200-1400 & 1900-0800; on arr park outside site bef registering at recep; resident storks; excel." ♦ 15 Mar-15 Nov. €11.60   2005*

RIBEAUVILLE *6E3* (4.5km S Rural) **Camp Intercommunal, 1 Route des Vins, 68340 Riquewihr [03 89 47 90 08; fax 03 89 49 05 63; camping.riquewihr@tiscali.fr]** Fr Strasbourg on N83/E25, take junc 21 (fr opp dir take junc 22) to Blebenheim/Riquewihr. D416 & D3 thro Blebenheim. At T-junc turn R onto D1B, site on R at rndabt. Lge, hdg pitch, pt sl, pt shd; htd wc; chem disp; mv service pnt; baby facs; shwrs inc; el pts (6A) €4.10 (poss rev pol); gas; lndtte; ice; shops 5km; tradsmn in ssn; snacks; playgrnd; dogs €1.20; poss cr; adv bkg; noise fr main rd; cc acc; CCI ess. "Cent of wine region; register 1st with recep, open 0830-1200 & 1300-2100 high ssn; 0830-1200 & 1330-1900 low ssn; rec arr early; gd for sm children; sports ground adj; friendly staff; san facs clean but need modernising; Riquewihr lovely town." ♦ Easter-31 Dec. €11.40   2004*

RIBEAUVILLE *6E3* (8km W Rural) **Camp Municipal de la Menere, 68150 Aubure [03 89 73 92 99]** Take D416 W fr Ribeauville for 7km, then turn L to Aubure. Foll rd to vill for 5km. Site 200m S of vill. Med, mkd pitch, terr, pt shd; wc; shwrs €0.75; el pts (6A) €2.50; gas; lndry rm; ice; shops 12km; playgrnd 50m; no statics; dogs €0.50; phone; Eng spkn; adv bkg (dep req); quiet; CCI. "Highest vill in Alsace (800m) & former medical spa; fresh & pleasant site in mountain; walking & cycling rtes nrby; peaceful & friendly." 15 May-20 Sep. €8.00   2003*

RIBERAC *7C2* (500m N Urban) **Camp Municipal La Dronne, Route d'Angouleme, 24600 Riberac [05 53 90 50 08 or 05 53 90 03 10; fax 05 53 91 35 13; ot.riberac@perigord.tm.fr]** Site on L of main rd D709 immed N of bdge over Rv Dronne on o'skts of Riberac. Med, some hdg pitches, pt shd; wc (cont for men); shwrs inc; el pts €1.90; lndtte; supmkt 500m; tradsmn; snacks; playgrnd; sw pool 1km; lake sw 10km; no twin-axles; quiet. "Pitches in cent hdgd; facs clean but inadequate, poss overstretched high ssn; vg, well-run site; walking distance to town cent; kingfishers on rv; vg lge Fri mkt in Riberac; conv by rd." ♦ 1 Jun-15 Sep. €10.00   2005*

RICHELIEU *4H1* (S Urban) **Camp Municipal, 6 Ave de Schaafheim, 37120 Richelieu [02 47 58 15 02 or 02 47 58 10 13 (Mairie); fax 02 47 58 16 42; commune-de-richelieu@wanadoo.fr]** Fr Loudun, take D61 to Richelieu, D749 twd Chatellerault; site sp. Sm, hdg/mkd pitch, pt shd; wc; chem disp; shwrs inc; el pts (5-15A) €1.52-3.05; shop 1km; playgrnd; pool 500m; fishing; tennis; quiet; CCI. "Phone ahead to check site open as open dates may vary; clean, gd facs but may need updating; poss itinerants; conv Loire chateaux & gardens of Richelieu; bureau open 0930-1030 & 1830-1930 low ssn & all day high ssn; €30 dep req for barrier key." ♦ 15 May-15 Sep. €6.70   2004*

RIEL LES EAUX *6F1* (2km SW Rural) **Camping du Plan d'Eau, 21570 Riel-les-Eaux [tel/fax 03 80 93 72 76]** On D965 NE twd Chaumont: after 6km turn N to Mosson on D118 & cont to Belan-sur-Ource. Join D13 sp Essoyes. Site on L after 3km. Well sp. Sm, hdg pitch, pt shd; wc; chem disp; shwrs inc; el pts (6A); tradsmn; snacks; bar; lake adj; fishing; Eng spkn; quiet; CCI. "Conv Champagne area; excel sh stay." ♦ 1 Apr-31 Oct. €9.15   2002*

RIEZ *10E3* (500m E Urban) **Camping Rose de Provence, 04500 Riez [tel/fax 94 92 77 75 45; rose-de-provence@wanadoo.fr]** Exit A51 junc 18 onto D82 to Greoux-les-Bains then D952 to Riez. On reaching Riez strt across rndabt, at T-junc turn L & immed R, site sp. Med, mkd pitch, pt shd; wc; chem disp (wc); shwrs inc; el pts (6A) €2.50; lndtte; rest, snacks, bar 500m; playgrnd; lake sw 10km; tennis adj; 5% statics; dogs €1.22; phone; adv bkg (dep & booking fee req); red low ssn; CCI. "Helpful owners; conv Verdon Gorge; vg long/sh stay." ♦ ltd. Easter-15 Oct. € 10.90   2003*

RIEZ *10E3* (10km S Rural) **Camping Le Coteau de la Marine, 04500 Montagnac-Montpezat [04 92 77 53 33; fax 04 92 77 59 34; www. homair-vacances.fr]** A51 exit 18, D82 to Greoux-les-Bains, then D952 & D11 & Montagnac, Montpezat & site sp. (Steep incline bef ent to site) Lge, hdg/mkd pitch, hdstg, pt sl, terr, pt shd; wc; chem disp; mv service pnt; 50% serviced pitch; shwrs inc; el pts (6-10A) €4; gas; lndtte; ice; shop; tradsmn; rest; snacks; bar; playgrnd; pool; tennis; fishing; boating; tennis; games area; games rm; entmnt; TV; dogs €2.50; statics; Eng spkn; adv bkg ess high ssn; quiet but poss noise fr night-flying helicopters in gorge; cc acc; CCI. "Gravel pegs req for awnings; gd sh stay." ♦ 1 May-25 Sep. € 19.00   2002*

RIEZ *10E3* (9km W) **Camp Municipal Les Lavandes, Route Puimoisson, 04210 Valensole [04 92 74 86 14]** 400m E of Valensole off D6, sp on N side of rd. Med, pt sl, shd; wc; shwrs inc; el pts (3A); shops; playgrnd; entmnt; pool 4km; quiet. "Hilltop site with basic facs." Jul-3 Sep.   2002*

RIOM *9B1* (5km NW) **Camp Municipal de la Croze, St Hippolyte, 63140 Chatelguyon [04 73 86 01 88 (Mairie); fax 04 73 86 08 51]** Fr A71 exit junc 13; ring rd around Riom sp Chatelguyon to Mozac, then D227. Site L bef ent St Hippolyte. Fr Volvic on D986 turn L at rndabt after Leclerc supmkt & L again to D227. Diff ent to site. Not rec to tow thro Riom. Lge, mkd pitch, pt sl, pt shd; wc; chem disp; shwrs inc; el pts (10A) inc; lndtte; ice; shops 2km; tradsmn; playgrnd; pool 3km; dogs; quiet; CCI. "€30 dep for barrier key; gd sightseeing area; v strict pitching rules, poss diff for British vans on sl pitches; vg long stay." 1 May-30 Sep. € 13.15   2003*

RIOM *9B1* (6km NW) **Camping Clos de Balanede, Route de la Piscine, 63140 Chatelguyon [04 73 86 02 47; fax 04 73 86 05 64; claude. poughon@wanadoo.fr; www.balanede.com]** Fr Riom take D985 to Chatelguyon, site on R on o'skts of town. Tight turn into ent. Lge, pt sl, pt shd; wc; shwrs inc; el pts (3-10A) €1.90-3.90; gas; lndtte; shop; rest; snacks; bar; playgrnd; pool; tennis; dogs €1.22; poss cr; Eng spkn; adv bkg; quiet. "V clean, well organised site." ♦ 15 Apr-30 Sep. € 11.10   2005*

RIOM ES MONTAGNES *7C4* (E Urban) **Camp Municipal Le Sedour, 15400 Riom-es-Montagnes [04 71 78 05 71]** Site on W of D678 Riom N to Condat rd, 500m out of town over bdge, sp fr all dirs, opp Clinique du Haut Cantal. Med, pt shd; wc; shwrs inc; el pts (2-10A) €2.10; lndtte; supmkt 200m; playgrnd; pool 5km; games area; TV rm; Eng spkn; adv bkg; some rd noise top end of site. " V helpful staff; vg." 1 Jun-30 Sep. € 6.00   2004*

RIOM ES MONTAGNES *7C4* (10km SW Rural) **Camp Municipal Le Pioulet, 15400 Trizac [04 71 78 64 20 or 04 71 78 60 37 (Mairie); fax 04 71 78 65 40]** D678 W fr Riom-es-Montagnes to Trizac. Site on R after leaving vill S twd Mauriac. Sm, hdg pitch, pt sl, pt shd; wc; chem disp; el pts (2-5A) €2; gas; tradsmn, rest, bar, shops 1km; BBQ; lndtte; playgrnd; tennis nr; sand beach; lake sw; quiet; Eng spkn; adv bkg; phone; CCI. "Excel for long stay; friendly site; spotless facs; vg walking area, lovely scenery." ♦ 16 Jun-15 Sep. € 7.00   2004*

RIOZ *6G2* (Rural) **Camp Municipal Les Platanes, Rue de la Faiencerie, 70190 Rioz [03 84 91 91 59 or 03 84 91 84 84 (Mairie); fax 03 84 91 90 45]** Site off D5 in vill of Rioz. Med, some hdg pitch, some hdstg, pt shd; htd wc; baby facs; shwrs inc; el pts (6A) €2.30; gas; shops adj; rests in vill; playgrnd; pool adj; dogs €1.50; quiet. "Site yourself, warden calls; gd facs; friendly vill." 1 Apr-30 Sep. € 10.00   2004*

RIOZ *6G2* (7km S Rural) **Camping L'Esplanade, Prairie de la Riviere, 70190 Cromary [03 84 91 82 00 or 03 84 91 85 84 (LS)]** F S on N57 take D14 E thro Devecey. At Vielley turn L onto D412. Site on L over rv. Fr N on N57 by-pass Rioz & take slip rd onto D15 sp Sorans. Turn L in vill, pass under N57 to They, then foll sp Cromary & site. Sm, hdg/mkd pitch, pt shd; wc (some cont); chem disp; shwrs inc; el pts (4-8A) €1.90-3.10; lndtte; ice; shop 3km; tradsmn; BBQ; playgrnd; rv sw adj; 40% statics; Eng spkn; adv bkg; quiet; cc acc. "Welcoming Dutch owners; well-kept site; vg long/sh stay." ♦ ltd. 1 May-15 Sep. € 6.10   2003*

RIQUEWIHR see Ribeauville *6E3*

RISCLE *8E2* (500m N Urban) **Camp Municipal Le Pont de l'Adour, 32400 Riscle [05 62 69 72 45 or 06 08 55 36 89 (mob); fax 05 62 69 72 45; camping.dupondeladour@wanadoo.fr]** On ent Riscle fr N on D935, site on L immed after x-ing Rv Adour. Med, pt shd, hdg pitch; wc (some cont); chem disp; shwrs inc; el pts (5-6A) inc; lndtte; ice; shop; rest; snacks; pool adj; playgrnd; entmnt; TV; dogs €1.52; quiet; red low ssn; CCI. ♦ ltd. 1 Apr-15 Oct. € 15.00   2005*

RIVIERE SAAS ET GOURBY see Dax *8E1*

FRANCE

At the entrance of the Gorges du Tarn

Le Peyrelade ****
F-12640 Riviere-sur-Tarn

Open from 15.5. till 15.9.
Mobile homes and bungalows to let
On the shores of a river and in the heart of the regional natural park of Grands Causses, this campsite offers one of the most beautiful beaches the region. Apart from swimming, you can also practise many outdoors activities: canoe, hiking, horseback riding, mountain bike, fishing, speleology, climbing, forest courses, hang-gliding.

Phone: +33 (0)5 65 62 62 54 • Fax: +33 (0)5 65 62 65 61
campingpeyrelade@wanadoo.fr • www.campingpeyrelade.com

RIVIERE SUR TARN *10E1* (Rural) Camping du Moulin de la Galiniere, Boyne, 12640 Riviere-sur-Tarn [05 65 62 65 60 or 05 65 62 61 81; fax 05 65 62 69 84; guycha@wanadoo.fr] Fr Millau N on N9 turn R onto D907 dir Gorges du Tarn; site ent bef Boyne vill, other side of bdge to Camping Le Pont, bef R turn. Site on bank Rv Tarn. Med, pt shd; wc; shwrs inc; el pts (6A) €2.03; lndtte; ice; shops adj; snacks; playgrnd; shgl beach; rv sw; fishing (permit req'd); birdwatching; dogs €0.70; quiet. "Excel, v clean facs; pleasant owner." 1 Jul-31 Aug. € 9.00   2002*

RIVIERE SUR TARN *10E1* (Rural) Camping Le Pont,   Boyne,   12640   Riviere-sur-Tarn [05 65 62 61 12] Fr Millau head N on N9, R after 7km onto D907 sp Gorges du Tarn, site in 9km on R on ent to vill. Sm, pt shd; wc (some cont); chem disp; shwrs inc; el pts €2; lndry rm; shops, rest adj; playgrnd; sw pool 2km; rv sw & fishing; adj; quiet; CCI. "Vg long stay; gd base for Tarn gorges; canoeing & climbing nrby; helpful owner has tourist info." 1 Jun-30 Sep. € 8.20   2004*

RIVIERE SUR TARN *10E1* (2km E Rural) Camping Le Peyrelade, Route des Gorges du Tarn, 12640 Riviere-sur-Tarn [05 65 62 62 54; fax 05 65 62 65 61; campingpeyrelade@wanadoo.fr;   www.camping peyrelade.com] Exit A75 junc 44.1 to Aguessac, then take D907 N thro Riviere-sur-Tarn to site in 2km. Fr Millau drive N on N9 to Aguessac, then onto D907 thro Riviere-sur-Tarn, & site sp on R. Lge, hdg/mkd pitch, terr, shd; wc; chem disp; mv service pnt; baby facs; shwrs inc; el pts (6A) €3; gas; lndtte; shop; tradsmn; rest; snacks; bar; BBQ; playgrnd; htd pool; rv beach & sw adj; canoeing; games rm; cycle hire 100m; entmnt; child entmnt; TV; dogs; adv bkg; quiet; cc acc; red low ssn; CCI. "Excel touring base in interesting area." ♦ 15 May-15 Sep. € 22.00
2005*

See advertisement above

RIVIERE SUR TARN *10E1* (2km SE Rural) Camping Le Papillon, Les Canals, 12640 La Cresse [tel/fax 05 65 59 08 42; canal2@wanadoo. fr; http://campsitelepapillon.monsite.wanadoo.fr] Fr N on A75 exit junc 44.1 onto D29 dir Aguessac. Cross rv & take D187 N, site in 1.5km on R. Sm, hdg/mkd pitch, terr, shd, pt shd; htd wc; chem disp; baby facs; fam bthrm; shwrs inc; el pnts (10A) €3; gas; lndtte; ice; shop; tradsmn; rest; snacks; bar; BBQ (not charcoal); sm playgrnd; rv sw 150m; entmnt; TV; 5% statics; dogs €1; Eng spkn; adv bkg (dep req); quiet; red 30+ days; CCI."Quiet & pleasant; vg." 25 Apr-3 Oct. € 14.50   2005*

> Some of these sites have changed their opening dates - we'd better fill in some site report forms and let the editor of the guide know.

RIVIERE SUR TARN *10E1* (SW Rural) Camping Les Peupliers, Rue de la Combe, 12640 Riviere-sur-Tarn [05 65 59 85 17; fax 05 65 61 09 03; lespeupliers12640@wanadoo.fr;   www.camping lespeupliers.fr] Heading N on N9 turn R in Aguessac onto D907 bis twd Riviere-sur-Tarn. Site on R bef vi ll. Med, hdg/mkd pitch, pt shd; wc (some cont); chem disp; mv service pnt; baby facs; shwrs inc; el pt (6A) €3; gas; lndtte; ice; shop 200m; tradsmn; rest; snacks; bar high ssn; BBQ; playgrnd; pool; waterslide; rv sw & shgl beach adj; fishing; watersports; games area; entmnt; child entmnt; internet; TV rm; some statics; dogs €1.50; phone; Eng spkn; adv bkg; quiet; red low ssn; cc acc; CCI. "Beautiful, peaceful, well-run, busy site; spotless san facs; excel pool area; friendly staff." ♦ 1 Apr-30 Sep. € 20.40 (CChq acc)   2005*

See advertisement opposite

ROANNE *9A1* (12km S Rural) **Camping Le Mars,** 42123 Cordelle [tel/fax 04 77 64 94 42; baznew@ wanadoo.fr] On D56 fr Roanne foll dir Lac Villarest; cross barrage & site 4.5km S of Cordelle well sp just off D56. Fr junc 70 on N7 to St Cyr-de-Favieres. Foll sp to Chateau de la Roche on D17 & site on D56. Fr S take D56 immed after Balbigny; single track app, with restricted visibility. Or fr N82 exit for Neulise onto D26 to Jodard, then D56 twd Cordelle. Site on L in 11km. Med, pt sl, terr, pt shd, hdg pitch; wc; chem disp; serviced pitch; mv service pnt; shwrs; child/baby facs; el pts (6A) inc; lndtte; ice; shop; tradsmn; snacks; bar; playgrnd; pool; lake sw, fishing & watersports 500m; mini-golf; entmnts; 40% statics; Eng spkn; adv bkg rec high ssn; quiet; red long stay; CCI. "Peaceful; lovely views; poss run down, scruffy low ssn." ♦ ltd. 2 Apr-30 Sep. € 19.50   2005*

ROANNE *9A1* (5km SW Rural) **Camping L'Oree du Lac,** 42300 Villerest [04 77 69 60 88 or 04 77 69 71 56 (LS); fax 04 77 69 60 88] Take D53 SW fr Roanne to Villerest; site sp in vill. Sm, mkd pitch, pt sl, pt shd; wc; chem disp (wc); shwrs inc; el pts (8-10A) inc; ice; rest; bar; playgrnd; pool; rv 300m; lake 100m; fishing; watersports; mini-golf; entmnts; TV; dogs; phone; adv bkg rec high ssn; quiet; CCI. "Attractive site; mini-train nrby; medieval vill; gd local wine." Easter-30 Sep. € 12.40   2002*

ROCAMADOUR *7D3* (6km NE) **Camp Municipal,** 46500 Alvignac [tel/fax 05 65 33 60 62 or 05 65 33 60 30; mairie-alvignace@wanadoo.fr; www.alvignac.net] Fr N140 turn E onto D371 sp Alvignac. Site sp fr vill cent & on R after Hotel de Poste. Sm, pt sl, unshd; wc (cont); shwrs; el pts €1.52; shop; rest; playgrnd; tennis; dogs €0.61; lake 1km; fishing. "Site yourself; attendant calls; opening dates subject to change, phone ahead to check." 15 Jun-15 Sep. € 6.70   2002*

ROCAMADOUR *7D3* (1km E) **Camping Les Cigales,** L'Hospitalet, Route de Rignac, 46500 Rocamadour [05 65 33 64 44 or 05 65 33 63 28 (LS); fax 05 65 33 69 60; camping-cigales@wanadoo.fr; www.camping- cigales.com] Fr N on N140 Brive-Gramat turn W on D36 approx 5.5km bef Gramat; in 3km site on R at L'Hospitalet. Med, mkd pitch, shd; wc (some cont); chem disp; shwrs; el pts (6A) €2.80 gas; lndtte; shop; rest; snacks; bar; playgrnd; pool & paddling pool; rv, canoeing 10km; mini-golf; games rm; TV; dogs €1.50; adv bkg dep & booking fee req; CCI. "Gd sh stay; busy, family site; facs poss stretched; gd pool." ♦ 1 Jul-31 Aug. € 14.50   2004*

ROCAMADOUR *7D3* (1km E) **Le Relais du Campeur,** L'Hospitalet, 46500 Rocamadour [05 65 33 63 28; fax 05 65 10 68 21] Fr S exit N20 (Brive-la-Gaillarde to Cahors) at Payrac; R on D673, 21km to L'Hospitalet. Fr N exit N20 at Cressenac for N140 to Figeac & Rodez; turn R at D673; site at x-rds after 4km; site behind grocer's shop on L. Avoid app fr W & coming thro Rocamadour (acute hair-pin & rd 2.2m wide). Med, pt sl, pt shd; wc (some cont); shwrs inc; el pts (6A) €2.50; gas; ice; shops; tradsmn; BBQ; playgrnd; pool; cycling; sailing; dogs €1; adv bkg; quiet; cc acc. "Ideal for Rocamadour; old facs but clean." 1 Apr-30 Sep. € 11.00   2005*

ROCAMADOUR *7D3* (1km NW Rural) **Aire Naturelle (Branche), Route de Souillac,** 46500 Rocamadour [05 65 33 63 37] Site on D247, 1km N of Rocamadour. Sm, pt shd; wc; (some cont); mv service pnt; shwrs inc; el pts inc; lndtte; shop 1km; BBQ; playgrnd; dogs; phone; quiet. "Gd, clean facs; spacious; friendly; easy walk to Rocamadour." 1 Apr-15 Nov. € 8.00   2004*

FRANCE

ROCHE BERNARD, LA *2G3* (500m S Urban) Camp Municipal Le Patis, Chemin de la Garenne, 56130 La Roche-Bernard [02 99 90 60 13 or 02 99 90 60 51 (Mairie); fax 02 99 90 88 28] Leave N165 junc 17 (fr N) junc 15 (fr S) & foll marina sp. Med, mkd pitch, pt shd; wc; chem disp; shwrs inc; el pts (10A) inc; lndtte; ice; shops & snacks 500m; playgrnd; pool 1km; sand beach 18km; rv adj; dogs €1; poss cr; Eng spkn; adv bkg; quiet but some rd noise; red low ssn; cc not acc. "Lovely position; excel clean site; v helpful staff; conv location; sailing, boating at marina adj; facs poss stretched high ssn; heavy o'fits phone ahead in wet weather; beautiful sm town; Thurs mkt day - do not exit/arr; rec." ♦ Easter-30 Sep. € 17.00   2005*

ROCHE CHALAIS, LA *7C2* (500m S Rural) Camp Municipal Gerbes, Rue de la Dronne, 24490 La Roche-Chalais [05 53 91 40 65; fax 05 53 90 32 01; camping.la.roche.chalais@wanadoo.fr] Fr S on D674 turn sharp L in vill at site sp. Site on R in 500m. Fr N take Coutras-Libourne rd thro vill; site sp on L beyond sm indus est. Med, mkd pitch, terr, pt shd; wc; shwrs inc; el pts (5-10A) €2.10-3.10; ice; lndtte; tradsmn; shops 500m; playgrnd; pool, tennis, cinema 800m; rv sw, fishing, boating & canoeing adj; leisure pk 5km; poss cr; adv bkg; rlwy & factory noise; CCI. "Day free per week; farm produce avail; spotless san facs; vg value; some terr plots leading down to rv; pitch N-side of site to avoid factory noise/smell; sh rvside walks; excel, clean, well-run site." ♦ 15 Apr-30 Sep. € 6.80   2005*

ROCHE DE GLUN, LA see Valence *9C2*

ROCHE DES ARNAUDS, LA see Veynes *9D3*

ROCHE POSAY, LA *4H2* (1.5km N Rural) Camp Municipal Le Riveau, Route de Lesigny. 86270 La Roche-Posay [05 49 86 21 23] Fr both E & W take new by-pass around N of town on D725; turn N onto D5; foll 'Hippodrome & Camping' sp; site on R 100m after D5/D725 junc; avoid town cent. Fr S bear L in town bef arch & foll sp. Lge, hdg/mkd pitch, shd; htd wc; shwrs inc; el pts (16A) inc (check pol); gas; lndtte; ice; shops 1km; rest; snacks; bar; BBQ (gas/elec); pool; playgrnd; rv sw & fishing 1.5km; tennis; cycle hire; entmnt; 10% statics; poss cr; Eng spkn; adv bkg; quiet; red long stay; CCI. "Excel, popular site; well-maintained; 1st class facs; pool planned 2006; barrier locks automatically 2300; parking avail outside; gd rests nrby; spa town." ♦ 4 Mar-22 Oct. € 15.20   2005*

ROCHE POSAY, LA *4H2* (3km E Rural) Camp Municipal Les Bords de Creuse, Rue de la Baignade, 37290 Yzeures-sur-Creuse [02 47 94 48 32 or 02 47 94 55 01 (Mairie); fax 02 47 94 43 32] Fr Chatellerault take the D725 E twds La Roche-Posay; after x-ing Rv Creuse, turn L onto D750 twds Yzeures-sur-Creuse; in vill cent turn R onto D104; site on R in 200m. Med, pt sl, pt shd; wc; chem disp; shwrs inc; el pts (10A) inc; lndtte; shops, pool, rv sw; tennis adj; ♦ 15 Jun-31 Aug.
2005*

ROCHE SUR YON, LA *2H4* (8km S Rural) Camping La Venise du Bocage, Le Chaillot, 85310 Nesmy [tel/fax 02 51 98 70 91 or 02 51 98 01 20; info@ot-roche-sur-yon.fr] Fr N take D747 dir La Tranche-sur-Mer. Take D36 twd Nesmy & site sp on R after 500m. Sm, mkd pitch, pt shd; wc (some cont); chem disp; shwrs inc; baby facs; el pts (6-10A) €2-2.50; lndtte; shop, rest, bar 3km; playgrnd; pool; tennis; 25% statics; dogs €1.07; phone; adv bkg; poss cr; quiet. "Vg long/sh stay; helpful, friendly owner; many games/sports avail; horseriding & golf 3km." ♦ 1 Apr-30 Sep. € 11.75   2004*

> Will you fill in the site report forms at the back of the guide, or shall I?

ROCHEBRUNE *9D3* (Rural) Camping Les Trois Lacs, 05190 Rochebrune [04 92 54 41 52; fax 04 92 54 16 14; direction@campingles3lacs.com; www.campingles3lacs.com] On D900 fr Serre-Poncon to Tallard, 2km after Espinasses turn L onto D951 & look for site sp. Turn R onto D56 after x-ing Rv Durance. Site on R in 2km. Sm, mkd/hdstg pitch, pt sl, shd; wc (some cont); chem disp; baby facs; shwrs €1; el pts (2-6A) €1.57-3.80; gas; lndtte; ice; shop 5km & supmkt 8km; tradsmn high ssn; snacks; bar; playgrnd; lake sw adj; fishing; tennis nrby; paragliding; go-karting; entmnt; 30% statics; dogs €2.50; poss cr; adv bkg; quiet; red long stay/low ssn; cc acc high ssn only; CCI. "Site among pine trees, poss diff for lge o'fits; lake access via security gate; gd sh stay/NH. ♦ 1 Apr-1 Oct. € 12.50   2003*

ROCHECHOUART *7B3* (3km S Rural) Camp Municipal Lac de Boischenu, 87600 Rochechouart [05 55 03 65 96] S fr Rochechouart on D675. Turn R onto D10 them immed L by lake into park. Site ent at far end of park by snack bar. Med, mkd pitch, pt sl, terr, shd; wc; shwrs; el pts (5A) €2.35 (long cable req some pitches); gas; shops 3km; rest adj; lake sw; 10% statics; poss cr; adv bkg; quiet. "V shady; open plan under trees; overlooking lake; poss busy w/e due to fishing; basic clean san facs; ltd facs low ssn; opening dates poss extended if gd weather." 15 May-15 Sep. € 9.10
2002*

ROCHECHOUART *7B3* (6km NW Rural) Camp Municipal, Rue de College, 16150 Chabanais [05 45 89 03 99 (Mairie); fax 05 45 89 13 83] D54/D29 NW fr Rochechouart to Chabanais. Sp fr town cent. Sm, pt shd; htd wc; shwrs inc; el pts (16A) €2.30; shop, rest, snacks, bar 200m; rv adj. 15 Jun-15 Sep. € 4.40   2004*

†ROCHEFORT *7B1* (1.5km N) **Camping Le Bateau, Rue des Pecheurs d'Islande, 17300 Rochefort [05 46 99 41 00; fax 05 46 99 91 65; lebateau@wanadoo.fr; www.campinglebateau. com]** Exit A837/E602 at junc 31 & take D733 dir Rochefort. At 1st rndabt by McDonalds, take D733 dir Royan. At next rndabt 1st R onto Rue des Pecheurs d'Islande. Site at end of rd on L. Med, hdg pitch, pt shd; wc; chem disp; shwrs inc; el pts (6A) inc; lndtte; shop; tradsmn; rest; snacks; bar; playgrnd; pool; waterslide; watersports; fishing; tennis; games rm; entmnt; 25% statics; dogs €1.40; site clsd Dec; quiet; CCI. "Helpful staff; no twin-axles; v clean san facs; lovely location adj to lake; ideal for touring area; gd cycling, walking." € 16.65   2004*

ROCHEFORT EN TERRE *2F3* (600m Rural) **Camping du Moulin Neuf, Route de Limerzel, 56220 Rochefort-en-Terre [02 97 43 37 52; fax 02 97 43 35 45]** Fr Redon W on D775 twd Vannes, approx 23km turn R onto D774 sp Rochefort-en-Terre at rlwy x-ing; immed after vill limit sp, turn sharp L up slope to ent; avoid vill. Med, hdg/mkd pitch, terr, pt sl, pt shd; mv service pnt; wc; chem disp; shwrs inc; el pts ltd (10A) €4.40 (check rev pol); lndtte; ice; shops in vill; tradsmn; rest nr; BBQ; play area; htd pool high ssn; lake sw 500m; dogs €3; poss cr; adv bkg; quiet; cc acc; CCI. "Well-run; peaceful base for touring area; easy walk to lovely town; no vehicle movements 2200-0700; British owners strictly maintain site; no twin-axles; vg long stay." ♦ ltd. 11 May-11 Sep. € 18.60   2005*

ROCHEFORT EN TERRE *2F3* (8km NE) **Camp Municipal La Digue, 56200 St Martin-sur-Oust [02 99 91 55 76 or 02 99 91 49 45; fax 02 99 91 42 94; st-martin-oust@wanadoo.fr]** On D873 14km N of Redon at Gacilly, turn W onto D777 twd Rochefort-en-Terre; site sp in 10km in St Martin. Med, pt shd; wc; shwrs; el pts (3-5A) €2; lndtte; ice; shops adj; BBQ; playgrnd; rv fishing 50m; dogs; adv bkg; quiet. "Towpath walks to vill & shops; clean facs but ltd low ssn; well-maintained site; site yourself, warden calls am & eve." 1 May-30 Sep. € 6.20   2003*

ROCHEFORT MONTAGNE see Mont Dore, Le *7B4*

ROCHEFORT SUR NENON see Dole *6H2*

ROCHEFOUCAULD, LA *7B2* (500m N Urban) **Camping des Flots, 16110 La Rochefoucauld [05 45 63 10 72 (HS) or 06 81 28 28 45; fax 05 45 62 14 55]** Foll camping sp on app to Rochefoucauld; site next to rv. Sm, shd; wc (cont); chem disp; shwrs inc; el pts €1.50; shops 500m in town; playgrnd; pool & tennis 300m; rv fishing 200m; adv bkg; quiet; CCI. "Chateau & cloisters worth visit; pitch near recep as other end adj to sewage plant; site run by fire brigade, use adj phone to ring fire stn for site key if no-one on site; excel clean san facs; vg sh stay." 15 May-15 Sep. € 6.50   2004*

†**ROCHEFOUCAULD, LA** *7B2* (6km E Rural) **Camping a la Ferme Rose Blanche (Gannicott), 16110 Malleyrand [tel/fax 05 45 63 07 56]** Take D13 E fr La Rochefoucauld, after 7km turn R onto D62 sp Malleyrand. Site in vill cent L past fire hydrant 100m. Sm, hdstg, pt sl, unshd; wc; chem disp; shwrs inc; el pts (16A) inc; lake sw nr; no dogs; adv bkg (dep req); quiet. "Friendly British owners; CL-type site; 2 bed apartment avail on site; meals to order; access poss diff for c'vans due steep slope & loose gravel; excel long/sh stay. " € 15.00   2004*

ROCHELLE, LA *7A1* (Urban/Coastal) **Camp Municipal Le Soleil, Ave Marillac, 17000 La Rochelle [05 46 44 42 53 or 05 46 51 51 25 (Mairie)]** App La Rochelle on N11, prepare to take L turn when 2 lge concrete water towers come into view sp Port des Minimes. Foll Port des Minimes to rlwy stn (clock tower). Turn R for site & immed L, then 2nd L (Quai Louis Prunier) to end. Turn R (Rue de Roux) over rlwy. Strt thro rndabt (Ave Henri Bacquerel), take 6th R (Ave M. Crepeau). Ent 1km on R. Or fr S on N137 take D937 sp Port des Minimes & rest as above. Lge, mkd pitch, unshd, some hdstg; wc; chem disp; mv service pnt adj; shwrs inc; el pts (6A) €3.20; shops 1km; tradsmn; BBQ area; beach 1km; some Eng spkn; adv bkg; some noise fr rd & port; CCI. "Easy walking dist cent La Rochelle & lge new yachting marina; sm pitches, facs basic; ltd space for tourers; free m'van o'night area immed opp camp ent; daily cover'd mkt in town; site poss full by 1400 - rec arr early; NH only." 15 May-15 Sep. € 10.75   2005*

ROCHELLE, LA *7A1* (12km N Rural/Coastal) **Camp Municipal Les Misottes, Rue de l'Ocean, 17137 Esnandes [05 46 35 04 07 or 05 46 01 32 13 (Mairie); lesmisottes@aol.com]** Fr N on D938 or N1327 turn W at Marans onto D105. In 7.5km turn S onto D9 then D202 to Esnandes. Enter vill, at x-rds strt, site on R in 200m adj Maison de la Mytiliculture. Fr La Rochelle D105 N to cent Esnandes, site sp. Med, mkd pitch, pt shd; wc; shwrs inc; el pts (10A) €2.40; lndtte; shops 500m; rest, bar 200m; snacks; playgrnd; pool; shgl beach 2km; canal fishing; 5% statics; dogs; Eng spkn; adv bkg; quiet; CCI. "Vg." 1 Apr-30 Sep. € 7.10   2004*

ROCHELLE, LA *7A1* (3km S Coastal) **Camping de la Plage, La Lizotiere, 66 Route de la Plage, 17440 Aytre [05 46 44 19 33; fax 05 46 45 78 21; contact@campingdelaplage17.com; www. campingdelaplage17.com]** S fr La Rochelle on N137 twd Rochefort; take exit sp Aytre. Site sp in town. Med, shd; wc; baby facs; shwrs inc; el pts (6A) €3; lndtte; snacks; playgrnd; htd, covrd pool; sand beach adj; games area; entmnt; some statics; dogs €1.70; poss cr; quiet. "Some sm pitches; new owners making improvements (2005)." 1 Feb-30 Nov. € 16.00   2005*

FRANCE

ROCHELLE, LA *7A1* (8km S Coastal) **Camping Les Chirats-La Platere, Route de la Platere, 17690 Angoulins-sur-Mer [05 46 56 94 16; fax 05 46 56 65 95; contact@campingleschirats.fr; www.campingleschirats.fr]** Turn off N137 S of La Rochelle & go thro Angoulins-sur-Mer. Foll site sp fr vill N twd Aytre. After 300m turn L across rlwy at stn. Foll sp 'plage' & site. Lge, hdg/mkd pitch, hdstg, pt sl, pt shd; wc (some cont); chem disp; sauna; serviced pitches; shwrs inc; el pts (6-10A) €4; gas; lndtte; shop & 2km; tradsmn; rest; snacks; bar; playgrnd; pools (1 htd, covrd); paddling pool; waterslide; jacuzzi; sand beach adj; fishing; fitness rm; games area; horseriding 1km; tennis 500m; TV rm; 10% statics; dogs €2.30; phone; poss cr; Eng spkn; adv bkg; quiet; cc acc; CCI. "Gd facs; site extended - new area unshd; aquarium worth a visit."
♦ 1 Apr-30 Sep. € 19.50   2005*

See advertisement opposite (top)

ROCHELLE, LA *7A1* (5km NW) **Camping au Petit Port de l'Houmeau, Rue des Sartieres, 17137 L'Houmeau [05 46 50 90 82; fax 05 46 50 01 33; info@aupetitport.com; www.aupetitport.com]** On ring rd N237 twd Ile-de-Re, take exit Lagord, across rndabt, after 300m turn R onto D104 to L'Houmeau. At T-junc in L'Houmeau turn R on D106, at 2nd boulangerie turn L & foll 1-way system/sp 'camping' thro vill (modern housing est). Site on L immed after sharp R-hand bend. Med, hdg/mkd pitch, hdstg; shd; wc; chem disp; mv service pnt; baby facs; shwrs inc; el pts (5-10A) €3.20-4; gas 800m; lndtte; lndry rm; ice; shops 800m; bar; BBQ (gas); playgrnd; shgl beach 1.5km; cycle hire; games rm; dogs €1.90; bus nr; poss cr; Eng spkn; adv bkg rec; quiet; red low ssn; cc acc; CCI. "Pleasant, friendly site; walking dist of boulangerie & rest; no vehicle access 2200-0800; lovely cycling fr site; vg." ♦ 1 Apr-31 Oct. € 15.00
                    2005*

See advertisement opposite (bottom)

†ROCHELLE, LA *7A1* (2km W) **Camp Municipal de Port Neuf, Blvd Aristide Rondeau, Port Neuf, 17000 La Rochelle [05 46 43 81 20 or 05 46 51 51 25 (Mairie)]** On ring rd fr N on N11 turn R onto N237 sp Ile-de-Re, after sp to city cent, foll sp 'Pont Neuf & Ile-de-Re' & site. Well sp on promenade rd on N side of harbour. If app fr airport side take care to avoid Ile-de-Re tollbooth. Lge, some hdstg, pt shd; wc; chem disp; baby facs; shwrs inc; el pts (6A) €2.90-3.20 (poss rev pol); gas; lndtte nr; pool 2km; sand beach 1.5km; dogs €1.85; bus; poss cr; Eng spkn; adv bkg; rd noise; red low ssn; CCI. "Conv city; clean facs but poss ltd low ssn; busy, poss shabby site; phone ahead to check open; office open 1100-1200 & 1700-1900 - some parking along rd adj football pitch; min stay 2 nights high ssn; m'vans not allowed in old part of town; cycle path along seafront to old town; bus stop on 1-way system." € 10.59   2005*

ROCHELLE, LA *7A1* (3km NW) **Camp Municipal Le Parc, Rue du Parc, 17140 Lagord [05 46 67 61 54 or 05 46 00 62 12 (Mairie); fax 05 46 00 62 01; contact@marie-lagord.fr]** On ring-rd round NW of La Rochelle, take exit for Lagord onto D105. Ignore 2 sps to site & take 3rd L (sharp turn). Pass sm rndabt & turn R in 100m, site on L, well sp. Fr N take sp to Lagord. At Lagord ignore 1st sp & go to rndabt sign. Turn L at mini rndabt & R at traff lts, site 50m on L. Med, hdg/mkd pitch, pt shd; wc; shwrs inc; el pts (3-10A) €2.15-4.30 (poss rev pol); lndtte; supmkt 2km; playgrnd; beach 4km; dogs €1.10; bus; quiet. "Gd facs & pitches; red facs low ssn; helpful staff; conv Ile de Re; twin-axles extra charge." ♦ 1 Jun-29 Sep. € 8.20   2005*

ROCHETTE, LA *(SAVOIE)* *9B3* (2km S Rural) **Camping du Lac St Clair, 73110 Detrier [04 79 25 73 55 or 04 79 25 50 32 (Mairie)]** Exit A41 at Pontcharra junc 22; foll D925 NE sp La Rochette & Albertville. Take 1st sp turn to La Rochette on R. Pass supmkt & boating pool. Site 300m on R. Med, pt sl, pt shd; wc (some cont); shwrs inc; baby facs; el pts (5-10A) €2.13; ice; lndtte; shop; tradsmn; child's pool adj; playgrnd; poss cr; dogs €0.91. "Base for W Alps; some rd noise." ♦ ltd. 1 Jun-30 Sep. € 14.00   2002*

†ROCROI *5C1* (3km SE Rural) **Camping La Muree, Rue Catherine-de-Cleves, 08230 Bourg-Fidele [tel/fax 03 24 54 24 45]** Site sp fr Rocroi on R. Sm, some hdstg, pt shd; wc; chem disp; shwrs inc; el pts (10A) €3.80; lndtte; shops 3km; rest; bar; playgrnd; lake sw 4km; 40% statics; dogs €1.60; some Eng spkn; adv bkg; quiet; cc acc; CCI. "Two lakes on site for fishing; pleasant site; gd sh stay/NH." ♦ € 16.00
                    2005*

†ROCROI *5C1* (8km SE) **Camp Departemental du Lac des Vieilles Forges, 08500 Les Mazures [tel/fax 03 24 40 17 31]** Fr Rocroi take D1 & D988 for Les Mazures/Renwez. Turn R D40 at sp Les Vieilles Forges. Site on R nr lakeside with lake views fr some pitches. Lge, mkd pitch, hdstg, pt sl, shd; wc; shwrs inc; el pts (6-10A) €2.50-4.30; lndtte; ice; shop; tradsmn; snacks; playgrnd; shgl beach by lake; boating, fishing & sw; tennis; cycle hire; entmnts high ssn; TV; 20% statics; dogs €1; poss cr; adv bkg; quiet. "Attractive walks; tennis & watersports lessons avail; vg site." ♦ € 9.30
                    2005*

Les Chirats-La Platère ★★★
Tel: 00 33.5.46.56.94.16 - Fax: 00 33.5.46.56.65.95
Owner: Marc Nadeau • Web: www.campingleschirats.fr

Campsite Les Chirats-La Platère is situated at 8 km of La Rochelle, at 100 m of a small sandy beach and at 3 km of the big beaches of Aytré and Châtelaillon. It has all modern facilities that one can expect to find on a 3 star campsite. You can enjoy the pleasures of several swimming pools with water slide with free entry for all ages. The sports and health centre (hammam, sauna, jacuzzi, solarium, heated swimming pool) as well as the 18 holes mini golf course have paid access. Angoulins sur mer has a wonderful micro climate that will provide your vacation with lots of sunshine. The village is situated in the heart of a wonderful holiday region (La Rochelle, Le Marais Poitevin, Rochefort, Saintes, Cognac and the islands of Ré and Oléron). The big playing area is situated directly on the seaside: on the top of the cliffs one can oversee the natural harbour of the Basque area (Fouras, Île d'Aix, Fort Boyard and Fort Enet). 4 hectares, 230 pitches. Tents, caravans, camping-cars, rental of chalets / Plane, grassy, lighted/ Electricity/ Hot showers, facilities equipped for disabled people / Restaurant, bar, grocery store, snacks/ TV/ Animations/ Fishing/ horse riding at 1 km/ Tennis at 0,5 Km/ Open from 01.04 till 30.09

ROCROI *5C1* (S Urban) **Camp Municipal Les Remparts, Ave du General de Gaulle, 08230 Rocroi [03 24 54 10 22 (Mairie)]** Fr N foll N51 thro town over bdge, site sp in 200m to R bef junc; site R 200m fr sp. Site outside town wall, v sm sp at rndabt. Sm, pt sl, pt shd; wc; shwrs; el pts (10A) €3 (check rev pol & earth); lndry rm; shops 500m; quiet; CCI. "Pleasant sm town nr for meals & shops; ground v soft after heavy rain; poss itinerants; no twin-axles." 1 May-15 Sep. € 6.00   2004*

ROESCHWOOG *5D3* **Camping du Staedly, Rue de l'Etang, 67480 Roeschwoog [03 88 86 42 18]** Fr traff lts in cent of Roeschwoog go W sp Luttenheim twd rlwy stn, cross rlwy turn L immed to site. Med, mkd pitch, pt shd; wc; chem disp; shwrs inc; el pts (6A) €3.10; gas; snacks; bar; shop & 1.5km; lake sw; many statics; adv bkg; noisy Fri & Sat (bar). "Cars parked outside." 1 Apr-31 Oct. € 9.00   2004*

ROMAGNE SOUS MONTFAUCON see Dun sur Meuse *5C1*

RODEZ *7D4* (1km NE Urban) **Camp Municipal de Layoule, 12000 Rodez [05 65 67 09 52; fax 05 65 67 11 43]** Clearly sp in Rodez town cent & all app rds. Access at bottom steep hill thro residential area. Med, hdg/mkd pitches, hdstg, pt shd; wc (poss cont only low ssn); chem disp; mv service pnt; shwrs inc; el pts (6A) €3; shop 1km; tradsmn; playgrnd; pool; golf; tennis nrby; no statics; phone; quiet; CCI. "Ideal for exploring Cevennes; clean facs; 20-25 min walk town cent with gd shops & numerous rests; gates clsd 2000-0700; warden insists on exit fr site uphill (another rte is avail) - poss v diff; excel long/sh stay." ♦ 1 Jun-30 Sep. € 12.00   2005*

ROMANS SUR ISERE *9C2* (10km N Rural) **Camping Les Falquets, Route de Marges, 26260 Charmes-sur-l'Herbasse [04 75 45 75 57 or 04 75 45 27 44 (LS); fax 04 75 45 66 17]** Exit A7 junc 13 onto D532 to Romans-sur-Isere. At Curson turn N onto D67 to Charmes, then D121 dir Marges. Site sp in vill. Med, pt shd; wc (some cont); chem disp; shwrs inc; el pts (6A) €2.50; lndtte; ice; shop 3km; tradsmn; bar; playgrnd; lake sw, waterslide, windsurfing & tennis 800m; 25% statics; phone; adv bkg rec high ssn; quiet; CCI. "Pleasant country site, well-kept; old facs but clean; sm rv on 1 side; red squirrels; gd long/sh stay/NH." ♦ 1 May-3 Sep. € 11.50   2005*

ROMANS SUR ISERE *9C2* (3km NE Rural) **Camp Municipal des Chasses, 26100 Romans-sur-Isere** [04 75 72 35 27] Fr W take D532 thro town, then N92, at sp for airport turn L, sp fr Thors. Fr E take A49, then N92, turn R at airport rndabt. Sm, hdg pitch, pt shd; wc (mainly cont); chem disp; mv service pnt; shwrs inc; el pts (10A) €2.35; ice; gas; lndtte; sm shop & 1km; tradsmn; bar; pool 2km; tennis; 10% statics; dogs €1; phone; Eng spkn; adv bkg rec; quiet; CCI. "Sm private airport adj; fantastic views of Vercors mountains; lax security; gd sh stay." ♦ ltd. 1 Apr-31 Oct. € 9.35   2005*

ROMANSWILLER see Wasselonne *6E3*

ROMIEU, LA *8E2* (Rural) **Le Camp de Florence, 32480 La Romieu** [05 62 28 15 58; fax 05 62 28 20 04; info@campdeflorence.com; www.campdeflorence.com] Take D931 N fr Condom & turn R onto D41, camp sp next to radio mast. Thro La Romieu & turn L at sp just bef leaving vill. Lge, hdg pitch, pt shd; wc; chem disp; mv service pnt; baby facs; shwrs inc; el pts (6A) inc (poss rev pol); lndtte; shops in vill; tradsmn; rest in 16thC farmhouse; snacks; BBQ; playgrnd; htd pool; tennis; cycle hire; games area; archery; clay pigeon shooting; internet; entmnt high ssn; TV/games rm; many statics; dogs €2; Eng spkn; adv bkg ess; quiet; red low ssn; cc acc; CCI. "Helpful & friendly; Dutch run; gd size pitches, most with views; clean facs; sh walk to historic La Romieu & Arboretum Coursiana; leisure complex 500m; many activities inc tour of town, magnificent views fr church tower; mkt Wed Condom; some noise fr disco, ask for pitch away fr bar; facs some dist fr touring pitches; poss muddy wet weather; lovely site; highly rec." ♦ 1 Apr-8 Oct. € 28.00 (CChq acc) ABS - D19   2005*

ROMORANTIN LANTHENAY *4G2* (E Urban) **Camping de Tournefeuille, Rue de Long-Eaton, 41200 Romorantin-Lanthenay** [02 54 76 16 60; fax 02 54 76 00 34; camping.romo@wanadoo.fr] Fr town cent on D724 to Salbis, foll sp thro several traff lts over bdge turn R into Rue de Long-Eaton, sp. Med, pt shd; htd wc; shwrs inc; el pts (6A) inc; gas; ice; shop 500m; snacks; pool adj; playgrnd; fishing; cycle hire; quiet. "Rv walk to town rec; office closed bet 1130 & 1600 but code is req for barriers. NB: May close earlier in ssn if quiet." May-30 Sep. € 18.50 (3 persons)   2005*

RONCE LES BAINS see Tremblade, La *7B1*

RONDE, LA see Courcon *7A2*

ROQUE D'ANTHERON, LA see Cadenet *10E3*

†**ROQUE ESCLAPON, LA** *10E4* (Rural) **Camp Municipal Notre Dame, Quartier Notre Dame, 83840 La Roque-Esclapon** [04 94 50 40 50 or 04 94 76 83; fax 04 94 50 40 51] Fr Castellane, take N85 for approx 14km & turn R onto D21 twd Comps-sur-Artuby. Turn L at sp for La Roque-Esclapon & foll sp to site. Sm, pt sl, pt shd; htd wc; chem disp; shwrs inc; el pts (6A) €3; ice; lndry rm; shop, rest, bar adj; BBQ; pool; playgrnd; tennis; paragliding; 65% statics; dogs; poss cr; quiet; phone adj; CCI. "Gd site in scenic area; gd for walks." € 8.15   2002*

ROQUE GAGEAC, LA see Sarlat la Caneda *7C3*

ROQUEBRUN *10F1* (Rural) **Camp Municipal Le Nice, Rue du Temps Libre, 34460 Roquebrun** [04 67 89 61 99 or 04 67 89 64 54 (Mairie); fax 04 67 89 78 15; otroquebrun@bechamail.com; http://tourisme.roquebrun.free.fr] N112 to St Chinian & take D20 dir Cessenon-sur-l'Orbe, turn L onto D14 twd Roquerbrun; site on L bef bdge over rv. Same recep as Campotel. Sm, mkd pitch, some hdstg, pt sl, terr, pt shd; wc (some cont); chem disp; shwrs inc; el pts (6A) €2; lndtte; ice; shops, rest, snack, bar 1km; playgrnd; rv sw & shg beach adj; canoe hire; tennis; entmnt; rv sw, fishing, sailing 50m; 5% statics; dogs €1.20; phone; poss cr; adv bkg; quiet; cc acc; CCI. "Excel cent for walking & cycling; beautiful scenery; gd sh/long stay." 15 Mar-15 Nov. € 11.20   2003*

ROQUEBRUNE SUR ARGENS see Frejus *10F4*

ROQUEFORT *8E2* (2km N Rural) **Camp Municipal de Nauton, 40120 Roquefort** [05 58 45 59 99 or 05 58 45 50 46; fax 05 58 45 53 63] Fr Roquefort N on D932 twd Bordeaux sp Langdon. Site on L after bend in rd in 2km. Sm, pt shd; wc; chem disp; shwrs inc; el pts (6A) inc (rev pol); shops 500m; rest, snacks, bar 2km; playgrnd; canoe/kayak, fishing 800m; games area; tennis adj; Eng spkn; adv bkg; quiet but some rd noise; CCI. "V clean but basic facs." ♦ ltd. 1 Jun-30 Sep. € 8.90   2004*

†**ROQUEFORT** *8E2* (12km NE Rural) **Camping Le Chateau (Raymond), 40120 Bourriot-Bergonce** [tel/fax 05 58 93 36 22; camping.de.bergonce. free.fr; http://camping.de.bergonce.free.fr] Fr Roquefort take D932 N. In approx 6km turn R onto D224 thro Retjons & Bourriot-Bergonce. Turn R onto D24, foll site sp. Fr N turn L onto D24 to site. Sm, pt shd; wc; chem disp; mv service pnt; shwrs inc; el pts (16A) €2.13; lndtte; shops 3km; tradsmn; rest 9km; bar 5km; 20% statics; dogs on lead; Eng spkn; adv bkg (dep req); quiet; CCI. "Wonderful setting in Landes forest; sale of farm produce; gd lakes & beaches, windsurfing & boating 30km; friendly owners; gd facs; CL-type site; phone ahead to check open low ssn." € 7.00   2005*

ROQUEFORT *8E2* (2.5km S Rural) **Camp Municipal, 40120 Sarbazan [05 58 45 64 93 (Mairie); fax 05 58 45 69 91]** Fr Roquefort take D934 S twd Villeneuve-de-Marsan & Pau. In 2km camp sp on L site in Sarbazan. Sm, pt sl, shd; wc (some cont); shwrs inc; el pts (5A) €1.60-2.40; lndtte; shops 2.5km; tradsmn; BBQ; playgrnd; tennis; quiet; red low ssn; CCI. "Peaceful, friendly; site yourself, warden calls am & pm; sports cent/health club adj; vg long stay; highly rec." ♦ ltd. 1 Apr-30 Oct. € 9.00   2005*

ROQUELAURE see Auch *8F3*

ROQUES see Toulouse *8F3*

ROSANS *9D3* (1.5km N Rural) **Camping Tamier Naturiste (Naturist), Route du Col de Pomerol, 05150 Tamier [04 92 66 61 55 or 04 92 87 47 24 (LS); fax 04 92 87 47 24; tamier@wanadoo.fr; www.alpes-campings.com]** On D94/D994 Serres to Nyons rd, turn N onto D25 at Rosans. Site sp in vill. Med, mkd pitch, terr, pt shd; wc; chem disp; shwrs inc; el pts (6A) inc; lndtte; ice; shop; tradsmn; rest; snacks; bar; playgrnd; pool; some statics; adv bkg; quiet. "Wonderful scenery; v friendly owners; excel long stay; v steep access rd; suggest park in upper car park nr ent bef going to recep." 1 May-15 Sep. € 19.65   2004*

ROSANS *9D3* (4km W Rural) **Aire Naturelle Le Gessy (Cagossi), 26510 Verclause [04 75 27 80 39]** Site sp fr vill; 2km up steep, narr rd. Sm, hdstg, sl, terr, pt shd; wc; chem disp (wc only); shwrs inc; el pts (16A) inc; supmkt & rest 2km; snacks; playgrnd; pool; 10% statics; Eng spkn; quiet; CCI. "Spacious pitches; gd views fr site." 1 Apr-15 Oct. € 12.00
2003*

ROSCANVEL *2E1* (Coastal) **Camp Municipal Le Kervian, Route du Camping, 29570 Roscanvel [02 98 27 43 23 or 02 98 27 48 51 (Mairie); fax 02 98 27 41 10]** Fr Crozon foll D355 dir Le Fret/Roscanvel. After Le Fret x-rds foll Municipal sp. Turn L just bef Roscanvel. Sm, mkd pitch, terr, unshd; wc (some cont); chem disp (wc only); shwrs inc; el pts (10A) €3; gas 1km; lndry rm; shop & bar 1km; tradsmn; sand beach 800m; horseriding nrby; dogs; phone adj; Eng spkn; quiet; cc not acc; CCI. "Panoramic views across valley to sea; gd long/sh stay." 15 Jun-15 Sep. € 6.70   2003*

ROSCOFF *1D2* (7km SW Coastal/Rural) **Camp Municipal du Bois de la Palud, 29250 Plougoulm [02 98 29 81 82 or 02 98 29 90 76 (Mairie); mairie-de-plougoulm@wanadoo.fr]** Fr D58 turn W on D10 sp Cleder/Plouescat; after 3km on ent Plougoulm foll sp to site. Sm, hdg/mkd pitch, terr, pt shd; wc; chem disp; shwrs inc; el pts (6A) €3; lndry rm; shop 800m; sand beach 500m; playgrnd; phone; some Eng spkn; adv bkg; quiet; CCI. "If arr late, site yourself & pay in morning; clean, tidy site; conv ferry; sh walk to vill; excel long stay." ♦ ltd
15 Jun-15 Sep. € 11.00   2004*

ROSCOFF *1D2* (3.5km W) **Camping des Quatre Saisons (formerly Camp Municipal de Perharidy), 29680 Le Ruguel [02 98 69 70 86; fax 02 98 61 15 74; camping.roscoff@wanadoo.fr]** Fr dock foll exit & camping sps SW; at rndbt exit N on D169 twd cent ville; in 800m turn W dir Santec, foll camping sps, pass travellers' site. Lge, hdg pitch, unshd; wc; chem disp; shwrs inc; baby facs; el pts (4-13A) €1.60-4.20; lndtte; ice; shops 2km; BBQ; playgrnd; sand beach; windsurfing; fishing; sailing; entmnt; dogs €1.70; poss cr; adv bkg rec high ssn; red low ssn; quiet. "Will open low ssn if bkd in adv; conv for ferry; cheap & cheerful; fair sh stay." ♦ 1 Apr-30 Sep. € 12.20   2005*

ROSIERS SUR LOIRE, LES *4G1* (1km N Urban) **Camping Le Val de Loire, 6 Rue Ste Baudruche, 49350 Les Rosiers-sur-Loire [02 41 51 94 33 or 01 40 33 93 33; fax 02 41 51 89 13; cledelles@aol.com; www.lescledelles.com]** Take D952 fr Saumur in dir Angers. Site on D59 1km N vill cent on L dir Beaufort-en-Vallee. Med, hdg/mkd pitch, pt shd; wc; chem disp; mv service pnt; baby facs; 50% serviced pitch; shwrs inc; el pts (10A) €5; gas; lndtte; ice; tradsmn; snacks; bar; BBQ; playgrnd; pool; lake sw 15km; waterslide; tennis; games rm; entmnt; TV; dogs €2.30; Eng spkn; adv bkg; quiet but some rlwy noise; red long stay/low ssn; CCI. "Close to Rv Loire; gd long stay cent for chateaux & Loire region; friendly & helpful; lge pitches; excel facs." ♦ 1 Apr-15 Oct. € 15.00   2005*

ROSIERS SUR LOIRE, LES *4G1* (1km S Urban) **Camping Le Bord de Loire, Ave Cadets-de-Saumur, 49350 Gennes [02 41 38 04 67 or 02 41 38 07 30; fax 02 41 38 07 12; aubord deloire@free.fr; www.cfp-gennes.com]** At Rv Loire bdge cross S to Gennes on D751B. Site on L. Ent to site thro bus terminus/stop on ent to Gennes. Lge, mkd pitch, pt sl, pt shd; wc (some cont); chem disp; shwrs; el pts (10A) €2.50; lndry rm; rest; bar; shop 500m in vill; playgrnd; htd pool in vill; dogs €0.60; rd noise; CCI. "Well maintained, excel san facs; vg sh/long stay." 1 May-30 Sep. € 7.50   2005*

ROSIERS SUR LOIRE, LES *4G1* (6km NW) **Camp Municipal Port St Maur, 49250 La Menitre [02 41 45 60 80; fax 02 41 45 65 65; info@loiredelumiere.com]** Exit Les Rosiers on D952 sp Angers. Site on L by rv. Med, mkd pitch, pt shd; wc; shwrs inc; el pts (5A); lndtte; shops 1km; rest; snacks; bar; playgrnd; games area; entmnt; boat trips on Loire; some rd & rlwy noise. "Access to san facs by steps; height barrier at ent; helpful warden." ♦ 1 Jun-15 Sep.   2004*

FRANCE

†ROSNAY *4H2* (N Rural) **Camp Municipal Rosnay, Route de St Michel-en-Brenne, 36300 Rosnay [02 54 37 80 17 (Mairie); fax 02 54 37 02 86; rosnay-mairie@wanadoo.fr]** NE on D27 fr Le Blanc to Rosnay; site sp 500m N of Rosnay on D44 rd to St Michel-en-Brenne. Med, mkd pitch, pt shd; wc (some cont); shwrs inc; el pts (6A) €1.90-3.20 (rev pol); lndry rm; rest & shop 500m; BBQ; playgrnd; cycling; tennis; bird-watching; dogs; phone; quiet; CCI. "Tranquil site; v popular; gd san facs; warden collects fees twice daily; lakeside, walks in National Park; fishing €2.50 per day; lge area for unmkd pitches." ♦ € 6.10   2005*

Mustn't forget to post our site report forms to The Club, otherwise sites might be deleted.

ROSPORDEN *2F2* (1km N Urban) **Camp Municipal de Roz an Duc, Route de Coray, 29140 Rosporden [02 98 59 90 27 or 02 98 66 99 00 (Mairie); fax 02 98 59 92 00; mairie.rosporden@ oleane.fr]** At Rosporden, take D36 N dir Chateauneuf-du-Faou. Site in leisure complex 500m fr rlwy stn. Sm, hdg/mkd pitch, pt sl, terr, pt shd; wc; chem disp; shwrs inc; el pts (3-6A) €2.30 (rev pol); gas; lndtte; shop, rest, snacks, bar in town; tradsmn; playgrnd; pool; tennis 100m; sand & shgl beach 15km; dogs €0.55; phone; poss cr; adv bkg; quiet; CCI. "Vg, well laid-out site; excel facs; conv to shops, etc." ♦ 13 Jun-4 Sep. € 8.00   2005*

ROSPORDEN *2F2* (12km NE Rural) **Camp Municipal de Kerisole, Rue Pasteur, 29390 Scaer [02 98 59 42 10 or 02 98 57 60 91; fax 02 98 57 66 89; mairie.scaer@altica.com; www. ville-scaer.fr]** Fr N165 take D70 to Rosporden, then N on D782, well sp in Scaer. Thro town foll sp to site. Med, mkd pitch, pt shd; wc; chem disp; mv service pnt; baby facs; shwrs; el pts (13A) €2.60; lndtte; ice; shop; tradsmn; rest; snacks; bar 250m; playgrnd; pool; few statics; dogs; phone; Eng spkn; adv bkg; quiet; CCI. "This is a gem at ent to forest with mkd walks; vill has great rests; excel san facs." ♦ 15 Jun-15 Sep. € 8.10   2004*

†ROSTRENEN *2E2* (2km S Rural) **Camping Fleur de Bretagne, Kerandouaron, 22110 Rostrenen [02 96 29 15 45; fax 02 96 29 16 45; info@ fleurdebretagne.com; www.fleurdebretagne.com]** Fr Rostrenen town cent foll dir Intermarche & take next R turn sp D31 Silfiac. In approx 1km turn L, site sp. Med, mkd pitch, pt sl, terr, pt shd; wc; chem disp; mv service pnt; shwrs inc; el pts (6A) €3.50; lndry rm; shop 2km; snacks; bar; BBQ; playgrnd; pool; fishing lake; watersports, horseriding nr; dogs €1; phone; Eng spkn; adv bkg; quiet; red long stay; CCI. "V helpful British owners; wooded walks; ltd opening Nov-Mar - phone ahead." ♦ € 12.00   2005*

ROUEN *3C2* (4km N Rural) **Camp Municipal, Rue Jules Ferry, 76250 Deville-les-Rouen [02 35 74 07 59]** Fr Rouen take N15 N twd Dieppe (avoid a'route); in Deville turn L at traff lts immed after Hotel de Ville, foll sp to site. Fr Le Havre at Barontin, turn R onto old N15, thro Maromme, turn R after 3 traff lts. Med, unshd, gravel pitch; wc; chem disp; mv service pnt; shwrs inc; el pts (10A) €2; supmkt 500m; playgrnd; pool 300m; some statics; poss cr; adv bkg; some noise fr adj factory & rd. "Facs clean but need updating; excel bus service to town; poss mkt traders on site; narr pitches; site office clsd Sat, Sun, local & national holidays; phone ahead to check site open low ssn; vg sh stay." 1 Mar-31 Dec. € 12.80   2004*

†ROUEN *3C2* (6km E) **Camping L'Aubette, 23 Rue du Vert Buisson, 76160 St Leger-du-Bourg-Denis [tel/fax 02 35 08 47 69]** Fr N31 Darnetal dir Beauvais. Site well sp as 'Camping' fr Rouen cent. Med, pt shd, pt sl, terr; wc (some cont); shwrs €1.55; el pts (3-10A) €1.50-5; shops 400m; sw pool in Rouen; 30% statics; poss cr. "Helpful staff; basic facs; poss untidy low ssn; extra charge for m'van water tank fill-up; in attractive rv valley; conv city cent; arrange with owner to leave early." € 7.60   2005*

ROUFFACH *6F3* (S Urban) **Camp Municipal, 68250 Rouffach [03 89 49 78 13; fax 03 89 78 03 09]** On N83 S fr Colmar bet Colmar & Cernay. Sm, pt shd; wc; chem disp; shwrs €1.50; el pts (4A) inc; lndry rm; shop 500m; cc not acc; CCI. "Clean site at start Alsace wine rte; ring bell on wall nr san facs block for warden; sh walk to town cent; vg sh stay/NH." Easter-30 Sep. € 8.90   2004*

ROUFFIGNAC *7C3* (300m N) **Camping Bleu Soleil, Domaine Touvent, 24580 Rouffignac [05 53 05 48 30; fax 05 53 05 27 87; infos@ bleusoleil.com; www.camping-bleusoleil.com]** On D6 in Rouffignac, take D31 NE twd Thenon. Site clearly sp on R after 300m. Med, hdg/mkd pitch, pt sl, terr, pt shd; wc; chem disp; 75% serviced pitches; shwrs inc; el pts (6-10A) €2.50; lndtte; ice; shop; tradsmn; rest, snacks & bar high ssn; BBQ; playgrnd; htd pool; tennis; games rm; TV rm; 10% statics; dogs €1; phone; Eng spkn; adv bkg (dep req); quiet; red long stay; cc acc; CCI. "Amazing views & scenery; v friendly owners; beautiful setting; caves nrby; poss diff for lge o'fits; excel." ♦ ltd. 1 Apr-15 Oct. € 15.00   2005*

ROUFFIGNAC *7C3* (6km SW Rural) **Camping Le Coteau de l'Herm (Naturist), 24580 Rouffignac [05 53 36 67 77; fax 05 53 05 74 87; info@ naturisme-dordogne.com]** Fr N89 (E70) 1.5km fr Thenon twd Perigeux, take D31 sp Rouffignac & Chateau de l'Herm, site well sp. In approx 10km turn R & after 3km site on L. Sm, mkd pitch, terr, pt sl, pt shd; htd wc; chem disp; shwrs inc; el pts (4A) €2.74; gas; ice; lndtte; shop; tradsmn; bar; snacks; BBQ; playgrnd; pool; cycle hire; dogs; quiet; adv bkg (dep req, bkg fee); Eng spkn; red 14 days; CCI. "Excel naturist site; excel facs; gd access; vg long stay; helpful Dutch owners; prehistoric sites; delightful location." 1 May-30 Sep. € 13.26   2004*

ROUSSILLON 10E2 (2.5km SW Rural) **Camping L'Arc-en-Ciel, Route de Goult, 84220 Roussillon** [04 90 05 73 96] Take N100 W out of Apt, then R on D201 sp Roussillon, then R on D4 for 1.5km, then L on D104 twd Roussillon. Take L fork twd Goult, site well sp 2.5km on L. No access for c'vans & m'vans in Roussillon vill. Med, mkd pitch, hdstg, terr, pt shd; wc; chem disp; serviced pitch; shwrs inc; el pts (4-6A) inc; gas; lndtte; ice; sm shop & 2.5km (uphill); tradsmn; snacks; playgrnd; children's pool; phone; adv bkg; quiet; CCI. "V helpful staff; tranquil site in old wooded ochre quarry; full of character; gd value; beware rd humps & drainage channels on site access rds; v quiet; lovely vills within easy reach; worth a detour; vg sh/long stay." ♦ 15 Mar-31 Oct. € 11.90   2004*

ROYAN 7B1 (6km NE Rural) **Camping Le Bois Roland, 82 Route de Royan, 17600 Medis [tel/fax 05 46 05 47 58; bois.roland@wanadoo.fr; www. le-bois-roland.com]** On N150 Saintes-Royan rd site sp in Medis. Med, pt shd; wc (some cont); chem disp; shwrs inc; el pts (5A) €3.90; gas; ice; lndtte; shop & 600m; tradsmn; snacks; bar; pool; sand beach 4km; playgrnd; entmnt; TV; dogs €3.50; adv bkg; Eng spkn; quiet; cc acc; CCI. "Attractive wooded site; family-run; friendly; facs poss stretched high ssn." ♦ 1 May-30 Sep. € 15.20   2003*

ROYAN 7B1 (6km E Rural) **Camping Le Clos Fleuri, 8 Impasse du Clos Fleuri, 17600 Medis** [05 46 05 62 17; fax 05 46 06 75 61; clos-fleuri@ wanadoo.fr] On N150 Saintes-Royan rd turn S in Medis twd Semussac. Well sp. Med, pt sl, shd; wc; shwrs inc; el pts (5-10A) €4.10-5.30; lndtte; shop in ssn & 6km; tradsmn; rest, snacks & bar in ssn; playgrnd; pool; sand beach 4km; table tennis; TV; mini-golf; boules; sauna; entmnt; dogs €3.20; quiet; adv bkg (dep req); Eng spkn; red low ssn; cc acc; CCI. "Family-run, rec for young families; lge indiv pitch; chalets for hire; excel long stay." ♦ 1 Jun-15 Sep. € 23.50   2005*

ROYAN 7B1 (4km SE Coastal) **Camping Ideal, Ave de Suzac, 17110 St Georges-de-Didonne** [05 46 05 29 04; fax 05 46 06 32 36; info@ ideal-camping.com] Fr Royan foll coast rd sp St Georges-de-Didonne. Site sp fr town. Lge, mkd pitch, shd; wc (some cont); chem disp; shwrs inc; el pts (3-6A) €2.85-3.90; gas; ice; lndtte; shop; tradsmn; rest; snacks; bar; playgrnd; sand beach 200m; phone; no dogs; poss noisy (bar); cc acc; red low ssn; CCI. ♦ ltd. 30 Apr-11 Sep. € 17.00 (3 persons)   2003*

†ROYAN 7B1 (4km SE Coastal) **Camping La Triloterie, 44 Ave d'Aquitaine, 17200 Royan** [05 46 05 26 91; fax 05 46 06 20 74; www.iroyan. com/triloterie] Fr Royan PO, foll sp Bordeaux N730, on E of rd. Med, shd; htd wc; chem disp (wc); shwrs inc; el pts (4A) inc (poss rev pol); shops 500m; waterslide; sand beach 1km; dogs; phone; poss cr/noisy high ssn; some rd noise; red low ssn. "Fair sh stay low ssn." € 16.16   2002*

ROYAN 7B1 (8km SE Coastal) **Parc Hotel Bois Soleil, 2 Ave de Suzac, 17110 St Georges-de-Didonne [05 46 05 05 94; fax 05 46 06 27 43; camping.bois.soleil@wanadoo.fr; www.bois-soleil.com]** Fr a'route A10 exit junc 35 dir Saintes dir Royan. Fr Royan foll seafront rd to S thro St Georges-de-Didonne, where rd turns inland, turn R in 100m sp Meschers. In 500m turn R into Ave Suzac & site ent on R. Site well sp. Lge, hdg/mkd pitch, terr, pt shd; htd wc (some cont); chem disp; mv service pnt; baby facs; shwrs inc; el pts (6A) inc (poss rev pol); gas; lndtte; ice; shop; tradsmn; rest; snacks; bar; BBQ (gas); playgrnd; 2 pools; sand beach adj; games area; 5% statics; dogs; phone; poss cr; Eng spkn; adv bkg (ess Jul/Aug); cc acc; red low ssn; CCI. "3 sep areas to site low ssn: pitches poss tight lge o'fits; wonderful location; war time bunkers nrby; vg shop & rest; popular site; bkg rec; vg." ♦ 1 Apr-31 Oct. € 31.00 (CChq acc)   2005*

ROYAN 7B1 (10km SE) **Camping Soleil Levant, 17132 Meschers-sur-Gironde [05 46 02 76 62; fax 05 46 02 50 56; soleil.levant.ribes@wanadoo.fr]** Take D145 coast rd fr Royan to Talmont. At Meschers turn R foll camp sp twd port; sp. Med, pt shd; wc (some cont); chem disp; shwrs inc; el pts inc; gas 1km; lndtte; ice; snacks; bar; shop; playgrnd; sand beach 1.5km; free pool & paddling pool; watersports & horseriding adj; 20% statics; no dogs; adv bkg; quiet; cc acc; CCI. "Visits to Cognac & Bordeaux distilleries; port & rest 300m; vill shop & daily mkt 500m." 15 Apr-15 Sep. € 20.20   2005*

ROYAN 7B1 (2km NW Urban) **Camping Le Royan, 10 Rue des Bleuets, 17200 Royan [05 46 39 09 06; fax 05 46 38 12 05; camping.le.royan@wanadoo. fr; www.le-royan.com]** Take D25 by-pass fr Royan dir La Palmyre. Site sp. Lge, mkd pitch, hdstg, pt sl, pt shd; wc (some cont); chem disp; mv service pnt; baby facs; shwrs inc; el pts (10A) inc; gas; lndtte; ice; shop; rest; snacks; bar; BBQ; playgrnd; htd pool; paddling pool; waterslide; sand beach 2.5km; lake sw 3km; solarium; games area; games rm; cycle hire; entmnt; child entmnt; TV; 25% statics; dogs €3; poss cr; adv bkg; quiet; cc acc; red low ssn/long stay/CCI. "Friendly, helpful owners; excel pool complex." ♦ 1 Apr-10 Oct. € 30.50 (3 persons)   2005*

See advertisement on next page

ROYAN 7B1 (4km NW Urban/Coastal) **Camping Clairefontaine, Allee des Peupliers, Pontaillac, 17200 Royan [05 46 39 08 11; fax 05 46 38 13 79; camping.clairefontaine@wanadoo.fr; www. camping-clairefontaine.com]** Foll Pontaillac sp fr Royan. Site sp in Clairefontaine (& Pontaillac). Lge, mkd pitch, pt shd; wc (some cont); chem disp; mv service pnt; fam bthrm; serviced pitches; shwrs inc; el pts (5A) €4; gas; lndtte; tradsmn; ice; shop; rest; snacks; bar; BBQ; playgrnd; 2 pools; sand beach 300m; tennis; TV rm; dogs; phone; Eng spkn; adv bkg; quiet; cc acc; CCI. "Gd family holiday; site patrolled; attentive staff; vg long/sh stay." ♦ 20 May-15 Sep. € 32.00 (3 persons)   2004*

Camping le Royan*** welcomes you on a woody and cozy family campsite of 3 hectares situated at the entry of Royan. At 2.5 km of the beaches with fine sand, our quality camp site offers the enthusiasts of mobile homes and cottages a wide range of rental possibilities. 100 marked pitches with grass are reserved for caravans or tents. The water park is open from the 1st of May. Installations: Heated water park of 270 m² in an exotic setting, water slide with multiple lanes, lagoon and paddle pool. Children's play park, volleyball, basketball, table tennis, jeu de boules, billiard, table-football, pinball, bicycle rental, television. Animation for children and sports activities in July and August, entertainment evenings.

www.le-royan.com

10, Rue des Bleuets-17200 Royan • Phone: (00 33) 05 46 39 09 06 • Fax: (00 33) 05 46 38 12 05 • E-Mail: camping.le.royan@wanadoo.fr

ROYBON *9C2* (1km S) **Camp Municipal Aigue Noire, Route de St Antoine, 38940, Roybon** [04 76 36 23 67; fax 04 76 36 33 02; roybon. campingaiguenoire@wanadoo; www.camping-aiguenoire.fr.st] Fr Roybon go S on D71 & foll sp. Med, mkd pitch, pt sl, pt shd; wc; chem disp; shwrs inc; el pts (6A) inc; shops 1km; playgrnd; sw & water sports in lake adj; dogs €1.30; adv bkg; quiet. "Very peaceful; walks adj; facs new & on solar power; vg all stays." ♦ 15 Apr-15 Oct. € 12.20   2004*

ROYERE DE VASSIVIERE *7B4* (6km SW Rural) **Camping Les Terrasses du Lac, Vauveix, 23460 Royere-de-Vassiviere** [05 55 64 76 77; fax 05 55 64 76 78; http://campings.vassiviere.free.fr/] Fr Eymoutiers take D43 for approx 10km then take D36 to Vauveix & foll sp. Med, hdg/mkd pitch, terr, pt shd; htd wc; chem disp; shwrs inc; el pts (10A) €3; lndtte; rest, bar 300m; snacks 500m; sand beach, sw & watersports adj; horseriding; walking; cycling; TV rm; dogs; phone 50m; quiet; CCI. "Helpful staff; lovely setting." ♦ 10 Apr-16 Oct. € 12.00   2004*

RUE *3B2* (7km N Rural) **Camping du Val d'Authie, 20 Route de Vercourt, 80120 Villers-sur-Authie** [03 22 29 92 47; fax 03 22 29 92 20; camping@valdauthie.fr; www.valdauthie.fr] Fr A16 take exit 24 onto N1 dir Boulogne. At ent to Vron turn W to Villers-sur-Authie & foll site sp. Lge, hdg/mkd pitch, pt sl, pt shd; htd wc; chem disp; shwrs inc; baby facs; el pts (6-10A) €5-8 (rev pol); gas; lndtte; ice; shop; tradsmn; snacks; bar; playgrnd; htd pool; paddling pool; sand beach 10km; tennis; games area; games rm; entmnt; TV; 60% statics; dogs €1.50; phone; poss cr; Eng spkn; adv bkg; quiet but poss noise fr chalets/statics; cc acc; CCI; "Helpful, friendly owners; v clean, unisex facs & spacious shwrs; sep area for tourers; gd pool; set in pleasant countryside; poss diff for lge o'fits; v cr & noisy high ssn." ♦ 1 Apr-31 Oct. € 23.50 (3 persons) (CChq acc)   2005*

RUE *3B2* (7km SE Rural) **Camping Sarl Chateau Gaillard, 18 Rue du Haut, 80120 Forest-Montiers** [tel/fax 03 22 23 97 33 or 06 11 63 51 95 (mob)] Fr N on A16 exit junc 24; turn L onto N1 twds Abbeville; site 500m on R. Fr S, N of Nouvion on L of N1 at Forest-Montiers. Med, hdg pitch, unshd; wc; chem disp; baby facs; shwrs inc; el pts (6A) €4; lndtte; shop 3km; tradsmn; bar; BBQ; playgrnd; htd pool; games rm; 80% statics; dogs; adv bkg; quiet; CCI. "V few touring pitches; NH only low ssn." ♦ 1 Apr-30 Oct. € 19.00 (4 persons)   2004*

RUFFEC *7A2* (3km E Rural) **Camping Le Rejallant, Les Grands Champs, 16700 Condac** [05 45 31 29 06 or 05 45 31 07 14; fax 05 45 31 34 76; cdc-ruffec-charente@wanadoo.fr] Site sp fr N10. App 1km fr turn-off. Med, hdg/mkd pitch, pt sl, shd; wc; chem disp (wc); shwrs inc; el pts (10A) €1.80; lndtte; tradsmn; snacks; rest & bar 100m; sm playgrnd; rv sw, fishing 100m; dogs; Eng spkn; quiet; cc not acc; CCI. "V clean facs - water poss v hot; gd for families; shwrs ltd; gates open 0700-2100 high ssn; no entry/exit 1100-1600 low ssn." 15 May-15 Sep. € 7.00   2005*

RUFFIEUX *9B3* (Rural) **Camping Le Saumont, 73310 Ruffieux** [04 79 54 26 26; fax 04 79 54 24 74; camping.saumont@wanadoo.fr; www.campingsaumont.com] N fr Aix-les-Bains take D991 N to Ruffieux, sp just bef Ruffieux at junc with D904. Sm, hdg/mkd pitch, pt shd; wc; chem disp; serviced pitch; shwrs; el pts (6-10A) €1.80-2.50; lndtte; ice; shop 1.5km; snacks; bar; BBQ; playgrnd; 2 pools (no shorts); tennis; watersports; sw lake & river 2-5km; cycle hire; 10% statics; dogs €1.20; adv bkg; quiet; red low ssn. "Dusty rd thro site when hot & dry; muddy after rain; sm pools." 1 May-30 Sep. € 13.50   2005*

RUFFIEUX *9B3* (4km W Rural) **Camping Le Colombier**, 01350 Culoz [tel/fax 04 79 87 19 00; camping.colombier@free.fr; http://camping.colombier.free.fr] W fr Ruffieux or N fr Bellay on D904, site sp off rndabt 1km E of Culoz. Med, hdg/mkd pitch, hdstg, pt shd; wc (some cont); chem disp; baby facs; shwrs inc; el pts (10A) €3; lndtte; shop 1km; tradsmn; rest; snacks; bar; playgrnd; lake sw adj; tennis; mini-golf; cycle hire; TV; phone; Eng spkn; adv bkg; quiet; cc acc; red CCI. "Gd touring base; conv Annecy; vg long/sh stay." ♦ 10 Apr-19 Sep. € 13.50   2003*

RUMILLY *9B3* (4km N) **Camping Les Charmilles**, 74150 Vallieres [04 50 62 10 60 or 06 18 06 34 51; fax 04 50 62 19 45; lescharmilles.camping@ wanadoo.fr] Exit N201 at either Albens or Alby sp Rumilly on D910. 4km N of Rumilly in Vallieres exit D910 on D14 sp Seyssel. Site on L in 500m. Med, mkd pitch, pt shd; wc; shwrs inc; el pts (6A) €2.75; gas; lndtte; shops 500m; tradmsn; rest; snacks; playgrnd; pool; entmnt; TV; dogs €0.50; adv bkg; quiet but noisy disco at w/e; red low ssn. 1 Apr-30 Oct. € 10.60   2003*

RUMILLY *9B3* (5km NE Rural) **Camping a la Ferme Fleurie (Andre), Route de Rumilly**, 74150 Marcellaz-Albanais [04 50 69 70 36] Fr Rumilly take D16 N thro Marcellaz-Albanais. Site sp 600m past vill on rd to Annecy. Sm, pt sl, pt shd; wc; chem disp (wc only); mv service pnt; shwrs inc; el pts (5A); shop & 5km; tradsmn; playgrnd; beach 10km; no statics; quiet; adv bkg; cc not acc; CCI. "Gd long/sh stay; excel activities & visits to local attractions; farm produce avail; mountain hikes; fondue nights; family atmosphere; poss diff access some pitches; service block across minor rd - poss unsuitable sm children." 15 Apr-15 Oct. € 11.80   2004*

RUOMS *9D2* (2km N Rural) **Camping Les Coudoulets**, 07120 Pradons [04 75 93 94 95; fax 04 79 39 65 89; camping@coudoulets.com; www.coudoulets.com] Site sp fr D579. Med, mkd pitch, shd; wc; chem disp; mv service pnt; shwrs inc; el pts (6A) €3.60; lndtte; shop 300m; rest; snacks; bar; playgrnd; htd pool; rv fishing nr; games area; 5% statics; dogs €2; Eng spkn; adv bkg; quiet. "Site o'looks Rv Ardeche; v friendly, careful owners; excel pool." ♦ 1 May-8 Sep. € 20.00   2005*

RUOMS *9D2* (8km NE Rural) **Camping Le Chamadou, Mas de Chaussy, 07120 Balazuc** [04 75 37 70 61 or 04 75 37 00 56; fax 04 75 37 70 61; www.camping-le-chamadou.fr.st] Fr Ruoms foll D579 dir Aubenas. After approx 9km turn R under viaduct, site sp. Keep R up narr rd to site. App recep on foot fr car pk. Med, hdg pitch, hdstg, pt sl, pt shd; wc (own san rec); chem disp; baby facs; fam bthrm; shwrs inc; el pts (5A) inc (some rev pol); lndtte; ice; shop 3km; tradsmn; snacks; bar; BBQ; playgrnd; pool; rv sw 2km; canoe & kayak hire; entmnt; TV rm; dogs €1.40; phone; poss cr; Eng spkn; adv bkg rec (dep req); v quiet; cc acc; CCI. "Excel site, superb panoramic views, well-run family site, most pitches v spacious." 1 Apr-30 Sep. € 17.95   2002*

RUOMS *9D2* (1km E) **Camping Le Ternis, Route de Lagorce**, 07120 Ruoms [04 75 93 93 15; fax 04 75 93 90 90; campternis@aol.com; www. camping-leternis.com] Fr Aubenas take D579 S to Ruoms; D559 E twd Lagorce, site outside town. Med, shd; wc; baby facs; shwrs inc; el pts (6A) €3.35; gas; lndtte; ice; shop; rest; snacks; playgrnd; htd pool; sand rv beach 2km; canoe & kayak hire; mini-golf; entmnt; TV rm; adv bkg; quiet; red low ssn; "Gorges d'Ardeche 2km; horseriding; games; walking." Easter-20 Sep. € 18.00   2002*

As we're travelling out of season, we'd better phone ahead to check that the site is actually open.

†**RUOMS** *9D2* (1km S Rural) **Camping Le Mas du Barry, Bevennes**, 07120 Ruoms [04 75 39 67 61; fax 04 75 39 76 33] by-pass Ruoms on D579 sp Vallon-Pont-d'Arc. On D579, 100m N of junc with D111. Site on R 2km S of Ruoms. Med, mkd pitch, sl, pt shd; wc; baby facs; shwrs; el pts (6A) inc; gas; lndtte; ice; shop; snacks; rest in ssn; bar; playgrnd; pool; some statics; poss cr; Eng spkn; adv bkg; rd noise; cc acc; CCI. "Quiet site in busy area; clean facs; helpful, welcoming manager." ♦ € 20.00   2004*

RUOMS *9D2* (3km S Rural) **Camping La Plaine**, 07120 Ruoms [04 75 39 65 83; fax 04 75 39 74 38; camping.la.plaine@wanadoo.fr; www.camping-la-plaine.com] Exit Ruoms S on D579 at junc 2km S foll D111 sp St Ambroix. Site on L. Lge, mkd pitch, pt sl, pt shd; wc; baby facs; shwrs inc; el pts (6A) €3.81; lndtte; ice; shop; rest; snacks; bar; BBQ; playgrnd; rv sw, fishing; red low ssn; CCI. 1 Apr-30 Sep. € 16.00   2002*

RUOMS *9D2* (4km SW) **Camping La Chapouliere**, 07120 Ruoms [tel/fax 04 75 39 64 98 or 04 75 93 90 72; campingla-chapouliere@ wanadoo.fr] Exit Ruoms S on D579. At junc 2km S, foll D111 sp St Ambroix. Site 1.5km fr junc. Med, mkd pitch, pt sl, shd; wc; baby facs; shwrs inc; el pts (6A) €4; gas; ice; lndtte; shop in ssn & 3km; rest; snacks; bar; pool; paddling pool; rv sw & fishing adj; tennis 2km; games area; entmnts; TV; dogs €1; adv bkg rec high ssn; quiet. "Beautiful pitches on rv bank; ltd facs low ssn." ♦ 19 Mar-30 Sep. € 23.50   2004*

FRANCE

RUOMS *9D2* (7km SW) **Camping Le Ranc Davaine,** 07120 St Alban-Auriolles [04 75 39 60 55; fax 04 75 39 38 50; camping.ranc.davaine@wanadoo. fr; www.camping-ranc- davaine.fr] Leave A7/E15 at Montelimar/Aubenas exit, foll sp twd Aubenas on N102. Just past Villeneuve-de-Berg turn L onto D103, thro St Germain, then join D579 to Ruoms. S of Ruoms leave D579 sp Gorges de l'Ardeche & join D111 twd Grospierres. At Les Tessiers turn R onto D246, sp St Alban-Auriolles. After x-ing Rv Chassezac turn L twd Chandolas. Ignore D246 turn to R, site after this turn on R. Lge, shd; wc; chem disp; baby facs; sauna; steam rm; shwrs inc; el pts (6-10A) inc; gas; lndtte; shop; rest; snacks; bar; BBQ (el only); playgrnd; pool complex (inc 1 htd, covrd); waterslide; rv sw; fishing; tennis; archery; mini-golf; games rm; fitness cent; entmnt; internet; TV rm; 75% statics; dogs €4.65; recep 0800-1930; adv bkg; quiet; cc acc. "Helpful staff; conv Gorges de l'Ardeche; public rd divides site; excel pool complex; mkt St Alban Mon; guided walks." ♦ 7 Apr-17 Sep. € 39.80 (CChq acc) ABS - C16
2005*

RUSSEY, LE see Maiche *6G3*

RUYNES EN MARGERIDE *9C1* (Rural) **Camp Municipal du Petit Bois,** 15320 **Ruynes-en-Margeride** [04 71 23 42 26 or 04 71 23 41 59; fax 04 71 23 90 01] Fr St Flour S on N9. After 7km turn L onto D4. Site in 7km, sp. Or exit junc 30 fr A75, turn R into vill & foll sp. Lge, pt sl, pt shd; wc (some cont); chem disp; mv service pnt; baby facs; shwrs inc; el pts (6-10A) €3.50; gas; lndtte; ice; shops, rest, bar 500m; playgrnd; pool adj; rv sw 15km; some log cabins; dogs €1; phone; Eng spkn; adv bkg; quiet; cc acc; CCI. "Excel scenery; v few flat pitches; gd cent for walking, horseriding, fishing; used as field work cent in term time; excel san facs." ♦ 1 May-30 Sep. € 11.00
2005*

RUYNES EN MARGERIDE *9C1* (4km E Rural) **Camping a la Ferme (Rolland),** 15320 Clavieres [04 71 23 45 50] Fr St Flour, S on N9. After 7km turn L onto D4 thro Claviers & foll sps. Site in Chirol, foll Chirol sp. Sm, wc; shwrs inc; el pts; farm food avail; shops 2.5km; playgrnd; rv 2.5km; pool, tennis, golf, horseriding 10km; sailing, fishing 15km; quiet. "Isolated, with beautiful views, gd facs for a basic site; long el lead req; pay at old white house in Chirol." Jun-Sep. € 4.57
2004*

SAALES *6E3* (NE) **Camp Municipal,** 67420 Saales [03 88 97 70 26 (Mairie); fax 03 88 97 77 39] Fr St Die take N420 twd Strasbourg, turn onto D32 in vill. Site on R just bef football pitch, well sp. Med, pt sl, terr, pt shd; wc; chem disp; shwrs inc; el pts inc; shop & rest 500m; tennis adj; quiet; 40% statics. "Gd sh stay; site yourself, warden calls am & pm." ♦ ltd 1 May-31 Aug.
2004*

SABLE SUR SARTHE *4F1* (10km NE Rural) **Camp Municipal,** 72430 Avoise [02 43 95 32 07 or 02 43 92 76 12; fax 02 43 95 62 48] Fr Sable take D309 twd Le Mans, after 10km thro vill of Parce-sur-Sarthe, cont twds Le Mans & cross bdge over Sarthe; sp for Avoise & camping sp on L, in cent Avoise on L 3rd car park. Sm, hdg pitch, pt shd; wc; shwrs inc; el pts inc; gas; ice; shops adj; Eng spkn; adv bkg; quiet; adj Rv Sarthe; CCI. "Pleasant, clean site, off beaten track; vg sh stay." 1 Jun-10 Sep. € 6.50
2003*

SABLE SUR SARTHE *4F1* (S Urban) **Camp Municipal de l'Hippodrome, Allee du Quebec,** 72300 Sable-sur-Sarthe [02 43 95 42 61; fax 02 43 92 74 82; camping-sable@wanadoo. fr; www.sable-sur-sarthe.com] W fr town cent (dir Angers) on Rue St Denis, Ave de Montreaux & Ave de la Vaige, sp in town (foll sm, white sp with c'van symbols or Hippodrome). Med, hdg pitch, pt shd; wc; shwrs inc; el pts (15A) €2.10; gas; ice; BBQ; lndry rm; sm shop; tradsmn; playgrnd; snacks; pool; boat & cycle hire; canoeing; archery; rv fishing; TV rm; Eng spkn; quiet; cc acc; red long stay low ssn. "Excel site; gd, clean facs; helpful owners; some pitches by rv, some diff for lge fits; 10 min walk to town; activities organised on site." ♦ 1 Apr-10 Oct. € 8.30
2004*

SABLE SUR SARTHE *4F1* (10km S) **Camping des Lices, Rue de la Piscine, 72300 Precigne** [02 43 95 46 13; fax 02 43 62 06 23] S on D24 fr Sable (sp Precigne & Durtal), site clearly sp on N o'skts opp stadium. Sm, hdg pitch, shd; wc; shwrs; el pts inc; lndry rm; shops 500m; pool adj; adv bkg; quiet but some rd noise; CCI. 1 Jun-15 Sep. € 6.50
2002*

SABLES D'OLONNE, LES *7A1* (4km N Urban) **Airotel Le Trianon, 95 Rue du Marechal Joffre, 85340 Olonne-sur-Mer** [02 51 23 61 61; fax 02 51 90 77 70; campingletrianon@free.fr; www. camping-le-trianon.com] S on N160 La Roche-sur-Yon twd Les Sables-d'Olonne; at Pierre Levee turn R onto D80 sp Olonne-sur-Mer. Also sp fr D80 N. V lge, hdg/mkd pitch, pt shd; wc; chem disp; shwrs inc; el pts (5A) inc (extra for 10-16A); lndtte; ice; shop; rest; snacks; bar; playgrnd; htd pool; waterslide; sand beach 5km; fishing & watersports 4km; tennis; golf; games area; entmnt; 40% statics; dogs €3.50; poss cr; adv bkg; quiet; red low ssn. "Pleasant situation; high kerbs into sm pitches; friendly, helpful staff; excel facs for families." ♦ 26 Mar-1 Oct. € 29.15   2005*

See advertisement opposite

SABLES D'OLONNE, LES *7A1* (4km N) **Camping de Sauveterre, 3 Rue des Amis de la Nature, 85340 Olonne-sur-Mer** [02 51 33 10 58; fax 02 51 21 33 97] Fr Les Sables-d'Olonne take D32 N to Olonne-sur-Mer; then D80 twds St Gilles-Croix-de-Vie for 3.5km; after 2nd rndabt site is on L. Med, mkd pitch, pt shd; wc (some cont); chem disp; shwrs inc; el pts (6A) €2.10; gas; ice; lndtte; shop; rest; snacks; bar; playgrnd; pool; sand beach 3km; many statics; dogs €1.20; poss cr; little Eng spkn; adv bkg rec high ssn; quiet; CCI. "Poss no water points; water avail fr sinks; site poss untidy; gd walking/ cycling; conv sandy beaches." 1 Apr-30 Sep.
€ 14.50   2004*

SABLES D'OLONNE, LES *7A1* (4km N Rural) **Camping Nid d'Ete, Rue de la Vigne Verte, 85340 Olonne-sur-Mer** [tel/fax 02 51 95 34 38; info@ leniddete.com] Fr Les Sables-d'Olonne take D32 N to Olonne-sur-Mer. L onto D80 twd St Gilles-Croix-de-Vie. Immed over rlwy bdge turn L, site on L immed past Camping Les Ormeaux. Med, hdg/mkd pitch, pt shd; wc; chem disp; baby facs; shwrs inc; el pts (6A) inc; lndtte; ice; shop & 2km; snacks; playgrnd; htd pool high ssn; beach 3km; entmnt; few statics; dogs €1.90; c'van winter storage; adv bkg; v quiet; CCI. "Pleasant site; surfing at La Plage Sauveterre 4km; vg sh stay."
1 Apr-30 Sep. € 17.80   2003*

SABLES D'OLONNE, LES *7A1* (5km N Coastal) **Camping La Loubine, 1 Route de la Mer, 85340 Olonne-sur-Mer** [02 51 33 12 92; fax 02 51 33 12 71; camping.la.loubine@wanadoo.fr] Fr Les Sables-d'Olonne take D32 N to Olonne-sur-Mer then D80 twd St Gilles-Croix-de-Vie for 3.5km; turn L at junc to Plage-de-Sauveterre; ent to site immed on L after turn. Lge, hdg/mkd pitch, pt sl, pt shd; wc; chem disp; mostly serviced pitches; shwrs inc; el pts (5A) €2.50; ice; gas; lndtte; shop; rest; snacks; bar; playgrnd; mini-golf; tennis; htd pool indoor & outdoor; sand beach 3km; entmnt; TV; poss cr; adv bkg; 70% statics; noise fr rd & nightclub; Eng spkn; cc acc; CCI. "Site lit & guarded at night; lge car park for late arrivals; ants poss a problem; ♦ 1 Apr-30 Sep. € 16.00   2002*

We're having a great holiday - must fill in some site report forms and send them to The Club as soon as possible.

SABLES D'OLONNE, LES *7A1* (8km N) **Camping L'Oree, Route des Amis de la Nature, 85340 Olonne-sur-Mer** [02 51 33 10 59; fax 02 51 33 15 16; loree@free.fr] Fr Olonne take D80 twd St Gilles-Croix-de-Vie for 4km - site on L after traff lts in Olonne-sur-Mer, well sp. Lge, hdg/mkd pitch, pt shd; wc; baby facs; shwrs inc; el pts (6A) inc; gas; lndtte; ice; shop; snacks; bar; playgrnd; htd pool; waterslide; sand beach 1.5km; tennis; horseriding; cycle hire; games area; games rm; entmnt; 10% statics; dogs €2.10; Eng spkn; adv bkg; quiet; CCI. "Pleasant walk (20 mins) thro forest to vg beach; c'vans & tents for hire; helpful owner; vg long/sh stay." ♦ 1 Apr-30 Sep. € 23.50   2003*

SABLES D'OLONNE, LES *7A1* (2km E Rural) **Camping Le Puits Rochais, 25 Rue de Bourdigal, 85180 Chateau-d'Olonne** [02 51 21 09 69; fax 02 51 23 62 20; BHJMP@wanadoo.fr; www. puitsrochais.com] Fr Les Sables-d'Olonne take D949 twd La Rochelle. Pass rndabt with sign to hypermrkt 'Magasin Geant' & turn R at 1st traff lts at Mercedes g'ge, then 1st L to site. Med, mkd pitch, pt shd; wc; chem disp; baby facs; shwrs inc; el pts (6-10A) inc; lndtte; shop; rest; snacks; bar; playgrnd; htd pool; waterslide; sand beach 2km; tennis; cycle hire; games area; games rm; entmnt; child entmnt; internet; TV; 60% statics; dogs €3; adv bkg; quiet; cc acc; red CCI. "Friendly, welcoming site; gd for families." ♦ 1 Apr-15 Oct. € 28.50   2005*

See advertisement on next page

Tennis, mini golf, ping pong, children's play area, bicycles, animation, performances, bar, snacks, games room and kids club (July and August)

Water Park
- **Heated swimming pool**
- **Waterslide**

Camping Caravanning Le Puits Rochais
25, rue de Bourdigal F- 85180 Le Château d'Olonne
Phone 00 33 (0)2 51 21 09 69 Fax 00 33 (0)2 51 23 63 20
bhjmp@wanadoo.fr • www.puitsrochais.com

Special rates for owners of the "International Camping Card"
Pack for 2 persons + 1 vehicle + electricity: € 14.50 p/n
During low season: from the 1st of April till the 1st of July
and from the 20th of August till the 30th of September

SABLES D'OLONNE, LES *7A1* (SE Urban/Coastal) CHADOTEL Camping Les Roses, Rue des Roses, 85100 Les Sables-d'Olonne [02 51 95 10 42 or 02 51 33 05 05 (LS); fax 02 51 33 94 04; chadotel@ wanadoo.fr; www.camping-chadotel.fr] Fr town cent foll dir Niort, turn down Blvd Ampere by Total petrol stn to Rue des Roses. Site opp take-away cafe & adj to hospital, lying bet D949 & sea front. Lge, hdg/mkd pitch, pt shd; htd wc; chem disp; shwrs inc; el pts (6A) inc; gas 1.5km; ice; lndtte; tradsmn; rest 500m; snacks; bar; BBQ (gas); playgrnd; htd pool; waterslide; sand beach 500m; entmnt; cycle hire; games rm; TV rm; 70% statics; dogs €2.90; phone; poss cr; Eng spkn; adv bkg; quiet; cc acc; CCI. "Conv for town & beach; close by harbour, shops, museums, salt marshes, shuttle buses." ♦ 1 Apr-5 Nov. € 26.50   2005*

SABLES D'OLONNE, LES *7A1* (3km SE) Camping Les Fosses Rouges, La Pironniere, 85180 Chateau-d'Olonne [02 51 95 17 95] Take D949 La Rochelle. At lge rndabt turn R, sp La Pironniere. Camp clearly sp on L in 1km. Lge, mkd pitch, shd; wc; shwrs inc; el pts (10A) inc; gas; lndtte; shop & 500m; snacks; bar; playgrnd; htd pool; sand beach 1.5km; entmnt; TV; 70% statics; poss cr; adv bkg; quiet; red low ssn. "Attractive site on o'skts town; interesting fishing port." ♦ 1 Apr-30 Sep. € 16.00
2003*

SABLES D'OLONNE, LES *7A1* (4km SW Coastal) CHADOTEL Camping La Dune des Sables, La Paracou, 85100 Les Sables-d'Olonne [02 51 32 31 21 or 02 51 33 05 05 (LS); fax 02 51 33 94 04; chadotel@wanadoo.fr; www. camping-chadotel.fr] Foll N160 to Les Sables-d'Olonne. Fr town foll sps to La Chaume & Les Dunes. Lge, mkd pitch, pt sl, unshd; htd wc; serviced pitches; shwrs inc; el pts (6A) inc; gas; lndtte; ice; shop; snacks; bar; BBQ (gas); playgrnd; pool; waterslide; sand beach 100m; tennis; cycle hire; games rm; entmnt; 75% statics; dogs €2.90; Eng spkn; adv bkg rec high ssn; red low ssn; CCI. "Helpful warden; great for family beach holiday; bowls tournaments & children's competitions weekly." ♦ 1 Apr-23 Sep. € 27.50   2005*

SABLES D'OR LES PINS *2E3* (1.2km NW Coastal/Rural) Camp Municipal La Saline, Rue du Lac, 22240 Plurien [02 96 72 17 40] Fr D786 turn N at Plurien onto D34 to Sables-d'Or. In 1km turn L & site on L after 200m. Med, pt sl, terr, pt shd; wc (some cont); chem disp; shwrs inc; el pts (6A) inc; lndtte; ice; shops 500m; playgrnd; sand beach 400m; dogs €0.50; phone; poss cr; Eng spkn; adv bkg; quiet; CCI. "Vg san facs; lovely hillside site, some pitches with views of tidal bay; office open 0800-1200 & 1400-1800, no pitching outside these hrs; gates clsd 2200-0700; family site; gd all stays." ♦ 1 Jun-15 Sep. € 11.60   2005*

SACQUENAY *6G1* (Rural) Aire Naturelle La Chenaie (Meot), 21260 Sacquenay S on N74 turn L onto D171A sp Occey, site sp. Sm, pt sl, pt shd; wc; shwrs inc; el pts (6A); ice; shop 400m; lndtte; playgrnd; poss v cr; adv bkg; quiet; red 10+ days; CCI. "Gd sh stay."   2003*

SADIRAC see Bordeaux *7C2*

SAHUNE see Remuzat *9D2*

SAIGNES see Bort les Orgues *7C4*

SAILLAGOUSE see Bourg Madame *8H4*

SAILLANS *9D2* (Rural) Camping Les Chapelains, 26340 Saillans [04 75 21 55 47] Fr Crest to Die on D93 turn onto D493. Site just bef Saillans vill boundary, well sp. Sm, hdg/mkd pitch, pt shd; wc; shwrs inc; el pts (4-10A) €2.30-4; gas; lndtte; ice; sm shop; tradsmn; snacks; bar; playgrnd; shgl beach; rv sw; dogs €1; Eng spkn; adv bkg; quiet; cc not acc; CCI. "Well-run, attractive site in area of stupendous beauty; some v sm pitches; san facs need updating; helpful warden; Rv Drome adj; vg sh/long stay." 15 Apr-15 Sep. € 7.50   2004*

SAILLANS *9D2* (3km E Rural) Camping Le Pont d'Espenel, 26340 Espenel [04 75 21 72 95 or 04 75 21 72 70] Fr Crest dir Die on D93, dir access to site on R. Med, mkd pitch, pt sl, pt shd; wc; chem disp; shwrs inc; el pts (6A) €2.45; lndtte; rest; bar; playgrnd; rv sw adj; canoeing; dogs; phone; Eng spkn; cc acc; CCI. "Excel long/sh stay." 1 May-30 Sep. € 8.25   2002*

SAILLANS *9D2* (5km E) **Camping Le Gap, 26340 Vercheny [04 75 21 72 62; fax 04 75 21 76 40; campingdugap@wanadoo.fr]** Bef Crest & Die on D93, 1km E of Vercheny. Access direct fr D93 on R. Med, mkd pitch, pt shd; wc (mainly cont); chem disp; shwrs; el pts (6A) €3.20s; ice; lndtte; snacks; bar; shop 1km; tradsmn; entmnt; playgrnd; pool; rv fishing/sw; TV; dogs €1.22; quiet; Eng spkn; adv bkg; CCI. "V friendly family-run site in lovely surroundings." May-15 Sep. € 12.10   2004*

SAILLANS *9D2* (8km E Rural) **Camp Municipal La Cocombe, 26340 Aurel [04 75 21 76 29 or 04 75 21 71 88; fax 04 75 21 76 40]** E of Saillans on N93 in vill of Vercheny turn S on D357. Bef vill of Auriel R by war memorial. Sm, shd; wc (cont); shwrs inc; el pts; shops 4km; rest; bar; pool; v quiet. "Mountain site, beautiful views; peaceful."   2003*

SAILLY LE SEC see Albert *3B3*

SAINTES *7B2* (1km N Urban) **Camping au Fil de l'Eau, 6 Rue de Courbiac, 17100 Saintes [05 46 93 08 00; fax 05 46 93 61 88; info@ campingsaintes.com; www.campingsaintes.com]** Well sp as 'Camping Municipal' fr rndbts on by-pass N & S on N150 & N137 (thro indus area). Lge, hdg/mkd pitch, pt shd; wc; chem disp; shwrs inc; el pts (5A) 3.20 (rev pol); lndtte; ice; shop; snacks; rest high ssn; bar; playgrnd; htd pool adj; rv sw, fishing & boating; mini-golf; some statics; dogs €0.85; cc acc; red low ssn; CCI. "Excel site; interesting Roman ruins in Saintes; guided tours around Cognac distilleries; v clean facs." ♦ 1 May-30 Sep. € 12.70   2005*

ST AFFRIQUE *8E4* (1km E Urban) **Camp Municipal, Parc des Sports, La Capelle Basse, 12400 St Affrique [05 65 98 20 00; fax 05 65 49 02 29]** Site on D99 Albi-Millau rd to St Affrique sp fr all dir in E end of town. Nr stn & sports complex. Med, pt shd; wc (cont); shwrs; el pts; ice; shop 1km; rest, snacks, bar 1km; pool; rv fishing & sw; tennis; adv bkg; quiet. 15 Jun-15 Sep.   2004*

ST AGREVE *9C2* (1km N) **Camping Chateau Lacour, 07320 St Agreve [04 75 30 27 09 or 04 75 30 12 19 (LS)]** Clearly sp in town. Med, mkd pitch, pt sl, pt shd; wc (cont); shwrs; el pts €2.74; lndtte; ice; shops 1km; horseriding; tennis 1km; playgrnd; quiet. "Spacious site; lge pitches; basic facs." 23 Jun-15 Sep. € 11.00   2002*

ST AGREVE *9C2* (12km S Urban) **Camp Municipal La Cheze, 07160 Le Cheylard [04 75 29 18 71; fax 04 75 29 46 75; zip-zap@wanadoo.fr]** Fr Le Cheylard take D264 SE & foll camping sp. App up steep hill & sharp bend into final app. Less steep app fr Valence on N86 & D20. Site 25km fr St Agreve by rd. Med, mkd pitch, terr, pt shd; wc (some cont); chem disp (wc); shwrs inc; el pts (5A) €3; lndtte; shops 1.2km; tradsmn; playgrnd; rv sw 2km; dogs; phone; security barrier; poss cr; Eng spkn; adv bkg; v quiet; 10% red CCI. "In grounds of chateau; lovely views over attractive town & mountains; gd walks nrby; vg long stay." ♦ 1 May-15 Sep. € 10.00   2003*

ST AIGNAN SUR CHER *4G2* (2km SE) **Camping Les Cochards (formerly Municipal), 1 Rue du Camping, Seigy, 41110 St Aignan-sur-Cher [02 54 75 15 59 or 06 83 79 45 44; fax 02 54 75 44 72; camping@lesclochards.com; www.lescochards.com]** On D17 heading SE fr St Aignan twd Seigy on S bank of Cher. Lge, mkd pitch, pt shd; htd wc; chem disp; mv service pnt; baby facs; shwrs inc; el pts (5A) €3.20; lndtte; ice; shop 3km; rest; snacks; bar; BBQ; playgrnd; pool; rv sw adj; rv fishing; canoeing; horseriding 3km; archery; entmnt; TV rm; 20% statics; dogs €1.10; phone; quiet; cc acc; CCI. "Nr several chateaux; fishing & boating; footpath to town; young, enthusiastic owners v helpful." ♦ ltd. Easter-15 Oct. € 15.50 (CChq acc)   2005*

ST AIGNAN SUR CHER *4G2* (4km NW Rural) **Camping du Port, 41110 Mareuil-sur-Cher [02 54 32 77 64]** Fr St Aignan take D17 twd Tours (on S bank of Cher); site in 4km in vill of Mareuil-sur-Cher behind church, thro new archway. Sm, mkd pitch, pt shd; wc; chem disp; shwrs inc; el pts (10A) €3; ice/gas 50m; shop 100m; supmkt adj; rest 4km; playgrnd; rv sw; fishing; dogs €1; quiet; CCI. "Beautiful, well-kept, rvside site; simple & quiet; gd touring area; wine-tasting nr; twin-axle vans not acc; spotless san facs but poss ltd low ssn; friendly staff; opening/closing dates variable, phone ahead to check; supplement for m'vans; if office clsd enquire at supmkt adj (same owners)." ♦ Easter-30 Sep. € 11.00   2005*

ST ALBAN AURIOLLES see Ruoms *9D2*

ST ALBAN DE MONTBEL see Chambery *9B3*

ST ALBAN SUR LIMAGNOLE see St Chely d'Apcher *9D1*

ST AMAND EN PUISAYE *4G4* (Urban) **Camp Municipal, 58310 St Amand-en-Puisaye [03 86 39 72 21 or 03 86 39 63 72 (Mairie); saintam.mairie@wanadoo.fr]** Fr N7 take D957 Neuvy-sur-Loire to St Amand, at rd junc in vill take D955 sp St Sauveur-en-Puisaye, site on R in 50m; clearly sp on all app to vill. Sm, mkd pitch, pt shd; wc (some cont); shwrs inc; el pts; quiet; sailing & fishing in adj reservoir; gates closd 2200-0700. 1 Jun-30 Sep. € 14.60   2004*

ST AMAND LES EAUX *3B4* (5km E Rural) **Camping Les Pommiers, Rue de la Haute Ville, 59970 Odomez [03 27 34 10 45]** Fr St Amand E on D954 sp Conde, after ent Bruille-St Amand rd goes sharp L, turn R at this bend. Site on L 1km. Sp fr bend at Bruille. Sm, shd; wc; chem disp; shwrs €1.25; el pts (3A) inc; shops 1.5km; playgrnd; pool 5km; 15% statics; dogs; adv bkg; quiet; CCI. "Danger of grounding at site ent; friendly owners; cycle/walking rte thro forest; rec NH only." 15 Mar-15 Oct. € 9.60   2003*

FRANCE

St-Amand-Montrond "City of gold, art and craft center", on the Jacques Coeur route

CAMPING MUNICIPAL
"LA ROCHE" ★★★

(A71 at 3 kilometers from the village direction Montluçon)

Calm and relaxed: a green and woody site of 4 hectares surrounded by the Berry canal and the Cher river. Fishing, children's games, swimming pool nearby, jeu de boules, tennis.

Phone / Fax 0033 (0)2.48.96.09.36 • E-mail: ot-sam@wanadoo.fr

---

ST AMAND LES EAUX *3B4* (3.5km SE) Camping du Mont des Bruyeres, 59230 St Amand-les-Eaux [tel/fax 03 27 48 56 87] Exit A23 m'way at junc 5 or 6 onto ring rd D169, site sp. Fr N exit E42 junc 31 onto N52/N507 then D169. Avoid St Amand cent. Med, hdg/mkd pitch, pt sl, terr, shd; htd wc; shwrs inc; el pts (6-10A) €3.60-4.50; lndtte; ice; shop; bar; playgrnd; pool 7km; 60% statics; adv bkg; quiet; CCI. "Attractive site on forest edge; access to some pitches diff due slopes; gd cycling; excel birdlife on site." 15 Mar-15 Nov. € 9.00   2005*

ST AMAND LES EAUX *3B4* (7km NW Rural) Camping La Gentilhommiere, 905 Rue de Beaumetz, 59310 Sameon [tel/fax 03 20 61 54 03] Fr A23 Paris-Lille, exit junc 3, sp St Amand, then L at rndabt foll Sameon. Site on R 300m in Sameon. Med, hdg pitch, shd; htd wc; chem disp; shwrs inc; el pts (3A) inc; gas; lndtte; ice; shop 8km; tradsmn; snacks; bar; BBQ; playgrnd; fishing; tennis; 90% statics; dogs €0.80; poss cr; quiet; CCI. "Well-maintained site; 5 touring pitches only; gd for Lille (park & ride fr a'route); gd local rest." ♦ 1 Apr-30 Sep. € 11.00   2005*

ST AMAND MONTROND *4H3* (3km SW) Camp Municipal La Roche, Chemin de la Roche, 18200 St Amand-Montrond [tel/fax 02 48 96 09 36; ot-sam@wanadoo.fr] Site off N144; fr S, turn L at rndabt on top of canal, site in 1km. Fr N thro town & turn R at rndabt on top of canal. Sm, white sp 'La Roche/Camping'. Med, shd, pt sl; wc (some cont); shwrs inc; chem disp; el pts (5A) €2.20; ice; lndry rm; shops 500m; playgrnd; pool nr' rv fishing; tennis; entmnt; dogs; phone; Eng spkn; quiet; CCI. "Spotless facs; helpful warden; top of site rec; vg." ♦ 1 Apr-30 Sep. € 8.30   2005*

See advertisement above

ST AMAND MONTROND *4H3* (8km NW) Camping Les Platanes, 18200 Bruere-Allichamps [02 48 61 06 69 or 02 48 61 02 68 (Mairie)] Site on N edge of town on rvside. Sm, pt shd; wc; chem disp; shwrs €1; el pts (10A) €2.50; ice; shops adj; tradsmn; snacks; playgrnd; rv fishing; quiet. "Friendly, relaxing rvside site; lovely surroundings; san block dated but spotless; v cent of France; level walk to interesting vill; excel." Jun-Sep. € 8.70   2005*

ST AMANS DES COTS *7D4* (5km S Rural) **LES CASTELS** Les Tours, 12460 St Amans-des-Cots [05 65 44 88 10 or 05 65 44 88 56 (LS); fax 05 65 44 83 07; camping-les-tours@wanadoo.fr; www.les-castels.com or www.les-tours.com] Foll D34/D97 fr Entraygues to St Amans, sp in vill. Site on Lac de la Selves. Med, hdg pitch, terr, pt shd; wc; chem disp; mv service pnt; serviced pitches; baby facs & fam bthrm; shwrs inc; el pts (6A) inc; lndtte; sm shop & 5km; rest; snacks; bar; BBQ; htd pool complex; paddling pool; lake & rv sw; windsurfing, boating on lake; tennis; horseriding; fishing; golf; gym; entmnt; 30% statics; dogs; adv bkg; quiet; red low ssn; cc acc. "Beautiful site on lake shores; san facs exceptionally clean & modern; v helpful staff; some unshd pitches - book early (Xmas) for shd pitch; 600m altitude so cold mornings & evenings; steep slope to san facs." ♦ 21 May-10 Sep. € 33.00 (CChq acc)   2005*

See advertisement opposite

ST AMANT ROCHE SAVINE see Ambert *9B1*

ST AMBROIX *9D2* (3km S Rural) Camping Beau Rivage, Route de Uzes, 30500 St Ambroix [04 66 24 10 17; fax 04 66 24 21 37; marc@camping-beau-rivage.fr] Site on D904, after Les Mages in 5km Camping sp on R. Foll sp approx 2-3km. Site off D37 twd Le Moulinet. Med, hdg/mkd pitch, pt sl, terr, pt sl, shd; wc (some cont); chem disp; shwrs inc; el pts (2-6A) €2.20-2.80; gas; lndtte; ice; shop 1km; tradsmn; rest, snacks 2km; bar 1km; playgrnd; pool 3km; paddling pool; rv sw; canoeing; dogs €2.50; poss cr; adv bkg; quiet; CCI. ♦ ltd. 1 Apr-15 Sep. € 15.00   2005*

ST AMBROIX *9D2* (200m W) **Camping Le Clos, Place de l'Eglise, 30500 St Ambroix** [04 66 24 10 08; fax 04 66 60 25 62] Fr S on D904, in St Amboix turn L immed bef church. Site in 300m. Foll intn'l camping sp. Sm, pt shd; wc; chem disp; shwrs inc; el pts (10A) €3.05; lndtte; rest; playgrnd; cycle hire; rv sw; fishing; sailing; TV rm; 20% statics; adv bkg. "Well-kept san facs; access poss diff for lge o'fits." ♦ 1 Apr-31 Oct. € 12.20   2004*

ST AMBROIX *9D2* (12km NW Rural) **Camping des Drouilhedes, Peyremale-sur-Ceze, 30160 Besseges** [04 66 25 04 80; fax 04 66 25 10 95; joost.mellies@wanadoo.fr; www.camping-drouilhedes.com] Leave D904 at St Ambroix onto D51 sp Besseges. In Besseges turn L over bdge sp Peyremale & in approx 1km turn R & foll camping sp. Med, hdg/mkd pitch, pt shd; wc (some cont); chem disp; baby facs; shwrs inc; el pts (6A) €3.40; gas; lndtte; ice; shop; tradsmn; rest; snacks; bar; BBQ (gas only); playgrnd; rv sw adj; tennis; games area; TV rm; 10% statics; dogs; phone; poss cr; Eng spkn; quiet; cc acc; CCI. "Well-run, scenic site with excel facs; ideal for children; v helpful Dutch owners." ♦ 1 Apr-30 Sep. € 17.70   2004*

ST AMOUR *9A2* (Urban) **Camp Municipal, Ave des Sports, 39160 St Amour** [03 84 48 71 68 or 03 84 44 02 00; fax 03 84 48 88 15] Sp S & N of vill. Ent by pool & tennis courts. Narr app. Med, pt sl, pt shd, some hdstdg; wc; chem disp; el pts inc; shwrs; shops 400m; playgrnd; pool adj; tennis; rv 5km; quiet. "Office open ltd hrs, site yourself, no barriers; effectively in public park; well-kept san facs; gd cycling; some rlwy noise at night; gd NH no longer." 1 Apr-30 Sep. € 14.60   2005*

STE ANASTASIE SUR ISSOLE see Brignoles *10F3*

ST ANDIOL see Cavaillon *10E2*

ST ANDRE D'ALLAS see Sarlat la Caneda *7C3*

ST ANDRE DE CUBZAC *7C2* (4km NW Rural) **Camping Le Port Neuf, 33240 St Andre-de-Cubzac** [tel/fax 05 57 43 16 44; camping.port.neuf@wanadoo.fr] Fr A10 or N10 take exit sp St Andre N137, site sp. Med, pt shd; wc; chem disp; mv service pnt; shwrs inc; el pts (2-6A) €2; ice; bar; playgrnd; pool; cycle hire; trout-fishing & boating in sm lake + rv 100m; many statics; dogs €1; quiet; Eng spkn. "NH only." 1 May-1 Oct. € 10.67   2002*

ST ANDRE DE LIDON see Cozes *7B1*

ST ANDRE DE SEIGNANX see Bayonne *8F1*

ST ANDRE DES EAUX see Baule, La *2G3*

ST ANDRE LES ALPES *10E3* (500m Urban) **Camp Municipal Les Iscles, Rue de Nice, 04170 St Andre-les-Alpes** [04 92 89 02 29; fax 04 92 89 02 56] Exit St Andre-les-Alpes SE on N202 to Nice turn E at edge of vill on wide service rd. Site almost immed on L fronted by lge car-park. Med, mkd pitch, shd; wc (some cont); chem disp; serviced pitches; shwrs inc; el pts (4A) inc; lndtte; supmkt adj; TV/games rm; Eng spkn; quiet. "Gd welcome; gd site in scenic area in pine woods on rough stony ground; lovely mountains & lakes; trains to Nice; Verdon Gorge & several Provence vills within reach." 1 May-30 Sep. € 11.05   2004*

†ST ANDRE LES ALPES *10E3* (6km NE Rural) **Camping L'Adrech, Route du Pont d'Allons, 04170 La Mure-Argens** [04 92 89 18 12; contact@adrech.com; www.adrech.com] Fr E or W on N202 to St Andre-les-Alpes, turn N onto D955 dir Colmars, Site on R. Do not app fr N fr Barcelonette via Col d'Allos. Sm, mkd pitch, pt sl, pt shd; wc; chem disp (wc); shwrs inc; el pts (3-6A) €3; snacks; bar; BBQ; watersports, lake sw nrby; 25% statics; dogs €1; Eng spkn; adv bkg; cc acc; CCI. "Family-run site; helpful, friendly owners; gd touring base in interesting area." € 13.50   2005*

ST ANGEAU see Mansle *7B2*

ST ANTOINE D'AUBEROCHE see Thenon *7C3*

ST ANTOINE DE BREUILH see Ste Foy la Grande *7C2*

FRANCE

ST ANTONIN NOBLE VAL 8E4 (Rural) Camping Ponget, Route de Caylus, 82140 St Antonin-Noble-Val [05 63 68 21 13 or 05 63 30 60 23 (Mairie); fax 05 63 30 60 54; camping-leponget@wanadoo.fr] Fr Caylus take D19 S to St Antonin; site on R just bef vill bef x-ing rv bdge; well sp. Sm, hdg pitch, pt shd; wc (some cont, own san rec); shwrs inc; el pts (3-6A) €2.50-3.60; gas; lndtte; shops, rest, snacks, bar 1km; playgrnd; sw 1km; phone; quiet; cc not acc; CCI. "Well-maintained site adj sports field; sh walk into medieval town; canoeing on Rv Aveyron; gd walking; new san facs 2004; poss diff lge o'fits." ♦ 1 May-30 Sep. € 12.10 2004*

ST ANTONIN NOBLE VAL 8E4 (6km N Rural) Camping Les Trois Cantons, Vivens, 82140 St Antonin-Noble-Val [05 63 31 98 57; fax 05 63 31 25 93; info@3cantons.fr; www.3cantons.fr] Fr Caussade take D926 dir Villefranche (do not take D5 or D19 sp St Antonin.) Site is on C5, sp. Fr St Antonin foll dir Caylus on D19. Just outside vill, after sm bdge where rd turns to R, turn L up hill. Foll this rd for 6km - narr rd. NB Hill steep & continuous. Med, mkd pitch, hdstg, pt sl, pt shd; htd wc (some cont); chem disp; mv service pnt; shwrs inc; el pts (2-10A) €2-6.50; gas; lndtte; ice; shop; supmkt 8km; BBQ; playgrnd; htd, covrd pool; rv sw 8km; tennis; cycle hire; horseriding nr; canoeing; entmnt; child entmnt; TV rm; dogs €1.25; poss cr; Eng spkn; adv bkg; quiet; cc acc; red low ssn; CCI. "V helpful owners; gd, peaceful, clean, well-managed, family holiday site in oak forest in unspoilt region." ♦ 15 Apr-30 Sep. € 18.75 (CChq acc) 2005*

ST ANTONIN NOBLE VAL 8E4 (1km E Rural) Camping d'Anglars, Marsac Bas, 82140 St Antonin-Noble-Val [05 63 30 69 76; fax 05 63 30 67 61] Fr Cassade on D926 dir Caylus for approx 5km, after Septfords take D5 then D958 twd St Antonin Noble-Val. Cont over rv & L thro tunnel then onto D115. Site in 1km on L twd Marsac. Med, hdg pitch, pt shd; wc; chem disp; mv service pnt; shwrs inc; el pts (3-6A) €2-3.60; lndtte; ice; shops; tradsmn; snacks; bar; playgrnd; sw & fishing rv adj; 5% statics; dogs €1.30; adv bkg; quiet; CCI. "Lge pitches with trees; shady; neat & tidy; friendly; best in area." ♦ 15 Apr-30 Sep. € 12.70 2005*

ST ANTONIN NOBLE VAL 8E4 (12km E Rural) Camping Pech Contal, Arnac, 82330 Varen [tel/fax 05 63 65 48 34] 8km fr St Antonin-Noble-Val on D115 Montauban-Cordes rd, turn L sp Arnac. Turn L in sq at Arnac, site 1.5km on R. App rd steep-poss diff lge o'fits. Sm, hdstg, pt sl, pt shd; wc; chem disp (wc only); 50% serviced pitches; shwrs inc; el pts (10A) inc; gas; lndtte; ice; shop & 8km; tradsmn; rest; snacks; bar; playgrnd; pool; entmnt; rv sw & fishing 1km; dogs €0.80; adv bkg; quiet; 5% red 7+ days; cc not acc; 5% red CCI. "V quiet & peaceful in beautiful area; gd cycling; Albi, Najac, Cordes & Gorges d' Aveyron nrby; golden orioles on site; mosquitoes poss a problem." ♦ 1 Apr-30 Sep. € 11.00 2003*

ST ARNOULT see Deauville 3D1

ST ASTIER 7C3 (Urban) Camp Municipal Le Pontet, 24110 St Astier [05 53 54 14 22 or 05 53 54 10 65; fax 05 53 04 39 36; info@ville-saint-astier.fr] Take N89 SW fr Perigueux; in 14km turn R at traff lts on D41 sp St Astier; site on R at town sp on banks of Rv Isle. Med, shd; wc; chem disp; shwrs inc; el pts (6A) €2.55; gas; lndtte; shops 400m; snacks; BBQ; playgrnd; pool; sand beach adj; entmnt; dogs €0.85; poss cr; adv bkg; v quiet; cc not acc; CCI. "Some areas soft in wet weather." 1 Apr-30 Sep. € 11.00 2003*

ST AUBAN 10E4 (300m S Rural) Camping La Pinatelle, 06850 St Auban [04 93 60 40 46; fax 04 93 60 42 45] Fr N85 take D2211, site well sp on R just bef vill. Sm, mkd pitch, pt shd; wc; chem disp (wc); shwrs; el pts €3.50; lndtte; supmkt 1km; tradsmn; rest; snacks; bar; playgrnd; sm pool; games area; dogs; phone; Eng spkn; adv bkg; quiet; CCI. "Friendly, helpful, family-run site; in beautiful countryside; easy access to gorges, coast & fishing." 1 Apr-30 Sep. € 11.40 2005*

ST AUBIN DE LUIGNE see Chalonnes sur Loire 2G4

514

SITES

ST AUBIN DU CORMIER 2E4 (Urban) Camp Municipal, Rue de l'Etang, 35140 St Aubin-du-Cormier [02 99 39 10 42 (Mairie); fax 02 99 39 23 25] Fr Vitre on D794 turn R on ent vill at car pk; sp in town. Poss diff for lge o'fits - narr app. Sm, pt sl, pt shd; wc; shwrs €1.05; el pts (6-10A) €1.90-2.70; ice; shops adj; forest walks; lake fishing; many statics; dogs; poss cr; adv bkg; quiet. 1 Apr-30 Sep. € 5.50   2003*

ST AUGUSTIN (CHARENTE MARITIME) see St Palais sur Mer 7B1

ST AVERTIN see Tours 4G2

ST AVIT DE VIALARD see Bugue, Le 7C3

†ST AVOLD 5D2 (1km N Urban) Camping Le Felsberg, Centre de Rencontre International, 57500 St Avold [03 87 92 75 05; fax 03 87 92 20 69; cis.stavold@free.fr] Fr A4 exit 39 & go S to St Avold, stay in L hand lane at 2nd traff lts & turn L; pass under N4 for 2km & turn R. Site well sp in & around town; app up steep incline. Sm, hdg/mkd pitch, hdstg, pt sl, pt shd; wc; chem disp; shwrs inc; el pts (6-10A) €3-5; lndtte; tradsmn; hypmkt 1.5km; rest, bar high ssn; playgrnd; 50% statics; dogs €1; poss cr; adv bkg; poss noisy youth groups; cc acc; red long stay; CCI. "German border 10km; coalmine & archaeological park nrby worth visit; heavy duty security gate at site ent - awkward; close to m'way; sm pitches; gd sh stay/NH." ♦ ltd.
€ 12.40   2004*

ST AYGULF 10F4 (Coastal) Camping de St Aygulf Plage, 270 Ave Salvarelli, 83370 St Aygulf [04 94 17 62 49; fax 04 09 81 03 16; camping.cote.d.azur.plage@wanadoo.fr; www.camping-cote-azur.com] Fr Roquebrune D7 at vill sp St Aygulf turn L on Rue du Gard. Keep turning L. Fr Frejus on N98, rd bends R after bdge over beach access, turn R bef rd climbs to L. V lge, mkd pitch, shd; wc; chem disp; shwrs inc; el pts (5A) inc; gas; lndtte; ice; shop; rest; snacks; bar; playgrnd; sand beach adj; watersports & sports facs nr; fishing; games area; entmnt; statics; adv bkg (dep & booking fee); cc acc; red 28+ days; CCI.
1 Apr-30 Oct. € 29.50   2004*

ST AYGULF 10F4 (4km S Coastal) Camping Le Pont d'Argens, 83370 St Aygulf [04 94 51 14 97; fax 04 94 51 29 44] Well sp fr N98 bet Frejus & St Aygulf. Situated by Rv Argens. If app fr W pass site on R & return via next rndbt. Lge, mkd pitch, pt shd; htd wc; chem disp; mv service pnt; baby facs; shwrs; el pts (5A) €3; gas; lndtte; ice; shop; tradsmn; rest; snacks; bar; playgrnd; pool; sand beach adj; cycle hire; TV rm; 5% statics; dogs €2.50; €30 barrier card; poss cr; Eng spkn; adv bkg; quiet; some rd noise; cc acc; CCI. "Excel, well-run site by rv & 10 mins walk to uncrowded beach (pt naturist); A1 facs; poss mosquitoes; excel pool." 1 Apr-15 Oct. € 23.00   2005*

ST AYGULF 10F4 (2km W) Camping Les Lauriers Roses, Route de Roquebrune, 83370 St Aygulf [04 94 81 24 46 or 04 94 81 03 58 (LS); fax 04 94 81 79 63; lauriersroses@cs.com; www.info-lauriersroses.com] Exit a'route A8 at Puget-sur-Argens onto N7 to Frejus. At 1st rndabt after Frejus town sp, turn R to Aygulf at junc immed after rndabt. Pass under rlwy bdge & turn R onto D8. After bdge with traff lts foll rd up to junc & turn L onto the D7, site in 1.5km on R. Med, mkd pitch, pt sl, terr, pt shd; wc; chem disp; baby facs; shwrs inc; el pts (5A) inc; gas; lndtte; ice; shop 500m; snacks; bar; BBQ (gas only); playgrnd; pool & paddling pool; sand beach 2km; games rm; entmnt; internet; 10% statics; dogs €1.80; Eng spkn; adv bkg; quiet; cc not acc; CCI. "Excel, family-run site site on hillside amongst trees; diff acc some pitches for lge o'fits (max 8m) - owner assists with siting c'vans; mkt Tue & Fri; no arrivals bet 1230-1500." ♦ ltd.
16 Apr-1 Oct. € 24.30   2004*

ST AYGULF 10F4 (2.5km W Coastal) Au Paradis des Campeurs, La Gaillarde-Plage, 83380 Les Issambres [04 94 96 93 55; fax 04 94 49 62 99; www.paradis-des-campeurs.com] Exit A8 (E80) at Puget onto N7 to by-pass Frejus, then onto N98 twd Ste Maxime. Site on R 2km after passing thro St Aygulf, on LH bend bef hill. Med, hdg/mkd pitch, hdstg, pt sl, terr, pt shd; htd wc; chem disp; mv service pnt; baby facs; shwrs inc; 30% serviced pitches (extra charge); el pts (6A) €3.50 (poss rev pol); gas 2km; lndtte; lndry rm; ice; shop; tradsmn; rest; snacks; bar; playgrnd; sand beach adj; cycle hire; golf 4km; games rm; TV rm; dogs €2.30; Eng spkn; quiet; red low ssn; cc acc; CCI. "V popular low ssn; direct access via underpass to beach; excel san facs; old rd to St Aygulf suitable for cycling; gd walks in wooded area behind site; superb views fr top level pitches - worth extra; gates shut at night & guarded; helpful owners; excel." ♦
28 Mar-16 Oct. € 22.00 (3 persons)   2005*

See advertisement opposite

ST AYGULF 10F4 (5km NW Rural) Camping L'Etoile d'Argens, Chemin des Etangs, 83370 St Aygulf [04 94 81 01 41; fax 04 94 81 21 45; info@etoiledargens.com; www.etoiledargens.com] Exit A8 at junc 37 Puget-sur-Argens onto N7 to Frejus & N98 to St Aygulf, or fr N7 take D7 to St Aygulf by-passing Frejus & turn onto D8 to site. Lge, hdg/mkd pitch, shd; 25% serviced pitches; wc; chem disp; baby facs; shwrs inc; el pts (10A) inc; gas; lndtte; ice; shop; tradsmn; rest; snacks; bar; no BBQ; playgrnd; htd pool; sand beach 3km; rv fishing; tennis; mini-golf; archery; golf 1.5km; entmnt; 40% statics; dogs €4; poss cr; Eng spkn; adv bkg; quiet; cc acc; red low ssn; CCI. "Standard, Comfort or Luxury pitches avail; busy low ssn; ferry down Rv Argens to beach in ssn; friendly owners; well-organised, excel site." ♦
1 Apr-30 Sep. € 49.00 (3 persons)   2005*

See advertisement on next page

Send your site reports by September   515   *Last year of report

FRANCE

2006

L'Etoile d'Argens

✳ ✳ ✳ ✳ *Camping-Caravaning*

ESE COMMUNICATION - DRAGUIGNAN - 04 94 67 06 00

www.etoiledargens.com

E-mail : info@etoiledargens.com

83370 St Aygulf - Tél. +33 4 94 81 01 41

FRANCE

†ST BEAT *8G3* (S) **Camp Municipal Clef de France**, 31440 St Beat [05 61 79 44 17] On N125 at S exit to town, sp on L. Med, pt shd; htd wc; shwrs inc; el pts (5A) inc; ice; shops 200m; pool 200m; fishing; boating; 95% statics; quiet. "Facs ltd low ssn; long walk to san facs; site bet two rvs & close to Spanish border; NH/sh stay only." € 8.20
2003*

ST BENOIT DES ONDES see Cancale *2E4*

ST BENOIT SUR LOIRE *4F3* (1.5km SE Rural) **Camping Le Port**, Rue du Port, 45730 St Benoit-sur-Loire [02 38 35 79 00; fax 02 38 35 77 19] Fr Sully-sur-Loire take D60 to St Benoit-sur-Loire. Foll sp fr vill, in 1.5km on L side of 1-way street. Sm, pt sl, shd; wc; shwrs inc; el pts (13A); gas 4km; shop, rest 1.5km; BBQ; playgrnd; sand beach adj; rv sw, fishing, canoeing adj; dogs; phone; poss cr; Eng spkn; quiet; CCI." ♦ 11 Apr-30 Sep. € 10.50
2004*

ST BERTRAND DE COMMINGES see Montrejeau *8F3*

ST BOIL *6H1* (Rural) **Camping Moulin de Collonge**, Route des Vins, 71940 St Boil [03 85 44 00 40 or 03 85 44 00 32; fax 03 85 44 00 40; millofcollonge@wanadoo.fr] S on A6 take N80 at Chalon-Sud; W dir Le Creusot; 9km turn S on D981 thro Buxy to St Boil; sp on L thro vill. Sm, hdg/mkd pitch, pt shd; wc (few cont); baby facs; shwrs inc; el pts (6A) €3.50; gas; lndtte; ice; shop & 2km; tradsmn; rest; snacks; bar; BBQ; playgrnd; htd, covrd pool; lake fishing; cycle hire; entmnt; dogs; v cr high ssn; some Eng spkn; adv bkg; quiet; CCI. " V busy but v quiet site away fr it all; v clean; modern facs; friendly owner; gd snacks; gd cycle ways nrby; two sm ponds with free fishing; excel vineyards on Bourgogne rte; chalet bungalows for rental; adv bkg essential for pizzeria." ♦ 1 Mar-30 Sep. € 19.00 (CChq acc)
2005*

ST BOMER LES FORGES see Domfront *4E1*

ST BONNET EN CHAMPSAUR *9D3* (800m SE Rural) **Camp V V F Le Roure**, 05500 St Bonnet-en-Champsaur [04 92 50 01 86; fax 04 92 50 11 85] On N85 rte Napoleon (90km S of Grenoble) exit for St Bonnet & site, foll VVF sp. Note St Bonnet 8km N of Col Bayard with 16% gradient. Sm, pt sl, shd; wc; shwrs inc; el pts (6A) €3.50; ice; lndtte; shops 600m; snacks; bar; BBQ; playgrnd; htd pool; rv 1km; lake 4km; fishing 2km; games area; entmnt; dogs €8; poss cr; adv bkg; quiet; red low ssn. 1 May-30 Sep. € 12.50
2004*

ST BONNET PRES ORCIVAL see Orcival *7B4*

*Last year of report

Southern Brittany

Les pierres couchées
Camping et locations ★★★★
300 meters from the sea!
Special offers on www.pierres-couchees.com
www.korbmarketing.com.tr
Have fun!

L'ERMITAGE 44250 SAINT-BRÉVIN-LES-PINS · tél : 00 33 (0)2 40 27 85 64 · fax : 00 33 (0)2 40 64 97 03

ST BONNET TRONCAIS see Cerilly *4H3*

†**ST BREVIN LES PINS** *2G3* (N Coastal) **Camp Municipal Le Mindin, 32-40 Ave du Bois, 44250 St Brevin-les-Pins** [02 40 27 46 41; fax 02 40 39 20 53; info@camping-de-mindin.com; www.camping-de-mindin.com] On beach rd at N end of St Brevin. Med, shd; htd wc; chem disp; baby facs; shwrs inc; el pts (6A) €4.20; lndtte; shop; rest; snacks; bar; playgrnd; paddling pool; sand beach adj; mainly statics; dogs €2; poss cr; adv bkg; cc acc; red low ssn; CCI. "Sm, sandy pitches; gd san facs." € 12.80   2005*

This site entry hasn't been updated for a while; we'd better fill in a site report form and send it to The Club.

†**ST BREVIN LES PINS** *2G3* (1km S Coastal) **Camp Municipal La Courance, 100-110 Ave Foch, 44250 St Brevin-les-Pins** [02 40 27 22 91; fax 02 40 27 24 59; francecamping@wanadoo.fr] Take Ave Foch fr cent of St Brevin, site on R, clearly sp. Lge, pt sl, shd; htd wc; baby facs; shwrs inc; el pts €3; gas; lndtte; ice; shops 1km; rest; snacks; bar; beach adj; some statics; dogs €1.40; quiet; red low ssn. € 10.80   2005*

ST BREVIN LES PINS *2G3* (2km S Coastal) **Camping Les Rochelets, Chemin des Grandes Rivieres, 44250 St Brevin-les-Pins** [02 40 27 40 25; fax 02 40 27 15 55; rochelets@wanadoo.fr; www.rochelets.com] Fr N or S on D213 exit sp Les Rochelets, site sp. Lge, hdg/mkd pitch, pt shd; wc (some cont); shwrs; el pts; lndtte; ice; tradsmn; rest; bar; playgrnd; pool; beach 100m; games area; games rm; entmnt & child entmnt; 30% statics; dogs; adv bkg; quiet; cc acc; red low ssn. "Gd site for families." 1 Apr-30 Oct. € 17.00   2002*

ST BREVIN LES PINS *2G3* (2.4km S Coastal) **Camping Le Fief, 57 Chemin du Fief, 44250 St Brevin-les-Pins** [02 40 27 23 86; fax 02 40 64 46 19; camping@lefief.com; www.lefief. com] Fr Nantes dir St Nazaire. After St Nazaire bdge S on D213. Pass Le Clerc & exit sp St Brevin-l'Ocean/La Courance. At rndabt foll sp Le Fief. Lge, hdg/mkd pitch, pt shd; wc; chem disp; baby facs; sauna; shwrs inc; el pts (5A) €5; gas; lndtte; ice; shop; tradsmn; rest; snacks; bar; BBQ (gas/charcoal); playgrnd; htd, covrd pool; jacuzzi; sand beach 800m; waterpark & waterslide etc adj; tennis; gym; games area; cycle hire nr; gym; entmnt; 30% statics; dogs €4; Eng spkn; adv bkg; quiet; cc acc; red low ssn. "Excel for families; vg leisure facs." ♦ 1 Apr-6 Nov. € 32.00   2005*

See advertisement on previous page

ST BREVIN LES PINS *2G3* (5km S Coastal) **Camping Village Club Les Pierres Couchees, Ave des Pierres Couchees, L'Ermitage, 44250 St Brevin-les-Pins** [02 40 27 85 64; fax 02 40 64 97 03; contact@ pierres-couchees.com; www.pierres-couchees. com] Sp fr D213 in St Brevin-L'Hermitage. Lge, mkd pitch, terr, pt shd; htd wc (some cont); baby facs; shwrs inc; el pts (10A); lndtte; shop & 3km; tradsmn; rest; snacks; bar; BBQ; playgrnd; htd pool; paddling pool; waterslide; sand beach 300m; tennis; games area; games rm; fitness rm; cycle hire; horseriding 300m; golf 12km; entmnt; child entmnt; TV; 75% statics; dogs €3.05; Eng spkn; adv bkg; quiet; cc acc; red low ssn; CCI. "Vg facs for families; friendly, helpful staff." ♦ 31 Mar-9 Oct. € 24.00   2005*

See advertisement above

Close to St Malo and Dinard

LE PONT LAURIN

Camping Le Pont Laurin
La Vallée Gatorge - 35800 St BRIAC
Phone 00 336 03 60 67 64
www.ouest-camping.com
The camping is situated at a 5 minutes walk
of the town centre of Saint-Briac and at 1 km
of the 8 beaches of fine white sand. It is a
very old fishing-village which has preserved
all its original charm.

It is considered one
of the pearls of the
Emeraude coast with
an ideal mix of sea
and nature tourism.

We are happy to
welcome you in the
pleasant and relaxed
environment along
the Frémur River
where you can make
your choice out of
pitches and rental
mobile home.

ST BRIAC SUR MER *2E3* (Urban/Coastal) Camping Emeraude, 7 Chemin de la Souris, 35800 St Briac-sur-Mer [tel/fax 02 99 88 34 55; camping.emeraude@wanadoo.fr; www.camping-emeraude.com] SW fr Dinard to St Lunaire on N786, after passing Dinard golf course, site is sp to L. Lge, pt shd; wc; chem disp; shwrs inc; el pts (6A) €3.70; gas; lndtte; ice; sm shop & 200m; tradsmn; snacks; bar; playgrnd; htd pool & paddling pool; water park; beach 300m & sand beach 1.5km; mini-golf; games area; entmnt; 40% statics; dogs €2; poss cr; adv bkg. "Excel, well-run & established site; close to sm vill with gd facs; many beaches adj; St Briac noted for its bathing, yachting & sports facs." ♦ Easter-30 Sep. € 24.40   2005*

> Some of these sites have changed their opening dates - we'd better fill in some site report forms and let the editor of the guide know.

ST BRIAC SUR MER *2E3* (400m S Coastal) Camping Le Pont Laurin, La Vallee Gatorge, 35800 St Briac-sur-Mer [02 99 88 34 64 or 06 03 60 67 64 (mob); fax 02 99 16 38 19; lepontlaurin@ouest.camping.com; www.ouest-camping.com] Fr St Briac, 500m S on D3. Lge, hdg/mkd pitch, hdstg, pt shd; wc (some cont); serviced pitches; chem disp; shwrs inc; el pts (6A) €3.60; lndtte; ice; shop & 400m; tradsmn; rest; snacks; playgrnd; sand beach 900m; sailing; canoe hire; sports cent adj; some statics; dogs €1.50; Eng spkn; adv bkg; quiet; CCI. "Welcoming, helpful staff; peaceful site; clean modern san facs; excel beaches; gd walking; sh walk to interesting vill; conv for St Malo, Mont St Michel; highly rec." Easter-30 Sep. € 14.10   2005*

See advertisement above

ST BRIAC SUR MER *2E3* (1km SW Coastal) Camp Municipal des Mielles, Rue Jules Jeunet, 22770 Lancieux [02 96 86 22 98 or 02 96 86 22 19; fax 02 96 86 28 20; marie.lancieux@wanadoo.fr] Fr S on D786 at 500m past windmill turn L into Rue du Fredy. Site on R in 300m, sp. Lge, mkd pitch, unshd; wc (some cont); chem disp; shwrs inc; el pts (6A) €2.60; lndtte; ice; shop 500m; playgrnd; sand beach 150m; watersports 150m; tennis; entmnts; 2% statics; dogs €1.30; poss cr; CCI. ♦. "Well-managed, & guarded in ssn; hot water ltd low ssn; excel facs; popular site." ♦ 1 Apr-30 Sep. € 12.85   2005*

ST BRICE SUR VIENNE see St Junien *7B3*

ST BRIEUC *2E3* (5km E Coastal) Camping Bellevue, Pointe de Guettes, 22120 Hillion [02 96 32 20 39 or 02 96 31 25 05 (HS); fax 02 96 32 20 39] Fr St Brieuc twds Dinan on N12 turn N at exit St Rene onto D712 to Hillion, then rd to Lermot. Site well sp. Med, unshd; wc; chem disp; shwrs; el pts (5-10A) €2-3 (poss rev pol); lndtte; shops 1.5km; playgrnd; quiet; red low ssn. "Gd sea views; coastal paths; well-maintained site; narr site rds poss diff lge o'fits; vg." 1 Apr-30 Sep. € 11.60   2005*

ST BRIEUC *2E3* (3km S Urban) Camping des Vallees, Parc de Brezillet, 22000 St Brieuc [tel/fax 02 96 94 05 05] Fr N12 take exit sp D700 Tregeux, Pleufragan & foll sp 'Des Vallees' for 3km. Med, hdg pitch, some hdstg, pt shd; wc (some cont); chem disp; mv service pnt; baby facs; shwrs inc; el pts (10A) €3.80; lndtte; shop; snacks; bar; playgrnd; htd pool, waterslide adj; sand beach 3km; 25% statics; dogs €2; adv bkg; cc not acc; CCI. "High kerb on ent to pitches." ♦ Easter-15 Oct. € 13.90   2004*

FRANCE

ST CALAIS *4F2* (500m N Urban) **Camp Municipal du Lac, Rue du Lac, 72120 St Calais** [02 43 35 04 81] Leave N157 at R angle bend by Champion supmkt; site in 100m. Site by lake on N edge of town, well sp fr cent. Med, hdg/mkd pitch, pt shd; wc; chem disp; mv service pnt; shwrs inc; el pts (3-6A) €1.60-2.50; lndtte; shops 500m; rest; snacks; bar adj; BBQ; playgrnd; pool adj; lake sw adj; poss cr; adv bkg; quiet; no cc acc; CCI. "Site v clean, pleasant, well-kept; warden friendly & helpful; spacious pitches esp nr lake; gd situation bet Le Mans & Vendome, close to Loire; gd touring base; plenty for children in high ssn." ♦ 1 Apr-15 Oct.
€ 7.00   2005*

ST CANNAT *10F2* (3km NW) **Provence Camping, Les Ponnes, 13410 Lambesc** [04 42 57 05 78; fax 04 42 92 98 02; provence.camping@wanadoo.fr; www.wwwprovencecamping.com] On N7 going S, at end of Lambesc by-pass turn R onto N517; site on L in 150m. Sm, pt sl, shd; wc; mv service pnt; shwrs inc; el pts (5-10A) €2.50-3.50; gas; lndry rm; ice; shop; bar; playgrnd; pool; horseriding; TV; entmnt; some statics; dogs €1.60; red low ssn; CCI. "Kerbs to pitches; o'nighters not particularly welcome." ♦ 1 Apr-30 Sep. € 12.90   2003*

ST CAST LE GUILDO *2E3* (Coastal) **Camping Les Mielles, Route de St Malo, 22380 St Cast-le-Guildo** [02 96 41 87 60; fax 02 96 41 98 08] Fr D786 at Matignon turn onto D13 into St Cast. Cross over staggered x-rds foll site sp down long gentle hill. R at next x-rds & site on R in 200m. Lge, unshd; wc (mainly cont); chem disp; shwrs inc; el pts (6A) €1.95; ice; lndtte; shop; snacks; sand beach 300m; pool; playgrnd; entmnt; poss cr; noisy. "Plenty of facs for teenagers." 1 Apr-20 Sep.
€ 16.00   2002*

ST CAST LE GUILDO *2E3* (500m N Coastal) **Camping Le Chatelet, Rue des Nouettes, 22380 St Cast-le-Guildo** [02 96 41 96 33; fax 02 96 41 97 99; chateletcp@aol.com; www. lechatelet.com] Site sp fr all dir & in St Cast but best rte via D13 fr Matignon into St Cast, turn L after passing Intermarche supmkt on R; foll sm site sp. Or app on D19 fr St Jaguel. Care needed down ramp to main site. (NB Avoid Matignon cent Wed due to mkt.) Med, hdg/mkd pitch, pt sl, terr, pt shd; wc; chem disp; baby facs; shwrs inc; el pts (8A) inc (50m cable req); gas; lndry rm; lndtte; ice; shop; snacks; bar; playgrnd; htd pool & paddling pool; dir access sand beach 150m (via steep steps); tennis; entmnt; cycle hire 500m; golf 2km; TV rm; 80% statics (tour ops); dogs €3.60; adv bkg; red low ssn; cc acc. "Overlkg sea & beautiful coast; extra for sea view pitches; gates clsd 2230-0730; helpful staff; steep climb to beaches; acc to some pitch diff for lge o'fits; mkt Mon." ♦ 28 Apr-10 Sep. € 37.00
ABS - B11   2005*

See advertisement opposite (bottom)

ST CAST LE GUILDO *2E3* (1km S Coastal) **Camping Les Bles d'Or, La Chapelle, 22380 St Cast-le-Guildo** [tel/fax 02 96 41 99 93]   App St Cast fr S on D19. Site sp opp beach N of Pen Guen. Med, hdg/mkd pitch; pt shd; wc; sp; mv service pnt; chem disp; 30 pitches with individ san facs (extra charge); shwrs inc; el pts (10A) €3; gas; lndtte; ice; supmkt 800m; tradsmn; rest 700m; snacks high ssn; bar; BBQ; playgrnd; htd pool; sand beach 700m; games rm; 30% statics; dogs; phone; adv bkg; quiet; red low ssn; cc acc; CCI. "Excel site; warm welcome." ♦ 1 Apr-31 Oct. € 12.00   2005*

ST CAST LE GUILDO *2E3* (3.5km S) **LES CASTELS Le Chateau de Galinee, 22380 St Cast-le-Guildo** [02 96 41 10 56; fax 02 96 41 03 72; chateau galinee@wanadoo.fr; www.chateaudegalinee. com or www.les-castels.com] Fr St Malo take 2nd exit (Toutes Direction) & branch R at junc with D301, sp Rennes, Dinard. At next rndabt take 2nd exit onto D168. At Ploubalay go thro vill & turn L at rndbt onto D768. Branch onto D786 at La Ville-es-Cointe & foll D786 thro Notre Dame-de-Guildo. Approx 2km after leaving Notre Dame-de-Guildo turn L into Rue de Galinee & foll sp to site. Med, hdg/mkd pitch, pt shd; wc; chem disp; baby facs; fam bthrm; shwrs inc; el pts (10A) inc; lndtte; sm shop; snacks; bar; BBQ; playgrnd; htd pool complex inc covrd pool; sand beach 4km; fishing pond; tennis; games area; mini-golf; cycle hire; horseriding 6km; golf 3km; games rm; entmnt; TV rm; 30% statics; dogs €3.20; recep 0900-0200 & 1400-1700; Eng spkn; adv bkg; red long stay; quiet; cc acc; CCI. "Excel site; facs poss ltd low ssn; mkts Fri (& Mon high ssn); excursions to Jersey; peaceful, family site; friendly, helpful staff." ♦ 6 May-10 Sep.
€ 30.30 (CChq acc) ABS - B27   2005*

See advertisement opposite (top)

ST CAST LE GUILDO *2E3* (6km SW) **Camping Le Vallon aux Merlettes, 43 Rue du Dr Jobert, 22550 Matignon** [02 96 41 11 61 or 06 70 31 03 22; giblanchet@wanadoo.fr] Fr E & W take D786 to Matignon; 500m fr town cent turn SW on D13 twds Lamballe. Med, pt sl, pt shd; wc (cont); chem disp; shwrs inc; el pts (10A) €2.20; gas; lndtte; shop; snacks; playgrnd; pool 4km; tennis; sand beach 6km; adv bkg rec; quiet; cc not acc; CCI. "Lovely site, on playing fields outside attractive town; vg clean facs." ♦ 29 Mar-29 Sep. € 9.80   2003*

STE CATHERINE DE FIERBOIS see **Ste Maure de Touraine** *4H2*

STE CECILE see **Chantonnay** *2H4*

FRANCE

ST CERE *7C4* (SE) Camping Le Soulhol, 46400 St Cere [05 65 38 12 37; fax 05 65 10 61 75; lesoulhol@sud-villages.com; www.campingle soulhol.com] Fr S on D940 twds St Cere turn onto D48 (Leyne); in 300m turn L (sp not easily seen); site in 200m. Site sp fr all dir to St Cere. Lge, pt shd; wc; chem disp; mv service pnt; baby facs; shwrs; el pts (10A) €2.50; gas; lndtte; ice; sm shop; tradsmn; rests in town; snacks; pool adj; entmnts; TV rm; 10% statics; dogs €1; phone; Eng spkn; red low ssn; CCI. "Friendly, helpful staff; excel walks in pleasant area; sh walk to town; san facs renovated 2004; far end of site bet 2 rvs v quiet; severe speed ramps; excel long/sh stay." ♦ 1 May-20 Sep. € 12.50 2004*

ST CHELY D'APCHER *9D1* (8km E Rural) Camping Le Galier, Route de St Chely, 48120 St Alban-sur-Limagnole [04 66 31 58 80; fax 04 66 31 41 83] Exit A75 junc 34 onto N106, then E on D987. Site 1.5km SW of St Alban on rvside. Sm, mkd pitch, pt sl; htd wc (some cont); shwrs inc; el pts (6A) €3.40; lndtte; shop 1.5km; snacks; bar; playgrnd; pool; dogs €1.40; poss cr; adv bkg; quiet; red low ssn/CCI; "V clean san facs; friendly owners; gd walking, fishing; vg NH to/fr S."♦ 1 Mar-15 Nov. € 12.50 2004*

ST CHELY D'APCHER *9D1* (N) Camp Municipal, 48200 St Chely-d'Apcher [04 66 31 03 24 or 04 66 31 00 67 (Mairie)] On E side of N9 to N end of town. Med, hdg pitch, unshd; wc; shwrs; el pts (10A) inc; shops in town; TV; poss cr; Eng spkn; adv bkg; quiet. "Friendly site; gd walks; gd NH." 15 Jun-15 Sep. € 10.00 2003*

ST CHERON *4E3* (3km SE Rural) Camping Heliomonde (Naturist), La Petite Beauce, 91530 St Cheron [01 64 56 61 37; fax 01 64 56 51 30; heliomonde@wanadoo.fr; www.heliomonde.fr] N20 S to Arpajon; then D116 to St Cheron. Site bet Arpajon & Dourdan. Sp in town. Med, shd; wc; chem disp; sauna; shwrs inc; el pts €3.30; lndtte; shop; rest; htd pool; paddling pool; games area; fitness rm; entmnt; some statics; adv bkg; quiet. 7 Mar-12 Nov. € 22.90 (CChq acc) 2005*

ST CHERON 4E3 (3.5km SE Rural) Camping Le Parc des Roches, La Petite Beauce, 91530 St Cheron [01 64 56 65 50; fax 01 64 56 54 50; contact@parcdesroches.com; www.parcdes roches.com] N20 S to Arpajon; then D116 to St Cheron. Site bet Arpajon & Dourdan. Sp in town. Lge, hdg/mkd pitch; pt shd; htd wc; chem disp; mv service pnt; baby facs; shwrs inc; el pts (4A) €2.60; gas 200m; Indtte; ice; shop 3lkm; tradsmn; rest; snacks; bar; BBQ; playgrnd; htd pool; paddling pool; tennis; solarium; games rm; games rm; 70% statics; dogs €1.70; train 3km; Eng spkn; adv bkg; quiet; cc acc; CCI. "Pleasant site; gd for walking; picturesque wooded setting; v helpful owner; some san facs new, others not; train to Paris 3km; historical sites; chateaux." ♦ 14 Apr-15 Oct. € 20.65   2005*

See advertisement

ST CHINIAN 10F1 (1km W) Camp Municipal Les Terrasses, Route de St Pons, 34360 St Chinian [04 67 38 28 28 (Mairie); fax 04 67 38 28 29; commune-de-st-chinian@wanadoo.fr] On main Beziers-St Pons rd, N112, heading W on o'skts of St Chinian. Site on L. Med, terr, unshd; wc; shwrs inc; el pts €2; shops 1km; poss cr; quiet. "Gd views." 15 Jun-31 Aug. € 6.90   2002*

†ST CIRQ LAPOPIE 7D3 (2km N Rural) Camping La Plage, 46330 St Cirq-Lapopie [05 65 30 29 51; fax 05 65 30 23 33; camping.laplage@wanadoo. fr; www.campingplage.com] Exit Cahors on D653, in Vers take D662 sp Cajarc. In 20km turn R at Tour-de-Faure over narr bdge, sp St Cirq-Lapopie, site 100m on R beside Rv Lot. Med, mkd pitch, shd; wc; baby facs; shwrs inc; el pts (6-10A) €3-4; Indtte; shop; rest; snacks; bar; BBQ; playgrnd; pool; rv sw; canoeing; watersports; entmnt; 5% statics; dogs €1.50; adv bkg; quiet; CCI. "Low ssn site yourself, pay later; clean, tidy site; gd rest in town 1-2km uphill; gd walking." ♦ € 16.00
        2005*

ST CIRQ LAPOPIE 7D4 (9km E Rural) Camping Ruisseau de Treil, 46160 Larnagol [05 65 31 23 39; fax 05 65 31 23 27; lotcamping@ wanadoo.fr; www.lotcamping.com] Fr Figeac foll D19 thro Cajarc. At top of hill leaving Cajarc turn R onto D662 sp Cahors & Larnagol. Site sp on R 300m bef Larnagol on blind bend. Sm, mkd pitch, pt sl, pt shd; wc; chem disp; child/baby facs; shwrs inc; el pts (6A) €3.40; gas; Indtte; ice; shop; tradsmn; snacks; bar; BBQ; playgrnd; 2 pools; rv sw, fishing, canoeing adj; horseriding; cycle hire; TV rm; 4% statics; dogs €3.40; poss cr; Eng spkn; adv bkg; quiet; 20-30% red low ssn & snr citizen; CCI. "Spotless san facs but inadequate when site full; guided walks in area; lovely, spacious, British-owned site in valley; conv many tourist attractions; pitches poss uneven." ♦ ltd. 7 May-17 Sep. € 18.30   2005*

ST CIRQ LAPOPIE 7D3 (2.5km S Rural) Camping La Truffiere, Route de Concots, 46330 St Cirq-Lapopie [05 65 30 20 22; fax 05 65 30 20 27; contact@camping-truffiere.com; www.camping-truffiere.com] Take D911, Cahors to Villefranche, then turn N onto D42 at Concots dir St Cirq for 8km - site clearly sp. Med, pt sl, terr, shd; htd wc; chem disp; mv service pnt; shwrs inc; el pts (6A) €3; Indtte; ice; shop & 4km; rest; snacks; bar; playgrnd; htd pool; paddling pool; rv sw & fishing 3km; cycle hire; entmnt; TV; dogs €1; phone; Eng spkn; adv bkg; quiet; 10% red low ssn; cc acc; CCI. "Excel facs but ltd low ssn; most pitches in forest clearings - pitches in open with temp el pts (no earth); site & rds not suitable v lge o'fits; some pitches steep; well-kept; hospitable; delightful site; gd rest; lovely pool." ♦ 1 Apr-30 Sep. € 15.00 (CChq acc)
        2005*

ST CIRQ LAPOPIE 7D3 (5km W Rural) Camp Municipal, 46330 St Gery [05 65 31 40 08 (Mairie); fax 05 65 31 45 65] Foll N side Rv Lot on D653. Fr Vers D662 sp Figeac. Thro St Gery, after rlwy x-ing turn R bef petrol stn. Sp. Sm, pt sl, shd; wc (cont); el pts (10A) inc (poss long lead req); shop 2km; rv & fishing adj; quiet. "V clean facs; warden calls 2000." € 8.80   2003*

ST CLAUDE *9A3* (2km SE Rural) **Camp Municipal du Martinet, 39200 St Claude [03 84 45 00 40 or 03 84 41 42 62 (LS); fax 03 84 45 11 30]** On ent town foll 1-way, under bdge mkd 4.1m high, then take R turn 'Centre Ville' lane to next traff lts. Turn R then immed L sp Geneve, turn R 300m after Fiat g'ge onto D290, site on R. Med, pt shd; wc (cont); chem disp; shwrs inc; el pts (5A) inc; gas; ice; shops 1km; rest; htd pool adj; tennis; fishing; poss cr; adv bkg; quiet; red low ssn; CCI. "In Jura mountains; clsd 1230-1400 & 2000; could do with some refurb; smoking pipe factory & museum nrby; excel walking; v attractive town; gd long/sh stay." 1 May-30 Sep.
€ 11.70   2004*

ST CLAUDE *9A3* (10km NW) **Camping Le Champ Renard, 39260 Moirans-en-Montagne [03 84 42 34 98; fax 03 84 42 60 50; camping. champ.renard@wanadoo.fr]** Fr St Claude foll Lons-Lyon rd (D436 to D470) to Moirans-en-Montagne (approx 25km by rd). Site opp sm indus est. Steep access rds. Med, mainly sl, terr, pt shd; wc; shwrs inc; el pts (6A) €2.50; shops 2km; tradsmn; snacks; pool; shgl beach & lake 6km; mini-golf; dogs €1.20; adv bkg; some rd noise; CCI. "V friendly & helpful warden; one of nicer sites in area; local town & lake attractive; 15thC church in vill; pleasant sp walks; gd sh stay." 15 Mar-15 Oct.
€ 13.90   2005*

ST COLOMBAN DES VILLARDS *9C3* (Rural) **Camping La Perriere, Route du Col du Glandon, 73130 St Colomban-des-Villards [tel/fax 04 79 56 50 26]** Exit A43 junc 26 onto D927. Site at end of vill. Access rd narr & winding in places. Sm, mkd pitch, hdstg; shwrs inc; el pts €4; lndtte; shop 200m; BBQ; playgrnd; games area; phone; quiet. "Access rd not rec long o'fits; excel long stay." ♦ 1 May-1 Nov. € 10.00   2002*

ST CONGARD see Malestroit *2F3*

ST CONNEC see Mur de Bretagne *2E3*

ST CONSTANT see Maurs *7D4*

ST COULOMB see St Malo *2E4*

ST CREPIN ET CARLUCET see Sarlat la Caneda *7C3*

STE CROIX EN PLAINE see Colmar *6F3*

ST CYBRANET see Sarlat la Caneda *7C3*

ST CYPRIEN *7C3* (1km S) **Camping du Garrit, 24220 St Cyprien [tel/fax 05 53 29 20 56; pbecheau@aol.com; www.campingdugarrit endordogneperigord.com]** Sp on D703 fr St Cyprien on rvside. Be sure to foll 'Camping du Garrit' sp & not other Le Garrit sps. Med, hdg/mkd pitch, pt shd; wc; chem disp; baby facs; shwrs inc; el pts (6A) €2.50; BBQ; lndtte; ice; shop; playgrnd; pool; canoeing; sailing; boat hire; fishing; rv adj; dogs €1; phone; Eng spkn; adv bkg (dep req); quiet; CCI. "Excel site; highly rec; friendly owner; easy walk to town; gd touring base."
1 May-15 Sep. € 13.50   2005*

ST CYPRIEN PLAGE *10G1* (3km S Coastal) **Camping Cala Gogo, La Vigie, 66750 St Cyprien-Plage [04 68 21 07 12; fax 04 68 21 02 19; calagogo@campmed.com; www.campmed.com]** Exit A9 at Perpignan Nord onto D617 to Canet-Plage, then D81; site sp bet St Cyprien-Plage & Argeles-Plage dir Les Capellans. V lge, mkd pitch; pt shd; wc; mv service pnt; baby facs; shwrs inc; el pts (6A) €3; gas; lndtte; ice; supmkt; rest; snacks; bar; playgrnd; 2 pools; paddling pool; sand beach adj; tennis; cycle hire; entmnt; TV; 20% statics; dogs €3.50; adv bkg; red low ssn; cc acc. "Suitable for partially-sighted." ♦ 15 May-25 Sep. € 25.50
                                                          2004*

ST CYPRIEN PLAGE *10G1* (1.5km SW Urban/Coastal) **CHADOTEL Camping Le Roussillon, Chemin de la Mer, 66750 St Cyprien [04 68 21 06 45 or 02 51 33 05 05 (LS); fax 02 51 33 94 04; chadotel@wanadoo.fr; www. camping-chadotel.fr]** Exit A9 Perpignan Nord onto N114 to Elne, D40 to St Cyprien. Site sp. Lge, hdg/mkd pitch, unshd; htd wc; baby facs; shwrs inc; el pts (6A) inc; gas; lndtte; shop; snacks; bar; BBQ (gas); playgrnd; htd pool; waterslide; sand beach 1km; cycle hire; games rm; TV rm; entmnt; bus to beach; dogs €2.90; Eng spkn; adv bkg; red long stay/low ssn; cc acc. "Vg family site; gd touring base." ♦ 1 Apr-23 Sep. € 28.00   2005*

ST CYPRIEN SUR DOURDOU see Conques *7D4*

ST CYR (VIENNE) see Jaunay Clan *4H1*

ST CYR SUR MER (VAR) see Bandol *10F3*

ST DENIS DU PAYRE see Lucon *7A1*

ST DIE *6E3* (10km E Urban) **Camp Municipal Le Violu, 88520 Gemaingoutte [03 29 57 70 70 (Mairie); fax 03 29 51 72 60; commune gemaingoutte@wanadoo.fr]** Take N59 Rte du Col fr St Die twd Ste Marie-aux-Mines. Site on L at ent to Gemaingoutte, 1km after junc with D23 Sm, pt sl, pt shd, mkd pitch; wc (some cont); chem disp; shwrs inc; el pts (5A) €2; lndtte; ice; shops 2.5km; tradsmn; playgrnd; rv adj; dogs €0.80; quiet; CCI. "Peaceful site on Rte du Vin; office only open at 1900-2030 daily; gd sh stay." ♦ 1 May-30 Sep.
€ 8.80   2005*

†ST DIE *6E3* (1km SE Urban) **Camping La Vanne de Pierre, 5 Rue du Camping, 88100 St Die [03 29 56 23 56; fax 03 29 42 22 23; vannede pierre@wanadoo.fr; www.vannede pierre.com]** Fr any dir twd town cent foll 'Stade du Breuil Camping' sp. Med, hdg/mkd pitch, terr, pt shd; htd wc (some cont); chem disp; shwrs inc; el pts (6-10A) €4-5; lndtte; shops 2km; tradsmn; rest in town; snacks; bar; playgrnd; htd pool; rv fishing; tennis 500m; entmnt; internet; TV rm; 2% statics; dogs €3; poss cr; adv bkg rec; quiet but some rd noise; cc acc; CCI. "Gd, clean san facs; lge pitches; well-kept site; card operated barrier (cash dep/passport req); office open 0900-1300 & 1500-2000; helpful staff." ♦ € 22.00 (CChq acc)   2005*

ST ELOY LES MINES *7A4* (SE Rural) **Camp Municipal La Poule d'Eau,** Vieille Ville, 63700 St Eloy-les-Mines [04 73 85 45 47; fax 04 73 85 07 75] On N144 fr S turn W at 1st rndabt at St Eloy-les-Mines (Vieille Ville) onto D10; site 200m clearly sp. Fr Montlucon/Montaigut, last rndabt; site by 2 lakes. Med, pt sl, shd; wc; shwrs; el pts (6A) inc; ice; shop adj; tradsmn; playgrnd; lake sw, fishing & watersports adj; entmnt; adv bkg; quiet. "For security san facs open at set times, site ent barrier clsd 1200-1600; nice location; warden v proud of his site; excel sh stay/NH." 1 Jun-30 Sep. € 7.35   2003*

ST EMILION *7C2* (3km N) **Camping Domaine de la Barbanne,** Route de Montagne, 33330 St Emilion [05 57 24 75 80; fax 05 57 24 69 68; barbanne@ wanadoo.fr; www.camping-saint-emilion.com] NB: Trailer c'vans not permitted in cent of St Emilion. Fr A10 exit junc 39a sp Libourne onto D670. In Libourne turn E on D243 twd St Emilion. On o'skts of St Emilion turn L onto D122 dir Lussac & Montagne, site on R by lake in 3km. Or fr S, foll site sp off D670 to Libourne, nr Les Bigaroux. NB D122 S of St Emilion unsuitable for c'vans. Lge, hdg/mkd pitch, shd; wc (some cont); chem disp; mv service pnt; baby facs; shwrs inc; el pts (10A) inc; gas; lndtte; ice; sm shop; tradsmn; rest, snacks high ssn; bar; BBQ; playgrnd; htd pools inc; fishing; watersports nr; tennis; mini-golf; cycle hire; children's club; excursions high ssn; TV; 20% statics; dogs €1.40; phone; poss cr; Eng spkn; adv bkg; quiet; cc acc; CCI. "Owners friendly & helpful; well-run, peaceful, professionally-managed site; activities inc in site fee; v clean facs; free bus/taxi service to St Emilion; facs poss stretched in high ssn & ltd in low ssn; facs used by long-dist coach firms; tree fluff a minor irritation in May; wine-tasting tours; shop sells wine at chateau prices; gd cycle rtes; vg family site; excel." ♦ 1 Apr-23 Sep. € 27.90 (CChq acc) ABS - D08   2005*

STE ENIMIE *9D1* (1.5km W Rural) **Camp Couderc,** Route de Millau, 48210 Ste Enimie [04 66 48 50 53; fax 04 66 48 58 59; camping couderc@wanadoo.fr] Leave Ste Eminie in dir Millau, site on L bank of Rv Tarn. Med, mkd pitch, pt sl, terr, pt shd; wc; chem disp; shwrs inc; el pts (6A); gas; shop; snacks; bar; playgrnd; pool; canoeing; Eng spkn; quiet; CCI. "Rd along gorge narr & twisting; busy, friendly site; gd sh stay." 1 Apr-30 Sep. € 13.00   2003*

ST ETIENNE DE BAIGORRY see St Jean Pied de Port *8F1*

ST ETIENNE DE CROSSEY see Voiron *9C3*

ST ETIENNE DE FONTBELLON see Aubenas *9D2*

†**ST ETIENNE DE MONTLUC** *2G4* (E) **Camp Municipal de la Colleterie,** Blvd de Tivoli, 44360 St Etienne-de-Montluc [02 40 86 97 44; fax 02 40 86 98 78] Well sp fr N165 (E60) in both dirs. Sm, hdg/mkd pitch, pt sl, pt shd; htd wc; chem disp; shwrs inc; baby facs; el pts (20A) €3.20; lndtte; shop, rest, bar 500m; playgrnd; fishing; dogs €0.75; adv bkg rec; CCI. ♦ € 6.60   2005*

ST ETIENNE DE VILLEREAL see Villereal *7D3*

ST ETIENNE DU BOIS (VENDEE) see Lege *2H4*

ST ETIENNE DU GRES see St Remy de Provence *10E2*

STE EULALIE EN BORN see Mimizan *7D1*

ST EVARZEC see Quimper *2F2*

ST EVROULT NOTRE DAME DU BOIS see Aigle, L' *4E2*

ST FARGEAU *4G4* (6km SE Rural) **Camp Municipal La Calanque,** 89170 St Fargeau [tel/fax 03 86 74 04 55] SE of St Fargeau, take D85 dir of St Sauveur-en-Puisaye for 6km. Well sp on lakeside. Lge, mkd pitch, shd; htd wc (some cont); shwrs inc; el pts (10A) €1.50-2.35; lndtte; ice; shop, rest, snacks, bar adj; playgrnd; lake & sand beach adj; fishing; 10% statics; quiet (noisy nr lake); adv bkg rec high ssn; CCI. "Pleasant site in birch woods with cycling, canoeing, horseriding nr." ♦ 15 Apr-30 Sep. € 8.00   2005*

ST FERREOL TRENTE PAS see Nyons *9D2*

ST FLORENT SUR CHER *4H3* (7km S Urban) **Camp Intercommunal,** 18400 Lunery [02 48 65 07 38 or 02 48 23 22 08; fax 0248 55 26 78; fercher@ wanadoo.fr] Fr N151 turn S onto D27 at St Florent-sur-Cher, cont for 7km, site in vill cent of Lunery. Sm, hdg/mkd pitch, pt shd; chem disp; mv service pnt; wc; shwrs inc; el pts (6A) inc; shop, rest in vill; fishing; entmnt; bus, train in vill; red long stay. "Charming, friendly site in peaceful location; friendly welcome; v quiet & v clean; liable to flooding low ssn; phone ahead to check open low ssn; gd long/sh stay." 15 May-15 Sep. € 11.00   2005*

ST FLORENTIN *4F4* (1km S Urban) **Camping L'Armancon,** 89600 St Florentin [tel/fax 03 86 35 11 86; ot.saint-florentin@wanadoo.fr] N fr Auxerre on N77 site on R app rv bdge S of town. Fr N pass traff islands, exit town up slope, x-ing canal & rv. Site immed on S side of rv bdge, not sp & easily missed. Diff to turn if app fr N. Lge, pt sl, pt shd; wc (cont); shwrs inc; el pts inc; gas; lndtte; shop adj; snacks; playgrnd; rv sw; fishing; dogs €0.15; poss cr; some rlwy & rd noise at night. "Friendly manager; close to town cent; excel pitches; v gd long/sh stay." 15 Apr-15 Oct. € 9.85   2005*

ST FLOUR *9C1* (2km N Rural) **Camping International La Roche Murat,** 15100 St Flour [04 71 60 43 63; fax 04 71 60 27 82; courrier@ camping-saint-flour.com; www.camping-saint-flour.com] Fr N or S on A75 exit junc 28; sp off rndabt on St Flour side of m'way. Med, hdg/mkd pitch, terr, pt shd; htd wc; chem disp; shwrs inc; el pts (10A) €2.40; gas; lndry rm; shops 4km; tradsmn; playgrnd; pool 2km; dogs; Eng spkn; adv bkg; quiet but some rd noise; cc not acc; CCI. "Busy site conv NH fr A75; v helpful warden; gd views; sunny & secluded pitches; gd clean facs; some pitches sm; when pitches waterlogged - use site rds; excel touring cent." ♦ 1 Apr-1 Nov. € 8.40   2005*

ST FLOUR *9C1* (SW Urban) **Camp Municipal Les Orgues, 19 Ave Dr Maillet, 15100 St Flour** [04 71 60 44 01] On A75 to St Flour, foll sps for 'ville haute'; at x-rds in town cent turn L (dir Aurillac). Ent in 250m, narr & steep on L bet houses, site sp opp poss obscured by parked cars. NB Site ent is on busy main rd & has 2m high barrier. If c'van over 2m, stop at barrier (c'van sticking out into rd), walk down to office & ask warden to unlock barrier - poss v dangerous. Med, mkd pitch, pt sl, pt shd; wc; shwrs inc; el pts (6A) €2.40; ice; shops, rest; bar 1km; playgrnd; covrd pool 1km; tennis; quiet; poss cr; CCI. "Facs need updated; Gd NH." ♦ 15 May-15 Sep. € 9.60   2005*

ST FORT SUR GIRONDE *7B2* (4km SW Rural) **Camping Port Maubert, 8 Rue de Chassillac, 17240 St Fort-sur-Gironde** [05 46 04 78 86; fax 05 46 04 16 79; bourdieu.jean-luc@wanadoo.fr; www.campingportmaubert.com] Exit A10 junc 37 onto D730 dir Royan. Foll sp Port Maubert & site. Sm, hdg/mkd pitch, shd; wc (some cont); chem disp; mv service pnt; shwrs inc; el pts (10A) €3.50; gas; lndtte; ice; shop 4km; tradsmn; bar; BBQ; playgrnd; pool; sand beach 25km; cycle hire; games rm; TV; some statics; dogs €2; Eng spkn; adv bkg; quiet; cc acc; red long stay/CCI. "Pleasant, well-run site." 1 May-30 Sep. € 12.20   2005*

STE FOY LA GRANDE *7C2* (1.5km NE Urban) **Camping de la Bastide (formerly Camp Municipal La Tuilerie), Ave Georges Clemenceau, 33220 Ste Foy-la-Grande** [tel/fax 05 57 46 13 84; camping@paysfoyen.com] Fr W go thro town & turn off at D130 to site, sp on Rv Dordogne. Med, mkd pitch, pt shd; wc; chem disp; mv service pnt; baby facs; shwrs inc; el pts (5-10A) inc (rev pol); lndtte; ice; tradsmn; shops, snacks & bar 500m, playgrnd; rv sw adj; fishing, canoeing; 10% statics; dogs; phone; poss cr; Eng spkn; adv bkg; v quiet; CCI. "Clean, well-cared for & pretty site; immac san facs; gd street mkt Sat; fairly high kerb stones onto pitches - poss diff lge o'fits; rvside path into interesting old town." ♦ Easter-31 Oct. € 13.90
                     2005*

STE FOY LA GRANDE *7C2* (6km W Rural) **Camping La Riviere Fleurie, 24230 St Antoine-de-Breuilh** [tel/fax 05 53 24 82 80; info@la-riviere-fleurie.com; www.la-riviere-fleurie.com] Turn S off D936 in St Antoine-de-Breuilh, site 2.7km fr main rd exit. Well sp adj Rv Dordogne. Med, mkd pitch, pt shd; wc; chem disp; baby facs; shwrs inc; el pts (10A) €2.90-€4; gas; lndtte; ice; shops 4km; hypmkt 5km; tradsmn; bar; BBQ; playgrnd; pool; games rm; rv sw adj; tennis, horseriding; golf; canoeing & fishing nrby; 10% statics; dogs €1.80; phone; Eng spkn; adv bkg; quiet except for church bells; red long stay; CCI. "Site & facs excel; v friendly, helpful owners; v gd cycling area; mkt Sat in Ste Foy; card barrier €20 dep; gets better every year." ♦ 1 Apr-30 Sep. € 16.00   2004*

STE FOY LA GRANDE *7C2* (10km W Rural) **Camping de La Plage, 24230 St Seurin-de-Prats** [tel/fax 05 53 58 61 07; info@camping-in-france.net; www.camping-in-france.net] Fr D936 W of Ste Foy take D11 at Les Reaux twrds Pessac. Site on R of D11 immed bef x-ing Rv Dordogne into Pessac. Med, pt hdg/mkd pitch, pt sl, pt shd; wc; chem disp; mv service pnt; shwrs inc; el pts (15A) €4; lndtte; ice; shops 500m; rest; snacks; bar; BBQ; playgrnd; pool; rv sw & shgl beach adj; boating; fishing; tennis; games area; games rm; sat TV; 4% statics; dogs €1.80; Eng spkn; adv bkg; quiet; CCI. "Beautiful rvside site; British owners; canoeing & kayaking nrby; golf course, aquapark, go-carting, bowling & animal pk nrby." 1 May-31 Oct. € 16.00
                     2005*

STE FOY L'ARGENTIERE *9B2* (7km SE) **Camp Municipal Les Verpillieres, 69850 St Martin-en-Haut** [04 78 48 62 16] Fr Craponne on W o'skts of Lyon SW on D11 to cent of St Martin-en-Haut. D11 W to St Symphorien, almost immed L to St Catherine, site on L in 3km. Fr St Foy take D489 SE to Duerne, D34 to St Martin-en-Haut, D11 W twd St Symphorien to site in 4km. This app not for lge o'fits, has 7-12% climbs out of St Foy & hairpins after Duerne. Med, pt sl, shd; wc; shwrs; el pts (5A); lndtte; shops 4km; snacks; playgrnd; entmnt; 75% statics; poss cr; adv bkg; quiet. "Lovely wooded site with red squirrels; busy at w/e." 1 Apr-31 Oct.
                     2002*

ST FRAIMBAULT see Domfront *4E1*

ST GALMIER *9B2* (15km NW Rural) **Campeole Le Val de Coise, 42330 St Galmier** [04 77 54 14 82; fax 04 77 54 02 45] Fr St Etienne take N82 N. In 7km turn R onto D12 sp St Galmier Or fr N on N82 look for sp to St Galmier about 1.5km S of Montrond-les-Bains & turn L onto D6 to St Galmier. On D12 in St Galmier at floral rndabt with fountain if app fr N go L & fr S go R, uphill & foll site sp. Site approx 1.5km fr rndabt. Med, terr, pt shd; wc; chem disp; shwrs inc; el pts (10A) €3.10; lndtte; ice; shop; playgrnd; pool & paddling pool; tennis 2km; fishing; TV rm; many statics; dogs €1.52; adv bkg; v quiet; cc acc. "Pretty hilltop town, off beaten track; helpful staff; pleasant site but access rd & site rds a little steep for c'vans - OK for m'vans; facs stretched high ssn." 1 Apr-30 Sep. € 12.50   2003*

ST GAUDENS *8F3* (1km W Rural) **Camp Municipal Belvedere des Pyrenees, Route de Tarbes Quartier du Lanta, 31800 St Gaudens** [05 62 00 16 03] Foll camping sp fr St Gaudens town cent on N117 dir Tarbes. Site ent at top of hill on N side. Last rd sp is 'Belvedere'. Med, pt shd; htd wc; mv service pnt; shwrs inc; el pts (13A) €3.80; gas; ice; rest nrby; playgrnd; no adv bkg; some rd noise; cc not acc. "Pleasant site; facs clean; some rd noise; gates clsd 2200, need key after; phone to check opening in low ssn; gd views of Pyrenees in gd weather." 1 Apr-30 Sep. € 10.20   2005*

Les Dômes de Miage
★ ★ ★
A new way to discover the mountains...

A campsite in the middle of untouched nature, in quiet location at the foot of the Mont-Blanc, the centre of many hiking paths. A wide choice of activities and services, sports centre with swimming pool, tennis, etc., at approx. 800 yards. The nearest towns are: Chamonix - 15 miles, St. Gervais - 1,2 miles, Megève - 7,5 miles.

**197 route des Contamines · F-74170 Saint-Gervais-les-bains
Phone: + 33 (0)4 50 93 45 96 · fax: + 33 (0)4 50 78 10 75
www.camping-mont-blanc.com · camping.st-gervais@wanadoo.fr**

ST GAULTIER *4H2* (Urban) **Camp Municipal L'Illon**, Rue de l'Image, 36800 St Gaultier [02 54 47 11 22 or 02 54 01 66 00 (Mairie); fax 02 54 01 66 09] Site well sp in town. Med, mkd pitch, pt sl, pt shd; wc; shwrs inc; el pts; ice; gas; shops 500m; playgrnd; rv & fishing 50m; quiet. € 7.20   2005*

STE GEMME see Cadeuil *7B1*

ST GENIES see Sarlat la Caneda *7C3*

ST GENIEZ D'OLT *9D1* (1km NE) **Camp Municipal La Boissiere**, Route de la Cascade, 12130 St Geniez-d'Olt [05 65 70 40 43; fax 05 65 47 56 39] Site 500m off D988 on D509; sp on D988 E of town. Lge, mkd pitch, pt sl, pt shd; wc (cont); baby facs; shwrs inc; el pts (6A); lndtte; shop & supmkt 1km; rest; snacks; bar; tennis adj; fairly quiet. "Pleasant town in Lot Valley; gd sh stay/NH." ♦ 20 Apr-Sep. € 18.00   2004*

ST GENIEZ D'OLT *9D1* (1.8km W Rural) **Camping Marmotel**, 12130 St Geniez-d'Olt [05 65 70 46 51; fax 05 65 47 41 38; info@marmotel.com; www.marmotel.com] Exit A75 at junc 41 onto D37 dir Campagnac. Then onto D202, D45 & D988. Site situated on W of vill by rv on D19. Lge, hdg pitch, pt shd; wc; chem disp; mv service pnt; some pitches with individual san facs; baby facs; sauna; shwrs inc; el pts (10A) inc; gas; lndtte; shop 500m; tradsmn; rest; bar high ssn; BBQ; playgrnd; htd pool; paddling pool; waterslide; tennis; games area; cycle hire; entmnt; TV rm; some statics; dogs €1.50; Eng spkn; adv bkg; quiet; red low ssn; cc acc; CCI. "Highly rec; some pitches poss tight lge o'fits; poss muddy when wet; gd pool & rest; easy walk into St Geniez medieval town; lovely countryside around." ♦ 1 May-19 Sep. € 23.50 (CChq acc)   2004*

ST GENIS LAVAL see Lyon *9B2*

ST GEORGES (PAS DE CALAIS) see Hesdin *3B3*

ST GEORGES DE DIDONNE see Royan *7B1*

ST GEORGES DU VIEVRE *3D2* (Rural) **Camp Municipal du Vievre**, Route de Nouards, 27450 St Georges-du-Vievre [02 32 42 76 79 or 02 32 56 34 29 (LS); fax 02 32 57 52 90; info@saintgeorgesduvievre.org; www.camping-normand.com] Fr traff lts on D130 in Pont Authou turn W onto D137 to St Georges-du-Vievre; in town sq at tourist info turn L uphill sp camping; site 200m on L. If app fr S on N138 at Bernay take D834 sp Le Havre to Lieurey. Turn R onto D137 to St Georges, then turn R at camping sp by sw pool. Sm, hdg pitch, pt shd; wc; chem disp; mv service pnt; serviced pitches; shwrs inc; el pts (5A) €2.10; gas 200m; lndry rm; shops 200m; playgrnd; pool 150m; tennis 50m; sw 100m; cycle hire; dogs; Eng spkn; adv bkg (rec high ssn); quiet; CCI. "Peaceful; gd facs & pitches; well-run site; v interesting area; excel long/sh stay." ♦ 1 Apr-30 Sep. € 7.40   2005*

ST GEORGES DU VIEVRE *3D2* (3km E Rural) **Camping La Brettonniere (Sejourne)**, 27450 St Gregoire-du-Vievre [02 32 42 82 67] At traff lts on D130 in Pont Authou turn W onto D137 twd St Georges-du-Vievre; after 7km turn L, sp Camping Rural; site in 1km. NB Steep rdway down & narr terrs poss unsuitable for c'vans. Sm, mkd pitch, terr, shd; wc; chem disp; shwrs inc; el pts €3; shop 1km; playgrnd; pool 4km; adv bkg; quiet; CCI. "Eggs & cider for sale; CL-type farm site; vg." 1 May-31 Oct. € 9.50   2002*

ST GEORGES LE GAULTIER *4E1* (2km W Rural) **Camping La Gendrie**, 72130 St Georges-le-Gaultier [tel/fax 02 43 33 87 21; info@french adventures.co.uk; www.frenchadventures.co.uk] 50km NW fr Le Mans; 8km W N138. In vill take rd by cafe, site 2km on L, dir St Mars-du-Desert. Sm, hdg pitch, pt sl, pt shd; wc; chem disp; shwrs inc; el pts inc; gas; lndtte; BBQ; shop, rest, snacks, bar, 2km; covrd pool; playgrnd; sand beach 15km; fishing 3km; cycle hire; games rm; adv bkg (dep) - tel 01925 630757 (UK); quiet. "Gd long/sh stay; British-owners; conv National Park; beautiful countryside; phone site for rd map; 2 hrs fr Caen ferry." ♦ ltd. Easter-31 Oct. € 17.00   2004*

ST GEOURS DE MAREMNE *8E1* (500m W Rural) Camping Les Platanes, 3 Route de Lecoume, 40230 St Geours-de-Maremne [tel/fax 05 58 57 45 35; info@platanes.com; www. campinglesplatanes.com] Fr N10 take junc sp St Geours-de-Maremne. Site sp fr town cent. Med, pt sl, pt shd; htd wc; chem disp; shwrs inc; el pts (6A) €3.50; gas; lndtte; ice; shop nr; tradsmn; rest; snacks; bar; BBQ; playgrnd; pool (high ssn); sand beach 8km; tennis; games area; TV; 50% statics; dogs €1.20; phone; poss cr; adv bkg; quiet; red low ssn/long stay; cc acc; CCI. "Great beaches, surfing & rafting nr; friendly British owners; diff to site on lower level; almost hilly site; OK upper level, poss diff lge o'fits; low ssn can be long, stumbling walk to san facs in dark; useful NH on N10; many muddy pitches if wet." 1 Mar-1 Nov. € 14.95   2005*

Will you fill in the site report forms at the back of the guide, or shall I?

ST GERAUD DE CORPS see Montpon Menesterol *7C2*

ST GERMAIN see Aubenas *9D2*

ST GERMAIN DU BEL AIR see Gourdon *7D3*

ST GERMAIN LES BELLES see Masseret *7B3*

ST GERMAIN L'HERM *9B1* (500m Rural) Camping St Eloy, 63630 St Germain-l'Herm [04 73 72 05 13 or 04 73 34 75 53 (LS)); fax 04 73 34 70 94; sogeval@wanadoo.fr; www.camping-massif central.com] Take D906 S fr Ambert to Arlanc, turn R onto D999A to St Germain, site sp on app to vill. Med, mkd pitch, pt sl, terr, pt shd; wc (some cont); chem disp; mv service pnt; el pts (8A) €3; lndry rm; shop 500m; tradsmn; rest 500m; BBQ; playgrnd; pool; 10% statics; dogs €1.50; phone; adv bkg; quiet. "Pleasant views; cycle & walking tracks fr vill; vg." ♦ ltd. 1 Jun-15 Sep. € 12.00   2004*

ST GERVAIS D'AUVERGNE *7A4* (N Rural) Camp Municipal L'Etang Philippe, 63390 St Gervais-d'Auvergne [tel/fax 04 73 85 74 84; camping. stgervais-auvergne@wanadoo.fr] Fr N144 3km S of St Eloy-les-Mines, take D987 S to St Gervais. Site on R just bef town. Lge, hdg pitch, pt shd; wc; chem disp; mv service pnt; shwrs inc; el pts (10A) inc; lndtte; ice; shop 500m; tradsmn (Jul/Aug); playgrnd; lake sw & beach adj; cycle hire; tennis; mini-golf; archery; entmnt; some statics; dogs; Eng spkn; adv bkg; quiet; CCI. "V clean facs; poss untidy low ssn & ltd facs; lovely setting by sm lake; many activities in town & on site in Jul/Aug." ♦ Easter-30 Sep. € 8.90   2004*

ST GERVAIS D'AUVERGNE *7A4* (8km E Rural) Camp Municipal Les Pres Dimanches, 63390 Chateauneuf-les-Bains [04 73 86 41 50 or 04 73 86 67 65 (LS); fax 04 73 86 41 71; mairie-chat-les-bains@wanadoo.fr] Fr Montaigut take N144 S twd Riom & Clermont-Ferrand. In 9km at La Boule S onto D987 to St Gervais. Take D227 E to Chateauneuf-les-Bains. In 7km L onto D109. Site thro vill on R. Sm, pt shd, hdg/mkd pitch; htd wc; shwrs inc; el pts (6A) inc; lndtte; shop 250m; rest adj; playgrnd; quiet; adv bkg; excel; CCI. "Nrby fishing, tennis, boules, canoeing, spa baths 500m; helpful warden; beautiful countryside." ♦ ltd. 15 May-15 Oct. € 10.00   2005*

ST GERVAIS LES BAINS *9B4* (10km SE Rural) Camping Le Pontet, Route de Notre-Dame-de-la-Gorge, 74170 Les Contamines-Montjoie [04 50 47 04 04; fax 04 50 47 18 10; camping dupontet@wanadoo.fr; www.campinglepontet. com] Fr St Gervais take the D902 to Les Contamines-Montjoie (sp); go thro vill & foll sp to Notre Dame-de-la-Gorge; site in 2km on L, clearly sp. Lge, mkd pitch, hdstg, pt shd; htd wc; chem disp; baby facs; shwrs inc; el pts (2-10A) €2.70-9.90; lndtte; shops 2km; tradsmn; rest; snacks; playgrnd; fishing; lake adj; leisure/sports park adj; tennis; mini-golf; horseriding; phone; Eng spkn; adv bkg; quiet. "Alpine walking on mkd walks in area; in winter ski lift 200m fr site." ♦ 1 Dec-30 Sep. € 15.00   2005*

ST GERVAIS LES BAINS *9B4* (2km S Rural) Camping Les Domes de Miage, 197 Route des Contamines, 74170 St Gervais-les-Bains [04 50 93 45 96; fax 04 50 78 10 75; camping. st-gervais@wanadoo.fr or info@camping-mont-blanc.com; www.camping-mont-blanc.com] Fr N thro St Gervais, at fork take L sp Les Contamines onto D902, site 2km on L. Med, mkd pitch, pt shd; htd wc (some cont); chem disp; mv service pnt; shwrs inc; el pts (3-10A) €2.90-3.90; gas; lndtte; ice; shop; tradsmn; rest; snacks; bar; playgrnd; pool; tennis 800m; fishing 1km; cycle hire; internet; TV rm; dogs €2; Eng spkn; adv bkg (bkg fee); quiet; cc acc; red low ssn; CCI. "Friendly, family-owned; vg walking in area; beautiful location; immac san facs; excel." ♦ 13 May-24 Sep. € 20.50 (CChq acc)   2005*

See advertisement

ST GERY see St Cirq Lapopie *7D3*

ST GILLES *10E2* (Urban) Camping de la Chicanette, Rue de la Chicanette, 30800 St Gilles [04 66 87 28 32; fax 04 66 87 49 85; camping.la. chicanette@libertysurf.fr] Site on N572 W fr Arles, sp in cent of town, behind Auberge de la Chicanette. Narr app rd, tight turn to ent. Med, hdg pitch, pt shd; wc; chem disp; shwrs inc; el pts (6A) inc (rev pol); lndtte; shop adj; snacks; bar; playgrnd; pool; entmnt; 20% statics; dogs €3; poss cr; quiet; red low ssn; CCI. "Sm pitches; site unkempt low ssn; interesting old town; bus to Nimes." 1 Apr-31 Oct. € 21.00   2004*

ST GILLES CROIX DE VIE *2H3* (3km NE Rural) Camping Aire Naturelle Le Petit Beauregard, Rue du Petit Beauregard, 85800 Le Fenouiller [02 51 55 07 98] N fr Les Sables d'Olonne take D38 twd St Gilles Croix-de-Vie. Turn R onto D754 sp Le Fenouiller for 3km. Turn R; site well sp in 500m. Sm, mkd pitch, pt shd; wc; chem disp; shwrs inc; el pts (6A) €2.50; lndtte; shop 1km; tradsmn; rest nr; BBQ; playgrnd; sand beach 3km; few statics; dogs; quiet; Eng spkn; adv bkg; CCI. "V friendly & helpful owner; excel san facs & v clean; gd beaches nrby; gd value long stay; rec; St Gilles v busy & cr; vg long stay." ◆ 1 May-30 Sep. € 11.00 2005*

ST GILLES CROIX DE VIE *2H3* (4km SE Urban/Coastal) CHADOTEL Le Domaine de Beaulieu, Route des Sables, 85800 Givrand [02 51 55 59 46 or 02 51 33 05 05 (LS); fax 02 51 33 05 06; chadotel@wanadoo.fr; www.camping-chadotel.fr] S on D38 fr St Gilles Croix-de-Vie, site sp on L. Lge, hdg/mkd pitch, pt shd; htd wc; serviced pitches; baby facs; shwrs inc; el pts (6A) inc; gas; lndtte; ice; shop; snacks; bar; BBQ (gas); playgrnd; 2 pools; waterslide; sand beach 1km; tennis; entmnt; mini-golf, golf 5km; TV; dogs €2.90; adv bkg; quiet; red long stay/low ssn; cc acc; CCI. "Lots to do on site - gd for families; red facs low ssn." ◆ 1 Apr-23 Sep. € 27.50 2005*

ST GILLES CROIX DE VIE *2H3* (3km NE) Camping Le Chatelier, Route de Nantes, 85800 Le Fenouiller [02 28 10 50 75] Fr St Gilles-Croix-de-Vie D754 NE, sp to Le Fenouiller, site on L. Med, mkd pitch, pt shd; wc; chem disp; shwrs inc; baby facs; el pts (6A) (rec long lead); gas; lndtte; tradsmn; shops 2km; snacks; bar; BBQ; playgrnd; htd pool high ssn; sand beach 3km; entmnt adj; TV rm; 50% statics; dogs; quiet. "Friendly owners; 10 mins cycle to town; vg long stay." ◆ ltd. Easter-15 Oct. € 16.00 2002*

ST GILLES CROIX DE VIE *2H3* (9km SE) Camping Les Alouettes, Route de St Gilles, 85220 La Chaize-Giraud [02 51 22 96 21; fax 02 51 22 92 68; pascal.chaillou@free.fr; www.lesalouettes.com] Take D38 S fr St Gilles dir Sables-d'Olonne: in 2.5km take D12 to La Chaize-Giraud. Site on L in 5km. Med, pt sl, pt shd; wc (some cont); chem disp; shwrs inc; el pts (6A) €3; gas; lndtte; shop; tradsmn; snacks; playgrnd; htd pool; sand beach 5km; lake sw 14km; games area; 75% statics; dogs €1.70; adv bkg; quiet; cc acc; CCI. "Few touring pitches; gd san facs." ◆ ltd. 18 Apr-14 Sep. € 14.30 2004*

ST GILLES CROIX DE VIE *2H3* (5km E) Camping Europa, Le Bois Givrand, 85800 Givrand [02 51 55 32 68; fax 02 51 55 80 10; contact@europacamp.com; www.europacamp.com] On D6 fr St Gilles Croix-de-Vie to Aizenay; site in approx 3km & seen fr rd on R, opp boat builders. Lge, mkd pitch, pt shd; wc (some cont); chem disp; serviced pitches; baby facs; shwrs inc; el pts (6-10A) inc; gas; lndtte; shop 3km; rest, snacks, bar high ssn; BBQ; playgrnd; pool complex; waterslide; sand beach 3km; rv fishing, boat hire adj; watersports 5km; horseriding, golf nr; tennis; mini-golf; games rm; entmnt; TV rm; 60% statics (sep area); recep 0830-1900; dogs €2.14; adv bkg; cc acc. "Vg; pleasant site but facs stretched high ssn." ◆ 1 Jun-20 Sep. € 26.70 ABS - A13 2005*

ST GILLES CROIX DE VIE *2H3* (1km S Coastal) Camping Les Cypres, Route du Pont Jaunay, 85800 St Gilles-Croix-de-Vie [02 51 55 38 98; fax 02 51 54 98 94; camping@free.fr] Site on S end of St Gilles-Croix-di-Vie off D38. after rndabt turn sharp L - hard to spot. Lge, hdg pitch, shd; wc; chem disp, mv service pnt, shwrs inc; el pts (10A) inc; gas; ice; lndtte; shop, tradsmn; rest; snacks; bar; playgrnd; indoor pool & jacuzzi; sand beach 600m; 12% statics; dogs €2.60; rv 100m; Eng spkn; adv bkg €7.62 fee; quiet; cc acc; red long stay/low ssn; CCI. "Excel for family hols; family-run site; chem disp in recep - long dist fr some pitches; some facs poss clsd low ssn." ◆ 1 Apr-15 Sep. € 21.00 2003*

ST GILLES CROIX DE VIE *2H3* (8km E) Camping Le Pont Rouge, Ave Georges Clemenceau, 85220 St Reverend [tel/fax 02 51 54 68 50; camping.pontrouge@wanadoo.fr] W fr Aizenay on D6 rd for St Gilles-Croix-de-Vie, turn R just past water tower into St Reverend. Foll sp to site. Sm, hdg pitch, pt sl, pt shd; htd wc; chem disp; shwrs inc; el pts (6A) €3; ice; BBQ; lndtte; tradsmn; shop 1km; rest 3km; playgrnd; htd pool; sand beach 8km; poss cr; dogs €2; quiet; Eng spkn; adv bkg; red low ssn; CCI. "Attractive, secluded site; gd long stay." ◆ 1 Apr-31 Oct. € 15.00 2003*

ST GILLES CROIX DE VIE *2H3* (2km S Coastal) CHADOTEL Camping Le Bahamas Beach, 168 Route des Sables, 85800 St Gilles-Croix-de-Vie [02 51 54 69 16 or 02 51 33 05 05 (LS); fax 02 51 33 94 04; chadotel@wanadoo.fr; www.camping-chadotel.fr] S fr St Gilles-Croix-de-Vie on Rte des Sables, sp. Lge, mkd pitch, unshd; wc; chem disp; shwrs inc; el pts (6A) inc; gas; lndtte; ice; shop; playgrnd; htd pool; waterslide; beach 1km; watersports; games rm; TV rm; cycle hire; entmnt; child entmnt; excursions; many statics; dogs €2.90; poss cr; Eng spkn; adv bkg; quiet; red long stay/low ssn; cc acc; CCI. "Gd holiday site for children; excel cycle rtes along coast." ◆ 1 Apr-23 Sep. € 28.00 2005*

ST GIRONS *8G3* (3km N Rural) **Camping Audinac,** 09200 Audinac-les-Bains [tel/fax 05 61 66 44 50; accueil@audinac.com; www.audinac.com] E fr St Girons take D117 twd Foix; after 2km uphill turn L onto D627; foll sp. Med, terr, pt shd; wc; chem disp (wc only); mv service pnt; shwrs inc; el pts (10A) €3; gas; lndtte; ice; shops 5km; tradsmn; rest in ssn; playgrnd; pool high ssn; no statics; dogs €1; no twin-axles; Eng spkn; adv bkg ess; quiet; cc acc; red low ssn; CCI. "Spacious, attractive, well appointed site; not all pitches are level; facs ltd low ssn; gd long/sh stay." ♦ 1 May-30 Sep. € 14.00
2004*

ST GIRONS *8G3* (3km SE Rural/Urban) **Camping du Pont du Nert, Route de Lacourt,** 09200 Encourtiech [05 61 66 58 48; dmmadre@aol.com] On E bank of Rv Salat at junc D33 & D3. Fr St Girons by-pass foll D618 sp Aulus-les-Bains. Site on L at junc to Rv Nert. Sm, pt sl, pt shd; wc; shwrs inc; el pts (8A) €2; playgrnd; fishing; tennis; quiet; CCI. 1 Jun-15 Sep. € 9.00
2004*

STE HERMINE *2H4* (11km NE Rural) **Camping Le Colombier (Naturist),** 85210 St Martin-Lars [02 51 27 83 84; fax 02 51 27 87 29; lecolombier.nat@wanadoo.fr] Fr junc 7 of A83 take N137 N thro Ste Hermine (do not foll sp for centre vill.) Just past town limit turn R onto N148 sp Niort & Thire. In 2km turn R sp Thire & in 500m turn R onto D8. Turn L onto D10 sp St Martin-Lars. 150m past St Martin-Lars turn R sp Le Columbier. Site ent on L in 200m. Med, pt sl, pt shd; wc; chem disp; shwrs inc; el pts (6-16A) €3-5; lndtte; ice; shops 2km; tradsmn; rest; snacks; bar; playgrnd; new pool; lake sw; 2% statics to let; dogs €3.20; poss cr; Eng spkn; adv bkg; quiet; cc acc; INF card req. "Excel, well-run site; lge pitches; vg facs; friendly Dutch owners; conv Mervent National Park; excel long stay." ♦ ltd. 1 Apr-1 Nov. € 14.40
2005*

STE HERMINE *2H4* (500m SW Rural) **Camp Municipal La Smagne,** 85210 Ste Hermine [02 51 27 35 54] On N137 500m S of vill cent. Med, mkd pitch; pt shd; wc; chem disp; serviced pitches; mv service pnt; shwrs inc; el pts (5A) €1.50; gas; lndtte; shops 500m; playgrnd; pool adj; tennis; quiet but some rd noise. "Nice site; pleasant vill; conv location just off A83; phone ahead to check open low ssn." 15 Jun-15 Sep. € 4.50
2004*

ST HILAIRE DE LUSIGNAN see Agen *8E3*

ST HILAIRE DE RIEZ *2H3* (Coastal) **Camp Municipal de La Plage de Riez, Ave des Mimosas,** 85270 St Hilaire-de-Riez [02 51 54 36 59; fax 02 51 60 07 84; riez85@free.fr] Fr St Hilaire take D6A sp Sion-sur-l'Ocean. Turn R at traff lts into Ave des Mimosas, site 1st L. V lge, pt sl, shd; wc; some serviced pitch; shwrs inc; el pts (10A) €3.10; gas; lndtte; ice; shop; rest; snacks; bar; playgrnd; pool 5km; sand beach adj; cycle hire; TV; entmnt; 30% statics; dogs; poss cr; Eng spkn; red low ssn. "Vg for dogs; exceptionally helpful manager." 8 Apr-1 Nov. € 13.90
2005*

ST HILAIRE DE RIEZ *2H3* (Coastal) **Camp Municipal de la Plage de Sion,** 85270 St Hilaire-de-Riez [02 51 54 34 23; fax 02 51 60 07 84; sion85@free.fr; www.souslespins.com] Fr St Hilaire, take D6A sp Sion-sur-l'Ocean, strt at traff lts. Site 200m on R. Lge, mkd pitch, pt shd; 80% serviced pitch; wc; chem disp; mv service pnt; shwrs inc; el pts (10A) €3.10; lndtte; ice; shop, rest, snacks, bar 400m; playgrnd; pool 1km; sand beach adj; 15% statics; dogs €2.40; phone; Eng spkn; adv bkg rec high ssn; quiet; CCI. "Gd for family holidays; vg long stay." ♦ 5 Apr-31 Oct. € 22.00 (3 persons)
2004*

ST HILAIRE DE RIEZ *2H3* (Coastal) **Camping La Ningle, Chemin des Roselieres,** 85270 St Hilaire-de-Riez [02 51 54 07 11 or 02 51 54 16 65 (LS); fax 02 51 54 99 39; camping delaningle@wanadoo.fr] Fr St Hilaire, take rd sp Sion-sur-l'Ocean. At traff lts/rndabt, foll sp 'Autres Campings' until site sp is seen. Med, hdg/mkd pitch, pt shd, wc; chem disp; serviced pitches; shwrs inc; el pts (6A) €2.13; gas; lndtte; shop; tradsmn; bar; playgrnd; pool; sand beach 500m; tennis; fitness rm; poss cr; adv bkg (dep req) & bkg fee; dogs €3; Eng spkn; red low ssn; CCI. "Highly rec; v friendly & personal; gd sized pitches; well-maintained; excel long stay." ♦ ltd. 15 May-15 Sep. € 17.50
2003*

ST HILAIRE DE RIEZ *2H3* (2km N Urban/Coastal) **Camping Cap Natur (Naturist), 151 Ave de la Faye,** 85270 St Hilaire-de-Riez [02 51 60 11 66; fax 02 51 60 17 48; info@cap-natur.com; www.cap-natur.com] Via D69 fr Challans after Le Pissot turn R at 1st rndabt; R at next rndabt; fork R in approx 300m; site on L approx 600m. Med, hdg/mkd pitch, pt sl, pt terr, pt shd; htd wc; chem disp; mv service pnt; baby facs; sauna; shwrs inc; el pts (10A) €4.20; gas; lndtte; ice; shop & 1km; tradsmn; rest; snacks; bar; BBQ; playgrnd; 2 htd pools (1 covrd); sand/shgl beach 800m (naturist beach 6km); games area; games rm; cycle hire; golf 10km; entmnt; many statics; dogs €2.20; poss cr; Eng spkn; adv bkg (dep req); quiet; 20% red 20+ days/low ssn; cc acc; INF card req (can purchase on site). "Gd cent for interesting area; v friendly staff; gd facs; v sm pitches; can by busy; excel." ♦ 3 Apr-1 Nov. € 27.50 (CChq acc)
2005*

ST HILAIRE DE RIEZ *2H3* (2km N Coastal) **Camping La Pomme de Pin, Ave des Becs,** 85270 St Hilaire-de-Riez [02 51 58 21 26; fax 02 51 59 52 23; www.homair-vacances.fr] Take coast rd SE fr St Jean-de-Monts. Foll sp Les Mouettes, site on L. Lge; wc; shwrs inc; el pts (6A) inc; lndtte; ice; supmkt 500m; tradsmn; rest; snacks; playgrnd; pool; sand beach 100m; games rm; poss cr; adv bkg; quiet. 1 May-25 Sep.
2003*

FRANCE

ST HILAIRE DE RIEZ *2H3* (6km N Rural) **Camping La Puerta del Sol, Les Borderies, 85270 St Hilaire-de-Riez** [02 51 49 10 10; fax 02 51 49 84 84; info@campinglapuertadelsol. com; www.campinglapuertadelsol.com] N on D38 fr Les Sables-d'Olonne; exit on D69 sp Soullan, Challans, Le Pissot. At next rndabt take 3rd exit & foll lge sp to site. Site on R in 1.5km. Lge, hdg/mkd pitch, pt sl, pt shd; wc (some cont); chem disp; serviced pitches; baby facs; shwrs inc; el pts (6A) inc (poss rev pol); gas; lndtte; ice; shop, rest, snacks, bar high ssn; BBQ (gas/elec); playgrnd; htd pool; paddling pool; waterslide; sand beach 5km; watersports 5km; fishing 2km; tennis; horseriding; golf; cycle hire; games area; games rm; entmnt; internet; TV rm; 15% statics; dogs €3.50; Eng spkn; adv bkg; quiet; cc acc; CCI. "Vg; red facs low ssn." ♦ 1 Apr-30 Sep. € 28.00 ABS - A19   2005*

Mustn't forget to post our site report forms to The Club, otherwise sites might be deleted.

ST HILAIRE DE RIEZ *2H3* (1km NW) **Camping Le Chateau Vieux, 50 Rue du Chateau Vieux, 85270 St Hilaire-de-Riez** [02 51 54 35 88; fax 02 51 54 33 97] Fr St Gilles-Croix-de-Vie head NW twd St Hilaire-de-Riez on D38B. Look for sp to L to site approx 1km out of St Hilaire just bef rndabt. Lge, pt shd; wc (some cont); shwrs inc; el pts (6A) inc; lndtte; ice; shop; farm produce 1km; playgrnd; htd pool; sand beach 5km; jacuzzi; TV; entmnt; poss cr; adv bkg; quiet. "Nr fishing port with beautiful beaches; excursions & excel seafood rest." 8 May-15 Sep. € 25.00 (3 persons)   2002*

ST HILAIRE DE RIEZ *2H3* (2km NW) **Camping Les Chouans, 108 Ave de la Faye, 85270 St Hilaire-de-Riez** [02 51 54 34 90 or 02 51 54 33 87; fax 02 51 55 33 87; leschouans@free.fr or idees@sunmarina.com; www.sunmarina.com] Take main rd fr St Gilles-Croix-de-Vie to St Hilaire. At rndabt foll sps for St Hilaire to 2nd rndabt. Foll sps for Sion cont for La Pege. Pass 2 sites, Les Chouans is 3rd. Lge, pt shd; wc; baby facs; shwrs inc; el pts (6-10A); lndtte; lndry rm; shop; rest; snacks; bar; BBQ (gas); playgrnd; htd pool; beach & waterslide 1.3km; games area; fitness rm; child club; entmnt; TV; 70% statics; dogs €3; quiet. "Lge pitches." ♦ 14 Apr-30 Sep. € 29.00 (3 persons)   2004*

ST HILAIRE DE RIEZ *2H3* (5km NW Coastal) **Camping La Paree Preneau, 23 Ave de la Paree Preneau, 85270 St Hilaire-de-Riez** [02 51 54 33 84 or 02 51 54 41 16 (LS); fax 02 51 55 29 57; camplapareepreneau@wanadoo.fr; www.camping lapareepreneau.com] Fr N on D38; on reaching St Hilaire-de-Riez at 1st rndabt take 1st exit sp Sion-sur-l'Olcean and St Hilaire-de-Riez centre. At next rndabt take 1st exit (petrol station on R) sp La Paree Preneau & bear R soon after rndabt again sp La Paree Preneau; site on L in 2km. Or fr Les Sables-d'Olonne N on D38, go thro St Gilles-Croix-de-Vie & pass St Hilaire-de-Riez; at rndabt turn L sp Sion-sur-l'Ocean & St Hilaire-de-Riez centre, then as above. Lge, mkd pitch, pt sl, pt shd; wc (some cont); baby facs; shwrs inc; el pts (6A) inc; lndtte; sm shop; tradsmn; bar; BBQ (charcoal/gas; playgrnd; 2 pools (1 htd/covrd); jacuzzi; beach 1km; fishing 1km; windsurfing 5km; cycle hire; entmnt; TV/games rm; dogs €2; recep 0900-1930; c'vans over 7m not acc; Eng spkn; adv bkg; red low ssn; cc acc high ssn (not Amex); CCI. "Gd, simple site; card op night barrier; pool poss unsupervised at times, care req with young children; some pitches poss tight lge o'fits; mkt Thu & Sun." ♦ 20 May-9 Sep. € 21.00 ABS - A29   2005*

ST HILAIRE DU HARCOUET *2E4* (1km W Urban) **Camp Municipal de la Selune, 50600 St Hilaire-du-Harcouet** [02 33 49 43 74 or 02 33 49 70 06; fax 02 33 49 59 40] Sp on N side of N176 twd Mont St Michel/St Malo/Dinan, on W side of town; well sp. Med, hdg pitch, pt sl, pt shd; wc; chem disp; shwrs inc; el pts (6A); lndry rm; shops 1km; snacks 500m; playgrnd; pool 300m; dogs; gate locked 2200-0730; 15% red 20+ days; 10% red CCI. "Easy access; v helpful & pleasant warden; vet practice on corner with N176; poss lge groups of noisy youths; excel long/sh stay low ssn." Easter-15 Sep. € 11.80   2004*

ST HILAIRE LA FORET *7A1* (Rural) **Camping La Grand' Metairie, 8 Rue de la Vineuse-en-Plaine, 85440 St Hilaire-la-Foret** [02 51 33 32 38; fax 02 51 33 25 69; grand-metairie@wanadoo.fr; www.la-grand-metairie.com] Fr D949 turn S onto D70, sp St Hilaire-la-Foret, or fr Avrille take D19. Site at ent to vill. Lge, hdg/mkd pitch, hdstg, pt shd; wc; chem disp; serviced pitches; sauna; shwrs inc; el pts (6A) inc; gas; lndtte; ice; shop; tradsmn; rest; snacks; bar; playgrnd; htd, covrd pool; paddling pool; sand beach 3km; tennis; jacuzzi; fitness rm; play rm; mini-golf; cycle hire; entmnt & child entmnt; table tennis; golf 15km; 80% statics; dogs €3; Eng spkn; adv bkg (dep req + bkg fee); quiet; red low ssn/long stay; cc acc; red CCI. "Gd base for beaches, La Rochelle, Ile de Re; friendly & helpful owners; excel." ♦ 25 Mar-23 Sep. € 26.00   2005*

ST HILAIRE LA FORET *7A1* (4km SW Rural) Camping Les Batardieres, 85440 St Hilaire-la-Foret [02 51 33 33 85] Fr Sables d'Olonne take D949 twd Avrille. 7km after Talmont-St-Hilaire fork R on D70 to St Hilaire-la-Foret. In 3km turn R on ent vill. Site 70m on L. Med, hdg pitch, pt shd; wc; chem disp; shwrs inc; el pts (6A) €3; lndtte; ice; shop adj; playgrnd; sand beach 5km; tennis; cycling; 75% statics; dogs €1.50; adv bkg; quiet; CCI. "Excel; spacious pitches; wide choice of beaches; excel for children & families; rec." 1 Jul-6 Sep. € 14.00
2002*

ST HILAIRE ST FLORENT see Saumur *4G1*

ST HIPPOLYTE *6G3* (Urban) Camping Les Grands Champs, 25190 St Hippolyte [03 81 96 54 53] To R of D121 fr St Hippolyte to Montecheroux, side rd thro sm housing est. Site sp next to stadium. Med, pt sl, terr, pt shd; wc; shwrs; el pts (10A) inc; lndtte; shops 750m; playgrnd; fishing; quiet; CCI. "Walks/scenery good; direct access to rv; vg long stay." 1 May-15 Sep. € 10.55
2003*

ST HONORE LES BAINS *4H4* (150m Rural) Camp Municipal Plateau du Guet, 13 Rue Eugene Collin, 58360 St Honore-les-Bains [03 86 30 76 00 or 03 86 30 74 87 (Mairie); fax 03 86 30 73 33; mairie-de-st-honore-les-bains@wanadoo.fr] On D985 fr Luzy to St Honore-les-Bains. In cent vill turn L on D106 twd Vandenesse. Site on L in 150m. Or N fr Chateau-Chinon 27km. Then D985 to St Honore. Med, pt hdstg, pt terr, pt shd; wc; shwrs inc; el pts (10A) €2.50; lndry rm; shop; snacks 100m; playgrnd; pool 1km; adv bkg; quiet; CCI. "V clean facs; excel site but town rather run down." ◆ 1 Apr-10 Oct. € 8.10
2005*

ST HONORE LES BAINS *4H4* (1km W Rural) Camping Les Bains, 15 Ave Mermoz, 58360 St Honore-les-Bains [03 86 30 73 44; fax 03 86 30 61 88; camping-les-bains@wanadoo.fr; www.campinglesbains.com] Fr St Honore-les-Bains foll site sp as 'Village des Bains' fr town cent on D106 twd Vandenesse. Med, hdg/mkd pitch, some hdstg, pt sl, shd; wc (some cont); chem disp; baby facs; shwrs inc; el pts (6A) inc; gas; lndtte; shop 1km; rest; snacks; bar; BBQ; playgrnd; pool; waterslide; fishing; tennis; mini-golf; horseriding 300m; cycle hire; entmnt; dogs €1.50; recep 0830-2200; c'vans over 8m not acc; Eng spkn; adv bkg; quiet low ssn; cc acc; CCI. "Vg site, helpful staff; adj Morvan Regional Nature Park; gd walking; sm pitches & poss waterlogged in wet weather; mkt Thu am." ◆ 15 Mar-31 Oct. € 18.70
ABS - L01
2005*

ST JACQUES DES BLATS *7C4* (Rural) Camp Municipal des Blats, Route de la Gare, 15800 St Jacques-des-Blats [04 71 47 06 00 or 04 71 47 05 90 (Mairie); fax 04 71 47 07 09; i-tourisme-st-jacques@wanadoo.fr] L of N122 Murat to Aurillac; 3km W of Horan Tunnel in vill of St Jacques-des-Blats; 300m fr N122 down steep app rd; sp in vill. Sm, hdg pitch, pt shd; wc; chem disp; shwrs; el pts (10A) €2.40; lndtte; ice; shops 500m; BBQ; playgrnd; mini-golf; TV; 30% statics; quiet; CCI. "Gd British-owned hotel for meals & bar nrby; 4 rests within walking dist; gd walking & VTT trails fr site; lift to summit Plomb de Cantal; vg mountain walks." 1 May-30 Sep. € 8.80
2005*

ST JANS CAPPEL see Bailleul *3A3*

ST JEAN D'ANGELY *7B2* (Urban) Camping du Val de Boutonne, Quai de Bernouet, 17400 St Jean-d'Angely [05 46 32 26 16; fax 05 46 32 29 54; ville@angely.net] Exit A10 at junc 34. Head SE on D939, site sp in town. Med, mkd pitch, shd; wc (mainly cont); chem disp; shwrs inc; el pts (6-10A) €2.80-3; tradsmn; playgrnd; pool nr; some statics; dogs €1; quiet; CCI. "Clean site by Rv Boutonne; v gd san facs; v friendly; camping area pleasant & flat; park with boating lake & rv adj." ◆ 15 May-30 Sep.
€ 11.50
2005*

ST JEAN DE CEYRARGUES see Ales *10E1*

ST JEAN DE COUZ see Echelles, Les *9B3*

ST JEAN DE LOSNE *6H1* Camping Essi Les Herlequins, 21170 St Jean-de-Losne [03 80 39 22 26; fax 03 80 29 05 48; www.saintjeandelosne.com] Site sp on ent town fr N on D968. Access fr town on Quai National & Rue du Port-Bernard on N bank of Rv Saone. Med, hdg/mkd pitch, hdstg, pt shd; wc (some cont); shwrs; el pts (10A); ice; rest; snacks; BBQ; playgrnd; sand beach; rv sw; dogs €1.14; poss cr; adv bkg; quiet. "Fair for sh stay; 10 mins walk fr town cent; v helpful, friendly owners." 1 May-30 Sep. € 13.60
2005*

ST JEAN DE LUZ *8F1* (3km N Coastal) Camping Bord de Mer, Erromardie, 64500 St Jean-de-Luz [tel/fax 05 59 26 24 61] Exit A63 junc 3 onto N10 dir St Jean-de-Luz. In 1km cross rlwy & immed turn sharp R sp Erromardie. Site on sharp turn L bef beach. Ent by plastic chain fence bef ent to prom, but easy to miss. Med, hdg pitch, pt sl; terr; wc (mainly cont); chem disp; mv service pnt; shwrs inc; el pts (6-10A) €3; lndry rm; tradsmn; snacks; bar; BBQ; playgrnd; sand beach adj; dogs; quiet. "Cliff walk to town; views over superb, clean beach; old facs ltd but clean; friendly owner; recept clsd 1300-1600; gd sh stay en route Spain." ◆ ltd.
1 Mar-30 Oct. € 18.00
2004*

FRANCE

ST JEAN DE LUZ *8F1* (3km N Coastal) Camping de la Ferme Erromardie, 64500 St Jean-de-Luz [05 59 26 34 26; fax 05 59 51 26 02] Exit A63 junc 3 onto N10 sp St Jean-de-Luz. After 1km x rlwy and turn immed sharp R sp Erromardie. Site ent on R in 1km just bef rest/bar. Lge, hdg/mkd pitch, shd; wc; chem disp; mv service pnt; baby facs; shwrs inc; el pts (4-6A) €2.30-3; gas; lndtte; tradsmn; rest; snacks; bar; playgrnd; beach adj; dogs €0.60; poss cr; Eng spkn; adv bkg; CCI. "Ideal for coastal walk into St Jean-de-Luz; Basque museum nrby; san facs down steps & poss stretched high ssn; gd long/sh stay." 15 Mar-15 Oct. € 18.50   2005*

ST JEAN DE LUZ *8F1* (3km N Urban/Coastal) Camping International Erromardie, Ave de la Source, 64500 St Jean-de-Luz [05 59 26 07 74; fax 05 59 51 12 11; camping-international@wanadoo.fr; www.erromardie.com] Fr A63 exit junc 3 sp St Jean-de-Luz. At traff lts at end of slip rd turn L onto N10 sp St Jean; in 1km cross rlwy & immed turn sharp R sp Erromardie, site on R in 1km opp beach. Lge, hdg/mkd pitch, pt sl, shd; wc (some cont); chem disp (wc); shwrs inc; el pts (5A) inc; lndtte; shop; rest; snacks; bar; BBQ (charcoal); playgrnd; pool; sand/shgl beach adj; fishing 2km; watersports 3km; golf, entmnt; TV rm; many statics; dogs €2; c'vans over 7m not acc high ssn; adv bkg; quiet; cc acc. "Mkt Tue & Fri am; some facs poss clsd & office clsd after 1800 low ssn; poss poor security; twin-axle c'vans acc." 8 Apr-30 Sep. € 29.00 ABS - A17   2005*

ST JEAN DE LUZ *8F1* (1.5km NE Coastal) Camping Iratzia, Chemin d'Erromardie, 64500 St Jean-de-Luz [05 59 26 14 89; fax 05 59 26 69 69] Fr A63 exit St Jean-de-Luz Nord. Join N10 twds St Jean; after Shell g'ge cross rlwy bdge & immed turn R sp Erromardie. Site on R in 500m. Lge, pt terr, pt sl, pt shd; wc; shwrs inc; el pts (6A) €3.50; lndry rm; ice; shop; rest; bar; playgrnd; sand beach 300m; TV; entmnt; dogs €1; phone; poss cr; adv bkg; red low ssn; CCI. "Poss some noise fr young tenters & chalets; many pitches diff access for long o'fits; friendly, well-kept, clean site." 1 May-30 Sep.
          2005*

ST JEAN DE LUZ *8F1* (3km NE Coastal) Camping Le Maya, Quartier Acotz, 64500 St Jean-de-Luz [05 59 26 54 91; CampingMaya@aol.com] Fr N exit A63 at Biarritz Sud onto N10 head SW. After passing thro Guethary turn W off N10 sp Acotz, foll camping sp. Or fr S exit junc 3 sp St Jean-de-Luz onto N10, as above. Med, mkd pitch, terr, pt shd; wc; chem disp; shwrs; el pts (6A) €3; gas; shops adj; hypmkt 1km; rest, snacks 300m; bar; playgrnd; sand beach 500m; dogs €2; adv bkg; quiet; Eng spkn; CCI. "Gd long stay/NH." 25 Jun-25 Sep. € 17.80   2004*

ST JEAN DE LUZ *8F1* (4km NE Rural) Camping Atlantica, Quartier Acotz, 64500 St Jean-de-Luz [05 59 47 72 44; fax 05 59 54 72 27; camping@club-internet.fr; www.campingatlantica.com] Exit A63 at junc 3 sp St Jean-de-Luz-Nord. Take (N10) twd Biarritz at top of hill sp Acotz Plage; site well sp. Lge, mkd pitch, pt sl, pt shd; wc; mv service pnt; shwrs inc; baby facs; el pts (6A) €3.80; lndtte; shop; rest; snacks; bar; playgrnd; pool; beach 500m; entmnt; games/TV rm; 35% statics; dogs €2.30; bus; poss cr; Eng spkn; adv bkg (dep €61 + bkg fee €15); quiet but some rd & train noise; cc acc; CCI. "Excel pool; facs ltd low ssn; excel all stays." ♦ 15 Mar-15 Sep. € 23.00   2004*

†ST JEAN DE LUZ *8F1* (4km NE Coastal) Camping Duna-Munguy, Plage Senisc, 64500 Acotz [05 59 47 70 70; fax 05 59 47 78 82] Exit A63 at junc 3 St Jean-de-Luz Nord. Take N10 twd Biarritz, turn L at 2nd rise then R at T-junc & down hill under rlwy bdge sp Acotz Plages. Site well sp. NB Steep downhill app. Sm, mkd pitch, hdstg, pt shd; htd wc; chem disp; shwrs inc; jacuzzi; el pts (10A) €3.50 (poss rev pol); lndtte; playgrnd; pool; sandy beach 300m; golf 5km; TV; 90% statics; dogs €3; phone; site clsd 15 Dec-15 Jan; poss cr; Eng spkn; adv bkg; quiet but rlwy noise; cc not acc; CCI. "Steep app poss diff long o'fits & ltd space on site; gd san facs; helpful owner; conv on way to Spain; site 1 of 10 in area; no sea views but sheltered in storms; pitches have patio, table/chairs & washing line; smart shwrs; excel." € 22.00   2005*

ST JEAN DE LUZ *8F1* (4km NE Coastal) **Camping Merko Lacarra, Plage d'Acotz, 64500 St Jean-de-Luz [05 59 26 56 76; fax 05 59 54 73 81; contact@merkolacarra.com; www.merkolacarra. com]** Exit A63 at junc 3 St Jean-de-Luz Nord. Take N10 twd Biarritz, turn L at 2nd rise then R at T-junc & down hill under rlwy bdge sp Acotz Plages, site on L. NB steep downhill app. Med, pt sl, pt shd; wc; chem disp; shwrs; el pts (16A) £3.80; lndtte; shop; snacks; bar; sand beach over rd; 15% statics; dogs €1.50; m'van o'night sep area; Eng spkn; quiet; cc acc; CCI. "Lovely walking/cycling along coast; poss cr high ssn; conv foothills Pyrenees." ♦ 27 Mar-30 Oct. € 23.00   2005*

ST JEAN DE LUZ *8F1* (4km NE Coastal) **Camping-Plage Soubelet, Quartier Acotz, 64500 St Jean-de-Luz [05 59 26 51 60]** Fr St Jean take N10 twd Biarritz. Bef Guethary turn L to Acotz/ Plages. Turn R down hill, under rlwy bdge & turn L. Site on R in 300m. Lge, mkd pitch, hdstg, pt shd; htd wc; chem disp; baby facs; shwrs inc; el pts (12A) €2.75; lndtte; shop; snacks; playgrnd; sand beach adj; 5% statics; poss cr; Eng spkn. "Gd sea views; peaceful, poss ltd san facs in low ssn & stretched high sssn, rec own san facs; poss unkempt; conv Bidart for rests, shops etc." Easter-30 Oct. € 16.60
                    2004*

ST JEAN DE LUZ *8F1* (5km NE Coastal) **Camping Inter-Plages, 64500 Acotz [05 59 26 56 94]** Fr St Jean-de-Luz take N10 twd Biarritz. Bef Guethary turn L at top of hill at sp Acotz/Plages. Foll rd over rlwy bdge to sea & site. Med, pt shd; wc; chem disp; baby facs; shwrs inc; el pts (6-10A) €3.50-4.50; lndtte; shop & rest adj; playgrnd; sand beach 150m; 10% statics; dogs €2; quiet; red low ssn. "Site at top of cliffs with steep path to beach; sea views fr some pitches; helpful family owners; v diff for lge o'fits - narr rds." ♦ 1 Apr-30 Sep. € 21.00
                    2003*

ST JEAN DE LUZ *8F1* (5km NE Coastal) **Camping Les Tarmaris Plage, 64500 St Jean-de-Luz [05 59 26 55 90; fax 05 59 47 70 15; contact@ tamaris-plage.com]** Fr A63 take St Jean-de-Luz Nord exit. Turn R sp Guethary. After 1km turn L sp Acotz, Campings-Plages. Then foll sps to Tamaris Plage. Med, mkd pitch, pt sl, pt shd; wc; chem disp; baby facs; shwrs inc; el pts (5A) inc; gas; lndtte; ice; shop, rest, snacks, bar 1.5km; BBQ; playgrnd; beach adj; child club; entmnt; TV rm; phone; poss cr; poss noisy; Eng spkn; red low ssn; CCI. "Under personal supervision of owner; do not arrive bet 1200-1400; luxurious facs block has fountain & flowers; excel." ♦ 1 Apr-30 Sep. € 29.00   2004*

ST JEAN DE LUZ *8F1* (5km NE Coastal) **Caravaning Playa, 64500 Acotz [tel/fax 05 59 26 55 85]** Fr St Jean-de-Luz take N10 twd Biarritz. Before Guethary turn L at sp Acotz-Plages. Turn L at T-junc & foll rd to site. Med, mkd pitch, terr, pt shd; wc; chem disp; shwrs inc; el pts (4A) inc; lndtte; shop; snacks; sand/shgl beach adj; fishing; boating; dogs; poss cr; noisy nr rd; cc acc; CCI. "V pretty site overlooking lovely beach." ♦ 1 Apr-30 Oct. € 23.60   2003*

ST JEAN DE LUZ *8F1* (6km E) **Camping d'Ascain, 64310 Ascain [05 59 54 40 61; fax 05 59 54 46 79; camping.ascain@wanadoo.fr]** Fr A63 exit junc 2 onto N10 to St Jean-de-Luz. Take D918 sp Ascain, St Pee. In 6km site on R after town sp. Med, shd; wc (most cont); chem disp; mv service pnt; shwrs inc; el pts (10-16A) €3; gas; ice; shop & 500m; playgrnd; pool adj; beach 6km; sea fishing 5km; cycle hire; entmnt & child entmnt; TV; no statics; dogs €1; Eng spkn; adv bkg; quiet; red low ssn. 1 Apr-30 Sep. € 17.00   2002*

As we're travelling out of season, we'd better phone ahead to check that the site is actually open.

ST JEAN DE LUZ *8F1* (6km SE Urban) **Camping Chourio, Luberriaga, 64310 Ascain [05 59 54 06 31 or 05 59 54 04 32]** Fr St Jean-de-Luz take D918 sp Ascain. In 6km turn R at traff lts, in 250m over rv bdge & turn L at mini-rndabt. Site sp in town. Med, pt shd; wc; chem disp; shwrs €1; el pts (6A) €2.40; tradsmn; rest, snacks, bar 1km; poss cr; quiet; CCI. "Conv Spanish border; facs tired but clean & adequate." 1 Apr-31 Oct. € 9.50   2004*

ST JEAN DE LUZ *8F1* (10km SE) **Camping d'Ibarron, 64310 St Pee-sur-Nivelle [05 59 54 10 43; fax 05 59 54 51 95; camping.dibarron@wanadoo. fr; www.camping-ibarron.com]** Fr St Jean take D918 twd St Pee, site 2km bef St Pee on R of rd. Lge, shd; wc (mainly cont); chem disp; shwrs inc; el pts (6A) €3.20; gas 3km; lndtte; shop, tradsmn, snacks high ssn; playgrnd; sand beach 10km; tennis; 5% statics; dogs €1.30; phone; Eng spkn; adv bkg; quiet; CCI. "Helpful, pleasant owner; excel site; ltd facs low ssn." ♦ 1 May-20 Sep. € 13.50
                    2004*

ST JEAN DE LUZ *8F1* (10km SE Rural) **Camping Goyetchea, Route d'Ahetze, 64310 St Pee-sur-Nivelle [05 59 54 19 59; c-goyetchea@wanadoo.fr; www.camping-goyetchea.com]** Fr St Jean-de-Luz take D918 twd St Pee-sur-Nivelle. Turn L at Hotel Bonnet at Ibarron D855. Site on R in 800m. Med, pt shd; wc (some cont); chem disp; baby facs; shwrs inc; el pts (6A) €3.50; gas; lndry rm; ice; shop; supmkt 800m; tradsmn; rest; snacks; BBQ; playgrnd; pool; sand beach 10km; lake sw 4km; games area; entmnt; 10% statics; dogs €1.50; adv bkg; quiet; cc acc; red low ssn; CCI. "Pleasant, quiet site; vg long/sh stay." ♦ 3 Jun-16 Sep. € 18.00   2005*

See advertisement

Camping du Col d'Ibardin

Basque Country

Located between Biarritz (25 kms) and San Sebastian (25kms), our campsite will please the chidren as much as their parents

Swimming Pool / Tennis / Playground / Bar/ Snack / Take Away / Launderette / Kid's Club / Mobil homes to rent...

Tél. : (00 33) 559 54 31 21 • Fax : (00 33) 559 54 62 28 • 64122 Urrugne • www.col-ibardin.com • info@col-ibardin.com

†ST JEAN DE LUZ 8F1 (3km SW) Camping Larrouleta, 64122 Urrugne [05 59 47 37 84; fax 05 59 47 42 54; info@larrouleta.com; www.larrouleta.com] Exit A63 junc 2 onto N10 S for 500m. Turn R & R again into site. Or fr S on N10, 2km beyond Urrugne vill (by-pass vill), turn L into minor rd, site 50m on R. Lge, hdg/mkd pitch, hdstg, pt shd; htd wc; chem disp; baby facs; shwrs inc; el pts (5A) €2; gas; lndtte; ice; shop; hypmkt 1.5km; tradsmn; rest (Jul/Aug); snacks; bar; playgrnd; htd pool; lake sw, fishing & boating; sand beach 3km; tennis; games; entmnt; dogs; phone; bus; poss cr; some Eng spkn; adv bkg ess high ssn; rd/rlwy noise & poss noise fr disco; red low ssn; cc acc; CCI. "Pleasant, well-maintained, clean site nr lake; excel san facs; friendly, helpful warden (ask for dir on departure to avoid dangerous bend); some pitches unreliable in wet but can park on site rds if site not busy; poss ltd facs low ssn; poor facs for disabled; conv a'route & Biarritz; excel en rte Spain." ♦ € 15.00   2005*

We're having a great holiday - must fill in some site report forms and send them to The Club as soon as possible.

ST JEAN DE LUZ 8F1 (4km SW Coastal) Camping Juantcho, Route de la Corniche, Socoa, 64122 Urrugne [tel/fax 05 59 47 11 97; camping.juantcho.com; www.camping-juantcho.com] Leave A63 at junc 2. Keep to L lane & immed after passing toll booth take exit to Socoa, site on R on cliff top rd. Lge, mkd pitch, terr, pt shd; wc; chem disp; shwrs inc; el pts (5A) inc; lndtte; ice; shop & snacks in ssn; playgrnd; beach, fishing & watersports 500m; entmnts 500m; some statics; dogs €1.20; poss cr; quiet; CCI. "V helpful staff; beautiful beach, 10 min walk fr site; rd busy & steep; ltd facs low ssn." 1 May-30 Sep. € 16.60   2004*

ST JEAN DE LUZ 8F1 (7km SW Rural) Camping Aire-Ona, 64122 Urrugne [tel/fax 05 59 54 30 32] S fr Bayonne on N10, take A63 by-passing St Jean-de-Luz. Take Urrugne exit, immed E sp Ascain & camping sp. Fr St Jean-de-Luz exit by N10, turn R sp 'Frontiere par Behobie' past m'way access & turn R in 1km. Site in 1km. Last 500m of app narr but surface gd. Med, pt sl, pt shd; wc; shwrs inc; el pts (4A) inc; gas; lndtte; ice; shop & 4km; BBQ; playgrnd; sand beach, sailing, watersports 5km; cycle hire; adv bkg; quiet. "Pleasant owners resident; gd views of Pyrenees foothills; La Rhune funicular 10km." 1 Jun-30 Sep. € 15.00   2004*

This site entry hasn't been updated for a while; we'd better fill in a site report form and send it to The Club.

ST JEAN DE LUZ 8F1 (7km SW Rural) Camping du Col d'Ibardin, Route d'Ascain, 64122 Urrugne [05 59 54 31 21; fax 05 59 54 62 28; info@col-ibardin.com; www.col-ibardin.com] Turn L off N10 onto D4; at rndbt foll sp Col d'Ibardin Ascain; site on R immed past minor rd to Col d'Ibardin. Med, hdg/mkd pitch, pt sl, pt terr, pt shd; 5% serviced pitch; wc; chem disp; baby facs; shwrs inc; el pts (4-10A) €3.50-5.20 (rev pol); gas; lndtte; ice; shop; tradsmn; supmkt 5km; rest, snacks & bar in ssn; BBQ; playgrnd; pool; paddling pool; sand beach 6km; cycle hire; tennis; TV; 5% statics; dogs €1.60; phone; Eng spkn; adv bkg; quiet; cc acc; CCI. "Helpful owner; mountain rlwy nr; excel san facs; gd walking; gd touring base for Pyrenees & N Spain." ♦ 1 Apr-30 Sep. € 21.00   2005*

See advertisement above

ST JEAN DE MAURIENNE *9C3* (Urban) Camp Municipal des Grands Cols, Ave du Mont-Cenis, 73300 St Jean-de-Maurienne [tel/fax 04 79 64 28 02; camping@saintjeandemaurienne.fr; www.saint jeandemaurienne.fr /tourisme/campfr.html] Site sp fr N6 in St Jean-de-Maurienne; site behind shops 100m fr Pont-d'Arvan twds town cent behind trees/parking. Med, hdg/mkd pitch, pt sl, pt shd; wc; chem disp; mv service pnt; 20% serviced pitches; shwrs inc; el pts (16A) €3; lndtte; ice; supmkt 1km; tradsmn; rest; snacks; bar; playgrnd; pool 1.5km; lake 3km; games rm; TV; dogs €1; Eng spkn; quiet; red low ssn; CCI. "V helpful staff; gd site rest; gd mountain views; conv interesting town cent; gd NH prior to Frejus tunnel; friendly staff; clean san facs; extremely kind, helpful manager." 15 May-30 Sep. € 11.00   2005*

ST JEAN DE MAURIENNE *9C3* (10km SW Rural) Camping Caravaneige du Col, Fontcouverte, 73300 La Toussuire [04 79 83 00 80; fax 04 79 83 03 67; campingducol@free.fr] Fr Chambery E on A43 to St Jean-de-Maurienne. In St Jean foll sp Vallee de l'Arvan. Site on L after vill of Fontcouverte, 1km bef vill of La Toussuire. Sm, terr, pt shd; htd wc (some cont); chem disp; mv service pnt; baby facs; shwrs inc; el pts (10A) €4.30; gas; lndry rm; rest; snacks; bar; playgrnd; TV: drying-room & skiboot storage; adv bkg; quiet; 5% red CCI. "Excel welcome; site owner runs navette to vill, 1km fr ski-lifts; clean san facs up external flight of stairs." 11 Jun-4 Sep & 15 Dec-30 Apr. € 10.65   2005*

ST JEAN DE MONTS *2H3* (Coastal) Camping Les Places Dorees, Route de Notre Dame de Monts, 85160 St Jean-de-Monts [02 51 59 02 93 or 02 40 73 03 70 (LS); fax 02 51 59 30 47; abridespins@aol.com; www.placesdorees.com] Fr Nantes dir Challons & St Jean-de-Monts. Then dir Notre Dame-de-Monts. Med, pt sl, shd; wc; chem disp; shwrs inc; el pts (2-10A); gas; lndtte; ice; shop adj; tradsmn; rest; snacks; sand beach 800m; htd pool; waterslides; sports area; games rm; entmnt; dogs €2.80; Eng spkn; adv bkg; quiet; CCI. "Vg; free entmnt children/adults; organised excursions; friendly family-run site; mountain views." ♦ 1 Jun-10 Sep. € 30.00 3 persons   2004*

ST JEAN DE MONTS *2H3* (Urban/Coastal) CCDF Les Sirenes, Ave des Demoiselles, 85160 St Jean-de-Monts [02 51 58 01 31; fax 02 51 59 03 67; secretariat@campingclub.asso.fr; www.camping club.asso.fr] Site in town cent; ent town on D753 fr dir Chalons, turn R at junct, then 1st L at church. Take 2nd L (Ave des Demoiselles). Site on L. V lge, pt sl, shd; wc; chem disp; shwrs inc; el pts (3-10A); gas; lndtte; ice; shops adj; rest; snacks; bar; pool 1km; sand beach 500m; fishing, watersports 500m; entmnt; dogs €1.70; adv bkg ess high ssn; quiet. "Sh walk thro pines to beach; mem'ship to CCDF avail." ♦ 28 Mar-30 Sep. € 18.60   2002*

ST JEAN DE MONTS *2H3* (2km Urban) Camping Le Bois Dormant, 168 Rue de Sables, 85167 St Jean-de-Monts [02 51 58 01 30; fax 02 51 59 35 30; boisdormant@siblu.fr; www.siblu.com] Fr Challans pass thro Le Perrier & on coming to St Jean-de-Monts, at 1st rndabt take last exit dir Les Sables d'Olonne. Foll Les Sables dirs to 4th rndabt, turn R, site on L. V lge, hdg/mkd pitch, pt shd; htd wc; chem disp; mv service pnt; serviced pitches; baby facs; shwrs inc; el pts (6A) inc; gas; lndtte; ice; shop; tradsmn; rest; snacks; bar; playgrnd; htd pool; waterslide; sand beach 2.5km; tennis; sports area; entmnt; child entmnt; TV/games rm; statics; no dogs; poss cr; Eng spkn; adv bkg; red low ssn; CCI. "Excel; access to sister site with disco & entmnt; various sports facs; children's club." ♦ 29 Apr-9 Sep. € 144.00 (7 nights)   2005*

See advertisement on next page

Some of these sites have changed their opening dates - we'd better fill in some site report forms and let the editor of the guide know.

ST JEAN DE MONTS *2H3* (2km N Coastal) Camping La Daviere Plage, Route de Notre Dame, 85160 St Jean-de-Monts [tel/fax 02 51 58 27 99; daviereplage@wanadoo.fr; www. daviereplage.com] Site on L off D38 Rte de Notre Dame fr St Jean & 2km W of Notre Dame. Well sp. Med, hdg/mkd pitch, pt shd; wc; chem disp; shwrs; el pts (10A) €3.50; gas; lndry rm; ice; shops adj; tradsmn; rest; snacks; bar; playgrnd; sand beach, watersports 700m; sports area; entmnt; TV rm; dogs €2.80; CCI. "Family site; mkd cycle & walking trails." 1 Jun-15 Sep. € 17.50   2004*

ST JEAN DE MONTS *2H3* (2km SE Urban) Camping Le Bois Masson, 149 Rue des Sables, 85167 St Jean-de-Monts [02 51 58 62 62; fax 02 51 58 29 97; boismasson@siblu.fr; www.siblu.com] Fr Challans pass thro Le Perrier & on ent to St Jean-de-Monts, at 1st rndabt take last exit dir Les Sables d'Olonne. Foll Les Sables at next rndabts & 4th rndabt turn R, site on R shortly after Camping Le Bois Dormant. V lge, hdg/mkd pitch, pt shd; htd wc; chem disp; baby facs; shwrs inc; el pts (6A) inc; gas; lndtte; shop; rest; snacks; bar; BBQ (gas); playgrnd; 2 htd pools (1 covrd); waterslide; sand beach 2.5km; fishing, windsurfing, watersports nrby; entmnt; child entmnt; internet; TV; 4% statics; no dogs; Eng spkn; adv bkg; quiet; 20% red low ssn. "Busy, popular site with narr access rds; excel family site; mkt Sat." ♦ 8 Apr-16 Sep.   2005*

See advertisement on next page

FRANCE

le bois
masson & le
bois dormant

★★★★ st jean-de-monts,
vendée

**To book, or request a
brochure, please call
0870 242 7777** quoting
code **CACLUB.**

Le Bois Masson & Le Bois
Dormant, 168 Rue
des Sables, 85167
St Jean-de-Monts, France
Tel: 00 33 251 58 62 62
Fax: 00 33 251 58 29 97
Email: boisdormant@siblu.fr

**Two great parcs with
swimming pools,
sports & family
activities. Enjoy the
lively life at Le Bois
Masson, or relax at
the more peaceful
Le Bois Dormant.**

■ 80m² standard pitch size

■ Superb spring
& autumn prices

■ Ferry inclusive package

■ Wide range of sports
and activities

■ Bilingual friendly staff

■ FREE use of superb
indoor & outdoor pools

■ FREE use of 3 children's
clubs for all ages

■ Le Bois Masson open
from: 8 March - 16 Sept
Le Bois Dormant
open from:
29 April - 9 Sept   v2819

ST JEAN DE MONTS *2H3* (7km SE Rural)
Camping La Yole, Chemin des Bosses, Orouet,
85160 St Jean-de-Monts [02 51 58 67 17; fax
02 51 59 05 35; contact@la-yole.com; www.
la-yole.com] Take D38 S fr St Jean-de-Monts to
Orouet. At 1st main rd on R turn R, in 500m turn L.
Site on L in 200m. Situated bet D38 & coast, 1km
fr Plage des Mouettes. On arr, park in carpark on R
bef registering. Lge, hdg/mkd pitch, shd; wc; chem
disp; serviced pitch; baby facs; shwrs inc; el pts
(10A) inc; gas; lndtte; ice; shop; rest; snacks; bar;
BBQ (gas only); playgrnd; 2 htd pools (1 covrd);
paddling pool; waterslide; jacuzzi; sand beach 2km;
tennis; fishing; horseriding 3km; watersports 6km;
games rm; entmnt; TV; some statics (tour ops); sm
dogs €5; recep 0800-1930; c'vans over 6m not acc
high ssn; poss cr; Eng spkn; adv bkg ess; cc acc;
CCI. "Gd; v busy site; clean facs; excel cycle paths;
gd beaches; mkt Wed & Sat am." ♦ 8 Apr-29 Sep.
€ 29.00 (CChq acc) ABS - A23   2005*

ST JEAN DE MONTS *2H3* (2km S) **Camping Les
Pins**, 166 Ave Valentin, 85160 St Jean-de-Monts
[02 51 58 17 42] Site sp fr D753 & D38. Med, mkd
pitch, terr, pt shd; wc; shwrs inc; baby facs; el pts
(6A) inc; gas; lndtte; ice; shop; snacks; bar;
playgrnd; pool; sand beach 1.6km; TV; quiet; Eng
spkn; CCI. "Close to beautiful, but cr beach; parking
in town & beach may be diff."
10 Jun-15 Sep. € 19.82 (3 persons)   2002*

ST JEAN DE MONTS *2H3* (2km S Rural/Coastal)
Camping Les Verts, 177 Ave Valentin, 85160
St Jean-de-Monts [tel/fax 02 51 58 47 63]   Sp on
D38 & coast rd. Lge, hdg/mkd pitch, pt sl, pt shd;
wc; shwrs inc; el pts (3-6A) inc; gas; lndtte; shop
high ssn; rest; snacks; bar; playgrnd; TV; htd pool;
sand beach 1.6km; 10% statics; poss cr; adv bkg;
20% red May/June/Sep; CCI. "Excel beach, v
welcoming; ltd facs low ssn; some pitches narr &
rough; vg long stay." 15 May-30 Sep. € 17.80
                                              2003*

ST JEAN DE MONTS *2H3* (5km S Coastal)
Camping Les Genets, Ave des Epines, Orouet,
85160 St Jean-de-Monts [02 51 58 93 94]
Fr St Jean-de-Monts foll coast rd twd St Hilaire-
de-Riez. At 1st rndabt after 4km turn L to site on R.
Lge, pt shd; wc; shwrs inc; baby facs; el pts (8A) inc;
gas; lndtte; ice; shops adj; rest; snacks; bar; BBQ;
playgrnd; htd, covrd pool; sand beach; cycle hire;
tennis; windsurfing, waterslide, sailing 1km;
children's club; TV; dogs €3; red low ssn; adv bkg;
quiet. "Gd facs." 1 May-15 Sep. € 27.00 (3 persons)
                                              2002*

ST JEAN DE MONTS *2H3* (1km W Coastal)
Camping Le Bois Joly, 46 Route de Notre
Dame-de-Monts, 85165   St   Jean-de-Monts
[02 51 59 11 63; fax 02 51 69 11 06; boisjoly@
compuserve.com; www.camping-leboisjoly.com]
N on D38 circular around St Jean-de-Monts; at
rndabt past junc with D51 turn R dir Notre Dame-de-
Monts, site on R in 300m. Lge, hdg/mkd pitch, pt
shd; wc; chem disp; serviced pitches; baby facs;
shwrs inc; el pts (6A) inc; lndtte; shops 1km; snacks
& bar high ssn; playgrnd; pool; sand beach 1km;
entmnt; TV rm; 25% statics; no dogs; phone; poss
cr; Eng spkn; adv bkg; cc acc; CCI. "Ideal for
families; excel san facs; lge pitches; coastal & inland
cycleways nrby; vg long stay." ♦ 1 Apr-29 Sep.
€ 23.00   2002*

ST JEAN DE MONTS *2H3* (1km NW Rural)
Camping La Buzeliere, 79 Rue de Notre Dame,
85169 St Jean-de-Monts [02 51 58 64 80; fax
02 28 11 03 61; buzeliere@aol.com]   Take D38
fr St Jean-de-Monts to Notre Dame-de-Monts. Site
on L. Med, hdg/mkd pitch, pt sl, pt shd; wc; chem
disp; baby facs; shwrs inc; el pts (10A) inc; lndtte;
shop & 1km; snacks; bar; BBQ; playgrnd; htd pool;
sand beach 1km; 20% statics; adv bkg; quiet; CCI.
"Many sports inc golf nr; red facs low ssn; excel all
stays." ♦ 1 May-30 Sep. € 22.00   2005*

SITES

ST JEAN DE MONTS *2H3* (3.5km NW Urban/Coastal) Camping Les Amiaux, 223 Rue de Notre-Dame-de-Monts, 85169 St Jean-de-Monts [02 51 58 22 22; fax 02 51 58 26 09; accueil@amiaux.fr; www.amiaux.fr] Site on D38 mid-way bet St Jean-de-Monts & Notre-Dame-de-Monts. V lge, hdg/mkd pitches, pt shd; wc; chem disp; serviced pitches; baby facs; shwrs inc; el pts (10A) inc; gas; lndtte; ice; sm shop; rest; snacks; bar; BBQ; playgrnd; htd & covrd pool; waterslides; sand beach 900m; tennis; cycle hire; mini-golf; games rm; archery; entmnt; 50% statics; dogs €2.10; Eng spkn; adv bkg; cc acc; red low ssn; CCI. "Excel site; gd facs; conv Oceanile water park & Puy du Fou theme park; rec long stay." ♦ 1 May-30 Sep. € 30.40   2005*

ST JEAN DE MONTS *2H3* (4km NW Coastal) Camping aux Coeurs Vendeens, 251 Route de Notre Dame-de-Monts, 85160 St Jean-de-Monts [02 51 58 84 91; fax 02 28 11 20 75; coeurs vendeens@free.fr] Take D38 fr St Jean-de-Monts to Fromentine, site on L after 4km. Med, hdg pitch, shd; wc; shwrs inc; el pts (6A) €1.50; lndtte; ice; shop; rest; snacks; bar; playgrnd; htd pool; sand beach 700m; cycle hire; mini-golf; sailing & windsurfing 700m; TV rm; entmnt; 10% statics; dogs €2.50; late night car park; poss cr; adv bkg rec high ssn; quiet; red low ssn. ♦ 1 May-30 Sep. € 22.00   2003*

ST JEAN DE MONTS *2H3* (6km NW Coastal) Camping La Foret, Chemin de la Rive, 85160 St Jean-de-Monts [02 51 58 84 63; www.chez. com/campinglaforet] Fr St Jean-de-Monts, take D38 twd Notre-Dame-de-Monts for 6km, over rndabt then turn L (last turning bef Notre-Dame-de-Monts) sp Pont d'Yeu, then immed L. site on L in 200m, on parallel rd to main rd. Med, hdg/mkd pitch, pt shd; wc; chem disp; shwrs inc; el pts (6A) €3.80; gas; lndtte; shop; tradsmn; snacks; pool; playgrnd; htd pool; sand beach 500m; TV; 30% statics; dogs €2; phone; poss cr; Eng spkn; adv bkg; quiet; Eng spkn; BBQ; CCI. "Track thro pine forest to beach in 500m; cycle tracks; not suitable twin-axles; some pitches diff c'vans." ♦ Ltd. 15 May-15 Sep. € 23.50   2005*

ST JEAN DE MUZOLS see Tournon sur Rhone *9C2*

ST JEAN DU BRUEL see Nant *10E1*

ST JEAN DU GARD *10E1* (1.5km N) Camping Les Sources, Route du Mialet, 30270 St Jean-du-Gard [04 66 85 38 03; fax 04 66 85 16 09; www. camping-des-sources.fr] Fr Ales take D907 twd Anduze & St Jean-du-Gard. Take by-pass twd Florac. R at traff lts on D983, foll camp sp. NB: Do not enter town cent when towing - v narr streets. Med, hdg pitch, terr, shd; htd wc; chem disp; shwrs inc; el pts (6A) inc; gas; ice; shop; tradsmn; snacks; bar; playgrnd; pool; rv sw; dogs €1.50; Eng spkn; adv bkg ess Jul/Aug; quiet. "Lovely, well laid-out site; pitches sm, not rec for lge o'fits; friendly family owners; steam rlwy nrby; conv National Park of Cevennes." ♦ 1 Apr-30 Sep. € 17.25   2004*

ST JEAN DU GARD *10E1* (5km N) Camping La Foret, 30270 Falguieres [04 66 85 37 00; fax 04 66 85 07 05; laforet30@aol.com] W thro St Jean on D907/D260 turn R fr by-pass on D983. Foll sp to Falguieres & site sp on narr winding rd for 2.5km. Med, pt sl, pt shd; wc; shwrs inc; el pts (4A) €2.50; gas; lndtte; ice; shop; rest 5km; bar; pool; rv sw 500m; adv bkg; quiet. "Site in wooded hill country; friendly family owners." 1 May-15 Sep. € 13.50   2002*

ST JEAN DU GARD *10E1* (2km W Rural) Camping Le Petit Baigneur, Route de la Corniche des Cevennes, 30270 St Jean-du-Gard [04 66 85 32 05; fax 04 66 85 35 48] Site on S side of D907 at W end of St Jean-du-Gard by-pass & 250m beyond D907/260 junc. If app fr W go past site ent & make U turn at layby opp D907/260 junc - due acute angle of site ent. Sm, pt shd; wc; chem disp (wc only); shwrs inc; el pts (6A) €2.30; lndtte; ice; shop 1.5km; tradsmn; rest, snacks, bar 1.5km; playgrnd; rv sw & shgl beach adj; fishing; TV; sm statics; dogs; phone; CCI. "Beautiful, family-run, rvside site; lovely quiet spot; vg facs; tourist steam train 1.5km." ♦ 1 Apr-15 Sep. € 11.40   2005*

ST JEAN EN ROYANS *9C2* (Rural) Camp Municipal, Ave de Provence, 26190 St Jean-en-Royans [04 75 47 74 60] Take N532 to St Nazaire-en-Royans. Shortly after passing under high rlwy arch in St Nazaire turn R on D76 to St Jean-en-Royans. Site at S end of St Jean; sp (different site fr Camp Municipal St Nazaire). Med, hdg pitch, pt shd; wc; chem disp; shwrs inc; el pts (10A) €1.90; shops 500m; rv fishing 50m; some statics; dogs €0.80; factory noise. "Lge pitches; some pitch no el pts; no twin-axle vans; rec drinking water fr toilet blk, not fr old water pumps; gd supmkt in vill; spectacular mountain rds in area; v pleasant site but let down by dated san facs; semi-parkland." 15 May-30 Sep. € 8.10   2005*

ST JEAN FROIDMENTEL see Cloyes sur le Loir *4F2*

ST JEAN LE CENTENIER *9D2* (Rural) Camping Les Arches, 07580 St Jean-le-Centenier [tel/fax 04 75 36 75 45] Situated midway Aubenas & Montelimar. Leave N102 just after St Jean-le-Centenier dir Mirabel, site in 500m (D458). Sm, hdg pitch, pt sl, terr, pt shd; wc; baby facs; shwrs; el pts (10A) €3; lndtte; rest; snacks; bar; playgrnd; rv sw; fishing; canoeing; dogs €1.50; Eng spkn; quiet. "Vg site; simple & immac; peaceful location; helpful owner." ♦ Easter-15 Sep. € 14.00   2005*

Site report forms at back of Guide   537   *Last year of report*

ST JEAN PIED DE PORT *8F1* (Urban) **Camp Municipal de Plaza Berri, 64220 St Jean-Pied-de-Port [05 59 37 11 19]** Fr N on D933 thro town & cross rv. In 50m bear L at sm rndabt, site in 200m, sp. Enquire at Hotel de Ville (Town Hall) off ssn. Some care needed on app as narr rds. Med, mkd pitch, pt sl, pt shd; wc; chem disp; shwrs inc; el pts (5A) €2 (poss rev pol); shops 400m; pool 500m; quiet; CCI. "If no-one at recep, take numbered pitch & contact recep later; lovely old walled town on rv; conv Pyrenees & Spanish frontier; street mkt Mon; facs well-kept & clean; gd NH; poss open until mid-Nov." ♦ Easter-30 Sep. € 7.00   2005*

Will you fill in the site report forms at the back of the guide, or shall I?

†**ST JEAN PIED DE PORT** *8F1* (9km N Rural) **Camping a la Ferme (Bachoc), Maison Etchemendigaraya, 64780 Suhescun [05 59 37 60 83; bruno.bachoc@wanadoo.fr]** Fr D933 fr St Palais to St Jean-Pied-de-Port, take D22 twd Suhescun. Site sp. Sm, pt sl, pt shd; wc; shwrs inc; el pts (3A) €2; lndry rm; ice; shop 3km; farm produce for sale; sand beach 45km; watersports nr; cycle hire; statics; adv bkg; quiet; red CCI. "CL-type site on working farm; vg family atmosphere; welcoming owners; conv en rte Spain." € 10.00   2004*

ST JEAN PIED DE PORT *8F1* (3km E Rural) **Aire Naturelle La Paix des Champs (Jasses), Ferme Asoritzia, Route de Jaxu, 64220 St Jean-le-Vieux [05 59 37 02 63]** E fr St Jean-Pied-de-Port on D933. In 2km turn L onto D22 sp Jaxu, site on R in 1km. Sm, pt shd, wc; chem disp (wc); shwrs inc; el pts (3A) inc; lndry rm; supmkt 1km; playgrnd; pool 2km; trout-fishing; walking; dogs; quiet; CCI. "Tranquil & beautiful; mountain views; san facs poss stretched high ssn; interesting old town on pilgrim rte to Santiago de Compostela." ♦ ltd. 15 Apr-10 Nov. € 10.00   2005*

ST JEAN PIED DE PORT *8F1* (2km W Rural) **Europ Camping, 64220 Ascarat [05 59 37 12 78; fax 05 59 37 29 82]** Site on D918 bet Uhart-Cize & Ascarat. Well sp. Med, hdg/mkd pitch, pt shd; wc; chem disp; serviced pitch; sauna; shwrs inc; el pts (6A) inc (check pol); lndtte; shop 2km; tradsmn; rest; snacks; bar; playgrnd; pool; 10% statics; dogs €1.98; adv bkg; quiet; cc acc; CCI. "Vg; helpful staff." ♦ Easter-30 Sep. € 22.30   2002*

ST JEAN PIED DE PORT *8F1* (3km W) **Camping Narbaitz, Route de Bayonne, 64220 Ascarat [05 59 37 10 13 or 05 59 37 09 22 (LS); fax 05 59 37 21 42; campingnarbaitz@wanadoo.fr; www.camping-narbaitz.com]** Site on L of D918 St Jean to Bayonne 3km fr St Jean, sp. Med, hdg/mkd pitch, pt sl, pt shd; wc (some cont); chem disp; mv service pnt; baby facs; shwrs inc; el pts (6A) €3 (poss rev pol); lndry rm; shop, snacks & bar in ssn; playgrnd; pool; child entmnt; canoeing; kayaking; cycling; 5% statics; dogs free; phone; poss cr; Eng spkn; adv bkg (dep req); quiet; cc acc high ssn; red low ssn; CCI. "Pleasant, clean site; new/refurbished facs; gd value; trout-fishing on Rv Nive; attractive site nr Spanish border (cheaper petrol); family-run; helpful owners; lovely views; organised activities inc guided walks." ♦ 12 Mar-30 Sep. € 18.00 (CChq acc)   2005*

ST JEAN PIED DE PORT *8F1* (8km W) **Camp Municipal L'Irouleguy, 64430 St Etienne-de-Baigorry [05 59 37 43 96 or 05 59 37 40 80; fax 05 59 37 48 20; comstetiennebaigorry@wanadoo.fr]** W on D15 fr St Jean-Pied-de-Port to St Etienne-de-Baigorry. Site on R, sp 300m past rlwy x-ing. Ent next to wine co-operative. Med, shd; wc; chem disp; shwrs inc; el pts €2.50; lndtte; supmkt adj; sw & tennis 100m; troutfishing; birdwatching; rv access; poss cr; adv bkg; quiet. "Out of ssn call at Mairie who will open site for NH." ♦ 1 Mar-5 Dec. € 10.00   2004*

ST JODARD *9B1* (Rural) **Camp Municipal, 42590 St Jodard [04 77 63 42 42; fax 04 77 63 40 01]** Fr Roanne take N7 S then N82 to Neulise. Exit at junc 72 & turn R onto D26 to St Jodard. Site in 6km on ent vill, sp. Sm, pt shd, wc (mainly cont); shwrs inc; el pts (3-5A) €2.90; ice; shops etc in vill; playgrnd; pool high ssn; lake 1.5km; fishing; boat hire; tennis; mini-golf; quiet; red low ssn; CCI. "Pleasant site; pretty, rural vill; site yourself - warden calls am & pm; vg sh stay." 1 May-30 Sep. € 5.20   2003*

ST JORIOZ see Annecy *9B3*

ST JORY DE CHALAIS see Thiviers *7C3*

ST JOUAN DES GUERETS see St Malo *2E4*

ST JOUIN BRUNEVAL see Etretat *3C1*

ST JOUIN DE MARNES *4H1* (Rural) **Camping Clos-aux-Peres, 18 Rue des Gentils-Lieux, 79600 St Jouin-de-Marnes [05 49 67 44 50; fax 05 49 67 47 89]** S of Thouars on D37 in dir Poitiers, site on L on ent to vill. Sm, mkd pitch, pt shd; wc; chem disp; shwrs inc; el pts (10A) €2.30; lndtte; tradsmn; shop, rest, bar in vill; BBQ; playgrnd; pool; phone; quiet; CCI." 1 Jun-30 Sep. € 12.50   2002*

ST JULIEN DE CONCELLES see Nantes *2G4*

ST JULIEN DE LAMPON see Sarlat la Caneda *7C3*

ST JULIEN DE PEYROLAS see Pont St Esprit *9D2*

ST JULIEN DES LANDES see Mothe Achard, La *2H4*

ST JULIEN EN BEAUCHENE *9D3* (7km N Rural) **Camp Le Champ La Chevre, 26620 Lus-La-Croix-Haute** [04 92 58 50 14; fax 04 92 58 55 92; info@campingchamplachevre.com; www.camping champlachevre.com] Turn E off N75 thru Lus vill, site SE of vill nr sw pool on D505. Med, mkd pitch, pt sl, terr, pt shd; wc; chem disp; shwrs €1; el pts (6A) €3.10; gas; lndtte; ice; shops 300m; snacks; playgrnd; htd pool adj; fishing; some statics; dogs €1.50; poss cr; adv bkg; quiet; cc acc; CCI. "Helpful staff; excel mountain views; many waymkd walks; excel pool; gd NH." ♦ ltd. 1 May-30 Sep. € 13.80   2005*

ST JULIEN EN BORN *8E1* (1.5km N Rural) Aire **Naturelle (Daret), Marregue, 40170 St Julien-en-Born** [tel/fax 05 58 42 72 35] Foll D652 N fr St Julian-en-Born, site 400m N of Cusson x-rd. Sm, shd; wc; shwrs inc; el pts; lndtte; shop 2km; playgrnd; sand beach 10km; fishing, sailing, horseriding 1km; Eng spkn; quiet. "Poss need long elec lead; vg." 15 Jun-30 Sep.   2004*

ST JULIEN EN BORN *8E1* (6km NE Rural) **Le Village Tropical Sen Yan, 40170 Mezos** [05 58 42 60 05; fax 05 58 42 64 56; reception@sen-yan.com; www.sen-yan.com] Fr Bordeaux on N10 turn W onto D38 at Laharie twd Mezos & after 12km turn L onto D63 to Mezos. Site 1.5km fr D63/D38 junc NE of Mezos. Take D652 N fr Lit-en-Mixe, take R turn onto D166 in St Julien-en-Born to Mezos. Lge, hdg/mkd pitch, shd; wc (some cont); chem disp; baby facs; sauna; shwrs inc; el pts (6A) inc; gas; lndtte; shop; rest; snacks; bar; BBQ (gas only); playgrnd; 3 pools (1 htd & covrd); sand beach 12km; rv adj; fishing; canoe hire 1km; watersports 15km; tennis; mini-golf; cycle hire; many sports & games; games/TV rm (cab/sat); fitness cent; internet; entmnt; 80% statics; dogs €2.30; phone; recep 0900-1230 & 1330-2000; code op barrier; max c'van 7m high ssn; Eng spkn; adv bkg; quiet; cc acc; CCI. "Pleasant & restful; excel facs for families; lively atmosphere with music in bar - but not audible fr camping area; mkt Miziman Fri." ♦ 1 Jun-15 Sep. € 34.00 ABS - A09   2005*

ST JULIEN EN GENEVOIS *9A3* (5km SE Rural) **Camping La Colombiere, Chef-Lieu, 74160 Neydens** [04 50 35 13 14; fax 04 50 35 13 40; la.colombiere@wanadoo.fr; www.camping-la- colombiere.com] Fr A40 junc 13 take N201 twd Annecy. Site is sp after approx 1.75km at Neydens. NB: Do not go into St Julien-en-Genevois when towing. Med, hdg/mkd pitch, pt sl, pt shd; htd wc; mv service pnt; baby facs; shwrs inc; el pts (6) inc, extra for 15A; lndry rm; ice; shops 500m; farm produce; rest; bar; BBQ (gas/elect/charcoal); playgrnd; htd pool; paddling pool; lake fishing 1km; cycle hire; archery; entmnt; internet; TV rm; 30% statics; dogs €1.70; bus; poss cr; quiet; cc acc; CCI. "Excel, clean, family-run site; gd facs; conv Swiss border & Lake Geneva; lovely vill walks; vg rest; excel tour of Geneva inc vineyard & wine-tasting; friendly & helpful staff." ♦ 1 Apr-30 Sep. € 28.50 (CChq acc) ABS - M08   2005*

ST JULIEN EN GENEVOIS *9A3* (6km S Rural) **Camping Le Terroir, 118 Chemin de Clairjoie, 74160 Presilly-la-Tuiliere** [04 50 04 42 07; fax 04 50 04 55 53; camping.le.terroir@wanadoo.fr] Fr St Julien-en-Genevois S on N201 for 5km. At traff lts after rndabt turn R twd Presilly. Site on L past vill on D18. Sm, mkd pitch, pt shd; htd wc; chem disp; shwrs inc; el pts (5-10A) €2.80-3.50; lndtte; tradsmn; rest 5km; snacks, bar 2km; BBQ; playgrnd; htd pool 6km; TV rm; some statics; dogs; poss cr; Eng spkn; adv bkg; quiet; CCI. "Gd touring base." 1 Jun-30 Sep. € 10.10   2005*

ST JULIEN EN ST ALBAN see Privas *9D2*

ST JULIEN MOLIN MOLETTE see Bourg Argental *9C2*

ST JUNIEN *7B3* (500m Urban) **Camp Municipal, Ave Corot, 87200 St Junien** [05 55 02 34 86; fax 05 55 02 34 88] Fr Limoges take N141 W to St Junien. Or 9km NE Rochechouart on D675. Site in town, sp. Med, hdg pitch, sl, shd; wc; chem disp; mv service pnt; shwrs inc; el pts (10A) €3.80; ice; playgrnd; htd pool 300m; rv fishing 200m; dogs; adv bkg (dep req). "Vg." 14 May-4 Sep. € 6.60   2005*

ST JUNIEN *7B3* (4km E Rural) **Camping de Chambery, 87200 St Brice-sur-Vienne** [05 55 02 18 13] Fr Limoges on N141 turn L at rndabt 5km fr St Junien sp St Brice. In vill turn L & L again at site sp, site on L in 500m. Sm, hdg/mkd pitch, hdstg, pt sl, pt shd; htd wc; chem disp; shwrs inc; el pts (10A) €3.10; lndtte; shop in vill; playgrnd; rv nr; dogs; adv bkg; CCI. "Lovely location; pitches overlook lake & countryside; site yourself, helpful warden calls early eve; conv Oradour-sur-Glane." ♦ 26 Apr-15 Sep. € 11.00   2004*

ST JUNIEN LA BREGERE see Bourganeuf *7B4*

ST JURS see Moustiers Ste Marie *10E3*

ST JUST (CANTAL) *9C1* (Urban) **Camp Municipal,** 15320 St Just [04 71 73 72 57; fax 04 71 73 71 44; commune.stjust@wanadoo.fr; www.saintjust. com] Exit junc 31 fr A75, foll sp St Chely-d'Apcher D909; turn W onto D448 twds St Just (approx 6km); sp with gd access. Med, mkd pitch, pt sl, terr, pt shd; htd wc; chem disp; shwrs inc; el pts (10A) €2; lndtte; ice; shop; snacks; bar; pool high ssn; fishing; tennis; cycle hire; v quiet. "Friendly warden; ltd facs low ssn; gd touring base; gd rest in vill."
1 May-30 Sep. € 9.00   2005*

ST JUST EN CHEVALET *9B1* (Urban) **Camp Municipal Le Verdille,** 42430 St Just-en-Chevalet [04 77 65 02 97] Exit A72 at junc 4, join D53 NE twd St Just-en-Chevalet. Foll sp in town to camping/piscine. Due to steep gradients avoid D1 when towing. Med, hdg pitch, pt sl, pt shd; wc (mainly cont); chem disp shwrs inc; el pts (16A) €2.20; lndtte; shops & supmkt 500m; rest 500m; snacks, bar adj; pool & tennis adj; 10% statics; phone; Eng spkn; adv bkg; quiet; CCI. "Friendly proprietors; v quiet site." € 7.70   2004*

ST JUST LUZAC see Marennes *7B1*

ST JUSTIN *8E2* (11km E Rural) **Aire Naturelle Municipal,** 40240 Creon d'Armagnac [05 58 44 81 07 (Mairie)] Fr Roquefort take D626 dir La Bastide, turn L onto D933. After 500m turn R onto D35, site on L after 11km on ent vill of Creon d'Armagnac. Sm, pt sl, pt shd; wc; chem disp; shop 1km; playgrnd; sports area; fishing; horseriding; quiet; CCI. "Gd NH."
1 May-30 Sep. € 4.00   2004*

ST JUSTIN *8E2* (2km NW) **Camping Le Pin, Route de Roquefort,** 40240 St Justin [tel/fax 05 58 44 88 91; campinglepin@wanadoo.fr] Fr St Justin D933, take D626 twd Roquefort. Site on L in 2km, well sp fr town. Sm, shd; wc; shwrs inc; el pts (6A) €3; lndtte; shop & 2km; rest; snacks; bar; playgrnd; pool; cycle hire; horseriding; rv fishing 2km; dogs €1.50; poss cr; Eng spkn; adv bkg; quiet; CCI. "Helpful owner; facs poss streched when site full; ongoing improvements; gd rest; beautiful vill." ♦
1 Apr-30 Oct. € 17.20   2004*

ST LAGER BRESSAC see Privas *9D2*

ST LAMBERT DU LATTAY *4G1* **Camp Municipal La Coudraye, Rue de la Coudray,** 49190 St Lambert-du-Lattay [02 41 78 49 31 or 02 41 78 44 26 (Mairie)] Fr Angers on N160 thro vill cent & foll N160 sp Chemille. Site sp on L adj wine museum in 200m. Sm, hdg pitch, pt sl, pt shd; wc (some cont); chem disp; shwrs inc; el pts (10A) inc; gas; lndry rm; ice; playgrnd; rv 500m; fishing 50m; entmnt; dogs €0.65; adv bkg rec; noisy. "Wine museums worth visiting; fair NH." ♦ 15 Mar-30 Oct.
€ 10.00   2004*

ST LARY SOULAN *8G2* (Rural) **Camp Municipal La Lanne,** 65170 St Lary-Soulan [05 62 39 41 58 or 05 62 40 87 85 (LS); fax 05 62 40 01 40; camping@saintlary-vacances.com] On Bielsa-Aragnouet rd, sp on on ent vill. Site in side street E of main rd & ent not sp. Look for ent with tall trees at each side. Med, mkd pitch, pt sl, shd; htd wc; chem disp; shwrs inc; el pts (6-10A) €5; gas; lndtte; shop 250m; rest, snacks, bar 400m; playgrnd; htd pool adj; TV rm; adv bkg; quiet; red low ssn. "Office clsd 1200-1430; vg san facs." ♦ 5 Dec-1 Oct.
€ 14.40   2005*

†**ST LARY SOULAN** *8G2* (2km N Rural) **Camping Le Rioumajou,** 65170 Bourisp [tel/fax 05 62 39 48 32; lerioumajou@wanadoo.fr; www.camping-le-rioumajou.com] On W side of D929 2km N of St Lary-Soulon & 500m N of Bourisp. Lge, hdg/mkd pitch, hdstg, shd; wc; chem disp; shwrs inc; el pts (4-10A) €3.50-6; gas; lndtte; shop; tradsmn; rest; snacks; bar; htd pool; playgrnd; tennis; entmnt; TV rm; phone; dogs €1; poss cr; Eng spkn; adv bkg; quiet; CCI. "Conv National Park & Bielsa tunnel; lots to do in area; St Lary-Soulan attractive; gd walking & watersports." € 14.00   2004*

†**ST LARY SOULAN** *8G2* (3km NE Rural) **Camping Le Lustou, Agos,** 65170 Vielle-Aure [05 62 39 40 64; fax 05 62 39 40 72; camping.lustou@libertysurf.fr] Exit A64 junc 16 & head S on D929. Thro Arreau & Guchen turn R onto D19 dir Vielle-Aure. Site on R just bef Agos. Med, mkd pitch, pt sl, pt shd; htd wc; chem disp; baby facs; shwrs inc; el pts (2-10A) €2.20-6.50; gas; lndtte; ice; shop 2km; snacks; bar; playgrnd; htd, covrd pool; fishing, canoeing, tennis nrby; TV rm; dogs €1.50; phone; adv bkg; some rd noise; CCI. "Family-owned site; excel walking, skiing; immac facs." ♦ € 11.60 (3 persons)   2004*

ST LAURENT DE CERDANS see Prats de Mollo la Preste *8H4*

ST LAURENT DE LA PREE see Fouras *7A1*

ST LAURENT DE NESTE see Montrejeau *8F3*

ST LAURENT DU PAPE see Voulte sur Rhone, La *9D2*

ST LAURENT DU PONT see Echelles, Les *9B3*

ST LAURENT DU VAR see Cagnes sur Mer *10E4*

ST LAURENT DU VERDON *10E3* (1.5km N Rural) **Camping La Farigoulette,** 04500 St Laurent-du-Verdon [04 92 74 41 62; fax 04 92 74 00 86] Turn L off D311 15km fr Riez onto D311. Turn R at x-rds, cont on D311. In St Laurent-du-Verdon vill cent, turn L onto D411 sp La Farigoulette. Site on R in 1.5km. Lge, pt sl, shd; wc; mv service pnt; shwrs inc; el pts (5A) €2.90; lndtte; ice; shop; rest; bar; playgrnd; 2 pools; lake sw adj; tennis; mini-golf; canoeing; watersports; fishing; cycle hire; entmnt; TV; poss cr; red low ssn. 15 Mar-15 Oct. € 16.00   2002*

ST LAURENT DU VERDON *10E3* (2km W Rural) Domaine Naturiste d'Enriou (Naturist), 04500 St Laurent-du-Verdon [04 92 74 41 02; fax 04 92 74 01 20; domaine.enriou@voila.fr] Fr Riez foll D11 S, site on D311 to St Laurent-du-Verdon & sp fr D11/D311 junc immed N of Quinson. Med, shd; wc; chem disp; shwrs inc; el pts (3-6A) €2.60-3.60; gas; ice; shops; rest; snacks; playgrnd; 2 pools; sw lake 500m; canoes; archery; fishing; entmnt; TV; few statics; adv bkg; v quiet; INF card req. "Friendly; long walks on site; peaceful; excel for visiting Gorges du Verdon; vg."
15 May-30 Sep. € 26.50   2005*

ST LAURENT EN BEAUMONT see Mure, La *9C3*

†**ST LAURENT EN GRANDVAUX** *6H2* (SE Urban) Camp Municipal Le Champs de Mars, Rue du Camping, 39150 St Laurent-en-Grandvaux [03 84 60 19 30 or 03 84 60 14 13 (Mairie); fax 03 84 60 19 72] E thro St Laurent on N5 twd Morez, site on R, sp 'Caravaneige' at ent. Med, mkd pitch, hdstg, pt sl, unshd; htd wc; chem disp; shwrs inc; some serviced pitches; el pts (6A) €1.80; lndtte; ice; shops in vill; playgrnd; TV rm; 20% statics; dogs; phone; site clsd Oct; adv bkg; quiet; CCI. "Gd site, pleasantly quiet in May; no dog walk area." ♦
€ 7.40   2004*

ST LAURENT EN GRANDVAUX *6H2* (10km W Rural) Camping L'Abbaye, Route du Lac, 39130 Bonlieu [03 84 25 57 04; fax 03 84 25 50 82; camping.abbaye@wanadoo.fr] Site on L of N78, 1km bef vill of Bonlieu, sp. Med, mkd pitch, pt sl, pt shd; wc; chem disp; baby facs; shwrs inc; el pts (6A) €2.70; lndtte; shop 4km; rest; snacks; bar; BBQ; playgrnd; lake sw nr; games area; dogs €0.80; Eng spkn; adv bkg; quiet; CCI. "Gd walks; gd dog walks; attractive area with Lac de Bonlieu 1km; bar/rest open low ssn; access to san facs poss diff elderly/disabled fr lower terraces." ♦ 1 May-30 Sep. € 12.10   2005*

ST LAURENT NOUAN see Beaugency *4F2*

ST LEGER SOUS BEUVRAY *4H4* (1km) Aire Naturelle Municipal, 71990 St Leger-sous-Beuvray [03 85 82 45 55 or 03 85 82 57 61] Take N81 SW fr Autun dir Bourbon-Lancy & in approx 13km, turn R onto D61 to St Leger. Site sp in vill. Sm, mkd pitch, pt sl, pt shd; wc (cont); chem disp (wc only); 70% serviced pitch; el pts €3.50; shops 1km; 5% statics; dogs; phone (emergency only) poss cr; quiet; CCI. "Simple, quiet site; in Morvan Regional Park; Mt. Beuvray 3km; museum 3km; warden on site high ssn only; fair sh stay."
15 Mar-15 Nov. € 7.00   2003*

ST LEON SUR VEZERE see Montignac *7C3*

ST LEONARD DE NOBLAT *7B3* (12km N) Camp Municipal du Pont du Dognon, 87240 St Laurent-les-Eglises [05 55 56 57 25 or 05 55 56 56 13; fax 05 55 56 55 17] Take N141 fr St Leonard-de-Noblat; after 1.5km turn L (N) on D19 thro Le Chatenet-en-Dognon. Site in approx 4km, bef St Laurent-les-Eglises. Med, mkd pitch, terr, pt shd; htd wc; shwrs inc; el pts (4A) €2.40; gas; lndtte; shop & 3km; rest; snacks; pool; rv sw; shgl beach; canoeing; tennis; cycle hire; entmnt; dogs €0.90; adv bkg; quiet. 15 Apr-15 Oct. € 10.20   2004*

ST LEONARD DE NOBLAT *7B3* (9km SE) Camp Municipal du Lac, 87460 Bujaleuf [05 55 69 54 54 or 05 59 60 59 04 (Mairie); fax 05 55 69 54 54; bujaleuf.informations@wanadoo.fr; www.camping-bujaleuf.com] Fr St Leonard take D13, D14 to Bujaleuf. Site 1km N of town on D16. Med, terr, pt shd; wc; shwrs; el pts (5A) €2; lndtte; shops 1km; playgrnd; rv sw; poss cr; quiet; red low ssn. "Site overlooks lake; no warden Sun or Mon; Bujaleuf sm mkt town." 15 May-30 Sep. € 7.00   2003*

ST LEONARD DE NOBLAT *7B3* (2km S Rural) Camp Municipal Beaufort, 87400 St Leonard-de-Noblat [05 55 56 02 79; fax 05 55 56 98 01; mairie-st-leonard-de-noblat@wanadoo.fr] Leave A20 S-bound at junc 34 dir St Leonard, onto N141. In 18km on ent St Leonard, 300m after x-ing Rv Vienne, fork R (sp). Site on R in 2km. Med, hdg pitch, pt sl, pt shd; htd wc; chem disp (wc); shwrs inc; el pts (5A) inc; ice; lndtte; shop & 4km; tradsmn; bar; playgrnd; rv sw; fishing; dogs; phone; poss cr & noisy; adv bkg; CCI. ♦ 15 Jun-15 Sep. € 12.40   2005*

ST LEU D'ESSERENT see Chantilly *3D3*

STE LIVRADE SUR LOT see Villeneuve sur Lot *7D3*

ST LO *1D4* (500m NE Urban) Camp Municipal de Ste Croix, Ave de Paris, 50000 St Lo [02 33 55 16 14 or 02 33 57 10 25; fax 02 33 57 27 52; sport.stlo@wanadoo.fr] On D972 on L exit St Lo on Bayeux rd climbing hill. Site on L at pedestrian traff lts. Sharp turn into site. Sm, hdg pitch, pt sl, pt shd, wc; chem disp; shwrs inc; el pts (6-10A) €1.22-2.45; lndry rm, shop 500m; tradsmn; rest, snacks, bar 500m; BBQ; playgrnd; htd pool 1km; sand beach 25km; dogs €0.45; adv bkg; quiet; CCI. "Well-kept site; warden present 0730-1200 & 1730-2030, barrier poss clsd other times."
1 Jun-12 Sep. € 8.90   2005*

ST LOUIS *6G4* (2km N) Camping au Petit Port, 8 Allee des Marronniers, 68330 Huningue [tel/fax 03 89 69 05 25] Exit N66 Mulhouse-Basle in St Louis. Foll sps to Huningue & strt, after level x-ing, site sp. Sm, shd; wc; shwrs inc; el pts (4A) inc; shop 1km; htd pool 2km; 50% statics; bus to Basle; poss cr; quiet. "Poss diff access lge o'fits; v helpful warden; gd site sh stay/NH." ♦ 1 May-30 Sep. € 10.70   2004*

ST LUNAIRE see Dinard *2E3*

FRANCE

ST LYPHARD 2G3 (300m E Rural) **Camping Les Brieres du Bourg, Route d'Herbignac, 44410 St Lyphard** [02 40 91 43 13 or 01 40 33 93 33 (LS); fax 02 40 91 43 03; cledelles@aol.com; www. lescledelles.com.fr] Fr Nantes on N165 dir Vannes, exit junc 15 dir La Roche-Bernard then in 2km turn L onto D574 then D774 sp Herbignac, Guerande. At Herbignac fork L onto D47. Pass 1st sp on R to St Lyphard, site on L in 1km. Med, hdg/mkd pitch, pt sl, shd; wc; chem disp; mv service pnt; baby facs; serviced pitch; shwrs inc; el pts (6A) €5; gas; lndtte; ice; shops 1km; tradsmn; rest 1km; snacks; bar; playgrnd; pool; sand beach 10km; lake sw adj; tennis; cycle hire; mini-golf; fishing; games rm; entnmt; child entnmt; TV; 10% statics; dogs €2.30; phone; Eng spkn; adv bkg; quiet; red long stay/low ssn; CCI. "Delightful vill; beautiful National Park; sports complex adj; site being refurbished (2003); gd sh stay." ♦ 1 Apr-15 Oct. € 15.00   2003*

†**ST MAIXENT L'ECOLE** 7A2 (SW) **Camp Municipal du Panier Fleuri, Rue P Drevin, 79400 St Maixent-l'Ecole** [05 49 05 53 21 or 05 49 76 13 77 (Mairie)] Take N11 twd Niort, at 2nd set of traff lts nr top of hill out of town turn L. Foll camping sps into ent. Med, pt sl, pt shd; wc (some cont); shwrs inc; el pts (10A) €5; tradsmn; playgrnd; pool adj; tennis; dogs €0.55; quiet; cc not acc. "Helpful warden on site 0930-1200 & 1700-2130, if locked for security go to house nr wc block; interesting town; medieval houses, abbey church & crypt adj; ltd/basic facs low ssn in Portakabin; NH en rte Spain." € 7.30   2005*

ST MALO 2E4 (500m Urban/Coastal) **Camp Municipal Cite d'Alet, Rue Gaston Buy, 35400 St Malo** [02 99 81 60 91 or 02 99 40 71 11 (LS); fax 02 99 40 71 37; camping@ville-saint-malo.fr; www.ville-saint-malo.fr/campings/]] Fr ferry terminal go twd St Malo, site sp at rndabt immed past docks. Fr all other dir foll sp for port/ferry, then site sp. Site off Place St Pierre, St Servan-sur -Mer. App thro old part of city poss diff for lge o'fits. Lge, mkd pitch, pt sl, pt shd; wc; chem disp; mv service pnt; shwrs inc; el pts (10A) inc (poss rev pol & long elec cable poss req); lndtte; shops, tradsmn, rest, snacks 500m; bar; playgrnd; sand beach 500m; dogs €2.15; bus; phone; poss cr; Eng spkn; adv bkg; cc acc; CCI. "Staff helpful & courteous; WW2 museum on site; nice views; conv for St Malo & ferries; gd views over harbour to old city; noise fr harbour, esp when foggy; gd shwr block; gd mkt Fri." ♦ Ltd. 1 Apr-30 Sep. € 15.50   2005*

Mustn't forget to post our site report forms to The Club, otherwise sites might be deleted.

ST MALO 2E4 (2km NE Coastal) **Camp Municipal du Nicet, Ave de la Varde, 35400 St Malo** [02 99 40 26 32; fax 02 99 21 92 62; camping@ ville-saint-malo.fr] Fr St Malo take coast (busy & narr) rd Ave JF Kennedy twd Cancale; pass Camping Nielles on L bef district of Rotheneuf; turn L at camping sp just after sm G'ge on L; turn L at T-junc; site in view. Lge, mkd pitch, pt sl, pt terr, unshd; wc; chem disp, shwrs inc; el pts (5-10A) inc (rev pol); lndtte; shops 800m; tradsmn; playgrnd; sand beach adj; dogs €2.14; poss cr & noisy high ssn; Eng spkn; adv bkg (dep req;) cc acc; CCI. "Clean, well-run site on cliff top; secluded beach via steep steps; can be exposed if pitched nr edge with sea view; some pitches sm; recep closd 1200-1630." ♦ 1 Jul-1 Sep. € 14.80   2003*

ST MALO 2E4 (4km NE Coastal) **Camping des Chevrets, Plage de Chevrets, La Guimorais, 35350 St Coulomb** [02 99 89 01 90; fax 02 99 89 01 16; campingdeschevrets@wanadoo.fr; www.camping deschevrets.com] St Malo to Cancale coast rd D201; La Guimorais on L 3km E of Rotheneuf, strt thro vill; fairly narr app. V lge, hdg/mkd pitch, pt sl, pt shd; wc (some cont); chem disp; mv service pnt; baby facs; shwrs inc; el pts (6A) €3.35; gas; lndtte; shop; rest; snacks; bar; playgrnd; sand beach adj; games area; cycle hire; internet; entmnt; 50% statics; dogs; poss cr; Eng spkn; adv bkg; cc acc; red low ssn/long stay; CCI. "Conv St Malo, Mont St Michel; vg site." ♦ 7 Apr-1 Nov. € 21.95   2005*

See advertisement opposite

ST MALO *2E4* (5km SE Rural) **Camping Le P'tit Bois, La Chalandouze, 35430 St Jouan-des- Guerets** [02 99 21 14 30; fax 02 99 81 74 14; camping. ptitbois@wanadoo.fr; www.ptitbois.com] Fr St Malo take N137 dir Rennes; after o'skts of St Malo turn R twd St Jouan-des-Guerets, site sp. Lge, hdg/mkd pitch, pt shd; wc (some cont); chem disp; mv service pnt; baby facs; shwrs inc; el pts (10A) inc; gas; lndtte; shop; rest; snacks; bar; BBQ (gas/elec); playgrnd; htd, covrd pool; paddling pool; waterslide; jacuzzi; sand beach 1.5km; tidal rv sw; watersports 2km; tennis; mini-golf; archery; games rm; internet; entmnt; TV; 50% tour ops/statics; dogs €4; adv bkg; cc acc; red low ssn/CCI. "30 mins fr port/ferries; gd quality site; friendly & helpful recep; gd for families; conv Le Mont St Michel." ♦ 8 Apr-9 Sep. € 42.30 (3 persons) ABS - B03   2005*

See advertisement opposite

ST MALO *2E4* (3km S) **Camping La Ville Huchet, Rue de la Passagere, 34500 St Malo** [02 99 81 51 89; fax 02 99 81 11 83; info@lavillehuchet. com] On N137 foll sp Rennes. Turn R after 5km to side rd sp Quelmer & La Passagere. Lge, pt sl, pt shd; wc; chem disp; shwrs· inc; el pts (4A) €4.05; lndtte; shop; rest; snacks; bar; sand beach 5km; playgrnd; pool; water park; cycle hire; table tennis; sports field; entmnt; TV; 40% statics; adv bkg; quiet, but some rd noise; "Spacious but insufficient water taps; poor san facs; excel pool." ♦ 1 May-15 Sep. € 25.70   2003*

ST MALO DU BOIS see Mortagne sur Sevre *2H4*

ST MARCEL D'ARDECHE see Pont St Esprit *9D2*

ST MARCELLIN *9C2* (10km NE Rural) **Camp Municipal La Vendee, 38470 Vinay** [04 76 36 91 00 or 04 76 36 70 37 (Mairie)] On N92 clear sp in vill to site. Med, pt shd; wc; chem disp; shwrs; el pts; ice; rest nr; shops nr; playgrnd; adults & paddling pool adj; rv fishing; quiet; adv bkg. "Gd sh stay/NH; helpful staff." 15 May-15 Sep.   2002*

ST MARCELLIN *9C2* (E Urban) **Camp Municipal, 38160 St Marcellin** [04 76 38 41 61 (Mairie)] Clearly sp fr both sides of town. Sm, pt shd; wc; shwrs; el pts; shops adj; pool 1km; quiet. "Spectacular scenery; lge mkt Sat." Jun-Aug.   2002*

ST MARCELLIN *9C2* (10km S) **Camp Municipal, 38680 Pont-en-Royans** [04 76 36 06 30 or 04 76 36 03 09 (Mairie); fax 04 76 36 10 77] App on D531 fr St Nazaire or D518 fr St Marcellin, site on R on ent to town. Sm, hdg pitch, hdstg, pt terr, pt shd; wc (mainly cont); chem disp; shwrs inc; el pts (4A) inc; gas in town; ice; shops 500m; lake 8km; rv adj; tennis; entmnts; poss cr; statics; quiet but some rd noise; CCI. "Site in 2 adj parts; helpful warden; rvside walk to Pont-en-Royans." 15 Apr-30 Sep. € 12.00   2004*

ST MARCELLIN *9C2* (7km SW Rural) **Camping Les Carrets (Farconnet), 38840 St Bonnet-de-Chavagne** [04 76 38 41 15] Fr St Marcellin on N92, D27 to Chatte, D68 to St Bonnet, keep L below vill about 2km, farm on L. Sm, pt sl, unshd; wc; chem disp (wc); shwrs inc; el pts (6A) €2 (long lead rec); quiet; adv bkg. "Outstanding farm site; spectacular views of Vercors; farm produce; excel sh stay." 15 Mar-15 Nov. € 7.50   2002*

ST MARCELLIN *9C2* (12km SW Rural) **Camp Municipal, 26190 St Nazaire-en-Royans** [04 75 48 41 18 or 04 75 48 40 63 (Mairie); fax 04 75 48 44 32] Site is on W edge of St Nazaire-en-Royans on D76, 700m fr cent, well sp. Med, hdg pitch, pt sl, pt shd; wc (some cont); chem disp; shwrs inc; el pts (3-6A) €2.60-3.40; lndtte; shops & rest 1km; playgrnd; dogs €1.22; quiet; CCI. "Immac facs; helpful warden; excel rest in vill; ideal for exploring scenic mountains of Vercors; medieval town nrby; aquaduct on Rv Isere a tourist attraction; gate clsd 2200-0700; excel sh stay/NH." ♦ 1 May-30 Sep. € 7.70   2003*

STE MARGUERITE SUR MER see Dieppe *3C2*

†**STE MARIE AUX MINES** *6E4* (1km E Rural) **Camping Les Reflets du Val d'Argent, Route Diechery, 68160 Ste Marie-aux-Mines** [03 89 58 64 83; fax 03 89 58 64 31; reflets@rmcnet.fr; www.valdargent.com/camping] Fr Selestat N59 into Ste Marie. Go thro vill to traff lts & turn L. 1km to site; sp. Med, mkd pitch, pt shd; wc; chem disp; shwrs inc; el pts (5-15A) €3.05-9.15; lndtte; shop & 1km; tradsmn; rest; snacks; bar; BBQ; playgrnd; pool; TV; 5% statics; dogs €3.50; phone; adv bkg; quiet; red low ssn; CCI. "Lovely peaceful site; vg swimming pool; ski in winter 5km; vg long stay." € 13.90   2003*

FRANCE

STE MARIE AUX MINES *6E4* (7km NW Rural)
Camp Municipal Vosges-Alsace, 68660 Liepvre
[03 89 58 90 14 (Mairie)] E on N59 turn L at 2nd
Camping sp in vill, opp Schmidt factory. Turn R
immed after rlwy bdge, site on L in 600m. Med,
pt sl, pt shd; wc (cont); shwrs; el pts; shops 1km;
poss cr; quiet. Apr-Oct. 2002*

STE MARIE DU MONT see Carentan *1D4*

†**STES MARIES DE LA MER** *10F2* (1km E Coastal)
Camping La Brise, Rue Marcel Carriere, 13460
Stes Maries-de-la-Mer [04 90 97 84 67; fax
04 90 97 72 01; labrise@saintesmaries.com]
Sp on o'skts on all rds. Take N570 fr Arles or D58
(N570) fr Aigues-Mortes. V lge, unshd; htd wc
(mainly cont); mv service pnt; shwrs inc; el pts (10A)
€4.30; lndtte; ice; shops 500m; 3 htd pools; fishing;
horseriding & birdwatching in 20km; dogs €4.20;
clsd mid Nov-mid Dec; red low ssn. "Under same
ownership as Le Clos du Rhone & can use their
facs; v efficient management; v cr Aug; card ent;
poss mosquitoes; m'vans can use free municipal car
park with facs; conv Camargue National Park; gd
security; vg winter NH." ♦ € 18.90 2005*

STES MARIES DE LA MER *10F2* (2km W Coastal)
Camping Le Clos du Rhone, 13460 Stes
Maries-de-la-Mer [04 90 97 85 99; fax 04 90 97 78
85; leclos@laposte.net; www.saintesmariesde
lamer.com] Fr Arles take D570 to Stes Maries;
fr Aigues Mortes, D58/D570. Lge, unshd; wc; some
serviced pitches; chem disp; shwrs inc; el pts (6-10A)
inc; gas; lndtte; ice; shop; rest; snacks; playgrnd; pool;
sand beach; entmnt; dogs; horseriding adj; poss cr;
quiet; adv bkg; cc acc. "Excel pool & facs; san facs
poss ltd & stretched low ssn; popular with families;
private gate to beach; mosquitoes."♦ Easter-30 Sep.
€ 26.00 2005*

ST MARTIAL DE NABIRAT see Gourdon *7D3*

ST MARTIAL ENTRAYGUES see Argentat *7C4*

ST MARTIN D'ARDECHE see Pont St Esprit *9D2*

ST MARTIN DE CRAU *10F2* (Urban) **Camping de
la Crau**, 13310 St Martin-de-Crau [04 90 47 17 09;
fax 04 90 47 09 92; camping.lacrau@wanadoo.fr;
www.hotelcampinglacrau.com] Fr W take N113
sp St Martin-de-Crau. L at 1st traff lts. Fr E take
N113 thro town & R at traff lts by Hotel. Site behind
Hotel de la Crau, 50m up side rd running N off N113
on D830B. Med, hdg/mkd pitch, shd; wc (some
cont); chem disp; shwrs inc; el pts (6A) €3.80; gas
in town; rest; snacks; bar; shop in high ssn & 300m;
tradsmn; lndtte; ice; playgrnd; pool; beach 35km; TV
rm; dogs €1.60; Eng spkn; adv bkg; red long
stay/low ssn; cc acc (Visa); CCI. "Poss itinerants;
site run down; adequate facs; provencal cooking
avail; special private pitch extra; noisy nr pool;
under-staffed low ssn; conv for Arles, St Remy, Les
Baux; gd for bird watchers (Camargue/Crau plain)."
♦ Easter-15 Oct. € 14.80 2003*

ST MARTIN DE LONDRES *10E1* (10km N Rural)
Camping Les Muriers, Chemin de Sauzèdes,
34190 Bauzille-de-Putois [04 67 73 73 63; fax
04 67 73 31 84 (Mairie)] Fr S on D986 twd Ganges
turn L at rndabt on ent Bauzille-de-Putois & foll sp.
Site in 500m on L. Med, pt shd; wc (cont); chem
disp (wc); mv service pnt; shwrs inc; el pts (5A) €3;
ice; lndtte; tradsmn; snacks; BBQ; playgrnd; sw rv
500m; dogs; phone; bus 500m; poss cr; quiet; cc not
acc; CCI. "Canoe hire on rv; coast 45km; gd sh
stay." 1 May-30 Aug. € 10.00 2004*

ST MARTIN DE LONDRES *10E1* (2km E Rural)
Camping Le Pic St-Loup, 34380 St Martin-
de-Londres [04 67 55 00 53; fax 04 67 55 00 04]
Fr Ganges take D986 S. In St Martin turn L onto
D122, site sp. Med, hdg/mkd pitch, pt sl, pt shd; wc;
chem disp; shwrs inc; el pts (6A) inc; gas; lndtte;
shop; ice; rest; snacks; bar; covered pool; playgrnd;
10% statics; poss cr; adv bkg; quiet but some rd
noise; 10% red for 10+ nights; cc not acc; CCI.
"V friendly site & helpful owner; some pitches v sm
for van, awning & car; larger pitches on lower terr,
but ltd elec; shwrs awkward to use." 1 Apr-30 Sep.
€ 15.90 2004*

**ST MARTIN DE QUEYRIERES see Argentiere la
Bessee, L'** *9C3*

ST MARTIN DE SEIGNANX see Bayonne *8F1*

ST MARTIN DES BESACES *1D4* (Rural) **Camping
Le Puits, La Groudiere**, 14350 St Martin-
des-Besaces [tel/fax 02 31 67 80 02; enquiries@
lepuits.com; www.lepuits.com] Fr Caen SW on
A84 dir Rennes, Villers-Bocage & exit junc 41 to
St Martin-des-Besaces. At traff lts in vill turn R & foll
site sp, site on L at end of vill in 500m. Fr Cherbourg
foll sp St Lo onto m'way. After Torini-sur-Vire at junc
with A84 foll sp Caen & exit junc 41, then as above.
Sm, hdg/mkd pitch, pt sl, pt shd; wc; chem disp; mv
service pnt; shwrs inc; el pts (6A) €4; gas; lndtte; ice;
shop 500m; tradsmn; rest 500m; snacks; bar; BBQ;
sm playgrnd; pool 10km; sand beach 35km; lake adj;
fishing; cycling; equestrian trails; entmnt; no statics;
dogs; adv bkg (dep req); quiet; red low ssn (3nts for
price of 2); cc acc; CCI. "V helpful, welcoming, British
owners; no arrivals bef 1400; excel facs; pleasant
CL-type orchard site; lge pitches with garden; B&B in
farmhouse; suitable for rallies up to 30 vans; owner
selects pitch for sh stays; conv for Caen ferries &
D-Day beaches; excel war museum in vill; gd for
c'van storage; san facs poss stretched high ssn & in
need of upgrading; excel long/sh stay." ♦
1 Mar-31 Oct. € 14.00 2005*

ST MARTIN EN CAMPAGNE *3B2* (3km N Coastal) Camping Les Goelands, Rue des Grebes, 76370 St Martin-en-Campagne [02 35 83 82 90; fax 02 35 83 21 79; info@camping-les-goelands. com; www.camping-les-goelands.com] Fr Dieppe foll D925 twd Le Treport & Abbeville. Turn L at rndabt on D113 twd St Martin-en-Campagne. Cont thro vill to St Martin-Plage (approx 3km) & foll 'Camping' sp to site on L. Lge, hdg/mkd pitch, hdstg, pt sl, terr, pt shd, hdstg; htd wc; 100% serviced pitches; chem disp; baby facs; shwrs inc; el pts (16A) inc (poss rev pol); gas; lndtte; shop 1km; tradsmn; snacks (& in vill), bar high ssn; BBQ; playgrnd; htd pool & waterslide 1km; sand/shgl beach 500m; fishing; tennis; mini-golf; cycle hire; golf 20km; horseriding, archery 15km; TV; 40% statics; dogs €1.50; Eng spkn; adv bkg; quiet; cc acc; red CCI. "Sports complex in St Martin; gd touring area; ltd recep hrs low ssn; no late arrivals area; poss resident workers; mkt Dieppe Sat am; vg site." ♦ 1 Mar-31 Oct. € 27.00 ABS - N08   2005*

> As we're travelling out of season, we'd better phone ahead to check that the site is actually open.

ST MARTIN EN HAUT see Ste Foy l'Argentiere *9B2*

ST MARTIN EN VERCORS see Chapelle en Vercors, La *9C3*

ST MARTIN LARS see Ste Hermine *2H4*

ST MARTIN SUR LA CHAMBRE *9C3* (Rural) Camping Le Bois Joli, 73130 St Martin-sur-la-Chambre [04 79 56 21 28 or 04 79 59 42 30; fax 04 79 56 29 95; camping.le.bois.joli@wanadoo. fr] Leave A43 at junc 26 onto D213 sp La Chambre & Col de la Madeleine; foll camping sp (rd narr & winding in places); site on L. Med, mkd pitch, terr, pt sl, pt shd; wc (some cont); chem disp; shwrs inc; el pts (10A) inc; gas; lndtte; ice; shop, snacks, bar 3km; tradsmn; rest; BBQ; playgrnd; pool; fishing; guided walks; entmnt; dogs €0.91; 20% statics; poss cr; quiet; Eng spkn; adv bkg; red long stay; phone; CCI. "V helpful warden; spectacular mountain scenery; gd location walking rtes & skiing; conv Frejus Tunnel." ♦ 1 Apr-15 Sep. € 13.00 2003*

ST MARTIN SUR OUST see Rochefort en Terre *2F3*

ST MARTIN VALMEROUX see Salers *7C4*

ST MATHIEU *7B3* (3km E) Camp Municipal Le Lac, Les Champs, 87440 St Mathieu [05 55 00 30 26 (Mairie); fax 05 55 48 80 62] On D699 heading E in dir of Limoges 1.8km fr vill turn on L (N). Sp fr vill cent. Med, hdg/mkd pitch, pt shd; wc; baby facs; shwrs; el pts; lndtte; shops 3km; rest adj; playgrnd; lake sw & beach; quiet. "Pleasantly situated nr lake; windsurfing; pedaloes; lge pitches." 1 May-15 Sep.   2004*

STE MAURE DE TOURAINE *4H2* (6km NE Rural) **LES CASTELS Le Parc de Fierbois, 37800 Ste Catherine-de-Fierbois** [02 47 65 43 35; fax 02 47 65 53 75; parc.fierbois@wanadoo.fr; www.les-castels.com or www.fierbois.com] S on N10 fr Tours, thro Montbazon & cont twd Ste Maure & Chatellerault. About 16km outside Montbazon nr vill of Ste Catherine look for site sp. Turn L off main rd & foll sp to site. Lge, hdg/mkd pitch, pt shd; wc; chem disp; mv service pnt; baby facs; shwrs inc; el pts €4; lndtte; shop; tradsmn; rest; bar; BBQ; playgrnd; htd, covrd pool; waterslide; sand/shgl beach at lake; boating; fishing; horseriding; tennis; games area; games rm; entmnt; chstatics; dogs €1.70; poss cr; Eng spkn; adv bkg; cc acc; CCI. "Helpful staff; peaceful low ssn; check el pts; rec site." ♦ 15 May-15 Sep. € 35.00   2005*

See advertisement on next page

STE MAURE DE TOURAINE *4H2* (1.5km SE Rural) Camp Municipal de Marans, Rue de Toizelet, 37800 Ste Maure-de-Touraine [02 47 65 44 93] Fr A10 take Ste Maure exit junc 25 & foll D760 twd Loches. At 4th rndabt turn L & then immed R. Site on R in 500m. Site sp fr m'way. Med, mkd pitch, pt shd; wc; chem disp; mv service pnt; shwrs inc; el pts (10A) €2.40 (poss long cables req); supmkt 500m; shops, rest, bar 1km; BBQ; playgrnd; pool 1.5km; fishing; tennis; roller blade court; dogs €1.30; phone; Eng spkn; adv bkg; quiet. "Excel, v clean facs, beautiful & well-kept; facs poss stretched when busy; excel disabled facs; office closed 1100-1200; barrier down 2200-0700; twin-axle vans not allowed; easy walk to town." ♦ 10 Apr-30 Sep. € 7.00   2005*

STE MAURE DE TOURAINE *4H2* (11km SW) Camp Municipal La Croix de la Motte, 37800 Nouatre-Marcilly [02 47 65 20 38 or 02 47 65 33 56] In Ste Maure, turn W off N10 onto D760 for 4km, turn L onto D58 twd Pouzay for 4km, turn S onto D18 for 4km, site on L on ent vill. Med, hdg/mkd pitch, pt shd; wc (some cont); chem disp; baby facs; shwrs inc; el pts (6A) €2.60; lndtte; ice; shop 1km; tradsmn; rest, snacks, bar 4km; playgrnd; rv sw adj; fishing; some Eng spkn; adv bkg; quiet; CCI. "Helpful warden; clean san facs; pitches private & gd size; v quiet, pleasant site; conv for Loire chateaux; canoes/kayaks for hire; no c'vans over 6m or twin-axles." 15 Jun-15 Sep. € 7.00   2003*

FRANCE

STE MAURE DE TOURAINE *4H2* (6km W Rural) Camping du Chateau de la Rolandiere, 37220 Trogues [tel/fax 02 47 58 53 71; contact@larolandiere.com; www.larolandiere.com] Exit A10 junc 25 onto D760 dir Chinon. Site sp. Sm, hdg/mkd pitch, pt shd; wc; chem disp; baby facs; shwrs inc; el pts (10A) €3.50; gas 6km; lndtte; shop & 6km; tradsmn; snacks; bar; BBQ; playgrnd; pool; paddling pool; rv sw & sand beach 4km; games rm; mini-golf; cycle hire; TV rm; dogs €2; Eng spkn; adv bkg; quiet; red low ssn; CCI. "Delightful site; ideal for Loire chateaux." ♦ 1 May-30 Sep. € 21.00   2005*

ST MAURICE DE LIGNON *9C1* (1km E Rural) Camping du Sabot, 43200 St Maurice-de-Lignon [04 71 65 32 68; cmegiraud@aol.com] Take N88 N fr Yssingeaux or S fr St Etienne. Site sp in St Maurice. Well sp. Med, mkd pitch, part terr, pt shd; htd wc (some cont); chem disp; shwrs; el pts (6A) €3.25; lndtte; shops; rest, snacks 250m: BBQ; playgrnd; 50% statics; dogs; phone; poss cr; Eng spkn; adv bkg; quiet. "New owners; major improvements 2004; mkd walks fr site; ltd no. touring pitches, blocks poss needed." 15 Apr-15 Oct. € 9.25   2004*

STE MAURE DE TOURAINE *4H2* (6km W Rural) Chlorophylle Parc, Les Allais, 37220 Trogues [02 47 58 60 60; fax 02 47 95 24 04; contact@chloro-parc.com] Exit A10 junc 25 onto D760 dir Chinon. Site sp. Lge, mkd pitch, pt shd; htd wc; chem disp; shwrs inc; el pts (6A) inc; lndtte; shop; tradsmn; snacks; bar; BBQ; playgrnd; htd pool; waterslide; fishing; tennis; games area; entmnt; TV; 80% statics; dogs; phone; poss cr; Eng spkn; adv bkg; cc acc; CCI. "Ltd facs low ssn & expensive; superb pool complex." ♦ ltd. 1 Feb-30 Nov. € 26.35   2003*

†**ST MAURICE LES CHARENCEY** *4E2* (Rural) Camp Municipal de la Poste, 61190 St Maurice-les-Charencey [02 33 25 72 98]   Vill on N12 halfway bet Verneuil-sur-Avre & Mortagne-au-Perche. Site in vill cent, adj post office. Sm, mkd pitch, pt sl, pt shd; wc; lndtte; el pts (3-5A) €2; shop & bar nrby; lake adj; fishing; phone; some rd noise. "Direct access to lake; phone ahead low ssn to check open; vg sh stay/NH." ♦ ltd. € 6.00   2003*

ST MAURICE D'ARDECHE see Aubenas *9D2*   **ST MAURICE SUR FESSARD see Montargis** *4F3*

†ST MAURICE SUR MOSELLE *6F3* (4.5km NE Urban) **Domaine de Champe, 14 Rue des Champs-Naves, 88540 Bussang [03 29 61 61 51; fax 03 29 61 56 90; info@domaine-de-champe. com; www.domaine-de-champe.com]** Fr N66/E512 in Bussang, site sp from town sq. Med, hdg/mkd pitch, pt sl, pt shd; wc; chem disp; mv service pnt; baby facs; shwrs; el pts (5-10A) €3.20-3.90; lndtte; ice; shop, tradmsn; rest 500m; snacks; bar; BBQ; playgrnd; pool; rv 1km; tennis; cycle hire; games area; w/e activities; TV; 10% statics; dogs €2; phone; bus 1km; poss cr; Eng spkn; quiet; adv bkg; CCI. "Lovely views; v helpful owners; excel walks in Vosges by Rv Moselle; gd rest in vill; san facs shabby low ssn & insufficient for size of site." ♦ € 16.00   2005*

ST MAURICE SUR MOSELLE *6F3* (10km E Rural) **Camp Municipal Benelux-Bale, Rue de la Scierie, 68121 Urbes [03 89 82 78 76 or 03 89 82 60 91 (Mairie); fax 03 89 82 16 61; mairie.urbes@ wanadoo.fr]** Site off N66 on N side of rd at foot of hill rising W out of Urbes. At foot of Col de Bessang. Lge, hgd/mkd pitch, pt shd; wc; chem disp; shwrs €0.95; el pts (4-10A) inc; gas in vill; ice; lndtte; bar; playgrnd; rv & lake sw & fishing adj; dogs €0.35; quiet; adv bkg rec high ssn; 60% statics; CCI. "Gd sh stay/NH; beautiful area nr Col de Bussang." 23 Apr-2 Oct. € 10.35   2005*

ST MAURICE SUR MOSELLE *6F3* (W Rural) **Camping Les Deux Ballons, Ave Pied des Ballons, 88560 St Maurice-sur-Moselle [03 29 25 17 14; fax 03 29 25 27 51; verocamp@aol.com; www.camping-deux-ballons.fr]** On N66 on E side of rd in vill, site on L before petrol stn. Clearly sp. Lge, mkd pitch, pt sl, pt shd; wc; chem disp; mv service pnt; baby facs; shwrs inc; el pts (4-15A) €4-5; gas; lndtte; ice; shop 500m; snacks; bar; pool; waterslide; tennis; games rm; internet; TV rm; dogs €2; phone; poss cr; Eng spkn; adv bkg; dep req + bkg fee; quiet; red low ssn; cc not acc; CCI. "Cycle path thro countryside fr site; some pitches sm; excel site, rec long/sh stay." ♦ 10 Apr-12 Sep. € 20.50   2004*

STE MAXIME *10F4* (1km N Rural) **Camping La Beaumette-Imbert, 83120 Ste Maxime [04 94 96 14 35 or 04 94 96 10 92; fax 04 94 96 35 38; camping@labeaumette.com]** Leave Ste Maxime on rd to Le Muy & a'route, site on L in 1km. Med, shd; wc (own san rec); chem disp; shwrs inc; el pts (16A) €4; lndry rm; shop 500m; beach 1km; dogs; 50% statics; phone; quiet; adv bkg; CCI. "Security vg but low ssn warden absent; €80 dep security gate; site liable to flooding in severe weather; all facs upstairs inc disabled; cold water only except shwrs; vg." ♦ v ltd. Easter-Oct. € 20.00   2004*

STE MAXIME *10F4* (5km NE Coastal) **Camping Les Cigalons, La Nartelle, 83120 Ste Maxime [04 94 96 05 51; fax 04 94 96 79 62; campingcigalon@ wanadoo.fr]** Site on N98 E of Ste Maxime, go thro La Nartelle & turn L into lane immed after seafood rest. Site on L after 25m. Med, mkd pitch, pt sl, shd; wc; chem disp; shwrs; el pts (6A); lndtte; sm shop; rest, snacks, bar adj; paddling pool; sand beach 50m; poss cr; adv bkg; v quiet. "Friendly owners; gd position; sm v hard compacted earth pitches; car parking poss diff." ♦ 1 Apr-30 Sep.   2004*

ST MAXIMIN LA STE BAUME *10F3* (3km SE) **Camping Caravaning Le Provencal, Chemin de Mazaugues, 83470 St Maximin-la-Ste Baume [04 94 78 16 97; fax 04 94 78 00 22; camping. provencal@wanadoo.fr]** Exit St Maximin on N560 twd Marseilles. After 1km turn L on a'route app rd, R on D64. Site on R after 2km. Lge, pt sl, shd; wc; mv service pnt; shwrs inc; el pts (10A) inc; gas; lndtte; shop & 3km; snacks; bar; pool; adv bkg; CCI. 1 Apr-30 Sep. € 16.90   2004*

ST MAYEUX see Mur de Bretagne *2E3*

STE MENEHOULD *5D1* (1km E Rural) **Camp Municipal de la Grelette, Chemin de l'Alleval, 51800 Ste Menehould [03 26 60 80 21 (Mairie); fax 03 26 60 62 54; services-administratifs@ ville-sainte-menohould.fr; www.ville-sainte-menohould.fr]** E on N3; turn R over 1st bdge after rlwy stn; foll sp for La Piscine; site on R after pool; sp fr town. Sm, mkd pitch, pt sl, pt shd; wc; shwrs inc; chem disp; el pts (4A) €1.85; tradmsn; supmkt 500m; rest, snacks, bar 1km; pool adj; dogs €0.70; poss cr; adv bkg; Eng spkn; no cc acc; CCI. "Helpful warden on site 0800-1100 & 1800-2000; lge o'fits won't get thro gate without warden, otherwise site yourself; workers resident on site Jun '03; gd sh stay/NH." 1 May-30 Sep. € 6.60   2004*

STE MERE EGLISE *1C4* (9.5km NE Coastal) **Camping Le Cormoran, 50480 Ravenoville-Plage [02 33 41 33 94; fax 02 33 95 16 08; lecormoran@ wanadoo.fr; www.lecormoran.com]** NE on D15 fr Ste Mere-Eglise to Ravenoville, turn L onto D14 then R back onto D15 to Ravenoville Plage. Turn R on D421, Rte d'Utah Beach, site on R in 1km. Or fr N13 sp C2 Fresville & ent Ste Mere-Eglise, then take D15. Lge, hdg/mkd pitch, some hdstg, unshd; wc; chem disp; mv service pnt; shwrs inc; el pts (6A) inc; gas; lndtte; ice; shop; tradmsn; snacks; bar; BBQ (not elec); playgrnd; htd pool; paddling pool; jacuzzi; sand beach adj; tennis; cycle hire; games area; archery; entmnt; internet; TV rm; 60% statics; dogs €3; poss cr; recep 0830-1300 & 1500-2000; Eng spkn; adv bkg; quiet; cc acc; CCI. "Excel, family-run site with vg facs for children; places of interest & museums relating to D-Day Landings; warm welcome; helpful reception; lge pitches; poss v windy; special pitches for early dep for Cherbourg ferry; m'vans o'night rate €13." ♦ 1 Apr-24 Sep. € 28.80 (CChq acc) ABS - N122005*

STE MERE EGLISE *1C4* (500m E Urban) **Camp Municipal, 6 Rue Airborne, 50480 Ste Mere-Eglise** [02 33 41 35 22; fax 02 33 41 79 15] Fr Cherbourg S on N13 to cent of Ste Mere-Eglise (avoiding by-pass); at vill sq turn L on D17 to site, next to vill sports ground. Med, some hdstg, pt sl, pt shd, wc (some cont); chem disp (wc); shwrs inc; el pts (10A) inc (poss rev pol); gas 500m; lndtte; ice; shop & bar 500m; rest, snacks, BBQ; playgrnd; sand beach 10km; tennis; 5% statics; phone; poss cr; little Eng spkn; adv bkg; CCI. "Nice site; clean facs; conv D-Day beaches, museums & Cotentin Peninsula; conv ferries; gates locked overnight but open 6 am for early departures; 5 min walk to town; access poss if warden absent & pay later; gd long/sh stay." ♦ 15 Mar-15 Nov. € 10.70   2005*

ST MICHEL EN GREVE *2E2* (1km N Coastal) **Camping Les Capucines, Kervourdon, Tredez-Locqueneau, 22300 St Michel-en-Greve** [02 96 35 72 28; fax 02 96 35 78 98; les.capucines@ wanadoo.fr; www.lescapucines.fr] Fr Lannion on D786 SW twd St Michel-en-Greve, sp Morlaix; approx 7km bef ent St Michel-en-Greve, turn R into narr rd & R again in 100m at x-rds. Fr Roscoff take D58 to join N12 at junc 17; NE of Morlaix at junc 18 turn onto D786 twd Lannion; site down narr app rd on L on leaving St Michel-en-Greve, then R at x-rds. Med, hdg/mkd pitch, pt sl, pt shd; wc; chem disp; 100% serviced pitches; baby facs; shwrs inc; el pts (7A) inc; gas; lndtte; ice; shop & 1km; tradsmn; rest 2km; snacks; bar; BBQ; playgrnd; htd pool; sand beach 8km; watersports 1km; tennis; mini-golf; cycle hire; games rm; 7% statics; phone; c'van max length 8m high ssn; Eng spkn; adv bkg; quiet; 1 night in 7 free; cc acc; CCI. "Excel; well-maintained, peaceful site; immac san facs; gd pool; gd size pitches; exceptionally helpful owners; lovely bays; gd base; mkt in Lannion Thu." ♦ 15 Mar-5 Nov. € 26.00 ABS - B13   2005*

We're having a great holiday - must fill in some site report forms and send them to The Club as soon as possible.

ST MICHEL CHEF CHEF see Pornic *2G3*

ST MICHEL ESCALUS see Leon *8E1*

ST MIHIEL *5D2* (14km NE Rural) **Camp Municipal Les Passons Madine 2, 55210 Heudicourt [03 29 89 36 08; fax 03 29 89 35 60]** Fr St Mihiel, take D901 NE to Chaillon. Turn R on D133 to Heudicourt. Bear L out of vill, still on D133 & after 1km turn R to Nonsard. Site on R in 1.5km, immed after sailing school at N end of Lake Madine. Lge, mkd pitch, pt sl, pt shd; wc (mainly cont); shwrs inc; el pts €2.50; rest; shop; lndry rm; lake sw adj; nautical sports & fishing; horseriding school & sailing school adj; many statics; CCI. "Sm, cramped pitches; san facs in need of basic repair; gd lake for watersports; fair NH - not well looked after low ssn." 1 Apr-30 Sep. € 8.30   2003*

ST MIHIEL *5D2* (2km W Urban) **Camping Base de Plein Air, Chemin du Gue Rappeau, 55300 St Mihiel [03 29 89 03 59; fax 03 29 89 07 18; base.de.plein.air@wanadoo.fr]** Site on W bank of rv. Sp app St Mihiel. Fr town cent take rd sp Bar-le-Duc (D901) 1st R after rv bdge. Med, mkd pitch, pt shd; wc (mainly cont); chem disp; shwrs inc; el pts (10A) lndtte; shops 2km; tradsmn; rest, snacks, bar 1km; playgrnd; games area; canoeing & sailing; 10% statics; adv bkg; quiet; CCI; "Site developed as youth cent; facs clean but tired; pleasant scenery; lge pitches." 15 Apr-15 Oct.   2005*

STE NATHALENE see Sarlat la Caneda *7C3*

ST NAZAIRE *2G3* (6km SW Rural/Coastal) **Camp Municipal de l'Eve, Route du Fort, St Marc-sur-Mer, 44600 St Nazaire [02 40 91 90 65 or 05 46 22 38 22; fax 02 40 91 76 59 or 05 46 23 65 10 camping-de-leve@wanadoo.fr; www.yukadi villages.com]** At St Nazaire (Ouest) stay on N171 La Baule rd. Exit N171 on D492 (Pornichet/La Baule) & cont to junc with D92 (end of D492); at lge island immed after Geant superstore & Big Mac sp, take 4th exit sp Universite/Camping de l'Eve. In 1km turn R at traff lts sp Camping de l'Eve; site on R in 2km. Lge, hdg/mkd pitch, hdstg, pt sl, shd; wc; chem disp; baby facs; shwrs inc; el pts (5A) €4 (poss rev pol); gas; lndtte; shop; tradsmn; supmkt 2km; rest, snacks, bar high ssn; playgrnd; htd pool; paddling pool; waterslide; sand beach (via subway); tennis; entmnt; child entmnt; 30% statics; dogs €2.30; bus; poss cr; Eng spkn; adv bkg; quiet; red low ssn; CCI. "Vg long/sh stay; vg facs; pleasant vill." ♦ 14 May-10 Sep. € 22.00   2005*

See advertisement opposite

ST NAZAIRE EN ROYANS see St Marcellin *9C2*

ST NECTAIRE *9B1* (SE Rural) **Camping La Cle des Champs, Les Sauces, 63710 St Nectaire [04 73 88 52 33; campingcledechamps@free.fr; www.campingcledeschamps.com]** S bound exit A75 at junc 6 to join D978 sp Champeix; N bound exit junc 14 to join D996 sp Champeix/St Nectaire; immed after St Nectaire sp turn L at VW/Audi g'ge on L (site sp); site 300m on L. Med, hdg/mkd pitch, pt sl, pt shd; wc (some cont); chem disp; mv service pnt; shwrs inc; el pts (2-5A) €2.10-6.40 (rev pol); gas; lndry rm; lndtte; ice; shops 1km; playgrnd; pool; dogs €0.50; poss cr; poss noisy high ssn; adv bkg (dep req); cc not acc; CCI. "Well-kept, clean site; helpful owner; gd long stay; facs stretched in high ssn; extra charge for water." ♦ 1 Apr-30 Sep. € 12.00   2003*

ST NECTAIRE *9B1* (1km SE) **Camp Municipal Le Viginet, 63710 St Nectaire [04 73 88 53 80 or 04 73 34 75 53 (Mairie); fax 04 73 34 75 99; sogeval@wanadoo.fr]** In St Nectaire (opp Ford g'ge) turn L up v steep hill, site on R in 250m. (Rec walk up hill bef taking van). Med, hdg/mkd pitch, pt sl, pt shd; wc; chem disp; mv service pnt; shwrs inc; el pts (10A) €3; gas; ice; lndtte; shops 2km; tradsmn; snacks; playgrnd; pool; adv bkg; quiet; cc not acc; CCI. "Gd facs; gd views; nice sm pool." ♦ 29 Apr-30 Sep. € 13.00   2002*

ST NECTAIRE *9B1* (2km SE) **Camping La Hutte des Domes, Saillant, 63710 St Nectaire [04 73 88 50 22]** Exit 6 fr A75 S of Clermont- Ferrand. Take D978 to Champeix. Turn R onto D996 sp St Nectaire. Site on L in Saillant, ent easily missed. Sm, mkd pitch, pt sl, pt shd; wc (some cont); chem disp; shwrs inc; el pts (4-6A) €2.45-2.90; shops 2km; tradsmn; dogs €0.45; quiet. "Exceptionally clean." 1 May-30 Sep. € 10.50   2003*

ST NIC *2E2* (1,5km SW Coastal) **Camping Ker'Ys, Pentrez-Plage, 29550 St Nic [02 98 26 53 95; fax 02 98 26 52 48; camping-kerys@wanadoo.fr; www.ker-ys.com]** Turn W off D887 onto D108 & into St Nic, & foll sp Pentrez-Plage & site. Lge, pt shd; wc; chem disp; baby facs; shwrs; el pts (10A) €3.20; gas; lndtte; shop; snacks; BBQ; bar; htd pool complex; waterslide; sand beach adj; watersports; tennis; games area; entmnt; child entmnt; TV rm; some statics; dogs €2.20; adv bkg; cc acc; red low ssn. "Gd family site in lovely location; vg beach; friendly, helpful staff." ♦ Easter-24 Sep. € 17.00
                    2005*

See advertisement on next page

ST NICOLAS DE LA GRAVE see Moissac *8E3*

Pentrez Plage - 29 550 SAINT NIC
Tel 00 33 (0)2 98 26 53 95
Fax 00 33 (0)2 98 26 52 48

Camping ★★★ **Ker-Ys**

www.ker-ys.com - camping-kerys@wanadoo.fr

At only 20 meters
from the beach,
situated in a beautiful
environment in the Bay
of Douarnenez.
Domaine de Ker-Ys
offers you pitches and
rental accommodations.

Open from Easter till
the 24th of September

Water park with heated
swimming pool,
children's pool, slides,
balneo, animation.

ST NICOLAS DU PELEM *2E3* (1.5km SW Rural) Camp Municipal de la Piscine, Rue de Rostrenen, 22480 St Nicolas-du-Pelem [02 96 29 51 27; fax 02 96 29 59 73] Fr Rostrenen, take D790 NE twd Corlay. In 11km, turn L sp St Nicolas-du-Pelem. Site in 500m on R, opp pool. Med, pt shd; wc (some cont); chem disp (wc); shwrs inc; el pts (5A) inc; gas, shops 1.5km; rest, snacks, bar adj; htd pool opp; dogs; quiet; CCI. "V clean, well-kept site; choose own pitch, warden will call; excel long stay." ♦ ltd. 15 Jun-15 Sep. € 4.50   2003*

ST NIZIER LE DESERT *9A2* (Rural) Camp Municipal La Niziere, 01320 St Nizier-le-Desert [04 74 30 35 16; fax 04 74 30 32 78] Fr Bourg-en-Bresse take N83 SW for 4km, L onto D22 to Dompierre-sur-Veyle (13km). Turn R onto D90 at camping sp & site in 2km on R by lakeside. Med, shd; wc; shwrs inc; el pts (6A) €2; lndry rm; shops 1km; playgrnd; fishing; tennis; 75% statics; quiet. "Unspoilt; rural off beaten track on side of sm lake; v peaceful; site yourself, warden calls each pm; access poss diff for c'vans." 1 Apr-30 Sep. € 9.80   2004*

ST OMER *3A3* (8km NE Rural) Camping La Chaumiere, 529 Langhemast Straete, 59285 Buysscheure [03 28 43 03 57; camping. lachaumiere@wanadoo.fr; www.campingla chaumiere.com] Take D928 fr St Omer (see NOTE) twd Bergues & Watten & foll sp St Momelin. Stay on rd until Lederzeele. In Lederzeele turn R onto D26 twds Cassel. After approx 2km turn R just bef rlwy bdge sp Buysscheure & site. Turn L after church, R, then site on L 500m. Single-track rd after church. NOTE on D928 fr St Omer height restriction over 3m; use adj level x-ing sp rte vehicles over 3m. Sm, hdg/mkd pitch, pt sl, unshd; wc; chem disp; mv service pnt; baby facs; shwrs inc; el pts (6A) inc; lndry rm; shop 1km; tradsmn; rest; snacks; bar; BBQ; playgrnd; pool; fishing; cycle hire; archery; entmnt; TV; dogs €1; Eng spkn; adv bkg; quiet, but some rlwy noise; red 10+ days; CCI. "Excel site; v clean & well-cared for; basic san facs; pitches poss diff lge o'fits; friendly welcome; office open 0800-2100; regional dishes served in rest; in interesting area; close to WW1 battlefields & WW2 sites; owner can advise on local vets." ♦ 1 Apr-30 Sep. € 16.00   2005*

ST OMER *3A3* (3km SE Urban) Camp Municipal Beausejour, Rue Michelet, 62510 Arques [tel/fax 03 21 88 53 66] Fr junc 4 of A26 foll sp Arques to town cent. Foll sp Hazebrouck. Ater x-ring canal site sp 'Camping ***' on L. Med, hdg/mkd pitch; wc; chem disp; mv service pnt; shwrs €1.10; el pts (4-6A) €3; lndtte; shops 1.5km; playgrnd; lake fishing; 75% statics; dogs; adv bkg; rlwy noise; cc not acc; CCI. "No twin-axle vans; nice, friendly site; office open am only low ssn; access poss diff for lge o'fits; site boggy if wet; lge pitches; conv visit to Cristal d'Arques; Pas de Calais or Belgium (Ypres 50km); useful NH." ♦ 1 Apr-31 Oct. € 9.35   2005*

> This site entry hasn't been updated for a while; we'd better fill in a site report form and send it to The Club.

ST OMER *3A3* (5km NW Rural) Camping Le Fremont, 62910 Serques [03 21 39 86 55; campinglefremont@aol.com] Fr N43 Calais-St Omer, site on L 1.5km SE of Moulle past Tilques exit (just over brow of hill on N45 - don't overshoot). Med, sl, terr, pt shd; wc; chem disp; shwrs €1.35; el pts (3-6A) €2.80; lndtte; shop; rest, snacks 2km; bar; pool 5km; golf 4km; 90% statics; adv bkg; some noise. "Helpful, friendly warden; conv Calais ferry; san facs clean but need refurb; easily found fr N43; basic site for NH only." ♦ 1 Apr-15 Oct. € 13.00   2005*

FRANCE

ST OMER *3A3* (10km NW Rural) **Camping Chateau du Gandspette**, 133 Rue du Gandspette, 62910 Eperlecques [03 21 93 43 93; fax 03 21 95 74 98; contact@chateau-gandspette.com; www.chateau-gandspette.com] Fr Calais SE on A26/E15 exit junc 2 onto N43 foll sp Nordausques-St Omer. 1.5km after Nordausques turn L onto D221 twd Eperlecques; site about 5km on L. Do not turn off D221 into Eperlecques. Or leave A16 at junc 24, foll D600 twd St Omer. After about 20km turn R at rndabt onto D207, site sp. (D300 & D600 are same rd but change number at rndabt.). Med, hdg/mkd pitch, pt hdstg, pt sl, pt shd; wc; chem disp; mv service pnt; baby facs; shwrs inc; el pts (6A) inc (some rev pol); gas; lndtte; ice; supmkt 800m; tradsmn; rest; snacks; bar; BBQ (not el); playgrnd; 2 pools; fishing 3km; tennis; cycle hire; horseriding, golf 3km; games rm; entmnt; TV; 40% statics; dogs €1; phone; recep 0800-2000; poss cr; Eng spkn; adv bkg (dep req high ssn + bkg fee); quiet; cc acc; CCI. "Lovely, well-run, efficient, busy site; tasteful landscaping; no shade if full; narr app on woodland track to far tourer field; site poss muddy in wet; ltd hdstg; 20km fr Calais; spacious, mainly sl pitches, various sizes; excel, clean facs; charming owners; super pool; excel rest; gd dog walks; local vet avail." ♦ 1 Apr-30 Sep. € 26.00 (CChq acc) ABS - P08 2005*

ST PAIR SUR MER see Granville *1D4*

ST PALAIS (GIRONDE) see Mirambeau *7C2*

ST PALAIS (PYRENEES ATLANTIQUES) *8F1* (1km S Rural) **Camp Municipal Ur-Alde**, 64120 St Palais [06 73 55 84 48 (mob) or 05 59 65 72 01 (Mairie); camping-ur-alde@wanadoo.fr] Fr S on D933 site bef rv bdge at ent of vill. Or foll sp fr cent St Palais. Med, hdg pitch, pt hdstg; pt terr, pt shd; wc; chem disp; shwrs inc; el pts €2.60; gas 400m; lndtte; ice; bar sells provisions; shops 400m; playgrnd; pool adj; fishing; horseriding adj; tennis; TV; adv bkg; quiet; CCI. "Lovely area; lge pitches, some with taps." 15 Jun-15 Sep. € 18.00 2005*

ST PALAIS SUR MER *7B1* (1km N Rural/Coastal) **Camping Le Logis**, 22 Rue des Palombes, 17420 St Palais-sur-Mer [05 46 23 20 23 or 05 46 22 38 22; fax 05 46 23 10 61 or 05 46 23 65 10; contact@ lelogis.com; www. www.yukadivillages.com] On rd N out of Royan, after vill of St Palais-sur-Mer, site sp on R after petrol stn. V lge, pt sl, shd; htd wc (some cont); chem disp; shwrs inc; el pts (6A) €4.80; gas 2km; lndtte; ice; shop & 2km; tradsmn; rest; snacks; bar; playgrnd; pool; paddling pool; waterslide; aquapark; shgl beach 1km; tennis; games area; entmnt; child entmnt; TV; 35% statics; dogs €4; poss cr; Eng spkn; adv bkg; red low ssn; CCI. "La Palmyre zoo & wine-tasting close by; excel water park." 14 May-10 Sep. € 25.50 2005*

See advertisement above

ST PALAIS SUR MER *7B1* (7km N) **Camping Le Logis du Breuil**, 17570 St Augustin [05 46 23 23 45; fax 05 46 23 43 33; camping.logis-du-breuil@wanadoo.fr; www.logis-du-breuil.com] N150 to Royan, then D25 dir St Palais- sur-Mer. Strt on at 1st rndabt & traff lts; at next rndabt take 2nd exit dir St Palais-sur-Mer. At next traff lts turn R dir St Augustin on D145; site on L. Lge, mkd pitch, pt shd, pt sl; wc (some cont); chem disp; baby facs; shwrs inc; el pts (6A) inc (50m cable poss req); gas; lndtte; ice; shop; supmkt; rest; snacks; bar; BBQ; playgrnd; pool; paddling pool; sand beach 5km; fishing 1km; tennis; games area; games rm; cycle hire; archery; horseriding 400m; golf 3km; excursions; entmnt; internet; TV rm; 10% statics; dogs €1.60; phone; recep 0800-2000; barrier, dep req €20; poss cr; Eng spkn; adv bkg; cc acc; CCI. "Lge pitches; gd alt to cr beach sites; san facs gd; friendly." ♦ 15 May-30 Sep. € 21.60 ABS - A04 2005*

ST PALAIS SUR MER *7B1* (8km N) **Camping Les Vignes**, 3 Rue des Ardilliers, 17570 St Augustin [tel/fax 05 46 23 23 51] On app Royan on D733, after x-ing D14 turn R sp St Palais (by-passing Royan cent). At rndabt on D25 foll sp St Augustin. Site on R. Med, mkd pitch, pt shd; wc (some cont); shwrs; el pts (10A) €3.20; gas; lndtte; ice; shop; tradsmn; rest; snacks; bar; playgrnd; pool 200m; cycle hire; entmnt; 70% statics; dogs €0.85; phone; adv bkg; red long stay/low ssn; CCI. "Excel rest/bar; gd value; v welcoming; site on wine producer's land, own produce sold; immac pools." ♦ ltd. 1 May-30 Sep. € 9.60 2004*

ST PALAIS SUR MER *7B1* (NE Coastal) **Parc ACCCF Marcel Taburiaux**, 2 Ave de Bernezac, 17420 St Palais-sur-Mer [05 46 39 00 71; fax 05 46 38 14 46] Foll sp off Royan-St Palais rd. Med, pt shd; wc; chem disp; mv service pnt; 50% serviced pitches; baby facs; shwrs inc; el pts (2-6A) €2-2.90; lndtte; ice; shop; rest; snacks; playgrnd; htd pool; TV; entmnt; lake fishing 1km; adv bkg. 15 Mar-15 Oct. € 16.00 2002*

ST PALAIS SUR MER *7B1* (1.5km NE Coastal) **Camping Les Ormeaux**, 44 Ave de Bernezac, 17420 St Palais-sur-Mer [05 46 39 02 07; fax 05 46 38 56 66] Foll sp off Royan-St Palais rd. Rec app ent fr R. Ent & camp rds narr. Lge, pt shd; wc; shwrs inc; el pts (6A) €4.50; gas; lndtte; ice; shop; snacks; bar; playgrnd; htd pool; sand beach 700m; entmnt; TV; some statics; dogs €2.50; quiet; red low ssn. 1 Apr-31 Oct. € 23.50 (3 persons) 2003*

ST PALAIS SUR MER *7B1* (2km E Coastal) **Camping Le Val Vert**, 10 Ave Frederic Garnier, 17640 Vaux-sur-Mer [tel/fax 05 46 38 25 51; camping-val-vert@wanadoo.fr; www.camping-val-vert.com] Fr Saintes on N150 dir Royan; join D25 dir St Palais-sur-Mer; turn L at traff lts dir Vaux-sur-Mer, Zone Artisanale & Val Vert; at rndabt 1st exit R to Vaux-sur-Mer; at traff lts turn L; at rndabt 3rd exit, then immed R. Site on R in 500m. Lge, hdg pitch; wc; chem disp; baby facs; shwrs inc; el pts (10A) inc; gas; lndtte; shop; rest; snacks; bar; gas/elec BBQ; playgrnd; htd pool; paddling pool; beach 1km; watersports; tennis 400m; horseriding; golf 5km; games rm; dogs €2.50; recep 0800-2100; no c'vans over 6.50m high ssn; adv bkg; cc acc. "Daily mkt in Royan; no twin-axle vans." ♦ 15 Apr-30 Sep. € 29.10 (3 persons) ABS - A25 2005*

ST PALAIS SUR MER *7B1* (2km SE Coastal) **Camping Nauzan (formerly Municipal)**, Ave de Nauzan, 17640 Vaux-sur-Mer [05 46 38 29 13; fax 05 46 38 18 43; camping@vaux-atlantique.com] Take either coast rd or inland rd fr Royan to Vaux-sur-Mer; site not well sp. Lge, mkd pitch, pt shd; wc; chem disp; baby facs; shwrs inc; el pts (6A) inc; gas; lndtte; ice; shop; supmkt 1km; rest; snacks; bar; playgrnd; sm pool; sand beach 500m; tennis 200m; 10% statics (sep area) dogs €2.75; adv bkg; quiet; 30% red low ssn; CCI. "Gd site, being improved (2005); helpful staff."♦ 1 Apr-30 Sep. € 24.40 (3 persons) 2005*

ST PALAIS SUR MER *7B1* (3km NW Coastal) **Camping La Cote de Beaute**, Ave de la Grande Cote, 17420 St Palais-sur-Mer [05 46 23 20 59; fax 05 46 23 37 32; phlDct@aol.com] Fr St Palais-sur-Mer foll sp to La Tremblade & Ronce-les-Bains. Site on D25, 50m fr beach, look for twin flagpoles of Camping Le Puits-de-l'Auture & lge neon sp on R; site in 50m. Med, shd; htd wc; baby facs; shwrs inc; el pts (6A) inc; lndtte; supmkt adj; tradsmn; rest; snacks; bar; playgrnd; sand beach 200m across rd; tennis, cycle hire adj; golf 2km; some statics; dogs €2; adv bkg; quiet. "Friendly staff; clean & tidy site; 8km of sand beach; steep descent to beach opp which is covrd at high tide; better beach 600m twd La Tremblade; cycle track to St Palais & Pontaillac." 1 May-30 Sep. € 22.10 (3 persons) 2004*

ST PALAIS SUR MER *7B1* (3km NW Coastal) **Camping La Grande Cote**, Ave de la Grande Cote, 17420 St Palais-sur-Mer [tel/fax 05 46 23 20 18] Fr Royan, take D25 thro St Palais, site on R where rd runs close to sea. Look for flags. Med, mkd pitch, pt shd; htd wc; baby facs; shwrs inc; el pts (6A) inc; gas; lndtte; ice; shop; rest; snacks; bar; sand beach 200m; dogs €1.50; bus; quiet. "Helpful staff; excel site; close to flagged area for safe bathing." ♦ 15 May-15 Jun. € 22.50 2004*

ST PALAIS SUR MER *7B1* (3km NW Coastal) **Camping Le Puits de l'Auture, La Grande Cote,** 17420 St Palais-sur-Mer [05 46 23 20 31; fax 05 46 23 26 38; camping-lauture@wanadoo.fr] Fr Royan take D25 onto new rd past St Palais foll sp for La Palmyre. At one way section turn back L sp La Grande Cote & site is 800m; rd runs close to sea, flags at ent. Lge, shd; wc (some cont); shwrs inc; el pts (6-10A) inc; gas; ice; shop; snacks; playgrnd; pool; sand beach 500m; fishing; internet; 40% statics; Eng spkn; adv bkg rec; red low ssn; cc acc. "Well-maintained, excel site; san facs stretched high ssn; poss cr but pitches carefully controlled; friendly staff." 1 May-1 Oct. € 35.00 (3 persons)   2005*

ST PALAIS SUR MER *7B1* (4km NW) **Camping Les Cotes de Saintonge, 11 Rue des Sables,** 17570 St Augustin [05 46 23 23 48; fax 05 46 39 48 37; lescotesdesaintonge@libertysurf.fr; www. lescotesdesaintonge.fr] Foll rd sp fr Royan to La Tremblade & St Augustin, site on R after sp end St Augustin. Med, shd; wc (some cont); shwrs inc; el pts (6A) inc; shop & 600m; rest; snacks; bar; playgrnd; pool; sand beach 3km; TV rm; entmnt; many statics; dogs €2.30; quiet. "Amongst oak trees; fine forests & beaches locally; poss clsd low ssn - phone to check." ♦ 1 Apr-15 Sep. € 22.30   2004*

ST PARDOUX *9A1* (4km SW Rural) **Camping Elan, Route de St Pardoux, 63440 Blot-l'Eglise** [04 73 97 44 94 or 06 10 21 40 58; campingelan@ hotmail.com] Fr N on N144 take D16 to Blot, fr S take D50, foll site sp. Med, hdg/mkd pitch, pt shd; wc; chem disp (wc); shwrs inc; el pts (5A) €2.25; lndry rm; shop, rest, bar 500m; playgrnd; rv fishing, canoeing 6km; tennis; dogs €1.50; poss cr; Eng spkn; adv bkg; quiet; red long stay; CCI. "New Dutch owners making improvements; new san facs & pool planned for 2006; gd walking area; conv Vulcania; c'van storage avail; site open low ssn by arrangement." 1 Apr-30 Sep. € 10.00   2005*

ST PARDOUX L'ORTIGIER see Donzenac *7C3*

ST PAUL DE FENOUILLET *8G4* (7km E Rural) **Camp Municipal Les Oliviers, 66460 Maury** [04 68 59 15 24 (Mairie)] Heading W on D117. Site immed after level x-ing on R 500m bef Maury. Sm, shd; wc (cont); shwrs inc; el pts; playgrnd; CCI. "Some rd noise fr level x-ing; vineyards & castles to visit; gd sh stay." 1 Jun-15 Sep. € 11.00   2004*

†**ST PAUL DE FENOUILLET** *8G4* (S Rural) **Camp Municipal de l'Agly, 66220 St Paul-de-Fenouillet** [04 68 59 09 09; fax 04 68 59 11 04; contact@ camping-agly.com] Heading W on D117; turn L at traff lts in St Paul; site on R in 200m, well sp. Sm, hdg/mkd pitch, pt sl, pt shd; wc; chem disp; shwrs inc; el pts (16A) €3.70; gas & supmkt 500m; pool 1km; rv sw 500m; quiet; CCI. "Gd site; friendly warden; beautiful mountain scenery; gd climbing & biking; poss unkempt low ssn; vg long stay." ♦ € 13.65   2005*

ST PAUL DE VARAX see Bourg en Bresse *9A2*

ST PAUL DE VEZELIN *9B1* **Camping d'Arpheuilles, 42590 St-Paul-de-Vezelin** [04 77 63 43 43] Take D53 fr Roanne 10km. Turn L onto D8 twd St German-Laval. Turn L at Dance onto D112 to St-Paul-de-Vezelin. Turn L on ent to vill. Or fr A72 exit junc 5 onto D8, then D112. V diff single track fr vill (3km) - v steep in places. Med, mkd pitch, pt sl, pt shd; wc (some cont); chem disp; mv service pnt; shwrs inc; el pts (6A) €2.90; gas; lndtte; ice; shop; tradsmn; rest; snacks; bar; BBQ; playgrnd; pool; lake/rv sw adj; sand beach adj; TV; 30% statics; dogs; phone; Eng spkn; adv bkg (dep req); 20% red 3+ days; quiet. "Beautiful location; helpful owner; various sports facs; excel long stay." 1 May-5 Sep. € 13.57   2002*

> Some of these sites have changed their opening dates - we'd better fill in some site report forms and let the editor of the guide know.

ST PAUL EN FORET see Fayence *10E4*

ST PAUL LE GAULTIER *4E1* (S Rural) **Camp Municipal, 72590 St Paul-le-Gaultier** [02 43 33 58 55 or 02 43 97 27 55] Located on D15, St Paul-le-Gaultier is 25km SW of Alencon. Sm; shwrs free; el pts (4A) inc; playgrnd; rv fishing. "Tranquil site; excel value; site by lake; office open 0900-1000 & 1700-1900." € 6.30   2004*

ST PEE SUR NIVELLE see St Jean de Luz *8F1*

ST PEREUSE *4H4* (SE Rural) **LES CASTELS Manoir de Bezolle, 58110 St Pereuse-en-Morvan** [03 86 84 42 55; fax 03 86 84 43 77; info@bezolle. com; www.bezolle.com or www.les-castels.com] 9km W of Chateau Chinon on D978 Autun-Nevers. Site sp; ent on N side of D978 on D11. Med, pt sl, pt terr, pt shd; wc; chem disp; mv service pnt; shwrs inc; el pts (10A) €4 (long lead poss req & avail on loan); gas; lndtte; ice; shop; rest; snacks; bar; playgrnd; sm pool; lakeside walks; fishing; tennis; mini-golf; horseriding; entmnt; TV rm; 25% statics; dogs €2; quiet; red low ssn; cc acc; CCI. "Friendly recep; well-kept site; med sized pitches; lge ones avail at extra cost; gd views; lovely situation in National Park; gd for touring Burgundy wine region." ♦ 1 May-15 Sep. € 30.00 (CChq acc)   2005*

See advertisement on next page

ST PHILIBERT see Carnac *2G3*

ST PIERRE D'ARGENCON see Aspres sur Buech *9D3*

FRANCE

ST PIERRE DE CHARTREUSE 9C3 (Rural) Camping de Martiniere, Route du Col de Porte, 38380 St Pierre-de-Chartreuse [04 76 88 60 36; fax 04 76 88 69 10; brice.gaude@wanadoo.fr; www.campingdemartiniere.com] Take D520 S fr Les Echelles to St Laurent-du-Pont, D512 thro Gorge-du-Guiers-Mort to St Pierre-de-Chartreuse. Site clearly sp about 2km S of vill on D512 rd to Grenoble. Med, mkd pitch, pt shd; htd wc (mainly cont); chem disp; mv service pnt; shwrs inc; el pts (2-6A) €2-3.90; gas; lndtte; ice; shop; tradsmn; rest; bar; playgrnd; pool; paddling pool; fishing; games area; library; dogs €1; Eng spkn; adv bkg rec (ess in winter ssn); red low ssn; CChq not acc; cc acc; CCI. "Grand Chartreuse Monastery 4km; spectacular mountain scenery; unspoilt vills; friendly owner." 30 Apr-18 Sep. € 15.00 (CChq acc) 2004*

ST PIERRE DU VAUVRAY see Pont de l'Arche 3D2

ST PIERRE LAFEUILLE see Cahors 7D3

ST PIERRE LE MOUTIER 4H4 (500m N Rural) Camp Municipal de Beaudrillon, Le Panama, Rue de Beaudrillon, 58240 St Pierre-le-Moutier [03 86 37 42 09 (Mairie)] Site on N7. Sp at either ent to town. Sm, hdg pitch, pt sl, pt shd; wc (cont); own san rec; chem disp; shwrs inc; el pts (6A) €2.95; ice; shops 2km; no adv bkg; quiet, some rd & rlwy noise; CCI. "Modern, clean san facs; warden present 0800-1000 & 1800-2000, otherwise go to Mairie; sh stay/NH only." ♦ 15 May-15 Sep. € 8.35 2005*

ST PIERRE LE MOUTIER 4H4 (7km W) Camp Municipal de St Mayeul, 03320 Le Veurdre [04 70 66 40 67 (Mairie); fax 04 70 66 42 88] Fr N7 at St Pierre-le-Moutier SW onto D978A to Le Veurdre. Site sp on far side of Le Veurdre. Med, pt shd; wc; shwrs inc; el pts inc; shops 500m; no statics; quiet. "Rec sh stay; friendly staff; pleasant quiet spot; site yourself, warden calls." 1 Jun-15 Sep. € 9.20 2005*

ST PIERRE LE MOUTIER 4H4 (8km NW Rural) Camping La Bruyere, 18600 Mornay-sur-Allier [02 48 74 57 01] Fr W on N76 turn R onto D45 & foll sp. Site just bef x-ing rv Allier. Sm, pt shd; wc; shwrs inc; el pts (3A) €1.55; quiet. "V tidy site with clean facs; site run by volunteers; pitch self & warden collects fees; excel NH." 1 May-15 Sep. € 6.15 2004*

ST PIERRE QUIBERON see Quiberon 2G3

ST PIERRE SUR DIVES 3D1 (1.5km SW) Camp Municipal, Route de Lieury, 14170 St Pierre-sur-Dives [02 31 20 73 28 or 02 31 20 97 90; fax 02 31 20 36 02; mairie.saint.pierre.sur.dives@wanadoo.fr] Fr Falaise on D511, site sp on app to town; turn R at 1st junc, do not foll by-pass. Sm, hdg/mkd pitch, pt shd; wc; shwrs; el pts (10A) €2; shops 650m; playgrnd; pool 500m; Eng spkn; adv bkg; quiet. "Delightful site, close to Caen & historic beaches of Normandy; warden lives on site; pleasant town on Rte du Fromage; conv ferry port; rec." ♦ 1 May-15 Sep. € 6.70 2005*

> Will you fill in the site report forms at the back of the guide, or shall I?

ST POINT see Cluny 9A2

ST POINT LAC see Pontarlier 6H2

ST POL DE LEON 1D2 (2km E Coastal) Camping Ar Kleguer, Plage Ste Anne, 29250 St Pol-de-Leon [02 98 69 18 81; fax 02 98 29 12 84; info@camping-ar-kleguer.com] In St Pol-de-Leon foll Centre Ville sp. At cathedral sq (2 towers), turn R foll sp for Plage. In 150m, bef church with tall belfry, turn L foll Plage & camping sp. On reaching sea turn L (N); site at end, well sp. Med, mkd pitch, terr, pt shd; wc (some cont); own san; chem disp; shwrs inc; el pts (2-10A) €2.90 (long lead poss req); lndtte; shops 500m; snacks; bar; htd pool; waterslide; beach; games rm; 40% statics; dogs €1.70; poss cr; adv bkg; poss noisy; CCI. "Modern facs; gd views; gd sh stay." 1 Apr-30 Sep. € 16.00 2003*

SITES

ST POL DE LEON *1D2* (2km E Coastal) **Camping de Trologot, Greve du Man, 29250 St Pol-de-Leon** [02 98 69 06 26 or 02 98 69 22 29 (LS); fax 02 98 29 18 30; camping-trologot@wanadoo. fr; www.camping-trologot.com] Fr E take N12/E50 twd Morlaix & join D58 to St Pol-de-Leon. In St Pol foll 'Campings' & 'Plages' sp along seafront for approx 600m. Site on L after a sharp L-hand bend, opp Greve du Man beach. Fr Roscoff on D58 turn L onto D769 sp St Pol. Foll 'Campings' & at graveyard turn L & strt on at rndabt. Turn L at seafront, then as above. Med, hdg/mkd pitch, unshd; wc; chem disp; mv service pnt; shwrs; el pts (10A) inc; gas; lndtte; shop 2km; tradsmn; BBQ (gas/charcoal only); playgrnd; pool; sand beach adj; entmnt; TV; 20% statics; €1.20; no c'vans over 7m high ssn; poss cr; adv bkg; quiet; cc acc; red long stay/low ssn/CCI. "Ideal NH for Roscoff ferry; excel refurbished site; v clean san facs; boat slipway on adj beach; gd sized pitches; helpful owners; highly rec." ♦ 1 May-30 Sep. € 19.90 (CChq acc) ABS - B29   2005*

ST POL DE LEON *1D2* (2km SE Rural) **Camping des Hortensias, Kermen, 29660 Carantec** [tel/fax 02 98 67 08 63 or 02 98 67 96 34] Fr Roscoff on D58 dir Morlaix. Turn L after approx 10km on D173, turn R at 1st rndabt for site sp. Sm, unshd; wc; chem disp; mv service pnt; shwrs inc; el pts (10A) €2; gas 3km; lndtte; shop 3km; playgrnd; beach 3km; dogs €0.80; adv bkg; quiet; CCI. "Gd touring base; conv ferry." ♦ 1 May-30 Sep. € 9.60   2005*

†ST POL DE LEON *1D2* (3km SE) **Camping Tal ar Mor, Kerlaudy, Pont de la Corde, 29420 Plouenan** [tel/fax 02 98 69 03 11] Fr Roscoff on D58 10km fr ferry, 1km fr Pont de la Corde. Site on R immed bef sharp L bend. Sm, hdg/mkd pitch, hdstg, pt sl, pt shd; wc; shwrs inc; el pts (6-10A) inc; lndry rm; shop 2km; rest; bar; playgrnd; sand beach 5km; 5% statics; dogs; phone; poss cr; Eng spkn. "Gd for ferry & touring; keen & helpful owner; some noise fr main rd." € 10.40   2004*

ST POL DE LEON *1D2* (5km SE Coastal) **Camping Village Les Mouettes, La Grande Greve, 29660 Carantec** [02 98 67 02 46; fax 02 98 78 31 46; camping@les-mouettes.com; www.les-mouettes.com] Fr Morlaix take D58 N, then cont on D173 coastal rd twd Carantec; on ent Carantec sp to site on L. Fr Roscoff take D58 sp Mortaix, then D173 to Carantec. Foll sp town cent, then site. Lge, mkd pitch, pt shd; wc; chem disp; mv service pnt; baby facs; shwrs inc; el pts (6A) inc (poss rev pol); gas; lndtte; ice; shop; snacks; bar; BBQ (charcoal/gas only); playgrnd; htd pool & paddling pool; waterslide; sand/shgl beach 1km; fishing; golf & watersports in town; child entmnt; games rm; internet; 50% statics; dogs €4; poss cr; Eng spkn; adv bkg; noise fr boatyard; red low ssn; cc acc; CCI. "Conv Roscoff ferry; sea views; €20 dep for key; mkt Carentec Thu." ♦ 1 May-10 Sep. € 42.00 ABS - B14   2005*

ST POL DE LEON *1D2* (6km S Urban) **Camp Municipal de Kerilis, 29670 Henvic** [02 98 62 82 10; fax 02 98 62 81 56; commune-henvic@ wanadoo.fr] Site on R of main rd bet St Pol-de-Leon & Morlaix. Foll sp for Henvic. Site 150m after exit main rd. Med, pt shd; wc; shwrs inc; el pts inc; lndry rm; supmkt nr; playgrnd; sand beach 8km; quiet; CCI. "Barrier closes 2200; helpful warden." 1 Jul-31 Aug. € 9.50   2003*

†ST POL DE LEON *1D2* (7km W Coastal) **Camp du Theven, Ports Misclic - Mogueriec, 29250 Sibiril** [02 98 29 96 86; fax 02 98 61 23 30; roudaut. theven.29@wanadoo.fr; http://perso.wanadoo. fr/camping.theven.29] Fr Roscoff ferry on D58, at junc with D10 take Sibiril/Cleder turn. In Sibiril pass church & turn R past water tower, foll sp Port de Mogueriec, site sp. Sm, hdg/mkd pitch, terr, pt shd; wc; shwrs €1; el pts (4-6A) €3; ice; lndtte; shop; supmkt 5km; snacks; bar; BBQ; playgrnd; sand/rocky beach adj; fishing; boat hire; entmnt; 6% statics; dogs €1; Eng spkn; adv bkg; quiet; CCI. "Friendly, helpful owner; hot water/shwrs coin op; liable to close for 10 day periods low ssn - phone ahead to check open; v ltd facs low ssn, poss no hot water." € 10.90   2004*

ST POL SUR TERNOISE *3B3* (5km NW Rural) **Camp de M. Vigneron, 62130 Croix-en-Ternois** [tel/fax 03 21 03 39 87 or 03 21 03 43 12] W fr St Pol-sur-Ternoise on N39 then into Croix-en-Ternois; foll camp sp. Sm, hdg pitch, pt shd; wc; shwrs €1.50; el pts (6A) inc; ice; shop 5km; bar; BBQ; playgrnd; mini-golf, fishing & horseriding nr; 50% statics; dogs; adv bkg; poss noise fr motorbike circuit. "Gd walks & cycling; poorly equipped san facs; vg sh stay." ♦ 1 Apr-Oct. € 15.00   2004*

†ST PONS DE THOMIERES *8F4* **Camp Municipal Les Cerisiers du Jaur, 34220 St Pons-de-Thomieres** [04 67 97 34 85; fax 04 67 97 34 87] Fr Castres on N112 go thro town cent under rlwy bdge. Turn L onto D908 sp Olargues. Site on R immed past block of flats. Med, mkd pitch, terr, pt shd; wc; mv service pnt; baby facs; shwrs inc; el pts (6A) inc; ice; lndry rm; tradsmn; snacks; playgrnd; poss cr; quiet; Eng spkn; phone; CCI. "Excel site; vg san facs inc spacious facs for disabled; friendly, helpful owner; 1km walk to vill." € 14.30   2004*

ST PONS DE THOMIERES *8F4* (4km N Rural) **Aire Naturelle La Borio de Roque, 34220 St Pons-de-Thomieres** [04 67 97 10 97; fax 04 67 97 21 61; info@borioderoque.com; www.borioderoque. com] On D907, R at sp, foll track for 1.2km to site. Sm, hdg pitch, terr, shd; wc; chem disp; shwrs inc; el pts (10A) inc; ice; bar; tradsman in ssn; lndtte; playgrnd; pool; adv bkg rec high ssn (€15.24 bkg fee); Eng spkn; CCI. "Exquisite & spotless site; welcoming; meals served if req; secluded & peaceful in wooded hills; diff access lge/underpowered o'fits down single, dirt track - no turning/passing." ♦ 15 May-15 Sep.   2003*

FRANCE

ST PONS DE THOMIERES *8F4* (8km NE Rural) **Camp Municipal Les Terrasses du Jaur, 34390 Premian [04 67 97 27 85 or 04 67 97 06 40 (Mairie)]** Go E on D908 fr St Pons-de-Thomieres twd Olargues for 8km. Imposs to turn R over rv to site, cont on D908, turn round & app fr E, turn L into site. Sm, hdg pitch, pt sl, terr, pt shd; wc; chem disp; shwrs inc; el pts (3A) €1.50; lndry rm; shop; rv sw & fishing 100m; quiet; 30% statics; adv bkg; CCI. "Hotel in vill serves meals & drinks; site in full operation bet dates shown, but pitching acc all year - ltd facs." 15 May-15 Oct. € 6.60 2002*

ST PONS DE THOMIERES *8F4* (11km W Rural) **Camp Municipal de Cabanes, Route de St-Pons, 81270 Labastide-Rouairoux [05 63 98 01 26 or 05 63 98 07 58; fax 05 63 98 01 99; tourisme@labastide-rouairoux.com]** E fr Labastide-Rouairoux twd St Pons on N112. Site adj N112 immed after leaving Labastide vill. Sm, hdg/mkd, terr, pt shd; wc; chem disp; shwrs €0.76; el pts inc; shop 1km; tradsmn; ice; adv bkg; some rd noise; CCI. "Lovely site, spotless facs; v pretty; poss diff lge o'fits due to terr." 15 Jun-15 Sep. € 11.00 2005*

ST POURCAIN SUR SIOULE *9A1* (Urban) **Camp Municipal Ile de la Ronde, Quai de la Ronde, 03500 St Pourcain-sur-Sioule [04 70 45 45 43]** On N9, 31km S of Moulins; sp in town, bordering rv. Med, hdg pitch, pt shd; wc; chem disp; mv service pnt; shwrs; el pts €2.05; lndtte; shops adj; playgrnd; pool 1km; adv bkg; quiet; CCI. "Barrier clsd 2000-0800; clean, well-maintained site; extra charge for lger pitches; gd sh stay." 1 Jun-31 Aug. € 8.85 2005*

ST POURCAIN SUR SIOULE *9A1* (500m NE Urban) **Camp Municipal de la Moutte, 03500 St Pourcain-sur-Sioule [04 70 45 91 94 or 04 70 45 35 27 (Mairie)]** Fr Moulins on N9 S twd St Pourcain-sur-Sioule. Site well sp on L. Sm, mkd pitch, pt shd; wc; chem disp; shwrs inc; el pts (4A) €2.05; lndtte; BBQ; sw adj; quiet. "Vg site in lovely town; spotless san facs; 5 mins to shops; gd sh stay." 15 May-30 Sep. € 7.80 2005*

ST POURCAIN SUR SIOULE *9A1* (6km E) **Camp Municipal Le Moulin du Pre, 03500 Paray-sous-Briailles [04 70 45 12 26 or 04 70 45 05 14 (Mairie); fax 04 70 45 69 14]** Fr St Pourcain take D46 twd Varennes. After approx 4km site sp to R, in 4km. Sm, pt shd; wc; shwrs inc; el pts; lndtte; rest; rv fishing; tennis; quiet. "V well-kept vill & site; poss itinerants on site." 2002*

ST PRIEST DE GIMEL see Tulle *7C4*

†ST PRIVAT *7C4* (400m N) **Aire Communale St Privat, Les Chanoux, 19220 St Privat [tel/fax 05 55 28 28 77 (Mairie); francois-michel.perrier@wanadoo.fr]** Fr Argentat on D980 for 17km dir Pleaux & Mauriac, rd steep & winding in parts. Sm, chem disp; mv service pnt; water fill €2 for 100 litres; el pts (10A) €2; shops, rests in vill; m'vans only. € 2.00 2003*

ST PRIVAT *7C4* (4km W Rural) **Camp Municipal du Lac de Feyt, 19220 St Privat [05 55 28 25 42]** Fr Argentat take D980 & D75 dir Servieres-le-Chateau. Thro Servieres to site in 4km on lakeside. Med, pt shd; wc (cont); shwrs inc; el pts (5A) €2; lndtte; shops 4km; tradsmn; playgrnd; lake sw; tennis adj; fishing; sailing; poss cr; adv bkg; quiet. "Beautiful countryside, gd long stay." 15 Apr-30 Sep. € 8.20 2003*

ST PRIVAT D'ALLIER see Monistrol d'Allier *9C1*

ST QUAY PORTRIEUX *2E3* (1km NW Coastal) **Camping Bellevue, 68 Blvd Quay du Littoral, 22410 St Quay-Portrieux [02 96 70 41 84; fax 02 96 70 55 46; campingbellevue@free.fr; www.campingbellevue.net]** Foll D786 thro St Quay-Portrieux twd Paimpol; fork R 500m after beach at St Quay (sp for camp); site on R. Lge, hdg/mkd/pitch, hdstg, terr, pt shd; wc (some cont); chem disp; mv service pnt; serviced pitch; baby facs; shwrs inc; el pts (6A) €3; gas; lndtte; ice; shop; tradsmn; snacks; BBQ; playgrnd; htd pool; paddling pool; sand beach 800m; games area; internet; TV; dogs free; Eng spkn; adv bkg; quiet; red low ssn; cc acc; CCI. "Beautiful position; direct access to sm cove, main beaches 800m St Quay; overlooks sea; friendly staff; gd, clean facs; gd long/sh stay." ♦ 29 Apr-16 Sep. € 16.70 2005*

ST QUENTIN *3C4* (1km SE) **Camp Municipal, Blvd Jean Bouin, 02100 St Quentin [03 23 06 94 05]** Fr all app rds foll sp Centre Ville/Auberge de Jeunesse (c'van on sign). Press intercom at barrier for ent. Not well sp. Sp 'Terrain de Camping'. Sm, mkd pitch, hdstg, unshd; wc (some cont); shwrs; el pts (6-10A) €2.25-3.50; supmkt 1km; pool adj; some rd noise. "Gd value; v helpful staff; dated san facs, poss stretched & unclean high ssn; lge gritty pitches; pleasant canal walk adj; gates clsd 2200-0700; poss itinerants; NH only." 1 Mar-30 Nov. € 8.90 2005*

ST QUENTIN *3C4* (10km SW Urban) **Camping Le Vivier aux Carpes, 10 Rue Charles Voyeux, 02790 Seraucourt-le-Grand [03 23 60 50 10; fax 03 23 60 51 69; camping.du.vivier@wanadoo.fr]** Fr A26 take exit 11 St Quentin/Soissons; S 4km on D1 dir Tergnier/Soissons. Fork R onto D8 to Essigny-le-Grand & in vill foll camping sp W to Seraucourt. Fr St Quentin, S 10km on D930 to Roupy, E on D32 5km to Seraucourt-le-Grand. Site is N of Seraucourt on D321. Med, hdg/mkd pitch, some hdstg, pt shd; wc; chem disp; mv service pnt; baby facs; shwrs inc; el pts (6A) inc (poss rev pol); gas; lndtte; shop & supmkt 200m; tradsmn; snacks; BBQ; playgrnd; pool nr; angling; golf, tennis, horseriding adj; games rm; 20% statics; dogs €0.80; Eng spkn; adv bkg; quiet; CCI. "Gd, clean san facs; gd low ssn; lge pitches (but prone to flooding); ltd hdstg; gd value; friendly, helpful staff; can arrange with vet for return journey; excel for restful holiday; WW1 cemeteries, memorials & museum; Disneyland Paris 90 mins; wildlife in woods & lakes; gd dog walks; mosquito problem late Jun; well organised & busy; storage & seasonal pitches avail; rec arr early; warn staff night bef if planning v early departure; excel." ♦ 1 Mar-31 Oct. € 16.30 2005*

Camping-Caravaning ★★★
LE CHAMP NEUF
en Saint Quentin en Tourmont

Situated at 500 m from the Ornithology Park of
Marquenterre, at 2 km of the bay.
Rental of mobile homes and chalets.
Marked pitches with electricity for
caravans and tents.

8, rue du Champ Neuf
80120 ST QUENTIN EN TOURMONT
Tel. : 00 33 (0)3 22 25 07 94
Fax : 00 33 (0)3 22 25 09 87

E-mail: contact@camping-lechampneuf.com
Internet: www.camping-lechampneuf.com

ST QUENTIN EN TOURMONT *3B2* (S Rural)
Camping Le Champ Neuf, 8 Rue du Champ Neuf,
80120 St Quentin-en-Tourmont [03 22 25 07 94; fax
03 22 25 09 87; contact@camping.lechampneuf.
com; www.camping-lechampneuf.com]
Exit N1 or A16 onto D32 to Rue, take D940 around
Rue   & foll sp St Quentin-en-Tourmont, Parc
Ornithologique & Domaine du Marquenterre to site.
Site sp fr D204 Lge, hdg/mkd pitch, shd; wc; chem
disp; mv service pnt; baby facs; shwrs inc; el pts
(5-10A) €3-3.50; lndtte; shop; snacks; bar; BBQ;
playgrnd; beach 2km; games area; cycle hire;
horseriding 500m; entmnt high ssn; some statics;
dogs €1; adv bkg; quiet; cc acc. "Excel Ornithology
Park adj; well-kept, pleasant site; friendly, helpful
owner." ♦ 1 Apr-31 Oct. € 14.60   2005*

See advertisement

ST QUENTIN EN TOURMONT *3B2* (3km S Rural)
Camping Le Bout des Crocs, 80120 St Quentin-
en-Tourmont [03 22 25 73 33; fax 03 22 25 75 17]
Exit N1 or A16 onto D32 to Rue. When W of Rue
turn off onto D4 heading W. In 2km turn R onto
D204 & foll sp Le Bout des Crocs, then Parc
Ornithologique. Site on R. Med, hdg pitch, pt shd;
wc; chem disp; baby facs; shwrs €1; el pts (6A)
€3.25; lndtte; tradsmn; playgrnd; TV rm; 60%
statics; quiet; CCI. "Tourers put at end of site 200m
fr (poor) shwrs; excel bird reserve 1km."
1 Apr-1 Nov. € 11.00   2005*

ST QUENTIN LA POTERIE see Uzes *10E2*

ST RAMBERT D'ALBON *9C2* (Urban) Camping
Les Claires, 26140 St Rambert-d'Albon [tel/fax
04 75 31 01 87] Fr a'route A7 exit junc 12 dir
Chanas, turn S onto N7. In 1km turn R to St Rambert,
turn R at rndabt by town hall, under rlwy bdge & foll
site sp. Med, pt sl, shd; wc; chem disp (wc); baby facs;
shwrs inc; el pts (6A) €3.60; gas; lndtte; ice; tradsmn;
rest; snacks; bar in vill; BBQ; playgrnd; pool; sports
area; entmnt; 50% statics; dogs; phone adj; Eng spkn;
some rlwy noise; CCI. "Excel sh stay/NH."
Easter-15 Oct. € 14.20   2005*

ST RAMBERT D'ALBON *9C2* (8km NE Rural)
Camping Le Temps Libre, Quartier Font Rozier,
38150 Bouge-Chambalud [04 74 84 04 09; fax
04 74 84 15 71; camping.temps-libre@
libertysurf.fr; www.temps-libre.fr] Fr A7 take exit
junc 12 Chanas onto D519, dir Grenoble for 8km. Or
fr N7 take exit D519 E sp Grenoble. Site sp at 1st
rndabt & well sp in vill. Med, hdg/mkd pitch, hdstg,
pt sl, terr, pt shd; wc; chem disp; serviced pitches;
shwrs inc; el pts (9A) €4 lndtte; shop in ssn &
supmkt 10km; tradsmn; rest high ssn; snacks; bar
high ssn; playgrnd; 3 htd pools with chutes; tennis;
mini-golf; fishing; pedal boats; 30% statics; dogs
€2.50; Eng spkn; adv bkg; poss noisy; red low ssn;
cc acc; CCI. "Useful NH S of Lyon; ltd facs low ssn."
♦ 1 Apr-30 Sep. € 20.00 (CChq acc)   2005*

ST RAMBERT D'ALBON *9C2* (5km SE) Camping
Le   Chateau   de   Senaud,   26140   Albon
[0475 03 11 31; fax 04 75 03 08 06; camping
desenaud@libertysurf.fr;   www.chateau-de-
senaud.com] Exit a'route at Chanas. S on N7 twd
Valence, in 10km L at sp Camping Senaud onto
D132. Foll sp to site (1.5km). access tight for lge
o'fits - narr rent & sharp bends. Med, mkd pitch, pt sl,
pt shd; wc (some cont); chem disp; mv service pnt;
shwrs inc; el pts (6-10A) inc; lndtte; shop high ssn;
rest; snacks; bar; playgrnd; pool; waterslide; fishing;
tennis; mini-golf; golf adj; 60% statics; dogs €2;
poss cr; some rd noise; cc acc. "Gd site but needs
facelift; facs ltd low ssn; poss diff access to some
pitches." ♦ 1 Mar-31 Nov. € 25.00   2005*

ST RAMBERT D'ALBON *9C2* (9km SE Rural)
Camping La Chataigneraie, Route de Mantaille,
26140 Anneyron [tel/fax 04 75 31 43 33; contact@
chataigneraie.com; www.chataigneraie.com]
Exit A7 junc 12 for Chanas & St Rambert d'Albon then
Anneyron. Site is on D161 3km S of Anneyron via
narr, winding rd - poss dff lge o'fits. Med, hdg/mkd
pitch, pt sl, terr, pt shd; wc; chem disp; shwrs inc; el
pts (6-10A) €3.70-€4.40; lndtte; shop; tradsmn; rest;
bar; BBQ; playgrnd; pool; tennis; 40% statics; dogs
€2; phone; adv bkg; quiet; cc acc; red low ssn. "V
peaceful site overlooking Rhone valley; friendly owner;
gd size pitch; vg long/sh stay/NH." ♦ ltd.
1 Apr-30 Sep. € 16.50   2005*

Camping MONPLAISIR ★★★

Chemin Monplaisir • F-13210 SAINT-REMY-DE-PROVENCE

PHONE: + 33 (0)4 90 92 22 70 · FAX: + 33 (0)4 90 92 18 57 · E-MAIL: reception@camping-monplaisir.fr

★ Overflowing swimming and paddling pool – Snack bar in high season – Laundry
★ 130 pitches, 2.8 ha of comfort, quietness and garden area.
★ Boules, children's games, table tennis, supermarket.
★ Chalets and mobile homes to let.

ST RAPHAEL *10F4* (Coastal) Camping Vallee du Paradis, Route de Gratadis, 83700 St Raphael [04 94 82 16 00; fax 04 94 82 72 21; info@camping-vallee-du-paradis.com] Turn off N98 inland for St Raphael via Valescure; cont past Le Verlaine site; Vallee du Paradis sp on L. Lge, pt shd; wc; shwrs; el pts (10A) €4.20; gas; lndtte; ice; shop; rest; snacks; playgrnd; sand/shgl beach 400m; boat-launching; rv fishing adj; entmnts; TV; 50%statics; poss cr; quiet; red low ssn. 15 Mar-15 Oct. € 34.00   2004*

ST RAPHAEL *10F4* (4.5km N) Camping Sunelia Douce Quietude, 3435 Blvd Jacques Baudino, 83700 St Raphael [04 94 44 30 00; fax 04 94 44 30 30; sunelia@douce-quietude.com; www.douce-quietude.com] Exit A8 at junc 38 onto D37 then D100 sp Agay. Foll sp Valescure-Boulouris, site sp. NB c'vans not permitted on St Raphael seafront. Lge, pt sl, pt shd; wc; chem disp; serviced pitch; shwrs; el pts (6A) inc; gas; lndtte; shop; rest; bar; BBQ (gas only); ice; playgrnd; pool; sand beach 6km; entmnt; excursions; TV; many tour ops statics; dogs €4; phone; poss v cr; cc acc. "Noisy disco nightly; excel facs; sm touring pitches mostly amongst statics." ♦ 1 Apr-14 Oct. € 44.00 (3 persons) (CChq acc)   2004*

ST REMEZE see Vallon Pont d'Arc *9D2*

ST REMY DE PROVENCE *10E2* (500m NE) Camp Municipal du Mas de Nicolas, Ave Plaisance-du-Touch, 13210 St Remy-de-Provence [04 90 92 27 05; fax 04 90 92 36 83; camping-mas-de-nicolas@wanadoo.fr] Heading N on N571 ignore 1st Cavaillon sp town; cont to rndabt & turn R on N99 sp Cavaillon, Noves. Turn L in 500m to site on L in 500m. Well sp on all app to St Remy & in town. Site ent narr. Med, mkd/ hdg pitch, pt sl, pt shd; wc (some cont); chem disp; baby facs; shwrs inc; el pts (6A) €3; gas; lndtte; shops 1km; tradsmn; bar in ssn; pool; playgrnd; sat TV; dogs 1.50; poss cr; adv bkg ess; quiet; red low ssn; cc acc. "Excel facs; some pitches with diff access long o'fits; recep closd 1200-1500 for arr but parking avail nrby; supmkt on N by-pass nr; 25 min walk into town; vg long/sh stay." ♦ ltd. 15 Mar-15 Oct. € 16.00   2004*

ST REMY DE PROVENCE *10E2* (500m E) Camping Pegomas, Ave Jean Moulin, 13210 St Remy-de-Provence [tel/fax 04 90 92 01 21; contact@campingpegomas.com; www.camping pegomas.com] On D99 W dir Cavaillon, ignore R fork to St Remy. Pass under concrete aquaduct to next rndabt, turn L (Champion sp). Pass twin stone sculptures on rndabt, at 2nd rndabt turn R, site in 400m - sharp turn into site - usually flags flying. Med, hdg/mkd pitch, pt shd; htd wc (few cont); chem disp; mv service pnt; baby facs; shwrs inc; el pts (6A) €2.80 (poss rev pol); gas; lndtte; ice; shop 300m; tradsmn; snacks; bar; playgrnd; pool & paddling pool high ssn; entmnt; TV; dogs €1; phone; poss cr; Eng spkn; adv bkg; quiet; red low ssn; cc acc; CCI. "Well-run site; well-situated to visit much of Provence; sh walk to town; lge o'fits poss diff some sm pitches; gd pool & sunbeds; san facs basic/dated; poss unclean low ssn; mkt Wed; gates clsd 2100-0800 - security code avail; vg long stay." ♦ 1 Mar-31 Oct. € 15.00   2005*

> Mustn't forget to post our site report forms to The Club, otherwise sites might be deleted.

ST REMY DE PROVENCE *10E2* (8km W) Camp Municipal, Ave Docteur Barberin, 13150 St Etienne-du-Gres [04 90 49 00 03; corinne.gervais@voila.fr] Fr Arles take N570 dir Avignon D99 E dir St Remy. Site sp on o'skts of St Etienne. Sm, hdg pitch, pt shd; wc (some cont); chem disp; mv service pnt; shwrs inc; el pts (6A) €2.50; ice; shop 1km; no statics; quiet; CCI. "Gd, peaceful site; gd grass pitches, poss muddy when wet; ltd wc/shwr facs - rec own san facs; conv Arles, Avignon & Nimes." 1 Apr-30 Sep. € 10.20   2005*

ST REMY DE PROVENCE *10E2* (1km NW Rural) Camping Monplaisir, Chemin Monplaisir, 13210 St Remy-de-Provence [04 90 92 22 70; fax 04 90 92 18 57; reception@camping-monplaisir.fr; www.camping-monplaisir.fr] Exit St Remy NW by D5 to Maillane, in 110m turn L & foll sp in 500m. Med, hdg/mkd pitch, pt shd; htd wc (some cont); chem disp; mv service pnt; baby facs; fam bthrm; shwrs inc; el pts (6A) €3.30 (poss rev pol); gas; lndtte; ice; shop; supmkt 500m; tradsmn; snacks; bar; BBQ; playgrnd; pool; child entmnt; internet; dogs €1.60; phone; bus 1km; Eng spkn; adv bkg (dep req); quiet; cc acc; red long stay/low ssn; CCI. "Some sm pitches poss diff lge o'fits; gd touring base; lovely town; immaculate, well-run site; clean, modern san facs; v highly rec." ♦ 1 Mar-10 Nov. € 17.50   2005*

See advertisement

ST REMY DE PROVENCE *10E2* (8km NW Rural) Camping Les Micocouliers, 445 Route de Cassoulen, 13690 Graveson [tel/fax 04 90 95 81 49; micocou@ifrance.com; http://micocou.free.fr] Leave A7 junc 25 onto D99 St Remy-de-Provence then D5 N past Maillane, site on R. Med, hdg/mkd pitch, unshd; wc; chem disp; mv service pnt; shwrs inc; el pts (4-13A) €2.85-5.20; lndtte; sm shop & 3km; BBQ; pool; 8% statics; dogs €1.60; phone; Eng spkn; adv bkg; CCI. "V helpful owners; immac san facs; gd pool & sun area." ♦ 15 Mar-15 Oct. € 14.30 (CChq acc)   2005*

ST REMY SOUS BARBUISE see Arcis sur Aube *4E4*

ST REVEREND see St Gilles Croix de Vie *2H3*

ST ROME DE DOLAN see Severac le Chateau *9D1*

†**ST ROME DE TARN** *8E4* (300m N Rural) Camping La Cascade des Naisses, 12490 St Rome-de-Tarn [05 65 62 56 59; fax 05 65 62 58 62; campingdelacascade@wanadoo.fr] Fr Millau take D992 to St Georges-de-Luzencon, turn R onto D73 & foll sp to St Rome. Diff, steep app for sm o'fits Med, hdg/mkd pitch, hdstg, terr, pt shd; wc; own san; chem disp; mv service pnt; shwrs inc; el pts (6A) inc; lndtte; shop; snacks; playgrnd; pool; tennis; cycle hire; dogs €6; adv bkg; quiet; CCI. "Ideal NH for m'vans - but inadvisable for disabled & for lge & underpowered o'fits due v steep rds & bends, particularly after rain; lovely rvside pitches; each level has a wc but steep walk to shwr block; sh walk into beautiful vill; ltd facs low ssn." ♦ € 25.00   2005*

ST ROME DE TARN *8E4* (10km W Rural) Camping La Tioule, 12400 St Victor-et-Melvieu [05 65 62 51 93; carriere.nic@wanadoo.fr; http://perso.wana doo.fr/campinglatioule/] Fr Millau or St Affrique on D999 at Lauras take D23 sp Tiergues, then D250/D50 sp St Victor-et-Melvieu. Other app not rec due narr, winding rds. Sm, mkd pitch, pt sl, terr, pt shd; wc; chem disp; shwrs inc; el pts (16A) €2.80; tradsmn; BBQ; playgrnd; pool; dogs; adv bkg; quiet; CCI. "Beautiful area; vg site." 15 Jun-31 Aug. € 12.00   2005*

ST SALVADOU see Villefranche de Rouergue *7D4*

ST SATURNIN (PUY DE DOME) *9B1* (Rural) Domaine La Serre de Portelas (Naturist), 63450 St Saturnin [04 73 39 35 25 or 04 73 91 21 31 (LS); fax 04 73 39 35 76; ffn-laserre@ifrance.com] On A75 S fr Clermont-Ferrand exit junc 5 onto D213 W-bound sp Tallende. In 4km turn N on D96 sp Chadrat. Site on L about 3.5km after Chadrat. Turn acute L at end of tel posts. Or take N89 S fr Clermont-Ferrand twd Theix, turn S onto D96 & foll rd to site, sp. Sm, pt sl, pt shd; wc; chem disp; shwrs inc; el pts (6A) €3; gas; ice; lndtte; sm shop & 6km; BBQ; playgrnd; games area; 35% statics; dogs; quiet; red low ssn; INF card req. "Panoramic views; gd base for Parc des Volcans d' Auvergne." 15 Jun-15 Sep. € 13.85   2005*

ST SATURNIN (PUY DE DOME) *9B1* (9km W Rural) Camping La Clairiere, Rouillas-Bas, 63970 Aydat [tel/fax 04 73 79 31 15; info@camping laclairiere.com] S fr Clermont-Ferrand exit A75 junc 5 onto D213 W & foll sp Lac d'Aydat. At x-rds at end Rouillas-Bas turn L, site 100m on L. Sm, hdg pitch, terr, pt shd; htd wc; chem disp; shwrs inc; el pts (10A) €3 (poss rev pol); lndtte; shop 600m; rest 250m; snacks high ssn; playgrnd; 10% statics; dogs €1; Eng spkn; adv bkg rec high ssn; quiet; red low ssn. "V pleasant, quiet site; excel walking Puy-de-Dome area; friendly, helpful owner; clean facs poss stretched when site full." 1 Apr-30 Sep. € 12.00   2005*

ST SAUVEUR DE MONTAGUT *9D2* (2km S Rural) Camping Le Chambourlas, 07360 Les Ollieres-sur-Eyrieux [04 75 66 24 31; fax 04 75 66 21 22; lechambourlas@aol.com; www.chambourlas.com] Fr Aubenas take N304 dir Privas. At Privas, turn R at 1st traff lts twd Le Cheylard (D2). Site on R in 14km at Les Ollieres. Steep site ent. Med, mkd pitch, shd; wc; chem disp; baby facs; shwrs inc; el pts (10A) inc; gas; lndtte; ice; shop; rest; snacks; bar; BBQ; playgrnd; pool; paddling pool; lake sw & fishing; canoe hire; sports area; organised excursions; TV rm; 10% statics; dogs €2.50; adv bkg; cc acc. "Warm welcome; some v lge pitches; gd nature walks fr site." ♦ Easter-2 Oct. € 23.50 (CChq acc)   2005*

ST SAUVEUR DE MONTAGUT *9D2* (2km S Rural) Camping Le Mas de Champel, Route de La Voulte-sur-Rhone, 07360 Les Ollieres-sur-Eyrieux [04 75 66 23 23; fax 04 75 66 23 16; masdechampel@wanadoo.fr; www.masde champel.com] Fr N86 W on D120 at La Voulte-sur-Rhone or D21 at Beauchastel. Rds join at St Laurent-du-Pape. Cont on D120, turn R soon after D2 on ent Les Ollieres bef descent into vill. Site sp. Med, terr, unshd; wc; chem disp; shwrs inc; el pts (10A) inc; lndtte; shops 1km; rest; snacks; bar; playgrnd; pool; paddling pool; rv sw; fishing; canoeing; guided walks; cycle hire; archery; solarium; entmnt; some statics; poss cr; adv bkg; quiet. "Pleasant site in lovely countryside." ♦ 28 Apr-22 Sep. € 24.00   2005*

FRANCE

ST SAUVEUR DE MONTAGUT *9D2* (4km S) Eyrieux Camping, La Fereyre, 07360 Les Olliers-sur-Eyrieux [04 75 66 30 08; fax 04 75 66 63 76; blotjm@aol.com] Exit N86 at Beachastel via D21 to D120. In 15km site on L bef ent Les Ollieres. App via 500m of steep, unmade single track rd with unexpected hairpin bend at bottom. For sm vans & experienced drivers only. Med, pt sl, terr, pt shd; wc; chem disp; shwrs inc; baby facs; el pts (6A) inc; ice; shop & 500m; rest; snack; bar; playgrnd; pool; rv sw; fishing; archery; cycle hire; mini-golf; tennis; entmnt; dogs €2; adv bkg; quiet. ♦ 1 Apr-14 Sep. € 17.60   2002*

ST SAUVEUR DE MONTAGUT *9D2* (4km S Rural) LES CASTELS Le Domaine des Plantas, 07360 Les Olliers-sur-Eyrieux [04 75 66 21 53; fax 04 75 66 23 65; plantas.ardeche@wanadoo.fr; www.domainedesplantas.com or www.les-castels.com] Exit A7 junc 16, cross Rv Rhone on N304 to Le Pouzin, then turn N thro La Voulte-sur-Rhone. Then take D120 sp St Fortunat, 20km to Les Ollieres; over bdge, turn L & foll site sp. Med, hdg/mkd pitch, hdstg, terr, pt shd; wc; chem disp; mv service pnt; baby facs; shwrs inc; el pts (10A) inc; gas; lndtte; ice; shop & 2km; rest; snacks; bar; playgrnd; htd pool (no boxer shorts); rv sw & sand beach adj; fishing; hiking; games rm; child entmnt; 30% statics; dogs €3; Eng spkn; adv bkg ess; quiet; cc acc; red low ssn; CCI. "Beautiful site in wondrous setting; renovated san facs; warm-hearted owners; v highly rec; c'vans can only leave when accompanied 0800, 0930 & 1100; 4x4 used to take c'vans up v steep exit; excel." ♦ 29 Apr-7 Sep. € 30.00 (CChq acc)   2005*

See advertisement

ST SAUVEUR DE MONTAGUT *9D2* (8.5km W Rural) L'Ardechois Camping, Le Chambon, 07190 Gluiras [04 75 66 61 87; fax 04 75 66 63 67; ardechois. camping@wanadoo.fr; www.ardechois-camping.fr] Fr N foll N86 fr Valence for 12km. Turn R onto D120 to St Sauveur dir Le Cheylard. In St Sauveur foll D102 dir Mezilhac & St Pierreville. Site approx 8km on bank Rv Glueyre. Med, hdg/mkd pitch, terr, shd; htd wc (mainly cont); chem disp; mv service pnt; shwrs inc; el pts (6-10A) inc; gas; lndtte; shop & 8km; tradsmn; rest high ssn; snacks; bar; playgrnd; htd pool; paddling pool; rv & sand beach adj; cycle hire; games area; internet; TV rm; 70% statics; dogs €4; Eng spkn; adv bkg ess in ssn; cc acc; red low ssn/snr citizens; CCI. "Excel; v friendly, family site in glorious countryside; organised walks + picnic; excel rest; v helpful Dutch owners." ♦ 15 Apr-31 Oct. € 25.50 (CChq acc)   2005*

ST SAUVEUR EN PUISAYE *4G4* (1km) Camping Les Joumiers, Route de Mézilles, 89520 St Sauveur-en-Puisaye [03 86 45 66 28 or 03 86 45 46 28; fax 03 86 45 60 27; campingmote ljourniers@wanadoo.fr] Fr A6 S, exit at sp Joigny-Toucy onto D955 thro Aillant-sur-Tholon to Toucy, then cont to St Sauveur. Or N fr St Sauveur on D7 sp Mezilles, site on R in 1.5km. Site well sp at main x-rds in town. Med, hdg/mkd pitch, pt shd; htd wc; chem disp; shwrs inc; el pts (5A) €2.75; gas; lndry rm; ice; tradsmn; rest; snacks; bar 2km; BBQ; playgrnd; htd pool; lake sw & beach adj; fishing; games area; cycle hire; 6 statics; dogs €1.20; phone; poss cr; no adv bkg; quiet; cc acc; 5% red long stay/CCI. "Helpful staff; lge pitches; lake views fr pitches; sm beach on lakeside." ♦ ltd. 15 Mar-15 Nov. € 11.60   2004*

ST SAUVEUR LE VICOMTE see Haye du Puits, La *1D4*

ST SAUVEUR LENDELIN see Coutances *1D4*

ST SAVIN *7A3* (1km N Urban) **Camp Municipal la Gassotte (formerly du Moulin), 10 Rue de la Gassotte, 86310 St Savin-sur-Gartempe [05 49 48 18 02; fax 05 49 48 28 56; saint.savin@ ag86.fr]** E fr Chauvigny on N151 to St Savin; fr St Savin N on D11; well sp; flagged ent on R. Fr S on D5 cross rv; meet N151, turn R & camp on R. Fr S on D11 use 'heavy vehicles' rec rte to meet N151. NB There are 3 sites in St Savin. Sm, pt shd; wc; chem disp; mv service pnt; shwrs inc; el pts (12A) €2.15; lndry rm; shop 500m; tradsmn; playgrnd; rv fishing adj; TV; quiet; CCI. "Famous murals in Abbey restored by UNESCO; attractive, peaceful site; old mill converted to social cent; v helpful warden; excel long stay." ♦ 7 May-15 Sep. € 5.80   2004*

ST SAVINIEN *7B2* (S) **Camping L'Ile aux Loisirs (La Grenouillette), 17350 St Savinien [05 46 90 35 11; fax 05 46 91 65 06; www.ileauxloisirs. com]** Fr St Jean-d'Angely take D18 to St Savinien. Site on S side of town; cross rv bdge in vill; site on L after 300m. Med, pt shd; wc; shwrs inc; el pts (6A) €3; (rev pol); lndtte; shops 250m; bar; snacks; playgrnd; pool adj; tennis & mini-golf nrby; entmnt; dogs €1; adv bkg; quiet, some rd noise; cc acc. 1 Jul-31 Aug. € 11.50   2004*

ST SAVINIEN *7B2* (5km SW Rural) **Camping du Petit Bonheur (formerly Municipal), 14 Rue du Port, 17350 Crazannes [tel/fax 05 46 74 44 25 or 06 64 74 71 10 (mob); petit-bonheur@wandadoo.fr]** Fr St Savinien take D18 for 1.5km, turn L onto D119. Site on L in 300m. Sm, pt sl, pt shd; wc; chem disp; shwrs inc; el pts (10A) €3; gas; lndtte; shops 300m; tradsmn; rest, snacks, bar 300m; playgrnd; pool; rv sw, fishing 100m; dogs €0.80; Eng spkn; quiet; CCI. "Peaceful, CL-type site nr Rv Charente; new san facs planned 2006; gd cycling." Easter-15 Sep. € 8.00   2005*

ST SEINE L'ABBAYE see Chanceaux *6G1*

ST SERNIN *7D2* (2km N Rural) **Camping du Moulin de Borie Neuve, 47120 St Sernin [055320 70 73; info@borieneuve.com; www. borieneuve.com]** S fr Ste Foy-la-Grande on D708 twd Duras. 2km after Villeneuve turn L, sp St Astier. Site on R in 100m. Sm, pt shd; wc; 60% serviced pitches; shwrs inc; el pts (5A) €2.75 (poss rev pol); gas 2km; lndry rm; ice; shop 2km; tradsmn; snacks; bar; BBQ; playgrnd; pool; lake sw 4km; dogs; poss cr; Eng spkn; adv bkg; quiet; 5% red 7+ days; cc not acc; CCI. "Dutch owners v helpful & friendly; excel eve meals cooked by hosts; local wine sold on site; lovely quiet site; lge pitches; superb pool; excel local activities & mkts; tourist attractions in area, castles, vineyards; gd walking/cycling; site will open outside these dates by special arrangement by tel 24 hrs ahead." ♦ ltd. 12 May-15 Oct. € 15.40   2003*

ST SERNIN SUR RANCE *8E4* (Rural) **Camping Bellevert, 12380 St Sernin-sur-Rance [05 65 99 61 72]** E of Albi on D999. Site well sp fr vill. At bottom of valley on Rv Rance. NB: avoid using bdge. Sm, mkd pitch, shd; wc (mainly cont); shwrs; el pts (6A); gas 1km; shops 1km; playgrnd; no statics; adv bkg; quiet; CCI. "Well-tended site on banks of trout stream." 1 Jul-31 Aug.   2003*

ST SEURIN DE PRATS see Ste Foy la Grande *7C2*

ST SEVER *8E2* (1km N Urban) **Camp Municipal Les Rives de l'Adour, Ave Rene Crabos, 40500 St Sever [05 58 76 04 60]** S on D933 fr Mont de Marsan, cross D924 then bdge over Rv Adour. Look immed for access rd on L bef rlwy x-ing & steep climb up to St Sever. Site sp, easy to find adj Parc des Sports. Med, shd; wc; shwrs inc; el pts €1.55; shops 1km; ice; lndry rm; playgrnd; pool; tennis; sailing; fishing; quiet. 22 Jun-3 Sep.   2002*

ST SEVER CALVADOS see Vire *1D4*

STE SEVERE SUR INDRE *7A4* (Rural) **Camp Municipal, Route de l'Auvergne, 36160 Ste Severe-sur-Indre [02 54 30 50 28 (Mairie); fax 02 54 30 63 39]** On D917 fr La Chatre, site on R 200m after g'ge on L. Sm, pt shd; wc (some cont); shwrs inc; el pts €1.60; gas, shop, rest, bar 500m; playgrnd adj; quiet. "Tiny site in pleasant vill; associations with Jacques Tati & Georges Sand; vg sh stay/NH." Easter-1 Nov. € 6.40   2002*

†STE SEVERE SUR INDRE *7A4* (6km SE Rural) **Camping Perassay, 36160 Perassay [02 54 30 63 25; camping@the-french-connection.net; www. the-french-connection.net]** Fr Ste Severe take D917 S & after approx 6km turn L onto D71 sp Perassay. Site on R in cent of vill opp tabac. Sm, pt sl, pt shd; wc; chem disp (wc); shwrs inc; el pts (10A) inc; lndtte; BBQ; lake sw 10km; 1 static; c'van storage; adv bkg; quiet. "British-owned CL-type site; vg." ♦ € 15.00   2005*

STE SIGOLENE see Monistrol sur Loire *9C1*

ST SULPICE see Brengues *7D4*

ST SYLVESTRE SUR LOT see Villeneuve sur Lot *7D3*

†ST SYMPHORIEN *7D2* (1km S Rural) **Camping La Hure, Route de Sore, 33113 St Symphorien [tel/fax 05 56 25 79 54 or 06 86 77 09 27; campingdelahure@libertysurf.fr]** S thro Langon on app to a'route. Foll sp Villandraut, St Symphorien. Sp fr vill 1km S on D220. Med, shd; wc; chem disp; shwrs inc; el pts (5A) €2.40; lndtte; shops; rest; snacks; playgrnd; pool; tennis; rv fishing; dogs €1.20; adv bkg; red low ssn. "Helpful staff; basic facs; in beautiful pinewoods; gd cycling, walks, beaches." € 11.30   2004*

ST SYMPHORIEN *7D2* (14km SW Urban) **Aire Naturelle Municipale**, 40430 Sore [05 58 07 60 06; fax 05 58 07 64 72] Fr St Symphorien, take D220/D43 to Sore, then take D651 sp Mont-de-Marsan. Lane to site on L, nr rv. Sm, pt sl, pt shd; wc; chem disp (wc); shwrs inc; el pts inc; lndtte; gas, shop, snacks, bar 1km; BBQ; playgrnd; pool, tennis & sports facs adj; no dogs; phone; quiet. "Site yourself & warden calls; some el pts don't work so long lead handy; pleasant wooded area." ♦ ltd. 15 Jun-15 Sep. € 9.50   2005*

> As we're travelling out of season, we'd better phone ahead to check that the site is actually open.

ST THEOFFREY *9C3* (E Rural) **Camping Ser-Sirant**, Petichet, 38119 St Theoffrey [04 76 83 91 97; fax 04 76 30 83 69; camping sersirant@wanadoo.fr; www.euro-campsite.com] N fr La Mure on N85 dir Grenoble. At traff lts in Petichet turn E, site on lakeside in 500m. Med, mkd pitch, pt terr, pt shd; wc; chem disp; shwrs inc; el pts (4-6A) €2.60-5.10; lndtte; shop 8km; tradsmn; rest 1km; lake sw & beach adj; watersports; phone; bus 1km; Eng spkn; adv bkg; quiet; CCI. "Lovely views; excel walking & cycling; v helpful owners; highly rec; excel long/sh stay." 1 May-30 Sep. € 14.50   2004*

ST TROPEZ *10F4* (6km SE) **Camping Moulin de Verdagne**, 83580 Gassin [04 94 79 78 21; fax 04 94 54 22 65] Foll N559 N out of Cavalaire for 6km. Take 1st R after town traff lts in La Croix-Valmer, site sp on R. Site in 2km, surrounded by vineyards. Rough app rd/track. Med, terr, pt shd; wc (some cont); chem disp; shwrs inc; el pts (10A) €3.95; lndtte; shop 4km; tradsmn; rest; snacks; playgrnd; pool; sand beach 8km; dogs €3.05; 60% statics; phone; poss cr; Eng spkn; quiet; cc acc. "Pool is 2m deep; many pitches diff to reach towing a c'van; tight bends & narr pitches poss diff long o'fits; site poorly maintained & unkempt low ssn." 1 Feb-30 Nov. € 18.70   2002*

ST THIBERY see Pezenas *10F1*

ST TROPEZ *10F4* (6km S Rural) **Parc Saint James Gassin, Route de Bourrian, 83580 Gassin [04 94 55 20 20; fax 04 94 56 34 77; info@camping-parcsaintjames.com; www.camping-parcsaintjames.com]** Exit A8 at junc 36 St Tropez; after Port Grimaud foll sp Cavalaire S on D559 where clearly sp. V lge, hdg/mkd pitch, pt sl, terr, pt shd; wc (some cont); chem disp; shwrs inc; el pts (6A) inc; gas; lndtte; ice; shop; rest; snacks; bar; BBQ; plagyrnd; htd pool; paddling pool; beach 2.5km; tennis; games area; games rm; solarium; entmnt (child & adult); cable TV; cycle hire; golf 12km; 50% statics; dogs €5; phone; Eng spkn; adv bkg ess high ssn; quiet but some rd noise; cc acc; 10% red + 14 days/low ssn; CCI. "Conv St Tropez; scenic drives; vg." ♦ 7 Jan-27 Nov. € 34.00   2005*

See advertisement

ST TROPEZ *10F4* (7km S Coastal) **Camping Kon-Tiki, Plage de Pampelonne, 83350 Ramatuelle [04 94 55 96 96; fax 04 94 55 96 95; kontiki@campazur.com; www.campazur.com]** Foll Ramatuelle sp fr St Tropez; site sp on L. V lge, mkd pitch, pt sl, pt shd; wc; chem disp; baby facs; shwrs inc; el pts (6A) €5; gas; lndtte; ice; shop; rest; snacks; bar; playgrnd; sand beach adj; tennis; archery; entmnt; TV; 50% statics; dogs; poss cr; adv bkg ess high ssn (dep req); quiet; red low ssn; cc acc; CCI. "Some sm pitches; ideal beach holiday; all watersports avail." 5 Apr-18 Oct. € 35.00   2003*

ST TROPEZ *10F4* (7km S) **Camping La Croix du Sud, Loumede, 83350 Ramatuelle [04 94 79 80 84; fax 04 94 79 89 21; www.campingcroixdusud.fr]** App St Tropez fr W on N98A, turn R at traff lts at W o'skts sp Ramatuelle. Site on R in 7km opp filling stn. Med, pt sl; wc; shwrs; el pts (3-6A) €4.50; gas; lndtte; ice; shops 4km; tradsmn; rest; snacks; playgrnd; htd pool; sand beach 2.5km; 25% statics; dogs €2.90; poss cr; no adv bkg; quiet; Eng spkn; CCI. "Fair." 1 Apr-15 Oct. € 29.30   2004*

ST TROPEZ *10F4* (8km S Coastal) **Camping La Cigale, Route de l'Escalet, 83350 Ramatuelle [04 94 79 22 53; fax 04 94 79 12 05; camping lacigale@wanadoo.fr; www.camping-lacigale.fr]** Fr A8 or N7 at Le Luc take D558 to Grimaud & D61, N98 & N98A to St Tropez. Bef St Tropez take D93 S for 7km minor rd to Plage de l'Escalet. Med, pt shd; wc; shwrs; el pts (6A) inc; shop; lndtte; rest; snacks; bar; playgrnd; htd pool; paddling pool; sand beach 800m; cycle hire; tennis 800m; golf 8km; 30% statics; dogs €5; no c'vans acc over 5m; poss cr; Eng spkn; quiet. "Gassin, Ramatuelle must see vills; gd rest; gd." 1 Apr-15 Oct. € 30.00   2005*

ST TROPEZ *10F4* (8km S Rural) **Camping Les Tournels, Route de Camarat, 83350 Ramatuelle [04 94 55 90 90; fax 04 94 55 90 99; info@tournels.com; www.tournels.com]** Exit A8 at Le Muy dir St Maxime, St Tropez. Take D61 dir Ramatuelle then foll sp 'La Plage' & Camarat lighthouse. V lge, mkd pitch, terr, shd; wc (some cont); chem disp; mv service pnt; some serviced pitch; sauna; shwrs inc; el pts (5-10A) inc; gas; lndtte; shop; rest; snacks; bar; playgrnd; htd pool; sand beach 1.5km; games area; fitness rm; mini-golf; cycle hire; entmnt; child entmnt; TV; 90% statics; dogs €3.50; adv bkg; quiet; Eng spkn; cc acc; cc acc; red low ssn; CCI. "Well-run site; v clean & well-maintained; lower pitches full long term winter vans; upper terr levels via v steep, narr rd; poss diff long o'fits; lovely views fr upper level; vg long/sh shay." 1 Mar-10 Jan. € 34.00   2004*

> We're having a great holiday - must fill in some site report forms and send them to The Club as soon as possible.

ST VALERY EN CAUX *3C2* (500m NE Coastal) **Camp Municipal Falaise d'Amont, Rue Traversiere, 76460 St Valery-en-Caux [02 35 97 05 07]** SW fr Dieppe on D925 to St Valery-en-Caux; site sp on R off D925 500m fr town cent. App rd v steep, not rec lge o'fits. Sm, mkd pitch, terr, unshd; wc; chem disp; shwrs inc; el pts (6A) €2.10; shop & gas 500m; lndtte; playgrnd; shgl beach 500m; quiet; CCI. "Panoramic views; conv WW2 memorials; unsuitable towed c'vans due terrs; v steep app rd poss problem for lge o'fits &/or lge m'vans." 15 Mar-15 Nov. € 6.00   2003*

†**ST VALERY EN CAUX** *3C2* (SW Coastal) **Camp Municipal d'Etenemare, Rue Traversiere, 76460 St Valery-en-Caux [tel/fax 02 35 97 15 79]** Fr Dieppe on D925 foll camping sp on ent town. Med, mkd pitch, pt shd; htd wc; chem disp; baby facs; shwrs inc; el pts (10A) €2.15; lndtte; shop; tradsmn; pool & tennis in town; shgl beach; adv bkg; quiet; cc acc; CCI. "Site poss clsd low ssn - phone to check; v clean, tidy site." ♦ € 13.40   2005*

†**ST VALERY EN CAUX** *3C2* (W Coastal) **Aire Communale, 76460 St Valery-en-Caux [02 35 97 00 63 or 02 35 97 00 22 (Mairie); fax 02 35 97 90 73]** Sp fr cent of St Valery-en-Caux along rv/seafront to harbour. Sm, chem disp; mv service pnt; water fill €2; el pts €2; shops, rests nr; phone; free parking for 48 hrs. € 3.00   2003*

ST VALERY SUR SOMME *3B2* (2km S Rural) **LES CASTELS** Le Domaine du Chateau de Drancourt, 80230 Estreboeuf [03 22 26 93 45; fax 03 22 26 85 87; chateau.drancourt@wanadoo.fr; www.chateau-drancourt.com or www.les- castels. com] Leave A28/E402 at junc 1 at Abbeville onto D40 twd Noyelles-sur-Mer. At rndabt with D940 turn L sp St Valéry-sur-Somme. Turn S onto D48 dir Estréboeuf. Turn immed L for Chateau de Drancourt, site sp on L. NB.1-way ent & exit system operates at recep area. Lge, mkd pitch, pt sl, pt shd; wc; chem disp; mv service pnt; baby facs; shwrs inc; el pts (6A) inc; gas; lndtte; shop; rest; snacks; bar; BBQ; playgrnd; 2 htd pools + paddling pool; sand beach 8km; fishing adj; watersports 2km; tennis; mini-golf; games rm; cycle hire; horseriding 12km; entmnt; 80% statics; dogs; Eng spkn; adv bkg; cc acc; CCI. "Conv, busy, popular NH; lge allocation of best pitches to tour op statics & fixed tents; golf lessons; trips to Paris; red facs low ssn; chem disp long walk fr site." ♦ 8 Apr-30 Oct. € 29.00 ABS - P06   2005*

ST VALERY SUR SOMME *3B2* (1km SW Urban/Coastal) **Camping Le Walric**, Route d'Eu, 80230 St Valery-sur-Somme [03 22 26 81 97; fax 03 22 60 77 26; info@campinglewalric.com; www. campinglewalric.com] Ringrd round St Valery D940 dir Le Treport. Cont to 2nd rndabt (1st rndabt Champion supmkt on L) 3km, & take 1st L sp St Valery & Cap Hornu D3. Site on R in 2km at ent to town sp. Lge, hdg/mkd pitch, pt shd; wc; chem disp; mv service pnt; baby facs; shwrs inc; el pts (6A) inc; gas; lndry rm; ice; shop 2km; tradsmn; snacks; bar; playgrnd; htd pool; paddling pool; beaches nr; fishing; boat & cycle hire; games area; tennis; entmnt; child entmnt; 50% statics; dogs €2; phone; Eng spkn; adv bkg; quiet; cc acc; red low ssn; CCI. "Excel location, cycle rtes, canal track, steam train; immac, clean san facs; rec long stay." ♦ 1 Mar-1 Nov. € 23.00   2005*

See advertisement

ST VALERY SUR SOMME *3B2* (3km SW Rural) **Camping de la Baie**, Routhiaville, 80230 Pende [03 22 60 72 72] Just off D940 twd Treport, well sp. Sm, hdg pitch; wc (some cont); chem disp; shwrs inc; el pts (3-6A) €1.80-3.50; lndtte; shop 2km; tradsmn; playgrnd; mini-golf; 95% statics; adv bkg; quiet; red low ssn; CCI. "Friendly, helpful owners; superbly run, clean, tidy site; san facs spotless; low trees in places need care; cycle rte to St Valery." Easter-15 Oct. € 10.20   2005*

†**ST VALERY SUR SOMME** *3B2* (10km W Coastal) **Camp Municipal de Brighton Les Pins**, Rue Guillaume-le-Conquérant, 80410 Cayeux-sur-Mer [tel/fax 03 22 26 71 04] Take D940 out of St Valery to Cayeux, then D102 NE for 2km & foll sp. Lge, mkd pitch, pt shd; htd wc; shwrs; chem disp; el pts (6-10A) €3.90-5.40; lndtte; shop; snacks; bar; playgrnd; beach 500m; sailing & fishing adj; cycle hire; mini-golf; horseriding; games rm; 50% statics; adv bkg. ♦ € 15.65   2005*

ST VALERY SUR SOMME *3B2* (6km NW Coastal) **Camping des Galets de la Molliere**, 80410, La Molliere [tel/fax 03 22 26 61 85] Fr Cayeux-sur-Mer take D102 N along coast for 3km. Site on R. Lge, mkd pitch, pt shd; wc; chem disp; mv service pnt; shwrs inc; el pts (10A) inc; gas; lndtte; shop; snacks; bar; BBQ; playgrnd; sand beach 1km; 15% statics; dogs €1.07; phone adj; quiet; CCI. "Spacious site with lge pitches; poss noise fr dogs barking; barrier & recep clsd 1230-1500 & 2300-0700." 1 Apr-31 Oct. € 20.00   2005*

ST VALLIER *9C2* (400m N Urban) **Camp Municipal Les Iles de Silon**, 26240 St Vallier [04 75 23 22 17 or 04 73 23 07 66] On N7 just N of town, clear sp in both dir. Med, hdg pitch, pt shd; wc; chem disp; shwrs inc; el pts (6A) €2 (rev pol & adaptor & poss long cable req); lndtte; shop & 500m; snacks; BBQ; playgrnd; pool 1km; tennis adj; watersports; dogs €1; Eng spkn; adv bkg; quiet but some rlwy noise; cc acc; CCI. "Views over rv; v friendly warden; c'vans over 5.50m not admitted; rec arr bef 1600 high ssn; site yourself, office opens eves; immac facs; vg sh stay/NH." ♦ ltd. 15 Mar-15 Nov. € 9.00   2004*

ST VALLIER *9C2* (5km W Rural) **Camping L'Oasis, Le Petit Chaleat, 07370 Eclassan** [04 75 34 56 23; fax 04 75 34 47 94; oasis.camp@ wanadoo.fr] Leave N7 at St Vallier, cross Rhone to Sarras. Then across N86 onto D6 sp St Jeure d'Ay, in 7km turn R foll sp to site. App rd twisting & narr, many sharp bends & no passing places. Sm, hdg/mkd pitch, terr, pt shd, 80% serviced pitch; wc; chem disp; shwrs inc; el pts (3-6A) €3-3.50; gas; lndtte; ice; shop; tradsmn; rest; snacks; bar; playgrnd; pool; rv adj; mini-golf; archery; golf 10km; 20% statics; dogs €2.20; Eng spkn; adv bkg; quiet; cc not acc; CCI. "In idyllic setting by rv; tractor takes c'vans to pitch; not rec NH due diff approach."
1 Apr-15 Oct. € 17.50   2004*

ST VALLIER DE THIEY see Grasse *10E4*

ST VARENT see Thouars *4H1*

ST VICTOR ET MELVIEU see St Rome de Tarn *8E4*

ST VINCENT DE COSSE see Sarlat la Caneda *7C3*

ST VINCENT DE PAUL see Dax *8E1*

ST VINCENT SUR JARD see Jard sur Mer *7A1*

ST YORRE *9A1* (5km SE Rural) **Camping des Marants, 70 Ave des Sources, 03270 Mariol** [04 70 59 44 70] Fr Vichy take D906 S & after 13.5 km take L turn sp Mariol. Site on L after 250m. Sm, pt shd; wc; chem disp; shwrs inc; el pts inc; lndry rm; playgrnd; pools; lake sw; tennis; games area; dogs; CCI. "V pleasant site; friendly staff; excel value."
€ 9.50   2005*

ST YORRE *9A1* (SW Rural) **Camp Municipal Les Gravieres, 03270 St Yorre** [04 70 59 21 00; fax 04 70 59 20 09; mairie.saint-yorre@wanadoo.fr] Fr A71 exit junc 12 sp Gannat. At Bellerive turn R onto D131 sp Hauterive. L over bdge to St Yorre. Foll camping sp. C'vans banned fr St Yorre town cent. Med, hdg pitch, pt shd; wc (some cont); chem disp; baby facs; shwrs inc; el pts (4-10A) €3.30; lndry rm; shops 1km; tradsmn; snacks; BBQ; playgrnd; pool adj; rv sw & fishing; games area; sports cent adj; dogs; phone adj; Eng spkn; adv bkg; quiet; CCI. "Gd touring base; helpful guardien." ♦
1 May-30 Sep. € 9.50   2005*

ST YRIEIX LA PERCHE *7B3* (1km N Urban) **Camp Municipal d'Eau, Plan d'Eau d'Arfeuille, 87500 St Yrieix-la-Perche** [05 55 75 08 75; camping@ saint-yrieix.com] Site well sp on L on D704 dir Limoges. Med, hdg pitch, terr, pt shd; htd wc; chem disp; baby facs; shwrs; el pts (6A) inc; playgrnd; lake sw & beach adj; quiet. 1 Jul-15 Sep. € 11.70
                    2005*

†ST YRIEIX LA PERCHE *7B3* (8km W Rural) **Camping Les Vigeres, 87500 Le Chalard** [05 55 09 37 22; fax 05 55 09 93 39; lesvigeres@ aol.com] Take N20 to Limoges then N704 to St Yrieix. In St Yrieix turn W on D901 to Chalus. 1st vill is Le Chalard & site is 1km after vill. Sm, hdg/mkd pitch, pt shd; wc; chem disp; shwrs inc; el pts (3-10A) €2.50-3.50; lndtte; shops 2km; BBQ; playgrnd; pool; lake sw & sand beach adj; fishing; library; adv bkg; v quiet; 10% red low ssn; CCI. "Vg, peaceful site; welcoming British owners; clean san facs; historic area; rec." ♦ € 11.00   2005*

ST YRIEIX LA PERCHE *7B3* (12km NW Rural) **Camp Municipal (de Bel Air), 87500 Ladignac-le-Long** [05 55 09 39 82 or 05 55 09 30 02 (Mairie); fax 05 55 09 39 80; camping-ladignac@wanadoo. fr] Exit Limoges S on N21 to Chalus. Turn E on D901 sp St Yrieix to Ladignac. Turn N to lakes at sp. Site on R. Med, pt shd, hdg pitch; wc; chem disp; serviced pitch; shwrs inc; el pts (10A) €2.50; lndtte; shop & 1km; tradsmn; playgrnd; lake sw 500m; 10% statics; dogs; phone; Eng spkn; adv bkg; quiet; red low ssn; CCI. "Beautiful lakeside site; v spacious pitches; spotless san facs; barrier with card operation - early ssn apply to Mairie in vill sq for card; cycling; walking; excel." 1 May-31 Oct. € 9.50   2005*

SALBRIS *4G3* (NE Urban) **Camp Municipal de Sologne, 8 Allee de la Sauldre, 41300 Salbris** [02 54 97 06 38; fax 02 54 97 33 13; camping desologne@wanadoo.fr] Exit A71 junc 4. Take D944 bypass, then take N20 N. Turn E onto D55 sp Pierrefitte; site on R in 200m on rvside. Med, hdg/mkd pitch, pt shd; wc (some cont); chem disp; baby facs; shwrs inc; el pts (10A) inc (some rev pol); gas; lndtte; shop 200m; hypmkt 1km; tradsmn; rest; snacks; bar high ssn; playgrnd; htd pool nr; lake adj; fishing; boat hire; karting 6km; TV rm; 25% statics; dogs €0.50; phone; poss cr; Eng spkn; adv bkg; cc acc; CCI. "Excel, well-maintained, lakeside site; friendly, helpful owners; adj lake with pool & sports facs; poss some noise fr rlwy, rd & motor circuit; gd san facs poss stretched if site busy; easy walk to town; gd dog walks adj." ♦
1 Apr-15 Oct. € 16.00   2005*

SALERNES *10F3* (Rural) **Camp Municipal Les Arnauds, 83690 Salernes** [04 94 67 51 95; fax 04 94 70 75 57; lesarnauds@ville-salernes.fr; www. ville-salernes.fr] W fr Draguignan on D557 thro Salernes; site sp on L on W o'skts of town; to avoid town cent turn R at rndabt on E o'skts sp Villecroze; take 1st L at next 2 rndabts & foll site sp. Med, hdg/mkd pitch, pt shd; wc; chem disp; baby facs; shwrs; el pts (10A) inc; lndtte; bar; playgrnd; rv sw adj; tennis; dogs €1.50; Eng spkn; adv bkg; quiet; red low ssn; CCI. "Excel; warm welcome; excel san facs; gd night lighting; pleasant location; some sm pitches poss diff lge o'fits; rvside site; no twin-axle vans; no entry 1200-1500; take torch into shwrs, lights on sh time switch." 1 May-30 Sep. € 18.50   2003*

FRANCE

SALERNES *10F3* (4km E Rural) **Camping Le Ruou, Les Esparrus, 83690 Villecroze-les-Grottes [04 94 70 67 70; fax 04 94 70 64 65; camping.leruou@wanadoo.fr; www.leruou.com]** Fr Draguignan take D557 thro Flayosc, then D560 dir Salernes. Site sp on L. Med, mkd pitch, terr, shd; htd wc; chem disp; mv service pnt; baby facs; el pts (6-10A) €4-5; gas; lndtte; ice; shop; rest; snacks; bar; BBQ: playgrnd; pool; paddling pool; waterslides; games area; fishing; archery; games/TV rm; adv bkg; 35% statics; dogs €2.50; adv bkg; quiet. ♦ 1 Apr-31 Oct. € 18.00 (CChq acc) 2004*

SALERNES *10F3* (4km W Rural) **Le Relais de la Bresque, 15, Rue de la Piscine, 83690 Sillans-la-Cascade [tel/fax 04 94 04 64 89; lerelaisde labresque@free.fr; www.lerelaisdelabresque.com]** D560 W fr Salernes. At vill take D22 N to site, 1km on R. Med, shd, mkd pitch; wc; chem disp; mv service pnt; shwrs inc; serviced pitch; el pts (5-10A) €2.60-4.10; lndtte; ice; rest; tradsmn; playgrnd; pool adj; rv 1.5km; cycle hire; horseriding; archery, fitness course; games rm; dogs €1; Eng spkn; quiet; adv bkg rec; red low ssn. 1 Feb-31 Dec. € 12.80 2004*

SALERS *7C4* (1km NE Rural) **Camp Municipal Le Mouriol, Route de Puy-Mary, 15410 Salers [04 71 40 73 09 or 04 71 40 72 33 (Mairie); fax 04 71 40 76 28]** Take D922 SE fr Mauriac for 2km, E on D22 to Salers. Or fr S turn R onto D680 to Salers; site 1km NE of Salers on D680 dir Puy Mary opp Hotel 'Le Gerfaut'; sp fr all dir. Med, hdg/mkd pitch, sl, pt shd, wc (some cont); chem disp (wc); shwrs inc; el pts (6A) inc (rev pol & long lead poss req); lndtte; shops 1km; BBQ; playgrnd; tennis; hill-walking; dogs; phone; no adv bkg; quiet; 10% red 14 days. "Salers o'stndg medieval vill & within walking dist for rest & museums; san facs stretched if site full; wheel wedges req most pitches; gd long/sh stay." ♦ ltd. 15 May-15 Oct. € 11.00 2005*

SALERS *7C4* (800m W Rural) **Camping a La Ferme (Fruquiere), Apcher, 15140 Salers [04 71 40 72 26]** D922 S fr Mauriac for 17km; L on D680 sp Salers; in lane on R sp Apcher - immed after passing Salers town sign. Sm, pt shd; wc (some cont), chem disp (wc); shwrs inc; el ptd (10A) €2.20; shop 300m; dogs; poss cr high ssn; quiet; CCI. "Sm farm site conv for Salers & exploring the Cantal; gd." 1 May-30 Sep. € 8.60 2005*

SALERS *7C4* (7km W Rural) **Camp Municipal Les Moulin du Teinturier, 15140 St Martin-Valmeroux [04 71 69 43 12; fax 04 71 69 24 52; mairie. saint-martin-valmeroux@wanadoo.fr]** Fr Mauriac D922 sp on D37, 500m on L. Med, hdg pitch, pt shd; wc; serviced pitch; shwrs; el pts (6A) €1; lndtte; shop; rest; BBQ; playgrnd; TV; quiet; rv fishing; walking; adj tennis, mini-golf, horseriding, pool. "Ideal exploring Auvergne; on Rv Maronne."♦ 15 Jun-15 Sep. € 9.76 2002*

SALIES DE BEARN *8F1* (2km NW Urban) **Camp Municipal de Mosqueros, Ave Al Cartero, 64270 Salies-de-Bearn [05 59 38 12 94]** Leave A64 at exit 7 S onto D430 sp Salies de Bearn. After 500m take D330 on R sp 'Casino' & turn R onto D17 at rndabt. Site sp in town, on D17 Bayonne rd NW of town. Site next to 'Base Plein Air des Mosqueros'. Med, hdg/mkd pitch, pt shd; wc; chem disp; shwrs inc; el pts inc (10A) inc; lndtte; shops 1km; rest 600m; pool, sports facs adj; fishing 1km; golf 2km; horseriding 3km; TV; quiet; "Excel; friendly recep; barrier closd 2200-0700; mkt Thu; poss diff for lge o'fits." ♦ 15 Mar-15 Oct. € 13.40 2004*

SALIES DU SALAT *8F3* (7km SE Rural) **Camping L'Estelas, 09160 Mauvezin-de-Prat [05 61 96 65 80]** Fr A64 a'route exit 20, SW on D117 dir St Girons; turn S on D133 sp Mauvezin & Francazal. Site on R in 200m. Sm, pt sl, shd; wc; shwrs; el pts (16A) €1.52; ice; lndtte; shops 2km; playgrnd; rv 2km; adv bkg rec high ssn. ♦ 15 Mar-15 Oct. € 9.15 2002*

SALIES DU SALAT *8F3* (2km S) **Camp Municipal La Justale, Chemin de St Jean, 31260 Mane [05 61 90 68 18; fax 05 61 97 40 18]** Fr A64 exit 20 onto D117, turn R in vill at sp 'Village de Vacances'. Site on R in approx 500m. Sm, pt shd; wc; mv service pnt; shwrs inc; el pts (6A) €2-2.75; lndtte; shops 500m; playgrnd; rv sw adj; fishing; tennis; horseriding; TV rm; dogs €1; adv bkg. "Pleasant sm site; excel facs; vg sh stay/NH." 1 May-31 Oct. € 10.40 2005*

SALIGNAC EYVIGNES see Sarlat la Caneda *7C3*

SALINS LES BAINS *6H2* (500m N) **Camp Municipal Salins-les-Bains, 39110 Salins-les-Bains [03 84 37 92 70]** SE fr Bescancon on N83. At Mouchard take D472 E to Salins. Turn L at rndabt at N of Salins, well sp. Sm, pt shd; wc; shwrs inc; el pts (10A) €2.50; lndry rm; supmkt 500m; playgrnd; adv bkg; quiet. "V clean, modern san facs; excel touring base N Jura; not often visited by British; site van at far end of site to avoid daytime rd noise." ♦ 1 Apr-30 Sep. € 13.30 2005*

SALLANCHES *9A3* (2km SE Urban) **Camping L'Ecreuil, 74700 Sallanches [04 50 58 43 67; fax 04 50 58 44 61]** App fr Chamonix on N205, turn R opp Ford g'ge ent Sallanches; strt on thro traff lts, over sleeping policemen, under rlwy bdge & fork R at Braconne rest; strt at next junc to site in 200m. Med, shd; wc; chem disp; shwrs inc; el pts (10A) €2.50; gas; lndtte; ice; shops 1km; tradsmn; rest (not every day); bar; playgrnd; pool nr; lake sw & sand/shgl beach; dogs €1; poss cr; quiet; cc acc; CCI. "Excel, v clean facs; plenty of trees; mountain views inc Mont Blanc; gd base for Mont Blanc region; vg all stays." 1 Apr-15 Oct. € 15.50 2003*

SALLANCHES *9A3* (2km SE Rural) **Camping Miroir du Mont Blanc Plage,** Chemin de Mont Blanc Plage, 74700 Sallanches [04 50 58 14 28 or 04 50 58 12 04 (LS); fax 04 50 93 95 23] Fr Geneva on N205 into Sallanches. Take 1st L after 2nd set of traff lts (by post office) sp Hospital. Foll rd thro traff lits & over rndabt when rd turns sharp R & runs alongside m'way. In 2km site ent on R beside rndabt. Park here & walk to recep to check in. Med, mkd pitch, shd; wc; shwrs; el pts (8A) €2.45; gas 2km; lndry rm; ice; shops 2km; tradsmn; rest; snacks; bar; playgrnd; pool; paddling pool; waterslide; lake sw & sand/shgl beach adj; tennis; fishing; sailing; windsurfing 50m; entmnt; TV rm; adv bkg rec; quiet; red low ssn. "Magnificent views." 15 May-15 Sep. € 12.30   2003*

SALLANCHES *9A3* (4km SE) **Escapades Terre Oceane Camping des Iles,** 245 Chemin de la Cavettraz, 74190 Passy [04 50 58 45 36 or 05 46 55 10 01; fax 04 46 55 10 00; info@ campingterreoceane.com; www.campingterre oceane.com] On N205 dir Chamonix t turn L (1st into filter to turn L) onto D199 3km after Sallanches. Turn L immed bef level x-ing. Site at end of rd. Lge, hdg/mkd pitch, pt shd; wc (some cont); baby facs; shwrs inc; el pts (8A) inc; lndtte; shop & 3km; snacks; playgrnd; htd pool; shgl lake beach & sw adj; fishing; entmnt; child entmnt; statics; dogs €2; phone; Eng spkn; adv bkg; quiet; cc acc high ssn; CCI. "Mountain views; conv Mt Blanc, glacier & Chamonix; vg site." ♦ 16 Jun-15 Sep. € 16.00   2005*

SALLELES D'AUDE see Narbonne *10F1*

SALLES (GIRONDE) *7D1* (Urban) **Camping du Val de l'Eyre,** Route du Lanot, 33770 Salles [05 56 88 47 03; fax 05 56 88 47 27; levalde leyre@free.fr] Exit 21 fr A63 a'route, foll dir to Salles on D3. On edge of Salles turn L on D108 at x-rds. Ent to site on L after rv opp Champion supmkt building. Lge, pt shd; wc; chem disp; baby facs; shwrs inc; el pts (6A) €3.50 (poss rev pol); gas; lndtte; shops adj; supmkt nr; rest; snacks; bar; BBQ; playgrnd; sports area; lake & rv sw; fishing; canoeing; mini-golf; tennis 500km; horseriding 8km; entmnt; dogs €2.50; quiet but entmnt poss noisy; cc acc; red low ssn. "Attractive site." ♦ 1 Mar-31 Oct. € 21.00   2005*

SALLES (GIRONDE) *7D1* (8km S Rural) **Camping La Cyprea,** 33830 Lugos [05 57 71 93 30] S fr Bordeaux on N10 to cent Belin; turn R onto D110; camp sp on wall facing you; stay on this rd thro pine forest. Camp on L just bef sp for Lugos (Gare). Sm, pt shd; wc; shwrs €0.60; el pts inc (2A) €2; lndry rm; tradsmn; pool; quiet; CCI. "Friendly owner; lovely sm pool; fair." 1 Jul-1 Sep. € 9.00   2003*

†**SALLES (GIRONDE)** *7D1* (4km SW Rural) **Camping Le Bilos,** 37 Route de Bilos, 33770 Salles [05 56 88 45 14 or 05 56 88 36 53; fax 05 56 88 45 14; http://pageperso.aol.fr/lebilos] Exit 21 fr A63. Foll sp Salles on D3. Turn L onto D108 sp Lanot, pass Champion supmkt on R; in 2km bear R & site on R in 2km. Med, pt shd; htd wc; chem disp; shwrs inc; el pts (3-10A) €1.90-5.30; gas; lndtte; shop; BBQ sep area; playgrnd; some statics; dogs; adv bkg; quiet. "Pleasant, peaceful farm in pine forest; not muddy when wet; friendly owners; phone to check open low ssn; conv for Arcachon, Bordeaux, Dune of Pyla; vg sh stay/NH en rte Spain, especially low ssn, but ltd facs low ssn." € 7.00   2005*

SALLES (LOT ET GARONNE) see Fumel *7D3*

SALLES CURAN *8E4* (Rural) **Camping Les Genets,** Lac de Pareloup, 12410 Salles-Curan [05 65 46 35 34 or 05 65 42 06 46; fax 05 65 78 00 72; contact@camping-les-genets.fr; www.camping-les-genets.fr] Fr D911 Rodez-Millau rd take D993 S for approx 9km, then R onto D577, site sp on R by lake. Lge, pt sl, shd; wc; shwrs; el pts (6A) inc; lndtte; shop; rest; pizzeria; bar; htd pool; cycle hire; sailing; fishing; lake sw & beach; child entmnt; 40% statics; dogs €4; adv bkg; red long stay. "On edge of lake in beautiful area; ltd facs low ssn." ♦ 1 Jun-11 Sep. € 28.00   2005*

SALLES SUR VERDON, LES *10E3* (500m Rural) **Camping La Source,** 83630 Les Salles-sur-Verdon [04 94 70 20 40; fax 04 94 70 20 74; contact@camping-lasource.com] Fr Moustiers on D957, site sp in vill via rd round vill. Med, hdg/mkd pitch, hdstg, pt terr; pt shd; wc (some cont); chem disp; child/baby facs; serviced pitches; shwrs inc; el pts (6-10A) €3-4.50; gas; lndtte; ice; shop, rest, snacks, bar 500m; playgrnd; TV rm; dir access to lake; lake sw & shgl beach adj; watersports; canoe hire; dogs €2; phone; Eng spkn; adv bkg; quiet; cc acc; red low ssn; CCI. "Excel facs; superb situation; well-run site conv Gorges du Verdon; direct access to vill; friendly, helpful owners; gates clsd 2200-0700 & recep clsd 1200-1400." ♦ 1 Apr-15 Oct. € 15.10   2005*

SALLES SUR VERDON, LES *10E3* (N Rural) **Camp Municipal Les Ruisses,** 83630 Les Salles-sur-Verdon [04 98 10 28 15; fax 04 98 10 28 16] Fr Moustiers foll D957, site on L just bef Les Salles. Lge, mkd pitch, pt shd; wc (some cont); shwrs inc; el pts (6A) €2.70; ice; lndtte; shop, snacks, bar high ssn; playgrnd; shgl lake 1km; fishing; no adv bkg; quiet; cc acc; CCI. "Pleasant site, easy access to nice lake." ♦ 15 Feb-15 Dec. € 10.50   2004*

FRANCE

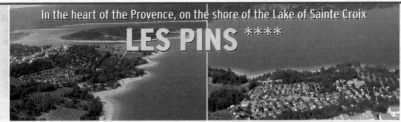

SALLES SUR VERDON, LES *10E3* (2km E Rural) Camping L'Aigle, Quartier St Pierre, 83630 Aiguines [tel/fax 04 94 84 23 75; www.aiguines. com] Fr D957 fr Les Salles or Moustiers turn onto D19 & cont for approx 7km. Site sp 1km beyond vill. Rd steep, winding & with hairpins. Med, terr, pt shd; wc; mv service pnt; baby facs; shwrs inc; el pts (2-10A) €2.50-3.70; lndtte; shops, rest 300m; BBQ; playgrnd; ent barrier; dogs €1.70; phone; Eng spkn; quiet; cc acc; CCI. "Panoramic views of lake; clean, modern facs; steep, twishing access to terr pitches poss diff lge o'fits; highly rec." Easter-30 Sep. € 11.40   2005*

SALLES SUR VERDON, LES *10E3* (3km E Rural) Camp Municipal Le Galetas, 83630 Aiguines [tel/fax 04 94 70 20 48; campinglegaletas@aol. com] Fr S foll D957 twd Moistiers-Ste Marie then take D71 to Aguines & foll sp. Lge, pt shd; wc; chem disp; mv service pnt; shwrs inc; el pts (6A) €2.50; lndtte; bar; rv sw; watersports. "Site is set back into hills; vg all stays." 1 Apr-15 Nov. € 12.50   2004*

SALLES SUR VERDON, LES *10E3* (W Rural) Camping Les Pins, Lac de Sainte Croix, 83630 Les Salles-sur-Verdon [04 98 10 23 80; fax 04 94 84 23 27; camping.les.pins@wanadoo.fr; www.campingles pins.com] Fr Moustiers on D957 to Les Salles-sur-Verdon. Site clearly sp in vill, via track round vill. Med, hdg/mkd pitch, hdstg, terr, pt shd; wc; chem disp; mv service pnt; serviced pitches; baby facs; shwrs inc; el pts (6A) inc; gas; lndtte; shop 200m, tradsmn; bar; playgrnd; shgl beach & lake sw 200m; fishing; watersports; dogs €1.50; Eng spkn; adv bkg; quiet; red low ssn/CCI. "On shore of Lake de Ste Croix; marvellous views; gd touring base; excel, friendly site." ♦ 1 Apr-21 Oct. € 20.75   2005*

See advertisement

SALON DE PROVENCE *10E2* (12km SE) Camping Durance et Luberon, Domaine du Vergon, 13370 Mallemort [04 90 59 13 36; fax 04 90 57 46 62] Fr Salon take the N538 (N) for approx 6km; turn E onto the D17/D23 twd Mallemort; go strt at N7 rnabt, into Mallemort cent; site sp fr there. Med, hdg/mkd pitch, pt shd; wc (some cont); chem disp; shwrs inc; el pts inc (6—10A) €2.80-3.40; ice; gas; lndtte; shop 3km; tradsmn; rest 1km; snacks; bar; BBQ; playgrnd; htd pool; tennis; cycle hire; horseriding adj; rv fishing 1km; 5% statics; dogs €1.60; phone; Eng spkn; adv bkg; quiet; 10% red long stays; cc not acc; CCI. "Friendly owners; lge pitches." 15 Apr-15 Oct. € 14.00   2004*

SALON DE PROVENCE *10E2* (3km NW) Camping Nostradamus, Route d'Eyguieres, 13300 Salon-de-Provence [04 90 56 08 36; fax 04 90 56 65 05; gilles.nostra@wanadoo.fr; www.camping-nost radamus.com] Exit A54/E80 junc 13 onto D569 N sp Eyguieres. After approx 1.5km turn R opp airfield onto D72d, site on R in approx 4km just bef T-junc. Med, hdg/mkd pitch, pt shd; wc; chem disp; mv service pnt; baby facs; shwrs inc; el pts (4-6A) €2.80-5; gas; lndtte; ice; shop; tradsmn; rest; snacks; bar; BBQ; playgrnd; pool; entmnt; TV; 15% statics; dogs €2.50; phone; Eng spkn; adv bkg (€12.20 bkg fee); quiet; cc acc; red low ssn; cc acc; CCI. "Pleasant site; owner v helpful & welcoming; poss diff access for lge o'fits; gd walking; exce." ♦ 1 Mar-31 Oct. € 15.00 (CChq acc)   2005*

SALORNAY SUR GUYE see Cluny *9A2*

†**SALSES LE CHATEAU** *10G1* (1km N Rural) Camp International du Roussillon, 66600 Salses-le-Chateau [04 68 38 60 72; fax 04 68 38 60 37] Ent on W side of N9. Site has hotel, rest & camping. Med, hdg pitch, hdstg, pt shd; wc; chem disp; shwrs inc; el pts (5-6A) €4.50 (poss rev pol); gas; lndtte; ice; shops 2km; tradsmn; rest; snacks; bar; BBQ (no elec); playgrnd; pool; 20% statics; dogs €3.50; phone; Eng spkn; adv bkg; some rlwy noise; 10% red 15+ days; cc acc; CCI. "Gd local wine sold at recep; red facs low ssn; on wine rte for Languedoc Roussillon & Herault; sh walk to castle; new owners 2005; popular NH." ♦ ltd. € 13.80   2005*

SALVETAT SUR AGOUT, LA *8F4* (Urban) Camping de la Blaquiere, Route de Lacaune, 34330 La Salvetat-sur-Agout [04 67 97 61 29 or 04 67 24 71 08] Fr Lacaune S on D607 to site in La Salvetat. Sp on ent to vill. Fr S heading N on D907 foll site sps thro vill, site on L just after sm supmkt. Med, mkd pitch, shd; wc; chem disp (wc); shwrs inc; el pts €2.50; ice lndry rm; shop, rest etc in vill; BBQ; playgrnd; rv adj; lake sw, fishing, watersports 3km; tennis; horseriding; 5% statics; adv bkg; quiet; CCI. "Spectacular scenery, esp for walking in Herault National Park; friendly owner." 1 Apr-31 Aug. € 8.40
2003*

SALVETAT SUR AGOUT, LA *8F4* (4km N Rural) Camping Goudal, Route de Lacaune, La Gache, 34330 La Salvetat-sur-Agout [04 67 97 60 44; fax 04 67 97 62 68; info@goudal.com; www.goudal.com] Fr St Pons-de-Thomieres take D907 N dir Lacaune. Go thro La Salvetat, site sp. Med, mkd pitch, pt sl, terr, pt shd; wc; chem disp; mv service pnt; shwrs inc; el pts (6A) €2.50; gas; lndtte; ice; shop; rest high ssn; BBQ; playgrnd; child entmnt high ssn; some statics; dogs €1.50; poss cr; Eng spkn; adv bkg; quiet; CCI. "Friendly Dutch owners; spacious site in woodland; lovely location; vg." 1 May-30 Sep. € 14.95
2005*

SALVETAT SUR AGOUT, LA *8F4* (10km E Rural) Camping Le Pioch, 34330 Fraisse-sur-Agout [04 67 97 61 72; NICO-OUDHOF@wanadoo.fr] Fr Salvetat take D14 E twd Fraise-sur-Agout. In 6km look for sp on L (2km bef Fraise). Site is up narr, steep rd but with passing places. Med, pt sl, pt shd; wc; shwrs inc; el pts (6A) €2.50; gas; lndtte; shop; tradsmn; rest; snacks; bar; BBQ; playgrnd; dogs; Eng spkn; adv bkg; quiet; CCI. "Excel walking area." 1 May-1 Oct. € 11.50
2005*

SAMEON see St Amand les Eaux *3B4*

†**SAMOENS** *9A3* (750m S Rural) Camping Caravaneige Le Giffre, La Gliere, 74340 Samoens [04 50 34 41 92; fax 04 50 34 98 84; camping@samoens.com; www.samoens.com] Leave A40 at junc 15 sp Fillinges/St Jeoire. Foll D907 thro Taninges E for 11km, sp Samoens. At W town boundary turn R immed after wooden arch over rd, foll sp to Parc des Loisirs. Site on R after sw pool & park. Lge, mkd pitch, pt shd; htd wc (few cont); chem disp; shwrs inc; el pts (6-10A) €2.70-4.30; gas 3km; lndtte; ice; shops 750m; tradsmn; rest, snacks adj; playgrnd; htd pool adj; fishing lake adj; drying rm; ski navette 25m; tennis; 5% statics; dogs €1.80; phone; poss cr; adv bkg ess high ssn (dep req); quiet; cc acc; red CCI. "Superb situation beside a lake & rv surrounded by mountains; friendly staff; v quiet even when full; price inc use of sw pool (ice rink in winter); v interesting tours of town & surrounding hamlets fr nrby tourist office; simple but excel snacks & rest; some facs ltd low ssn; on arr, park on rdside - book in bef ent site; recep open 0800-1200 & 1400-1800; card op barrier (€30 dep)." € 15.80
2005*

†**SAMOENS** *9A3* (5km W Rural) Camp Municipal Lac et Montagne, 74440 Verchaix [04 50 90 10 12] Fr Taninges take D907 sp Samoens for 6km, site to R of main rd in Verchaix. Med, shd; shwrs; el pts (5-10A) lndtte; ice; shops nr; rest, bar adj; playgrnd; rv & lake adj; tennis; mini-golf; some statics; adv bkg; quiet. "Gd base Haute Savoie; recep closd 1230-1430; car park by barrier; dep req for barrier." ♦ € 13.11
2004*

SAMOREAU see Fontainebleau *4E3*

SAMPZON see Vallon Pont d'Arc *9D2*

SANARY SUR MER *10F3* (4km NE) Campasun Mas de Pierredon, 652 Chemin Raoul Coletta, 83110 Sanary-sur-Mer [04 94 74 25 02; fax 04 94 74 61 42; campasun@free.fr; www.campasun.fr] Take D11 fr Sanary, cross m'way & 1st L. Site on R in approx 1km. Med, shd; htd wc; chem disp; mv service pnt; shwrs inc; el pts (10A) €4.60; ice; lndtte; shop; rest; snacks; bar; playgrnd; htd pool; paddling pool; beach 3km; tennis; entmnt; TV; dogs €3.95; poss cr; adv bkg rec; quiet; red low ssn; red CCI. "Noise fr m'way & youth groups high ssn; ltd facs low ssn; gd family site." ♦ 15 Mar-30 Oct. € 22.35 (CChq acc)
2004*

SANARY SUR MER *10F3* (1.5km W Coastal) Camping Mogador, Chemin de Beaucours, 83110 Sanary-sur-Mer [04 94 74 53 16; fax 04 94 74 10 58; mogador@infonie.fr; www.camping-mogador.fr] Fr A50 take exit 12 dir Bandol. Site sp on R bef Sanary. Lge, pt shd; wc; shwrs inc; el pts inc; gas; lndtte; shop; rest; snacks; bar; playgrnd; pool; shgl beach 800m; fishing, watersports 1km; entmnt; TV; 30% statics; dogs €4 (not acc Jul/Aug); adv bkg rec; quiet. 1 Apr-30 Sep. € 15.00 (3 persons) (CChq acc)
2005*

SANARY SUR MER *10F3* (3km W Coastal) Camping Les Girelles, 1003 Chemin de Beaucours, 83110 Sanary-sur-Mer [04 94 74 13 18; fax 04 94 74 60 04; www.lesgirelles.com] Fr Sanary on D559 to Bandols; site on L, well sp. Med, mkd pitch, terr, pt shd; wc; shwrs inc; el pts (4A) €3.70; gas; lndtte; shop; snacks; bar; no BBQ; playgrnd; paddling pool; shgl beach adj; some statics; dogs €4; poss cr; quiet; CCI ess. "Gd site in 2 parts; lower level overlooks bay but haphazard & dusty; upper level better." Easter-25 Sep. € 23.00
2005*

SANCERRE 4G3 (4km N Rural) Camping Le Rene Foltzer, 18300 St Satur [02 48 54 04 67 or 02 48 54 02 61 (Mairie); fax 02 48 54 01 30; otsi. saint.satur@wanadoo.fr] Fr Sancerre on D955 thro cent St Satur & St Thibault. Turn L immed bef Loire bdge. Site on R in 100m. Med, hdg pitch, shd; wc; chem disp; shwrs inc; el pts (10A) €2.50; gas; lndtte; shop 500m; rest 500m; playgrnd; pool 200m; tennis; entmnt; rv sw, canoe hire adj; golf 1km; 50% statics; poss cr; some Eng spkn; adv bkg (dep req); quiet; CCI. "Friendly & helpful staff; gd san facs; poss unkempt grounds; rvside walks; gd touring cent; some sm pitches; some pitches at one end overlooking Loire; mixed reports on water temperature - poss lukewarm, poss v hot; gates clsd 2200-0700; recep clsd 1200-1600; gd all stays." ♦
1 May-30 Sep. € 11.50   2005*

SANCHEY see Epinal 6F2

SANDUN see Guerande 2G3

SANGUINET 7D1 (3km N Rural) Camping Lou Broustaricq, Route de Langeot, 40460 Sanguinet [05 58 82 74 82; fax 05 58 82 10 74; loubrousta@ wanadoo.fr; www.lou-broustaricq.com] Take Arcachon exit off Bordeax-Bayonne m'way. After 5km twd S on D3 & D216 to Sanguinet. Site sp in town off Bordeaux rd. V lge, mkd pitch, pt shd; htd wc (some cont); chem disp; shwrs inc; el pts (10A) €3.30; lndtte; shop; rest, snacks, bar high ssn; BBQ; playgrnd; pool; waterslide; lake sw & sand beach 500m; watersports; sailing school; tennis; walking tracks; games area; cycle hire; entmnt; child entmnt; golf nr; TV rm; 60% statics; dogs €2.30; Eng spkn; adv bkg (dep req + bkg fee); quiet; red low ssn; cc acc; CCI. "In lovely wooded area; close to freshwater lake with sandy beaches; gd cycle tracks; gd for children; vg." ♦ 15 Mar-15 Nov. € 26.80   2005*

See advertisement below

SANGUINET 7D1 (1.5km S Rural) Camping Le Lac, 526 Rue de Pinton, 40460 Sanguinet [05 58 82 70 80; fax 05 58 82 14 24; camping. lelac@wanadoo.fr; www.camping-lelac.com] Foll Le Lac sp at rndabt in Sanguinet, turn L on lakeside, site on L in 600m. Lge, mkd pitch, pt shd; shwrs inc; el pts (6-10A) €2.60-3.80; snacks; shops 500m; tradsmn; lndtte; ice; playgrnd; sand beach; lake sw & sailing nrby; dogs €1.75; poss cr; quiet; CCI. "Spacious site in pine woods 2 min walk to lake & beach; cycle path around lake; san facs poss run down low ssn; poss itinerants; friendly, helpful staff."
10 Mar-15 Nov. € 11.30   2004*

SANGUINET 7D1 (2km SW) Camping Les Grands Pins, Route du Lac, 40460 Sanguinet [05 58 78 61 74; fax 05 58 78 69 15; info@ campinglesgrandspins.com; www.campingles grandspins.com] Foll Le Lac sp at rndabt in Sanguinet. Turn L at lakeside. Site on L in 450m opposite yacht club. Lge, hdg pitch, shd; wc; chem disp; (wc); shwrs inc; child/baby facs; el pts (3-10A) €3.50; lndtte; ice; rest; snacks; bar; playgrnd; pool; sand beach; lake sw; boating; windsurfing; fishing, canoeing; tennis; mini-golf; cycle hire; TV; 50% statics; dogs; poss cr; Eng spkn; adv bkg; poss noisy; CCI. "Clean site; rest & bar poss clsd low ssn; free parking for m'vans adj (charge in Jul/Aug)." ♦
1 Apr-31 Oct. € 28.50   2004*

SARLAT LA CANEDA 7C3 (10km N Rural) Camping La Bouquerie, 24590 St Genies [05 53 28 98 22; fax 05 53 29 19 75; labouquerie@ wanadoo.fr; www.labouquerie.com] On D704 Sarlat-Montignac rd, turn E twd St Genies. Site in 1.5km, sp off this rd. Lge, hdg/mkd pitch, terr, pt shd; serviced pitches; htd wc; mv service pnt; chem disp; shwrs inc; el pts (6-10A) inc; lndtte; shop; tradsmn; rest; snacks; bar; playgrnd; 3 pools; sand beach 10km; tennis; fishing; entmnt; TV rm; adv bkg rec high ssn; quiet; cc acc; CCI. ♦ 5 Apr-27 Sep. € 23.80   2003*

SARLAT LA CANEDA 7C3 (12km N) Camping Les Tailladis, 24200 Marcillac-St Quentin [05 53 59 10 95; fax 05 53 29 47 56; tailladis@aol.com] N fr Sarlat on D704 dir Montignac. After 7km turn L & foll sp to site. Med, hdg pitch; pt sl, terr, pt shd; wc; chem disp; mv service pnt; shwrs inc; el pts (6A) €3.40; gas; lndtte; ice; shop; rest; snacks; bar; pool; lake sw; horseriding; fishing; canoeing; 6% statics; dogs €1.95; phone; poss cr; Eng spkn; adv bkg (dep req & bkg fee); cc acc; red CCI low ssn. "Free glass wine on arrival; meals rec; v friendly & helpful Dutch owners; clean san facs; 1 week horseriding course avail; vg long stay." ♦ 15 Mar-31 Oct.
€ 16.50   2005*

SARLAT LA CANEDA 7C3 (5km NE) Camping Le Val d'Ussel, 24200 Proissans [05 53 59 28 73; fax 05 53 29 38 25; valdussel@online.fr; www. valdussel.com & www.homair-vacances.fr] Fr Sarlat, take D704 N & foll sps to Proissans. Fr Perigueux, take N89 to Thenon, D67 to Chambon, D704 to sps to Proissans. Fr Brive, N89 twd Perigueux, D60 S. Med, pt sl, pt shd; wc; chem disp; shwrs inc; baby facs; el pts (6-10A) €3-3.75; gas; lndtte; ice; tradsmn; rest; snacks; bar; BBQ; playgrnd; 2 htd pools; lake adj; fishing; shgl beach 15km; tennis; games area; child entmnt; TV; statics; dogs €1.75; adv bkg; quiet; red low ssn.
19 May-25 Sep. € 20.00   2004*

SARLAT LA CANEDA 7C3 (8km NE) Camping La Chataigneraie, 24370 Prats-de-Carlux [05 53 59 03 61; fax 05 53 29 86 16; lachataigneraie@ wanadoo.fr; www.lachataigneraie24.com] Avoid app fr Sarlat as rd winds around steep hill. Instead, take D703 W fr Souillac & in 14km turn R onto D61 sp Carlux. On o'skirts of Carlux fork L onto D47B. Site in 6km on R. Med, hdg/mkd pitch, terr, pt shd; wc; chem disp; baby facs; shwrs inc; el pts (6A) inc (poss rev pol); gas; lndtte; snacks; sm bar; BBQ (gas only); playgrnd; pool; waterslide; tennis, mini-golf; entmnt (Jul/Aug); games rm; dogs €2; max van length high ssn 7m; poss cr; quiet; cc acc. "Excel; friendly & helpful owners; mkt Sarlat Wed & Sat am; some pitches diff due position of trees; vg pool area; vg san facs." ♦ 1 Jun-16 Sep. € 26.40
ABS - D13   2005*

SARLAT LA CANEDA 7C3 (8km NE Rural) Camping Maillac, Ste Nathalene, 24200 Sarlat-la-Caneda [05 53 59 22 12; fax 05 53 29 60 17; campingmaillac@wanadoo.fr] Take D47 out of Sarlat to Ste Nathalene. After 4km turn L at x-rds (if missed next 2 turnings also lead to site), v well sp. Med, mkd pitch, pt sl, pt shd; wc; chem disp; mv service pnt; shwrs inc; el pts (6A) €2.80; gas; lndtte; ice; shop; rest; snacks; bar; BBQ; playgrnd; pool; 10% statics; dogs €0.85; poss cr Jul/Aug; some Eng spkn; adv bkg; quiet; red low ssn; cc acc; CCI. "Spacious pitches; excel, gd value rest in vill; lovely area; gd long stay." 15 May-30 Sep. € 14.10
                                                          2003*

SARLAT LA CANEDA 7C3 (9km NE) Camping La Palombiere, Ste Nathalene, 24200 Sarlat-la- Caneda [05 53 59 42 34; fax 05 53 28 45 40; la.palombiere@ wanadoo.fr; www.lapalombiere.com] Take D47 out of Sarlat to Ste Nathalene, thro vill, past Mill Rest, fork L on o'skts. Site sp. Med, terr, shd; wc; chem disp; baby facs; shwrs inc; el pts (6-10A) inc; lndtte; shop; rest; snacks; bar; BBQ; htd pool; tennis; games rm; games area; mini-golf; entmnt; TV; 60% statics; Eng spkn; adv bkg; quiet; 10% red low ssn. "Highly rec; tour ops on site; poss diff for lge o'fits due trees & pitch sizes." ♦ 13 Apr-29 Sep. € 30.00   2004*

SARLAT LA CANEDA 7C3 (10km NE Rural) Camping Les Peneyrals, Le Poujol, 24590 St Crepin-et-Carlucet [05 53 28 85 71; fax 05 53 28 80 99; camping.peneyrals@wanadoo.fr; www.peneyrals.com] Fr Sarlat N on D704; D60 E dir Salignac-Eyvignes to Le Poujol; S to St Crepin. Site sp. Lge, hdg pitch, pt sl, terr, pt shd; htd wc; chem disp; mv service pnt; all serviced pitch; baby facs; shwrs inc; el pts (5-10A) €3.60; lndtte; ice; shop; rest; snacks; bar; playgrnd; 4 pools (1 htd, covrd); paddling pool; waterslide; fishing; tennis; games area; mini-golf; boules; entmnt; 50% statics; dogs €2; phone adj; Eng spkn; adv bkg; quiet; red low ssn; cc acc. "Friendly owners; excel family & touring site." ♦ 13 May-16 Sep. € 25.00   2005*

See advertisement below

FRANCE

SARLAT LA CANEDA *7C3* (12km NE Rural) Camping Le Temps de Vivre, Route de Carlux, 24590 Salignac-Eyvignes [tel/fax 05 53 28 93 21; camping.letempsdevivre@wanadoo.fr; www. temps-de-vivre.com] Fr Sarlat N on D704, bear R onto D60 to Salignac-Eyvigues. Fr Salignac take D61 S dir Carlux, site sp in 1.5km on R. Sm, mkd/hdg pitch, terr, pt shd; wc; chem disp; baby facs; fam bthrm; shwrs inc; el pts (10A) €2; gas; ice; lndtte; shop; tradsmn; BBQ; supmkt 2km; rest; snacks; bar; pool; playgrnd; games area; golf; tennis; fishing; dogs €1.85; 50% statics; poss cr; quiet; adv bkg (fee); Eng spkn; cc acc; CCI. "Attractive site; gd touring base Dordogne; friendly owners; highly rec." ♦ 1 Apr-31 Oct. € 14.50   2005*

SARLAT LA CANEDA *7C3* (1km E) Camping Les Perieres, Route de Ste Nathalène, 24200 Sarlat-la-Caneda [05 53 59 05 84; fax 05 53 28 57 51; www.lesperieres.com] Site on R of D47 to Proissons & Ste Nathalene. NB steep access rds. Med, mkd pitch, terr, pt shd; wc; mv service pnt; shwrs inc; el pts (6A) inc; gas; lndry rm; ice; shop; tradsmn; bar; htd covrd pool & outdoor pool; games rm; tennis; adv bkg; quiet; cc acc +2% charge. "Highly rec; walking dist of Sarlat in grounds of holiday vill; every facility; spotlessly clean; friendly & helpful; conv Sarlat; excel site." ♦ Easter-30 Sep. € 31.90 (3 persons)   2005*

SARLAT LA CANEDA *7C3* (6km E Rural) Camping Les Grottes de Roffy, 24200 Ste Nathalene [05 53 59 15 61; fax 05 53 31 09 11; roffy@perigord.com; www.roffy.fr] Fr N end of Sarlat take D47 NE for Ste Nathalene. Site on R 1km bef vill. Fr Souillac (E) exit junc 55 onto N703/704 to Carlux. Turn N onto D61 then D47 to Ste Nathalene, site thro vill on L. Lge, hdg/mkd pitch, terr, pt shd; htd wc; chem disp; baby facs; shwrs inc; el pts (6A) inc; gas; lndtte; ice; shop 5km; tradsmn; rest; playgrnd; 4 pools; tennis; entmnt; child entmnt; 40% statics (inc tour ops); dogs €1.90; extra for 'comfort' pitches; Eng spkn; adv bkg (ess Jul/Aug - write Jan 1); noisy high ssn; CCI. "Excel rest & shop; helpful staff." ♦ 1 May-18 Sep. € 25.05   2005*

SARLAT LA CANEDA *7C3* (10km E Rural) Camping Les Ombrages de la Dordogne, Rouffillac, 24370 Carlux [05 53 28 62 17; fax 05 53 28 62 18; ombrages@perigord.com; www. ombrages.fr] 12km W thro Souillac on D703. Turn L at x-rds in Rouffillac & immed turn L bef rv bdge into site. Med, some mkd pitch, pt shd; wc; chem disp; shwrs inc; el pts (6-10A) €2.50-3.50; gas 1km; lndtte; ice; shop 1km; tradsmn (high ssn); rest 100m; snacks; bar; BBQ; playgrnd; pool adj; rv sw adj; fishing; tennis; games area; cycle & canoe hire; internet; TV rm; 2% statics; dogs €1.50; phone; poss cr; Eng spkn; adv bkg; quiet but some rd noise; cc acc; CCI. "Pleasant, well-maintained, rvside site; enthusiastic owners live on site; pitching poss diff due trees; facs poss stretched high ssn; canoe trips arranged; cycle track; vg." 1 Apr-31 Oct. € 12.40   2005*

SARLAT LA CANEDA *7C3* (12km E Rural) Camp Municipal, 24370 St Julien-de-Lampon [05 53 29 83 39 or 05 53 29 46 11 (Mairie); fax 05 53 59 69 18] Fr Sarlat-la-Caneda take D704/703 E, cross rv at Rouffillac sp St Julien-de-Lampon. Site on L 200m after bdge. Med, mkd pitch, pt shd; wc; chem disp; shwrs inc; el pts (6A) inc; lndtte; ice; shop 500m; tradsmn; rest, snacks & bar 200m; playgrnd; rv sw adj; fishing; canoe hire; tennis; dogs; phone; Eng spkn; quiet; CCI. "Lovely location with mature trees; poss tight pitches for lge o'fits; football stadium on site & public use rest, bar & picnic area; site is NH for canoe safaris; gd walking." 1 Jun-15 Sep. € 13.70   2003*

SARLAT LA CANEDA *7C3* (12km E Rural) Camping Le Mondou, 24370 St Julien-de -Lampon [tel/fax 05 53 29 70 37; lemondou@camping-dordogne.info; www.mondou.club.tip.nl] Fr Sarlat-la-Caneda take D704/D703 E; cross rv at Rouffillac, ent St Julien-de-Lampon & turn L at x-rds; site sp. Med, hdg pitch, pt shd; wc; chem disp; baby facs; shwrs; el pts (6-10A) €2.50; gas 700m; ice; lndry rm; shop 500m; rest; bar; BBQ; playgrnd; pool & paddling pool; cycle hire; rv sw, fishing & waterports 300m; games rm; games area; 10% statics; dogs €1; phone; Eng spkn; adv bkg rec, dep req; quiet. "Helpful owners; beautiful views; excel." ♦ 1 May-15 Oct. € 12.00   2004*

SARLAT LA CANEDA *7C3* (5km SE Rural) Camping Les Acacias, Route de Cahors, 24200 Sarlat-la-Caneda [05 53 31 08 50; fax 05 53 59 29 30; camping_acacias@wanadoo.fr; www. acacias.fr] Foll sp La Caneda vill & site fr D704 S fr Sarlat. NB Last few metres of app v narr rd. Med, hdg/mkd pitch, pt sl, shd; wc; chem disp; mv service pnt; baby facs; shwrs inc; el pts (6A) €2.50; gas; lndtte; ice; supmkt 3km; tradsmn; rest; snacks; bar; playgrnd; 2 pools; dogs; phone; bus; adv bkg; quiet; cc acc; CCI. "Clean, modern san facs; helpful, enthusiastic owners; ideal touring base; gd mkt in Sarlat Wed & Sat; vg long/sh stay." 1 Apr-30 Sep. € 13.00   2005*

SARLAT LA CANEDA *7C3* (7km SE Rural) Camping Aqua Viva, 24200 Carsac-Aillac [05 53 31 46 00; fax 05 53 29 36 37; aqua-viva@perigord.com; www.aquaviva.fr] Fr N or S take N20/A20 to Souillac. Foll D703 twd Sarlat. Just past Calviac-en-Perigord, turn R onto D704a, site on L in 3km. Ent easily missed; app with care as busy rd. Lge, mkd pitch, pt terr, pt sl, pt shd; wc; chem disp; baby facs; shwrs inc; el pts (6A) inc (poss rev pol); gas; lndtte; ice; shop; rest; snacks; bar; BBQ; playgrnd; pool; sw & boating in sm lake; fishing; cycle hire; games rm; internet; playgrnd 2; recep 0900-1900; poss cr; Eng spkn; adv bkg ess; cc acc; CCI. "Nice, friendly staff; excel, lively site for families; basic but gd value rest; facs stretched high ssn." ♦ 15 Apr-23 Sep. € 27.00 ABS - D17   2005*

SARLAT LA CANEDA *7C3* (7km SE Rural) Camping Le Rocher de la Cave, 24200 Carsac-Aillac [05 53 28 14 26; fax 05 53 28 27 10; rocherdelacave@wanadoo.fr; www.rocherdela cave.com] Fr Sarlat-la-Caneda take D704 S twd Carsac-Aillac & turn L bef vill. Follow sp. Med, hdg/mkd pitch, pt shd; wc; shwrs inc; el pts (10A) €2.60; gas; lndtte; shops 2km; tradsmn; rest; snacks; bar; playgrnd; pool; rv sw; canoe hire; tennis 500m; 5% statics; dogs; phone; quiet. "Rv site with chalets avail; 20% red low ssn; gd long/sh stay." ♦ ltd. 1 May-15 Sep. € 15.30 2004*

SARLAT LA CANEDA *7C3* (8km SE) Camping Le Plein Air des Bories, 24200 Carsac-Aillac [tel/fax 05 53 28 15 67] Take D704 SE fr Sarlat sp Gourdon; diff RH turn to site after Carsac vill. Easier access on D703 fr Vitrac. Med, pt sl, shd; wc (male cont); baby facs; shwrs; el pts (3-6A) inc; gas; lndtte; lndry rm; sm shop in ssn; shops 1.5km; tradsmn; snacks; bar; rv sw; htd pool; canoe hire; boating & fishing; tennis 700m; poss cr; quiet; Eng spkn; CCI. "Vg long/sh stay; friendly owners; clean, shady rv-side site." ♦ 1 Jun-15 Sep. € 18.00 2004*

SARLAT LA CANEDA *7C3* (8km SE Rural) Camping Les Chenes Verts, Route de Sarlat, 24370 Calviac-en-Perigord [05 53 59 21 07; fax 05 53 31 05 51; chenes-verts@wanadoo.fr; www. chenes-verts.com] S fr Chateauroux on A20 leave at Souillac exit. Join D703 heading W twd Sarlat; branch R onto D704a soon after Calviac-en-Perigord, site on R in 2km. Or take D704/704A SE fr Sarlat. Site in 8km on L; clearly sp & flags at ent. Med, hdg/mkd pitch, pt sl, pt shd; wc (some cont); chem disp; mv service pnt; baby facs; shwrs inc; el pts (6A) inc (25m cable rec); gas; lndtte; sm shop; tradsmn; rest; snacks; bar; BBQ (gas/charcoal only); playgrnd; 2 pools (1 htd, covrd); canoeing; cycle hire; horseriding; golf 7km; games area; games rm; entmnt; TV rm; 70 statics (sep area); no dogs; recep 0830-1200 & 1400-1900; Eng spkn; adv bkg; quiet but some noise fr bar; red long stay; cc acc; CCI. "Pleasant, peaceful site; gd size pitches but sandy, so muddy when wet; v helpful owners; wine-tastings; excel pool; mkt Sat Sarlat; basic san facs, ltd low ssn; v gd location for Dordogne." ♦ 15 May-15 Sep. € 20.30 ABS - D04 2005*

SARLAT LA CANEDA *7C3* (9km SE) Camping La Butte, 24250 La Roque-Gageac [tel/fax 05 53 28 30 28; contact@camping-la-butte.com; www. camping-la-butte.com] On D703 1km fr Vitrac bet Vitrac & Cenac. Med, hdg pitch, shd; wc; shwrs inc; el pts (4-10A) €2.60-3.30; gas; lndtte; ice; shop; rest; snacks; bar; BBQ; pool; rv sw; fishing; boating; dogs €2; poss cr; adv bkg; red low ssn. "Many interesting chateaux & towns in easy reach; in beautiful part of Dordogne; rather run down; NH/sh stay only." Easter-Oct. € 14.70 2003*

SARLAT LA CANEDA *7C3* (10km SE) Camping Les Granges, 24250 Grolejac [05 53 28 11 15; fax 05 53 28 57 13; lesueur.francine@wanadoo.fr; www.lesgranges-fr.com] Fr Sarlat take D704 SE, sp Gourdon. Site sp nr cent of Grolejac on R. Care on acute corner after rlwy bdge. Med, hdg, terr, pt shd; wc; chem disp; baby facs; shwrs inc; el pts (6A) €3.50; gas; lndtte; shop; rest; snacks; bar; playgrnd; htd pool; paddling pool; cycle hire; entmnt; mini-golf; rv & lake fishing 1km; TV; 40% statics; dogs €3; poss cr; Eng spkn; adv bkg; cc acc; CCI. "Historical & beautiful area." 2 May-15 Sep. € 33.40 (4 persons) 2005*

SARLAT LA CANEDA *7C3* (13km SE Rural) Camp Municipal Le Roc Perce, Plan d'Eau, 24250 Grolejac [05 53 59 48 70; fax 05 53 29 39 74] On D704 SE fr Sarlat twd Goudon, Grolejac in 11km. In vill cent, foll sp 'Plan d'Eau'; pass thro vill & turn R in front of La Marais Rest, in 100m turn L dir Nabirat. Site on L in 500m. Med, hdg pitch, pt shd; wc; chem disp; baby facs; shwrs; el pts (10A) inc; gas 1km; lndtte; shop 1km; rest 500m; playgrnd; sand beach; lake sw, fishing & watersports; dogs; Eng spkn; adv bkg; quiet; no cc acc CCI. "Popular site on created lake with artificial sand beach; rest walking dist; v quiet (lonely) low ssn." ♦ 15 Jun-15 Sep. € 12.00 2005*

SARLAT LA CANEDA *7C3* (13km SE Rural) Camping La Noyeraie, Le Barthe, 24250 Grolejac [05 53 28 14 59] Fr Sarlat SE twds Gourdon on D704; in Grolejac turn L sp Milhac; site well sp in 1km. Access rd steep, narr & winding. Sm, pt sl, pt shd; wc; shwrs inc; el pts (10A) inc; shop/gas 2km; lndtte; ice; playgrnd; pool; TV rm; dogs €0.50; Eng spkn; adv bkg; quiet; no cc acc; CCI. "Excel, pleasant, tranquil site for touring Dordogne, Cahors; v helpful owners; farm produce avail; v clean facs." ♦ Apr-Sep. € 12.50 2005*

SARLAT LA CANEDA *7C3* (6km S Rural) Camping La Bouysse de Caudon, 24200 Vitrac [05 53 28 33 05 or 06 80 17 19 93 (mob); fax 05 53 30 38 28; la-bouysse.24@wanadoo.fr; www.labouysse.com] On D46 turn L onto D703 sp to Souillac. In 3km turn R & foll site sp, site on L. Well sp. Med, hdg/mkd pitch, terr, pt sl, pt shd; wc; chem disp; mv service pnt; shwrs inc; el pts (6-10A) €3-3.40; gas; BBQ (gas); lndtte; shop; rest; snacks; bar; tradsmn; rv sw; pool (no shorts); playgrnd; entmnt; tennis; games area; fishing; canoe hire; phone; dogs; poss cr; adv bkg (dep); Eng spkn; quiet; cc acc; CCI. "Excel for all stays; red facs low ssn; family-run on banks of Rv Dordogne; helpful staff; plenty of gd, clean san facs but poss ltd low ssn; many Bastides in area." ♦ ltd. Easter-30 Sep. € 17.60 2004*

FRANCE

SARLAT LA CANEDA *7C3* (6km S Rural) Camping Soleil-Plage, Caudon-par-Montfort, 24200 Vitrac [05 53 28 33 33 or 06 07 33 96 54 (LS); fax 05 53 28 30 24; info@soleilplage.fr; www. soleilplage.fr] On D46, 6km S of Sarlat twd Vitrac, turn L onto D703, to Chateau Montfort, R to site dir Caudon, sp. Site beyond Camping La Bouysse on rvside, 2km E of Vitrac. Narr rds on site. Lge, hdg pitch, pt shd; wc; chem disp; mv service pnt; baby facs; serviced pitches; shwrs inc; el pts (10A) €3.50; gas; lndtte; shop & 7km; rest; snacks; bar; playgrnd; pool; paddling pool; waterslide; rv sw & beach adj; fishing; canoeing; tennis; cycle hire; mini-golf; golf 1km; entmnt; internet; TV; 45% statics; dogs €2.20; phone; Eng spkn; adv bkg ess Jul/Aug; quiet; cc acc; red low ssn/groups; CCI. "Farm rest adj; farm produce avail; v friendly, welcoming owner; variety of pitches - extra for serviced; san facs v clean; superb pool; excel." ♦ 1 Apr-30 Sep. € 24.90   2005*

See advertisement

SARLAT LA CANEDA *7C3* (9km S Rural) Camping Beau Rivage, Gaillardou, 24250 La Roque-Gageac [05 53 28 32 05; fax 05 53 29 63 56; camping.beau.rivage@wanadoo.fr; www.camping-beau-rivage.com] On S side of D703, 1km W of Vitrac, E of Elf petrol stn, adj Rv Dordogne. Lge, mkd pitch, shd; htd wc (some cont); chem disp; baby facs; shwrs inc; el pts (6A) €4; gas; lndtte; ice; shops 2km; snacks; bar; playgrnd; pool; canoes; tennis; games area; cycle hire; horseriding; archery; golf 2km; entmnts; TV; dogs €1.60; poss cr; adv bkg rec high ssn; quiet. "Conv Domme." ♦ 1 Mar-30 Sep. € 17.50   2004*

SARLAT LA CANEDA *7C3* (9km S Rural) Camping La Plage, 24220 Vezac [05 53 29 50 83] On banks of Rv Dordogne, 500m W of La Roque-Gageac on D703. Med, mkd pitch, shd; wc; chem disp (wc); shwrs inc; el pts (4-6A) €1.90-4; gas; sm shop 1km; BBQ; playgrnd; shgl beach; rv sw; fishing; canoeing; poss cr; adv bkg; quiet; CCI. "Attractive site; magnificent rvside location; excel pitches; basic san facs but v clean; highly rec." 1 Apr-30 Sep. € 10.00   2003*

SARLAT LA CANEDA *7C3* (9km S Rural) Camping Le Pech de Caumont, 24250 Cenac-et-St-Julien [05 53 28 21 63 or 05 53 28 30 67; fax 05 53 29 99 73; jmilhac@pech-de-caumont.com; www.pech-de-caumont.com] D46 fr Sarlat to Cenac, cross rv into vill; site sp fr main st. Do not go thro Domme. Med, hdg/mkd pitch, pt sl, terr, pt shd; wc; chem disp; shwrs inc; el pts (6A) €2.50; lndtte; ice; shops 1km; snacks; sm bar; BBQ; playgrnd; pool; rv sw 2km; TV rm; 4% statics; dogs; phone; poss cr; Eng spkn; adv bkg; quiet; red low ssn; cc acc; CCI. "Excel views; v helpful owners; modern, clean san facs; family-run site, popular with British; excel long/sh stay." 1 Apr-30 Sep. € 17.85   2004*

SARLAT LA CANEDA *7C3* (10km S Rural) Camp Municipal, 24250 Cenac-et-St Julien [05 53 28 31 91 or 05 53 31 41 31 (Mairie)] D46 fr Sarlat to Vitrac then Cenac; cross rv & site on L on ent Cenac. Med, mkd pitch, pt shd; wc; shwrs inc; el pts (6A) inc; lndtte; shop, rest, snacks, bar 200m; rv sw, boating & fishing adj; quiet. "V pleasant site; lovely vill nrby with gd rest, shops etc; site opens earlier if demand; expensive for ltd facs low ssn; facs clean but well-used, superb location compensates." 1 Jun-15 Sep. € 13.90   2005*

SARLAT LA CANEDA *7C3* (10km S Rural) Camping La Riviere, 24250 Domme [05 53 28 33 46; fax 05 53 29 56 04; sarl-camping-larivdomme@wanadoo.fr] Fr Sarlat take D46 to Vitrac. Cross rv bdge on D46E. In 1km at T-junc turn R on D50 & in 1km turn R at sp into site. Sm, pt shd; wc; chem disp; shwrs inc; el pts (10A) €2.60; lndtte; shops 4km; playgrnd; pool; few statics; adv bkg; quiet; red low ssn. "Generous pitches; v pleasant owner." 1 May-15 Sep. € 10.40   2005*

SARLAT LA CANEDA *7C3* (10km S Rural) Camping Le Bosquet, La Riviere, 24250 Domme [05 53 28 37 39; fax 05 53 29 41 95; info@ lebousquet.com] Fr Sarlat take D46 S to Vitrac cross rv on D46E. Sp at junc, site 500m on R. Sm, hdg/mkd pitch, pt shd, wc; chem disp; shwrs inc; el pts (6A) €2.40 (long lead poss req); gas; lndtte; sm shop; tradsmn; snacks; pool; rv sw & fishing 500m; 50% statics; dogs; Eng spkn; adv bkg; quiet; CCI. "Friendly, helpful warden; excel clean facs but poss stretched high ssn; gd shd but sm pitches; gd value in popular area." ♦ 1 Apr-30 Sep. € 11.30   2005*

SARLAT LA CANEDA *7C3* (10km S Rural) Camping Le Perpetuum, 24250 Domme [05 53 28 35 18; fax 05 53 29 63 64; www.homair-vacances.fr] Fr Sarlat take D46 to Vitrac; cross rv bdge to D46E; in 1km turn R onto D50, R again in 1km at site sp. Med, hdg/mkd pitch, pt shd; wc; chem disp; mv service pnt; baby facs; shwrs inc; el pts (10A) inc; lndry rm; lndtte; ice; shop (farm produce); tradsmn; snacks; bar; BBQ; playgrnd; pool; rv sw (Rv Dordogne); canoeing adj; tennis; games area; entmnt; statics; no dogs; poss cr; Eng spkn; adv bkg (dep req); quiet; red low ssn; cc acc; CCI. "V relaxed, friendly atmosphere; hospitable & helpful owners; Eng spkn but French appreciated; conv many tourist attractions; gd local walks; vg long/sh stay." ♦ 1 May-25 Sep. € 19.62   2004*

SARLAT LA CANEDA *7C3* (12km S Rural) Camping Bel Ombrage, 24250 St Cybranet [05 53 28 34 14; fax 05 53 59 64 64; belombrage@wanadoo.fr; www.belombrage.com] S on D57 fr Sarlat to Vezac, turn L sp Castelnaud. Fork L sp St Cybranet onto D57; site on L in 1km outside vill. Lge, hdg pitch, shd; wc; chem disp; shwrs inc; el pts (10A) inc; gas 800m; lndtte; tradsmn; supmkt, rest, snacks nr; BBQ; playgrnd; 3 pools; rv sw & beach; fishing; canoeing; tennis 600m; cycle hire; horseriding 2km; games area; games rm; library; dogs free; c'vans over 8m not acc high ssn; adv bkg; quiet; cc not acc; CCI. "Attractive, well-managed site; beautiful setting; popular with British; recep clsd lunchtime & after 1900; mkt Thu; ideal base for Dordogne." ♦ 1 Jun-5 Sep. € 20.80 ABS - D01   2005*

SARLAT LA CANEDA *7C3* (2km SW Rural) Camping Le Montant, St Andre d'Allas, 24200 Sarlat-la-Caneda [05 53 59 18 50; fax 05 53 59 37 73; contact@camping-sarlat.com] Turn R off D57 2km fr Sarlat, site sp. Med, terr, hdg/mkd pitch, pt shd; wc; chem disp; baby facs; shwrs inc; el pts (3-10A) €2.60; gas 2km; lndtte; ice; shop 2km; tradsmn; rest 500m; snacks; bar; playgrnd; htd pool; jacuzzi; children's club; games area; cycle hire; canoeing; fishing; golf nr; beach 6km; entmnt; 5% statics; adv bkg rec high ssn; quiet; red low ssn; cc acc; CCI. "Set in the heart of Perigord Noir; many sports activities." ♦ Easter-15 Sep. € 15.70   2004*

SARLAT LA CANEDA *7C3* (7km SW Rural) Camping La Cabane, 24220 Vezac [05 53 29 52 28; fax 05 53 59 09 15; camping.la.cabane@wanadoo.fr] Fr Sarlat-La-Caneda take D57 thro Vezac. On leaving Vezac turn L immed bef rlwy bdge, site sp on R on bank of Rv Dordogne. Lge, hdg/mkd pitch, pt shd; wc; shwrs inc; el pts (3-10A) inc; gas; lndtte; shop high ssn; rest & snacks 3km; bar; BBQ; playgrnd; htd covrd pool; rv sw adj; shgl beach adj; TV rm; phone; poss cr; Eng spkn; adv bkg (dep req); quiet; CCI. "Well shd, rvside site; lge pitches; conv all attractions; easy rvside walk to Beynac chateau; boat trips, light aircraft flights & canoe hire locally; many sports; poss untidy low ssn; vg long/sh stay." ♦ ltd. 1 Apr-31 Oct. € 11.30   2004*

†SARLAT LA CANEDA *7C3* (8km SW Rural) Camping Les Deux Vallees, 24220 Vezac [05 53 29 53 55; fax 05 53 31 09 81; les2v@perigord.com; www.les-2-vallees.com] Fr W leave D703 onto D49 - ignore 1st sp to site & cont onto D57 sp Sarlat. 250m fr junc foll 2nd site sp. Fr E leave D703 onto D57; 250m after junc with D49 turn L & foll sp to site. Med, hdg/mkd pitch, shd; htd wc; chem disp; baby facs; shwrs inc; el pts (6A) €3.50; ice; gas; lndtte; shop; tradsmn; rest; snacks; bar; BBQ; playgrnd; 3 pools; shgl beach 500m; cycle hire; games rm; entmnt July/Aug; 6% statics; dogs €1; Eng spkn; adv bkg ess Jul/Aug (dep req + bkg fee); quiet but rlwy adj; cc acc; red low ssn/long stay; CCI. "Beynac chateau & caves 1km, Castlenau 3km; helpful Dutch owners; ltd san facs low ssn; poss uneven pitches & muddy when wet; gd." ♦ € 16.75   2005*

This site entry hasn't been updated for a while; we'd better fill in a site report form and send it to The Club.

FRANCE

SARLAT LA CANEDA *7C3* (9km SW Rural) Camping Le Tiradou, Chemin du Grand-Fosse, 24220 St Vincent-de-Cosse [05 53 30 30 73; fax 05 53 31 16 24; francis@letiradou.fr; www.letiradou.fr] Take the D703 fr La Roque-Gageac thro Beynac & onto St Vincent; site is 2km fr Beynac on R. Med, hdg/mkd pitch, shd; wc; chem disp (wc only); shwrs inc; el pts (6A) inc; ice; BBQ; lndtte; snacks, bar, shop, tradsmn avail high ssn; playgrnd; pool; rv fishing, boating, watersports & beach adj; TV; quiet; phone; Eng spkn; adv bkg; cc acc. "Gd touring base along Dordogne Rv." ♦ Easter 30 Sep. € 12.50   2004*

SARLAT LA CANEDA *7C3* (10km SW Rural) Camping Le Capeyrou, 24220 Beynac-et-Cazenac [05 53 29 54 95; fax 05 53 28 36 27; lecapeyrou@wanadoo.fr; www.campinglecapeyrou.com] Fr W on D703 on R (opp petrol stn) immed past vill of Beynac. Or fr N on D57 fr Sarlat; in vill immed on L on rv. Med, hdg pitch, pt shd; wc; chem disp; mv service pnt; baby facs; shwrs inc; el pts (6-10A) €3-4; lndtte; shop adj; snacks; bar; playgrnd; pool; dogs €1; poss cr; Eng spkn; adv bkg; quiet; 20% red low ssn; cc acc. "Rvside walk into attractive vill with castle; excel lge pool; v helpful, friendly owners; excel site." ♦ Easter-30 Sep. € 17.00   2005*

SARLAT LA CANEDA *7C3* (10km SW Rural) Camping-Caravaning Maisonneuve, Vallee de Ceou, 24250 Castelnaud-la-Chapelle [05 53 29 51 29; fax 05 53 30 27 06; campmaison@aol.com; www.campingmaisonneuve.com] D57 SW fr Sarlat sp Beynac. Cross Rv Dordogne at Castelnaud; site sp 1km on L out of Castelnaud on D57 twd Daglan. Foll narr rd across bdge (or alt ent sp 500m for vans). Med, hdg pitch, shd; htd wc (some cont); chem disp; child/baby facs; fam bthrm; shwrs inc; el pts (6-10A) €3.20-4; gas; lndtte; ice; shop, tradsmn, rest, snacks & bar high ssn; BBQ; playgrnd; pool; rv & shgl beach; fishing; mini-golf; games rm; TV rm; no statics; dogs €1; Eng spkn; adv bkg ess high ssn; quiet; red low ssn; Eng spkn; cc acc; CCI. "Vg, modern facs; lovely rural setting in heart of Perigord Noir; spacious; gd walking, cycling; helpful owners." ♦ 1 Apr-15 Oct. € 16.60   2005*

See advertisement above

SARLAT LA CANEDA *7C3* (18km SW Rural) Domaine Le Cro Magnon, 4220 Allas-les-Mines [05 53 29 13 70; fax 05 53 29 15 79; contact@domaine-cro-magnon.com; www.domaine-cro-magnon.com] Fr Sarlat on D57/D703 two Le Buisson turn L onto D48 sp site & Berbiguieres. Do not foll any earlier sp to site as rds impassable to c'vans & m'vans. App steep, narr & twisting but gd surface. Med, pt shd; wc; chem disp; baby facs; sauna; shwrs inc; el pts (6A) inc; gas; lndtte; rest; snacks; bar; BBQ (gas/elec); playgrnd; 2 pools (1 htd); rv fishing 800m; watersports; games area; cycle hire; entmnt; TV; adv bkg; quiet. 1 May-15 Sep. € 27.80 ABS - D24   2005*

SARLAT LA CANEDA *7C3* (5km W Rural) Camping Les Charmes, Malartigue, 24200 St Andre-d'Allas [05 53 31 02 89; fax 05 53 31 06 32; les.charmes@wanadoo.fr] Fr Sarlat to St Cyprien on D25 site on R 200m bef rd forks with D35 to Le Bugue; 8km along narr rd; poss hard to find. Med, pt sl, pt shd; wc; shwrs inc; el pts (4A) €2.30; lndtte; shop; snacks; bar; BBQ; playgrnd; pool; tennis; entmnt; some statics; dogs €0.76; adv bkg; quiet; red low ssn. "Friendly & helpful." Easter-15 Oct. € 11.50   2002*

SARLAT LA CANEDA *7C3* (9km W Rural) LES CASTELS Le Moulin du Roch, Route des Eyzies, St Andre d'Allas, 24200 Sarlat-la-Caneda [05 53 59 20 27; fax 05 53 59 20 95; moulin.du.roch@wanadoo.fr; www.moulin-du-roch.com or www.les-castels.com] Fr A20 take exit 55 at Souillac dir Sarlat. At rndabt in Sarlat (just under rlwy viaduct) take 1st exit & foll sp thro Sarlat dir Perigueux. As come to end of Sarlat turn L onto D6 dir Les Eyzies (bcomes D47 in 2km). Site on L in approx 11 km on D47. Lge, hdg/mkd pitch, terr, pt shd; htd wc; chem disp; baby facs; shwrs inc; el pts (6A) inc; gas; lndtte; shop; rest; snacks; bar; BBQ (gas/charcoal only); playgrnd; htd pool & paddling pool (proper sw trunks only - no shorts); lake sw 8km; fishing; tennis; canoeing & horseriding 10km; games rm; entmnt; child entmnt; internet; TV rm; 45% static tents/vans; no pets; Eng spkn; adv bkg rec Jun-Aug; quiet; red low ssn/long stay; cc acc; CCI. "Gd rest; mkt Sat; many sports in area; gd rest & pool; v clean facs; strict rules pool area; arr bef 2000; guided walks; v well-run site." ♦ 29 Apr-16 Sep. € 30.00 (CChq acc) ABS - D02   2005*

See advertisement opposite (top)

†SARREGUEMINES *5D3* (5km S Rural) Camping Etang St Vit, 14 Rue de Roth, 57910 Neufgrange [03 87 98 13 83; fax 03 87 98 63 79] Fr Sarreguemines, clearly sp 5km S on N61 twd a'route & also S on D919. Lge, pt shd; wc; shwrs €1; el pts (6A) €1.60-2.60; ice; lndtte; cooking facs; sm shop in ssn & 800m; rest; snacks; playgrnd; sports area; lake sw; fishing; windsurfing; fitness rm; tennis 800m; dogs €1.70; mostly statics; some Eng spkn; CCI. "Adj to lake; big field; little shd; family-run; dep for san facs key; poss itinerants; owners plan serviced pitches". ♦ € 8.80   2005*

SARZEAU *2G3* (10km E Coastal) **Camp Municipal, Rue de la Plage de Rouvran, 56370 Le Tour-du-Parc [02 97 67 30 88; fax 02 97 67 39 02]** On N165 fr Vannes dir Nantes, exit sp Sarzeau onto D780. Just S of St Armel turn L onto D199 & in 3km onto D199A for Le Tour-du-Parc, then foll sp for site. Med, mkd pitch, pt sl, pt shd; wc; chem disp (wc); shwrs inc; el pts (5A) €2.50; gas; lndtte; lndry rm; ice; shop; tradsmn; rest; snacks; playgrnd; sand beach adj; watersports adj; tennis; cycle hire & routes; 5% statics; dogs €0.80; phone adj; poss cr; Eng spkn; adv bkg; quiet; CCI. "Megaliths & menhirs nrby; medieval city of Vannes 12km; boat trips around Golfe du Morbihan 8km; fair long stay." ♦ ltd. 1 Apr-15 Sep. € 8.55   2004*

SARZEAU *2G3* (10km E Coastal) **Camping Le Cadran Solaire, 56370 Le Tour-du-Parc [02 97 67 30 40 or 02 97 67 30 38]** Take N165 fr Vannes twds Nantes, turn R for Sarzeau (D780), nr St Armel turn L on D199 & in 3.2km on D199A for Le Tour-du-Parc. In Le Tour-du-Parc turn R at water tower, sp Sarzeau, site on R in 1km. Med, hdg pitch, pt shd; wc; chem disp; shwrs inc; el pts (6A) inc; lndtte; shop; playgrnd; shgl beach adj; tennis; some statics; phone; poss cr; quiet; cc acc; CCI. "Situated by lake; vg san block; fair sh stay." ♦ 1 Apr-30 Sep. € 17.50   2003*

SARZEAU *2G3* (7km SE Coastal) **Camping La Madone, Manoir de Ker An Poul, Penvins, 56370 Sarzeau [02 97 67 33 30; fax 02 97 67 44 83; campinglamadone@wanadoo.fr; www.camping-lamadone.fr]** Fr E exit N165 1km E of Muzillac, sp Sarzeau D20 & cont approx 20km to junc of D20 & D199, S on D199 sp Penvins. Fr W, 6km E of Vannes, exit N165 onto N780 sp Sarzeau, in 9.5km S onto D199 sp Penvins. Lge, pt sl, pt shd; wc (some cont); chem disp; baby facs; shwrs inc; el pts (6A); gas; lndtte; ice; shop; rest adj; snacks; bar; htd pool; sand beach 600m; playgrnd; entmnt; 10% statics; poss cr; adv bkg; quiet; red low ssn; CCI. ♦ Easter-31 Oct. € 17.30   2002*

SARZEAU *2G3* (2km S Coastal) **Camping La Ferme de Lann Hoedic, Route de Roaliguen, 56370 Sarzeau [02 97 48 01 73; fax 02 97 41 72 87; contact@camping-lannhoedic.fr; www.camping-lannhoedic.fr]** Fr Vannes on N165 turn onto D780 dir Sarzeau. Do not ent Sarzeau, but at Super U rndabt foll sp La Roaliguen. After 1.5km turn L to Lann Hoedic. Med, hdg/mkd pitch, pt shd; wc; chem disp; mv service pnt; baby facs; shwrs inc; el pts (10A) €2.70; gas; lndtte; ice; shop 800m; tradsmn; rest 2km; snacks; bar 1km; playgrnd; sand beach 800m; 5% statics; dogs €1.50; phone; poss cr; Eng spkn; adv bkg; quiet; CCI. "Conv St Malo; peaceful, well-run site." ♦ 1 Apr-31 Oct. € 15.90 (CChq acc)   2005*

See advertisement below

FRANCE

Some of these sites have changed their opening dates - we'd better fill in some site report forms and let the editor of the guide know.

SARZEAU *2G3* (4km S Coastal/Rural) **Camping An Treste, Route de la Plage de Roaliguen, 56370 Sarzeau [02 97 41 79 60; fax 02 97 41 36 21; letreste@campingletreste.com; www.campingletreste.com]** Fr E on D780 turn L at 1st rndabt nr Super U supmkt sp Le Roaliguen, site sp on L. Lge, hdg/mkd pitch, pt sl, pt shd; wc (some cont); chem disp; baby facs; shwrs inc; el pts (10A) €3.30; gas; lndtte; ice; supmkt 2km; tradsmn; snacks; bar in ssn; playgrnd; htd pool & paddling pool; waterslide; sand beach 800m; tennis, horseriding, golf 3km; TV rm; 5% statics; dogs €1.50; phone; Eng spkn; adv bkg; quiet; 20% red low ssn; cc acc; CCI. "Well-run site; gd base for exploring region; lots to do in area; helpful owners; excel long stay." ♦ 24 May-10 Sep. € 20.70   2005*

SARZEAU *2G3* (2km SW Rural) **Camping Le Bohat, Route d'Arzon, 56370 Sarzeau [02 97 41 78 68; fax 02 97 41 70 97; lebohat@campinglebohat.com; www.campinglebohat.com]** Fr Vannes on N165, exit onto D780 to Sarzeau. Do not turn off this main rd to Sarzeau but cont twd Arzon; 1km after 2nd rndabt turn L for Le Bohat. Fr Nantes on N165 take D20 at Muzillac, cont to end & join D78. Rest as above. Lge, hdg/mkd pitch, pt shd; wc (some cont); chem disp; mv service pnt; baby facs; shwrs inc; el pts (10A) inc; gas; lndtte; ice; shop 3km; tradsmn; takeaway; bar; BBQ (gas/charcoal); playgrnd; htd pool & paddling pool; sand beach, watersports 5km; cycle hire 2km, golf 6km; horseriding 2km; games rm; entmnt; TV rm; 4% statics; dogs €1.70; phone; recep 0830-1930 high ssn; c'vans over 7.50m not acc high ssn; poss cr; Eng spkn; adv bkg; quiet; cc acc; CCI. "Arrivals field no el pts; busy, family-run site; lge pitches; excel, helpful staff; cycle tracks; Chateau de Suscinio & local zoo worth visit; boat trips round Golfe du Morbihan & local islands; mkt Thu." ♦ 26 Apr-16 Sep. € 21.55
ABS - B07   2005*

See advertisement

SARZEAU *2G3* (5km SW Coastal) **Camping Saint Jacques, 1 Rue Pratel Vihan, 56370 Sarzeau [02 97 41 79 29; fax 02 97 48 04 45; info@ camping-stjacques.com; www.camping stjacques. fr]** Fr Sarzeau on D780, at 2nd rndabt foll dir St Jacques, site sp. Lge, mkd pitch, pt shd; wc (come cont); chem disp; baby facs; shwrs inc; el pts (6A) €2.40; gas; lndtte; ice; shop; snacks; bar; BBQ; playgrnd; sand beach adj; tennis; fishing; sailing school; mini-golf; cycle hire; entmnt; 10% statics; dogs; Eng spkn; adv bkg; quiet; red low ssn; cc acc; CCI. "Excel beach & dunes." ♦ 1 Apr-30 Sep. 2003*

SAUCHY LESTREE see Cambrai *3B4*

SAUGNACQ ET MURET *7D1* (Rural) **Camping Le Muretois, 40410 Saugnacq-et-Muret [tel/fax 05 58 09 62 14 or 05 58 09 60 45]** In vill of Le Muret, by-passed by N10, within 500m of N10 at junc with D20, sp. At rear of Hotel Caravaniers. Sm, mkd pitch, pt shd; wc (own san rec); chem disp (wc); shwrs; el pts (10A) (some rev pol); gas; ice; shop 500m; rest 100m; snacks; bar; playgrnd; rv fishing 3km; tennis; cycle hire; dogs; phone; poss cr; adv bkg rec high ssn; quiet; CCI. "Friendly, basic site; gd NH; watch elec points!" Apr-Sep. € 8.00 2003*

SAUGUES *9C1* (Urban) **Camp Municipal, 43170 Saugues [04 71 77 80 62 or 04 71 77 81 21; fax 04 71 77 66 40]** 500m W fr Saugues on D589 twd Paulac, turn R into Ave de Gevaudan. Site on L in 100m. Well sp. Med, mkd pitch, pt shd; wc; chem disp; baby facs; shwrs inc; el pts (10A) inc; shop; snacks; bar; lndtte; BBQ; rv sw; fishing; boating; canoeing; sports area; adv bkg; cc not acc; CCI. "Gd cent for gorges of Allier & Le Puy-en-Velay; barriers clsd at night; lge grass pitches; vg long/sh stay." 15 Jun-15 Sep. € 13.50 2004*

SAUJON *7B1* (2km N Rural) **Aire Naturelle La Lande (Renouoleau), Route de L'Illate, 17600 Saujon [05 46 02 84 31; fax 05 46 02 22 47]** Fr Saintes on N150 turn R at 2nd sp Saujon. At intersection turn L onto D131. In 500m at x-rds, turn L at rndabt in front of fire stn. Site sp at x-rds. Site on R immed after R bend. Sm, pt sl, pt shd; wc; chem disp; shwrs; el pts (6A) €2.30; lndry rm; shop, rest, snacks & bar 2km; playgrnd; beach 12km, poss cr. "Excel CL-type site with full facs; very quiet; spotless facs." Apr-Oct. € 9.10 2002*

SAULCE, LA *9D3* (2km E Rural) **Camping du Lac, Route Napoléon, Curbans, 05110 La Saulce [04 92 54 23 10]** S fr Gap on N85 twd Sisteron for 16km; R to La Saulce over a'route; in vill turn L onto D19 & over canal. Turn L again. Site 1km on L. Med, pt shd; wc; chem disp; shwrs inc; el pts (6A) inc; lndtte; shop 2km; tradsmn; rest; playgrnd; pool; paddling pool; walking; cycling; fishing; 10% statics; poss cr; Eng spkn; adv bkg; quiet; CCI. "Enthusiastic family owners; lge pitches; excel long stay." ♦ 1 Apr-10 Oct. € 17.00 2004*

SAULIEU *6G1* (1km N Rural) **Camp Municipal du Perron, Route de Paris, 21210 Saulieu [tel/fax 03 80 64 16 19 or 03 80 64 09 22 (Mairie); saulieu. tourisme@wanadoo.fr]** On N6 on L of rd on ent fr N. Sp. Lge, hdg/mkd pitch, pt sl, pt shd; htd wc; chem disp; shwrs inc; el pts (10A) €2.50; gas; lndtte; ice; sm shop; tradsmn; rest in ssn; bar; playgrnd; pool; tennis; dogs €0.76; adv bkg; quiet, but rd noise; red low ssn; CCI. "No twin-axle vans; gates clsd 2200-0700; office clsd 1200-1500; gd cent touring Morvan Reg Park; many gd rests; fishing in lake; gd walking area." ♦ ltd. May-Sep. € 12.05 2003*

†SAULXURES SUR MOSELOTTE *6F3* (1.5km W Rural) **Camping Le Lac de la Moselotte, 336 Route des Amias, 88290 Saulxures-sur- Moselotte [03 29 24 56 56; fax 03 29 24 58 31; lac-moselotte@ ville-saulxures-mtte.fr; www.ville-saulxures-mtte.fr]** Sp fr D43. Med, hdg/mkd pitch, pt sl, pt shd; htd wc; chem disp; shwrs inc; el pts (10A) €6; lndtte; shop; tradsmn; snacks; bar; playgrnd; lake sw & sand beach adj; watersports; canoe & cycle hire; fishing; games rm; entmnt; TV; 40% statics; phone; Eng spkn; adv bkg; quiet; cc acc; red long stay/CCI. "Pleasant, beautifully situated site." ♦ € 15.00 2004*

Will you fill in the site report forms at the back of the guide, or shall I?

SAUMUR *4G1.* **See also sites listed under Bourgueil, Coutures, Doue la Fontaine, Montsoreau, Les Rosiers sur Loire and Vernantes.**

SAUMUR *4G1* (1km N Urban) **Camping L'Ile d'Offard, Rue de Verden, 49400 Saumur [02 41 40 30 00; fax 02 41 67 37 81; iledoffard@ wanadoo.fr; www.cvtloisirs.com]** Fr N or S on N147 turn off for town cent at rndabt N of Saumur. Ent town past rwly station & cross Rv Loire brdge; take 1st L to site; foll sp. Lge, hdg/mkd pitch, hdstg, pt sl, pt shd; htd wc; chem disp; mv service pnt; shwrs inc; el pts (6-10A) €3 (rev pol); ice; gas; lndtte; shops in ssn; tradsmn; rest; snacks; bar; playgrnd; htd, covrd pool adj; lake sw 500m; fishing, boating adj; tennis; cycle hire; games area; child entmnt; TV rm; 10% tour ops statics; dogs €1; poss cr; Eng spkn; adv bkg (non-refundable bkg fee); some rlwy noise; red low ssn; cc acc; CCI. "Pleasant, busy, well-managed site; helpful staff; recep open 0800-1900 daily, clsd 1200-1400 or 1600 (w/e), clsd 1200-1700 winter; code for barrier; most pitches lge but some v sm pitches bet statics; lge o'fits check in advance; sh rvside walk to town; gd cycle rtes; hdstg pitches in winter; vg sh/long stay." ♦ ltd. 1 Mar-30 Sep. € 19.50 (CChq acc) 2005*

FRANCE

SAUMUR *4G1* (8km NE Rural) **Camping Le Po Dore, 49650 Allonnes** [02 41 38 78 80; fax 02 41 38 78 81] NE fr Saumur on N147/E60 to D10. Site 3km W of Allonnes on R. Med, hdg/mkd pitch, pt shd; wc; chem disp; shwrs inc; el pts (6-10A) €2.80-4 (rev pol); gas 3km; lndtte; tradsmn; rest; snacks; bar; playgrnd; pool; mountain cycle hire; 10% statics; dogs €1; phone; poss cr; some Eng spkn; some noise fr rlwy; red low ssn; cc acc; CCI. "Well-managed, friendly & helpful owners; access to el pts diff fr some pitches; farm animals; conv for wine rtes, caves & museums; barrier clsd 2200-0700; 10 mins fr a'route." ♦ 1 Apr -31 Oct. € 15.20   2005*

SAUMUR *4G1* (6km E Rural) **LES CASTELS L'Etang de la Breche, 5 Impasse de la Breche, 49730 Varennes-sur-Loire** [02 41 51 22 92; fax 02 41 51 27 24; mail@etang-breche.com; www. etang-breche.com] Exit Saumur on N152 twd Tours & site sp fr either dir. Site on N side of rd (6km W of Varennes) app fr lge lay-by giving easy ent. Lge, hdg pitch, pt shd; wc; chem disp; mv service pnt; 20% serviced pitch; baby facs; shwrs inc; el pts (10A) €3; gas; lndtte; ice; shop; tradsmn; rest; snacks; bar; playgrnd; 2 htd pools (no shorts); waterslide; cycle hire; tennis; games rms; entmnt; internet; TV rm; 30% statics; dogs; phone; Eng spkn; adv bkg (ess Jul/Aug), dep req; quiet but rd noise in some areas; 40% red low ssn; cc acc; CCI. "Excel facs; auto barrier clsd 2300-0700; plenty of space for children's play; easy access; lge pitches; v helpful staff; excel rest; conv Loire chateaux & wine-tastings; gd long stay." ♦ 15 May-15 Sep. € 30.00   2005*

SAUMUR *4G1* (10km SE) **Centre Naturiste La Herpiniere (Naturist), 49730 Turquant** [02 41 51 74 81] Saumur to Montsoreau on D947, turn R at vill sq & foll sp Herpiniere FFN. X-rds at windmill, site on L at end of rd. Med, pt shd; wc (some cont); chem disp; shwrs; el pts (4A) €1.52; ice; tradsmn; bar; playgrnd; pool; tennis; mini-golf; entmnts; adv bkg; quiet; INF card. "Sells own wine; huge grounds for naturist walks; facs run down (2001)." ♦ 1 Apr-30 Oct. € 10.70   2002*

SAUMUR *4G1* (5km NW Rural) **Camping de Chantepie, 49400 St Hilaire-St-Florent** [02 41 67 95 34; fax 02 41 67 95 85; info@camping chantepie.com; www.campingchantepie.com] Take D161, then D751 on S bank of rv sp Gennes. Site is on L of rd bet Le Pointrineau & La Croix, approx 5km fr N147 junc. Or fr N after x-ing rv on N147, take turn sp St Hilaire-St-Florent & join D751 for Gennes; well sp fr D751. NB Easy to miss turning. Long access rd to site with poor rd surface. Lge, hdg/mkd pitch, pt shd; wc; chem disp; mv service pnt; baby facs; shwrs inc; el pts (10A) inc (poss rev pol); gas; lndtte; ice; shop; tradsmn; rest; snacks; bar; BBQ; playgrnd; htd, covrd pool; paddling pool; rv beach 200m; fishing; tennis 2km; mini-golf; cycle hire; golf 2km; horseriding, boating 5km; entmnt; TV rm; internet; 10% statics; dogs €2; c'vans over 8m not acc; Eng spkn; adv bkg; quiet; red low ssn; cc acc; CCI. "Excel site; helpful staff; care with access to pitches for lge o'fits; recep 0800-1930; wine-tastings & visits; excel san facs inc for disabled; mkt Sat Saumur." ♦ 15 May-15 Sep. € 29.00 ABS - L06   2005*

See advertisement on page 218

SAUMUR *4G1* (8km NW Rural) **Camp Municipal La Croix Rouge, 49160 St Martin-de-la-Place** [02 41 38 09 02; fax 02 41 45 65 65] Fr Saumur, take N147 N then turn L onto D952 dir Angers. At St Martin-de-la-Place foll sp for site. Med, mkd pitch, pt shd; wc; chem disp; mv service pnt; shwrs; el pts (8A) €2; lndry rm; ice; shop, rest, 600m; bar 200m; playgrnd; rv sw, sailing adj; dogs; bus 150m; Eng spkn; adv bkg; quiet; cc not acc; CCI. "Beautiful, tranquil site on bank of Rv Loire; rv views on some pitches; no twin-axles." ♦ ltd. 1 Jun-15 Sep. € 8.00   2005*

SAUSHEIM see Mulhouse *6F3*

SAUVETERRE DE BEARN *8F1* (S Rural) **Camping du Gave, Ave de la Gare, 64390 Sauveterre-de-Bearn [05 59 38 53 30; fax 05 59 36 19 88; camping-du-gave@wanadoo.fr]** Site on D933 on S side of town. Ent immed off rndabt at end of rv bdge. Med, mkd pitch, shd; wc (some cont); chem disp; shwrs; el pts (6A); lndtte; shop & 200m; tradsmn; rest 1km; snacks; bar; playgrnd; rv sw; canoeing; 10% statics; dogs; poss cr; adv bkg; quiet. "Lovely medieval town; site by rv; facs poss stretched in ssn; gd security; friendly management; footpath fr site to town." ♦ 1 Apr-15 Oct. € 6.00   2004*

SAUVETERRE DE GUYENNE *7D2* (8km NW Rural) **Camping Chateau Guiton (Naturist), 33760 Frontenac [05 56 23 52 79; fax 05 56 23 99 40; accueil@chateau-guiton.com; www.chateau-guiton.com]** Approx 6km N of Sauveterre-de-Guyenne turn W onto D123 sp Frontenac. Turn L just bef vill sp Chateau Guiton. Sm, mkd pitch, pt sl, pt shd; wc; chem disp; sauna; shwrs; el pts (10A) €3.50; gas; lndtte; ice; shop; tradsmn; rest & bar 4km; playgrnd; pool; TV rm; bus 6km; phone; Eng spkn; adv bkg; quiet; cc acc; IFN card req; "V friendly owner; site is converted chateau, part open, part wooded; in cent wine region; communal meal twice a week high ssn; close to Bordeaux; vg long/sh stay." 1 May-15 Oct. € 17.50   2004*

SAUVETERRE LA LEMANCE see Villefranche du Perigord *7D3*

SAUXILLANGES see Issoire *9B1*

SAUZE VAUSSAIS *7A2* (Rural) **Camp Municipal, Route de Chef Boutonne, 79190 Sauze-Vaussais [05 49 07 60 53 (Mairie); fax 05 49 07 78 49; mairie-sauze@marcireau.fr]** Fr Poitiers-Angouleme (N10), turn onto D948 at Les Maisons-Blanches to Sauze. Site sp in vill. Med, pt sl, pt shd; wc (cont); shwrs inc; el pts €2.40; shops 1km; BBQ; playgrnd; pool (public); tennis; quiet. "Comfortable, value-for-money; fair sh stay/NH." 22 Jun-7 Sep. € 5.30   2003*

SAVENAY *2G3* (3km E) **Camp Municipal du Lac, 44260 La Moere [02 40 58 31 76]** Site well sp in Savenay. Med, mkd pitch, terr, pt shd; wc; shwrs inc; el pts (5A) inc; gas adj; lndtte; ice; shop; snacks; sm playgrnd; free pool adj; fishing; quiet; cc not acc. "Lge pitches in attractive park adj to lake; vg site; conv La Baule, St Nazaire; v clean site; 45 mins drive to excel beaches." ♦ 1 May-30 Sep. € 11.00   2004*

SAVERDUN *8F3* (6km SW Rural) **Domaine de Pauliac (Naturist), 09700 Saverdun [05 61 60 43 95; fax 05 61 60 48 50; info@pauliac.com; www.pauliac.com]** Fr N20 Toulouse-Pamiers rd in Saverdun take D14, sp Pauliac FFN; fork L in 2km to site. Lge, terr, pt shd; wc; chem disp; sauna; shwrs inc; el pts (6A) €3.20; gas; ice; shop; tradsmn; rest; bar; 2 pools; cycle hire; children's playrm; archery; some statics; dogs €1.50; adv bkg; quiet; INF cards req. "Superb views; excel rest; gd base for Cathar country & visit Andorra; sep car pk." ♦ 1 Jun-1 Sep. € 21.50 2005*

SAVERNE *6E3* (1.3km SW Urban) **FFCC Camping de Saverne, Rue Pere Libermann, 67700 Saverne [03 88 91 35 65 or 03 88 71 52 82 (Mairie); fax 03 88 91 35 65; camping-saverne@ffcc.fr]** Take Saverne exit fr A4. Site well sp nr town cent. Med, hdg/mkd pitch, hdstg, pt sl, pt shd; wc; chem disp; mv service pnt; shwrs inc; el pts (16A) €2.40 (poss rev pol); gas; lndry rm; ice; shop 1km; hypmkt 4km; snacks; playgrnd; pool 1km; 30% statics; dogs; poss cr; Eng spkn; adv bkg; quiet; cc acc; 10% red CCI. "Pleasant, busy site on edge of town; excel san facs; 30 mins walk into Saverne; hourly trains to Strasbourg; helpful warden; aire de service nr ent." ♦ 1 Apr-30 Sep. € 10.20   2005*

SAVERNE *6E3* (5km SW) **Camping au Paradis Perdu, Rue de Hirschberg, 67440 Thal-Marmoutier [03 88 70 60 59]** Fr Saverne, use minor rds rather than by-pass; foll sp Thal-Marmoutier then foll camp sps to St Gall & site; access thro archway - poss tight for lge vans. Sm, pt sl, pt shd; wc; chem disp; shwrs; el pts (3-6A) €1.85-€3.70; rest; snacks; shops 3km; adv bkg; 20% statics; dogs €1; quiet. "Pleasant setting at rear of rest; facs basic but gd." 1 Apr-15 Oct. € 9.00   2002*

SAVERNE *6E3* (13km SW) **Camping du Rocher, 57850 Dabo [03 87 07 47 51; fax 03 87 07 47 73; ot-dabo@claranet.fr; www.ot-dabo.fr]** Fr Saverne take D132 to Lutzelbourg, then D98 to Haselbourg & D45 to Dabo. Go thro vill; site sp on R in 2km. Sm, mkd pitch, pt shd; wc; shwrs €1.50; el pts (6-10A) €2-3.30; shop 2km; playgrnd; cycling; fishing; quiet. "Site yourself; warden calls; fair sh stay/NH." ♦ ltd. Easter-1 Nov. € 8.30   2004*

SAVIGNY EN VERON *4G1* (W Rural) **Camp Municipal La Fritillaire, Rue Basse, 37420 Savigny-en-Veron [02 47 58 03 79; fax 02 47 58 03 81; camping@cc-veron.fr; www.cc-veron.fr/camping]** Fr Montsoreau on D751 or D7 on S bank of Rv Loire, foll sp to Savigny-en-Veron & site. Med, mkd pitch, pt shd; htd wc; chem disp; mv service pnt; baby facs; some serviced pitches; shwrs inc; el pts (10A) €2.75; lndtte; rest, snacks, bar adj; BBQ; playgrnd; htd, covrd pool 4km; games area; tennis; cycle hire; some statics; dogs €0.70; Eng spkn; adv bkg; quiet; CCI. "Excel, peaceful site; gd touring base Loire chateaux; vg cycling." ♦ 15 Apr-30 Sep. € 13.00   2005*

See advertisement opposite

SAVINES LE LAC *9D3* **Camping Le Grand Morgon, 05160 Savines-le-Lac [04 92 44 27 75]** N94 to Savines fr Gap; cross bdge over lake; turn R onto D954 & site on R in 3km. No sp at ent, only 250m bef. Med, pt sl, pt shd; wc (cont); chem disp; shwrs; lake sw 400m; watersports; adv bkg; quiet; CCI. "Scenic views; gd sh stay." ♦ ltd. 20 Jun-15 Sep.   2003*

SAVINES LE LAC *9D3* (2km SW Rural) **Camp Municipal Les Eygoires, 05160 Savines-le-Lac [04 92 44 20 48 or 04 92 44 20 03 (Mairie); fax 04 92 44 39 71; camping.municipal.savinelelac@ wanadoo.fr]** Take N94 to Savines. Site on D954 on N side of rd. Lge, terr, pt shd; wc (some cont); baby facs; shwrs; el pts (5A) €3; lndtte; shop; snacks; bar; playgrnd; lake sw & shgl beach; sailing; some statics; dogs €1; adv bkg; quiet. "Security barrier operated by key fr office, clsd 1200-1600." 1 Jun-30 Sep. € 10.45   2003*

> Mustn't forget
> to post our site report
> forms to The Club, otherwise
> sites might be deleted.

SAVINES LE LAC *9D3* (5km SW Rural) **Camping La Palatriere, 05160 Le Sauze-du-Lac [tel/fax 04 92 44 20 98; lapalatriere@wanadoo.fr; www. lapalatriere.com]** Take N94 fr Gap thro Chorges, turn R after bdge at Savines-le-Lac onto D954 for 5km twds Le Sauze-du-Lac. Sm, mkd pitch, terr, pt shd; wc; shwrs inc; el pts (6A) inc; lndtte; shop; rest; snacks; bar; BBQ; playgrnd; lake sw; 25% statics; dogs €1; entmnt; TV; cc acc. "Family-run; beautiful views of mountains & lake; gd sh stay/NH." 1 May-30 Nov. € 20.00   2004*

SCEAUX DU GATINAIS *4F3* **Camp Municipal, 45490 Sceaux-du-Gatinais [02 38 87 40 27]** Take D40 N fr Montargis. At Prefontaines turn sharp L on D38. After about 250m fork R onto D31, sp Corbeilles. Sceaux-du-Gatinais in 8km, site behind church. Sm, pt shd; wc; shwrs; el pts; shop; snacks; playgrnd; tennis; rv fishing; quiet. "Vg sh stay; out-of-the-way." 2002*

SCHOENAU *6E3* (800m S) **Camping Schoenau Plage, 67390 Schoenau [03 88 85 22 85]** Fr Selestat take D424 twd German border then L to D20. On D20 turn L just bef Rhone Bdge; site on L. Lge, mkd pitch, pt shd; wc; chem disp; shwrs; el pts (10A); gas; ice; shops 1km; tradsmn; snacks; bar; playgrnd; lake sw; boating; fishing; 60% statics; poss cr; quiet; red CCI. "V pleasant, friendly site." 1 Apr-30 Sep.   2004*

SECONDIGNY *4H1* (S) **Camp Municipal du Moulin des Effres, 79130 Secondigny [05 49 95 61 97 or 05 49 63 70 15 (Mairie); fax 05 49 63 55 48; secondigny@marcireau.fr]** D949bis to Secondigny, S onto D748. Site sp 800m on L immed after lake. Med, pt sl, pt shd; wc (some cont); shwrs inc; el pts (6A) inc; rest 400m; snacks; shops 500m; lndry rm; pool; tennis; TV; entmnt; lake fishing; poss cr; quiet; CCI. "Warden calls pm; in pleasant surroundings nr attractive vill." 1 Jun-15 Sep. € 10.40   2002*

SEDAN *5C1* (11km SE) **Camp Municipal du Lac, Route de Mouzon, 08140 Douzy [03 24 26 31 19 or 03 24 26 31 48 (Mairie); fax 03 24 26 84 01]** On N43 fr Sedan-Metz to Douzy. Turn R (S) at traff lts in Douzy & site in 500m on L. Clearly sp. Med, pt shd; wc; 60% serviced pitch; shwrs inc; el pts (6A) inc; gas 1km; lndtte; shops 1km; tradsmn; snacks; bar; playgrnd; shgl beach & lake sw adj; waterslides; tennis; dogs €1.50; poss cr; Eng spkn; adv bkg; 10% red 8+ days; CCI. "V helpful staff; 3 modern san facs blocks; gd lndry facs; few pitches have shade; pitches uneven; gd site for Ardennes, Verdun; vg long/sh stay." ♦ 1 May-1 Oct. € 13.50   2003*

SEDAN *5C1* (1km W Urban) **Camp Municipal de la Prairie, Prairie de Torcy, Blvd Fabert, 08290 Sedan [tel/fax 03 24 27 13 05 or 03 24 27 73 73]** Fr A203/E44 exit junc 4 dir Sedan cent. Cont strt over viaduct, site visible on R, turn R at next traff lts, site 100m on R. Med, pt shd; wc (some cont); mv service pnt; shwrs inc; el pts (10A) inc; lndtte; shop 300m; rest 500m; snacks; bar; BBQ; sm playgrnd; pool 500m; fishing; phone; poss cr; adv bkg; quiet; red long stay; CCI. "Pleasant site by rv; san facs basic; useful for m'vans - can walk to everything; interesting town; wonderful castle with Eng tour; poss waterlogging in wet weather; bureau open 0800-2000; barrier." ♦ 1 Apr-30 Sep. € 8.20   2005*

SEDERON *9D3* (Rural) **Camping Les Routelles (Naturist), 26560 Sederon [04 75 28 54 54; fax 04 75 28 53 14; davine.bernard@wanadoo.fr; www.routelles.com]** Best app fr Sisteron on D946. immed bef Sederon turn R onto D225B (opp Renault g'ge), & foll sp 2km. At ent owner will tow up steep track to pitch. Med, sl, terr, pt shd; wc; chem disp; shwrs inc; el pts (6A) €1.83; rest; bar; BBQ (subject to pitch); playgrnd; pool; sw 3km; TV rm; dogs €1.67; quiet; phone; some Eng spkn; adv bkg; red low ssn. "Excel site; v clean san facs; excel rest; v friendly & helpful owner; eagles fly overhead; stunning views; owner pitches vans with 4WD; highly rec; unsuitable for disabled." 30 Apr-31 Dec. € 18.30   2003*

SEES *4E1* (S Urban) **Camp Municipal Le Clos Normand, Route d'Alencon, 61500 Sees [02 33 28 87 37 or 02 33 28 74 79 (LS); fax 02 33 28 18 13; office-tourisme.sees@wanadoo.fr]** Heading S cont to end of by-pass & exit twd town. C'vans & lge m'vans best app fr S - twd rndabt at S end of by-pass (ess to use this rndabt as other routes are dangerous). Well sp. Narr ent. Sm, hdg pitch, pt shd; wc; chem disp; mv service pnt; shwrs inc; el pts (6A) inc; gas; lndtte; ice; shop, snacks & bar 100m; rest 500m; playgrnd; pool 2km; fishing; 10% statics; dogs €1.10; Eng spkn; adv bkg; slight rd noise; CCI. "Helpful, friendly warden; cathedral nrby; pitches spacious & well-cared for; gd san facs; excel mv service pnt; gates clsd 2000 (1800 low ssn), ent thro exit & find pitch." ♦ 1 May-30 Sep. € 13.00   2005*

†SEGRE *2F4* (5km W Rural) **Pageant Camping a la Ferme, Le Petit Villeprouve, 49500 Nyoiseau [02 41 61 74 03]** W fr Segre on D775 dir Pouance. At start dual c'way go under rd bdge & at next rndabt take exit sp Bourg d'Ire, L'Arbre Vert (tractors, cyclists only). In 500m turn R after pond on R, in 500m turn L after 2nd house on L (old rails in rd), sp to site in 200m. Sm, hdstg, pt sl, pt shd; htd wc; shwrs inc; el pts (10A) inc; lake sw; Eng spkn; adv bkg; red long stay. "CL-type site; British owners." € 15.00   2004*

SEGRE *2F4* (7km NW Rural) **Camping du Parc de Loisir St Blaise, 49520 Noyant-la-Gravoyere [02 41 61 75 39; fax 02 41 61 53 25]** Fr Segre take dir Pouance to Noyant, site/park sp in vill on R. Sm, hdg pitch, terr, pt shd; wc; chem disp (wc); serviced pitches; shwrs inc; el pts (5A) inc; shop & 1km; tradsmn; rest; bar; playgrnd; lake sw adj; entmnt; dogs; phone; CCI. "Clean, well-maintained site in leisure park; gd views; slate mine worth visit (not an eyesore)." ♦ 1 May-30 Sep. € 10.00   2003*

SEIGNOSSE see Hossegor *8E1*

SEILHAC *7C4* (4km SW Rural) **Camp Municipal La Barthe, 19700 Lagrauliere [05 55 73 71 04; fax 05 55 73 25 28; mairie.lagruliere@wanadoo.fr; www.lagrauliere.correze.net]** S fr Uzerche N120 twd Tulle R on D167. Site sp to vill. Sm, mkd pitch, pt shd; wc; chem disp; shwrs inc; el pts (3-6A) €1.53; gas 2km, shop 700m; rest, snacks, bar 1km; BBQ; playgrnd; htd pool; dogs €0.31; phone adj; Eng spkn; quiet; CCI. "V quiet, clean site, nr pleasant vill; warden calls." ♦ ltd. 15 Jun-15 Sep. € 4.28   2002*

SEILHAC *7C4* (2.5km NW Rural) **Camp Municipal Le Lac de Bournazel, 19700 Seilhac. [05 55 27 05 65]** Fr Seilhac W on N120 for 1.5km turn R at rndabt for 1km, clearly sp. Lge, mkd pitch, terr, pt shd; wc; chem disp; baby facs; shwrs inc; el pts (10A) €2.70; lndtte; shop in ssn; rest 1km; snacks & bar 500m; BBQ; playgrnd; lakeside beach sw adj; 25% statics; dogs €1; Eng spkn; adv bkg; CCI. "Excel long/sh stay; v lge pitches; v clean; beach surveillance in ssn; pedaloes on lake." 1 Apr-30 Sep. € 12.50   2005*

SELESTAT *6E4* (Urban) **Camp Municipal Les Cigognes, Rue de la 1ere DFL, 67600 Selestat [03 88 92 03 98 or 03 88 58 87 20]** Site sp N83 & D424. Fr S town cent turn E off N83 & foll sps to site adj schools & playing fields. Med, pt shd; wc; mv service pnt; chem disp; shwrs inc; el pts (10A) inc; gas; lndtte; ice; shops 300m; playgrnd; pool 300m; enmnts; rv & lake nrby; dogs €0.76; poss cr; Eng spkn; adv bkg rec high ssn; quiet but some noise fr local football area; CCI. "Gd sh stay; helpful staff; gd train service Strasbourg - 10 mins walk to stn." ♦ 1 May-15 Oct. € 11.00   2002*

SELESTAT *6E4* (4km N) **Camping a la Ferme, 67600 Ebersheim [03 88 85 71 80; fax 03 88 85 71 05]** Exit Selestat on N83 to N & site on R in approx 4km, sp. Sm, pt shd; wc; chem disp; mv service pnt; shwrs €1; el pts inc; gas 1km; ice; lndtte; shops 1km; snacks; rest & bar Sat eve; playgrnd; horseriding, tennis 1km; no dogs; adv bkg; quiet; CCI. "Working farm with animals; CL-type site; friendly owner; excel bakery in vill." Easter-1 Nov. € 7.00   2003*

SELESTAT *6E4* (5km N Rural) **Camping Rural, 17 Rue du Buhl, 67600 Ebersheim [03 88 85 72 97]** Fr S or N on N83 in vill of Ebersheim foll green Camping Rural sps. Sm, pt shd; wc; shwrs inc; el pts inc; shop 500m; cooking facs; quiet; adv bkg; cc not acc; CCI. "Vg; gd touring base & friendly, helpful warden; Alsace wine sold on site." 15 Jun-15 Sep. € 9.40   2005*

SELESTAT *6E4* (6km N Rural) **Camp Municipal Le Wasen, Route d'Ebersheim, 67650 Dambach-la-Ville [03 88 92 48 60; fax 03 88 92 60 09 (Mairie); info.tourisme@dambach-la-ville.fr]** Exit A37 at junc 16 for N422 dir Obernai. After approx 20km take D210 for Dambach-la-Ville & foll sp. Med, mkd pitch, pt shd; wc; chem disp; shwrs inc; el pts (3A) inc; shop, rest, snacks, bar 1km; BBQ; lndtte; playgrnd; sports area; tennis adj. "Attractive medieval town; recep clsd fr 1200-1430; no access when barrier down as rd too narr for waiting; vg long/sh stay." ♦ 1 Jun-30 Sep. € 10.60   2004*

SELESTAT *6E4* (12km W Rural) **Camping du Haut-Koenigsbourg, 68660 Liepvre [03 89 58 43 20; fax 03 89 58 98 29; camping.haut-koenigsbourg@wanadoo.fr]** Fr Selestat W on N59 twd Liepvre vill then R at factory car park & foll site sps. Fr Ste Marie-aux-Mines on N59 turn L at rndabt after tunnel. Med, mkd pitch, pt sl, pt shd; htd wc; mv service pnt; shwrs inc; el pts (4-8A) €2.50-3.50; lndtte; ice; shop 1km; tradsmn; bar; BBQ; playgrnd; TV rm; 10% statics; dogs €1.50; poss cr; quiet; CCI. ♦ 15 Mar-15 Nov. € 9.50   2004*

SELESTAT *6E4* (5km NW Rural) **Aire Naturelle (Palmer), 11 Rue Faviers 67759 Scherwiller [03 88 92 94 57; fax 03 88 82 05 39]** Fr N foll N83 to Ebersheim then D81 to Scherwiller. Site sp off D35 at N end vill. Sm, pt shd; wc; shwrs €2.05; el pts €1.60; shop 1km; tradsmn; pool 5km; cc acc; CCI. "Vg; many tourist attractions nr." 15 May-15 Sep. € 8.70   2005*

SELONGEY *6G1* (S Rural) **Camp Municipal Les Courvelles, Rue Henri-Jevain, 21260 Selongey [03 80 75 52 38 or 03 80 75 70 74 (Mairie); fax 03 80 75 56 65; info@selongey.com]** Fr exit 5 on A31 N of Dijon take N74 N for 3km to Orville: turn W in Orville sp Selongey & site; site in approx 2km. Sm, some hdstg, unshd; wc; shwrs inc; el pts (6A) inc; shop 1km; tennis; quiet; CCI. "Warden calls 1900-2000 only; site yourself; rec arr early bef 1700 as busy & office open 1900-2000; no twin-axle vans; lovely clean, friendly site; patisserie nrby; conv NH; vg site; exceptional value." ♦ 1 May-30 Sep. € 9.00   2005*

FRANCE

SELTZ *5D3* (1km S Rural) **Camping Die Grune Les Peupliers, 67470 Seltz** [03 88 86 52 37] Fr Seltz on D468, turn L in 1km at sp. Lge, pt shd; wc; chem disp; mv service pnt; shwrs; el pts (6A) €2.50; rest; bar; playgrnd; lake fishing & boating adj; 85% statics; cc acc; CCI. "Sm pitches; 1 old & 1 modern shwr block; direct access to lake." ♦
€ 12.60   2005*

SEMUR EN AUXOIS *6G1* (3.5km S Rural) **Camp Municipal du Lac de Pont, 21140 Pont-et- Massene** [03 80 97 01 26 pr 03 80 97 25 72 (Mairie); camping-lac@worldonline.fr; www.lacdepont.com] Exit A6 junc 23 twd Semur-en-Auxois on D980; after sh dist turn R sp 'Lac de Pont'. Med, some hdg pitch, pt shd; wc; chem disp; shwrs inc; el pts (6A) inc; gas; lndry rm; ice; shop; tradsmn; rest; snacks; bar; lake sw; tennis; games rm; cycle hire; watersports; 30% statics; dogs €1.55; phone; poss cr; quiet; CCI. "Watersports on lake; conv ancient town; gd touring base; easy access; vg sh stay."
1 May-15 Sep. € 13.20   2002*

SEMUR EN AUXOIS *6G1* (11km W Urban) **Camp Municipal Les Libellules, Place de la Piscine, 21460 Epoisses** [03 80 96 31 91] Fr Semur, take D954 W dir Epoisses. In Epoisses turn R at sp 'Piscine/Camping'. Site on R in 600m, adj to pool. Med, hdg/mkd pitch, pt shd; wc; chem disp; shwrs inc; el pts (10A) €1.85; lndtte; shops 500m; rest, snacks, bar 600m; BBQ; playgrnd; pool adj; dogs; phone; quiet. "Pleasant vill with lovely chateau; famous for cheeses; conv Semur, Avallon & Vezelay; key deposit on site €15; if barrier clsd on ent to site, use phone R of wc (phone numbers listed at barrier); gd sh stay."
1 May-30 Sep. € 5.70   2004*

SENNECEY LE GRAND *6H1* (6km E Rural) **LES CASTELS Domaine du Chateau de L'Eperviere, 71274 Gigny-sur-Saone** [03 85 94 16 90; fax 03 85 94 16 97; domaine-de-leperviere@wanadoo.fr; www.domaine-eperviere.com or www.les-castels.com] Fr N6 at Sennecey-le-Grand turn E onto D18, site sp 1km S of Gigny-sur-Saone. Lge, mkd pitch, pt shd; htd wc; chem disp; baby facs; jacuzzi/sauna; shwrs inc; el pts (10A) inc; gas; lndtte; ice; sm shop; tradsmn; rest; snacks; pizzeria; bar high ssn; BBQ; playgrnd; 2 pools (1 htd, covrd); paddling pool; lake & rv nr; fishing; tennis 400m; cycle hire; entmnt; internet; TV rm; tour op statics & chalets; dogs €2.50; poss v cr; recep 0800-1900; Eng spkn; adv bkg; quiet; cc acc; CCI. "Excel, top-quality site; excel for chateau visits, wine-tastings, cycling; vg rest & gd value meals; san facs clean & modern; pleasant staff; popular site with tour ops; boggy when wet." ♦ 1 Apr-30 Sep.
€ 28.70 (CChq acc) ABS - L12   2005*

SENNECEY LE GRAND *6H1* (6km NW Rural) **Camping La Heronniere, Les Lacs de Laives, 71240 Laives** [tel/fax 03 85 44 98 85 or 03 85 44 89 67; camping.laives@wanadoo.fr; http://perso.wanadoo.fr/camping.laives] Turn W off N6 Chalon-Macon rd at Sennecey-le-Grand to Laives. Site sp on D18. Med, hdg/mkd pitch, pt shd; wc; chem disp; shwrs inc; el pts (6A) €3.70; lndry rm; rest 300m; snacks; shop; playgrnd; htd pool; lake sw & beach nrby; fishing; windsurfing; pedalo; sail boarding; cycle hire; dogs €1.50; Eng spkn; quiet; adv bkg; CCI. "Vg; busy site when fine; pop with bikers; gd shwrs; rest at lakeside; level site, gd for wheelchair users." ♦ 1 May-15 Sep. € 15.30 (CChq acc)   2005*

SENONCHES *4E2* (Urban) **Camp Municipal du Lac, 28250 Senonches** [02 37 37 94 63 or 02 37 37 76 76 (Mairie); fax 02 37 37 92 92] NE on D928, take D25, sp, to Senonches fr cent of La Loupe. Site clearly sp by sports facs & piscine adj to site (by sm lake). Sm, hdg/mkd pitch, pt shd; wc (cont); chem disp (wc); shwrs inc; el pts (6A) €2.10; shops 100m; pool & lake adj; phone; quiet. "Gd site." 1 May-30 Sep. € 4.20   2005*

SENONES see Raon l'Etape *6E3*

SENS *4F4* (1km S Urban) **Camp Municipal Entre Deux Vannes, Ave de Semigallia, 89100 Sens** [03 86 65 64 71; fax 03 86 95 39 41] NW on N6 take rd into Sens; site bet town cent & N6 on E side of N360, 1km to S of town cent; foll sp. Med, mkd pitch, pt shd; wc (some cont); chem disp (wc only); mv service pnt; baby facs; shwrs inc; el pts (16A) €1.30; lndtte; shops 1km; tradsmn high ssn; rest nrby; playgrnd; adv bkg rec; some noise fr rd & commercial premises nrby during day; cc acc; CCI. "Friendly, helpful warden; san facs old but clean; conv town cent; gate locked 2200."
1 May-1 Oct. € 10.20   2005*

SENS DE BRETAGNE *2E4* (Rural) **Camp Municipal La Petite Minardais, Rue du Clos Bertrand, 35490 Sens-de-Bretagne** [02 99 39 51 33 (Mairie)] Take N175 fr Antrain twd Rennes. Turn R at camping sp in Sens-de-Bretagne & foll sp to site. Sm, pt shd; wc; shwrs inc; el pts (4A); shop 500m; quiet. "Pleasant sm park & lake adj; CL-type site." 1 May-30 Sep.   2004*

SEPPOIS LE BAS see Altkirch *6F3*

SERAUCOURT LE GRAND see St Quentin *3C4*

SERENT see Ploermel *2F3*

SERIGNAC see Puy l'Eveque *7D3*

SERIGNAC PEBOUDOU see Cancon *7D3*

SERIGNAN DU COMTAT see Orange *10E2*

SERIGNAN PLAGE *10F1* (Coastal) **Camping Le Beausejour, 34410 Serignan-Plage [04 67 39 50 93; fax 04 67 32 01 96; info@camping-beausejour.com; www.camping-beausejour.com]** Fr A9/E15, exit Beziers-Est onto D64 S. In 4km turn L onto D37 E to Serignan-Plage. Site on R just bef shops. Lge, hdg/mkd pitch, pt shd; wc; chem disp; mv service pnt; shwrs inc; el pts (6A) inc; gas; lndtte; ice; shop, supmkt 8km; tradsmn; rest; snacks; bar; BBQ; playgrnd; sand beach adj; entmnt; 50% statics; dogs; poss v cr; Eng spkn; adv bkg (dep req + bkg fee); quiet; cc acc; CCI. "Direct access to excel beach; weekly mkts in vill; excel hypmkt nrby; vg long/sh stay." ♦ 1 Apr-30 Sep. € 28.50   2003*

SERIGNAN PLAGE *10F1* **Camping Le Clos de Ferrand (Naturist), 34410 Serignan Plage [04 67 32 14 30; fax 04 67 32 15 59]** Fr Beziers take D19 twd Valras-Plage. At Serignan town turn L on D37E to Serignan-Plage 5km. Med, hdg/mkd pitch, pt shd; wc; chem disp; shwrs inc; el pts (2-6A) inc; ice; lndtte; shop; snacks; rest; bar; playgrnd; TV rm; beach adj; rv 1km; fishing; boat hire; quiet; Eng spkn; adv bkg; cc not acc; INF card req; CCI. "V pleasant with direct access to beach; well-run, gd sized pitches divided by trees; san facs excel." ♦ ltd 15 May-15 Sep. € 30.00   2005*

SERIGNAN PLAGE *10F1* (Coastal) **Camping Le Clos Virgile, 34410 Serignan-Plage [04 67 32 20 64; fax 04 67 32 05 42; le.clos.virgile@wanadoo. fr; www.leclosvirgile.com]** Take Beziers Est exit fr A9 twd Les Plages, turn R onto N112 at Villeneuve-les-Beziers. Foll D37 for 5km to Serignan-Plage. Lge, mkd pitch; shd; wc; shwrs inc; el pts (5A) inc; gas; lndtte; ice; shop & 500m; rest; snacks; bar; playgrnd; htd/covrd/paddling pools; waterslide; entmnt; sand beach & watersports 500m; entmnt; 33% statics; dogs €3; phone; adv bkg; cc acc; quiet. "V friendly; constant hot water; money change on site; cycle hire & horseriding adj." ♦ 15 May-15 Sep. € 30.00   2004*

SERIGNAN PLAGE *10F1* (Coastal) **Camping Le Serignan-Plage Nature (Naturist), Ste Amat, 34410 Serignan-Plage [04 67 32 09 61; fax 04 67 32 26 36; info@leserignannature.com; www.leserignannature.com]** Fr Beziers take D19 twd Valras-Plage. At Serignan town turn L on D37E to Serignan-Plage. After 4km turn R on single-lane dual c'way. At T-junc turn L & immed L again in 50m to site. Lge, mkd pitch, pt shd; wc (some cont); chem disp; mv service pnt; shwrs inc; el pts (5A) inc; gas; lndry rm; ice; shop; rest; snacks; bar; playgrnd; pool complex; sand beach; mini-golf; golf 15km; internet; beauty cent; child entmnt; TV rm; 75% statics; dogs €3; poss cr; Eng spkn; adv bkg; quiet but some noise fr disco; red long stay/low ssn; CCI. "Excel, immac san facs; helpful staff; Camping Le Serignan Plage (non-naturist) adj with use of same private beach & facs; pool also shared - for naturists' use 1000-1200 only." 22 Apr-20 Sep. € 36.00 (CChq acc)   2005*

SERIGNAN PLAGE *10F1* (Coastal) **Camping-Village Le Grand Large, 34410 Serignan-Plage [04 67 39 71 30; fax 04 67 32 58 15; legrandlarge wanadoo.fr; www.camping- grandlarge.com]** Fr A9 exit Beziers-Est; take D64, D37E to Serignan-Plage then turn R at Centre Commercial. Lge, pt shd; wc; chem disp; mv service pnt; shwrs; el pts (10A) inc; gas; lndtte; shop; ice; rest; snacks; bar; 3 htd pools; 2 waterslides; playgrnd; games area; tennis; sand beach adj; watersports; entmnt; children's club high ssn; red low ssn CCI. "Nice family site nr beach." ♦ 26 Apr-14 Sep. € 29.00   2002*

SERIGNAN PLAGE *10F1* (Coastal) **Yelloh! Village Le Serignan-Plage, Ste Amat, 34410 Serignan-Plage [04 67 32 35 33; fax 04 67 32 26 36; info@ leserignanplage.com; www.yellohvillage.com or www.serignanplage.com]** Exit A9 junc 35. After toll turn L at traff lts onto N112 & at 1st rndabt strt on to D64. In 5km turn L onto D37E Serignan-Plage, turn R on narr 1-way rd to site. Adj to Camping Serignan-Plage Nature (Naturist site). V lge, hdg pitch, pt shd; wc (some cont); chem disp (wc); mv service pnt; baby facs; shwrs inc; el pts (5A) inc; gas; ice; lndtte; shop; hypmkt 6km; rest; snacks; bar; playgrnd; htd, covrd pool; Club Nautique - sw, sailing & water-ski tuition on private beach; tennis; horseriding; disco; entmnt; TV; 60% statics; dogs €3; use of naturist private beach & facs adj; poss v cr; Eng spkn; adv bkg; poss noisy; red low ssn; no cc acc; CCI. "V busy & tightly packed; excel pool but poss v cr." 22 Apr-24 Sep. € 43.00 (CChq acc)   2005*

SERIGNAN PLAGE *10F1* (3.5km W Rural) **Camping Domaine Les Vignes d'Or, Route de Valras, 34350 Serignan [04 67 32 37 18; fax 04 67 32 00 80]** Exit A9 junc 35 onto D64 to Serignan then foll sp. Med, hdg/mkd pitch, pt shd; wc; shwrs inc; el pts (6A) inc; beach 2.5km; 95% statics; dogs; quiet; CCI. "Ltd touring pitches; gd NH only." ♦ ltd. 1 Apr-15 Sep. € 22.00   2004*

SERIGNAN PLAGE *10F1* (5km W) **Camping Le Paradis, Route de Valras-Plage, 34410 Serignan [tel/fax 04 67 32 24 03]** 13km fr Beziers on D64, sp Valras-Plage. Site on L 1km after exit Serignan. Exit m'way at Beziers Est & site on L on rndabt S end of Serignan by-pass. Med, mkd pitch, pt shd; wc; chem disp; shwrs; el pts (6A) inc; gas; lndtte; ice; shop; supmkt opp; rest; snacks; playgrnd; pool; sand beach 2km; no dogs; poss cr; Eng spkn; adv bkg rec; quiet except for twice weekly disco to 0030; red low ssn; CCI. "Excel family-run site; immac san facs." ♦ 15 Apr-15 Sep. € 19.50 (3 persons)   2003*

SERQUES see St Omer *3A3*

SERRES *9D3* (800m SE) **Domaine des Deux Soleils, 05700 Serres [04 92 67 01 33; fax 04 92 67 08 02; dom.2.soleils@wanadoo.fr]** Take N75 S fr Serres to Super-Serres thro wood & up winding mountainside rd, site sp. Med, mkd pitch, sl, terr, pt shd; wc; shwrs inc; el pts (6A) inc; lndtte; shop; rest; snacks; playgrnd; 2 pools; TV; phone; entmnt; guided walks; fishing, horseriding adj; adv bkg; quiet. 1 May-30 Sep. € 23.95   2003*

FRANCE

SERRIERES *9C2* (3km W) **Camping Le Bas Larin**, 07340 Felines [tel/fax 04 75 34 87 93; camping. baslarin@wanadoo.fr] On N7, exit at Serrieres onto N82; cross canal & rv; cont over rndabt up winding hill, camp on L nr hill top. Well sp fr N7 & N82. Med, terr, shd; wc; chem disp; shwrs inc; el pts (4A) €2.30; lndtte; shops 2km; rest adj; playgrnd; pool; paddling pool; dogs €1.10; Eng spkn; some rd noise. "Beautiful views; friendly, family-run site; v popular with Dutch; gd sh stay." ♦ 1 Apr-30 Sep. € 13.00   2003*

As we're travelling out of season, we'd better phone ahead to check that the site is actually open.

SERVON see Pontaubault *2E4*

SETE *10F1* (6km N Urban) **Camp Municipal Chemin des Bains, Ave de Montpelier**, 34540 Balaruc-les-Bains [04 67 48 51 48 or 04 67 46 81 46 (LS)] Fr N113, take D2/D129 to Balaruc, passing Balaruc-le-Vieux. Ent cent of vill & then foll sps. Lge, hdg/mkd pitch, hdstg, shd; wc; shwrs inc; el pts (6A) inc; lndtte; shops adj; BBQ; playgrnd; thermal baths; dogs €1.30; poss cr; adv bkg (ess Jun-Sep); quiet. "Delightful holiday resort; facs old but clean; sm pitches; v busy, popular site; no warden Sun - list of reserved pitches on noticeboard; vg long/sh stay." Easter-12 Oct. € 12.00   2003*

SETE *10F1* (6km N) **Camp Municipal Pech d'Ay, Ave de la Gare**, 34540 Balaruc-les-Bains [04 67 48 50 34] Fr N113, take D2 twd Sete. Ignore 1st Balaruc sp, fork R onto D2F; turn R sp Balaruc, site on Prom. Lge, mkd pitch, pt sl, pt shd; wc; chem disp; shwrs; el pts (5A) €2.44; shops adj; playgrnd; shgle beaches nrby; poss cr; adv bkg rec (even low ssn); poss noisy; CCI. "Gd site; delightful holiday resort; thermal baths in vill offering courses of therapy treatment; busy all ssn; san facs clean but old & in need of upgrading." 28 Feb-12 Dec. € 11.40   2003*

SETE *10F1* (7km N Coastal) **Camping Les Vignes**, 34540 Balaruc-les-Bains [04 67 48 04 93; fax 04 67 18 74 32; camping.lesvignes@free.fr] Fr N113 take D2 sp Sete, turn W sp Balarac-les-Bains, after 2nd rndabt turn R, well sp in 100m on R. Med, hdg/mkd pitch, pt shd; wc (some cont); chem disp; mv service pnt; shwrs inc; el pts (4-10A) inc; lndtte; shops 1km; snacks; bar; playgrnd; pool; shgl beach 1km; sand beach 7km; fishing, horseriding & tennis nr; dogs; 30% statics; poss cr; adv bkg; quiet; cc acc; CCI. "V tight for long o'fits; narr rds on site; Sete worth a visit." ♦ ltd. 1 Apr-31 Oct. € 19.50   2005*

SETE *10F1* (7km NE Coastal) **Camping Le Mas du Padre, 4 Chemin du Mas du Padre**, 34540 Balaruc-les-Bains [04 67 48 53 41; fax 04 67 48 08 94; info@mas-du-padre.com; www. mas-du-padre.com] Fr Sete N on D2. In Balaruc turn R after traff lts 1km fr vill, then 2nd on R onto local rd for 500m. Well sp. Fr A9 exit junc 33 on N300 sp Sete; foll sp Balaruc-les-Bains on D2 for 2 rndabts, then turn R on D2E6 sp campings. Med, hdg/mkd pitch, pt sl, terr, shd; wc; chem disp; baby facs; shwrs inc; el pts (6A) inc; gas; lndtte; ice; shops 3km; tradsmn; playgrnd; pool; sand beach 8km; lake sw, fishing & boating 2km; tennis; entmnt; TV; 10% statics; dogs €1.95; poss cr; Eng spkn; adv bkg rec high ssn; quiet; cc acc; CCI. "Pretty site nr beaches; thoughtfully equipped & well kept; immac facs; extra for lger pitches; owner v helpful; excel." ♦ 31 Mar-12 Oct. € 21.20   2005*

SETE *10F1* (11km SW Coastal) **Camping Le Castellas, Cours Gambetta**, 34200 Sete [04 67 51 63 00; fax 04 67 53 63 01; camping. lecastellas@wanadoo.fr; www.le-castellas.com] SW fr Sete foll sp for La Corniche; pick up N112 & foll sp for 'Plages-Agde'. Lge, hdg pitch, pt shd; wc; chem disp; shwrs inc; el pts (6A) inc; gas; lndtte; ice; shop; rest; snacks; bar; playgrnd; 2 htd pools; sand beach 150m (across busy rd); tennis; mini-golf; games area; cycle hire; entmnt; poss cr; Eng spkn; adv bkg; rd & rlwy noise; red 7+ days; CCI. "Bull-fighting in ssn; Sete worth visit; superb beach; twin-axles welcome." 30 Apr-25 Sep. € 35.00   2004*

SEURRE *6H1* (500m S Urban) **Camping de La Raie Mignot, Rue de la Peche a l'Oiseau**, 21250 Seurre [03 80 20 32 63 or 03 80 21 09 11 (Mairie)] Fr A36 exit 1, foll D976 to Seurre, past supmkt on R, next R, foll sp, site 1km approx. Sm, pt shd; wc (cont); 50% serviced pitches; shwrs inc; el pts (5A) €1.30; ice; shops 1km; BBQ; statics; playgrnd; rv fishing; dogs; poss cr. "Fair NH; beside Rv Saone." 1 May-30 Sep. € 6.50   2002*

SEURRE *6H1* (600m W) **Camp Municipal de la Piscine**, 21250 Seurre [03 80 20 49 22 or 03 80 21 15 92 (Mairie); fax 03 80 20 34 01] Exit Seurre on D973 Dijon/Beaune rd; site on R over bdge adjoining municipal pool. Lge, hdstg, pt shd; wc; chem disp; shwrs inc; el pts (10A) inc (rev pol); gas; lndry rm; shops 600m; rest; snacks; bar; playgrnd; pool adj; 25% statics; adv bkg ess high ssn; quiet; CCI. "Vg san facs but inadequate when full; gd rest; twin-axles acc." ♦ ltd. 15 May-15 Sep. € 9.50   2004*

SEURRE *6H1* (3km NW) **Camping Les Sables, Chemin de la Plage, 21250 Pouilly-sur-Saone [03 80 20 43 50; les.sables@tiscali.fr]** Exit A36 at junc 1 onto D976 for Seurre then onto D973 to D996 to Pouilly-sur-Saone. Fr A31 exit junc Nuits-St Georges & take D35 dir Gerland & Bagnot. At D996 turn R for Pouilly in 7km. Site well sp. Sm, mkd pitch, pt shd; wc; chem disp (wc); shwrs inc; el pts (6A) €2.30; ice; shop 5km; tradsmn; BBQ; playgrnd; pool 2km; fishing adj; dogs €0.80; Eng spkn; adv bkg; quiet; CCI. "Excel CL-type site sh walk fr Rv Saone; v helpful British owners; facs basic but spotless; conv Beaune, Dijon & local mkts." ♦ ltd.
1 May-30 Sep. € 8.50   2004*

SEVERAC LE CHATEAU *9D1* (1km Urban) **Camping Les Calquieres (formerly Municipal), 12150 Severac-le-Chateau [05 65 47 64 82; contact@camping-calquieres.com; www.camping-calquieres.com]** Exit N9 at sp. App fr N thro main st, fork L, descent to site below chateau. Well sp. Med, terr, pt shd; wc (some cont); 50% serviced pitches; shwrs inc; el pts (6A) €2.50; lndry rm; shop 250m; playgrnd; pool adj; games area; fishing; tennis; some statics; dogs €1.50; adv bkg; quiet; red long stay; CCI. "Updated clean facs; friendly owners; lovely old town & chateau; gd hotel rest short walk into town." ♦
4 Apr-30 Sep. € 13.10   2005*

SEVERAC LE CHATEAU *9D1* (12km SE Rural) **Camp Municipal, 48500 St Rome-de-Dolan [04 66 48 80 66 or 04 66 48 83 59; fax 04 66 48 87 46]** Exit A75 junc 42 to Severac, then take D995 fr Severac-le-Chateau then E thro Le Massegros to St Rome-de-Dolan. Site on R at ent to vill. V diff app fr Les Vignes, Gorges du Tarn. Sm, pt sl, pt terr, pt shd; wc; chem disp; shwrs inc; el pts (6A) €2; lndtte; ice; shop 5km; tradsmn; rest, snacks, bar 5km; BBQ; playgrnd; rv sw 5km; dogs €1; phone 50m; Eng spkn; adv bkg; quiet; CCI. "CL-type, basic site on edge of Gorges du Tarn: stunning views; birdwatching; walking; vg sh stay/NH." ♦
1 Jun-30 Sep. € 8.80   2005*

SEYNE *9D3* (800m W) **Camping Les Prairies, Haute Gruyeres, 04140 Seyne [04 92 35 10 21; fax 04 92 35 26 96; info@campinglesprairies.com; www.campinglesprairies.com]** Fr Digne-les-Bains, take D900 N to Seyne. Turn L on ent Seyne, site sp. Med, mkd pitch, pt shd; wc; chem disp; mv service pnt; shwrs inc; el pts (6A) €3.50; gas; lndtte; shop 800m; tradsmn; rest 800m; snacks; BBQ; playgrnd; htd pool; table tennis; dogs €2.50; phone; Eng spkn; adv bkg; quiet; cc acc; CCI. "Immac site, v clean & tidy; excel long/sh stay." 26 Apr-15 Sep.
€ 18.00   2003*

†**SEYNE SUR MER, LA** *10F3* (2km W) **Camping St Jean, Ave de la Collegiale, 83140 Six-Fours-les-Plages [04 94 87 51 51; fax 04 94 06 28 23; info@campingstjean.com; www.campingstjean.com]** Fr Toulon exit m-way sp La Seyne. Turn R at 2nd x-rds onto N559, sp Six-Fours. Site sp 1km on R, diff turn. Lge, hdg pitch, shd; wc; shwrs inc; el pts €3.50; gas; lndtte; ice; shop; snacks; playgrnd; pool; paddling pool; sand beach 3km; games rm; entmnt; TV; some statics; dogs €3; phone; adv bkg rec Jul/Aug; quiet. "Generous pitches; facs clean but a little dated." € 24.00 (3 persons)   2005*

SEYSSEL *9B3* (Urban) **Camp Municipal du Nant Matraz, 74270 Seyssel [tel/fax 04 50 59 03 68]** Nr town cent on L of D992 N of Seyssell sp Frangy. Lge supmkt on opp side of rd. Med, pt shd; wc; mv service pnt; shwrs inc; el pts (10A) inc; ice; lndtte; shops adj; BBQ; playgrnd; games rm; pool in town; boat hire; rv fishing; dogs €1; adv bkg; quiet; Eng spkn; cc acc. "On banks of Rhone." 28 Apr-14 Sep.
€ 12.60   2002*

SEZANNE *4E4* (11km E Rural) **Camp Municipal Parc du Chateau, 51230 Connantre [03 26 81 08 76 or 03 26 81 07 16 (Mairie)]** On N4; site sp both dir. Med, hdg pitch, few hdstg, pt shd; wc; chem disp; shwrs inc; el pts (5-10A) €1.50-2.30 (rev pol) gas; ice; shops 1km; playgrnd; pool 5km; beach; lake sw 500m; 15% statics; dogs €1.10; adv bkg; some noise fr N4; 20% red 2+ days; CCI. "Clean, neat camp; friendly recep; excel facs; no twin-axles."
1 Apr-31 Oct. € 8.40   2005*

†**SEZANNE** *4E4* (6km SW Rural) **Camping La Traconne, 4 Impasse de Rouge Coq, 51120 Le Meix-St Epoing [03 26 80 70 76; fax 03 26 42 74 98; laurent.dudot@tiscali.fr; www.camping-traconne.com]** Turn S off N4 at Moeurs-Verdey about 2.5km W of Sezanne. Foll sp to vill/site on D239, site sp. Med, hdg/mkd pitch, pt shd; htd wc; chem disp; mv service pnt; baby facs; shwrs inc; el pts (6A) €3 (poss rev pol); lndtte; ice; shops 5km; tradsmn; BBQ; playgrnd; pool & waterslide 5km; fishing adj; games rm; 30% statics; dogs; adv bkg; quiet; CCI. "Peaceful, restful site in forest; vg san facs; local wine sold on site; excel cycling & walking." ♦
€ 12.00   2005*

See advertisement on next page

SEZANNE *4E4* (500m NW) **Terrain de Camping Municipal, Route de Launat, 51120 Sezanne [03 26 80 57 00]** W'bound on N4 Sezanne by-pass onto D373 & foll site sp. No access fr N4 E'bound. If app fr S foll camping sps (sm & yellow), but avoid town cent, turn L immed after 2nd set of traff lts. Med, mainly sl, pt shd; serviced pitches; wc (some cont); shwrs inc; shop, el pts (10A) €2; shop 500m; rest in town 1km; sm playgrnd; pool adj; waterslide; some rd noise; no cc acc; CCI. "Helpful manager; vg site; levelling blocks needed; request for gate opening/closing at back bungalow of two opp site (playing field)." ♦
1 Apr-15 Oct. € 9.00   2003*

SIBIRIL see St Pol de Leon *1D2*

SIERCK LES BAINS *5C2* (Rural) **Camp Municipal, Allee des Tilleuls, 57480 Sierck-les-Bains** [03 82 83 72 39] Fr W or S foll sp for Treves (Trier) on E bank of Moselle. Town & site sp. Fr N town is 3km S of frontier at SE corner of Duchy of Luxembourg. Sm, pt shd; wc (cont); own san rec; chem disp; shwrs; el pts (5A) €2.59; ice; shops 500m; snacks 500m; pool 1km; playgrnd; rv fishing; some statics; CCI. "San facs worn & poss ltd/unclean in ssn; train noise nuisance; fair NH only." 30 Mar-30 Sep.
€ 10.00   2002*

†SIGEAN *10G1* (5km N Rural) **Camping La Grange Neuve, Route de la Reserve Africaine, 11130 Sigean** [tel/fax 04 68 48 58 70] Take Sigean exit fr a'route A9; pass under A9; foll sp La Reserve Africaine. Med, hdg/mkd pitch, hdstg, pt sl, terr, pt shd; wc; chem disp; shwrs inc; el pts (6A) €3.60; lndtte; shop; rest; snacks, bar; playgrnd; pool; waterslide; sand beach 5km; TV rm; 5% statics; dogs €2.30; poss cr; adv bkg; quiet but some rd noise; red low ssn; CCI. "Easy access; ltd facs low ssn; NH only; ring ahead to check open low ssn." ♦ € 14.00   2004*

SIGEAN *10G1* (8km E Urban) **Camp Municipal du Golfe, 406 Blvd Francis Vals, 11210 Port-la-Nouvelle** [04 68 48 08 42; fax 04 68 40 37 90] Exit A9/E15 junc 39 onto N139 to Port-la-Nouvelle; at cement works rndbt R into D709; in 1km L over rlwy; L at rndbt; immed L into site. Lge, some hdg/mkd pitch, pt shd; wc; shwrs inc; el pts (6A) inc; lndry rm; shop 500m; playgrnd; sand beach 1km; dogs €1.10; some rlwy & rd noise; red low ssn; CCI. "Useful NH off A9 or N9." ♦ ltd. 1 Apr-30 Sep. € 15.00   2005*

SIGEAN *10G1* (8km SE) **Camping Le Clapotis (Naturist), 11480 Lapalme** [04 68 48 15 40] On N9 Narbonne-Perpignan rd turn L 8km S of Sigean. After 350m turn R at camping sp. Site in 150m. Final app rd narr but negotiable for lge vans. Lge, mkd pitch, pt shd; wc (cont); shwrs inc; el pts; gas; ice; rest in ssn; pool; poss cr; adv bkg; quiet; 10% red low ssn; Naturists INF card req. "Subject to strong winds; helpful management; gd windsurfing." Easter-Sep. € 20.50
                                            2003*

SIGNES *10F3* (Urban) **Camping Les Promenades, 13 Ave du Cheval Blanc, 83870 Signes** [04 94 90 88 12; fax 04 94 90 82 68; les. promenades@wanadoo.fr] Fr Aubagne take N8 twd Toulon, turn L at Camp du Castellet, on D2 for 10km to Signes, site on L behind petrol stn. Or fr m'way A8, exit at Brignoles. Fr Brignoles take N7 W, then D5 S to Meounes-les-Montrieux, D2 to Signes & site. Med, pt shd; wc; shwrs inc; el pts (6A) €3.50; lndtte; ice; shops adj; rest; snacks; bar; playgrnd; pool; tennis adj; games area; entmnt; TV rm; many statics; dogs €3; adv bkg. "Quiet mountain area; edge of lovely vill." ♦ 1 Mar-31 Oct. € 17.80   2004*

SIGNY L'ABBAYE *5C1* (Urban) **Camp Municipal de l'Abbaye, 08460 Signy-l'Abbaye** [03 24 52 87 73] Take D985 N twd Belgium fr Rethel to Signy-l'Abbaye. Foll sp fr town cent to Stade & Camping. Site by sports stadium. Med, hdg/hdstg pitch, pt sl, pt shd; htd wc; chem disp; shwrs inc; el pts (16A) €2.60 (poss rev pol); lndry rm; shops, rest 500m; playgrnd; rv fishing adj; dogs €0.53; little Eng spkn; adv bkg; v quiet; CCI. "Lovely, gd value site adj to sports cent; v friendly warden; san facs excel (shared with public fr sports cent); gravel surfaced hdg pitches - v strong awning pegs req, or can park on open grassed area; pleasant vill with vg rest; conv Zeebrugge & Ostend." ♦ ltd. 1 May-30 Sep.
€ 5.60   2005*

SIGOULES *7D2* (1.5km N Rural) **Camp Municipal La Gardonnette, Les Coteaux de Sigoules, 24240 Sigoules** [tel/fax 05 53 58 81 94; camping delagardonnette@wanadoo.fr; www.camping delagardonnette.com] S fr Bergerac take D933 S. After 6km at top of hill turn R by La Grappe d'Or Rest onto D17 sp Pomport/Sigoules. Thro Pomport, site at bottom of hill on R by lake. Med, mkd pitch, pt sl; wc; chem disp; shwrs inc; el pts (6A) €2; lndtte; lndry rm; shop, snacks, bar 1km; playgrnd; lake sw; fishing; canoeing; tennis; games area; entmnt; TV; 25% statics; dogs €1.50; phone; Eng spkn; adv bkg dep req; cc acc; CCI. "Barrier ent; facs clean but well worn & in need of refurb; gd security; gd value."
1 Apr-30 Sep. € 11.50   2005*

SILLE LE GUILLAUME *4F1* (3km N Rural) **Camp Municipal La Foret, Sille-Plage, 72140 Sille-le-Guillaume [02 43 20 11 04; fax 02 43 20 84 82; campingdelaforet@wanadoo.fr]** Exit Sille on D304 sp Mayenne. After 2km at x-rds turn R; across next x-rds & turn L at next x-rds; sp Sille-Plage; site immed on R visible. Sp fr other dir. Lge, pt shd; wc; shwrs inc; el pts (10A) €2.20; gas; shop; tradsmn; playgrnd; tennis; boating; lake sw; fishing; 20% statics; dogs €1; poss cr; rd noise; CCI. "Pleasant lakeside & forest scenery (some pitches amongst trees)." 1 Apr-31 Oct. € 7.10   2002*

SILLE LE GUILLAUME *4F1* (11km SE Urban) **Camp Municipal de la Gironde, 72240 Conlie [02 43 20 81 07 or 02 43 20 50 35 (Mairie); fax 02 43 20 99 37; camping.conlie@wanadoo.fr]** SE fr Sille-le-Guillaume on D304 twd Conlie. Ent vill & site sp in vill to R. Sm, hdg/mkd pitch, pt sl, shd; wc; chem disp (wc only); shwrs inc; el pts (6A) €2.50; lndtte; shops 200m; playgrnd adj; pool 5km; dogs; phone; adv bkg, quiet; CCI. "No resident warden, access poss diff; phone ahead to check open if travelling low ssn; v pleasant site." ♦ 1 Apr-31 Oct. € 5.00   2005*

SILLE LE GUILLAUME *4F1* (2km NW Rural) **Camping Le Landereau, Le Grez, 72140 Sille-le-Guillaume [02 43 20 12 69]** Exit Sille on D35 Rennes rd (route verte), after 2km at x-rds, turn R to site in 150m on L, easily visible & sp. Sp fr Sille Plage. Med, pt sl, pt shd; wc; chem disp; baby facs; shwrs; el pts (2-10A) inc; gas; lndtte, ice; shop 2km; rest; snacks; bar; playgrnd; rv/lake sw 2km; 50% statics; dogs €0.91; CCI. "Beautiful site but outdated plumbing; lovely lake at Sille Plage; nice town." Easter-1 Nov. € 11.50   2004*

SILLE LE PHILIPPE *4F1* (2km SW Rural) **LES CASTELS Le Chateau de Chanteloup, 72460 Sille-le-Philippe [02 43 27 51 07 or 02 43 89 66 47; fax 02 43 89 05 05; chanteloup.souffront@wanadoo.fr; www.chateau-de-chanteloup.com or www.les-castels.com]** Leave A11/E50 at junc 7 Sp Le Mans Z1 Nord. After toll turn L onto N138. Foll this & turn L onto D313 sp Coulaines & Ballon. Take D301 (just bef lge supmkt) & approx 13km site is sp just after ent to Sillé-le-Philippe. Avoid ent Sille-le-Philippe. Med, some mkd pitch, pt sl, pt shd; wc; chem disp; baby facs; shwrs inc; el pts (6A) inc (poss rev pol); lndtte; ltd shop & 2km; tradsmn; rest high ssn; snacks; bar; BBQ; playgrnd; pool; lake fishing; tennis; cycle hire; horseriding & golf 10km; games area; entmnt; internet; TV rm; dogs; c'vans over 8m not acc; sep o'night area with elec & water; poss v cr; Eng spkn; adv bkg; quiet; cc acc; CCI. "Excel, friendly site; clean facs & gd rest; recep 0815-2300; breakfast avail; gd for 24hr car race (Le Mans w/e); rest & shop poss clsd after Le Mans w/e; chateaux & wine tours arranged." 1 Jun-3 Sep. € 33.00 ABS - L13   2005*

SISTERON *10E3* (1.5km N) **Camp Municipal Les Pres Hauts, 04200 Sisteron [tel/fax 04 92 61 00 37 or 04 92 61 19 69; office-de-tourisme- sisteron@wanadoo.fr]** On W of D951 3km N of Sisteron. Fr S on N85 take R turn 300m after thro tunnel exit town & cross rv; L after 2km. Lge, hdg pitch, pt sl, pt shd; wc; chem disp; serviced pitches; shwrs inc; el pts (6A) €3 (poss rev pol); lndtte; shop & 1.5km; playgrnd; pool; tennis; fishing; entmnt; dogs €1; Eng spkn; quiet; cc acc; CCI. "Vg facs; friendly warden; gd views; Citadelle a must; pleasant old town; lge pitches; ltd facs low ssn; vg sh stay/NH." ♦ 1 Mar-31 Oct. € 13.00   2005*

SIVRY SUR MEUSE see Dun sur Meuse *5C1*

SIX FOURS LES PLAGES see Seyne sur Mer, La *10F3*

SIXT SUR AFF see Gacilly, La *2F3*

SIZUN *2E2* (Rural) **Camp Municipal du Gollen, 29450 Sizun [02 98 24 11 43 or 02 98 68 80 13 (Mairie); fax 02 98 68 86 56]** Fr Roscoff take D788 SW onto D69 to Landivisiau, D30 & D764 to Sizun. In Sizun take D18 at rndabt. At end of by-pass, at next rndabt, take 3rd exit. Site adj pool. Sm, pt shd; wc (some cont); shwrs inc; el pts (10A) inc (poss rev pol); lndry rm; shops 500m; playgrnd; htd pool adj high ssn; phone; poss cr; no adv bkg; quiet; cc not acc; CCI. "Site in Armorique Nature Park; friendly recep; site yourself if warden not avail; no twin-axle vans." 15 Apr-30 Sep. € 12.20   2005*

†**SOISSONS** *3D4* (1km N Urban) **Camp Municipal, Ave du Mail, 02200 Soissons [03 23 74 52 69; fax 03 23 59 67 72; officedetourisme@ville-soissons.fr; www.ville-soissons.fr]** Fr N on D1; foll town cent sp to 1st rndabt; turn R, cross rv & immed R; du Mail, cul-de-sac, on W bank of Rv Aisne, N of town, sp Camping Piscine. Site well sp beside sw pool. Rd humps & tight ent on last 500m of access rd. (Poss to avoid tight ent by going 150m to rndabt & returning.) Med, hdg/mkd pitch, hdstg, pt shd; htd wc; chem disp (wc); shwrs inc; el pts (6A) inc (poss rev pol); lndry rm; sm shop 600m; tradsmn; rest; snacks; bar 1km; BBQ; playgrnd; pool adj; excursions; 5% statics; dogs €1; phone; poss cr; quiet but some rd noise in ev; cc not acc; CCI. "Well-run; lovely site in interesting area; gd sized pitches; helpful staff; gd san facs; gd rvside walks, cycling, dog walks; flat, easy walk to town; poss itinerants; mkt Wed & Sat in vill; vg winter NH." ♦ € 16.00   2005*

SOLIGNAC SUR LOIRE see Puy en Velay, Le *9C1*

FRANCE

SOMMIERES *10E1* (3km SE) **Camping Les Chenes, Les Teullieres Basses, 30250 Junas [04 66 80 99 07 or 06 03 29 36 32; fax 04 66 51 33 23; chenes@wanadoo.fr]** Fr Sommieres take D12 S (sp Gallargues) 3km to junc with D140 L (N) for 1km. Site on R 300m up side rd. Sp. Med, pt sl, shd; wc (cont); chem disp; shwrs inc; el pts (3-10A) €2.05-3.10 (long lead poss req); lndtte; shops 1km; playgrnd; pool; beach & rv sw 2km; games area; some statics; dogs €2.20; phone; sep car park; security barrier; adv bkg; quiet; CCI. "Gd shade; gd san facs; friendly, helpful staff; vg." Easter-15 Oct. € 9.50   2005*

SOMMIERES *10E1* (500m NW Urban) **Camp Municipal Le Garanel, Rue Eugene Rouche, 30251 Sommieres [tel/fax 04 66 80 33 49]** Fr A9 exit junc 27 N & foll D34 then take N110 twd Sommieres. By-pass town on N110, over rv bdge; turn L for D4, site thro car park. Fr N on N110 turn L at 4th junc sp "Ville Vieille" & site adj rv. Site sp fr N110 fr N. Sm, hdg/mkd pitch, pt shd; wc (some cont); chem disp; mv service pnt; shwrs inc; el pts (4-10A) €2.45-3.60; lndtte; shops, rest, snacks 300m; tradsmn; bar 200m; BBQ; beach 25km; tennis adj; bus 500m; twin-axle restrictions; poss cr; Eng spkn; adv bkg; quiet; CCI. "Friendly, helpful warden; sh walk to historic town; some open views; rv walks; Sat mkt." 1 Apr-30 Sep. € 12.50   2005*

SONZAY *4G1* (W Rural) **Camping L'Arada Parc, 88 Rue de la Baratiere, 37360 Sonzay [02 47 24 72 69; fax 02 47 24 72 70; laradaparc@free.fr; www. laradaparc.com]** Exit A28 junc 27 Neuille-Pont-Pierre onto D766 to Sonzay; turn R in town cent. Site on R on o'skirts immed past new houses; sp. Med, hdg/mkd pitch, pt sl, pt shd; wc; chem disp; mv service pnt; 20% serviced pitches; child/baby facs; shwrs inc; el pts (10A) €3.50 (poss rev pol); gas; lndtte; ice; shop; tradsmn; rest; snacks; bar; BBQ; playgrnd; htd pool; paddling pool; tennis; lake sw 9km; rv fishing 500m; mini-golf; cycle hire; games area; entmnt; internet; TV rm; 15% statics; dogs €1.50; phone; bus to Tours; Eng spkn; adv bkg; quiet; cc acc; red long stay; CCI. "Conv Loire chateaux & vineyards; gd views; 60km fr Le Mans circuit; poss diff for lge o'fits when site full/cr; friendly, helpful owners; excel rest; immac facs; excel pool." ♦ 1 Apr-1 Nov. € 17.50 (CChq acc)   2005*

See advertisement

SOREDE see Argeles sur Mer *10G1*

†SORGUES *10E2* (E Urban) **Camping La Montagne, 944 Chemin de la Montagne, 84700 Sorgues [04 90 83 36 66 or 04 90 39 46 15; fax 04 90 39 82 94; camping.lamontagne@wanadoo.fr]** Exit A7 at Avignon Nord junc 23 twd Carpentras on D942, then N on D6 to Sorgues; site sp fr a'route but foll 'Zone Industrielle' sps. App via steep ramp. Med, shd; wc; shwrs inc; el pts (15A) €3.10; lndtte; shop; rest; snacks; bar; playgrnd; pool; TV; entmnt; dogs €1.60; adv bkg; quiet but m'way noise. € 13.20   2003*

SOSPEL *10E4* (4km NW) **Domaine Ste Madeleine, Route de Moulinet, 06380 Sospel [04 93 04 10 48; fax 04 93 04 18 37; camp@camping-sainte-madeleine.com; www.camping-sainte- madeleine. com]** Take D2566 fr Sospel NW to Turini & take 4km on L; sp fr town. Rd to site fr Menton steep with many hairpins. Med, pt sl, pt terr, shd; wc; chem disp; shwrs €0.50; el pts (10A) €3; gas; ice; lndtte; pool; beach 20km; rv 3km; dogs €1; Eng spkn; adv bkg rec high ssn; quiet; 10% red low ssn; CCI. "Friendly, busy site; gd facs; pool has no shallow end." 25 Mar-30 Sep. € 18.00   2004*

SOUBES see Lodeve *10E1*

SOUILLAC *7C3* (5km SE Rural) **Camp Municipal,** 46200 Pinsac [05 65 37 85 83 or 05 65 37 06 02] S on N20 thro Souillac, turn L on o'skts onto D43 immed bef Rv Dordogne. Site in 5km. Sm, pt shd; wc; shwrs inc; el pts (5A) €2.50; lndry rm; ice; shop 1km; rest & bar 100m; snacks; fishing; Eng spkn; quiet. "Useful NH/sh stay espec low ssn; lovely rvside position; warden calls pm; conv for Rocamadour & local attractions; basic facs." 1 Jun-30 Sep. € 8.10   2005*

SOUILLAC *7C3* (1km S Rural) **Camping du Pont,** 46200 Lanzac [05 65 37 02 58 or 05 65 37 88 53; fax 05 65 37 02 31] S on N20 thro Souillac; immed after x-ing Rv Dordogne site visible on R of N20. Sm, shd; wc (mainly cont); chem disp; shwrs inc; el pts (6-10A) €2.33; gas; shops 1km; tradsmn; snacks; adv bkg; CCI. "Easy stroll into Souillac along rv; lovely location but poss itinerants; unreliable opening dates - phone ahead." ♦ 15 Jun-15 Sep. € 11.80   2005*

SOUILLAC *7C3* (5km S Rural) **Camping Verte Rive,** 46200 Pinsac [05 65 37 85 96; fax 05 65 32 67 69] Fr Souillac, S on N20. Turn L immed bef Dordogne rv bdge on D43 to Pinsac. Site on R in 2km. Med, hdg/mkd pitch, shd; wc (some cont); chem disp; baby facs; shwrs inc; el pts (6A) €3; gas; lndtte; shop & 1km; rest; snacks; bar; playgrnd; pool; rv sw; canoeing; 20% statics; dogs €1; poss cr; Eng spkn; adv bkg ess high ssn (bkg fee & dep req); quiet; CCI. "Friendly, peaceful, wooded site on banks Rv Dordogne; mosquitoes by rv; beautiful scenery; v peaceful low ssn; gd long/sh stay." ♦ Easter-30 Sep. € 15.00   2004*

SOUILLAC *7C3* (5km SW) **Camp Municipal de la Borgne,** 24370 Cazoules [05 53 29 81 64 or 05 53 29 73 29 (Mairie)] Fr Souillac, take D703 twd Sarlat. In 4km in vill Cazoules turn L foll site sps. Lge, pt shd; wc; baby facs; shwrs inc; el pts €2; lndry rm; sm shop; supmkt 4km; BBQ; playgrnd; pool; tennis adj; rv sw; canoe trips; boat hire; fishing; quiet low ssn. "Mosquito problem; on bank of Dordogne; helpful staff; excel rest in vill; excel long/sh stay." ♦ 15 Jun-31 Aug. € 12.00   2003*

SOUILLAC *7C3* (10km SW Rural) **Camping Le Heron, Mareuil, 46200 Le Roc** [tel/fax 05 65 37 67 38; vpassingham@free.fr; www. heroncamping.com] Fr Souillac, take D804 (D703) W sp Sarlat & in 300m turn L onto D255 (later becomes D43) sp Le Roc, over rv bdge (take care sharp bend & single track). Cont on D43 thro Le Roc. Foll sp L onto D12 sp Gourdon, site in 200m on L. Sm, pt shd; wc; chem disp; fam bthrm; shwrs inc; el pts (6-10A) inc; gas 6km; lndtte; ice; shop & 4km; tradsmn; rest, snacks, bar 4km; htd pool; rv nr; fishing; watersports; dogs €2; Eng spkn; adv bkg; quiet but some rd/rlwy noise; no cc acc; red long stay/CCI. "Friendly British owners; lge pitches; chateau & caves nrby; beautiful scenery for walks & cycling." ♦ 1 Apr-31 Oct. € 16.90   2005*

SOUILLAC *7C3* (1km W Urban) **Escapades Terre Oceane Camping Les Ondines, 46200 Souillac** [05 65 37 86 44 or 05 46 55 10 01; fax 05 46 55 10 00; info@campingterreoceane.com; www.campingterreoceane.com] Turn W off N20 in cent Souillac onto D703 sp Sarlat. In 200m turn L at sp into narr rd. Ent 400m on R adj rv. Lge, mkd pitch, pt sl, pt shd; wc; chem disp; shwrs inc; el pts (5A) €3; lndtte; shop; rest 1km; BBQ; playgrnd; htd pool & aquatic park nrby; rv sw; tennis; fishing; canoeing; tennis; mini-golf; horseriding; gd walking; entmnt; child entmnt; some statics; dogs; phone; Eng spkn; quiet; CCI. "Conv for Rocamadour & caves." ♦ 17 Jun-16 Sep. € 15.00   2005*

†SOUILLAC *7C3* (6km W Rural) **Camping a la Ferme (Levet), Le Perigourdine, 24370 Peyrillac-et-Millac** [05 53 29 72 12] Fr cent of Souillac, W on D703 to Peyrillac-et-Millac; in vill turn L at sp to site. Drive past farmhouse, ent 75m on R. Sm, pt shd; htd wc; mv service pnt; shwrs inc; el pts (16A) €2.50; lndry rm; shop, rest, bar etc 5km; BBQ; playgrnd; pool; rv 2km; adv bkg; quiet; no cc acc; CCI. "Excel CL-type site; gd touring cent & gd NH en rte Spain; easy to find; not suitable lge o'fits as access narr, sloping & sharp bend." € 10.00   2005*

SOUILLAC *7C3* (6km W Rural) **Camping au P'tit Bonheur, 24370 Peyrillac-et-Millac** [tel/fax 05 53 29 77 93; contact@camping-auptitbonheur. com] Exit Souillac by D703 sp Sarlat. At Peyrillac turn R to Millac, about 2km on minor & narr rd uphill (13%) to plateau. Well sp fr D703. Med, terr, hdg/mkd pitch, pt shd; wc (some cont); chem disp; shwrs inc; el pts (10A) €2.80; gas; shops 2km; tradsmn; snacks; bar; playgrndhtd pool; 5% statics; dogs €3; Eng spkn; adv bkg; quiet; 10% red low ssn; cc acc high ssn only; CCI. "Excel; peaceful, well-run site with views; owners pleasant; app rd steep mostly single track; pitches diff for twin-axles." ♦ 1 Apr-15 Sep. € 13.00   2004*

SOUILLAC *7C3* (8km NW) **LES CASTELS Le Domaine de la Paille Basse, 46200 Souillac** [05 65 37 85 48; fax 05 65 37 09 58; paille. basse@wanadoo.fr; www.lapaillebasse.com or www.les-castels.com] Exit Souillac by D15 sp Salignac, turn onto D165 at Bourzolles foll sp to site in 3km. Steep & narr app, few passing places. Lge, hdg pitch, terr, pt shd; wc; chem disp; mv service pnt 800m; shwrs inc; el pts (3-6A) inc; shop; rest; snacks; bar; gas; ice; lndtte; shop; rest; bar; playgrnd; pool; paddling pool; waterslide; games rm; tennis; mini-golf; sports area; golf 5km; organised outdoor activities; entmnt; internet; TV rm; dogs €3.50; adv bkg; red low ssn; quiet; cc acc; red low ssn. "Excel site; v clean facs; friendly, helpful staff; restored medieval vill; excel rest & gd shop." ♦ 15 May-15 Sep. € 26.50 (CChq acc)   2005*

FRANCE

SOULAC SUR MER *7B1* (2km S Coastal) **Camp L'Amelie Plage, 33780 Soulac-sur-Mer [05 56 09 87 27; fax 05 56 73 64 26; camping.amelie. plage@wanadoo.fr]** S fr Soulac to L'Amelie down minor rd, diff app. Lge, pt sl, pt shd; wc; shwrs inc; el pts (4-10A) €3.20-4; lndtte; shop; rest; snacks; bar; BBQ; playgrnd; sand beach adj; fishing, windsurfing; tennis; cycle hire; entmnt; TV; some statics; dogs; poss cr; adv bkg; poss noisy; red low ssn; "Tractor used to pull c'vans onto sandy area or up steeper slopes." 26 Apr-20 Sep. € 23.00   2003*

SOULAC SUR MER *7B1* (13km S Coastal) **Camp Municipal du Gurp, 33590 Grayan-et-L'Hopital [05 56 09 44 53; fax 05 56 09 54 73]** Take D101 fr Soulac. Turn R after 5km sp Grayan & R at x-rds. Site clearly sp. V lge, hdstg, shd; wc; chem disp; shwrs inc; el pts (4A); lndtte; shop; rest; snacks; bar; playgrnd; sand beach adj; tennis; games area; entmnt; TV; dogs; poss cr; quiet. "In pine forest; gd, vast beaches." 1 Jun-10 Sep. € 10.67   2005*

SOULAC SUR MER *7B1* (13km S Coastal) **Centre Naturiste Euronat La Depee (Naturist), 33590 Grayan-et-L'Hopital [05 56 09 33 33; fax 05 56 09 30 27; info@euronat.fr; www.euronat.fr]** Fr Soulac, take D101 twd Montalivet, turn W at camp sp onto rd leading direct to site. Fr Bordeaux, take N215 sp Le Verdon-sur-Mer. Approx 8km after Lesparre-Medoc turn L onto D102. In Venday-Montalivet bear R onto D101. In 7.5km turn L sp Euronat. V lge, mkd pitch, hdstg, shd; wc (some htd); chem disp; shwrs inc; el pts (10A) inc; gas; lndtte; ice; shop; rest; snacks; bar; BBQ; playgrnd; htd, covrd pool; sand beach adj; tennis; horseriding; cinema; archery; cycle hire; golf driving range; internet; TV; 75% statics; dogs €3; phone; Eng spkn; adv bkg (dep req); quiet; red low ssn; INF card req. ◆ 27 Mar-7 Nov. € 38.90 (CChq acc)   2004*

SOULAC SUR MER *7B1* (1.5km SW Coastal) **Camping Les Sables d'Argent, Blvd de l'Amelie, 33780 Soulac-sur-Mer [05 56 09 82 87; fax 05 56 09 94 82; camping.sables.d.argent@ wanadoo.fr; www.sables-d-argent.com]** Drive S fr Soulac twd L'Amelie-sur-Mer. Clearly sp on R. Med, mkd pitch, pt sl, pt shd; wc; shwrs inc; el pts (10A) €3.90; lndtte; shop; rest; snacks; bar; private sand beach adj; fishing; tennis; entmnt; TV; 10% statics; dogs €2.50; poss cr. "Ideal seaside with lge uncr beach & some surf; Soulac sm, lively mkt town." 1 Apr-30 Sep. € 18.60   2005*

SOULAINES DHUYS *6E1* (500m Rural) **Camp Municipal de la Croix Badeau, 10200 Soulaines-Dhuys [03 25 92 77 44 or 03 25 92 77 85]** 500m N of junc D960 & D384, behind lge church of Soulaines-Dhuys, well sp. Sm, hdg/mkd pitch, hdstg, pt shd; wc ltd (some cont); chem disp (wc); shwrs inc; el pts (15A) €1.52 (rev pol); lndry rm; ice; shop 500m; playgrnd; tennis; rv 300m; phone; Eng spkn; quiet; CCI. "Excel, clean site in fascinating vill; twin-axle €25 extra; security gate clsd 24 hrs, phone ahead for code to open gate; warden calls evenings; security card req for facs block; hourly church bells." 1 May-30 Sep. € 7.61   2005*

SOULLANS *2H3* (500m NE Urban) **Camp Municipal Le Moulin Neuf, Rue St Christophe, 85300 Soullans [02 51 68 00 24 (Mairie); fax 02 51 68 88 66]** Fr Challans ring rd take D69 sp Soullans. Site sp on L just bef town cent. Med, hdg/mkd pitch, pt shd; wc (some cont); shwrs inc; el pts (4A); gas 500m; lndtte; shop 500m; playgrnd; beach 12km; tennis; phone adj; poss cr; adv bkg; quiet; CCI. "Vg; lovely walks & cycling; simple site." 15 Jun-15 Sep. € 8.80   2005*

SOUPPES SUR LOING *4F3* (1km SW) **Camp Municipal Les Bords du Loing, Chemin des Mariniers, 77460 Souppes-sur-Loing [01 64 29 72 63 or 01 64 78 57 77]** Fr A77 take exit 17 onto N7 dir Nemours, site sp on SW side of rd over rlwy x-ing alongside Loing canal. Lge, pt shd; wc (cont); shwrs inc; el pts (6A); gas; lndtte; ice; shops 1km; BBQ; playgrnd; child club; sports area; lake 50m; fishing, tennis, kayak 400m; horseriding 3km; golf 7km; entmnt; statics; adv bkg;. "Poss noisy at w/e & hols; fair sh stay." ◆ 1 Apr-31 Oct. € 8.38   2004*

SOURAIDE see Cambo les Bains *8F1*

SOURDEVAL *2E4* (N Urban) **Aire Naturelle de Camp Municipal, 50150 Sourdeval [02 33 59 61 97 or 02 33 79 35 55 (Mairie); fax 02 33 79 35 59; otsourdeval@wanadoo.fr]** Well sp fr all dirs on D977 11km N Mortain. Sm, pt sl, un shd; wc; shwrs; el pts (10A); playgrnd; fishing; tennis; quiet. "Municipal site in sm vill; NH only." 1 Jun-30 Sep.   2004*

SOURSAC *7C4* (1km NE) **Camp Municipal de la Plage, Centre Touristique du Pont Aubert, 19550 Soursac [05 55 27 55 43 or 05 55 27 52 61 (Mairie); fax 05 55 27 63 31; centrepontaubert@ wanadoo.fr]** Fr Mauriac take D678 to Chalvignac. Bear R onto D105 at 3km (12% descent) to cross Barrage de l'Aigle & 2km 12% ascent on D105E/D16, winding rd. In further 3km pass junc to Latronche, 1st R to site. Med, terr, pt sl, shd; wc; mv service pnt; baby facs; shwrs inc; el pts (6A) €2.10; lndtte; ice; shop 1km; rest planned 2006; snacks; playgrnd; pool & waterslide nrby; lake sw; archery; cycle hire; mini golf; games area; TV; adv bkg; quiet; "V gd clean san facs; attractive by lake; well worth detour; excel." ◆ 15 Jun-15 Sep. € 8.80   2005*

SOUSTONS *8E1* (6km NE) **Camping Village La Paillotte, 40140 Azur [05 58 48 12 12; fax 05 58 48 10 73; info@paillotte.com; www.paillotte.com]** Fr N10 turn W at Magescq onto D150 (site about 8km fr this junc); join D50 to Azur. Turn L at church in Azur; foll site sp. Lge, mkd pitch, pt shd; wc (some cont); baby facs; shwrs inc; el pts (10A) inc; gas; lndtte; shop; rest; snacks; bar; BBQ (gas/elec); playgrnd; pool; paddling pool; lake sw & sand beach adj; hot springs; dinghy sailing; windsurfing; fishing; cycle hire; games rm; entmnt; internet; TV; statics (tour ops); no dogs; bus; recep 0900-2100; adv bkg; cc acc; CCI. "Facs ltd low ssn; lakeside site; mkt Soustons Mon." ◆ 22 Apr-24 Sep. € 37.00 ABS - A22   2005*

SOUSTONS *8E1* (6.5km NE) **Camping Azu'Rivage, 720 Route des Campings, 40140 Azur [tel/fax 05 58 48 30 72; info@caming azurivage.com; www.campingazurivage.com]** Exit m'way A10 at exit Megescq & take D150 W for 8km to Azur, site sp fr church adj La Paillotte. Med, pt shd; wc; baby facs; shwrs inc; el pts (10A) inc; lndtte; sm shop & 6km; rest; snacks; playgrnd; pool; sand beach & lake sw; tennis; boating; watersports; entmnt; TV rm; dogs €1.65; poss cr; adv bkg; red long stay; quiet. "Delightful forest setting adj lake; rec." ♦ 15 Jun-15 Sep. € 17.40   2005*

SOUSTONS *8E1* (2km W) **Camp Municipal L'Airial, 61 Ave de Port d'Albret, Quartier Nicot, 40140 Soustons [05 58 41 12 48; fax 05 58 41 53 83; contact@camping-airial.com; www.camping-airial.com]** On D652 (Mimizan/ Labenne), opp Etang de Soustons. Foll site sp fr Soustons. Lge, mkd pitch, shd; wc; chem disp; shwrs inc; el pts (6A) inc; lndtte; shop; snacks; bar; playgrnd; htd pool; sand beach 7km; boating; watersports; fishing; TV rm; entmnt; dogs; phone; poss cr; adv bkg; quiet; red low ssn. "V pleasant site; gd shade & many birds; gd, clean facs but ltd low ssn; gd long stay." Easter-15 Oct. € 16.30   2003*

†**SOUTERRAINE, LA** *7A3* (2km E Urban) **Camping Suisse Ocean, Le Cheix, 23300 La Souterraine [05 55 63 33 32 or 05 55 63 59 71; fax 05 55 63 21 82]** Fr W on N145/E62 take 2nd La Souterraine exit (Mazeirat) twd town, strt thro 1st rndabt, at 2nd rndabt turn R, then L to L'Etang de Cheix. Fr E on N145 take D72 sp La Souterraine. Med, hdg/mkd pitch, hdstg, pt sl, terr, pt shd; htd wc (some cont); chem disp; mv service pnt; shwrs inc; el pts (10A) €2.60; lndtte; ice; sm shop & 2km; tradsmn; rest; snacks; bar; playgrnd; sand lake beach adj; tennis, fishing, sailing adj; diving (summer); 10% statics; dogs €0.80; poss cr; Eng spkn; adv bkg; quiet but night noise fr factory nrby; cc acc; CCI. "V attractive site; gd rest; ltd facs low ssn inc el pts & stretched when site full; pleasant sm town; superb location; v lge pitches; extremely sl rds on site could ground some lge o'fits - walk site bef pitching; gd sh/long stay." ♦ € 8.40   2004*

SOUTERRAINE, LA *7A3* (10km S Rural) **Camping Intercommunal, 23290 St Pierre-de-Fursac [05 55 63 65 69 or 05 55 63 61 28 (Mairie); fax 05 55 63 68 20]** Exit A20 at junc 23.1 onto D1 S twd St Pierre-de-Fursac. Site on L at ent to vill dir 'Stade'. Sm, mkd pitch, pt sl, pt shd; wc; shwrs inc; el pts (6A) €1.50 (poss rev pol); shop 500m; playgrnd; phone; quiet. "Well-kept site; pleasant situation overlooking vill; no rest but vill hotel has excel menu; many walks sp." ♦ ltd. 15 Jun-30 Sep. € 4.00   2005*

STENAY *5C1* (2km W Urban) **Camp Municipal (formerly Les Pasquis), 55700 Stenay [03 29 80 64 22; fax 03 29 80 62 59; otsistenay@ wanadoo.fr]** 2km W of Stenay on D964 or D947. Sp fr rndabt in cent of Stenay. Lge, pt shd; wc; own san; chem disp; shwrs; el pts; gas; shop; rv adj; adv bkg; quiet; CCI. "Museum of Beer in town." 1 Jun-30 Sep.   2003*

STRASBOURG *6E3* (3km W Urban) **FFCC Camping La Montagne Verte, 2 Rue Robert Forrer, 67000 Strasbourg [03 88 30 25 46; fax 03 88 27 10 15; lamontagneverte@ffcc.fr]** Fr m'way A35 (Colmar/St Die) about 2km S of Strasbourg exit junc 4 for Montagne Verte. Foll camp sp, 1st R to site on R in approx 1km. Sp off N4 & D392 to W of city, 1km fr town side of Boulevard de Lyon. Fr town cent foll sp for St Die/Colmar as camp sp intermittent. Height limit 3.3m on app rd. Lge, mkd pitch, pt shd; wc; chem disp; baby facs; shwrs inc; el pts (6A) €3.50; gas; lndry rm; shop, rest nr; tradsmn; bar; BBQ; playgrnd; covrd pool; tennis; games area; few statics; dogs €1; Eng spkn; noise fr aircraft, rlwy & church clock; cc acc; 10% red CCI. "Gd site adj rv; easy access to city; undergrnd car park at Petit-France; €6 all day; well-maintained but poss unkempt low ssn & red unclean facs; san facs need update; pitches v soft after rain; gates clsd 1900-0700 & 1200-1530 low ssn; €30 dep barrier card; gd cycle tracks by rv to town; mixed reports early ssn; poss itinerants; gd for dog walks." 15 Mar-31 Dec. € 11.20   2005*

SUEVRES see Blois *4G2*

SUHESCUN see St Jean Pied de Port *8F1*

†**SULLY SUR LOIRE** *4F3* (2km N Rural) **Camping Hortus - Le Jardin du Sully, Route d'Orleans, St Pere, 45600 Sully-sur-Loire [tel/fax 02 38 36 35 94; camping-hortus@wanadoo.fr; www.camping-hortus.com]** Fr N on D948 to Sully then turn R at rndabt immed bef x-ing bdge over Rv Loire onto D60 dir Chateauneuf-sur-Loire. Sp to site in 200m. Fr S thro Sully on D948, cross Rv Loire & turn L at rndabt onto D60. Med, hdg/mkd pitch, hdstg, pt shd; htd wc; chem disp; mv service pnt; serviced pitches; shwrs inc; el pts (6A) (poss rev pol); gas 800m; lndtte; shop 800m; snacks; bar; BBQ; htd, covrd pool; playgrnd; rv beach adj; child entmnt; sat TV; dogs; adv bkg rec; quiet; cc acc. "Site excel; new facs planned 2006, inc pool, shop & pizzeria; v organised, friendly site; gd cycling; nature reserve adj; fairy-tale chateau in Sully; some sm pitches." ♦ € 15.00   2005*

See advertisement on next page

SURGERES *7A2* (1km S Urban) **Camp Municipal de la Geres, 17700 Surgeres [05 46 07 79 97 or 05 46 07 00 23 (Mairie); fax 05 46 07 53 98 (Mairie)]** Site sp in Surgeres, on banks of Rv Geres, & fr Surgeres by-pass. Sm, pt shd; wc (cont); mv service pnt; shwrs; el pts (5A) €2.50-3.00; shop 200m; rest, snacks & bar 800m; pool & tennis 800m; dogs €1; phone; poss cr; cc acc; CCI. "Adj to park; m'vans extra charge; poss itinerants; NH only." 1 Apr-30 Oct. € 7.63   2005*

FRANCE

HORTUS, LE JARDIN DE SULLY

CAMPING *** with 100% pitches for tourism

- At 135 km of Paris
- Covered swimming pool
- Rental of mobile homes and tent bungalows

Open all year long

www.camping-hortus.com

Photo M.G. EDITIONS - Cartes Postales

---

†SURIS *7B3* (1km N Rural) **Camping La Blanchie, 16270 Suris [tel/fax 05 45 89 33 19; lablanchie@ wanadoo.fr; www.lablanchie.co.uk]** Fr N141 halfway bet Angouleme & Limoges take the D52 S at La Peruse to Suris. In 2km turn E up a narr lane to site. Sm, some hdstg, pt sl, pt shd; wc; chem disp; shwrs inc; el pts (10A) €2.50; lndtte; playgrnd; tennis, golf, Futuroscope nrby; lake/rv sw & sand beach 2.5km; some statics; no dogs; c'van storage; adv bkg; quiet; red long stay; CCI. "V welcoming British owners; v clean site in lovely area; ltd facs; pool planned for 2006; gd touring base." ♦ 1 Apr-30 Oct. € 16.00   2005*

†SURTAINVILLE *1C4* (1km W Coastal) **Camp Municipal Les Mielles, 80 Route des Laguettes, 50270 Surtainville [02 33 10 12 40 or 02 33 04 31 04 (Mairie); mairie.surtainville@wanadoo.fr]** S fr Cherbourg on D650, take D66 W thro Surtainville, site on R. Med, pt sl, unshd; htd wc (male cont); chem disp; shwrs inc; el pts (4A) €2.50; lndtte; playgrnd; sand beach 100m; 30% statics; dogs €1; adv bkg; quiet; CCI. "Excel beach." ♦ ltd. € 8.25   2005*

SUSSAC see Eymoutiers *7B4*

SUZE SUR SARTHE, LA *4F1* (Rural) **Camp Municipal Le Port, 72210 La Suze-sur-Sarthe [02 43 77 32 74 or 02 43 77 30 49; fax 02 43 77 28 77]** Take D23 S of Le Mans fr N226 ring rd for 6.5km. Turn R at sp for La Suze-sur-Sarthe & foll sp for Camping & Piscine. Turn R just bef pool 200m fr rv bdge in vill & adj to pool. Rec use D23 sp for lorries fr E of town. Med, mkd pitch, pt shd; wc; own san; chem disp; mv service pnt (in adj car park); shwrs inc; el pts (8A) €2.15; shops, snacks 300m; BBQ; playgrnd adj; htd pool adj; rv adj; fishing; boating; tennis; TV; dogs; many statics; adv bkg; red 7+ days. "Narr gate to site; ample hdstg & ltd free el pts for m'vans in adj car park; fair sh stay/NH." ♦ ltd. 1 May-30 Sep. € 4.20   2002*

TADEN see Dinan *2E3*

†TAIN L'HERMITAGE *9C2* (5km NE Rural) **Camping Chante-Merle, 26600 Chantemerle-les-Bles [04 75 07 49 73; fax 04 75 07 45 15; chantemerlecamp@aol.com]** Exit A7 at Tain L'Hermitage. After exit toll turn L twd town, next turn R (D109) to Chantemerle; site sp. Cont for 5km, site on L. Sm, hdg/mkd pitch, pt shd; htd wc; chem disp; serviced pitches; baby facs; shwrs inc; el pts (6A) €2.50; lndtte; ice; shops 500m; rest & snacks high ssn; bar; playgrnd; pool; 10% statics; dogs; site clsd Jan; quiet but some rd noise; CCI. "Helpful manager; lovely, quiet site; excel facs." ♦ € 14.80   2005*

> This site entry hasn't been updated for a while; we'd better fill in a site report form and send it to The Club.

TAIN L'HERMITAGE *9C2* (S Urban) **Camp Municipal Les Lucs, 24 Ave Roosevelt, 26600 Tain l'Hermitage [04 75 08 32 82 or 04 75 08 30 32; fax 04 75 08 32 06; camping. tainlhermitage@wanadoo.fr]** At S end of town on W N7 just past bdge to Tournon on R when going S. Alongside Rv Rhone via gates (locked o/night). Well sp adj sw pool/petrol stn. Med, hdg/mkd pitch, pt shd; wc (mainly cont); chem disp; shwrs inc; el pts (6A) inc (poss rev pol); lndtte; shops, snacks adj; playgrnd; pool adj high ssn; dogs €1.05; phone; no twin-axles & no access for lge m'vans over 6m; Eng spkn; red low ssn; cc not acc; CCI. "Popular NH; well-organised & well-controlled; friendly recep; immac site; excel pool complex adj open 1 Jun; v secure site, access via barrier code; poss rd noise fr N7; pleasant walks by rv to Tain & Tournon; nr chocolate factory; no o'fits over 5.50m; highly rec." 15 Mar-30 Oct. € 15.70   2005*

TALLARD see Gap *9D3*

TALLOIRES see Annecy *9B3*

TANINGES see Cluses *9A3*

TARADEAU see Vidauban *10F3*

TARASCON *10E2* (6km N Rural) **Camping Lou Vincen, 30300 Vallabregues [04 66 59 21 29; fax 04 66 59 07 41; campinglouvincen@wanadoo.fr; www.campinglouvincen.com]** N fr Tarascon on D81A, then D183A. Med, hdg/mkd pitch, hdstg, shd; htd wc (some cont); chem disp; mv service pnt; shwrs inc; el pts (6A) €3.20; gas; lndtte; ice; shop, rest, snacks, bar 100m; playgrnd; pool; tennis; fishing; horseriding 3km; TV; dogs €1; adv bkg; quiet; cc acc; red long stay/low ssn; CCI. "Hdg pitches poss diff v lge o'fits; gd base for Camargue." 2 Apr-20 Oct. € 13.80   2005*

TARASCON *10E2* (2km W) **Camp Municipal Le Rhodanien, Au Champ de Foire, 30300 Beaucaire [04 66 59 25 50 or 04 66 59 26 57; fax 04 66 59 68 51]** Take D999 W fr Tarascon to Beaucaire, across Rv Rhone. At end of bdge immed turn R at Camping sp to site in 1km. Fr W on D999 turn N on W o'skts of town twd Chateau, adj Rv Rhone. Med, shd; wc (some cont); shwrs; gas; ice; el pts (10A) €3.05; shops 200m; playgrnd; pool; fishing; sailing; windsurfing; tennis; games area; adv bkg; quiet, but some rd noise; CCI. 1 Jul-31 Aug. € 12.36
2002*

TARASCON SUR ARIEGE *8G3* (4km N Rural) **Camping Le Lac, Hotel de Plein Air, 09400 Mercus-Garrabet [tel/fax 05 61 05 90 61 or 05 61 02 67 40 (LS); info@campinglac.com; www.campinglac.com]** N20 S fr Foix, after 10km exit Mercus over N20 sp, cross rlwy line. At T-junc turn R thro Mercus, site of R over level x-ing. Tight bend into site off long, narr ent drive. Med, hdg/mkd pitch, terr, shd; wc (some cont); chem disp; baby facs; shwrs inc; el pts (4-10A) €3-4.50; ice; lndtte; shop; tradsmn; supmkt 4km; BBQ; pool; rv & lake sw, fishing & watersports adj; games rm; dogs €1.50; phone; adv bkg (fee); rd & rlwy noise; red long stay; CCI. "V clean facs; v friendly owners; diff ent for long c'vans; sm pitches; 60km Andorra; a real find; excel long stay." ♦ ltd. Easter-15 Oct.
€ 15.00   2003*

†**TARASCON SUR ARIEGE** *8G3* (1.5km SE Rural) **Camping Le Pre-Lombard, Route d'Ussat, 09400 Tarascon-sur-Ariege [05 61 05 61 94; fax 05 61 05 78 93; leprelombard@wanadoo.fr; www.prelombard.com]** Travelling S twd Andorra join N20 to Tarascon. Approx 15km S of Foix after 3 rndabts & x-ing a bdge, at 4th rndabt turn L & foll site sp after rlwy. This rte avoids cent of Tarascon. Lge, mkd pitch, pt shd; htd wc; chem disp; mv service pnt; shwrs inc; el pts (6A) inc; gas; lndtte; ice; shop & snacks high ssn only; rest & supmkt in town; bar; BBQ (gas/elec/charcoal); playgrnd; htd pool; pading pool; rv fishing, watersports & sw adj; tennis 1km; archery; entmnt; TV; dogs €2; Eng spkn; adv bkg rec high ssn; quiet; red low ssn; clsd mid Nov - late Jan; cc acc; CCI. "Excel winter NH en rte to Spain; vg location by rv (gd walks); excel facs; spacious pitches; helpful owner; poss noisy at night; conv Andorra; prehistoric caves nrby." ♦ € 25.00 (CChq acc) ABS - D23   2005*

TARASCON SUR ARIEGE *8G3* (2km S Rural) **Camping Ariege Evasion, 09400 Ornolac-Ussat -Les-Bains [tel/fax 05 61 05 11 11; contact@ariege-evasion.com; www.ariege-evasion.com]** S on N20 fr Foix to Tarascon-sur-Ariege then 2km to Ornalac-Ussat-Les-Bains. Foll camp sp over narr bdge & R at T-junc. In 750m turn L & immed R at staggered x-rds, site in 100m. Med, hdg/mkd pitch, pt shd; wc (cont); chem disp; mv service pnt; shwrs inc; el pts (3-10A) €2-4; gas 1km; lndtte; shop 1km; tradsmn; rest; playgrnd; rv sw; trout-fishing; canoe hire; 5% statics; Eng spkn; adv bkg; quiet; red low ssn; CCI. "Prehistoric caves nr; largest cave in Europe in vill; conv Andorra." 1 Mar-15 Oct. € 12.50   2004*

†**TARASCON SUR ARIEGE** *8G3* (15km SW) **Camping La Bexanelle, 09220 Vicdessos [tel/fax 05 61 64 82 22 or 05 61 64 88 25 (Mairie); camping-la-bexanelle@wanadoo.fr]** Fr N8 at Tarascon take D8 W sp Vicdessos. Site on L at ent to vill, sp. Lge, hdg pitch, pt shd; wc; chem disp; serviced pitch; shwrs; el pts (5-10A) €1.50-2.80; gas; lndtte; rest in ssn; BBQ; playgrnd; pool; TV; rv fishing; red low ssn; adv bkg; CCI.
€ 9.15   2002*

TARASCON SUR ARIEGE *8G3* (1.5km NW Rural) **Camping Le Sedour, Florac, 09400 Surba [05 61 05 87 28; fax 05 61 01 49 33; info@campinglesedour.com]** Fr rndbt 1km N of Tarascon take 1st R sp Massat. Turn R in 100m, site on L in Surba vill. Med, hdg/mkd pitch, pt sl, pt shd; wc; chem disp; some serviced pitches; shwrs inc; el pts (10A) inc; lndtte; supmkt 1km; tradsmn; rest, bar 300m; playgrnd; 60% statics; dogs €1; poss cr; some Eng spkn; adv bkg; quiet; CCI. "Conv for Ariege valleys & prehistoric park; mountain views; friendly, helpful owners; gd facs; poss diff access lge o'fits." ♦ 1 Mar-3 Nov. € 18.00   2004*

†**TARBES** *8F2* (9km SW) **Camping La Bergerie, Rue des Chenes, 65380 Lanne [tel/fax 05 62 35 40 05; pierre.denoune@wanadoo.fr]** Fr Tarbes take N21 twd Lourdes. Site on L after airport sps & long brick wall on R. Med, mkd pitch, shd; wc; shwrs; el pts (10A) €2.10; gas; ice; shop; playgrnd; pool high ssn; tennis; dogs €0.80; bus 200m; adv bkg; quiet but some aircraft & rd noise; red low ssn; CCI. "Well-run site; friendly owners; gd san facs." ♦ € 9.60   2004*

TARDETS SORHOLUS *8F1* (1km S) **Camping du Pont d'Abense, 64470 Tardets-Sorholus [tel/fax 05 59 28 58 76 or 05 59 39 75 61]** Take D918 S to Tardets, turn R to cross bdge onto D57. Site sp on R. Tardets cent narr. Med, mkd pitch, shd; wc; chem disp; shwrs inc; el pts (3A) inc; lndry rm; shop, rest, snacks & bar 500m; tradsmn; rv sw 1km; quiet; adv bkg; CCI. "Gd walks in Pyrenees fr site; helpful family; vg." Easter-Oct. € 15.00   2003*

LE PANORAMIC**
Campsite of the "SITES et PAYSAGES de FRANCE" chain

Camping LE PANORAMIC
Route de la Plage
29560 TELGRUC SUR MER
Phone: 02 98 27 78 41
Fax: 02 98 27 36 10
Info@camping-panoramic.com
www.camping-panoramic.com

Quiet family camping at the seaside (beach at 700m), in the Regional Natural Park of Armorique. Situated on the peninsula of CROZON where one can discover all the different faces of Brittany: the beaches, the steep cliffs, the dunes, the harbours, the islands, the forests.... 200 pitches, swimming pool, Jacuzzi, tennis, restaurant, bar. Rental of mobile homes.

TARDETS SORHOLUS *8F1* (1km W) **Camping a la Ferme Carrique (Iriart), 64470 Tardets-Sorholus** [05 59 28 50 25] S fr Mauleon on D918 to Tardets-Sorholus. Turn W on D24 to Alos over single c'way bdge. Site 500m on L after Alos. Sm, pt shd; wc; shwrs inc; el pts (5A) inc; shops 2km; rv sw 2km; quiet. "CL-type farm site; friendly family; clean facs; excel." ♦ 1 Jun-31 Oct. € 10.00   2004*

TAUPONT see Ploermel *2F3*

TAUTAVEL see Estagel *8G4*

†**TEILLET** *8E4* (S Rural) **Relais de l'Entre-Deux-Lacs, 81120 Teillet** [05 63 55 74 45; fax 05 63 55 75 65; contact@camping-entredeuxlacs.com; www.camping-entredeux lacs.com] Fr Albi by-pass take D81 SE to Teillet. Site on R at S end of vill. Med, hdstg, terr, shd; wc; chem disp; shwrs inc; el pts inc (6A) inc (poss no earth & long lead poss req); gas; lndtte; shops 200m; rest, snacks bar high ssn; playgrnd; pool high ssn; 10% statics; dogs €2; adv bkg (dep & admin fee); quiet; red 5+ nights Sep-Jun. "Farm welcomes children; friendly; steep site rds; few water points; heavily wooded; fair sh stay." ♦ € 17.00   2003*

TELGRUC SUR MER *2E2* (Coastal) **Camping Les Mimosas, 106 Rue de la Plage, 29560 Telgruc-sur-Mer** [tel/fax 02 98 27 76 06 or 06 78 02 55 66 (mob)] Fr D887 Crozon-Chateaulin rd turn SW onto D208 into Telgruc. Fr town sq foll sp Trez-Bellec-Plage. 300m after exiting town, turn L & L, site clearly sp. Med, hdg pitch, terr, pt shd; wc; chem disp; shwrs inc; el pts (10A) €1.70; lndtte; shop 600m; sand beach 600m; playgrnd; tennis; dogs €0.80; poss cr; adv bkg rec high ssn; quiet; CCI. "Gd; excel coastal scenery; lots of trees."1 Apr-30 Sep. € 9.20   2005*

TELGRUC SUR MER *2E2* (Coastal) **Camping Pen-Bellec, 29560 Telgruc-sur-Mer** [02 98 27 31 87 or 02 98 27 71 95] Take D887 Chateaulin-Crozon, turn S on D208 for Telgruc-sur-Mer. In Telgruc take rd mkd 'Plage Trez Bellec'. At Plage cont to far end where rd rises & turns inland. Sm, unshd, mkd pitch; wc; shwrs €1; el pts (3A) €2.50; shop & 2km; lndtte; ice; sand beach adj; watersports adj; cycle hire; dogs €0.90; poss cr; noisy. "Conv beach; v clean; beautiful views; gd cliff walking." 15 May-30 Sep. € 11.00   2004*

TELGRUC SUR MER *2E2* (1km S Coastal) **Camping Le Panoramic, 130 Route de la Plage, 29560 Telgruc-sur-Mer** [02 98 27 78 41; fax 02 98 27 36 10; info@camping-panoramic.com; www.camping-panoramic.com] Fr D887 Crozon-Chateaulin rd, turn W on D208 twd Trez-Bellec Plage, site sp on R in approx 1.5km. Med, hdg/mkd pitch, terr, pt shd, wc (some cont); chem disp; mv service pnt; baby facs; shwrs inc, el pts (6-10A) €3.10-4.50; lndtte; shop; rest; snacks; bar; BBQ; playgrnd; covrd pool; jacuzzi; sand beach 700m; tennis; cycle hire; games rm; TV; some statics; dogs €1.60; adv bkg; cc acc; red low ssn; CCI. "Access to pitches poss diff due trees; vg, well-run, welcoming site." ♦ 1 Jun-15 Sep. € 22.00   2005*

See advertisement

TELGRUC SUR MER *2E2* (1.2km S Coastal) **Camping L'Armorique, Plomodiern, 29560 Telgruc-sur-Mer** [02 98 27 77 33; fax 02 98 27 38 38; contact@campingarmorique.com; www.campingarmorique.com] D887 Chateaulin to Crozon; turn S on D208 at sea end of Telgruc-sur-Mer. Steep hairpins on access rd, poss diff for long/low powered o'fits. Med, terr, pt shd; wc; shwrs inc; el pts (5A) €2.80; shop; lndtte; snacks; playgrnd; pool; sand beach 750m; games area; deep-sea diving, climbing, horseriding schools nrby; entmnt; games/TV rm; 20% statics; dogs €1.50; adv bkg; quiet; cc acc; CCI. "Pleasant, well-wooded site." ♦ ltd. 1 Apr-15 Sep. € 18.25   2004*

TENCE *9C2* (9km S Rural) **Camping Les Hirondelles, Route de la Suchere, 43400 Le Chambon-sur-Lignon** [04 71 59 73 84; fax 04 71 65 88 80; les.hirondelles.bader@wanadoo.fr] Fr cent of Le Chambon foll site sp S. Cross rv, bear R & after 200m turn L up hill & camp ent 300m on R. Med, hdg/mkd pitch, pt terr, pt shd; htd wc; chem disp; shwrs inc; el pts (2-6A) inc; lndtte; lndry rm; shop & 1km; rest; snacks; bar; playgrnd; paddling pool; canoeing, horseriding nrby; sports area; games/TV rm; 50% statics; dogs €1.05; adv bkg (ess Jul/Aug); quiet; CCI. ♦ 25 Jun-1 Sep. € 16.00   2004*

TENDE *10E4* (9km S Rural) **Camp Municipal, Quartier Barbanin**, 06540 Fontan [04 93 04 52 01; fax 04 93 04 52 02] Site is on N204 200m N of Fontan. Sm, pt sl, pt shd; wc (some cont); shwrs inc; el pts; lndtte; rshop, est, snacks, bar 200m; dogs; phone; adv bkg; some rd noise; CCI. "Pleasant site close to scenic vill of Saorge; site yourself if recep shut (ltd open hrs)." 1 Apr-15 Sep. 2004*

THANN *6F3* (7km NW) **Camp La Mine d'Argent, Rue des Mines**, 68690 Moosch [03 89 82 30 66 or 03 89 60 34 74; fax 03 89 42 15 12; serge. sorribas@free.fr] Turn L off N66 Thann-Thillot rd in cent of Moosch opp church; foll sps for 1.5km, ent on R, narr app. Med, mkd pitch, pt sl, pt terr, pt shd; wc; chem disp; shwrs inc; el pts (4-10A) €2.60-5; gas; lndtte; tradsmn; shops 1.5km; playgrnd; 5% statics; dogs €0.60; phone; adv bkg; quiet; red low ssn; no cc acc; CCI. "In heavily wooded valley; v clean & well-kept site; v enjoyable stay; helpful wardens; excel walking; busy w/e; highly rec." 15 Apr-15 Oct. € 10.20 2005*

THARON PLAGE see Pornic *2G3*

THEIX see Vannes *2F3*

THENON *7C3* (3km SE Rural) **Camping Jarry-Carrey, Route de Montignac**, 24210 Thenon [05 53 05 20 78; fax 05 53 05 57 66; lejarry carrey@wanadoo.fr] Sp fr N89, take D67 fr Thenon to Montignac. Site on R in 4km. Med, mkd pitch, pt sl, terr, pt shd; wc; chem disp (wc); shwrs inc; el pts (10A) €3.50; shops 2km; tradsmn; snacks; bar; ice; gas; lndtte; playgrnd; pool; dogs €1.50; adv bkg; quiet; 20% statics; dogs €1.37; Eng spkn; quiet; CCI. "Beautiful setting away fr tourist bustle but easy reach attractions; 2 lakes on site - fishing; excel base for area; friendly owners." ♦ 1 Apr-30 Sep. € 12.50 2005*

THENON *7C3* (10km W Rural) **Camping de la Pelonie, La Bourgie**, 24330 St Antoine-d'Auberoche [05 53 07 55 78; fax 05 53 03 74 27; lapelonie@aol.com] Fr Perigueux on N89 twd Brive; 5km past St Pierre-de-Chignac, site sp on L; turn L at Picnic area - go under rlwy bdge; site ent on L. Med, mkd pitch, pt shd; wc; chem disp; shwrs inc; el pts (6A) €3.05 (poss req long cable); lndtte; gas; ice; shop; rest; bar; playgrnd; htd pool; paddling pool; TV; 10% statics; dogs; phone; poss cr; Eng spkn; adv bkg; quiet; red low ssn; no cc acc; CCI. "A delightful, welcoming site; charming owners; gd facs & v clean; supmkt at Perigueux." ♦ 18 Apr-27 Sep. € 16.20 2003*

THERONDELS see Pierrefort *7C4*

THIEMBRONNE *3A3* (Rural) **Camping Les Pommiers**, 62560 Thiembronne [03 21 39 50 19 or 03 21 66 25 47 (LS); fax 03 21 95 79 20] SW fr St Omer for 25km on D928 to Fauquembergues. NW on D158 for 4km past water tower. Site sp. Med, sl, shd; wc; chem disp; shwrs inc; el pts inc; lndtte; shop 1km; snacks; playgrnd; pool; games area; entmnt; TV; 75% statics; poss cr; adv bkg; quiet. 15 Mar-15 Oct. € 20.00 2003*

THIERS *9B1* (6km NE) **Camp Municipal Les Chanterelles**, 63550 St Remy-sur-Durolle [tel/fax 04 73 94 31 71; mairie-saint-remy-sur-durolle@ wanadoo.fr] On A72/E70 W dir Clermont-Ferrand, exit at junc 3 sp Thiers. Foll sp twd Thiers on N89 into L Monnerie. Fr vill, take D20 & foll sp St Remy. In St Remy, foll 'Camping' sp. Do not app thro Thiers as narr rds v diff for lge o'fits. Med, terr, pt shd; wc; chem disp; mv service pnt; shwrs inc; el pts (10A) €2.90; gas; lndtte; ice; shops 3km; tradsmn; BBQ; playgrnd; pool & lake 300m; tennis; windsurfing; dogs €0.90; adv bkg; quiet; CCI. "Many attractions by water with beach; site beautifully situated with lovely views; gd facs; some noise at w/e fr statics." ♦ 1 May-30 Sep. € 9.00 2005*

THIERS *9B1* (8km SW Rural) **Camp Municipal Pont Astier**, 63190 Orleat [tel/fax 04 73 53 64 40; sogeval@wanadoo.fr] On A72 take exit 2 onto D906 S for 2.5km. Turn R on N89 for Clermont-Ferrand. Turn R at Pont-de-Dore onto D224. Site 3km on R. Med, hdg pitch, pt sl, pt shd; wc; chem disp; shwrs inc; el pts (10A) €3; lndry rm; ice; shop 3km; tradsmn; snacks; bar; BBQ; playgrnd; pool; fishing; tennis; dogs €1.50; Eng spkn; adv bkg; red low ssn; CCI. "Park nrby; by Rv Dore; lge pitches, but some damp; poss mosquito prob; ent poss diff." ♦ 1 Apr-30 Sep. € 12.00 2005*

THIERS *9B1* (4km NW Rural) **Camping Base de Loisirs Iloa, Courty**, 63300 Thiers [04 73 80 92 35 or 04 73 80 14 90; fax 04 73 80 88 81] Exit A72 junc 2 for Thiers; at rndabt turn L sp Vichy but take D44 sp Dorat; pass under m'way, site beyond Courty on L sp Les Rives-de-Thiers. Sm, mkd pitch, pt shd; wc (some cont); chem disp; mv service pnt; some serviced pitches; shwrs inc; el pts (6A) €2; gas 5km; lndtte; supmkt 5km; tradsmn; playgrnd; pool high ssn adj; lake fishing; tennis; mini-golf; entmnt; TV rm; dogs; noisy; CCI. "Well-maintained; v gd, clean san facs; excel sports facs adj; friendly warden; vg long/sh stay." ♦ ltd. 15 Apr-15 Oct. € 11.00 (3 persons) 2005*

THIEZAC see Vic sur Cere *7C4*

†**THILLOT, LE** *6F3* (1km NW) **Camp Municipal Clos des Chaume**, 88160 Le Thillot [03 29 25 10 30; fax 03 29 25 25 87; campingmunicipal-lethillot88@ laposte.net] Site sp on N o'skts of town N on N66, on R behind sports cent. Med, pt sl, pt shd; htd wc; shwrs inc; el pts (6A) €1.55; gas; lndry rm; shops 1km; playgrnd; pool; tennis adj; few statics; adv bkg; quiet. € 5.50 2004*

THILLOT, LE *6F3* (2km NW) **Camping Le Clos Martin, 5 Rue du Clos-Martin**, 88160 Ramonchamp [03 29 25 05 38] At Ramonchamp on N66 (travelling E) turn R & foll sp. Sm, pt shd; wc; chem disp; shwrs €1.25; el pts (6A) €2 (poss rev pol); lndtte; shops, rest 200m; BBQ; playgrnd; rv fishing; dogs €0.50; phone; CCI. "Nice, quiet site; helpful owners; gd walking & cycling." 1 Apr-15 Sep. € 6.80 2005*

THIONVILLE *5C2* (NE Urban) **Camp Municipal, 6 Rue du Parc, 57100 Thionville [03 82 53 83 75; fax 03 82 53 91 27]** Fr town cent take D153F sp Manom with park on R. Turn R at end of park. Camping sp easily visible app town to & fr cent. Sm, mkd pitch, some hdstg, pt shd; wc (some cont); chem disp; shwrs inc; el pts (3-10A) €2-4; shop 250m; tradsmn; rest snacks, bar 250m; playgrnd; pool 1km; boating; fishing; poss v cr; Eng spkn; adv bkg; quiet; CCI. "Well kept site, poss untidy low ssn; helpful & friendly warden; many long-term residents; rv walk to town; some pitches with rvside views; barrier open 0800-1200 & 1600-2000; vg short stay." ♦ 1 May-30 Sep. € 9.00   2005*

Some of these sites have changed their opening dates - we'd better fill in some site report forms and let the editor of the guide know.

†THIVIERS *7C3* (10km N Rural) **Camping Le Touroulet, Moulin du Tourelet, 24800 Chaleix [tel/fax 05 53 55 23 59; touroulet@hotmail.com]** Fr Limoges on N21 S twd Perigueux, thro vill of La Coquille, in about 4.5km turn R onto D98 twd St Jory-de- Chalais & Chaleix. In 4km turn L to vill & site 1km further on. Sm, pt sl, some hdstg, pt shd; pt htd wc; chem disp; shwrs inc; el pts (8A) inc; lndtte; ice; shop 1.5km; tradsmn; rest; bar; BBQ; lake sw & sand/ shgl beach; fishing; games rm; entmnt; dogs; adv bkg; quiet; CCI. "Spacious, attractive rvside site; well-kept, tidy; welcoming, helpful British owners; gd rest; weekly BBQs in ssn; excel Xmas package." € 14.00   2005*

THIVIERS *7C3* (10km N) **Camping Maisonneuve, 24800 St Jory-de-Chalais [tel/fax 05 53 55 10 63; camping.maisonneuve@wanadoo.fr; www. camping-maisonneuve.com]** N fr Thiviers on N21 for 6km; turn L on D98 thro Chaleix; Maisonneuve on L bef ent St Jory-de-Chalais. Other rtes v narr. Sm, hdg/mkd pitch, pt sl, pt shd; wc; chem disp; mv service pnt; shwrs inc; el pts (10A) €3.50; lndtte; shop 500m; rest; snacks; bar; playgrnd; pool; fishing lake; games rm; TV; 10% statics; dogs €1; Eng spkn; adv bkg; quiet; red 7+ days; CCI. "Excel; v helpful owners; in attract countryside; pretty site; lge pitches." ♦ 1 Apr-31 Oct. € 16.00   2005*

THIVIERS *7C3* (1.5km E Urban) **Camp Municipal Le Repaire, 24800 Thiviers [tel/fax 05 53 52 69 75]** N21 to Thiviers; at traff lts take D707 E twd Lanouaille; site in 1.5km on R. Med, hdg/mkd pitch, pt sl, terr, pt shd; wc; chem disp; mv service pnt; shwrs inc; el pts (5A) inc; lndry rm; shop 2.5km; tradsmn; snacks; playgrnd; pool high ssn (caps ess); TV rm; lake fishing; sw 800m; 5% statics; dogs €1.60; poss cr; adv bkg; quiet; red 7+ days; CCI. "Many chateaux, museums; walks; gd cent for N Perigord; some pitches unrel in wet weather; vg sh stay." ♦ 1 May-30 Sep. € 16.72   2002*

THOISSEY *9A2* (1km S) **Camp-Plage Municipal, 01140 Thoissey [04 74 04 02 97 or 04 74 04 04 25 (LS); fax 04 74 69 76 13; thoissey@wanadoo.fr]** S on N6 turn L onto D9. Turn sharp R on Plage immed after x-ing Rv Saone. Lge, mkd pitch, pt shd; wc (some cont); shwrs inc; el pts (6-10A) inc; lndtte; shop; rest; snacks; bar; playgrnd; htd pool (high ssn); watersports; rv beach & sw adj; TV; 75% statics; poss cr; quiet; CCI. "Excel family site; helpful staff; full facs for children; ltd facs low ssn, poss unclean; lge pitches; v muddy when wet; conv for vineyards." Easter- 20 Sep. € 17.00   2005*

THOLY, LE *6F3* (Rural) **Camp de Noir Rupt, 5 Chemin de L'Etang, 88530 Le Tholy [03 29 61 81 27; fax 03 29 61 83 05; www. jpvacances.com]** Fr Gerardmer, take Remiremont rd, turn R in Le Tholy up hill. Site on L on secondary rd to Epinal & sp. Med, pt shd; wc; shwrs inc; el pts (6A) €4.60; gas; lndtte; shops 1km; snacks; pool; tennis inc; poss cr; v quiet. "Sm pitches; vg." 15 Apr-15 Oct. € 16.20   2002*

THOLY, LE *6F3* (6km N Rural) **Camping Le Barba, Le Village, 88640 Rehaupal [tel/fax 03 29 66 35 57 or 03 29 66 21 17; camping.barba@wanadoo.fr]** Fr Gerardmer on D417 after 8km site sp on R 2km bef Le Tholy. Foll sp to Rehaupal, site on R on ent to vill. Sm, mkd pitch, pt shd; wc; chem disp; shwrs inc; el pts (3-6A) €2-3; gas; lndtte; ice; shop adj; tradsmn; rest; dogs €1; Eng spkn; quiet. "Excel base for Alsace; beautiful scenery; friendly owner." 1 May-30 Sep. € 9.00   2004*

THONAC see Montignac *7C3*

THONNANCE LES MOULINS *6E1* (2km W Rural) **LES CASTELS La Forge de Ste Marie, 52230 Thonnance-les-Moulins [03 25 94 42 00; fax 03 25 94 41 43; la.forge.de.sainte.marie@ wanadoo.fr; www.laforgedesaintemarie.com or www.les-castels.com]** Fr N67 exit sp Joinville-Est, foll D60 NE sp Vaucouleurs. In 500m turn R onto D427 sp Poissons & Neufchateau. Site on R in 11km. NB Wide turn into site fr main c'way, not fr what appears to be a run in. Med, hdg/mkd pitch, pt terr, shd; wc; serviced pitches; baby facs; shwrs; el pts (6A) inc; gas; lndtte; shop; tradsmn; rest; snacks; bar; BBQ; htd, covrd pool & paddling pool; lake; boating; freshwater fishing; cycle hire; gd walking; games rm; entmnt; internet; 75% statics; dogs; adv bkg (dep req); cc acc; CCI. "Vg site; access diff to some terr pitches; v friendly & helpful owners; clean, well-kept site; sharp bends on app rds to pitches poss diff lge o'fits; mkt Fri; vg rest." ♦ 29 Apr-15 Sep. € 29.00 (CChq acc) ABS - J04   2005*

THONON LES BAINS *9A3* (2km NE Urban) Camping St Disdille, 74207 Thonon-Les-Bains [04 50 71 14 11; fax 04 50 71 93 67] Fr W on N5 thro Thonon on HGV rte twds Evian; at rndabt with Lidl supmkt, foll sp to site or to St Disdille. Fr E on N5 sp app town; site by Lac Leman. Lge, mkd pitch, shd; wc; shwrs; el pts (6-10A); gas; lndtte; ice; shop; rest; playgrnd; lake sw 200m; games area; petanque; fishing; many statics; adv bkg ess; cc acc; CCI. ♦ 2002*

†**THONON LES BAINS** *9A3* (9km SE Rural) Camping La Prairie, 74500 Champanges [04 50 73 40 68; fax 04 50 73 48 46] Rec rte for c'vans & lge m'vans: D32 fr Thonon & foll sp Marin & Vallee d'Abondance/Champanges. Turn R into vill, site on R. Med, pt sl, terr, pt shd; wc; chem disp (wc); mv service pnt; baby facs; shwrs inc; el pts (4A) inc; lndtte; ice; shop 200m; rest; snacks; bar; playgrnd; lake sw in Thonon; tennis; games area; entmnt; TV rm; 10% statics; dogs; CCI. "Gd walking." ♦ ltd. € 8.10 2002*

THONON LES BAINS *9A3* (10km W) Camping La Pinede, 74140 Excenevex [04 50 72 85 05 or 04 50 72 81 27 (Mairie); fax 04 50 72 93 00] On N5 to Geneva, 10km fr Thonon, turn R at Camping sp. Lge, shd; htd wc; shwrs inc; chem disp; 2 serviced pitches; el pts (10A) inc; gas; lndtte; ice; shop; rest; snacks; bar; BBQ; playgrnd; sports area; tennis; lake sw, fishing, watersports & sand beach; horseriding 1km; entmnt; TV; 75% statics; dogs €2; poss cr; adv bkg; quiet; "Friendly & efficient staff; excel lakeside situation; supmkts close." 1 Apr-31 Oct. € 17.00 2004*

THONON LES BAINS *9A3* (10km W) Camping Mathieu Le Leman I, 74140 Yvoire [04 50 72 84 31; fax 04 50 72 96 33] Exit N5 bet Geneve & Thonon onto Rd 25 sp Yvoire; site in 10km; at Yvoire foll camping sp; fr Douvaine foll Lac Leman lakeside sp. Med, mkd pitch, pt sl, pt shd; wc (mainly cont); chem disp; shwrs inc; el pts (6A) €2.50; lndtte; ice; shop 150m; tradsmn; snacks; bar; playgrnd; lake sw 500m; 50% statics; dogs €1; Eng spkn; adv bkg (dep req); quiet; red low ssn; CCI. "Overlooking medieval vill; v friendly proprietor; v lge pitches; adj site Mathieu Le Leman II open Jul-Aug only; same ownership, sep recep & facs; excel long stay." 1 May-30 Sep. € 13.50 2005*

THORE LA ROCHETTE see Vendome *4F2*

THORENS GLIERES *9A3* (Rural) Camp Nantizel, 74570 Thorens-Glieres [04 50 22 43 42] Fr A40/A41 exit 19. Take N203 twd Annecy. In 10km after S-bend take D5 E to Thorens-Glieres & foll camping sp to site. Sm, pt sl, pt shd; wc; own san rec; chem disp; el pts (3A) €2; shops 4km; playgrnd; dogs €0.80; v quiet. "CL-type site on alpine farm with superb views; highly rec; quiet base; gd sh stay." 15 Jun-15 Sep. € 10.00 2005*

THORENS GLIERES *9A3* (3km SE Rural) Camping Rural Les Combes d'Usillon, 461 Chemin des Combes d'Usillon, 74570 Thorens-Glieres [04 50 22 81 10; campingville@aol.com] Fr Thorens-Glieres take D5 S twd Aviernoz. In 1km turn L twd La Louvatiere. Site sp Camping Rural in 2km on rvside. Sm, pt shd; shwrs inc; el pts €1.85; lndtte; shop 2.5km; rest; dogs; v quiet. "Pleasant owner; gd walking fr site." 15 May-15 Sep. € 10.00 2005*

THORENS GLIERES *9A3* (3km NW Rural) Aire Naturelle Le Moulin Dollay, 206 Rue du Moulin Dollay, 74570 Groisy [tel/fax 04 50 68 00 31] Fr Annecy take N203 N. At Champion supmkt fork L to Groisy. Thro Groisy & over rv bdge, turn R sp La Roche-sur-Foron, site on L. Sm, mkd pitch, pt shd; htd wc; chem disp; mv service pnt; baby facs; fam bthrm; shwrs inc; el pts (6A) €3; gas 1km; lndtte; shops 1km; tradsmn; snacks; BBQ; bar 5km; playgrnd; rv sw adj; sand beach 12km; TV rm; no dogs; train 500m; phone; adv bkg 25% dep; quiet; 10% red 8+ days; cc not acc. "Excel site with immac san facs; v friendly owner; highly rec." ♦ 15 May-15 Sep. € 15.00 2004*

THOUARCE *4G1* (SW) Camp Municipal de l'Ecluse, Ave des Trois Ponts, 49380 Thouarce [02 41 54 14 36 (Mairie); fax 02 41 54 09 11; mairie.thouarce@wanadoo.fr] Exit A87 junc 24 onto N160/D56 dir Beaulieu-sur-Layon & Thouarce. Site sp. Sm, pt shd; wc (cont for men); shwrs inc; el pts €1.60; gas; ice; shops & supmkt 400m; playgrnd; pool; fishing; adv bkg; quiet; CCI. 15 Apr-15 Oct. € 3.70 2002*

THOUARS *4H1* (1km E) Camp Municipal, 79100 Thouars [05 49 68 22 80; fax 05 49 66 16 09; laurence-morin@ville-thouars.fr] Sp fr cent of town. Ent down 1 in 5 hill, narr & winding; access diff lge o'fits. Sm, pt shd; wc; shwrs; el pts (5-10A) €2-3; snacks; playgrnd; pool nr; fishing. "Security gate closes at 2200; warden on site for 1 hour am only low ssn; fair sh stay." 6 Jun-30 Sep. € 8.00 2003*

THOUARS *4H1* (10km S Urban) Camp Municipal La Grande Versenne, 79330 St Varent [05 49 67 62 11 (Mairie); fax 05 49 67 67 87] Site sp on D938 at Boiulle. Fr Thouars turn R on D28 sp St Varent. Thro vill over bdge, turn R behind college; site sp. Sm, hdg pitch, pt shd; wc; shwrs inc; el pts (10A) €2.50; playgrnd; pool adj; supmkt nr; no statics; dogs €0.50; adv bkg; quiet. "Friendly staff; gd NH." ♦ 1 Apr-31 Oct. € 8.00 2003*

THOUARS *4H1* (6km NW) Camp Municipal des Planches, 79290 Argenton-l'Eglise [05 49 67 02 14 (Mairie)] Fr Thouars, take D759 twd Argenton-Chateau. In 4km turn R immed past rv bdge D61. Site sp thro Argenton-l'Eglise, by rv. Sm, pt shd; wc; own san adv; shwrs; el pts (10A); shops 500m; poss cr; rv fishing; tennis adj; adv bkg." 2002*

THUEYTS *9D2* (1.5km E Rural) **Camping du Pont de Mercier, 07330 Thueyts [tel/fax 04 75 36 46 08]** Clearly sp fr N102. Narr app rd. Med, pt sl, pt shd; wc; shwrs inc; el pts (3A) €2.20; gas; lndtte; ice; shop 1km; playgrnd; rv fishing; games area; dogs €1; adv bkg; quiet but some rd noise; red low ssn. "On banks of Ardeche with gd views & walks; ample shops & rests in Thueyts; Pont de Diable worth visit." 15 Apr-10 Sep. € 11.50   2002*

THUEYTS *9D2* (4km E Rural) **Camping Le Ventadour, Pont de Rolandy, 07380 Meyras [tel/fax 04 75 94 18 15]** Sp fr N102. Med, pt shd; htd wc; shwrs inc; el pts (3-10A) €1.90-2.90 (poss rev pol); lndtte; ice; shop; supmkt 5km; snacks; bar; gas BBQ; playgrnd; rv sw; fishing; some statics; dogs €1.20; Eng spkn; adv bkg; quiet. "Owners v helpful; easy access; gd, clean facs; attractive site; ideal base for touring Cevennes; excel; vg long/sh stays." 1 Apr-30 Sep. € 13.00   2004*

THURY HARCOURT *3D1* (Rural) **Camping de la Vallee du Traspy, Rue du Pont Benoit, 14220 Thury-Harcourt [02 31 79 61 80 or 02 31 52 53 54; fax 02 31 84 76 19]** App fr N on D562 fr Caen take L fork into town after pool complex. In 100m turn L at Hotel de la Poste, 1st L to site clearly sp. Med, mkd pitch, terr, pt shd; wc (cont); chem disp; serviced pitches; shwrs inc; el pts (6A) €3.10; gas; lndtte; ice; shop 1km; tradsmn; snacks; bar; BBQ; playgrnd; htd pool nr; sauna & spa; rv adj & lake nrby; fishing; entmnt; dogs €1.80; phone; poss cr; Eng spkn; adv bkg rec high ssn; quiet; CCI. "Friendly owners; quiet & close to town; approx gd for walking & canoeing on Rv Orne; gd sh stay." ♦ 1 Apr-14 Sep. € 12.30   2004*

THURY HARCOURT *3D1* (8km SE) **Camp Municipal des Rochers du Parc (formerly Moulin du Vey), Le Vey, 14570 Clecy [02 31 69 70 36; fax 02 31 66 96 08; camping.clecy@free.fr]** Fr Conde take D562 to Caen. R turn sp to Clecy. Foll camp sp. Med, mkd pitch, pt sl, pt shd; wc; shwrs inc; el pts (6A) €3; lndtte; shop 1km; tradsmn; snacks; playgrnd; rv sw; fishing; canoeing; games area; some statics; dogs €1.10; phone; quiet. "Excel cent for walking; lovely rvside site; friendly staff; gd facs but ltd low ssn." 1 Apr-15 Oct. € 12.00
2005*

TIL CHATEL *6G1* (2km E Rural) **Camping Les Sapins, 21120 Til-Chatel [03 80 95 16 68]** Leave A31 junc 5 onto N74 twd Til Chatel. Site on R in 500m adj Rest Les Sapins. Sm, pt sl, pt shd, serviced pitch; wc (some cont); shwrs inc; el pts (10A) inc; shops 2km; rest; snacks; bar; poss cr; Eng spkn; adv bkg; rd noise; CCI. "Poss v overcr high ssn; twin-axles not acc; facs need upgrade but v conv NH." Easter-31 Oct. € 15.00   2005*

TIL CHATEL *6G1* (5km W Rural) **Camp Municipal des Capucins, 21120 Is-sur-Tille [03 80 95 02 08; fax 03 80 95 08 33; mairiedis@wanadoo.fr]** Leave A31 at junc 5 S onto N74 dir Til-Chatel. Turn R onto D959 to Is-sur-Tille. Site on L at sports grnd. Well sp. Sm, shd; wc (cont); chem disp; shwrs inc; el pts (3A) inc; lndry rm; shops 1km; tradsmn; pool adj; poss cr; quiet. "Site yourself; warden calls am & pm; facs old but clean, useful NH." 1 Jun-30 Sep. € 7.90
2004*

TINTENIAC *2E4* (Urban) **Camp Municipal du Pont L'Abbesse, Rue du 8 Mai 1945, 35190 Tinteniac [02 99 68 09 91 or 02 99 68 02 15 (Mairie); fax 02 99 68 05 44]** Sp in cent of Tinteniac. Site behind Auberge La Halage, on canal de l'Ille et Rance. Sm, hdg/mkd pitch, pt sl, pt shd; wc; shwrs; el pts €2; shops, rest, snacks & bar adj; playgrnd; 30% statics; quiet; CCI. "V nice site; backs on canal with fishing & boating; vg rest adj; lovely walk/cycle on canal bank." ♦ 1 Mar-31 Oct. € 6.00   2004*

TINTENIAC *2E4* (2km S Rural) **Camping Les Peupliers, La Besnelais, 35190 Tinteniac [02 99 45 49 75; fax 02 99 45 52 98; camping. les-peupliers@wanadoo.fr]** On N137 Rennes to St Malo rd; after Hede foll rd to Tinteniac about 2km; site on main rd on R, sp. Med, hdg/mkd pitch, pt sl, pt shd; wc (some cont); chem disp; mv service pnt; shwrs inc; el pts (6A) €2.70 (poss rev pol); lndtte; ice; shops 2km; tradsmn high ssn; rest; snacks; bar; playgrnd; htd pool; lake fishing; tennis; games area; TV rm; 30% statics; dogs €1.55; phone; adv bkg; quite but some rd noise; CCI. "V quiet, clean, tidy site amongst fir trees; barrier with card operation; on Pilgrim Rte to Santiago de Compostela." ♦ ltd. 1 Apr-31 Oct. € 16.05   2005*

TOCANE ST APRE see Lisle *7C3*

TONNEINS *7D2* (500m SE Urban) **Camp Municipal Robinson, 47400 Tonneins [05 53 79 02 28 or 05 53 79 22 79 (LS)]** On N113, bet Marmande & Agen. Med, shd, hdstg; wc; shwrs inc; el pts inc; lndtte; rest; hypermkt 3km; quiet, some rd & rlwy noise. ♦ 1 Jun-15 Sep. € 10.25   2003*

TONNERRE *4F4* (600m N Urban) **Camp Municipal de la Cascade, Ave Aristide Briand, 89700 Tonnerre [tel/fax 03 86 55 15 44; ot.tonnerre@ wanadoo.fr]** Best app via D905 (E by-pass); turn at rndabt twd town cent L after x-ing 1st rv bdge. Foll site sp to avoid low bdge. On banks of Armancon & nr Canal de l'Yonne. Med, pt shd (lge pitches); wc (some cont); chem disp; mv service pnt; shwrs; el pts (5A) inc; lndry rm; ice; shops; tradsmn; rest; snacks; bar; playgrnd; htd pool 1km; rv sw adj; fishing; entmnt; TV rm; 5% statics; Eng spkn; adv bkg; quiet; cc acc; CCI. "Excel san facs; gd long stay." ♦ 1 Apr-15 Oct. € 11.60   2004*

TONNOY *6E2* (N Rural) **Camp Municipal Le Grand Vanne**, 54210 Tonnoy [03 83 26 62 36; fax 03 83 26 62 33] On A330 S fr Nancy sp Epinal/, exit junc 7 sp Flavigny. Site on L on banks of Rv Moselle. Lge, pt shd; wc (cont); shwrs inc; el pts (3-6A) inc; ice; shops 500m; snacks; BBQ; playgrnd; rv sw; fishing; 75% statics; dogs; poss cr; quiet. "Gd sh stay." 15 Jun-15 Oct. € 11.30   2003*

†**TORCY** *3D3* (3km N Urban) **Camping Le Parc de la Colline**, Route de Lagny, 77200 Torcy [01 60 05 42 32; fax 01 64 80 05 17; camping.parc. de.la.colline@wanadoo.fr; www.camping-de-la-colline.com] Exit A104 junc 10 W onto D10 sp Torcy/Noisiel. Site on L in 1km. Lge, hdg/mkd pitch, terr, pt shd; htd wc (some cont); chem disp; mv service pnt; shwrs inc; el pts (2A) inc (€3 for 6A); lndtte; shop; hypmkt 3km; playgrnd; htd pool; waterslide; lake beach & sw 1km; tennis; internet; TV rm; some statics; dogs €4.50; poss cr; adv bkg; cc acc; CCI. "Conv Disneyland, Parc Asterix & Paris; conv RER to Paris or Disneyland by site minibus; v helpful Eng-spkg staff; steep app to pitches but tow avail." ♦ € 24.10   2005*

See advertisement

TORIGNI SUR VIRE *1D4* (500m S Rural) **Camp Municipal du Lac 2**, Route de Vire, 50160 Torigni-sur-Vire [02 33 56 91 74 or 02 33 56 71 44 (Mairie); fax 02 33 56 13 35] Site sp fr N174 opp municipal stadium; adj Camp Municipal du Lac 1 (1 star). Sm, hdg pitch; wc; chem disp; shwrs inc; el pts €3 (long lead poss req); playgrnd; TV; Eng spkn; quiet. "Warden in house opp, helpful; pleasant, well-laid out site; basic san facs; gd NH." 1 May-31 Oct. € 7.30   2004*

TORIGNI SUR VIRE *1D4* (500m S Rural) **Camp Municipal du Lac No. 1**, 50160 Torigni-sur-Vire [02 33 56 91 74; fax 02 33 56 71 44] On L of N174 heading SE to Vire opp Municipal stadium, adj Camp Municipal du Lac 2 (3 star). Sp at gate, ent 4m. Care needed in wet. Med, pt sl, pt shd; wc; chem disp; shwrs inc; el pts €1.60; lndtte; shops 1km; playgrnd; quiet but early morning lorries; CCI. "Gd basic NH; warden in house opp; interesting town." 15 Mar-31 Oct. € 4.60   2004*

TORREILLES PLAGE *10G1* (Coastal) **Camping Club Les Tropiques**, Blvd de la Mediterranee, 66440 Torreilles-Plage [04 68 28 05 09; fax 04 68 28 48 90; camping-les-tropiques@ wanadoo.fr; www.camping-les-tropiques.com & www.homair-vacances.fr] Exit A9 junc 41 onto D83 E twd Canet-Plage. Torreilles-Plage sp. Lge, mkd pitch, shd; wc (some cont); chem disp; mv service pnt; shwrs inc; el pts (6A) inc; gas; lndtte; ice; shop; rest; snacks; bar; playgrnd; pool; sand beach 300m; tennis; archery; games area; entmnt; internet; TV rm; 80% statics; dogs €4; poss cr; Eng spkn; cc acc; red low ssn; CCI. "Gd family-run site; purchase camp bracelet to join in entmnts." ♦ 9 Apr-9 Oct. € 33.00 (CChq acc)   2005*

Will you fill in the site report forms at the back of the guide, or shall I?

TORREILLES PLAGE *10G1* (Coastal) **Camping Le Calypso**, 66440 Torreilles-Plage [04 68 28 09 47; fax 04 68 28 24 76; www.camping-calypso.com] Take D617 fr Perpignan sp Canet-Plage & D81 to St Laurent. 1.7km prior to St Laurent on R hand side of rd. 2nd site on L on way to beach. Med, shd; wc; chem disp; baby facs; shwrs; el pts (6A); gas; lndtte; shop adj; playgrnd; pool; sand beach 300m; rv 1km; TV; entmnts; 40% statics; no dogs; poss cr; adv bkg rec high ssn; quiet; cc acc. "Interesting trips to vineyards." ♦ 29 Mar-30 Sep. € 23.00   2002*

TORREILLES PLAGE *10G1* (Coastal) **Camping Les Dunes**, 66440 Torreilles-Plage [04 68 28 38 29 or 04 68 28 30 32] Exit a'route at Perpignan Nord on D83 dir Le Barcares. After 10km at int'chge bear R on D81 sp Canet-Plage. In 3km turn L; site sp. Lge, mkd pitch, pt shd; wc; shwrs inc; el pts; rest; snacks; bar; shops adj; sand beach 200m; pool; poss cr; adv bkg (rec Jul/Aug); many statics; CCI. "Ltd facs low ssn; strong awning pegs ess; dusty when wind blows." 15 Mar-15 Oct. € 21.50   2002*

FRANCE

TORREILLES PLAGE *10G1* (Coastal) CHADOTEL Camping Le Trivoly, Blvd des Plages, 66440 Torreilles-Plage [04 68 28 20 28 or 02 51 33 05 05 (LS); fax 04 68 28 16 48; chadotel@wanadoo.fr; www.camping-chadotel.fr] Torreilles-Plage is sp fr D81, site is cent vill. Lge, hdg/mkd pitch, pt shd; htd wc; serviced pitches; shwrs inc; el pts (6A) inc; gas; lndtte; ice; shop; snacks; bar; playgrnd; htd pool; waterslide; sand beach 800m; tennis; cycle hire; watersports; games rm; TV rm; entmnt; dogs €2.90; Eng spkn; adv bkg; quiet; cc acc. "Gd walking in Pyrenees; vg." ♦ 2 Apr-23 Sep. € 28.00   2005*

Mustn't forget to post our site report forms to The Club, otherwise sites might be deleted.

TORREILLES PLAGE *10G1* (8km N Coastal) Camping La Palmeraie, Blvd de la Plage, 66440 Torreilles-Plage [04 68 28 20 64; fax 04 68 59 67 41; info@camping-la-palmeraie.com; www.camping-la-palmeraie.com] Exit A9/E15 junc 41 at Perpignan Nord onto D83 twd Le Barcares for 10km. At int'chge turn R at junc 9 onto D81 dir Canet-Plage, cont for 3km to lge rndabt & turn L sp Torreilles-Plage, site on R. Lge, hdg/mkd pitch, shd; wc; chem disp; shwrs inc; el pts (5-10A) €3.50-6.60; gas; lndtte; ice; shop; rest; snacks; bar; BBQ (gas only); playgrnd; pool; sand beach 600m; tennis; horseriding nr; games rm; entmnt; child entmnt; TV rm; some statics; dogs; Eng spkn; adv bkg; quiet; red low ssn; cc acc; CCI. "Attractive site; friendly, helpful staff." ♦ 27 May-30 Sep. € 23.70
2005*

TOUCY *4F4* (Urban) Camp Municipal Base de Loisirs Le Patis, 89130 Toucy [03 86 44 13 84 or 03 86 44 28 44; fax 03 86 44 28 42] On D3, 25km SW of Auxerre, Site on S bank of Rv Quanne almost in town cent; sp. Med, pt shd; wc; shwrs inc; el pts (3A) €2.50; shops 500m; pool; fishing; poss cr; adv bkg; quiet. "Friendly warden; excel rests in town; vg mkt Sat; no twin-axles." 1 May-30 Sep. € 6.00
2004*

TOUL *6E2* (7km E Rural) Camping de Villey-de-Sec, 34 Rue de la Gare, 54840 Villey-le-Sec [tel/fax 03 83 63 64 28] Exit Toul E on D909 or take junc 15 fr A31 onto D909. In vill site S by Rv Moselle. V steep app rd. Med, hdg/mkd pitch, hdstg, pt shd; wc; chem disp; mv service pnt; baby facs; shwrs inc; el pts (6A) inc; gas; lndtte; ice; shop; rest; snacks; bar; BBQ; playgrnd; games area; dogs; phone; Eng spkn; no adv bkg; quiet; cc acc; red long stay. "Friendly, beautifully-situated, clean site on rvside." ♦ 3 Apr-30 Sep. € 10.00   2004*

†TOULOUSE *8F3* (5km N Urban) Camp Municipal du Pont de Rupe, 21 Chemin du Pont de Rupe, 31000 Toulouse [05 61 70 07 35; fax 05 61 70 93 17] N fr Toulouse on N20, sp. Poss tricky app fr N for long vans, suggest cont past Pont de Rupe traff lts to next rndabt & double back to turn. Fr S on ring rd exit junc 33A (after junc 12), turn immed R & foll sport sp. Lge, hdg/mkd pitch, hdstg, pt shd; htd wc; own san; chem disp; mv service pnt; shwrs inc; el pts (6-10A) €3.35-4.45; lndtte; shop; rest; snacks; playgrnd; lake fishing; games rm; TV; 90% statics; dogs €1; phone; bus; poss cr (esp public hols); Eng spkn; adv bkg; cc acc; CCI "Well-organised but poss unkempt low ssn; many shabby statics; access by barrier card."
€ 13.00   2005*

TOULOUSE *8F3* (10km S) Camp Municipal du Ramier, 31120 Roques [05 61 72 56 07; fax 05 61 72 57 52] Take Muret exit off A6 S of Toulouse on N117 to Roques. Site on banks of Rv Garonne. Med, pt shd; wc (most cont); shwrs inc; el pts (6-10A) inc; lndtte; shop; playgrnd; bus to city; poss cr; rd noise. "Grubby facs; poss itinerants & workers on site; poss light aircraft noise; v quiet at night; NH only." 1 May-31 Oct. € 15.50   2004*

TOUQUES see Deauville *3D1*

TOUQUET PARIS PLAGE, LE *3B2* (5km N Rural) Camping La Dune Blanche, Route de Camiers, 62176 Camiers [03 21 09 78 48 or 06 86 15 69 32; fax 03 21 09 79 59; camping@duneblanche.com; www.duneblanche.com] Leave A16 junc 26 dir Etaples or junc 27 dir Neufchatel onto D940 dir Etables, Le Touquet. Site well sp. Lge, mkd pitch, pt sl, shd; wc; chem disp; baby facs; shwrs inc; el pts (4-6A) €3.80-5.80; gas; lndtte; shops 2km; tradsmn; bar; BBQ; playgrnd; sand beach 3km; entmnt; TV; 90% statics; dogs €2; phone; bus to beach at Ste Cecile; poss cr; Eng spkn; adv bkg; quiet; red long stay; cc acc; CCI. "Amongst trees; conv Le Touquet, Calais; staff friendly & helpful; san facs need upgrade; gd sh stay." ♦ 1 Apr-2 Nov. € 15.00
2005*

TOUQUET PARIS PLAGE, LE *3B2* (1km S Coastal) Camp Municipal Stoneham, Ave Godin, Paris Plage, 62520 Le Touquet [03 21 05 16 55; fax 03 21 05 06 48] Fr N39 (Etaples) trav to rndabt 7 then 4th set of traff lts. Turn L sp site Stoneham & foll sp. Ent on L. Lge, hdg pitch, pt shd; wc; shwrs inc; el pts (6A) €4.30; lndtte; shops 1km; tradsmn; playgrnd; htd pool 2km; sand beach 1km; 95% statics; dogs €1.25; poss cr even low ssn; adv bkg rec; CCI. "Excel facs; fair NH." 15 Feb-30 Nov.
€ 15.10   2005*

†TOUQUIN *4E4* (2km SE Rural) **Camping Chateau de Chambonnieres, 77540 Le Plessis-Feu-Aussous [01 64 04 15 85; fax 01 64 04 13 36]** Fr A1, exit at Senlis & travel to Meaux. Take A140 & A4 to junc 15, then N36. At the obelisk take D231, to Plessis-Feu-Assous. Site sp on L Med, mkd pitch, pt shd; wc (some cont); chem disp; baby facs; shwrs inc; el pts (6A) inc; gas; lndtte; shop; supmkts 25km; tradsmn; BBQ; sm playgrnd; tennis; horseriding; games area; games rm; dogs €1.50; phone; poss cr; Eng spkn; adv bkg ess in ssn; quiet; cc not acc; CCI. "Modern, clean san facs, but poss long walk & ltd low ssn; v hospitable, friendly, & helpful owners; drive to Peripherique & use metro for Paris; gd NH area with elec & water; gd base Disneyland, Paris, Versailles & Fontainebleau." ♦ € 27.10 ABS - P04
2005*

TOUQUIN *4E4* (2km W Rural) **Camping Les Etangs Fleuris, Route de la Couture, 77131 Touquin [01 64 04 16 36; fax 01 64 04 12 28; contact@ etangs-fleuris.com; www.etangsfleuris.com]** On D231 fr Provins, turn R to Touquin. Turn sharp R in vill & foll sp to site on R in approx 2km. Or fr Coulommiers, take D402 SW twd Mauperthuis, after Mauperthuis L twd Touquin. Foll sp in vill to site 2km W of vill. Med, some hdg pitch, pt shd; wc; chem disp; mv service pnt; shwrs inc; el pts (10A) inc; gas; lndtte; ice; sm shop; tradsmn; hypmkt nr; snacks; bar; playgrnd; htd pool; paddling pool; lake fishing; mini-golf; entmnt; 80% statics; phone; adv bkg; quiet; cc not acc; CCI. "Conv Paris & Disneyland; tour ops on site; no twin-axle c'vans high ssn; v rural & quiet." 1 Apr-18 Sep. € 19.80 (CChq acc)
2005*

TOUR DU MEIX, LA see Clairvaux les Lacs *6H2*

TOUR DU PARC, LE see Sarzeau *2G3*

TOURCOING *3A4* (5km SW Rural) **Camping Les Ramiers, 1 Chemin des Ramiers, 59910 Bondues [tel/fax 03 20 23 12 32]** A19 junc 2, S on N17 twd Menen & Tourcoing, exit Bondues sp to site. Med, pt shd; wc; chem disp; shwrs €1; el pts (3A) €2; ice; BBQ; playgrnd; 50% statics; bus 2km; phone adj; adv bkg; quiet; CCI; "Sh stay/NH, conv Lille & TGV 1 hr Paris." 15 Apr-31 Oct. € 9.00
2002*

TOURNAN EN BRIE *4E3* (1km S Rural) **Caravaning Fredland, 77220 Tournan-en-Brie [01 64 07 96 44; fax 01 64 42 00 61]** Foll N4 E fr Paris. 15km beyond junc with N104 turn R onto D10 sp Liverdy. Site immed on R on lakeside Med, mkd pitch, pt sl, pt shd; wc; chem disp; shwrs inc; el pts (6A) inc; lndtte; rest; snacks; bar; BBQ; playgrnd; htd pool; fishing; games area; 75% statics; poss cr; adv bkg. "Conv for Paris visits; 10 min walk to stn; v nice site beside lake." 1 Mar-31 Oct.
€ 21.50
2005*

TOURNEHEM SUR LA HEM see Ardres *3A3*

†TOURNIERES *1D4* (Rural) **Camping Le Picard, 14330 Tournieres [02 31 22 82 44; fax 02 31 51 70 28; paul.palmer@wanadoo.fr; www.camp-france.com]** Fr Bayeux foll D5/D15 W to Tournieres, 5km past Le Molay-Littry. Fr N13 Cherbourg-Bayeux, E of Carentan turn S onto N174 then E on D15 to Tournieres. Site sp opp Tournieres church. Sm, pt shd, hdg pitch; wc; chem disp; serviced pitches; shwrs inc; el pts (10A) €3.05; lndtte; shop 5km; tradsmn; rest; snacks; bar; playgrnd; htd pool; sand beach 20km; boating; fishing; phone; adv bkg; quiet; cc acc; CCI. "Delightful, British-owned site with rustic atmosphere; conv Normandy beaches, Bayeux Tapestry, Cherbourg ferry; v popular with British tourists; van storage; helpful owners bake croissants & will do laundry; ample hot water." ♦ € 15.30
2004*

As we're travelling out of season, we'd better phone ahead to check that the site is actually open.

†TOURNON SUR RHONE *9C2* (Urban) **Camping de Tournon, 1 Promenade Roche-de-France, 07300 Tournon-sur-Rhone [tel/fax 04 75 08 05 28; camping@camping-tournon.com; www.camping -tournon.com]** Fr Tain l'Hermitage cross Rhone, turn R onto N86. In approx 1km R at end of car park. Turn L after 50m, site on R. Med, shd; wc (some cont); chem disp; mv service pnt; shwrs inc; el pts (6-10A) €2.40-4; gas; lndtte; shop, rest, snacks, bar nr; playgrnd; pool 1km; some statics; dogs €1; phone; site clsd 3rd week Jan & last week Nov; c'van storage avail; poss cr; Eng spkn; adv bkg rec; red long stay; cc acc high ssn; CCI. "Gd facs but inadequate high ssn; easy walk into town; nr steam rlwy; canoeing; friendly owners; lovely views of Rhone fr some pitches; fr mid-Jun rock concerts held nrby at w/e; Mistral can make site v dusty; vg." ♦ € 11.70
2005*

TOURNON SUR RHONE *9C2* (6km N Rural) **Camping L'Iserand, Rue Royal, 07610 Vion [04 75 08 01 73; fax 04 75 08 55 82; iserand@ tele2.fr]** Take N86 N fr Tournon, site 1km N of Vion on L. Med, hdg/mkd pitch, sl, terr, pt shd; htd wc; chem disp; mv service pnt; baby facs; shwrs inc; el pts (10A) €3; ice; gas; lndtte; shop & 1km; tradsmn; rest 1km; snacks; bar; BBQ; playgrnd; pool; beach; cycle hire; canoeing 1km; entmnt; TV rm; 15% statics; no dogs; bus 1km; phone; poss cr; adv bkg; Eng spkn; quiet but some rd & rlwy noise; red low ssn; CCI. "Steam rlwy to mountains adj; v friendly owner lives on site - & will take low ssn visitors; excel." 1 Apr-30 Sep. € 13.00
2005*

La Mignardière

Camping ★★★★ 37510 BALLAN-MIRÉ

At 8 km southwest of TOURS/LOIRE VALLEY
Relax Tranquillity Free time
Large pitches with trees – first class sanitary –
swimming pools, tennis, playing garden, TV room,
grocery, kids club, Fun Park at 50 m
Rental of chalets and mobile homes
(Off season 3rd week for free)

Open from 27/03 till 23/09/2006

Tel.: +33 (0)2 47 73 31 00 - Fax:+33 (0)2 47 73 31 01
www.mignardiere.com - info@mignardiere.com

TOURNON SUR RHONE *9C2* (3km SW Rural) Camping Le Manoir, 222 Route de Lamastre, 07300 Tournon-sur-Rhone [04 75 08 02 50 or 06 70 00 06 13; fax 04 75 08 57 10; info@ lemanoir-ardeche.com; www.lemanoir-ardeche. com] Leave Tournon on D532 just bef x-ing rv, dir Lamastre. Site on R after 3km (4th site). Med, mkd pitch, pt shd; wc (50% cont); chem disp; mv service pnt; shwrs inc; el pts (10A) inc; ice; BBQ; lndtte; shop 2.5km; tradsmn; snacks; bar; playgrnd; pool; rv sw adj; TV rm; entmnt; 20% statics; dogs; phone; poss cr; adv bkg; quiet but some rd noise; cc acc; CCI. "Vg rvside site, ideal for walking; vineyard tours; friendly, hard working staff; gd long/sh stay." ♦ 1 Apr-30 Sep. € 14.50   2003*

TOURNON SUR RHONE *9C2* (2.5km W Rural) Camping Les Acacias, 07300 Tournon-sur-Rhone [tel/fax 04 75 08 83 90; acacias-camping@ wanadoo.fr] Fr N86 Tournon turn W onto D532 dir Lamastre, site on R in approx 2km. Med, pt shd; wc (some cont); chem disp; shwrs; el pts (6A) €3; gas; lndtte; rest; shop 2km; playgrnd; pool; dogs €1; poss cr; Eng spkn; rd noise; adv bkg; CCI. "Nr steam rlwy; gd pitches; some noise fr sawmill; friendly; vg site." ♦ 1 Apr-30 Sep. € 14.50   2005*

TOURNON SUR RHONE *9C2* (4km W) Camping Le Castelet, 07300 St Jean-de-Muzols [04 75 08 09 48; fax 04 75 08 49 60; courrier@ camping-lecastelet.com] Exit Tournon on N86 N; in 500m turn L on D532 twd Lamastre; in 4km turn R on D532 over bdge & turn immed R into site. Med, terr, pt shd; wc (some cont); chem disp; shwrs inc; el pts (5A) inc; gas; lndtte; ice; shop & supmkt 4km; tradsmn; bar; playgrnd; pool; rv sw; entmnt; adv bkg; quiet, but some rd noise; red low ssn; cc not acc. "Steam rlwy adj; owner will arrange to have train stop; spotless san facs." 1 Apr-28 Sep. € 14.90   2003*

TOURNUS *9A2* (1km N Urban) **Camp Municipal en Bagatelle**, 71700 Tournus [03 85 51 16 58; fax 03 85 51 04 13] Fr N6 at N of town turn E opp rlwy stn & rest 'Le Terminus;' foll site sp. Med, some mkd pitch, pt sl, pt shd; wc (some cont); chem disp; mv service pnt; shwrs inc; el pts (10A) inc (long lead poss req); gas; lndtte; ice; shops; BBQ; playgrnd; htd pools adj high ssn; rv 250m; TV; dogs €0.50; Eng spkn; quiet but some rlwy noise; CCI. "Excel, peaceful site nr rv; popular NH - rec arr early; conv A6; spotless facs but v stretched high ssn & ltd low ssn; easy walk to interesting town on rv; v helpful staff." ♦ 1 May-30 Sep. € 13.30   2005*

TOURNUS *9A2* (6km S Rural) Camping Le National 6, 71113 Uchizy [tel/fax 03 85 40 53 90] Exit A6 junc 27 & foll N6 S; sp on L, turn L over bdge on lane to site on L. Adj Rv Saone. Med, shd; wc; shwrs inc; el pts (6A) €3; gas; shop; snacks; playgrnd; pool; fishing; boat hire; poss cr; adv bkg; quiet; red low ssn. "Site in attractive setting on rv bank; gd new san facs; well-maintained site; helpful staff." 1 Apr-30 Sep. € 12.50   2004*

TOURNUS *9A2* (10km W Rural) Aire Naturelle de Camping a La Ferme de Malo (Goujon), Champlieu, 71240 Etrigny [03 85 92 21 47 or 03 85 92 23 40; fax 03 85 92 22 13; fam@ aubergemalo.com; www.aubergemalo.com] S on N6 to Tournus; after rwly stn turn R onto D14; after passing under rlwy DO NOT fork L to foll D14 - cont strt onto D215 dir St Gengoux-le-National; in 8km, in Nogent, turn R at lge stone drinking trough onto D159 (not mkd); at 2nd x-rds turn L onto D459 (sp Champlieu); at 1st x-rds turn L into Champlieu; site on L 500m after vill, bef rv. Sm, mkd pitch, pt shd; wc (cont); shwrs inc; el pts (6-10A) €3; lndtte; tradsmn; rest 1km; playgrnd; horseriding; sw, fishing & boating 10km; tennis 3km; adv bkg ess high ssn; quiet; no cc acc; CCI. "Adj to Rv Grison; farm produce avail; baker calls Tues & Fri; eve meals avail in farmhouse 1km fr campsite; v pleasant & quiet site close to Maconnais wine rte; san facs poss stretched in high ssn; additional pitches & pool opp main site; vg sh stay." 1 May-30 Sep. € 10.80   2004*

†TOURS *4G2* (6km E) **Camping Les Acacias (formerly Municipal), Rue Berthe Morizot, 37700 La Ville-aux-Dames [02 47 44 08 16 or 02 62 19 18 08 (LS); fax 02 47 46 26 65; camplvad.@.aol.com]** Fr Tours take D751 sp Amboise, in 6km 1st sp La Ville-aux-Dames to R, in 200m turn R, site sp. Med, shd; htd wc; chem disp; mv service pnt; serviced pitch; shwrs; el pts (4-10A) €2.50-4.60; gas; Indtte; ice; sm shop; supmkt 1km; playgrnd; pool 500m; boules; tennis 600m; fitness trail, mountain bike circuit, fishing 100m; dogs €1.50; adv bkg; quiet, but rd & rlwy noise; CCI. "V helpful owners; excel san facs; gd site; conv town cent." ♦ € 10.50   2005*

TOURS *4G2* (8km E Rural) **Camp Municipal des Peupliers,   37270   Montlouis-sur-Loire [02 47 50 81 90 or 02 47 45 85 85; fax 02 47 45 15 74; tourisme-montlouis@wanadoo. fr; www.ville-montlouis-loire.fr]** On D751, Tours to Amboise rd, 2km W of vill of Montlouis. Fr N foll sp to Vouvray (keep on N side of Loire to avoid Tours) & cross rv by new bdge to Montlouis. Sp at last minute. Lge, hdg pitch, pt shd; htd wc; chem disp; mv service pnt; baby facs; shwrs inc; el pts (6-16A) €2.70; ice; Indtte; shop 2km; tradsmn; playgrnd; tennis; dogs €1.55; card-operated barrier €20 dep; adv bkg; quiet except at w/e; slight rd noise; red long stay; CCI. "Superb site; conv Tours, vineyards & chateaux; lge pitches; excel san facs; friendly site; vg value; some rd & rlwy noise but quality of site compensates; red facs low ssn; excel." ♦ 15 Mar-15 Oct. € 7.95   2005*

TOURS *4G2* (5km SE Urban) **Camping Les Rives du Cher, 61 Rue de Rochepinard, 37550 St Avertin [02 47 27 27 60; fax 02 47 25 82 89; contact@camping-lesrivesducher.com]** Fr Tours, take N76 S of rv sp Blere/Vierzon into St Avertin vill. Take next L at traff Its over 1st of 2 bdges. Site on R in 450m, not well sp. Med, hdg/mkd pitch, some hdstg, pt shd; wc (some cont); chem disp; mv service pnt; shwrs inc; el pts (4-10A) €2.75-4.40 (poss rev pol); Indtte; shops 400m; rest, snacks & bar adj; playgrnd; htd pool adj; tennis; fishing; dogs €1.10; phone; adv bkg; quiet; cc acc; CCI. "Friendly warden; camp neat, clean but needs modernising; some resident workers; pitches on rd side of site noisy in morning rush hour; poss late night noise fr adj parks & clubs; conv." ♦ 1 Apr-15 Oct. € 12.65   2005*

TOURS *4G2* (10km SE Urban) **Camp Municipal Les Isles, 37270 Veretz [02 47 50 50 48; fax 02 47 35 70 10; mairie.veretz@wanadoo.fr; www. mairie.veretz@wanadoo.fr]** Exit Tours N76 dir Vierzon to Veretz; site 1km past rv bdge on L (S) bank of Rv Cher. Med, hdg/mkd pitch, pt shd; wc (some cont); chem disp; mv service pnt; shwrs inc; el pts (6A) inc; Indtte; ice; supmkt 500m; playgrnd; pool 5km; table tennis; fishing; TV rm; poss cr; Eng spkn; adv bkg ess high ssn; red 14+ days; 10% red CCI. "Vg site; gd welcome; facs adequate, clean; pitches among tall trees by rv overlooking Chateau Veretz; friendly recep; gd security; gd all stays." ♦ 20 May-30 Sep. € 9.30   2003*

TOURS *4G2* (8km SW Urban) **Camping La Mignardiere, 27 Ave des Aubepines, 37510 Ballan-Mire [02 47 73 31 00; fax 02 47 73 31 01; info@mignardiere.com; www.mignardiere.com]** Fr A10 exit junc 24 onto N585 & D37 by-pass. At exit for Joue-les-Tours foll sp Ballan-Mire onto D751. Turn R at 1st set traff Its & foll site sp to W of lake. Lge, hdg/mkd pitch, hdstg, pt shd; htd wc; chem disp; mv service pnt; 10% serviced pitch; baby facs; shwrs inc; el pts (6-10A) €3; Indtte; sm shop; tradsmn; snacks; bar 200m; BBQ; playgrnd; htd pools; windsurfing & fishing 1km; tennis; cycle hire; squash; internet; entmnt; child entmnt; TV rm; dogs; phone; Eng spkn; adv bkg; quiet; red low ssn; CCI. "Conv Loire Valley & chateaux; unisex facs low ssn; gd cycle paths; vg site." ♦ 27 Mar- 23 Sep. € 20.00 (CChq acc)   2005*

See advertisement

TOURS *4G2* (8km W Rural) **Camping L'Islette, 23 Rue   de   Vallieres,   37230   Fondettes [02 47 42 26 42]** Foll N152 W fr Tours twd Saumur. In approx 6km turn L at traff Its onto D276 at Port de Vallieres. Site on L in approx 2km. Sm, hdg pitch, pt shd; wc (some cont); shwrs inc; el pts (10A) €1.70; shop 2km; playgrnd; pool 4km; dogs; bus; poss cr; adv bkg; quiet; CCI. "V pleasant site; helpful owners; facs poss stretched if site full." ♦ ltd. 1 Apr-30 Oct. € 7.00   2004*

TOURS *4G2* (10km W Rural) **Camping de la Confluence, Route de Bray, 37510 Savonnieres [tel/fax 02 47 50 15 71]** Fr Tours take D7 on S of Rv Cher. Site on R on ent Savonnieres on rvside. Med, hdg/mkd pitch, hdstg, pt shd; wc (some cont); chem disp; mv service pnt; baby facs; shwrs inc; el pts (10A) inc; Indtte; ice; shops 500m; tradsmn; rest 100m; bar adj; BBQ; playgrnd; canoe hire; tennis adj; dogs; phone; bus 200m; Eng spkn; adv bkg (dep req); quiet; red 15 days; CCI. "Refurbished 2005; gd views of Rv Cher; gd birdwatching; gd cycling area; poss noisy youths." ♦ 1 Jun-15 Sep. € 13.00   2005*

TOURS *4G2* (11km W Rural) **Camp Municipal Les Granges, 37230 Luynes [02 47 55 60 85 or 02 47 55 50 31 (Mairie); fax 02 47 55 52 56; mairie@luynes.fr]** Fr Tours take N152 twd Saumur. Turn R at Porte-de-Luynes, sp to Luynes & site. Med, hdg/mkd pitch, pt shd; wc; shwrs inc; el pts (6A) inc; shops 500m; tradsmn; playgrnd; pool 800m; fishing 500m; games rm; quiet. "Pleasant views." ♦ 7 May-16 Sep. € 10.10   2003*

TOURY *4F3* **Camp Municipal, Rue de Boissay, 28310 Toury [02 37 90 50 60 (Mairie)]** Fr Orleans take N20 N. Site well sp. Sm, shd; wc; chem disp; shwrs inc; el pts (5A) €3; gas 1km; shop, rest, snacks, bar 1km; BBQ; playgrnd; dogs; poss cr. "NH only; site unattended; rd & rlwy noise; several statics; not many pitches avail; arrive bef 1600 to ensure pitch." 1 Apr-15 Oct. € 10.00   2002*

TOUSSAINT see Fecamp *3C1*

TOUTAINVILLE see Pont Audemer *3D2*

FRANCE

TOUZAC see Fumel *7D3*

TRANCHE SUR MER, LA *7A1* (500m N Urban/Coastal) **Camp Municipal Le Vieux Moulin, Ave Maurice Samson, 85360 La Tranche-sur-Mer** [02 51 27 48 47] On ent town foll sp for Gendarmerie, sp adj supmkt. Lge, mkd pitch, some hdstg, pt sl, pt shd; wc (chem closet); own san; chem disp; shwrs inc; el pts (6A) €1.83; lndry rm; shop 400m; sand beach 500m; 50% statics; poss cr; adv bkg (dep); quiet; CCI. "Some sm pitches; town cent & beach 5 mins walk; gd long stay."
1 Apr-30 Sep. € 14.50   2004*

TRANCHE SUR MER, LA *7A1* (2km NE Coastal) **Camping Le Clos Cottet, 85700 Angles** [02 51 28 90 72; fax 02 51 28 90 50; info@camping-closcottet.com; www.camping-clos cottet.com] S on D747 twd La Tranche-sur-Mer, site is on R sp after passing Angles. Lge, mkd pitch, unshd; wc; chem disp; mv service pnt; serviced pitch; baby facs; shwrs; el pts (5A); gas; lndtte; shop; rest; snacks; bar; playgrnd; htd, covrd, pool; archery, mini-golf; beach 5km; fishing, sailing, windsurfing; waterslide 5km; entmnts; statics; dogs €2.50; CCI. "Vg long stay." Easter-30 Sep. € 18.00   2002*

TRANCHE SUR MER, LA *7A1* (5km NE Rural) **Campings Moncalm et L'Atlantique, 85750 Angles** [02 51 97 55 50; fax 02 51 28 91 09; camping-apv@wanadoo.fr; www.camping-apv. com] Fr La Tranche-sur-Mer take D747 NE for approx 5km. Site 300m bef vill of Angles. Lge, pt shd, wc; shwrs; baby facs; el pts (3-10A) €2.50; lndtte; ice; shop 300m; rest; snacks; bar; BBQ; playgrnd; htd pool; rv fishing; canoeing; waterschute; sailing; windsurfing; entmnt; TV; dogs €2; adv bkg ess; red low ssn. Easter-30 Sep.
€ 21.00   2002*

TRANCHE SUR MER, LA *7A1* (500m E Coastal) **Camping Bel, Rue de Bottereau, 85360 La Tranche-sur-Mer** [02 51 30 47 39; fax 02 51 27 72 81] Ent La Tranche on D747, take 2nd R at rndabt, R at traff lts, ent on L. Med hdg/mkd pitch, pt shd; wc; chem disp; baby facs; shwrs inc; el pts (6A) inc; lndtte; shops rest adj; snacks; bar; tradsmn; playgrnd; pool & children's pool; table-tennis; TV; 70% statics; phone; poss cr; Eng spkn; adv bkg; quiet; CCI "Ideal for families with young children; cycle hire nearby; excel long/sh stay". ♦ 25 May-7 Sep. € 20.00   2004*

TRANCHE SUR MER, LA *7A1* (500m E Coastal) **Camping La Baie d'Aunis, 10 Rue de Pertuis, 85360 La Tranche-sur-Mer** [02 51 27 47 36; fax 02 51 27 44 54; info@camping-baiedaunis.com; www.camping-baiedaunis.com] App on D747 fr La Roche-sur-Yon, turn 2nd R at rndabt sp 'Centre Ville', strt at traff lts & rest on L. Well sp. Med, hdg/mkd pitch, hdstg, pt shd; htd wc (some cont); chem disp; mv service pnt; baby facs; shwrs inc; el pts (10A) €3.85; gas; ice; lndtte; shop 600m; tradsmn; rest; snacks; bar; BBQ; playgrnd; htd pool; sand beach adj; sailing; sea-fishing; watersports; tennis 500m; cycle hire adj; games rm; entmnt; TV; 10% statics; dogs (not Jul/Aug) €2; Eng spkn; adv bkg (ess Jul/Aug); quiet; cc acc; red low ssn; CCI. "Vg, friendly site; excel facs & rest; boat trips to Ile de Re; lovely area, gd beaches; poss diff ent lge o'fits." ♦ 28 Apr-17 Sep. € 24.00   2005*

See advertisement opposite (top)

TRANCHE SUR MER, LA *7A1* (4km E Coastal) **Camping Le Jard, 123 Blvd du Lattre de Tassigny, 85360 La Tranche-sur-Mer** [02 51 27 43 79; fax 02 51 27 42 92; info@camping-du-jard.fr; www.homair-vacances.fr] Foll D747 S fr La Roche-sur-Yon twd La Tranche-sur-Mer; at rndabt turn L (3rd exit) onto D1046 sp La Faute-sur-Mer; cont for approx 5km. At rndabt turn R (1st exit) sp La Faute-sur-Mer, then R at next rndabt onto D46 sp La Tranche-sur-Mer 'par la cote' & La Griere-Plage (ignore all previous La Griere sp); cont for approx 1.5km; site on R. Rough app rd. Lge, hdg pitch, unshd; wc (some cont); chem disp; serviced pitch; baby facs; sauna; shwrs inc; el pts (10A) inc; lndtte; shop; rest; snacks; bar; BBQ; playgrnd; 2 pools (1 htd, covrd); paddling pool; waterslide; sand beach 800m; tennis; games area; games rm; fitness cent; mini-golf; cycle hire; horseriding 10km; golf 20km; internet; entmnt; TV; 30% statics (tour ops); no dogs; c'vans over 10m not acc high ssn; adv bkg; rd noise; red low ssn; red C'van Club; cc acc; CCI. "Clean, tidy, well-run site; pitches liable to flood in wet weather; recep 0800-2100; some sm pitches; gd pool; mkt Tue & Sat." ♦ 21 May-15 Sep. € 28.50 ABS - A03   2005*

TRANCHE SUR MER, LA *7A1* (2km S) **Camping Les Blancs Chenes, Route de la Roche-sur-Yon, 85360 La Tranche-sur-Mer** [02 51 30 41 70 or 02 51 27 37 80 (reservation); fax 02 51 28 84 09; vagues.oceanes@wanadoo.fr; www.camping-vagues-oceanes.com] Site sp on rd D747 Lge, mkd pitch, pt shd; mv service pnt; wc; baby facs; shwrs inc; el pts (5A) inc; gas; lndtte; shop; tradsmn; rest; snacks; bar; playgrnd; htd, covrd pool; waterslide; sand beach 1.8km; tennis; games area; entmnt; statics; dogs €2.60; quiet; Eng spkn; adv bkg; cc acc; CCI. ♦ 1 Apr-28 Sep. € 23.00   2002*

TREBES see Carcassonne *8F4*

TREBEURDEN *1D2* (4km N Coastal) **Camping L'Esperance, Penvern, 22560 Trebeurden** [02 96 91 95 05; fax 02 96 91 98 12; accueil@camping-esperance.com; www.camping-esperance.com] Fr Lannion on D65 to Trebeurden, then D788 sp Tregastel, site in 5km. Med, hdg/mkd pitch, pt shd; wc (some cont); chem disp; mv service pnt; baby facs; shwrs inc; el pts (5-10A) €2.80-3.50; gas; lndtte; ice; shop 2km; playgrnd; sand beach adj; golf adj; TV; 10% statics; dogs €1.50; bus; Eng spkn; adv bkg; quiet; cc not acc; CCI. "V pleasant site; nr GR34 long dist walking rte." ♦ 1 Apr-30 Sep. € 14.20   2005*

TREBEURDEN *1D2* (1km S Coastal) **Camping Armor Loisirs, Pors-Mabo, Rue de Kernevez, 22560 Trebeurden** [02 96 23 52 31; fax 02 96 15 40 36; info@armorloisirs.com or armorloisirs@aol.com; www.armorloisirs.com] N fr Lannion twds Trebeurden on D65. Turn L at 1st mini rndabt, then immed fork R into Rue de Kernevez, site on R in 800m, foll sp Pors-Mabo. Med, hdg/mkd pitch, pt sl, pt shd; wc; chem disp; baby facs; serviced pitches; shwrs; el pts (10A) inc; gas; lndtte; ice; shop 1km; tradsmn; snacks; bar; BBQ; playgrnd; htd pool; sand beach 500m; watersports; fishing; games rm; entmnt; internet; TV; 40% statics; dogs; Eng spkn; adv bkg; quiet; cc acc; red low ssn/CCI. "Steep 'sleeping policemen'; some pitches poss diff for long o'fits; peaceful, well-run site; gd sea views; vg." ♦ 1 Apr-30 Sep. € 20.00   2005*

See advertisement opposite (bottom)

TREBEURDEN *1D2* (4km S Coastal) **Camping Les Plages de Beg Leguer, Route de la Cote, 22300 Lannion** [02 96 47 25 00 or 02 99 83 34 81 (LS); fax 02 96 47 27 77; info@campingdesplages.com; www.campingdesplages.com] Fr Lannion take rd out of town twd Trebeurden then twd Servel on D65, then head SW off that rd twd Beg Leguer (sp). Lge, hdg/mkd pitch, pt shd; wc (some cont); mv service pnt; chem disp; shwrs inc; el pts (6-10A) €3-4.50; gas; lndtte; shop; tradsmn; rest; snacks; bar; playgrnd; htd pools; sand beach 350m; fishing; sailing; windsurfing; tennis; mini-golf; 10% statics; dogs €1; Eng spkn; adv bkg; quiet; red long stay; cc acc; CCI. "V pleasant, peaceful site; lge pitches; excel coast." ♦ Easter-1 Nov. € 17.00   2005*

TREDION *2F3* (1.5km S Rural) **Camp Municipal l'Etang aux Biches, 56350 Tredion** [02 97 67 14 06; fax 02 97 67 13 41] E fr Vannes on N166 for 15km to Elven; in town foll sps N for Tredion. Site on L in 5km. Sm, hdg/mkd pitch, pt sl, pt shd; wc; shwrs inc; el pts (3A) inc; ice; shop 1.5km; tradsmn; playgrnd; quiet. "V peaceful; inland fr v busy coast; helpful staff." ♦ 1 Jul-31 Aug. € 7.30   2003*

TREGASTEL *1D2* (1.5km N Coastal) Tourony Camping, Route de Poul Palud, 22730 Tregastel [02 96 23 86 61; fax 02 96 15 97 84; contact@ camping-tourony.com; www.camping-tourony. com] On D788 fr Trebeurden dir Perros Guirec, site on R immed after exit Tregastel town sp & immed bef bdge over Traouieros inlet, opp Port de Ploumanac'h. Med, hdg/mkd pitch, pt shd; wc (some cont); chem disp; mv service pnt; baby facs; shwrs inc; el pts (6A) €2.80; gas; ice; lndtte; shop 400m; tradsmn; snacks; bar; BBQ; playgrnd; sand beach adj; lake fishing; tennis; cycle hire; games area; golf, horseriding nrby; entmnt; TV; 15% statics; dogs €1; Eng spkn; adv bkg; quiet; cc acc; red long stay/low ssn; CCI. "V pleasant site in gd location; friendly, helpful management; gd touring base Granit Rose coast." ♦ 8 Apr-23 Sep. € 15.80   2005*

See advertisement above

TREGASTEL *1D2* (4km SW Coastal) Camp Municipal Le Dourlin, L'Île Grande, 22560 Pleumeur-Bodou [02 96 91 92 41 or 02 96 23 91 17 (Mairie)] Off D788 SW of Tregastel. Foll minor rd thro vill to site on coast. Med, unshd; wc (some cont); shwrs inc; el pts inc; lndtte; ice; shops 500m; bar adj; playgrnd; shgl beach; sailing; fishing; sports area; quiet; CCI. "Fine sea views; gd walking, cycling; ornithological stn nr; excel." ♦ 8 Jun-30 Sep. € 10.50   2004*

TREGASTEL *1D2* (4km W Coastal/Rural) Camping du Port, Chemin des Douaniers, Landrellec, 22560 Pleumeur-Bodou [02 96 23 87 79; fax 02 96 15 30 40; renseignements@camping-du-port.com; www. camping-du-port.com] Turn off D788 to Landrellec & foll rd thro vill past shop for 100m, take care tight turn L. Site in 500m. Med, hdg/mkd pitch, terr, pt shd; htd wc; chem disp; mv service pnt; serviced pitches; baby facs; shwrs inc; el pts (6-16A) €2.60; gas; lndtte; ice; shop; rest; snacks; bar; BBQ; playgrnd; pool 2km; direct access to sandy/shgl beach adj; fishing, boating, waterskiing; cycle hire; games rm; entmnt; internet; TV rm; dogs €2; Eng spkn; adv bkg; quiet; cc acc; red low ssn; CCI. "Immac, family-owned site; beautiful location; direct access beach; coastal path runs thro site; narr pitches by shore; telecoms museum worth visit." ♦ 1 Apr-8 Oct. € 16.50   2005*

See advertisement below

TREGASTEL *1D2* (1.5km NW Coastal) Camping Le Golven, Route de la Corniche, 22730 Tregastel-Plage [02 96 23 87 77 or 02 99 60 08 34] On D788 beyond Tregastel sp, on L side opp g'ge (twd Trebeurden). Lge, shd; wc; shwrs; el pts; gas; lndtte; ice; shop; rest; snacks; bar; playgrnd; pool; beach 1km; games area; mini-golf; TV; entmnt; bus; adv bkg. "Scenic coast."   2002*

TREGUENNEC see Pont l'Abbe *2F2*

TREGUIER *1D3* (8km N Coastal) **Camp Municipal de Beg-Ar-Vilin, 22820 Plougrescant** [02 96 92 56 15 or 02 96 92 51 18 (Mairie); fax 02 96 92 59 26] Take D8 N out of Treguier to Plougrescant. At St Gonery/Plougrescant turn R foll sp. Med, pt shd; wc; shwrs inc; lndtte; shops 2km; el pts €3.15; beach sand/rock adj; phone; quiet. "Gd; busy, cr site high ssn." ♦ 1 Jun-15 Sep. € 8.80
2005*

TREGUIER *1D3* (10km N Coastal) **Camp du Gouffre, 22820 Plougrescant** [tel/fax 02 96 92 02 95] On D8 N fr Treguier to Plougrescant. R at 2nd church & foll site sp. Med, mkd pitch, pt sl, unshd; wc; chem disp; mv service pnt; shwrs inc; el pts (6-15A) €2.50; lndtte; shop 2km; tradsmn (bread only); ice; playgrnd; sand/shgl beach adj; quiet; adv bkg; cc acc; CCI. "Facs well designed & immac." ♦ 15 Apr-15 Sep. € 10.00
2004*

†TREGUIER *1D3* (10km N) **Camping Le Varlen, Route de Pors-Hir, 22820 Plougrescant** [02 96 92 52 15; fax 02 96 92 50 34] Take D8 N out of Treguier to Plougrescant. Go past old chapel then immed bef church turn R sp Pors-Hir to site in 1km on R. Sm, mkd pitch, pt sl, pt shd; wc; mv service pnt; baby facs; shwrs inc; el pts (10A) inc (poss rev pol); lndtte; ice; shop; bar; playgrnd; sports area; shgl beach 200m; 90% statics; adv bkg; quiet; cc acc. "Shwrs v clean but avoid shwr behind house/bar due dangerous electrics; beautiful coastal walks; some pitches sm & poss diff lge o'fits/m'vans; v helpful owners." € 16.00
2005*

TREGUIER *1D3* (9km NE Coastal) **Camping Port La Chaine, 22610 Pleubian** [02 96 22 92 38; fax 02 96 22 87 92; info@portlachaine.com; www. portlachaine.com] Fr Paimpol take old D786 W & pick up new D786 over rv & thro Lezardrieux. After 3km at x-rds turn R (N) onto D33 thro Pleumeur-Gautier; exit on D20 twds Larmor-Pleubian, turn L after 2km twd coast & foll site sp. Lge, mkd pitch, pt sl, pt shd; wc (some cont); chem disp; serviced pitch; baby facs; shwrs inc; el pts (6A) inc; gas; lndtte; ice; shop; tradsmn; snacks; bar; BBQ; playgrnd; pool; shgl beach adj; watersports nr; tennis; mini-golf, cycle hire in vill; games rm; child entmnt; internet; TV; 30% statics; dogs €1.60; poss cr; Eng spkn; adv bkg ess; quiet; cc acc. "Lovely, peaceful site; excel views fr some pitches; gd facs; helpful owners." ♦ 1 May-9 Sep. € 24.50
ABS - B23
2005*

TREIGNAC *7B4* (4.5km N) **Camping de la Plage, 19260 Treignac** [05 55 98 08 54; fax 05 55 98 16 47; laplage@sud-vacances.com] On D940 opp Lac Barriousses, 4.5km N of Treignac. Med, mkd pitch, pt sl, terr, shd; htd wc; chem disp; mv service pnt; shwrs inc; el pts (5A) inc; lndtte; sm shop & 4.5km; rest 500m; snacks; lake sw, boating, fishing adj; 5% statics; poss cr; adv bkg (booking fee); quiet; CCI. "Vg long/sh stay; levelling blocks for m'vans most pitches; excel, v clean site; beautiful area & outlook." ♦ 1 Apr-30 Sep. € 14.30
2002*

TREIGNAC *7B4* (10km NW Rural) **Camp Municipal Le Merle, 19370 Chamberet** [05 55 98 30 12 (Mairie); fax 05 55 98 79 34] S fr Eymoutiers on D30 or N fr Treignac on D16. In Chamberet foll sp Camping Badinage, opp lake take rd up past some houses, site 250m at end. Sm, pt sl, terr, shd; wc; shwrs; el pts; playgrnd nr; lake sw, quiet. "Peaceful site." ♦ 1 Jul-15 Sep. € 6.50
2003*

TRELEVERN see Perros Guirec *1D2*

TREMBLADE, LA *7B1* (1km N) **Camping La Pignade, 40 Ave du Monard, 17390 Ronce-les-Bains** [05 46 36 25 25 or 05 46 36 15 35; fax 05 46 36 34 14 or 05 46 85 52 92; info@ camping-lapignade.com; www.camping-la pignade.com] Fr A10 exit junc 35 dir Saintes onto D728 twd Ile d'Oleron. After 15km at Marennes turn L at rndabt dir La Tremblade, still on D728. After rv bdge turn R at rndabt twd Ronce-les-Bains. After 1km turn L, site at end of rd. Lge, mkd pitch, pt shd; wc (some cont); chem disp; shwrs inc; baby facs; some serviced pitch; el pts (6A) inc; gas; lndtte; ice; shop; snacks; rest; bar; BBQ; playgrnd; htd pool & paddling pool; waterslide; sand beach 2km; games area; entmnt; child entmnt; TV rm; 70% statics; no dogs; Eng spkn; adv bkg; poss cr & noisy high ssn; red long stay/low ssn; cc acc; red long stay; CCI. "Children's clubs; archery; sports co-ordinator; golf practice; gd for families; rec." ♦ 30 Apr-18 Sep. € 33.00
2004*

TREMBLADE, LA *7B1* (2km N) **Camping La Clairiere, Rue des Roseaux, Ronce-les-Bains, 17390 La Tremblade** [05 46 36 36 63; fax 05 46 36 06 74; Clairiere.La@wanadoo.fr; www. camping-la-clairiere.com] Fr N on A10 exit Saintes, foll sp La Tremblade; site sp. Med, pt shd; wc; baby facs; shwrs; el pts (6A) €4; lndtte; shop; rest; snacks; bar; BBQ (gas); playgrnd; 2 pools; paddling pool; waterslide; beach 2.5km; fishing; watersports; tennis; cycle hire; games area; entmnt; TV; statics; dogs €2; poss cr; adv bkg; quiet. 1 May-15 Sep. € 18.00
2003*

TREMBLADE, LA *7B1* (3km W) **Camping La Pacha, Rue Buffard, 17390 La Tremblade** [05 46 36 14 44 or; fax 05 46 36 71] App fr Saujon on D14 turn L soon after passing rd sp with name of town. If overshot turn L at 1st traff lts. Foll sps. Site on R after 3km. Med, shd; wc; shwrs inc; el pts (6A) €3.05; ice; shop; rest; snacks; playgrnd; pool; beach 6km; TV; entmnt; statics; dogs €1.06; quiet. "Peaceful amongst pine trees." Easter-30 Sep. € 15.00
2002*

TREMOLAT see Bugue, Le *7C3*

FRANCE

TREPORT, LE *3B2* (Urban) **Camp Municipal Les Boucaniers, Ave des Canadiens, 76470 Le Treport** [02 35 86 35 47; fax 02 35 86 55 82] Fr Eu take minor rd sp to Le Treport under low bdge. On ent o'skts of Le Treport, turn R at 2nd traff lts, camp ent 100m on R. Site nr stadium. Lge, pt shd; htd wc; shwrs inc; el pts (6A) €3.60; lndtte; shop; rest; snacks; bar; playgrnd; sand beach 2km; games rm; entmnt; TV; 10% statics; dogs; quiet; red facs low ssn. "Gd seafood rests 15 mins walk." ♦ 1 Apr-30 Sep. € 10.40   2005*

TREPORT, LE *3B2* (1km E Coastal) **Camp International du Golf, Route de Dieppe, 76470 Le Treport** [02 27 28 01 50; fax 02 27 28 01 51] Fr Dieppe, take D925 NE twd Le Treport for 20km bef taking D940 sp Floques/Le Treport. Site on L at top of hill on o'skts of Le Treport. Foll sp. Lge, mkd pitch, shd; wc; chem disp; mv service pnt; 30% serviced pitches; shwrs inc; el pts (5A) €4.50; ice; shop 1km; rest, snacks, bar 1km; playgrnd; shgl beach 900m; fishing; sailing; windsurfing; dogs €3; poss cr; adv bkg; quiet; red low ssn; cc acc; CCI. "Pleasant site; poor san facs low ssn; conv town; Le Treport down fairly steep hill fr site, lovely but poss cr." 1 Apr-15 Sep. € 12.00   2003*

TREPT *9B2* (2.5km E) **Domaine des Trois Lacs du Soleil, 38460 Trept** [04 74 92 92 06; fax 04 74 92 93 35; info@les3lacsdusoleil.com; www.yellohvillage-3-lacs-du-soleil.com] Exit A432 at junc 3 or 3 & head twd Cremieu then Morestel. Trept bet these 2 towns on D517, site sp by lakes. Lge, pt shd; wc; baby facs; shwrs inc; el pts (6A) inc; lndtte; shop; rest; snacks; bar; BBQ (gas); playgrnd; pool complex; waterslides; lake sw & beach adj; fishing; tennis; archery; horseriding 2km; mini-golf; entmnt; internet; TV rm; 5% statics; dogs €1.50; adv bkg; Eng spkn; quiet; cc acc; red low ssn. ♦ 1 May-10 Sep. € 31.00 (CChq acc)   2004*

†**TRETS** *10F3* (4km SW Rural) **Camping Le Devancon, Chemin de Pourachon, 13790 Peynier** [04 42 53 10 06; fax 04 42 53 04 79; infos@ledevancon.com; www.ledevancon.com] Leave a'route A8 at Canet or Pas de Trets or leave D6 at Trets & take D908 to Peynier. In vill cont on D908 sp Marseille. Site on R at end vill after g'ge. Med, mkd pitch, all hdstg, pt sl, shd; htd wc; chem disp; mv service pnt; shwrs inc; el pts (3-10A) €2-10; gas; ice; lndtte; shop; tradsmn; rest; snacks; bar, BBQ; playgrnd; pool; paddling pool; sand beach 30km; tennis; entmnt; TV rm; 50% statics; dogs €2; some Eng spkn; adv bkg; quiet; cc acc; red long stay/CCI. "V helpful owner; poss diff manoeuvring onto pitches for lge o'fits; few water points; gd touring area; gd, clean site." ♦ € 17.00   2004*

TREVIERES *1D4* (Rural) **Camp Municipal, Rue des Eccles, 14710 Trevieres** [02 31 22 57 52 or 02 31 92 89 24] Turn S off N13 onto D30 sp Trevieres. Site on R on ent to vill. Med, pt shd, hdg pitch; wc (cont); chem disp; mv service pnt; shwrs inc; el pts (10A) €2.30; lndtte; shop 500m; rest; playgrnd; sand beach 10km; rv fishing adj; poss cr; adv bkg rec high ssn; quiet; CCI. "Excel long/sh stay; lge pitches; ideal for D-Day beaches; set in apple orchard." ♦ Easter-15 Sep. € 8.00   2002*

We're having a great holiday - must fill in some site report forms and send them to The Club as soon as possible.

TREVIERES *1D4* (3km NE Rural) **Camping La Roseraie, Rue de l'Eglise, 14710 Surrain** [tel/fax 02 31 21 17 71] Take N13 fr Bayeux twds Cherbourg. In approx 12km take D208 sp Surrain. Site sp in vill. Med, mkd pitch, pt sl, pt shd; wc; el pts (6A) €3.40; lndtte; ice; shop; snacks; playgrnd; htd pool; tennis; entmnt; 20% statics; Eng spkn; adv bkg; quiet. "Friendly recep; conv for Bayeux Tapestry & D-Day Museums." ♦ Easter-30 Oct. € 14.20 (CChq acc)   2004*

TREVOUX see Villefranche sur Saone *9B2*

TRIE SUR BAISE *8F2* (2.5km NE Rural) **Camping Fontrailles, Le Quartier Lanorbe, 65220 Fontrailles** [05 62 35 62 52; detm.paddon@free.fr; www.fontraillescamping.com] Fr N on N21 leave Mirande & turn L (S) at end of town sp Trie-sur-Baise onto D939. After St Michel look out for silos on R after 7km, site sp. Fr S at Mielan turn onto D3/17 sp Trie-sur-Baise to Fontrailles. Sm, pt sl, pt shd; wc; chem disp (wc); shwrs inc; el pts (9A) €2; ice; shop, rest, snacks & bar 3km; BBQ; playgrnd; pool; tennis; fishing; dogs; Eng spkn; adv bkg; quiet; red long stay; CCI. "Delightful CL-type site; well kept in orchard; excel pool & tennis in nrby communal oak wood; gd base for area; gd walking; helpful British owners; conv Lourdes, Pyrenees & Spain; mkt Trie-sur-Baise Tues." 1 Jul-30 Sep. € 14.00   2005*

TRINITE SUR MER, LA see Carnac *2G3*

TRIZAC see Riom es Montagnes *7C4*

TROCHE see Uzerche *7B3*

TROGUES see Ste Maure de Touraine *4H2*

TROYES *4E4* (2km NE Urban) **Camping de Troyes (Municipal), 7 Rue Roger Salengro, 10000 Pont Ste Marie [03 25 81 02 64; fax 03 25 42 34 09; www.troyescamping.net]** Fr Troyes on D960 twd Nancy, 2km fr town cent on L opp Stade & bet Esso g'ge & car wash. Fr N site on R on N77 just pass junc with D960. Foll sp fr all dirs to Pont Ste Marie & site. To avoid busy town cent when towing, app fr N on by-pass using D960, site on R. Fr S on A26 exit junc 23 onto N19, then D960 ring rd twd Troyes Cent. Site on R. Well sp fr all dirs & in town. Med, some hdg/mkd pitch, few hdstg, pt shd; wc; chem disp; mv service pnt; shwrs inc; el pts (5A) €2.70 (long lead poss req); gas; lndtte; ice; shop; tradsmn; supmkt adj; vg rest nrby; snacks; playgrnd; pool 2km; TV; dogs €1; bus opp; poss cr; Eng spkn; adv bkg; cc acc; red 3+ nights low ssn; church bells at night; CCI. "Twin-axles poss not admitted; peaceful parkland but busy site; lge pitches divided by trees/shrubs; v friendly, hardworking wardens; tourist info office on site; rec arr early as v popular; gd bus service to town or 20 min walk; Troyes Cathedral, museums & old quarter worth visit; lge clothing outlet nrby; gd fruit & fish mkts; reduced facs low ssn." ♦ 1 Apr-15 Oct. € 13.80   2005*

TROYES *4E4* (12km E Rural) **Camping La Fromentelle, 10220 Dosches [tel/fax 03 25 41 52 67]** Exit A26 junc 23 onto D48 to Dosches. In Dosches turn R onto D8, in 4km turn R onto D1, site on R in 1km. Sm, mkd pitch, pt sl, unshd; wc; chem disp (wc); mv service pnt; shwrs inc; el pts (6A) €2.60 (long lead poss req); BBQ; playgrnd; sand beach 6km; lake sw 5km; dogs €0.50; adv bkg; quiet; CCI. "Clean, pleasant site; warm welcome; gd for birdwatching, sailing, watersports on lakes; conv Troyes." ♦ 30 Apr-30 Sep. € 9.20   2005*

TROYES *4E4* (10km SE Rural) **Camping Plan d'Eau des Terres Rouges, 10390 Clerey [03 25 46 04 45; fax 03 25 46 05 86; terres-rouges@wanadoo.fr]** SE fr Troyes on N71 dir Bar-sur-Seine, foll sp Clerey. Site well sp. Sm, hdg pitch, pt shd; wc (some cont); chem disp; mv service pnt; shwrs €1; el pts (5A) €2.60; shops 4km; tradsmn; rest; snacks; bar; playgrnd; tennis; lake sw inc; fishing, waterskiing, boating; 10% statics; phone; adv bkg; no cc acc; CCI. "Gd, basic NH; friendly owners; conv fr a'route to Calais; excel NH." ♦ Easter-30 Sep. € 13.80   2005*

TULLE *7C4* (2km NE) **Camp Municipal Bourbacoup, Ave du Lieutenant-Colonel-Faro, 19000 Tulle [05 55 26 75 97 or 06 87 84 90 60]** Fr Tulle, take N120 NW dir Limoges. Foll site sp. Med, mkd pitch, pt shd; wc (some cont); shwrs inc; el pts inc; supmkt 3km; rest, bar 1km; pool 1km; rv adj; dogs; quiet. "Pretty site on bank of rv; easy cycle ride to town; poss itinerants; dated but v clean san facs."♦ 1 Jul-31 Aug. € 10.50   2005*

TULLE *7C4* (12km NE Rural) **Camping L'Etang de Ruffaud, 19800 St Priest-de-Gimel [05 55 21 26 65 or 05 55 26 42 12 (LS)]** Sp on N89 Tulle- Clermont-Ferrand rd & 3km S of this rd. Med, shd, pt sl; wc; shwrs inc; el pts; gas; lndtte; ice; shop; rest; playgrnd; shgl beach adj; rv fishing; boating; windsurfing; cycle hire; tennis; TV; entmts; quiet; Eng spkn; CCI 15 Jun-15 Sep.   2002*

TULLE *7C4* (4km SE Rural) **Camping Le Pre du Moulin, 19150 Laguenne [tel/fax 05 55 26 21 96; lepredumoulin@wanadoo.fr]** Exit Tulle on N120 twd Aurillac, pass ATAC commercial cent on R cross bdge & 1st L to camp site. Last 1km on unmade rd, but not diff. Sm, pt sl, pt shd; wc; chem disp; shwrs inc; el pts (6A) €2.50; gas; lndtte; shops 2km; tradsmn; snacks; pool; rv fishing adj; cycle hire; no dogs high ssn, low ssn; €2.30; adv bkg rec high ssn; dep req; quiet; CCI. "Attractive, peaceful; adequate san facs; steep climb to san facs - diff for disabled; British owners." 15 Apr-30 Sep. € 15.50   2005*

TURBALLE, LA see Guerande *2G3*

TURCKHEIM see Colmar *6F3*

TURQUANT see Saumur *4G1*

TURSAC see Eyzies de Tayac, Les *7C3*

UCHIZY see Tournus *9A2*

UGINE *9B3* (7km NW) **Camping Champ Tillet, 74210 Marlens [04 50 44 40 07; champtillet@ caramail.com]** N508 S fr Annecy after leaving Lake. Take new by-pass past Faverges to Ugine. After rndabt, site on R at junc bef Marlens. Look for baker's shop. Sp. Med, pt shd; wc (some cont); shwrs inc; el pts (3-10A) inc; lndtte; bar; rest; snacks; ice; shops adj; supmkts 3km; pool; playgrnd; rv 500m; cc acc. "Gd walks, lovely views; barrier clsd 2300-0700." ♦ 1 Apr-30 Oct. € 20.30   2004*

URBES see St Maurice sur Moselle *6F3*

URDOS *8G2* (500m N Rural) **Camp Municipal Le Gave d'Aspe, 64490 Urdos [05 59 34 88 26; fax 05 59 34 88 86; legavedaspe@aol.com]** Turn W off N134 onto site access rd by disused Urdos stn approx 1km bef vill, clear sp. Other access rds in vill v diff lge o'fits. Sm, mkd pitch, pt sl, pt shd; wc; chem disp; shwrs inc; el pts (30A) €2.30; shop, rest, bar 500m; tradsmn; BBQ; playgrnd; paddling pool; rv sw; phone; poss cr; Eng spkn; adv bkg; quiet; cc acc; CCI. "Adj Rv Aspe; 14km fr Col du Somport/Tunnel; surrounded by mountains; conv x-ing into Spain; ltd facs; vg." 1 May-15 Sep. € 9.00   2004*

URRUGNE see St Jean de Luz *8F1*

SITES

†URT *8F1* (E Rural) **Camping Ferme Mimizan,** 64240 Urt [05 59 56 21 51] E fr Bayonne on A64/E80, exit junc 4 sp Urt; in vill turn sharp R at PO & foll sps; site on R in 1km. Fr N on D12 cross Rv Adour by metal bdge & turn L immed past church, site on R in 1.5km. Med, pt shd; wc; shwrs inc; el pts (10A) €2.50; farm rest; playgrnd; pool; 98% statics; adv bkg; poss noise fr static residents; red low ssn; CCI. "Gd walking & cycling; conv coast & Pyrenees; friendly owners; v peaceful out of ssn; NH only."
€ 14.00   2004*

URT *8F1* (500m S Rural) **Camping Etche Zahar,** Allee des Mesples, 64240 Urt [05 59 56 27 36; fax 05 59 56 29 62; camping.etche-zahar@wanadoo. fr; www.etche-zahar.fr] Exit A64 at junc 4 dir Urt. Fr N on N10 exit junc 8 at St Geours-de-Maremne onto D12 S to Urt, site sp. Fr town cent head W, L at rndabt, L again to site. Sm, hdg pitch, pt sl, pt shd; wc; chem disp; shwrs inc; el pts (10A) €2.80; lndtte; shop 500m; tradsmn; snacks; bar; BBQ; rest 500m; playgrnd; pool & children's paddling pool; fishing; games area; cycle hire; bird sanctuary nrby; entmnt; internet; 25% statics; dogs €2; phone; Eng spkn; adv bkg; quiet; CCI. "Peaceful site; welcoming & pleasant owners; gd walking & cycling; conv Belloc Abbey & Bayonne." ♦ 23 Mar-14 Nov. € 16.00
                                                                    2005*

UZER *9D2* (3km SE Rural) **Camping La Turelure,** Fontanne, 07110 Uzer [04 75 36 87 47; fax 06 87 14 75 46; laturelure@free.fr] S fr Aubenas on D104, 1km S of Uzer. Site well sp; app rd narr. Sm, hdg/mkd pitch, pt shd; wc (some cont); chem disp; mv service pnt; shwrs; el pts (3-6A) €2.30-3.50; gas; lndtte; shop 1km; tradsmn high ssn; rest 1km; snacks 5km; BBQ; playgrnd; rv sw; fishing; canoeing; games area; 10% statics; dogs; phone; poss cr; some Eng spkn; adv bkg; quiet; red low ssn; cc not acc; CCI. "V pleasant farm site bet vineyard & rv; situated in cherry orchard; v friendly owner; regional wines & produce avail; excel base for touring S Ardeche; peaceful with beautiful views; vg long/sh stay." ♦ ltd. 1 Apr-31 Oct. € 10.00
                                                                    2004*

UZERCHE *7B3* (8km NE Rural) **Camping Aimee Porcher (Naturist),** 19140 Eyburie [05 55 73 20 97 or 0031 264 436285 (N'lands) (LS); fax 0031 264 436285; info@aimee-porcher.com; www.aimee-porcher.com] Fr Uzerche take D3 NE to Eyburie & in Eyburie turn R at site sp (Cheyron/Pingrieux). In 1km turn L at site sp; site at end of narr lane. Sm, mkd pitch, terr, pt shd; wc; chem disp; shwrs inc; baby facs; el pts (6A) inc (poss long lead req); lndtte; ice; tradsmn; snacks; bar; BBQ; playgrnd; lake & rv sw adj; no statics; dogs €2; Eng spkn; adv bkg; quiet; red long stay; CCI. "Beautiful views; friendly & helpful Dutch owners; v lge site with pitches well spread out; facs basic but clean; excel all stays." ♦ 1 Jun-1 Sep.
€ 19.50   2005*

UZERCHE *7B3* (200m SE Rural) **Camp Municipal La Minoterie, Route de la Minoterie,** 19140 Uzerche [05 55 73 12 75 or 05 55 73 17 00 (Mairie); fax 05 55 98 44 55] Fr N exit A20 at junc 44 for Uzerche. After x-ing town bdge turn L & proceed thro tunnel. Site clearly sp on ent to town on rvside. Steep app rd & sharp bend. NB Narr app rd used by lorries fr nrby quarry. Site well sp. Med, mkd pitch, pt sl, shd; wc; chem disp; shwrs inc; el pts (10A) €2.40; lndtte; shops 200m; playgrnd; fishing; kayak hire; rock-climbing; quiet; CCI. "Rvside site; excel value; office in building at ent to camping area; poss risk of flooding; sh walk to beautiful old vill; gd local walks; conv NH."
1 May-30 Sep. € 10.00   2005*

UZERCHE *7B3* (9km SW Rural) **Camp Municipal du Lac du Pont-Charal,** 19410 Vigeois [05 55 98 90 86 or 05 55 98 91 93 (Mairie); fax 05 55 98 99 79] Fr A20 exit 45 onto D3 & D7. Med, pt sl, shd; wc; chem disp; shwrs inc; el pts (15A) €2.50; gas; lndtte; ice; shop; rest; snacks; bar; playgrnd; lake sw & beach; fishing; watersports; sports area; tennis 2km; entmnt; TV; dogs €0.80; adv bkg; quiet. "Delightful, well-kept site; new san facs 2005; facs excel." ♦ 1 Jun-15 Sep. € 7.60
                                                                    2005*

UZERCHE *7B3* (9km SW Rural) **Camping a la Ferme Domaine Vert,** Les Magnes, 19230 Troche [tel/fax 05 55 73 59 89; www.ledomainevert.nl] Exit A20 junc 45 onto D3 to Vigeois, 2km after Vigeois turn R onto D50 sp Lubersac. After 5km (ignore sp to Troche) foll site sp to R. Sm, pt shd; wc; shwrs; lndry rm; meals avail; fishing 4km; canoeing nr, lake sw; Eng spkn; quiet. "Peaceful, farm site; surrounded by woodland; welcoming, friendly Dutch owners." 15 Apr-30 Sep.   2004*

UZERCHE *7B3* (12km SW Rural) **Aire Naturelle du Bois Coutal (Veysseix),** Perpezac-le-Noir, 19410 Vigeois [05 55 73 71 93; fax 05 55 73 27 66; boiscoutal@wanadoo.fr] Exit A20/E09 S fr Uzerche at junc 46 onto D920 & foll sp Perpezac le-Noir. Go thro Perpezac on D156 N dir Vigeois & foll site sp. Site 4km fr Perpezac. Sm, sl, pt shd; wc; chem disp; shwrs inc; el pts inc (6A) inc; lndtte; shop, rest, snacks, bar 3km; playgrnd; pool; few statics; dogs; poss cr; Eng spkn; adv bkg; quiet. "Friendly, helpful owner; v clean facs; vg long/sh stay." 1 Apr-31 Oct. € 12.00   2003*

UZES *10E2* (800m N Urban) **Camping La Paillote,** Mas Franval, Quartier de Grezac, 30700 Uzes [04 66 22 38 55; fax 04 66 22 26 66; info@ paillotte.com; www.paillote.com] Exit A9 junc 23 sp Remoulins. Fr Remoulins take D981 to Uzes. Aim for town cent one-way ring rd. Site sp clearly. Narr rds for 800m passing cemetery. Med, mkd pitch; shd; wc; shwrs inc; el pts (10A) inc; gas; lndtte; shop; tradsmn; rest; snacks; bar; playgrnd; pool; paddling pool; lake sw & fishing; cycle hire; games area; games rm; entmnt; some statics; dogs €2; Eng spkn; adv bkg; quiet; CCI. "Poolside rest; facs clean but water temperature poss variable; extra for lakeside pitches." Easter-30 Oct. € 35.00   2005*

UZES *10E2* (3km E Rural) **Camping Le Moulin Neuf**, 30700 St Quentin-la-Poterie [04 66 22 17 21; fax 04 66 22 91 82; le.moulin.neuf@wanadoo.fr; www.le-moulin-neuf.com] Take D982 out of Uzes, after 3km turn N, site in 400m. Med, mkd pitch, pt shd; wc; chem disp; shwrs inc; el pts (5A) inc; lndtte; shop & 2km; snacks; bar; playgrnd; tennis; htd pool; cycle hire; mini-golf; fishing; horseriding; poss cr; v quiet. "Site off beaten track; conv Gorges d'Ardeche, Avignon, Arles & Nimes; barrier clsd 2230-0700; mosquito problem."♦ 10 Apr-15 Oct. € 18.20
2004*

UZES *10E2* (3km SW Rural) **Camping Le Mas de Rey, Route d'Anduze, 30700 Arpaillargues** [tel/fax 04 66 22 18 27; info@campingmasderey. com; www.campingmasderey.com] Sp fr Uzes. Exit by D982 sp Anduze. After 2.5km cross narr bdge, turn L in 100m on site app rd. Med, hdg/mkd pitch, hdstg, pt sl, pt shd; wc; chem disp; fam bthrm; shwrs inc; el pts (10A) €3 (rev pol); lndtte; ice; shop & 3km; tradsmn; rest, snacks; bar; BBQ; playgrnd; pool; rv sw 6km; TV rm; dogs €1.60; phone; poss cr; Eng spkn; adv bkg (dep req); quiet; CCI. "Helpful owners & staff; gd for sm children; some v lge pitches; pleasant town; gd long stay." ♦ 10 Apr-15 Oct. € 16.00
2005*

VACQUEYRAS see Carpentras *10E2*

VAISON LA ROMAINE *9D2* (500m Urban) **Camping du Theatre Romain, Quartier des Arts, Chemin du Brusquet, 84110 Vaison-la-Romaine** [04 90 28 78 66; fax 04 90 28 78 76; camping.du. theatre.romain@wanadoo.fr] Fr town cent foll sp for Theatre Romain & site. Ent to Chemin du Busquet on rndabt at Theatre Romain. Or site sp off the Orange-Nyons rd thro town (do not ent town cent). Med, hdg/mkd pitch, pt shd; wc; chem disp (wc); mv service pnt; serviced pitches; baby facs; shwrs inc; el pts (5-10A) €2.80-3.90; lndtte; ice; shop & gas 500m; bar; BBQ; playgrnd; pool; dogs €2; Eng spkn; adv bkg ess high ssn (bkg fee); quiet; cc acc; CCI. "Helpful owner may accept visitors out of ssn - phone ahead; mkt Tues; v attractive Provencale town; Roman remains; summer concerts in amphitheatre; v busy site even low ssn; scrupulously clean & tidy; rec arr early or adv book; highly rec." ♦ 15 Mar-15 Nov. € 19.00   2005*

VAISON LA ROMAINE *9D2* (4km NE Rural) **Camping L'Ayguette, 84110 Faucon** [04 90 46 40 35 or 06 18 47 33 42 (mob); fax 04 90 46 46 17; info@ayguette.com; www. ayguette.com] Exit Vaison NE on D938, R on D71, thro St Romain-en-Viennois. Then R onto D86 sp Faucon. Site on R, well sp. Med, mkd pitch, terr, shd; htd wc; chem disp; baby facs; shwrs inc; el pts (10A) €2.50 (poss long lead req); lndtte; ice; shop, supmkt 4km; tradsmn; snacks; bar; BBQ; playgrnd; htd pool; dogs €1.50; adv bkg; quiet; cc acc; CCI. "V helpful owners; tractor tow available; excel mod facs inc hairdryers & children's shwrs; excel long stay in scenic area." 1 Apr-30 Sep. € 17.40
2005*

VAISON LA ROMAINE *9D2* (4km NE Rural) Camping Le Soleil de Provence, Route de Nyons, Quartier Trameiller, 84110 St Romain-en- Viennois [04 90 46 46 00; fax 04 90 46 40 37; info@ camping-soleil-de-provence.fr; www.camping-soleil-de-provence.fr] Leave A7 at junc 19 Bollene onto D94 dir Nyons. After Tullette turn R onto D20 & then D975 to Vaison-la-Romaine; fr Vaison take D938 sp Nyons; in 4km R & in 150m L to site; well sp. Med, terr, hdg/mkd pitch, pt shd; wc; chem disp; some serviced pitches; shwrs inc; el pts (10A) €2.50; gas; lndtte; ice; shop; tradsmn; rest high ssn; snacks; bar; playgrnd; pool; entmnt; dogs: poss cr; adv bkg; quiet; CCI. "Stunning views, lovely town & countryside; mkt Tues; v quiet, friendly, family-run site; excel, popular site." ♦ 15 Mar-31 Oct. € 17.00
2005*

VAISON LA ROMAINE *9D2* (800m SE Rural) Camping Club International Carpe Diem, Route de St Marcellin, 84110 Vaison-la-Romaine [04 90 36 02 02; fax 04 90 36 36 90; contact@ camping-carpe-diem.com; www.camping-carpe-diem.com] S on A7 exit Orange; foll sp to Vaison; at Vaison on Nyons rd (D938) turn S at rndabt by supmkt dir Carpentras. In 1km turn L at junc to St Marcellin, site immed on L. Lge, hdg/mkd pitch, terr, pt shd; wc (some cont); chem disp; mv service pnt; shwrs inc; el pts (6-10A) €2.70-3.70; gas; lndtte; shop & 800m; tradsmn; pizzeria, snacks, bar high ssn; playgrnd; 2 pools; paddling pool; rv sw 5km; mini-golf; entmnt; internet; TV rm; 10% statics; dogs €2.50; poss cr; Eng spkn; adv bkg (dep req + bkg fee); cc acc; CCI. "Lively; helpful staff; conv Roman ruins; summer concerts; gd cent for Provence region; gd facs but poss stretched high ssn; vg." ♦ 1 Mar-5 Nov. € 20.00 (CChq acc)
2004*

VAISON LA ROMAINE *9D2* (6km SE) Camping Les Trois Rivieres, Quarter des Jonches, 84340 Entrechaux [04 90 46 01 72; fax 04 90 46 00 75; www.camping-les3rivieres.com] Take D938 fr Vaison twd Malaucene for 3.5km. Turn E onto D54 to Entrechaux; site well sp rndabts at both ends of vill. Narr app rd. Med, pt sl, shd; wc; shwrs inc; el pts (3-10A) €2.50-4; gas; lndtte; ice; shop 2km; rest; snacks; bar; playgrnd; rv shgl beach, sw & fishing; horseriding; some statics; internet; entmnt; TV; dogs €1.50; poss cr; quiet; adv bkg; 20% red Jun & Sep. "Gd clean rv bathing; rds rough & twisty, access v diff for lge o'fits; quiet & shd." 1 Apr-30 Sep. € 12.00
2005*

VAISON LA ROMAINE *9D2* (5km NW Rural) Camping Domaine de La Cambuse, Route de Villedieu, 84110 Vaison-la-Romaine [tel/fax 04 90 36 14 53; brun.pierre@club-internet.fr] Fr Vaison-la-Romaine N on D51 sp Villedieu. After 4km fork R onto D94 sp Villedieu. Site on R after 300m. Sm, terr, pt shd; wc (some cont); chem disp; shwrs inc; el pts (15A) €2.35; gas 4km; ice; tradsmn; snacks, bar in ssn; pool; 5% statics; phone; poss cr; quiet; CCI. "Site on side of hill with slate-topped sandstone pillars within working vineyard; v friendly & helpful owners; gd long/sh stays." 1 May-30 Sep. € 10.60   2004*

VAL ANDRE, LE *2E3* (3km S Coastal) Camp Municipal des Monts Colleux, 22370 Pleneuf-Val-Andre [02 96 63 13 00 or 02 96 72 95 10; fax 02 96 63 10 49] Site 800m off D786 & off D78, sp fr Pleneuf town cent. Lge, pt sl, pt shd; wc; mv service pnt; shwrs inc; el pts (6A) €2.75; ice; lndry rm; shops 500m; playgrnd; BBQ; sand beach 500m; adv bkg; red low ssn; dogs €1. "V helpful staff; cliff top walks & mussel fishing." 1 May-12 Sep. € 12.10 2002*

VAL D'AJOL, LE see Plombieres les Bains *6F2*

VAL DE VESLE see Reims *3D4*

VAL D'ISERE *9B4* (1km E Rural) Camping Les Richardes, 73150 Val d'Isere [tel/fax 04 79 06 26 60] Leave Val d'Isere going E twds Col de l'Iseran on D902, site on R. Med, pt sl, unshd; wc; shwrs €1; el pts (3-6A) €1.90-3.80; pool 1.5km; dogs €0.40; quiet; CCI. "Situated in beautiful mountains." 15 Jun-15 Sep. € 9.50 2003*

VALBONNAIS see Mure, La *9C3*

VALENCAY *4H2* (1km W Urban) Camp Municipal Les Chenes, Route de Loches, 36600 Valencay [tel/fax 02 54 00 03 92 or 02 54 00 32 32] App town fr E on D960 or N/S on D956, foll sp for D960 Lucay-le-Male. Ignore 1st sp for camping (Veuil); D960 is next L in town. Foll sp for pool & camping. Med, hdg/mkd pitch, pt shd; wc; chem disp; shwrs inc; el pts (4-10A) €1.65-3.40 (poss rev pol); lndtte; shops 1km tradsmn; BBQ; playgrnd; htd pool & tennis adj; fishing; adv bkg; quiet; 10% red 7+ days; CCI. "Excel site; gd, clean facs; poss muddy after heavy rain; gate clsd 1200-1500 & 2200-0700; landscaped grounds around lake; gd car museum in town; chateau; son et lumiere Jul/Aug; day's drive to Calais or Le Havre for ferries." 1 May-30 Sep. € 9.40 2005*

VALENCE *9C2* (12km SE Rural) Camping Sunelia Le Grand Lierne, 26120 Chabeuil [04 75 59 83 14; fax 04 75 59 87 95; contact@grandlierne.com; www.grandliernne.com] Fr m'way A7 S take Valence Sud exit dir Grenoble. After 8km take D68 on R twd Chabeuil. Turn L at rndabt on o'skts of vill & foll site sp using by-pass; do not go into vill. On arr, park in lay-by at end of app rd & walk to recep to book in. Med, some mkd pitch, pt shd; wc; chem disp; baby facs; shwrs inc; el pts (10A) inc; gas; lndtte; shop; rest; snacks; bar; BBQ (gas & el only); playgrnd; pool & whirlpool; tennis; archery; games area; games rm; golf 3km; entmnt; internet; many statics; dogs €2.50 (no dogs Jul/Aug); poss cr; Eng spkn; adv bkg rec; poss noisy high ssn; cc acc; CCI. "Site set in oak forest; friendly staff; gd facs & all-round entmnt; one half of site some sm pitches - poss diff twin-axle & lge o'fits; gd for families; barrier clsd 2200-0700; mkt Chabeuil Tue; regimented!" ♦ ltd. 28 Apr-10 Sep. € 35.30 (CChq acc) ABS - M04 2005*

†VALENCE *9C2* (1km S Urban) Camp Municipal de l'Eperviere, Chemin de l'Eperviere, 26000 Valence [04 75 42 32 00; fax 04 75 56 20 67; eperviere@vacanciel.com] Leave A7 a'route at Valence Sud & turn N onto N7, site well sp fr N7. When app fr S on N7 turn L at traff lts 500m after Geant supmkt. Fr N on N7 look for R turn 2km S of Valence. Lge, hdg pitch, hdstg, pt shd; htd wc; shwrs inc; el pts (10A,) €4.70; lndtte; supmkt 500m; rest adj; rest; snacks; bar; playgrnd; htd pool; fishing in Rhone; watersports cent adj; games area; TV; 30% statics; site clsd mid-Dec to mid-Jan; poss cr; Eng spkn; no adv bkg; rd noise; cc acc; red low ssn; CCI. "Popular NH; poss itinerant workers; not well maintained or supervised low ssn; generous pitches." ♦ ltd. € 15.80 2005*

VALENCE *9C2* (9km NW) Camp Municipal Les Vernes, 26600 La Roche-de-Glun [04 75 84 54 11 or 04 75 84 60 52 (Mairie)] Turn W off N7 at Pont d'Isere. On ent La Roche-de-Glun foll camping sp. Sm, hdg/mkd pitch, pt shd; wc (some cont); serviced pitches; chem disp; shwrs inc; el pts (10A) inc; lndtte; ice; shop 500m; BBQ; free pool adj in ssn; sports cent adj; phone; poss cr; adv bkg; quiet; no cc acc; CCI. "V pleasant site; gd & v clean san facs; friendly warden resident; gd sh stay/NH; barrier clsd 2200-0700." 1 May-30 Sep. € 12.50 2003*

VALENCE D'AGEN *8E3* (1km S) Camp Municipal, Route des Charretiers, 82400 Valence-d'Agen [05 63 39 61 67; tourisme.valencedagen@wanadoo.fr] Exit town on D953 sp Auch, turn R after x-ing rv 1st L. Site sp behind sw baths on R. Sm, pt shd; wc (cont); shwrs; el pts; shops 1km; rest, snacks adj; playgrnd; games area; poss cr; quiet. 1 Jul-31 Aug. 2004*

VALENSOLE see Riez *10E3*

VALLABREGUES see Tarascon *10E2*

VALLET *2G4* (1km N) Camp Municipal, 44330 Vallet [02 40 33 95 03] 1km N of Vallet on N763; leave Vallet on N763; on R approx 1.2km after last rndabt on by-pass; foll sp. Med, mkd pitch, pt shd; wc (some cont); shwrs inc; el pts (6A) inc; lndry rm; shop 2km; pool 2km; fishing; tennis; quiet; poss rd noise; gate opening hrs Jul/Aug 0700-2100; CCI. "NH/sh stay only; clean & comfortable; 20 mins walk to town cent; cent of wine-growing area; narr ent; gd mkt Sun am." 15 May-Sep. € 6.00 2002*

VALLIERES see Rumilly *9B3*

Camping Nature Park ★★★★
L'Ardéchois
VALLON PONT D'ARC ARDÈCHE - SÜD

Bordering the Ardèche

Pont d'Arc: 3 km
Village: 1 km

Open : 08.04 - 30.09

- Heated waterpark
- Heated sanitary + family bathrooms
- Mobilhome rents
- Comfortable sites
- Bar, Restaurant, Supermarket
- Canoe Nature Paradise
- Animations for children
- Tennis
- Midget golf
- LudoPark (Multisports)
- English spoken
- Off-season reduction

Camping Nature Park l'Ardéchois - Route des Gorges de l'Ardèche
F-07150 Vallon pont d'Arc - Tel. 33 (0)4 75 88 06 63 - Fax 33 (0)4 75 37 14 97
www.ardechois-camping.com - e-mail: ardecamp@bigfoot.com

FRANCE

VALLOIRE *9C3* (500m N Rural) **Camping Caravaneige Ste Thecle,** 73450 Valloire [04 79 83 30 11; fax 04 79 83 35 13; camping-caravaneige@valloire.net] Exit A43 junc 29 onto N6 to St Michel-de-Maurienne, then onto D902 to Valloire. At vill mkt turn R over rv to site. Climb fr valley 15% gradient max. Med, mkd pitch, some hdstg, unshd; htd wc (cont); chem disp; mv service pnt; baby facs; fam bthrm; shwrs €1; el pts (10A) €2; gas 1km; lndtte; shop 300m; rest 500m; bar 200m; playgrnd; skiing, iceskating, pool nr; TV rm; dogs; phone 100m; bus; Eng spkn; adv bkg; quiet; red long stay; cc acc. "Superb mountain scenery for walking & cycling; excel long stay." ♦ ltd.
1 Dec-1 May & 1 Jun-30 Sep. € 13.20   2003*

VALLON EN SULLY *7A4* (Rural) **Camp Municipal, Les Soupirs,** 03190 Vallon-en-Sully [04 70 06 50 96 or 04 70 06 50 10 (LS); fax 04 70 06 51 18; mairie.vallonensully@wanadoo.fr] N fr Montlucon on N144; in 23km at traff lts where D11 crosses N144 turn L & foll camping sp for Vallon-en-Sully. After bdge over Rv Cher turn L in 50m. Site in 100m. If N or S on A71 exit at junc 9 Vallon-en-Sully; turn N on N144; in 3km at traff lts turn L. Lge, shd; wc; shwrs; el pts (6-20A) €2-4 shops 500m; snacks & rest adj; TV rm; adv bkg; quiet. "On banks of rv & bounded by canal; risk of flooding in wet." 15 Jun-15 Sep. € 6.00   2005*

VALLON PONT D'ARC *9D2* (5km N) **Camping a la Ferme Charoussas,** 07150 Lagorce [04 75 88 02 73] Fr Aubenas on D104 turn L on D579 sp Vallon-Pont-d'Arc; in 10.5km turn L on D1 for Lagorce. In 10km turn R at wine co-op bef vill. Site 200m on R. Or fr S by-pass Vallon N to Lagorce, thro vill, turn L at bottom of hill at co-operative. Sm, pt sl, pt shd; wc; shwrs inc; el pts inc; shops 500m; pool; adv bkg; quiet. "Friendly & peaceful; conv Gorges d'Ardeche; vg CL-type site." 1 Jun-30 Sep. € 13.75   2003*

VALLON PONT D'ARC *9D2* (9km E) **Camping Carrefour de l'Ardeche,** Route de Bourg-St Andeol, 07700 St Remeze [04 75 04 15 75; fax 04 75 04 35 05; carrefourardeche@worldonline.fr] D4 E fr Vallon-Pont-d'Arc. Site on L on bend after St Remeze vill. Med, mkd pitch, pt shd; wc; chem disp; shwrs inc; el pts inc; gas; lndtte; ice; snacks; bar; playgrnd; pool; TV rm; cycle hire; canoeing; fishing 5km; entmnt; adv bkg; quiet; cc acc. "On plateau surrounded by vineyards." ♦ Easter-30 Sep. € 23.50   2003*

VALLON PONT D'ARC *9D2* (1km SE Rural) **Camping L'Ardechois,** Route des Gorges, 07150 Vallon-Pont-d'Arc [04 75 88 06 63; fax 04 75 37 14 97; ardecamp@bigfoot.com; www.ardechois-camping.com] Fr Vallon take D290 rte des Gorges & site on R bet rd & rv. Lge, mkd pitch, hdstg, pt sl, shd; htd wc; chem disp; mv service pnt; baby facs; fam bthrm; serviced pitch; private bthrm €15 (by reservation); shwrs inc; el pts (6-10A) inc; gas; lndtte; ice; shop; tradsmn; rest; snacks; bar; BBQ; playgrnd; htd pool & paddling pool; rv sw; tennis; canoeing; games area; entmnt; TV rm; 80% statics; dogs €6.30; Eng spkn; adv bkg; quiet; cc acc; red low ssn; CCI. "Spectacular scenery; excel rvside site; v helpful staff; town 15 mins walk; price depends on size of pitch; gd san facs; excel." ♦
8 Apr-30 Sep. € 39.00   2005*

See advertisement

VALLON PONT D'ARC *9D2* (1km SE Rural) **Camping Le Provencal,** 07150 Vallon-Pont-d'Arc [04 75 88 00 48; fax 04 75 37 18 69; camping.le.provencal@wanadoo.fr] Fr Aubenas take D579 thro Vallon-Pont-d'Arc to S. Turn L on D290 N of rv; site on R in 500m (middle of 3 sites). Fr Ales, N on D904/D104, turn R onto D111 & D579 to Vallon-Pont-d'Arc. Lge, pt shd; htd wc; shwrs inc; el pts (8A) inc; gas; lndtte; ice; shop; rest; snacks; bar; playgrnd; htd pool; rv sw; canoeing; fishing; sailing; tennis; poss cr; Eng spkn; adv bkg; quiet; cc acc. "Friendly helpful staff; site at NW end of spectacular Gorges de l'Ardeche." ♦ Easter-20 Sep. € 31.60   2004*

VALLON PONT D'ARC *9D2* (1.5km SE Rural) Mondial Camping, Route des Gorges, 07150 Vallon-Pont-d'Arc [04 75 88 00 44; fax 04 75 37 13 73; reserv-info@mondial-camping. com; www.mondial-camping.com] Fr N exit A7 Montelimar Nord junc 17 dir Le Teil, Villeneuve-de-Berg, Vogue, Ruoms then Vallon-Pont-d'Arc. Take D290, Rte des Gorges de l'Ardeche to site in 1.5km. Fr S exit A7 junc 19 at Bollene, dir Bourg-St Andeol, then D4 to St Remeze & Vallon-Pont-d'Arc. Lge, hdg/mkd pitch, shd; htd wc; chem disp; mv service pnt; serviced pitches; baby facs; shwrs inc; el pts (6-10A) €4.20; gas; lndtte; ice; shop; rest; snacks; bar; playgrnd; 2 htd pools; waterslides & aqua park; rv sw; canoeing; tennis adj; games rm; entmnt; internet; TV; some statics; dogs €4.70; poss cr; Eng spkn; adv bkg; quiet; red low ssn; cc acc; CCI. "Dir access to rv, Ardeche gorges & canoe facs; gd touring base; additional charge for serviced pitches; excel long stay." ♦ 20 Mar-30 Sep. € 30.00   2005*

See advertisement above

VALLON PONT D'ARC *9D2* (2km SW) Camping Le Casque Roi, 07150 Salavas [04 75 88 04 23; fax 04 75 37 18 64; casqueroi@aol.com]   Take D579 S fr Vallon-Pont-d'Arc; site on R 500m after bdge over Ardeche. Sm, shd; wc (some cont); baby facs; shwrs inc; el pts (10A) inc; lndtte; shop; snacks; bar; playgrnd; htd pool; rv sw 1km; cycle hire; entmnt; 10% statics; dogs €1; poss cr; quiet; CCI. "Gd touring base for Ardeche gorges; canoeing & guided walks." 1 Apr-11 Nov. € 20.00   2003*

VALLON PONT D'ARC *9D2* (800m W Urban) Camping La Roubine, Route de Ruoms, 07150 Vallon-Pont-d'Arc [tel/fax 04 75 88 04 56; roubine. ardeche@wanadoo.fr;   www.camping-roubine. com] Site on W side of Vallon-Pont-d'Arc off D579, well sp by rvside. Med, hdg/mkd pitch, pt shd; htd wc; chem disp; mv service pnt; baby facs; shwrs inc; el pts (6A) €4; gas; lndtte; ice; shop; rest; snacks; bar; playgrnd; htd pool; rv sw & sand beach adj; fishing; canoeing; tennis; cycle hire; games area; mini-golf; child entmnt; TV rm; some statics; dogs €3; Eng spkn; adv bkg; quiet; cc acc. "Excel, well-run site in lovely area." ♦ 22 Apr-16 Sep. € 30.00   2005*

See advertisement below

VALLON PONT D'ARC *9D2* (2km W Rural) Camping La Plage Fleurie, Les Mazes, 07150 Vallon-Pont-d'Arc [04 75 88 01 15; fax 04 75 88 11 31; info@laplagefleurie.com; www.laplagefleurie.com] Site on main 'Route Touristique' of Ardeche: D579, 4.5km SE of Ruoms turn R at sp La Plage Fleurie in 1.5km. Fr N sp easily missed; no sp fr S. Lge, mkd pitch, pt sl, terr, shd; wc; shwrs inc; chem disp; el pts (10A) inc; gas; lndtte; ice; shop & 1.5km; tradsmn; snacks; rest; bar; playgrnd; pool; sand beach for rv sw; canoe hire; fishing; sailing; entmnt; TV rm; 10% statics; dogs €2.50; Eng spkn; adv bkg rec high ssn; quiet; red low ssn; CCI. "Conv Gorges de l'Ardeche; vg; gd position on rvside; excel san facs." ♦
26 May-15 Sep. € 22.00   2003*

VALLON PONT D'ARC *9D2* (2km W) Camping L'Arc en Ciel, Route de Ruoms, 07150 Les Mazes [04 75 88 04 65; fax 04 75 37 16 99; info@arcenciel-camping.com] Take D579 W fr Vallon. After 1.1km bear L for Les Mazes (poor sp). Pass thro vill & in about 1.7km bear L at far side at camp sp. Lge, pt sl, pt shd; wc; shwrs; el pts (3-6A) inc; lndtte; ice; shop; snacks; bar; playgrnd; shgl beach & rv sw; games rm; poss cr; adv bkg; quiet; cc acc. "Pleasant site on rv bank; excel." ♦ Easter-14 Sep. € 19.00   2003*

VALLON PONT D'ARC *9D2* (2km W) Camping Le Beau Rivage, 07150 Les Mazes [04 75 88 07 62; fax 04 75 88 03 54; a.massot@worldonline.fr; www.ardeche-tourisme.com] Take D579 W fr Vallon. After approx 1.1km bear L for Les Mazes (badly sp). After 800m turn L down side rd for site. Med, mkd pitch, terr, shd; wc (some cont); baby facs; shwrs; el pts (6A) inc; gas; lndry rm; ice; shop & 2km; tradsmn; rest 2km; bar; BBQ; playgrnd; htd pool; rv sw; fishing; sailing; canoe hire; entmnt; TV rm; 5% statics; dogs €1.60; phone; poss cr; Eng spkn; cc acc; CCI. "Vg quality site; dir access to rv; excel long stay." 1 May-15 Sep. € 24.60   2003*

VALLON PONT D'ARC *9D2* (3km W Rural) Camping Le Chassezac, Route d'Ales, 07120 Sampzon [04 75 39 60 71; fax 04 75 39 76 35; info@campinglechassezac.com; www.campinglechassezac.com] Fr Aubenas S on D579. Approx 2.5km past Ruoms at rndabt, turn R onto D111. Foll sp 2km to site on R. Med, mkd pitch, pt shd; wc (some cont); chem disp; baby facs; shwrs inc; el pts (6A) €3.80; lndtte; lndry rm; ice; shop; rest; snacks; bar; BBQ (gas only); playgrnd; pool; rv sw adj; fishing; cycle, canoe hire; horseriding; TV; 15% statics; dogs €2; phone; poss cr; Eng spkn; adv bkg dep req; quiet; CCI. "Friendly, helpful staff; vg all stays." ♦ ltd. 1 Apr-30 Sep. € 17.00   2004*

VALLON PONT D'ARC *9D2* (5km NW) Camping Le Riviera, 07120 Sampzon [04 75 39 67 57; fax 04 75 93 95 57; leriviera@wanadoo.fr] Take D579 W fr Vallon-Pont-d'Arc. After 6.5km cross narr bdge over Ardeche on D161. Site immed on L. Lge, mkd pitch, pt shd; wc; chem disp; mv service pnt; shwrs inc; el pts (10A) inc; gas; lndry rm; ice; shop 100m; rest; snacks; bar; BBQ; playgrnd; pool; paddling pool; rv sw adj; shgl beach; tennis; games rm; cycle hire; horseriding; entmnt; TV rm; some statics; dogs €3; poss cr; some rd noise. "Attractive pools." 1 Apr-30 Sep. € 27.00
                    2005*

> This site entry hasn't been updated for a while; we'd better fill in a site report form and send it to The Club.

VALLON PONT D'ARC *9D2* (5km NW Rural) Camping Soleil Vivarais, 07120 Sampzon [04 75 39 67 56 or 04 66 73 97 39; fax 04 75 39 64 69; info@soleil-vivarais.com; www.camping-soleil-vivarais.fr or www.yellohvillage.com] Take D579 fr Vallon-Pont-d'Arc. After 6km turn L onto D161, cross narr bdge over Ardeche. Site immed on R. Lge, hdg/mkd pitch, shd; wc; chem disp; mv service pnt; baby facs; shwrs inc; el pts (10A) inc; gas; lndry rm; ice; shop; rest; snacks; bar; playgrnd; htd pool; shgl beach & rv sw 500m; canoe hire; tennis; games rm; entmnt Jul/Aug; TV; 50% statics; dogs €3; poss cr; Eng spkn; adv bkg; quiet; cc acc. "V interesting area; busy site in gd location; sm pitches poss diff lge o'fits; gd entmnt." ♦ 3 Apr-11 Sep. € 38.00   2004*

VALLON PONT D'ARC *9D2* (6km NW) Le Domaine de la Bastide, 07120 Sampzon [04 75 39 64 72; fax 04 75 39 73 28; camping.bastide@wanadoo.fr; www.camping-la-bastide.fr] Fr Vallon take D579 W & turn L onto D111. Cross rv, site sp on L. Lge, mkd pitch, pt shd; wc; chem disp; shwrs; el pts (3-5A) inc; gas; lndtte; shop high ssn; tradsmn; rest, bar high ssn; BBQ (gas); playgrnd; 2 htd pools; sauna; rv sw; tennis; mini-golf; entmnt; horseriding; TV rm; canoeing; fishing; sailing; 70% statics; dogs; Eng spkn; adv bkg (dep req); quiet; cc acc; CCI. "Lovely scenery nr Ardeche gorge; well-run site; excel long/sh stay." ♦ 1 Apr-14 Sep. € 30.00   2003*

VALLOUISE see Argentiere La Bessee, L' *9C3*

VALOGNES *1C4* (1km N Urban) **Camp Municipal Le Bocage**, Rue Neuve, 50700 Valognes [02 33 95 82 00 or 06 10 84 59 33 (mob)] Off N13 Cherbourg to Carentan take 1st exit to Valonges, turn L just past Champion at Lidl sp. Site sp bef town, easily missed. Fr Carentan dir, take 3rd R after 4th set traff lts. Sm, hdg/mkd pitch, hdstg, pt shd; wc (cont); chem disp (wc); shwrs inc; el pts (6-10A) €2 (poss rev pol); gas; shop 300m; rest, snacks, bar nr; dogs €0.50; poss cr; quiet; cc not acc; CCI. "Excel site; vg san facs; friendly staff; ideal NH & conv Cherbourg ferries (27km); sh walk to attractive town; poss itinerants; warden calls 1900-2000, site self if office not open; vg sh stay." ♦1 Apr-30 Sep. € 9.00   2005*

VALRAS PLAGE *10F1* (N Coastal) **Camping L'Occitanie**, Chemin de Querelles, 34350 Valras-Plage [04 67 39 59 06; fax 04 67 32 58 20; campingoccitanie@wanadoo.fr; www.camping occitanie.com] Fr A9/E15 exit junc 35 at Beziers Est & join D64 sp Valras-Plage. Site is immed on L after rndabt at ent of Valras-Plage Est. Lge, hdg/mkd pitch, hdstg, pt sl, pt shd; htd wc; chem disp; mv service pnt; baby facs; shwrs inc; el pts (5A) inc (poss rev pol); lndtte; ice; shop 1km; tradsmn; rest; snacks; bar; BBQ (gas/charcoal only); playgrnd; pool; sand beach 1km; sailing; fishing; mini-golf; games rm; entmnt; TV rm; 25% statics; dogs €2.75; recep 0800-2100; c'van/mvan max 7m Jul/Aug; poss cr; Eng spkn; adv bkg; quiet; red low ssn/long stay; cc acc; CCI. "Lively town; mkt Mon & Fri am; excel, family site." ♦ 27 May-9 Sep. € 24.00 ABS - C12   2005*

See advertisement opposite (bottom)

Some of these sites have changed their opening dates - we'd better fill in some site report forms and let the editor of the guide know.

VALRAS PLAGE *10F1* (7km NE Coastal) **Camping Les Sablons**, 34420 Portiragnes-Plage [04 67 90 90 55 or 04 67 90 89 07; fax 04 67 90 82 91; les.sablons@wanadoo.fr; www. les-sablons.com] Fr A9 a'route exit Beziers Est junc 35 onto N112. Then take D37 S to Portiragnes-Plage & foll sp. V lge, mkd pitch, shd; wc; chem disp; mv service pnt; baby facs; shwrs inc; el pts (6A) inc; gas; lndtte; ice; shop; rest; snacks; bar; BBQ; playgrnd; 2 htd pools; waterslide; sand beach adj; diving; boating; fishing; tennis; games area; entmnt; 50% statics; dogs €4; phone; poss cr; Eng spkn; adv bkg (dep & bkg fee, min 3 wks Jul/Aug); cc acc; quiet. "Gd site on beach; modern san facs; nightly disco but quiet after midnight; resident doctor; grottoes & local excursions; vg long stay." ♦ ltd. 1 Apr-30 Sep. € 38.00   2003*

VALRAS PLAGE *10F1* (3km SW Coastal) **Airotel Les Vagues**, Chemin des Montilles, 34350 Vendres-Plage [04 67 37 33 12; fax 04 67 37 50 36; pleinairdeschenes@free.fr; www.lesvagues.net] Exit A9 junc 36 onto D64 to Valras then Vendres-Plage. Site sp. Lge, pt shd; wc; baby facs; shwrs inc; el pts inc; lndtte; shop; rest; snacks; bar; playgrnd; htd pool complex; paddling pool; waterslides; jacuzzi; sand beach 300m; games area; horseriding 5km; entmnt; TV rm; 75% statics; dogs €6; adv bkg; red low ssn. ♦ 1 Apr-30 Sep. € 38.00 (CChq acc)   2004*

VALRAS PLAGE *10F1* (3km SW Coastal) **Camping Domaine de la Yole**, 34350 Valras-Plage [04 67 37 33 87; fax 04 67 37 44 89; layole34@aol. com; www.campinglayole.com] Leave A9/E15 at Beziers-Ouest; foll D64 twd Valras-Plage, then Valras-Plage-Ouest & site sp. V lge, hdg/mkd pitch, hdstg, shd; wc (some cont); chem disp; baby facs; shwrs inc; el pts (5A) inc; gas; lndtte; ice; supmkt; rest; snacks; bar; BBQ; playgrnd; 2 pools & paddling pool; sand beach 400m; tennis; cycle hire; games area; games rm; entmnt; internet; tour ops statics; dogs €3.30 (not on beach); poss cr; Eng spkn; adv bkg; quiet but noisy nr rd; cc acc; red low ssn; CCI. "Excel; gd for all age groups; special offers families & children; mkt Mon & Fri." ♦ 29 Apr-23 Sep. € 34.90 ABS - C03   2005*

See advertisement opposite (top)

VALRAS PLAGE *10F1* (5km SW Rural) **Camp Municipal Les Cardonilles**, 34350 Vendres [04 67 39 57 14 or 04 67 32 60 50 (Mairie); fax 04 67 32 60 45; vendres.camp@wanadoo.fr] A9 fr Narbonne exit junc 36 & foll sp to Valras-Plage, at rndabt take R, site sp. Sm, mkd pitch, pt shd; wc; shwrs inc; el pts; ice; BBQ; playgrnd; sand beach 5km; 75% statics; dogs; quiet; CCI. "Steel pegs req high ssn." Easter-30 Sep. € 5.25   2002*

VALRAS PLAGE *10F1* (2.5km W Urban/Coastal) **Camping Blue Bayou**, Vendres-Plage-Ouest, 34350 Valras-Plage [04 67 37 41 97; fax 04 67 37 53 00; bluebayou@infonie.fr; www. bluebayou.fr] Exit Beziers Ouest fr A9 twd Valras-Plage & Vendres-Plage-Ouest. Lge, pt shd; wc; own san; shwrs inc; el pts inc; gas; lndtte; shop; snacks; bar; playgrnd; pool; sand beach 300m; adv bkg; quiet; CCI. "Poss dusty/windy end Jul/Aug, gd beach & pool; basic san facs." 1 May-30 Sep. € 25.92   2002*

VALREAS *9D2* (1km N) **Camping La Coronne,** Route de Pegue, 84600 Valreas [04 90 35 03 78; fax 04 90 35 26 73] Fr Nyons take D538 W to Valreas. Exit town on D10 rd to Taulignan, immed after x-ing bdge over Rv Coronne turn R into D196 sp Le Pegue. Site on R in 100m on rvside. Sp app fr E but easy to miss; app fr W; well sp in Valreas. Med, hdg/mkd pitch, pt sl, pt shd; wc (some cont); chem disp; mv service pnt; shwrs inc; el pts (3-10A) €1.37-3.04; gas; lndtte; ice; shop; tradsmn; rest; snacks; bar; BBQ; playgrnd; pool; paddling pool; fishing; entmnt; TV; dogs €0.80; phone; poss cr; Eng spkn; adv bkg (dep req); quiet; cc acc; CCI. "Sm pitches; excel pool; facs could do with refurb; site clsd 2200-0700." ♦ ltd. 1 Mar-30 Sep. € 12.00
2004*

VALREAS *9D2* (8km SE) **Camping de l'Herein,** Route de Bouchet, 84820 Visan [04 90 41 95 99; fax 04 90 41 91 72] E fr Bollene on D94/D994 twd Nyons; after Tulette turn L (N) onto D576 dir Visan & Valreas; sp in vill opp PO; turn L onto D161 Bouchet rd; site on L in 800m just over sm bdge. Med, hdg/mkd pitch, pt shd; wc; chem disp; shwrs inc; el pts (6-10A) €2.50-3.00; gas; ice; lndtte; shop & 1km; tradsmn; snacks; bar; playgrnd; pool; dogs €1.50; quiet; adv bkg rec; cc acc; CCI. "Lge pitches; facs poss stretched high ssn; vg." ♦ ltd 15 Mar-15 Oct. € 13.50
2005*

VALREAS *9D2* (8km W Rural) **Camping Les Truffieres,** 26230 Grignan [tel/fax 04 75 46 93 62; info@lestruffieres.com; www.lestruffieres.com] Fr A7 take D133 E twds Grignan. On W o'skts of vill turn S on D71. In 1km turn L at sp. Site is 200m on R. Fr Nyons take D538 W to Grignan. Sm, mkd pitch; shd; wc; chem disp; mv service pnt; shwrs inc; el pts (10A) €4.20; gas; lndtte; ice; shop 1km; tradsmn, rest, snacks high ssn; bar; communal BBQ only; playgrnd; pool; fishing; 5% statics; Eng spkn; adv bkg; quiet; CCI. "Pleasant owners; 20 min stroll to town; gd pool area; some pitches diff access; excel long stay." ♦ 20 Apr-30 Sep. € 16.00
2005*

Will you fill in the site report forms at the back of the guide, or shall I?

VALS LES BAINS see Aubenas *9D2*

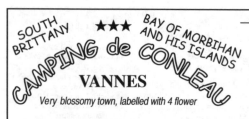
VANDENESSE EN AUXOIS *6G1* (Rural) Camping Le Lac de Panthier, 21320 Vandenesse-en- Auxois [03 80 49 21 94; fax 03 80 49 25 80; franckcoellier@wanadoo.fr; www.lac-de- panthier.com] Fr Arnay le Duc on N6 take N81 NE twd Dijon. After 14km take 1st exit at rndabt sp Creancy D114. 2km beyond Creancy at x-rds turn R. Site on R in 1km beside lake adj Camping Les Voiliers. Fr Somernon take D977bis S to Vandenesse. Fr A6 exit at Pouilly-en-Auxois; foll D16/D18 to Vandenesse; turn L on D977bis, site on L. Lge, hdg/mkd pitch, pt sl, pt shd; wc; chem disp; mv service pnt; sauna; shwrs inc; el pts (6A) inc (some rev pol); lndtte; shop & 6km; rest; snacks; bar; playgrnd; 2 pools (1 htd, covrd); waterslide; lake beach 50m; cycle hire; entmnt; sat TV; dogs €2.50; adv bkg ess; red low ssn; CCI. "Lovely area; this site & Les Voiliers adj operate as one; lge pitches; gd cycling & walks round lake; well-run site; facs poss stretched high ssn; vg." ♦ 9 Apr-15 Oct. € 23.40 (CChq acc)   2005*

VANDIERES see Dormans *3D4*

†**VANNES** *2F3* (5km N Rural) Camping du Haras, Aerodrome Vannes-Meucon, 56250 Monterblanc [02 97 44 66 06 or 06 71 00 05 59 (mob LS); fax 02 97 44 49 41; camping-vannes@wanadoo.fr; http://campingvannes.free.fr] App fr N165 turn L onto D767 sp Airport. Go N for 7km & turn R onto D778 for 1km & turn R again. After 1km approx, turn L onto Airport Perimeter Rd, site sp on W side. App fr N on D767, join D778 & as above. Med, hdg/mkd pitch, hdstg, pt shd; htd wc; chem disp; mv service pnt; fam bthrm; shwrs inc; el pts (4-10A) €2-6; gas; lndtte; ice; shop 5km; tradsmn; snacks; bar; BBQ; playgrnd; htd pools; waterslide; sand beach 12km; lake sw 3km; fishing; horseriding 300m; cycle hire; games rm; dogs €3; Eng spkn; adv bkg; quiet with minimal aircraft noise; cc acc; red CCI. "Lovely site; ltd space for tourers." ♦ € 17.00   2005*

See advertisement (right)

VANNES *2F3* (6km SE Rural) Camping Le Rhuys, Le Poteau Rouge, 56450 Theix [02 97 54 14 77; fax 02 97 75 98 54] Fr junc N166 on Vannes, Nantes is 5km, turn R on D780 Sarzeau, site sp on R in 400m. Med, hdg pitch, pt sl, unshd; wc (cont); chem disp; mv service pnt; shwrs inc; baby facs; el pts (5-10A) €2.25-4; lndtte; ice; shops 2km; tradsmn; rest; bar; playgnrd; htd sm pool; TV; entmnts; rv 300m; sand beach & lake 3km; waterslide; fishing; tennis; statics; dogs €1; Eng spkn; adv bkg; quiet. ♦ 30 Mar-31 Oct. € 18.50   2002*

VANNES *2F3* (10km SE) **Camping La Peupleraie, Le Marais, 56450 Theix [tel/fax 02 97 43 09 46]** Exit N165 into Theix foll sp dir Trefflean, site off D116; site 2.5km NE of Theix (sp easily missed). Med, shd; wc; chem disp; shwrs inc; el pts (5A) €2 (rev pol); lndtte; shops 3km; tradsmn; playgrnd; games area; adv bkg; quiet; 10% red CCI. "Fruit & veg fr farm; san facs in need of update; gd NH for Vannes." 15 Apr-15 Oct. € 9.40   2003*

VANNES *2F3* (4km S) **Camping Moulin de Cantizac, 199 Route de Vannes, 56860 Sene [02 97 66 90 26]** S fr Vannes on D199 twds Sene. Site on L at rndabt beside rv. Med, hdg pitch, pt sl, pt shd; wc (some cont); shwrs inc; el pts (6A) €3; lndtte; tradsmn; ice; sand beach 4km; boating; dogs €1.20; quiet. "Superb cent for bird watching, starting with estuary outside site ent; Vannes of historical interest." 1 May-15 Oct. € 14.00   2005*

VANNES *2F3* (3km SW Coastal) **Camp Municipal de Conleau, 188 Ave Marechal Juin, 56000 Vannes [02 97 63 13 88; fax 02 97 40 38 82; camping@ mairie-vannes.fr; www.mairie-vannes.fr]** Exit N165 at Vannes Ouest, foll sp for 'Centre Ville' & look for site sp fr 1st rndabt. Site on R of rd to Conleau. If on N165 fr Auray take 1st exit sp Vannes & at 2nd rndabt R (sp) to miss town cent. C'vans not allowed thro town cent. Lge, mkd pitch, pt sl, pt shd; wc; chem disp; mv service pnt; shwrs; el pts (6A) €3.50 (some rev pol); lndtte; ice; tradsmn; playgrnd; sea water pool nr; sand beach 500m; entmnt; TV; dogs €1.30; Eng spkn; adv bkg; quiet; cc acc. "Vannes interesting; pleasant walk along estury to old city; fishing; boating; sep area m'vans; vg sh stay." ♦ 1 Apr-30 Sep. € 17.30   2005*

See advertisement opposite (top)

VANNES *2F3* (5km SW Coastal) **Camping de Penboch, 9 Chemin de Penboch, 56610 Arradon [02 97 44 71 29; fax 02 97 44 79 10; camping. penboch@wanadoo.fr; www.camping-penboch.fr]** Exit Brest-Nantes N165 Vannes by-pass onto D101 & foll sp Arradon. Site well sp. Med, hdg/mkd pitch, pt shd; wc (some cont); chem disp; mv service pnt; baby facs; shwrs inc; el pts (6-10A) €3.20-4.20 (poss rev pol); gas; lndtte; ice; sm shop & 2km; tradsmn; snacks; bar; BBQ; playgrnd; htd pool; waterslide; sand beach 200m; games rm; internet; TV rm; 50% statics; dogs €3.50 (high ssn); Eng spkn; adv bkg rec high ssn; quiet; red low ssn; CCI. "Boat trips around Morbihan; steel pegs req; overflow has 50 pitches with all facs; plenty of activities for youngsters." ♦ 8 Apr-23 Sep. € 29.80   2005*

VANNES *2F3* (6km SW Coastal) **Camping de l'Allee, Rue du Moustoir, 56610 Arradon [02 97 44 01 98; fax 02 97 44 73 74; camping delallee@free.fr]** Fr Vannes take D101 & D101A to Arradon. Take by-pass & take 1st exit at rndabt & foll sp. Site to SW of Arradon. Fr Auray on D101 site sp fr Moustoir. Med, hdg/mkd pitch, pt sl, pt shd; wc; chem disp; shwrs inc; el pts (6-10A) €2.80-3.50 (rev pol & poss long leads req); gas; lndtte; ice; sm shop & 2km; snacks; playgrnd; htd pool; shgl beach 600m; games/TV rm; dogs €1.50; poss cr; quiet; 20% red low ssn; CCI. "A delightful site; restful area; family-run; excel san facs but poss stretched high ssn; pitches in apple orchard; dinghy launching & boat mooring nrby; gd rests in Arradon; gd walks." ♦ 1 Apr-30 Sep. € 16.80   2004*

VANS, LES *9D1* (2.5km E) **Domaine des Chenes, Chassagnes, 07140 Les Vans [04 75 37 34 35; fax 04 75 37 20 10; reception@domaine-des-chenes. fr]** Fr town cent take the D104, head twd Chassagnes on the E side of town, turn R at garden cent, site after 3km; sp. Med, pt sl, pt shd; wc (some cont); baby facs; shwrs inc; el pts (10A) €3.70; lndtte; shop; rest; snacks; bar; BBQ; playgrnd; pool; 80% statics; poss cr; adv bkg; quiet; cc acc; CCI. "Fair sh stay; lovely shady site ideal for birdwatchers." 1 Apr-30 Sep. € 16.50   2003*

VANS, LES *9D1* (5km E Rural) **Camping La Rouveyrolle, 07460 Berrias-et-Casteljau [04 75 39 00 67; fax 04 75 39 07 28; rouv@ club-internet.fr]** Heading S on D104, S of Maison Neuve turn W twd Casteljau; site sp approx 2km. Med, hdg/mkd pitch, shd; wc; chem disp; serviced pitches; shwrs inc; el pts (5A) €3.60; lndtte; shop & 1km; tradsmn; rest; snacks; bar; playgrnd; htd pool; rv sw 500m; tennis 500m; 45% statics; Eng spkn; adv bkg (dep req); quiet; red low ssn; cc acc; CCI. "Excel long stay." ♦ 1 Apr-30 Sep. € 21.00   2002*

VANS, LES *9D1* (5km NW Rural) **Camping Les Gorges de Chassezac, Champ d'Eynes, 07140 Malarce-sur-la-Thines [04 75 39 45 12]** Fr Les Vans cent, dir Graviere, approx 5km thro Graviere cont, site on L. Med, mkd pitch, pt sl, shd; wc (many cont); chem disp; shwrs; el pts (6A) €2.20; gas; lndtte; ice; shop; snacks; bar; playgrnd; rv sw adj; TV; entmnt; adv bkg; Eng spkn; poss cr; quiet; CCI; "Vg long stay." ♦ ltd. 1 May-31 Aug. € 10.00   2002*

VARADES see Ancenis *2G4*

VARCES ALLIERES ET RISSET see Grenoble *9C3*

VAREN see St Antonin Noble Val *8E4*

VARENNES EN ARGONNE *5D1* **Camp Municipal Le Paquis, 55270 Varennes-en-Argonne [03 29 80 71 01 (Mairie); fax 03 29 80 71 43]** On D946 Vouziers/Clermont-en-Argonne rd; sp by bdge in vill, on banks of Rv Aire, 200m N of bdge. Med, pt shd; wc; shwrs inc; el pts (3-6A) €2.30; ice; lndtte; shops adj; BBQ; fishing; dogs €0.30; quiet. "Vg sh stay." Easter-30 Sep. € 7.30   2002*

Between Nice - Cannes - Grasse - Vence

Les Pinèdes ★★★

F-06480 La Colle sur Loup

Tel.: 00 33 04 93 32 98 94 • Fax: 00 33 04 93 32 50 20

Open from 15.03 to 30.09

Les Pinèdes is beautifully situated at a 10 minutes drive from the Mediterranean coast and between the most interesting villages of the Côte d'Azur. Everything you need for a splendid vacation is available on the camping: luxury sanitary facilities, large pitches, swimming pool, restaurant, etc. It is a family camping with sports and leisure activities for young and old with the atmosphere and colours of the Provence.

camplespinedes06@aol.com

www.lespinedes.com

VARENNES SUR ALLIER 9A1 (9km N Rural) Camp Municipal, 03340 St Gerand-de-Vaux [04 70 45 08 83 (Mairie)] N on D105 fr Varennes-sur-Allier; sp cent of St Gerand-de-Vaux to side of fishing lake. Sm, mkd pitch, terr, pt shd; wc; shwrs inc; el pts (6A); lndry rm; playgrnd; quiet; CCI. "Site alongside fishing lake; rec check opening dates." ♦ ltd. May-Sep. 2002*

VARENNES SUR ALLIER 9A1 (3km NW Rural) Camping Le Chateau de Chazeuil, 03150 Varennes-sur-Allier [tel/fax 04 70 45 00 10; camping-de-chazeuil@ifrance.internet; www.camping-de-chazeuil.com] Ent to Chateau grounds at traff lts at junc of N7 & D46. (E & immed L bet tall iron gates). Med, pt shd; wc (some cont); chem disp; shwrs inc; el pts (6A) €2.75 (long lead poss req); lndtte; ice; shops, rest, snacks & bar 2km; tradsmn; BBQ; playgrnd; pool; fishing; dogs €1; Eng spkn; adv bkg; quiet; CCI. "Superb, quiet site in grounds of chateau; gd supmkt in town; friendly owners; well off main rds; excel pool & san facs tho shortage of wcs & el pts." ♦ 15 Apr-15 Oct. €16.25 2004*

VARENNES SUR LOIRE See Saumur 4G1

VARILHES 8G3 (Urban) Camp Municipal du Parc du Chateau, Ave de 8 Mai 1945, 09120 Varilhes [05 61 67 42 84; fax 05 61 60 55 54] Exit N20 at sp Varilhes. Turn N in town on D624. Site 250m on L (sp) just bef leisure cent. Med, mkd pitch, pt shd; wc; shwrs inc; el pts (5-10A); shops adj & 200m; lndry rm; rest 200m; snacks; playgrnd; pool adj; rv fishing adj; 20% statics; adv bkg; quiet. 1 Apr-15 Sep. €5.34 2003*

VARILHES 8G3 (7km SE Rural) Camping Mille Fleurs (Naturist), Le Tuilier, 09120 Gudas [tel/fax 05 61 60 77 56; info@camping-millefleurs.com; www.camping-millefleurs.com] Fr S at Foix town on N20, turn R onto D1 at traff lts. In 6.5km sharp bend L onto D13 sp Mirepoix. In 500m turn L at sp Gudas. Site in 2km on L. NB Do not app fr Varilhes thro Dalou & Gudas, rd too narr for c'vans. Sm, hdg/mkd pitch, terr, pt shd; wc; chem disp; mv service pnt; shwrs inc; child/baby facs; fam bthrm; el pts (4-8A) €2.50-3.25; gas 10km; shop 8km; tradsmn; rest, snacks; bar; BBQ; no statics; dogs €1.75; phone; Eng spkn (dep €50); quiet; red low ssn; INF card req. "Excel site; lovely owners; gd pitches; v clean facs; guided mountain walks arranged; gd base Andorra, Toulouse & Carcassonne; gd views; communal meal twice a week in high ssn; adv bkg rec high ssn." ♦ 1 Apr-15 Oct. €14.85 2005*

†VARILHES 8G3 (3km NW Rural) Camping Les Mijeannes, Route de Ferries, 09120 Rieux-de-Pelleport [05 61 60 82 23; fax 05 61 67 74 80; lesmijeannes@wanadoo.fr; www.campingsmijeannes.com] Exit N20 sp Varilhes; on app Varilhes cent join one way system; 1st R at Hotel de Ville; over rv bdge; foll camp sps; site 2km on R. Med, hdg pitch, pt shd; wc; chem disp; shwrs inc; el pts (4-10A) €2.80-3.80; tradsmn; bar; BBQ; playgrnd; pool; fishing; games area; TV; dogs €1.10; phone; some Eng spkn; adv bkg; quiet; CCI. "V helpful owner; local interest info avail on site; storage & equip hire; gd size pitches; poss ltd facs low ssn; excel, peaceful site; vg long/sh stay." €15.20 2004*

VARREDDES see Meaux 3D3

VARZY 4G4 (1.5km N) Camp Municipal du Moulin Naudin, 58210 Varzy [03 86 29 43 12; fax 03 86 29 72 73] On D977 fr Clamecy to Nevers, sp. Sm, unshd; wc; shwrs inc; el pts (5A) €1.83; shops 1.5km; fishing; tennis nrby; quiet. May-Sep. €10.60 2003*

VATAN *4H3* (Urban) **Camp Municipal de la Ruelle au Loup, Rue du College**, 36150 Vatan [02 54 49 91 37 or 02 54 49 76 31 (Mairie); fax 02 54 49 93 72; mairie@vatan-en-berry.com] Exit A20 junc 10 onto D922 to town cent. Take D2 foll site sp - 2nd on L (easily missed). Med, hdg/mkd pitch, pt shd; wc; mv service pnt; shwrs inc; el pts (6A) €2 (rev pol); lndtte; shops, rests 200m; playgrnd; pool adj; adv bkg; quiet; cc not acc; CCI. "V pleasant, clean & well-kept site in park; spacious pitches; easy access fr a'route; conv Loire chateaux; excel value." ♦ 15 Apr-15 Sep. € 8.00   2005*

VATAN *4H3* (8km N) **Camp Municipal St Phalier**, 18310 Gracay [02 48 51 24 14 or 02 48 51 42 07 (Mairie); fax 02 48 51 25 92] Leave A20 at junc 9 & take D83 to Gracay. On o'skts of vill turn L & immed turn L foll sp to Cent Omnisport & site. Sm, mkd pitch, pt shd; wc (some cont); chem disp; shwrs inc; el pts (10A) €2; rest, bar & shop 1km; tradsmn; playgrnd & pool adj; fishing; dogs €0.56; phone; Eng spkn; quiet; CCI. "Clean site; excel san facs; sm lake & sm park adj; overhead barrier 1.90m at ent, stop & wait for warden to activate; vill in walking dist; gd NH for A20." 1 May-15 Sep. € 7.20   2005*

VATAN *4H3* (1km S Rural) **Camping Le Moulin de la Ronde (Naturist)**, Route de la Ronde, 36150 Vatan [02 54 49 83 28] Fr town cent take rd S twds A20; at Champion supmkt turn R; site on L 500m; sp. Sm, pt shd; wc; chem disp; shwrs inc; el pts (10A) inc; gas 1km; shop, rest, bar & snacks 1km; playgrnd; pool; dogs; adv bkg; quiet; INF card req. "Basic site & facs; take great care with el pts; fair sh stay only." 1 Apr-30 Oct. € 18.50   2003*

VAUVERT *10E2* (5km E Rural) **Camping Les Mourgues**, Gallician, 30600 Vauvert [tel/fax 04 66 73 30 88; info@masdemourgues.com; www.masdemourgues.com] Exit A9 junc 26 onto N313/N572. Site on R at x-rds to Gallician & Stes Marie-de-la-Mer. Med, hdg/mkd pitch, pt shd; wc; chem disp; shwrs inc; el pts (6A) €2.50; lndtte; ice; shop; snacks; pool; games area; dogs €1.70; phone; adv bkg (25% dep req); rd & farming noise; cc acc; CCI. "Gd; v helpful British owners; some diff, long narr pitches; ground stony; facs poss stretched high ssn." ♦ 1 Apr-30 Sep. € 12.00   2005*

VAUX SUR MER see St Palais sur Mer *7B1*

VAYRAC *7C3* (3.5km S) **Camping Les Granges**, 46110 Vayrac [05 65 32 46 58; fax 05 65 32 57 94; info@les-granges.com] App Vayrac on D703, turn S at traff lts in town. Site in 3.5km sp in Vayrac on banks of Rv Dordogne. Lge, pt shd; wc (some cont); shwrs; el pts (4A) €2.60; gas; lndtte; shop; rest; snacks; bar; playgrnd; pool; entmnt; TV; adv bkg; quiet. "Vg children's amenities; poss mosquitoes." 15 May-15 Sep. € 12.60   2002*

VAZERAC *8E3* (Rural) **Camping Latapie**, 82220 Vazerac [tel/fax 05 63 67 70 92; camping-latapie@compuserve.com] Fr Moissac take D927 to Lafrancaise, on D20, L turn D109 to Vazerac, foll sp to site. Sm, pt sl, pt terr, pt shd; wc; shwrs; el pts; lndtte; ice; rest; bar; playgrnd; lake fishing adj; adv bkg; Eng spkn; quiet. 1 Apr-1 Nov.   2002*

VEDENE see Avignon *10E2*

VEIGNE see Montbazon *4G2*

VELLES see Chateauroux *4H2*

Mustn't forget to post our site report forms to The Club, otherwise sites might be deleted.

VENAREY LES LAUMES *6G1* (1km W) **Camp Municipal Alesia**, Rue du Docteur-Roux, 21150 Venarey-les-Laumes [tel/fax 03 80 96 07 76 or 03 80 96 01 59 (Mairie); mairie.vll@worldonline.fr] SE fr Montbard on D905, site well sp fr Venarey on D954. Med, hdg/mkd pitch, pt shd, some hdstg; htd wc; chem disp; shwrs inc; el pts (6A) €2.50; lndtte; shops 1km; tradsmn; BBQ; playgrnd; sand beach 50m; lake sw; cycle hire; TV rm; dogs €0.30; phone; poss cr; Eng spkn; adv bkg; some rlwy noise; red low stay; cc acc; CCI. "V scenic area, much to explore; barrier clsd 2200-0700; warden cooks meals on request; friendly staff." ♦ 1 Apr-15 Oct. € 9.00   2005*

VENCE *10E4* (8km S Rural) **Camping Les Pinedes**, Route de Pont de Pierre, 06480 La Colle-sur-Loup [04 93 32 98 94; fax 04 93 32 50 20; camples pinedes06@aol.com; www.lespinedes.com] Exit A8 junc 47 Cagnes-sur-Mer & foll dir Villeneuve-Loubet Vill. At vill turn L at traff lts onto D6 to La Colle-sur-Loup, site sp. Lge, hdg/mkd pitch, hdstg, terr, pt shd; wc; chem disp; mv service pnt; serviced pitches; shwrs inc; el pts (10A) inc; lndtte; ice; shop high ssn & 1.5km; tradsmn; rest adj; snacks; bar; BBQ (gas/elec); pool; paddling pool; beach 3km; rv sw & fishing adj; tennis, horseriding 1km; games area; TV rm; 20% statics; dogs €1.90; c'vans over 6m & m'vans over 8m not acc high ssn; Eng spkn; adv bkg; quiet; cc acc; red long stay/low ssn/CCI. "V helpful, friendly manager; steep access to pitches but gd rd surface; not suitable for disabled; excel for touring Cote d'Azur; excel site." 15 Mar-30 Sep. € 29.40 ABS - C30   2005*

See advertisement

VENCE *10E4* (6km SW) **Caravaning Les Rives du Loup**, Route de la Colle, 06140 Tourrettes-sur-Loup [tel/fax 04 93 24 15 65; rdl@net-up.com] On D6 rd, Rte de la Colle. Sm, pt shd; wc; baby facs; shwrs inc; el pts (3-5A) €2.50-3 (poss rev pol); lndtte; ice; shop; snacks; playgrnd; pool; fishing; tennis; guided walks; horseriding 5km; 60% statics; dogs €2.50; adv bkg; quiet. "Many outdoor activities avail; beautiful location." 1 Apr-30 Sep. € 18.50   2003*

VENCE *10E4* (8km SW Rural) **Camping des Gorges du Loup, Chemin des Vergers, 06620 Le Bar-sur-Loup** [04 93 42 45 06; info@goregedu loup.com; www.lesgorgesduloup.com] Fr A8 exit junc 47 & foll sp Vence then to Pont du Loup. Site well sp. App fr other dirs is diff. Med, mkd pitch, some hdstg, terr, pt shd; wc (some cont); chem disp; shwrs inc; el pts (4-10A) €2.50-4 (poss rev pol); gas; lndtte; ice: shop; playgrnd; pool; shgl beach; TV rm; 20% statics; dogs €2; phone; bus 1km; Eng spkn; adv bkg 25% dep & bkg fee req; quiet; cc not acc; CCI. "Vg site with helpful, pleasant owners; spotless san facs; superb views; not suitable disabled; not suitable lge o'fits; vg long stay."
1 Apr-30 Sep. € 23.70   2004*

VENCE *10E4* (3km W) **Domaine La Bergerie, Camping Estate, Route de la Sine, 06140 Vence** [04 93 58 09 36; fax 04 93 59 80 44] Fr A8 exit junc 47 & foll sp Vence thro Cagnes-sur-Mer. Take detour to W around Vence foll sp Grasse/Tourrette-sur-Loup. At rndabt beyond viaduct take last exit, foll site sp S thro La Sine town long, narr rd to site, up driveway on R. Lge, mkd pitch, hdstg, pt sl, shd; wc; chem disp; mv service pnt; shwrs inc; el pts (2-5A) inc; gas; lndtte; ice; shop & 5km; tradsmn; rest; snacks; bar; playgrnd; pool; tennis; dogs; poss cr; Eng spkn; no adv bkg; quiet; 5-10% red 10-20+ days; cc acc; CCI. "Office clsd 1230-1500; helpful owner; waiting area if full; access to san facs diff for disabled & many pitches long way fr san facs; Vence lovely & excel touring base; Antibes gd sand beach (30km); Italian border 40km; poss neglected & scruffy low ssn."
25 Mar-15 Oct. € 29.00 (CChq acc)   2005*

VENDAYS MONTALIVET *7C1* (6km NE Rural) **Camping du Vieux Moulin, Route du Moulin, 33590 Vensac** [tel/fax 05 56 09 45 98; camping_vieuxmoulin@hotmail.com] Turn off N215 sp Vensac. Well sp in vill adj windmill. Med, pt shd, mkd pitch; wc; chem disp; shwrs inc; el pts (5A) €3; lndtte; ice; shop; tradsmn; rest; snacks; bar; playgrnd; pool; sand beach 8km; entmnt; TV; 7% statics; Eng spkn; adv bkg; quiet. "Excel ambiance; v friendly; improved site." 1 May-31 Oct. € 11.50
                    2005*

VENDAYS MONTALIVET *7C1* (1km S) **Camping Les Peupliers, Route de Sarnac, 33930 Vendays-Montalivet** [tel/fax 05 56 41 70 44; lespeupliers33@hotmail.com; www.chez.com/ campinglespeupliers] NW fr Lesparre on N215 for 9km. Then W on D102 to Vendays-Montalivet. In town cent foll D101 twd Hourtin. Turn L in 100m (sp), site on L in 200m. Med, mkd pitch, shd; wc; chem disp; baby facs; shwrs inc; el pts (4-10A) €2.30-4.35; gas; lndtte; ice; shop 400m; tradsmn; snacks; BBQ; playgrnd; sand beach 10km; entmnt; fitness rm; TV rm; cycle hire; 10% statics; dogs €1.25; phone; adv bkg; quiet; red long stay/low ssn; cc acc; CCI. "Friendly owners; conv Medoc vineyards; excel cycle paths adj; excel san facs; €20 dep barrier key; vg long stay." ♦ 1 Apr-30 Sep.
€ 11.00   2004*

VENDAYS MONTALIVET *7C1* (3km W Rural) **Camping Le Merin, 33930 Vendays-Montalivet** [tel/fax 05 56 41 78 64] NW fr Lesparre Medoc on N215 for 9km; then W on D102 to Vendays-Montalivet. Cont on D102 twds Montalivet-les-Bains. Site on L in 3km. Lge, hdg pitch, pt shd; wc; shwrs; el pts (6-10A) €2.40-2.90; lndtte; shop 3km; tradsmn in ssn; playgrnd; sand beach 4km; fishing; cycle hire; entmnt; 5% statics; dogs €0.80; adv bkg; CCI. "Working farm." 12 Apr-1 Nov. € 8.80
                    2003*

VENDAYS MONTALIVET *7C1* (6km W Coastal) **Camp Municipal de Montalivet, Ave de l'Europe, 33930 Vendays-Montalivet** [05 56 09 33 45] Take D101 fr Soulac to Vendays, D102 to Montalivet-les-Bains. Site sp bef ent to Montalivet. Turn L at petrol stn, site 500m on L. V lge, mkd pitch, shd; wc; chem disp; mv service pnt; shwrs inc; el pts inc; lndtte; shop; rest; snacks; bar; playgrnd; paddling pool; beach 700m; dogs €1.80; quiet; adv bkg. "Site in pine forest; gd mkt 1km; naturist beaches N & S of Montalivet." ♦ 1 May-30 Sep. € 14.20   2004*

VENDEUVRE SUR BARSE *6F1* (8km NW Rural) **Camping de la Voie Colette, Rue du Lac, 10140 Mesnil-St Pere** [tel/fax 03 25 41 27 15; voiecolette@yahoo.fr] On N19 foll sps Lac de La Foret d'Orient. Approx 10km fr Vendeuvre or 20km fr Troyes turn on D43, thro Mesnil-St Pere; site at far end of lakeside promenade. Lge, pt sl, pt shd; wc (most cont); chem disp (wc); shwrs inc; el pts (2-6A) €1.30-2.60; gas; lndtte; ice; shop; snacks; playgrnd; sand beach 1km; lake sw 200m; fishing; sailing; games rm; dogs €0.50; phone; quiet; CCI. "Huge lake with sw & yachting facs; conn charge el pts 1st night; poss v cr high ssn; san facs stretched high ssn & ltd low ssn; fair sh stay." ♦ ltd. 1 Apr-7 Oct.
€ 11.20   2004*

VENDOME *4F2* (8km NE Rural) **Camp Municipal Les Ilots, 41100 Pezou** [02 54 23 40 69 (Mairie) or 02 54 23 67 35; fax 02 54 23 62 40; commune. pezou@wanadoo.fr] N fr Vendome on N10, turn R at traff lts (sp) immed after La Poste in cent vill of Pezou; site on R in 400m over rv bdge at junc D12/D34; sp. NB Ent poss diff wide vans (ent deliberately narr to stop itinerants). Sm, level, pt shd; wc (some cont); chem disp; shwrs inc; el pts (16A) €1.20; gas; shops 400m; playgrnd; tennis; rv fishing 20m; quiet. "Gd NH; pleasant but poss itinerants outside main gates using site facs; poor security on site; site yourself - warden calls daily." ♦
4 May-17 Sep. € 7.20   2003*

VENDOME *4F2* (500m E Urban) **Camp Municipal Les Grands Pres, Rue Geoffroy-Martel, 41100 Vendome [02 54 77 00 27 or 02 54 89 43 51; fax 02 54 89 43 58; camping.vendome@free.fr]** Fr N10 by-pass foll sp for town cent. In town foll sp Loisirs & Sports. Site adj to pool 500m. Or fr D957 foll sp to Loisirs & Sports for 2km. Lge, mkd pitch, pt shd; wc; chem disp; all serviced pitches; shwrs inc; el pts (4-6A) €2.60-3.85; gas 500m; lndtte; shop high ssn; rest in town; snacks; playgrnd; pool adj; rv fishing adj; entmnt; 5% statics; dogs €0.85; poss cr; some Eng spkn; adv bkg rec high ssn; quiet but some rd noise; CCI. "Pleasant setting; friendly staff; v clean san facs a trek fr outer pitches; sports cent, pool & theatre adj; gd shopping, historic town; beautiful site but diff to find & noise fr N10; vg sh stay." ♦ 10 Jun-31 Aug. € 8.00   2005*

VENDOME *4F2* (8km W Rural) **Camp Municipal de la Bonne Aventure, 41100 Thore-la-Rochette [02 54 72 00 59; fax 02 54 89 41 01; enora. conan@cpvendome.com]** Fr Vendome take D917 twd Montoire. After 6km turn R onto D82 for Thore; thro vill & cont to vill exit sign, foll site sp. Beware there are 2 rds to Montoire - foll sp to vill. Med, pt shd; wc; chem disp; shwrs; el pts (5A) €2.20; lndtte; shop 2km; tradsmn; snacks; rv sw, fishing & watersports adj; playgrnd; tennis; entmnts; games area; dogs €0.85; adv bkg; CCI. "Peaceful site; v pretty & quiet setting by Rv Loir; worth effort to find; well-kept facs; code for barrier; helpful warden; excel long stay." 15 May-30 Sep & Easter & Whitsun. € 6.70   2005*

VENDRES see Valras Plage *10F1*

VENOSC see Bourg d'Oisans, Le *9C3*

VENSAC see Vendays Montalivet *7C1*

VERCHAIX see Samoens *9A3*

VERDIERE, LA *10E3* (N Rural) **Camp Municipal Fontvielle, Route de Manosque, 83560 La Verdiere [04 94 04 12 10 (Mairie); fax 04 94 04 19 73]** Fr D13 at Montmeyan take D30 W twds La Verdiere. Then D554 out of vill. Site sp. Sm, pt sl, pt shd; wc; shwrs inc; el pts; shop 1km; pool; quiet; "Warden visits am & pm; poss disturbance fr local youths." 15 Jun-15 Sep.   2003*

VERDON SUR MER, LE *7B1* (Rural/Coastal) Camping Le Royannais, 88 Route de Soulac, 33123 Le Verdon-sur-Mer [05 56 09 61 12; fax 05 56 73 70 67; camping.le.royannais@wanadoo.fr; www.royannais.com] Fr Bordeaux N215 tw Le Verdon-sur-Mer (Royan), L D1 twd Soulac then R, site on L. Med, mkd pitch, hdstg, pt shd; htd wc; chem disp; baby facs; serviced pitches; shwrs inc; el pts (4A) €4; gas; lndtte; ice; shop; snacks; bar; BBQ; playgrnd; beach 400m; cycle hire; 40% statics; dogs €2.10; phone; bus; site clsd 16 Dec-14 Jan; Eng spkn; adv bkg; quiet; red long stay; CCI. "Conv Soulac; ferry to Royan 30 mins; charming site, lots of trees; gd shwrs;." ♦ 1 Apr-15 Oct. € 13.50   2005*

VERDON SUR MER, LE *7B1* (1km Coastal) Camping La Pointe du Medoc, Ave de la Pointe de Grave, 33123 Le Verdon-sur-Mer [05 56 73 39 99; fax 05 56 73 39 96; info@camping-lapointedumedoc.com; www.camping-lapointedumedoc.com] App Le Verdon-sur-Mer on N215, site sp. Lge, terr, pt shd; wc (some cont); chem disp; mv service pnt; 30% serviced pitch; shwrs; el pts (6A) inc; lndtte; shop & 1km; tradsmn; rest; snacks; bar; playgrnd; htd pools; sand beach 1km; watersports; fishing; horseriding; mini-golf; entmnt; TV rm; 20% statics; dogs €5; adv bkg; quiet; red low ssn; cc acc. ♦ 9 Apr-30 Sep. € 26.00   2005*

As we're travelling out of season, we'd better phone ahead to check that the site is actually open.

VERDUN *5D1* (W Urban) Camping Les Breuils, Allee des Breuils, 55100 Verdun [03 29 86 15 31; fax 03 29 86 75 76; contact@camping-lesbreuils. com; www.camping-lesbreuils.com] Fr A4/E50 exit junc 31. Site sp nr Citadel. Avoid Verdun town cent due to 1-way streets. Fr on D964 turn R over 1st rv bdge, foll sp Chalons & site sp. Lge, hdg/mkd pitch, some hdstg, pt sl, pt shd; wc; chem disp; mv service pnt; baby facs; shwrs inc; el pts (6A) €3.80 (some rev pol); gas; lndtte; shop 2km; tradsmn, rest, snacks & bar (high ssn); playgrnd; pool with flumes high ssn; cycle hire; dogs €1.50; phone; poss cr; Eng spkn; adv bkg (dep req) rec high ssn; quiet; cc acc; red 10+ days; CCI. "Helpful, friendly, family-owned for last 30 years; v clean, pleasant site; some site rds tight lge o'fits; gd pool 1400-2000; excel, modern san block (locked o'night); long walk to water taps; pretty lake; lovely lakeside pitches; walking dist to town; WWI museums local; citadel in Verdun; excel hypmkt 3km fr town twd Metz." ♦ ltd. 1 Apr-30 Sep. € 14.20   2005*

VERDUN SUR LE DOUBS *6H1* (500m W Rural) Camp Municipal La Plage, 71350 Verdun-sur-le-Doubs [03 85 91 55 50 or 03 85 91 52 52; fax 03 85 91 90 91] SE on D970 fr Beaune to Verdun-sur-le-Doubs & foll sp in town. Or on D973 or N73 twd Chalons fr Seurre, turn R onto D115 to Verdun; site on bank of Rv Saone. Lge, some hdg/mkd pitch, pt sl, pt shd; wc (some cont); chem disp; shwrs inc; ltd el pts €0.80; shops 500m; rest, snacks & bar 500m; BBQ; playgrnd; pool adj; waterslide; gd cycling & fishing; phone; quiet. "Lovely rvside location; interesting sm town; v clean; nr town cent; welcoming; lge pitches; excel." 1 May-30 Sep. € 8.10   2005*

VERMENTON *4G4* (500m W Rural) **Camp Municipal Les Coullemieres, 89270 Vermenton** [03 86 81 53 02 or 03 86 81 50 01 (Mairie); fax 03 86 81 63 95; mairie.vermenton@free.fr; www.vermenton.fr] Lies W of N6. Well sp in vill, over rlwy x-ing & site adj to rv. Med, hdg/mkd pitch, pt shd; htd wc (some cont); chem disp; shwrs inc; el pts (6A) €2.50; lndtte; shop 500m; rest 200m; playgrnd; tennis; rv boating, fishing & sw 20m; cycle hire; TV rm; dogs €1; bus; Eng spkn; adv bkg rec high ssn; quiet; cc acc. "Friendly, helpful management; peaceful, clean, well-run site; gd facs; gd location by rv; gd walks & cycling; beautiful town with 12thC church; no twin-axle vans; weight limit on access rds & pitches; excel long/sh stay." ♦ 1 May-30 Sep. € 10.50   2005*

VERMENTON *4G4* (2km W) **Camp Municipal, 89460 Accolay** [03 86 81 54 47] N fr Vermenton on N6 twd Auxerre; in 2km turn L sp Accolay. Cross bdge, turn R thro vill; site on R at 500m. Med, pt shd; wc; chem disp; 4 serviced pitches; shwrs; el pts (3-10A) €1.22-1.85; gas; shops 300m; lndry rm; playgrnd; rv adj; adv bkg; quiet; 10% red long stay; cc acc; CCI. "Site yourself; caves 11km; v beautiful country by pleasant sm vill; grassy pitches can be boggy; helpful warden avail most of day; gd sh stay; €6.55 if c'van 5m+ long; poss itinerants on site." 1 Apr-30 Sep. € 5.60   2002*

VERNANTES *4G1* (2km E Rural) **Camping Intercommunal de la Grande Pature, 49390 Vernantes** [02 41 51 45 39; fax 02 41 51 57 20] Fr Saumur on N147. Take D767 to Vernantes then D58 dir Vernoil. Site sp. Sm, pt shd; wc; shwrs inc; el pts (10A); shop 200m; playgrnd; tennis, fishing adj; adv bkg; quiet; CCI. 15 Jun-30 Sep.   2004*

†**VERNANTES** *4G1* (9km NW Rural) **Camping Le Chant d'Oiseau, 49390 Mouliherne** [02 41 67 09 78; info@loire-gites.com] Fr Saumur take D767 twd Noyant. Turn L in Vernantes then R onto D58 twd Mouliherne.Turn off D58 3km SE Mouliherne opp wooden cross. Foll rd for 2km. Site sp on L. Sm, pt sl, pt shd; wc; chem disp; shwrs inc; el pts (6A) €2.50; BBQ; v quiet; adv bkg; Eng spkn. "Gd, clean, CL-type site; peaceful paradise for birdwatchers; gd facs; helpful & friendly British owners; excel." ♦ ltd. € 10.00   2005*

VERNET see Auterive *8F3*

†**VERNET LES BAINS** *8G4* (1km N Rural) **Camping L'Eau Vive, Chemin de St Saturnin, 66820 Vernet-les-Bains** [04 68 05 54 14; fax 04 68 05 78 14; leauv@club-internet.fr; www.leau-vive.com] On app to town cent on D116 turn R over rv & site 1st R 1km at end of rd. Med, mkd pitch, terr, pt shd; wc; chem disp; serviced pitch; mv service pnt; shwrs inc; el pts (10A) €1.50; lndtte; shop 1km; tradsmn; rest; snacks; bar; BBQ; playgrnd; lake sw; waterslide; tennis 500m; games area; TV rm; 40% statics; dogs €2.50; site clsd Nov to mid-Dec; Eng spkn; quiet. "V helpful, friendly Dutch owners; beautiful area; gd walking." ♦ € 22.00 (3 persons) (CChq acc)   2005*

VERNET LES BAINS *8G4* (1.2km N Urban) **Camping Del Bosc, 68 Ave Clemenceau, 66820 Vernet-les-Bains** [04 68 05 54 54; fax 04 68 05 51 62] Fr Villefranche to Vernet on D116, site on o'skirts of town on L opp Ecomarche. Med, pt sl, shd; wc; chem disp; shwrs inc; el pts (3-10A) €1.70-2.20; lndtte; shop; playgrnd; entmnt; Eng spkn; adv bkg rec Jul/Aug; quiet; CCI. "Conv Tet valley & 'Little Yellow Train'; some pitches v sm & some steep; v clean facs; hot water to shwrs only." ♦ 1 Apr-1 Oct. € 9.60   2005*

VERNET LES BAINS *8G4* (2km N Rural) **Camping Les Closes, Route de Fillois, 66820 Corneilla-de-Conflent** [04 68 05 64 60 or 04 68 05 64 48] Fr Villefranche twd Vernet-Les-Bains on D116. Turn L into Corneilla-de-Conflent. Foll sp, site approx 1km. Med, mkd pitch, pt sl, terr, pt shd; wc (some cont); chem disp; shwrs inc; el pts (10A) €2.30; lndtte; shop 500m; playgrnd; pool; dogs; phone; adv bkg; CCI. "Beautiful views; helpful owners; interesting area." ♦ 1 Apr-30 Sep. € 9.00   2004*

VERNET LES BAINS *8G4* (2km NE) **Camping Les Sauterelles, Col de Milleres, 66820 Fillols** [tel/fax 04 68 05 63 72] Fr Perpignan take N116 to Prades, D27 passing thro L'Abbaye de St Michel-de-Cuxa, foll sps to Chalet des Cortalets. Suitable for sm o'fits. Med, pt sl, pt shd; wc (cont); mv service pnt; shwrs; el pts (5A) €2; ice; snacks; bar; shop; playgrnd; pool; no dogs; adv bkg; quiet. "Mountain walking; caves; vineyards; historical locations; panoramic views." ♦ 1 Jun-30 Sep. € 8.50   2002*

†**VERNET LES BAINS** *8G4* (3km NW Rural) **Camping Le Rotja, 66820 Fuilla** [tel/fax 04 68 96 52 75; campinglerotja.ellenetwim@wanadoo.fr; www.prades-tourisme.com/ campinglerotja] Take N116 fr Prades dir Mont-Louis, 500m after Villefranche-de-Conflens turn L onto D6 sp Fuilla. In 3km just bef church, turn R at sp to site. Sm, mkd pitch, pt sl, terr, pt shd; htd wc; chem disp; baby facs; shwrs inc; el pts (10A) inc; gas; lndtte; ice; shop 2km; rest 100m; snacks; BBQ (gas); playgrnd; pool; rv sw adj; 10% statics; dogs €1; phone; Eng spkn; adv bkg (dep req); quiet; cc acc; red long stay; CCI. "Views of Mount Canigou; peaceful site; friendly Dutch owners; gd hiking." ♦ € 18.00   2004*

VERNET, LE *9D3* (500m N Rural) **Camping Lou Passavou, 04140 Le Vernet** [04 92 35 14 67; fax 04 92 35 09 35; loupassavous@wanadoo.fr; www.loupassavous.com] Fr N on A51 exit junc 21 Volonne sp Digne. Fr Digne N on D900; site on R. Fr S exit A51 junc 20 Les Mees onto D4, then N85 E to Digne, then as above. Med, pt shd; wc; chem disp; baby facs; shwrs inc; el pts (6A) €3; lndtte; shop; tradsmn; rest; snacks; bar; playgrnd; pool; fishing; games area; TV; dogs €1; poss cr; Eng spkn; adv bkg; quiet; cc acc; CCI. "Excel scenery; gd walking." ♦ ltd. 15 Apr-15 Sep. € 13.00   2003*

†VERNEUIL SUR AVRE *4E2* (1km W Rural) Camping Le Vert Bocage, Ave Edmond Demolins, 27130 Verneuil-sur-Avre [02 32 32 26 79] On ent Verneuil-sur-Avre join ring rd & foll sp for N26 to L'Aigle-Argentan. Site clearly sp on o'skts on L. Med, hdg/mkd pitch, pt shd; wc; chem disp; shwrs inc; el pts (6A) inc; lndry rm; shops 1km; rest, snacks, bar & pool 200m; playgrnd; fishing adj; tennis; sports in town; 15% statics; dogs; site clsd Jan; no adv bkg; quiet but some traff noise; CCI. "Expensive for facs avail; clean facs but old & v ltd low ssn; site scruffy low ssn; NH only." € 25.00
2004*

VERNIOZ see Auberives sur Vareze *9B2*

VERNON *3D2* (2km W Rural) Camping Les Fosses Rouges (formerly Municipal), Chemin de Reanville, 27950 St Marcel [02 32 51 59 86 or 02 32 51 21 74] Fr E5/A13 m'way exit 16 twd Vernon onto D181; in 2km at rndabt L on D64; foll sp Les Fosses Rouge - take care as rd bends to R onto D64; at tall wireless mast bear L off main rd; site on L down lane. Med, mkd pitch, pt sl, pt shd; wc (some cont); own san rec; chem disp; shwrs inc; el pts (6A) €3.20 (poss rev pol); gas; ice; shops 600m; tradsmn; BBQ; playgrnd; pool 4km; 70% statics; adv bkg; quiet; no cc acc; CCI. "Conv Monet's garden at Giverny, approx 11km; gd views; lovely little village; friendly, helpful warden & avail late eves; new san facs 2005; parking for m'vans - cont past site over rndabt for 900m, turn v sharp L past hotel on R & parking on R." 1 Mar-31 Oct. € 9.50
2005*

VERRUYES *7A2* Camping de la Fragnee, 79310 Verruyes [tel/fax 05 49 63 21 37; camping-verruyes@district-parthenay.fr; www.district-parthenay.fr] On Parthenay-Niort rd D743 turn SE at Mazieres-en-Gatine for Verruyes; sp 'Verruyes Plan d'Eau'. Med, mkd pitch, shd; wc; chem disp; shwrs inc; el pts (6A) inc; lndtte; gas; ice; shop; tradsmn; rest; snacks; bar; playgrnd; tennis; entmnts; sand beach for lake sw; cycle hire; fishing; dogs €1.07; Eng spkn; adv bkg; quiet; cc acc. "Friendly site; pitches muddy when wet." 15 Apr-31 Oct. € 11.60
2002*

VERS *7D3* (Urban) Camp Municipal de l'Arquette, 46090 Vers [05 65 31 41 94] Fr Cahors foll D653 N side Rv Lot to Vers; in vill turn R over bdge onto D662 sp St Cirq-Lapopie; turn R in 100m, foll site sp. Med, mkd pitch, shd; wc; chem disp (wc); shwrs inc; el pts (10A) €1.80 (rev pol); shop & rest 200m; playgrnd adj; phone; poss cr; Eng spkn; adv bkg; quiet; cc not acc; CCI. "Friendly staff; attractive rvside site but poss flood risk; facs basic; gd rests in vill; pleasant, local walks, views; conv Peche-Merle cave paintings." 1 May-30 Sep. € 11.50   2005*

VERS *7D3* (Rural) Camping La Cheneraie, Le Cuzoul, 46090 Vers [05 65 31 40 29; fax 05 65 31 41 70; lacheneraie@free.fr] Exit Cahors on D653 sp Figeac. In Vers turn L at rlwy x-ing, site on R in 50m, clearly sp. App steep & siting lge o'fits poss diff. Sm, pt sl, pt shd; wc; chem disp (wc); shwrs inc; el pts (10A) inc; gas; lndtte; rest; bar; playgrnd; pool; tennis; dogs; Eng spkn; adv bkg ess high ssn; quiet; cc acc; CCI. "Lovely scenery in Lot Valley; well-run, friendly site; vg long/sh stay." 19 Apr-13 Sep. € 16.80
2003*

VERS PONT DU GARD see Remoulins *10E2*

VERSAILLES *4E3* (3km E Urban) Camping Huttopia de Versailles, 31 Rue Berthelot, Porchefontaine, 78000 Versailles [01 39 51 23 61; fax 01 39 53 68 29; versailles@huttopia.com; www.huttopia.com] Fr Chateau on N10 take Ave de Paris & turn R at 4th set traff lts (after bend & immed after twin gate lodges); sp. Lge, sl, shd; wc (some cont); mv service pnt; chem disp; shwrs inc; el pts inc (5-16A) inc; gas; lndtte; rest 100m; snacks; bar high ssn; shop; tradsmn; pool 200m; playgrnd; bus 500m; dogs €3; adv bkg (dep); Eng spkn; 20% statics; red low ssn/long stay; cc acc; CCI. "Sl, uneven pitches poss diff; site dark due trees; conv Paris (RER stn 400m) & Versailles Chateau (2km); excel clean shwrs; vg management." ♦ ltd. 1 Apr-15 Dec. € 24.00
2005*

VERSAILLES *4E3* (7km S Urban) Le Parc Etang de St Quentin-en-Yvelines, 78180 Montigny-le-Bretonneux [01 30 58 56 20; fax 01 34 60 07 14] Fr A12, N10 or N286 foll sp for Bois d'Arcy. Then foll Base de Loisirs sp. At rndabt surrounding sm lake & lge blue arch, take exit sp camping, site 200m on R. Lge, hdg pitch, pt shd; wc (some cont); chem disp; shwrs inc; el pts (6-10A) €3.30-€4; gas; lndtte; ice; sm shop; tradsmn; rest; no BBQ; playgrnd; pool; fishing; sailing adj; 20% statics; dogs €2.10; poss cr; Eng spkn; adv bkg (dep req); some rd/rlwy noise; CCI. "Conv Palace Versailles; 10 min walk to rlwy for 40 min to Paris; country park adj; excel shopping cent 5 mins in car; helpful staff; office & gate clsd Sat noon to Mon am low ssn; pitches liable to flood; ageing facs & a little shabby; poss itinerants; gd sh stay." ♦ 1 Mar-31 Oct. € 14.00   2005*

VERTEILLAC *7C2* (Urban) Camp Municipal Le Pontis Sud-Est, 24320 Verteillac [05 53 90 37 74 or 05 53 91 60 39 (Mairie)] N fr Riberac or S fr Mareuil on D708; in Verteillac turn R at sp Camping-Tennis-Piscine; turn L at Gendamerie & next R; site at end of park access rd. Sm, hdg pitch, unshd, pt sl; wc; chem disp; mv service pnt; shwrs inc; 50% statics, red low ssn; el pts (6A); sw 500m; CCI. "San facs gd but ltd low ssn; clean, tidy & quiet site; site yourself, warden calls." ♦ 15 May-Sep. € 7.60
2002*

FRANCE

VERTEILLAC *7C2* (8km NW Rural) **Camping Petit Vos,** 24320 Nanteuil-Auriac-de-Bourzac [05 53 90 39 46; petitvos@aol.com] On D674 S fr Angouleme to Libourne, turn L at Montmoreau-St Cybard onto D24 to Salles-Lavalette (11km), then take D1 to Nanteuil-Auriac (4.5km). Go thro vill & foll sp 'Petit Vos' up to x-rds. Turn R sp Vendoire, then 2nd R. Site immed on R. Sm, pt sl, pt shd; wc; chem disp (wc only); shwrs inc; el pts (10A) inc; lndtte; shops & bar 4.5km; rest 2km; BBQ; rv sw & sand beach 15km; dogs €1; Eng spkn; adv bkg ess (dep req); quiet; CCI. "CL-type, British owned site; excel facs but ltd; wonderful views fr site; v peaceful; vg long stay." € 8.50   2003*

VERVINS *3C4* (7km N) **Camping Le Val d'Oise, Route de Mont-d'Origny,** 02580 Etreaupont [03 23 97 48 04] Site to E of Etreaupont off N2, Mons-Reims rd. Site adj football pitch on banks of Rv Oise. Sm, mkd pitches, pt shd; wc (some cont); shwrs inc; el pts (6A) €3 (poss rev pol); ice; shop 500m; tradsmn; playgrnd; tennis; sports field adj; rv & fishing adj; dogs €1; quiet. "Pretty site; warm welcome; uninspiring vill; supmkt in Hirson; conv rte to Zeebrugge ferry (approx 200km); gd NH/sh stay." Easter-30 Oct. € 10.60   2005*

VESOUL *6G2* (1.5km W) **Camping International du Lac,** 70000 Vesoul [03 84 76 22 86; fax 03 84 75 74 93] 2km fr N19, sp fr W end of by-pass, pass new indus est to lge lake on W o'skts. Ent opp Peugeot/Citroen factory on lakeside. Lge, pt shd; wc; shwrs inc; el pts (10A) €2; gas; lndtte; shops 2km; rest; bar; lake sw; fishing; tennis; dogs €1.70; adv bkg; red CCI. "Super site with gd size pitches & excel aqua park nr with red for campers; screened fr indus est by trees; gd cycle rtes; pitches poss soft after rain." 1 Mar-31 Oct. € 15.90   2004*

VEULES LES ROSES *3C2* (3.5km E) **Camp Municipal Le Mesnil,** 76740 St Aubin-sur-Mer [02 35 83 02 83] On D68 2km W of St Aubin-sur-Mer. Med, hdg pitch, terr, unshd; htd wc; shwrs inc; el pts (10A) inc; gas; lndtte; shop; tradsmn; playgrnd; sand beach 1.5km; cc acc; CCI. ♦ 1 Apr-31 Oct. € 15.45   2003*

VEULES LES ROSES *3C2* (6km E) **Camping Les Garennes de la Mer,** 76740 Le Bourg-Dun [tel/fax 02 35 83 10 44; didpoulain@spray.fr] Fr Veules-les-Roses, take D925 twd Dieppe. Site sp in Le Bourg-Dun. Sm, mkd pitch, pt sl, pt shd; wc; shwrs inc; el pts (16A) €3; gas; lndry rm; shops 250m; supmkt 5km; tradsmn; shgl beach 3km; 60% statics; Eng spkn; poss cr; adv bkg; quiet; cc acc; CCI. "Beautifully laid out, v clean & tidy." ♦ ltd. 1 Apr-15 Oct. € 10.40   2005*

VEULES LES ROSES *3C2* (10km E Coastal) **Camp Municipal de la Plage,** 76860 Quiberville-sur-Mer [02 35 83 01 04 or 02 35 04 21 33 (Mairie); fax 02 35 83 67 33; campingplage@normandnet.fr] Fr Dieppe on D75, site on R in Quiberville. Lge, unshd; wc; shwrs; el pts (6-10A); lndtte; rest in vill; playgrnd; tennis adj; adv bkg. "Conv Dieppe ferry." ♦ 1 Apr-2 Nov. € 18.90   2002*

VEULES LES ROSES *3C2* (500m S Coastal) **Camp Municipal des Mouettes, Ave Jean Moulin,** 76980 Veules-les-Roses [02 35 97 61 98 or 02 35 97 64 11 (Mairie); fax 02 35 97 33 44] On ent vill fr Dieppe on D925, turn R onto D68, site in 500m up hill (14%). Med, mkd pitch, pt sl, pt shd; htd wc; shwrs inc; el pts (6A) €3.80; lndry rm; shops 300m; snacks; bar; pool 7km; beach 300m; games area; TV; 50% statics; dogs €1.05; poss cr; Eng spkn; quiet. "Immac site & vg facs; interesting/pleasant area; v helpful warden." 15 Feb-30 Nov. € 14.00   2005*

VEULES LES ROSES *3C2* (500m W Coastal) **Camping Communal Le Paradis, Chemin de Manneville,** 76980 Veules-les-Roses [02 35 97 61 42] Turn R off D925 (Dieppe/Fecamp) approx 1.5km W of Veules. Site well sp. Diff app over 2km of single track rds with few passing places. Sm, pt sl, pt shd; wc (cont); shwrs inc; el pts (10A) inc; gas; lndry rm; ice; shops 300m; snacks; playgrnd; beach 300m; fishing; sailing; windsurfing; 60% statics; adv bkg; quiet; CCI. "Tarmac rds; although sl, all pitches level; no vehicles & camp lights off at 2200; poor san facs; interesting vill with gd cafe; rec check opening dates." 15 Jun-15 Sep. € 14.00   2004*

VEURDRE, LE see St Pierre le Moutier *4H4*

VEYNES *9D3* (6km NE) **Camping Mon Repos,** 05400 Montmaur [04 92 58 03 14; serranicolas@viola.fi] Fr D994 Veynes-Gap rd, foll D937 N, turning R at bdge to keep on D937. Site sp. Sm, pt sl, shd; wc (cont); own san; chem disp; mv service pnt 6km; shwrs inc; el pts (5A) €2.80; gas; ice; lndry rm; shop; tradsmn; snacks; playgrnd; pool 6km; rv sw; entmnt; TV rm; 30% statics; dogs €0.76; quiet; Eng spkn; CCI. "Friendly, family-run site; excel area for walking." 1 May-15 Sep. € 10.00   2002*

†VEYNES *9D3* (15km NE Rural) **Camping Caravaneige au Blanc Manteau, Route de Ceuse,** 05400 La Roche-des-Arnauds [02 97 57 82 56] Take D994 fr Veynes twd Gap; site sp in vill of La Roche-des-Arnauds on D18 in 1km. Med, pt shd; htd wc (some cont); chem disp; shwrs inc; el pts (2A) inc; lndtte; shops 750m; snacks; bar; pool; playgrnd; tennis; adv bkg. "Gd sized pitches; v scenic." ♦ € 19.55   2003*

VEYNES *9D3* (2km SW Rural) **Camping Les Rives du Lac, Les Iscles,** 05400 Veynes [04 92 57 20 90; fax 04 92 58 16 82; muretr@aol.com; www.camping-lac.com] Off D994. Sp on lakeside. Med, mkd pitch, hdstg, pt sl, pt shd; wc; chem disp; mv service pnt; baby facs; shwrs; el pts (10A) €3l; lndtte; ice; shop; tradsmn; snacks; bar; BBQ; playgrnd; pool; lake sw & beach adj; water sports; mountain biking; climbing; dogs €2; bus 500m; phone; adv bkg; quiet; cc acc; CCI. "V attractive, well-managed, clean site located on shore of sm lake; san facs excel; welcoming staff; vg." 14 May-17 Sep. € 16.50   2005*

FRANCE

VEYNES *9D3* (1.5km W) **Camping Solaire du Petit Buech, Les Iscles, 05400 Veynes** [04 92 58 12 34; fax 04 92 58 00 47; contact@camping-solaire. com; www. camping-solaire.com] Sp fr rndabt at ent to Veynes fr Serres on N994. Lge, shd; wc; chem disp; shwrs inc; el pts (5A) €3; gas; lndtte; ice; shop; tradsmn; rest; snacks; bar; 2 pools; games area; entmnt; some statics; dogs €2; phone; adv bkg; quiet. "Helpful staff" 1 May-30 Oct. € 13.40
2005*

VEZAC see Sarlat la Caneda *7C3*

VEZELAY *4G4* (3km N Rural) **Camp Municipal Le Patis, Route de Givry, 89450 Asquins** [03 86 33 30 80; mairie. asquins@wanadoo.fr] Fr Vezelay take D951 N to Asquins, & turn R to site on rvside - tight turn. Site sp. Sm, pt shd; wc; chem disp (wc); shwrs inc; el pts €3; ice; shop 500m; BBQ; playgrnd; dogs; poss cr; quiet; CCI.
15 Jun-15 Sep. € 8.00   2005*

VEZELAY *4G4* (2km SE) **Camp Municipal, 89450 St Pere** [03 86 33 36 58 or 03 86 33 26 62 (Mairie); fax 03 86 33 34 56; cme.saint-pere@libertysurf. fr] Fr Vezelay take D957, turn onto D36 to St Pere. Site sp. Med, pt shd; wc (cont); shwrs inc; el pts (10A) €2; ice; shops 500m; playgrnd; rv sw adj; fishing; canoeing; tennis; poss cr; quiet. "Conv Morvan National Park; basic facs but pleasant; quiet site with gd walking area." Easter-30 Sep. € 8.60
2005*

VEZELAY *4G4* (600m S) **Camping L'Ermitage, Route de l'Étang, 89450 Vezelay** [tel/fax 03 86 33 24 18] Foll sp fr cent of Vezelay to 'Camping Vezelay' & Youth Hostel. Sm, pt sl, pt shd; wc; some serviced pitches; shwrs inc; el pts (10A) €2.50 (rev pol); shops 500m; tradsmn (high ssn); sw 13km; poss cr; Eng spkn; quiet; no cc acc; CCI. "Peaceful site with modern facs; little shade, beautiful outlook; 10 mins walk to Vezelay with superb abbey church, many rests & other attractions; blocks req; some pitches diff lge o'fits; 1 day free in 10; vg NH/sh stay." 1 Apr-30 Oct. € 9.00
2005*

VIAS *10F1* (4km E) **Sunelia Le Domaine de la Dragonniere, 34450 Vias** [04 67 01 03 10; fax 04 67 21 73 39; dragonniere@wanadoo.fr; www. dragonniere.com] Exit A9 junc 35 onto D64 twd Valras, then N112 dir Agde & Vias. Site on R. V lge, mkd pitch, pt shd; wc; chem disp; mv service pnt; shwrs inc; el pts (5A) inc; lndtte; shop; rest; snacks; bar; playgrnd; htd pool; paddling pool; sand beach 5km (free shuttle high ssn); tennis; games area; cycle hire; entmnt; child entmnt; TV rm; internet; statics; dogs €5; Eng spkn; adv bkg; cc acc. "Excel for children high ssn; many activities." ♦
1 Apr-30 Sep. € 35.00 (3 persons) (CChq acc)
2005*

VIAS *10F1* (2km S Coastal) **Camping Cap Soleil,** 34450 Vias-Plage [04 67 21 64 77; fax 04 67 21 70 66; cap.soleil@wanadoo.fr; www. capsoleil.fr] N112 W fr Agde to Vias. Turn S in town & foll sps for Vias-Plage over canal bdge & sps to site. Lge, shd; wc; baby facs; baby facs; shwrs inc; el pts (6A) inc; lndtte; ice; shop in ssn; rest; snacks; bar; BBQ; playgrnd; htd pool; waterslide; naturist pool 1/7-31/8; sand beach 800m; rv sw 600m; tennis; entmnt; TV rm; 90% statics; dogs €5; private washrms avail; adv bkg; quiet; red facs low ssn. "Sm pitches." 1 Apr-30 Sep. € 35.00   2005*

VIAS *10F1* (3km S Coastal) **Camping Californie Plage,** 34450 Vias-Plage [04 67 21 64 69; fax 04 67 21 54 62; californie-plage@wanadoo.fr; www.californie-plage.fr] W fr Agde on N112 to Vias; turn S in town & foll sps 'Mer' over canal bdge & sp to site. Lge, mkd pitch, shd; wc; chem disp; shwrs inc; el pts inc (3A) inc (5-10A) €1.60-3.20; lndtte; rest; supmkt; snacks; bar; gas; ice; playgrnd; cvrd/htd pool; waterslide; sand beach adj; cycle hire; TV rm; entmnt; 10% statics; dogs €4.60; adv bkg; Eng spkn; CCI. ♦ 1 Apr-15 Sep. € 31.00   2004*

VIAS *10F1* (3km S Coastal) **Camping Mediterrannee Plage,** 34450 Vias [04 67 90 99 07; fax 04 67 90 99 17; camping.med@wanadoo.fr; www.mediterranee-plage.com & www.homair-vacances.fr] Fr N112 bet Beziers & Sete in Vias vill cross Canal du Midi & turn R & foll sps for Cite Ouest. Lge, unshd; wc (cont); chem disp; shwrs; baby facs; el pts (6A); gas; lndtte; ice; shop; rest; snacks; bar; BBQ; playgrnd; pool; sand beach; tennis; entmnt; child entmnt; TV; mini-golf; horseriding; cycle hire; archery; canoeing; fishing; boating; no dogs; adv bkg; cc acc. ♦ 3 Apr-18 Sep. € 24.10   2002*

VIAS *10F1* (3km S Coastal) **Yelloh! Village Le Club Farret,** 34450 Vias-Plage [04 67 21 64 45; fax 04 67 21 70 49; info@yellohvillage-club-farret. com or farret@wanadoo.fr; www.yellohvillage-club-farret.com or www.farret.com] Fr A9, exit Agde junc 34. Foll sp Vias-Plage on D137. Sp fr cent of Vias-Plage on L, immed after Gendarmerie. V lge, mkd pitch, pt shd; wc; chem disp; mv service pnt; baby facs; shwrs inc; el pts (6A) inc; gas; lndtte; ice; shop; rest; snacks; bar; playgrnd; htd pool; sand beach adj; watersports; tennis; cycle hire; fitness rm; games area; games rm; entmnt; child entmnt; TV; 20% statics; Eng spkn; quiet; cc acc; red low ssn; CCI. "Camp guarded at night; excel facs, entmnt & lessons; excursions." ♦ 6 Apr-23 Sep. € 42.00   2005*

See advertisement on previous page

VIAS *10F1* (5km SW Coastal) **Camping La Carabasse, Route de Farinette,** 34450 Vias-Plage [04 67 21 64 01; fax 04 67 21 76 87; lacarabasse@ siblu.com; www.siblu.com] Fr S on A9 exit 34 & take 1st exit onto N312 sp Vias & Agde. After 8km take RH lane twd Beziers on N112. Branch R to Vias-Plage & at rndabt foll sp for Vias-Plage on D137. Site 1km on L. V lge, hdg/mkd pitch, pt shd; wc; chem disp; baby facs; shwrs inc; some pitches with indiv san facs; el pts (6A) inc (poss rev pol); gas; lndtte; ice; shop; rest; snacks; bar; BBQ; playgrnd; 2 htd pools; waterslide; sand beach 600m; tennis; mini-golf; watersports; golf 10km; entmnt; child entmnt; TV; 70% statics; no dogs; Eng spkn; adv bkg ess; quiet but poss noisy high ssn; red low ssn; CCI. "Vg local produce inc wines; organised activities; pitches poss tight med/lge o'fits due trees; excel for young families." ♦ 15 Apr-14 Sep. € 144.00 (7 nights)   2005*

See advertisement opposite

VIAS *10F1* (5km SW Coastal) **Camping Les Flots Bleus, Cote Ouest,** 34450 Vias-Plage [04 67 21 64 80; fax 04 67 01 78 12; camping lesflotsbleus@wanadoo.fr; www.camping-flotsbleus.com] Fr N112 at Vias, take D137 sp Vias-Plage. After x-ing Canal du Midi turn R sp Cote Ouest, site sp. Lge, some hdg/mkd pitch, hdstg, pt shd; wc (some cont); chem disp; mv service pnt; baby facs; shwrs €0.30; el pts (6A) inc; lndtte; ice; shop; tradsmn; rest; snacks; bar; playgrnd; htd pool; waterslide; sand beach adj; games area; cycle hire; entmnt; 50% statics; dogs €3.50; adv bkg; quiet; CCI. "Europark 2km; facs clean but poss stretched high ssn; gd." 15 Apr-15 Sep. € 29.00   2005*

VIC LE COMTE see Issoire *9B1*

VIC SUR CERE *7C4* (6km NE) **Camp Municipal La Bedisse, Route de Raulhac,** 15800 Thiezac [04 71 47 00 41 or 04 71 47 01 21 (Mairie); fax 04 71 47 02 23; otthiezac@wanadoo.fr] Sp fr N122 on D59. Med, mkd pitch, pt shd; wc (some cont); shwrs inc; el pts €2; lndry rm; shops 500m; playgrnd adj; pool 3km; tennis; poss cr; quiet. "Gd walking in Cantal; helpful owner; clean facs; excel long/sh stay." 1 Jun-15 Sep. € 7.60   2003*

VIC SUR CERE *7C4* (1km E) **Camp Municipal du Carlades, Ave des Tilleuls,** 15800 Vic-sur-Cere [04 71 47 51 04 or 04 71 47 51 75 (Mairie); fax 04 71 47 50 59] Fr Aurillac on N122 site sp on ent Vic-sur-Cere on R. Lge, pt shd; wc (cont); shwrs inc; el pts (6A) inc; supmkt 100m; pool 500m; playgrnd; tennis & mini-golf nrby; rv fishing; poss cr; adv bkg; quiet. "Gate clsd 2000; office clsd Sun; no pitching without booking in." ♦ 1 Apr-30 Sep. € 11.30   2005*

FRANCE

VIC SUR CERE *7C4* (3km SE) **Camping La Pommeraie**, 15800 Vic-sur-Cere [04 71 47 54 18; fax 04 71 49 63 30; pommeraie@wanadoo.fr; www.camping-la-pommeraie.com] Fr Vic-sur-Cere take D54 twd Pierrefort & Chaudes-Aigues, initially sp Salvanhac. Foll yellow site sp over rv, under rlwy bdge. Foll D154 up steep, narr, winding hill for 1.5km. Foll camp sp. R into narr lane. NB Lioran Tunnel on N122 NE of Vic-sur-Cere not rec when towing in poor weather; check with police in Murat or Aurillac. Med, terr, pt shd; wc (some cont); serviced pitches; shwrs inc; el pts (6A) inc; bar; rest; snacks; BBQ; shop; baby facs; lndtte; ice; pool; playgrnd; tennis; fishing; entmnt for young people; dogs €2; many statics; poss cr; adv bkg rec; noise fr bar at night; cc acc. "No BBQs; shop not open low ssn; best pitches at top of site but v steep acc; not suitable elderly or infirm; wonderful views; peaceful; mkt Tue & Fri." ♦ 1 May-15 Sep. € 21.00 2004*

VIC SUR CERE *7C4* (5km SW) **Camp Municipal Val-de-Cere**, 15800 Polminhac [04 71 47 41 03 or 04 71 47 40 07 (Mairie)] Fr Vic-sur-Cere or Aurillac take N122 to Polminhac. In vill turn S on D57 (sp) site 800m on L immed bef rv bdge. Med, hdg pitch, pt shd; wc; shwrs inc; el pts (4A) €2; shops 800m; paddling pool; sm dogs free; quiet. 15 Jun-15 Sep. € 11.40 2002*

VICDESSOS see Tarascon sur Ariege *8G3*

VICHY *9A1* (1km SW Urban) **Camping Les Acacias**, Rue Claude Decloître, 03700 Bellerive-sur-Allier [04 70 32 36 22; fax 04 70 32 88 52; camping-acacias@club-internet.fr; www.camping-acacias.com] Cross bdge to Bellerive fr Vichy, turn L at 2nd rndabt onto D1083 (past Conforma), then turn L at next rndabt sp 'piscine'. Foll sm camping sps. Or fr S leave D906 at St Yorre & cross Rv Allier, then foll sp to Bellerive. Site sp at rndabt on app to Bellerive adj Rv Allier. Med, hdg/mkd pitch, shd; wc; chem disp; baby facs; shwrs inc; el pts (10A) €3; gas; ice; shops 1km; snacks; BBQ; playgrnd; pool (high ssn); fishing; boating; TV; 20% statics; adv bkg; quiet; cc acc; CCI. "Helpful owner; beware sleeping policeman bumps nr & in town; facs need updating; easy walk into town." 1 Apr-10 Oct. € 14.50 2005*

VICHY *9A1* (1.5km SW) **Camping Beau Rivage**, Rue Claude Decloitre, 03700 Bellerive-sur-Allier [04 70 32 26 85; fax 04 70 32 03 94; camping-beaurivage@wanadoo.fr; www.camping-beaurivage.com] Fr Vichy take N209 dir Gannat. After x-ing bdge over Rv Allier, turn L at rndabt sp Camping, sp to Beau Rivage. Site on L on rv bank. Med, shd; wc (mainly cont); chem disp; baby facs; shwrs inc; el pts (10A) €3; gas; lndtte; ice; shop; supmkt 1km; rest; BBQ; playgrnd; 2 pools & waterslide; tennis 2km; fishing; canoeing; boating; archery; entmnt; TV; poss cr. 1 Apr-22 Oct. € 14.40 2005*

VICHY *9A1* (5km SW Rural) **Camping La Roseraie**, Route de Randan, 03700 Brugheas [04 70 32 43 33; fax 04 70 32 26 23; campingla roseraie@wanadoo.fr] Fr Vichy on D1093, foll sp to Brugheas. Site well sp. Med, hdg/mkd pitch, pt shd; wc; chem disp; baby facs; shwrs inc; el pts (6A) €2.50; gas; lndtte; ice; shop 3km; tradsmn; snacks; bar high ssn; BBQ; playgrnd; pool; TV rm; games area; mini-golf; 10% statics; dogs; adv bkg; quiet; red long stay; CCI. "Sm chateau in Brugheas; smokerie opp site selling excel smoked salmon." ♦ ltd. 1 Apr-30 Oct. € 12.60 2004*

VIDAUBAN *10F3* (500m N) **Camp Municipal Les Bords d'Argens**, 83550 Vidauban [04 94 73 61 02 or 04 94 73 10 28 (Mairie); fax 04 94 73 07 82; ot_83@club-internet.fr] Fr A8 exit junc 13 onto N7 dir Vidauban. Site sp on ent to vill. Med, pt shd; wc; chem disp; shwrs inc; el pts (6-8A) €1.90; ice; shops 500m; rest, snacks, bar 1km; pool; rv adj; sand beach 27km; dogs; quiet; CCI. "Trains to Monaco fr Les Arcs 5km; friendly site; gates locked 2200-0700; gd sh stay." 1 Jun-30 Sep. € 10.00 2002*

†**VIDAUBAN** *10F3* (5km N Rural) **Camping La Vallee de Taradeau** (formerly La Musardiere), La Plan Guille, 83460 Taradeau [04 94 73 09 14] Exit A8 at Le Muy W or Le Luc E & take N7 to Vidauban, then D48 twd Lorgues; D73 N twd Taradeau. Site on R in 4km - rough app rd. Med, mkd pitch, shd; wc; shwrs inc; el pts (2-8A) €2.30-4.70; lndtte; rest; snacks; bar; pool; some statics; dogs €1.20; adv bkg; quiet; CCI. "Friendly, helpful staff." € 21.20 2004*

VIEILLE BRIOUDE 9C1 (1.5km SE) **Camp Intercommunal La Bageasse, 43100 Brioude** [04 71 50 07 70] Off N102 fro S foll camp sps on SE side of town at boundary sp. Narr app rd. Med, mkd pitch, terr, pt shd; wc (some cont); chem disp (wc); shwrs inc; el pts (6A) (some rev pol); lndtte; ice; shop 2km; tradsmn; snacks; BBQ; playgrnd; pool 2km; rv/lake sw, fishing & boating adj; canoe hire; 8% statics; dogs; phone; Eng spkn; adv bkg; quiet; red long stay; CCI. "V clean site; helpful warden; phone ahead to check open low ssn; interesting basilica; gd long/sh stay." ♦
20 May-30 Sep. € 9.00   2003*

We're having a great holiday - must fill in some site report forms and send them to The Club as soon as possible.

VIELLE ST GIRONS see Leon 8E1

†**VIELMUR SUR AGOUT** 8F4 **Camping Le Pessac, 81570 Vielmur-sur-Agout** [tel/fax 05 63 74 30 24] W on D112 fr Castres after 13km turn L D92 S. 200m after level x-ing turn L, site in 100m, sp. Sm, mkd pitch, pt shd; wc; mv service pnt; shwrs; el pts (6A) €3; lndtte; ice; shop; bar; playgrnd; pool; 20% statics; dogs €0.92; CCI.
€ 8.20   2003*

VIERZON 4G3 (2.5km SW Urban) **Camp Municipal de Bellon, Route de Bellon, 18100 Vierzon** [02 48 75 49 10 or 02 48 75 20 03 (LS); fax 02 48 53 00 79] Fr N on A71 take A20 twd Chateauroux, leave at junc 7 onto D320 & then D27, turn 2nd L off D27 after Intermarche supmkt. Site 1km on R, sp. Med, hdg pitch, pt sl, pt shd; wc (some cont); chem disp; mv service pnt; shwrs inc; el pts (6A) €2.30 (some rev pol); gas; lndry rm; ice; shop 500m; rest; snacks; playgrnd; fishing; boat hire; phone; poss cr; Eng spkn; adv bkg; quiet; CCI. "Attractive site by rv but unkempt & poss itinerants low ssn; gd sized pitches but some poss diff to negotiate; poss some rlwy noise; gates clsd 2300-0700; warden on site 1700-2200." ♦
1 May-30 Sep. € 10.80   2004*

VIEUX BOUCAU LES BAINS 8E1 (1.5km N Coastal) **Camping La Cote, Route de Vieux Boucau, 40660 Messanges** [05 58 48 94 94; fax 05 58 48 94 44; lacote@wanadoo.fr; www.campinglacote.com] On D652 2km S of Messanges. Med, pt shd; wc; chem disp; shwrs inc; el pts (6-10A) €3-4.10; lndtte; supmkt/shop 1km; rest; snacks; bar; playgrnd; sand beach 1km; golf 2km; 5% statics; dogs €1.50; phone; adv bkg; Eng spkn; quiet; red low ssn; CCI. "Peaceful, clean, tidy site on edge of pine woods; gd access to beaches." ♦ 1 Apr-30 Sep. € 13.40   2005*

VIEUX BOUCAU LES BAINS 8E1 (4km N Coastal) **Airotel Le Vieux Port, Route des Lacs, 40660 Messanges** [05 58 48 22 00; fax 05 58 48 01 69; contact@levieuxport.com; www.levieuxport.com] Fr S take D652 past Vieux-Boucau, site sp. V lge, mkd pitch, pt sl, pt shd; wc (some cont); chem disp; mv service pnt; shwrs inc; el pts (6A) €5.50; gas; lndtte; ice; shop; tradsmn; rest; snacks; bar; playgrnd; htd, covrd pool; waterslide; sand beach 400m; tennis; games area; cycle hire; horseriding; quadbikes; mini-golf; boules; beach train; entmnt; child entmnt; dogs €3.50; adv bkg, dep req; poss cr; quiet; red low ssn; cc acc. ♦ Easter-30 Sep.
€ 33.00 (CChq acc)   2005*

VIGAN, LE (GARD) 10E1 (9km NE) **Camping Le Pied de l'Aigoual, Domaine de Pateau, 30570 Valleraugue** [04 67 82 24 40; fax 04 67 82 24 23] Fr Le Vigan, take D999 E to Pont l'Herault then take D896 N. Site 1km N of Valleraugue on R. Well sp. Med, shd; wc; shwrs inc; chem disp; el pts (3-6A) €2.50-3; ice; lndtte; shops in vill; snacks; bar; playgrnd; pool; fishing; tennis 2km; 4% statics; dogs €0.80; phone; bus; Eng spkn; adv bkg; quiet; CCI. "Excel base for Cevennes National Park; 1 hr drive fr Mediterranean; well positioned site in valley; pretty vill." 1 Jun-30 Sep. € 9.00   2004*

VIGAN, LE (GARD) 10E1 (2km E) **Camping Le Val d'Arre, 30120 Le Vigan** [04 67 81 02 77 or 06 82 31 79 72; fax 04 67 81 71 23; valdelarre@wanadoo.fr; www.camping-france.com/valdelarre] E fr Vigan on D999. Turn R at 1st rndabt over bdge. Turn L immed after bdge; site in 400m, well sp. Height limit 3.10m. Lge, mkd pitch, pt sl, pt shd; wc (some cont); chem disp; shwrs inc; el pts inc (10A) €2.74; gas & 2km; lndtte; ice; tradsmn; shop & 2km; rest; snacks; playgrnd; htd pool; rv sw & fishing 4km; entmnt; games rm; TV; dogs €1.52; phone; Eng spkn; adv bkg; noisy high ssn; red low ssn; cc acc; CCI. "V helpful owners; gd touring base for Les Grand Causses & gorges." ♦ 1 Apr-30 Sep.
€ 13.42   2003*

VIGAN, LE (LOT) see Gourdon 7D3

VIGEOIS see Uzerche 7B3

VIGNES, LES 9D1 (6km NE Rural) **Camping La Blaquiere, 48210 Les Vignes** [tel/fax 04 66 48 54 93; camping.blaquiere@wanadoo.fr] On Gorges du Tarn D907 fr Le Rozier to St Enimie, camp is on R 6km after Les Vignes. Sm, mkd pitch, shd; wc; chem disp; shwrs inc; el pts (4-6A) €2.50; ice; lndry rm; shop; tradsmn; rest; BBQ; snacks; playgrnd; rv sw & fishing; 50% statics; dogs €1.60; phone; Eng spkn; quiet; red low ssn. "Superb location on rvside; rec sh stay." 1 May-15 Sep.
€ 11.00   2003*

VIHIERS *4G1* (1km Urban) **Camp Municipal du Lys, Etang du Lys, 49310 Vihiers [02 41 75 00 14 or 02 41 75 80 60 (Mairie); ville.vihiers@wanadoo.fr]** W of Vihiers leave D960 at foot of hill, twds Valanjou, & within 150m bear L at 1st fork in rd. Sm, mkd pitch, pt shd; wc; shwrs inc; el pts (5A) €2.20; ice; lndry rm; shop; playgrnd; boules; mini-golf; coarse fishing; 15% statics; some rd noise; CCI. "Surcharge for twin-axles; site thoroughly rec; san facs excel, warden v helpful; narr ent to some pitches; busy public rd rather close; vg sh stay." ♦ 20 May-15 Sep. € 6.00   2003*

†**VIHIERS** *4G1* (10km SE Rural) **Camping Le Serpolin, St Pierre-a-Champ, 49560 Clere-sur-Layon [02 41 52 43 08; fax 02 41 52 39 18; lynn.cluer@wanadoo.fr; www.campingleserpolin.com]** Take D748 S fr Vihiers by-pass sp Argenton Chateau. In 2km turn L at sp Clere-sur-Layon onto D54. Cont thro vill to 1st mkd x-rd, turn R, site last house along this lane. Sm, unshd; htd wc; chem disp; shwrs inc; el pts (10A) inc; lndtte; BBQ; fishing; no children; c'van storage; Eng spkn; adv bkg rec (dep req); quiet. "Peaceful, CL-type site nr vineyards; adults only; must phone prior to arrival; v helpful British owners; fruit & vegetables in ssn; rallies by arrangement; v clean san facs; conv major towns, chateaux, mkts & Futuroscope." € 12.50   2005*

VIJON *7A4* (3.5km E Rural) **Camping Les Petouilleres, 36160 Vijon [02 54 30 63 47]** Fr Boussac-Bourg take D917 N for 11km; site on D917 well sp bef vill of Marembert, opp rd to Vijon. Sm, hdg/mkd pitch, pt shd; wc; chem disp; mv service pnt; shwrs inc; el pts (6-10A) €1.70-2.20; lndry rm; ice; playgrnd; dogs €0.25; Eng spkn; adv bkg rec high ssn; quiet. "Welcoming & helpful owners; v clean facs; lge pitches; a little gem; excel long/sh stay." 1 Apr-31 Oct. € 6.85   2003*

VILLARD DE LANS *9C3* (800m N Rural) **Camping Caravaneige L'Oursiere, 38250 Villard-de-Lans [04 76 95 14 77; fax 04 76 95 58 11; info@camping-oursiere.fr; www.camping-oursiere.fr]** Site clearly visible on app to town fr D531 Gorges d'Engins rd (13km SW Grenoble). App fr W on D531 not rec for c'vans. Lge, terr, unshd; htd wc (some cont); chem disp; mv service pnt; baby facs; shwrs inc; el pts (6-10A) €5-6; gas; ice; lndtte; shops; snacks; rest; BBQ; playgrnd; pool, waterspark 800m; drying rm; 20% statics; poss cr; adv bkg; quiet; cc acc; CCI. "Excel all winter sports; friendly, helpful owners." ♦ 3 Dec-2 Oct. € 15.25   2005*

†**VILLARD DE LANS** *9C3* (10km N Rural) **Camping Caravaneige Les Buissonnets, 38112 Meaudre [04 76 95 21 04; fax 04 76 95 26 14; camping-les-buissonnets@wanadoo.fr; www.camping-les-buissonnets.com]** NE o'skts of Meaudre off D106, approx 30km SW of Grenoble by rd & 18km as crow flies. Med, sl, unshd; htd wc; chem disp; mv service pnt; shwrs inc; el pts (2-10A) €2.20-8; lndtte; shops 500m; snacks; rest 500m; pool 300m; playgrnd; games area; bus to ski slopes; site clsd 5 Nov-mid-Dec; Eng spkn; quiet; higher price in winter. "Gd skiing cent; conv touring Vercours." ♦ € 8.00   2005*

VILLARS COLMARS see Colmars *9D4*

VILLARS LES DOMBES *9A2* (Urban) **Camp Municipal Les Autieres, Ave des Nations, 01330 Villars-les-Dombes [04 74 98 00 21 or 06 61 70 36 51]** N fr Lyon on N83, site in town cent on R by sw pool. Lge, pt shd; wc; shwrs inc; el pts €3; lndtte; ice; shop; rest; snacks; BBQ; playgrnd; pool adj; tennis; mini-golf; rv adj; entmnts; 50% static. "Popular NH; fine bird park 10 mins walk; tight security, barrier & pedestrian gate." ♦ 1 Apr-25 Sep. € 12.30   2004*

VILLECROZE LES GROTTES see Salernes *10F3*

VILLEDIEU LES POELES *1D4* (500m S Urban) **Camp Municipal le Pres de la Rose, 2 Impasse du Pré de la Rose, 50800 Villedieu-les-Poeles [02 33 61 02 44; camping-bougourd@wanadoo.fr]** Exit A84 junc 38 & foll town cent sp. At bottom of hill at traff lts turn next L opp church. In 200m turn L into car park access & foll sp to site. Med, hdg/mkd pitch, pt shd; wc (some cont); chem disp; mv service pnt; shwrs inc; baby facs; el pts (6-8A) €2.50 (poss rev pol); lndtte; ice; shop 500m; supmkt 2km; rest, snacks, & bar 500m; playgrnd; rv fishing; boating; tennis; entmnt; TV rm; no statics; phone; poss cr; Eng spkn; adv bkg; quiet; red low ssn; cc acc; CCI. "Peaceful site; sh walk to historic town founded by Knights of St John; copper, pewter & lace workshops in Villedieu, bell foundry worth visit (clsd Sun/Mon); mini-train avail Jul/Aug; delightful town; pleasant area; lge pitches; kerbs around pitches poss diff lger o'fits; site gates clsd 2200-0700; avoid arr Tue am due mkt; conv NH for Cherbourg ferry." ♦ ltd. Easter-15 Sep. € 8.80   2005*

VILLEFORT (LOZERE) *9D1* (600m S) **Camp Municipal Les Sedaries, Route d'Ales, 48800 Villefort [04 66 46 84 33]** On D906 heading S fr Villefort twd Ales. Sm, terr, pt shd; wc; chem disp (wc); shwrs inc; el pts (6A) inc; shops, rest, bar in town; BBQ; lake sw 1km; phone; poss cr; quiet; CCI. "Attractive in beautiful mountain scenery; Lozere mountains & gorges of Borne & Chassezac; access all hrs, bureau clsd 1000-1830; diff access upper terr." 15 Apr-Sep. € 8.50   2002*

VILLEFRANCHE DE CONFLENT see Prades *8G4*

FRANCE

†VILLEFRANCHE DE LAURAGAIS *8F3* (10km SW Rural) Camping Le Lac de la Thesauque, Nailloux, 31560 Montgeard [05 61 81 34 67; fax 05 61 81 00 12; camping-thesauque@caramail. com] Fr S exit A61 at Villefrance-de-Lauragais junc 20 onto D622, foll sp Auterive then Lac after Gardouch vill, site sp. Fr N turn off A61 at 1st junc after tolls S of Toulouse onto A66 (sp Foix). Leave A66 at junc 1 & foll sp Nailloux. Turn L on ent vill onto D662 & in 2km turn R onto D25 & immed R to site, sp. Med, mkd pitch, hdstg, terr, pt shd; wc; chem disp; shwrs inc; el pts (6-10A) €3-4; lndtte; shop; rest; snacks; bar; playgrnd; fishing; boating; 70% statics; dogs €0.80; poss cr; red low ssn; CCI. "Lovely, peaceful location; scenic walk around lake; sm terr pitches; v ltd facs low ssn; gd security; gd for m'vans; helpful staff." € 14.00   2005*

VILLEFRANCHE DE ROUERGUE *7D4* (10km N) Aire Naturelle Municipal, 12260 Villeneuve-d'Aveyron [05 65 45 60 38 (Mairie); fax 05 65 81 60 38] N on D922 Villefranche-Figeac rd. Sp in town. Sm, pt sl, unshd; wc (cont); shwrs; el pts; shop 300m; pool 1km; v quiet. "Vg sh stay." 1 Jul-31 Aug.   2002*

VILLEFRANCHE DE ROUERGUE *7D4* (9km SE) Camping Le Muret, 12200 St Salvadou [05 65 81 80 69 or 05 65 29 84 87] Fr Villefranche on D911 twd Millau, R on D905A sp camping & foll camping sp 7km. Sm, hdg/mkd pitch, shd; wc (some cont); shwrs inc; el pts (16A) €3; gas & ice at farm; lndtte; shops 9km; tradsmn; rest; snacks; bar; lake adj; fishing; dogs; phone; adv bkg; v quiet; red long stay; CCI. "Attractive farmland setting." ♦ 17 Jun-30 Aug. € 12.00   2003*

VILLEFRANCHE DE ROUERGUE *7D4* (1.5km SW Urban) Camping Le Rouergue (formerly Municipal Les Teulels), Ave de Fondies, 12200 Villefranche-de-Rouergue [05 65 45 16 24 or 05 65 45 13 18 (LS); fax 05 65 45 55 58; infos@ villefranche.com] Best app fr N on D922; site well sp on D47; avoid 1-way system in town; ent thro sports stadium. Med, hdg/mkd pitch, pt shd; wc (some cont); chem disp; baby facs; serviced pitches; shwrs inc; el pts (16A) €2.50; lndtte; shop; tradsmn; ice; playgrnd; pool adj; TV rm; dogs €1; Eng spkn; adv bkg (30% dep); quiet; cc acc; CCI. "Clean & well-kept; sports stadium adj; nr Najac medieval vill; rvside path to town 15 min; excel san facs; m'van services outside site; lge pitches; v helpful wardens; gd security; gd value; open dates variable - phone ahead to check." 1 May-30 Sep. € 16.00   2005*

VILLEFRANCHE DE ROUERGUE *7D4* (10km W Rural) Camping Lac du Moulin de Bannac, 12200 Martiel [05 65 29 44 52; fax 05 65 29 43 84] On rd D911 to S bet Martiel & Limogne. Med, hdg/mkd pitch, pt sl, pt shd; wc; chem disp; mv service pnt; shwrs; el pts; lndtte; shop 1km; snacks; bar; playgrnd; pool; fishing; quiet; Eng spkn; CCI. "Wooded setting with lake; excel sh stay." ♦ 1 Apr-30 Oct. € 10.00   2002*

VILLEFRANCHE DU PERIGORD *7D3* (11km NE) Camp Municipal du Plan d'Eau, 46250 Cazals [05 65 22 84 45 or 05 65 22 82 84 (Mairie); fax 05 65 22 87 15] Site on D673 bet Frayssinet & Salviac at Cazals. Med, pt shd; wc; shwrs; el pts €2.50; ice; lndry rm; shops 500m; playgrnd; entmnt; lake sw; poss cr; quiet. Apr-Oct. € 7.50   2002*

VILLEFRANCHE DU PERIGORD *7D3* (6km SW) Camping Moulin du Perie, 47500 Sauveterre-la-Lemance [05 53 40 67 26; fax 05 53 40 62 46; moulinduperie@wanadoo.fr; www.camping-moulin-perie.com] Fr Perigueux foll dir Brive; after 8km turn R onto D710 & foll rd S. Rd numbers change briefly to D31, D51 & D25 bet Le Bugue & Siorac-en-Perigord & then cont D710. In dir of Fumel after turn off to Villefranche-du-Perigord, in Sauveterre-la-Lemance turn L at traff lts nr PO, over level x-ing. Cont strt down main rd & turn L bef cemetary (sp) & foll camping sp for 3km dir Loubejac to site on R. Med, pt sl, pt shd; wc; chem disp; mv service pnt; baby facs; shwrs inc; el pts (6A) inc; gas; lndtte; ice; shop; rest; snacks; bar; BBQ; playgrnd; pool; sm lake & beach; trout fishing - current British licence helpful; tennis 3km; games rm; organised activities; horseriding 18km; golf 25km; cycle hire; archery; microlight flying; 25% statics; dogs €3.40; poss cr; Eng spkn; adv bkg rec; quiet; cc acc; CCI. "Extremely well-run site; attention to detail maintained even low ssn; v warm welcome; gd touring base; site rds narr; highly rec." ♦ ltd. 5 May-23 Sep. € 25.00 (CChq acc) ABS - D09   2005*

VILLEFRANCHE DU QUEYRAN see Casteljaloux *7D2*

VILLEFRANCHE SUR CHER *4G3* (9km SE) Camp Municipal Val Rose, Rue de Val Rose, 41320 Mennetou-sur-Cher [02 54 98 11 02 or 02 54 98 01 19 (Mairie)] Site sp fr N76 fr Villefranche; site on R at end of vill of Mennetou. Sm, pt shd; wc; chem disp; shwrs inc; lndtte; snacks & shops adj; rest in town; playgrnd; pool adj; rv sw 1km; adv bkg; quiet. "Pretty walled town 5 mins walk along rv; gate clsd fr 1200-1430; excel san facs; narr rd diff for turning; friendly warden; mkt Thurs; gd NH/sh stay." ♦ 7 May-1 Sep. € 8.00   2004*

VILLEFRANCHE SUR CHER *4G3* (10km SE Rural) Camp Municipal Les Saules, 41320 Chatres-sur-Cher [02 54 98 04 55 or 02 54 98 03 24 (Mairie); fax 02 54 98 09 57; chatres-sur-cher@cg41.fr] Site off N76 in Chatres-sur-Cher bet Villefranche & Vierzon. Med, pt shd; wc; shwrs inc; el pts (5A) €1.80; ice; shops & rests nrby; playgrnd; sand beach adj; rv sw, fishing & watersports adj; 10% statics; adv bkg; quiet; CCI. "Pleasant site on rv; friendly warden; facs old but v clean; gd sh stay/NH." 1 May-31 Aug. € 6.25   2005*

VILLEFRANCHE SUR SAONE *9B2* (3km E Urban) Camp Municipal Plan d'Eau (also called La Plage), 2788 Route de Riottier, 69400 Villefranche-sur-Saone [04 74 65 33 48; fax 04 74 60 68 18]   Exit A6 (Lyon-Paris) junc 31 Villefranche; turn R on leaving 'peage' (toll), cont to site on R bef Rv Saone. Look for sp on rndabt. Med, unshd; wc (some cont); chem disp; mv service pnt; shwrs inc; el pts (6A) inc (poss rev pol); gas; lndry rm; shop 1km; tradsmn; snacks in ssn; bar; lake sw adj; fishing; 10% statics; adv bkg; quiet; cc acc; CCI. "Easy access & nr a'route but quiet; gd walking." ♦ 30 Apr-22 Sep. € 15.30   2005*

VILLEFRANCHE SUR SAONE *9B2* (3km E) Camping Entre Saone et Dombes, Ave de la Plage, 01480 Jassans-Riottier [tel/fax 04 74 60 95 44] Cross Rv Saone fr Villefranche or exit A6 junc 31 onto D904 to Jassans. Turn N onto D933 in cent of Jassans, 1st L to site on rv bank N of rd bdge. Lge, pt sl, shd; wc (cont); snacks; shwrs; el pts inc; gas; ice; shop; 2 pools; tennis; 60% statics; poss cr; poss noisy. "Nice site; gd NH." May-Sep. € 11.50   2003*

VILLEFRANCHE SUR SAONE *9B2* (10km E) Camp Municipal du Bois de la Dame, 01480 Ars-sur-Formans [04 74 00 77 23 or 04 74 00 71 84 (Mairie); fax 04 74 08 10 62] Fr Villefranche on N6; then E on D904. Med, mkd pitch, pt sl, terr, pt shd; wc (cont); chem disp; shwrs inc; el pts (6A) €2; lndtte; playgrnd; fishing lake; 60% statics; dogs €1.22; poss cr; adv bkg rec high ssn; CCI. "Ltd facs low ssn; twin-axle vans not acc; office clsd 1400-1600; pilgrimage vill; museum; excel." ♦ 1 Apr-30 Sep. € 8.00   2003*

VILLEFRANCHE SUR SAONE *9B2* (6km SE) Camp Municipal La Petite Saone, 01600 Trevoux [tel/fax 04 74 00 14 16 or 04 74 08 73 73 (Mairie)] Fr Villefranche take N6 S to Anse. Turn L onto D39 then D4 for Trevoux, site sp in town, on bank of Rv Saone. Lge, pt shd; wc (mainly cont); shwrs; el pts (10A); shops 1km; playgrnd; rv fishing & sw adj; entmnts; 75% statics; adv bkg high ssn; quiet; 10% red CCI. "Spacious site; clean facs; some pitches taken up by permanent vans; gd sh stay." 1 Apr-30 Sep. € 16.60   2005*

VILLEFRANCHE SUR SAONE *9B2* (5km S Urban) Camping Les Portes du Beaujolais, Chemin des Grandes-Levees, 69480 Anse [04 74 67 12 87; fax 04 74 09 90 97; campingbeaujolais@wanadoo.fr; www.camping-beaujolais.com] N6 S to Lyon, exit to Anse, cont thro town on N6. Site sp off D39, on banks of Rvs Saone & L'Azergues. Lge, hdg/mkd pitch, hdstg, pt shd; wc (some cont); chem disp; shwrs inc; el pts (6-10A) inc; lndtte; shop; snacks; bar; playgrnd; pool; rv sw; 10% statics; dogs €3.20; phone; Eng spkn; adv bkg; quiet, but poss some noise Fr A6 nrby; CCI. "Friendly; super pitches; gd base for Beaujolais region; Anse 10 mins walk; narr gauge rlwy adj; ltd facs low ssn; gd long/sh stay; conv NH." ♦ 1 Mar-31 Oct. € 18.70 (CChq acc) 2005*

VILLENEUVE D'AVEYRON see Villefranche de Rouergue *7D4*

VILLENEUVE DE BERG *9D2* (E) Camping Domaine Le Pommier, 07170 Villeneuve-de-Berg [04 75 94 82 81; fax 04 75 94 83 90; info@ campinglepommier.com] Site off rndabt at E end of by-pass to Villeneuve-de-Berg on N102. If app fr Aubenas do not go thro town. Steep incline, poss req tractor. Lge, terr, pt sl; wc; shwrs inc; el pts €3.50; lndtte; ice; shop; rest; snacks; htd pool; waterslides; entmnt; crazy golf; sound-proofed disco high ssn; internet; dogs €4; poss cr; adv bkg; quiet; red low ssn. "Superb pool complex; excursions high ssn; excel san facs." 1 Apr-15 Sep. € 25.00   2002*

VILLENEUVE DE LA RAHO see Perpignan *8G4*

VILLENEUVE LES GENETS see Bleneau *4G3*

VILLENEUVE LOUBET see Cagnes sur Mer *10E4*

†VILLENEUVE SUR LOT *7D3* (7km E Rural) Camping Le Sablon, 47140 St Sylvestre-sur-Lot [05 53 41 37 74] In Villeneuve turn E onto D911 sp Cahors, after 5km on ent St Sylvestre site on R behind supmkt. Sm, hdg pitch, shd; wc; shwrs; el pts (6-10A) €2.50-3.50; lndry rm; snacks; playgrnd; pools & paddling pool; waterslide; fishing; mini-golf; 25% statics; quiet. "Pleasant, family-owned; interesting local sights; gd facs but run down low ssn; muddy when wet - no hdstg; poss itinerants; barrier clsd 1200-1400." € 7.00   2005*

VILLENEUVE SUR LOT *7D3* (8km E Urban) Camping Les Berges du Lot, Place de la Mairie, 47140 St Sylvestre-sur-Lot [05 53 41 22 23 or 05 53 41 24 58 (Mairie)] Exit Villeneuve on D911 sp Cahors. Site in cent of St Sylvestre-sur-Lot. Foll Camping sp to rear of La Mairie (Town Hall) & adj car park supmkt to R of main rd. Sm, mkd pitch, pt shd; wc; chem disp; shwrs inc; el pts (16A) €2.50; shops adj; rest, bar 1km; sm pool; boating; fishing; birdwatching; Eng spkn; quiet. "Recep open 0800-1000 & 1600-2000; popular site; helpful staff; immac; gd views; Lot Valley cycle rtes." ♦ 15 May-30 Sep. € 6.50   2005*

VILLENEUVE SUR LOT *7D3* (S Urban) Camp Municipal du Rooy, Rue de Rooy, 47300 Villeneuve-sur-Lot [05 53 70 24 18] Foll camping sp in town on E of N21. Med, mkd pitch, pt sl, terr, pt shd; wc (some cont); chem disp; shwrs inc; el pts (6-10A) €1.52-2.29; shops 2km; tradsmn; BBQ; pool nrby; rv 5m; 15% statics; dogs €0.30; phone; poss cr; quiet; CCI. "Nice, friendly site; helpful warden; some pitches poss flooded in bad weather (keep to L of site); toilets v old, but freshly painted & clean; excel sh stay." 15 Apr-30 Sep. € 6.55   2003*

VILLENEUVE SUR LOT *7D3* (8km W) Camp Municipal Fonfrede, Route de Villeneuve, 47110 Ste Livrade-sur-Lot [05 53 01 00 64] Exit Villeneuve-sur-Lot on D911 to Ste Livrade-sur-Lot. Site clearly sp on R 1km bef vill. Med, pt shd; wc; shwrs; el pts (4A) €1.70; lndtte; shops 1km; playgrnd; pool 400m; tennis; quiet. 24 Jun-8 Sep. € 7.20   2002*

†VILLENEUVE SUR YONNE *4F4* (250m Urban) Camping Le Saucil, Chemin du Saucil, 89500 Villeneuve-sur-Yonne [03 86 87 00 69 or 03 86 87 08 32 (LS)] Ent town on N6. Turn W in town at camping sp, cross rv, 1st turn L. Med, pt shd; wc (mainly cont); chem disp (wc); shwrs inc; el pts (5A) inc; lndtte; ice; shops adj; playgrnd; sports area; fishing; 20% statics; dogs; quiet but noisy rlwy. "Tatty site, poor facs, NH only." ♦ 2004*

VILLEQUIER see Yvetot *3C2*

VILLEREAL *7D3* (2km N) Camping Le Chateau de Fonrives, Route d'Issigeac, 47210 Villereal [05 53 36 63 38; fax 05 53 36 09 98; chateau.de. fonrives@wanadoo.fr; www.campingchateau fonrives.com] Fr Bergerac take N21 S for 8km, turn L onto D14 thro Issigeac; site is just outside vill of Rives. Med, pt sl, pt shd; wc; baby facs; shwrs inc; el pts (6A) inc; gas; lndtte; ice; shop; rest; bar; BBQ; playgrnd; pool; waterslide; lake sw; fishing; golf; cycle hire; games rm; entmnt; some statics; dogs €1.90; Eng spkn; adv bkg; quiet but some noise fr weekly disco; cc acc; CCI. "Site in Chateau grounds; B&B avail; gd, lge pool; spacious grounds; interesting town; van poss manhandled on some shady pitches; easier access new pitches without shade; v friendly owners; mkt Sat am." ♦ 1 May-30 Sep. €27.50 2004*

VILLEREAL *7D3* (7km NE Rural) Camping Le Moulin de Mandassagne, 47210 Parranquet [tel/fax 05 53 36 04 02; ipimougu@fr.packardbell. org] Fr Monpazier take D2 twd Villereal, site sp 200m off rd. Fr Villereal take D104 twd Monpazier. Sm, mkd pitch, pt shd; wc; chem disp; shwrs inc; el pts (6A); gas; lndry rm; ice; shop adj; snacks; playgrnd; pool; sand beach 6km; tennis; fishing; entmnt; TV; Eng spkn; adv bkg; v quiet. "Lovely countryside." ♦ 1 May-1 Oct. €12.80 2004*

VILLEREAL *7D3* (3km SE Rural) Camping Les Ormes, Fauquie-Haut, 47210 St Etienne-de-Villereal [05 53 36 60 26; fax 05 53 36 69 90; info@campinglesormes.com; www.campingle sormes.com] Take D255 SE fr Villereal. At fork in rd in 1km, take RH rd sp St Etienne-de-Villereal. Site on R in 2km. Med, mkd pitch, pt shd; wc; chem disp; shwrs inc; el pts (4A) inc; gas; lndtte; ice; shop; tradsmn; snacks; bar; BBQ; playgrnd; pool; lake fishing; tennis; games rm; entmnt; TV; 10% statics; dogs; phone; poss cr; Eng spkn; adv bkg; quiet; red low ssn; CCI. "Excel site; highly rec early & late summer; busy high ssn; vg long stay." 1 Apr-31 Oct. €23.00 2003*

VILLEREAL *7D3* (3km NW Rural) Aire Naturelle de Bergougne (Bru), 47210 Rives [05 53 36 01 30; fax 05 53 36 05 41; info@camping-de-bergougne. com; www. camping-de-bergougne.com] Fr Villereal, take D207 NW sp Issigeac/ Bergerac. In 1km turn L onto D250 W sp Doudrac. Foll sm green sp to site. Sm, hdg pitch, pt sl, unshd; wc; chem disp; shwrs inc; el pts inc; lndtte; rest, bar 3km; playgrnd; fishing; games rm; adv bkg (dep req). "Gd sh stay." 15 May-30 Sep. €12.00 2003*

FRANCE

VILLERS BOCAGE *3D1* (7km S Urban) **Camp Municipal La Closerie, Rue de Caen, 14260 Aunay-sur-Odon [02 31 77 32 46; fax 02 31 77 70 07; mairie.aunay.sur.odon@wanadoo.fr]** Exit A84 junc 43 sp Villers-Bocage/ Aunay & take D6 twd Aunay. In approx 5km bef Aunay town sp, turn L sp 'Zone Industrielle', in 200m turn R at rndabt. Site on R in 100m. Sm, mkd pitch, pt sl, pt shd; wc; chem disp; shwrs inc; el pts €2.75; gas, shops 500m; games area; quiet, but rd noise at rush hour; CCI. "Barrier clsd 2200-0800." ♦ ltd. 1 Jul-31 Aug. € 10.05
2003*

VILLERS BOCAGE *3D1* (6km SW Rural) **Camping Vallee de Graham, 14240 Cahagnes [02 31 73 02 26 or 06 72 12 10 40 (mob)]** Fr cent Cahagnes on D54 then take D193 for 2km; sp fr town sq; 1.5km narr app rd is one way. Med, pt sl, pt shd; wc; shwrs inc; el pts (6A) €1.80; lndry rm; shops 3km; snacks; fishing; boating; quiet. "Excel view over lakes & countryside; poss to stay low ssn; site yourself, warden calls; dated facs; still v peaceful." € 10.00
2005*

VILLERS COTTERETS *3D4* (7km NE) **Camping Castel des Biches, Parc du Château Alexandre Dumas, 02600 Villers-Helon [03 23 72 93 93; fax 03 23 72 93 33; acceuil@castel-des-biches.com; www.castel-des-biches.com]** Site S of Soissons bet N2 & D1; exit Soissons S on D1 sp Chateau-Thierry, turn R sp Villers-Helon, foll sp. Med, mkd pitch, pt shd; htd wc; shwrs inc; el pts (10A) €3.90; gas; lndtte; playgrnd; paddling pool; fishing; cycle hire; games area; 80% statics; adv bkg; quiet.
1 Apr-31 Oct. € 13.10
2004*

VILLERS HELON see Villers Cotterets *3D4*

VILLERS LES NANCY see Nancy *6E2*

VILLERS SUR AUTHIE see Rue *3B2*

VILLES SUR AUZON see Mormoiron *10E2*

†**VILLEVAUDE** *3D3* (2km E Rural) **Camping Le Parc, Rue Adele Claret, Montjay-la-Tour, 77410 Villevaude [01 60 26 20 79; fax 01 60 27 02 75; camping.leparc@ club-internet.fr; www.campingleparc.fr]** Fr N, A1 twds Paris, then A104 to Marne-la-Valle, exit at junc 6B (Paris Bobigny), then D105 to Villevaude, then to Montjay & site sp. Fr S exit A104 at junc 8 to Meaux & Villevaude. Lge, hdg/mkd pitch, pt shd; htd wc; serviced pitches; chem disp; mv service pnt; baby facs; shwrs inc; el pts (6A) inc; lndtte; shop 5km; tradsmn; rest high ssn; snacks; bar; playgrnd; pool 4km; lake sw & sand beach 5km; tennis 200m; games area; TV rm; 30% statics; dogs; phone; Eng spkn; adv bkg; cc acc; CCI. "V conv Disneyland; Paris; Parc Asterix; gd san facs." ♦ € 24.00
2005*

See advertisement above

VILLIERS LE MORHIER see Maintenon *4E2*

This site entry hasn't been updated for a while; we'd better fill in a site report form and send it to The Club.

†**VILLIERS SUR ORGE** *4E3* (600m SE Urban) **Camping Le Beau Village, 91700 Villiers-sur-Orge [01 60 16 17 86 or 01 60 16 17 88; fax 01 60 16 31 46; le-beau-village@wanadoo.fr; www.beau-village.com]** Rec app fr N20, exit sp La Ville-du-Bois & Carrefour. Take rd for Villiers-sur-Orge & turn R at traff lts with sm Renault g'ge. Site sp 200m on L. Care needed on app due to narr rds. Med, hdg pitch, pt shd, htd wc; chem disp; shwrs inc; el pts (10A) €3.50 (poss rev pol); gas; lndtte; shops 1km; tradsmn; bar; playgrnd; kayaking; dogs €2; phone; train 700m; site clsd mid-Dec to mid-Jan; poss cr; quiet; red low ssn. "Well-run site but poss neglected statics; pleasant orchard; train to Paris 25 mins; ltd space for lge o'fits." € 14.50
2005*

VIMOUTIERS *3D1* (700m NW Urban) **Camp Municipal La Campiere, Blvd Dentu, 61120 Vimoutiers [02 33 39 30 29 or 02 33 39 18 86 (Mairie); fax 02 33 36 51 43; mairie.vimoutiers@wanadoo.fr]** App on D579 or D916 or D979 bet Lisieux & Argental. Site nr stadium. Sm, hdg pitch, pt shd; htd wc; chem disp; shwrs inc; el pts (6A) €1.95; lndry rm; shop 200m; rest, snacks 800m; playgrnd adj; pool 2km; rv fishing, sw & boating 2km; tennis; cycle hire; 10% statics; dogs €1.10; poss cr; adv bkg; noise fr nrby factory; 5% red 7+ days; CCI. "Excel, well-maintained site at cent of Camembert cheese indus; attractive town within easy walk; sports facs 2km; helpful warden; vg san facs; ent poss tight for lge o'fits." ♦ 4 Mar-2 Nov. € 9.40   2005*

VINAY see St Marcellin *9C2*

VINCA see Prades *8G4*

VINCELLES see Auxerre *4F4*

VINON SUR VERDON see Greoux les Bains *10E3*

VINSOBRES see Nyons *9D2*

VIOLES see Orange *10E2*

VION see Tournon sur Rhone *9C2*

VIRE *1D4* (1km SE) **Camp Municipal La Piscine, 14500 Vire [02 31 67 20 34]** Fr Vire on D577 head S immed turn after rndabt & foll D175, sp Maisoncelles-la-Jourdan. Site sp in 1km & adj lge sw pool complex. Sm, pt shd; wc (cont); shwrs inc; el pts inc; shop, rest in town; pool adj; mainly static. "Pleasant NH; conv for Cherbourg peninsula; site yourself, warden calls; noisy pm & eve fr adj pools; poor security; v sm pitches." 1 May-30 Sep. € 6.25   2002*

VIRE *1D4* (12km W Rural) **Camp Municipal, 14380 St Sever-Calvados [02 31 68 82 63; fax 02 31 67 95 15]** Fr A84 E onto D524 or fr Vire W on D524, site sp on E app only. Med, pt shd; wc; chem disp; shwrs inc; el pts (5A) €2.50; shops 500m; rsnacks; bar; sand beach 30km; Rv Vire adj; fishing; boating; tennis adj; playgrnd; dogs; adv bkg rec high ssn; quiet. "V peaceful site on hill in forest area; gd walking; great for families with young children; warden on site fr Jun; barrier open 1200-1330 & 1700-2100 only, otherwise apply to bar; spotless site; gd long/sh stay." Easter-1 Oct. € 6.30   2004*

VIRIEU LE GRAND *9B3* (5km NE Rural) **Camp Municipal au Vaugrais, 01510 Artemare [04 79 87 37 34 or 04 79 87 32 64 (Mairie); fax 04 79 87 37 46]** N fr Belley on D904 turn N into Virieu, foll sp Belmont/Haute Ville. Well sp fr D904 on rvside. Sm, pt shd, hdg pitch; wc (some cont); chem disp (wc); shwrs inc; el pts (5A) €2.40; ice; shop 500m; playgrnd; pool 1km; fishing; dogs €1; adv bkg; quiet; CCI. "Charming site; v friendly/ helpful warden; v clean san facs; lge pitches with gd views; Artemare within walking dist; interesting area; excel long stay." ♦ 1 May-30 Sep. € 6.80   2005*

VIRIEU LE GRAND *9B3* (1km S Rural) **Camping du Lac, 01510 Virieu-le-Grand [tel/fax 04 79 87 82 02]** Fr D904 site sp on L 1km past Virieu-le-Grand. Uneven app. Med, terr, hdg pitch, pt shd; wc; shwrs inc; el pts (6A) inc; ice; tradsmn; shops 4km; playgrnd; cycle hire; lake beach, sw & fishing; some rd & rlwy noise. "Clean, pleasant lakeside site; v clean facs; helpful owner; views of lake fr most pitches." Jun-15 Sep. € 13.50   2004*

VISAN see Valreas *9D2*

VITRAC see Sarlat la Caneda *7C3*

VITRE *2F4* (N Rural) **Camp Municipal du Lac, 35210 Chatillon-en-Vendelais [02 99 76 06 32 or 02 99 76 06 22 (Mairie); fax 02 99 76 12 39]** Take D178 fr Vitre to Fougeres. In 11km branch L onto D108, sp Chatillon-en-Vendelais. Foll sp thro vill for 'Camping du Lac' in 1km Med, pt sl, pt shd; wc; shwrs inc; el pts (6A) €2.70; lndtte; ice; shop & 1km; playgrnd; tennis; lake adj; fishing; 10% statics; quiet; CCI. "Nature reserve (birds) nr; warden on site 0930-1030 only; pleasant site; v quiet low ssn; gd walks, birdwatching; clean vg san facs; gd sh stay." 15 May-30 Sep. € 7.00   2005*

VITRE *2F4* (2km SE Urban) **Camp Municipal Ste Etienne, Route d'Argentre-du-Plessis, 35500 Vitre [02 99 75 25 28 or 02 99 74 43 53; fax 02 99 74 04 12]** Exit A11 at junc 5 onto D857 twd Vitre. Take Vitre ring rd twd Rennes; 500m fr ring rd S on D88 twd Argentre-du-Plessis & foll camp sp. Sm, hdg pitch, pt sl, shd; wc (some cont); chem disp (wc only); mv service pnt; shwrs inc; el pts (10A) €2; ice; shop 1km; supmkt 800m; 25% statics; dogs; quiet; cc not acc; CCI. "Fair sh stay; pitch yourself; no security; acc to many pitches diff; adj to sports complex; ltd office hrs; gd rests in town." 1 Apr-31 Oct. € 7.00   2005*

VITRY AUX LOGES *4F3* (3.5km N Rural) **Camping Etang de la Vallee, Seichebrieres, 45530 Vitry-aux-Loges [02 38 46 82 92]** Fr junc of N60, E60 & D952 N of Chateauneuf-sur-Loire take D10 N. In Vitry-aux-Loges foll sp Seichbrieres, site sp of R just outside vill. Lge, mkd pitch, shd; htd wc; chem disp; shwrs inc; el pts inc; lndtte; tradsmn; snacks, bar 100m; lake sw 100m; phone; adv bkg; quiet; CCI. "Gd forest walking; conv Orleans; fishing & watersports nr; vg long/sh stay." ♦ 1 Apr-1 Nov. € 12.00   2002*

VITRY LE FRANCOIS *6E1* (4km SE Rural) **Aire Naturelle Camping Nature (Scherschell), 13 Rue de l'Evangile, 51300 Luxemont-et-Villotte [03 26 72 61 14 or 06 83 42 83 53 (mobile)]** Fr Chalons sp on N4 at E end of Vitry-le-Francois by-pass, foll sp to R, then foll 3km to site. Fr S take exit for Vitry & pass lorry park. Foll site sp for 1km, turn L at rndabt. Sm, pt sl, pt shd; htd wc (most cont); own san facs; chem disp; shwrs inc; el pts (5-10A) inc (poss rev pol); gas 2km; shop 6km; tradsmn; BBQ; playgrnd; lake sw 500m; fishing; 15% statics; adv bkg; quiet; CCI. "Delightful quiet site in trees & farmland; v helpful & friendly owners; v peaceful; a great site; no twin-axle c'vans; excel." 1 Apr-1 Oct. € 13.50   2005*

VITRY LE FRANCOIS *6E1* (2km W Urban) **Camp Municipal La Peupleraie, Quai des Fontaines, 51300 Vitry-le-Francois [03 26 74 20 47 or 03 26 41 22 77 (Mairie); fax 03 26 41 22 88]** Fr N on N44 turn R at lge gate (sp Paris) & cont on dual c'way for approx 1km. Turn R on side rd, site sp nr lge parking area. Med, hdg pitch, pt shd; wc; shwrs inc; el pts (5A) inc; gas; shops adj; rest, snacks, bar 500m; dogs €2; quiet, but some rd noise. "Delightful site; tight ent poss diff lge o'fits." 1 Jun-30 Sep. € 9.40   2005*

VITTEAUX *6G1* (1km W Rural) **Camp Municipal La Gare, 21350 Vitteaux [03 80 49 60 87 or 03 80 49 61 25 (Mairie)]** Sp fr vill nr Hippodrome. Sm, hdg pitch, shd; wc; chem disp (wc); shwrs inc; el pts (6A) €2.50; lndry rm; rest, snacks & bar 1km; BBQ; playgrnd; htd covrd pool nr; dogs €1; quiet. "In cent Burgundy; part of sports complex; new facs 2005; warden calls am & pm; pick your spot; no security barrier; vg sh stay." ♦ 15 Mar-1 Nov. € 6.50   2005*

VITTEL *6F2* (1km NE) **Camp Municipal, Rue Claude Bassot, 88800 Vittel [03 29 08 02 71]** Fr Chaumont/Dijon at traff lts take Epinal/Nancy rd into Place Gen de Gaulle; turn L over bdge & foll sp. Fr Epinal turn R over bdge at Place Gen de Gaulle & foll sp. Med, hdg/mkd pitch, hdstg, pt shd; wc (mainly cont); chem disp; shwrs inc; el pts (10A) inc; lndtte; shop 1km; tradsmn; pool. tennis 2km; poss cr; Eng spkn; adv bkg; quiet; CCI. "Excel; walking & cycling rtes; spa town; friendly warden; gd sh stay." 26 Apr-30 Sep. € 9.00   2004*

VIVIER SUR MER, LE see Dol de Bretagne *2E4*

VIVIERS see Montelimar *9D2*

VIVONNE *7A2* (500m E) **Camp Municipal, Chemin de Prairie, 86370 Vivonne [05 49 43 41 05 (Mairie); fax 05 49 43 34 87; vivonne@cg86.fr]** Exit N10 where it by-passes Vivonne & ent town. Site in municipal park to E of town. Med, pt shd; wc; shwrs inc; el pts €2.15; lndtte; playgrnd; pool; waterslide adj; noisy fr busy rlwy & at w/e & at nights. "Warden resident on site; v welcoming & helpful; v clean facs; gd for wheelchair users." ♦ 20 May-15 Sep. € 7.40   2004*

VIZILLE *9C3* (500m N urban) **Camping Le Bois de Cornage (formerly Municipal), Chemin du Camping, 38220 Vizille [tel/fax 04 76 68 12 39; campingvizille@wanadoo.fr]** Site sp at x-rds of Rte Napoleon (N85) & Rte de Briancon (N91). Site on N outskirts of town. Well sp Med, hdg/mkd pitch, pt sl, terr, shd; wc; chem disp; baby facs; shwrs inc; el pts (6-10A) €2.80 (long lead poss req); gas 500m; lndry rm; shops 200m; supmkt, rest bar, 500m; tradsmn; snacks; playgrnd; gd cycling & climbing nrby; 10% statics; dogs €0.80; no vans over 5m permitted; poss cr; Eng spkn; adv bkg rec high ssn; quiet; red long stay/low ssn; CCI. "V helpful owner; excel clean facs; pizzaria on site; mkd walks nrby; visit Chateau de Vizille; La Mure tourist rlwy; Grenoble, Vercors & Chartreuse Monastry; gd long/sh stay." 25 Apr-30 Sep. € 14.00   2005*

VIZILLE *9C3* (7km S) **Camp Municipal, 38220 Laffrey [04 76 73 10 21 or 04 76 73 11 37]** Exit Grenoble on N85. S thro Vizille to Laffrey. Steep climb on narr rd. Site 200m S of vill at top of steep hill on Rte Napoleon. Site sp fr town but beware 1-way system outside camp gates. Med, pt sl, pt shd; wc; shwrs inc; el pts (6A) €3.10; shop in ssn; sw & watersports in lake; dogs €1; some rd noise. "Sm pitches; adj attractive lake with mountain views." 15 Jun-15 Sep. € 14.70   2005*

VOGUE see Aubenas *9D2*

VOIRON *9C3* (4km NE) **Camp Municipal de la Grande Foret, 38960 St Etienne-de-Crossey [04 76 06 05 67]** Site sp on main rd D520 fr both Voiron & St Laurent-du-Pont bet Voiron & Chambery. Clearly sp in vill sq. Site also sp fr N75 Les Abrets-Voiron rd at Le Fagot. Sm, pt shd; wc; shwrs; el pts inc (6A); shops 200m; playgrnd; quiet. "Well-laid out & maintained; ltd facs low ssn, but full price; pitches badly worn & muddy end of ssn (Sep)." 15 Jun-15 Sep. € 12.50   2004*

VOIRON *9C3* (10km E Rural) **Camping Le Balcon de Chartreuse, 950 Chemin de la Forêt, 38380 Miribel-les-Echelles [04 76 55 28 53; fax 04 76 55 25 82; balcondechartreuse@wanadoo.fr; www.camping-balcondechartreuse.com]** Fr N520 out of Voiron to St Etienne-de-Crossey. Then take D49 to Mirabel. Do not app with c'van fr Les Echelles. Med, terr, pt shd; wc; chem disp; shwrs inc; el pts (6A) €3.50; lndtte; ice; shop 4km; rest; snacks; bar; playgrnd; pool; paddling pool; horseriding; tennis 1km; games area; entmnt; TV; 30% statics; dogs €1; poss cr; adv bkg rec; quiet; CCI. 1 Apr-30 Oct. € 12.50   2005*

VOLONNE see Chateau Arnoux *10E3*

VOLVIC *9B1* (6km S) **Camp Municipal, Chemin de Ratiers, 63530 Volvic [04 73 33 63 39 or 04 73 33 50 38 (Mairie)]** Exit Riom on D986: foll sp for Pontgibaud & Volvic. Site on L at x-rds to vill after passing lge sp on R for Volcanic Park, nr junc with D15, along unmade rd. Ent poss diff lge o'fits. Sm, shd; wc (some cont); chem disp; shwrs inc; shops 1km; tradsmn; sm dogs free; adv bkg; rd noise. "Site is guarded 0800-2100 but itinerants use site facs; NH only." 15 Jun-15 Sep. € 9.00   2003*

VONNAS *9A2* (1km W Rural) **Camp Municipal Le Renom, 01540 Vonnas [04 74 50 02 75]** Fr Bourg-en-Bresse take N79 W sp Macon. In 15km take D26 S to Vonnas; turn R in town cent & site on R in 1km by leisure cent. Med, pt shd; wc; chem disp; shwrs inc; el pts (10A) inc; shop 1km; BBQ; pool; rv; fishing; quiet. "Gd mkt Thurs am." ♦ ltd. Apr-Oct. € 9.60   2002*

FRANCE

VOREY *9C1* (4km E Rural) **Domaine du Pra de Mars, 43800 Vorey-sur-Arzon** [tel/fax 04 71 03 40 86; leprademars@free.fr] On D103 dir Retournac. Med, hdg/mkd pitch, pt sl, pt shd; htd wc (some cont); chem disp; some serviced pitches; mv service pnt; baby facs; fam bthrm; shwrs inc; el pts (5A) €2.90; lndtte; rest; snacks; bar; BBQ; htd pool; rv sw; dogs €1.10; bus; phone; Eng spkn; adv bkg; quiet; cc acc; CCI. "Vg site; welcoming owners; beautiful location; gd walking area." 1 Apr-30 Sep. € 13.00   2003*

VOREY *9C1* (W) **Camping Les Moulettes, Chemin de Feline, 43800 Vorey-sur-Arzon** [04 71 03 70 48; fax 04 71 03 72 06; campinglesmoulettes@ libertysurf.fr] Fr Le Puy take D103 sp Vorey. Site sp in vill; L in main sq. Sm, hdg pitch, pt shd; wc; shwrs inc; el pts (10A) inc; lndtte; shops in vill; snacks; playgrnd; pool, waterslide adj; fishing adj; Eng spkn; adv bkg; quiet. "Excel rest nrby - site will make res." 1 May-15 Sep. € 13.60   2003*

VOUECOURT *6E1* (Rural) **Camp Municipal Rives de Marne, 52320 Vouecourt** [03 25 02 44 66 (Mairie)] N fr Chaumont on N67; sp to site in 17km; thro vill by Rv Marne; well sp. Sm, pt shd; wc (some cont); chem disp; shwr; el pts (10A) €2.20 (poss rev pol); gas; shop 6km; tradsmn; playgrnd; rv sw; fishing; CCI. "Perfect location; baker calls am; warden calls each evening; rv known to flood in winter; excel sh stay." 1 May-30 Sep. € 6.50
                                                                          2005*

VOUILLE *4H1* **Camp Municipal, 86190 Vouille** [05 49 51 90 10 (after 1800) or 05 49 54 20 30 (Mairie)] Fr Parthenay take the N149 twds Vouille; go thro Vouille & turn R onto the D43 by the Super U. At bottom of hill turn R twds town cent; site sp behind Cheval Blanc rest. Sm, mkd pitch, shd; wc; chem disp (wc); shwrs inc; el pts (3A) €2; ice; lndry rm; shop 500m; playgrnd adj; pool; quiet. "Site yourself; useful NH; excel rest adj; ideal Futuroscope." ♦ 1 May-15 Sep. € 6.00   2003*

VOULTE SUR RHONE, LA *9D2* (4km N Rural) **Camping La Garenne, 07800 St Laurent-du-Pape** [tel/fax 04 75 62 24 62; campinglagarenne@ freesurf.fr] Well sp fr La Voulte. Fr Valence S on N86 La Voulte, approx 15km turn W onto D120; 300m after St Laurent-du-Pape cent, turn R bef PO. Med, pt terr, pt shd; wc; chem disp; shwrs inc; el pts (4A) inc; gas; lndtte; ice; shop 1km; rest; snacks; bar; playgrnd; pool; dogs €1.70; poss v cr; Eng spkn; adv bkg; quiet; red long stay; CCI. "V helpful owners; magnificent view fr terr pitches; excel long stay." ♦ 1 Mar-1 Nov. € 28.50   2004*

VOULTE SUR RHONE, LA *9D2* (4km NE) **Camp Municipal Les Voiliers, 07800 Beauchastel** [04 75 62 24 04; fax 04 75 62 42 32] Site 30km S of Tournon on N86, 500m E of Beauchastel sp in town, over canal, past hydro. Med, shd; wc (cont); snacks; shwrs inc; el pts (5A) inc; lndtte; ice; shops 500m; pool; playgrnd; dogs €1.07; poss cr; quiet. "V friendly; gd san facs." 1 Apr-31 Oct. € 13.50
                                                                          2003*

VOUVRAY *4G2* (500m S Urban) **Camp Municipal du Bec de Cisse, 37210 Vouvray** [02 47 52 68 81; fax 02 47 52 67 76] Travelling E on N152 fr Tours for about 6km, turn R at traff lts in Vouvray; site on L in 200m adj to rv bdge & opp tourist office. Do not turn L into town cent. Sm, hdg/mkd pitch, pt shd; wc; chem disp; shwrs; el pts (10A) €2.80; gas; lndtte; ice; shop 500m; tradsmn; rest, snacks, bar 300m; playgrnd; sw 1km; dogs 41; Eng spkn; adv bkg rec high ssn; quiet but some traff noise; CCI. "Pleasant, well-run site; helpful owner; san facs v clean but deteriorating; bus tours - old town worth a visit; vg long/sh stay." ♦ 1 May-26 Sep. € 10.50   2005*

VRAIGNES EN VERMANDOIS see Peronne *3C3*

VUILLAFANS see Ornans *6G2*

WACQUINGHEN see Marquise *3A3*

WARLINCOURT LES PAS *3B3* (Rural) **Domaine La Kilienne, 1 Rue du Moulin, 62760 Warlincourt-les-Pas** [03 21 73 03 03; fax 03 21 22 64 14; lakilienne@wanadoo.fr] Fr Arras or Doullens turn S fr N25. Site 2.5km on L, in vill. Lge, hdg/mkd pitch, terr, pt shd; wc; chem disp; mv service pnt; shwrs inc; el pts (10A) inc; lndtte; ice; tradsmn; snacks; bar; BBQ; htd pool; playgrnd; fishing; mini-golf; TV; entmnt; some statics; dogs €1; poss cr; adv bkg. "Attractive site with watermill; St Kilien Spring & chapel." ♦ 1 Apr-31 Oct. € 15.00   2005*

WASSELONNE *6E3* (1km W Urban) **Camp Municipal, Route de Romanswiller, 67310 Wasselonne** [tel/fax 03 88 87 00 08] Fr N4 take D244 to site Med, mkd pitch, terr, pt shd; wc; mv service pnt; shwrs inc; el pts (5-10A) €2.10-3.50; gas; lndtte; shop; rest; snacks; bar; playgrnd; htd, covrd pool high ssn; 30% statics; dogs €0.60; quiet; CCI. "Pleasant town; views over hills." 15 Apr-15 Oct. € 11.00   2005*

WASSELONNE *6E3* (6km NW Urban) **Camp Municipal, 67310 Romanswiller** [tel/fax 03 88 87 45 54 or 03 88 87 05 57 (Mairie)] Fr Saverne take N4 twd Strasbourg. 1km N of Wasselonne turn R onto D260 & cont twd town cent, turn R onto D224 sp Romanswiller & 'Camping Piscine'. 2km N at o'skts turn L into 'Centre des Loisirs'. Sm, hdg pitch, pt shd; wc; chem disp; all serviced pitches; shwrs inc; el pts (10A) inc; lndry rm; ice; shops 2km; rest; snacks; BBQ; playgrnd; htd pool; tennis; cycle hire; 90% statics; poss cr; some Eng spkn; poss noisy; CCI. "Helpful warden; v well kept site in sports complex; pleasant town; views over hills." 1 Apr-15 Sep. € 12.70   2002*

WATTEN *3A3* (W Rural) **Camping Le Val Joli, Wattendam, 59143 Watten [03 21 88 23 26 or 03 21 88 24 75]** NW fr St Omer on N43; 6km N of Tilques turn N on D600; in 5km turn R to D205 sp Watten; at T-junc turn L; cross rv; thro town; site sp on L; 1st L after PO; 1st L again; site on R not sp - look for gap in railings. Med, pt sl, pt shd; wc; chem disp; shwrs €1.60; el pts (3A) inc; shops adj; playgrnd; fishing & cycling along river/canal; 90% statics; poss noisy; CCI. "Spacious, attractive site; conv ferries & glass works at Arques; gd clean san facs; friendly, helpful warden; vet 20 mins walk; gd NH/sh stay." 1 Apr-31 Oct. € 10.75   2005*

Some of these sites have changed their opening dates - we'd better fill in some site report forms and let the editor of the guide know.

WATTWILLER see Cernay *6F3*

†WIMEREUX *3A2* (5km N Rural) **Camping Le Beaucamp, 10 Rue de Ferquent, 62164 Ambleteuse [03 21 32 62 10]** Exit A16 junc 7 onto D191E dir Ambleteuse, site in 6km in R. Lge, hdg pitch, unshd; htd wc; chem disp; shwrs €1.83; el pts (5A) €3.05; gas; ice; lndtte; shop; snacks; bar; BBQ; playgrnd; pool 10km; sand beach 1.5km; entmnt; 90% statics; dogs; quiet; cc acc; CCI. "Gd sh stay/NH; sep area for tourers; lge pitches." € 15.50   2002*

WIMEREUX *3A2* (1km S Coastal) **Camp Municipal Olympic, Rue de la Liberation, 62930 Wimereux [03 21 32 45 63]** A16 exit 32 Wimereux Sud to site on R fr rndbt. Or N fr Boulogne on D940, at vill sp Wimereux & rndabt, turn R. Med, hdg/mkd pitch, pt sl, unshd; wc; chem disp; baby facs; shwrs inc; el pts (4A) €3.20 (rev pol); BBQ; lndry rm; shop adj; tradsmn; rest; playgrnd; pool 4km; beach 800m; sailing; fishing; 30% statics; dogs €1; Eng spkn; some noise fr rds & rlwy; CCI. "Conv Boulogne & NH; office open fr 0800; ent card dep €5; site unkempt low ssn; hot water runs out early; gd all stays." 15 Mar-26 Oct. € 12.20   2005*

†WIMEREUX *3A2* (1.5km S Coastal) **Caravaning L'Ete Indien, Hameau de Honvault, 62930 Wimereux [03 21 30 23 50; fax 03 21 30 17 14; eteindien@eracotedopale.com]** Fr Calais A16 SW exit junc 32 sp Wimereux Sud. Thro Terlincthun R after x-ing rlwy, site in 700m on R. Med, mkd pitch, pt sl, unshd; htd wc; chem disp; mv service pnt; serviced pitches; baby facs; shwrs inc; el pts (6A) inc; lndtte; snacks; bar; BBQ (gas); playgrnd; sandy beach 1.5km; 95% statics; dogs; Eng spkn; adv bkg; some rlwy noise; red 14+ days. "Conv A16, Calais ferries; rec low ssn phone to check site open; mainly statics but tourers welcome although no dedicated pitches or elec." ♦ € 19.50   2005*

WINGEN SUR MODER *5D3* (W Rural) **Aire Naturelle Municipal, 67290 Wingen-sur-Moder [03 88 89 71 27 (Mairie); fax 03 88 89 86 99; mairie@wingen-moder.com]** W fr Haguenau on D919 to W end Wingen-sur-Moder. Site sp by rlwy arch. Sm, mkd pitch, terr, pt shd; wc; chem disp; shwrs inc; el pts (13A) €2; rest nr; shop 500m; Eng spkn; adv bkg; quiet; 7th day free; CCI. "Excel site; v peaceful but adj sports field poss used by youth groups/motorbikers high ssn; clean facs; warden calls am & pm; gd walking/cycling." 1 May-30 Sep. € 10.40   2005*

WISSANT *3A2* (Coastal) **Camp Municipal La Source, Rue de la Source, 62179 Wissant [03 21 35 92 46; fax 03 21 00 19 11]** Fr Calais exit Wissant. At D940 bear L twd Boulogne. In 1.5km turn R at camping sp into Rue de la Source. Site on L in 300m. Lge, hdg/mkd pitch, pt shd; htd wc; chem disp; shwrs inc; el pts (5A) inc; gas; 500m; ice; lndtte; shops 500m; tradsmn; rest adj; playgrnd; sand beach 500m; entmnt; 80% statics; dogs €0.76; poss cr; quiet; Eng spkn; phone; CCI. "Friendly, helpful manager; scruffy site & statics; poor pitches at far end site; poss unclean san facs; lovely scenery; gd walking/cycling." 1 Mar-11 Nov. € 15.30   2003*

WISSANT *3A2* (6km NE Coastal/Rural) **Camping Cote d'Opale Le Blanc Nez, 18 Rue de la Mer, 62179 Escalles [tel/fax 03 21 85 27 38; camping. blancnez@laposte.net]** Fr A16 take junc 40 to Cap Blanc-Nez. Site situated on W edge of Escalles on D940 twd sea. Med, mkd pitch, pt sl, unshd; wc; chem disp; mv service pnt; shwrs €1; el pts (4-10A) €4-10 (long lead poss req); gas; lndry rm; ice; shop; tradsmn; rest; snacks; bar; playgrnd; sand/shgl beach 1km; 60% statics; dogs €1.30; phone; bus 100m; poss cr; adv bkg; quiet; CCI. "Ltd hot shwrs/hot water, but v clean san facs; diff access for lge o'fits due parked cars; sm pitches; elec linked to pitch number - no choice; excel rest; gd location & walking; security barrier; gd NH." 1 Apr-10 Nov. € 15.50   2005*

WISSANT *3A2* (6km NE Coastal) **Camping Les Erables, 17 Rue du Chateau d'Eau, 62179 Escalles [03 21 85 25 36]** Fr A16 take exit 11 & go thro Peuplinges. Site sp on ent Escalles. Sm, mkd pitch, terr, unshd; wc; chem disp; mv service pnt; showrs inc; el pts (6A) €3; lndtte; shops, bar 3km; tradsmn; rest 1km; sand beach 3km; dogs; quiet; CCI. "New site 2004; helpful owner; lge pitches: steep ent access; sea views; gates close 2200; excel all stays." ♦ Easter-1 Nov. € 12.40   2004*

FRANCE

WISSANT *3A2* (4km E Rural) **Camping La Vallee, 901 Rue Principale, 62179 Hervelinghen** [03 21 36 73 96 or 03 21 85 15 43] Fr Calais exit A16 onto D244 & foll sp St Inglevert. Site on L at end Hervelinghen vill. Sm, hdg/mkd pitch, unshd; htd wc; chem disp; shwrs €1; el pts (6A) €3.30 (poss rev pol); lndry rm; rest; snacks; bar; BBQ; playgrnd; sand/shgl beach 3km; 75% statics; dogs €1; Eng spkn; adv bkg; quiet; CCI. "Family-run site; immac san facs but no stand pipes or waste water emptying point; attractive countryside; conv Calais, Cite Europe, ferry; gd walking in area." ♦ ltd. 1 Apr-31 Oct. € 14.50   2005*

XONRUPT LONGEMER see Gerardmer *6F3*

YCHOUX *7D1* (10km E Rural) **Camp Municipal du Lac des Forges, 40160 Ychoux** [05 58 82 35 57 or 05 58 82 36 01 (Mairie); fax 05 58 82 35 46] Fr Bordeaux take N10 S & turn onto D43 at Liposthey W twd Parentis-en-Born. Site in 8km on R, past vill of Ychoux. Sm, pt sl, pt shd; wc; chem disp; shwrs; el pts inc (rev pol); ice; lndtte; shops 1km; snacks; rest; playgrnd; TV rm; lake adj; fishing; sailing; quiet. "Levelling blocks poss req; unisex, open-plan san facs; pitches nr rd poss noisy." 15 Jun-15 Sep. € 12.00   2005*

YENNE *9B3* (300m N Rural) **Camping Le Flon, Ave du Rhone, 73170 Yenne** [04 79 36 82 70 or 04 79 36 90 76; fax 04 79 36 92 72; ccyenne@wanadoo.fr] Fr N504 ent Yenne, site visible. E on rd to Tunnel du Chat, site sp on banks Rv Rhone. Med, mkd pitch, shd; wc (cont); shwrs inc; el pts €2.50; shops 500m; rest, snacks, bar 500m; playgrnd; fishing; canoeing; dogs €1.10; adv bkg; some rd noise. 15 Jun-31 Aug. € 8.85   2004*

YENNE *9B3* (8km E Rural) **Camp Municipal Le Lamartine, 73370 Bourdeau** [04 79 25 03 41 (Mairie); fax 04 79 25 35 73] N fr Chambery on N504 sp Bourg-en-Bresse on W side of lake. 2km N of Le Bourget turn R opp g'ge sp Bourdeau. Thro car park in front of Mairie. Fr N or W fr Yenne turn L just after Tunnel du Chat. Sm, pt sl, pt shd; wc (some cont); shwrs inc; el pts (6A) inc; shop 200m; rest adj; BBQ; lake 1.5km; dogs; adv bkg; quiet; CCI. "Gd views; nice walks nr." 15 Jun-15 Sep. € 10.00   2004*

YPORT *3C1* (1km SW Coastal) **Camping Le Rivage, Rue Hottieres, 76111 Yport** [02 35 27 33 78] Fr D940 bet Etretat & Fecamp take D11 2km NE of Les Lages, meeting up with D211 & head twd Yport. Site on D211. Med, pt sl, terr, unshd; wc; chem disp; shwrs; el pts (6A) inc; ice; shops 1km; snacks; bar; shgl beach 300m; games rm; TV rm; phone; adv bkg; quiet. "Views overlkg sea; steep descent to beach; san facs inadequate high ssn; rec stop at top of site & walk to recep bef pitching, as turning poss diff lge o'fits; conv Etretat, Fecamp & Benedictine palace." 27 Jun-7 Sep. € 12.50   2004*

YSSINGEAUX *9C1* (300m SE Urban) **Camp Municipal de Choumouroux, 43200 Yssingeaux** [04 71 65 53 44 or 04 71 59 01 13 (Mairie); fax 04 71 65 19 35] N88 Le Puy to St Etienne on R bef Yssingeaux; ent next to school, opp petrol stn. Sm, pt shd; wc (cont); shwrs inc; el pts (10A) €2.30; shops 500m; playgrnd; fishing; 10% statics; dogs €1.20; quiet. 1 May-30 Sep. € 6.60   2004*

YVETOT *3C2* (10km N) **Camp Municipal de la Durdent, 76560 Hericourt-en-Caux** [02 35 96 38 08 or 02 35 96 42 12 (Mairie); fax 02 32 70 02 59; officedetourisme.doudeville@wanadoo.fr] Fr Le Havre on N15 L at traff lts in Yvetot on D131 sp Cany to Hericourt. After passing thro vill turn L on D149. Site on L in 300m. Or exit A29 junc 8 dir Fecamp. After 3.5km at rndabt outside Fauville turn R sp Hericourt 10km. Site visible on R below rd on ent vill. Sm, mkd pitch, pt sl, unshd; wc (some cont); shwrs inc; el pts (6A) €2; lndry rm; shops 500m; poss cr; quiet; cc not acc; CCI. "Site by trout stream, excel rests in vill; pitch yourself; warden calls; pleasantly situated; basic facs but well-maintained; gd sh stay." 15 Apr-30 Sep. € 10.00   2005*

YVETOT *3C2* (12km S Rural) **Camp Municipal de Barre-y-Va de la Commune de Caudebec-en-Caux, Route de Villequier, 76490 Villequier** [02 35 96 26 38 or 02 35 95 90 10 (Mairie)] Fr Caudebec take D81 W on rv twd Villequier & site on R in 1km next to Rv Seine. Med, pt shd; wc (male cont); chem disp; shwrs inc; el pts (5A) €3.50 (rev pol); lndtte; ice; shops 1km; tradsmn; playgrnd; pool 300m; rv fishing & boating adj; some statics; phone; Eng spkn; some noise fr rd, rv & nrby disco; CCI. "Site adj Rv Seine; interesting area; popular, clean & well kept; san block ltd - lights controlled fr outside cubicles & you could be left in the dark!; NH only." 1 Apr-30 Sep. € 7.95   2005*

YVOIRE see Thonon les Bains *9A3*

CORSICA

AJACCIO *10H2* (11km SE) **Camping U Prunelli, Pont de Pisciatello, 20166 Porticcio** [04 95 25 19 23; fax 04 95 25 16 87; prunelli.camp@infonie.fr] Fr Ajaccio E twd Sartene on N196. SW onto D55. Site immed on R at junc. Med, pt shd; wc; shwrs inc; el pts (16A) inc; gas; lndtte; shop; rest; snacks; bar; playgrnd; pool; sand beach 3km; poss cr; adv bkg; quiet but some rd noise. 28 Mar-31 Oct. € 24.40   2003*

AJACCIO *10H2* (4km W) **Camping de Barbicaggia, Rue de Sanguinaires, 20000 Ajaccio** [04 95 52 01 17] Fr Ajaccio take D111 twds Iles Sanguinaires. Site on R after 4km. Med, hdg/mkd pitch, hdstg, terr, shd; wc (some cont); chem disp; shwrs inc; el pts; lndtte; sand beach 100m; 5% statics; phone adj; bus 200m; poss v cr; Eng spkn. "Sea views over bay; ltd space for vans; steep entry not suitable for lge units; rec check pitch bef ent site; gd long/sh stays." ♦ ltd. € 16.70   2004*

AJACCIO *10H2* (1km NW Coastal) **Camping Les Mimosas, Route d'Alata, 20000 Ajaccio [04 95 20 99 85; fax 04 95 10 01 77]**
Foll D194 round N of Ajaccio & then directions to Super U; 1st R off rndabt immed after Super U. Med, hdg/mkd pitch, hdstg, pt sl, shd; wc; chem disp; serviced pitches; shwrs inc; el pts (5-10A) gas 1km; lndtte; ice; sm shop & 1km; tradsmn; rest; snacks; bar; playgrnd; shgl beach 1km; 5% statics; dogs; phone; adv bkg; quiet; 10% red CCI. "Conv Ajaccio; gd rest on site; gd long/sh stay." ♦ ltd.
1 Apr-15 Oct. € 15.30   2005*

ALERIA *10H2* (3km Coastal) **Camping Marina d'Aleria, 20270 Aleria [04 95 57 01 42; fax 04 95 57 04 29; info@marina-aleria.com]**
S fr Bastia on N198; bef Aleria turn E on N200 to Plage de Padulone. Lge, hdg pitch, pt shd, wc; mv service pnt; shwrs inc; el pts (6A) €3.60; lndry rm; shop; rest; snacks; bar; BBQ; playgrnd; sand beach adj; tennis; cycle hire; entmnt; cc acc. "Superb site on sea shore; Roman ruins in Aleria."
Easter-15 Oct. € 25.00   2003*

ALERIA *10H2* (7km N Coastal) **Camping-Village Riva-Bella (Naturist), 20270 Aleria [04 95 38 81 10 or 04 95 38 85 97; fax 04 95 38 91 29; rivabella@wanadoo.fr; www.rivabella-corsica.com]**
Fr Bastia S on N198 for 60km, site sp to L. Med, pt shd; wc; mv service pnt; shwrs; el pts €3.80; shop; lndtte; rest; snacks; bar; playgrnd; sand beach adj; fishing; watersports; tennis; cycle hire; fitness rm; internet; entmnt; excursions; TV rm; 10% statics; dogs €3; adv bkg; quiet; red low ssn; INF card req.
9 Apr-31 Oct. € 31.00 (CChq acc)   2005*

ALGAJOLA *10G2* (800m E Coastal) **Camping de la Plage, 20220 Algajola [04 95 60 71 76; fax 04 95 60 75 10]**
Site 6km W fr L'lle-Rousse on N197 (D199) dir Algajola. On R opp Hotel Pascal Paol bef Algajola. Med, pt shd; htd wc (some cont); chem disp; mv service pnt; shwrs inc; el pts (6A) €2.80; lndtte; shop; rest; snacks; bar; playgrnd; sand beach; entmnt; no statics; tram; poss cr; adv bkg; quiet; cc acc. "Rest, snacks & bar poss clsd low ssn; tram to l'lle-Rousse & Calvi fr site gd for touring inland; gd all stays." 15 Mar-30 Oct. € 15.60
                                                          2003*

BASTIA *10G2* (5km N Coastal) **Camping Casablanca (formerly Les Orangers), Licciola, 20200 Miomo [04 95 33 24 09; fax 04 95 33 23 65]**
Foll main coast rd D80 N 4km fr ferry. Site well sp on L of rd. Sm, shd; wc; shwrs; el pts €2.45-3.10; ice; shop; tradsmn; rest; snacks; bar; TV; sandy/shgl beach adj; quiet; CCI. "Poss run down low ssn; friendly owners; vg rest; site ent tight for lge o'fits; poss unreliable opening dates." 1 Apr-1 Oct.
€ 13.10   2004*

BASTIA *10G2* (11km S Coastal) **Camping San Damiano, Lido de la Marana, 20620 Biguglia [04 95 33 68 02; fax 04 95 30 84 10; l.pradier@wanadoo.fr; www.campingsandamiano.com]**
S fr Bastia on N193 for 4km. Turn SE onto Lagoon Rd (sp Lido de Marana). Site on L in 7km. Lge, pt shd; wc; chem disp; baby facs; shwrs inc; el pts (6A) €3; lndtte; shop; rest; playgrnd; sandy beach adj; cycle path; games area; games rm; dogs €0.50; Eng spkn; cc acc; CCI. ♦ 1 Apr-20 Oct. € 20.00
                                                          2005*

BELGODERE see lle Rousse, L' *10G2*

BIGUGLIA see Bastia *10G2*

BONIFACIO *10H2* (15km N Coastal) **Camping Rondinara, Suartone, 20169 Bonifacio [04 95 70 43 15; fax 04 95 70 56 79; reception@rondinara.fr; www.rondinara.fr]** Fr Bonifacio take N198 dir Porte-Vecchio for 10km, then turn R onto D158 dir Suartone (lge camp sp at turning). Site in 5km. NB D158 single track, many bends & hills. Med, pt sl, pt shd; wc; mv service pnt; shwrs inc; el pts (6A) €3.30; lndtte; ice; shop; rest; snacks; bar; BBQ; playgrnd; pool; sand beach 400m; water sports; volleyball; dogs €1.60; poss cr; Eng spkn; no adv bkg; quiet; red low ssn; cc acc; CCI. "Excel rest; idyllic location; excel long/sh stay."
15 May-30 Sep. € 19.70   2005*

BONIFACIO *10H2* (4km NE Rural) **Camping Pian del Fosse, Route de Santa Manza, 20169 Bonifacio [tel/fax 04 95 73 16 34; pian.del.fosse@wanadoo.fr]** Leave Bonifacio on D58 dir Sta Manza, site on L in 4km. Sm, hdg/mkd pitch, terr, shd; wc; chem disp; shwrs inc; el pts (4A) €3.80; lndtte; shop; tradsmn; snacks; BBQ; playgrnd; sand/shgl beach 3km; 20% statics; dogs €3.20; poss cr; Eng spkn; quiet. "Pitches poss diff lge m'vans due overhanging trees; vg." ♦ ltd.
Easter-15 Oct. € 21.50   2004*

BONIFACIO *10H2* (4km NE Rural) **Pertamina Village U Farniente, 20169 Bonifacio [04 95 73 05 47; fax 04 95 73 11 42; pertamina@wanadoo.fr; www.camping-pertamina.com]**
Fr Bonifacio take RN198 N, site on R in 4km. Med, hdg/mkd pitch, pt sl, pt shd; wc (some cont); chem disp; mv service pnt; baby facs; shwrs inc; el pts (6A) inc; gas; lndtte; ice; shop; rest; snacks; bar; playgrnd; htd pool; waterslide; beach 4km; tennis; archery; entmnt; TV rm; 50% statics; dogs; poss cr; adv bkg; cc acc; CCI. "Access to pitches diff; excel."
♦ 1 Apr-15 Oct. € 27.00 (CChq acc)   2005*

CALVI *10G2* (Coastal) **Camping La Pinede, Route de la Pinede, 20260 Calvi [04 95 65 17 80; fax 04 95 65 19 60]**
S fr L'lle-Rousse on N197; well sp ent Calvi; 1st ent on R to Rte de la Pinede, 2nd ent 1km after 1st. Lge, shd; shwrs; el pts (6A) €3.50; shop; supmkt nrby; rest; pool; superb beach 250m; mini-golf; no dogs; train to Calvi & lle-Rousse 250m; cc acc. "Too shd; clean facs." 1 Apr-1 Oct. € 22.00   2005*

FRANCE

CALVI *10G2* (1.8km SE Coastal) **Camping Paduella, Route de Bastia, 20260 Calvi [04 95 65 13 20 or 04 95 65 06 16; fax 04 95 65 17 50]** On N197 fr Calvi; on R 200m after rndabt by casino supmkt. Med, mkd pitch, pt sl, terr, pt shd; wc chem disp; baby facs; shwrs inc; el pts (6A) €3.30; lndtte; ice; shop/supmkt; snacks; bar; playgrnd; sand beach 400m; 25% statics; poss cr; quiet; CCI. "Poss best site at Calvi; immac san facs but slippery when wet, especially disabled ramp; vg." ♦ 10 May-15 Oct. € 18.80   2005*

CALVI *10G2* (4km SE Coastal) **Camping La Dolce Vita, Route de Bastia, 20260 Calvi [04 95 65 05 99; fax 04 95 65 31 25]** N197 twd L'lle Rousse. Site on L, by rest, immed after x-ing rv bdge. Adj Bastia-Calvi a'route. Lge, shd; wc; shwrs inc; el pts (10A) €3.50; gas; lndtte; ice; shop; rest; snacks; bar; playgrnd; sand beach 150m; TV rm; dir access to rv; fishing; sailing windsurfing; poss cr; quiet, but some aircraft noise. 1 May-30 Sep. € 21.60   2005*

CARGESE *10H2* (3km N) **Camping Le Torraccia, 20130 Cargese [04 95 26 42 39 or 04 95 20 40 21 (LS); fax 04 95 20 40 21; contact@ camping-torraccia.com]** N fr Cargese twd Porto on D81 for 3km. Site on L. Med, terr, pt shd; wc; shwrs inc; ltd el pts (10A) €2.50; lndry rm; shop; rest; snacks; bar; playgrnd; sports area; sand beach 3km; adv bkg; red low ssn. "Nearest site to Porto without diff traffic conditions." 1 May-30 Sep. € 17.00   2004*

†CENTURI *10G2* (800m S Rural/Coastal) **Camping L'Isulottu, Morsiglia, 20238 Centuri [04 95 35 62 81; fax 04 95 35 63 63; isulottu@ wanadoo.fr]** Fr St Florent N on D35/D80, site on L. Med, hdstg, pt sl, pt shd; wc; shwrs inc; el pts €3.30; gas; lndtte; ice; shop; rest; snacks; playgrnd; shgl beach 200m; watersports; TV; poss cr; quiet; adv bkg. € 16.00   2003*

CERVIONE *10G2* (7km NE Coastal) **Camping Merendella, Moriani-Plage, 20230 San Nicolao [04 95 38 53 47 or 04 95 38 50 54; fax 04 95 38 44 01; merendel@club-internet.fr; www. merendella.com]** Site 44km S of Bastia at Moriani-Plage; foll N193 & N198 fr Bastia to Moriani Plage, on E (beach side) of N198, 700m after supermkt. Med, hdg/mkd pitch, shd; wc; chem disp; mv service pnt; shwrs inc; el pts (5A) €4; lndtte; ice; shop & supmkt 1km; rest; bar; playgrnd; dir access to beach adj; tennis 500m; TV rm; no dogs; adv bkg (€15.24 dep req); quiet; cc acc; CCI. "Friendly; efficient staff; idyllic beachside pitches." ♦ 15 May-15 Oct. € 18.00   2004*

CERVIONE *10G2* (6km SE Coastal) **Camping Calamar, Prunete, 20221 Cervione [04 94 38 00 94; fax 04 95 38 00 82; camille. zucca@wanadoo.fr; www.campingcalamar.com]** On N198 S fr Prunete for 6km. Turn L at x-rds, site in 500m beside beach, sp. Sm, pt shd; wc; shwrs inc; el pts €2; lndtte; shop 500m; snacks; bar; BBQ; sand beach adj; sailing; watersports; Eng spkn; adv bkg; quiet; red low ssn. "Friendly owner; pleasant site with trees & shrubs; close to mountains; 30 mins fr Bastia; excel long/sh stay." 1 Apr-31 Oct. € 11.80   2002*

CORBARA see lle Rousse L' *10G2*

CORTE *10G2* **Camping U Sognu, Route de la Restonica, 20250 Corte [04 95 46 09 07]** At rndabt turn W off N193 sp Centre Ville. Immed L after bdge onto D623 sp La Resonica & site. Site on R in 200m. Med, pt shd; wc; shwrs inc; el pts (6A) €3; ice; shop; tradsmn; rest; bar; rv & lake 200m; sw & fishing; poss v cr; cc not acc. "Gd views of old university capital town; clean but inadequate facs high ssn; gd rest & bar; conv walking Resonica & Tavignano gorges." 1 Apr-25 Oct. € 19.00   2003*

CORTE *10G2* (E Urban) **Camping Le Restonica, Faubourg St Antoine, 20250 Corte [tel/fax 04 95 46 11 59; vero.camp@worldonline.fr]** Fr N193 Ajaccio to Corte, twd cent of town. Pass petrol stn on R then sharp turn R before x-ing bdge (acute angle). Site on R bet rv bdge in 200m. Sharp turn down hill to ent. Med; wc; shwrs inc; el pts €3.50; gas; ice; shops 200m; rest; sports complex 150m; adv bkg; quiet. "Corte beautiful old town; gd walking & horseriding." 1 May-30 Sep. € 16.00   2004*

GHISONACCIA *10H2* (4km E Coastal) **Camping Arinella Bianca, Route de la Mer, Bruschetto, 20240 Ghisonaccia [04 95 56 04 78; fax 04 95 56 12 54; arinella@arinellabianca.com; www.arinellabianca.com]** S fr Bastia on N193/ N198 approx 70km to Ghisonaccia. At Ghisonaccia foll sp opp pharmacy to beach (plage) & Rte de la Mer. In 3km turn R at rndabt & site well sp. NB When towing keep to main, coastal rds. Lge, hdg/mkd pitch, shd; wc (some cont); chem disp; mv service pnt; baby facs; shwrs inc; el pts (6A) €3.50 (rev pol); gas; lndtte; ice; shop; tradsmn; rest; snacks; bar; BBQ; playgrnd; pool; sand beach adj; fishing; watersports & activities; tennis; horseriding adj; cycle hire; games rm; internet; entmnt; TV rm; 45% statics; recep 0830-2100; dogs €2.50; Eng spkn; adv bkg (dep req); barrier (dep €15); red low ssn; cc acc; CCI. "V clean, well-run site; attractive lake in cent; trees make access to pitches diff; v helpful owner & staff." ♦ 16 Apr-30 Sep. € 33.00 (CChq acc)   2005*

GHISONACCIA *10H2* (5km E Coastal) **Camping Marina d'Erba Rossa, Route de la Mer, 20240 Ghisonaccia [04 95 56 25 14 or 04 95 56 21 18; fax 04 95 56 27 23; erbarossa@wanadoo.fr; www.homair-vacances.fr]** Drive into town on N198. Site sp down D144 (easy to miss). Take D144 E to coast & site on R after 5km. Lge, hdg/mkd pitch, shd; wc; chem disp; shwrs; el pts (5-6A) inc (long lead rec); lndtte; ice; shop; rest; pizzaria; snacks; playgrnd; pool; private sand beach; watersports; tennis; cycle hire; mini-golf; horseriding; entmnt; child entmnt; some statics; adv bkg. ♦ 3 Apr-23 Oct. € 31.80   2004*

ILE ROUSSE, L' *10G2* (6km SE) **Camping Le Clos des Chenes, Route de Belgodere, Lozari, 20226 Belgodere [04 95 60 15 13 or 04 95 60 41 27 (LS); fax 04 95 60 21 16; cdc.lozari@wanadoo.fr; www.closdeschenes.fr]** E on fr L'Ile Rousse on N197 E twd Bastia. After 7km turn S at Lozari onto N197 sp Belgodere; site on R after 1.5km. Lge, sl, pt shd; wc; shwrs inc; baby facs; chem disp; el pts (10A) inc (long cable req); gas; lndtte; ice; shop; tradsmn; rest; bar; pizzeria; BBQ; playgrnd; pool & children's pool; sand beach 2km; tennis; games rm; 10% statics; dogs €2.70; poss cr; some Eng spkn; adv bkg; red low ssn; cc acc; CCI. "V tranquil, few pitches with view of mountains, most amongst sm oaks haphazardly placed; v ltd facs low ssn; gd touring cent; daily mkt; vg long stay." ♦ Easter-30 Sep. € 26.00   2004*

ILE ROUSSE, L' *10G2* (3km S Urban/Coastal) **Camping Les Oliviers, Route de Bastia, 20220 Monticello [04 95 60 19 92; fax 04 95 60 30 91]** Fr town take rd dir Bastia. Site on L in 800m. Lge, mkd pitch (some), pt sl, pt shd; wc; chem disp; shwrs inc; el pts (6A) €3.50; gas 800m; ice; lndtte; shop 800m; tradsmn; rest; snacks; bar; shgl beach 500m; 5% statics; dogs; phone; tram 1km; poss cr; adv bkg; cc acc. "Pleasant site but facs stretched & cr high ssn; ltd el pts; quiet at night but some rd noise in parts of site; gd location; coastal path to town." ♦ ltd 1 May-30 Sep. € 18.00   2004*

ILE ROUSSE, L' *10G2* (4km SW) **Aire Naturelle Balanea (Savelli de Guido), Route d'Algajola, 20256 Corbara [04 95 60 06 84 or 04 95 60 11 77 (ssn); fax 04 95 60 06 84; balanea@balanea.com]** Off N197 turn S down dirt rd at Lada Garage (nrly opp Mobiclub). Med, pt shd; wc; shwrs inc; el pts; shops 5km; snacks; beach 3km; CCI. Easter-30 Sep.
2003*

LECCI *10H2* (Rural) **Camping Mulinacciu, 20137 Lecci [04 95 71 47 48; fax 04 95 71 54 82; info@ campingmulinacciu.com; www.camping-mulinacciu.com]** N fr Porto-Vecchio on N198 for approx 10km. Cross double bdge over Rv Oso & turn L onto unmade rd app turning to San Sipriunu. Site sp down this rd. Med, pt shd; wc; shwrs inc; el pts; lndtte; shop; playgrnd; pool; waterslide; sand beach 7km; tennis; fishing; games area; TV; Eng spkn; quiet. "Access to rv; friendly owner; vg long/sh stay." 1 Jun-15 Sep. € 15.00   2002*

MACINAGGIO *10G2* (500m N Coastal) **Camping de la Plage U Stazzu, 20248 Macinaggio [04 95 35 43 76]** In Macinaggio foll sp fr D80. Med, sl, pt shd; wc (cont); chem disp (wc); shwrs inc; no el pts; gas, shop, snacks 500m; rest; bar; BBQ; playgrnd; shgl beach adj; dogs; quiet; phone. "Fair sh stay; conv for Cap Corse; no lighting except bar area; tent area shd, c'van area unshd, bare & sl." ♦ ltd 1 Apr-30 Sep. € 12.50   2002*

OLMETO *10H2* (3km S Coastal) **Camping Vigna Maggiore, 20113 Olmeto-Plage [04 95 76 02 07; fax 04 95 74 62 02; www.vignamaggiore.com]** Site is approx 5km N of Propriano at junc N196 & D157 Med, terr, pt shd; wc; chem disp; mv waste; shwrs inc; el pts €3.50; lndtte; rest; bar; playgrnd; pool; sand beach 1km; games area; some statics; poss cr; adv bkg; CCI. 1 Apr-30 Sep. € 18.40
2005*

OLMETO *10H2* (4km SW Coastal) **Camping L'Esplanade, Tour de la Calanca, 20113 Olmeto-Plage [04 95 76 05 03; fax 04 95 76 16 22; infos@camping-esplanade.com; www.camping esplanade.com]** S fr Olmeto on N196 twd Propriano; turn R onto D157; site in 1km. Med, mkd pitch, pt sl, terr, shd; wc; shwrs; el pts (10A) inc; shop; rest; snacks; ice; tradsmn; playgrnd; lndtte; beach adj; sep car park. 10 Apr-21 Oct. € 20.00
2004*

OLMETO *10H2* (6km SW Coastal) **Camping Abartello, Route Porto Pollo, 20113 Olmeto-Plage [04 95 74 05 12; fax 04 95 74 04 95; jpvogli@aol.com]** Fr Propriano take N196 N & turn onto D157 dir Porto Pollo to site. Med, shd; wc; chem disp; shwrs inc; el pts (10A) €2.75; ice; lndtte; shop, rest, snacks & bar nrby; tradsmn; supmkt 8km; beach adj; some statics; dogs; phone; poss cr; quiet; CCI. "Excel site for beach sw, exploring megalithic sites & mountain drives; basic facs poss unclean." 1 May-30 Sep.   2005*

PIANA *10G2* (11.5km W Coastal) **Camping Plage d'Arone, 20115 Piana [04 95 20 64 54]** Tho SW of Porto, rec c'vans arr fr Carese in S. Fr Carese head N on D81 to Piana. Turn L in vill onto D824 (sp), site on R in 11km. Med, pt shd; wc; chem disp; shwrs inc; el pts inc; lndtte; shop high ssn; supmkt in Piana; tradsmn; playgrnd; sand beach 350m; no statics; quiet; CCI. "Access fr site to excel sandy bay with 2 rests/bars; excel sh stay." ♦ 15 May-30 Sep.
€ 20.60   2004*

PIANOTTOLI CALDARELLO *10H2* (3.5km SE Coastal) **Camping Kevano Olage, 20131 Pianottoli-Caldarello [04 95 71 83 22; fax 04 95 71 83 83]** Turn off N196 in Pianottoli at x-rds onto D122 for 1km. Turn R just bef Caldarello, site on L in 2km. Med, mkd pitch, pt sl, terr, pt shd; wc; chem disp; mv service pnt; shwrs inc; el pts (4-6A) €2.50; lndtte; ice; shop; tradsmn; pizzeria; snacks; bar; playgrnd; sand beach 400m; entmnt; TV; phone; poss cr; Eng spkn; adv bkg rec high ssn; quiet; cc acc; CCI. "Site in macchia amongst huge boulders; beautiful site nr gd beaches; family-run site; no dogs on beach Jul/Aug." ♦ Ltd. 1 May-30 Sep. € 29.00   2005*

FRANCE

PIETRACORBARA *10G2* (Coastal) **Camping La Pietra**, 20233 Pietracorbara [04 95 35 27 49; fax 04 95 35 28 57] Fr Bastia on D80 N. In 20km ent vill L onto D232. Site on R in 1km at marina beach. Well sp. Sm, hdg/mkd pitch, shd; wc; shwrs inc; el pts (20A) inc; lndtte; ice; shop; tradsmn; playgrnd; sand beach 300m; tennis; Eng spkn; red low ssn; cc acc; CCI. "Excel facs; helpful owners." ♦
1 Apr-15 Oct. € 26.00   2003*

PORTICCIO see Ajaccio *10H2*

PORTO *10G2* (1km E Rural) **Camping Sole e Vista**, Rue d'Ota, 20150 Porto [04 95 26 15 71; fax 04 95 26 10 79] On D81 Ajaccio-Calvi rd. Ent thro Spar/Timy supmkt car park in Porto. NB rd fr Calvi diff for c'vans. Lge, mkd pitch, pt sl, terr, shd; wc; chem disp; shwrs inc; el pts (16A) €3.20; gas; lndtte; shop adj; snacks; bar; BBQ; playgrnd; shgl beach 1.5km; some statics; poss cr; Eng spkn; adv bkg; quiet; red CCI. "National Parks area; vg."
1 Apr-31 Oct. € 15.50   2003*

PORTO *10G2* (1.5km e Coastal) **Camping Les Oliviers**, 20150 Porto [04 95 26 14 49; fax 04 95 26 12 49; www.campinglesoliviers.com] On D81 fr Porto on R bank of Rv Porto nr Pont de Porto. Site nr rv a sh distance downhill fr Cmp Sole e Vista. Check for access, poss ltd space for c'vans. Lge, terr, shd; wc; baby facs; shwrs; el pts (5A) inc; lndry rm; ice; shop high ssn; tradsmn; snacks; bar; BBQ; playgrnd; beach 1km; rv sw; sailing & windsurfing 1km; tennis; cycle hire; mini-golf; archery; entmnt; TV; quiet. "Gd, clean, modern facs; dir access to rv; ent to upper levels of site v steep."
1 Apr-31 Oct. € 27.50   2004*

PORTO POLLO *10H2* (Coastal) **Camping Alfonsi-U-Cassedu**, Porto-Pollo, 20140 Serra-di-Ferro [04 95 74 01 80; fax 04 95 74 07 67] Turn W onto D157 off N196 Propriano-Olmeto rd sp Porto-Pollo. After narr rv bdge turn L. Site in 4km on L bef Porto-Pollo vill. Med, pt shd; wc; mv service pnt; shwrs; el pts inc; lndry rm; shop high ssn; supmkt in vill; rest high ssn; snacks; beach; poss cr; poss noisy; CCI. ♦ 1 Jun-30 Sep. € 27.00
                                              2003*

PORTO VECCHIO *10H2* (5km N Rural/Coastal) **Camping La Vetta**, Ste Trinite, 20137 Porto-Vecchio [04 95 70 09 86; fax 04 95 70 43 21; campinglavetta@multimania.com; www.multi mania.com/campinglavetta] On L (W) of N198 N of Ste Trinite. Sp in advance fr N & S. Med, pt sl, shd; wc; shwrs inc; el pts €3; gas; lndtte; ice; shop 500m; supmkt 3km; rest; snacks; playgrnd; sports are; sand beach 4km; pool; Eng spkn; quiet but some rd noise. "Excel bay for snorkelling, sw & windsurfing." 1 May-30 Sep. € 19.00   2004*

PORTO VECCHIO *10H2* (5km N Coastal) **Camping Les Ilots d'Or, La Trinite, Route de Marina di Fiori**, 20137 Porto-Vecchio [04 95 70 01 30 or 04 95 36 91 75; fax 04 95 70 01 30] Turn E off N198 5km N of Porto-Vecchio at La Trinite twd San Ciprianu. Turn only poss fr S, turn round if app fr N. In 1km fork R, site in 1km. Med, pt sl, pt terr, shd; wc (cont); shwrs inc; el pts (6A) inc; gas; ice; shop; poss cr; quiet. "Well organised with beach on gulf of Porto Vecchio; helpful family owners; lovely part of Corsica with many v gd beaches within easy reach; vg long stay."15 Apr-10 Sep. € 20.00   2004*

PORTO VECCHIO *10H2* (2km S Rural) **Camping U-Stabiacciu, Route de Palombaggia**, 20137 Porto-Vecchio. [04 95 70 37 17; fax 04 95 70 62 59; stabiacciu@wanadoo.fr; www. stabiacciu.com] Foll ring-rd N198 to S Porto-Vecchio, take 1st L sp Palombaggia. Site in 50m. Med, shd; wc (some cont); shwrs; el pts (10A) €2.80; ice; lndtte; shop in ssn; tradsmn; snacks; bar; BBQ; playgrnd; mini-golf; sand beach nrby; 3% statics; dogs; phone; Eng spkn; cc acc; CCI. "Gd all stays; excel beaches; gd base for exploring region."
1 Apr-20 Oct. € 18.50   2002*

PORTO VECCHIO *10H2* (5km SW) **Camping U Pirellu, Route de Palombaggia**, 20137 Porto-Vecchio [04 95 70 23 44; fax 04 95 70 60 22; u.pirellu@wanadoo.fr] On N198 fr Porto-Vecchio 2km S, L on rte de Palombaggia & site in 6km. Med, hdg pitch, terr; pt shd; wc; chem disp; shwrs; el pts (6A) €2.50; lndtte; ice; shop; rest; snacks; bar; playgrnd; pool; tennis; TV; dogs €0.76; red low ssn; CCI. "Steep slope fr ent gate; gd long/sh stay."
1 Apr-30 Sep. € 21.90   2004*

PORTO VECCHIO *10H2* (8km W Coastal) **Club la Chiappa** (Naturist), 20137 Porto-Vecchio [04 95 70 00 31; fax 04 95 70 07 70; chiappa-club@wanadoo.fr; www.chiappa.com] On N198 fr Bastia heading S thro Porto-Vecchio. 2km S turn L to Ponta de la Chiappa & foll camp sp. Lge, pt shd; wc; chem disp; shwrs; el pts inc; lndtte; ice; shop; rest; bar; playgrnd; pool; sauna; watersports; sand beach; tennis; horseriding; entmnt; TV rm; 10% statics; adv bkg; quiet; red low ssn. "Set in naturist reserve with 3km of private beach." 20 May-7 Oct. € 30.00   2003*

†PROPRIANO *10H2* (2km NE Coastal) **Camping Le Tikiti, Route de Baracci**, 20110 Propriano [04 95 76 08 32; fax 04 95 76 18 25; campingtikiti@fr.st; www.campingtikiti.fr.st] Fr Sartene, take by-pass to Ajaccio; 1km after meeting coast rd, turn R up winding, unmade rd; site in 500m. Lge, pt shd, terr; wc; chem disp; shwrs inc; el pts €3; gas; lndtte; ice; shop high ssn; rest; playgrnd; sand beach 300m; windsurfing 500m; Eng spkn; poss v cr; red low ssn; cc not acc. "Phone to check site open low ssn; facs poss stretched low ssn; superb views fr site; Propriano excel base for S Corsica." € 19.50   2004*

SAGONE *10H2* (2km N) **Camping La Sagone, Route de Vico, 20118 Sagone** [04 95 28 04 15; fax 04 95 28 08 28; sagone.camping@wanadoo.fr; www.camping-sagone.com] Fr Sagone dir Cargese then D70 dir Vico, site sp. Lge, mkd pitch, pt shd; wc; baby facs; shwrs inc; el pts inc; lndtte; ice; shop; rest; snacks; bar; BBQ; playgrnd; pool; beach 1.5km; tennis 100m; horseriding 1km; entmnt; TV rm; 10% statics; dogs €1.75; adv bkg; quiet. ♦ 1 May-30 Sep. € 24.25 (CChq acc)
2004*

ST FLORENT *10G2* (500m W Coastal) **Camping U Pezzo, Route de la Plage, 20217 St Florent** [tel/fax 04 95 37 01 65; jean-marc.wohlgemuth@wanadoo.fr] Exit St Florent for L'Ile-Rousse on N199. After 2km sharp R immed after x-ing bdge. Med, pt shd; wc (cont); shwrs; el pts (10A) €3; lndtte; shop; snacks; bar; beach adj; fishing; sailing; windsurfing; waterslide; horseriding; CCI. "Sh walk to town." 1 Apr-15 Oct. € 13.00
2003*

ST FLORENT *10G2* (2.5km W Coastal) **Camping Kalliste, 20217 St Florent** [04 95 37 03 08; fax 04 95 37 19 77] Fr St Florent twd L'Ile-Rousse on N199, after 2km sharp R immed after x-ing bdge. Site sp in 500m. Lge, unshd; wc; mv service pnt; shwrs inc; el pts (10A) €3; lndry rm; lndtte; ice; shop high ssn; rest; snacks; bar; tennis; horseriding; rv beach; fishing; sailing; windsurfing; poss cr; adv bkg; CCI. 1 Apr-30 Sep. € 20.00
2002*

SARTENE *10H2* (5km N Rural) **Camping Olva Les Eucalyptus, Route de la Castagna, 20100 Sartene** [04 95 77 11 58 or 04 95 77 14 09; fax 04 95 77 05 68] Fr Sartene, take D69 twd Ste Lucie, site in 5km. Med, pt sl, pt shd; wc; shwrs; el pts (6A); gas; shop; rest; beach 8km; adv bkg; quiet. "V friendly." 1 Apr-30 Sep. € 15.30   2002*

SERRA DI FERRO see Porto Pollo *10H2*

VENACO *10G2* (4km E Rural) **Camping La Ferme de Peridundellu, 20231 Venaco** [tel/fax 04 95 47 09 89] S on N200 fr Corte for 15km; R on D143; at bdge keep R towards Venaco; site on L in 1.5km on bend. Sm, pt sl, pt shd; htd wc; chem disp (wc); shwrs inc; el pts (6-10A) inc; lndtte; ice; shop 2km; tradsmn; rest; snacks & bar 2km; quiet; cc acc; CCI. "CL-type site; beautifully situated; gd walking country; friendly owner whose wife cooks evening meals in rest." € 18.00   2005*

VIVARIO *10G2* (5km N) **Aire Naturelle Le Soleil (Marietti), Tattone, 20219 Vivario** [04 95 47 21 16 or 04 95 47 23 08] N fr Ajaccio on N193 twds Corte. Well sp by the stn in Tattone. Sm, hdstg, terr, shd; wc; chem disp; shwrs; el pts inc; ice; pizzeria; fishing; quiet. "Nice, clean site; superb views; train to Corte & Ajaccio stops on request; ideal walking; friendly owners; sm area for tourers; facs stretched high ssn; ring ahead low ssn; excel long/sh stay." 1 Jun-30 Oct. € 16.00   2003*

ILE DE RE

ARS EN RE *7A1* (300m Coastal) **Airotel Le Cormoran, Route de Radia, 17590 Ars-en-Re** [05 46 29 46 04; fax 05 46 29 29 36; info@cormoran.com; www.cormoran.com] Fr La Rochelle take D735 onto Ile-de-Re, site sp fr Ars-en-Re. Med, hdg/mkd pitch, hdstg, pt shd; wc; chem disp; mv service pnt; baby facs; sauna; shwrs inc; el pts (10A) €4.50; lndtte; ice; shop 800m; tradsmn; rest; snacks; bar; playgrnd; htd pool; beach 500m; tennis; cycle hire; games area; games rm; golf 10km; entmnt; some statics; dogs €4; Eng spkn; adv bkg; quiet; cc acc; CCI. "Delightful vill; vg site." ♦ 3 Apr-3 Oct. € 36.75   2003*

COUARDE SUR MER, LA see St Martin de Re *7A1*

> Will you fill in the site report forms at the back of the guide, or shall I?

PORTES EN RE, LES *7A1* (800m E Urban/Coastal) **Camping La Providence, Route de la Trousse-Chemise, 17880 Les Portes-en-Re** [05 46 29 56 82; fax 05 46 29 61 80; campingprovidence@wanadoo.fr; www.campingprovidence.com] On N11 & N137 to La Rochelle foll sp to Ile de Re. Cross toll bdge & foll D735 to Les Portes-en-Re at far end of island. Site adj to Plage de la Redoute. Lge, hdg/mkd pitch, pt shd; htd wc (few cont); chem disp; mv service pnt; baby facs; shwrs inc; el pts (10A) €4.50; gas; lndtte; shop; rest; snacks; bar; playgrnd; sand beach adj; sailing, watersports, tennis, golf nrby; cycle hire; games rm; mini-golf; 50% statics; dogs €3.50; poss cr; Eng spkn; adv bkg; CCI. "Easy access to beach & town; gd, flat cycling on island & across bdge to mainland; lge pitches." ♦ 1 Apr-15 Oct. € 25.00 (3 persons)
2005*

See advertisement on next page

ST CLEMENT DES BALEINES *7A1* (Coastal) **Airotel La Plage, 17590 St Clement-des-Baleines** [05 46 29 42 62; fax 05 46 29 03 39; info@la-plage.com; www.la-plage.com or www.cormaran.com] Fr La Rochelle on D735 to far end of Ile de Re; site 500m fr Baleines lighthouse, sp. Med, hdg/mkd pitch, hdstg, unshd; htd wc (some cont); chem disp; mv service pnt; baby facs; fam bthrm; shwrs inc; el pts (10A) €4.50; gas 1km; lndtte; ice; shop 1.5km; tradsmn; rest; snacks; bar; playgrnd; htd pool; sand beach adj; games area; games rm; cycle hire; entmnt; child entmnt; dogs €5; Eng spkn; adv bkg; quiet; cc acc; red low ssn; CCI. "Delightful vill; excel facs for families; vg." ♦ 3 Apr-3 Oct. € 36.75 (3 persons)   2003*

FRANCE

ST CLEMENT DES BALEINES *7A1* (Coastal) **Camping La Cote Sauvage (formerly Municipal),** 336 Rue de la Foret, 17590 St Clements-des-Baleines [05 46 29 46 63; fax 05 46 29 49 72] Fr cent of vill, foll sp to site at edge of forest. Lge, mkd pitch, pt sl, pt shd; wc; chem disp; mv service pnt; baby facs; shws inc; el pts (10A) €3.70; shop 300m; sand beach adj; cycle routes adj; sw; dogs €1.50; phone; quiet; Eng spkn; CCI. "Gd location; excel san facs." ♦ 1 Apr-15 Oct. € 12.50   2005*

ST MARTIN DE RE *7A1* (2km SE Coastal) **Camping Les Peupliers,** 17630 La Flotte-en-Re [05 46 09 62 35; fax 05 46 09 59 76; camping@ lespeupliers.com; www.les-peupliers.com] Site sp fr D735. Lge, pt shd, wc; chem disp; shws inc; el pts (5A) inc; lndtte; shop; snacks; playgrnd; pool; sand beach 800m; games area; entmnt; TV; 80% statics; dogs €4; adv bkg; CCI. "Sea views; gd sports facs." 1 May-17 Sep. € 28.00 (3 persons)   2005*

ST MARTIN DE RE *7A1* (5km SE Coastal) **Camping Antioche, Route de Ste Marie, 17580 Le Bois-Plage-en-Re** [05 46 09 23 86; fax 05 46 09 43 34; camping. antioche@wanadoo.fr; www.antioche.com] Fr toll bdge fr La Rochelle, at 1st rndabt take D201 sp Le Bois-Plage. In about 9km, site on L. Med, hdg/mkd pitch (sandy), pt shd; wc; chem disp; mv service pnt; shws inc; el pts (6A) inc; lndtte; shop & 3km; playgrnd; snacks; bar; sand beach adj; entmnt; some statics; dogs €4; phone; poss cr; Eng spkn; adv bkg (dep req); cc acc; red long stay/CCI. "Direct access to beach & cycle path; friendly staff; v clean facs." ♦ 9 Apr-24 Sep. € 33.00 (3 persons)   2005*

ST MARTIN DE RE *7A1* (5km SE Rural) **Camping La Grainetiere, Route St Martin, 17630 La Flotte** [05 46 09 68 86; fax 05 46 09 53 13; lagrainetiere@ free.fr; www.la-grainetiere.com] 10km W fr toll bdge, site sp on La Flotte ring rd. Med, pt shd; wc; chem disp; mv service pnt; baby facs; shwrs inc; el pts (10A) €3.50; gas; lndtte; shop; tradsmn; playgrnd; htd pool; sand beach 3km; cycle hire; TV rm; 70% statics; dogs €2.50; poss cr; Eng spkn; adv bkg; CCI. "Beautiful wooded site kept spotlessly clean; generous pitches; immac refurbished san facs; helpful owners." ♦ 15 Mar-15 Nov. € 20.00   2004*

ST MARTIN DE RE *7A1* (7km SE Coastal) **Camp Municipal La Cote Sauvage, La Basse Benee** 17740 Ste Marie-de-Re [05 46 30 21 74; fax 05 46 30 15 64; info@mairie-sainte-marie-de-re. fr] Fr vill cent, foll sp to site. Med, mkd pitch, pt shd; wc; chem disp; mv service pnt; shwrs inc; el pts (10A) €2.50; shop; snacks; bar playgrnd; sand beach adj; boat hire; fishing; Eng spkn; quiet; CCI. "Excel location; highly rec site; many cycle tracks." 1 Jun-22 Sep. € 12.00   2002*

ST MARTIN DE RE *7A1* (800m S Urban) **Camp Municipal Les Remparts, Rue les Remparts, 17410 St Martin-de-Re** [05 46 09 21 96; fax 05 46 09 94 18; camping.stmartindere@wanadoo.fr] Foll D735 fr toll bdge to St Martin; sp in town fr both ends. Med, hdg/mkd pitch, pt sl, pt shd; wc; chem disp; mv service pnt; shwrs inc; el pts (10A) inc; lndtte; shop; snacks; BBQ; playgrnd; pool 3km; sand beach 1.3km; dogs €1.55; Eng spkn; adv bkg; quiet; CCI. "Lovely port vill; ltd facs low ssn; some pitches boggy in wet weather; excel cycling on island." ♦ 12 Feb-15 Nov. € 14.50 (3 persons)   2005*

ST MARTIN DE RE *7A1* (3km SW Coastal) **Parc Club Interlude, Plage de Gros Jonc, 17580 Le Bois-Plage-en-Re** [05 46 09 18 22; fax 05 46 09 23 38; infos@interlude.fr; www.interlude.fr] Fr toll bdge at La Rochelle foll D201 to Gros Jonc. Turn L at rndabt at site sp. Site 400m on L. Lge, mkd pitch, hdstg, pt shd; htd wc; chem disp; mv service pnt; baby facs; sauna; shwrs inc; el pts (10A) €4; gas; lndtte; shop; rest; snacks; bar; BBQ; playgrnd; 2 pools (1 htd, covrd); sand beach; watersports; jacuzzi; solarium; tennis nr; games area; boat & cycle hire; fitness rm; child entmnt; TV rm; 45% statics; dogs €7; poss cr; Eng spkn; o'night spaces/facs for m'vans; adv bkg ess; quiet. "Excel, v quiet, relaxing site; mature trees & birdsong; well-run & customer oriented; cramped, sandy pitches - extra for lger pitches; nrby sandy beaches excel." ♦ 3 Apr-19 Sep. € 27.50 (CChq acc)   2005*

ST MARTIN DE RE *7A1* (6km W) **Camping de l'Ocean, 17670 La Couarde-sur-Mer [05 46 29 87 70; fax 05 46 29 92 13; campingde locean@wanadoo.fr; www.campingocean.com]** Fr La Rochelle take D735 over bdge to Ile de Re. Past St Martin-de-Re & La Couarde. Site on R, 2.5km after La Couarde. Lge, mkd pitch, shd; wc; chem disp; mv service pnt; baby facs; shwrs inc; el pts (5-10A) €3.50-4.90; lndtte; shop; rest; snacks; bar; playgrnd; htd pool; paddling pool; sand beach adj; watersports; tennis; games area; cycle hire; horseriding 1.5km; golf 6km; 40% statics; dogs €4.30; poss cr; adv bkg; rd noisy. "Spacious site; lge, well-laid out pitches, but site rds & ent to pitches v narr; twin-axles not rec; friendly staff; busy holiday area; St Martin v pretty; excel." ♦ 1 Apr-30 Sep. € 36.00 (3 persons) (CChq acc)
2005*

STE MARIE DE RE see St Martin de Re *7A1*

ST MARTIN DE RE *7A1* (6km W Coastal) **Camping La Tour des Prises, Route d'Ars, 17670 La Couarde-sur-Mer [05 46 29 84 82; fax 05 46 29 88 99; camping@lesprises.com; www.camping-la-tour-des-prises.com]** Fr toll bdge foll D735 or D201 to La Couarde, then Rte d'Ars for 1.8km to R turn; site sp & 200m on R. Med, hdg/mkd pitch, pt shd; wc; chem disp; mv service pnt; shwrs inc; el pts (16A) inc; lndtte; ice; shop; tradsmn; playgrnd; htd, covrd pool; beach 600m; sailing school; games rm; cycle hire in vill; 30% statics; dogs €2; adv bkg; quiet; red low ssn; CCI. "Excel site; v clean; lge indiv pitch; many cycle/walking tracks; all watersports on island; beach 10 mins walk; helpful owner & staff." 1 Apr-30 Sep. € 34.10 (3 persons)   2005*

ILE D'OLERON

BREE LES BAINS, LA *7A1* (Coastal) **Camp Municipal Le Planginot, Allee du Gai Sejour, 17840 La Bree-les-Bains [05 46 47 82 18; fax 05 46 75 90 74]** N fr St Pierre d'Oleron on D734, turn R for La Bree on D273, site sp. Lge, mkd pitch, pt shd; wc; shwrs; el pts (5A) €2; lndtte; snacks; rest in high ssn; playgrnd; pool; beach adj; adv bkg; quiet. "Immac facs; gd location for beach & cycle path." ♦ 15 Mar-15 Oct. € 10.80   2004*

BREE LES BAINS, LA *7A1* (3km NW Coastal) **Camp Municipal, Blvd d'Antioche, 17650 St Denis-d'Oleron [05 46 47 85 62; fax 05 46 47 81 51]** Clear sp fr D734 in St Denis-d'Oleron town cent. Lge, mkd pitch, pt shd; htd wc; mv service pnt; shwrs inc; el pts (6A) €3.40; gas; lndtte; ice; shop; rest; snacks; playgrnd; pool; sand beach adj; fishing; tennis; dogs €1.75; poss cr; quiet. "Gd facs; some pitches v soft; ideal for beach holiday with children." 15 Mar-15 Oct. € 12.05 (3 persons)   2005*

CHATEAU D'OLERON, LE *7B1* (1km W Coastal) **Airotel Domaine d'Oleron, Domaine de Montravail, 17480 Le Chateau- d'Oleron [05 46 47 61 82; fax 05 46 47 79 67; info@camping-airotel-oleron.com; www.camping-airotel- oleron.com]** Clearly sp fr D734 after x-ing bdge. Med, mkd pitch, pt shd; wc; shwrs inc; el pts (10A) €3.80 (poss rev pol); gas; lndtte; ice; shop & 500m; snacks; bar; BBQ; playgrnd; htd pool; sand beach 1km; fishing; tennis; horseriding; games area; cycle hire; some statics; dogs €2.40; poss cr; Eng spkn; adv bkg; quiet; red low ssn/CCI. ♦ 1 Apr-15 Oct. € 21.00
2005*

CHATEAU D'OLERON, LE *7B1* (2.5km NW Coastal) **Camping La Brande, Route des Huitres, 17480 Le Chateau-d'Oleron [05 46 47 62 37; fax 05 46 47 71 70; info@camping-labrande.com; www.camping-labrande.com]** Fr Chateau-d'Oleron stay on D734 to La Gaconnierre D240 NE to site. Lge, shd; wc; mv service pnt; baby facs; sauna; steam room; shwrs inc; el pts (6-10A) €3.20-4; gas; lndtte; shop; rest in ssn; snacks; bar; BBQ; playgrnd; 3 pools (1 htd, covrd); waterslide; sand beach 300m; tennis; mini-golf; games area; golf 6km; entmnt; TV rm; 60% statics; dogs €2.50; Eng spkn; adv bkg; quiet; red low ssn. "V pleasant owners; gd rest on site; 10 min cycle ride into town." 15 Mar-15 Nov. € 26.00 (CChq acc)   2004*

ST GEORGES D'OLERON *7A1* (Rural) **CHADOTEL Camping Le Domaine d'Oleron, La Jousseliniere, 17190 St Georges -d'Oleron [05 46 76 54 97 or 02 51 33 05 05 (LS); fax 02 51 33 94 04; chadotel@wanadoo.fr; www. camping-chadotel.fr]** Foll sp to St Georges-d'Oleron on D734 to LeClerc rndabt where turn R. At 2nd rndabt turn L twd site, sp. Med, shd; wc; chem disp; baby facs; shwrs inc; el pts (6A) inc; gas; lndtte; shop; snacks; bar; BBQ (gas only); playgrnd; pool; waterslide; sand beach 2.5km; games rm; cycle hire; TV; 25% statics; dogs €2.90; adv bkg; red long stay; quiet; barrier card €15 dep. ♦ 1 Apr-23 Sep. € 27.50 ABS - A41   2005*

ST GEORGES D'OLERON *7A1* (5km E Coastal) **Camping La Gautrelle, Plage des Saumonards, 17190 St Georges-d'Oleron [05 46 47 21 57; fax 05 46 75 10 74; secretariat@campingclub.asso. fr]** Fr viaduct, take D734 to St Pierre. At 3rd traff lts, turn R to Sauzelle, thro vill & L for St Georges & immed to R sp CCDF La Gautrelle (if you pass a shop/bar you've gone too far). Site is end of lane in approx 1.5km & adj to beach. Lge, mkd pitch, shd; wc; shwrs inc; el pts (4A) inc (long cable req); shops adj; sand beach; fishing; dogs €1; adv bkg; quiet; CCI. "Splendid beaches; forest walks, fishing; ltd el pts." 28 Mar-30 Sep. € 16.60   2003*

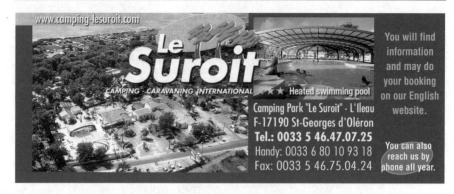

ST GEORGES D'OLERON *7A1* (6km E Coastal)
Camping Signol, Ave des Albatros, Boyardville, 17190 St Georges-d'Oleron [05 46 47 01 22; fax 05 46 47 23 46; contact@signol.com; www.signol.com] Cross bdge onto Ile d'Oleron & cont on main rd twd St Pierre-d'Oleron. Turn R at Dolus-d'Oleron for Boyardville & foll sp in vill. Lge, hdg/mkd pitch, pt sl, pt shd; wc (some cont); mv service pnt; chem disp; baby facs; shwrs inc; el pts; gas; lndtte; shops adj; tradsmn; bar; playgrnd; htd pool; paddling pool; sand beach 800m; some statics; Eng spkn; adv bkg. "Ltd facs low ssn." ♦ 1 Apr-30 Sep. 2005*

ST GEORGES D'OLERON *7A1* (2km SE) Camping Verebleu, La Jousseliniere, 17190 St Georges-d'Oleron [05 46 76 57 70; fax 05 46 76 70 56; verebleu@wanadoo.fr; www.verebleu.tm.fr] Foll D734 thro St Pierre-d'Oleron. On NW o'skts of town at St Gilles turn R (sp La Jousseliniere), cross over D273. After 1km take 1st turn L (sp St Georges, La Jousseliniere). Site 500m on L. Lge, hdg/mkd pitch, pt shd; wc (some cont); chem disp; mv service pnt; shwrs inc; el pts (4-8A) €3.50-€4; gas; lndtte; ice; sm shop; supmkt 1.5km; rest; snacks; bar; playgrnd; htd pool; sand beach 3km; entmnt; 30% statics; dogs €3.20; poss cr; adv bkg ess high ssn (30% dep req + bkg fee); quiet; cc acc; CCI. "V efficient management; excel; Oleron is a sm, unspoilt island; lovely beaches; gd for families." ♦ ltd. 15 May-12 Sep. €23.00 2003*

ST GEORGES D'OLERON *7A1* (3km W Coastal)
Camping Le Suroit, L'Ileau, 17190 St Georges-d'Oleron [05 46 47 07 25 or 06 80 10 93 18 (mob); fax 05 46 75 04 24; camping@lesuroit.fr; www.camping-lesuroit.com] Fr Domino cent foll sp for beach, turn L for L'Ileau. Strt at x-rds. Fork L for La Cotiniere, 150m site on R. Lge, mkd pitch, shd; htd wc; baby facs; shwrs inc; el pts (10A) €4; gas; lndtte; ice; shop; rest; snacks; bar; playgrnd; htd, covrd pool; sand beach adj; tennis; games area; cycle hire; entmnt; TV; some statics; dogs €3; adv bkg; quiet; red low ssn. "Excel site." ♦ 1 Apr-30 Sep. € 21.00 2005*

See advertisement

ST GEORGES D'OLERON *7A1* (3km W Coastal)
Camping Les Grosses Pierres, Les Sables Vigniers, 17190 St Georges-d'Oleron [05 46 76 52 19 or 02 51 27 37 80 (reservation); fax 05 46 76 54 85 or 02 51 28 84 09; vagues-oceanes@wanadoo.fr; www.camping- vagues-oceanes.com] Site sp fr D734. Lge, mkd pitch; terr, pt shd; wc; shwrs inc; el pts (10A) inc; gas; lndtte; shop; rest; snacks; bar; playgrnd; htd, covrd pool; sand beach 900m; 95% statics; Eng spkn; adv bkg; cc acc; CCI. 12 Apr-20 Sep. € 26.00 2003*

ST PIERRE D'OLERON *7B1* (400m N Rural)
Camping La Pierriere, 18 Route de St Georges, 17310 St Pierre-d'Oleron [05 46 47 08 29; fax 05 46 75 12 82; camping-la-pierriere@ewanadoo.fr] On island foll sp into St Pierre. Turn R at 3rd traff lts then L. Sp to La Pierriere-Piscine are clear. Med, mkd pitch, pt shd; some serviced pitch; wc; chem disp; shwrs inc, el pts (4-10A) €3.50-3.80; lndtte; ice; rest; snacks; bar; playgrnd; htd pool; sand beach 4km; dogs €2; poss cr; Eng spkn; adv bkg; quiet; cc acc; CCI. "Gd for cycling; daily mkt in town; some facs clsd Sep." ♦ 5 Apr-19 Sep. € 20.20 2002*

ST PIERRE D'OLERON *7B1* (3km W Coastal)
Camping La Perroche Leitner, 18 Rue de Renclos de la Perroche, 17310 St Pierre-d'Oleron [05 46 75 37 33; fax 05 49 85 12 57] Site about 10km fr bdge on W coast of Ile d'Oleron. Fr bdge foll sp to Grande Village/Vert-Bois/La Remigeasse & La Perroche. Well sp. Med, hdg/mkd pitch, hdstg, terr, pt shd; wc; mv service pnt; shwrs inc; el pts (5A) inc; gas; lndtte; ice; shop; tradsmn; playgrnd; direct access sand beach 200m; games area; Eng spkn; quiet; cc acc. ♦ 1 Jun-15 Sep. € 25.00 2005*

ST TROJAN LES BAINS *7B1* (1km SW Coastal)
Camp Municipal Montplaisir, Ave Les Bris, 17370
St Trojan-les-Bains [05 46 76 01 03 or
05 46 76 00 30 (Mairie); fax 05 46 76 13 80]
App St Trojan-les-Bains on D126, strt thro rndabt
with figure sculpture & R at next rndabt, site sp. Site
in fork in 1km. Lge, pt sl, pt shd; wc; chem disp;
baby facs; fam bthrm; shwrs inc; el pts (3-6A)
€2.30-3.05; gas 200m; ice; lndtte; shop 200m;
tradsmn; rest; snacks; bar; BBQ; sm playgrnd; sand
beach 1km; horseriding, tennis, cinema & fun park
nrby; dogs; phone; no adv bkg; cc acc; CCI. "Gd
value; site in forest; adequate, clean facs." ♦
1 Jul- 31 Aug. € 10.40   2002*

†**ST TROJAN LES BAINS** *7B1* (1.5km SW Coastal)
Camp Municipal Les Martinets, 11 Ave des Bris,
17370 St Trojan-les-Bains [05 46 76 02 39; fax
05 46 76 42 95; lesmartinets@free.fr; http://monsite.
wanadoo.fr/lesmartinets] Fr D26 cont on toll bdge
rd then L onto D126 to Trojan-les-Bains. Foll sp for
'Campings' & 'Plage' then sp for Gatseau Plage.
Lge, mkd pitch, pt sl, pt shd; wc (few cont); chem
disp; shwrs inc; el pts (6A) €3.15; gas 500m; lndtte;
ice; shops 300m; tradsmn; snacks high ssn;
playgrnd; sand beach 1km; cycle hire; 5% statics;
dogs €1.25; phone; adv bkg dep req; cc acc; CCI.
"Gd site." ♦ ltd. € 11.45   2004*

ST TROJAN LES BAINS *7B1* (1.5km SW)
Camping La Combinette, Ave des Bris, 17370
St Trojan-les-Bains [05 46 76 00 47; fax
05 46 76 16 96; la-combinette@wanadoo.fr]
Fr toll bdge stay on D26 for 1km, L onto D275 & L
onto D126 to St Trojan-les-Bains. Strt ahead at
rndabt with figure sculpture, then R at next rndabt sp
Campings. In 1km turn L at rd fork, site on R in 1km.
Lge, shd; wc; serviced pitches; shwrs inc; el pts
(10A) inc; gas; lndtte; ice; shop; snacks; rest;
playgrnd; beach 2km; cycle hire; entmnt; quiet. "V cr
high ssn & facs stretched." 1 Apr-1 Nov. € 15.40
                                                2002*

FRANCE

FRANCE – NORTH-WEST

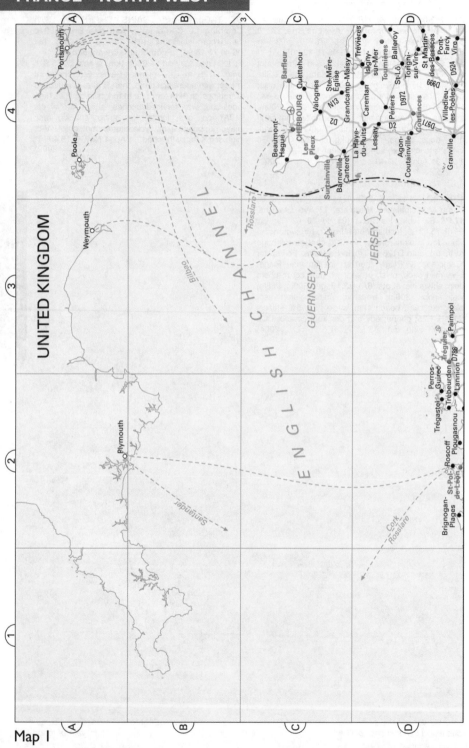

Map 1

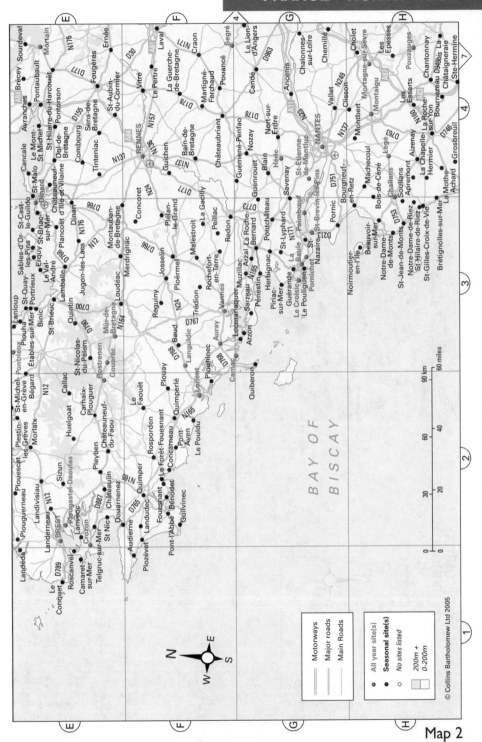

Map 2

© Collins Bartholomew Ltd 2005

FRANCE – CENTRAL

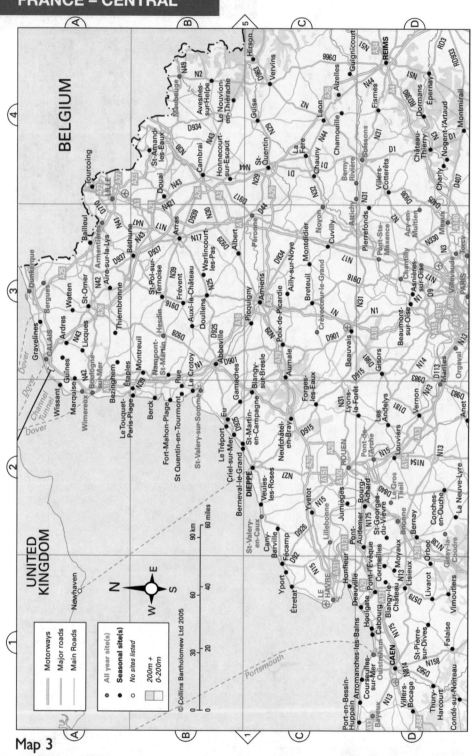

Map 3

© Collins Bartholomew Ltd 2005

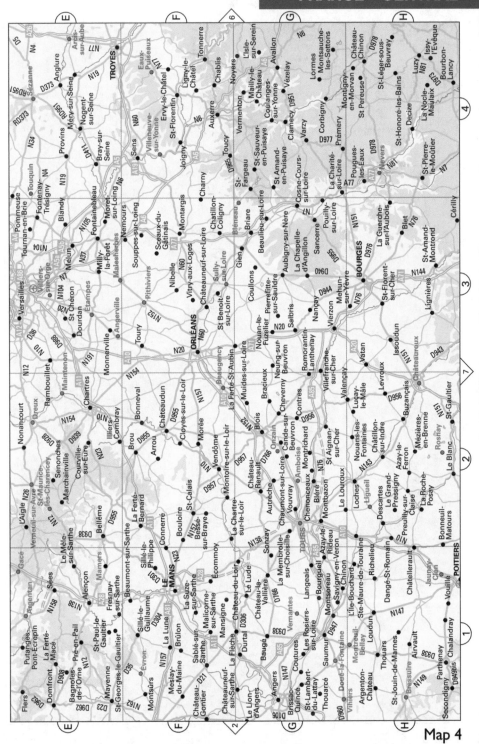

Map 4

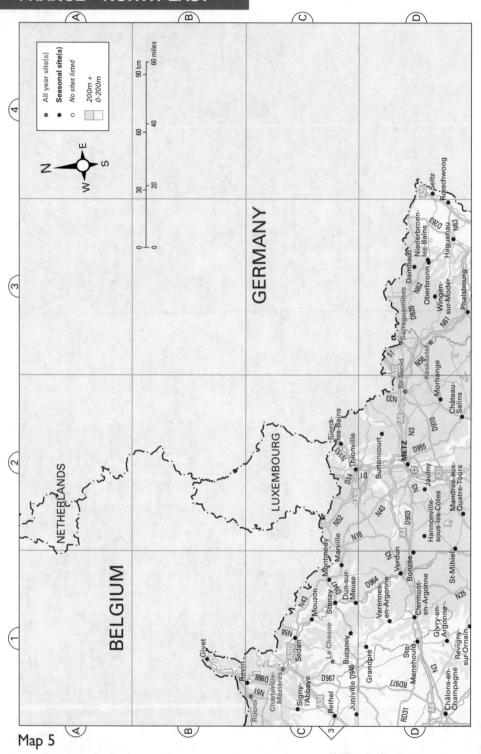

Map 5

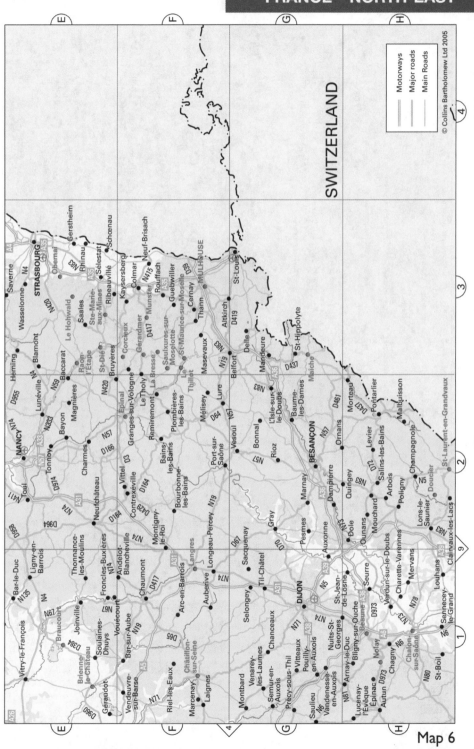

SWITZERLAND

Motorways
Major roads
Main Roads

© Collins Bartholomew Ltd 2005

Map 6

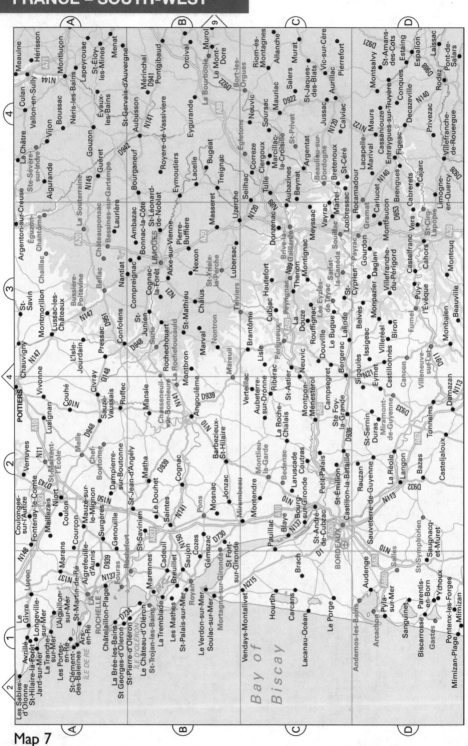

Map 7

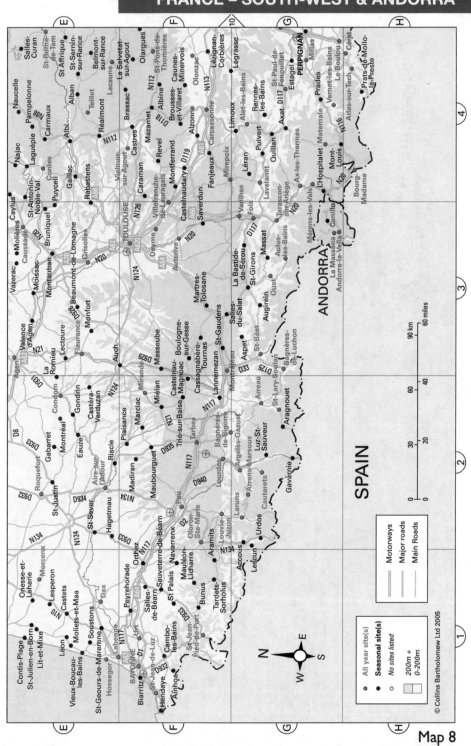

Map 8

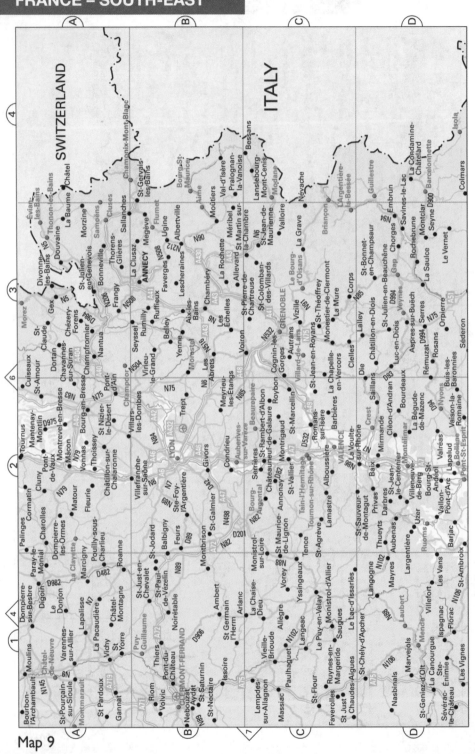

Map 9

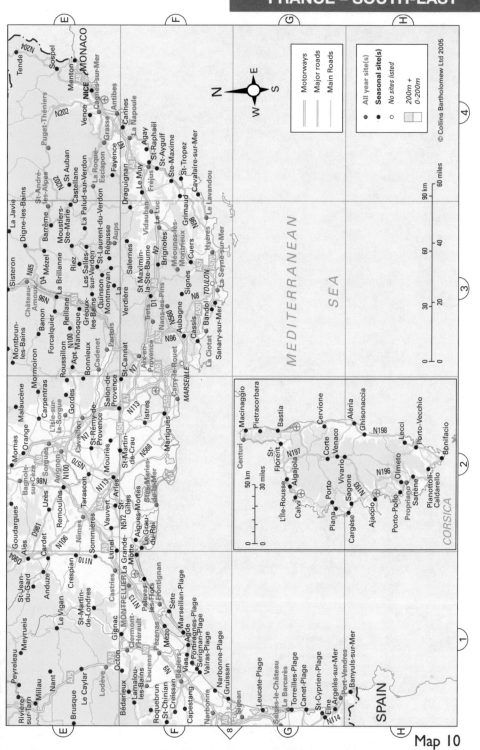

MEDITERRANEAN SEA

CORSICA

SPAIN

Motorways
Major roads
Main Roads

All year site(s)
Seasonal site(s)
No sites listed

200m +
0-200m

Map 10

PORTUGAL

One of the oldest nation-states in Europe and Britain's oldest ally, Portugal has a rich, seafaring history. It is now a modern, forward-looking country and is a founding member of NATO. The diversity of its geography and natural features, together with its mild climate, make Portugal a popular year-round holiday destination.

ESSENTIAL FACTS

Capital: Lisbon (population 2.6 million)
Area: 92,951 sq km (inc Azores and Madeira)
Bordered by: Spain
Terrain: Rolling plains in south; mountainous and forested north of River Tagus
Climate: Temperate climate with no extremes of temperature; wet winters in the north influenced by the gulf stream; elsewhere Mediterranean with hot, dry summers and short, mild winters
Coastline: 1,793 km
Highest Point (mainland Portugal): Monte Torre 1,993 m
Population: 10.5 million
Language: Portuguese
Religion: 97% Roman Catholic
Government: Parliamentary democracy
Local Time: GMT/BST, ie the same as the UK all year
Currency: Euro divided into 100 cents; 1 = € 1.47, € 1 = 67 pence*

TOURIST INFORMATION

PORTUGUESE TOURIST OFFICE
11 BELGRAVE SQUARE
LONDON SW1X 8PP
Tel: 0845 3551212
Personal visits: Mon-Fri 8am-5pm
www.visitportugal.com
info@visitportugal.com

OPENING HOURS

Banks – Mon-Fri 8am-3pm; some banks in city centres also open 6pm-11pm Mon-Sat.

Museums – Tue-Sun 10am-5pm; closed Monday.

Post Offices – Mon-Fri 9am-6pm; in main towns open on Saturday morning.

Shops – Mon-Fri 9am-1pm & 3pm-7pm, Sat 9am-1pm; food shops remain open Mon-Fri until 8pm & during the lunch hour; large supermarkets open Mon-Sat until 10pm & Sunday.

PUBLIC HOLIDAYS 2006

Jan 1; Feb 28 (Carnival); Apr 14, 25 (Day of Liberty); May 1; Jun 10 (Portugal Day), 15; Aug 15; Oct 5 (Republic Day); Nov 1; Dec 1 (Independence Day), 8, 25. Other local holidays and saints' days are celebrated,

according to region, eg Jun 13 in Lisbon (St Anthony), Jun 24 in Porto (St John the Baptist). School summer holidays run from the last week in June to the last week in September.

TELEPHONING AND THE INTERNET

From the UK dial 00351 for Portugal. All numbers have 9-digits, including the area code which starts with a 2. The area code must be dialled even for local calls. To call the UK from Portugal dial 0044, omitting the initial zero of the area code.

Mobile phones – roaming agreements with all major GSM networks; use of hand-held phone is prohibited when driving.

Public phones – international calls from phone boxes with blue and white 'internacional' sign; phones operate with phone cards; some accept credit cards.

Internet – internet cafés in most towns charging € 2.5-€ 5 an hour; internet booths in post offices using pre-paid cards.

Emergency numbers – Police 112; Fire brigade 112; Ambulance 112.

* Exchange rates as at October 2005

The following chapter should be read in conjunction with the important information contained in the Handbook chapters at the front of this guide.

CAMPING AND CARAVANNING

There are approximately 170 campsites in Portugal, many of which are situated along the coast. Sites are rated from 1 to 4 stars. A Camping Card International (CCI) is essential in lieu of a passport at those sites belonging to the Portuguese Camping Federation, and may entitle the holder to a reduction in tariff.

There are 23 Orbitur sites on the Portuguese mainland which are privately owned and of a high standard, as indeed are municipal sites. Orbitur sites are open to all and caravanners can join the Orbitur Camping Club to obtain generous discounts off current rates. Senior citizens may join this Club free, otherwise the cost is € 15. Membership can be arranged at any Orbitur site, or by completing the enrolment form on the Orbitur website or via their head office at:

RUA DIOGO DO COUTO 1-8
P-1149-042 LISBOA
Tel: 00351 21 8117000 Fax: 00351 21 8148045
www.orbitur.pt
info@orbitur.pt

Casual/wild camping is not permitted.

All place names used in the Site Entry listings which follow can be found in Michelin's Touring & Motoring Atlas for Spain & Portugal, scale 1:400,000 (1 cm = 4 km).

Affiliated National Clubs

FEDERAÇAO PORTUGUESA DE CAMPISMO E CARAVANISMO
AVENIDA EDUARDO GALHARDO 24D
P-1199-007 LISBOA
Tel: 21 3642370 Fax: 21 3619284
www.fpcampismo.pt
info@fpcampismo.pt

COUNTRY INFORMATION

Cycling – Transportation of Bicycles

Legislation stipulates that the exterior dimensions of a vehicle should not be exceeded and, in practice, this means that only caravans or motor caravans are allowed to carry bicycles/motorbikes at the rear of the vehicle. Bicycles may not extend beyond the width of the vehicle or more than 45 cms from the back. However, bicycles may be transported on the roof of ordinary cars provided that an overall height of 4 metres is not exceeded. Cars carrying bicycles/motorbikes on the back may be subject to a fine.

If you are planning to travel from Portugal to Spain please note that slightly different regulations apply and these are set out in the Spain Country Introduction.

Electricity and Gas

The power supply in Portugal is 220 volts with a current on campsites of 6 to 15 amps. Plugs have two round pins. CEE connections are commonplace.

The full range of Campingaz cylinders is available.

Entry Formalities

Holders of British and Irish passports may visit Portugal for up to 90 days without a visa. Registration formalities are carried out by campsite reception staff.

Regulations for Pets

See Pet Travel Scheme under Documents in the section PLANNING AND TRAVELLING.

Medical Services

For treatment of minor conditions go to a pharmacy (farmacia). Staff are generally well-trained and are qualified to dispense drugs which may only be available on prescription in Britain. In large towns there is usually at least one pharmacy whose staff speak English. All municipalities have a health centre. A doctor will charge you for treatment but basic emergency hospital treatment is free on production of your British passport. You will have to pay for prescribed medicines as well as dental treatment. Nationals of other EU countries resident in the UK will require a European Health Insurance Card (EHIC).

For serious illness you can obtain the name of an English-speaking doctor from the local police station or tourist office or from a British or American consulate. There is a British hospital in Rua Saraiva de Carvalho, Lisbon.

Normal precautions should be taken to avoid mosquito bites, including minimum possible exposure of the body, use of insect repellents and mosquito nets, especially during the night.

You are strongly recommended to obtain comprehensive travel and medical insurance before travelling to Portugal, such as the Caravan Club's Red Pennant Motoring & Personal Holiday Insurance.

See Medical Matters in the section PLANNING AND TRAVELLING.

Safety and Security

See Safety and Security in the section DURING YOUR STAY.

The crime rate is comparatively low but pickpocketing, bagsnatching and thefts from cars are becoming increasingly common in major tourist areas. Be particularly vigilant on public transport, at crowded tourist sites and in public parks, where it is wise to go in pairs. Keep car windows closed and doors locked while driving in urban areas at night. Pedestrians, particularly the elderly, are advised not to wear valuable jewellery or watches in public areas.

Forest fires occasionally cause road and rail closures. You should be aware of this and be prepared for possible delays. You should be extremely careful when visiting isolated areas in the affected regions and should be guided by local fire service authorities at all times. No smoking is allowed in woodland areas and barbecues should be avoided. Don't waste water during your visit.

Portugal shares with the rest of Europe a threat from international terrorism. Attacks could be indiscriminate and against civilian targets in public places, including tourist sites.

British Embassy

RUA DE SÃO BERNARDO 33, P-1249-082 LISBOA
Tel: 21 3924000
www.uk-embassy.pt
consular@Lisbon.mail.fco.gov.uk

There are also British Consulates in Porto and Portimão.

Irish Embassy

RUA DA IMPRENSA A ESTRELA 1-4, P-1200-684 LISBOA
Tel: 21 3929440

CUSTOMS REGULATIONS

See also Customs Regulations in the section PLANNING AND TRAVELLING.

Caravans and Motor Caravans

Dimensions must not exceed 4 metres in height, 2.50 metres in width, 12 metres in length and combined length of car + caravan of 18 metres.

Currency

Euro exceeding € 12,470 must be declared on arrival. There are no restrictions on the import and export of foreign currency.

DOCUMENTS

See Documents in the section PLANNING AND TRAVELLING.

Proof of Identity

The Portuguese authorities stipulate that proof of identity bearing the holder's photograph and signature (such as a passport, photocard driving licence or International Driving Permit) should be carried at all times. Failure to do so may incur a fine.

You must carry your vehicle registration certificate, proof of insurance and MOT certificate (if appropriate). There are heavy on-the-spot fines for those who fail to do so.

MONEY

- Travellers' cheques may be cashed in banks and are widely accepted as a means of payment in shops, hotels and restaurants displaying the appropriate logo or sign. Commission charges can be high.

- The major credit cards are widely accepted and may be used to obtain cash from machines throughout the country.

- Cardholders are recommended to carry their credit card issuer/bank's 24-hour UK contact number in case of loss or theft.

- Recent visitors report that small change appears to be in short supply and you may well be asked for it in shops.

MOTORING

It is a fact that many Portuguese drive erratically and extreme vigilance is advised. By comparison with the UK, the accident rate is very high. Particular blackspots are the N125 along the south coast, especially in the busy holiday season, and the coast road between Lisbon and Cascais. In rural areas you may encounter horse-drawn carts and flocks of sheep or goats.

There are no special difficulties in driving except for Lisbon and Porto, which are unlimited 'free-for-alls'.

Alcohol

The maximum legal level of alcohol in the blood is less than in the UK, at 0.05%. It is advisable to adopt the 'no drink and drive' rule at all times.

Breakdown Service

The Automovel Club de Portugal (ACP) operates a 24-hour breakdown service covering all roads in mainland Portugal. Its specially equipped vehicles are coloured red and white. Emergency telephones are located at 2 km intervals on main roads and motorways. Visiting motorists in need of assistance are

PORTUGAL

advised to telephone the ACP breakdown service as follows:

- In Lisbon or the region south of Pombal: 21 9429103

- In Porto or north of Pombal: 22 8340001

In Aveiro, Braga, Coimbra, Faro, Grandola, Lisbon, Portimao, Porto, Setúbal and Santarém a special mobile breakdown service is in operation seven days a week.

This service is available to members of AIT and FIA affiliated clubs, such as the Caravan Club, and comprises on-the-spot repairs taking up to a maximum of 45 minutes and, if necessary, the towing of vehicles. The charges for breakdown assistance and towing vary according to distance, time of day and day of the week, plus motorway tolls if applicable. Payment is required in cash.

Police patrols (GNR/Brigada de Transito) can assist motorists on some motorways.

Essential Equipment

Reflectorised Jackets

A driver whose vehicle is immobilised on the carriageway must wear a reflectorised jacket or waistcoat when getting out of the vehicle. Sensibly, any passenger who gets out to assist should also wear one. This rule does not apply to foreign-registered vehicles, but as you will need to buy a reflectorised jacket to comply with Spanish law while driving through Spain to Portugal, it would be sensible to observe the rule in Portugal.

Seat Belts

All passengers must wear a seat belt at all times. Children under 12 years are not allowed to travel in the front passenger seat.

Warning Triangles

It is compulsory to use a warning triangle if, for any reason, a stationary vehicle is not visible for at least 100 metres.

See Equipment and Essential Equipment Table under Motoring in the section PLANNING AND TRAVELLING.

Fuel

See also Fuel under Motoring in the section PLANNING AND TRAVELLING.

Unleaded petrol and diesel are readily available throughout the country. Super petrol with a lead substitute has replaced leaded petrol. LPG is available, but filling stations may be few and far between. Credit cards are accepted at most filling stations but a small extra charge may be made. There are no automatic petrol pumps.

Mountain Roads and Passes

There are no mountain passes or tunnels in Portugal. Roads through the Serra da Estrela near Guarda and Covilha may be temporarily obstructed for short periods after heavy snow; otherwise motorists will encounter no difficulty in motoring during winter.

Parking

There are no road markings indicating parking restrictions but parking is prohibited near intersections, pedestrian crossings, tram or bus stops and illegally parked vehicles may be clamped or towed away. Vehicles must be parked facing in the direction of traffic. Blue zone parking areas operate in Lisbon and there are parking meters in the centre of main towns.

Parking for the Disabled

On roads and in car parks, parking places reserved for disabled people are marked with a wheelchair symbol. Do not park if a space is marked with a name or vehicle registration number.

Do not park on roads where parking is prohibited. You must pay to park on roads where payment is required and must not exceed the time paid for. You must not exceed time limits on roads where time restrictions apply. Do not drive or park in pedestrian zones. Car parks do not generally offer concessions.

See also Parking Facilities for the Disabled under Motoring in the section PLANNING AND TRAVELLING.

Priority

In general, at intersections and road junctions, road users must give way to vehicles approaching from the right. At roundabouts vehicles already on the roundabout have right of way.

Roads

The national roads are surfaced with asphalt, concrete or stone setts. Main roads generally are well-surfaced but not always very wide. Roads in the south of the country are generally in good condition, but, despite recent extensive road improvement schemes, many sections in the north are still in a very poor state. All roads, with the exception of motorways, should be treated with care; even a good section may suddenly deteriorate and potholes may be a hazard. Roads in towns are often cobbled and rough.

Drivers entering Portugal from Zamora in Spain will notice an apparently shorter route on the C527/N221 road via Mogadouro. Although this is actually the signposted route, the road surface is poor in places and this route is not recommended for trailer caravans. The recommended route is via the N122 to Bragança.

Road Signs and Markings

See European Road Signs under Motoring in the section PLANNING AND TRAVELLING.

Road signs conform to international standards. Road markings are white or yellow.

You may be fined on-the-spot for crossing a continuous single or double white or yellow line in the centre of the road when overtaking or when executing a left turn into or off a main road, despite the lack of any other 'no left turn' signs. If necessary, drive on to a roundabout or junction to turn, or turn right as directed by arrows.

Speed Limits

See Speed Limits Table under Motoring in the section PLANNING AND TRAVELLING.

Exceptions

Drivers must maintain a speed between 40 km/h (25 mph) and 60 km/h (37 mph) on the 25th April Bridge over the Tagus. Speed is controlled by radar.

Motor caravans over 3,500 kg are restricted to 50 km/h (31 mph) in built-up areas, 70/80 km/h (44/50 mph) on the open road, and 90 km/h (56 mph) on motorways.

Visitors who have held a driving licence for less than one year must not exceed 90 km/h (56 mph) and must display a '90' disc on the rear of their vehicle. This can be obtained at the frontier.

It is prohibited to use a radar detector or to have one installed in a vehicle.

Towing

Motor caravans are permitted to tow a car on a four-wheel trailer, ie so that all four wheels are off the ground. Towing a car on an A-frame (two back wheels only on the ground) is not permitted.

Traffic Jams

Traffic jams are most likely to be encountered around the two major cities of Lisbon and Porto and on roads to the coast, such as the A1 Lisbon-Porto and the A2 Lisbon-Setúbal, which are very busy on Friday evenings and Saturday mornings. The peak periods for holiday traffic are the last weekend in June and the first and last weekends in July and August.

Around Lisbon bottlenecks occur on the bridges across the Tagus, the road to Cascais, the A1, N10 (Vila Franca de Xira), A8 (Loures and Malveira) and on the secondary road from Setúbal via Almada.

Around Porto you may encounter traffic jams on the Arribada Bridge on the A1, the N1 at Vila Nova de Gaia, the N13 from Póvoa de Varzim and near Vila de Conde, the N12, N13 and the N15.

Major motorways are equipped with suspended signs which indicate the recommended route to take when traffic is disrupted.

Violation of Traffic Regulations

Speeding, illegal parking and other infringements of traffic regulations are heavily penalised. The police are authorised to impose on-the-spot fines and a receipt must be given. Foreign motorists must pay in cash.

MOTORWAYS

Portugal has more than 1,800 km of motorways (auto-estradas) and tolls (portagem) are payable on most sections. It is permitted to spend the night on a motorway rest or service area with a caravan, although the Caravan Club does not recommend this practice for security reasons. It should be noted that toll tickets are only valid for 12 hours and fines are incurred if this period of time is exceeded.

Motorway Tolls

Class 1   Vehicle with or without trailer with height from front axle less than 1.10 m.

Class 2   Vehicle with or without trailer with height from front axle over 1.10 m.

Class 3   Vehicle with 3 axles with height from front axle over 1.10 m.

Class 4   Vehicle with 4 axles with height from front axle over 1.10 m.

(See table on following page)

Toll Bridges

25th April Bridge and Vasco da Gama Bridge

The 2 km long 25th April Bridge in Lisbon crosses the Tagus River. Tolls are charged for vehicles travelling in a south-north direction only. Tolls also apply on the Vasco da Gama Bridge, north of Lisbon, but again only to vehicles travelling in a south-north direction.

PORTUGAL

Road No.	Route	km	Class 1	Class 2	Class 3	Class 4
A1	Lisboa to Porto	304	17.75	31.10	39.85	44.25
A2	Lisboa to Algarve	238	16.80	29.40	37.85	42.05
A3	Porto to Valenca	108	7.15	12.50	16.10	17.95
A4	Porto to Amarente	54	3.35	5.90	7.45	8.35
A5	Lisboa to Cascais	25	1.10	2.20	2.20	2.20
A6	A2 to Caia (Spanish border)	156	10.60	18.65	23.95	26.75
A7	Povoa de Varzim to Guimaraes-Basto	60	4.50	8.00	10.20	11.40
A8	Lisboa to Leiria	131	7.85	13.60	17.40	19.35
A9-A1-A5	Alverca to A5 (Estadio Nacional)	33	2.65	4.55	6.00	6.65
A10	A9 to junction A10/A13 Benavente	8	1.05	1.90	2.40	2.70
A11	Barcelos-Braga (A3) to Guimaraes (A7)	12	1.30	2.20	2.85	3.15
A12	Setúbal to Montijo (Vasco de Gama Bridge)	25	1.70	3.00	3.85	4.30
A13	Almeirim to Marateca (A2/A6)	76	6.00	10.45	13.50	15.05
A14	Figueira da Foz to Coimbra North	38	2.05	3.60	4.55	5.15
A15	Caldas da Rainha to Santarém (A1)	42	3.20	5.55	7.20	7.85
	Vasco da Gama Bridge (S to N)	17	2.00	4.75	7.10	9.25
	25 April Bridge (S to N)	2	1.15	2.85	4.15	5.40

Toll charges in euros. Some exits have automatic tollbooths. Credit cards accepted on the following motorways: A1, A2, A3, A4, A5, A6, A9, A10, A12, A13, A14, otherwise payment in cash.

In case of breakdown, or if you need assistance, you must keep as near to the right-hand side as possible and wait inside your vehicle until a patrol arrives. It is prohibited to carry out repairs, to push vehicles physically or to walk on the bridge. If you run out of petrol, you must wait for a patrol vehicle.

TOURING

- Some English is spoken in large cities and tourist areas. Elsewhere a knowledge of French could be useful.
- A Lisboa Card entitles the holder to free unrestricted access to public transport, free entry to a number of museums, monuments and other places of interest in Lisbon and surrounding area, and discounts in shops and places offering services to tourists. It is obtainable from tourist information offices, travel agents, some hotels and Carris ticket booths.
- Portuguese cuisine is rich and varied and makes the most of abundant, locally grown produce; seafood is particularly good. The national speciality is the bacalhau, dried, salted cod, for which there are 365 recipes, one for each day of the year. Aside from port, many excellent and inexpensive

wines are produced, both red and white, including the famous vinho verde (verde means young and fresh, not green!) Do ensure when eating out that you understand exactly what you are paying for; appetisers put on the table are not free.

- Each town in Portugal devotes several days in the year to local celebrations which are invariably lively and colourful. Carnivals and festivals during the period before Lent, during Holy Week and at wine harvest can be particularly spectacular.

- During the summer months bullfights are generally held each Sunday. In Portugal the bull is not killed.

- Ferry services operate across the Rio Minho, which forms the northern border between Portugal and Spain, at Vila Nova de Cerveira and Monçáo (every 30 minutes between 8am and 10pm) and across the Guadiana river between Vila Real de Santo Antonio and Ayomonte (every 30 minutes between 8am and 7.30pm). Another service operates between Alcoutim and Sanlucar. A bridge (N431) crosses the Guadiana River. The border is open 24 hours a day.

- A passenger and vehicle ferry crosses the Sado estuary from Setúbal to Trioa and there are frequent services for cars and passengers across the Tagus River from Lisbon to Cacilhas, Barreiro, Montijo and Porto Brandao. There is a bridge across the border with Spain on the River Minhos from Salvatierra to Moncao.

PORTUGAL

PORTUGAL

Distances are shown in kilometres and are calculated from town/city centres along the most practicable roads, although not necessarily taking the shortest route.
1km = 0.62 miles

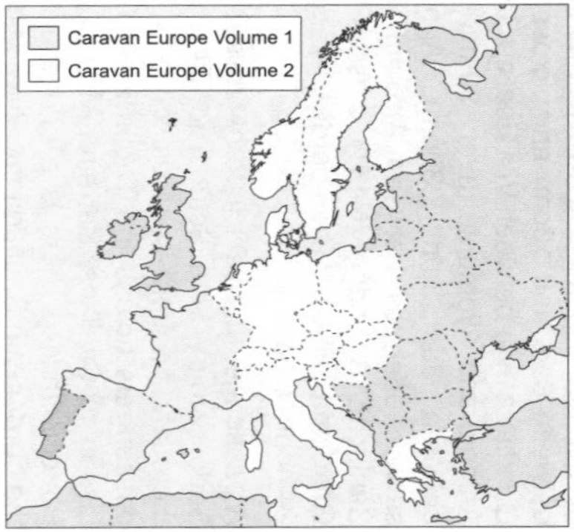

Miranda do Douro to Vila Real de Santo António = 688km

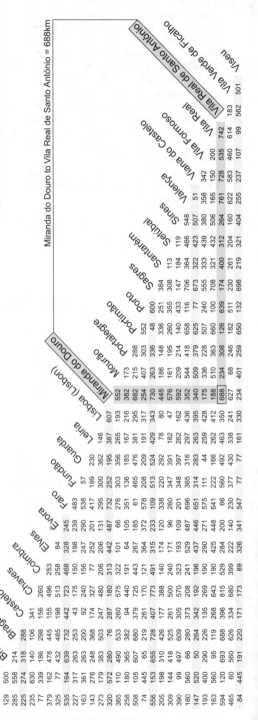

	Aveiro	Beja	Braga	Bragança	Castelo Branco	Chaves	Coimbra	Elvas	Évora	Faro	Fundão	Guarda	Leiria	Lisboa (Lisbon)	Miranda do Douro	Mourão	Portalegre	Portimão	Porto	Sagres	Santarém	Setúbal	Sines	Valença	Viana do Castelo	Vila Formoso	Vila Real	Vila Real de Santo António	Vila Verde de Ficalho
Beja	408																												
Braga	129	500																											
Bragança	285	558	214																										
Castelo Branco	225	274	318	288																									
Chaves	235	630	140	106	341																								
Coimbra	77	339	186	298	156	260																							
Elvas	379	162	478	445	155	496	253																						
Évora	325	77	432	485	198	513	258	84																					
Faro	535	164	639	732	442	723	468	328	245																				
Fundão	227	317	263	253	43	175	150	198	239	483																			
Guarda	163	361	263	200	92	240	156	247	290	538	57																		
Leiria	143	276	248	368	174	327	77	252	201	417	199	230																	
Lisboa (Lisbon)	273	179	383	503	247	480	206	206	131	295	300	362	146																
Miranda do Douro	320	572	280	76	287	180	313	442	487	732	252	195	387	607															
Mourão	365	110	490	533	260	575	322	101	66	276	303	356	265	193	552														
Portalegre	258	180	365	382	94	440	191	64	105	351	136	185	167	216	382	173													
Portimão	508	105	607	680	379	725	443	267	185	61	465	476	381	295	682	215	288												
Porto	74	445	65	219	261	170	121	364	372	578	208	209	191	317	254	407	303	552											
Sagres	556	153	655	728	407	773	491	315	233	109	513	524	429	343	730	263	336	48	600										
Santarém	205	198	310	426	177	388	140	174	120	338	220	292	78	80	445	186	148	336	251	384									
Setúbal	309	144	418	525	261	500	240	171	96	260	347	391	182	47	576	161	195	260	355	308	113								
Sines	390	99	497	609	305	570	323	193	109	201	348	397	262	162	592	209	214	140	433	147	184	119							
Valença	180	560	66	280	373	208	241	529	487	696	365	316	297	436	352	544	418	658	116	706	364	466	548						
Viana do Castelo	147	520	50	264	342	192	196	437	446	651	314	283	263	395	340	509	379	625	77	673	322	423	507	51					
Vila Formoso	193	400	290	226	135	269	190	290	271	575	111	44	259	428	175	336	228	507	240	555	333	439	380	358	342				
Vila Real	163	560	95	119	268	643	190	425	448	641	222	166	262	412	188	510	363	660	100	708	321	432	506	165	150	200			
Vila Real de Santo António	594	120	693	688	396	815	529	284	200	66	560	492	463	350	688	234	308	126	639	174	400	312	264	761	728	535	742		
Vila Verde de Ficalho	465	60	560	626	334	680	399	222	140	230	377	430	338	241	627	68	246	182	511	230	261	204	160	622	583	460	614	183	
Viseu	84	445	191	220	171	173	89	326	341	547	77	77	161	330	234	401	259	650	132	698	219	321	404	255	237	107	99	562	501

SITES IN PORTUGAL

†ABRANTES *B3* (2km S Urban) **Clube de Campismo de Abrantes, Travessa do Cavaco, no. 2, 2205-059 Rossio ao Sul do Tejo [(241) 331743]** Exit IP6 sp Abrantes & foll sp Rossio ao Sul do Tejo. Head S thro Abrantes & cross Rv Tejus on N2 & turn L at traff island down hill to rv. Site in 200m on R, (walled). Sm, pt shd; wc (own san rec); chem disp (wc); shwrs inc; el pts (9A) €1.25; Indry rm; shop, rest, snacks, bar 200m; BBQ; playgrnd; pool 200m; rv sw adj; fishing; canoeing; entmnt high ssn; TV rm; no statics; bus 300m; rlwy stn 600m; poss cr; rd noise; CCI. "Friendly, helpful warden; unmkd pitches; san facs poss neglected low ssn." € 7.50   2005*

We're having a great holiday - must fill in some site report forms and send them to The Club as soon as possible.

ABRANTES MARTINCHEL see Tomar *B2*

AGUEDA *B2* (6km S Rural) **Club de Campismo de Aguada de Baixo, Largo do Rossio, 3780-031 Aguada de Baixo [(234) 666327]** S on rd IC2, site sp at S end of vill of Aguada de Baixo. Med, pt shd; wc; chem disp; mv service pnt; shwrs inc; el pts (4A) inc; shop 500m; bar; rest 1.5km; snacks; bar; BBQ; playgrnd; pool; fishing; boating 5km; TV; bus 500m; Eng spkn; quiet. "Friendly staff; adj typical farming vill." 1 Apr-30 Sep. € 9.00   2004*

ALANDROAL *C3* (13km S Rural) **Camping Rosario, Monte das Mimosas, Rosario, 7250-999 Alandroal [(268) 459566; info@campingrosario.com; www.campingrosario.com]** Fr E exit IP7/A6 at Elvas W junc 9; at 3rd rndabt take exit sp Espanha, immed 1st R dir Juromenha & Redondo. Onto N373 until exit Rosario. Fr W exit IP7/A6 junc 8 at Borba onto N255 to Alandroal, then N373 E sp Elvas. After 1.5km turn R to Rosario & foll sp to site. Sm, hdstg, pt sl, pt shd; wc; chem disp; shwrs inc; el pts (6A) €2.10; gas 2km; Indtte; ice; shop 2km; tradsmn; rest; bar; playgrnd; pool; lake sw adj; boating; fishing; TV; no statics; dogs €1 (not acc Jul/Aug); Eng spkn; adv bkg; quiet; red long stay/low ssn; CCI. "Remote new site being developed by enthusiastic young Dutch couple beside Alqueva Dam; excel touring base; ltd to 50 people max." 15 Mar-15 Oct. € 12.10   2004*

†ALBUFEIRA *B4* (2km NE Urban) **Camping Albufeira, Estrada de Ferreiras, 8200-555 Albufeira [(289) 587629 or 587630; fax (289) 587633; campingalbufeira@mail.telepac.pt; www.roteiro-campista.pt/Faro/albufeir.htm]** Exit IP1/E1 sp Albufeira onto N125. Turn R down slip rd sp Albufeira; camp on L approx 1km. NB Care needed with speed bumps at barrier. V lge, some mkd pitch, terr, pt shd, htd wc; chem disp; mv service pnt; shwrs inc; el pts (10A) €2.75; gas; Indtte; ice; shop; supmkt; rest; snacks; bar; playgrnd; 3 pools; sand beach 2km; tennis; sports park; cycle hire; disco (soundproofed); entmnt; TV; 70% statics; dogs; phone; car wash; cash machine; security patrols; dep for barrier key; poss cr; Eng spkn; no adv bkg; some rd noise; cc acc; long stay/low ssn red up to 50%; red 10% CCI. "Friendly, secure site; excel pool area/rest/bar; excel, modern, clean san facs; some pitches lge enough for US RVs; pitches on lower part of site prone to flooding in heavy rain; conv beach & town; poss lge rallies during Jan-Apr; camp bus to town." ♦€ 21.45   2005*

See advertisement below

PORTUGAL

*Last year of report

†ALBUFEIRA *B4* (10km W Rural) **Camping Canelas, Alcantarilha,** 8365-908 Armacao de Pera [(282) 312612 or 314718; fax (282) 314719; turismovel@mail.telepac.pt www.roteiro-campista.pt/Faro/canelas.htm] Fr Lagos take N125, turn R (S) at Alcantarilha twd Armacao de Pera, site in 1.5km on R. Fr IP1/A22 Algarve coastal m'way, take Alcantarilha exit & turn L on N125 into vill, turn R at traff lts. Site on R in 1.5km just bef 2nd rndabt. V lge, pt sl, pt shd; wc; chem disp; mv service pnt; shwrs €0.50; el pts (5-10A) €2.75-3.50; gas; lndtte; ice; shop in ssn; rest; snacks; bar; playgrnd; 3 solar htd pools; sand beach 1.5km; tennis; entmnt; 5% statics; dogs; phone; poss cr; Eng spkn; cc not acc; red low ssn & long stay; CCI. "Vg security at ent; excel cent for Algarve; v popular in winter; spacious & shady site; check el pts bef using." ♦ € 17.00   2005*

See advertisement above

This site entry hasn't been updated for a while; we'd better fill in a site report form and send it to The Club.

†ALBUFEIRA *B4* (10.5km W Coastal) **Parque de Campismo de Armacao de Pera,** 8365-184 Armacao de Pera [(282) 312260; fax (282) 315379; www.roteiro-campista.pt/Faro/armpera.htm] Fr Lagos take N125 coast rd E. At Alcantarilha turn S, sp Armacao de Pera & Campismo. Site in 2km on L. V lge, pt sl, shd; wc; chem disp; mv service pnt; shwrs inc; el pts (6-10A) €2.50-4; gas; lndtte; shop; rest; snacks; bar; playgrnd; pool & paddling pool; sand beach 1km; tennis; cycle hire; games area; entmnt; TV rm; 5% statics; phone; bus adj; car wash; poss cr; Eng spkn; adv bkg; quiet; red low ssn. "Min stay 3 days Oct-May; easy walk to town; friendly, popular & attractive site." ♦ € 20.50   2005*

See advertisement below

†ALCACER DO SAL *B3* (1km NW) **Parque de Campismo Municipal de Alcacer do Sal,** Olival do Outeiro, 7580-125 Alcacer do Sal [(265) 612303; fax (265) 610079; cmalcacer@mail.telepac.pt] Heading S on A2/IP1 turn L twd Alcacer do Sal on N5. Site on R 1km fr Alcacer do Sal. Sp at rndabt. Site behind supmkt. Med, hdg/mkd pitch, pt sl, pt shd; wc; chem disp; mv service pnt; shwrs; el pts (12A) €1.29; gas; ice; lndtte; shops, rest, snacks & bar 50m; BBQ; playgrnd; pool; sand beach 24km; TV rm; dogs; phone; Eng spkn; quiet; red long stay; CCI. "Excel facs but poss grubby; site manager not resident." ♦ € 7.75   2005*

ALCOBACA *B2* (N Urban) **Campismo Municipal de Alcobaca, Avda Joaquim V Natividade, 2460-071 Alcobaca [(262) 582265]** Turn W off A8/ IC1at junc 21 onto N8 Alcobaca. Site on L on ent town, well sp. Lge, hdg pitch, hdstg, pt sl, terr, shd; wc; chem disp; shwrs inc; el pts (3A) €0.90; gas; lndtte; shop 100m, tradsmn; rest, snacks 200m; bar; playgrnd; pool 200m; TV; some statics; bus 200m; poss cr; Eng spkn; some noise fr rd & flats opp; quiet; red low ssn/CCI. "Well-run, clean, tidy site; friendly staff; vg facs; Batalha & monastery worth a visit; fascinating Mon mkt nrby; pleasant sm town with gd rests; bus service to Lisbon." ♦
1 Feb-31 Dec. € 9.05   2005*

ALCOBACA *B2* (3km S Urban) **Camping Silveira, Capuchos, 2460-479 Alcobaca [(262) 509573; silveira.capuchos@clix.pt]** S fr Alcobaca on N 8-6 sp Evora de Alcobaca. Site on L in 3km after Capuchos. Med, hdg pitch, pt shd; wc; shwrs inc; el pts (6A) €1.50; gas; lndtte; shops 1.5km; rest, snacks, bar 1km; pool 3km; sand beach 10km; games rm; no statics; Eng spkn; quiet; CCI. "Vg, wooded, CL-type site; friendly owner; gd views; excel facs; walks; excel touring base."
1 Jun-30 Sep. € 12.00   2004*

†ALJEZUR *B4* (3km N) **Camping Serrao, Herdade so Serrao, 8670-121 Aljezur [(282) 990220; fax (282) 990229; camping-serrao@clix.pt]** Site off N120 to Praia Amoreira & Campsite. Driving fr N 4km after Rogil turn by cafe on R on slight bend. Lge sp 200m bef turn. Driving fr S 4km after Aljezur (camp sp 1.3km). Turn on L. Lge, shd; wc (some cont); chem disp; mv service pnt; shwrs inc; el pts (6A) €2; gas; lndtte; shop 4km; rest; snacks; bar; BBQ; pool; sand beach 3km; tennis; games area; cycle hire; fishing; entmnt; TV; phone; quiet; adv bkg; cc acc; red low ssn; CCI. "No mkd pitches, pitch between lines of trees; helpful owner; gd san facs; much quieter area than S coast." ♦ € 15.10
                    2002*

ALVOR see Portimao *B4*

AMARANTE *C1* (2km NE Rural) **Camping Penedo da Rainha, Rua Pedro Alveollos, Gatao, 4600-099 Amarante [(255) 437630; fax (255) 437353; ccporto@mail.telepac.pt]** Fr IP4 Vila Real to Porto foll sp to Amarante & N15. On N15 cross bdge for Porto & immed take R slip rd. Foll sp thro junc & up rv to site. Lge, mkd pitch, some hdstg, pt sl, terr, shd; wc; chem disp (wc); mv service pnt; shwrs inc; el pts (4A) €1.17; gas 2km; lndtte; shop in ssn & 2km; rest; snacks 100m; bar; playgrnd; sm pool & 3km; rv adj; fishing; canoeing; cycling; entmnt; dogs; phone; bus to Porto fr Amarante; some Eng spkn; adv bkg; quiet; red CCI. "Excel facs but some pitches far fr facs; few touring pitches; well-run site; friendly, helpful recep; in woodland/parkland; plenty of shd; steep slopes - take advice or survey rte bef driving to pitch; conv Amarante old town & Douro Valley; Sat mkt." ♦ 1 Feb-30 Nov. € 11.00   2005*

†ARGANIL *C2* (3km NE Rural) **Camp Municipal de Arganil, 3300-432 Sarzedo [(235) 205706; fax (235) 205423; campingma@hotmail.com; www. cm-arganil.pt]** Fr Coimbra on N17 twd Guarda; after 50km turn S sp Arganil on N342-4; site on L in 4km in o'skts of Sarzedo bef rv bdge; avoid Gois to Arganil rd fr SW. Med, terr, shd; wc; mv service pnt; shwrs inc; el pts (5-15A) €2.20; gas; lndtte; ice; shop 100m; rest; snacks; bar; playgrnd; rv sw, fishing & canoeing adj; ski in Serra da Estrela 50km Dec/Jan; TV; phone; Eng spkn; quiet; red low ssn/long stay/snr citizens; cc acc; CCI. "Vg, well-run site; friendly owner; fine views; gd cent for touring."
€ 8.40   2002*

ARMACAO DE PERA see Albufeira *B4*

†AVEIRO *B2* (3km S Coastal) **Parque de Campismo Gafanha da Nazare, Rua dos Balnearios do C. Despostivo, 3830-640 Gafanha da Nazare [(234) 366565; fax (234) 365789]** Exit Gafanha da Encarnacao, 3km S of Aveiro. Foll Campismo sp. Lge, hdstg, pt shd; wc; own san rec; shwrs inc; el pts (4A) €0.95; gas; ice; shop 1km; rest; snacks; bar; playgrnd; pool 2km; sand beach 3km; fishing; canoeing; cycle hire; entmnts; TV; quiet; 90% statics; CCI. "Gd security; gd." ♦ ltd.
€ 6.82   2004*

†AVEIRO *B2* (6km SW Coastal) **Camping Costa Nova, Quinta dos Patos, 3830 Gafanha da Encarnacao, Ilhavo [(234) 393220; fax (234) 394791; info@campingcostanova.com; www.campingcostanova.com]** Site on Barra-Vagueira coast rd 1km on R after Costa Nova. V lge, mkd pitch, terr, pt shd; htd wc; chem disp; mv service pnt; shwrs inc; el pts (2-6A) €2.20; gas; lndtte; shop & 1.5km; tradsmn; rest in ssn; snacks; bar; BBQ; playgrnd; pool 4km; sand beach; fishing; cycle hire; games area; games rm; entmnt; internet; TV rm; some statics; dogs €1.50; phone; Eng spkn; adv bkg; quiet; cc acc; red long stay; CCI. "Peaceful setting adj nature reserve ; sm pitches; helpful staff." ♦ €16.40   2005*

See advertisement on previous page

†AVEIRO *B2* (10km W Coastal) **Parque de Campismo Praia da Barra, Rua Diogo Cao 125, 3830-772 Ilhavo [tel/fax (234) 369425; camping barra@iol.pt; www.campingbarra.com]** Fr Aveiro foll sp to Barra on A25/IP5; foll one-way sp to site. Lge, shd; wc (some cont); shwrs inc; el pts €1.80; gas; lndry rm; shop; rest; snacks; bar; playgrnd; pool 500m; sand beach 100m; phone; bus adj; poss cr w/e; Eng spkn; cc acc; CCI. "All pitches in pine trees - poss diff; bird reserve nrby; v strict security; gates clsd 2200-0700." €13.70   2004*

AVEIRO *B2* (8km NW Coastal) **Camping ORBITUR-Sao Jacinto, EN327, Km 20, 3800-901 Aveiro [(234) 838284; fax (234) 838122; info@orbitur.pt; www.orbitur.com]** Fr Porto take A29/IC1 S & exit sp Ovar onto N327. (Note the long detour fr Aveiro itself - 30+ km.) Site in trees to N of Sao Jacinto. Lge, terr, shd; wc; chem disp; mv service pnt; shwrs inc; el pts (5-15A) €2.25 (poss rev pol); gas; lndtte; shop; rest; snacks; bar; BBQ; playgrnd; pool 5km; sand beach 2.5km; fishing; TV; dogs €1.20; phone; bus; red low ssn/long stay/snr citizens; cc acc; CCI. "Excel site; best in area; 15 min ferry (foot passengers only); gd, clean san facs." ♦ 1 Feb-30 Nov. €17.20   2005*

AVO see Oliveira do Hospital *C2*

†BEJA *C4* (S Urban) **Parque de Campismo Municipal de Beja, Avda Vasco da Gama, 7800-397 Beja [(284) 311911; fax (284) 311895]** Fr S (N122) take 1st exit into Beja. In 600m turn R & foll sp for site in 300m. Fr any other dir take by-pass S (sp Faro) & after passing Ford depot on R turn N twd town; then as fr S. Med, pt shd, gravel pitches; wc; shwrs inc; el pts (6A) €1.66; supmkt 500m; rest 500m; snacks 200m; bar adj; pool, tennis & football stadium adj; bus 50m; rlwy stn 1km; noisy in ssn; red low ssn; CCI. "C'van storage facs; helpful staff; san facs old but clean; NH only." €9.15   2005*

†BRAGA *B1* (1km S Urban) **Parque Municipal da Ponte, Sao Lazaro, 4710 Braga [(253) 273355; fax (253) 613387]** Fr Porto N14 N to Braga, then fr ring rd exit junc 2 onto N101 dir Guimaraes. After Guimaraes bear L for underpass sp hospital & other rtes. Site by old football stadium 200m on R (do not confuse with new stadium). Fr N drive thro city, foll sp Guimaraes, bear L for underpass (no max height shown) sp hospital & other rtes. Sm, hdstg, pt sl, terr, pt shd; chem disp; wc; own san rec; shwrs inc; el pts (16A) €1.55; gas; shop 200m; playgrnd; pool adj; rd noise. "Not rec for disabled; terr pitches steep for vans, check site/pitch bef driving in; poss scruffy pitches & unclean shwrs; conv Porto, Geres National Park; easy walk to city cent; NH only." €11.35   2005*

BRAGANCA *D1* (6km N Rural) **Camp Municipal Rio Sabor, EN103.7, Rabal/Portelo, Km 6, 5300 Braganca [(273) 331535; fax (273) 304299]** Fr Braganca N for 6km on N103.7 twd Spanish border. Site on R on bend with no app warning. Med, hdstg, pt sl, terr, pt shd; wc; chem disp; shwrs inc; el pts (12A) inc; gas; lndry rm; ice; shop & 6km; tradsmn; rest in ssn; snacks; bar; playgrnd; fishing; rv sw; cycle hire; dogs; bus; poss cr; Eng spkn; quiet but barking dogs; CCI. "On S boundary of National Park; rv runs thro site; young trees; rudimentary electrics; Braganca citadel worth visit." 1 May-30 Sep. €10.00   2004*

BRAGANCA *D1* (10km W Rural) **Cepo Verde Camping, Gondesende, 5300-561 Braganca [(273) 999371; fax (273) 323577]** Fr IP4 fr W take N103 fr Braganca for 8km. Site sp fr IP4 ring rd. R off N103, foll lane & turn R at sp. Steep ascent. NB Camping sp to rd 103-7 leads to different site (Sabor) N of city. Med, mkd pitch, hdstg, terr, pt shd; wc; chem disp; shwrs inc; el pts some (6A) €1.40; lndtte; shop; rest; snacks; bar; playgrnd; pool; phone; bus 1km; dogs; Eng spkn; adv bkg; quiet; CCI. "Remote, scenic site adj Montesinho National Park; wc not suitable for disabled due to steep steps; facs tired." 1 Apr-30 Sep. €10.20   2004*

BUDENS see Vila do Bispo *B4*

CABECEIRAS DE BASTO *C1* (4km N Rural) **Clube de Campo Valsereno, 4860-431 Cabeceiras de Basto [(962) 599055]** Fr N206 or IC5 turn N twd Cabeceiras. Site sp on N311 by Rio Douro. Sm, pt shd; wc; shwrs inc; el pts (12A) €1.50; lndtte; shop 4km, bar; rest, snacks 4km; BBQ; playgrnd; pool; rv sw; TV; carwash. "Magnificent mountain setting." 1 Jun-15 Sep. €10.00   2002*

CABRIL see Geres *C1*

†CALDAS DA RAINHA *B3* (8km W Rural) Camping ORBITUR, Rua Maldonado Freitas, 2500-516 Foz do Arelho [(262) 978683; fax (262) 978685; info@orbitur.pt; www.orbitur.com] Take N360 fr Caldas da Raina twds Foz do Arelho. Site on L; well sp. Lge, terr, shd; wc (some cont); chem disp; shwrs; el pts (5-15A) €2.25; gas; lndtte; shop; rest high ssn; snacks; bar; BBQ; playgrnd; pool high ssn; sand beach 2km; cycle hire; games rm; TV rm; 5% statics; dogs €1.20; Eng spkn; adv bkg; quiet; cc acc; red low ssn; CCI. "Lagoon Obidos 2km; interesting walled town; attractive area; well-maintained, much improved, well-run site; excel san facs." ♦ € 20.40   2005*

CALDAS DAS TAIPAS see Guimaraes *B1*

†CAMINHA *B1* (4.5km NE) Parque Natural, 4910 Vilar de Mouros [tel/fax (258) 727472; casa-da-anta@mail.telepac.pt; www.casa-da-anta.com] Fr Caminha take N13 NE twd Valenca. In approx 5km, after Seixas, turn R onto rd sp Vilar de Mouros (Camping 1.5km). Foll camping sp, site on R. Lge, pt sl, terr, pt shd; wc; chem disp; shwrs inc; el pts (10A) €2.30; lndtte; shop; rest; snacks; playgrnd; pool; fishing; tennis; entmnt; poss cr; 10% statics; phone; site clsd Dec; adv bkg; quiet; cc acc; CCI. "Excursion to mountains; mosquito repellant fr recep; site looking tired; gd sh stay." € 14.50   2004*

CAMINHA *B1* (2km SW Coastal) Camping ORBITUR-Caminha, Mata do Camarido, N13, Km 90, 4910-180 Caminha [(258) 921295; fax (258) 921473; info@orbitur.pt; www.orbitur.com] Foll seafront rd N13/E1 fr Caminha dir Viana/Porto, at rest turn R, site in approx 1km. Long o'fits take care at ent. Lge, terr, shd; wc; mv service pnt; chem disp; shwrs inc; el pts (5-15A) €2.25-2.75; gas; lndtte; shop; rest; snacks; bar; BBQ; playgrnd; pool 2.5km; sand beach 150m; rv sw; fishing; cycle hire; 5% statics; dogs €1.20; Eng spkn; adv bkg; fairly quiet; cc acc; red low ssn/long stay/snr citizens; CCI. "Care in shwrs - turn cold water on 1st as hot poss scalding; Geres National Park & Viana do Castelo worth visit; poss to cycle to Caminha; vg site." 16 Jan-30 Nov. € 19.40   2005*

†CAMPO MAIOR *C3* (4km W Rural) Parque de Campismo de Campo Maior, Barragem do Caia, 7370 Campo Maior [(268) 689493; info@parqueverde.pt; www.parqueverde.pt] Fr Elvas on N373 or Badajoz on N371 turn L on edge of Campo Maior onto N243 sp Barragem do Caia. Site on R in 4km just bef reservoir, sp Faisao Rest. V lge, hdstg, terr, pt shd; wc; chem disp; shwrs inc; el pts (6A) €1.10 (long lead poss req); lndtte; rest; snacks; bar; shop; pool 4km; lake sw adj; playgrnd; games area; boating; fishing; 98% statics; dogs; phone; poss cr/noisy high ssn & w/e; CCI. "Gd welcome; superb views fr top terrs; poss muddy pitches; site untidy & poss litter-strewn low ssn." ♦ € 8.90   2004*

†CASCAIS *A3* (5km NW Coastal) Camping ORBITUR-Guincho, N247-6, Lugar de Areia, Guincho, 2750-053 Cascais [(214) 870450 or 871014; fax (214) 872167; info@orbitur.pt; www.orbitur.com] Fr Lisbon take A5 W, at end m'way foll sp twd Cascais. At 1st rndabt turn R sp Birre & Campismo. Foll sp for 2.5km. App rd bumpy - care needed. V lge, some hdg/mkd pitch, terr, shd; wc; mv service pnt; chem disp; shwrs inc; el pts (15A) €2.25; gas; lndtte; supmkt & 500m; rest; snacks; bar; BBQ; playgrnd; sand beach 800m; watersports & fishing 1km; tennis; cycle hire; horseriding 500m; golf 3km; entmnt in ssn; car wash; 50% statics; dogs on lead €1.20; phone; Eng spkn; adv bkg; some rd noise; red low ssn/long stay/snr citizens; cc acc; CCI. "Buses to Cascais for train to Lisbon; sandy, wooded site behind dunes; plenty of nice, open pitches with views for tourers; gd rest; ltd facs in winter & poss itinerants; charge for awnings; v busy high ssn; vg low ssn." ♦ € 22.00 ABS - E10   2005*

CASTELO BRANCO *C2* (2.5km N) Camp Municipal Castelo Branco, 6000-113 Castelo Branco [(272) 330361 or 322577; fax (272) 322578] Fr IP2 take Castelo Branco Norte, at 1st rndabt site sp. Turn L just bef Modelo supmkt, site 2km on L. Lge, pt sl, shd; wc; shwrs; chem disp; mv service pnt; el pts (3A) €2; gas; lndtte; ice; shop; rest 2km; playgrnd; pool; lake 500m; Eng spkn; quiet but some rd noise; CCI. "Useful NH on little used x-ing to Portugal; gd site but rds to it poor." 2 Jan-15 Nov. € 5.00   2003*

CASTRO DAIRE *C2* (8km S Rural) Camping Castro Daire, Termas do Carvalhal, 3600 Castro Daire [tel/fax (254) 613918; naturimont@mail.telepac.pt; www.naturimont.com] S fr Castro Daire or N fr Viseu on N2 at km 144, site clearly sp. Site on E of rd. Med, sl, terr, shd; wc; shwrs inc; el pts (5-12A) €2; gas; lndry rm; shop; bar; playgrnd; pool adj; tennis; cycle hire; entmnt; TV; phone; adv bkg; some rd noise. "Thermal spa opp site." 1 Jun-30 Sep. € 11.50   2005*

CHAVES *C1* (4km S Rural) Camp Municipal Quinta do Rebentao, Largo de Camoes, 5400-764 Chaves [tel/fax (276) 322733] Fr o'skts Chaves take N2 S. After about 3km in vill of Vila Nova Veiga turn E at sp thro new estate, site in about 500m. Med, hdstg, terr, pt shd; wc; chem disp; mv service pnt; shwrs inc; el pts (6A) €1.20; gas 4km; lndry rm; shop 1km; rest; snacks; bar; BBQ; pool €0.50 km; rv sw & fishing 4km; cycle hire; dogs; phone; bus 800m; adv bkg; Eng spkn; red CCI. "Gd site in lovely valley but remote; v helpful staff; facs block quite a hike fr some terr pitches; Chaves interesting, historical Roman town; scenic area." ♦ 1 May-31 Oct. € 11.00   2004*

COSTA DE CAPARICA see Lisboa *B3*

PORTUGAL

†COVILHA *C2* (4km NW Rural) **Camping Piao**, 6200-036 Covilha [tel/fax (275) 314312 or 327932; cccc.piao@portugalmail.com; www.clubecamp ismocovilha.web.pt] App Covilha, foll sp to cent, then sp to Penhas da Saude; after 4km of gd but twisting climbing rd; site on L. Lge, terr, pt shd; wc; shwrs €0.70; el pts (6A) €1.20; gas; shop; rest; snacks; bar; playgrnd; 2 pools; tennis; entmnt; 60% statics; phone; poss cr; Eng spkn; CCI. "Gd walking fr site." ♦ € 10.95   2003*

DARQUE see Viana do Castelo *B1*

ELVAS *C3* (1.5km W Urban) **Parque de Campismo da Piedade**, 7350-901 Elvas [(268) 628997 or 622877; fax (268) 620729] Take old N4 thro town, foll sp Estremoz. Site on L after site sp without distance; look carefully for site ent down track 100m. Med, mkd pitch, hdstg, mostly sl, pt shd; wc; chem disp; shwrs inc; el pts (16A) inc; gas; lndry rm; rest; snacks; bar; BBQ; playgrnd; pool adj; no statics; no dogs; phone; bus 500m; poss cr; CCI. "Attractive aqueduct & walls; Piedade church & relics adj; traditional shops; nice walk to town; v quiet site, even high ssn; excel san facs." 1 Apr-15 Sep. € 11.50   2003*

ENTRE AMBOS OS RIOS see Ponte da Barca *B1*

†ERICEIRA *B3* (1km N Coastal) **Camp Municipal Mil Regos**, 2655-319 Ericeira [(261) 862706; fax (261) 866798; geral@cm-mafra.pt; www.cm-mafra. pt] On N247 coast rd, well sp N of Ericeira. V lge, pt sl, pt shd; wc; shwrs inc; el pts €2.30; gas; shop; rest; playgrnd; pool adj; beach 200m; fishing; entmnt; 90% statics; phone; quiet. "Easy reach Mafra & Sintra Palaces; overlooks sea; san facs basic; busy site." ♦ € 18.00   2005*

†ESPINHO *B1* (Urban) **Camp Municipal de Espinho**, 4500-082 Espinho [(227) 335871; fax (227) 322680] Foll N109 fr Porto to Espinho; on app town site sp at junc on R. V lge, sl, pt shd; wc; chem disp; shwrs inc; el pts (10A) €1.37; gas; shop; snacks; bar; playgrnd; pool; paddling pool; sand beach 500m; fishing; no dogs; poss cr; adv bkg; rd noise; CCI. "Sep secure area for cars; if pitched at bottom of site must climb to get to facs; frequent trains to Porto." € 12.00   2003*

†ESPINHO *B1* (11km S) **Camping Cortegaca Os Nortenhos, Praia de Cortegaca**, 3885-000 Ovar [(265) 752199; fax (256) 755177; clube-nortenhos@ netvisao.pt] Fr Espinho foll rd thro Esmoriz twd Aveiro to Cortegaca vill. Turn R to beach (Praia), site on L at beach, sp fr vill. V lge, pt shd; wc (cont); shwrs; el pts €2.25; gas; shop; snacks; bar; playgrnd; sand beach adj; entmnt; TV; 95% statics; no dogs; phone; bus 500m; poss cr; quiet; cc acc; CCI. "V helpful, friendly staff; v ltd tourer pitches & poss v cr high ssn; facs ltd at w/e; conv Porto; guarded at ent; sun shelters over pitches." ♦ € 12.40   2004*

ESTELA see Povoa De Varzim *B1*

†EVORA *C3* (2km SW Rural) **Camping ORBITUR, Estrada das Alcacovas, Herdade Esparragosa**, 7000-703 Evora [(266) 705190; fax (266) 709830; info@orbitur.pt; www.orbitur.com] Fr N foll N18 & by-pass, then foll sps for Lisbon rd at each rndabt or traff lts. Fr town cent take N380 SW sp Alcacovas, foll site sp, site in 2km. NB Narr gate to site & sharp turn to recep. Lge, hdstg, terr, pt shd; wc; chem disp; shwrs inc; el pts (5-15A) €2.25 (long lead poss req); gas; lndtte; shop; supmkt 500m; tradsmn; rest; snacks; bar; BBQ; playgrnd; pool; tennis; games area; no statics; dogs €1.20; phone; bus; rlwy stn 2km; Eng spkn; adv bkg ess; quiet; cc acc; red low ssn/long stay/snr citizens; red CCI. "Conv town cent, Evora World Heritage site with wealth of monuments; cycle path to town; poss flooding some pitches after heavy rain; helpful staff; well-kept site." ♦ € 20.40   2005*

†FERNAO FERRO *B3* (4km E Rural) **Parque Verde, Rua da Escola 9, Fontainhas, Casal do Sapo, 2840 Fernao Ferro** [(212) 108956; fax (212) 103263; info@parqueverde.pt; www. parqueverde.pt] Fr Sesimbra take N378 N, turn R at major junc Marco do Grilo. In approx 3km turn R by factory, site on L in 1km. Med, pt sl, pt shd; wc; chem disp; shwrs inc; el pts (2A) €1.60 (long lead rec); gas; shop; rest; snacks; bar; playgrnd; pool; sand beach 13km; tennis; entmnt; some statics; bus; phone; poss cr; quiet; cc acc. "In forest." € 11.00   2002*

FERRAGUDO see Portimao *B4*

†FIGUEIRA DA FOZ *B2* (4km S Coastal) **Camping ORBITUR-Gala, N109, Km 4, Gala, 3090-458 Figueira da Foz** [(233) 431492; fax (233) 431231; info@orbitur.com; www.orbitur.com] Fr Figueira da Foz on N109 dir Leira for 3.5km. After Gala site on R in approx 400m. Ignore sp on R 'Campismo' after long bdge. Lge, terr, shd; wc; chem disp; mv service pnt; shwrs; el pts (6-10A) €2.25-2.75; gas; lndtte; shop; rest; snacks; bar; BBQ; playgrnd; sand beach 400m; fishing 1km; tennis; entmnt; dogs €1.20; phone; red low ssn/long stay/snr citizens; cc acc; CCI. "Gd." ♦ € 19.40   2005*

FIGUEIRA DA FOZ *B2* (6km S Coastal) **Camping Foz do Mondego, Cabedelo-Gala, 3080-661 Figueira da Foz** [(233) 402740/2; fax (233) 402749; foz.mondego@fcampismo.pt; www. fpcampismo.pt] Fr S on N109 turn L bef bdge sp Gala. Foll site sp. V lge, mkd pitch, htd wc; chem disp; mv service pnt; baby facs; shwrs inc; el pts (2A) inc; gas; lndtte; lndry rm; shop 2km; rest; snacks; bar; BBQ; playgrnd; sand beach adj; fishing; surfing; TV; 40% statics; dogs €0.50; phone; CCI. "Wonderful sea views; excel." ♦ 8 Jan-14 Nov. € 13.00   2004*

FOZ DO ARELHO see Caldas da Rainha *B3*

†FUNDAO *C2* (1.5km SW Urban) **Camping Quinta do Convento, 6234-909 Fundao [(275) 753118; fax (275) 771368]** Fr N thro town cent; when almost thro town take L fork at triangle dir Silvares; site 1km uphill on L. Site well sp fr A23. Med, hdstg, terr, shd; wc (some cont); chem disp; mv service pnt; shwrs inc; el pts (6-10A) €1.75; lndtte; shop; rest; snacks; bar; playgrnd; pool; entmnt; TV; bus 1.5km; adv bkg; quiet. "Guarded; no vehicle access after 2300; gd, friendly site with nice atmosphere." ♦ ltd. € 9.00   2005*

> Some of these sites have changed their opening dates - we'd better fill in some site report forms and let the editor of the guide know.

FUZETA see Olhao *C4*

GAFANHA DA NAZARE see Aveiro *B2*

†GERES *C1* (1km N Rural) **Parque de Campisto de Cerdeira, Campo do Geres, 4840-030 Terras do Bouro [(253) 351005 or 357065; fax (253) 353315; info@parquecerdeira.com; www.parquecerdeira.com]** Fr N103 Braga-Chaves rd, 28km E of Braga turn N onto N304 at sp to Poussada. Cont N for 18km to Campo de Geres. Site in 1km; well sp. V lge, shd; wc; chem disp; shwrs inc; el pts (5-10A) €2.10-3.15; gas; lndry rm; rest; bar; shop; playgrnd; lake sw; TV rm; cycle hire; fishing 2km; canoeing; few statics; no dogs; bus 500m; entmnt; poss cr; quiet; adv bkg; Eng spkn; cc acc; CCI. "Beautiful scenery; unspoilt area; fascinating old vills nrby & gd walking; ltd facs low ssn." ♦ € 17.35   2005*

GERES *C1* (2km N Rural) **Vidoeiro Camping, Lugar do Vidoeiro, 4845-081 Geres [(253) 391289; fax (258) 452450; aderepg@mail.telepac.pt; www.adere-pg.pt]** NE fr Braga take N103 twds Chaves for 25km. 1km past Cerdeirinhas turn L twds Geres onto N308. Site on L 2km after Caldos do Geres. Steep rds with hairpins. Cross bdge & reservoir, foll camp sps. Lge, mkd pitch, hdstg, terr, pt shd; wc; chem disp; shwrs inc; el pts (12A) inc; lndry rm; tradsmn; rest; bar 500m; pool 500m, lake sw 500m; phone; quiet. "V attractive site in National Park; gd, clean facs; thermal spa in Geres." ♦ 15 May-15 Oct. € 10.20   2005*

†GERES *C1* (10km E Rural) **Camping Outeiro Alto, 5470-013 Cabril [tel/fax (253) 659860; trote-geres@hotmail.com]** Fr N103 turn N to Cabril, site sp. App poss difficult. Med, terr, pt shd; wc; shwrs inc; el pts inc; lndtte; shop 800m; rest 350m; snacks; bar; BBQ; TV rm; entmnt; rv sw; fishing; boating. "A white knuckle app; spectacular scenery; sm area for tourers." € 10.00   2002*

†GOIS *C2* (1km S Rural) **Camp Municipal do Castelo, 3330-309 Gois [(235) 778585; fax (235) 770129; casa.antonio@netc.pt; www.goiscamping.com]** Fr Coimbra take N17/N2 E to Gois, site sp to W of rv. Med, terr, shd; wc (some cont); chem disp; baby facs; shwrs inc; el pts (4-16A) €2.20; gas; lndry rm; ice; shop; tradsmn; rest 150m; snacks; bar; BBQ; playgrnd; pool 200m; sand beach 15km; rv sw 500m; tennis; fishing; canoeing; cycle hire; 15% statics; dogs €1.30; poss cr; Eng spkn; adv bkg; quiet; red low ssn/CCI. "Quiet, clean site in beautiful wooded countryside; helpful owners." ♦ € 11.40   2003*

†GOUVEIA *C2* (6km NE) **Camping Quinta das Cegonhas, Nabainhos-Melo, 6290-122 Gouveia [tel/fax (238) 745886; cegonhas@cegonhas.com; www.cegonhas.com]** Turn S at 114km post on N17 Seia-Celorico da Beira. Site sp thro Melo vill. Sm, pt shd; wc; chem disp; mv service pnt; shwrs; el pts (4A) €2; lndtte; shop 300m; rest; snacks; bar; playgrnd; pool; entmnt; TV; dogs €0.60; bus 300m; Eng spkn; adv bkg; quiet; 5-10% red 7+ days; CCI. "Vg; friendly Dutch owners; site based on vill manor house & grounds; well-run; conv Torre & Serra da Estrella; gd walks; highly rec." ♦ € 11.50   2005*

†GUARDA *C2* (500m SW Urban) **Camp Municipal da Guarda, Avda do Estadio Municipal, 6300-705 Guarda [(271) 221200; fax (271) 210025]** Exit A23 junc 35 onto N18 to Guarda. Foll sp cent & sports centre. Site adj sports cent off rndabt. Med, hdstg, sl, shd; wc (some cont, own san rec); chem disp (wc); shwrs inc; el pts (15A) €1.25; gas; lndry rm; shop; rest, snacks, bar high ssn; BBQ; playgrnd; pool 2km; TV; phone; bus; Eng spkn; poss noise fr rd & nrby nightclub; CCI. "Highest city in Portugal, poss v cold at night; access to several pitches diff for c'vans, OK for m'vans; run down facs, site poss negelected low/mid ssn; walking dist to interesting town; music festival 1st week Sep." ♦ € 8.50   2005*

†GUIMARAES *B1* (5km N) **Camping Taipas Turitermas, Largo das Termas, 4800-360 Caldas das Taipas [(253) 576274]** Exit N101 heading S fr Braga, site lkm fr rd (8km N fr Guimaraes). Pass junc on L sp Citania, turn L in 150m at sp Piscina, R in 300m to site opp sw baths; 2.8m ent. On Mon street mkt blocks route & alt route S thro a sh 1-way system can be used. Med, shd; wc; chem disp; mv service pnt; shwrs; el pts (4-10A) €1.25; shops 300m; rest; bar; playgrnd; pool; fishing; entmnts; no dogs; bus 500m; quiet. "Conv Braga Cathedral, castle & palace at Guimaraes; spa." ♦ 1 Jun-30 Sep. € 10.50   2004*

PORTUGAL

GUIMARAES *B1* (6km SE) **Parque da Penha, Montanha da Penha, 4800 Guimaraes** [(253) 515912; fax (253) 515085] Take N101 SE fr Guimaraes. Turn R at sp for Penha. Site sp. Lge, hdstg, pt sl, terr, shd; wc; shwrs; el pts (6A) €1.50; gas; lndry rm; shop; rest; snacks; bar; playgrnd; pool, sand beach adj; fishing; no statics; bus 150m, teleferic (tram) 200m; rlwy stn 1.5km; no dogs; phone; car wash; poss cr; Eng spkn; adv bkg; quiet; CCI. "Excel staff; san facs poss need upgrading; hilltop site with wonderful views overlooking Guimaraes World Heritage site; gd sh stay." ♦ ltd. 1 Apr-30 Sep. € 9.40   2004*

Will you fill in the site report forms at the back of the guide, or shall I?

†IDANHA A NOVA *C2* (8km NE Rural) **Camping ORBITUR-Idanha-a-Nova, EN354-1, Km 8, Barragem de Idanha-a-Nova, 6060 Idanha a Nova** [(277) 202793; fax (277) 202945; info@orbitur.pt; www.orbitur.com] Fr Castelo Branco NE on N233. R on N240 to Ladoeiro. At Ladoeiro L on N354 sp Idanha-a-Nova. Foll site sp. Alt rte fr NW on N353, then by-pass around vill to N354, site sp. V lge, pt sl, shd; wc; chem disp (wc); shwrs inc; el pts (6A) €2.25; lndtte; lndry rm; shop; tradsmn; rest; snacks; bar; BBQ; playgrnd; pool; lake sw, fishing; watersports 150m; tennis; entmnt; TV rm; 10% statics; dogs €1.20; phone; Eng spkn; adv bkg; quiet; red long stay/low ssn/snr citizens; cc acc. "Uphill to town & supmkts; excel." ♦ € 17.90   2005*

ILHAVO see Aveiro *B2*

†LAGOS *B4* (5km W Rural) **Turiscampo Espiche, N125 Espiche, 8600-109 Luz-Lagos** [(282) 789265; fax (282) 788578; info@turiscampo.com; www.turiscampo.com] N125 fr Lagos dir Sagres, site 5km on R. Lge, mkd pitch, some hdstg, pt sl, terr, shd; htd wc; chem disp; mv service pnt; baby facs; shwrs inc; el pts (6-10A) €2.75-3.50; gas; lndtte; ice; supmkt; tradsmn; rest; snacks; bar; playgrnd; pool; paddling pool; sand beach 2km; fishing 2.5km; cycle hire; games rm; entmnt; child entmnt; internet; TV rm; some statics; dogs €1.50; phone; bus; Eng spkn; adv bkg; cc acc; red long stay/low ssn/CCI. "Excel site for long winter stays; superb views; lovely vill & beach; much improved site - new san facs 2005; helpful staff; gd value for money." ♦ € 19.80 (CChq acc)   2005*

See advertisement opposite

†LAGOS *B4* (7km W Coastal) **Camping ORBITUR-Valverde, Estrada da Praia da Luz, Valverde, 8600-148 Lagos** [(282) 789211 or 789212; fax (282) 789213; info@orbitur.pt; www.orbitur.com] Foll coast rd N125 fr Lagos to Sagres for 3km. Turn L at traff lts sp Luz, site 2km on R, well sp. V lge, hdg/mkd pitch, terr, shd; wc; mv service pnt; shwrs inc; el pts (6A) €2.25; gas; lndtte; supmkt; rest; snacks; bar; BBQ: playgrnd; 2 pools; waterchute; sand beach 3km; tennis; sports facs; cycle hire; games area; games rm; entmnt; TV rm; dogs €1.20; bus; Eng spkn; adv bkg; quiet; red low ssn/long stay/snr citizens/Orbitur card; cc acc; CCI. "Well-run site; v friendly staff; gd, clean san facs; access to pitches tight due trees; disabled facs not suitable wheelchair users (steps); spacious low ssn; charge for awnings; excel for long, winter stays; narr, busy rd to beach/town." ♦ € 23.90 ABS - E09   2005*

LAMAS DE MOURO *C1* (1km S Rural) **Camping Lamas de Mouro, 4960-170 Lamas de Mouro** [(251) 465129; info@versana.pt; www.versana.pt] Fr N202 at Melgaco foll sp Peneda National Park, site sp in Lamas de Mouro. Med, pt shd; wc; chem disp; mv service pnt; shwrs inc; el pts (10A) €2.30; lndry rm; shop; tradsmn; rest; snacks; bar; cooking facs; phone; poss cr; quiet; CCI. "Ideal for walking in National Park; park ranger v helpful & speaks gd Eng." 1 Apr-30 Nov. € 13.20   2004*

LAMEGO *C1* (5km W Rural) **Parque de Campismo de Lamego, Serra das Meadas, 5100 Lamego** [tel/fax (254) 613918; naturimont@oninet.pt] Fr Lamego, foll rd dir Almasave/Resende. In 500m turn L sp 'Serra das Meadas, Complexo Turistico Turisserra.' Site in 4km uphill. Sm, pt sl, pt shd, wc; serviced pitch; shwrs (cold only) inc; el pts (12A) €1.50; gas; lndry rm; shop; rest; snacks; bar; playgrnd; pool 5km; lake sw 6km; fishing; canoeing; tennis; cycle hire; entmnt; TV rm; no statics; bus 4km; phone; Eng spkn; quiet. "Site situated at height of approx 1000m; spectacular views." 1 Jun-30 Sep. € 10.00   2003*

LAVRA see Porto *B1*

†LISBOA *B3* (10km SW Coastal) **Camping ORBITUR-Costa Caparica, Ave Afonso de Albuquerque, Quinta de S. Antonio, 2825-450 Costa de Caparica** [(212) 901366 or 903894; fax (212) 900661; info@orbitur.pt; www.orbitur.com] Take A2/IP7 S fr Lisbon; after Rv Tagus bdge turn W to Costa de Caparica. At end of rd turn N twd Trafaria, & site on L. Well sp fr a'strada. Lge, terr, shd; wc; chem disp; mv service pnt; shwrs inc; el pts (6A) €2.25; gas; lndtte; shop; rest; snacks; bar; BBQ; playgrnd; pool 800m; sand beach 500m; fishing; entmnt; TV; 25% statics; dogs €1.20; phone; car wash; bus; Eng spkn; cc acc; red low ssn/long stay/snr citizens/Orbitur card; CCI. "Slightly run-down resort; beach adequate, app on foot; heavy traff into city; rec use free parking at Monument to the Discoveries & tram to city cent; ferry to Belem; ltd facs low ssn; pleasant, helpful staff." ♦ € 22.00   2005*

†LISBOA *B3* (5km NW) **Parque Municipal de Campismo de Monsanto, Estrada da Circunvalacao, 1400-061 Lisboa [(217) 623100; fax (217) 623105]** Fr W on A5 foll sp Parque Florestal de Monsanto/Buraca. Fr S on A2, cross toll bdge & foll sp for Sintra; join expressway, foll up hill; site well sp; stay in RH lane. Site sp fr all major rds. V lge, mkd pitch, hdstg, pt sl, terr, pt shd; wc; chem disp; mv service pnt; 80% serviced pitches; shwrs inc; el pts (6-16A) inc; gas; ice; lndtte; shop; tradsmn; rest; snacks; bar; playgrnd; pool; sand beach 10km; tennis; mini-golf; entmnt; bank; post office; car wash; TV rm; frequent bus to city nrby; rlwy station 3km; Eng spkn; adv bkg; some rd noise; red low ssn; cc acc; red CCI. "Well laid-out; spacious, guarded site in trees; ltd mv service pnt; excel excursions booked at tourist office on site; friendly, helpful staff; conv bus for Lisbon; in high ssn some o'fits placed on sloping forest area (quiet); few pitches take awning; take care hygiene at chem disp/clean water tap." ♦ € 21.50
2005*

LOURICAL *B2* (4km SW Rural) **Campismo o Tamanco, Casas Brancas 11, 3100-231 Lourical [tel/fax (236) 952551; campismo.o.tamanco@ mail.telepac.pt; www.campismo-o-tamanco. com]** On N109 fr Figuera da Foz S twds Leiria, take 2nd exit to Lourical N342. Site 800m on L. Med, hdg/mkd pitch, pt shd; wc; chem disp; shwrs inc; el pts inc (6-16A) €2-3.25; gas; lndtte; shop; tradsmn; rest; snacks; bar; pool; sand beach 12km; lake sw adj; cycle hire; entmnt; TV; dogs €0.50; poss cr; Eng spkn; adv bkg; rd noise; 10% red low ssn 7+ days; CCI. "Excel; Dutch owners; chickens & ducks roaming site; superb mkt on Sun at Lourical; a bit of the real Portugal; gd touring base."
1 Feb-31 Oct. € 13.15   2004*

†LUSO *B2* (1.5km S Rural) **Camping ORBITUR-Luso, N336, Pampilhosa, Quinta do Vale do Jorge, 3050-246 Luso [(231) 930916; fax (231) 930917; info@orbitur.pt; www.orbitur.com]** S fr Luso on N336, sp. Lge, pt sl, pt shd; wc; mv service pnt; shwrs inc; el pts (5-15A) €2.25; gas; lndtte; shop; tradsmn; rest; snacks; bar; BBQ; playgrnd; pool 1km; sand beach 35km; tennis; TV rm; dogs €1.20; adv bkg; Eng spkn; quiet; red low ssn/long stay/snr citizens; cc acc; CCI. "Some sm pitches unsuitable for c'vans + awnings." ♦ € 17.20
2005*

MEDAS GONDOMAR see Porto *B1*

MIRA *B2* (7km SW Coastal) **Camp Municipal de Mira, 3070-721 Praia de Mira [(231) 472173; fax (231) 458185]** S fr Aveiro on N109, turn R in Mira onto N334, sp Praia de Mira. Foll rd to seafront, turn L, foll rd S out of town, site in 300m. V lge, pt shd; wc; chem disp; shwrs €0.80; el pts (6A) €1; shop; rest; snacks; bar; playgrnd; pool 300m; sand beach 500m; no dogs; phone; bus 1km. "Gd beach; Costa Nova & Aveiro worth a visit." ♦ 1 May-30 Sep.
€ 12.50   2004*

†MIRA *B2* (3km W Rural) **Camping Vila Caia, Lagoa de Mira, 3070-176 Mira [(231) 451524; fax (231) 451861; vlcaia@portugalmail.com; www. vilacaia.com]** S fr Aveiro on N109 for 29km; at Mira take N334 for 5km. Site sp on R 500m W of Lagoa de Mira. Lge, hdstg, pt shd; wc (some cont); chem disp; mv service pnt; shwrs inc; el pts (4A) €2.20; gas; lndtte; shop; rest; snacks; bar; playgrnd; pool; sand beach 3km; fishing; tennis; cycle hire; entmnt; TV; some statics; no dogs; phone; bus adj; clsd Dec; Eng spkn; no adv bkg; quiet; cc acc; red low ssn; CCI. ♦ € 14.80   2004*

MIRA *B2* (7km NW Coastal) **Camping ORBITUR-Mira, E Florestal 1, Km 2, Dunas de Mira, 3070-792 Praia de Mira [(231) 471234; fax (231) 472047; info@orbitur.pt; www.orbitur.com]** Fr N109 in Mira turn W to Praia de Mira, foll site sp. Lge, terr, unshd; wc; chem disp; mv service pnt; shwrs inc; el pts (5-15A) €2.25-2.75; gas; lndtte; shop (in ssn); tradsmn; rest, snacks, bar high ssn; playgrnd; pool 7km; sandy, surfing beach & dunes 200m; entmnt; fishing; boating; cycle hire; TV rm; 5% statics; dogs €1.20; phone; Eng spkn; poss noisy w/e; red low ssn/long stay/snr citizens; cc acc; CCI. "Friendly, helpful staff; suitable for cycling; gd low ssn facs; nature reserve opp site." ♦
1 Feb-30 Nov. € 19.40   2005*

PORTUGAL

MIRANDA DO DOURO *D1* (500m W Urban) Campismo Santa Luzia, Rua do Parque de Campismo, 5210-190 Miranda do Douro [(273) 431273 or 431216; fax (273) 431075; mirdouro@mail.telepac.pt] Fr Spain on ZA324/N221, cross dam & thro town, site well sp. Do not enter walled town. Lge, pt sl, terr, pt shd; wc; chem disp; shwrs inc; el pts (5A) €1.25; shop, rest & 1km; snacks, bar; playgrnd; pool 100m; phone; bus 500m; Eng spkn; quiet; CCI. "Interesting ent into N Portugal; old walled town; spectacular rv gorge; boat trips." ♦ 1 Jun-30 Sep. € 9.50   2004*

†**MIRANDELA** *C1* (4km N Rural) Camping Tres Rios Maravilha, 5370-555 Mirandela [tel/fax (278) 263177; clube.ccm@oninet.pt] Fr IP4 take Mirandela N exit. Foll town cent sp at 1st rndabt. At 2nd rndabt take 1st exit, site on L in approx 2km, adj Rv Tuela. Lge, mkd pitch, pt shd; wc; chem disp; shwrs inc; el pts (12A) €1.50 (poss rev pol); gas; Indtte; tradsmn; rest; snacks; bar; playgrnd; pool; canoeing; fishing; tennis; entmnt; TV; 60% statics; dogs; phone; bus, train 2km; Eng spkn; poss cr & noisy; red low ssn/CCI. "Busy site but v quiet low ssn; friendly owner; excel san facs; attractive pool." ♦ € 12.00   2005*

MOGADOURO *D1* (1km S Rural) Camp Municipal Quinta da Agueira, Complexo Desportivo, 5200-244 Mogadouro [(279) 340230; camera mogadouro@mail.telepac.pt] Fr Miranda do Douro on N221 or fr Braganca on IP2 to Macedo then N216 to Mogadouro. Site sp adj sports complex. Lge, shd; wc; chem disp; mv service pnt; shwrs inc; el pts (15A) €1.50; gas; Indry rm; rest 500m; bar; BBQ; playgrnd; pool adj; beach 10km; tennis; car wash; entmnt; TV; dogs €1; phone; bus 500m; adv bkg; quiet. "In lovely area; gd touring base." ♦ 1 Apr-30 Sep. € 9.00   2005*

See advertisement above

MONCARAPACHO see Olhao *C4*

†**MONTARGIL** *B3* (5km N Rural) Camping ORBITUR, EN2, 7425-017 Montargil [(242) 901207; fax (242) 901220; info@orbitur.pt; www.orbitur.com] Fr N251 Coruche to Vimieriro rd, turn N on N2, over dam at Barragem de Montargil. Fr Ponte de Sor S on N2 until 3km fr Montargil. Site clearly sp bet rd & lake. V lge, terr, shd; wc; chem disp; mv service pnt; shwrs inc; el pts (6-10A) €2.25-2.75; gas; Indtte; shop & 3km; tradsmn; rest; snacks; bar; playgrnd; rv beach adj; boating; watersports; fishing; tennis; TV; 50% statics; dogs €1.20; phone; Eng spkn; adv bkg; quiet; cc acc; red low ssn/long stay/snr citizens; CCI. "Clean, well-equipped site in area of natural beauty; vg." ♦ € 19.40   2005*

†**NAZARE** *B2* (2km N Rural) Camping Vale Paraiso, EN242, 2450-138 Nazare [(262) 561800; fax (262) 561900; info@valeparaiso.com; www.valeparaiso.com] Site thro pine reserve on N242 fr Nazare to Leiria. V lge, mkd pitch, hdstg, terr, shd; wc (some cont); chem disp; mv service pnt; baby facs; shwrs inc; el pts (4-10A) €2.50; gas; Indtte; ice; supmkt; rest; snacks & takeaway; bar; playgrnd; 2 pools; sand beach 2km; lake 1km; fishing; sports area; organised activities; games rm; cycle hire; child entmnt; TV; 1% statics; dogs €2; bus; site clsd 6-26 Dec; Eng spkn; adv bkg; quiet; cc acc; red low ssn/long stay; CCI. "Gd security; pitches vary in size & price, & divided by concrete walls, poss not suitable lge o'fits." ♦ € 18.60 (CChq acc)   2005*

NAZARE *B2* (2km E Rural) Camping ORBITUR-Valado, EN8, Km 5, Valado, 2450-148 Nazare-Alcobaca [(262) 561609; fax (262) 561137; info@orbitur.pt; www.orbitur.com] Site on N of rd to Alcobaca & Valado (N8-4), opp Monte de Sao Bartolomeu. V lge, terr, shd; wc; mv service pnt; shwrs inc; el pts (6A) €2.25; gas; Indtte; shop & 2km; rest; snacks; bar; BBQ; playgrnd; pool 3km; sand beach 1.8km; tennis; TV rm; 10% statics; dogs €1.20; phone; adv bkg; red low ssn/long stay/snr citizens; cc acc. "Excel site; helpful manager; visits to Fatima, Alcobaca, Balhala rec." 1 Feb-30 Nov. € 17.90   2005*

†ODEMIRA *B4* (1km S) **Camping Sao Miguel,** 7630-592 Odemira [(282) 947145; fax (282) 947245; camping.sao.miguel@mail.telepac.pt] Fr N120 site ent 2km fr Odeceixe. V lge, pt sl, shd; wc; chem disp; mv service pnt; shwrs inc; el pts (6A) €2.10; gas; lndtte; ice; shop; rest; snacks; bar; BBQ; playgrnd; pool; sand beach 5km; tennis; TV; no dogs; phone; adv bkg; quiet; red low ssn/long stay. € 19.50   2003*

Mustn't forget to post our site report forms to The Club, otherwise sites might be deleted.

†ODIVELAS *B3* (3km NE Rural) **Camping Markadia, Barragem de Odivelas, 7920-999 Alvito [(284) 763141; fax (284) 763102]** Fr Ferreira do Alentejo on N2 N twd Torrao. After Odivelas turn R onto N257 twd Alvito & Barragem. Site in 7km. Med, hdstg, pt sl, pt shd; wc (some cont); chem disp; mv service pnt; shwrs inc; el pts (10A) €2.40; gas; lndtte; ice; shop; tradsmn; rest; snacks; bar; playgrnd; pool 50m; sand beach, lake sw 500m; boating; fishing; horseriding; tennis; no dogs Jul-Aug; phone; car wash; adv bkg; v quiet; red low ssn/CCI. "Exceptionally beautiful, superb, secluded site on banks of reservoir; site lighting poor." ♦ ltd. € 19.20   2005*

†OLHAO *C4* (10km NE Rural) **Camping Caravanas Algarve, Sitio da Cabeca Moncarapacho, 8700-623 Moncarapacho [(289) 791669]** Exit IP1/A22 sp Moncarapacho. In 2km turn L sp Fuzeta. At traff lts turn L & immed L opp supmkt in 1km. Turn R at site sp. Site on L. Sm, hdstg, pt sl, unshd; own san facs; chem disp; el pts (10A) inc; gas 3km; lndtte; shop, rest, snacks, bar 1.5km; sand beach 4km; 10% statics; dogs; adv bkg dep req; Eng spkn; quiet; 10% red CCI. "Situated on a farm in orange groves; Spanish border 35km; National Park Ria Formosa 4km." € 15.00   2004*

†OLHAO *C4* (10km NE Rural) **Campismo Casa Rosa, 8700 Moncarapacho [(289) 794400; fax (289) 792952; casarosa@sapo.pt; www. casarosa.com.pt]** Fr A22 (IP1) E twd Spain, leave at exit 15 Olhao/Moncarapacho. At rndabt take 2nd exit dir Moncarapacho. Cont past sp Moncarapacho Centro direction Olhao. In 1km at Lagoao, on L is Café Da Lagoao with its orange awning. Just past café is sp for Casa Rosa. Foll sp. Sm, hdstg, terr, unshd; htd wc; chem disp; shwrs inc; el pts (6A) inc; gas 3km; lndtte; ice; rest & snacks 2km; pool; shgl beach 6km; rv sw 6km; sat TV; no dogs; Eng spkn; adv bkg (dep req); noise fr construction yard adj; CCI. "CL-type site adj holiday apartments; adults only; helpful, friendly owners; evening meals avail; access poss diff lge o'fits; elec supply poss erratic; ideal for touring E Algarve; conv Spanish border; rec." ♦ ltd. € 10.00   2005*

†OLHAO *C4* (1km E) **Camping de Olhao, Pinheiros de Marim, 8700-912 Olhao [(289) 700300; fax (289) 700390 or 700391; parque.campismo@sbsi. pt; www.sbsi.pt/camping]** Turn S twd coast fr N125 1km E of Olhao by filling stn. Clearly sp on S side of N125, adj Ria Formosa National Park. V lge, hdg/mkd pitch, pt sl, pt shd, wc (some cont); chem disp; mv service pnt; shwrs inc; el pts (6A) €1.50; gas; lndtte; ice; supmkt; bar; rest; ice cream parlour; playgrnd; pool; paddling pool; fishing 2km; tennis; games rm; games area; cycle hire; horseriding 1km; TV; sep car park; car wash; security guard; 20% statics; phone; bus to Faro, rlwy station 1km; some rlwy noise; 50% red Oct-May & 30% red 30+ days; cc acc. "Pleasant staff; gd, clean facs; excel pool; v pop long stay low ssn; many sm pitches, some diff access for lge o'fits; excel rest; pop with lge youth groups in high ssn; gd for cycling, bird-watching; ferry to islands." ♦ € 18.80   2005*

See advertisement below

PORTUGAL

†OLHAO *C4* (9km E Coastal/Urban) **Parque Campismo de Fuzeta, 2 Rua do Liberdade, 8700-019 Fuzeta [(289) 793459 or 794351; fax (289) 794034]** Fr N125 Olhao-Tavira rd, turn S at traff lts at Alfandanga sp Fuzeta & foll sp to site. Lge, some hdstg, pt shd; wc; chem disp; shwrs €0.25; el pts (6A) €1.30; gas; lndtte; shop & 1km; rest adj; snacks; bar; BBQ; playgrnd adj; sand beach adj; 5% statics; dogs; phone; Eng spkn; no adv bkg; noise fr rd & adj bars; red long stay. "Pleasant staff; popular with long-stay m'vanners; haphazard pitching; elec cables run across site rds; poss flooding after heavy rain; areas of soft sand; v clean san facs but hot water to shwrs only; gd security; gd value; gd shopping in town & train service to Algarve towns; attractive area." ♦ ltd. € 10.60   2005*

†OLIVEIRA DE AZEMEIS *B2* (1.5km E Urban) **Camping La Salette, 3720-222 Oliveira de Azemeis [(256) 674373]** Fr N1 turn E onto N224 to Vale de Cambra, foll sp Parque de La Salette. Med, shd; wc; shwrs €0.75; el pts (6A) €0.50; gas; lndtte; shop 100m; rest, snacks, bar adj; BBQ; playgrnd 300m; pool adj; TV; phone; bus 200m; Eng spkn; quiet. "Picturesque area." ♦ € 10.00   2005*

†OLIVEIRA DO HOSPITAL *C2* (6km SE) **Parque de Sao Giao, 3400-570 Sao Giao [(238) 691154; fax (238) 692451]** Fr N17 Guarda-Coimbra rd turn S almost opp N230 rd to Oliveira do Hospital, dir Sandomil. Site on R in about 3km over rv bdge. Lge, shd; wc; chem disp; shwrs; el pts (6A) €1.50; gas; lndtte; shop; rest; bar; BBQ; rv sw; pool 7km; playgrnd; fishing; phone; quiet. "Facs basic but clean; working water mill; app/exit long, steep, narr, lane." € 10.50   2002*

†OLIVEIRA DO HOSPITAL *C2* (15km S Rural) **Parque de Campismo Ponte Das Tres Entradas, Santa Ovaia, 3400-591 Avo [(238) 670050; fax (238) 670055; ponte3entradas@mail.telepac.pt; www.ponte3entradas.com]** On N17 Guarda-Coimbra rd after town of Oliveria do Hospital turn S at Pousada sp onto N230. Site sp by Rv Alva at Avo in approx 12km. Med, pt shd; wc; shwrs inc; el pts (4A) €1.60; gas; lndtte; shop; rest; snacks; bar; BBQ; rv sw; fishing; playgrnd; tennis; games area; TV; entmnt; cycle hire; phone; quiet; cc acc; site clsd Nov; cc acc; CCI. "Pretty site in mountains." ♦ € 9.00   2002*

OVAR see Espinho *B1*

PENACOVA *B2* (3km N Rural) **Camp Municipal de Vila Nova, Rua dos Barqueiros, Vila Nova, 3360-204 Penacova [(239) 477946; fax (239) 478098; penaparque@iol.pt]** IP3 fr Coimbra, cross Rv Mondego N of Penacova & foll sp R onto N2 to site. Med, pt shd; wc; shwrs inc; el pts (6A) inc; rest 150m; snacks; bar; BBQ; playgrnd; rv sw; fishing; no dogs; phone; red CCI. "Open, attractive site." 1 Apr-31 Oct. € 12.30
                                                                          2002*

PENACOVA *B2* (1km S Rural) **Camping Penacova, Estrada da Carvoeira, 3360 Penacova [tel/fax (239) 477464; penacova@fpcampismo.pt; www.fpcampismo.pt]** On N2 S of Penacova on E bank of rv. Fairly steep app needing care. Lge, pt shd; wc; chem disp; shwrs inc; el pts (4A) €1.30; gas 500m; shop; rest/snacks; bar; playgrnd; rv sw; fishing; canoeing; entmnt; 70% statics; phone; no dogs; quiet but poss noisy w/e; red low ssn; CCI. "Impeccable; lovely site; friendly helpful owner; pretty, rural area; heavily wooded; strenuous trek up to Penacova." ♦ 17 Jan-14 Nov. € 12.15   2004*

PENELA *B2* (500m SE Rural) **Parque Municipal de Campismo de Panela, Rua de Coimbra, 3230-284 Penela [(239) 569256; fax (239) 569400]** Fr Coimbra S on IC2, L at Condeixa a Nova, IC3 dir Penela. Thro vill foll sp to site. Sm, hstg, pt sl, terr, pt shd; wc; chem disp; shwrs inc; el pts (6A) €0.50; shop, rest, snacks, bar, pool 500m; some statics; some traff noise; CCI. "Attractive sm town; restful, clean, well-maintained site." ♦ ltd. 1 Jun-30 Sep. € 4.50   2002*

†PENICHE *B3* (1.5km E Coastal) **Camping Peniche Praia, Estrada Marginal Norte, 2520 Peniche [(262) 783460; fax (262) 789447; penichepraia@hotmail.com; www.penichepraia. pt]** Travel S on IP6 then take N114 sp Peniche; fr Lisbon N on N247 then N114 sp Peniche. Site on R on N114 1km bef Peniche. Lge, unshd; wc; shwrs inc; el pts (6A) €2.20; gas; lndtte; ice; shop; tradsmn; rest, snacks, bar high ssn; playgrnd; pool; sand beach 1km; cycle hire; entmnt; TV; phone; bus 2km; poss cr; Eng spkn; adv bkg rec; quiet; red long stay/low ssn; CCI. "Sm pitches." € 14.20   2004*

†PENICHE *B3* (3km E Coastal) **Camp Municipal de Peniche, Ave Monsenhor M Bastos, 2520-206 Peniche [(262) 789696; fax (262) 789529; www. cm-peniche.pt]** Site 2km E fr Lourinha after N114 (fr Obidos) joins N247; rd crosses bdge & site on R. V lge, terr, pt shd; wc; shwrs inc; el pts (4A) €1.30; gas; lndtte; shop; rest; bar; playgrnd; pool adj; beach 200m; fishing; tennis; 40% statics; phone; bus 100m; red low ssn; v quiet; cc acc. "Friendly staff; interesting area; gd NH." ♦ € 10.00   2004*

POCO REDONDO see Tomar *B2*

PONTE DA BARCA *B1* (4km N Rural) **Camping Travanca, Lugar de Boucas Donas, 4970-094 Arcos de Valdevez [(258) 526105 or (258) 452280; fax (258) 452450; aderepg@mail.telepac.pt; www.adere-pg.pt]** Fr Arcos de Valdevez on N202 twd Mezio, turn L sp Boucas Donas. Foll sp National Park & site. Sm, hdstg, pt shd; wc (some cont); baby facs; showrs inc; el pts (16A); shop; tradsmn; bar; BBQ; playgrnd; TV rm; no statics. "A new National Park site high up in glorious country; vg walking." 1 Jun-30 Aug. € 9.75   2004*

PONTE DA BARCA *B1* (14km E Rural) **Camping Entre-Ambos-os-Rios, Lugar da Igreja, Entre-Ambos-os-Rios, 4980-613 Ponte da Barca [(258) 588361 or 452250; fax (258) 452450; aderepg@ mail.telepac.pt; www.adere-pg.pt]**
N203 E fr Ponte da Barca, pass ent sp for vill. Site sp N twd Rv Lima, after 1st bdge. Lge, pt sl, shd; wc; shwrs inc; el pts (12A) inc; gas; lndry rm; rest 300m; snacks; bar; playgrnd; rv sw; canoeing; fishing; entmnt; TV; phone; bus 100m; adv bkg; CCI. "Beautiful site in National Park." 15 May-30 Sep.
€ 6.70   2005*

As we're travelling out of season, we'd better phone ahead to check that the site is actually open.

PORTALEGRE *C3* (5km NE Rural) **Camping ORBITUR, Quinta da Saude, Estrada da Serra, 7300-435 Portalegre [(245) 308384; fax (245) 308385; info@orbitur.com; www.orbitur.com]**
Fr Portalegre town on SE side take N246-2 dir Parque Serra de Sao Mamede. Go uphill in NE dir. Site on R in 5km at Quinta de Sande. NB. N246-2 is a loop rd. Do not take it fr N of Portalegre. Lge, pt sl, shd; wc; chem disp; mv service pnt; shwrs inc; el pts (5-15A) €2.25; gas; lndtte; shop adj; tradsmn; rest adj; bar; BBQ; playgrnd; pool adj; dogs €1.20; phone; quiet but poss some noise fr club adj to ent; cc acc; red low ssn/long stay/snr citizens; CCI. "Few level pitches; pitches in woodland glades."
15 Mar-15 Oct. € 17.20   2005*

†PORTIMAO *B4* (3km SE Coastal) **Camping Ferragudo, 8400-280 Ferragudo [(282) 461121; fax (282) 461355; geral@clubecampismolisboa. pt]** Leave N125 at sp Ferraguda, turn L at traff lts at end of Parchal vill. Turn R over waterway in Ferraguda, foll sp. V lge, terr, pt shd; cont wc; shwrs inc; el pts (4-6A) inc; gas; lndry rm; shop; rest; snacks; bar; playgrnd; pool; sw & fishing 800m; entmnt; TV; no dogs; phone; bus 100m; v cr Jul/Aug; CCI. "Helpful staff; bus to Portimao at ent; shop/recep 1.5km fr pitches; unsuitable lge motor homes; housing bet site & beach." € 26.40   2005*

†PORTIMAO *B4* (10km SW Urban) **Parque de Campismo da Dourada, 8500 Alvor [tel/fax (282) 459178]** Turn S at W end of N125 Portimao by-pass sp Alvor. Site on L in 4km bef ent town. V lge, pt sl, pt shd; wc; chem disp; shwrs €0.50; el pts (6A) €2.50; gas; lndtte; shop high ssn; rest; snacks; bar; playgrnd; pool 800m; sand beach 1km; fishing; sports area; entmnt; TVrm; dogs €1.75; bus 50m; poss noisy; red long stay/low ssn. "Friendly & helpful family-run site; facs ltd & poss poor low ssn; office frequently unattended in winter; pool planned for 2006." ♦ € 15.75   2005*

†PORTO *B1* (11km N Coastal) **Camping ORBITUR-Angeiras, Rua de Angeiras, Matosinhos, 4455-039 Lavra [(229) 270571 or 270634; fax (229) 271178; info@orbitur.pt; www. orbitur.com]** Fr m'way ICI/A28 take turn-off sp Lavra, site sp at end of slip rd. Site in approx 3km. V lge, pt sl, shd; wc (some cont); chem disp; mv service pnt; shwrs inc; el pts (5-15A) €2.25; gas; lndtte; shop; rest; snacks; bar; BBQ; playgrnd; pool; beach 400m; tennis; fishing; games area; games rm; TV; few statics; dogs €1.20; phone; bus to Porto; Eng spkn; adv bkg; red low ssn/long stay/snr citizens; cc acc; CCI. "Fish & veg mkt in Matosinhos; friendly staff; clean; gd pitches." ♦ € 20.40   2005*

†PORTO *B1* (16km SE Rural) **Campidouro Parque de Medas, Lugar do Gavinho, 4515-397 Medas-Gondomar [(224) 760161; fax (224) 769082; campidouro@iol.pt]** Take N12 dir Gondomar off A1. After 1st rndabt pick up N108 dir Entre-os-Rios. Sp for Medas on R, thro hamlet & foll sp for site on R. New concrete access/site rds. Lge, mkd pitch, hdstg, terr, pt shd; wc; chem disp; mv service pnt; serviced pitches; shwrs inc; el pts (6A) €2.40; gas; lndtte; shop, rest (w/e only low ssn); bar; playgrnd; pool & paddling pool; rv sw, fishing, boating; tennis; games rm; entmnt; TV rm; 90% statics; phone; bus; poss cr; quiet; cc acc; 20% red CCI. "Helpful owners; gd rest; v clean facs; hot water for shwrs only; sm level area (poss cr by rv) for tourers; some sm pitches; bus to Porto rec as parking diff; beautiful site on Rv Douro; long steep descent; excel."
€ 15.75   2005*

†PORTO *B1* (8km SW Coastal) **Camping Marisol, Rua Alto das Chaquedas 82, Canidelo, 400-356 Vila Nova de Gaia [(227) 135942; fax (227) 126351]** Fr Porto ring rd IC1 take N109 exit sp Espinho. In 1km take exit Madalena. Site sp on coast rd. Med, hdg pitch, pt shd; wc; chem disp; mv service pnt; shwrs inc; el pts (6A) inc; gas; lndry rm; shop; rest; bar; BBQ; playgrnd; pool 800m; sand beach adj; games area; car wash; TV; 50% statics; bus 150m; poss cr; Eng spkn. "Conv for Porto; gd." ♦ € 10.25   2004*

†PORTO *B1* (10km SW Coastal) **Camping ORBITUR-Madalena, Rua do Cerro 608, Praia da Madalena, 4405-736 Vila Nova de Gaia [(227) 122520 or 122524; fax (227) 122534; info@ orbitur.pt; www.orbitur.com]** Fr Porto ring rd IC1/A44 take N109 exit dir Espinho. In 1km take exit sp Madalena opp Volvo agent. Watch for either 'Campismo' or 'Orbitur' sp to site along winding, cobbled rd. V lge, terr, pt sl, pt shd; wc; chem disp; mv service pnt; serviced pitches; shwrs inc; el pts (5-15A) €2.25; gas; lndtte; shop; rest, snacks, bar in ssn; BBQ; playgrnd; pool; sand beach 250m; tennis; games area; entmnt; TV rm; 40% statics; dogs €1.20; phone; bus to Porto; Eng spkn; adv bkg; cc acc; red low ssn/long stay/snr citizens; CCI. "Site in forest; restricted area for tourers; slight aircraft noise; excel for visits Porto & wine cellars; do not take c'van into Porto; some uneven pitches; poss ltd facs low ssn; excel bus to Porto cent fr site ent; vg." ♦ € 20.40   2005*

Serra dos Mangues
2460-697 S. Martinho do Porto
☎ 351.262 989 764
🖷 351.262 989 763
E-mail: parque.colina.sol@clix.pt
Site: www.colinadosol.com

COLINA DO SOL

Open
All
Year

Free Swimming Pools – Beautifull Beaches – Restaurant – Bar – Children's Playground

†PORTO *B1* (3km NW Urban) **Parque de Campismo da Prelada, Rua Monte dos Burgos, 4250-318 Porto** [(228) 312616; www.roteiro-campista.pt/Porto/prelada.htm] Fr all dirs take Via de Centura Interna (central ring rd) IC23. NW of city cent take N13/14 Via Norte dir Braga & airport. Take 1st slip rd R dir, turn L under flyover dir Matosinhos. At 1st traff lts turn L. Site on R in 800m, sp. V lge, pt sl, shd; wc (some cont); mv service pnt; shwrs inc; el pts (2-6A) €1.85-3.69; gas; lndtte; shop; rest; snacks; bar; playgrnd; pool 3km; rocky beach 6km; tennis; phone; bus to city; rd noise on S side nr m'way; facs ltd low ssn; Eng spkn; CCI. "Tours of wine lodges, maintenance of facs poor out of ssn; fair." ♦ ltd. € 14.00   2004*

PORTO COVO see Sines *B4*

†POVOA DE VARZIM *B1* (13km N Coastal) **Camping ORBITUR-Rio Alto, EN13, Km 13, Lugar do Rio Alto, Estela, 4470-275 Povoa de Varzim** [(252) 615699; fax (252) 615599; info@orbitur.pt; www.orbitur.com] N on Povoa by-pass, in 11km turn L 1km N of Estela at Golf sp, in 3km turn R to camp ent. V lge, hdg/mkd pitch, terr, shd; wc; chem disp; shwrs inc; el pts (5-15A) €2.25; gas; lndtte; shop; rest; snacks; bar; BBQ; playgrnd; pool; sand beach 150m; tennis; games area; games rm; golf adj; entmnt; TV; 10% static/semi-statics; dogs €1.20; phone; Eng spkn; adv bkg; poss cr; red low ssn/long stay/snr citizens; cc acc; CCI. "Vg rest on site; direct access to vg beach; excel touring base." ♦ € 22.00   2005*

PRAIA DE MIRA see Mira *B2*

†PRAIA DE QUIAIOS *B2* (Coastal) **Camping ORBITUR, Praia de Quiaios, 3080-515 Quiaios** [(233) 919995; fax (233) 919996; info@orbitur.pt; www.orbitur.com] Fr N109 turn W onto N109-8 dir Quiaios, foll sp 3km to Praia de Quiaios & site. Lge, terr, shd; wc; shwrs inc; el pts (10A) €2.25; gas; lndtte; supmkt; rest; snacks; bar; BBQ; playgrnd; pool 500m; sand beach 500m; tennis; cycle hire; games rm; TV; entmnt; dogs €1.20; phone; cc acc; red low ssn/snr citizens/long stay; CCI. "Interesting historical area; vg touring base; peaceful site." € 17.90   2005*

†QUARTEIRA *C4* (2km N Coastal) **Camping ORBITUR-Quarteira, Estrada da Fonte Santa, Ave Sa Carneira, 8125 Quarteira** [(289) 302826 or 302821; fax (289) 302822; info@orbitur.pt; www.orbitur.com] Fr E & IP1/A22 take exit junc 3 at Loule onto N396 to Quarteira; on ent town L at rndabt by g'ge, cont on dual c'way to bottom of hill, turn L at 2nd traff lts, site on R in 2km. V lge, pt sl, terr, shd; wc; chem disp; mv service pnt; shwrs inc; el pts (6-10A) €2.25 (long lead req some pitches); gas; lndtte; supmkt 200m; rest; snacks; bar; playgrnd; pool; waterslide; sand beach 600m; tennis; disco; TV rm; 5% statics; dogs €1.20; phone; bus 50m; Eng spkn; aircraft noise fr Faro; red low ssn/long stay/snr citizens; cc acc; CCI. "Lovely site; popular winter long stay; some new san facs (2005); some el pts in need of update; caterpillar prob Jan-Mar; easy walk to town." ♦ € 23.90   2005*

ROSARIO see Alandroal *C3*

†SAGRES *B4* (2km W Coastal) **Camping ORBITUR, Cerro das Moitas, 8650-998 Sagres** [(282) 624371; fax (282) 624445; info@orbitur.pt; www.orbitur.com] On N268 to Cape St Vincent; well sp. V lge, hdg/mkd pitch, pt shd; wc; chem disp; mv service pnt; shwrs inc; el pts (6-10A) €2.25-2.75; gas; lndtte; shop; rest; snacks; bar; playgrnd; sand beach 2km; cycle hire; TV rm; dogs €1.20; Eng spkn; adv bkg; quiet; red long stay/low ssn/snr citizens; cc acc. "Vg, clean, tidy site in pine trees; cliff walks." ♦ € 19.40   2005*

SANTO ANTONIO DAS AREIAS *C3* (3km SE Rural) **Camping Asseiceira, Asseiceira, 7330-204 Santo Antonio das Areias** [tel/fax (245) 992940; michaellake40@sn.com] Fr N246-1 turn off sp Marvao/Santo Antonio das Areias. Turn L to Santo Antonio das Areias then 1st R on ent town then immed R again, up sm hill to rndabt. At rndabt turn R then at next rndabt cont straight on. There is a fuel station on R, cont down hill for 400m. Site on L. Sm, pt sl, pt shd; wc; chem disp; shwrs inc; el pts (16A) €2.50; gas 500m; shop, rest, snacks, bar 3km; pool 500m; no statics; bus 1km; quiet; CCI. "Clean, tidy, remote site; gd for walking, birdwatching; British owners; nr Spanish border." ♦ ltd. 1 Mar-30 Oct. € 14.50   2005*

†SAO MARTINHO DO PORTO *B2* (1.5km N Coastal) **Parque de Campismo Colina do Sol, Serra dos Mangues, 2460-697 Sao Martinho do Porto [(262) 989764; fax (262) 989763; parque.colina. sol@clix.pt; www.colinadosol.com]**
Leave A8/IC1 SW at junc 21 onto N242 W to Sao Martinho, by-pass town on N242 dir Nazare. Site on L northside of Sao Martinho. V lge, mkd pitch, pt sl, terr, pt shd; wc; chem disp; mv service pnt; shwrs inc; el pts (6A) €2.35; gas; lndtte; ice; shop 1km; rest; snacks; bar; BBQ; playgrnd; pool; paddling pool; sand beach 1.5km; fishing; TV; 10% statics; dogs €1; phone; poss cr; Eng spkn; adv bkg; quiet; cc acc; CCI. "Gd touring base on attractive coastline; vg." ♦ € 16.50   2005*

See advertisement

†SAO PEDRO DE MOEL *B2* (N Urban/Coastal) **Camping ORBITUR, Rua Volta dos Sete, Sao Pedro de Moel, 2430 Marinha Grande [(244) 599168; fax (244) 599148; info@orbitur.pt; www.orbitur.com]** Site at end of rd fr Marinha Grande to beach; turn R at 1st rndabt on ent vill. Site S of lighthouse. V lge, some hdg/mkd pitch, pt terr, shd; wc; chem disp; mv service pnt; shwrs inc; el pts (6A) €2.25; gas; lndtte; shop; rest; snacks; bar; BBQ; playgrnd; pool; waterslide; sand beach 500m (heavy surf); fishing; tennis; cycle hire; TV rm; dogs €1.20; phone; adv bkg; Eng spkn; quiet; red low ssn/long stay/snr citizens; cc acc; CCI. "Friendly, well-run, clean site; easy walk to shops, rests; site in pinewoods; Sao Pedro smart resort; ltd facs low ssn." ♦ € 22.00   2005*

†SAO TEOTONIO *B4* (7km W Coastal) **Camping Monte Carvalhal da Rocha, Praia do Carvalhal, Brejao, 7630-569 Sao Teotónio [(282) 947293; fax (282) 947294; geral@montecarvalhalr-turismo. com; www.montecarvalhalr-turismo.com]** Turn W off N120 dir Brejao, Carvalhal. Site sp. Med, shd; wc; shwrs inc; el pts (16A) €2.50; gas; lndry rm; shop, rest, snacks, bar high ssn; BBQ; playgrnd; sand beach 500m; fishing; cycle hire; TV; some statics; no dogs; phone; bus 2km; car wash; Eng spkn; adv bkg; quiet; cc acc; red low ssn. "Beautiful area; friendly, helpful staff." € 19.50   2005*

†SAO TEOTONIO *B4* (7km W Coastal) **Parque de Campismo da Zambujeira, Praia da Zambujeira, 7630-740 Zambujeira do Mar [(283) 961172; fax (283) 961320]** S on N120 twd Lagos, turn W when level with Sao Teotonio on unclass rd to Zambujeira. Site on L in 7km, bef vill. V lge, pt sl, pt shd; wc; chem disp; mv service pnt; shwrs €0.50; el pts (6-10A) €2; gas; shop, rest, snacks, bar high ssn; playgrnd; sand beach 1km; tennis; TV; some statics; phone; quiet; red low ssn/long stay. "In pleasant rural setting; sh walk to unspoilt vill with some shops & rest; cliff walks; coastal scenery; v welcoming, friendly owners." € 17.00   2003*

SATAO *C2* (10km N Rural) **Camping Quinta Chave Grande, Casfreires, Ferreira d'Aves, 3560-043 Satao [tel/fax (232) 655552; bert@mail. telepac.pt; www.chave-grande.com]** Leave IP5 Salamanca-Viseu rd onto N229 to Satao, site sp in Satao. Med, terr, pt shd; wc; chem disp; mv service pnt; shwrs inc; el pts (4A) €2; gas; lndtte; ice; shop 3km; tradsmn; rest 3km; snacks; bar; playgrnd; pool; tennis; TV; quiet; Eng spkn; red long stay. "Gd walks fr site; new friendly Dutch owners 2005; gd touring base; excel." 1 Apr-31 Oct. € 15.60   2004*

†SERPA *C4* (1km SE Urban) **Parque Municipal de Campismo Serpa, Largo de Sao Pedro, 7830-303 Serpa [(284) 544290; fax (284) 540109]** Sp fr most directions. Fr 2nd exit off N260 fr N not sp - need to take 1st R at 1st rndabt then foll sp. Do not ent walled town. V lge, pt sl, pt shd; wc; chem disp; shwrs inc; el pts (6A) €1.25; gas; lndtte; rest, snacks, bar 50m; BBQ; shop 100m; daily mkt 500m; supmkt nr; pool adj; rv sw 5km; 20% statics; dogs; phone; adv bkg; poss noise fr rd & barking dogs; no cc acc; CCI. "Popular, well-kept, basic site; simple, high quality facs; many facs poss not open low ssn; v pretty town, developing rapidly." ♦ € 7.74   2004*

SESIMBRA *B3* (2km W Coastal) **Camp Municipal Forte do Cavalo, Porto de Abrigo, 2970 Sesimbra [(212) 288508; fax (212) 288265; dscdet@ mun-sesimbra.pt; www.mun-sesimbra.pt]** Fr Lisbon S on A2/IP7 turn S onto N378 to Sesimbra. Turn R immed after town ent sp Campismo & Porto. Fork R again sp Porto; L downhill at traff lts to avoid town cent. Turn R at sea front to site by lighthouse. Steep uphill app. V lge, pt sl, terr, shd; wc; shwrs inc; el pts (6A) €1.80; gas; ice; shop; rest 200m; bar 500m; BBQ; playgrnd; beach 800m; fishing; boating; phone; no dogs; poss cr; quiet. "Pitches ltd for tourers; gd views; lovely, unique fishing vill; castle worth visit." 1 Apr-31 Oct. € 9.40   2004*

†SETUBAL *B3* (4km W Coastal) **Parque de Campismo do Outao, Estrada de Figueirinha, 2900-182 Setubal [(265) 238318; fax (265) 228098]** Fr Setubal take coast rd W twd Outao, site on L. V lge, pt shd; wc (some cont); chem disp; shwrs inc; el pts (5A) €2; gas; shop; rest; bar; playgrnd; sand beach adj; 90% statics; poss cr; some rd noise; red low ssn; 10% red CCI. ♦ € 13.10   2004*

†SINES *B4* (15km SE) **Parque de Campismo de Porto Covo, 7250-437 Porto Covo [(269) 905136; fax (269) 905239]** S fr Sines on N120 twd Cercal, turn R after 13km dir Porto Covo & site 200m bef vill. V rough app rd to site. Med, hdstg, pt sl, unshd; wc (cont); chem disp; mv service pnt; shwrs inc; el pts (4-10A) €2; gas; shop; rest; snacks; bar; BBQ; playgrnd; pool; sand beach; games area; cycle hire; boat trips; TV; mostly statics; dogs; bus 200m; phone; poss cr; poss noisy high ssn; adv bkg; red low ssn. "Not rec for tourers; few touring pitches & v sm, diff access; pleasant site; lovely vill." ♦ € 12.50   2003*

PORTUGAL

TOMAR *B2* (7km NE Rural) **Camping Rural Pelinos 77, Olalhas, 2300-093 Tomar** [(249) 301814; op100936@mail.telepac.pt] N fr Tomar on N110, turn R to Calcadas at traff lts opp g'ge, foll site sp. Sm, terr, pt shd; wc; chem disp (wc); serviced pitches; shwrs inc; el pts (8A) €2; lndtte; shop 100m; rest; snacks; bar; BBQ (winter only); playgrnd; pool; lake sw, watersports, fishing 5km; TV; dogs; phone; quiet; Eng spkn; adv bkg; red low ssn; CCI. "Owner will assist taking o'fits in/out; vg." 15 Jan-15 Nov. € 10.00   2002*

TOMAR *B2* (10km E Rural) **Camping Redondo, Rua do Casal Rei, 2300-035 Poco Redondo** [tel/fax (249) 376421; hansfromme@hotmail. com; http://home.wanadoo.nl/edvols] Fr N or S on N110, take IC3 for Tomar, then take 1st exit sp Albufeira do Castelo de Bode/Tomar. Foll site sp (red hearts) for 7km. Steep drop at site ent. Sm, pt sl, pt shd; wc; chem disp; mv service pnt; shwrs inc; el pts (4-6A) €1.95-2.20; lndtte; shop 2km; rest; snacks; bar; playgrnd; pool; waterslide; lake beach 4.5km; TV rm; few statics; phone; bus; poss cr; Eng spkn; adv bkg; red low ssn; CCI. "Due steep drop at ent, site owner tows c'vans out." 15 Mar-1 Oct. € 12.50   2005*

TOMAR *B2* (10km SE Rural) **Camping Castelo do Bode, 2200 Abrantes-Martinchel** [(241) 849262; fax (241) 849244; castelo.bode@fcmportugal. com] S fr Tomar on N110, in approx 7km L onto N358-2 dir Barragem & Castelo do Bode. Site on L in 6km immed after dam; steep ent. Med, mkd pitch, hdstg, terr, pt shd; wc (some cont); chem disp; shwrs inc; el pts (2A) inc; gas; ice; supmkt 6km; tradsmn; rest, snacks 2km; bar; playgrnd; lake sw adj; boating; fishing; dogs €0.50; phone; bus to Tomar 1km; no adv bkg; quiet; CCI. "Lovely site on edge of 60km long lake with excel watersports; old san facs, but clean; helpful staff; a gem of a site; lge free carpark on ent Tomar." 14 Jan-14 Nov. € 11.25
                                                                     2005*

†**VAGOS** *B2* (6km W) **Parque de Campismo da Vagueira, 3840-254 Vagueira** [(234) 797618 or 797526; fax (234) 797093; www.roteiro-campista. pt/Aveiro/vagueira.htm] Fr Aveiro take N109 S twd Figuera da Foz. Turn R in Vagos vill. After 6km along narr poor rd, site on R bef reaching Vagueira vill. V lge, shd; wc; chem disp; shwrs inc; el pts (6A) inc; gas; lndtte; ice; rest; bar; playgrnd; pool 1.5km in Vagos; sand beach 500m; fishing adj; tennis; entmnt; 90% statics; adv bkg; quiet; cc acc; red CCI. "Poss diff access to pitches for lge o'fits; areas soft sand. ♦ € 14.40   2002*

VALHELHAS *C2* (1km W Rural) **Camp Municipal Rossio de Valhelhas, 6300-235 Valhelhas** [(275) 487160; fax (275) 487372; jfvalhelhas@ clix.pt; www.valhelhas.com] Fr Manteigas, site is on R of N232 on ent Valhelhas. Lge, shd; wc; shwrs inc; el pts (4A) inc (long lead req); lndry rm; shop 150m; rest 300m; snacks; bar; playgrnd; rv sw adj; fishing; games area; few statics; no dogs; phone; bus 100m; poss cr; quiet; cc not acc; CCI. "Pleasant, woodland site; conv for touring Serra da Estrella; rv dammed to make natural sw pool; friendly, helpful staff." 1 May-30 Sep. € 9.10   2005*

VALPACOS *C1* (6km E Rural) **Campismo Rabacal-Valpacos, Lugar de Faixo, Rio Rabacal, 5430 Valpacos** [(278) 759354] Fr E82/IP4 turn N onto N213 to Valpacos, turn R onto N206, site sp. Lge, pt shd; wc; shwrs inc; el pts (6A) €1; lndtte; rest; snacks; bar; BBQ; fishing; rv sw; playgrnd; phone; quiet; red CCI. "Friendly staff; beautiful rvside setting." ♦ 1 May-30 Sep. € 6.75
                                                                     2002*

VALVERDE see Lagos *B4*

†**VIANA DO CASTELO** *B1* (3km S Coastal) **Parque de Campismo Inatel do Cabedelo, Rua Dos Trabalhadores, Cabedelo, 4900-164 Darque** [(258) 322042; fax (258) 331502] Fr Viana take N13 over old bdge twd Porto. Take immed R sp Cabedelo & Campismo. In 2km turn L into site app rd. Lge, mkd pitch, hdstg, pt sl, pt shd; wc (some cont); shwrs inc; el pts (6A) inc; gas; lndtte; shop; tradsmn; snacks; bar; sand beach adj; entmnt; 30% statics; no dogs; phone; adv bkg; quiet; CCI. "V secure; gd for children; hourly ferry to Viana; spacious pitches under pines; poss poor facs low ssn & in need of refurb; site clsd 10 Dec-15 Jan." ♦ € 12.50   2005*

†**VIANA DO CASTELO** *B1* (2km SW Coastal) **Camping ORBITUR-Cabedelo, Rua Diogo Alvares, Cabedelo, 4900-161 Darque** [(258) 322167; fax (258) 321946; info@orbitur.pt; www. orbitur.com] On N13 twd Porto fr Viana do Castelo (rec do not take bdge on A28/IC1). Turn 1st R after bdge over Rv Lima sp Cabedelo & Camping. Foll sp for 2km to site. Site in park on L. Lge, pt sl, shd; wc; mv service pnt; shwrs inc; el pts (5-15A) €2.25; gas; lndtte; shop; rest; snacks; bar; BBQ; playgrnd; pool; lge sand beach adj; surfing; fishing; entmnt; TV; dogs €1.20; phone; Eng spkn; adv bkg; quiet; red low ssn/long stay/snr citizens; cc acc; CCI. "Site in pinewoods; friendly staff; gd facs; plenty of shade; major festival in Viana 3rd w/e in Aug; lge mkt in town Fri am; sm passenger ferry over Rv Lima to town; beach access fr site." ♦ € 20.40
                                                                     2005*

VIEIRA DO MINHO *C1* (1.5km S Urban) **Parque de Campismo de Cabreira, Lugar de Entre os Rios, 4850 Vieira do Minho [(253) 648665; fax (253) 648667; bina.vc@mil.telepac.pt]** Take N103 E fr Braga for 30km; foll sp to Vieira Do Minho, site sp in Vieira at 1.5km. Lge, pt shd; wc; chem disp (wc); shwrs inc; el pts (5A) €2.50; gas; lndtte; shop; rest; snacks; bar; playgrnd; 2 pools adj; rv sw adj; sports area; cycle hire; entmnt; phone; bus 1km; Eng spkn; quiet; CCI. "V friendly; good, level grassy site; conv for Geres National Park." ♦ ltd. 1 Feb-31 Oct. € 14.50   2005*

We're having a great holiday - must fill in some site report forms and send them to The Club as soon as possible.

†VILA DO BISPO *B4* (8km SE Coastal/Rural) **Parque de Campismo Quinta dos Carricos (Part Naturist), Praia de Salema, 8650-196 Budens [(282) 695201; fax (282) 695122; quintacarrico@oninet.pt]** Take N125 out of Lagos twd Sagres. In approx 14km at sp Salema, turn L. Site on R 300m. V lge, pt terr (tractor avail); pt shd; wc; chem disp; mv service pnt; shwrs €0.60; el pts (6A) €2.30 (metered for long stay); gas; lndtte; ice; shop; rest; snacks; bar; pool 1km; sand beach 1km; golf 1km; 8% statics; dogs €1.15; phone; bus; Eng spkn; adv bkg (ess high ssn); quiet; cc acc; red long stay; CCI. "Naturist section in sep valley; apartments avail on site; friendly Dutch owners; tractor avail to tow to terr; area of wild flowers in spring; no music allowed; beach 30 mins walk; buses pass ent for Lagos, beach & Sagres; excel." ♦ € 19.70   2005*

†VILA DO BISPO *B4* (3km S Rural/Coastal) **Camping Praia da Ingrina, Raposeira, 8650 Vila do Bispo [tel/fax (282) 639242; manuel.carlos-361@clix.pt]** Fr Vila do Bispo take N125 E to Raposeira. At traff lts turn R sp Ingrina. After 1km bear R & foll sp to site. Last km of access rd rough. Med, terr, pt shd; wc; chem disp (wc); shwrs inc; el pts (6A) €2.60; gas; shop; rest & 1km; snacks; bar; BBQ; playgrnd; sand beach 600m; dogs €2.50; phone; red long stay; CCI. "Basic CL-type site; gd cliff walks to unspoilt beaches/surfing beaches; el pts ltd - long lead req; fair." € 14.50   2003*

†VILA FLOR *C1* (2.5km SW Rural) **Camp Municipal de Vila Flor, Barragem do Peneireiro, 5360-303 Vila Flor [(278) 512350; fax (278) 512380; cm.vila.flor@mail.telepac.pt]** Site is off N215, sp fr all dirs. Bumpy app rd. V lge, terr, pt shd; wc; chem disp (wc); shwrs; el pts (16A) €1.50; gas; lndry rm; shop; snacks; bar; BBQ; playgrnd; pool adj; tennis adj; TV rm; 10% statics; dogs; phone; poss v cr; adv bkg; CCI. "Friendly staff; v pleasant." ♦ ltd. € 8.50   2005*

†VILA FRANCA DE XIRA *B3* (1km NE) **Camp Municipal Vila Franca de Xira, 2600-125 Vila Franca de Xira [(263) 275258; fax (263) 271511; xiracamping@cm-vfxira.pt]** Fr A1/IP1 exit junc 3 onto N1 dir Vila Franca. Immed cobble stone rd to town seen, turn R & site well sp. Sm, hdstg, terr, pt shd; wc (some cont); chem disp (wc); shwrs inc; el pts (12A) €0.85; playgrnd; pool; fishing 800m; canoeing 400m; entmnt; 40% statics; bus 200m, rlwy stn 1km; site clsd Dec; poss cr; Eng spkn; some rd noise; red long stay; CCI. "Conv trains to Lisbon; gd NH." € 10.30   2004*

VILA NOVA DE CACELA see Vila Real de Santo Antonio *C4*

VILA NOVA DE GAIA see Porto *B1*

†VILA NOVA DE MILFONTES *B4* (Coastal) **Camping Campiferias, 7645-301 Vila Nova de Milfontes [(283) 996409; fax (283) 996581; novaferias@oninet.pt]** S fr Sines on N120/IC4 for 22km; turn R at Cercal on N390 SW for Milfontes on banks of Rio Mira; clear sp. If driving thro Vila Nova twd coast, look out for site sp on R. V lge, shd; wc; chem disp; shwrs inc; el pts (5A) €1.90; shop 50m; rest; snacks; bar; playgrnd; beach 800m; entmnt; TV; no dogs; site clsd 2-25 Dec; adv bkg; quiet; red low ssn. "V clean site; trees may make pitching diff; conv for beach & shops; mkt opp." ♦ € 13.30   2004*

†VILA NOVA DE MILFONTES *B4* (1km N Coastal) **Parque de Campismo de Milfontes, 7645-300 Vila Nova de Milfontes [tel/fax (283) 996104; parquemilfontes@netc.pt]** S fr Sines on N120/IC4 for 22km; turn R at Cercal on N390 SW for Milfontes on banks of Rio Mira; clear sp. V lge, pt shd; wc; chem disp; shwrs inc; el pts (4-9A) €2); gas; lndtte; shop supmkt & mkt 5 mins walk; rest; snacks; bar; playgrnd; sand beach 800m; TV; phone; poss cr; quiet; cc acc; 10% red CCI. "Pitching poss diff for lge o'fits due trees & statics; nr fishing vill at mouth Rv Mira with beaches & sailing on rv; poss probs with elec supply; nice site." ♦ € 15.00   2003*

†VILA NOVA DE MILFONTES *B4* (5km N Coastal) **Sitava Camping, Brejo da Zimbreira, 7645-017 Vila Nova de Milfontes [(283) 890100; fax (283) 890109; sitava@mail.telepac.pt; www.sitava.pt]** S fr Sines on N120/IC4. At Cercal take dir Vila Nova de Milfontes. At Brunheiras turn R at site sp; site in 4km on L. Lge, mkd pitch, pt sl, pt shd; wc (cont); serviced pitches; chem disp; shwrs inc; el pts (6A) €2; gas; lndtte; shop; rest; snacks; bar; BBQ; playgrnd; pool; sand beach 600m; tennis; entmnt; TV; 60% statics; no dogs; phone; bus 100m; poss cr; Eng spkn; adv bkg; quiet; red low ssn/CCI. "Friendly staff; bus to beach; excel facs but ltd low ssn; vg security." ♦ € 12.90   2005*

PORTUGAL

SITES

VILA PRAIA DE ANCORA *B1* (7km S) **Parque de Campismo do Paco, Estrade do Paco, 4910-024 Vila Praia de Ancora [tel/fax (258) 912697; camping.paco@sapo.pt]** Fr N13 Caminha-Viana do Castelo, site sp 1km S of Ancora, km 81. Med, pt shd; wc; chem disp; mv service pnt; shwrs inc; el pts (6A) €2; gas; lndtte; ice; shop; tradsmn; rest; snacks; bar; BBQ; playgrnd; pool 1.5km; rv sw; sand beach 1km; fishing; canoeing; games area; TV; phone; car wash; adv bkg (dep req); Eng spkn; quiet; cc acc; red CCI. "Pleasant staff; excel san facs; vg touring base; gd beaches nr."
15 Apr-30 Sep. € 13.30   2003*

VILA REAL *C1* (1km NE Urban) **Clube de Campismo de Vila Real, Rua de Dr Manuel Cardona, 5000-558 Vila Real [(259) 324724 or 325665]** On IP4/E82 take Vila Real N exit & head S into town. At Galp g'ge rndabt, turn L & in 30m turn L again Site at end of rd in 400m. Site sp. Lge, pt sl, terr, pt shd; wc; chem disp; shwrs inc; el pts (6A) inc; gas; sm shop adj; rest; snacks; bar; BBQ; playgrnd; pool complex adj; tennis; 10% statics; dogs; phone; bus 200m; site clsd mid-Dec to mid Jan; poss cr; 10% red CCI. "Conv upper Douro; old-fashioned facs ltd when site full; gd mkt in town."
♦ ltd. 1 Mar-30 Nov. € 12.50   2005*

†VILA REAL DE SANTO ANTONIO *C4* (3km W Coastal) **Parque Municipal de Campismo, 8900 Monte Gordo [(281) 510970; fax (281) 510003; cmvrsa@mail.telepac.pt]** Fr Faro on N125 turn R sp Monte Gordo. Site on sea front in 500m. Or fr Spain over bdge at border, exit junc 9 to Vila Real over rlwy line. Strt over rndabt & turn R at T-junc, site sp just bef ent town. V lge, pt sl, shd; wc (some cont); chem disp; shwrs inc; el pts (10A) €1.52; gas; lndtte; lndry rm; ice; shop & 1km; tradsmn; rest; snacks; bar; BBQ; playgrnd; sand beach 100m; canoeing; TV; 10% statics; dogs; phone; bus; train to Faro 3km; v cr in ssn; Eng spkn; no adv bkg; quiet; cc acc; red low ssn/long stay/snr citizens; CCI. "V lge pitches but poss v overcr high ssn; caution soft sand makes some pitches unreliable, esp in wet; ground poss too soft for lge o'fits; san facs poor & site unkempt; lovely area; gd birdwatching; gd security." ♦ € 16.74   2005*

†VILA REAL DE SANTO ANTONIO *C4* (10km W) **Camping Calico, Sitio do Calico, 8900-907 Vila Nova de Cacela [(281) 951195; fax (281) 951548; transcampo@mail.telepac.pt; www.roteiro-campista.pt]** On N side of N125 Vila Real to Faro rd. Sp on main rd & in Vila Nova de Cacela vill, visible fr rd. Rds have been re-surfaced for 95% of the way. Lge, pt sl, shd; wc; chem disp; shwrs inc; el pts (6A) inc; gas; lndtte; shop; rest; bar; playgrnd; pool; sand beach 4km; cycle hire; many statics; phone; Eng spkn; adv bkg; noisy in ssn & rd noise; red long stay/low ssn; CCI. "Friendly staff; site slowly being renovated; NH only." € 17.00   2003*

VILAR DE MOUROS see Caminha *B1*

VISEU *C2* (2km E Urban) **Camping ORBITUR-Fontelo, Rua do Fontelo, Barrio Santa Eugenia 3500-033 Viseu [(232) 436146; fax (232) 432076; info@orbitur.pt; www.orbitur.com]** Take exit Viseu Este fr rd IP5, at 1st rndabt (approx 2km) foll sp to site. Steep rd access fr recep. Lge, sl, shd; wc; chem disp; mv service pnt; shwrs inc; el pts (6A) €2.25; gas; lndtte; shop; rest 100m; snacks; bar; BBQ; playgrnd; pool 10km; TV; dogs €1.20; phone; Eng spkn; adv bkg; quiet; cc acc; red low ssn/long stay/snr citizens; CCI. "Very helpful & friendly; interesting cathedral, museum & art gallery nrby; excel san facs; surrounding country beautiful; poss diff to manoeuvre on site amongst trees; excel carnival 24 June annually." ♦ 15 Mar-15 Oct.
€ 17.20   2005*

This site entry hasn't been updated for a while; we'd better fill in a site report form and send it to The Club.

†VOUZELA *C2* (3km E) **Parque Campismo Municipal Vouzela, Senhora do Castelo, 3670-250 Vouzela [(232) 740020; fax (232) 711513; parquecampismo@cm-vouzela.pt]** Fr Vouzela foll N228; turn R sp Sra do Castelo. Site well sp fr town cent. Steep app. V lge, pt sl, terr, pt shd; wc; chem disp; mv service pnt; shwrs inc; el pts (6-15A) €1.25; gas; lndry rm; shop; rest; snacks; bar; playgrnd; pool; tennis; cycle hire; entmnt; TV; 95% statics; phone; quiet except w/e; CCI. "Lovely location; poss diff to find pitch bet statics; access to higher terrs by steep hill." ♦ € 8.50   2005*

ZAMBUJEIRA DO MAR see Sao Teotonio *B4*

SPAIN

Legend:

Motorways
Major roads
Main Roads

- All year site(s)
- Seasonal site(s)
- No sites listed

200m +
0-200m

N
W E
S

0   30   60   90   120 150 km
0   20   40   60   80   100 miles

© Collins Bartholomew Ltd 2005

VALENÇA
Lamas de Mouro
Caminha
Ponte da Barca
Vila Praia de Âncora
VIANA DO CASTELO
Geres
BRAGANÇA
N103
Vieira do Minho
CHAVES
Valpaços
N218
Cabeceiras de Basto
Mirandela
N216
MIRANDA DO DOURO
BRAGA
Guimarães
IP4
Póvoa de Varzim
N2
Amarante
IP4
Vila Flor
Mogadouro
PORTO
VILA REAL
N220
Espinho
Lamego
Castro Daire
N226,IC26
Oliveira de Azeméis
N102,IP2
N221
Vouzela
Satão
VILAR FORMOSO
VISEU
AVEIRO
IP5
A25,IP5
Vagos
IP3
Gouveia
N17
GUARDA
Mira
N23A
Oliveira do Hospital
Valhelhas
Luso
Penacova
Covilhã
N238
Praia de Quiaios
COIMBRA
Arganil
FUNDÃO
Figueira da Foz
Góis
Louriçal
Penela
N112
Idanha-a-Nova
São Pedro de Moel
LEIRIA
IC8
CASTELO BRANCO
Nazaré
N113
Tomar
São Martinho do Porto
Alcobaça
Abrantes
IP6
IP2
Caldas da Rainha
Santo Antonio das Areias
Peniche
Santo Antonio das Areias
PORTALEGRE
SANTARÉM
N119
Vila Franca de Xira
IP2
Ericeira
Montargil
Campo Maior
N245
ELVAS
N251
A6,IP7
Cascais
N114
N4
A6,IP2,IP7
Alandroal
Fernão Ferro
LISBOA
ÉVORA
N254
Sesimbra
SETÚBAL
N18,IP2
N256
Alcácer do Sal
MOURÃO
IC1
Odivelas
N261
IP2
N121
SINES
N18
BEJA
N260,IP8
Vila Nova de Milfontes
N2
Serpa
VILA VERDE DE FICALHO
Odemira
N263
IP2
N122
São Teotónio
A2,IP1
Aljezur
IC1
Vila do Bispo
N268
N125
PORTIMÃO
Quarteira
A22,IP1
VILA REAL DE SANTO ANTÓNIO
SAGRES
Lagos
Albufeira
Olhão
N125
FARO

SPAIN

At the crossroads of Europe and Africa and the third largest country in western Europe, Spain has some of Europe's most popular holiday resorts and areas of outstanding natural beauty. Most visitors converge on the 'costas' but the mountains, national parks, towns and villages of the interior reflect a rich culture, history and artistic legacy combined with wonderful scenery.

ESSENTIAL FACTS

Capital: Madrid (population 3.1 million)
Area: 504,782 sq km (inc Balearic & Canary Islands)
Bordered by: Andorra, France, Portugal
Terrain: High, rugged central plateau, mountains to north and south
Climate: Temperate climate; hot summers, cold winters in the interior; more moderate summers and cool winters along the northern and eastern coasts; very hot summers and mild/warm winters along the southern coast; The best time to visit northern Spain is summer; the centre is best in autumn and the south best in winter and spring
Coastline: 4,964 km
Highest Point (mainland Spain): Mulhacen (Granada) 3,478 m
Population: 40.3 million
Languages: Castilian Spanish, Catalan, Galician, Basque
Religion: 90% Roman Catholic
Government: Parliamentary democracy and monarchy
Local Time: GMT/BST + 1, ie 1 hour ahead of the UK all year
Currency: Euro divided into 100 cents; £1 = € 1.47, € 1 = 67 pence *

TOURIST INFORMATION

SPANISH TOURIST OFFICE
(Visits by appointment only)
79 NEW CAVENDISH STREET
LONDON W1W 6NB
P.O. BOX 4009, LONDON W1A 6NB
Tel: 0845 9400180 (brochure requests) or
020 7486 8077 (Mon-Fri 9.15am-4.15pm)
www.tourspain.co.uk
info.londres@tourspain.es

OPENING HOURS

Banks – Mon-Fri 9am-2pm, Sat 9am-1pm.

Museums – Tue-Sat 10am-8pm, Sun 10am-2pm; closed Monday.

Post Offices – Mon-Fri 8.30am-2/30pm & 5pm-8pm, Sat 9am-1pm.

Shops – Mon-Sat 10am-1pm & 4pm-8pm.

PUBLIC HOLIDAYS 2006

Jan 1, 6; Apr 13, 14, 17; May 1; Aug 15; Oct 12 (National Holiday); Nov 1; Dec 6 (Constitution Day), 8, 25. Several other dates for fiestas according to region. School summer holidays stretch from mid-June to mid-September.

TELEPHONING AND THE INTERNET

From the UK dial 0034 for Spain. All numbers have 9 digits, starting with 9, which incorporate the area code. Mobile phone numbers start with a 6. To call the UK from Spain dial 0044, omitting the initial zero of the area code. To call Gibraltar dial 00350.

Mobile phones – roaming agreements with all major GSM networks; use of hand-held phones is hibited when driving; mobile phones must not be used at all at petrol stations.

Public phones – operated with coins or cards.

Internet – access is widely available at cyber cafés and computer shops. Expect to pay from € 2 to € 6 per hour.

Emergency numbers – Police 112; Fire brigade 112; Ambulance 112.

Exchange rates as at October 2005

SPAIN

The following introduction to Spain should be read in conjunction with the important information contained in the Handbook chapters at the front of this guide.

CAMPING AND CARAVANNING

Casual Camping

Before camping on private property it is necessary to obtain the owner's permission. In order to camp on municipal or communal land, permission must be obtained from the local authority or tourist office of the area. Camping is prohibited less than one kilometre from a campsite, near residential buildings and other populated centres or near a beach.

Organised Camping and Caravanning

There are approximately 1,200 campsites in Spain with something to suit all tastes, from some of the best and biggest holiday parks in Europe, to a wealth of attractive small sites offering a personal, friendly welcome. Most campsites are located near the Mediterranean, especially on the Costa Brava and Costa del Sol, as well as in the Pyrenees and other areas of tourist interest. Spanish campsites are indicated by blue road signs. In general pitch sizes are small at about 80 square metres.

Whereas many sites claim to be open all year, this cannot always be relied on and if planning a visit out of season it is advisable to check first. Some 'all year' sites open only at the weekends during the winter and facilities may be very limited. If staying on sites in the popular coastal areas between late spring and October, or in January and February, it is advisable to arrive early in the afternoon or to book in advance.

An International Camping Card (CCI), while not compulsory, is recommended and is increasingly required when checking into Spanish sites. Senior citizens may be eligible for a discounted prices at some sites on presentation of proof of age.

All place names used in the Site Entry listings which follow can be found in Michelin's Touring & Motoring Atlas for Spain & Portugal, scale 1:400,000 (1 cm = 4 km).

Affiliated National Club

FEDERACIÓN ESPANOLA DE CAMPING Y CARAVANING (FECC)
APTDO DE CORREOS 221
E-28850 MADRID
Tel: 914-39 08 04 Fax: 914-39 61 02
campistasfecc@terra.es

COUNTRY INFORMATION

Cycling

There are more than 70 dedicated cycle paths in Spain, many of which follow disused railway tracks. Known as 'Vias Verdes' they can be found in northern Spain, in Andalucia, around Madrid and inland from the Costa Blanca. For more information see the website www.viasverdes.com or contact the Spanish Tourist Office.

It is compulsory for all cyclists, regardless of age, to wear a safety helmet on all roads outside built-up areas. The helmet may be removed on long hills or when the weather is extremely hot! At night, in tunnels or in bad weather, bicycles must have front and rear lights, together with reflectors at the rear and on wheels and pedals. Cyclists must also wear a reflecting device while riding at night on roads outside built-up areas (to be visible from a distance of 150 metres) or when visibility is bad.

Strictly speaking, cyclists have right of way when motor vehicles wish to cross their path to turn left or right, but great care should be taken. Do not proceed unless you are sure that a motorist is giving way.

Transportation of Bicycles

Spanish regulations stipulate that bicycles may be carried on the rear of a vehicle providing the rack to which the motorcycle or bicycle is fastened has been designed for the purpose. Lights, indicators, number plate and any signals made by the driver must not be obscured and the rack should not rest on the vehicle's tow bar or compromise the carrying vehicle's stability.

An overhanging load, such as bicycles, may exceed the length of the vehicle by up to 10% (up to 15% in the case of indivisible items) and the load must be indicated by a 50 cm square panel with reflectorised red and white diagonal stripes. These panels may be purchased in the UK from motor caravan or caravan dealers/accessory shops. There is currently no requirement for bicycle racks to be certified or pass a technical inspection.

If you are planning to travel from Spain to Portugal please note that slightly different official regulations apply which are set out in the Portugal Country Introduction.

Electricity and Gas

The power supply in Spain is 230 volts and the current on campsites is 4 amps or more. Plugs have two round pins. Most campsites do not yet have CEE connections.

Campingaz is widely available in 901 and 907 cylinders. The Cepsa Company sells butane gas cylinders and regulators, which are available in large stores and petrol stations, and the Repsol Company sells butane cylinders at their petrol stations throughout the country. It is understood that Repsol and Cepsa depots will refill cylinders, but the Caravan Club does not recommend this practice.

See Electricity and Gas in the section DURING YOUR STAY.

Entry Formalities

Holders of British and Irish passports are permitted to stay up to 90 days without a visa. If planning to stay longer, an application must be made to the local police for a residence card (tarjeta de residencia).

Regulations for Pets

See Pet Travel Scheme under Documents in the section PLANNING AND TRAVELLING.

Dogs must be kept on a lead in a public place and in a car they should be isolated from the driver by means of bars or netting.

Medical Services

Basic emergency health care is available free from practitioners in the Spanish National Health Service on production of a European Health Insurance Card (EHIC). In some parts of the country you may have to travel some distance to attend a surgery or health clinic operating within the health service. In any event, it is probably quicker and more convenient to use a private clinic, but the Spanish health service will not refund any private healthcare charges. Dental treatment is not generally provided under the state system and you will have to pay for treatment.

Medicines prescribed by health service practioners can be obtained from any pharmacy (farmacia) and are free to EU pensioners. In an emergency go to the casualty department (urgencias) of any major hospital. Urgent treatment is free in a public ward at a public hospital on production of an EHIC; for other treatment you will have to pay 40% of the cost.

RTFB Publishing produces a useful quick reference health guide for travellers priced £4.99, plus health phrase books in French and Spanish, priced £1.99 each. Telephone 023 8022 9041 or see www.whatshouldido.com for further details and orders.

You are strongly recommended to obtain comprehensive travel and medical insurance before travelling to Spain, such as the Caravan Club's Red Pennant Motoring & Personal Holiday Insurance.

See Medical Matters in the section PLANNING AND TRAVELLING.

Safety and Security

See Safety and Security in the section DURING YOUR STAY.

Street crime is common in many Spanish cities, towns and holiday resorts. It is occasionally accompanied by violence. You should avoid carrying passports, credit cards, travel tickets and money together in handbags or pockets and you should keep all valuable personal items, such as cameras or jewellery, out of sight. The authorities have stepped up the police presence in tourist areas. Nevertheless, you should remain alert in all areas (including airports, train and bus stations, and even in supermarkets and their car parks). In Madrid particular care should be taken in the Puerto de Sol and surrounding streets, including the Plaza Mayor, Retiro Park and Lavapies, and on the metro. This advice also applies to the Ramblas and Monjuic areas of Barcelona and to the Plaza Catalunya. Visitors should be wary of approaches by strangers either asking directions or offering any kind of help. These approaches, at times made by bogus police officers, are sometimes ploys to distract attention while they or their accomplices make off with valuables and/or take note of credit card numbers for future illegal use. Beware also muggers who use children or babies to distract your attention while you are being robbed.

The incidence of rape and sexual assault is very low; nevertheless visitors are advised not to lower their personal security awareness because they are on holiday. They should also be alert to the availability and possible use of 'date rape' drugs in Spain.

Motorists travelling on motorways, particularly those north and south of Barcelona, those in the Madrid area, in some parts of Andalucia and around Alicante and Murcia, should be alert for 'highway pirates' who target foreign registered and hire cars (the latter have a distinctive number plate), especially those towing caravans. Be suspicious when parked in lay-bys or picnic areas of approaches by other motorists asking for help.

Motorists are sometimes targeted in service areas, followed and subsequently tricked into stopping on the hard shoulder. The usual ploy is for the driver or passenger in a passing vehicle, which may be 'official-looking', to suggest by gesture that there is something seriously wrong with a rear wheel or exhaust pipe (a tyre having been punctured earlier, for example in a petrol station). The Club has received reports of the involvement of a second vehicle whose occupants also indicate a problem at the rear of your vehicle and that you should pull over onto the hard shoulder. If flagged down by other motorists or a motorcyclist in this way, be extremely wary. The Spanish Tourist Office advises holidaymakers not to pull over but to wait until they reach a service area or toll station. If you do get out of your car when flagged down, take care it is locked while you check outside, even if someone is left inside. Car keys should never be left in the ignition.

A few incidents have been reported of visitors being approached by a bogus uniformed police officer asking to inspect their wallet for fake euro notes or to check their identity by punching their credit card PIN into an official-looking piece of equipment carried by the officer. If approached in this way refuse to comply with the request and offer instead to go to the nearest police station.

Spanish police have set up an emergency number with English-speaking staff for holidaymakers (902-10 21 12) offering round-the-clock assistance in Alicante, Barcelona, Madrid, Malaga, Seville and Valencia. Tourists still have to report to a police station if they have an accident, or have been robbed or swindled. They will be told on the phone where to find the nearest police station.

Despite the Madrid train bombings in March 2004, together with a series of small bomb explosions in tourist resorts, the threat to British citizens is low but, given the possibility of further incidents, there is a risk that tourists could be caught up in terrorist attacks. Future bombings may not carry advance warnings and bombs may explode prematurely. Visitors throughout Spain should be alert to the situation and immediately report anything of a suspicious nature to the police, including bags or other objects.

The terrorist group, ETA, has warned that it will continue to target tourist facilities. There are also regular incidents of street violence in the Basque country involving organisations sympathetic to ETA, and directed against the security forces, political parties and banks. Similar incidents happen elsewhere in the country and other possible targets include multinational companies with operations in Spain. There is a heightened risk of incidents occurring during local fiestas.

If travelling to Spain with the intention of buying property, you are strongly advised to engage an experienced local lawyer and to deal only with established and reputable estate agents. Some general guidance notes on the subject are available from the Spanish Desk in the Consular Division of the Foreign & Commonwealth Office, Room G/105/6, Old Admiralty Building, Whitehall, London SW1A 2PA, and from British Consular offices in Spain.

During the summer months stinging jellyfish frequent Mediterranean coastal waters. Coast guards operate a beach flag system to indicate the general safety of water: red – do not enter water; yellow – take precautions; green – all clear. Coast guards operate on most of the popular beaches, so if in doubt, ask.

There is a high risk of forest fires during the hottest months and you should avoid camping in areas with limited escape routes. It is likely that the Spanish government will introduce a total prohibition on the lighting of fires (including barbecues) in forest areas throughout Spain.

If you are planning a skiing holiday you should contact the Spanish Tourist Office before travelling for advice on safety and weather conditions. Information about Spanish ski resorts can be obtained from the website www.goski.com/spain

British Embassy

CALLE DE FERNANDO EL SANTO 16, E-28010 MADRID
Tel: 917-00 82 00
www.ukinspain.com
madridconsulate@ukinspain.com

British Consulates-General

EDIFICIO TORRE DE BARCELONA
AVDA DIAGONAL 477-13º, E-08036 BARCELONA
Tel: 933-66 62 00
barcelonaconsulate@ukinspain.com

Alameda de Urquijo 2-8°, E-48008 Bilbao
Tel: 944-15 76 00
bilbaoconsulate@ukinspain.com

PASEO DE RECOLETOS 7/9, E-28004 MADRID
Tel: 915-24 97 00
madridconsulate@ukinspain.com

There are also British Consulates in Alicante, Málaga and Vigo, and Honorary Consulates in Benidorm (via Consulate in Alicante), Cadiz, Santander and Seville.

Irish Embassy

IRELAND HOUSE, PASEO DE LA CASTELLANA 46-4
E-28046 MADRID
Tel: 914-36 40 93
embajadairlanda@terra.es

There are also Irish Honorary Consulates in Alicante, Barcelona, Bilbao, El Ferrol, Fuengirola and Seville.

CUSTOMS REGULATIONS

Caravans and Motor Caravans

The maximum permitted height of a caravan or motor caravan including load is 4 metres, width 2.5 metres and length of motor vehicle, caravan or trailer, 12 metres. Maximum combined length of car + caravan 18.75 metres.

Currency

There is no restriction on the import or export of euro bank notes, foreign currency, travellers' cheques, etc. However, amounts over an equivalent of € 6,010 must be declared on entry.

Duty-Free Imports

Duty-free shopping is permitted in Andorra but there are strict limits on the amount of goods which can be imported into Spain, and Customs checks are frequently made. Each person is permitted to import the following items from Andorra free of duty or tax:

1.5 litres of spirits

5 litres of table wine

300 cigarettes or 150 cigarillos or 75 cigars or 400 gm of tobacco

75 gm of perfume and 375 ml of eau de toilette

Other items up to the value of € 525

Alcohol and tobacco allowances apply only to persons aged 17 or over.

Tobacco

Under Spanish law the number of cigarettes which may be exported from Spain is set at eight hundred. Anything above this amount is regarded as a trade transaction which must be accompanied by the required documentation. If travellers are apprehended with more than 800 cigarettes but without the necessary paperwork, they face seizure of the cigarettes and a large fine.

See **Customs Regulations** in the section *PLANNING AND TRAVELLING.*

DOCUMENTS

Visitors must be able to show some form of identity if requested to do so by the police.

Carry photocopies of the relevant pages or your passport, or a photocard driving licence.

Although motor insurers have progressed to remove the need to provide motorists with bail cover, as a precautionary measure it will continue to be provided with the Caravan Club's Red Pennant Motoring & Personal Holiday Insurance and is also available if you arrange your motor insurance through the Club's MotorCover Motor Insurance scheme.

The British three part EU-format pink and green driving licence is recognised in Spain. Holders of the old-style green driving licences are advised to apply for a photocard driving licence. Alternatively, the old-style licence may be accompanied by an International Driving Permit available from the AA, Green Flag or the RAC.

At all times when driving in Spain it is compulsory to carry your driving licence, vehicle registration certificate, insurance certificate and MOT certificate, if applicable. Vehicles imported by a person other than the owner must have a letter of authority from the owner.

See **Documents** and **Insurance** in the section *PLANNING AND TRAVELLING.*

MONEY

- All bank branches offer foreign currency exchange, as do many hotels and travel agents. Many exchange agencies in cities and centres of tourism are open 24 hours. Travellers' cheques are widely accepted as a means of payment in hotels, shops and restaurants and can be changed at banks and bureaux de change. However, recent visitors are still reporting difficulties cashing euro travellers' cheques and you should not rely on them for all your immediate cash needs.

- The major credit cards are widely accepted as a means of payment at shops, restaurants and petrol stations. Cash machines are widespread. Smaller retail outlets in non-commercial areas may not accept payments by credit card – check before buying. When shopping it is advisable to carry your passport or photocard driving licence if paying with a credit card as you will almost certainly be asked for photographic proof of identity.

- Cardholders are recommended to carry their credit card issuer/bank's 24-hour UK contact number in case of loss or theft.

SPAIN

- Keep a supply of loose change as you could frequently be asked for it in shops and at kiosks.

MOTORING

Drivers should take particular care as driving standards can be erratic, eg excessive speed and dangerous overtaking. Pedestrians should take particular care when crossing roads (even at zebra crossings) or walking along unlit roads at night.

Alcohol

The maximum limit for the level of alcohol in the blood is 0.05%, ie less than in the UK. After a traffic accident all road users have to undergo a breath test. Penalties for refusing a test or exceeding the legal limit are severe and may include immobilisation of vehicles, a heavy fine and three month's suspension of driving licence. This limit applies to cyclists as well as drivers of private vehicles.

Breakdown Service

The Real Automóvil Club de España (RACE) operates a breakdown service and assistance can be obtained 24 hours a day by telephoning the national centre in Madrid on 915-94 93 47. After hearing a message in Spanish press the number 1 to access the control room where English is spoken.

RACE breakdown vehicles are blue and yellow and display the words 'RACE Asistencia' on the sides. There are assistance points throughout mainland and insular Spain and vehicles patrol the main towns and roads. This service provides on-the-spot minor repairs and towing to the nearest garage. Charges vary according to type of vehicle and time of day, but payment for road assistance must be made in cash.

If you request assistance at an SOS post on a motorway, make sure that the tow truck that serves you bears the Autopistas symbol or that it is the one you requested.

Essential Equipment

Glasses

Spanish drivers requiring glasses to drive must carry a spare pair at all times when driving. Visiting motorists are advised to do so in order to avoid any difficulties with the local authorities.

Lights

Dipped headlights should be used in built-up areas, in tunnels and at night on motorways

and fast roads – even if they are well lit. Spare bulbs and fuses should be carried, together with the tools to fit them if required.

Dipped headlights must be used at all times on 'special' roads, eg temporary routes created at the time of road works such as the hard shoulder, or in a lane travelling in the opposite of the normal direction.

Emergency flashing lights should be used if you are unable to reach the minimum required speed – 60 km/h (37 mph) – or to alert drivers behind you to danger ahead.

Reflectorised Jackets

If your vehicle is immobilised on the carriageway outside a built-up area at night, or in poor visibility, you must wear a reflectorised jacket or waistcoat (to make you visible from distance of 150 metres) when getting out of your vehicle. This rule also applies to passengers who may leave the vehicle, for example, to assist with a repair.

Seat Belts

The wearing of seat belts is compulsory on front and rear seats of cars. Children over three years of age and under 1.5 metres (5 feet) in height must use an approved child restraint if available. Children under three must always be placed in a restraint system adapted to their size.

Warning Triangles

Foreign-registered vehicles are only required to carry one warning triangle, whereas Spanish-registered vehicles require two. Visiting motorists are recommended to carry two triangles in order to avoid any local difficulties which may arise. Warning triangles must conform to EU standards and should be placed 50 metres behind and in front of broken-down vehicles.

*See also **Essential Equipment** and **Essential Equipment Table** under **Motoring** in the section **PLANNING AND TRAVELLING**.*

Fuel

Credit cards are accepted at most service stations, but you should be prepared to pay cash if necessary in remote areas.

For diesel (gasoleo) supplies in the Santurtzi/Bilbao area a visitor has advised using the fuel station at the Carrefour supermarket about halfway between Santurtzi and Bilbao. Follow the signs to Sestao from the adjacent motorway.

LPG, formerly only available for public service vehicles, can now be purchased by private motorists from some Repsol filling stations. Visit the Repsol website, www.repsolypf.com and look under Products and Services for Autogas, commercial information. This will lead you to a map showing the location of their LPG stations throughout Spain, together with addresses.

See also Fuel under Motoring in the section PLANNING AND TRAVELLING.

Mountain Passes and Tunnels

Some passes are sometimes blocked in winter following heavy falls of snow. Information on road conditions can be obtained by telephoning the Central Traffic Division on 900-12 35 05.

See Mountain Passes and Tunnels in the section PLANNING AND TRAVELLING.

Parking

Yellow road markings indicate parking restrictions. Vehicles must be parked on the right-hand side of the carriageway except in one-way streets where parking may be allowed on both sides. Illegally parked vehicles may be towed away or clamped.

Parking meters and traffic wardens operate in large cities. Signs indicate blue zones (zona azul); the maximum period of parking is 90 minutes between 8am and 9pm hours. Parking discs are available from town halls, hotels and travel agencies. In the centre of some towns there is a 'zona ORA' where parking is permitted for up to 90 minutes against tickets bought in tobacconists.

Recent visitors to tourist areas on Spain's Mediterranean coast report that the parking of motor caravans on public roads and, in some instances in public parking areas, may be prohibited in an effort to discourage 'wild camping'. The Club has been unable to obtain confirmation of such regulations which may vary according to region or province. Specific areas where visitors have encountered this problem include Alicante and Palamos. It is understood that the owners of a number of motor caravans have been fined in the Alicante and Denia areas for parking on sections of the beach belonging to the local authority.

Parking for the Disabled

On roads and in car parks, parking places reserved for disabled people are marked with a wheelchair symbol.

Do not park on roads where waiting is prohibited, or in pedestrian zones, unless local concessions permit it. Fees and time limit concessions vary; check locally. Do not drive or park in pedestrian zones unless local concessions allow. Most car parks offer concessions to vehicles displaying a Blue Badge.

See also Parking Facilities for the Disabled under Motoring in the section PLANNING AND TRAVELLING.

Pedestrians

Jaywalking is not permitted. In main towns pedestrians may not cross a road unless a traffic light is at red against the traffic, or a policeman gives permission. Offenders may be fined on-the-spot.

Priority

As a general rule traffic coming from the right has priority at intersections but when entering a main road from a secondary road drivers must give way to traffic from both directions. Traffic already on a roundabout has priority over traffic joining the roundabout. Trams and emergency vehicles have priority at all times over other road users.

Motorists must give way to cyclists on a cycle lane, cycle crossing or other specially designated cycle track. They must also give way to cyclists when turning left or right.

Roads

All national roads and roads of tourist interest are in good condition and well-signposted, and driving is straightforward. Hills often tend to be longer and steeper than in parts of the UK and some of the coastal roads are very winding, so traffic flows at the speed of the slowest lorry. Local roads are prefixed with the letter C.

As far as accidents are concerned the N340 coast road, especially between Malaga and Fuengirola, is notorious, as is the Madrid ring road, and special vigilance is necessary.

Road humps are making an appearance on Spanish roads and recent visitors report that they may be high, putting low stabilisers at risk.

Road Signs and Markings

See European Road Signs under Motoring in the section PLANNING AND TRAVELLING.

Road signs conform to international standards. Lines and markings are white. In the Basque and Catalan regions place names may appear in local and national form, eg Girona/Gerona, Irunea/Pamplona, Donostia/San Sebastian, and road atlases usually show both. The following may also be seen:

Carretera de peaje – *Toll road*
Ceda el paso – *Give way*
Cuidado – *Caution*

SPAIN

Curva peligrosa – *Dangerous bend*
Despacio – *Slow*
Desviación – *Detour*
Dirección única – *One-way street*
Embotellamiento – *Traffic jam*
Estacionamiento prohibido – *No parking*
Estrechamiento – *Narrow lane*
Gravillas – *Loose chippings/gravel*
Inicio – *Start*
Obras – *Roadworks*
Paso prohibido – *No entry*
Peligro – *Danger*
Salida – *Exit*

Many ordinary roads have a continuous white line on the near (verge) side of the carriageway. Any narrow lane between this line and the side of the carriageway is intended primarily for pedestrians and cyclists and not for use as a hard shoulder.

A continuous line also indicates 'no stopping'; even if it is possible to park entirely off the road, it should be treated as a double white line and not crossed except in a serious emergency. If your vehicle breaks down on a road where there is a continuous white line along the verge, it should not be left unattended as this is illegal and an on-the-spot fine may be levied.

Many road junctions have a continuous white centre line along the main road. This line must not be crossed to execute a left turn, despite the lack of any other 'no left turn' signs. If necessary, drive on to a 'cambio de sentido' (change of direction) sign to turn.

The Club has received reports that the traffic police are keen to enforce both the above regulations.

Watch out for traffic lights which may be mounted high above the road and hard to spot. Green, amber and red arrows are used on traffic lights at some intersections. Two red lights mean no entry.

Speed Limits

*See **Speed Limits Table** under **Motoring** in the section **PLANNING AND TRAVELLING**.*

In built-up areas, speed is limited to 50 km/h (31 mph) except where signs indicate a lower limit. On motorways and dual carriageways in built-up areas, speed is limited to 80 km/h (50 mph) except where indicated by signs.

Outside built-up areas motor caravans of any weight are limited to 90 km/h (56 mph) on motorways and dual carriageways, to 80 km/h (50 mph) on other main roads with more than one lane in each direction, and to 70 km/h (44 mph) on secondary roads.

Reduce your speed to 20 km/h (13 mph) in residential areas.

The installation and use of radar detectors is prohibited. Drivers are not allowed to make signals to warn other drivers of the presence of police, eg headlight-flashing.

Towing

Motor caravans are prohibited from towing a car unless the car is on a special towing trailer with all four wheels off the ground.

Any towing combination in excess of 10 metres must keep at least 50 metres from the vehicle in front except in built-up areas, on roads where overtaking is prohibited or where there are several lanes in the same direction.

Traffic Jams

Roads around the large Spanish cities such as Madrid, Barcelona, Zaragoza, Valencia and Seville are extremely busy on Friday afternoons when residents leave for the mountains or coast, and again on Sunday evenings when they return. The coastal roads along the Costa Brava and the Costa Dorada may also be congested. The coast road south of Torrevieja is frequently heavily congested as a result of extensive holiday home construction.

Summer holidays extend from the end of June to the end of September and the busiest periods are the last weekend in July, the first weekend in August and the period around the Assumption holiday in mid-August.

The Autovía de la Cataluña Central now provides a rapid east-west link between Gerona and Lleida via Vic, Manresa and Cervera and an 88 km section of the A6/NVI has opened between Manzanal del Puerto and Benevente which means faster access from the north-west to Madrid.

Traffic jams occur on the busy A7 from the French border to Barcelona during the peak summer holiday period. An alternative route now exists from Malgret de Mar along the coast to Barcelona using the A19 where tolls are lower than on the A7.

Violation of Traffic Regulations

The police are empowered to impose on-the-spot fines. There is usually a 30% reduction for immediate settlement; an official receipt should be obtained. Visiting motorists must pay immediately unless they can give the name of a person or company in Spain willing to guarantee payment. Failure to pay immediately may result in confiscation of vehicles. A form is issued specifying the offence and the amount paid (check that the amount written on the form is the same as the amount actually paid). An appeal may be made within 15 days and there are instructions on the back of the form in English. RACE can provide legal advice – tel 902-40 45 45.

Accidents

The Central Traffic Department runs an assistance service for victims of traffic accidents linked to an SOS telephone network along motorways and some roads. Motorists in need of help should ask for 'auxilio en carretera' (road assistance). The special ambulances used are connected by radio to hospitals participating in the scheme.

MOTORWAYS

The Spanish motorway system has been subject to massive expansion in recent years and there are now approximately 7,000 km of motorways (autopistas) and dual carriageways, with more under construction or planned. Many sections are toll-free. The website www.autopistas.com features maps of all motorway sections with rest areas, together with traffic and weather conditions. Autovias are dual carriageways with motorway characteristics, but not necessarily with a central reservation, and are toll-free. Autovia road numbers are prefixed with the letter A or N. Autopista road numbers are prefixed with the letters AP and tolls are charged.

Rest areas with parking facilities, petrol stations and coffee shops are strategically placed and well-signposted. Emergency telephones are located on both sides of the carriageway at 2 km intervals.

Exits on motorways are numbered consecutively from Madrid. Exits on dual carriageways (autovias) are numbered according to the kilometre point from Madrid.

Motorway signs near Barcelona are confusing. To avoid the city traffic when heading south, follow signs for Barcelona but the moment signs for Tarragona appear follow these and ignore Barcelona signs.

Motorway Tolls

Class 1* Motorcycle; private car with or without single axle caravan; minibus with 2 axles and 4 wheels

Class 2* Private car or minibus with caravan with twin axles; lorry with 2 or 3 axles.

These categories are given as an indication only, as classification of vehicles varies according to different motorway companies.

(See table on following page)

TOURING

- One of Spain's greatest attractions is undoubtedly its cuisine. Spanish cooking is rich and varied with many regional specialities and traditional dishes which have achieved worldwide fame such as paella, gazpacho and tapas. Seafood in particular is excellent and plentiful. Fixed-price menus or 'menu del dia' invariably offer good value. Spain is one of the world's top wine producers, enjoying a great variety of high quality wines of which rioja and sherry are probably the best known. Local beer is low in alcohol content and is generally drunk as an aperitif to accompany tapas. Service is generally included in restaurant bills but a tip of approximately 50-60 cents per person up to 10% of the bill is appropriate if you have received good service.

- Perhaps due to the benign climate and long hours of sunshine, Spaniards tend to get up later and stay out later at night than their European neighbours. Out of the main tourist season and in 'non-touristy' areas it may be difficult to find a restaurant open in the evening before 9pm. Taking a siesta is still common practice, although it is becoming more common for businesses to stay open during the traditional siesta hours.

- Spain's many different cultural and regional influences are responsible for the variety and originality of fiestas held each year. Over 200 have been classified as 'of interest to tourists' while others have gained international fame. A full list can be obtained from the Spanish Tourist Office in London, from Real Automóvil Club de Espana (RACE), or from provincial tourist offices.

- The Madrid Card, valid for one, two or three days, gives free use of public transport, free entry to various attractions and museums, including the Prado, Reina Sofia and Thyssen-Bornesmisza collection, as

SPAIN

Road No.	Route	km	Class 1	Class 2
AP1	Burgos (Castañares) to Miranda de Ebro (A68)	84	8.30	8.95
AP2	Junction A7 to Alfajarin (Zaragoza)	215	16.50	24.40
AP4	Sevilla (Dos Hermanas) to Cádiz (Puerto Real)	104	6.00	10.55
AP6	Madrid (Villalba) to Adanero	70	7.85	15.70
AP7	Frontier to Granollers		9.45	15.15
	Barcelona (Molins de Rei) to Salou		7.05	12.57
	Tarragoma to Valencia	227	17.75	23.95
	Valencia (Silla) to Alicante (San Juan)	150	11.75	15.90
	Alicante to Cartagena	76	*2.65	*3.10
	Malaga to Estepona		2.15	3.50
AP9	La Coruña to Vigo		10.60	18.10
AP15	Pamplona (Noain) to Valtierra (A68)	83	6.90	
C16	Manresa to Terrasa to AP7	42	*5.29	*5.73
C32	Barcelona (Mongat) to Palafolls	49	3.05	4.89
AP51	Avila to Villacastin		*1.75	2.25
AG55	Coruña to Carballo	32.6	1.85	2.80
AG57	Vigo to Baiona		1.25	1.85
AP61	Segovia to San Rafael		*2.95	3.15
AP66	Oviedo (Campomanes) to León	75	8.95	16.25
AP68	Bilbao to Zaragoza	294.4	21.55	39.15

*Toll charges in euros. Payment in cash or by credit card. *Variable toll depending on time of day.*

well as free tours and discounts at restaurants and shows. You can buy the card from www.madridcard.com, by telephoning 0034 917-13 04 44, from the City Tourist Office in Plaza Mayor or on Madrid Visión tour buses. Similar generous discounts can be obtained with the Barcelona Card, valid from one to five days, which can be purchased from tourist offices and from El Corte Ingles department stores; see www.barcelonaturisme.com

- Bullfighting is still a very popular entertainment in Spain and fights take place in the bullrings or plazas of main towns during the summer. In addition, every year each town celebrates its local Saint's Day which is always a very happy and colourful occasion.

- BBC World Service radio in English can be heard on the following local frequencies: Marbella 101.6 FM, Nerja 97.7 FM, Malaga 96.8 or 107 FM.

- Ferries are operated by Transmediterranea from Spain to North Africa, the Balearic Islands and the Canary Islands (weekly). All enquiries should be made through their UK agents:

SOUTHERN FERRIES
30 CHURTON STREET
LONDON SW1V 2LP
Tel: 020 7976 6340
www.sncm.fr

- Gibraltar – for information on Gibraltar contact:

GIBRALTAR GOVERNMENT TOURIST OFFICE
ARUNDUL GREAT COURT
179 STRAND
LONDON WC2R 1EH
Tel: 020 7836 0777
www.gibraltar.gi or www.gibraltar.gov.uk
info@gibraltar.gov.uk

- There are no campsites on the Rock. The only direct access to Gibraltar from Spain is via the border at La Linea which is open 24 hours a day. You may cross on foot and it is also possible to take cars or motor caravans to Gibraltar, but be prepared for long queues. As roads in the town are extremely narrow and bridges low, it is advisable to park on the outskirts; visitors advise against leaving vehicles on the Spanish side of the border owing to the high risk of break-ins. An attraction to taking the car into Gibraltar is an English-style supermarket and a wide variety of competitively priced goods free of VAT. There is currently no charge for visitors or cars to enter Gibraltar but Spanish border checks can cause delays to travellers crossing between Spain and Gibraltar.

- Disabled visitors to Gibraltar may obtain a temporary parking permit from the police station on production of evidence confirming their disability. This permit allows parking for up to two hours (between 8am and 10pm) in parking places reserved for disabled people.

SPAIN

SPAIN / ANDORRA

Distances are shown in kilometres and are calculated from town/city centres along the most practicable roads, although not necessarily taking the shortest route.

1km = 0.62 miles

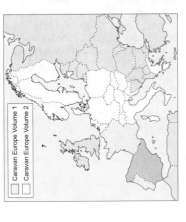

Caravan Europe Volume 1
Caravan Europe Volume 2

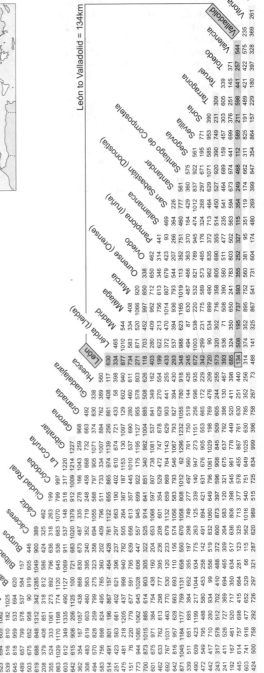

León to Valladolid = 134km

REGIONS AND PROVINCES OF SPAIN

ANDALUCIA
4   Alméria
11   Cádiz
14   Córdoba
18   Granada
21   Huelva
23   Jaén
29   Málaga
41   Sevilla

ARAGON
22   Huesca
44   Teruel
50   Zaragoza

ASTURIAS
33   Asturias

BALEARIC ISLANDS
7   Balearic Islands

CANARY ISLANDS
35   Las Palmas
38   Sta. Cruz de Tenerife

CANTABRIA
39   Cantabria

CASTILLA-LA MANCHA
2   Albacete
13   Cuidad Real
16   Cuenca
19   Guadalajara
45   Toledo

CASTILLA Y LEON
5   Ávila
9   Burgos
24   León
34   Palencia
37   Salamanca
40   Segovia
42   Soria
47   Valladolid
49   Zamora

CATALUÑA
8   Barcelona
17   Gerona
25   Lérida
43   Tarragona

COMUNIDAD VALENCIANA
3   Alicante
12   Castellón
46   Valencia

EXTREMADURA
6   Badajoz
10   Cáceres

GALICIA
15   La Coruña
27   Lugo
32   Ourense
36   Pontevedra

LA RIOJA
26   La Rioja

MADRID
28   Madrid

MURCIA
30   Murcia

NAVARRA
31   Navarra

PAIS VASCO
1   Álava
20   Guipúzcua
48   Vizcaya

SPANISH ENCLAVES
51   Ceuta
52   Melilla

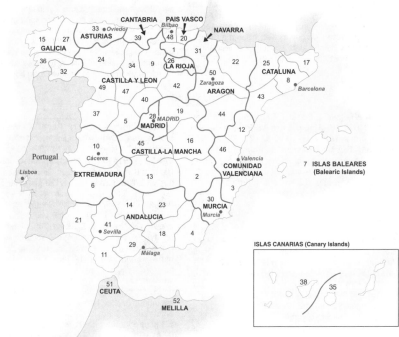

The first two digits of a Spanish postcode correspond to the number of the province in which that town or village is situated

Source : Spanish National Tourist Office

SPAIN

ABEJAR *3C1* (800m NW Rural) **Camping El Concurso, Ctra de Molinos de Duero s/n, 42146 Abejar (Soria) [975-37 33 61; fax 975-37 33 96]** N234 W fr Soria to Abejar. Turn onto rd SO840 dir Molinos de Duero, site on L. Lge, mkd pitch, pt sl, pt shd; wc; chem disp; mv service pnt; shwrs inc; el pts (5A) inc; gas; lndtte; shop & 500m; tradsmn; rest; snacks; bar; playgrnd; pool; lake 2km; phone; poss cr & noisy in ssn; cc acc; CCI. "Nr lake & National Park, v beautiful." ♦ ltd. Easter & 1 Jun-30 Sep. € 18.00   2004*

†**ABIZANDA** *3B2* (Rural) **Fundacion Liguerre de Cinca, Ctra A138, Km 28, 22393 Abizanda (Huesca) [974-50 08 00; fax 974-50 08 30; icinca@ aragon.ugt.ore; www.liguerredecinca.com]** A138 N fr Barbastro, site sp at km 29 or S fr Ainsa, site sp at km 27, 18 km S of Ainsa. Med, mkd pitch, terr, shd; wc; chem disp; shwrs inc; baby rm; el pts (10A) €3.75; gas; lndtte; shop, rest, snacks, bar high ssn; playgrnd; pool; lake sw 1km; watersports; tennis; games rm; horseriding; cycle hire; car wash; 10% statics; dogs; phone; poss cr; Eng spkn; adv bkg (dep & bkg fee); quiet; cc acc; red long stay; CCI. "Excel facs; v highly rec; site in 2 parts sep by ravine, bottom terr muddy in wet; trees may be diff for lge o'fits; v helpful staff & lovely site; few British; nearest shops at Ainsa; excel long stay." € 15.75
                                              2003*

†**ADRA** *2H4* (5km E Coastal) **Camping La Habana, Ctra N340 Motril-Almería, Km 64, Puente del Rio, 04770 Adra (Almeria) [950-52 21 27 or 619-45 41 34]** Exit N340 junc 391 to Puente del Rio, foll site sp. Med, pt shd; wc; shwrs; el pts; gas; lndtte; shop; rest; bar; beach adj; horseriding; phone; bus 3km; CCI. "Narr app rd & ent; site rather tatty."
                                              2004*

†**AGUILAR DE CAMPOO** *1B4* (3km W Rural) **Monte Royal Camping, Ave Virgen del Llano, s/n: 34800 Aguilar de Campoo (Palencia) [979-12 30 83]** App site fr S on N611 fr Palencia. At Aguilar de Campoo turn W at S end of rv bdge at S end of town. Site on L in 3km; sp at edge of reservoir. If app fr N cont thro town cent & turn R after x-ing rv. Lge, mkd pitch, pt sl, shd; wc; chem disp (wc only); baby facs; shwrs €0.60; el pts (3-5A) inc; gas; lndry rm; ice; shops 3km; rest in ssn; bar; playgrnd; sand beach nr lake; watersports; horseriding; fishing; TV; 20% statics; dogs; phone; cc acc; CCI. "Useful NH 2 hrs fr Santander; site in beautiful area but v ltd/basic facs low ssn; facs poss stretched high ssn; barking dogs poss problem; friendly staff; gd walking, cycling & birdwatching in National Park." ♦ € 18.00   2004*

†**AGUILAS** *4G1* (3km NE Rural) **Camping Aguilas, Ctra Cabo Cope, Los Geraneos, 30880 Aguilas (Murcia) [968-41 92 05; fax 968-41 92 82]** Fr Lorca take N332 dir Aguilas; avoid town cent when towing & foll sp L to Calabardina/Cabo Cope; site on L within 3km. Med, mkd pitch, hdstg, pt shd; wc; chem disp; shwrs inc; el pts (15A) €3.20; gas; lndtte; shop high ssn; rest; snacks; bar; playgrnd; pool; sand beach 4km; tennis; 30% statics; phone; poss full Jan-Feb; quiet; adv bkg; Eng spkn; red low ssn/long stay; cc acc; CCI. "Vg for quiet holiday; all pitches shaded with trees or netting; clean facs; v helpful warden; excel." € 15.30   2005*

†**AGUILAS** *4G1* (3km SW Coastal) **Camping Bellavista, Ctra de Vera, Km 3, 30880 Aguilas (Murcia) [968-44 91 51; fax 968-44 93 27; info@ campingbellavista.com; www.campingbellavista. com]** On N332 Aguilas to Vera rd. Well marked by flags. Sm, hdg pitch, hdstg, pt sl, pt shd; wc; chem disp; shwrs inc; el pts (6-10A) €3.65; gas; lndtte; shop 2km; tradsmn; rest; snacks; bar; BBQ; playgrnd; sand beach 500m; cycle hire; poss cr; Eng spkn; adv bkg; quiet; cc acc; red long stay/low ssn; CCI. "Gd winter stay; clean, tidy site with excel facs & rest; security gates (€10 dep); ltd pitches for lge vans; v helpful owner; fine views; poss barking dogs at night on 1 side of site & rd noise at other end; 30 min walk to town; excel town & vg beaches."
€ 16.00   2004*

†**AINSA** *3B2* (2.5km N Rural) **Camping Pena Montanesa, Ctra Ainsa-Bielsa, Km 2.3, 22360 Labuerda (Huesca) [974-50 00 32; fax 974-50 09 91; info@penamontanesa.com; www. penamontanesa.com]** E fr Huesca on N240 for approx 50km, turn N onto N123 just after Barbastro twd Ainsa. In 8km turn onto A138 N for Ainsa & Bielsa. Or S fr St Lary Soulan on D929 in French/Spanish border, cross via Bielsa Tunnel to join A138 S to Ainsa & Bielsa. Site 2km N of Ainsa on this rd. NB: Bielsa Tunnel sometimes clsd bet Oct & Easter due to weather. Lge, mkd pitch, shd; htd wc; chem disp; baby facs; sauna; shwrs inc; el pts (6A) inc; gas; lndtte; shop 2km; supmkt; rest; snacks; bar; BBQ (gas/elec only); playgrnd; htd pools (1 covrd) + paddling pool; lake sw 2km; canoeing; cycle hire; horseriding; games area; entmnt child & adult; disco; TV; many statics; dogs €3 kept on lead; phone; recep 0800-0000; adv bkg (bkg fee €60.10 min 7 nights); quiet; cc acc; red low ssn; cc acc; CCI. "Friendly staff; pitches poss tight due trees; site nr beautiful medieval town & Ordesa National Park; local map given at recep & info on excursions; excel." ♦ € 37.66 ABS - E12   2005*

See advertisement

AINSA *3B2* (1km E Rural) **Camping Ainsa, Ctra Ainsa-Campo, 22330 Ainsa (Huesca) [tel/fax 974-50 02 60]** Fr Ainsa take N260 E dir Pueyo de Araguas, cross rv bdge, site sp L in 200m. Foll lane to site. Sm, terr, pt shd; wc; shwrs inc; el pts €3.70; gas; lndtte; shop 1km; rest, snacks bar high ssn; playgrnd; pool; 50% statics; dogs; phone; poss cr; some indus noise mornings; cc acc; CCI. "Pleasant, welcoming, well-maintained site; fine view of old city." Holy Week-30 Oct. € 17.75   2005*

†AINSA *3B2* (6km NW Rural) **Camping Boltana, Ctra N260, Km 442, 22340 Boltana (Huesca) [974-50 23 47; fax 974-50 20 23; info@ campingboltana.com]** Fr Ainsa head into Boltana, turn L over rv & foll sp. Site is 2km E of Boltana, final 300m on single track rd. Med, mkd pitch, pt sl, terr, pt shd; htd wc; chem disp; baby facs; shwrs inc; el pts (4-10A) €3.90; gas; lndtte; shop & 2km; tradsmn; rest; snacks; bar; playgrnd; pool; paddling pool; rv sw & fishing 600m; tennis 1km; horseriding 500m; games area; cycle hire; adventure sports; 70% statics; dogs €2.45; phone; clsd 21 Dec-9 Jan; poss cr; Eng spkn; adv bkg; poss noisy; cc acc; red CCI. "Many activities avail; conv Ordesa National Park; poss diff for disabled travellers; san facs stretched high ssn; friendly, helpful staff; excel." ♦ € 20.70 (CChq acc)   2005*

ALBARRACIN *3D1* (1km E Rural) **Camp Municipal Ciudad de Albarracin, Casco Urbano, Junto Polideportivo, 44100 Albarracin (Teruel) [978-71 01 97 or 978-71 01 07; fax 978-71 01 07]** On TE901 app Albarracin, pass g'ge on R, turn L over bdge just bef Albarracin (sp). L again after 1km, R to site. Med, pt sl, pt shd; wc; chem disp; baby facs; shwrs inc; el pts (16A) €2; gas; lndtte; shop & adj; rest; snacks; bar; BBQ; playgrnd; pool in ssn; phone; poss cr; adv bkg; quiet; cc acc; CCI. "Excel site; immac san facs; sh walk to quaint town for shops & rests; sports cent adj; rec." 1 Apr-31 Oct. € 11.56   2003*

ALBERCA, LA *1D3* (2km N Rural) **Camping Al-Bereka, Ctra Salamanca-La Alberca, Km 75.6, 37624 La Alberca (Salamanca) [923-41 51 95]** Fr Salamanca S on N630/E803 take C515 to Mogarraz, then SA202 to La Alberca. Site on L at km 75.6 bef vill. Rte fr Ciudad Real OK but bumpy in places. Med, mkd pitch, terr, shd; wc; chem disp; shwrs inc; el pts €2.50; lndry rm; ice; shop; rest 2km; snacks; bar; BBQ; playgrnd; pool; paddling pool; some statics; dogs; quiet; cc acc; CCI. "Beautiful countryside; La Alberca is a gem; beautifully restored medieval vill with abbey; helpful owner; nice, quiet site." ♦ 1 Mar-30 Oct. € 21.40   2005*

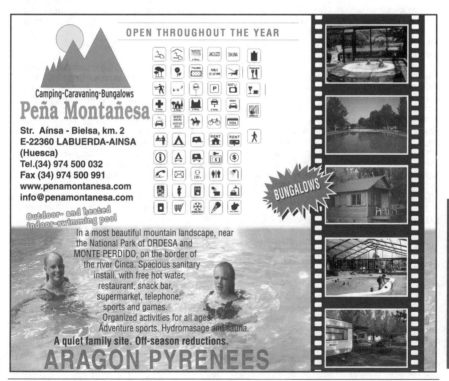

ALBERCA, LA *1D3* (6km N) **Camping Sierra de Francia, 37623 Nava de Francia (Salamanca)** [923-45 40 81; fax 923-45 40 01] Fr Cuidad Rodrigo take C515. Turn R at El Cabaco, site on L in approx 2km. Med, shd; wc; shwrs; el pts €3.20; gas; lndtte; shop; rest; bar; pool; playgrnd; horseriding; cycle hire; quiet; cc acc. "Conv 'living history' vill of La Alberca & Monasterio de la Pena; excel views." 1 Apr-30 Sep. € 17.15   2002*

ALBERCA, LA *1D3* (10km SE Rural) **Camping Vega de Francia, Ctra Sotoserrano-Bejar, Paraje Vega de Francia, 37657 Sotoserrano (Salamanca)** [tel/fax 923-16 11 04] Fr Sotoserrano take Ctra de Bejar for 3km sp Lagunilla & El Cerro. Bef Roman bdge turn L onto rd sp Camping Vega de Francia for 500m to site. Single track in places. Sm, hdg pitch, hdstg, terr, shd; wc; chem disp; mv service pnt; baby facs; shwrs inc; el pts (3A) €2.25; lndry rm; shop; tradsmn; rest; snacks; bar; BBQ; playgrnd; rv sw adj; TV rm; 50% statics; dogs; phone; Eng spkn; adv bkg dep req; quiet; 20% red 15+ days; cc acc. "V friendly family-run site; excel bar-rest popular with locals; shop sells local produce; owner makes wine, olive oil & honey; gd walking & views; app poss not suitable for lge o'fits; excel long/sh stays." ♦ 1 Mar-3 Oct. € 17.00   2004*

ALBOLOTE see Granada *2G4*

†**ALCALA DE GUADAIRA** *2G3* (3km SE Rural) **Camping Oromana, Camino del Maestre s/n, 41500 Alcala de Guadaira** [955-68 32 57; fax 955-68 18 44; oromana@campingoromana.es; www.campingoromana.es] Leave A92 at junc 12, foll sp to Alcala & Utrera. Cross rv bdge; turn L into Utrera rd & L again Hotel Oromano; turn R at fork to site; sp. Fr A376 take C432 to Alcala, site sp on R on ent Alcala at bottom of hill. Lge, mkd pitch, hdstg, pt sl, pt shd; wc; chem disp; shwrs inc; el pts €3.25; lndtte; shop 2km; rest, snacks & bar high ssn; playgrnd; pool in ssn; 50% statics; phone; poss cr; Eng spkn; quiet; cc acc; red long stay; CCI. "Bus every 30 mins to Seville (12km), 2km walk fr site; lovely setting in pine park; friendly recep; poss itinerants & unclean/ltd facs low ssn & neglected vans; noise fr nrby shooting range & disco high ssn; muddy after rain." ♦ € 16.00   2005*

†**ALCALA DE LOS GAZULES** *2H3* (4km E Rural) **Camping Los Gazules, Ctra de Patrite, Km 4, 11180 Alcala de los Gazules (Cadiz)** [956-42 04 86; fax 956-42 03 88; www.camping losgazules.com] Well sp in Alcala down dead-end rd to Patrite. Med, mkd pitch, pt sl, pt shd; wc; chem disp (wc); shwrs inc; el pts €3.45; lndtte; shop; rest; bar; playgrnd; pool; 90% statics; phone; adv bkg; red long stay; CCI. "Well-maintained site extended & upgraded; take care canopy frames; v friendly & helpful staff; attractive town with v narr streets, leave car in park at bottom & walk; gd walking, birdwatching; lack of proper shelter fr wind; activities avail - hiking, cycling/mountain biking, canoeing; ltd facs low ssn." € 14.00   2005*

ALCANAR *3D2* (3km N Coastal) **Camping Los Alfaques, 43530 Alcanar (Tarragona)** [977-74 05 61] Clearly sp on main rd N340, approx 3km S of San Carlos de la Rapita. Lge, pt sl, shd; wc; chem disp; shwrs €0.20; el pts (5A) €2.60; gas; lndtte; ice; shop & 2km; rest; bar; playgrnd; pool 200m; steep, shgl beach; fishing; 50% statics; phone; some rd noise. "Vg for boat-launching, fishing; conv ancient town of Morella." 15 Mar-30 Sep. € 16.00   2003*

We're having a great holiday - must fill in some site report forms and send them to The Club as soon as possible.

ALCANTARA *2E2* (4km NW Rural) **Camping Puente de Alcantara, Finca Los Cabezos, 10980 Alcantara (Caceres)** [927-39 09 47] W fr Alcantara to Roman bdge over Rv Tagus. Turn R at camping sp over cattle grid. Med, pt sl, unshd; wc; chem disp; shwrs inc; el pts (5A) €3.25; gas; lndtte; shop; snacks; bar; playgrnd; pool; watersports; tennis; adv bkg; quiet; cc acc; CCI. "Nice views; attractive vill with many storks; gd birdwatching area; friendly owner; ltd facs low ssn." ♦ 1 Apr-30 Sep. € 15.00   2004*

†**ALCARAZ** *4F1* (6km E Rural) **Camping Sierra de Penascosa, Ctra Penascosa-Bogarra, Km 1, 02313 Penascosa (Albacete)** [967-38 25 21; fax 967-21 10 14; sercofin@navegalia.com] Fr N322 turn E bet km posts 279 & 280 sp Penascosa. In vill foll site sp for 1km beyond vill. Gravel access track & narr ent. Sm, mkd pitch, hdstg, terr, shd; wc; chem disp; shwrs; el pts (6A) €2.80; gas; lndtte; shop; rest high ssn; snacks; bar; playgrnd; pool; cycle hire; dogs; v quiet; cc acc; CCI. "Not suitable lge o'fits or faint-hearted; pitches sm, uneven & amongst trees - care needed when manoeuvring; gd for exploring Sierras; historical sites nr." ♦ € 17.50   2005*

ALCOSSEBRE *3D2* (3km NE Coastal/Rural) **Camping Ribamar, Camino Ribamar s/n, 12579 Alcossebre (Castellon)** [tel/fax 964-76 11 63] Exit AP7 at junc 44 into N340 & foll sp to Alcossebre. At 1st rndabt foll Las Fuentes sp, then site sp. Med, hdg/mkd pitch, hdstg, pt sl, terr, pt shd; wc; chem disp; baby facs; shwrs inc; el pts (10A) inc; gas; lndtte; shop; tradsmn; rest; bar; playgrnd; pool; sand beach 200m; paddling pool; tennis; games area; 25% statics; dogs €1.25; poss cr; adv bkg; quiet; red long stay/low ssn; CCI. "Pleasant site; realistic pitch size." 1 Apr-30 Sep. € 18.70   2004*

CAMPING CABO DE GATA

Camping Cabo de Gata is situated in the south-east of the province of Almeria. It is a volcanic area wich offers the visitant beautiful beaches, incredible landscapes, traditional cooking and a lot of sun and calm places. From the camp site you can visit the natural park, the desert of Tabernas (the only desert all arround Europe), the sorbas caves (the most important gypsum karst in the world), the minihollywood (where you will be the wildest cowboy, for one day), and many more things. Come and enjoy it! • Bar-restaurant, supermarket, social hall, tennis, petanca & volley-ball, swimming pool • Beach situated at 900 mts. • English spoken. **OPEN THROUGHOUT THE YEAR**

PARQUE NATURAL
Cabo de Gata – Níjar

Costa de almeria

Andalucía - Spain

Tel.: (34) 950 16 04 43
Fax: (34) 950 52 00 03
Ctra. Cabo de Gata, s/n. - Cortijo Ferrón
E-04150 CABO DE GATA (Almería)

SPECIAL OFFER AUTUMN-WINTER-SPRING
2 adults + car & caravan or camping-car + electricity (6 Amp.):

1 month: 260 €	2 months: 505 €	
3 months: 750 €	4 months: 995 €	+ 7% VAT
5 months: 1.240 €	6 months: 1.485 €	

Extra electr. 10 Amp. + 15 € per month; 16 A,p. + 25 € per month

Bungalows

Special offer in spring, winter and autumn for
Bungalows: 2 person

1 month: 500 €   2 months: 940 €
3 months: 1.280 €   4 months: 1.680 €
5 months: 1.900 €   6 months: 2.000 €
www.campingcabodegata.com
info@campingcabodegata.com

---

†ALCOSSEBRE *3D2* (2.5km S Coastal) **Camping Playa Tropicana**, 12579 Alcossebre (Castellon) [964-41 24 63; fax 964 41 28 05; info@ playatropicana.com; www.playatropicana.com] Fr AP7 exit junc 44 onto N340 dir Barcelona. At km 1018 turn on CV142 twd Alcossebre. Just bef ent town turn R sp 'Platjes Capicorb', turn R at beach in 2.5km, site on R. Lge, mkd pitch, pt terr, pt shd; wc; chem disp; baby facs; serviced pitches (extra charge); shwrs inc; el pts (6A) inc; gas; lndtte; shop; rest; snacks; bar; playgrnd; pool; sand beach adj; watersports; games area; TV; car wash; no dogs; poss cr; adv bkg rec high ssn; quiet; cc acc; 50% red low ssn/long stay & special offers. "Excel facs & security; superb well-run site; vg low ssn; poss rallies Jan-Apr; management v helpful; poss flooding after heavy rain; take fly swat!" ♦ € 44.00 (CChq acc) 2005*

†ALCOSSEBRE *3D2* (500m W Coastal) **Camping Alcossebre**, 12579 Alcossebre (Castellon) [964-41 28 89] Turn off N340 twds Alcossebre. Site 500m bef town & sm beach & narr app rd. Sm, shd; wc; shwrs; el pts €2.50; gas; snacks; bar; pools; playgrnd; watersports; fishing; CCI. € 18.90 2004*

†ALHAMA DE MURCIA *4F1* (5km NW Rural) **Camping Sierra Espuna, El Berro**, 30848 Alhama de Murcia (Murcia) [968-66 80 38; fax 968-66 80 79; info@campingelberro.com; campingsierraespuna.com] Fr Alhama de Murcia take C3315 sp Mula. Take 2nd sp to site sp El Berro, site on edge of vill. 15km by rd - narr & twisty, diff for lge o'fits. Med, hdstg, terr, pt shd; wc; chem disp; baby facs; shwrs; el pts (6A) inc; gas; lndtte; shop 500m; snacks; bar; playgrnd; pool; tennis; minigolf; organised activities; 30% statics; dogs €2; phone; poss cr; adv bkg; quiet but poss noise w/e; red long stay; cc acc; CCI. "In Sierra Espuna National Park on edge of unspoilt vill; gd walking, climbing, mountain biking area; v friendly staff; highly rec." ♦ € 14.00 2004*

†ALICANTE *4F2* (8km NE Coastal) **Camping Costa Blanca, Calle Convento 143**, 03560 El Campello (Alicante) [tel/fax 965-63 06 70; info@ campingcostablanca.com; www.campingcosta blanca.com] Exit AP7/E15 junc 67 onto N332, site visible on L at turn for El Campello. Med, hdg pitch, hdstg; shd; htd wc; chem disp; mv service pnt; shwrs inc; baby facs; el pts (6A) €3.60; gas; lndtte; shop; rest; snacks; bar; playgrnd; pool; waterslides; sand beach 500m; watersports; tennis 800m; horseriding 1km; golf 3km; TV cab/sat; 80% statics; dogs; train 1km; sep car park; poss cr; adv bkg; some noise fr rlwy; red long stay; CCI. "Pleasant site nr archaeological site & fishmkt; modern facs; friendly, helpful staff; not suitable RVs & lge o'fits due narr access to pitches; pitches sm & low canvas awnings; gd security." ♦ € 30.20 (CChq acc) 2005*

†ALICANTE *4F2* (10km NE Coastal) **Camping Bon Sol, Camino Real de Villajoyosa 35, Playa Muchavista**, 03560 El Campello (Alicante) [tel/fax 965-94 13 83] Exit AP7 N of Alicante at junc 67 onto N332 sp Playa San Juan; on reaching coast rd turn N twds El Campello; site sp. Sm, mkd pitch, hdstg, pt shd, all serviced pitches; wc; chem disp; shwrs; el pts (4A) €4; lndtte; shop; rest; bar; sand beach adj; 50% statics; adv bkg; cc acc; red long stay/low ssn; CCI. "Diff ent for c'vans; helpful staff; noisy w/e; vg." ♦ € 24.60 2004*

†ALLARIZ *1B2* (1.5km W Rural) **Camping Os Invernadeiros, Crta Allariz-Celanova, Km3**, 32660 Allariz (Ourense) [988-44 01 26; fax 988-44 20 06] Well sp off N525 Orense-Xinzo rd & fr A52. Sm, pt shd; wc; shwrs inc; el pts €2.40; gas; lndtte; shop; snacks; bar; playgrnd; pool 1.5km; horseriding; cycle hire; quiet; red long stay; cc acc; CCI. "Vg; site combined with horseriding stable; rv walk adj." € 13.60 2004*

ALMAYATE see Torre del Mar *2H4*

SPAIN

†ALMERIA *4G1* (23km SE Coastal/Rural) **Camping Cabo de Gata, Ctra Cabo de Gata s/n, Cortijo Ferron, 04150 Cabo de Gata (Almeria)** [950-16 04 43; fax 950-52 00 03; info@ campingcabodegata.com; www.campingcabo degata.com] Exit m'way N340/344/E15 junc 460 or 467 sp Cabo de Gata onto N471 dir San Jose, foll sp. Lge, hdg/mkd pitch, pt shd; wc; chem disp; baby facs; shwrs inc; el pts (6-16A) €3.85; gas; lndtte; ice; supmkt high ssn; tradsmn; rest; snacks; bar; playgrnd; pool; diving cent; sand beach 900m; tennis; games area; excursions; cycle hire; TV; 2% statics; dogs €2.25; Eng spkn; adv bkg; cc acc; red long stay/low ssn/CCI. "M'vans with solar panels/TV aerials take care with metal framed sun shd; occasional power cuts; poss long walk to water point; gd for cycling, birdwatching esp flamingoes; popular at w/e; poss resident workers; isolated, dry area of Spain with many interesting features; warm winters; exchange 2nd hand Eng books avail; excel." ♦ € 20.50   2005*

See advertisement on previous page

This site entry hasn't been updated for a while; we'd better fill in a site report form and send it to The Club.

†ALMERIA *4G1* (4km W Coastal) **Camping La Garrofa, Ctra N340a, Km 435.4, 04002 Almeria** [950-23 57 70; info@lagarrofa.com; www. lagarrofa.com] Site sp on coast rd bet Almeria & Aguadulce. Med, some hdstg, pt sl, pt shd; wc; chem disp; shwrs inc; el pts €3.60; gas; lndtte; shop; rest; snacks; shgl beach adj; 10% statics; dogs €1.80; bus; sep car park; m'wy noise; CCI. "V pleasant site; helpful staff; clean facs." ♦ € 17.80   2005*

†ALMERIA *4G1* (10km W Coastal) **Camping Roquetas, Ctra Los Parrales s/n, 04740 Roquetas de Mar (Almeria)** [950-34 38 09; fax 950-34 25 25; info@campingroquetas.com; www.camping roquetas.com] Fr A7 take exit 429; at rndabt turn L twd Aguadulce, turn R 500m nr pedestrian lts; foll sp to site. V lge, pt shd; wc; chem disp; shwrs inc; el pts (6A) €3.75; gas; lndtte; ice; shop; snacks; bar; 2 pools; paddling pool; shgl beach 400m; tennis; TV rm; 10% statics; dogs €1.60; phone; Eng spkn; adv bkg rec all year; quiet; cc acc; red low ssn/long stay/CCI. "Many long term visitors in winter; double-size pitches in winter; helpful staff; gd clean facs; poss dusty; artificial shade." ♦ € 14.40   2003*

†ALMUNECAR *2H4* (6km W Coastal) **Nuevo Camping La Herradura, Paseo Maritimo Andres Segovia (Pena Parda), 18690 La Herradura (Granada)** [958-64 06 34; fax 958-64 06 42; laherradura@nuevocamping.com; www.nuevo camping.com] Turn S off N340 sp La Herradura & foll rd to seafront. Turn R to end of beach rd. Med, mkd pitch, pt terr, pt shd; wc; chem disp; serviced pitches; shwrs inc; el pts (5A) €2.60; gas 500m; lndtte; shop; rest; snacks; bar; playgrnd; shgl beach adj; 20% statics; dogs €1; phone; bus; poss v cr; adv bkg; quiet; cc acc; red low ssn/long stay; CCI. "Friendly site in avocado orchard; mountain views some pitches; height restriction lge m'vans, some sm pitches - v tight to manoeuvre; vg san facs but ltd low ssn; popular winter long stay." ♦ € 18.10   2005*

†ALTEA *4F2* (4km S Coastal) **Camping Cap-Blanch, Playa de Albir, 03530 Altea (Alicante)** [965-84 59 46; fax 965-84 45 56; capblanch@ctv.es] Exit AP7/E15 junc 64 Altea-Collosa onto N332, site bet Altea & Benidorm, dir Albir. 'No entry' sps on prom rd do not apply to access to site. Lge, pt shd, hdstg; wc; chem disp; mv service pnt; baby facs; shwrs inc; el pts (5A) €4.20; gas; shop 100m; lndtte; rest; bar; playgrnd; shgl beach adj; watersports; tennis; golf 5km; TV; carwash; poss cr; Eng spkn; adv bkg; quiet; cc acc; red low ssn/long stay. "Poss cr in winter with long stay campers; Altea mkt Tues; buses to Benidorm & Altea; most pitches hdstg on pebbles; excel long stay." ♦ € 35.00   2003*

†AMETLLA DE MAR, L' *3C2* (2.5km S Coastal) **Camping L'Ametlla Village Platja, Paratge Stes Creus s/n, 43860 L'Ametlla de Mar (Tarragona)** [977-26 77 84; fax 977-26 78 68; info@ campingametlla.com; www.campingametlla. com] Exit AP7 junc 39, foll sp to site. Lge, hdg/mkd pitch, hdstg, terr, pt shd; htd wc; chem disp; mv service pnt; baby facs; shwrs inc; el pts (5A) inc; gas; lndtte; ice; shop high ssn; rest; snacks; bar; BBQ; playgrnd; pool; paddling pool; shgl beach 400m; diving cent; games area; fitness rm; cycle hire; entmnt; TV; some statics; dogs; phone; Eng spkn; adv bkg; quiet; cc acc; red long stay; CCI. "Conv Port Aventura & Ebro Delta National Park; excel site & facs." ♦ € 27.90   2005*

See advertisement opposite

AMPOLLA, L' *3C2* (Coastal) **Camping Sant Jordi, Calle del Mar 5, 43895 L'Ampolla (Tarragona)** [tel/fax 977-46 04 15; campingsantjord@teleline. es] Turn off N340 for L'Ampolla at km stone 1098. Fr harbour 500m NE. 1st site reached. Med, terr, pt shd; wc (cont); own san rec; chem disp; shwrs inc; el pts (6A) inc; gas; lndtte; ice; shop & 500m; rest; snacks; bar; playgrnd; sand beach adj; 10% statics; dogs; phone; Eng spkn; adv bkg; quiet; red long stay; cc acc; CCI. "V helpful manager/owner; unspoilt coast; poss itinerants on site; facs poss poor low ssn; gd sh stay." ♦ 20 Apr-15 Oct. € 28.80   2004*

†ARANDA DE DUERO *1C4* (3km N Urban) **Camping Costajan, Ctra A1/E5, Km 164-165, 09400 Aranda de Duero (Burgos) [947-50 20 70; fax 947-51 13 54; campingcostajan@telefonica. net]** Sp on N1 Madrid-Burgos rd, exit km 164 Aranda Norte & foll sp to Aranda & site 500m on R. Med, pt sl, shd; wc; chem disp; mv service pnt; shwrs inc; el pts (10A) €4.30 (poss no earth); gas; lndtte; shop; tradsmn; supmkt 1km; rest high ssn; snacks; bar; BBQ; playgrnd; pool high ssn; tennis; games area; 10% statics; dogs €2; phone; bus 2km; adv bkg; quiet, but some traff noise; red low ssn but ltd facs; cc acc; CCI. "Sm mkt 1km; lovely site under pine trees; poultry farm adj; diff pitch access due to trees & sandy soil; v friendly, helpful owner; site poss clsd late Nov-13 Jan - phone ahead to check; low ssn recep opens 1830 - site yourself, many facs also clsd low ssn; excel facs for disabled; poss cold/tepid shwrs low ssn; gd winter NH." € 18.00
2005*

†ARANJUEZ *1D4* (1.5km NE Urban) **Camping Soto del Castillo, Ctra N-IV Km 40, 28300 Aranjuez (Madrid) [918-91 13 95; fax 918-91 41 97]** Fr N (Madrid) turn off N1V exit 37 onto M305. On ent town turn L bef rv, after petrol stn on R. Take L lane & watch for site sp on L, also mkd M305 Madrid. Site in 500m on R. (If missed cont around cobbled rndabt & back twd Madrid.) Fr S turn off N1V for Aranjuez & foll Palaceo Real sp. Join M305 & foll sp for Madrid & camping site. Warning: rd surface rolls, take it slowly on app to site. Med, pt shd; wc; chem disp; shwrs inc; el pts (6A) €3.50 (poss no earth, rev pol); gas; lndtte; shop; hypmkt 3km; rest; snacks; bar; playgrnd; pool & paddling pool; cycle hire; 45% statics & lge area tents only; phone; cc acc; red low ssn; 10% red CCI. "Busy transit site low ssn - poss run down; some v shabby statics; haphazard siting; some pitches damaged & el pts not working; gd clean facs but ltd low ssn; hot water for everything; friendly staff; pleasant town; conv Madrid by train; conv Royal Palace & gardens; some pitches damaged - check mud & ruts as diff when wet; v busy/noisy at w/e; site poss clsd early 2006 for pitch renovation - phone ahead to check." ♦€ 17.60   2005*

ARBON *1A3* (Rural) **Camping La Cascada, 33718 Arbon (Asturias) [985-62 50 81]** Approx 20km W of Luarca on N634, turn S onto AS25 for approx 10km. Immed bef town of Navia, site sp. Winding rd. Med, sl, pt shd; wc; chem disp (wc); shwrs inc; el pts (3-4A) €2; gas; shop & 1km; snacks; bar; BBQ; playgrnd; pool; sand beach 12km; 15% statics; dogs; phone; Eng spkn; adv bkg; quiet; CCI. "V friendly, family-run site in beautiful area; excel info fr local tourist office." Easter-30 Sep. € 10.50
2005*

†ARCOS DE LA FRONTERA *2G3* (1km E) **Camping Lago de Arcos, 11630 Arcos de la Frontera (Cadiz) [956-70 83 33; fax 956-70 80 00]** On A382 at Arcos turn E at sp El Bosque onto A372. Turn L at sp El Santiscal & site, site on R. Med, pt shd; wc; shwrs inc; el pts (5A) €2.75; gas; lndtte; sm shop; snacks; bar; playgrnd; pool high ssn; phone; poss cr; quiet; cc acc; CCI. "Noisy at Easter - young people attending Running Bull Festival on Easter Sunday; tel to check open in low ssn; friendly staff; most pitches have canopy frames." ♦ ltd. € 15.10   2005*

†ARDALES *2G3* (6km N Rural) **Camping Parque Ardales, Bda Los Embalses, s/n, 29550 Ardales (Malaga) [tel/fax 952-11 24 01; rey@camping parqueardales.com]** Fr Antequera on A382 W to Campillos, then A357 S dir Ardales. Foll sp twd Embalse del Conde de Guadalhorce. V steep ent & exit not suitable towed c'vans. Sm, hdstg, pt sl, shd; wc; chem disp (wc); shwrs inc; el pts (10A) €3.50; shop high ssn; BBQ; lake sw & beach adj; dogs; poss cr; quiet; cc acc. "Forested site around lake with steep sl & sharp corners; stunning views; mainly for tenters; helpful owner; hot water only 2hrs am & pm; conv walk to Camino del Rey & drive to Bobastro." € 14.25   2005*

SPAIN

†ARENAS DE SAN PEDRO *1D3* (8km N Rural) Camping Prados Abiertos, Ctra Avila-Talavera, N502, Km 72, 05410 Mombeltran (Avila) [tel/fax 920-38 60 61; derivera@telepolis.com]
N fr Arenas de San Pedro, site is 3km S of Mombeltran, 600m past junc with AV923, on R adj hotel. Med, mkd pitch, terr, shd; wc; chem disp; shwrs inc; el pts (5A) inc; gas; lndtte; shop; rest; snacks; bar; playgrnd; pool; paddling pool; tennis; cycle hire; TV; 20% statics; phone; site clsd 19 Dec-6 Jan; poss cr; cc acc; CCI. "Ltd pitches accessible with c'van; in Gredos mountains."
€ 16.40   2005*

†ARENAS DEL REY *2G4* (Rural) Camping Los Bermejales, Km 360, Embalse Los Bermejales, 18129 Arenas del Rey (Granada) [958-35 91 90; fax 958-35 93 36; camping@losbermejales.com; www.losbermejales.com]
On A44/E902 S fr Granada, exit at junc 139 dir La Malaha onto A385. In approx 10km, turn L onto A338 dir Alhama de Granada & foll sp for site. Fr A92 foll sp Alhama de Granada, then Embalse Los Bermejales. Med, mkd pitch, hdstg, terr, pt shd; wc; chem disp; mv service pnt; shwrs inc; el pts (9A) €2.45; gas; lndtte; ice; shop; rest; snacks; bar; BBQ; playgrnd; pool; lake sw & sand/shgl beach adj; fishing (licence req); pedalos; tennis; TV rm; 50% statics; dogs; phone; poss cr high ssn; little Eng spkn; adv bkg; quiet. "Ideal base for touring Granada; Roman baths 12km at Alhama de Granada; vg disabled facs." ♦ € 14.70   2005*

ARENAS, LAS *1A4* (1km E Rural) Camping Naranjo de Bulnes, Las Vegas, 33554 Arenas de Cabrales (Asturias) [tel/fax 985-84 65 78]
Fr Unquera on N634, take N621 S to Panes, AS114 23km to Las Arenas. Site E of vill of Las Arenas de Cabrales, both sides of rd. V lge, mkd pitch, pt sl, pt shd; wc; chem disp; baby facs; shwrs inc; el pts (10A) €2.90; lndtte; ice; shop; rest; snacks; bar; playgrnd; rv sw; TV rm; poss cr; some Eng spkn; adv bkg; some rd noise; cc acc; CCI. "Lovely site by rv; beautifully situated; attractive, rustic-style san facs; N side san facs up 22 steps, S side san facs level ground; rds thro site poor; poor security; conv Picos de Europa; mountain-climbing school; guides; excursions; mountain scenery, walking; excel value rest." 1 Mar-31 Oct. € 21.00   2005*

ARENYS DE MAR *3C3* (3km NE Coastal) Camping Globo Rojo, Ctra N11, Km 660.9, 08360 Canet de Mar (Barcelona) [tel/fax 937-94 11 43; camping@globo-rojo.com; www.globo-rojo.com]   On N11 500m N of Canet de Mar. Site clearly sp on L. Gd access. Med, hdg/mkd pitch, hdstg, shd; wc; chem disp; baby facs; shwrs; el pts (10A) €4; gas; lndtte; shop; tradsmn; rest; snacks; bar; BBQ; playgrnd; pool; paddling pool; shgl beach & watersports adj; games area; tennis 50m; horseriding 2km; cycle hire; child entmnt; internet; TV rm; 8% statics; dogs €3.50; phone; sep car park; Eng spkn; adv bkg (dep req); cc acc; red low ssn/long stay/CCI. "Excel facs; friendly, family-run site; conv Barcelona by train (38km); highly rec." ♦ 1 Apr-30 Sep. € 24.75   2005*

ARES see Ferrol *1A2*

†ARNES *3C2* (Rural) Camping Els Ports, Ctra Arnes-Horta San Joan, Km 2, 43597 Arnes (Tarragona) [tel/fax 977-43 55 60]   Exit AP7 at junc Tortosa onto C12 sp Gandesa. Turn W onto T333 at El Pinell de Brai, then T330 to site. Med, pt shd; htd wc; shwrs inc; el pts €3.85; lndtte; shop; rest; bar; pool; paddling pool; games area; cycle hire; horseriding 3km; entmnt; TV rm; some statics; phone; bus 1km; quiet; cc acc. "Nr nature reserve & many sports activities." ♦ ltd. € 17.20   2005*

AURITZ *3A1* (3km SW) Camping Urrobi, 31694 Espinal (Navarra) [tel/fax 948-76 02 00]
NE fr Pamplona on N135 twd Valcarlos thro Erro; 1.5km after Auritzberri (Espinal) turn R on N172. Site on N172 at junc with N135 opp picnic area. Med, pt shd; wc; chem disp; mv service pnt; shwrs inc; el pts (3A) €4.25; gas; lndtte; shop; tradsmn; supmkt 1.5km; rest; snacks; bar; BBQ; playgrnd; pool; rv adj; tennis; mini-golf; cycle hire; horseriding; 20% statics; phone; Eng spkn; adv bkg; quiet; cc acc; CCI. "Excel site & facs, walks in surrounding hills; solar htd water." ♦ 1 Apr-31 Oct. € 16.00
                                                     2005*

AVIN see Cangas de Onis *1A3*

†AYERBE *3B2* (1km Rural) Camping La Banera, Ctra Loarre Km.1, 22800 Ayerbe (Huesca) [tel/fax 974 38 02 42; labanera@wanadoo.es] Take A132 NW fr Huesca dir Pamplona. Turn R at 1st x-roads at ent to Ayerbe. Site 1km on R on A1206. Med, mkd pitch, terr, pt shd; wc; chem disp; baby facs; fam bthrm; shwrs inc; el pts (6A) €2.40; gas; lndtte; ice; shop 1km; rest; snacks; bar; cooking facs; TV rm; dogs; some Eng spkn; adv bkg; quiet; cc acc; red long stay; CCI. "V friendly, well-maintained, family-run site; excel peace & quiet; helpful owners; facs clean; wonderful views; excel rest, vg value; close to Loarre - one of best castles in Spain; care req by high o'fits as many low trees." ♦ € 10.50
                                                     2005*

AYERBE *3B2* (10km NE Rural) Camping Castillo de Loarre, 22809 Loarre (Huesca) [tel/fax 974-38 27 22; campingloarre@ctv.es]
NW on A132 fr Huesca, turn R at ent to Ayerbe to Loare sp Castillo de Loarre. Pass 1st site on R (La Banera) & foll sp to castle past Loarre vill on L; site on L. App rd steep & twisting. Med, pt sl, pt shd; wc; chem disp; shwrs inc; el pts (6A) inc; gas; lndtte; ice; shop; tradsmn; rest; snacks; bar; playgrnd; sm pool; cycle hire; 10% statics; dogs; phone; poss cr; Eng spkn; quiet; cc acc; CCI. "Elevated site in almond grove beneath castle; superb scenery & views, esp fr pitches on far L of site; some pitches ltd el pts; excel birdwatching - many vultures/eagles at eye level; gd touring area; site open w/e in winter; v busy high ssn & weekends; pitching poss diff lge o'fits due low trees; worth the journey." ♦ 9 Apr-4 Nov.
€ 14.80   2005*

Càmping Esponellà

E-17832 ESPONELLÀ (GIRONA)

At 35km from the French border, 8 km from Banyoles and 30 km from the Costa Brava. If you come from France, exit 3; if you come from the south, exit 6. Next to a typical Catalan village of only 300 inhabitants. At the border of the river Fluvia (fishing and renting of kayaks) and surrounded by mountains with numerous excursion possibilities by foot, bike or mountain bike. The site has good san. installations with hot water in showers and washing up basins. Sites w. electr., water and ablution. Swimming pool and 2 heated pools, minigolf, tennis, bar-musical (karaoke) organised leisure, bungalows for hire. Massages and natural therapies.

Open throughout the year.

Tel.: (34) 972 59 70 74
Fax: (34) 972 59 71 32
www.campingesponella.com
informa@campingesponella.com

†AYORA *4F1* (4km S Rural) **Valle de Ayora Caravan Park, Km 110, Ctra N330 Almansa-Ayora, 46620 Ayora (Valencia) [676-94 60 21; ayoracamping@terra.es]** N fr Almansa on N330 dir Ayora, site sp at km 110. Sm, pt shd; wc; chem disp; shwrs inc; no el pts; shop, rest, snacks, bar 4km; pt shd 4km; htd child pool; dogs; adv bkg; quiet; red long stay; CCI. "Peaceful, British-owned, CL-type site; gd walking; fishing; climbing; bird-watching; ltd to 5 o'fits - phone ahead to check space avail." € 20.00   2004*

BAIONA *1B2* (2km NE Urban/Coastal) **Camping Playa America, Ctra Vigo-Baiona, Km 9.250, 36350 Nigran (Pontevedra) [986-36 71 61; fax 986-36 54 04; oficina@campingplayaamerica. com; www.campingplayaamerica.com]** Sp on rd PO552 fr all dirs (Vigo/Baiona/La Guardia) nr beach. Med, mkd pitch, pt shd; wc; chem disp; mv service pnt; baby facs; shwrs inc; el pts (6A) €3; gas; lndtte; shop; tradsmn; rest; snacks; bar; BBQ; playgrnd; pool; sand beach 500m; cycle hire; 60% statics; dogs; bus 500m; poss cr; Eng spkn; adv bkg; CCI. "Friendly staff; gd long stay." ♦ 16 Mar-16 Oct. € 19.50   2004*

†BAIONA *1B2* (1km E Coastal) **Camping Bayona Playa, Ctra Vigo-Baiona, Km 19, Sabaris, 36393 Baiona (Pontevedra) [986-35 00 35; fax 986-35 29 52; campingbayona@bme.es]** Fr Vigo on PO552 sp Baiona. Or fr A57 exit Baiona & foll sp Vigo & site sp. Site clearly sp for 25km around. Lge, mkd pitch, pt shd; wc (some cont); chem disp; mv service pnt; shwrs inc; el pts (3A) €2.80; gas; lndtte; ice; shop; rest; snacks; bar; playgrnd; pool; waterslide; sand beach adj; 20% statics; dogs; phone; poss cr; adv bkg (esp high ssn); quiet; red long stays; CCI. "Area of o'stndg natural beauty with sea on 3 sides; well-organised site; excl facs; avoid access w/e as v busy." ♦ € 26.40   2005*

BAIONA *1B2* (7km S Coastal) **Camping Mougas, 36309 Mougas (Pontevedra) [986-38 50 11; fax 986-38 29 90; campingmougas@vigonet.com; www.campingmougas.com]** Fr Baiona take coastal rd PO552 S; site sp. Med, pt shd; wc; chem disp; shwrs; el pts €3.05; lndtte; supmkt; rest; snacks; bar; playgrnd; pool; beach adj; tennis; horseriding; fishing; entmnts; statics; red low ssn. "Excel staff; lovely site; gd for watching sunsets; gd long/sh stay." Holy Week-30 Sep. € 17.90   2004*

†BALAGUER *3C2* (8km N Rural) **Camping La Noguera, 25615 Sant Llorenc de Montgai (Lleida) [973-42 03 34; fax 973-42 02 12; www. campinglanoguera.com]** Fr Lleida, take N11 ring rd & exit at km 467 onto C13 NE dir Andorra & Balaguer. Head for Balaguer town cent, cross rv & turn R onto LV9047 dir Gerb. Site on L in 8km thro Gerb. App fr Camarasa not rec. Lge, mkd pitch, hdstg, terr, pt shd; wc; chem disp; mv service pnt; baby facs; shwrs inc; el pts (6A) €4.60; gas; lndtte; ice; supmkt; tradsmn; rest; snacks; bar; BBQ; playgrnd; pool; games area; TV rm; 50% statics; dogs €3.10; phone; poss cr; Eng spkn; adv bkg; quiet; cc acc; red long stay; CCI. "Next to lake & nature reserve; gd cycling." ♦ ltd. € 18.40   2005*

BANOS DE FORTUNA see Fortuna *4F1*

BANOS DE MONTEMAYOR see Bejar *1D3*

†BANYOLES *3B3* (8km N Rural) **Camping Esponella, Ctra Banyoles-Figueres, Km 8, 17832 Esponella (Gerona) [972-59 70 74; fax 972-59 71 32; informa@campingesponella.com; www.camping esponella.com]** Heading S fr French frontier, turn R (W) at Figueras on C260. After 13km turn L at junc to Banyoles. Site 6.4km S. Lge, pt shd; htd wc (some cont); chem disp; shwrs inc; rest; el pts (5A) €3.40; lndtte; ice; shop; rest; bar; BBQ; playgrnd; 2 htd covrd pools; tennis; games area; cycle hire; mini-golf; rv fishing; horseriding; entmnt; some statics; dogs €1.38; quiet; red long stay/CCI. "Banyoles Lake (boating) 10km; Costa Brava 50km, S side of Pyrenees 30km; gd walks; check el pts earthing; excl facs; v busy w/e." € 23.10   2005*

See advertisement

CAMPING BEGUR
CARAVANING-BUNGALOW

CRA. D'ESCLANYA KM.2, 17255 BEGUR-COSTA BRAVA-SPAIN TEL. 972 623 201-FAX. 972 624 566 EMAIL: INFO@CAMPINGBEGUR.GP5:41.9404°N-3.1989° E

WWW.CAMPINGBEGUR.COM

†BANYOLES *3B3* (2km W Rural) **Camping Caravaning El Llac, 17834 Porqueres (Gerona)** [tel/fax 972-57 03 05] Fr Gerona enter Banyoles & foll sp Olot. Site adj Lago de Banyoles, sp fr rd GI524. Lge, mkd pitch; pt shd; wc; shwrs; el pts €3.65; lndtte; shop; snacks; bar; pool; lake sw; 80% statics; dogs €2.10; bus 1km; site clsd mid-Dec to mid-Jan; poss cr; quiet but noisy rest/disco adj in high ssn; red long stay. "Museums & ancient churches; ltd facs low ssn; facs stretched high ssn." ♦ € 17.20   2004*

> Some of these sites have changed their opening dates - we'd better fill in some site report forms and let the editor of the guide know.

BARBATE see Vejer de la Frontera *2H3*

BARCELONA see sites listed under El Masnou, Gava and Sitges

†BECERREA *1B2* (15km E Rural) **Camping Os Ancares, Ctra N-V1, Liber, 27664 Mosteiro-Cervantes (Lugo)** [tel/fax 982-36 45 56] Fr A6 exit Becerrea S onto LU722 sp Navia de Suarna. After 10km in Liber turn R onto LU723 sp Doiras, site in 7km just beyond Mosteiro vill; site sp. Site ent poss diff lge o'fits & lge m'vans. Med, terr, shd; wc; shwrs inc; el pts (6A) €2.40; gas; lndry rm; rest; snacks; bar; playgrnd; pool; fishing; horseriding; poss cr; quiet; CCI. "Isolated site; a little run down; gd rest & san facs; ltd facs low ssn; outstanding mountain scenery; gd walking." € 13.30   2005*

BEGUR *3B3* (N Coastal) **Camping El Maset, Playa Sa Riera, 17255 Begur (Gerona)** [972-62 30 23; fax 972-62 39 01; elmaset@jazzfree.com] Fr Begur take rd N twd Sa Riera. Med, shd; wc; chem disp; baby facs; shwrs inc; el pts €4.30; gas; lndtte; shop; snacks; rest; bar; pool; fishing; playgrnd; games area; beach nr; phone; no dogs; cc acc. ♦ 22 Mar-24 Sep. € 23.65   2002*

BEGUR *3B3* (1.5km S) **Camping Begur, Ctra d'Esclanya, Km 2, 17255 Begur (Gerona)** [972-62 32 01; fax 972-62 45 66; info@camping begur.com; www. campingbegur.com] Exit AP7/E15 junc 6 Girona onto C66 dir La Bisbal & Palamos. At x-rds to Pals turn L dir Begur, then turn R twd Esclanya, site on R, clearly sp. Slope to site ent. Lge, pt sl, shd; wc; chem disp; baby facs; fam bthrm; serviced pitches; shwrs inc; el pts (10A) inc; gas; lndtte; supmkt; rest; snacks; bar; BBQ; playgrnd; pool; beach 2km; tennis; games area; gym; internet; 10% statics; dogs €4.80; phone; Eng spkn; adv bkg; cc not acc; red long stay/CCI. "Adj castle & magnificent views; narr site rds poss diff lge o'fits; excursions arranged; excel, peaceful site." ♦ 14 Mar-30 Sep. € 32.10   2005*

See advertisement above

BEJAR *1D3* (6km S Rural) **Camping Cinco Castanos, 37710 Candelario (Salamanca)** [923-41 32 04; fax 923-41 32 82] In cent of Bejar S turn L sp Candelario. Thro Candelario foll sp for 3km. Steep bends & narr app rd. Sm, mkd pitch, pt sl, pt shd; htd wc; chem disp (wc); baby facs; shwrs inc; el pts €2.75; gas; lndtte; ice; shop 1km; rest; bar; playgrnd; pool; no dogs; phone; quiet; CCI. "Mountain vill; friendly owner; no facs in winter; no lge o'fits as steep site; vg long stay." ♦ Holy Week-30 Sep. € 16.60   2003*

†BEJAR *1D3* (15km SW Rural) **Camping Las Canadas, Ctra N630, Km 432, 10750 Banos de Montemayor (Caceres)** [927-48 11 26; fax 927-48 13 14; info@lascanadas.net; www. campinglascanadas.net] Fr Plasencia turn off new A630 m'way at 437km stone to Heruns then take old N630 twd Bejar. Site at 432km stone, behind 'Hervas Peil' (leather goods shop). Lge, mkd pitch, pt sl; shd (net shdg); htd wc; chem disp; baby facs; shwrs inc; el pts (5A) inc; gas; lndtte; shop; rest; snacks; bar; playgrnd; pool in high ssn; fishing; TV rm; 60% statics; dogs; poss cr; Eng spkn; quiet but rd noise; cc acc; 15% red long stay; CCI. "Gd san facs but poss cold shwrs; poss untidy low ssn; high vehicles take care overhanging trees; gd walking country; NH/sh stay." ♦ ltd. € 18.70 (CChq acc)   2005*

†BELLVER DE CERDANYA *3B3* (2km E Rural) Camping Bellver, Ctra N260, Km 193, 17539 Isovol (Gerona) [973-51 02 39; fax 973-51 07 19; camping@bellver.org; www.campingbellver.com] On N260 fr Puigcerda to Bellver; site on L. Well sp. Lge, mkd pitch, shd; htd wc; chem disp (wc); shwrs inc; el pts (5A) €3.10; gas; lndtte; rest; snacks; bar; playgrnd; pool; 80% statics; dogs; phone; poss cr; Eng spkn; quiet; cc acc; CCI. "Friendly helpful staff; gd stopover for Andorra; lovely pitches along rv; san facs immac; v quiet low ssn." € 18.50   2004*

†BELLVER DE CERDANYA *3B3* (1km W Rural) Camping La Cerdanya, Ctra N260, Km 200, 25727 Prullans (Lleida) [973-51 02 62; fax 973-51 06 72; campingcerdanya@ctv.es] Fr Andorra frontier on N260, site sp. Lge, shd; wc; baby facs; mv service pnt; shwrs inc; el pts (4A) €3.60; gas; lndtte; shop; rest; snacks; pool; paddling pool; entmnt; 80% statics; phone; poss cr; adv bkg; quiet; red long stay; cc acc. ♦ € 20.80   2003*

BENABARRE *3B2* (500m Urban) Camping Benabarre, 22580 Benabarre (Huesca) [974-54 35 72; fax 974-54 34 32] Fr N230 S, turn L after 2nd camping sp & into vill. Ignore brown camping sp (part of riding cent). Med, pt shd; wc; shwrs inc; el pts (10A) inc; shops 500m; bar; pool; tennis; no statics; phone; quiet. "Excel simple site; houses built along one side; gd facs; lovely vill with excel chocolate shop; conv Graus & mountains; interesting vill; friendly site - a real find; gd value for money; v quiet low ssn; warden calls 1700; mkt on Fri." Holy Week-30 Sep. € 11.60   2005*

BENAMAHOMA see Ubrique *2H3*

†BENASQUE *3B2* (3km N Rural) Camping Aneto, 22440 Benasque (Huesca) [974-55 11 41; fax 974-55 16 63; anetocamping.3066@cajavural.com] Fr Vielha N230 then N260 to Castejon de Sos, foll sp to Benasque, site on L in 3km. Med, pt sl, pt shd; wc; chem disp; shwrs inc; el pts (10A) €3.60; gas; ice; lndtte; shop in ssn & 3km; tradsmn; rest in ssn; snacks; bar; BBQ; playgrnd; TV; sw 3km; poss cr; quiet; 75% statics; cc acc; Eng spkn; phone; CCI. "Vg long stay; highly rec; unspoilt countryside; stunning app via gorges fr S; gd walking, wildflowers; friendly owners; access to pitches poss diff lge o'fits." € 15.00   2002*

SPAIN

BENAVENTE *1B3* (11km SW Rural) **Camping Rio Tera, 49698 Mozar de Valverde (Zamora)** [980-64 05 50; fax 980-64 05 73; campingriotera@ terra.es; www.campingriotera.com] W fr Benavente on N525; in about 12km camp sp just bef Colinas de Trasmonte. Turn L & go thro Villanazar. Turn R at T-junc, cross rv. Site in 100m on R. Med, mkd pitch, pt shd; wc; chem disp; shwrs inc; el pts (5A) €3; lndry rm; shop; rest; snacks; bar; playgrnd; tennis; 10% statics; dogs; quiet; cc acc; CCI. 1 Apr-30 Sep. € 15.50   2004*

Mustn't forget to post our site report forms to The Club, otherwise sites might be deleted.

BENICARLO see also Peniscola *3D2*

†**BENICARLO** *3D2* (2km NE Urban/Coastal) **Camping La Alegria del Mar, Ctra N340 Km 1046, Calle Playa Norte, 12580 Benicarlo (Castellon)** [964-47 08 71] Sp off main N340 app Benicarlo. Take slip rd mkd Service, go under underpass, turn R on exit & cont twd town, then turn at camp sp by Peugeot dealers. Sm, mkd pitch, pt shd; wc; shwrs; el pts (4-6A) €3.50; gas; lndtte; shop 500m; rest; snacks; bar; playgrnd; sm pool; beach adj; games rm; phone; poss cr; quiet but rd noise at night; red long stay/low ssn; cc acc. "Eng-owned; access to pitches poss diff in ssn; facs old/basic but clean; Xmas & New Year packages; fair sh/long stay." € 16.00   2003*

†**BENICASIM** *3D2* (500m NE Coastal) **Camping Bonterra Park, Avda de Barcelona 47, 12560 Benicasim (Castellon)** [964-30 00 07; fax 964 30 00 08; info@campingbonterra.com; www. campingbonterra.com] Fr N exit AP7 junc 45 onto N340 dir Benicasim. In approx 7km turn R Benicasim N; strt ahead to traff lts, then turn L, site on L 500m after rlwy bdge. Fr S on AP7 exit junc 46 onto N340 dir Benicasim. In approx 8km turn R sp Benicasim (not Benicasim Playas) into vill main street Calle Santo Tomas past rlwy bdge, site on L in 500m. Lge, mkd pitch, pt sl, shd; htd wc; chem disp; mv service pnt; baby facs; shwrs inc; el pts (6A) inc; gas; lndtte; shop; rest; snacks; bar; playgrnd; 2 pools (1 covrd & htd); paddling pool; sand beach 300m; tennis; cycle hire; entmnt (daytime only); games area; games rm; internet; 15% statics; dogs (except Jul/Aug); train; sep car park; Eng spkn; adv bkg; quiet; cc acc; red long stay/low ssn; red CCI. "V clean, well-managed site; excel walks; many long-stay winter residents; access to pitches poss diff due trees; highly rec." ♦ € 45.05 ABS - E19   2005*

See advertisement on previous page

†**BENICASIM** *3D2* (4.5km NW Coastal) **Camping Azahar, 12560 Benicasim (Castellon)** [964-30 31 96; fax 964-30 25 12] Fr AP7 junc 45 take N340 twd Valencia; in 5km L at top of hill (do not turn R to go-karting; foll sp. Turn R under rlwy bdge opp Hotel Voramar. Lge, mkd pitch, pt sl, terr, unshd; htd wc; chem disp; mv service pnt; baby facs; shwrs inc; el pts (4-6A) €2.57 (extension leads req); gas; lndtte; rest; snacks; bar; playgrnd; pool; sand beach 300m across rd; tennis at hotel; cycle hire; 25% statics; dogs €3.54; phone; poss cr high ssn; Eng spkn; adv bkg; red long stay/low ssn/snr citizens; cc acc; CCI. "Popular site, esp in winter; organised events; gd walking & cycling; gd touring base; access poss diff for m'vans & lge o'fits; poss uneven pitches." ♦ ltd. € 24.80   2005*

†**BENIDORM** *4F2* (3km Coastal) **Camping La Torreta, Avda Dr Severo Ochoa s/n, 03500 Benidorm (Alicante)** [965-85 46 68; fax 965-80 26 53] Exit AP7/E15 junc 65 onto N332. Foll sp Playa Levante, site sp. Lge, mkd pitch, hdstg, pt sl, terr, pt shd (bamboo shades); wc (some cont); mv service pnt; shwrs inc; el pts (10A) €3; gas; lndtte; ice; shop; rest; bar; playgrnd; pool & paddling pool; sand beach 1km; 10% statics; dogs; bus; no adv bkg; quiet; red 15+ days; CCI. "Take care siting if heavy rain; some pitches v sm; popular long stay winter visitors; gd long stay." ♦ € 24.90   2003*

†**BENIDORM** *4F2* (1km N) **Camping Arena Blanca, Avda Dr Severo Ochoa 44, 03500 Benidorm (Alicante)** [965-86 18 89; fax 965-86 11 07; info@camping-arenablanca.es; www.camping-arenablanca.es] Fr AP7 exit junc 65 onto N332 dir Playa Levante. Site sp. Med, terr, pt shd; wc; chem disp; some serviced pitches; shwrs inc; el pts (16A) €3; gas; lndtte; supmkt; rest; snacks; bar; playgrnd; pool; paddling pool; sand beach 1km; cash machine; sat TV conn all pitches; 30% statics; dogs; phone; bus 200m; adv bkg; quiet; red long stays; cc acc. ♦ € 32.50   2005*

†**BENIDORM** *4F2* (2km N Urban) **Camping Villamar, Ctra del Albir, Km 0.300, 03503 Benidorm (Alicante)** [966-81 12 55; fax 966-81 35 40; camping@ampingvillamar.com; www.campingvillamar.com] Exit AP7 junc 65. Down hill twd town, turn L at traff lts into Ctra Valenciana, turn R where 2 petrol stns either side of rd, site on L. V lge, mkd pitch, terr, pt shd; wc; chem disp; serviced pitches; shwrs; el pts €3.50; gas; lndtte; shop; rest; bar; playgrnd; 2 pools (1 covrd/htd); sand beach 2km; entmnt; games rm; sat TV; phone; no dogs; adv bkg; quiet; red long stay/low ssn. "Excel site, esp winter; gd security; v welcoming; gd walking area." ♦ € 27.80   2002*

†BENIDORM *4F2* (3km N Urban) **Camping Villasol, Avda Bernat de Sarria s/n, 03500 Benidorm (Alicante) [965-85 04 22; fax 966-80 64 20; campingvillasol@dragonet.es; www.camping-villasol.com]** Leave AP7 at junc 65; thro several traff lts close to m'way; after going down hill, turn sharp L at next traff lts (get in L lane bef lts); ignore 1st camp sp, R at 1km, foll rd to end, turn R, site on R. Care - dip at ent, poss grounding. Lge, mkd pitch, pt shd; wc; baby facs; shwrs inc; el pts (10A) €3.60; gas; lndtte; supmkt; rest; bar; playgrnd; 2 pools (1 htd); sand beach 1.3km; sat TV all pitches; medical service; currency exchange; 5% statics; no dogs; phone; poss cr; Eng spkn; rd noise at bottom site; cc acc; red low ssn/long stay. "Some sm pitches; excel in winter; friendly staff." ♦ € 30.70   2005*

†BENIDORM *4F2* (2km NE Urban) **Camping El Raco, Avda Dr Severo Ochoa s/n, Raco de Loix, 03500 Benidorm (Alicante) [965-86 85 52; fax 965-86 85 44; info@campingraco.com; www. campingraco.com]** Turn off A7 m'way at junc 65 then L onto A332; take turning sp Benidorm Levante Beach; ignore others; L at 1st traff lghts; strt on at next traff lts, El Raco 1km on R. Lge, hdg/mkd pitch, hdstg, pt sl, pt shd; wc; chem disp; 50% serviced pitches; shwrs inc; el pts (10A) €3; gas; lndtte; shop; bar; BBQ; rest; playgrnd; pool; beach 1.5km; games area; TV; 30% statics; poss v cr in winter; quiet; red 15+ days low ssn; cc acc. "Excel site; v popular winter long stay but strictly applied rules about leaving c'van unoccupied; easy 30 min walk to Benidorm; vg local sightseeing; el pts metered for long stay." ♦ € 26.00   2004*

†BENIDORM *4F2* (3km NE Urban) **Camping Benisol, Avda de la Comunidad Valenciana s/n, Benidorm 03500 (Alicante) [965-85 16 73; fax 965-86 08 95; campingbenisol@yahoo.es]** Exit AP7/E15 junc 65 onto N332. Foll sp Benidorm, Playa Levante (avoid by-pass). Site ent easy to miss. Lge, hdg pitch, hdstg, shd; wc; chem disp; serviced pitches; shwrs inc; el pts (4-6A) €2.25; gas; lndtte; shop; rest; snacks; bar; playgrnd; pool; sand beach 4km; TV; 40% statics; bus to Benidorm; Eng spkn; adv bkg with dep; some rd noise; red long stay/low ssn; CCI. "Helpful staff; well-run, clean site; excel sh/long stay." ♦ € 24.00   2003*

†BENIDORM *4F2* (3km NE Rural) **Camping Excalibur, Camino Viejo del Albir s/n; Alfaz del Pi, 03500 Benidorm (Alicante) [966-86 71 39; fax 966-86 69 28; c-m@camping-medieval.com; www.camping-medieval.com]** Exit AP7/E15 at junc 65 onto N332, foll sp Alfaz & Playa Levante. Foll sp 'Castillo Conde de Alfaz' to site. Lge, mkd pitch, terr, hdstg, pt shd; wc; chem disp; 100% serviced pitches; sauna; shwrs inc; el pts (15A) €3.13; gas; lndry rm; lndtte; supmkt; rest; snacks; bar; playgrnd; htd pool; sand beach 3km; tennis; jacuzzi; solarium; gym; games area; cycle hire; disco; entmnt; child entmnt; TV; 75% statics; dogs; phone; bus; poss cr & noisy in ssn; cc acc; 50% red long stay; CCI. "Purpose-built, busy medieval theme site; visitors coached in for medieval banquets at w/e; holiday camp atmosphere." ♦ € 20.00   2003*

BESALU *3B3* (2km E Rural) **Camping Masia can Coromines, Ctra N260, Km 60, 17851 Maia del Montcal (Gerona) [tel/fax 972-59 11 08; coromines@grn.es]** NW fr Gerona on C150 to Besalu. Turn R sp Figueras (N260) for 2.5km. At 60km sp turn into driveway on L opp fountain for approx 300m. Narr app. Sm, pt shd; wc; serviced pitch; shwrs inc; el pts (12A) €3; gas; lndtte; ice; shop 2.5km; rest high ssn; snacks; bar; playgrnd; pool; Eng spkn; adv bkg; quiet with some rd noise; cc acc; CCI. "Friendly, family-run site in beautiful area, narr ent; gd walks, cycle hire." ♦ 13 Apr-31 Oct. € 18.25   2003*

BETANZOS *1A2* (6km NW Rural) **Camping Santa Marta-Coruna, Babio 23, 15165 Bergondo (La Coruna) [tel/fax 981-79 58 26; info@camping santamarta.com; www.campingsantamarta.com]** Fr AP/E19 exit junc sp Bergondo/Sada, foll sp to site. Lge, some hdg/mkd pitch, sl, pt shd; wc; chem disp; baby facs; shwrs inc; el pts (10A) €3.50 (poss rev pol); gas; lndtte; ice; shop, tradsmn; rest high ssn; snacks; bar; BBQ; playgrnd; pool high ssn; sand beach 2km; tennis; cycle hire; TV; dogs; Eng spkn; adv bkg; quiet; CCI. "V peaceful, friendly, under-used site; clean facs; req blocks for levelling; gd touring base." ♦ 1 Jun-30 Sep. € 18.00   2004*

BIELSA *3B2* (8km W Rural) **Camping Pineta, Ctra del Parador, Km 7, 22350 Bielsa (Huesca) [tel/fax 974-50 10 89; www.pirineo.com/camping.pineta]** Fr A138 in Bielsa turn W & foll sp for Parador Monte Perdido & Valle de Pineta. Site on L after 8km (ignore previous campsite off rd). Lge, terr, pt sl, pt shd; wc; chem disp; baby facs; shwrs inc; el pts (6A) €4.20 (poss rev pol); gas; lndtte; shop & 8km; rest; snacks; bar; BBQ; playgrnd; pool; games area; cycle hire; some statics; phone; cc acc; CCI. "Well-maintained site; clean facs; glorious location in National Park." Holy Week-30 Sep. € 21.00   2005*

†BIESCAS *3B2* (3km SE Rural) **Camping Gavin, Ctra N260, Km 503, 22639 Gavin (Huesca) [974-48 50 90 or 659-47 95 51; fax 974-48 50 17; info@campinggavin.com; www.campinggavin. com]** Take N330 N fr Huesca, then N260. Site is at Km 503 fr Huesca, bet Biescas & Gavin. Foll sp for Gavin & look for sp for site. Lge, mkd pitch, terr, pt shd; htd wc; chem disp; mv service pnt; baby facs; fam bthrm; shwrs inc; el pts (10A) €4.10; gas; lndtte; ice; shop; tradsmn; snacks; bar; playgrnd; pool; tennis; cycle hire in National Park; internet; TV; 20% statics; dogs; phone; bus 1km; adv bkg; quiet; CCI. "Wonderful site on edge of Ordesa National Park; super views; barrier ent; immac san facs; excel." ♦ € 21.40 (CChq acc)   2005*

†BILBAO *1A4* (14km N Coastal) **Camping Sopelana, Ctra Bilbao-Plentzia, Km 18, Playa Atxabiribil s/n, 48600 Sopelana (Vizcaya) [946-76 19 81; fax 944-21 50 10; recepcion@ campingsopelana.com; www.campingsopelana. com]** In Bilbao cross rv by m'way bdge sp to airport, foll 637/634 N sp Las Arenas & Plentzia. At km 21 strt on at rndabt then L at next rndabt. Cont thro Sopelana & foll sp on L. Med, hdg pitch, sl, terr; wc (some cont); chem disp; mv service pnt; baby facs; shwrs; el pts (10A) €3.50; gas; lndtte; shop, rest (w/e only low ssn); snacks; bar; playgrnd; pool; sand beach 200m; 70% statics; poss cr; Eng spkn; adv bkg ess high ssn; quiet but noise fr disco adj; red long stay; CCI. "Conv Bilbao & Guggenheim museum; metro stn 1km; poss stong sea winds; v ltd space for tourers; pitches sm, poss flooded after heavy rain; ltd facs low ssn, poss no hot water for shwrs; used by local workers; poor security in city cent/Guggenheim car park; v helpful manager; NH/sh stay only." ♦ € 25.00   2005*

BLANES *3C3* (1km S Coastal) **Camping Bella Terra, Playa S'Abanell, 17300 Blanes (Gerona) [972-34 80 17 or 972-34 80 23; fax 972-34 82 75; info@campingbellaterra.com; www.camping bellaterra.com]** Exit A7 junc 9 via Lloret or junc 10 via Tordera. On app Blanes, all campsites are sp at rndabts; all sites along same rd. Lge, mkd pitch, shd; wc; chem disp; mv service pnt; baby facs; shwrs inc; el pts (5A) inc; gas; lndtte; ice; shop; tradsmn; rest; snacks; bar; BBQ; playgrnd; pools; sand beach adj; tennis; games area; games rm; cycle hire; entmnt; internet; TV; 50% statics; dogs €4.50; poss cr; Eng spkn; quiet; cc acc; red long stay/CCI."Split site - 1 side has pool, 1 side adj beach; pitches poss diff for lge o'fits - pitches on pool side lger; vg site." ♦ 1 Apr-30 Sep. € 34.40   2005*

See advertisement above

†BLANES *3C3* (1km S Coastal) **Camping Blanes, Avda Villa Madrid 33, 17300 Blanes (Gerona) [972-33 15 91; fax 972-33 70 63; info@camping blanes.com; www.campingblanes.com]** Fr N on AP7/E15 exit junc 9 onto NII dir Barcelona. In 15km at 1st traff lts turn L & foll sp Blanes. Fr S to end of C32, then NII dir Blanes. On app Blanes, foll camping sps & Playa S'Abanell - all campsites are sp at rndabts; all sites along same rd. Site adj Hotel Blau-Mar. Lge, mkd pitch, shd; htd wc; chem disp; mv service pnt; shwrs inc; shop; el pts (5A) inc; gas; lndtte; supmkt; snacks high ssn; bar; playgrnd; pool; dir access to sand beach; watersports; cycle hire; games rm; entmnt; internet; dogs; phone; poss cr; Eng spkn; quiet; cc acc; red low ssn. "Easy walk to town cent; trains to Barcelona & Gerona; some sm pitches with low hanging trees; excel." ♦ € 28.35   2005*

See advertisement opposite

BLANES *3C3* (1km S Coastal) **Camping El Pinar, Calle Villa de Madrid, 17300 Blanes (Gerona) [972-33 10 83; fax 972-33 11 00; camping@ elpinarbeach.com]** Exit A7 junc 9 via Lloret or junc 10 via Tordera. On app Blanes, all campsites are sp at rndabts; all sites along same rd. V lge, pt shd; wc; chem disp; mv service pnt; baby facs; shwrs inc; el pts (5A) inc; gas; lndtte; ice; shop; snacks; shop; rest; snacks; bar; BBQ; playgrnd; pool; sand beach adj; TV; 50% statics; dogs; phone; poss cr; adv bkg; poss noisy (music); 50% red for 30+ days; cc acc; CCI. "Nice site; gd facs." ♦ ltd 1 Apr-1 Oct. € 27.53   2004*

†BLANES *3C3* (1km S Coastal) **Camping S'Abanell, Avda Villa de Madrid 7-9, 17300 Blanes (Gerona) [972-33 18 09; fax 972-35 05 06]** Take coast rd S fr cent Blanes. Site well sp on L in 1km. Lge, mkd pitch, pt sl, shd; wc; chem disp; serviced pitches; shwrs; el pts (3A) inc; gas; lndtte; shop adj; rest; snacks; bar; sand beach steeply shelving; 5% statics; phone; site clsd 25 Dec-6 Jan; poss cr; adv bkg; rd noise; red low ssn/snr citizens; CCI. "Friendly, helpful staff; lge o'fits need manhandling due trees & pitch layout; san facs poss unclean low ssn; gd sh stay." € 27.50   2004*

†BLANES *3C3* (1.5km SW Urban/Coastal) **Camping La Masia, Calle Colon 44, 17300 Blanes (Gerona)** [972-33 10 13; fax 972-33 31 28; info@ campinglamasia.com; www.campinglamasia.com] Fr A7 exit junc 9 sp Lloret de Mar, then Blanes. At Blanes foll sp Blanes Sur & Campings, site immed past Camp S'Abanell. V lge, hdstg, pt shd; htd wc; chem disp; mv service pnt; 25% serviced pitch; sauna; steam rm; shwrs inc; el pts (2-5A) inc; lndtte; shop; rest; snacks; bar; playgrnd; 2 pools (1 htd, covrd); sand beach adj; watersports; tennis; weights rm; internet; entmnt; TV rm; 70% statics; dogs; poss cr; Eng spkn; adv bkg; poss noisy; red long stay; CCI. "Well-maintained site; helpful staff." ♦ € 30.70 (CChq acc)   2004*

> As we're travelling out of season, we'd better phone ahead to check that the site is actually open.

BOCA DE HUERGANO see Riano *1A3*

†BOCAIRENT *4F2* (9km E Rural) **Camping Les Fonts de Mariola, Ctra Bocairent-Alcoi, Km 9, 46880 Bocairent (Valencia)** [962-13 51 60; fax 962-13 50 31; info@campingmariola.com; www. campingmariola.com] Fr N330 turn E at Villena onto CV81. N of Banyeres & bef Bocairent turn E sp Alcoi up narr, steep hill with some diff turns & sheer drops; site sp. Lge, pt shd; wc (cont); shwrs inc; el pts (6A) €3; shop; snacks; bar; playgrnd; rv sw 1km; phone; 50% statics; cc acc; CCI. "In Mariola mountains; gd walking; lonely out of ssn; site under development spring 2004 - v poor facs." € 15.00
2004*

BOLTANA see Ainsa *3B2*

†BONANSA *3B2* (2km E Rural) **Camping Baliera, Ctra N260, Km 355.5, Castejon de Sos, 22523 Bonansa (Huesca)** [974-55 40 16; fax 974-55 40 99; info@baliera.com; www.baliera. com] S fr Vielha on N230 for approx 35km, past km 130 turn R onto N260 over bdge opp Elf stn & Ribagorza rest, then onto A1605 sp Bonansa, site 100m on L. Site sp fr N230. Lge, mkd pitch, pt sl; terr, shd; htd wc; chem disp; mv service pnt; baby facs; shwrs inc; el pts (5-10A) €4; gas; lndtte; ice; shop; tradsmn; rest in ssn; snacks; bar; playgrnd; pool (caps ess); lake sw 10km; horseriding 4km; golf 4km; weights rm; TV; 25% statics; dogs €2.10; phone; poss cr; Eng spkn; quiet; cc acc; red low ssn; CCI. "Well-run, peaceful site in parkland setting; part of site v sl; walking in summer, skiing in winter; excel cent for touring; conv Vielha tunnel; gd mountain rds; helpful owner proud of his site; spotless facs." ♦ € 20.00 (CChq acc)   2005*

†BOSSOST *3B2* (3km SE) **Camping Prado Verde, 25551 La Bordeta de Vilamos (Lleida)** [973-64 71 72; fax 973-64 04 56] On N230 at km 176.4 on banks of Rv Garona. Med, shd; wc; baby facs; shwrs; el pts €4; lndtte; shop & 3km; snacks; bar; playgrnd; pool; fishing; cycle hire; TV; no dogs; quiet; cc acc; CCI. "V pleasant NH." € 16.80
2003*

BOSSOST *3B2* (4km S Rural) **Camping Bedura Park, Ctra N230, Km 174.5, 25551 Era Bordeta (Lleida)** [973-64 82 93; fax 973-64 70 38; info@ bedurapark.com; www.bedurapark.com] Fr N on N230, R over rv behind Camping Forcanada. Fr S on N230, 10km fr Viela, L turn over rv. Site is 12km fr French border. Med, mkd pitch, terr, pt shd; wc; chem disp; baby facs; shwrs; el pts (5A) €3.50; gas; lndtte; shop; rest; BBQ; playgrnd; htd pool; fishing; cycle hire; 20% statics; no dogs; phone; bus 200m; poss cr; Eng spkn; adv bkg (dep req); CCI. "Skiing, walking in area; excel." ♦ 1 Apr-30 Sep. € 21.50   2004*

SPAIN

BROTO *3B2* (3km N Rural) **Camping Rio Ara, Ctra Ordesa s/n, 22376 Torla (Huesca)** [974-48 62 48; fax 974-48 63 52] Fr Torla sp on N260. R down v steep narr rd for 1km. Med, pt sl, pt shd; wc; chem disp (wc); shwrs inc; el pts €3.70; lndtte; shop; bar; no statics; phone; cc not acc; CCI. "Attractive well-kept site; mainly tents; conv for Torla; bus to Ordesa National Park; not rec for lge o'fits due to steep app." 1 Apr-31 Oct. € 12.50   2004*

BROTO *3B2* (5km N Rural) **Camping Ordesa, 22376 Torla (Huesca)** [974-48 61 25; fax 974-48 63 81] Fr Ainsa on N260 twd Torla. Pass Torla turn R onto A135 (Valle de Ordesa twd Ordesa National Park. Site 2km N of Torla, adj Hotel Ordesa. Med, pt shd; wc; chem disp; serviced pitch; baby facs; shwrs; el pts (6A) €3; gas 2km; lndtte; shop 2km, tradsmn; rest high ssn; bar; playgrnd; pool; tennis; some statics (sep area); phone; bus 1km; poss cr; Eng spkn; adv bkg (ess Jul/Aug); quiet; red low ssn; cc acc; CCI. "V scenic; recip in adj Hotel Ordesa; excel rest; v helpful staff; facs poss stretched w/e; long, narr pitch & lge trees on access rd poss diff lge o'fits; ltd facs low ssn; no access to National Park by car Jul/Aug, shuttlebus fr Torla." Holy Week-12 Oct. € 16.90   2005*

BROTO *3B2* (1.2km W Rural) **Camping Oto, Afueras s/n, 22370 Oto-Broto (Huesca)** [974-48 60 75; fax 974-48 63 47; info@campingoto.com; www.campingoto.com] On N260 foll camp sp on N o'skts of Broto. Diff app thro vill but poss. Lge, pt sl, pt shd; wc; chem disp; baby facs; shwrs inc; el pts (10A) €3.30 (poss no earth); gas; lndtte; shop; snacks; bar; BBQ; playgrnd; pool; paddling pool; entmnt; adv bkg; quiet; cc acc. "Conv Ordesa National Park; excel, clean san facs; excel bar & café; friendly owner; pitches below pool rec; some noise fr adj youth site." 1 Apr-15 Oct. € 14.70
2005*

†**BROTO** *3B2* (6km W Rural) **Camping Viu, Ctra N260 Biescas-Ordesa, Km 484.2, 22378 Viu de Linas (Huesca)** [974-48 63 01; fax 974-48 63 73; info@campingviu.com; www.campingviu.com] Lies on N260, 4km W of Broto. Fr Broto, N for 2km on rd 135; turn W twd Biesca at junc with Torla rd; site approx 4km on R. Med, sl, pt shd; htd wc; chem disp; mv service pnt; shwrs inc; el pts (5-8A) €4; gas; lndtte; shop; rest; BBQ; playgrnd; games rm; cycle hire; horseriding; walking, skiing & climbing adj; car wash; phone; adv bkg; quiet; cc acc; CCI. "Friendly owners; gd home cooking; fine views; highly rec; clean, modern san facs." € 16.50
2005*

BURGO DE OSMA, EL *1C4* (17km N Rural) **Camping Canon del Rio Lobos, 42317 Ucero (Soria)** [975-36 35 65] On SO 920 17km N fr El Burgo de Osma. Med, hdg/mkd pitch, hdstg & grass, shd; wc; chem disp; shwrs inc; el pts €3.61; ice; lndtte; rest; snacks; bar; BBQ; playgrnd; pool; no dogs; quiet; no cc acc; CCI. "Sm pitches/tight turning; help avail; heart of canyon of Rv Lobos; v pretty location; vg long stay; gd base walking, cycling, climbing; bird watcher's paradise." Holy Week & 1 Jul-30 Sep. € 20.00   2002*

†**BURGOS** *1B4* (4km NE Urban) **Camping Rio Vena, Km 245 Burgos-Irun, 09192 Villafria de Burgos (Burgos)** [947-48 41 20]   Leave m'way AP1 Palencia-Bilbao at junc 2. Foll N1 twd city. On sight of 1st camp sp take service rd (parallel to N1) for 1km to site on R bet industrial units. Sp quite poor. Important to get into service rd early as no direct access fr N1 dual c'way to site. Sm, pt sl, pt shd; wc; shwrs inc; el pts (10A) €4.20 (no earth); gas; lndtte; tradsmn; rest; bar; shop; bus to Burgos at gate; poss cr; rd noise; cc acc; CCI. "Clean facs; delightful owner; v helpful staff; sm uneven, dusty pitches; many trees - poss diff lge o'fits; conv Burgos cathedral; indus est nrby; heavy traffic noise; NH only." € 14.40   2005*

†**BURGOS** *1B4* (22km NE) **Camping Picon del Conde, Ctra N1 Madrid-Irun, Km 263, 09292 Monasterio de Rodilla (Burgos)** [tel/fax 947-59 43 55] Fr Burgos, leave E80 at junc 3 & join N1 twd Burgos. Site is on L after passing under 2nd m'way bridge. Fr S or W head N on AP1/E80 & leave at junc 2, head N on N1 over pass (max gradient 12%). Site about 500m past Monasterio de Rodilla on R. Med, hdg/mkd pitch, shd; htd wc; chem disp; shwrs inc; el pts (5A) €3.30; gas; lndry rm; shop; rest; snacks; bar; playgrnd; pool; 75% statics; dogs; phone; rd noise; cc acc; CCI. "2 hrs drive fr Bilbao ferry; ltd facs low ssn; poss migrant workers; caution el pts; awkward access to san facs & wash-up on 1st floor, shwrs on 2nd; sculpture gallery adj worth a visit; site muddy in wet weather; friendly staff; fair NH only." ♦ € 13.90   2005*

BURGOS *1B4* (3.5km E Rural) **Camping Fuentes Blancas, Ctra Cartuja Miraflores, Km 3.5, 09193 Burgos** [tel/fax 947-48 60 16] Fr N foll sp for N1 Madrid S thro Burgos. Turn R then foll sp twd Leon then under rd, onto S bank of rv, site sp. Fr W on N620 keep rv on L, site eventually sp. Fr m'way exit junc 238, 1st R sp Cortes then L sp Burgos; over rlwy x-ing, turn R onto S bank of rv, site sp. Lge, mkd pitch, shd; wc; chem disp; mv service pnt; baby facs; shwrs inc; el pts (6A) inc; gas; ice; lndtte; shop high ssn & 3km; rest; snacks; bar; playgrnd; pool high ssn; games area; dogs; phone; bus; poss cr; Eng spkn; quiet, some rd noise; cc acc. "V clean facs; neat, roomy site but some sm pitches; poss v muddy in wet; recep open 0800-2200; gd bar/rest; easy access town car parks; Burgos lovely town with art gallery & cathederal; cycle paths & attractive walk into city; ltd facs low ssn & poss itinerants." 1 Apr-30 Sep. € 20.75   2005*

CABO DE GATA see Almeria *4G1*

†**CABRERA, LA** *1D4* (4km S Rural) **Camping d'Oremor, 28721 Cabanillas de la Sierra (Madrid)** [918-43 90 34; fax 918-43 94 09; doremor@doremor.com; www.doremor.com] Fr Madrid, N on E5/N1; exit junc 50; go N parallel to E5/N1. Site clearly sp in 3km. Med, shd; htd wc; chem disp; mv service pnt; shwrs inc; el pts €4; gas; lndtte; shop; rest; snacks; bar; playgrnd; pool; lake sw & fishing adj; tennis; statics; no dogs; poss cr; adv bkg; quiet; cc acc. "Windsurfing on lake & skiing in area in winte; conv NH." ♦ € 16.00   2005*

†CABRERA, LA *1D4* (1km SW Rural) **Camping Pico de la Miel, Ctra N1 Km 58, Finca Prado Nuevo, 28751 La Cabrera (Madrid) [918-68 80 82 or 918-68 81 20; fax 918-68 85 41; pico-miel@ picodelamiel.com]** Fr Madrid on N1/E5, exit junc 60 sp La Cabrera, site sp bef vill. Lge, mkd pitch, pt sl, pt shd; htd wc; chem disp; shwrs inc; el pts (10A) €4; gas; lndtte; shop high ssn; supmkt 1km; rest, snacks, bar high ssn & w/e; playgrnd; Olympic-size pool; paddling pool; sailing; fishing; windsurfing; tennis; games area; squash; mountain-climbing; car wash; 75% statics; dogs; phone; v cr high ssn & w/e; some Eng spkn; adv bkg; quiet; cc acc; red CCI. "Attractive walking country; 30 mins fr Madrid; touring area not v attractive & has frames too low for vans with aerial; interesting park adj; excel san facs." ♦ ltd. € 20.60   2005*

†CABRERA, LA *1D4* (15km SW Rural) **Camping Piscis, Ctra Guadalix de la Sierra, Km.20.9, 28729 Navalafuente (Madrid) [918-43 22 68; fax 918-47 13 41; campiscis@campiscis.com]** Fr N1/E5 exit 50 dir Guidalix de la Sierra, foll sp to Navalafuente & site. Lge, hdg pitch, hdstg, pt sl, pt shd; wc; chem disp; shwrs; el pts (5A) €3.40 (long lead req); gas; lndtte; shop 6km; rest; snacks; bar; playgrnd; pool; 75% statics; quiet; adv bkg; Eng spkn; 10% red 6+ days low ssn; cc acc; CCI. "Mountain views; walking; tennis; pool & watersports 10km; bus to Madrid daily outside gate, 1 hr ride; spacious pitches; ltd facs low ssn." ♦ € 20.50   2005*

CADAQUES *3B3* (1km N Coastal) **Camping Cadaques, Ctra Port Lligat 17, 17488 Cadaques (Gerona) [972-25 81 26; fax 972-15 93 83; info@ campingcadaques.com]** At ent to town, turn L onto tarmac rd thro narr streets, site in about 1.5km on L. NB App to Cadaques on busy, narr mountain rds, not suitable lge o'fits. If raining, roads only towable with 4WD. Lge, mkd pitch, hdstg, sl, pt shd; wc; chem disp; shwrs; el pts (5A) €3.70; gas; lndtte; shop; rest; bar; playgrnd; pools; shgl beach 600m; no dogs; sep car park; poss cr; Eng spkn; no adv bkg; quiet; cc acc. "Cadaques home of Salvador Dali; sm pitches; medical facs high ssn; san facs poss poor low ssn; fair sh stay;." 10 Apr-30 Sep. € 22.15   2004*

CADAQUES *3B3* (8km NW Coastal) **Camping L'Arola, 17489 El Port de la Selva (Gerona) [972-38 70 05]** Off N11 at Figueras, sp to Llanca on N260. In 20km turn R to El Port de la Selva. Site on L (N side of coast rd) bef town. Sm, hdstg, unshd; wc; chem disp; shwrs; el pts (10A) inc; lndry rm; shops 1km; tradsmn; rest; bar; shgl beach adj; 5% statics; bus; poss cr; adv bkg; CCI. "Nr sm, pleasant town with gd shops, rests, harbour, amusements for all ages; scenic beauty; v friendly owner." 1 Jun-30 Sep. € 18.10   2003*

CADAQUES *3B3* (8km NW Coastal) **Camping Port de la Vall, 17489 El Port de la Selva (Gerona) [972-38 71 86; fax 972-12 63 08; info@camping portdelavall.com; www.campingportdelavall.com]** On coast rd fr French border at Llanca take minor rd twd El Port de la Selva. Site 2km fr El Port de la Selva on L. Easily seen. Lge, pt shd; wc; shwrs; el pts (3-5A) €4.87; gas; lndtte; ice; shop; rest; snacks; bar; playgrnd; shgl beach adj; internet; some statics; dogs €2.40; phone; poss cr; adv bkg; poss noisy; cc acc; red low ssn. "Easy walk to harbour; gd site but facs showing age; sm pitches & low branches poss diff - check bef siting; overpriced." 1 Apr-31 Oct. € 47.10 (4 persons)   2005*

CADAVEDO see Luarca *1A3*

†CALATAYUD *3C1* (15km N Rural) **Camping Savinan Parc, Ctra El Frasno-Illueca, Km 7, 50299 Savinan (Zaragoza) [tel/fax 976-82 54 23]** Exit A2/E90 (Zaragoza-Madrid) at km 255 to T-junc. Turn R to Savinan for 6km, foll sps to site 1km S. Lge, hdstg, terr, pt shd; wc; chem disp; mv service pnt; shwrs; el pts (5A) €3.60 (adaptor req); gas; lndry rm; shop 1.5km; rest; snacks; bar; playgrnd; pool high ssn; tennis; horseriding; phone; dogs €3.60; cc acc; CCI. "Beautiful scenery; helpful, friendly staff; some sm narr pitches; rec identify pitch location to avoid stop/start on hill; terr pitches have steep, unfenced edges; many pitches have fixed sunscreen frames & diff for long o'fits; all hot water on coin slots; modern facs block but cold in winter & poss stretched high ssn; many permanent chalets; site poss clsd Feb." € 16.00   2005*

CALATAYUD *3C1* (3km E) **Camping Calatayud, Ctra Madrid-Barcelona, Km 239, 50300 Calatayud (Zaragoza) [976-88 05 92]** Fr W exit NII sp Calatayud; site on S side of old N11 (parallel to new dual c'way) at km stone 239a. Med, pt shd; wc; chem disp; shwrs inc; el pts (5-10A) €3.80 (rev pol - rec do not use); gas; lndtte; snacks; shop 2km; pool; some rd noise; cc acc; CCI. "Site area bleak; facs, inc pool, poorly maintained; interesting town, Moorish features; excel excursion to Monasterio de Piedra; NH only." 1 Apr-15 Oct. € 17.30   2005*

CALELLA *3C3* (2km NE Coastal) **Camping Caballo de Mar, Passeig Maritim 52-54, 08397 Pineda de Mar (Barcelona) [937-67 17 06; fax 937-67 16 15; info@caballodemar.com; www.caballodemar.com]** Fr N exit AP7 junc 9 & immed turn R onto NII dir Barcelona. Foll sp Pineda de Mar & turn L twd Paseo Maritimo. Fr S on C32 exit 122 dir Pineda de Mar & foll dir Paseo Maritimo. Lge, mkd pitch, shd; wc; chem disp; baby facs; shwrs inc; el pts (3-6A) €3.10-4.90; gas; lndtte; ice; shop; tradsmn; rest; snacks; bar; BBQ; playgrnd; pool; sand beach adj; games area; games rm; entmnt; internet; 10% statics; dogs €2.60; rlwy stn 2km (Barcelona 30 mins); Eng spkn; adv bkg; quiet; cc acc; red long stay/CCI. "Excursions arranged; gd touring base & conv Barcelona; gd, modern facs; excel." ♦ 18 Mar-30 Sep. € 21.40   2004*

†CALELLA *3C3* (1km S Coastal) **Camping Botanic Bona Vista Kim**, Ctra N11, Km 665, 08370 Calella de la Costa (Barcelona) [937-69 24 88; fax 937-69 58 04; info@botanic-bonavista.net; www. botanic-bonavista.net] A19/C32 exit sp Calella onto NII coast rd, site is sp S of Calella on R. Care needed on busy rd & sp almost on top of turning (adj Camp Roca Grossa). Lge, mkd pitch, hdstg, terr, pt shd; shwrs inc; wc; chem disp; mv service pnt; sauna; shwrs inc; el pts (6A) €4.40 (rev pol); lndtte; supmkt; rest; snacks; bar; BBQ/picnic area; playgrnd; pool; sand beach adj; solarium; jacuzzi; TV; 20% statics; dogs €3.30; phone; poss cr; Eng spkn; adv bkg; some rd noise; CCI. "V steep access rd to site - owner prefers to tow c'vans with 4WD, poss diff v lge m'vans; all pitches have sea view; v friendly owner; spotless facs; train to Barcelona fr St Pol (2km); vg long stay." ♦ € 22.00   2004*

CALELLA *3C3* (1km SW Coastal) **Camping Roca Grossa**, Ctra N-11, Km 665, 08370 Calella (Barcelona) [937-69 12 97; fax 937-66 15 56; rocagrossa@rocagrossa.com; www.rocagrossa. com] Situated off rd N11 at km stone 665. Sp. Lge, sl, terr, shd; wc; chem disp; mv service pnt; shwrs inc; el pts (6A) €4.50; gas; ice; lndtte; shop; rest; snacks; bar; games rm; TV rm; pool; playgrnd; beach adj; windsurfing; tennis; phone; dogs €3.40; statics; adv bkg; Eng spkn; cc acc. "Conv for Barcelona; v friendly, family-run site; v steep access rd to site; modern facs; excel pool & playgrnd on top of hill; steep site - tractor pull avail; scenic drive to Tossa de Mar." 1 Apr-30 Sep. € 21.20   2005*

CALONGE see Playa de Aro *3B3*

†CALPE *4F2* (2km N Urban/Coastal) **Camping La Merced**, Ctra de la Cometa, 03710 Calpe (Alicante) [965-83 00 97] Exit A7/E15 at junc 63 & foll sp Calpe down hill to traff lts & turn L. At 4th traff island, turn L & site on R in 400m. Med, mkd pitch, hdstg, pt terr, shd; htd wc; chem disp; mv service pnt; shwrs inc; el pts (10A) inc (poss long cable req); gas; lndtte; shop; rest 150m; snacks; bar; BBQ; pool adj; sand beach 500m; TV rm; no statics; dogs; phone; bus 50m; poss cr; Eng spkn; adv bkg; poss noisy; red long stay/low ssn; CCI. "Unkempt low ssn; refurbished san facs." ♦ ltd. € 23.50   2004*

†CAMARASA *3B2* (23km N Rural) **Zodiac Camping II**, Ctra C13, Km 66, 25615 Camarasa (Lleida) [973-29 21 57; fax 973-45 50 03; zodiac@ campingzodiac.com] Fr C13 Lleida to Balaguer. N of Balaguer take C147 & foll sp for Camarasa & site. Med, hdstg, pt sl, terr, pt shd; wc; chem disp; baby facs; shwrs; el pts (5A) €4; shop; lndtte; rest; snacks; bar; playgrnd; pool; rv sw adj; tennis; TV; 60% statics; phone; Eng spkn; quiet; cc acc. "Site on resevoir; some sm pitches; excel views & walks." ♦ ltd. € 18.80   2004*

CAMBRILS see also Salou *3C2*

†CAMBRILS *3C2* (1km N Coastal) **Camping Amfora d'Arcs**, Ctra N340, Km 1145, Vinyols I Els Arcs, 43850 Cambrils (Tarragona) [977-36 12 11; fax 977-79 50 75] Exit A7 junc 37 onto N340 & watch for km sp, site bet 1145 & 1146km. Lge, hdg pitch, hdstg, pt shd; wc; chem disp; shwrs inc; el pts (5A) inc; gas; lndtte; supmkt opp; rest high ssn; bar; playgrnd; pool; beach 1.5km; 60% statics; phone; poss cr; Eng spkn; adv bkg; noisy espec at w/e; cc acc; red 7+ days low ssn; site clsd Jan; CCI. "Sm pitches; high ssn elec mandatory; NH only." € 23.50   2003*

CAMBRILS *3C2* (1.5km N Urban/Coastal) **Camping Playa Cambrils Don Camilo**, Ctra Salou-Cambrils, Km 1.5, Aptdo de Correos 315, 43850 Cambrils (Tarragona) [977-36 14 90; fax 977-36 49 88; camping@playacambrils.com; www. playacambrils. com] Exit A7 junc 37 dir Cambrils. Foll dir Port then coast rd N twd Salou on N340. Site sp on L after rv bdge opp watch tower on R approx 2km fr port. Slow app req not to overshoot. V lge, hdg/mkd pitch, shd; wc; chem disp; baby facs; shwrs inc; el pts (5A) inc; gas; lndtte; ice; supmkt; rest; snacks; bar; playgrnd; htd pool; sand beach adj; tennis; games rn; boat hire; cycle hire; watersports; entmnt; children's club; cinema; TV rm; 25% statics; bus to Port Aventura; cash machine; doctor; 24-hour security; dogs €3.50; Eng spkn; adv bkg ess high ssn; quiet; cc acc; 25-45% red long stay/low ssn; 10% red CCI. "Excel site; lge pitches; helpful, friendly staff; sports activities avail; bus to Port Aventura 5km." ♦ 15 Mar-12 Oct. € 34.66 (CChq acc)   2005*

See advertisement above

†CAMBRILS *3C2* (S Urban/Coastal) **Camping La Llosa**, Ctra N340, Km 1143, 43850 Cambrils (Tarragona) [977-36 26 15; fax 977-79 11 80; campinglallosa@telefonica.net; www.camping-lallosa.com] Exit A7/E15 at junc 37 & join N340. Head S into Cambrils & at traff lts turn R. Site sp on L within 100m. V lge, hdstg, shd; wc; shwrs inc; el pts (10A) €3.40; gas; lndtte; ice; shop; rest; snacks; bar; playgrnd; pool; sand beach; entmnt high ssn; car wash; 50% statics; dogs €1.75; phone; poss cr; Eng spkn; some rd & rlwy noise; cc acc; red long stay. "Interesting fishing port; v clean wc; excel pool; gd supmkt nrby; poss diff siting for m'vans due low trees; excel winter NH." ♦ € 20.80   2005*

We're having a great holiday - must fill in some site report forms and send them to The Club as soon as possible.

CAMBRILS *3C2* (2km S Coastal) **Camping Joan, Calle Pedro III 14**, 43850 Cambrils (Tarragona) [977-36 46 04 or 977-36 15 57; fax 977-36 46 04; info@campingjoan.com; www.campingjoan.com] S on N340, km 1.141 dir Valencia to petrol stn & hotel Daurada, foll site sp. Lge, hdg/mkd pitch, shd; wc; chem disp; baby facs; shwrs inc; el pts (5A) €3.40; gas; ice; lndtte; supmkt; snacks; bar; BBQ; playgrnd; pool & paddling pool; sand beach adj; watersports; fishing; games area; sat TV; 10% statics; phone; currency exchange; car wash; red low ssn/long stay/CCI. "Conv Port Aventura; family site; v clean san facs; friendly welcome; some sm pitches; vg." ♦ 12 Mar-3 Oct. € 17.60   2005*

See advertisement above

CAMBRILS *3C2* (7km SW Coastal) **Camping Els Prats**, Ctra N340, Km 1137, 43892 Miami Playa (Tarragona) [977-81 00 27; fax 977-17 09 01; info@campingelsprats.com; www.campingelsprats.com] Exit A7 junc 37 onto N340 twds Valencia. At km 1137 turn dir Camping Marius, under rlwy bdge & turn R to site. Lge, mkd pitch, shd; wc; chem disp; mv service pnt; baby facs; shwrs; el pts (5A) inc; lndtte; shop; rest; snacks; bar; playgrnd; pool; sand beach adj; watersports; games area; tennis; horseriding 3km; golf 6km; cycle hire; TV; 20% statics; no dogs Jul/Aug; adv bkg; quiet; cc acc. "Pleasant, family site." ♦ 10 Mar-15 Oct. € 26.45 (CChq acc)   2004*

CAMBRILS *3C2* (5km SW Coastal) **Camping Oasis Mar**, Ctra de Valencia, 43892 Montroig (Tarragona) [977-17 95 95; fax 977-17 95 16; oasis@anit.es] Fr A7 exit 37; N340 Tarragona-Valencia rd, at Montroig, km 1139. Lge, mkd pitch, pt shd; wc; chem disp; shwrs inc; baby facs; el pts (6A) €3.75; gas; lndtte; ice; shop; rest; snacks; bar; BBQ; playgrnd; pool; sand beach adj; watersports; 30% statics; dogs €4; Eng spkn; red long stay/low ssn. "Helpful staff; busy at w/e when statics occupied; vg." 1 Mar-31 Oct. € 22.00   2004*

CAMBRILS *3C2* (7km SW Coastal) **Camping Marius**, N-340 Km 1137, Miami Playa, 43892 Montroig (Tarragona) [977-81 06 84; fax 977-17 96 58; schmid@teleline.es; www.campingmarius.com] On N340 Tarragona-Valencia rd, thro Cambrils, site ent on E of rd, sp. Lge, shd; wc; baby facs; shwrs inc; gas; lndtte; ice; el pts (6A) inc; shop; snacks; bar; playgrnd; shgl beach; poss cr; adv bkg (ess Jul-Aug; overflow v cramped); dogs; phone; cc acc. "Traditional campsite; well-managed by Swiss owners; poss noise fr night club, rd & rlwy." ♦ Easter-15 Oct. € 30.00   2003*

SPAIN

CAMBRILS *3C2* (8km SW Coastal) **Campingpark Playa Montroig, N340, Km1138, Montroig, 43300 Montroig (Tarragona)** [977-81 06 37; fax 977-81 14 11; info@playamontroig.com; www.playamontroig.com] Exit A7 fr m'way 37, W onto N340. Site has own dir access onto N340 bet Cambrils & Hospitalet, well sp fr Cambrils. V lge, hdg/mkd pitch, pt sl, shd; htd wc; chem disp; mv service pnt; serviced pitches; baby facs; shwrs inc; el pts (10A) inc; gas; lndtte; ice; supmkt; rest; snacks; bars; playgrnd; 3 htd pools; sand beach adj; tennis; games area; skateboard track; sports & child club; disco; mini-golf; cycle hire; golf 3km; cash machine; excursions; doctor; entmnt; child entmnt; internet; 40% statics; no dogs; phone; security guards; poss cr; Eng spkn; adv bkg (dep req); some rd & rlwy noise; cc acc; red snr citizens low ssn; CCI. "Magnificent site; unbelievably clean; private, swept beach; some sm pitches & low branches; 4 grades pitch/price; highly rec." ♦ 16 Mar-29 Oct. € 45.00   2005*

See advertisement inside front cover

> This site entry hasn't been updated for a while; we'd better fill in a site report form and send it to The Club.

CAMBRILS *3C2* (8km W Coastal) **Camping La Torre del Sol, Ctra N340, Km 1136, 43892 Montroig Del Camp (Tarragona)** [977-81 04 86; fax 977-81 13 06; info@latorredelsol.com or info@latorredelsol.net; www.latorredelsol.com & www.latorredelsol.net] Leave A7 Valencia/Barcelona m'way at junc 37 & foll sp Cambrils. After 1.5km join N340 coast rd S for 6km. Watch for site sp approx 4km bef Miami Platja. Leave N340 via slip rd, foll sp under main rd to site at km 1136. Site ent narr, alt ent avail for lge o'fits. Lge, hdg/mkd pitch, shd; wc; chem disp; mv service pnt; baby facs; sauna; shwrs inc; el pts (6A) inc (10A avail); gas; lndtte; ice; shop; tradsmn; rest; snacks; bar; BBQ; luxury playgrnd; 3 pools; paddling pool; whirlpool; private sand beach; tennis; squash; cycle hire; golf 4km; cinema; disco; ent & child entmt; live shows high ssn; day-care cent for children; excursions; internet; TV; doctor; cash machine; 40% statics; no dogs; poss v cr; Eng spkn; adv bkg; quiet, but some rd/rlwy noise & disco; low ssn/snr citizen red. "Guarded; radios/TVs to be used inside vans only; conv Port Aventura, Aquaparc, Aquopolis; no c'vans over 7m high ssn; excel." ♦ 15 Mar-22 Oct. € 42.00 (CChq acc) ABS - E14   2005*

See advertisement opposite

†CAMPELL *4E2* (1km S Rural) **Camping Vall de Laguar, 03791 Vall de Laguar (Alicante)** [965-57 74 90 or 699-77 35 09; info@camping laguar.com; www.campinglaguar.com] Exit A7 junc 62 sp Ondara. Turn L to Orba onto CV733 dir Benimaurell & foll sp to Vall de Laguar. In Campell vill (narr rds) fork L & foll site sp uphill. Steep ent to site. Lge o'fits ignore sp in vill & turn R to Fleix vill. In Fleix turn L to main rd, downhill to site sp at hairpin. Med, mkd pitch, hdstg, terr, pt shd; htd wc; chem disp; shwrs €0.50; el pts (5-10A) €2; gas; lndtte; ice; shop 500m; rest; snacks; bar; BBQ; pool; sand beach 18km; 50% statics; dogs; phone; Eng spkn; adv bkg; quiet; cc acc; red long stay; CCI. "Sm pitches diff for lge o'fits; m'vans 7.50m max; excel home-cooked food in rest; ideal site for walkers; mountain views; friendly owners live on site; excel but rec sm o'fits & m'vans only." ♦ ltd. € 19.40   2005*

CAMPELLO, EL see Alicante *4F2*

CANDELARIO see Bejar *1D3*

CANET DE MAR see Arenys de Mar *3C3*

†CANGAS DE ONIS *1A3* (16km E Rural) **Camping Picos de Europa, Ctra Cangas de Onis-Cabrales, Km 6, 33556 Avin (Asturias)** [985-84 40 70; fax 985-84 42 40; info@picos-europa.com; www.picos-europa.com] N625 fr Arriondas to Cangas, then AS114 dir Panes for approx 15km. Go thro Avin vill, site on R. Med, terr, pt shd; wc; chem disp; baby facs; shwrs inc; el pts (5A) €4; gas; lndtte; shop; rest; snacks; bar; pool; beach 20km; horseriding; canoeing on local rvs; some statics; phone; poss cr; Eng spkn; adv bkg; some rd noise & goat bells; cc acc; CCI. "Owners v helpful; beautiful, busy, well-run site; vg value rest; san facs stretched in ssn; poss diff access due narr site rds & cr; some sm pitches - lge o'fits may need 2; conv local caves, mountains, National Park, beaches; vg rest." € 18.00   2005*

CANGAS DE ONIS *1A3* (3km SE Rural) **Camping Covadonga, 33589 Soto de Cangas (Asturias)** [tel/fax 985-94 00 97] N625 fr Arriondas to Cangas de Onis, then AS114 twds Covadonga & Panes, cont thro town sp Covadonga. At rndabt take 2nd exit sp Cabrales, site on R in 100m. Med, mkd pitch, pt shd; wc; chem disp; shwrs; el pts (3A) €2.40 (no earth); shop; supmkt in town; rest; snacks; bar; poss cr; adv bkg; quiet, but slight rd noise; 10% red long stay; CCI. "V sm pitches (approx 5 x 6m); take care with access; site rds v narr; conv for Picos de Europa; gd." Holy Week & 1 Jun-30 Sep. € 15.70   2004*

CAPMANY see Figueres *3B3*

CARAVIA ALTA see Colunga *1A3*

CAMPING CARAVANING BUNGALOW RESORT
LA TORRE DEL SOL
Cat. 1 ★★★★

catalunya sud

CATALUNYA

HOLIDAYS MEAN CHANGE OF SCENARY

LA TORRE DEL SOL,
SUBTROPICAL HOLIDAY
PARK AT THE BEACH
WITH ACTIVITIES
AND FACILITIES.
FROM 15th MARCH
TILL 20th OCTOBER

CAMPING
RESORTS

soleil
VILLAGE

 E-43300 MONT-ROIG DEL CAMP (TARRAGONA) · Phone.: +34 977 810 486 · Fax: +34 977 811 306
www.latorredelsol.com · info@latorredelsol.com   www.latorredelsol.net · info@latorredelsol.net

CARBALLO *1A2* (Coastal) **Camping As Nevedas, 15105 Noicela (La Coruna)** [tel/fax 981-73 95 52] On C552 fr La Coruna dir Carballo, turn R approx 3km bef Carballo sp Noicela 8km. Site on R in vill. Sm, hdg pitch, pt sl, pt shd; wc; chem disp (wc); serviced pitch; shwrs inc; el pts (5A) €1.80; gas; lndtte; shop; tradsmn; rest; bar; BBQ; playgrnd; pool; sand beach 2km; golf 2km; 20% statics; dogs; bus fr ent; phone; poss cr; Eng spkn; adv bkg; quiet; red long stay; cc acc; CCI. "Santiago de Compostela 45km; water amusement park 15km; excel." 15 Apr-30 Sep. € 13.82   2003*

†**CARBALLO** *1A2* (6km N Coastal) **Camping Baldayo, Rebordelos, 15684 Carballo (La Coruna)** [981-73 95 29] Not sp fr rd. On rd AG55 La Coruna-Finisterre turn R 5km bef Carballo, sp Noicela. In Noicela fork R sp Caion, next L & site sp when app dunes. App fr Arteijo diff for lge vans. Sm, pt sl, pt shd; wc; chem disp; shwrs; el pts inc; lndtte; shop; snacks; bar; playgrnd; sand beach 500m; 95% statics; no dogs; phone; poss cr; quiet. "Sm pitches; narr camp rds; poss unkempt low ssn." € 14.00   2005*

CARCHUNA see Motril *2H4*

CARIDAD, LA (EL FRANCO) *1A3* (1km SE Coastal) **Camping Playa de Castello, 33758 La Caridad (El Franco) (Asturias)** [985-47 82 77] On N634/E70 Santander dir Coruna, turn N at km 532. Site in 200m fr N634, sp fr each direction. Sm, mkd pitch, pt shd; wc; chem disp; shwrs inc; el pts (2-5A) inc; gas; lndtte; shop, tradsmn, bar high ssn only; shgl beach 800m; no statics; Eng spkn; adv bkg; quiet; red long stay/CCI. "A green oasis with character; gd." Holy Week & 1 Jun-30 Sep. € 13.00   2003*

†**CARLOTA, LA** *2G3* (1km NE Rural) **Camping Carlos III, Ctra de Madrid-Cadiz Km 430, 14100 La Carlota (Cordoba)** [957-30 03 38; fax 957-30 06 97; campingcarlos@navegalia.com] Approx 25km SW of Cordoba on A4/E5, exit at km 432 turning L under autovia. Turn L at rndabt on main rd, site well sp on L in 800m. Lge, mkd pitch, hdstg, pt sl, pt shd; htd wc (some cont); chem disp; shwrs inc; el pts (5-10A) €3.40; gas; lndtte; shop; rest; bar; BBQ; playgrnd; pool; horseriding; 30% statics; dogs; phone; Eng spkn; adv bkg; cc acc; red long stay; CCI. "V efficient, well-run site; bus to Cordoba every 2 hrs; less cr than Cordoba municipal site; excel pool; gd, clean facs; if pitched under mulberry trees, poss staining fr berries."♦ € 17.60   2005*

†CAROLINA, LA *2F4* (12km NE Rural) **Camping Despenaperros, Calle Infanta Elena s/n, Junto a la Autovia de Andulucia, Km 257, 23213 Santa Elena (Jaen) [953-66 41 92; fax 953-66 19 93; info@ campingdespenaperros.com; www.camping despenaperros.com]** Leave A4/E5 at junc 257, yellow site sp to N side of vill - municipal leisure complex. Med, mkd pitch, hdstg, pt shd; wc; chem disp; mv service pnt; all serviced pitches; shwrs inc; el pts (10A) €3.20 (poss rev pol); gas; lndtte; sm shop; tradsmn; rest high ssn; snacks; bar; playgrnd; pool; TV & tel points all pitches; dogs; phone; adv bkg; poss noisy w/e high ssn; 20% red 28+ days; 10% red CCI. "Gd winter NH but ltd facs; gd size pitches; gd walking area; friendly, helpful staff; v clean san facs; disabled facs (wc only) only useable with manual wheelchair; pleasant wooded location; conv National Park de Despenaperros & m'way; gd rest; sh walk to vill & shops (ltd opening hrs low ssn)." ♦ ltd. € 14.50   2005*

CARRION DE LOS CONDES *1B4* (Urban) **Camping El Eden, Camino de Santiago, Km 200, 34120 Carrion de los Condes (Palencia) [979-88 11 52]** Site sp E & W ents to town off N120 adj Rv Carrion at El Plantio. App poorly sp down narr rds to rv. Not well sp. Med, pt shd; wc; shwrs; el pts (5A) €2.25; gas; lndtte; rest; bar; playgrnd; bus 500m; cc acc. "Pleasant walk to town; basic rvside site; phone ahead to check opening dates; fair NH." ♦ € 11.70   2004*

CARRIZO DE LA RIBERA *1B3* (Urban) **Camping Orbigo, Calle Las Eras, 24270 Carrizo de la Ribera (Leon) [987-35 82 50; fax 987-35 78 98]** Fr Leon take LE441 W 20km thro Villanueva & cross bdge onto LE240. Immed after bdge turn R at traff lts, site in 300m. Med, pt shd; wc; shwrs €0.65; el pts (6A) €1.60; shop; rest 300m; bar; playgrnd adj; pool 500m; fishing; 50% statics; no dogs; phone; bus 500m; poss cr w/e; some rd noise; CCI. "Pleasant, grassy, rvside site." ♦ ltd. 15 Jun-15 Sep. € 9.50   2005*

†CARTAGENA *4G1* (10km SW Coastal/Rural) **Camping Naturista El Portus (Naturist), 30393 Cartagena (Murcia) [968-55 30 52; fax 968-55 30 53; elportus@elportus.com; www. elportus.com]** Fr N332 Cartagena to Mazarron rd take E20 to Canteras. In Canteras turn R onto E22 sp Isla Plana & in 500m turn L onto E21 sp Galifa/El Portus. In 2km at rndabt, site ent on L. Lge, mkd pitch; some hdstg, pt shd; wc; chem disp; mv service pnt; shwrs inc; el pts (6A) inc; gas; lndtte; ice; shop; rest; snacks; bar; playgrnd; htd, covrd pool & paddling pool; shgl beach adj; tennis; games area; golf 15km; internet; entmnt; 30% statics; dogs €3.90; phone; poss cr; Eng spkn; cc acc; red low ssn/long stay; INF card req. "Ltd facs; restful low ssn; gd situation; many long-stay winter visitors; helpful staff; random pitching; Cartagena interesting old town." ♦ ltd. € 30.00   2005*

CASPE *3C2* (12km NE Rural) **Lake Caspe Camping, Ctra N211, Km 286.7, 50700 Caspe (Zaragoza) [tel/fax 976-63 24 86]** E fr Zaragoza on N11. S at Bujaraloz onto C230. E thro Caspe on N211. In 16km on L at km 286.7, sp. Med, hdg/mkd pitch, hdstg, pt shd; wc; chem disp; baby facs; shwrs inc; el pts (5A) €4.40; gas; ice; lndtte; shop; rest; snacks; bar; playgrnd; pool high ssn; rv fishing; sailing; 10% statics; dogs €3; phone; poss cr; Eng spkn; adv bkg; quiet; CCI. "Excel site but avoid on public hols; beautiful surroundings; sm pitches nr lake; mosquitoes." 18 Mar-5 Nov. € 17.25   2005*

CASTANARES DE LA RIOJA see Haro *1B4*

CASTELLBO see Seo de Urgel *3B3*

CASTELLO D'EMPURIES *3B3* (5km NE Urban) **Camping Mas Nou, Ctra Figueras-Rosas, Km 38, 17486 Castello d'Empuries (Gerona) [972-45 41 75; fax 972-45 43 58; info@campingmasnou.com; www.campingmasnou.com]** On m'way A7 exit 3 if coming fr France & exit 4 fr Barcelona dir Rosas (E) C260. Site in 10km once past Castello d'Empuries, on L at ent to Empuriabrava - use rndabt to turn. Lge, shd, mkd pitch; wc; chem disp; baby facs; shwrs inc; el pts (10A) €4; lndtte; ice; shops 200m; rest; snacks; bar; BBQ; playgrnd; pool; beach 2.5km; tennis; games area; mini-golf; entmnt; TV; car wash; 5% statics; dogs €1.50; phone; Eng spkn; red long stay/low ssn; cc acc; CCI. "Aqua Park 4km, Dali Museum 10km; Roman Monastery; gd touring base; helpful staff; well-run site; excel san facs; sports activities & children's club." ♦ 8 Apr-1 Oct. € 33.60 (CChq acc)   2005*

See advertisement

CASTELLO D'EMPURIES *3B3* (4km SE Coastal) **Camping Nautic Almata, 17486 Castello d'Empuries (Gerona) [972-45 44 77; fax 972-45 46 86; info@almata.com; www.almata. com]** Fr A7 m'way exit 3; foll sp to Rosas. After 12km turn S (R) for St Pere Pescador & site on L in 5km. Site clearly sp on rd Castello d'Empuries-St Pere Pescador. Lge, pt shd; wc; chem disp; shwrs inc; el pts (10A) inc; rest; gas; shop; lndtte; playgrnd; pool; sand beach adj; sailing school; tennis; games area; horseriding; cycle hire; TV; disco bar on beach; entmnt; dogs €4.90; poss cr; adv bkg; quiet; 50% red low ssn. "Excel, clean facs; boats & moorings avail; ample pitches; sports facs inc in price; helpful staff; direct access to nature reserve; waterside pitches rec." ♦ 13 May-24 Sep. € 45.60   2005*

SPAIN

CASTELLO D'EMPURIES *3B3* (1km S Coastal) **Camping Castell Mar, Playa de la Rubina, 17486 Castello d'Empuries (Gerona) [972-45 08 22; fax 972-45 23 30; cmar@campingparks.com; www.campingparks.com]** Exit A7 at junc 3 sp Figures; turn L onto C260 sp Rosas, after traff lts cont twd Rosas, turn R down side of rest La Llar for 1.5km, foll sp Playa Rubina. Lge, hdg/mkd pitch, pt shd; wc; chem disp; serviced pitches; baby facs; shwrs inc; el pts (6A) inc; gas; lndtte; shop; tradsmn; rest; snacks; bar; BBQ; playgrnd; pool; sand beach 100m; games rm; entmnt; excursions; TV; 30% statics; dogs; phone; Eng spkn; adv bkg; quiet; red low ssn; CCI. "Sm pitches, poss unsuitable lge o'fits; excel for families; gd sh/long stay." ♦ 13 May-24 Sep. € 38.00   2004*

CASTELLO D'EMPURIES *3B3* (5km S Coastal) **Camping-Caravaning Laguna, Platja Can Turias, 17486 Castello d'Empuries (Gerona) [972-45 05 53 or 45 20 33; fax 972-45 07 99; info@camping laguna.com or reservas@campinglaguna.com; www.campinglaguna.com]** Exit AP7 junc 4 dir Roses. After 12km at rndabt take 3rd exit, site sp. Site in 4km; rough app track. V lge, mkd pitch, pt shd; wc; chem disp; mv service pnt; serviced pitches (inc gas); baby facs; shwrs inc; el pts (5A) €3.50; gas; lndtte; ice; supmkt; rest; snacks; bar; playgrnd; htd pool; sand beach; sailing; watersports; tennis; games area; multisports area; cycle hire; mini-golf; horseriding; entmnt; child entmnt; 4% statics; dogs free; Eng spkn; adv bkg; quiet; red snr citizens/long stay; cc acc; CCI. "Spotless san facs rin renovated block; site continues to improve; gd birdwatching; excel." ♦ 16 Mar-22 Oct. € 29.60   2005*

See advertisement

CASTRO URDIALES *1A4* (1km N Coastal) **Camping de Castro, Barrio Campijo, 39700 Castro Urdiales (Cantabria) [942-86 74 23; fax 942-63 07 25; info@camping.castro.com]** Fr Bilbao turn off A8 at 2nd Castro Urdiales, km 151. Camp sp on R by bullring. V narr, steep lanes to site - no passing places. Lge, pt sl, pt terr, unshd; wc; shwrs inc; el pts (6A) €2.50; lndtte; ice; shop; rest; bar; playgrnd; pool (caps req); sand beach 1.5km; 75% statics; dogs; phone; bus; poss cr; Eng spkn; adv bkg; quiet; CCI. "Facs OK but water supply unreliable; great care req on v narr, steep access rd for 1km; not rec for c'vans; poss tatty low ssn." ♦ ltd. Easter & 1 Jun-30 Sep. € 19.20   2004*

CASTROPOL see Ribadeo *1A2*

CAZORLA *2F4* (6km E Rural) **Camping Puente de las Herrerias, El Vadillo del Castril, 23470 Cazorla (Jaen) [953-72 70 90; puenteh@ infonegocio.com]** Fr Cazorla foll sp for Parador & then Puente de la Herrerias. Driving distance 25km fr Cazorla on narr rd with many bends & two passes - not rec trailer c'vans. Lge, pt shd; wc; shwrs; el pts (16A) inc; gas; shop; rest; bar; playgrnd; pool; horseriding; cycle hire; phone; quiet. "Stunning scenery in National Park." Easter-9 Dec. € 21.20   2004*

CAZORLA *2F4* (2km SW Rural) **Camping San Isicio, 23470 Cazorla (Jaen) [tel/fax 953-72 12 80]** Fr W on A319, turn R bef Cazorla, foll sp. Sm, pt shd; wc; shwrs; el pts €2.10; pool; quiet. "Perched on steep hill; towing service for c'vans but really only suitable sm m'vans; ltd facs but a gem of a site." 1 Mar-1 Nov. € 11.70   2003*

CEE *1A1* (6km NW Coastal) **Camping Ruta Finisterre, Ctra Coruna-Finisterre, Km 6, Playa de Estorde, 15270 Cee (La Coruna) [tel/fax 981-74 63 02; estorde@finisterrae.com; http://finisterrae.com/camping/rutafinisterre/]** Foll sp thro Cee & Corcubion on rd AC445 twd Finisterre; site easily seen on R of rd (no thro rd). Med, terr, shd; wc; chem disp; shwrs inc; el pts (10A) €2.80; gas; lndtte; ice; shop & 1km; rest; snacks; bar; playgrnd; sand beach 100m; dogs; phone; poss cr; adv bkg; some rd noise; cc acc; CCI. "Site in pine trees - check access to pitch & el pts bef positioning; 5km to Finisterre; clean beach adj; peaceful." Holy Week & 15 Jun-15 Sep. € 19.00   2005*

†**CHILCHES** *4E2* (1km S Coastal) **Camping Mediterraneo, Avda Mare Nostrum s/n, 12592 Chilches (Castellon) [tel/fax 964-58 32 18]** Exit AP7 junc 49 onto N340, exit junc 947-948 twds Chilches. Site at extreme S end Chilches, sp. Lge, mkd pitch, hdstg, shd; wc; chem disp; shwrs inc; el pts inc; gas; lndtte; ice; shop; tradsmn; rest; snacks; bar; playgrnd; pool; sand beach 500m; solarium; TV rm; some statics; dogs; phone; bus 1km; poss cr; adv bkg; cc acc; red long stay/CCI. ♦ ltd. € 21.40   2005*

†**CHIPIONA** *2H3* (2km S Coastal) **Camping El Pinar de Chipiona, Ctra Chipiona-Rota, Km 3, 11550 Chipiona (Cadiz) [956-37 23 21]** Site on R on A491 to Rota. Lge, mkd pitch, hdstg, pt shd; wc; chem disp; shwrs inc; el pts (5-10A) €2.70; gas; lndtte; shop; rest; snacks; bar; playgrnd; sand beach 1km; 20% statics; dogs; quiet but some rd noise; Eng spkn; red low stay; CCI. "Many pitches perm awnings; some san facs clsd low ssn; gd sh/long stay." ♦ € 17.50   2004*

CIUDAD RODRIGO *1D3* (1km S Rural) **Camping La Pesquera, Huerta de la Toma, 37500 Ciudad Rodrigo (Salamanca) [923-48 13 48]** Fr Salamanca on E80/N620. At W end of Ciudad Rodrigo, foll sp Portugal/Caceras. Keep in L lane, site sp in 300m on L on rvside. Med, mkd pitch, pt shd; wc; shwrs inc; el pts (3A) €2.90; lndtte; shop; snacks; rv sw, fishing adj; TV; phone; poss cr; no adv bkg; noisy; cc acc; CCI. "Medieval walled city worth visit; low ssn phone ahead to check open; facs dated but clean; poss scalding water; site yourself low ssn." ♦ 1 Apr-30 Sep. € 12.40   2005*

CLARIANA DE CARDENER see Solsona *3B3*

COLERA see Llanca *3B3*

COLOMBRES see Unquera *1A4*

COLUNGA *1A3* (1km N Coastal) **Camping Costa Verde, Playa La Griega de Colunga, 33320 Colunga (Asturias) [tel/fax 985-85 63 73]** N632 coast rd, fr E turn R twd Lastres in cent of Colunga; site 1km on R. Med, mkd pitch, unshd; wc; chem disp; baby facs; shwrs; el pts (5A) €2.40; gas; lndtte; shop; rest; bar; BBQ; sand beach 500m; games area; cycle hire; 50% statics; adv bkg; quiet but v noisy campers high ssn; cc acc; CCI. "Beautiful sandy beach; lovely views to mountains & sea; some site access rds used for winter storage; gd, plentiful facs; ltd hot water low ssn; vg sh stay." Holy Week & 1 Jun-30 Sep. € 18.40   2003*

Some of these sites have changed their opening dates - we'd better fill in some site report forms and let the editor of the guide know.

COLUNGA *1A3* (8km E Coastal) **Camping Arenal de Moris, Ctra de la Playa s/n, 33344 Caravia Alta (Asturias) [985-85 30 97; fax 985-85 31 37; moris@desdeasturias.com; www.arenalde moris.com]** Fr E70/A8 exit junc 337 onto N632 to Caravia Alta, site clearly sp. Lge, mkd pitch, terr, unshd; wc; chem disp; shwrs inc; el pts (5A) inc; lndtte; shop; rest; snacks; bar; playgrnd; pool; sand beach 500m; tennis; adv bkg; quiet but rd noise; cc acc; CCI. "Lovely views to mountains & sea; excel, clean san facs." Easter & 1 Jun-15 Sep. € 19.00   2005*

COMILLAS *1A4* (1km E Coastal) **Camping Comillas, 39520 Comillas (Cantabria) [942-72 00 74; fax 942-21 52 06]** Site on coast rd C6316 at E end of Comillas by-pass. App fr Santillana or San Vicente avoids town cent & narr streets. Lge, mkd pitch, pt sl, unshd; wc; chem disp; shwrs inc; el pts (3A) €2.60; lndtte; shop; rest 1km; snacks; bar; sand beach 100m; poss cr; adv bkg; quiet; cc acc; CCI. "Clean, ltd facs low ssn (poss no hot water); vg site in gd position; easy walk to interesting town; gd beach across rd." 1 Jun-30 Sep. € 18.50   2002*

COMILLAS *1A4* (4km E Rural) **Camping El Helguero, 39527 Ruiloba (Cantabria) [942-72 21 24; fax 942-72 10 20; elhelguero@ctv. es; www.campingelhelguero.com]** Exit A8 junc 249 dir Comillas onto CA135 to km 7. Turn dir Ruiloba onto CA359 & thro Ruiloba & La Iglesia, fork R uphill. Site sp. Lge, mkd pitch, pt sl, pt shd; wc; chem disp; shwrs inc; el pts (6A) €3; lndtte; shop, rest, snacks, bar in ssn; playgrnd; pool; sand beach 3km; 10% statics; dogs; night security; poss v cr high ssn; Eng spkn; poss noisy high ssn; cc acc; CCI. "Attractive site, gd touring cent; helpful staff; sm pitches poss muddy in wet." ♦ 1 Apr-30 Sep. € 15.80 (CChq acc)   2005*

†COMILLAS *1A4* (2km W Coastal) **Camping Playa de Oyambre, Finca Pena Gerra 39540 Oyambre (Cantabria) [tel/fax 942-71 14 61]** Fr N634 turn N at km 265.5 sp Comillas. Site on L in 3km; gd new rd (2005). Lge, mkd pitch, terr, pt sl, pt shd; wc; chem disp; mv service pnt; shwrs inc; el pts (10A) €4; gas; lndtte; shop & 4km; tradsmn; rest; snacks; bar; pool; beach 1km; 40% statics; Eng spkn; adv bkg; cc acc; CCI. "V well-kept site; v quiet week days low ssn; friendly staff; gd base for N coast & Pyrenees; 4WD avail to tow to pitch if wet; some sm pitches; new rd to site planned 2005." € 18.30   2005*

†COMILLAS *1A4* (3km W Rural/Coastal) **Camping Rodero, 39528 Oyambre (Cantabria) [942-72 20 40; fax 942-72 26 29]** Exit A8 dir San Vicente, cross bdge over estuary & take R fork. Foll sp Oyambre & site. Lge, mkd pitch, pt sl, terr, pt shd; wc; chem disp; shwrs inc; el pts (6A) €2.68; gas; lndtte; ice; shop; tradsmn; rest; snacks; bar; playgrnd; sm pool (caps ess); sand beach 200m; 10% statics; no dogs; phone; bus 300m; poss v cr; adv bkg; cc acc; CCI. "Lovely views; friendly owners; site noisy but happy - owner puts Dutch/English in quieter part; sm pitches; poss run down low ssn; Comillas & San Vicente de la Barquera worth visit." ♦ € 26.00   2005*

SPAIN

CONIL DE LA FRONTERA *2H3* (3km N Coastal) Camping Cala del Aceite (Part Naturist), Ctra del Puerto Pesquero, Km 4, 11140 Conil de la Frontera (Cadiz) [956-44 29 50; fax 956-44 09 72; info@caladelaceite.com; www.caladelaceite. com] Sp fr N340 Cadiz to Algeciras in both dir. In Conil turn R to Fuente di Gallo, site on L. V lge, mkd pitch, pt shd; wc; chem disp; fam bthrm; sauna; shwrs inc; el pts (10A) inc; gas; lndtte; ice; supmkt; rest; snacks; bar; playgrnd; pool; sand beach 200m; 20% statics; dogs €1.25; phone; poss cr; Eng spkn; adv bkg; quiet; red long stay; CCI. "Friendly, helpful staff; gd interesting region; gd cliff-top walking; lge pitches; facs showing their age; naturist bathing in pool after 1800; sep naturist beach." ♦
1 Apr-15 Oct. € 21.00   2005*

Will you fill in the site report forms at the back of the guide, or shall I?

†CONIL DE LA FRONTERA *2H3* (1.3km NW Rural/Coastal) Camping La Rosaleda, Ctra del Pradillo, Km 1.3, 11140 Conil de la Frontera (Cadiz) [956-44 33 27; fax 956-44 33 85; info@ campinglarosaleda.com; www.campingla rosaleda.com] Fr N340 turn L onto C321 sp Conil. In 2km turn R at rndabt on ent Conil (do not go strt), 2nd site on R; sp. Lge, mkd pitch, pt sl, terr, pt shd; wc; chem disp; mv service pnt; shwrs inc; el pts (5-10A) inc; ice; gas; lndtte; shop & 1.3km; tradsmn; rest; snacks; bar; playgrnd; pool; sand beach 1.3km; entmnt; internet; 10% statics; no dogs 15 Jun-15 Sep, otherwise in sep area; phone; car wash; Eng spkn; adv bkg; quiet; red low ssn/long stay; CCI. "Friendly staff; poss noisy w/e; sea views; historical, interesting area; conv Seville, Cadiz, Jerez, ferries to Canaries & day trips Morocco etc; sm pitches not suitable lge o'fits but double-length pitches avail; pitches soft when wet; poss cold & windy in winter; lge rally on site in winter; gd walking & cycling." ♦ € 28.00   2005*

†CONTADOR, EL *4G1* (1km S Rural) Camping La Tala, 04825 El Cantador (Almeria) [619-01 77 59 or 666-46 00 07] Fr Almeria head for Granada or Murcia then for Chirivel on A92. Look for sp to El Cantador, thro vill, site sp on R 1.5km fr A92. Sm, hdg pitch, pt shd; wc; chem disp; shwrs inc; el pts €3; lndry rm; rest; snacks; bar; playgrnd; Eng spkn (dep req); quiet; red long stay; cc acc. "New site opened 2003; pool & shwr/wc for disabled planned 2004; v friendly, helpful owners open to suggestions for development of site; vg long/sh stay/NH."
€ 13.00   2003*

†CORDOBA *2F3* (8km N Rural) Camping Los Villares, Parque Periurbano, Avda de la Fuensanta 8, 14071 Cordoba (Cordoba) [957-33 01 45; fax 957-33 14 55; campingvillares@latinmail.com] Best app fr N of city on N432: fr N o'skts of Cordoba foll sp 'Parque Forestal Los Villares', rd CP45 Cerro Muriano. Site on L after approx 7km shortly after golf club. Last 5-6km of app rd v narr & steep, but well-engineered. Or fr N432 turn W onto CP45 1km N of Cerro Muriano. Or fr city cent foll sp for Parador until past municipal site on R. Shortly after, turn R onto CP45 & foll sp Parque Forestal Los Villares as above. Sm, hdstg, sl, shd; wc; chem disp; shwrs inc; el pts (15A) €3 (poss rev pol); gas; lndry rm; shop; rest; quiet; red long stay; CCI. "In nature reserve; peaceful; cooler than Cordoba city with beautiful walks, views & wildlife; sm, close pitches; basic facs; mainly sl site in trees; strictly run." ♦ € 13.30   2005*

†CORDOBA *2F3* (1km NW Urban) Camp Municipal El Brillante, Avda del Brillante 50, 14012 Cordoba [957-40 38 36; fax 957-28 21 65; elbrillante@campings.net; www.campingel brillante.com] Fr N1V take Badejoz turning N432. Take rd Cordoba N & foll sp to Parador. Turn R into Paseo del Brilliante which leads into Avda del Brilliante; white grilleblock wall surrounds site. Alt, foll sp for 'Macdonalds Brilliante.' Site on R 1km beyond Macdonalds on main rd going uphill away fr town cent. Site poorly sp. Med, hdg/mkd pitch, hdstg, pt shd; wc; chem disp; mv service pnt; serviced pitches; shwrs inc; el pts (6-10A) €3.10 (poss no earth); gas; lndry rm; shop; tradsmn; hypmkt nrby; rest in ssn; snacks; bar; playgrnd; pool adj in ssn; phone; bus; poss cr; Eng spkn; no adv bkg; quiet but traff noise & barking dogs off site; cc not acc; CCI. "Well-run, v busy, clean site; friendly staff; easy walk/gd bus service to town; rec arr bef 1500 - popular site; poss cramped pitches; poss itinerants low ssn (noisy); gd for wheelchair users; highly rec." ♦ € 19.00   2005*

CORUNA, A see Coruna, La *1A2*

CORUNA, LA *1A2* (5km E Coastal/Rural) Camping Bastiagueiro, Oleiros Playa Bastiagueiro, 15179 Santa Cruz (La Coruna) Exit La Coruna by NVI twd Betanzos. After bdge, take LC173 sp Santa Cruz. At 3rd rndabt, take 3rd exit sp Camping. In 100m, turn R up narr rd. Site on R in 150m. Sm, pt shd; wc (some cont); chem disp; shwrs inc; el pts (6A) €2.70; gas; lndtte; shop; snacks; bar; playgrnd; sand beach 500m; dogs; phone; poss cr; adv bkg; quiet; CCI. "Friendly owners; lovely views of beach; care req going thro narr ent gate; gd sh stay/NH."
Holy Week & 1 Jun-30 Sep. € 14.74   2003*

CORUNA, LA *1A2* (9km E Rural) **Camping Los Manzanos**, Olieros, 15179 Santa Cruz (La Coruna) [981-61 48 25; info@camping-los manzanos.com; www.camping-losmanzanos. com] App La Coruna fr E on NVI, bef bdge take AC173 sp Santa Cruz. R at traff lts in Santa Cruz cent, foll sp, site on L. Fr AP9/E1 exit junc 3, turn R onto NVI dir Lugo. Take L fork dir Santa Cruz/La Coruna, then foll sp Meiras. Site sp. Lge, pt shd; wc; chem disp; shwrs; el pts (6A) €3; gas; lndtte; shop; rest; snacks; playgrnd; pool; TV; 10% statics; dogs; phone; cc acc; CCI. "Conv for Santiago de Compostela; excel rest; helpful owners."
5 Apr-15 Sep. € 20.00   2004*

†**COTORIOS** *4F1* **Camping Llanos de Arance, Ctra Sierra de Cazorla/Beas de Segura, Km 22, 23478 Cotorios (Jaen)** [953-71 31 39; fax 953-71 30 36] Fr Jaen-Albecete rd N322 take junc E, onto A1305 N of Villanueva-del-Arzobispo sp El Tranco. In 26km to El Tranco lake, turn R & cross over embankment. Cotorios at km stone 53, approx 25km on shore of lake & Rio Guadalaquivir. App fr Cazorla or Beas definitely not rec if towing. Lge, shd; wc; shwrs; el pts (5A) €2.67; gas; shops 1.5km; rest; snacks; bar; BBQ; playgrnd; pool; rv sw; 2% statics; no dogs; phone; poss cr; quiet; cc acc; red low ssn; CCI. "Excel walks & bird life, boar & wild life in Cazorla National Park; gd rd surface fr Villanueva; lovely site." € 14.90   2003*

†**COTORIOS** *4F1* (500m Rural) **Camping Chopera, Cazorla-Cotorios, Km.21, Santiago Pontones, 23478 Cotorios (Jaen)** [tel/fax 953-71 30 05] Fr Jaen-Albacete rd N322 turn onto A1305, nr Villanueva del Arzobispo, sp El Tranco. In 26km at app to El Tranco lake (sh distance after exit fr tunnel), turn R & cross over embankment. Cotorios at km 52-53, approx 25km on shore of lake & Rio Guadalquivir. Warning, if towing c'van, do not app via Cazorla as rds are tortuous. Only app & return fr Villanueva as rd well surfaced, but still some steep sections. Med, shd; wc; shwrs; el pts (16A); lndtte; gas; shop; snacks; bar; playgrnd; rv adj; dogs; phone; car wash; cc acc. "In cent of beautiful National Park; lots of wildlife." ♦   2005*

†**COVARRUBIAS** *1B4* (500m E Rural) **Camping Covarrubias, Ctra Hortiguela, 09346 Covarrubias (Burgos)** [947-40 64 17; fax 983-29 58 41] Take N1/E5 or N234 S fr Burgos, turn onto C110 after approx 35km. Site sp on C110 - easy to miss. Med, pt sl, pt shd; wc; shwrs; el pts (12A) inc; gas; lndtte; shop 500m; rest; bar; playgrnd; pool & paddling pool; 50% statics; phone; poss cr; cc acc. "Ltd facs low ssn; charming vill; Santo Domingo de Silos monastery 18km; poss vultures; poss barking dogs." € 16.80   2005*

CREIXELL see Vendrell, El *3C3*

CREVILLENTE see Elche *4F2*

†**CUBILLAS DE SANTA MARTA** *1C4* (1km S Rural) **Camping Cubillas, Ctra N620, Km 102, 47290 Cubillas de Sta Marta (Valladolid)** [983-58 50 02; fax 983-58 50 16; camping cubillas@verial.es; www.campingcubillas.com] N620 Valladolid-Palencia, turn W at km 102 over m'way bdge. Site on L just over bdge. Lge, some hdg/mkd pitch, pt sl, unshd; wc; chem disp; mv service pnt; shwrs inc; el pts (2-5A) €2.75; gas; lndtte; sm shop; tradsmn; rest; snacks & bar in ssn; BBQ; playgrnd; pool; entmnt; 30% statics; dogs; phone; site clsd 19 Dec-7 Jan; red long stay/low ssn; cc acc; CCI. "Gd NH; conv visit Palencia & Valladolid; rd, rlwy & disco noise at w/e until v late."
♦ ltd. € 20.50   2005*

CUDILLERO *1A3* (2km SE Rural) **Camping Cudillero, Ctra Playa Aguilar, 33150 Cudillero (Asturias)** [tel/fax 985-59 06 63] Fr E on N632 (E70) fr Aviles twd La Coruna, turn R at sp El Pito past km 120.8. Foll camping sp where rd bends to L, then turn R at camp sp on rd to Playa Aguilar. Site on R in 1km. Do not app thro Cudillero; streets v narr & steep; much traffic. Med, hdg/mkd pitch, pt shd; wc; chem disp; baby facs; shwrs inc; el pts (3-5A) €2.50; gas; lndtte; ice; shop; snacks high ssn; bar; playgrnd; sand beach 1.2km; entmnt high ssn; TV; phone; adv bkg; quiet; CCI. "Nr vg sandy beach; pretty harbour vill." ♦
Easter & 1 Jun-15 Sep. € 17.00   2004*

CUDILLERO *1A3* (2km S Rural) **Camping L'Amuravela, El Pito, 33150 Cudillero (Asturias)** [tel/fax 985-59 09 95; camping@lamuravela.com; www.lamuravela.com] Fr E take N632 & turn R at junc El Pito-Cudillero. Foll sp to site for 500m, R turn to site then on R after bend. Do not app thro Cudillero as streets narr & steep; much traffic. Med, mkd pitch, pt sl, unshd; wc; chem disp; shwrs inc; el pts €2.60; gas; shop; snacks; bar; pool; sand beach 2km; 50% statics (sep area); poss cr; cc acc high ssn. "Hillside walks into Cudillero, attractive fishing vill with gd fish rests; gd clean facs; red facs low ssn; gd sh stay." Easter & 1 Jun-15 Sep. € 16.15
2004*

CUENCA *3D1* (6.5km N Rural) **Camping Cuenca, Ctra Ciudad Encantada Km 8, 16147 Cuenca** [tel/fax 969-23 16 56] Fr Madrid take N400/A40 dir Cuenca. Take by-pass/ring rd N onto CM2110. In 7km rd splits, take CM2105 to site in 1km on L. Lge, pt sl, pt terr, pt shd; wc; chem disp; shwrs inc; el pts (6-10A) €2.90; gas; lndtte; ice; shop; snacks; bar; playgrnd; pool high ssn; jacuzzi; tennis; games area; dogs €1; phone; poss cr esp Easter w/e; Eng spkn; adv bkg; quiet; CCI. "Nice green site; gd touring cent in fascinating area; well-kept; friendly, helpful staff; excel san facs but ltd low ssn; mv service pnt by appointment; interesting rock formations at Ciudad Encantada." ♦ 31 Mar-15 Oct. € 19.50   2005*

CUEVAS DE ALMANZORA see Garrucha *4G1*

CULLERA see Sueca *4E2*

DEBA *3A1* (6km E Coastal) **Camping Itxaspe, 20829 Itziar (Gipuzkoa) [tel/fax 943-19 93 77; itxaspe@campingitxaspe.com; www.camping itxaspe.com]** Exit m'way A8 junc 13 twds Deba. Fr Deba foll sp to vill of Itziar. Well sp. Sm, mkd pitch, pt sl, pt shd; wc; chem disp; shwrs; el pts (5A) €2; gas; shop; rest, bar adj; BBQ; playgrnd; pool; solarium; shgl beach 4km; some statics; adv bkg; quiet; red low ssn; CCI. "Excel site; helpful owner; w/ends busy." ♦ ltd. 1 Apr-30 Sep. € 16.55   2004*

†**DEBA** *3A1* (5km W Coastal) **Camping Aitzeta, Ctra Deba-Guernica, Km. 3.5, 20930 Mutriku (Gipuzkoa) [943-60 33 56; fax 943-60 31 06]** On N634 San Sebastian-Bilbao rd thro Deba & on o'skts turn R over level x-ing & over rv sp Mutriku. Site on L after 3km on narr & winding rd up short steep climb. Med, terr, unshd; wc; shwrs; el pts (4A) €2.10; gas; sm shop; rest 300m; snacks; bar; seawater pool 3km; sand beach 1km; dogs; phone; quiet. "Easy reach of Bilbao ferry; gd views; not suitable lge o'fits; ltd pitches for tourers." € 21.00
2005*

DELTEBRE *3D2* (8km E Coastal) **Camping L'Aube, 43580 Deltebre (Tarragona) [tel/fax 977-26 70 66]** Exit A7 junc 40 or 41 onto N340 dir Deltebre. Fr Deltebre foll T340 sp Riomar for 8km. At info kiosk branch R, site sp 1km on R. Lge, mkd pitch, hdstg, pt shd; wc; chem disp; mv service pnt; shwrs inc; el pts (3-10A) €2.30-5; lndtte; shop; rest; bar; snacks; pool; playgrnd; phone; sand beach adj; 40% statics; poss cr low ssn; red long stay; CCI. "At edge of Ebro Delta National Park; excel bird-watching; ltd facs in winter; san facs tired." ♦ ltd. 1 Mar-31 Oct. € 15.60   2005*

†**DELTEBRE** *3D2* (8km E Coastal) **Camping Riumar, Calle Aquila Peixetera 1, 43580 Deltebre (Tarragona) [tel/fax 977-26 76 80]** Exit A7 junc 41 dir Deltebre, then further 8km to Riumar. Med, pt shd; wc; mv service pnt; shwrs; el pts inc; lndtte; shop; rests in Riumar; snacks; bar; playgrnd; pool; sandy beach 200m; tennis; cycle hire; 10% statics; phone; bus 100m; CCI. "In Ebro delta, of outstanding interest to birdwatchers; site has potential but is run down, dirty & untidy low ssn." € 14.80   2005*

DELTEBRE *3D2* (10km SE Coastal) **Camping Eucaliptus, Playa Eucaliptus 43870 Amposta (Tarragona) [tel/fax 977-47 90 46; eucaliptus@ campingeucaliptus.com; www.camping eucaliptus.com]** Leave A7-E15 at junc 41. Foll sp to Amposta but don't go into town. Take sp for Els Muntells on TV3405 then Eucaliptus beach. Site on R 100m fr beach. Lge, mkd pitch, pt shd; wc; chem disp; shwrs; el pts (5A) €3.60; gas; ice; lndtte; shops; rest; snacks; bar; BBQ area; playgrnd; pool; sand beach adj; watersports; cycling; fishing; 20% statics; poss cr; adv bkg; noisy w/e & high ssn; red 7+ days; CCI. "V quiet area in Parc Natural; excel birdwatching; poss mosquito problem; gd long/sh stay." € 15.50 6 Mar-24 Oct   2004*

†**DENIA** *4E2* (6km N Coastal) **Camping Diana I & II, Ctra Denia por la Costa, Km 6, Llac Maracaibo 12, 03700 Denia (Alicante) [966-47 41 85; fax 966-47 53 89; camping-diana@camping-diana. com; www.camping-diana.com]** N fr Denia on coast rd, site on R in 6km. Med, mkd pitch, hdstg, pt shd; wc; chem disp; baby facs; shwrs inc; el pts (6A) €3.65; lndtte; shop & 1km; rest high ssn; bar; sand beach adj; games area; 10% statics; dogs; phone; bus adj; adv bkg; cc acc; red low ssn/CCI. "Well-maintained site in 2 sections - old part adj beach with gd shade, new part back fr beach with young trees." € 26.35   2004*

DENIA *4E2* (2km SE Coastal) **Camping Tolosa, Les Rotes, 03700 Denia (Alicante) [965-78 72 94]** Fr E end of Denia Harbour take Javea/Las Rotas rd. In approx 2km keep L at fork exit Javea rd on R. In approx 1km site app clearly sp on L; site 300m twd sea. Med, mkd pitch, hdstg, pt shd; wc; chem disp; shwrs inc; el pts (6A) €3; gas; shop; supmkt adj; bar; BBQ; shgl beach adj; 40% statics; phone; poss cr; quiet; 10% red long stay. "Well-managed; pleasant staff; sm pitches; gd all stays." Holy Week & 1 Apr-30 Sep. € 22.00   2002*

†**DENIA** *4E2* (3.5km SE Coastal) **Camping Los Pinos, Les Rotas, 03700 Denia (Alicante) [965-78 26 98]** Fr N332 foll sp to Denia then dir Las Rotas/Javea, site sp. Narr access rd poss diff lge o'fits. Med, mkd pitch, pt shd; wc; chem disp; shwrs inc; el pts (6-10A) €7.20; gas; lndtte; shop adj; tradsmn; BBQ; cooking facs; playgrnd; shgl beach; TV rm; 25% statics; dogs; phone; bus 300m; poss cr; Eng spkn; adv bkg; quiet; red long stays/low ssn; CCI. "Friendly, well-run site; excel value; access some pitches poss diff due trees - not suitable lge o'fits or m'vans; many long-stay winter residents; cycle path into Denia; social rm with log fire; interesting area; naturist beach 1km, v private but rocky shore." ♦ € 22.50   2005*

†**DENIA** *4E2* (9km W Coastal) **Camping Los Llanos, Playa de Vergel, 03700 Denia (Alicante) [965-75 51 88]** Take N332 Valencia-Alicante, site on L immed after sp to Denia. Med, pt shd; wc; chem disp; shwrs inc; el pts; lndtte; shop & 2km; rest 500m; snacks; bar; playgrnd; pool; paddling pool; sand beach 300m; 30% statics; phone; poss cr; adv bkg; quiet; cc acc. € 19.30   2003*

DOLORES see Guardamar del Segura *4F2*

†**DOS HERMANAS** *2G3* (500m N Urban) **Camping Club de Campo, Avda de la Libertad 13, 41700 Dos Hermanas (Sevilla) [954-72 02 50; fax 954-72-63-08]** Turn off NIV Seville-Cadiz rd (S of Seville) at sp Bellavista, Dos Hermanas; cont to 2nd Dos Hermanas town sp; turn L at BP filling stn; pass under rlwy then sharp L at next junc; sp. Med, hdstg, pt shd, sm pitches; wc; shwrs inc; el pts (5A) €2.90; gas; lndry rm; rest; snacks; bar; sm shop; supmkt 200m; ice; playgrnd; pool in ssn; poss v cr; rlwy & rd noise; cc acc; bus to Seville; CCI. "Fair sh stay/NH only; mixed reports san facs & poss ltd low ssn; site somewhat run down." € 20.00   2002*

†DOS HERMANAS *2G3* (1km W Urban) **Camping Villsom, Ctra Sevilla/Cadiz NIV, Km 554.8, 41700 Dos Hermanas (Sevilla)** [tel/fax 954-72 08 28; villsom@autovia.com] Fr AP4/E5 Seville-Jerez, exit junc 8, site on L on ent Dos Hermanas. Lge, mkd pitch, hdstg, pt sl, pt shd; wc (some cont); chem disp; shwrs inc; el pts (5-10A) €2.50; gas; lndtte; sm shop; hypmkt 1km; snacks in ssn; bar; playgrnd; pool in ssn; mini-golf; bus to Seville 1km fr gate over bdge; site clsd 23 Dec-7 Jan; poss cr; Eng spkn; adv bkg; rd noise & barking dogs adj; cc acc; CCI. "Adv bkg rec Holy Week; poss sm pitches; helpful staff; clean, tidy, well-run site; poss v cr & noisy high ssn; height barrier at Carrefour hypmkt - ent via deliveries." € 16.00   2005*

Mustn't forget to post our site report forms to The Club, otherwise sites might be deleted.

†ELCHE *4F2* (10km SW Urban) **Camping Internacional Las Palmeras, Ctra Murcia-Alicante, Km 45.3, 03330 Crevillente (Alicante)** [965-40 01 88; fax 966-68 06 64; laspalmeras@laspalmeras-sl.com; www.laspalmeras-sl.com] Exit A7 junc 77 onto N340 to Crevillente. Site on R well sp, access rd down side of hotel. Sm, mkd pitch, hdstg, pt shd; wc; chem disp; shwrs inc; el pts (10A) inc; lndtte; supmkt 300m; rest; bar; pool; paddling pool; 20% statics; dogs; cc acc; CCI. "Useful NH; report to recep in hotel; helpful staff; gd cent for touring Murcia; gd rest in hotel." € 16.00   2004*

ERRATZU *3A1* (E Rural) **Camping Baztan, Ctra Francia, s/n, 31714 Erratzu (Navarra)** [948-45 31 33; fax 948-45 30 85] Fr N121B km 62 marker take NA2600 sp Erratzu. In vill strt on at staggered x-rds & foll sp dir France, site on R outside vill 100m after Y junc. App rd thro vill narr with tight turns. Med, hdg/mkd pitch, shd; wc; chem disp; shwrs inc; el pts inc; lndtte; ice; shop; rest; playgrnd; pool; dogs €3.75; poss cr; adv bkg; quiet; cc acc. "Gd walking; lovely scenery; site manned w/e only low ssn." ♦ Holy Week-31 Oct. € 25.70   2005*

ESCALA, L' *3B3* (500m Urban/Coastal) **Camping Riells, Camp Rabassa, s/n, 17130 L'Escala (Gerona)** [tel/fax 972-77 00 27] Exit A7/E15 junc 5, foll GI623. On o'skirts of L'Escala foll sp for L'Escala, Riells, Montgo, site sp. Lge, mkd pitch, pt sl, shd; wc; chem disp; shwrs inc; el pts (5A); gas; lndtte; shop & 500m; rest; snacks; bar; playgrnd; pool; sand beach 500m; tennis; watersports 750m; phone; poss cr; adv bkg; quiet; cc acc; CCI. "Within 500m of beach, shops, rests, bars & cafes on promenade; c'van storage avail; sandy site; lge pitches; security boxes; recep open 0900-2200." 1 Jun-30 Sep.   2003*

†ESCALA, L' *3B3* (2km E Coastal) **Camping Cala Montgo, Ave Montgo s/n, 17130 L'Escala (Gerona)** [972-77 08 66; fax 972-77 43 40; calamontgo@betsa.es] On N11 thro Figueras approx 3km on L sp rd C252 L' Escala. Thro town & camp sp. V lge, pt sl, pt shd; wc; chem disp; baby facs; shwrs inc; el pts (5A) €3.40; gas; lndtte; ice; shop; tradsmn; rest; bar; playgrnd; pool; sand beach 200m; fishing; sports area; cycle hire; minigolf; 30% statics; dogs; poss cr; adv bkg; quiet; cc not acc; red low ssn; CCI. "Nr trad fishing vill; excel rest; facs ltd/run down & v quiet low ssn; poss dusty site." ♦ € 31.20   2005*

ESCALA, L' *3B3* (3km E Coastal) **Camping Neus, Cala Montgo, 17130 L'Escala (Gerona)** [972-77 04 03 or 972-20 86 67; fax 972-77 27 51 or 972-22 24 09; info@campingneus.com; www.campingneus.com] Leave A7 at exit 5 twd L'Escala then turn R twd Cala Montgo & foll sp. Med, mkd pitch, shd; wc; chem disp; shwrs inc; el pts (4A) €3.60; gas; lndtte; ice; shops; rest; snacks; bar; playgrnd; pool & paddling pool; sand beach; fishing; table tennis; tennis; TV rm; no statics; dogs; phone; bus 3km; Eng spkn; adv bkg dep req; quiet; cc acc; CCI. "Nice clean site; gd san facs; vg all stays." 1 Jun-17 Sep. € 26.70   2004*

ESCALA, L' *3B3* (S Urban/Coastal) **Camping L'Escala, Cami Ample 21, 17130 L'Escala (Gerona)** [972-77 00 08; fax 972-55 00 46] Fr exit 4 or 5 off A7 turn R outside L'Escala for L'Estartit. 1st turn L, 1st R, site sp, do not app thro L'Escala. Lge, shd; wc; chem disp; all serviced pitches; shwrs inc; el pts (6A) inc; gas; shop; rest; snacks; bar; playgrnd; beach 300m; some statics; dogs; phone; car wash; poss cr; quiet. "Empurias ruins 5km; sm pitches access poss diff lge o'fits; helpful, friendly staff; excel sh stay/NH." Easter-30 Sep. € 20.20   2004*

ESCALA, L' *3B3* (1km S Coastal) **Camping Maite, Playa de Riells, Ave Montgo, 17130 L'Escala (Gerona)** [tel/fax 972-77 05 44] Exit A7 junc 5 dir L'Escala. Thro town dir Riells to rndabt with supmkts on each corner, turn R to site. Lge, mkd pitch, some terr, shd; wc; chem disp; mv service pnt; shwrs inc; el pts (6A) €3.50; gas; ice; shop adj; rest; bar; playgrnd; beach 200m; TV; adv bkg; red long stay; cc acc; CCI. "Well-run site; quiet oasis in busy resort; steep site rds; some pitches narr access; gd long stay." 1 Jun-15 Sep. € 18.00   2003*

ESCALA, L' *3B3* (2km S Coastal) **Paradis Camping Caravaning, Ave De Montgo 260, 17130 L'Escala (Gerona)** [972-77 02 00 or 77 17 95; fax 972-77 20 31; info@campingparadis.com] On N11 thro Figueras, approx 3km on L sp C31 L'Escala; in town foll sp for Montgo & Paradis. Lge, terr, pt shd; wc; chem disp; mv service pnt; baby facs; shwrs inc; el pts (5A) €3.25; gas; lndtte; ice; shop; rest; bar; playgrnd; 2 pools; shgl/rocky beach adj; tennis; 5% statics; dogs €2.40; Eng spkn; adv bkg ess high ssn; quiet; CCI. "V well-run site, spacious pitches; no depth marking in pool." ♦ ltd. 18 Mar-15 Oct. € 30.75   2004*

SPAIN

†ESCARRILLA *3B2* (500m Rural) **Camping Escarra, Ctra Huesca-Francia, Km.85, 22660 Escarrilla (Huesca)** [974-48 71 28; fax 974-48 76 42; info@campingescarra.com; www.campingescarra.com] On A136 bet Sabinanigo & Portalet Pass, sp in Escarrilla. Lge, pt sl, pt shd; wc; chem disp; shwrs inc; el pts (6A) €4.45; gas; lndtte; shop; rest; snacks; bar; pool; games area; tennis; horseriding; phone; poss cr; adv bkg; 80% statics; quiet; cc acc. "Conv Ordesa National Park; mountain & adventure sports." € 20.70   2005*

†ESCORIAL, EL *1D4* (6km NE Rural) **Camping-Caravaning El Escorial, Crta Guadarrama a El Escorial, Km 3.5, 28280 El Escorial (Madrid)** [918-90 24 12; fax 918-96 10 62; info@camping elescorial.com; www.campingelescorial.com] Exit AP6 NW of Madrid junc 47 El Escorial/Guadarrama, onto M600 & foll sp to El Escorial, site on L at km stone 3,500. Fr S foll sp fr El Escorial to Guadarrama on M600, site on R in 5km. V lge, pt shd, hdstg, mkd pitch; htd wc; chem disp; shwrs inc; baby facs; el pts (5A) inc (long cable rec); gas; lndtte; shop, rest, bar in ssn & w/e; hypmkt 5km; snacks; BBQ; playgrnd; 3 pools; tennis; golf, horseriding 7km; games rm; child entmnt; excursions; 25% statics (sep area); dogs; cash machine; adv bkg; some Eng spkn; poss cr & noisy at w/e; cc not access; CCI. "Gd base for sightseeing; clean facs; helpful staff; gd security; sm pitches poss diff to access due trees but able to use 2 low ssn; facs ltd low ssn; overhead canopies, strong awning pegs rec; day trips to Segovia & Avila (high ssn); trains & buses to Madrid nr; Valle de Los Caidos & Palace at El Escorial well worth visit; gd views of mountains; easy parking in town for m'vans if go in early; mkt Wed." ♦ € 28.10 ABS - E13
2005*

See advertisement opposite

ESPINAL see Auritz *3A1*

ESPONELLA see Banyoles *3B3*

ESPOT *3B2* (500m SE Rural) **Camping Sol I Neu, Ctra. Sant Maurici s/n, 25597 Espot (Lleida)** [973-62 40 01; fax 973-62 41 07; camping@solineu.com] N fr Sort on C13 turn L to Espot on rd LV5004, site on L in approx 6.5km. Med, mkd pitch, pt shd; wc; chem disp; baby facs; shwrs inc; el pts (6-10A) inc; gas; lndtte; shop, bar high ssn; playgrnd; pool; paddling pool; TV; quiet; cc acc; CCI. "Excel facs; site 4km fr ent to National Park; Landrover taxis fr Espot take walkers into heart of park (no private vehicles allowed)." 15 Jun-15 Sep. € 24.85   2004*

ESPOT *3B2* (1km W Rural) **Camping Voraparc, Ctra Sant Maurici s/n Prat del Vedat, 25597 Espot (Lleida)** [973-62 41 08 or 973-25 23 24; fax 973-62 41 43; cvoraparc@jazzire.com; www.voraparc.com] Fr Sort N on C13 N. At sp turn L for Espot, go thro vill then turn R for National Park. Site in 1.5km on R. Well sp. Med, mkd pitch, pt sl, terr, shd; wc; chem disp (wc); baby facs; shwrs inc; el pts (6A) €3.80 (poss rev pol); gas; lndtte; lndry rm; shop; tradsmn; rest; snacks; bar; BBQ; playgrnd; htd pool; watersports nrby; walks; cycle hire; TV/games rm; no statics; dogs; phone; Eng spkn; adv bkg; quiet; 10% red 15+ days; cc acc; CCI. "Access rd narrow & needs care; conv for National Park in walking/cycling distance; gd birdwatching; gd long/sh stay." ♦ Easter-10 Oct. € 20.00   2004*

ESTARTIT L' *3B3* (Coastal) **Camping Rifort, Ctra de Torroella s/n, 17258 L'Estartit (Gerona)** [972-75 04 06; fax 972-75 17 22; campingrifort@retemail.es] Site on rndabt at ent to L'Estartit. Med, hdg/mkd pitch, terr, pt shd; wc; chem disp; shwrs; baby facs; el pts €3; gas; lndtte; shop 50m; snacks; bar; pool; sand beach 500m; tennis 150m; watersports; dogs €1.50; phone; bus adj; Eng spkn; adv bkg; noise fr adj main rd & entmnt; red low ssn; cc acc. "Family-run; excel, immac facs." ♦ 7 Apr-12 Oct. € 20.40   2005*

ESTARTIT, L' *3B3* (Coastal) **Camping Estartit, Calle Villa Primevera 12, 17258 L'Estartit (Gerona)** [972-75 19 09; fax 972-75 09 91; www.campingestartit.com] On N11 fr Figueras-Gerona turn L onto C66, then G642 dir Torroella de Montgri & L'Estartit; fork L on ent L'Estartit, foll site sps. Med, pt sl, shd; htd wc; chem disp; baby facs; shwrs inc; el pts (2-6A) €2.20-3.10; gas; lndtte; ice; shop; rest adj; snacks; bar; playgrnd; htd pool; paddling pool; sand beach 400m; entmnt; child entmnt; 15% statics; no dogs 20/6-20/8; phone; poss cr; Eng spkn; red long stay. "Friendly staff; 100m Fr vill cent; gd security; gd walks adj nature reserve; bar/rest & night club adj; facs poss stretched high ssn." 1 Apr-30 Sep. € 19.00   2005*

ESTARTIT, L' *3B3* (500m Urban/Coastal) **Camping La Sirena, La Platera s/n, 17258 L'Estartit (Gerona)** [972-75 15 42; fax 972-75 09 44; info@camping-lasirena.com] Fr Torroella foll sp to L'Estartit. On o'skts of vill turn R at Jocs Amusements, site on L 200m. Lge, pt shd; wc; chem disp; baby facs; shwrs inc; el pts (6-10A) €3.30; gas; lndtte; shop; rest; snacks; bar; BBQ; playgrnd; htd pool; sand beach adj; scuba diving; TV; money exchange; car wash; 10% statics; dogs; Eng spkn; quiet; red long stay/low ssn; CCI. "V ltd facs low ssn; gd value boat trips; nature reserve adj." ♦ 18 Apr-12 Oct. € 19.20   2004*

†ESTARTIT, L' *3B3* (2km Coastal) **Camping Les Medes**, Paratge Camp de l'Arbre s/n, 17258 L'Estartit (Gerona) [972-75 18 05; fax 972-75 04 13; info@campinglesmedes.com; www.campingles medes.com] Fr Torroella foll sp to L'Estartit. In vill turn R at town name sp (sp Urb Estartit Oest), foll rd for 1.5km, turn R, site well sp. Lge, mkd pitch, shd; htd wc; chem disp; mv service pnt; serviced pitches; baby facs; sauna; shwrs inc; el pts (6A) €3.75, extra charge for 10A (poss no earth); gas; lndtte; ice; shop; rest; snacks; bar; playgrnd; htd indoor/outdoor pools; sand beach 800m; watersports; solarium; tennis; games area; horseriding 400m; cycle hire; car wash; games rm; entmnt; TV; 7% statics; no dogs; phone; site clsd Nov; poss cr; Eng spkn; adv bkg (bkg fee €30.05); quiet; red long stay/low ssn (pay on arrival); cc not acc; CCI. "Excel, family-run & well organised site; welcome pack; gd facs & constant hot water; gd for children; conv National Park; no twin-axle vans." ♦ € 32.70   2005*

See advertisement on next page

ESTARTIT, L' *3B3* (1km S Coastal) **Camping El Molino**, 17258 L'Estartit (Gerona) [tel/fax 972-75 06 29] Fr N11 junc 5, take rd to L'Escala. Foll sp to Torroella de Montgri, then L'Estartit. Ent town & foll sp. V lge, hdg pitch, pt sl, pt shd; wc; shwrs; el pts inc; gas; ice; supmkt high ssn & 2km; rest; bar; playgrnd; sand beach 1km; games rm; poss cr; adv bkg. "Site in 2 parts - 1 in shd, 1 at beach unshd; gd facs; quiet location outside busy town." Holy Week & 1 May-30 Sep. € 14.60   2003*

ESTARTIT, L' *3B3* (W Coastal) **Camping Castell Montgri**, Ctra de Torroella, Km 4.7, 17258 L'Estartit (Gerona) [972-75 16 30; fax 972-75 09 06; cmontgri@campingparks.com; www.camping parks.com] Exit A7 junc 5 onto GI 623 dir L'Escala. Foll sp on rd C252 fr Torroella de Montgri to L'Estartit. Site on L clearly sp. V lge, hdg pitch, terr, hdstg, shd; wc; mv service pnt; chem disp; baby facs; shwrs inc; el pts (6A) inc; gas; lndtte; shop; rest; snacks; bar; playgrnd; 3 pools; waterslide; beach 1km; tennis; games area; watersports; entmnt; excursions; internet; TV; car wash; money exchange; 30% statics; dogs free; phone; poss cr; adv bkg; red long stay. "Gd views; help given to get to pitch; excel." ♦ 13 May-1 Oct. € 41.00   2005*

SPAIN

Only 2 km from L'Estartit, one of the most beautiful and ecological-minded villages of the Costa Brava, only 800m from the Beach. On our family site you will enjoy a fabulous holiday in the midst of nature. We have high quality installations: modern sanitary instal. With baby-baths, install. for the handicapped and free hot water, swimming pool (also indoors heated) bar, restaurant and supermarket... Leisure activities for the whole family: children's playground, watersports, bicycles for rent and a large programme of activities for all ages. And to relax a dive in our swimming pool with solarium and sauna.

telf.+34 972 751 805 –fax.+34 972 750 413 – www.campinglesmedes.com - info@campingslesmedes.com
paratge Camp de l'Arbre, apartado de correos, 140 - 17258 l'ESTARTIT, Girona   COSTA BRAVA

As we're travelling out of season, we'd better phone ahead to check that the site is actually open.

ESTARTIT, L' *3B3* (1km W Coastal) **Camping L'Emporda, Ctra Torroella de Montgri, Km 4.8, 17258 L'Estartit (Gerona) [972-76 06 49; fax 972-75 14 30; info@campingemporda.com; www. campingemporda.com]** Exit AP7 junc 5 onto GI623 dir L'Escala. Bef L'Escala turn S onto C31 dir Torroella de Montgri, then at Torroella take rd GI641 dir L'Estartit. Site bet L'Estartit & Torroella, opp Castell Montgri. Lge, pt shd; wc; chem disp; shwrs inc; baby facs; el pts (6A) €3.10; gas; lndtte; ice; shop; snacks; bar; playgrnd; pool; paddling pool; sand beach 1km; tennis; entmnt; organised walks; TV; dogs €1.70; phone; bus 70m; car wash; poss cr; adv bkg; quiet; red low ssn/long stay; CCI. "Family-run, pleasant & helpful; easy walking dist town cent; lge pitches." ♦ Holy Week-25 Sep. € 18.90   2005*

See advertisement opposite

†**ESTELLA** *3B1* (2km S Rural) **Camping Lizarra, Ordoiz s/n, 31200 Estella (Navarra) [948-55 17 33; fax 948-55 47 55]** N111 Pamplona to Logrono. Leave N111 sp Estella, turn R at T-junc, bear R at traff lts & turn R immed after rd tunnel, site sp. Pass factory, site on L in 1.5km. Well sp thro town. Lge, mkd pitch, wide terr, pt sl, unshd; htd wc (cont); chem disp; mv service pnt; baby facs; shwrs inc; el pts (6A) inc; gas; lndtte; shop; rest; snacks; bar; BBQ; playgrnd; pool; 80% w/e statics; phone; bus at w/e; poss cr; Eng spkn; noisy; cc acc; CCI. "Poss school parties, interesting old town; excel birdwatching in hills; on rte Camino de Compostella." ♦ € 21.50   2005*

†**ESTEPAR** *1B4* (2km NE Rural) **Camping Cabia, Ctra Burgos-Valladolid, Km 17, 09196 Cabia (Burgos) [947-41 20 78]** Site 15km SW of Burgos on N side of N620, adj Hotel Rio Cabia. Ent via Campsa petrol stn, W'bound exit 17, E'bound exit 18. Site sp fr N620 via service rd. Med, pt shd; wc; chem disp; shwrs inc; el pts (6A) €2; shops 15km & basic supplies fr rest; rest; bar; playgrnd; pool; 20% statics; constant rd noise; cc acc; CCI. "Friendly, helpful owner; gd rest; conv for m'way for Portugal but poorly sp fr W; ground poss v wet in winter; vg NH." € 11.00   2005*

CAMPING L'EMPORDÀ
Our camp site is small, quiet and familiar. It is situated at 1 km from the village l'Estartit and at the same distance from a fine sandy beach of 5 km, where you can enjoy a fabulaous view on the isles of Medas.

Road Torroella-l'Estartit, km 4,8
E- 17258 L'ESTARTIT
(Girona) COSTA-BRAVA
Tel.: 0034 972 75 06 49
Fax: 0034 972 75 14 30
www.campingemporda.com
info@campingemporda.com

†ESTEPONA *2H3* (7km E Coastal) **Camping Parque Tropical, Ctra N340 Km 162, 29680 Estepona (Malaga) [tel/fax 952-79 36 18]** On N side of N340 at km 162, 200m off main rd. Med, hdg/mkd pitch, terr, pt shd; wc; chem disp; mv service pnt; serviced pitch; shwrs inc; el pts (10A) inc; shop; gas; lndtte; ice; shop; rest; snacks; bar; sm playgrnd; htd, covrd pool; sand/shgl beach 1km; golf, horseriding nrby; wildlife park 1km; 60% statics; dogs; phone; bus 500m; poss cr; Eng spkn; adv bkg; rd noise; red low ssn/long stay; CCI. "Regimented, but gd site." ♦ € 24.00   2005*

†ESTEPONA *2H3* (11km SW Coastal) **Camping Chullera 2, Km 142.8, 29691 Manilva (Malaga) [tel/fax 952-89 01 96]** Travelling E on N340 site is at km post 142. Travelling W pass km post 142 until next rndabt, turn to return to site. Med, pt sl, pt shd; wc; chem disp; shwrs €0.50 tokens fr recep; el pts (15A) inc; gas; lndtte; shop; rest; bar; beach adj; playgrnd; 30% statics; dogs; phone; noisy at w/e high ssn; red long stay/low ssn; cc acc. "Immac san facs; site partly overlooked by high buildings; sunshades over pitches poss diff high o'fits; bus to La Linea for Gibraltar (passport req) & Estepona; poss itinerants." € 27.00   2005*

ESTEPONA *2H3* (11km SW Coastal) **Camping Chullera No 3, Sabinillas, 29691 Manilva (Malaga) [952-89 03 20; fax 952-89 01 96]** SW fr Estepona on N340, site on L, ent on main rd. Med, pt sl, unshd; wc; chem disp; shwrs; el pts €2.75; gas; ice; lndtte; shop; rest; snacks; bar; playgrnd; car wash; sand beach adj; TV; bus adj; quiet; cc acc. "Vg facs, friendly manager, rec." 15 Jun-15 Sep. € 14.00   2002*

ETXARRI ARANATZ *3B1* (2km) **Camping Etxarri, 31820 Etxarri-Aranatz (Navarra) [tel/fax 948-46 05 37; info@campingetxarri.com; www.campingetxarri.com]** S on AP15, turn W at Irurtzun onto N240A/N1 dir Vitoria/Gasteiz. Go thro Etxarri vill, turn L & cross old bdge, then take new rd over rlwy. Turn L, site sp. Med, pt shd; wc; shwrs inc; el pts €3.60; gas; lndtte; shop; rest; bar; BBQ; pool; playgrnd; sports area; archery; horseriding; cycling; hang-gliding; paragliding; entmnt; 80% statics; phone; poss cr; Eng spkn; noise fr youths; cc acc; CCI. "Wooded site; gd walks; interesting area; conv NH to/fr Pyrenees; youth hostel on site." 1 Apr-12 Oct. € 18.20 (CChq acc)   2005*

EUSA see Pamplona *3B1*

FARGA DE MOLES, LA see Seo de Urgel *3B3*

FERROL *1A2* (5km S Coastal) **Camping El Raso, Ctra de Redes, 15624 Ares (La Coruna) [981-46 06 76]** Turn W off N651 Betanzos-El Ferrol N of Pontedeume, foll sp to Playa El Raso & site. Med, hdg pitch, pt sl, terr, pt shd; wc; serviced pitches; shwrs inc; el pts (10A) €3.50 (check earth); gas; lndtte; shop in ssn & 1km; tradsmn; rest; bar; snacks; BBQ; sand beach adj; playgrnd; 5% statics; poss cr w/e; noisy (beach); Eng spkn; cc acc; CCI. "Rec inspect pitch bef accepting; access diff lge vans; fair sh stay." ♦ ltd 15 May-3 Sep. € 12.00   2002*

†FIGUERES *3B3* (1km N Urban) **Camping Pous, Ctra N11, Km 763, 17600 Figueres (Gerona) [972-67 54 96; fax 972-67 50 57]** Exit AP7/E15 S at junc 3 & join N11. Then foll N11A S twd Figueres. Site on L in 2km, ent adj Hotel Androl. Site recep in hotel. No access to N11A fr junc 4. Med, mkd pitch, shd; wc; chem disp; shwrs inc; el pts (10A) inc; shop 1km; rest; snacks; bar; playgrnd; few statics; dogs €2.50; Eng spkn; quiet with some rd noise; cc acc. "Gd, clean site; easy access; pleasant owner; excel rest; sh walk to town & Dali museum; 18km fr Rosas on coast." ♦ € 23.30   2005*

SPAIN

†FIGUERES *3B3* (12km N Rural) **Camping Les Pedres**, Calle Darnius 15, 17750 Capmany (Gerona) [972-54 91 92] S fr French border on N11, turn L sp Capmany, site 2km on L. Med, mkd pitch, pt sl, pt shd; htd wc; chem disp; shwrs inc; el pts (6A) inc; lndry rm; shop 1km; rest; snacks; bar; pool; sand beach 25km; 20% statics; dogs; phone; Eng spkn; adv bkg; quiet; cc acc; CCI. "Helpful Dutch owner; lovely views; gd touring & walking cent." ♦ € 22.90   2005*

FIGUERES *3B3* (8km NE Rural) **Camping Vell Emporda, Ctra Rosas/La Jonquera s/n, 17780 Garriguella (Gerona) [972-53 02 00 or 972-57 06 31 (LS); fax 972-55 23 43; vellemporda@ vellemporda.com; www. vellemporda.com]** On A7/E11 exit junc 3 onto N260 NE dir Llanca. Nr km 26 marker, turn R sp Garriguella, then L at T-junc N twd Garriguella. Site on R shortly bef vill. Lge, hdg/mkd pitch, terr, pt shd; wc; chem disp; baby facs; shwrs inc; el pts (10A) €3.50; gas; lndtte; ice; shop; tradsmn; rest; snacks; bar; playgrnd; pool & paddling pool; sand beach 6km; games area; games rm; TV; entmnt; 20% statics; dogs €2; phone; poss cr; Eng spkn; adv bkg; quiet; red long stay/low ssn; cc acc; CCI. "Conv N Costa Brava away fr cr beaches & sites; 20 mins to sea, at Llanca; overhanging trees poss diff high vehicles; excel." 1 Feb-1 Dec. € 25.50   2005*

See advertisement

†FIGUERES *3B3* (15km NW Rural) **Camping La Fradera, 17732 Sant Llorenc de la Muga (Gerona)** [tel/fax 972-54 20 54] Fr cent Figueras take N260 W dir Olot. After 1km turn R at mini-rndabt (supmkt on L), pass police stn to rd junc, strt on & cross over A7 m'way & pass thro Llers & Terades to Sant Llorenc. Site 1km past vill on L. Med, mkd pitch, pt shd; wc; chem disp; shwrs inc; el pts (6A) inc; lndtte; shop 2km; tradsmn; snacks; rest in vill; playgrnd; htd pool; rv sw 1km; few statics; poss cr; adv bkg; quiet; red long stay. "Vg site in delightful vill in foothills of Pyrenees; fiesta 2nd w/e Aug; v pleasant staff." ♦ ltd. € 16.30   2005*

FORNELLS DE LA SELVA see Gerona *3B3*

†FORTUNA *4F1* (1.5km N) **Castillejo Camping, 30709 Banos de Fortuna (Murcia) [968-68 70 62 or 619-00 32 58; www.elysiumcamping.com]** Exit A7 junc 83, 7km after Murcia onto C3223. Site sp on L. Sm, hdstg, unshd; wc; chem disp; mv service pnt; el pts (15A) €2; gas; lndry rm; shop 1km; tradsmn; rest; snacks; bar; playgrnd; htd pool; 10% statics; dogs free; adv bkg; quiet; red long stay; CCI. "Nr Fortuna natural hot springs & thermal treatment cent; flat site suitable disabled; new British owners 2004; excel long/sh stay." € 12.00
2004*

†FORTUNA *4F1* (3km N Rural) **Camping Fuente, Camino de la Bocamina s/n, 30709 Banos de Fortuna (Murcia) [tel/fax 968-68 51 25; informacion@campingfuente.com; www. campingfuente.com]** Fr Murcia on A7/E15 turn L onto C3223 sp Fortuna, thro town dir Balneario to Banos de Fortuna. Site on R down narr rd, sp. Med, mkd pitch, hdstg, pt sl, unshd; htd wc; chem disp; serviced pitches; indiv san facs some pitches; shwrs; el pts (10-16A) €1.50 or metered; gas; lndtte; shop; tradsmn; rest; snacks; bar; BBQ; playgrnd; htd pool; spa, jacuzzi; internet; some statics; dogs €1; phone; adv bkg; cc acc; red long stay; CCI. "Gd san facs; excel pool; secure overflow parking area; gd rest; many long-stay winter visitors; ltd recep hrs low ssn; poss sulpherous smell fr thermal baths." ♦ € 15.50   2005*

†FORTUNA *4F1* (3km N) **Camping Las Palmeras, 30709 Banos de Fortuna (Murcia) [968-68 51 23; fax 968-68 51 25]** Exit A7 junc 83 Fortuna; cont on C3223 thro Fortuna to Balneario de Fortuna; turn R & foll sp. Concealed R turn on crest at beg of vill. Med, mkd pitch, pt shd; wc; chem disp; shwrs; el pts (6A) €3; gas; lndry rm; shops 300m; tradsmn; rest; snacks; bar; natural hot water mineral pool 200m; 5% statics; poss cr; quiet; adv bkg acc; 20% red long stay; cc acc; CCI. "Gd value, friendly site; san facs run down; lge pitches; thermal baths also at Archena (15km)." ♦ ltd. € 9.00   2004*

†FOZ *1A2* (2km E Coastal) **Camping Benquerencia**, 27792 Benquerencia-Barreiros (Lugo) [tel/fax 982-12 44 50 or 679-15 87 88; contacto@campingbenquerencia.com; www. campingbenquerencia.com] Fr junc of N642 & N634 S of Foz; E twd Ribadeo; in 1km past Barreiros at km stone 566 turn L at site sp. Site on R in 1.5km. Med, mkd pitch, pt sl, pt shd; wc; shwrs inc; el pts (6A) €3; gas; lndtte; shop in ssn & 2km; rest; bar; playgrnd; sand beach 400m; tennis; games area; phone; quiet; cc acc; CCI. "Hot water to shwrs only; NH only." € 15.70   2005*

FOZ *1A2* (2.5km W Coastal) **Camping San Rafael, Playa de Peizas**, 27789 Foz (Lugo) [tel/fax 982-13 22 18; info@campingsanrafael.com] Site sp. Med, unshd; wc; chem disp; shwrs inc; el pts (5A) €3; gas; lndtte; shop; tradsmn; rest; snacks; bar; sand beach adj; games area; dogs; poss cr; adv bkg; quiet; 15% red long stay; cc acc; CCI. 1 Apr-30 Sep. € 14.00   2004*

†FRAGA *3C2* (1km SE Urban) **Camping Fraga, Ctra N11-Seros, Km 437, Pollígono 5, Parcelas 32-34, Ptda Vicaneta**, 22520 Fraga (Huesca) [974-34 52 12] Fr W pass thro Fraga town on N11. After about 500m turn R into indus est just past petrol stn. Turn R again in indus est, foll site sp. Fr E turn L into indus est just bef petrol stn. Sm, mkd pitch, hdstg, terr, pt shd; wc; chem disp; mv service pnt; shwrs inc; el pts (4A) inc (rev pol); lndtte; hypmkt 1km; tradsmn; rest; snacks; bar; playgrnd; pool; TV rm; some statics; dogs €2; phone; poss cr; adv bkg; red low ssn; CCI. "Conv NH bet Zaragoza & Tarragona; unspoilt town in beautiful area." ♦ € 40.00   2005*

FRANCA, LA *1A4* (1km NW Coastal) **Camping Las Hortensias, Ctra N634, Km 286, 33590 Playa de la Franca** (Asturias) [985-41 24 42; fax 985-41 21 53; lashortensias@campinglashortensias.com; www. campinglashortensias.com] Turn L off N634 on leaving vill of La Franca, foll sp 'Playa de la Franca' & cont past 1st site & thro car park to end of rd. Med, mkd pitch, pt sl, pt terr, pt shd; wc; chem disp; baby facs; shwrs inc; el pts (3-10A) €3.15; gas; lndtte; shop; rest, snacks; bar adj; playgrnd; sand beach adj; tennis; cycle hire; phone; dogs (but not on beach) €3; poss cr; Eng spkn; adv bkg; cc acc; red CCI. "Beautiful location nr scenic beach; sea views fr top terr pitches; vg." 1 Jun-15 Sep. € 19.70   2005*

FRIAS *1B4* (1.5km NW Rural) **Camping Frias, 09211 Frias** (Burgos) [947-35 71 98; fax 947-35 71 99; camfrias@burgos.net; www. campingfrias.com] Fr AP1 take N232 & N629 to Trespaderne. Turn sharp R (dir Miranda) & E for 10km. Turn R at Frias & camping sp. Site on R in 3km bef rv bdge. Med, mkd pitch, pt shd; wc; chem disp; mv service pnt; shwrs €0.60; el pts €2.50; ice; shop; rest; bar; 3 pools; rv adj; fishing; archery; cycle hire; 95% statics; dogs €2.50; phone; poss cr w/e; quiet; cc acc. "Interesting vill with castle & Roman bdge; open w/e only in winter, but phone ahead to check; sh stay/NH only." 11 Apr-16 Dec. € 20.40   2004*

†FUENGIROLA *2H4* (3km E Urban) **Camping La Rosaleda, Avda Las Salinas, Los Boliches, 29640 Fuengirola** (Malaga) [952-46 01 91; fax 952-58 19 66] Fr N340 Malaga-Marbella take rd to Los Boliches after Benalmadena. Site on R at rndabt. Med, mkd pitch, hdstg, pt sl, pt shd; wc; chem disp; shwrs inc; el pts (5A) inc; gas; lndtte; shop; tradsmn; rest; bar; sand beach 1.5km; dogs; phone; poss cr; Eng spkn; adv bkg; quiet but some rd noise; red long stay/low ssn. "Friendly, helpful staff; attractive area; magnificent views; easy walk Los Boliches; gd train & bus service; not for lge o'fits; sm pitches; some noise & dust fr adj building development (2005)." € 25.00   2005*

†FUENGIROLA *2H4* (4km SW Coastal) **Camping Fuengirola, Ctra Cadiz-Malaga Km 207, 29640 Fuengirola** (Malaga) [tel/fax 952-47 41 08] On R of N340 Malaga-Algeciras rd opp hotel immed at km stone 207. Go slowly down service stn exit (if missed, next rndabt is 2km). Lge, shd; wc; chem disp; serviced pitches; shwrs inc; el pts (6A) inc; gas; lndtte; ice; shop; rest; bar; playgrnd; pool; sand beach adj; watersports; TV; adv bkg; Eng spkn; some rd noise; red long stay; cc acc; CCI. "Sea views; clean facs; helpful staff." € 23.50   2003*

†FUENGIROLA *2H4* (9km W Coastal) **Camping Los Jarales, Ctra N340, Km 197 Calahonda, 29650 Mijas-Costa** (Malaga) [tel/fax 952-93 00 03] Fr Fuengirola take N340 W twd Marbella, turn at km 197 stone; site located to N of rd. Lge, mkd pitch, hdstg, pt sl, pt shd; wc; chem disp; serviced pitch; shwrs inc; el pts (5A) €2.90; gas; ice; lndtte; shop adj; rest; snacks; bar; playgrnd; pool; sand beach 400m; tennis; TV; poss cr; Eng spkn; adv bkg; rd noise; red long stay/CCI. "Well-run site; buses to Marbella & Fuengirola." ♦ € 18.70   2005*

†FUENTE DE PIEDRA *2G4* (700m S Urban) **Camping Fuente de Pedra** (formerly La Laguna), **Camino de la Rabita, Km 132 N334, 29520 Fuente de Piedra** (Malaga) [952-73 52 94; fax 952-73 54 61] Turn off A92 at km 132 sp Fuente de Piedra. Sp fr vill cent. Or to avoid town turn N fr A382 just W of turn for Bobadilla Estacion, sp Sierra de Yeguas. In 2km turn R into nature reserve, cont for approx 3km, site on L at end of town. Sm, mkd pitch, hdstg, pt sl, terr, pt shd; wc; shwrs inc; el pts (10A) €4.50; gas; lndry rm; ice; shop; rest; snacks; bar; BBQ; playgrnd; pool in ssn; internet; 25% statics; dogs; phone; bus 700m; Eng spkn; poss noise fr adj public pool; cc acc; red long stay/CCI. "Mostly v sm pitches, but some now avail for o'fits up to 7m; gd rest; wc clean but dated & poss stretched; adj lge lake with many flamingoes; interesting visits in region." ♦ ltd. € 19.00   2005*

FUENTE DE SAN ESTABAN, LA *1D3* (1km E Rural) Camping El Cruce, Ctra A62, Km 291 (E80), 37200 La Fuente de San Estaban (Salamanca) [923-44 01 30]
On A62/E80 (Salamanca-Portugal) km stone 291 immed behind hotel on S side of rd. Fr E watch for sp 'Cambio de Sentido' to cross main rd. Med, pt shd; wc; chem disp; shwrs; el pts (6A) €3 (poss no earth); rest adj; snacks; bar; gas; playgrnd; Eng spkn; some rd noise; cc acc; CCI. "Conv NH/sh stay en rte Portugal; friendly." 1 Jul-15 Sep. € 14.00
2004*

†**FUENTEHERIDOS** *2F3* (600m SW Rural) Camping El Madronal, Ctra a Castano del Robledo, Km 0.6, 21292 Fuenteheridos (Huelva) [959-50 12 01] Fr Zafra S on N435n turn L onto N433 sp Arancena, ignore first R to Fuenteheridos vill, camp sp R at next x-rd 500m on R. Med, mkd pitch, pt sl, pt shd; wc; chem disp; shwrs; el pts inc; gas; lndry rm; shop & 600m; snacks; bar high ssn; BBQ; 2 pools; cycle hire; horseriding; 5% statics; dogs; phone; carwash; quiet; CCI. "Tranquil site in National Park of Sierra de Arancena; lge pitches among chestnut trees; nrby vill streets diff for lge o'fits." € 14.00
2005*

GALENDE see Puebla de Sanabria *1B3*

†**GALLARDOS, LOS** *4G1* (4km N Rural) Camping Los Gallardos, 04280 Los Gallardos (Almeria) [950-52 83 26; fax 950-52 83 24; questions@almeriaonline.com] Leave N340 at junc 525; foll sp to Los Gallardos; pass under a'route after 800m; turn L into site ent. Med, mkd pitch, hdstg, pt shd; wc; chem disp; serviced pitch; mv service pnt; shwrs inc; el pts (5-10A) inc; gas; lndtte; ice; supmkt; rest (clsd Thurs); snacks; bar; pool; sand beach 10km; 2 grass bowling greens; golf; tennis adj; dogs €1.80; 40% statics; poss v cr; m'way noise; adv bkg; reds long stay/low ssn; cc acc; CCI. "British owned; 90% British clientele low ssn; gd social atmosphere; sep drinking water supply nr recep; prone to flooding wet weather." ♦ € 16.00
2004*

†**GANDIA** *4E2* (2km N Coastal) Camping L'Alqueria, Ctra Gandia-Grao de Gandia s/n; 46730 Grao de Gandia (Valencia) [962-84 04 70; fax 962-84 10 63; laqueria@laqueria.com; www.lalqueria.com] Fr A7 exit 60 onto N332 dir Grao de Gandia. Site sp. Lge, shd; wc; baby facs; shwrs inc; el pts €2.90; gas; lndtte; shop; rest; bar; htd, covrd pool; sand beach 800m; games area; entmnt; cycle hire; poss cr; adv bkg; quiet; cc acc; red long stay. "Excel facs; clean, pleasant site; popular at Easter; helpful family owners; easy walk to town & stn; nrby Denia is windsurfers' paradise." ♦ € 27.50
2004*

†**GARGANTILLA DEL LOZOYA** *1C4* (2km Rural) Camping Monte Holiday, 28739 Gargantilla del Lozoya (Madrid) [tel/fax 918-69 52 78; monte holiday@campings.net; www.sierranorte.com/holiday] Fr N on N1/E5 Burgos-Madrid rd turn R on M604 at km stone 69 sp Rascafria; in 8km turn R immed after rlwy bdge & then L up track in 300m, foll site sp. Do not ent vill. Lge, terr, pt sl, pt shd; wc; chem disp; baby facs; shwrs inc; el pts (7A) €3; lndtte; shop 6km; rest; bar; pool; rv sw; 80% statics; phone; little Eng spkn; adv bkg; quiet; cc acc; red CCI. "Interesting site; vg san facs; gd views; lovely area but site isolated in winter & poss heavy snow; friendly; conv NH fr m'way & for Madrid & Segovia; easy to find; some facs clsd low ssn." ♦ € 19.60
2004*

GARRIGUELLA see Figueres *3B3*

†**GARRUCHA** *4G1* (6km N Coastal) Camping Cuevas Mar, Ctra Garrucha-Villaricos, Palomares, 04610 Cuevas de Almanzora (Almeria) [tel/fax 950-46 73 82; cuevasmar@arrakis.es; www.campingcuevasmar.com] Exit N340 at junc 537 sp Cuevas del Almanzora, after 4km turn R sp Vera. In 2km turn L sp Palomares & turn R at site sp at rndabt immed bef Palomares, site on L in 1.5km. Fr S exit N340 at junc 520, by-pass Garrucha, site on L in 6km. Med, hdg/mkd pitch, hdstg, pt shd; wc; chem disp; mv service pnt; baby facs; shwrs inc; el pts (6A) €3.22; gas 3km; lndtte; ice; shop; tradsmn; rest 500m; bar; BBQ; playgrnd; pool; jacuzzi; sand/shgl beach 250m; 10% statics; dogs €1.90; poss cr; adv bkg; noisy barking dogs; red low ssn/long stay; CCI. "Vg san facs; immac, well-maintained site; lge pitches; only 1 tap for drinking water; friendly owner; beautiful coastline; mosquito problems; Fri mkt Garrucha; popular long stay site." ♦ ltd. € 20.10
2005*

†**GARRUCHA** *4G1* (4km NE Coastal) Camping Almanzora (Naturist), Ctra Garrucha-Palomares, 04620 Vera (Almeria) [950-46 74 25; fax 950-46 73 82] SE on N340 Murcia-Almeria rd, exit Vera, foll sp Garrucha. In 5km L & foll site sp. At junc with Garrucha & Villaricos rd turn L, then R at Vera Playa Hotel. Site on L at rndabt on hotel access rd. Lge, pt shd, wc; chem disp; mv service pnt; shwrs inc; baby facs; el pts (16A) inc (rec long lead); gas; lndtte; shop; tradsmn; rest; snacks; bar; playgrnd; pools; sand beach 300m; tennis; phone; quiet; poss cr; few statics; adv bkg rec; dogs; Eng spkn; cc acc; reds for long stay; CCI. "Excel site but part overlooked fr main rd; non-naturist part of site sold for development but improvements made to naturist site (2004); many long-stay winter visitors; naturist beach adj; adj hotel naturist until 8pm; many pitches have shade awnings but sm & poss diff for lge o'fits; Friday mkt at Garrucha." € 30.00
2005*

GATA *1D3* (4km W Rural) **Camping Sierra de Gata, Ctra EX109 a Gata, Km 4.100, 10860 Gata (Caceres) [tel/fax 927-67 21 68; sierradegata@campingsonline.com; www.campingsierra degata.com]** Foll sp Gata fr rd EX109/C526, site sp on unmkd rd on rvside. Med, shd; wc; chem disp; shwrs; el pts (5-10A); lndry rm; shop; rest 100m; snacks; playgrnd; pool; rv sw; fishing; paddling pool; tennis; games area; cycle hire; TV; quiet. "Peaceful, family-run site in beautiful area." ♦ ltd.
12 Mar-31 Oct. (CChq acc)   2004*

GAVA *3C3* (5km S Coastal) **Camping Tres Estrellas, C31, Km 186.2, 08850 Gava (Barcelona) [936-33 06 37; fax 936-33 15 25; fina@camping3estrellas.com; www.camping3 estrellas.com]** Fr S take C31 (Castelldefels to Barcelona), exit 13. Site at km 186.2 300m past rd bdge. Fr N foll Barcelona airport sp, then C31 junc 13. Slip rd immed under rd bdge, cross m'way, turn R then R again to join m'way heading N for 400m. Lge, mkd pitch, pt sl, pt shd; htd wc; chem disp; mv service pnt; shwrs inc; el pts (6A) €4.38 (poss rev pol &/or no earth); gas; lndtte; ice; shop; rest; snacks; bar; playgrnd; htd pool; sand beach adj; tennis; entmnt; internet; TV; 20% statics; phone; bus to Barcelona 400m; poss cr; Eng spkn; adv bkg; some aircraft & rd noise; cc acc; red snr citizens; CCI. ♦
15 Mar-15 Oct. € 26.80 (CChq acc)   2004*

GERONA *3B3* (8km S Rural) **Camping Can Toni Manescal, Ctra Llambillas, Km 2, 17458 Fornells de la Selva (Gerona) [972-47 61 17; fax 972-47 67 35; campinggirona@campinggirona. com]** Fr N leave AP7 at junc 7 onto N11 dir Barcelona. In 2km turn L to Fornells de la Selva; in vill turn L at church (sp); over rv; in 1km bear R & site on L in 400m. Sm, mkd pitch, pt sl, pt shd; wc; chem disp; baby facs; shwrs inc; el pts (5A) €2.70 (poss long lead req); gas; lndtte; shop, rest 2km; snacks, bar 4km; playgrnd; pool; sand beach 23km; dogs; phone; bus 1.5km; Eng spkn; adv bkg; quiet; cc acc; CCI. "V pleasant, open site; gd base for lovely medieval city Gerona - foll bus stn sp for gd, secure m'van parking; san facs poss dirty low ssn; welcoming & helpful owners; lge pitches; cold water only to washbasins; local rlwy stn; excel cycle path into Gerona, along old rlwy line; Gerona mid-May flower festival rec."
16 Jun-15 Sep. € 15.00   2005*

GETAFE see Madrid *1D4*

†**GIJON** *1A3* (4km E Rural) **Camping Deva-Gijon, Parroquia de Deva, 33394 Deva (Asturias) [985-13 38 48; fax 985-13 38 89; cdeva@campingdeva.com; www.campingdeva-gijon. com]** Leave Gijon on N632 twd Ribadesella & Santander. Site sp on R at km 64.875 just bef climbing hill to plateau. Lge, mkd pitch; pt sl, terr, pt shd, serviced pitches; wc; chem disp; shwrs inc; el pts (16A) €3.30; lndtte; ice; shop, rest, snacks in ssn; bar; pool & paddling; sand beach 4km; tennis; cycle hire; golf 3km; 50% statics; bus; car wash; sep car park; poss cr; noisy visitors & nr rd; cc acc; CCI. "Gd touring base; facs ltd low ssn & v open san facs not rec winter." ♦ € 24.60   2005*

GIJON *1A3* (13km NW Coastal) **Camping Buenavista, Candas, 33491 Perlora (Asturias) [tel/fax 985-87 17 93]** Fr Gijon take AS19 sp Tremanes & foll rd for approx 5km. On sharp L bend take exit on R (Aviles) & immed L onto AS239 sp Candas/Perlora, site sp. Med, terr, pt shd; wc; chem disp; shwrs; el pts €2.56; gas; lndtte; shop; rest; snacks; bar; playgrnd; sand beach 500m; 70% statics; poss cr; noisy; CCI. "Oviedo historic town worth a visit; quite steep pull-out, need gd power/weight ratio; gd sh stay." 1 Feb-30 Nov.
€ 15.70   2003*

†**GIJON** *1A3* (13km NW Coastal) **Camping Perlora, Ctra Candas, Km 12, 33491 Candas (Asturias) [985-87 00 48]** Fr A8 take exit Candas & foll rd to seafront, site sp at end promenade in Candas. Med, pt sl, unshd; wc; chem disp; mv service pnt; some serviced pitches; shwrs €0.50; el pts (5A) €2.30; gas; lndtte; ice; shop; rest; playgrnd; sand beach 1km; tennis; watersports; fishing; 80% statics; phone; poss cr; Eng spkn; quiet; no cc acc; red long stay; CCI. "Excel; v helpful staff; lovely, immac site on dramatic headland; ltd space for tourers; superb san facs, ltd low ssn." ♦ € 17.80   2005*

GIRONELLA *3B3* (500m Urban) **Camping Gironella, Ctra. C16/E9, Km 86.750 Entrada Sud Gironella, 08680 Gironella (Barcelona) [tel/fax 938-25 15 29; gironella@campinggironella.com; www.campinggironella.com]** Site is bet Berga & Puig-reig on C16/E9. Well sp. Med, mkd pitch, hdstg, pt shd; htd wc; chem disp; serviced pitch; baby facs; shwrs inc; el pts (3-10A) €2.15-6.50; gas; lndtte; shop; tradsmn; rest; snacks; bar; playgrnd; htd pool; games rm; entmnt; TV rm; 90% statics; dogs; phone; poss cr; Eng spkn; adv bkg (dep req); quiet; CCI. "Excel sh stay/NH but ltd touring pitches (phone ahead)." ♦ Holy Week,
1 Jul-15 Sep & w/e low ssn. € 16.00   2005*

GORLIZ *1A4* (700m Coastal) **Camping Arrien, Uresarantze Bidea, 48630 Gorliz (Bizkaia) [946-77 19 11; fax 946-77 44 80; arrien@teleline. es; www.campingarrien.com]** Fr Bilbao foll m'way to Getxo, then 637/634 thro Sopelana & Plentzia to Gorliz. In Gorliz foll sp to site on L. Lge, pt sl, pt shd; wc; chem disp; shwrs inc; el pts (3-5A) €3.60; lndtte; gas; shop; rest; snacks; bar; BBQ; playgrnd; sand beach 700m; 60% statics; dogs; phone; bus 150m; poss cr; Eng spkn; cc acc; 10% red CCI. "Useful base for Bilbao & ferry (approx 40 mins); bus to Plentzia every 20 mins, fr there can get metro to Bilbao; friendly, v helpful staff; unoccupied long stay tourers give shabby appearance." 1 Mar-31 Dec. € 22.00   2005*

SPAIN

GRANADA *2G4* (4km N Rural) **Camping Granada, Cerro de la Cruz s/n, 18210 Peligros (Granada) [tel/fax 958-34 05 48]** S on A44 fr Jaen twd Granada; take exit 121 & foll sp Peligros. Turn L at rndabt after 1km by Spar shop, site access rd 300m on R. Single track access 1km. Med, hdstg, terr, pt shd; wc; chem disp; shwrs inc; el pts (10A) €3; gas; lndtte; shop; rest; bar; playgrnd; pool; tennis; dogs €1.30; poss cr; some Eng spkn; adv bkg; quiet; cc acc; CCI. "Friendly, helpful owners; well-run site in olive grove; vg facs, superb views; gd access for m'vans but poss diff for v lge o'fits; pitches poss uneven & muddy after rain; site rds & access steep; conv Alhambra." ♦ ltd. 15 Mar-15 Oct. € 19.80
2005*

GRANADA *2G4* (4km N) **Camping Motel Sierra Nevada, Avda de Madrid 107, 18014 Granada [958-15 00 62; fax 958-15 09 54; campingmotel@ terra.es; www.campingsierranevada.com]** App Granada S-bound on A44 & exit at junc 123, foll dir Granada. Site on R in 1.5km just beyond bus stn & opp El Campo supmkt, well sp. Lge, shd; wc; chem disp; mv service pnt; baby facs; shwrs inc; el pts (6A) €3.45; gas; lndtte; ice; supmkt opp; rest; snacks; BBQ; playgrnd; 2 pools adj; sports facs; bus to city cent; poss cr (arr early); noisy at w/e; cc acc; CCI. "V helpful staff; excel san facs, but poss ltd low ssn; motel rms avail; can book Alhambra tickets at recep (24 hrs notice)." ♦ 1 Mar-1 Nov. € 22.00
2005*

†GRANADA *2G4* (9km N Rural) **Camping Cubillas, Ctra Bailen-Motril, Km 115, 18220 Albolote (Granada) [958-45 33 28; fax 958-45 32 65]** Exit A44/E902 junc 116 dir El Chaparral, site sp. Sm, mkd pitch, pt sl, pt shd; wc; chem disp; shwrs inc; el pts (5-10A) €2.50; gas; shop; snacks; bar; lake sw; playgrnd; boating & fishing adj; dogs; quiet; 10% red long stay & CCI. "Useful NH for Granada; some bird-watching; friendly staff; ltd facs low ssn." ♦ € 15.00
2005*

†GRANADA *2G4* (13km E Rural) **Camping Las Lomas, 11 Ctra de Guejar Sierra, Km 6.5, 18160 Guejar Sierra (Granada) [tel/fax 958-48 47 42; laslomas@campings.net]** Fr A44 exit onto by-pass 'Ronda Sur', then exit onto A395 sp Sierra Nevada. In approx 4km exit sp Cenes, turn under A395 to T-junc & turn R sp Guejar Sierra, Embalse de Canales, site sp bef vill. Med, hdg/mkd pitch, terr, pt shd; htd wc; chem disp; mv service pnt; baby facs; fam bthrm; shwrs inc; el pts (10A) €3 (poss no earth); gas; lndtte; shop; rest; snacks; bar; playgrnd; pool; waterskiing nrby; internet; poss cr; Eng spkn; adv bkg ess; quiet; red long stay; cc acc; CCI. "Helpful, friendly site; conv Granada (bus at gate); acc poss diff for lge o'fits; excel san facs; gd shop & rest; beautiful mountain scenery; excel site." ♦ ltd. € 22.00
2005*

We're having a great holiday - must fill in some site report forms and send them to The Club as soon as possible.

†GRANADA *2G4* (3km SE Urban) **Camping Reina Isabel, Ctra de La Zubia, Km 4, 18140 La Zubia (Granada) [958-59 00 41; fax 958-59 11 91; info@ reinaisabelcamping.com; www.reinaisabel camping.com]** Exit A44 nr Granada at junc sp Ronda Sur, dir Sierra Nevada, Alhambra, then exit 2 sp La Zubia. Foll site sp. Med, hdg/mkd pitch, pt shd; htd wc; chem disp; mv service pnt; shwrs inc; el pts (5A) €2.50 (poss rev pol); gas; lndtte; shop; supmkt 1km; rest; snacks; bar; pool high ssn; TV; dogs; phone; bus; Eng spkn; poss cr; quiet except during festival in May & disco adj; cc acc; 20% red 7+ days low ssn; red CCI. "Well-run, v busy site, gd rest; poss shwrs v hot/cold - warn children; easy to find, helpful staff; sm pitches; bus to Granada every 30 mins at w/e, every 20 mins fr 0700 in week; v busy; conv Sierra Nevada & Alhambra (order tickets at site to avoid queues peak periods)." € 18.25
2005*

See advertisement

GRANADA *2G4* (11km S Rural) **Camping Suspiro del Moro, 107 Avda de Madrid, 18630 Otura (Granada) [958-55 54 11; fax 958-55 51 05; suspirodelmoro@eresmas.com]** On A44/E902 dir Motril, exit junc 139. Foll camp sp fr W side of rndabt; site visible at top of slight rise on W side of A44. Med, mkd pitch, hdstg, shd; wc; chem disp; mv service pnt; shwrs inc; el pts (5A) €2.40 (poss no earth); ice; gas; lndry rm; snacks & rest in ssn; bar; shop; playgrnd; lge pool; tennis; games area; 10% statics; phone; bus; Eng spkn; rd noise & noisy rest at w/e; 35% red low ssn; cc acc; CCI. "Decent site; reasonable pitches; quiet low ssn; clean facs but few hot shwrs; san facs inadequate for site this size; rest poss noisy; hourly bus to Granada." ♦ ltd. 1 Mar-1 Nov. € 15.00   2004*

†**GRANADA** *2G4* (10km W Rural) **Camping Maria Eugenia, Avda Andalucia 190, Santa Fe, 18014 Granada [958-20 06 06; fax 958-20 68 17]**
On A329/A92 fr Granada dir Antequerra. Nr airport; site on main rd, well sp. Sm, mkd pitch, shd; wc; chem disp; mv service pnt; shwrs inc; el pts €3; lndtte; shop; snacks; bar; pool; TV; 30% statics; dogs; phone; bus fr site ent; rd noise. "Friendly, family-run site." € 15.40   2005*

†**GRAUS** *3B2* (7km S Rural) **Camping Bellavista & Subenuix, Embalse de Barasona, Ctra Graus N123, Km 23, 22435 La Puebla de Castro (Huesca) [974-54 51 13; fax 974 34 70 71; info@hotelcampingbellavista.com; www.hotelcamping bellavista.com]** Fr E on N230/N123 ignore 1st sp for Graus. Cont to 2nd sp 'El Grado/Graus' & turn R. Site on L in 1km. Med, mkd pitch, terr, pt shd; htd wc; chem disp; shwrs inc; el pts (10A) €3.50; gas; lndry rm; shop; rest; snacks; bar; playgrnd; pool; lake sw adj; watersports; fishing; tennis; horseriding; entmnt; internet; TV rm; 50% statics; dogs €1.50; phone; Eng spkn; adv bkg; noisy at w/e; red low ssn; cc acc; CCI. "Hotel also on site; excel rest; v helpful staff; sm pitches; beautiful position above lake; mountain views." € 17.90   2005*

GRAUS *3B2* (5km SW Rural) **Camping Lago de Barasona, Ctra N123A, Km 25, 22435 La Puebla de Castro (Huesca) [974-54 51 48 or 974-24 69 06; fax 974-54 52 28; info@lagobarasona.com; www.lagobarasona.com]** Fr E on N123, ignore 1st sp for Graus. Cont to 2nd sp 'El Grado/Graus/Benasque' & turn R. Site on L in 2km. Lge, hdg/mkd pitch, hdstg, sl, terr, shd; htd wc; chem disp; mv service pnt; shwrs inc; el pts (6A) €3.70; gas; lndry rm; ice; shop; tradsmn; rest; snacks; bar; BBQ; playgrnd; 2 pools; lake beach & sw 100m; watersports; sailing; tennis; horseriding 1km; entmnt; TV rm; 15% statics; dogs; Eng spkn; adv bkg; quiet; cc acc; red long stay; CCI. "Excel, well-equipped site; lge pitches; v helpful staff; highly rec." ♦ 1 Apr-30 Sep. € 21.50 (CChq acc)   2005*

†**GUADALUPE** *2E3* (1.5km S Rural) **Camping Las Villuercas, Ctra Villanueva-Huerta del Río, Km 2, 10140 Guadalupe (Caceres) [927-36 71 39; fax 927-36 75 61]** Exit NV/E90 Madrid-Menda at junc 178 onto EX118 to Guadalupe. Do not ent town. Site sp on R at x'rds at foot of hill. Med, shd; wc; shwrs; el pts €2.50; lndtte; shop; rest; bar; playgrnd; pool; tennis; phone; cc acc. "Excel; helpful owners; ltd facs low ssn; some pitches poss not avail in wet weather; nr famous monastery." € 12.50   2005*

†**GUARDA, A** *1B2* (1km E Coastal) **Camping Santa Tecla, Salcidos, Ctra Tui-A Guarda, 36780 A Guarda (Pontevedra) [986-61 30 11; fax 986-61 30 63; campingstatecla@navegalia.com; www.campingsantatecla.com]** S fr Vigo on C550. Site well sp thro A Guarda. Lge, mkd pitch, pt shd; wc; chem disp; mv service pnt; shwrs; el pts €3; gas; lndtte; shop; rest; bar; playgrnd; pool; rv sw adj; games area; dogs; bus 1km; Eng spkn; quiet. "Views across estuary to Portugal; 2km fr ferry; excel san facs; ltd facs low ssn." ♦ € 15.00   2004*

†**GUARDAMAR DEL SEGURA** *4F2* (2km N Rural/Coastal) **Camping Marjal, Ctra N332, Km 73.4, 03140 Guardamar de Segura (Alicante) [966-72 70 70 or 966-72 50 22; fax 966-72 66 95; camping@marjal.com; www.campingmarjal.com]** Fr N exit A7 junc 72 sp Aeropuerto/Santa Pola; in 5km turn R onto N332 sp Santa Pola/Cartagena, U-turn at km 73.4, site sp on R at km 73.5. Lge, hdg/mkd pitch, hdstg, pt shd; all serviced pitches; wc; chem disp; baby facs; sauna; shwrs inc; el pts (16A) €3 or metered; gas; ice; lndtte; supmkt; rest; snacks; bar; BBQ; playgrnd; 2 htd pools (1 covrd); sand beach 1km (inc naturist); lake sw 15km; tennis; sports cent; cycle hire; entmnt; child entmnt; internet; TV rm; 20% statics; dogs €3; phone; recep 0800-2300; adv bkg rec; Eng spkn; quiet; red long stay/low ssn/snr citizens; cc acc; CCI. "Gd facs; friendly, helpful staff; poss mosquitoes; excel family entmnt & activities; excel long stay." ♦ € 44.00   2005*

See advertisement on next page

GUARDAMAR DEL SEGURA *4F2* (3km S Urban) **Camping Mare-Nostrum, Ctra N332, Km 67, 03140 Guardamar del Segura (Alicante) [tel/fax 965-72 80 73; cmarenostrum@cesser.com; www.costablanca.org/marenostrum.asp]** Entrance to site immed off N332 on L fr Guardamar del Segura dir Torrevieja. Med, mkd pitch, hdstg, pt shd; htd wc; chem disp; baby facs; shwrs inc; el pts (5A) €2.50; gas; lndry rm; lndtte; shop; snacks; bar; playgrnd; pool high ssn; sand beach adj; 10% statics; dogs; bus; phone; some daytime rd noise; cc acc. "Rec sh stay/NH, dir access to beach thro pine woods." Holy Week-15 Sep. € 16.40   2002*

SPAIN

†GUARDAMAR DEL SEGURA *4F2* (3.5km W Rural) Camping Rincon de Luna, Ctra CV920, Km 3.5, 03140 Guardamar de Segura (Alicante) [966-72 74 00; fax 966-72 61 58; info@rinconluna.com; www.rinconluna.com] Fr N332 twds Cartagena; at km 71.8 turn W onto CV920 (C3323) twds Rojales & Formentera; site on L in 3km. Med, mkd pitch, pt shd; htd wc; chem disp; serviced pitches; sauna; shwrs inc; el pts (15A) metered; gas; lndtte; supmkt; rest; playgrnd; htd, covrd pool; sand beach 3.5km; sports area; gym; jacuzzi; 5% statics; dogs €1.20; phone; minibus; Eng spkn; adv bkg ess winter; quiet; red low ssn/snr citizens; cc acc; CCI. "Excel, well-run site; helpful staff; in historic area; gd birdwatching; excel rest; v popular winter long-stay." ♦ € 27.85   2005*

See advertisement above

> This site entry hasn't been updated for a while; we'd better fill in a site report form and send it to The Club.

GUARDAMAR DEL SEGURA *4F2* (12km W Rural) Camping Quinta Mare, Vereda Los Nigues, 03150 Dolores (Alicante) [678-39 81 57; cabinsncamping@vodafone.es] A7 fr Alicante twd Murcia. At junc 77 take A37 twd Dolores then turn L onto CV3321 fr rndabt. Cont over two more rndabts onto CV855 then L at junc & after 100m site just after stables on L. Sm, hdg pitch, hdstg, unshd; wc; chem disp; shwrs; el pts (10A) inc; gas; lndtte; shops, rest, snacks, bar 3km; BBQ; playgrnd; pool; sand beach 10km; 33% statics; dogs; phone 3km; Eng spkn; adv bkg dep req; quiet; cc not acc; CCI. "14km fr historical cent (Elche); excel shopping malls in town; old Arab Quarter; El Hondo Nature Reserve (5km), gd birdwatching; gd cycling area; gd long stay." € 11.00   2004*

†GUARDIOLA DE BERGUEDA *3B3* (3.5km W Rural) Camping El Bergueda, Ctra B400, Km 3.5, 08694 Guardiola de Bergueda (Barcelona) [938-22 74 32; campingbergueda@worldonline.es; www.campingbergueda.com] On C16 S take B400 W dir Saldes. Site is approx 10km S of Cadi Tunnel. Med, mkd pitch, some hdstg, terr, pt shd; wc; chem disp; baby facs; shwrs; el pts (2-6A) € 2.30-4 (poss rev pol); gas; lndtte; ice; shop; tradsmn; rest; snacks; bar; BBQ; playgrnd; pool; paddling pool; games area; games rm; TV; some statics; phone; dogs; Eng spkn; quiet; CCI. "V helpful staff; vg san facs; beautiful situation with mountain views; gd walking; a gem of a site." ♦ € 17.50   2005*

GUEJAR SIERRA see Granada *2G4*

GUITIRIZ *1A2* (1km N Rural) Camping El Meson, 27305 Guitiriz (Lugo) [982-37 32 88] On A6 NW fr Lugo, exit km 535 sp Guitiriz, site sp. Sm, pt sl, pt shd; wc; chem disp (wc); shwrs inc; el pts (6A) inc; gas; supmkt 1km; rest; bar; playgrnd; pool 6km; rv sw 500m; phone; bus adj; quiet. 15 Jun-15 Sep. € 11.80   2004*

†HARO *1B4* (500m N Urban) Camping de Haro, Avda de Miranda 1, 26200 Haro (La Rioja) [941-31 27 37; fax 941-31 20 68; campingdeharo@fer.es; www.campingdeharo.com] Fr N or S on N124 take exit on E side of rd sp Haro. In 500m at rndabt take 1st exit, under rlwy bdge, cont to site on R immed bef rv bdge. Exit 9 on AP68 & fr W on N232 fr Pancorbo, at ent to town on LR111, bear L; down hill, over rv bdge; foll site sp. Avoid cont into town cent. Med, hdg/mkd pitch, pt shd, wc; chem disp; mv service pnt; shwrs inc (am only in winter); el pts (3-5A) €2.40; gas; lndry rm; shop & 600m; snacks; bar; playgrnd; htd pool high ssn; 70% statics; dogs €1.75; phone; bus 800m; car wash; site clsd 11 Dec-9 Jan; poss cr; Eng spkn; adv bkg; quiet (not w/e), some rd noise; cc acc; CCI. "Highly rec, clean, tidy site but dusty rds; friendly owner; spacious pitches; excel facs; busy at w/ends; v pleasant, fascinating town nr vineyards & mountains; sh walk to town & Rioja bodegas; 2 hrs to Bilbao ferry." ♦ € 16.00 (CChq acc)   2005*

SPAIN

†HARO *1B4* (10km SW) **Camping La Rioja, Ctra de Haro/Sto Domingo de la Calzada, Km 8.5, 26240 Castanares de la Rioja (La Rioja)** [941-30 01 74; fax 941-30 01 56] Exit AP68 junc 9, take rd twd Santa Domingo de la Calzada. Foll by-pass round Casalarreina, site on R nr rvside just past vill on rd LR111. Lge, hdg pitch, pt shd; htd wc; chem disp; shwrs; el pts (10A) €2.85 (poss rev pol); gas; lndtte; shop; rest; snacks; bar; pool high ssn; tennis; cycle hire; entmnt; dogs; clsd 10 Dec-8 Jan; poss cr; adv bkg; 90% statics; dogs; quiet; cc acc. "Gd site; ltd facs in winter & few touring pitches; conv for Rioja wine cents; Bilbao ferry." € 20.00
2004*

†HECHO *3B1* (8km N Rural) **Camping Borda Bisaltico, Ctra Gabardito, Km 2, 22720 Hecho (Huesca)** [974-37 53 88] Fr Jaca W on N240 dir Pamplona, after 25km at Puente la Reina de Jaca turn R onto A176 then take HU210. Foll sp. Site in 8km.Take care, 1.5km narr, winding rd. Med, sl, terr, pt shd; wc; chem disp; mv service pnt; baby facs; shwrs inc; el pts (6A) €3; gas; lndtte; tradsmn; rest; bar; no statics; dogs; phone; bus; quiet; CCI. "Well-organised site; friendly owners; camping area around mountain inn; beautiful views; excel san facs; gd walking, climbing, birdwatching." € 14.30
2005*

†HECHO *3B1* (1km S Rural) **Camping Valle de Hecho, Ctra Puente La Reina-Hecho, 22720 Hecho (Huesca)** [tel/fax 974-37 53 61] Leave Jaca W on N240. After 25km turn N on A176 at Puente La Reina de Jaca. Site on W of rd, o'skts of Hecho/Echo. Med, mkd pitch, pt sl, pt shd; htd wc; chem disp; mv service pnt; shwrs inc; el pts (5-15A) €3.60; gas; lndtte; shop; rest; snacks; bar; playgrnd; pool; games area; 50% statics; phone; bus 200m; quiet; cc acc; CCI. "Pleasant site in foothills of Pyrenees; excel, spotless facs but poss inadequate hot water; gd birdwatching area; Hecho fascinating vill; shop, bar clsd low ssn except w/e; v ltd facs & poss neglected low ssn." € 16.00   2005*

HERRADURA, LA see Almunecar *2H4*

HONDARRIBIA see Irun *3A1*

†HORCAJO DE LOS MONTES *2E4* (200m Rural) **Camping El Mirador de Cabaneros, Calle Canada Real Segoviana s/n, 13110 Horcajo de los Montes (Ciudad Real)** [926-77 54 39; fax 926-77 50 03; camping-cabaneros@hortur.com; www.campingcabaneros.com] At km 53 off the Horcajo-Alcala rd, 200m fr vill. Med, mkd pitch, hdstg, terr, pt shd; htd wc; chem disp; mv service pnt; baby facs; shwrs; el pts €2.50; gas; shop 500m; rest; bar; BBQ; playgrnd; pool; rv sw 12km; games area; games rm; tennis 500m; cycle hire; entmnt; TV; 10% statics; phone; adv bkg rec high ssn; quiet; red long stay; cc acc; CCI. "Beside Cabaneros National Park; beautiful views." ♦ € 15.90 (CChq acc)   2005*

HORNOS *4F1* (Rural) **Camping Montillana, 23292 Hornos de Segura (Jaen)** [953-12 61 94] Fr Jaen-Albacete rd N322 take junc E, N of Villanueva del Arzobispo; sp El Tranco; in 26km at El Tranco lake strt on; site in 4.5km. Gradient less steep at 2nd ent. Med, some hdg/mkd, pt sl, terr, pt shd; wc; chem disp; shwrs; el pts (10A) €2.75; gas; lndtte; shop; rest; snacks; bar; pool; lake adj; phone; quiet; some Eng spkn; CCI. "Gd long stay; beautiful area; conv Segura de la Sierra, Cazorla National Park." Holy Week-30 Sep. € 13.95   2002*

HOSPITAL DE ORBIGO *1B3* (S Urban) **Camping Don Suero de Quinones, 24286 Hospital de Orbigo (Leon)** [987-36 10 18; fax 987-38 82 36] N120 rd fr Leon to Astorga, km 30. In Hospital cross rv, turn R thro narr streets; site at exit L in cent narr bdge, sp. Med, hdg pitch, pt shd; wc; shwrs; el pts (6A) €1.50; lndtte; shop; bar; rest adj; BBQ; pool adj; bus to Leon nr; 50% statics; dogs; phone; poss cr; Eng spkn; cc acc; CCI. "Statics v busy w/ends, facs stretched; poss noisy; fair NH; phone ahead to check site open if travelling close to opening/closing dates." ♦ 1 May-30 Sep. € 15.00   2002*

†HOSPITALET DE L'INFANT, L' *3C2* (2km S Coastal) **Camping Cala d'Oques, Via Augusta, 43890 L'Hospitalet de l'Infant (Tarragona)** [977-82 32 54; fax 977-82 06 91; eroller@nil.fut. es; www.fut.es/~eroller/] Exit AP7 junc 38 onto N340. Take rd sp L'Hospitalet de l'Infant at km 1123. Lge, terr, shd; htd wc; mv service pnt; baby facs; shwrs; el pts (5A) €3.45; gas; lndtte; shop; rest; bar; playgrnd; sand/shgl beach adj; entmnt; dogs €2.95; phone; poss cr; quiet; ltd facs low ssn; CCI. "Excel winter NH; sea views." € 30.00   2004*

HOSPITALET DE L'INFANT, L' *3C2* (2km S Coastal) **Camping El Templo del Sol (Naturist), Playa del Torn, 43890 L'Hospitalet de l'Infant (Tarragona)** [977-82 34 34; fax 977-82 34 64; info@eltemplodelsol.com; www.eltemplodelsol. com] Leave A7 at exit 38 or N340 twds town cent. Turn R (S) along coast rd for 2km. Ignore 1st camp sp on L, site 200m further on L. Lge, hdg/mkd pitch, pt sl, pt shd; wc; chem disp; serviced pitch; shwrs inc; el pts (6A) inc; gas; lndtte; ice; shop; rest; snacks; bar; playgrnd; pools; solar-energy park; jacuzzi; official naturist sand/shgl beach adj; cinema/theatre; TV rm; 5% statics; poss cr; Eng spkn; adv bkg (dep); some rlwy noise rear of site; 15% red 14+ days; cc acc. "Excel naturist site; no dogs, radios or TV on pitches; lge private wash/shwr rms; pitches v tight; conv Port Aventura; mosquitoes a problem; poss strong winds - take care with awnings." ♦ 21 Mar-22 Oct. € 41.00   2005*

---

† Site open all year   746   *Tell us about the sites you visit*

†HOSPITALET DE L'INFANT, L' *3C2* (8km S Coastal) **Camping La Masia, Playa de l'Almadrava, Km 1121, N340, 43890 L'Hospitalet de l'Infant (Tarragona)** [977-82 31 02 or 82 05 88; fax 977-82 33 54; info@campinglamasia.com; www.campinglamasia.com] Site sp on sea side of N340 at km 1121. Med, hdstg, sl, terr, pt shd; wc; chem disp (wc); jaccuzi; baby facs; shwrs inc; el pts (5A) inc; lndtte; shop; rest; bar; BBQ; playgrnd; pool; beach adj; gym; sauna; tennis; games area; squash; minigolf; cycle hire; horseriding 5km; golf 6km; entmnt; games/TV rm; internet; 80% statics; phone; poss cr; rlwy noise. "Not rec lge o'fits due poss diff access to pitches; gd long/sh stay." ♦ € 32.35
2004*

HOYOS DEL ESPINO *1D3* (4km E) **Camping Navagredos, Ctra de Valdecasas, 05635 Navarredonda de Gredos (Avila)** [920-20 74 76 or 983-29 58 41; fax 983-29 58 41] Fr N take N502 S. Then W on C500 twd El Barco. Site sp in Navarredonda on L in 2km, just bef petrol station. Med, pt sl, pt shd; wc; chem disp; mv service pnt; shwrs inc; el pts (10A) inc; lndry rm; shops 2km; tradsmn; rest & snacks in ssn; bar; phone; quiet. "Excel walking in Gredos mountains; some facs poorly maintained low ssn; rd app site steep with bends; site open w/ends until mid-Nov." ♦ 1 May-30 Sep. € 16.80
2005*

HOYOS DEL ESPINO *1D3* (1.5km S Rural) **Camping Gredos, Ctra de la Plataforma, Km.1.8, Puente del Duque, 05634 Hoyos del Espino (Avila)** [920-20 75 85; campingredos@camping redos.com; www.campingredos.com] Fr N110 turn E at El Barco onto AV941 for approx 41km; at Hoyos del Espino turn S twd Plataforma de Gredos. Site on R in 1.8km. Or fr N502 turn W dir Parador de Gredos to Hoyos del Espino, then as above. Sm, pt sl, pt shd; wc; chem disp; shwrs inc; el pts €2.90; gas; lndtte; shop 1km; snacks; playgrnd; rv sw adj; cycle hire; horseriding; adv bkg; quiet; CCI. "Lovely mountain scenery." ♦ Holy Week & 1 May-1 Oct. € 12.20
2004*

†HUELVA *2G2* (8km SE Coastal) **Camping Playa de Mazagon, 21130 Mazagon** [959-37 62 08; fax 959-53 62 56] Fr A49 ent Huelva & eventually pick up & foll sp twds indus zone. Head for coast, keep sea on R; over bdge & strt on twds Mazagon; site on R clearly sp off rd up hill. Lge, mkd pitch, pt shd; wc; chem disp; shwrs inc; el pts (10A) €4.07; gas; lndry rm; ice; shop; rest; snacks; bar; playgrnd; pool; sand beach adj; 75% statics; dogs €2; phone; poss cr; quiet; cc acc; red CCI. "Close to Donana National Park; poss exposed low ssn; poss unclean; some pitches v soft; more sites along coast; fair sh stay/NH only." ♦ € 18.00
2003*

HUESCA *3B2* (1.5km SW Urban) **Camping San Jorge, C/ Ricardo del Arco s/n, 22004 Huesca** [tel/fax 974-22 74 16; contacto@camping sanjorge.com; www.campingsanjorge.com] Site sp fr town cent on N123 dir Zaragoza. In municipal sports park, foll sp for pool. Med, shd; wc; chem disp (wc); shwrs inc; el pts (10A) €3.15; lndtte; shop; snacks; bar; 2 pools; dogs; cc acc; CCI. "Shabby site; grassy pitches; san facs run down & stretched; superb pool; friendly; poss probs with hot water; conv town cent." 1 Apr-15 Oct.
€ 14.20
2005*

†IRUN *3A1* (2km N Rural) **Camping Jaizkibel, Ctra Guadalupe Km 22, 20280 Hondarribia (Gipuzkoa)** [943-64 16 79; fax 943-64 26 53] Fr Hondarribia/Fuenterrabia inner ring rd foll sp to site below old town wall. Do not ent town. Med, hdg pitch, pt hdstg, terr, pt shd; wc; shwrs; el pts (2-6A) inc (check earth); lndtte; tradsmn; rest; bar; BBQ; playgrnd; sand beach 1.5km; tennis; 90% statics; no dogs; phone; bus 1km; adv bkg; quiet; red low ssn; cc acc; CCI. "Easy 20 mins walk to historic town; v scenic area; gd walking; gd touring base but ltd space on site for tourers." € 23.50
2005*

†IRUN *3A1* (3km S) **Camping Oliden, Ctra Madrid-Irun, Km 470, 20180 Oiartzun (Gipuzkoa)** [943-49 07 28] On S side of N1 at E end of vill bet km 470. Lge, pt sl, pt shd; wc; chem disp; shwrs; el pts (5A) €3.40; shops adj; bar; playgrnd; pool in ssn; beach 10km; rlwy & factory noise. "Steps to shwrs, diff access for disabled; grass pitches v wet low ssn; poor facs; NH only." € 18.60
2004*

†ISABA *3B1* (13km E Rural) **Camping Zuriza, Ctra Anso-Zuriza, Km 14, 22728 Anso (Huesca)** [974-37 01 96; www.lospirineos.info/camping zuriza] On NA 137 N fr Isaba, turn R 4km onto NA 2000 to Zuriza. Foll sp to site. Fr Anso, take HU 2024 N to Zuriza. Foll sp to site; narr, rough rd not rec for underpowered o'fits. Lge, pt sl, pt shd; wc; some serviced pitches; shwrs inc; el pts €2.70; lndry rm; shop; tradsmn; rest; bar; playgrnd; 50% statics; phone; quiet; cc acc; CCI. "Beautiful, remote valley; no vill at Zuriza, nearest vills Isaba & Anso; no direct route to France; superb location for walking." € 14.80
2005*

ISLA *1A4* (1km NW Coastal) **Camping Playa de Isla, Calle Ardanal 1, 39195 Isla (Cantabria)** [tel/fax 942-67 93 61] Turn off E70/A8 at km 185 Beranga sp Noja & Isla. Foll sp Isla, site well sp in town. App on narr lane for 1km. Med, mkd pitch, terr, pt shd; wc; chem disp; shwrs inc; el pts (6A) inc; gas; lndtte; shop & 1km; snacks; bar; playgrnd; sand beach adj; 30% statics; no dogs; phone; bus 1km; poss cr; quiet; cc acc; CCI. "Beautiful situation; spotless san facs; gd shop; excel long/sh stay." Easter-30 Sep. € 21.00
2003*

†ISLA CRISTINA *2G2* (1.5km E Coastal) Camping Giralda, Ctra La Antilla, Km 1.5, 21410 Isla Cristina [959-34 33 18; fax 959-34 32 84; campinggiralda@infonegocia.com; www.campinggiralda.com] Exit A49 sp Isla Cristina & go thro town heading E (speed bumps in town). Or exit A49 at km 117 sp Lepe. In Lepe turn S on H4116 to La Antilla, then R on coast rd to Isla Cristina & site. V lge, mkd/hdstg/sandy pitches; shd; wc; chem disp; mv service pnt; baby facs; shwrs inc; el pts €3.95; gas; lndtte; shop; rest; snacks; bar; playgrnd; pool high ssn; paddling pool; sand beach nrby; windsurfing; TV rm; 20% statics; dogs €1.50; poss cr; Eng spkn; red long stay/low ssn; cc acc. "V helpful staff; some pitches muddy in wet weather; diff for lge o'fits; gd winter stay." ♦ € 19.00 (CChq acc) 2005*

†ISLA CRISTINA *2G2* (4km E Coastal) Camping Playa Taray, Ctra La Antilla-Isla Cristina, Km 9, 21430 La Redondela (Huelva) [959-34 11 02; fax 959-34 11 96; www.campingtaray.com] Fr W exit A49 sp Isla Cristina & go thro town heading E. Fr E exit A49 at km 117 sp Lepe. In Lepe turn S on H4116 to La Antilla, then R on coast rd to Isla Cristina & site. Lge, pt shd; wc; shwrs; el pts €3.50; gas; lndry rm; shop; bar; rest; playrnd; sand beach adj; some statics; phone; dogs; bus; quiet; cc acc; red long stay/low ssn; CCI. "Gd birdwatching, cycling; less cr than other sites in area in winter; poss untidy low ssn & ltd facs; poss diff for lge o'fits; friendly, helpful owner." ♦ € 18.20 2005*

†ISLA CRISTINA *2G2* (7km E Coastal) Camping Luz, Ctra La Antilla-Isla Cristina, Km 5, 21410 Isla Cristina (Huelva) [959-34 11 42; fax 059-48 64 54] Fr W exit A49 sp Isla Cristina & go thro town heading E. Fr E exit A49 at km 117 sp Lepe. In Lepe turn S on H4116 to La Antilla, then R on coast rd to Isla Cristina & site. Med, pt sl, pt shd; wc; shwrs inc; el pts (5A) €4; gas; lndtte; shop & 3km; tradsmn; rest; snacks; bar; BBQ; playgrnd; pool; beach 200m; 40% statics; dogs; phone; bus 50m; poss cr; rd noise/noisy at w/e; red long stay; CCI. "V friendly staff, well-managed; vg shwrs; ltd facs low ssn; uneven pitches; poss diff for lge o'fits." € 31.20 2005*

ISLA PLANA see Puerto de Mazarron *4G1*

ISLARES see Orinon *1A4*

ITZIAR see Deba *3A1*

JARANDILLA DE LA VERA *1D3* (2km W Rural) Camping Yuste, N501, Km 47, 10440 Aldeaneuva de la Vera (Caceres) [927-57 26 59] Fr Plasencia head E on EX203 following sp for Parador, site at km stone 47 in Aldeaneuva de la Vera. Clearly sp down narr rd. Med, shd; wc; shwrs; el pts €2.57; gas; snacks; bar; pool; tennis; phone; quiet. "Most attractive in mountain country." 1 Apr-30 Sep. € 12.20 2002*

JARANDILLA DE LA VERA *1D3* (1km NW Urban) Camping Jaranda, Ctra EX 203, Km 47, 10450 Jarandilla de la Vera (Caceres) [927-56 04 54; fax 927-56 05 87; campingjaranda@eresmas.com] Site sp. Med, pt sl, terr, shd; wc; chem disp; mv service pnt; baby facs; shwrs; el pts (5A) €3.60; gas; lndtte; ice; shop; rest; snacks; bar; playgrnd; pool; paddling pool; games area; cycle hire; 30% statics; dogs €1.60; poss cr; adv bkg; quiet; cc acc. ♦ 15 Mar-15 Sep. € 14.50 2005*

†JAVEA/XABIA *4E2* (1km S) Camping Javea, Ctra Cabo de la Nao, Km 1, 03730 Javea (Alicante) [965-79 10 70; fax 966-46 05 07; info@camping-javea.com; www.camping-javea.com] Exit N332 for Javea on A132, cont in dir Port on CV734. At rndabt & Lidl supmkt, turn R sp Arenal Platges & Cap de la Nau. Strt on at next rndabt to site sp & slip rd 100m sp Autocine. If you miss slip rd go back fr next rndabt. Lge, mkd pitch, pt shd; wc; chem disp; baby facs; shwrs inc; el pts (8A) €3.10 (long lead rec); gas; lndtte; ice; shop 1km; tradsmn; rest; snacks; bar; BBQ; playgrnd; pool; paddling pool; sand beach 1.5km; games area; 15% statics; dogs €2; adv bkg; quiet; cc acc; red low ssn/long stay; cc acc; red long stay; CCI. "Excel site; lge pitches; mountain views; helpful staff." € 21.50 2005*

See advertisement above

†JAVEA/XABIA *4E2* (3km S Coastal) **Camping El Naranjal, Ctra Cabo de la Nao, Ptda dels Morers 15, 03730 Javea (Alicante)** [965-79 29 89; fax 966-46 02 56; naranjal@teleline.es; www.campingelnaranjal.com] Exit A7 junc 62 or 63 onto N332 Valencia/Alicante rd. Exit at Gata de Corgos to Javea. Foll sp Camping Javea/Camping El Naranjal. Access rd by tennis club, foll sp. Lge, mkd pitch, hdstg, pt shd; wc; chem disp; shwrs inc; el pts (10A) €3.15 (poss rev pol); gas; lndtte; ice; shop & 1km; rest; snacks; bar; shop; playgrnd; pool inc; paddling pool; sand beach 300m; tennis 300m; cycle hire; golf 3km; entmnt; 25% statics; dogs; phone; bus 500m; adv bkg; Eng spkn; quiet; red long stay/low ssn; CCI. "Gd scenery & beach; pitches poss tight lge o'fits; c'van storage; excel rest; rec." ♦ € 22.25   2005*

See advertisement above

†JIMENA DE LA FRONTERA *2H3* (NW Rural) **Camping Los Alcornocales, Ctra CC3331/A369, 11330 Jimena de la Frontera (Cadiz)** [956-64 00 60; fax 956-64 12 90; alcornocales@terra.es] Site sp fr A369 Ronda to Algeciras rd. Rec app fr N onto C3331, turn L at camping sp at top of bank, site on R in 100m. Do not enter Jimena - narr rds. Med, hdg/mkd pitch, pt sl, terr, shd; wc; chem disp; shwrs inc; el pts €3.37; gas; lndtte; shop; rest; bar; cycle hire; 90% statics; dogs; phone; adv bkg; quiet; cc acc; red CCI. "Conv Gibraltar; wonderful flora, fauna & scenery in National Park; excursions arranged; v friendly owner; 5 mins walk fr attractive hill town; poss unkempt & ltd facs low ssn; unsuitable lge o'fits." ♦ ltd. € 16.80   2005*

LABUERDA see Ainsa *3B2*

LAREDO *1A4* (Urban/Coastal) **Camping Carlos V, Travacia Derechos Humanos s/n, 39770 Laredo (Cantabria)** [942-60 55 93] Leave A8 at Junc to Laredo, foll yellow camping sp, site on W side of town. Med, mkd pitch, pt shd; wc; mv service pnt; baby facs; shwrs inc; el pts inc; gas; lndry rm; shop & 100m; rest; bar; sand beach 200m; poss cr; noisy; CCI. "Well sheltered & lively resort during sh ssn; fair sh stay." Holy Week & 6 May-15 Sep. € 22.50   2003*

LAREDO *1A4* (W Coastal) **Camping Laredo, Ctra Rep. de Filipinas s/n, 39770 Laredo (Cantabria)** [942-60 50 35; fax 942-61 31 80] Fr A8 exit junc 172 sp Laredo; cont N at rndabt into Laredo Playa, L at traff lts & foll site sp. Lge, mkd pitch, pt shd; wc; chem disp; mv service pnt; shwrs; el pts (5A) €2.25; gas; lndtte; shop (high ssn) snacks; bar; pool; playgrnd; sand beach 500m; TV; cycle hire; horseriding; phone; 20% statics; no dogs; poss cr; noisy; adv bkg; 10% red CCI. 1 Jun-15 Sep. € 17.44   2002*

> Some of these sites have changed their opening dates - we'd better fill in some site report forms and let the editor of the guide know.

LAREDO *1A4* (2km W Coastal) **Camping Playa del Regaton, El Sable 8, 39770 Laredo (Cantabria)** [tel/fax 942-60 69 95] Fr W leave A8 junc 172, under m'way to rndabt & take exit sp Calle Rep Colombia. In 800m turn L at traff lts, in further 800m turn L onto tarmac rd to end, passing other sites. Fr E leave at junc 172, at 1st rndabt take 2nd exit sp Centro Commercial N634 Colindres. At next rndabt take exit C/Rep Colombia, then as above. Lge, mkd pitch; pt shd; wc; chem disp; mv service pnt; shwrs inc; el pts (2A) inc; gas; lndtte; shop; rest; bar; sand beach adj; 75% statics; Eng spkn; adv bkg; quiet; cc not acc; red long stay/CCI. "Clean site by beach; sep area for tourers; horseriding nrby; wash up facs every pitch." ♦ Easter-25 Sep. € 17.60   2005*

LASPAULES *3B2* **Camping Laspaules, Ctra N260, Km 369, 22471 Laspaules (Huesca)** [974-55 33 20; camping@laspaules.com] Approx 20km NW Pont de Suert, in cent of vill adj rv. Med, pt shd; wc; baby facs; shwrs; el pts (6A) €4.12; gas; lndry rm; shop & in vill; tradsmn; snacks; bar; snacks; playgrnd; pool; paddling pool; TV; quiet; cc acc; CCI. "V pleasant; pitches well back fr rd." 1 Jun-30 Sep. € 13.30   2003*

SPAIN

†LEKEITIO 3A1 (3km S Coastal) **Camping Leagi, Calle Leagi s/n, 48289 Mendexa (Vizcaya) [tel/fax 946-84 23 52; leagi@campingleagi.com; www.campingleagi.com]** Foll N634 go twds Lekeitio. At x-rds in cent of town turn dir of church, clearly visible after x-ing bridge; turn R uphill. Site in 1km, v steep with hairpin bends. Steep tarmac ent to site. Med, mkd pitch, pt sl, unshd; wc; chem disp; mv service pnt; serviced pitch; shwrs inc; el pts (5A) €3.20 (rev pol); lndtte; shop; rest; snacks; bar; playgrnd; sand beach 1km; poss cr; quiet; cc acc; CCI. "Ltd facs low ssn; dogs roam (& foul) site Aug 05); beautiful scenery; excel local beach; lovely town; gd views; gd walking." € 21.20   2005*

LEKUNBERRI 3A1 (500m SE) **Aralar Camping, Plazaola 9, 31870 Lekunberri (Navarra) [tel/fax 948-50 40 11 or 948-50 40 49; info@campingaralar.com; www.campingaralar.com]** Exit fr AP15 at junc 124 dir Lukunberri & foll sp for site. Site on R after v sharp downhill turn. Med, all hdstg, pt sl, terr, pt shd; htd wc; chem disp; shwrs inc; el pts (5A) inc; gas; lndtte; shop; rest; snacks; bar; playgrnd; pool; cycle hire; horseriding; TV; dogs €2; 70% statics; phone; some Eng spkn; quiet; cc acc. "Beautiful scenery & mountain walks; only 14 touring pitches; v pleasantly arranged site; avoid Pamplona mid-Aug during bull-run; site also open at w/e & long w/e all year except Jan/Feb; gd sh stay/NH." 1 Jun-30 Sep. € 18.50   2004*

LEON 1B3 (5km SE Rural) **Camping Ciudad de Leon, 24195 Golpejar de la Sobarriba [987-26 90 86; fax 987-21 47 98]** SE fr Leon on N601 twds Valladolid, L at top of hill & foll site sp Golpejar o Sobarriba. Sm, pt sl, shd; wc; chem disp; shwrs inc; el pts inc (4A) €2.50; gas; lndry rm; shop; rest; snacks; bar; playgrnd; pool; paddling pool; tennis; cycle hire; bus 200m; quiet; adv bkg; poss cr; Eng spkn; CCI. "Excel welcome; helpful staff; easy access to beautiful city; clean, pleasant site; access some pitches poss diff." ♦ 1 Jun-20 Sep. € 14.50   2005*

LEON 1B3 (14km SE Rural) **Camp Municipal Esla, N-601, Km 310, 24210 Mansilla de las Mulas (Leon) [987-31 00 89; fax 987-31 18 10; aytomansilla@infonegocio.com]** N601 SE fr Leon, turn W onto N625 twd Mansilla. In 200m, turn L onto slip rd sp to site. Site in 1km. Heading N on N601 twd Leon, exit junc 21 sp Leon. Turn L into Mansilla & drive thro town. Site sp on R immed after bdge. Med, pt shd; wc; chem disp; shwrs inc; el pts inc; bar; playgrnd; rv sw nrby; adv bkg; quiet; CCI. "Gd base for Leon; conv Mansilla; vg all stays." 29 Jun-1 Sep. € 17.00   2003*

LEON 1B3 (12km SW Urban) **Camping Camino de Santiago, Ctra N120, Km 324.4, 24392 Villadangos del Paramo (Leon) [tel/fax 987-68 02 53]** Access fr N120 to W of vill, site sp. Ent concealed fr E. Lge, mkd pitch, pt shd; wc; chem disp; shwrs inc; el pts €3.10; gas; lndtte; shop; rest; snacks; bar; pool; 50% statics; phone; bus 1km; poss cr; adv bkg; rd noise; cc acc; 10% red 15+ days; CCI. "Conv for Leon; poss no hot water low ssn; pleasant, helpful staff; mosquitoes; vill church worth visit; gd NH." ♦ Easter-30 Sep. € 14.00   2005*

LERIDA/LLEIDA 3C2 (11km NE) **Camping Raco d'en Pep, Ctra Puigcerda Km 8.3, 25690 Vilanova de la Barca [973-19 00 47; fax 973-21 20 80]** Around Lleida on N11 a'via, exit 467 onto C13 heading NE for 8km, site on L of rd nr vill, immed after rlwy/rv bdge. Med, hdstg pitch (some hdg), gravel, pt shd; wc; own san; shwrs inc; el pts inc (poss no earth); gas; lndtte; rest; snacks; bar; playgrnd; pool; entmnt; phone; poss cr; noisy entmnt at w/e; cc acc; CCI. "Pleasant, well-kept site; gd pitches; ltd facs low ssn; gd pool; easy access Lleida; pleasant cycling thro fruit area; care req by lge o'fits due to low trees; site reported unkempt & used by workers Jun 05." Holy Week-30 Sep. € 19.00   2005*

†LINEA DE LA CONCEPCION, LA *2H3* (S Urban/Coastal) **Camping Sureuropa, Camino de Sobrevela s/n, 11300 La Linea de la Concepcion (Cadiz) [956-64 35 87; fax 956-64 30 59; sur-europa@hotmail.com]** Fr S on E5/N340 onto N351 coast rd. Just bef Gibraltar turn R up lane, in 200m turn L into site. Fr N on AP7, exit junc 124 onto A383 dir La Linea; foll sp Santa Margarita & site. Med, hdg/mkd pitch, hdstg, pt shd; wc; chem disp (wc); shwrs inc; el pts €2.50; lndtte; bar; sand beach 500m; sports club adj; phone; bus 1.5km; poss cr; Eng spkn; adv bkg; quiet; CCI. "Clean, flat, pretty site (gd for disabled); vg san facs; ideal for Gibraltar 4km." ♦ € 11.00   2005*

> Will you fill in the site report forms at the back of the guide, or shall I?

LLAFRANC see Palafrugell *3B3*

†**LLANCA** *3B3* (500m N Coastal) **Camping L'Ombra, Ctra Bisbal-Portbou, Km 13, 17490 Llanca (Gerona) [tel/fax 972-12 02 61; lombra@lycos.com]** Fr Figueres on N260 dir Portbou, site on L 500m N of traff lts at Llanca turn off. Med, mkd pitch, pt sl, pt shd; wc; chem disp; shwrs inc; el pts €4; lndtte; shop; supmkt 1km; bar; playgrnd; beach 1km; 75% statics; train 1km; quiet; red low ssn. "Useful winter base for coastal towns when other sites clsd; fair sh stay." € 28.45   2004*

LLANCA *3B3* (2km N Coastal) **Camping Garbet, 17469 Colera (Gerona) [972-38 90 01; fax 972-12 80 59]** On L of main rd fr Portbou to Cadaques (narr, twisting rd) 2km after vill of Colera. Easier app fr Llanca dir Portbou, site on R 2m bef Colera. Site easily seen on beach. Med, hdstg, pt shd; wc; shwrs; el pts €3.20; gas; lndtte; ice; shop; rest; snacks; bar; shgl beach; TV; rlwy stn 100m; poss cr; adv bkg; quiet but rd & rlwy noise; cc acc. "Situated in v sheltered bay; fishing, boating & historical attractions." 1 Apr-15 Oct. € 20.00   2005*

LLANCA *3B3* (4km N Coastal) **Camping Caravaning Sant Miquel, 17469 Colera (Gerona) [tel/fax 972-38 90 18; info@campingsantmiquel. com; www.campingsantmiquel.com]** Take main rd fr Portbou to Cadaques. After 7km turn L into Colera vill, then 1st R over bdge, turn L into site in 200m, well sp. Lge, mkd pitch, pt shd; wc; chem disp; shwrs inc; el pts (6-10A) €4.25; gas; lndtte; ice; shop; rest; snacks; bar; playgrnd; htd pool; shgl beach 1km; watersports; diving; cycle hire; entmnt; TV rm; 10% statics; dogs €2; poss cr; Eng spkn; adv bkg; quiet; cc acc; CCI. "Friendly site; gd rest & pool; v cr high ssn with students; conv local fishing ports & Dali Museum." ♦ 1 Mar-30 Sep. € 21.10 (CChq acc)   2005*

LLANES *1A4* (10km E Coastal) **Camping La Paz, Ctra N634, Km 292, 33597 Playa de Vidiago (Asturias) [985-41 10 12; fax 985-41 12 35; delfin@campinglapaz.com; www.campinglapaz.com]** Take N634/E70 fr Unquera to Ribadesella. Turn R at sp to site bet km stones 292 & km 293 bef Vidiago. Site access via narr 1km lane. Stop bef bdge & park on R, staff will tow to pitch. Narr site ent & steep to pitches. If coming fr Santander, foll Way Out/Salida to m'way A67 for Terrelavega. Lge, mkd pitch, terr, shd; wc; chem disp; mv service pnt; baby facs; shwrs inc; el pts (9A) €3.15 (poss rev pol); gas; lndtte; ice; shop; rest; bar; BBQ; sand beach adj; playgrnd; fishing; watersports; horseriding; mountain sports; no statics; dogs €2.15; phone; poss cr w/e; Eng spkn; adv bkg; quiet; cc acc; CCI. "Steep hill fr recep to pitches, free Landrover tow to pitch; excel views; superb beaches in area; exceptionally helpful owner & staff; excel." ♦ Easter-31 Oct. € 19.75   2005*

See advertisement

LLANES *1A4* (5km W Coastal) **Camping Playa de Troenzo, Ctra de Celerio-Barro, 33595 Llanes (Asturias) [985-40 16 72; fax 985-74 07 23; troenzo@telepolis.com]** Fr E take E70/A8 past Llanes & exit at junc 307 to Celorio. At T-junc with AS263 turn L dir Celorio & Llanes. Turn L on N9 (Celorio) thro vill & foll sp to Barro. Site on R after 500m (after Maria Elena site). Lge, terr, pt shd; wc; chem disp; shwrs inc; el pts (6A) €3; gas; lndtte; shop; rest; snacks; bar; playgrnd; sand beach adj; 75% statics; dogs; phone; poss cr; Eng spkn; adv bkg; CCI. "Lovely, old town; for pitches with sea views go thro statics to end of site; gd rests in town; nr harbour." 15 Feb-15 Dec. € 17.60   2004*

LLAVORSI *3B2* (3km N Rural) **Camping Riberies, Ctra Vall d'Arau 55, 25595 Llavorsi (Lleida) [973-62 21 51; fax 973-62 20 02]** On C147 3km N of Llavorsi. Fr S site is immed bef rv bdge on ent Riberies. Med, shd; wc; shwrs; el pts €3.20; shop in vill; rest adj; bar; phone; kayaking; rafting; quiet but some rd noise; Eng spkn. 1 Apr-15 Sep. € 16.00   2002*

†**LLAVORSI** *3B2* (9km N Rural) **Camping La Borda del Pubill, Ctra de Tavescan, Km 9.5, 25570 Ribera de Cardos (Lleida) [973-62 30 80; fax 973-62 30 28; info@campinglabordadelpubill. com; www.campinglabordadelpubill.com]** Fr France on A64 exit junc 17 at Montrejeau & head twd Spanish border. At Vielha turn E onto C28/C1412 to Llavorsi, then L504 to Ribera. Fr S take N260 fr Tremp to Llavorsi, then L504 to site. Lge, pt shd; htd wc; baby facs; shwrs; el pts €3.75; gas; lndtte; shop, rest high ssn; snacks; bar; playgrnd; htd pool; paddling pool; rv sw & fishing; kayaking; trekking; adventure sports; quad bike hire; horseriding; skiing 30km; games area; games rm; TV; 10% statics; dogs €3; phone; car wash; adv bkg; quiet; cc acc. "In beautiful area; excel walking; gd rest." ♦ € 21.70 (CChq acc)   2005*

LLORET DE MAR *3B3* (1km S Coastal) **Camping Tucan**, Ctra Blanes-Lloret, 17310 Lloret de Mar (Gerona) [972-36 99 65; fax 972-36 00 79; info@campingtucan.com; www.campingtucan.com] Fr N exit AP7 junc 8 & take 2nd exit on R sp Lloret de Mar. At x-rds foll sp Blanes, site on R. Fr S take last exit fr C32 & foll sp Lloret de Mar, site on L, sp. Lge, mkd pitch, terr, shd; wc; chem disp; shwrs inc; el pts (3A) €3.20; gas; lndtte; ice; shop; rest; snacks; bar; BBQ; playgrnd; pool; paddling pool; sand beach 600m; games area; golf 500m; entmnt; internet; TV rm; 25% statics; dogs €1.60; phone; bus; car wash; Eng spkn; adv bkg; quiet; cc acc; red long stay/snr citizens/CCI. "Well-appointed site; friendly staff." ♦ 1 Apr-24 Sep. € 23.80   2004*

†**LLORET DE MAR** *3B3* (1km SW Coastal) **Camping Santa Elena Ciutat**, Ctra Blanes/Lloret, 17310 Lloret de Mar (Gerona) [972-36 40 09; fax 972-36 79 54; santaelena@betsa.es] Exit A7 junc 9 dir Lloret. In Lloret take Blanes rd, site sp at km 10.5 on rd GI 682. V lge, pt sl; wc; baby facs; shwrs; el pts €3.50; gas; lndtte; shop; rest; snacks; bar; playgrnd; pool; shgl beach 800m; games area; phone; cash machine; poss cr; Eng spkn; noisy disco & traffic on adj main rd; red facs low ssn; CCI. "Ideal for teenagers; vg long stay." ♦ € 29.50   2004*

†**LOGRONO** *3B1* (500m N Urban) **Camping La Playa**, Avda de la Playa s/n, 26006 Logrono (La Rioja) [tel/fax 941-25 22 53; info@campinglaplaya.com; www.campinglaplaya.com] N of Rv Ebro. Leave city by bdge 'Puente de Piedra', then turn L at traff lts. Site well sp in town & fr N111, adj sports cent Las Novias. Avoid old bdge as weight limit poss a prob for lge o'fits. Med, hdg pitch, shd; wc; shwrs inc; el pts (5A) €3; gas; lndtte; ice; shop; snacks, bar in ssn; playgrnd; pool; rv sw adj; tennis; 10% statics; red CCI. "Sh walk to town cent; vg." € 19.80   2005*

†**LOGRONO** *3B1* (10km W) **Camping Navarrete**, Ctra La Navarrete-Entrena, Km I.5, 26370 Navarrete (La Rioja) [941-44 01 69; fax 941-44 06 39] Fr AP68 exit junc 11, at end slip rd turn L. At x-rds in Navarette, go strt over into town (site sp), turn R for site & R again onto LR137 sp Entrena. Site 1km on R. Lge, mkd pitch, pt shd; wc; chem disp; mv service pnt; baby facs; shwrs inc; el pts (5A) €3.30; gas; lndtte; shop; snacks; bar; BBQ; playgrnd; pool & paddling pool; tennis; horseriding; car wash; 95% statics; no dogs; site clsd 10 Dec-7 Jan; Eng spkn; noisy at w/e; cc acc; red low ssn/long stay. "Professionally run, v clean & tidy site; excel san facs; helpful staff; some sm pitches; local wine sold at recep; Bilbao ferry 2 hrs via m'way; interesting area." € 18.80   2005*

LORCA *4G1* (8km W Rural) **Camping La Torrecilla**, Ctra de Granada, 30817 Lorca (Murcia) [tel/fax 968-44 21 96] Leave N340/E15 at junc 585. In 1km turn L, site well sp. Med, mkd pitch, hdstg, pt sl, pt shd; htd wc; chem disp; mv service pnt; shwrs inc; el pts (6A) €3; gas; lndtte; shop 2km; tradsmn; rest; snacks; bar; playgrnd; pool; tennis; games area; TV rm; 5% statics; dogs; phone; bus 1km; poss cr; Eng spkn; quiet; cc acc; red long stay. "Friendly, helpful staff; excel pool; vg san facs." ♦ 11 May-31 Dec. € 12.00   2005*

LOREDO see Santander *1A4*

†**LUARCA** *1A3* (1km NE Coastal) **Camping Los Cantiles**, Ctra N634, km.502.7, 33700 Luarca (Asturias) [tel/fax 985-64 09 38] Fr E leave N632 sp Luarca onto N634 S, then take exit to Barcia/Almuna onto rd 754 to sea; site sp. Not rec to ent town fr W. Cont on N634/N632 to exit for Oviedo (N634) then take exit to Barcia/Almuna, then as for app fr E. Med, hdg pitch, pt shd; wc; chem disp; baby facs; shwrs inc; el pts inc (3-6A) €2.55; gas; lndtte; shop; tradsmn; rest high ssn; snacks; bar; pool 300m; shgl beach at foot of cliff; phone; poss cr; Eng spkn; adv bkg; quiet; 10% red long stay; CCI. "Beautiful, clean, guarded site on cliff top; superb views; friendly owner; facs ltd low ssn; some narr site rds; acc to beach diff due to steep climb down, but beach in next bay full rock pools; go E down concreted track." ♦ € 16.20   2005*

†**LUARCA** *1A3* (12km E Rural/Coastal) **Camping La Regalina**, Ctra de la Playa s/n, 33788 Cadavedo (Asturias) [985-64 50 56; fax 985-64 50 14; info@laregalina.com] Fr N632 dir Cadavedo, site sp. Med, pt shd; wc; chem disp; shwrs inc; el pts (5-8A) inc; gas; shop; rest; snacks; bar; pool; beach 1km; TV; 10% statics; phone; bus 600m; adv bkg; quiet; cc acc high ssn; red long stay. "Attractive mountain scenery by coast; pretty vill; ltd facs low ssn & some in need of renovation; gd." € 17.20   2005*

LUARCA *1A3* (2km W Coastal) **Camping Playa de Tauran**, 33700 Luarca (Asturias) [tel/fax 985-64 12 72] Fr Luarca, take N634 W & turn R at rndabt, sp El Chano. If missed, another sp in 1km. Cont 3.5km on long, narr, rough access rd. Rd thro Luarca unsuitable for c'vans. Med, some hdg pitch, pt sl, pt shd; wc; chem disp; baby facs; shwrs inc; el pts (5A) €2.50; gas; ice; lndtte; shop; tradsmn; rest; snacks; bar; BBQ; paddling pool; shgl beach 200m; sand beach 2km; cycle hire; phone; dogs €1; quiet; red long stays; CCI. "Superb sea views & mountain views; off beaten track; conv fishing & hill vills; excel; v peaceful, restful, attractive, well-kept site." 1 Apr-30 Sep. € 14.00   2003*

LUMBIER *3B1* (Rural) **Camping Iturbero, Termino de Iturbero s/n, 31440 Lumbier (Navarra)** [948-88 04 05; fax 948-88 04 14] SE fr Pamplona on N240 twds Yesa Reservoir. In 30km L on NA150 twds Lumbier. In 3.5km immed bef Lumbier turn R at rndabt then over single track bdge, 1st L to site. Well sp fr N240. Med, hdg/mkd pitch, some hdstg, pt shd; wc; chem disp; mv service pnt; shwrs inc; el pts (4A) €4; gas; lndtte; ice; shop 1km; rest; snacks; bar; BBQ; playgrnd; pool 100m; tennis; hang-gliding; 25% statics; dogs €2; bus 1km; quiet; CCI. "Beautiful, well-kept site; excel touring base; eagles & vultures in gorge & seen fr site; v helpful staff, little Eng spkn but lge selection of guides in Eng avail; Lumbier lovely sm town." 19 Feb-18 Dec. € 17.00
2005*

†**MADRID** *1D4* (8km NE) **Camping Osuna, Ruta el Aeropuerto (N11), Km 8, Avda de Logrono s/n, 28042 Madrid** [917-41 05 10; fax 913-20 63 65] Fr M40, travelling S clockwise (anti-clockwise fr N or E) exit junc 8 at Canillejas sp 'Avda de Logrono'. Turn L under m'way, then R under rlwy, immed after turn R at traff lts. Site on L corner - white painted wall. Travelling N, leave M40 at junc 7 (no turn off at junc 8) sp Avda 25 Sep, U-turn at km 7, head S to junc 8, then as above. Med, hdg/mkd pitch, pt sl, pt shd; wc; chem disp; shwrs inc; el pts (5A) €4.50 (long lead rec); lndtte; shop 600m; playgrnd; metro to town 600m; 10% statics; phone; poss cr; rd & aircraft noise; Eng spkn; red low ssn; CCI. "Sm pitches poss diff lge o'fits; helpful staff; conv city cent; clean site but poss neglected low ssn & facs tired." ♦ ltd. € 25.00
2005*

†**MADRID** *1D4* (13km S Urban) **Camping Alpha, Ctrade Andalucía, Km 12.4 (NIV), 28906 Getafe (Madrid)** [916-95 80 69; fax 916-83 16 59] Fr S on A4/E5 twd Madrid, leave at km 12.4 to W dir Ocana & foll sp. Fr N on A4/E5 exit at km 13b to change dir back onto A4, then exit 12b sp 'Pol. Ind. Los Olivos' to site. Lge, hdstg, hdg pitch, pt shd; wc; chem disp; mv service pnt; shwrs inc; el pts (15A) €5.40; ice; lndtte; shop; rest; snacks; bar; playgrnd; pool (caps ess) high ssn; tennis; games area; 20% statics; dogs; phone; poss cr; Eng spkn; adv bkg; cc acc; 10% red CCI. "Lorry depot adj; poss vehicle movements 24 hrs, minimal noise; bus & metro to Madrid 30-40 mins; sm pitches poss tight for space; clean facs but ltd hot water low ssn; v helpful staff; NH only." € 24.00
2005*

†**MADRIGAL DE LA VERA** *1D3* (500m E Rural) **Camping Alardos, Ctra Madrigal-Candeleda, 10480 Madrigal de la Vera (Caceres)** [tel/fax 927-56 50 66; mirceavd@hotmail.com] Fr Jarandilla take EX203 E to Madrigal. Site sp in vill nr rv bdge. Med, mkd pitch, pt shd; wc; chem disp; shwrs inc; el pts (6-10A) €3; ice; lndtte; shop & 1km; rest; snacks; bar; BBQ; playgrnd; pool; rv sw adj; TV; 10% statics; no dogs; phone; poss cr Jul/Aug; Eng spkn; adv bkg; cc not acc. "Friendly owners; superb site; ltd facs low ssn; beautiful scenery; excel touring area; ancient Celtic settlement at El Raso 5km." € 16.00
2005*

MAGDALENA, LA *1B3* (9km SE Rural) **Camping Astur-Leones, 24276 Santibanez de Ordas (Leon)** [987-59 02 12] Exit AP66 at La Magdalena. At ent to town turn sharp L (S) on LE420 (sp 'Hospital de Orbigo'). After 7km in Rioseco de Tapia turn W & site sp at far end of Santibanez. Sm, sl, shd; wc; chem disp; shwrs; el pts (10A) €1.71; gas; lndtte; shop; bar; playgrnd; pool; TV; phone; poss cr; quiet. ♦ ltd. 10 Jun-8 Sep. € 9.40
2003*

Mustn't forget to post our site report forms to The Club, otherwise sites might be deleted.

MAGDALENA, LA *1B3* (10km NW Rural) **Camping Mirantes de Luna, 24147 Mirantes de Luna (Leon)** [987-58 13 03 or 646-90 55 75; fax 987-25 26 60] Fr N take Villablino exit off AP66 & foll C623 & camping sp for 10km around E side of lake twds La Magdalena. Sm, mkd pitch, terr, pt shd; wc; chem disp; shwrs; el pts €2.10; gas; lndtte; rest; bar; playgrnd; phone; quiet; CCI. "Pleasant, friendly site; conv for caves at Valporquero; helpful owner with gd knowledge of area." 15 Jun-15 Sep. € 13.00
2004*

†**MALGRAT DE MAR** *3C3* (500m SW Coastal) **Camping Bon Repos, Pg Maritim s/n, 08398 Santa Susanna (Barcelona)** [937-67 84 75; fax 937-76 85 26; info@campingbonrepos.com; www.campingbonrepos.com] App fr Gerona on rd N11, site sp. Track leaves on L of N11; foll camp sp for 680m & turn R at sea-front T-junc. Cont thro Santa Susanna, down underpass & turn L in middle, rough app rd to site on beach behind rlwy stn; sp. V lge, shd; wc; chem disp; baby facs; shwrs inc; el pts (5A) €6; gas; lndtte; supmkt; rest; bar; playgrnd; 2 pools; beach adj; watersports; tennis; entmnt; 10% statics; dogs €2.50; poss cr; poss noisy; red low ssn; cc acc. "Conv rlwy stn - trains to Barcelona; site has pitches next to sea with el pts; vg." ♦ € 28.60
2005*

†**MAMOLA, LA** *2H4* (500m Coastal) **Camping Castillo de Banos, 18750 La Mamola (Granada)** [958-82 95 28; fax 958-82 97 68; info@campingcastillo.com; www.campingcastillo.com] On N340/A7 site sp at km 360, 500m fr vill of Castillo de Banos. Lge, mkd pitch, hdstg, pt shd; wc; chem disp; mv service pnt; shwrs inc; el pts (5A) €2.80; gas; lndtte; shop; tradsmn; rest; snacks; bar; playgrnd; pool; private shgl beach adj; fishing; cycle hire; entmnt; internet; dogs; adv bkg; quiet; cc acc; quiet; red CCI. ♦ € 19.00 (CChq acc)
2005*

†MANGA DEL MAR MENOR, LA *4G2* (2km W
Coastal) **Camping La Manga, Ctra El Algar/Cabo
de Palos, Km 12, 30370 La Manga del Mar Menor
(Murcia) [968-56 30 14 or 56 30 19; fax
968-56 34 26; lamanga@caravaning.es; www.
caravaning.es]** Leave autovia MU312 at junc 15
sp Playa Honda; site sp fr La Manga. Ent visible
beside dual c'way with flags flying. V lge, hdg/mkd
pitch, hdstg, pt shd; wc; chem disp; mv service pnt;
sauna; serviced pitches; shwrs inc; el pts (10A) inc;
gas; lndtte; ice; supmkt; rest; snacks; bar; BBQ;
playgrnd; 2 pools - 1 htd, covrd Oct-Mar (caps ess);
paddling pool; sand beach adj; fishing; windsurfing;
jacuzzi, gym (Oct-Mar); tennis; open-air cinema high
ssn; mini-golf; games rm; internet; cab TV/TV rm;
30% statics; dogs €1; phone; recep 0700-2300;
poss cr; Eng spkn; adv bkg ess (dep req & bkg fee);
cc acc; red long stay/low ssn; CCI. "Gd,
well-maintained, winter site; Mar Menor shallow &
warm lagoon; gd for families; 2 pitch sizes - sm ones
unsuitable o'fits over 5m; some narr site rds & trees;
additional area for m'vans; regional park 5km; gd
walking; mountain biking; bird sanctuary; excel
beaches; many dogs on site; poss lge rallies on site
Dec-Mar; conv Roman ruins Cartagena, Murcia,
Alicante; excel." ♦ ltd. € 25.50 (CChq acc)
ABS - E16   2005*

See advertisement

†MANZANARES EL REAL *1D4* (8km NE Rural)
**Camping La Fresneda, Ctra 608, Km 19.5, 28791
Soto del Real (Madrid) [tel/fax 918-47 65 23]**
Fr AP6/NV1 turn NE at Collado-Villalba onto M608
to Cerceda & Manzanares el Real. Foll rd round lake
to Soto del Real, site sp at km 19.5. Med, shd; wc;
chem disp; baby facs; shwrs €0.15; el pts (4-8A)
inc; gas; lndtte; shop; snacks; bar; playgrnd; pool;
tennis; phone; quiet; cc acc. ♦ € 28.00   2004*

†MANZANARES EL REAL *1D4* (3km NW Rural)
**Camping El Ortigal, Montaneros 19, La Pedriza,
28410 Manzanares el Real (Madrid) [918-53 01 20]**
Fr AP6/NV1 turn NE at Collado- Villalba onto M608
to Cerceda & Manzanares el Real. In 6km take L sp
to Manzanares, cross rv & immed L. Sp at this junc;
site further 3km on poor rd. Not many sp to site or
Pedriza. Lge, pt sl; wc; shwrs; el pts (10A) €3.85;
gas; shop; rest; bar; playgrnd; 99% statics/chalets;
phone; red low ssn. "Attractive country & views;
excel walking in adj sm National Park - narr
mountain tracks; old castle in Manzanares; sm area
for tourers; arr early to ensure pitch; warm welcome;
ltd facs low ssn." ♦ ltd. € 25.70   2004*

†MANZANERA *3D2* (1km NE Rural) **Camping Villa
de Manzanera, Partida Las Bateas s/n, Ctra 1514,
Km 10.5, 44420 Manzanera (Teruel) [978-78 17 48
or 978-78 19 21; fax 978-78 17 09]** Fr N234 Teruel-
Sagunto at Mora, onto A1514 at site sp. Site on L by
petrol stn bef vill. Med, mkd pitch, unshd; htd wc;
chem disp; shwrs inc; el pts (10A) €2; gas; lndtte;
shop 1km; rest; snacks; bar; playgrnd; pool;
30% statics; dogs; phone; bus 200m; poss cr; noisy;
cc acc; CCI. "Site much enlarged, popular with
young tenters; close wintersports area; obliging
staff; excel san facs but poss stretched high ssn;
some pitches worn & uneven; site a little run down;
excel, gd value rest; site controlled fr adj filling stn;
ltd facs in winter." ♦ ltd. € 9.70   2005*

†MARBELLA *2H3* (6km E Coastal) **Camping La
Buganvilla, 29600 Marbella (Malaga) [952-83 19 73
or 952-83 19 74; fax 952-83 19 74; info@
campingbuganvilla.com; www.campingbuganvilla.
com]** E fr Marbella for 6km on N340/E15 twds
Malaga. Pass site & cross over m'way at Elviria &
foll site sp. Fr Malaga exit R off autovia immed after
189km marker. Lge, terr, shd; wc; chem disp; shwrs;
el pts (10A) €3.20; gas; lndtte; ice; shop & 250m;
rest; bar & sun terr; playgrnd; pool; sand beach
350m; games rm; internet; TV; phone; no dogs
Jul-Aug; Eng spkn; adv bkg; poss noisy at w/e;
15% red 7+ days & 5% for snr citizens; cc acc; CCI.
"Relaxed, conv site; helpful staff; excel beach." ♦
€ 22.00   2005*

†MARBELLA *2H3* (10km E Coastal) **Camping Marbella Playa, Ctra N340, Km 192.8, 29600 Marbella (Malaga) [952-83 39 98; fax 952-83 39 99; info@campingmarbella.com; www. campingmarbella.com]** Fr Marbella on E15/N340 coast rd & site is on R bef 193 km stone & just bef pedestrian bdge over N340, sp 'to beach'. Fr Malaga U-turn on m'way as follows: pass 192km mark & immed take R slip rd to Elviria to turn L over bdge, back onto N340. Turn R bef next bdge. Lge, mkd pitch, hdstg, pt shd; wc; chem disp; mv service pnt; baby facs; shwrs; el pts (10-20A) €3.40-5.55; gas; ice; supmkt; rest; snacks; bar; BBQ; playgrnd; pool; sand beach adj; watersports; tennis 50m; TV; 30% statics; phone; bus nr; poss cr; cc acc; red long stay/snr citizens/CCI. "Pitches tight; friendly, helpful manager; gd base Costa del Sol; noisy peak ssn & w/ends; rd noise poss." ♦ € 23.70 ABS - E07
2005*

†MARBELLA *2H3* (12km E Coastal) **Camping Cabopino, Ctra N340/A7, Km 194.7, 29600 Marbella (Malaga) [tel/fax 952-83 43 73; info@ campingcabopino.com; www.campingcabopino. com]** Fr E site is on N side of N340/A7; turn R at km 195 'Salida Cabopino' past petrol stn, site on R in 500m. Fr W on A7 turn R at 'Salida Cabopino' km 194.7, go over bdge to rndabt, turn R for site in 300m. Lge, mkd pitch, pt sl, pt shd; wc; chem disp; mv service pnt; shwrs inc; el pts (10A) inc; lndtte; shop; rest; snacks; bar; BBQ; playgrnd; 2 pools (1 covrd); sand beach/dunes 200m; watersports; marina 300m; games area; archery; golf driving range; internet; 40% statics; dogs €2.25; bus 100m; Eng spkn; rd noise & lge groups w/enders; red low ssn; cc acc; CCI. "Popular low ssn; ltd waste-water disp; tourers ltd to lower half of site - flooding danger in heavy rain; access to some pitches diff due drops; poss power cuts; ltd security; excel rest at site ent; gd, clean san facs; v nice site." ♦ € 30.70 (CChq acc) ABS - E21
2005*

†MARIA *4G1* (8km W Rural) **Camping Sierra de Maria, Ctra Maria a Orce, Km 7, Paraje La Piza, 04838 Maria (Almeria) [950-16 70 45 or 660-26 64 74; fax 950-48 54 16; campingsierra demaria@cajamar.es; www.campingsierrade maria.com]** Exit A92 at junc 408 to Velez Rubio, Velez Blanco & Maria. Foll A317 to Maria & cont dir Huescar & Orce. Site on R. Med, mkd pitch, pt sl, pt shd; wc; chem disp; shwrs; el pts (6-10A) €3.50; shop high ssn; bar; cycle hire; horseriding; dogs; adv bkg; quiet; cc acc; CCI. "Lovely, peaceful, ecological site in mountains; much wildlife; variable pitch sizes; facs poss stretched high ssn; v cold in winter." ♦ € 14.20
2004*

†MARINA, LA *4F2* (2km S Coastal) **Camping Internacional La Marina, Ctra N332a, Km 76, 03194 La Marina (Alicante) [965-41 92 00; fax 965-41 91 10; info@campinglamarina.com; www.campingla marina.com]** On N332 coast rd Alicante/ Cartagena; app La Marina on edge of town turn L twd sea after lge g'ge, site sp in 1km. V lge, hdg/mkd pitch, hdstg, terr, shd; htd wc; chem disp; mv service pnt; 50% serviced pitches; baby facs; fam bthrm; sauna; solarium; shwrs inc; el pts (10A) inc; gas; lndtte; ice; supmkt; rest; snacks; bar; playgrnd; 2 pools (1 htd/covrd); waterslides; sand beach 500m; fishing; watersports; tennis; games area; games rm; fitness cent; entmnt; child entmnt; internet; TV rm; 10% statics; dogs €2; phone; bus 50m; car wash; security; Eng spkn; adv bkg; cc acc; 30-76% red long stay/varying pitch size; CCI. "Almost full late Feb; v busy w/e; spotless facs; popular winter site; bus fr gate; m'van services; gd security; gd rest; excel family site." ♦ € 42.60
2005*

See advertisement on next page

As we're travelling out of season, we'd better phone ahead to check that the site is actually open.

†MASNOU, EL *3C3* (Coastal) **Camping Masnou, Ctra Camil Fabra 33, 08320 El Masnou (Barcelona) [tel/fax 935-55 15 03]** App site fr N on N11. Pass El Masnou rlwy station on L & go strt on at traff lts. Site on R on N11. Not clearly sp. Med, pt sl, shd; wc; mv service pnt; shwrs inc; el pts €5.35; shop, snacks, bar high ssn; BBQ; playgrnd; pool high ssn; sand beach opp; internet; dogs; phone; train to Barcelona nr; poss v cr; Eng spkn; noise fr N11; cc not acc; CCI. "Gd pitches, no awnings; some sm pitches, poss shared; facs vg, though poss stretched when site busy; no restriction on NH vehicle movements; well-run, friendly site." ♦ ltd. € 23.50
2005*

MATARO *3C3* (2km N Coastal) **Camping Playa Sol, Ctra NII, Km 650, 08304 Mataro (Barcelona) [937-90 47 20; fax 937-41 02 82; playasol@ campingsonline.com; www.campingplayasol. com]** Exit AP7 onto C60 sp Mataro. Turn N onto NII dir Gerona, site sp. Lge, pt shd; wc; chem disp; mv service pnt; shwrs; el pts (6A) €4; lndtte; shop; rest; snacks; bar; playgrnd; pool; paddling pool; sand beach nr; games area; internet; TV; 50% statics; bus; adv bkg; cc acc. "Conv Barcelona 28km." ♦ 11 Mar-9 Oct. € 29.00 (CChq acc)
2005*

MAZAGON see Huelva *2G2*

MENDEXA see Lekeitio *3A1*

SPAIN

†MENDIGORRIA *3B1* (S Rural) **Camping El Molino, Ctra Larraga, 31150 Mendigorria (Navarra)** [948-34 06 04; fax 948-34 00 82; info@campingelmolino.com; www.campingelmolino.com] Fr Pamplona on N111 turn L at 25km in Puente La Reina onto NA601 sp Mendigorria. Site sp thro vill dir Larraga. App fr S feasible but requires towing thro' Tafalla - congestion. Med, some mkd pitch, pt shd; wc; chem disp; mv service pnt; serviced pitches; baby facs; shwrs inc; el pts (6A) inc; gas; lndtte; ice; shop; tradsmn; rest; snacks; bar; playgrnd; pool; tennis; games area; child entmnt; TV; statics (sep area); dogs; phone; poss cr at w/e; Eng spkn; clsd 24 Dec-6 Jan; adv bkg; poss noisy at w/e; cc acc; CCI. "Gd clean facs; excel." ♦ € 21.00 (CChq acc) 2005*

MEQUINENZA *3C2* (Urban) **Camping Octogesa, Ctra N211 s/n, Km 314, 50170 Mequinenza (Zaragoza)** [974-46 44 31; fax 974-46 50 31; rai@fuibol.e.telefonica.net] W fr Lerida on N11 for 29km; turn S 2km W of Fraga onto N211. On ent Mequinenza just past wooded area on L, turn L thro break in service rd, site well sp. Tight ent poss unsuitable lge o'fits. Med, hdg/mkd pitch, terr, pt shd; wc; chem disp (wc); shwrs inc; el pts (6A) inc; lndry rm; shop 1km; rest; snacks; bar; BBQ; playgrnd; 2 pools high ssn; tennis; dogs; phone; Eng spkn; adv bkg; quiet but noise fr arr of fishing parties; cc acc; CCI. "Site part of complex on bank of Rv Segre surrounded by hills & used as base for fishing trips - site will supply equipment; sm pitches unsuitable lge o'fits; inadequate recep; only bottled water avail, no supply to site; NH only." 15 Mar-15 Oct. € 20.00 2005*

†MERIDA *2E3* (2km SE Urban) **Camping Complejo Merida, Avda Reina Sofia s/n, 06800 Merida (Badajoz)** [924-30 34 53; fax 924-30 03 98; proexcam@jet.es; www.pagina.de/campingmerida] Fr E on A5/E90 exit junc 333 to Merida, site on L in 2km. Fr W on A5/E90 exit junc 346, site sp. Fr N strt along dual c'way dir Merida. At rndabt under rd bdge turn L onto old Madrid rd, site on R in 2km. Med, hdg/mkd pitch, pt sl, pt shd; wc; chem disp; shwrs inc; el pts (6-10A) inc (long lead poss req); gas; lndtte; ltd shop high ssn & 3km; hypmkt 6km; rest; snacks; bar; 2 free pools; TV; phone; Eng spkn; quiet but some rd & dog noise; cc acc; CCI. "Roman remains & National Museum of Roman Art worth visit; excel, clean, modern san facs but ltd hot water; poss diff lge o'fits manoeuvring onto pitch due trees & soft ground after rain; occasional problems with pump supplying site's water; gd seafood rest; ltd facs low ssn." ♦ € 19.00 2005*

†MIAJADAS *2E3* (10km SW Rural) **Camping-Restaurant El 301, Km 301 Ctra Madrid-Lisbon, 10100 Miajadas (Caceres)** [tel/fax 927-34 79 14] Leave A5/E90 just bef km stone 301 & foll sp 'Via de Servicio' with rest & camping symbols; site in 500m. Med, pt shd; wc; chem disp; shwrs inc; el pts (5-10A) €2.70 (poss no earth); gas; lndtte; shop; rest; snacks; bar; playgrnd; pool; phone; m'way noise & dogs; cc acc; CCI. "Well-maintained, clean site; OK wheelchair users but steps to pool; gd NH." € 14.10 2005*

MIJAS COSTA see Fuengirola *2H4*

MIRANDA DEL CASTANAR *1D3* (500m Rural) **Camping El Burro Blanco, Camino de las Norias s/n, 37660 Miranda del Castanar (Salamanca)** [tel/fax 923-16 11 00; elburroblanco@internet-rural.com; www.elburroblanco.internet-rural.com] Fr Ciudad Rodrigues take C515 to El Cabaco then R onto C512 for 2km sp Miranda del Castanar. In 2km turn L onto concrete/dirt rd for 700m. Site on R. Sm, mkd pitch, terr, pt shd; wc; chem disp; shwrs inc; el pts (2-10A) €2.50-4.80; lndtte; shop, rest, snacks 1km; tradsmn; bar; pool; no statics; dogs; phone 1km; Eng spkn; quiet; 10% red 3+ days; CCI. "Nice scenery, set in oak wood; medieval hill-top town 500m; tight ent to some pitches, manhandling req; excel." 1 Apr-1 Oct. € 18.20 2004*

MOANA *1B2* (3km W Coastal) **Camping Tiran, Ctra Cangas-Moaña, Km 3, 36957 Moana (Pontevedra)** [986-31 01 50; fax 986-44 72 04] Exit AP9 junc 146 & foll sp Moana/Cangas. Site beyond Moana. Med, hdg pitch, terr, pt shd; wc; shwrs inc; el pts (6A) inc; lndry rm; shop; tradsmn; rest; snacks; bar; playgrnd; beach adj; TV; 80% statics; no dogs; phone; adv bkg; quiet. "Site on v steep hill - only suitable m'vans & single-axle c'vans with powerful tow car; gd touring base S Galicia." Apr-Nov. € 23.00 2005*

†MOIXENT *4E2* (12km N Rural) **Camping Sierra Natura (Naturist), Finca El Tejarico, Ctra Moixent-Navalon, Km 11.5, 46810 Enguera (Valencia)** [962-25 30 26; fax 962-25 30 20; s_natura@terra.es; www.sierranatura.com] Exit N430 junc 618 or 623 at Moixent onto CV589 sp Navalon. At 11.5km turn R sp Sierra Natura - gd rd surface but some hairpin bends. Sm, pt sl, pt shd; wc; chem disp; baby facs; sauna; shwrs inc; el pts (10A) €2.80; lndry rm; ice; shop & 12 km; rest; snacks; bar; playgrnd; pool; 10% statics; dogs €3; phone; poss cr; Eng spkn; adv bkg; quiet; red long stay. "Tranquil, family-run site in remote area; stunning mountain scenery; naturist walks on site; excel pool & rest complex." ♦ ltd. € 15.80 2004*

†MOJACAR *4G1* (9km S Rural) **Camping Sopalmo, Sopalmo, 04638 Mojacar (Almeria)** [950-47 84 13; fax 950-47 30 02] Exit N340/E15 at junc 520 sp Mojacar Playa. Foll coast rd S to Carboneras, site sp on W of rd about 1km S of Agua de Enmedio. Sm, hdstg, pt shd; wc; chem disp (wc); shwrs; el pts (15A) €2.50; ice; gas; lndtte; sm shop (high ssn); tradsmn; rest, snacks 6km; bar; shgl beach 1.7km; internet; 10% statics; dogs €1; Eng spkn; adv bkg; some rd noise; cc not acc; red low ssn; CCI. "V clean, pleasant, popular site - constantly improving; friendly young owner; gd walking; remote but intimate & peaceful, poss windy; poss busy in low ssn; nr National Park; patchy mobile phone signal." ♦ € 18.20   2005*

†MOJACAR *4G1* (4km SW Coastal) **Camping Cueva Negra, Camino Lotaza, 2, 04638 Mojacar (Almeria)** [950-47 58 55; fax 950-47 57 11; info@ campingcuevanegra.com; www.campingcueva negra.com] Leave N340/E15 at junc 520 for AL151 twd Mojacar Playa. Turn R onto coastal rd. Site 500m fr Hotel Marina on R. App steep but new rd under construction (2004). Med, hdg/mkd pitch, all hdstg, terr, unshd; wc; chem disp; mv service pnt; shwrs inc; el pts (22A) inc; gas; lndtte; shop; tradsmn; rest; snacks; bar; pool; sand beach adj; entmnt; TV; 5% statics; dogs €1.90; poss cr; adv bkg; quiet; red 30+ days; CCI. "Well-kept, beautifully laid-out site; v clean san facs; pleasant atmosphere; gd touring base; facs stretched when site full." ♦ € 31.70   2005*

†MOJACAR *4G1* (1km W Rural) **Camping El Quinto, Ctra Mojacar-Turre, Aptdo Correos 628, 04638 Mojacar (Almeria)** [950-47 87 04; fax 950-47 21 48; campingelquinto@hotmail.com] Fr E15 (N340) exit 520 sp Turre & Mojacar. Site on R in approx 13km at bottom of Mojacar vill. Sm, hdg/mkd pitch, hdstg, pt shd; wc; chem disp; mv service pnt; shwrs inc; el pts (6-10A) €2.95; gas; lndtte; ice; shop 4km; tradsmn; rest 3km; snacks; bar; BBQ; playgrnd; pool; sand beach 3km; dogs; phone; poss cr; Eng spkn; adv bkg (dep req); quiet but some rd noise; red long stay; CCI. "Neat, tidy site; easy walk to vill; gd mkt Wed; close National Park; excel beaches; metered 6A elect for long winter stay; popular in winter, poss cr & facs stretched; security barrier; poss mosquitoes; drinking water ltd to 5L a time." ♦ € 20.50   2005*

MOMBELTRAN see Arenas de San Pedro *1D3*

MONASTERIO DE RODILLA see Burgos *1B4*

†MONCOFA *3D2* (2km E Coastal/Urban) **Camping Monmar, Ctra Serratelles s/n, 12593 Platja de Moncofa (Castellon)** [tel/fax 964-58 85 92; campingmonmarmoncofa@wanadoo.es] Exit 49 fr A7 or N340, foll sp Moncofa Platja passing thro Moncofa & foll sp beach & tourist info thro 1-way system. Site sp. Lge, hdstg, pt shd; htd wc; chem disp; all serviced pitches; baby facs; shwrs inc; el pts (6A) inc; gas; lndtte; shop & 1km; tradsmn; rest; snacks; bar; BBQ; playgrnd; pool; sand/shgl beach 200m; entmnt; internet; 10% statics; no dogs; phone; poss cr; Eng spkn; adv bkg; quiet; cc acc; red low ssn/long stay; CCI. "V helpful owner & staff; rallies on site Jan-Apr; poss v cr & dusty; mini-bus to stn & excursions; sunshades over pitches poss diff high o'fits; excel clean, tidy site." ♦ € 23.00   2005*

†MONCOFA *3D2* (2km S Coastal) **Camping Los Naranjos, Camino Cabres, Km 950.8, 12953 Moncofa (Castellon)** [964-58 03 37; fax 964-76 62 37] Fr N340 at km post 950.8 turn L at site sp, site 1km on R. Med, mkd pitch, hdstg, pt shd; wc; chem disp; mv service pnt; shwrs inc; el pts (10A) inc; gas; lndtte; ice; shop; tradsmn; rest; snacks; bar; playgrnd; pool; paddling pool; beach 300m; games area; 20% statics; phone; bus 1km; poss cr; adv bkg; quiet; red long stay. "Gd long/sh stay." € 22.00   2004*

MONTERROSO *1B2* (1km S Rural) **Camping Monterroso, Avda de la Playa s/n, 27569 Monterroso (Lugo)** [982-37 75 01; fax 982-37 74 16; aged@cinsl.es; www.campingmonterroso.com] Fr N540 turn W onto N640 to Monterroso. Fr town cent turn S on LU212. In 100m turn sharp R then downhill for 1km; 2 sharp bends to site. Sm, hdg/mkd pitch, unshd; wc; chem disp; serviced pitches; shwrs inc; el pts (10A) €2.90; shop 1km; rest 1km; bar; pool adj; games area; internet; Eng spkn; quiet; CCI. "Helpful staff; v quiet & ltd facs low ssn." ♦ 1 Mar-30 Sep. € 15.00   2005*

MONTROIG see Cambrils *3C2*

†MORAIRA *4F2* (1km SW Coastal) **Camping-Caravanning Moraira, Camino Paelleroso, 03724 Moraira-Teulada (Alicante)** [965-74 52 49; fax 965-74 53 15; campingmoraira@camping moraira.com; www.campingmoraira.com] A7, exit 63. Foll sp Teulada & Moraira. Turn W 1km S of Moraira onto AP1347, then site 500m up hill. Med, mkd pitch, hdstg, terr, shd; wc; chem disp; 15% serviced pitches; shwrs inc; el pts (6A) €3; lndtte; ice; shop & 650m; tradsmn; rest; snacks; bar; htd pool; sand beach 1km; no statics; dogs; phone; Eng spkn; adv bkg; poss noisy w/e high ssn; red low ssn/long stay; cc not acc; CCI. "Coastal town with harbour; modern site; relaxed informal atmosphere; gd touring base; ltd facs low ssn, san facs stretched high ssn; pitching poss diff for lge o'fits." ♦ ltd. € 18.50   2003*

†MORATALLA *4F1* (8km NW Rural) **Camping La Puerta, 30440 Moratalla (Murcia) [tel/fax 968-73 00 08; lapuerta@forodigital.com; www. campinglapuerta.com]** Fr Murcia take C415 dir Mula & Caravaca. Foll sp Moratalla & site. Lge, shd; htd wc; shwrs inc; el pts (10A) €3.80; gas; lndtte; shop; rest; bar; BBQ; playgrnd; pool; rv sw; tennis; games area; internet; TV rm; statics; dogs; adv bkg; quiet; cc acc. ♦ € 14.30 (CChq acc)   2005*

MORELLA *3D2* (35km S Rural) **Camping El Llosar, Partida Vegas Tejería, 12150 Vilafranca del Cid (Castellon) [964-44 14 09]** S fr Morella on CV125 to La Iglesuela del Cit, then rd CV15 to Vilafranca del Cid, site 800 W of Vilafranca on L. Med, hdstg, terr, pt shd; wc; shwrs, el pts (10A); gas; shop; rest; bar; playgrnd; pool; tennis; phone; adv bkg; quiet; cc acc. "Nr desert; rock climbing; phone ahead to check if open." ♦
Holy Week & 1 Jun-30 Sep. € 11.40   2004*

MOSTEIRO CERVANTES see Becerrea *1A2*

†MOTILLA DEL PALANCAR *4E1* (10km NW) **Camping Pantapino, Paraje de Hontanar, s/n, 16115 Olmedilla de Alarcon (Cuenca) [969-33 92 33; fax 969-33 92 44; paralelo40@ paralelo40.org]** Fr cent of Motilla foll NIII; turn NW onto rd CM2100 at sp for Valverde de Jucar; site on L just bef 12 km marker - rough app rd. Med, mkd pitch, pt sl, pt shd; wc; chem disp; mv service pnt; serviced pitches; baby facs; shwrs inc; el pts (10A) €3; gas; lndtte; shop; rest, bar high ssn; BBQ; playgrnd; pool; tennis; games area, mini-golf; horseriding; cycle hire; 40% statics; dogs €2.40; adv bkg; quiet; ltd facs low ssn; cc acc; 10% red CCI. "Clean, attractive site but tatty statics; poor facs; owners v hospitable & generous, live on site; gd size pitches; gd for Cuenca & Alarcon; poss clsd in winter - phone ahead to check; vg sh stay." ♦
€ 15.00   2004*

†MOTRIL *2H4* (12km SE Coastal) **Camping Don Cactus, N340, Km 343, 18730 Carchuna (Granada) [958-62 31 09; fax 958-62 42 94; camping@ doncactus.com; www.doncactus.com]** On N340 SE fr Motril 1km W of Calahonda. Ignore site sps; turn off opp church down made-up rd to shore; turn L to site in 500m - unmade rd. Lge, hdstg, shd; wc; chem disp; mv service pnt; shwrs; el pts (5A) €5 (no earth); gas; lndtte; supmkt; rest; snacks; bar; BBQ; playgrnd; pool; shgl beach adj; tennis; archery; golf 6km; entmnt; internet; TV; 60% statics; no dogs Jul & Aug; poss cr; no adv bkg; quiet; cc acc; red 30+ days; CCI. "No views but conv caves of Nerja, Calahonda, Motril, Granada, & Sierra Nevada; many plastic greenhouses around site; sm pitches; helpful staff; NH only." ♦ € 19.60 (CChq acc)   2005*

†MOTRIL *2H4* (3km W Urban/Coastal) **Camping Playa de Poniente de Motril, 18600 Motril (Granada) [958-82 03 03; fax 958-60 41 91]** Turn off coast rd N340 to port bef flyover; at rndabt take rd for Motril. Turn R in town, site sp. Lge, pt shd; htd wc; chem disp; baby facs; shwrs; el pts €2.50; gas; lndtte; ice; shop; supmkt 4km; rest, bar in ssn; beach adj; pool; playgrnd; golf; tennis; horseriding; cycle hire; 70% statics; dogs €1.50; bus; Eng spkn; adv bkg; cc acc; red low ssn/long stay. "Well-appointed site but surrounded by flats; gd, clean facs; helpful recep; gd shop; access diff for lge o'fits; poss lge flying beetles; excel long stay winter." ♦
€ 17.00   2004*

MOZAR DE VALVERDE see Benavente *1B3*

†MUNDAKA *3A1* (1km S Coastal) **Camping Portuondo, Ctra Amorebieta-Bermeo, Km 43, 48360 Mundaka (Bilbao) [946-87 77 01; fax 946-87 78 28; recepcion@campingportuondo. com; www.campingportuondo.com]** Leave E70 E of Bilbao onto B1631 to Bermeo. Keep on coast rd to Mundaka, site 1km on L. Ess to app fr Bermeo due to steep ent. Do not drive past recep until booked in due steep access. Med, terr, pt shd; wc; shwrs inc; el pts (6A) €3.25; lndtte; rest; snacks; bar; playgrnd; pool; paddling pool; beach 500m; 30% statics; dogs; train 800m; poss v cr w/ends; cc acc. "Clean, modern facs; pitches tight; popular with surfers; conv Bilbao - walk to stn for train to Bilbao/ connect to Guggenheim; site suitable sm m'vans only." € 20.10   2005*

†MURCIA *4F1* (10km SW Rural) **Camping La Paz, Ctra 340 Murcia-Granada, Km 321, 30835 Sangonera La Seca (Murcia) [968-89 39 29; fax 968-80 13 37]** Tourist complex La Paz off A7 at exit 647; lge notices both dirs. Behind service stn dir Granada, Almeria. Med, hdg/mkd pitch, hdstg, unshd; wc; chem disp; serviced pitches; shwrs inc; el pts inc (rev pol); lndtte; ice; shop; tradsmn; rest; snacks; bar; BBQ; playgrnd; pool; tennis; games area; TV; 95% statics; dogs; phone; cash machine; Eng spkn; adv bkg; red long stay/low ssn; cc acc; CCI. "V helpful staff; gd tour base but v ltd no touring pitches; conv Murcia." ♦ € 17.20   2005*

MUROS *1B1* (500m W Coastal/Rural) **Camping San Francisco, 15291 Louro (La Coruna) [981-82 61 48; fax 981-57 19 16; ofmsan@ planalfa.es]** Fr Muros cont on C550 coast rd for 3km to San Francisco vill. Site sp to R up narr rd. Med, mkd pitch, pt shd; htd wc; chem disp; mv service pnt; shwrs; el pts (5-8A) €3.10; gas; lndtte; ice; rest; snacks; bar; sand beach 400m; playgrnd; dogs; phone; adv bkg; Eng spkn; quiet; cc acc; CCI. "Clean; lovely surroundings; vg rest; excel long/sh stay." ♦ 20 Jun-20 Sep. € 19.10   2004*

SPAIN

MUROS *1B1* (7km W Coastal) **Camping Ancoradoiro, Ctra Corcubión-Muros, Km.7.2, 15250 Louro (La Coruna)** [981-87 88 97; fax 981-87 85 50] Foll AC550 W fr Muros. Site on L (S) thro pine wood, well sp. Med, hdg/mkd pitch, terr, pt shd; wc; chem disp; mv service pnt; shwrs inc; el pts (6A) €3.37; lndtte; ice; shop 2km; rest; bar; playgrnd; sand beach 500m; watersports; entmnt; no statics; no dogs; phone; poss cr; Eng spkn; adv bkg; quiet; CCI. "Beautiful beaches; scenic area; vg." 15 Mar-15 Sep. € 11.50   2004*

We're having a great holiday - must fill in some site report forms and send them to The Club as soon as possible.

MUTRIKU see Deba *3A1*

MUXIA *1A1* (10km E Coastal) **Camping Playa de Leis, Playa Berreira, Leis, 15124 Muxia (La Coruna)** [981-73 03 04] Fr Ponte do Porto turn L sp Muxia; foll camp sp. Site is 1st after Leis vill on R. Med, mkd pitch, terr, pt shd; wc; chem disp; shwrs inc; el pts €1.70; lndtte; shop; rest; bar; BBQ; playgrnd; sand beach 100m; dogs; TV; quiet; cc acc; CCI. "Beautiful situation on wooded hillside; dir acces to gd beach; ltd facs low ssn; facs in need of update; mkt in Muxia Thurs." 1 Jun-20 Sep. € 12.80   2005*

NAJERA *3B1* (500m S Urban) **Camping El Ruedo, San Julien 24, 26300 Najera (La Rioja)** [941-36 01 02] Take Najera town dirs off N120. In town turn L bef x-ing bdge. Site sp. Sm, pt shd; wc; chem disp; shwrs inc; el pts (10-16A) inc (rev pol); gas; lndtte; shop & phone; rest; bar; BBQ; snacks; pool 1km; playgrnd; TV; entmnt; poss cr; adv bkg; quiet; cc acc; CCI. "Pleasant site in quiet location, don't be put off by 1st impression of town; monastery worth visit." 1 Apr-10 Sep. € 15.12   2002*

†NAVAJAS *3D2* (1km Rural) **Camping Altomira, Ctra Navajas/Pantano del Regajo, 12470 Navajas (Castellon)** [964-71 32 11 or 964-71 09 46; fax 964-71 35 12; reservas@campingaltomira.com; www.campingaltomira.com] Fr Sagunto take A23 for approx 35km to Segorbe, then foll sp Navajas. Site on L just past R turn into vill. Med, hdstg, terr, pt shd; htd wc; chem disp; mv service pnt; serviced pitches; baby facs; shwrs; el pts (6A) €2.80; gas; lndry rm; shop & 1km; tradsmn; rest; snacks; bar; playgrnd; pool; paddling pool; tennis; cycle hire; 30% statics; dogs; phone; adv bkg; poss noisy w/e & public hols; red 15+ days/low ssn; cc acc; red CCI. "Superb welcome; friendly staff; panoramic views fr upper level; red squirrels on site; gd birdwatching; sh walk to vill; walking/cycling rte adj site; ltd facs low ssn; steep app to touring pitches on upper levels & kerbs to pitches; excel san facs; some sm pitches poss diff for lge o'fits without motor mover; poss clsd low ssn - phone ahead to check; excel." ♦ € 17.50 (CChq acc)   2005*

See advertisement above

NAVALAFUENTE see Cabrera, La *1D4*

NAVALENO *1C4* (Urban) **Camping Fuente del Boton, Ctra Sagunto-Burgos, 42149 Navaleno (Soria)** [975-37 43 38; fax 975-22 55 55] W fr Soria/Abejar on N234. Site on R side of rd on o'skts of Navaleno. Med, mkd pitch, pt sl, pt shd; wc; shwrs; el pts €2; lndtte; shop; rest; bar; playgrnd; pool; paddling pool; tennis; some rd noise; cc acc. ♦ ltd. 15 Jun-15 Sep. € 14.50   2004*

NAVARREDONDA DE GREDOS see Hoyos del Espino *1D3*

NAVARRETE see Logrono *3B1*

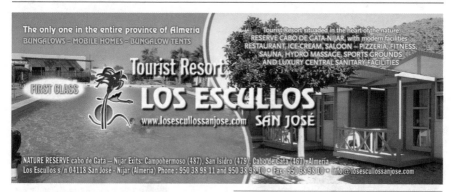

†NEGRAS, LAS *4G1* (1km N Coastal) **Camping Nautico La Caleta, Parque Natural del Cabo de Gata, 04116 Las Negras (Almeria) [tel/fax 950-52 52 37; campinglacaleta@arrakis.es]** Exit N344 at km stone 487 twd Las Negras. Site sp at ent to vill on R. Med, hdg pitch, hdstg, shd; wc; chem disp; mv service pnt; shwrs inc; el pts (10A) €3.20; gas; lndtte; ice; shop & 1km; tradsmn; rest; snacks; bar; playgrnd; pool; sand/shgl beach adj; cycle hire; dogs €1.60; phone; poss cr; quiet; red long stay/low ssn; 10% red for 8 days to 60% for 90 days; CCI. "Lge o'fits need care on steep app rd; vans over 2.50m take care sun shades on pitches; gd walking area; picturesque; excel rest in vill o'lkg sea; ltd facs low ssn; vg." ♦ € 18.90   2005*

NERJA *2H4* (4km E Rural) **Nerja Camping, Ctra N340, Km 297, 29787 Nerja (Malaga) [952-52 97 14; fax 952-52 96 96]** E fr Nerja 700m beyond end of new N340 a'via, on ordinary N360, turn acute L at camping sp. Foll partly surfaced rd to site on hillside. Fr Almunecar on N340, site on R approx 20km. Med, pt sl, terr, pt shd; wc; chem disp; shwrs inc; el pts (5A) €3.70 (check earth); gas; lndry rm; ice; shops; tradsmn; rest; snacks; bar; playgrnd; sm pool; sand beach 2km; cycle hire; Eng spkn; adv bkg rec; rd noise; red long stay/low ssn/CCI. "5 mins to Nerja caves; mkt Tue; annual carnival 15/05; diff access lge o'fits; gd horseriding; site rds steep but gd surface; gd views; friendly owners; san facs in need of refurb but clean." ♦ ltd. 1 Apr-30 Sep. € 22.90   2004*

†NERJA *2H4* (8km W Urban) **Camping El Pino, N340, Km 285-3, 29793 Torrox Costa (Malaga) [tel/fax 952-53 25 78]** Exit N340 at km 285, at rndabt turn L & foll sp Torrox Costa N340a; in 1.5km at rndabt turn R to Torrox Costa, then L onto rndabt sp Nerja, site well sp in 4km. App rd steep with S bends. Lge, mkd pitch, hdstg, pt sl, terr, pt shd; wc; chem disp; shwrs inc; el pts €3 (long lead req); lndtte; shop; rest; snacks adj; bar; playgrnd; 2 pools; 80% statics; dogs €2; phone; adv bkg; red low ssn/long stay; CCI. "Gd size pitches but high kerbs; helpful owner; narr, rough rd to beach in 2km; annoying tannoy; gd hill walks; conv Granada, Ronda; gd security." ♦ ltd. € 18.00   2004*

†NIJAR *4G1* (23km SE Coastal) **Camping Los Escullos San Jose, Paraje Los Escullos s/n, 04118 San Jose-Nijar (Almeria) [950-38 98 11 or 950-38 98 10; fax 950-38 98 10; info@los escullossanjose.com; www.losescullossanjose. com]** Fr E15/N344 (dir Almeria) exit junc 487 dir Campohermoso/San Jose. Then foll sp for El Pozo de los Frailes, Los Escullos & site; fr N on N340 exit 479 & foll sps. Lge, hdg/mkd pitch, hdstg, pt sl, pt shd; wc; chem disp; mv service pnt; baby facs; sauna; shwrs inc; el pts (10A) €4; gas; lndtte; ice; shop; rest; snacks; bar; playgrnd; pool; beach 700m; watersports; diving; tennis; cycle hire; fitness rm; entmnt; excursions arranged; internet; TV; 40% statics; dogs; Eng spkn; adv bkg; cc acc; red long stay/CCI. "Set in National Park on coast; many secluded beaches & walks; excel for watersports; vg pool & rest; helpful staff; excel." ♦ € 22.50   2004*

See advertisement above

This site entry hasn't been updated for a while; we'd better fill in a site report form and send it to The Club.

†NOIA *1B2* (5km SW Coastal) **Camping Punta Batuda, Playa Ornanda, 15970 Porto do Son (La Coruna) [981-76 65 42; camping@puntabatuda. com; www.puntabatuda.com]** Fr Santiago take C543 twd Noia, then C550 5km SW to Porto do Son. Site on R approx 1km after Boa. Lge, mkd pitch, terr, pt shd; htd wc; chem disp; shwrs inc; el pts (3A) €2.80; gas; lndtte; ice; shop; rest w/e only; snacks; bar; tradsmn; playgrnd; htd pool w/e only; sand beach adj; tennis; 50% statics; phone; some Eng spkn; adv bkg; quiet; red 15 days; CCI. "Wonderful views; exposed to elements low ssn, poss windy; some pitches v steep &/or sm; gd facs for disabled; naturist beach 5km S; gd long stay." ♦ € 17.00   2004*

SPAIN

Some of these sites have changed their opening dates - we'd better fill in some site report forms and let the editor of the guide know.

NOJA *1A4* (Coastal) **Camping Los Molinos, Playa del Ris, 39180 Noja (Cantabria)** [942-63 04 26; fax 942-63 07 25] Exit m'way A8 (Bilbao-Santander) at km 185. Go N foll sp to Noja, then L at Playa del Ris. Site sp. V lge, hdg pitch, pt shd; wc; chem disp; mv service pnt; shwrs; baby facs; el pts (3A) €2.45; gas; lndtte; shop; rest; snacks; bar; BBQ; playgrnd; pool; paddling pool; sand beach 500m; tennis; car wash; entmnt; 75% statics; dogs; poss cr; Eng spkn; adv bkg (dep req); cc not acc; CCI. "Gd site; lovely beach; some noise fr karting circuit until late evening but noise levels strictly curtailed at midnight." ♦ Holy Week & 1 Jun-30 Sep. € 18.30   2003*

NOJA *1A4* (700m Coastal) **Camping Playa Joyel, Playa del Ris, 39180 Noja (Cantabria)** [942-63 00 81; fax 942-63 12 94; playajoyel@telefonica.net; www.playajoyel.com] Fr Santander or Bilbao foll sp A8/E70. Approx 15km E of Solares exit m'way at Beranga onto CA147 N twd Noja & coast. On o'skirts of Noja turn L sp Playa de Ris, foll rd approx 1.5km to rndabt, site sp to L, 500m fr rndabt. V lge, mkd pitch, pt sl, pt shd; wc (cont); chem disp; mv service pnt; baby facs; shwrs inc; el pts (3A) inc (rev pol), 6A avail; gas; lndtte; ice; supmkt; tradsmn; rest; snacks; bar; BBQ (gas/charcoal on pitches); playgrnd; pool & paddling pool (caps ess); sand beach adj; windsurfing; sailing; tennis; games rm; entmnt; disco nightly high ssn but not noisy; hairdresser; car wash; cash dispenser; internet; 15% statics; no dogs; phone; recep 0800-2200; poss v cr w/e & high ssn; Eng spkn; adv bkg; cc not acc; CCI. "Well-organised; spotless facs; pleasant staff; gd location; conv Santander, Santillana; lovely sheltered bay with coves; some narr site rds + kerbs & sm pitches; midnight silence enforced; superb site; highly rec." ♦ 8 Apr-30 Sep. € 35.10 (CChq acc) ABS - E05   2005*

See advertisement on bookmark

NUEVALOS *3C1* (Rural) **Camping Lago Park, Ctra Alhama-Nuevalos Km 39.150, 50210 Nuevalos (Zaragoza)** [976-84 90 38 or 976-84 90 57; fax 976-84 90 38] Fr E on NII/E90 exit junc 231 to Nuevalos, turn R sp Madrid. Site 1.5km on L when ent Nuevalos. Fr W exit junc 204, site well sp. Steep ent fr rd. V lge, mkd pitch, terr, pt shd; wc; chem disp; child/baby facs; shwrs inc; el pts (4A) €3.90; gas; lndtte; shop, rest, snacks high ssn; bar 500m; BBQ; playgrnd; pool; lake nrby; fishing; boating; dogs; poss cr; adv bkg; quiet but noisy w/e high ssn; red long stay; CCI. "Nr wonderful beauty spot of Monasterio de Piedra & Tranquera Lake; excel facs but stretched high ssn & poss long, steepish walk; gd birdwatching; only site in area." 1 Apr-30 Sep. € 20.00   2004*

OCHAGAVIA *3A1* (500m S) **Camping Osate, 31680 Ochagavia (Navarra)** [tel/fax 948-89 01 84; www.campingsnavarra.com] On N135 SE fr Auritz, turn L onto NA140 & cont for 24km bef turning L twd Ochagavia on NA140. Site sp in 2km on R, 500m bef vill. Lge, mkd pitch, pt shd; wc; some serviced pitches; shwrs inc; el pts €3.05; shop; rest high ssn; snacks; bar; BBQ; 50% statics. "Attractive, remote vill; gd site; touring pitches under trees, sep fr statics; well-maintained; facs poss stretched high ssn; gd all stays." 6 Jan-31 Oct. € 13.55   2003*

†OLITE *3B1* (2km S Urban) **Camping Ciudad de Olite, 31390 Olite** [948-74 10 14; fax 948-74 06 04; colite@can.es] Fr Pamplona S on AP15 exit 50 twd Olite. At rndabt turn L, then in 300m turn R onto N115, site sp on L past Netto in 2km. Lge, mkd pitch, pt shd; wc; chem disp; serviced pitches; baby facs; shwrs inc; el pts (5A) inc; shop 2km; rest; bar; playgrnd; htd pool (caps ess); tennis; entmnt; games area; 70% statics; poss cr; Eng spkn; phone; cc acc; CCI. "Close to m'way; ltd space for tourers; site mostly used by Spanish for w/e; narr site rds; Olite historic vill with fairytale castle; bleak in winter; NH only." ♦ ltd. € 17.50   2005*

†OLIVA *4E2* (2km E Coastal) **Camping Kiko Park, Ptda Clotet de Mestre s/n, 46780 Playa de Oliva (Valencia)** [962-85 09 05; fax 962-85 43 20; kikopark@kikopark.com; www.kikopark.com] Exit A7/E15 junc 61; fr toll turn R at T-junc onto N332. Drive S thro Oliva, exit at km 212. Take rd to beach, 200m bef beach turn L & R & to end (private beach). Access poss diff on app rds due humps. Site not well sp fr town. Lge, hdg/mkd pitches, hdstg, shd; htd wc; chem disp; mv service pnt; some serviced pitches; baby facs; fam bthrm; shwrs inc; el pts (16A) inc; gas; lndtte; ice; supmkt; rest; snacks; BBQ; playgrnd; pool planned 2006; sand beach adj; watersports; windsurfing school; tennis 1km; games area; cycle hire; entmnt; child entmnt; internet; TV; dogs €2.20; phone; pitch price variable; Eng spkn; adv bkg; quiet; cc acc; red snr cititzens/long stay/low ssn; red CCI. "Excel rest in Michelin Guide; v helpful staff; excel clean, family-run site; vg san facs; lots to do in area." ♦ € 37.75 ABS - E20   2005*

See advertisement opposite

†OLIVA *4E2* (4km E Coastal) **Camping Azul, 46780 Playa de Oliva (Valencia)** [962-85 41 06; fax 962-85 40 96; campingazul@ctv.es] Exit A7/E15 junc 61; fr toll turn R at T-junc onto N332. Drive S thro Oliva, site sp, turn twds sea at km 209.8. Poor app over unmade rd. Med, pt shd; wc; mv service pnt; shwrs inc; el pts (10A) €2.70; gas; lndtte; shop; rest; bar; playgrnd; cycle hire; golf 1km; 20% statics; dogs; quiet; cc acc; red long stay/low ssn. "Gd site." ♦ € 17.73   2003*

Will you fill in the site report forms at the back of the guide, or shall I?

OLIVA *4E2* (5km SE Coastal) **Camping El Rancho, 46780 Playa de Oliva (Valencia)** [tel/fax 962-85 75 18; campingrancho@mx3.redestb.es] Exit A7/E15 junc 61 onto N332 sp Oliva. Turn twds sea at km 210.2, site sp. Lge, hdg/mkd pitch, hdstg (hard sand), shd; wc; chem disp; mv service pnt; shwrs €0.20; el pts (6A) €2.60; lndtte; ice; shop & 400m; tradsmn; rest; snacks; bar; sand beach adj; tennis; entmnt; no dogs; phone; adv bkg; (deposit & bkg fee) cc acc; red long stay; CCI. "Some v lge pitches; excel clean beach with lifeguards high ssn; excel rest facing beach; Ibiza visible on fine day." 1 Jun-15 Sep. € 25.50   2004*

†OLIVA *4E2* (5km SE Coastal) **Camping Pepe, 46780 Playa de Oliva (Valencia)** [962-85 75 19; fax 962-85 75 22; campingpepe@futurnet.es; www.campingpepe.com] Exit A7 junc 61; fr toll turn R at T-junc onto N332. Drive S thro Oliva & in 3.5km at km 210, move R to service rd sp 'Urbanizacion'. Cont past service stn & across flyover. At 1st rndabt, take 2nd exit past golf club ent, then 1st exit at next rndabt, turn L sp ' Camping Pepe' & others. Site down narr rd on L. Lge, hdg/mkd pitch, hdstg, pt shd; wc; chem disp; baby facs; shwrs; el pts (5A) inc; gas; lndtte; ice; shop & 1km; tradmn; rest high ssn; snacks; bar; BBQ; playgrnd; sand beach adj; golf club nr; 30% statics; dogs €1.90; phone; poss cr; Eng spkn; quiet; red long stay/low ssn; CCI. "Well-managed, friendly, busy site; 5 san facs blocks; hot water avail all day for all needs; high kerb to some pitches; barrier locked at night; beautiful beach; vg long/sh stay esp winter." ♦ ltd. € 25.80   2004*

SPAIN

EUROCAMPING lies directly on the fine, sandy beach of Oliva. Pitches with plenty of shade. Modern sanitary instalations with free hot water. Supermarket, Bar-Restaurant, children's playground. Special rates. **OPEN ALL YEAR ROUND. BUNGALOWS.**

Tel. +34 96 285 40 98 - Fax +34 96 285 17 53   Apartado n° 7 46780 OLIVA (Valencia)   e-mail: eurocamping@interbook.net   www.eurocamping-es.com

†OLIVA *4E2* (3km S Coastal) **Eurocamping, Ctra Valencia-Oliva, Aptdo 7, Partida Rabdells s/n, 46780 Playa de Oliva (Valencia)** [962-85 40 98; fax 962-85 17 53; info@eurocamping-es.com; www. eurocamping-es.com] Exit A7/E15 junc 61; fr toll turn R at T-junc onto N332. Drive S thro Oliva, turn R at km 213; at 1st rndabt foll sp to Valencia; at 2nd take 1st exit (site sp). Fr S by N332 turn R at km 209 (sp Urbanization), L at rndabt & foll camping sp to site. Lge, hdg/mkd pitch, hdstg, pt shd; htd wc; chem disp; mv service pnt; baby facs; shwrs inc; el pts (6-10A) €3.35-5.45; gas; lndtte; ice; shop; tradsmn; rest; snacks; bar; BBQ; playgrnd; sand beach adj; cycle hire; entmnt; TV; dogs €1.65; phone; poss cr; quiet but some noise fr adj bar; up to 65% red low ssn/long stay; cc acc; red long stay/low ssn/CCI. "Gd facs; busy, well-maintained, clean site; poss only warm shwrs; major housing development adj; helpful British owners; beautiful clean beach; gd beach walks; cycle rte thro orange groves to town; pitch far fr recep if poss, night noise fr generators 1700-2400; highly rec." ♦ € 36.15 (CChq acc)   2005*

See advertisement above

†OLIVA *4E2* (4km S Coastal) **Camping Ole, Partida Aigua Morta s/n, 46780 Playa de Oliva (Valencia)** [962-85 75 17; fax 962-85 75 16 or 962-85 11 34; campingole@hotmail.com; www.camping-ole. com] Exit A7/E15 junc 61 onto N332 dir Denia. At km 209.9 turn twds coast sp Oliva Nova. Site sp. Lge, hdg/mkd pitch, hdstg, shd; wc; chem disp; baby facs; shwrs inc; el pts (6-10A) €4.18; gas; lndtte; ice; supmkt; rest; snacks; bar; playgrnd; sand beach adj; fishing; tennis 600m; horseriding 2km; golf adj; entmnt; 15% statics; dogs €2.27; phone; Eng spkn; adv bkg; quiet; cc acc; red long stay/low ssn; CCI. "Many sports & activities; direct access to beach; excel." ♦ € 16.80   2005*

See advertisement opposite

†OLIVA *4E2* (7km S Coastal) **Camping Rio Mar, Ctra N332, Km 207, 46780 Playa de Oliva (Valencia)** [962-85 40 97; fax 962-83 91 32; riomar@campingriomar.com] Exit A7/E15 junc 61; fr toll turn R at T-junc onto N332. Drive S thro Oliva, site sp at km 207. Med, shd; wc; chem disp; shwrs; el pts (6A) €2.95; gas; lndtte; supmkt high ssn; rest, bar high ssn; playgrnd; sand beach adj; 20% statics; dogs €1.70; phone; poss cr; adv bkg; quiet; cc acc; red low ssn/snr citizens; CCI. "Friendly, family-run site; Fri mkt in Oliva." € 22.00   2002*

OLMEDILLA DE ALARCON see Motilla del Palancar *4E1*

†OLOT *3B3* (3km SE Rural) **Camping Fageda, Batet de la Serra, Ctra Olot-Santa Pau, Km 4, 17800 Olot (Gerona)** [tel/fax 972-27 12 39; campingfaged@garrotxa.com; www.campingla fageda.com] E fr Olot on GR524 to Banyoles, site on L of minor rd (C150) at 3.8km. Med, mkd pitch, pt sl, terr, pt shd; htd wc; chem disp; shwrs inc; el pts (10A) €4.65; gas; lndtte; shop; snacks; rest & bar high ssn; playgrnd; htd pool high ssn; 90% statics; phone; adv bkg (dep); quiet; cc acc; CCI. "Situated in beautiful area with extinct volcanoes & forests; walks fr site; diff access to water pnts for m'vans; isolated site, few visitors low ssn; v friendly, helpful staff." ♦ € 18.60   2005*

†OLOT *3B3* (7km SE Rural) **Lava Camping, Ctra Olot/Sta Pau, Km 7, 17811 Santa Pau (Gerona)** [972-68 03 58; fax 972-68 03 15; touristic@ garrotxa.com; www.garrotxa.com/turisme] Take rd Gl 524 fr Olot, site at top of hill, well sp & visible fr rd. Lge, mkd pitch, pt shd; wc; chem disp (wc); shwrs inc; baby facs; el pts €3.54; gas; lndtte, tradsmn; rest; snacks; bar; shop 2km; playgrnd; pool; horseriding adj; phone; adv bkg; Eng spkn; dogs; quiet; cc acc. "V helpful staff; gd facs; v interesting area; in volcanic region; v busy with tourists all ssn; walks sp fr site; Pyrenees museum in Olot; tourist train fr site to volcano; excel rests in medieval town; excel long/sh stay." € 19.54   2003*

OLOT *3B3* (9km NW Rural) **Camping La Vall de Bianya, Ctra C26, Km.215, 17813 La Vall de Bianya (Gerona)** [972-29 00 57; fax 972-29 01 28; informacio@campingbianya.com; www.camping bianya.com] Fr Olot N on C26, site sp. Med, mkd pitch, sl, pt shd; wc; chem disp; mv service pnt; baby facs; shwrs inc; el pts (10A) €4.15; lndtte; gas; shop; rest; snacks; bar; playgrnd; pool; games rm; games area; entmnt; TV rm; 50% statics; dogs €2.40; phone; poss cr; quiet; cc acc. "Modern, clean facs; some pitches soft in wet; gd sh stay." ♦ 1 Apr-31 Dec. € 16.80   2004*

†ORGANYA *3B2* (500m NW Rural) **Camping Organya, Calle de les Piscines s/n, 25794 Organya (Lleida)** [973-38 20 39; fax 973-38 35 36] Site sp to E of C14 adj sports cent/football pitch. Sharp rise off rd & narr access, not rec for lge o'fits. Med, pt shd; wc; shwrs; el pts (3A) €3; shop, rest 1km; bar; playgrnd; pools adj; tennis; paragliding tuition avail; mainly statics; dogs €2; phone; some rd noise; CCI. "Excel mountain scenery & interesting vill; new, clean san facs; pleasant pools adj; NH only - phone ahead low ssn to check site open." € 15.70   2004*

†ORGIVA *2G4* (2km S Rural) **Camping Orgiva, Ctra A348, Km 18.9, 18400 Orgiva (Granada)** [tel/fax 958-78 43 07; campingorgiva@wanadoo. es; www.descubrelaalpujarra.com] Fr N or S on Granada-Motril rd suggest avoid A348 via Lanjaron (narr & congested). Fr N323/A44 turn E nr km 179, 1km S of lge dam sp Velez de Benaudalla, over multi-arch bdge, turn L sp Orgiva. Foll rd (easy climb) turn L after sh tunnel over rv bdge; site 2nd building on R. Sm, pt sl, pt shd; wc; chem disp; serviced pitches; baby facs; shwrs inc; el pts (10A) €2.70 (rev pol); gas; ice; lndtte; supmkt 2km; rest; snacks; bar; playgrnd; pool; shgl beach 30km; bus 2km; adv bkg; cc acc; some Eng spkn; red low ssn/long stay; cc acc; 10% red CCI. "Immac san facs; vg value rest open all yr; magnificent scenery; gd base for mountains & coast; Thurs mkt in town; fiesta 27/9-1/10; pleasant walk thro orange & almond groves to vill; area popular for new-age travellers - festival early Mar; excel, friendly site." ♦ € 17.50   2005*

†ORGIVA *2G4* (2km NW Rural) **Camping Puerta de la Alpujarra, Ctra Lanjaron-Orgiva (Las Barreras), 18418 Orgiva (Granada)** [958-78 44 50; puertalpujarr@yahoo.es; www.campings.net/ puertadelaalpujarra] Fr Orgiva take A348 to Lanjaron. Site on L in 2km. Lanjaron poss diff for long o'fits. Med, mkd pitch, hdstg, terr, pt shd; wc; chem disp; shwrs inc; el pts (16A) inc; gas 2km; lndtte; shop; rest; bar; pool, paddling pool high ssn; dogs; bus adj; Eng spkn; adv bkg; quiet; 10% red 7+ days. "New site 2003; scenic area with gd views fr site; excel walking." € 19.00   2004*

SPAIN

1st CATEGORY
E-17211 LLAFRANCH-Palafrugell

Tel. (34) 972-30 11 56   Fax. (34) 972-61 08 94
Internet: http://www.campingkims.com
E-Mail: info@campingkims.com

CAMPING
KiM'S
LLAFRANC
1ᴬ CATEGORIA ★★★

One of the most beautifully situated camp sites on the Costa Brava in a landscaped green belt zone. 2 swimming pools, children's playground, bar, restaurant, supermarket. Only 325 sites (70-100-120m²) on a surface of 62.500 sq.m. at 500 m from the sea.

Bungalows and mobile homes for hire. Family atmosphere.

Open: Easter - 30.9.

ORIHUELA DEL TREMEDAL *3D1* (1km S) **Camping Caimodorro, Subida Fuente Colladillos s/n, 44366 Orihuela del Tremedal (Teruel)** [978-71 43 55] Fr Albarracin on A1512 head twd Orihuela. Turn R twd vill & R after petrol stn, sp. Sm, unshd; wc; shwrs; el pts €2.10; lndtte; shop; bar; pool; phone; Eng spkn; quiet; cc acc. "Elevated, breezy situation overlooking mountain vill; friendly owner; vg sh stay." Holy Week-31 Oct. € 11.30
2002*

ORINON *1A4* (Rural/Coastal) **Camping Orinon, 39797 Orinon (Cantabria)** [tel/fax 942-87 86 30; info@campingorinon.com] Exit A8/E70 at km 160 to Orinon. Med, mkd pitch, pt sl, unshd; wc; chem disp; mv service pnt; shwrs inc; el pts (4A) €2.50; gas; lndtte; shop; rest; snacks; bar; playgrnd; sand beach adj; TV; 90% statics; dogs; phone; Eng spkn; quiet. "Excel surfing beach adj; v clean site; helpful staff; vg." ♦ ltd. 1 Apr-30 Sep. € 16.00
2004*

ORINON *1A4* (2km E Coastal) **Camping Playa Arenillas, 39798 Islares (Cantabria)** [tel/fax 942-86 31 52; cueva@mundivia.es] Exit A8 at km 156 Islares. Turn W on N634. Site on R at W end of Islares. Steep ent. Lge, mkd pitch, pt shd; wc; chem disp; baby facs; shwrs inc; el pts (5A) €3.75 (poss no earth); gas; lndtte; ice; shop; tradsmn; rest adj; snacks; bar; BBQ; playgrnd; sand beach 100m; horseriding; cycle hire; games area; TV; 40% statics; no dogs; phone; bus; poss cr; Eng spkn; adv bkg rec Jul/Aug; some rd noise; cc acc; CCI. "Facs ltd low ssn & stretched in ssn; well-staffed; facs constantly cleaned; rec arr early for choice of own pitch; conv Guggenheim Museum; excel NH for Bilbao ferry." 1 Apr-30 Sep. € 20.00
2005*

ORIO see Zarautz *3A1*

†**OROPESA** *3D2* (3km NE Coastal) **Camping Torre La Sal 'Maria', Cami L'Atall s/n, 12595 Ribera de Cabanes (Castellon)** [964-31 95 96; fax 964-31 96 29] Leave AP7 at exit 45 & take N340 twd Tarragona. Foll camp sp fr km 1000 stone. Site next after Torre La Sal 2. Lge, mkd pitch, hdstg, pt shd; htd wc; chem disp; shwrs inc; el pts €4; gas; lndtte; shop; rest high ssn; BBQ; playgrnd; htd, covrd pool; sand/shgl beach adj; 10% statics; dogs (except Jul/Aug); phone; bus 200m; poss cr; Eng spkn; adv bkg; quiet; cc acc; red long stay/snr citizens; CCI. "Clean, well-maintained site." ♦ ltd.
€ 21.70
2004*

†**OROPESA** *3D2* (3.5km NE Coastal) **Camping Oasis, Ctra L'Atall, 12594 Oropesa (Castellon)** [tel/fax 964-31 96 77] Leave A7 at exit 45 & take N340 twds Tarragona. Turn R after km stone 999, site sp R at beach rd. Med, hdg pitch, hdstg, shd; wc; chem disp; shwrs; el pts (5A) €2.70; gas; shop & 500m; tradsmn; lndtte; rest; snacks; bar; pool; playgrnd; sand beach 200m; entmnt; TV rm; car wash; phone; 20% statics; quiet but some rd/rlwy noise; Eng spkn; red long stay & snr citizens; CCI. "Gd rest; friendly, helpful staff." € 22.00   2002*

†**OROPESA** *3D2* (3.5km NE Coastal) **Camping Torre La Sal 2, Cami L'Atall s/n, 12595 Ribera de Cabanes (Castellon)** [964-31 97 77; fax 964-31 97 44; camping@torrelasal2.com; www.torrelasal2.com] Leave AP7 at exit 45 & take N340 twd Tarragona. Foll camp sp fr km 1000 stone. Site adj Torre La Sal 'Maria'. Lge, hdg/mkd pitch, hdstg, pt shd; htd wc; chem disp; sauna; serviced pitch; shwrs inc; el pts (10A) €5.06; gas; lndtte; shop; tradsmn; supmkt adj; rest; snacks; bar; playgrnd; shgl beach adj; 4 pools (2 htd & covrd); tennis; games area; entmnt; library; TV rm; some statics; Eng spkn; adv bkg; quiet; red long stay/low ssn/snr citizens; CCI. "Clean, peaceful site; lge pitches; more mature c'vanners v welcome; poss diff for lge o'fits; water points few & far between." ♦
€ 26.60
2005*

OSSA DE MONTIEL *4E1* (10km SW Rural) **Camping Los Batanes, Ctra Lagunas de Ruidera, Km 8, 02611 Ossa de Montiel (Albacete) [926-69 90 76; fax 926-69 91 71; camping@ losbatanes.com; www.losbatanes.com]** Fr Munera twd Ossa de Montiel on N430. In Ossa foll sp in vill to site in 10km. Fr Manzanares on N430 app to Ruidera, cross bdge; turn immed R alongside lagoon, camp at 12km. Lge, pt shd; htd wc; chem disp; mv service pnt; shwrs; el pts (5A) €3; lndtte; ice; shops 10km; tradsmn; rest 200m; snacks; bar; playgrnd; pool, paddling pool high ssn; lake sw adj; cycle hire; TV; 10% statics; dogs €1.90; phone; Eng spkn; adv bkg; noisy at w/e; cc acc; 10% red CCI. "Lovely area of natural lakes; excel birdwatching & walking; friendly owners; low ssn phone to check open." ♦ 25 Febr-11 Dec. € 23.40 (CChq acc)
2005*

Will you fill in the site report forms at the back of the guide, or shall I?

OTURA see Granada *2G4*

PALAFRUGELL *3B3* (5km E Coastal) **Camping Tamariu, 17212 Tamariu (Gerona) [tel/fax 972-62 04 22; campingtamariu@teleline.es]** In Tamariu, app fr Palafrugell, turn L at bottom of hill on ent vill, site sp. Lge, pt sl, part terr, shd; wc; chem disp; shwrs; el pts €3; gas; lndtte; shop; snacks; bar; shgl beach 600m; pool; playgrnd; phone; poss cr; quiet. "On beautiful part of coast away fr main rds; gd grocers shops & rests in vill; steep app to terr pitches; poss more suitable for tents; conv parking for vill & beach."
Easter & 1 May-30 Sep. € 18.62
2002*

PALAFRUGELL *3B3* (2km SE Rural) **Camping La Siesta, Chopitea 110, 17210 Calella de Palafrugell (Gerona) [972-61 51 16; fax 972-61 44 16; info@ campinglasiesta.com; www.campinglasiesta. com]** On main rd to Gerona-Palamos turn L (E) on rndabt onto GI654 & foll sp Calella. Site on R just bef Calella. V lge, mkd pitch, pt sl, pt shd; wc; chem disp; el pts inc; gas; lndtte; shops; rest; snacks; 2 bars; no BBQ; playgrnd; 2 lge pools; beach 1.3km; tennis; horseriding; entmnt; statics; no dogs; bus; site open w/ends Nov-March; Eng spkn; adv bkg (dep req); noisy at w/e; red low ssn; CCI. "Excel beaches at Llafranch & Calella de Palafrugell; mkt at Palafrugell; many beaches & coves adj; narr, winding paths thro pines to pitches; most vans have to be manhandled onto pitches; twin-axles acc; Eng newspapers same day." Easter-30 Oct. € 39.60
2004*

PALAFRUGELL *3B3* (3km S Coastal) **Kim's Camping, Pseo Font d'en Xeco s/n, 17211 Llafranc (Gerona) [972-30 11 56; fax 972-61 08 94; info@campingkims.com; www.campingkims. com]** Exit m'way AP7 at junc 6 Gerona Nord if coming fr France, or junc 9 fr S dir Palamos. Foll sp for Palafrugell, Playa Llafranc. Lge, hdg/mkd pitches, hdstg, pl sl, terr, pt shd; wc; chem disp; baby facs; shwrs inc; el pts (6A) inc; gas; lndtte; ice; shop; rest; snacks; bar; BBQ; playgrnd; 2 pools; sand beach 500m; watersports; tennis nrby; games rm; games area; cycle hire; TV; entmnt; excursions; golf 10km; car wash; some statics; dogs; phone; guarded; poss cr; Eng spkn; adv bkg; quiet; cc acc; red low ssn/long stay; CCI. "Excel, beachside site; steep site rds; friendly, well-organised; high ssn w/e noise fr adj site; excel, new san facs inc bthrm for disabled." ♦ 7 Apr-30 Sep. € 37.00
2005*

PALAFRUGELL *3B3* (4km S Coastal) **Camping Moby Dick, Costa Verda 16-28, 17210 Calella de Palafrugell (Gerona) [972-61 43 07; fax 972-61 49 40; info@campingmobydick.com; www.campingmobydick.com]** Fr Palafrugell foll sps to Calella. At rndabt just bef Calella turn R, then 4th L, site clearly sp on R. Med, hdstg, sl, terr, pt shd; wc; chem disp; baby facs; shwrs inc; el pts (6-10A) €3.50; lndtte; shop; supmkt 100m; rest 100m; snacks; bar; playgrnd; shgl beach 150m; 15% statics; dogs; phone; bus 100m; poss cr; Eng spkn; adv bkg; quiet; CCI. ♦ 1 Apr-15 Oct. € 19.50
2005*

PALAMOS *3B3* (1km N Coastal) **Camping Benelux, Paraje Torre Mirona s/n, 17230 Palamos (Gerona) [972-31 55 75; fax 972-60 19 01]** Turn E off Palamos-La Bisbal rd (C66) at km stone 40.7. Site in 800m on minor metalled rd, to sea at Playa del Castell. Lge, hdstg, pt sl, pt shd; wc; chem disp; mv service pnt; shwrs inc; el pts (6A) inc; gas; lndtte; ice; shop; tradsmn; supmkt; rest (w/e only low ssn); snacks; bar; playgrnd; pool; sand beach 1km; safe dep; car wash; currency exchange; TV; 50% statics; dogs; poss cr; Eng spkn; adv bkg; noisy at w/e; red low ssn/long stay; cc acc; CCI. "In pine woods; many long stay British/Dutch; gd shop on site; excel supmkt in town; gd rests nrby; v friendly owner; clean facs poss ltd low ssn; poss flooding in heavy rain; poss diff for disabled; rough ground; vg long stay." ♦ ltd. 1 Apr-30 Sep. € 23.00
2004*

SPAIN

PALAMOS *3B3* (1km N Coastal) **Camping Internacional de Palamos**, Aptdo Correos 100, Cami Cap de Planes s/n, 17230 Palamos (Gerona) [972-31 47 36; fax 972-31 76 26; campingpalamos@infonegocio.com] Fr N leave A7 at junc 6 to Palamos on C66. Fr Palafrugell turn L 16m after o/head sp to Sant Feliu-Palamos at sm sp La Fosca & camp sites. Winding app thro La Fosca. Fr S, take exit 9 dir Sant Feliu & Lloret, then C253 to Sta Christina-Palamos, then La Fosca. Lge, pt shd; wc (mainly cont); chem disp; mv service pnt; baby facs; serviced pitches; shwrs inc; el pts; (5A) €4.40; lndry rm; shop; rest; snacks; bar; playgrnd; pool & paddling pool; sand beach 500m; solarium; mini-golf 200m; windsurfing, sailing & diving 1km; golf 15km; TV; car wash; 20% statics; phone; quiet. "Attractive site; superb san facs; highly rec." ♦ 19 Mar-30 Sep. € 31.90 (CChq acc)   2005*

PALAMOS *3B3* (1km N Coastal) **Camping Palamos**, Ctra La Fosca 12, 17230 Palamos (Gerona) [972-31 42 96; fax 972-60 11 00] App Palamos on C66/C31 fr Gerona & Palafrugell turn L 16m after o/head sp Sant Feliu-Palamos at sm sp La Fosca & campsites. Lge, pt sl, terr, pt shd; wc; shwrs; baby facs; el pts (4A) €2.50; gas; lndtte; ice; shop; rest 400m; playgrnd; 2 pools; shgl/rocky beach 500m; tennis; golf; 30% statics; dogs €2; phone; cc acc. 29 Mar-30 Sep. € 27.60   2003*

PALAMOS *3B3* (3km N Coastal) **Camping Relax Ge**, Barrio Roqueta s/n, 17253 Mont-Ras (Gerona) [972-30 08 18; fax 972-60 11 00; info@camping relaxnat.com; www.campingrelaxge.com] C31 Palafrugell-Palamos rd at km 39, site sp. Med, mkd pitch, pt shd; wc; chem disp; shwrs (5A) €2; gas; lndtte; ice; shop; rest; snacks; bar; playgrnd; htd pool & paddling pool; sand beach 1km; 10% statics; adv bkg (dep req); quiet; CCI. "Friendly, family-run site; exceptional beaches; conv Gerona, Barcelona; vg long stay." 1 Apr-30 Sep. € 26.75   2004*

PALAMOS *3B3* (5km N) **Camping Relax-Nat** (Naturist), Barrio Roqueta s/n, 17253 Mont-Ras (Gerona) [972-30 08 18; fax 972-60 11 00; info@ campingrelaxnat.com] Fr C66 Palafrugell-Palamos rd, turn E after km stone 38. Site in 1.5km on metalled rd. Lge, pt shd; wc; chem disp; shwrs; el pts (2A) €2; lndtte; shop; snacks; playgrnd; sand beach 4km; pool; playgrnd; tennis; games area; entmnt; adv bkg; quiet. "Naturist families & mixed groups min 2 people; diff pitch access for lge o'fits." 1 Apr-30 Sep. € 27.50   2003*

PALAMOS *3B3* (3km SW Coastal) **Camping Costa Brava**, 17252 Sant Antoni de Calonge (Gerona) [tel/fax 972-65 02 22; campingcostabrava@ campingcostabrava.net; www.campingcosta brava.net] Foll sp St Antoni de Calonge fr C31, site sp. Lge, mkd pitch, shd; wc; chem disp; baby facs; shwrs inc; el pts (5A) €3.30; lndtte; ice; shop adj; rest; snacks; bar; BBQ; playgrnd; pool & child pool; sand beach 300m; watersports; games rm; entmnt; car wash; dogs; phone; bus; poss cr; adv bkg; quiet; cc acc. "Well-managed, family-run site; rec arr early high ssn to secure pitch; pleasant, helpful owners." ♦ 1 Jun-20 Sep. € 25.00   2005*

PALAMOS *3B3* (3km SW Coastal) **Eurocamping, Ctra Palamos-Playa de Aro 15, Km 49.2, Avda Catalunya 15, 17252 Sant Antoni de Calonge (Gerona)** [972-65 08 79; fax 972-66 19 87; info@ euro-camping.com; www.euro-camping.com] Exit A7 junc 6 dir Palamos on C66 & Sant Feliu C31. Take exit Sant Antoni; on ent Sant Antoni turn R at 1st rndabt. Visible fr main rd at cent of Sant Antoni. V lge, mkd pitch, shd; wc; chem disp; mv service pnt; 20% serviced pitch; baby facs; shwrs inc; el pts (5A) inc; gas; lndtte; ice; supmkt; rest; snacks; bar; BBQ; playgrnd; 2 pools & paddling pool; sand beach 150m; waterpark 5km; tennis; cycle hire 200m; mini-golf; golf 7km; games area; games rm; fitness rm; doctor Jul & Aug; car wash; entmnt high ssn; internet; TV rm; 15% statics; dogs €3.37; phone; Eng spkn; adv bkg; quiet; cc acc; red long stay/low ssn; CCI. "Excel facs for families; lots to do in area; vg." ♦ 8 Apr-24 Sep. € 39.75   2005*

See advertisement

PALAMOS *3B3* (2.5km W Rural) **Camping Castell Park**, 17253 Vall-Llobrega (Gerona) [tel/fax 972-31 52 63; info@camingcastellpark.com; www.campingcastellpark.com] Exit m'way at junc 6 & take C66/C31 to Palamos. Site on R sp after 40km stone. Lge, mkd pitch, terr, shd; wc (some cont); chem disp; baby facs; shwrs inc; el pts (5A) inc; gas; lndtte; supmkt; rest; snacks; bar; BBQ; playgrnd; pool; paddling pool; sand beach 2.5km; golf 11km; games rm; entmnt; TV rm; 6% statics; dogs free; Eng spkn; adv bkg; quiet; red long stay; CCI. "Quiet family site with friendly atmosphere; rallies & single c'vanners welcome; c'van storage avail." ♦ 8 Apr-17 Sep. € 27.70   2005*

PALS *3B3* (4km NE Coastal) **Camping Playa Brava, Playa Pals, 17256 Pals (Gerona)** [972-63 68 94; fax 972-63 69 52; info@ playabrava.com] App Pals on rd 650 fr N or S. Avoid Pals cent. Fr by-pass take rd E sp Playa de Pals at rndabt. In 4km turn L opp shops, in 400m turn L past golf course, site on L bef beach. Avoid Begur & coast rd. Lge, shd; wc; chem disp; baby facs; shwrs; el pts inc; gas; lndtte; supmkt adj; rest; snacks; bar; playgrnd; pool; sand beach adj; tennis; cycle hire; car wash; no dogs; adv bkg; quiet; 30% low ssn red. "Guarded; gd facs for children & families." ♦ 13 May-17 Sep. € 33.75   2002*

PALS *3B3* (5km NE Coastal) **Camping Interpals, Avda Mediterranea s/n, Km 45, 17256 Playa de Pals (Gerona)** [972-63 61 79; fax 972-66 74 76; interpals@interpals.com; www.interpals.com] Exit A7 junc 6 dir Palamos onto C66. Turn N sp Pals & foll sp Playa/Platja de Pals, site clearly sp. Lge, pt sl, terr, shd; htd wc; chem disp; mv service pnt; baby facs; shwrs inc; el pts (5-10A) inc; lndtte; rest; snacks; bar; playgrnd; pool; sand beach 300m (naturist beach 1km); watersports; tennis; golf 1km; internet; TV; 5% statics; dogs (no Pitbulls or Rottweilers) €2.75; phone; adv bkg; quiet; 10% red CCI. "Set in pine forest; poss diff lge o'fits; modern, well-maintained facs." ♦ 31 Mar-30 Sep. € 39.00 (CChq acc)   2005*

†**PALS** *3B3* (1km E) **Camping Resort Mas Patoxas Bungalow Park, Ctra Torroella- Palafrugell, Km 339, 17256 Pals (Gerona)** [972-63 69 28; fax 972-66 73 49; info@campingmaspatoxas.com; www.campingmaspatoxas.com] AP7 exit 6 onto C66 Palamos/La Bisbal, turn L via Torrent to Pals. Turn R & site on R almost opp old town of Pals on rd to Torroella de Montgri. Or fr Palafrugell on C31 turn at km 339. Lge, mkd pitch, terr, shd; htd wc; 30% serviced pitches; chem disp; mv service pnt; baby facs; shwrs inc; el pts (5A) inc; gas; ice; lndtte; supmkt; tradsmn; rest; snacks; bar; playgrnd; pool; sand beach 4km; games area; entmnt; tennis; cycle hire; mini-golf; golf 4km; TV; dogs €3; phone; site clsd 18 Dec-12 Jan; recep clsd Monday low ssn; Eng spkn; adv bkg ess high ssn; quiet; red long stay/low ssn; gd security; cc acc; CCI. "Excel." ♦ € 39.00   2005*

PALS *3B3* (2km E Coastal) **Camping Cypsela, Rodors 7, 17256 Playa de Pals (Gerona)** [972-66 76 96; fax 972-66 73 00; info@cypsela. com; www.cypsela.com] Exit a'pista AP7 junc 6, rd C66 dir Palamos. 7km fr La Bisbal take dir Pals & foll sp Playa/Platja de Pals, site sp. V lge, mkd pitch, shd; wc; chem disp; 25% serviced pitches; baby facs; private bthrms; shwrs inc; el pts (6A) €2.70; gas; lndtte; ice; supmkt; rest; snacks; bar; playgrnd; pool (caps ess); shd beach 1.5km; tennis; mini-golf & other sports; cycle hire; golf 1.5km; entmnt; child entmnt; internet; TV; free bus to beach; no dogs; Eng spkn; adv bkg; cc acc; red long stay/CCI. "Noise levels controlled after midnight; excel san facs; 4 grades of pitch/price." ♦ 13 May-24 Sep. € 42.30   2005*

See advertisement on next page

†**PAMPLONA** *3B1* (7km N Rural) **Camping Ezcaba, Ctra N121, Km 7, 31194 Eusa (Navarre)** [948-33 03 15; fax 948-33 13 16; info@ campingszcaba.com; www.campingezcaba.com] Fr N leave AP15 onto NA30 (N ring rd) to N121A sp Francia/Iruna. Pass Arre & Oricain, turn L foll site sp 500m on R dir Berriosuso. Site on R in 500m - fairly steep ent. Or fr S leave AP15 onto NA32 (E by-pass) to N121A sp Francia/Iruna, then as above. Med, mkd pitch, pt sl, pt shd; wc; shwrs inc; el pts €3.60; gas; lndtte; ice; shop; rest; snacks; bar; pool; horseriding; tennis; dogs €1.90; phone; bus 1km; poss cr; adv bkg; rd noise; red low ssn. "V helpful & friendly staff; should be open all yr but phone to check; sm pitches unsuitable lge o'fits & poss diff due trees, esp when site full; nice walks fr site; attractive setting with surrounding hills; gd pool, bar & rest; in winter use as NH only." ♦ € 17.00   2005*

†**PANCORBO** *1B4* (3km NE Rural) **Camping El Desfiladero, Ctra Madrid-Irun, Km.305, 09280 Pancorbo (Burgos)** [947-35 40 27; fax 947-35 42 35] Fr A1/E5 exit junc 4 onto N1 dir Vitoria/Gasteiz, site on L in 2km at hostal. Med, mkd pitch, some hdstg, terr, pt shd; wc; chem disp; shwrs inc; el pts (8A) €3.20; lndtte; shop 3km; rest; snacks; bar; playgrnd; pool; tennis; 25% statics; dogs; train 3km; some rd & rlwy noise; cc acc; red CCI. "Access diff lge o'fits due steep ent; recep in hostal rest low ssn; friendly, helpful owner; fair sh stay/NH." ♦ € 11.70   2005*

†**PANCORBO** *1B4* (7km NE Rural) **Camping Monumento Al Pastor, 09219 Ameyugo (Burgos)** [947-34 43 55; fax 947-35 42 90] Fr W take slip rd to R sp Ameyugo & rest area. Pass under AP1 & foll sp to rest area & site. Site is 500m beyond Ameyugo on N side of AP1 at km stone 308, easily seen by monument of shepherd & lamb. If app fr E, take R turn on climbing hill on A1. Recep is in rest, sp 'Monumento al Pastor' fr rd. Med, terr, unshd; wc; shwrs inc; el pts (6-10A) inc; shop; rest; snacks; bar; playgrnd; tennis; 90% statics; no dogs; phone; poss cr; quiet but some rd noise; cc acc. "V ltd space for tourers & no easy alternative if they are occupied; facs ltd low ssn; vg rest, bar; beautiful views; conv NH for Bilbao." € 16.00   2004*

PELIGROS see Granada *2G4*

PENAFIEL *1C4* (Rural) **Camping Riberduero, Avda Polideportivo 51, 47300 Penafiel [tel/fax 938-88 16 37; camping@campingpenafiel.com; www.campingpenafiel.com]** Fr Valladolid 56km or Aranda de Duero 38km on N122. In Penafiel take VA223 dir Cuellar, foll sp to sports cent/camping. Med, mkd pitch, hdstg, shd; htd wc; chem disp; mv service pnt; baby facs; fam bthrm; shwrs inc; el pts (7.50A) €3.20; gas; lndtte; shop; rest; snacks; bar; playgrnd; pool; rv 1km; cycle hire; TV; 20% statics; dogs €1.50; phone; site open w/e only low ssn; poss cr; Eng spkn; adv bkg (50% dep req); quiet; cc acc; 10% red 15 days. "Excel, well-kept site; interesting, historical area; ideal for wheelchair users." ♦ 1 Apr-30 Sep. € 15.90   2005*

PENASCOSA see Alcaraz *4F1*

†**PENISCOLA** *3D2* (Urban/Coastal) **Camping Las Moreras, Avda Papa Luna 113, 12598 Peniscola (Castellon)** Fr N340 or A7 foll sp to cent Peniscola. Site well sp behind Hotel Casablanca. Sm, mkd pitch, hdstg, pt shd; own san; mv service pnt; el pts; shops, rests, snacks, bars nr; beach 150m; m'vans only. "Conv NH." € 15.00   2003*

†**PENISCOLA** *3D2* (500m Urban/Coastal) **Camping Bellavista, 12598 Peniscola (Castellon) [964-48 01 35; fax 964-48 16 49]** Site 500m fr cent of Peniscola. Leave town by Castillon rd. After rndabt 'Plaza de la Constitution' turn L by 'Foto Rita' & foll camp sp, site on R in 200m. Med, some hdstg, pt sl, terr, pt shd; wc; baby facs; shwrs inc; el pts (16A) inc; gas; lndtte; rest; snacks; bar; playgrnd; pool; sand beach 200m; 80% statics; guarded; poss cr; adv bkg; red long stay; CCI. "Few touring pitches; walking dist old town; castle worth visit; diff access to pitches." € 27.60   2004*

†**PENISCOLA** *3D2* (1km N Coastal) **Camping El Eden, Ctra CS501 Benicarlo-Peniscola Km 6, 12598 Peniscola (Castellon) [964-48 05 62; fax 964-48 98 28; camping@camping-eden.com; www.camping-eden.com]** Leaving Peniscola on rd to Benicarlo via sea front, take L turn at site sp (poss obscured by trees). Lge, hdg/mkd pitch, pt shd; htd wc; chem disp; baby facs; shwrs inc; el pts (10A) €3.30; gas; lndry service; shop 300m; rest, snacks; bar; playgrnd; pool; sand/shgl beach adj; 40% statics; dogs; cash dispenser; poss cr; rd noise in ssn; cc acc; red long stay/low ssn. "Ltd facs low ssn; san facs refurbished & v clean; cats on site & barking dogs; beach adj cleaned daily; gd security; excel pool; easy access to sandy/gravel pitches but many sm trees poss diff for awnings or high m'vans; poss vicious mosquitoes at dusk; easy walk/cycle to town; NB: 4 diff sizes of pitch (some with tap, sink & drain) with different prices." ♦ € 34.00   2005*

†PENISCOLA *3D2* (2km N) **Camping El Cid, Azagador de la Cruz s/n, 12598 Peniscola** [964-48 03 80] Exit A7 at junc 43. Take N340 sp Valencia for sh distance, turn L sp Peniscola. Approx 2km look for yellow sp to site. Med, mkd pitch, shd; wc; chem disp; shwrs inc; el pts (10A) €3.10; gas; lndtte; shop; supmkt 2km; rest; snacks; bar; playgrnd; pool; sand beach 3km; 50% statics; poss cr; cc acc; red long stay/low ssn; CCI. "Well-run site; pop with Spanish families; v friendly staff; vg long stay." € 16.75   2004*

†PENISCOLA *3D2* (2km W) **Camping Los Pinos, Ctra Abellars, 12598 Peniscola (Castellon)** [964-48 03 79] Exit A7 junc 43 or N340 sp Peniscola. Site sp on L. Med, pt shd; wc; chem disp; mv service pnt; baby facs; shwrs; el pts €2.73; gas; lndtte; shop; rest; snacks; bar; BBQ; playgrnd; pool; phone; bus fr site. "Narr site rds, lots of trees; poss diff access some pitches." € 13.67   2002*

†PENISCOLA *3D2* (2km NW Rural) **Camping Azahar Residencial, Partida Villarroyos s/n, Playa Montana, 12598 Peniscola-Benicarlo (Castellon)** [tel/fax 964-47 54 80; info@campingazahar.com; www.campingazahar.com] Exit AP7 junc 43, turn R immed after toll, site sp in 1.5km twd Benicarlo. Fr N340 site sp at km 1.041 fr S or km 1.039 fr N. Site nr go-kart track. Med, mkd pitch, hdstg, pt shd; htd wc; chem disp; mv service pnt; serviced pitches; sauna; shwrs inc; el pts (10A) inc; gas; lndtte; ice; shop; tradsmn; rest; snacks; bar; playgrnd; htd pool; jacuzzi; sand beach 2.5km; gym; 20% statics; dogs; phone; bus 500m; c'van storage; Eng spkn; adv bkg; some rd noise; cc acc; red long stay/snr citizens; CCI. "V helpful, enthusiastic staff & owners; improving site; gd cycling." ♦ € 25.90   2005*

See advertisement above

PINEDA DE MAR see Calella *3C3*

PINEDA, LA see Salou *3C2*

PITRES *2G4* (500m Rural) **Camping El Balcon de Pitres, Ctra Orgiva-Ugijar, Km 51, 18414 Pitres (Granada)** [958-76 61 11; fax 958-80 44 53] S fr Granada on N323, turn E onto A348. At Orgiva take GR421 to Pitres. Sm, terr, shd; wc; chem disp; el pts (10A) €2.53; gas; lndtte; ice; shop; rest; snacks; bar; playgrnd; pool; cycle hire; some statics; poss cr Aug; adv bkg; quiet; red long stay; cc acc; CCI. "Site in unspoilt Alpujarras region of Sierra Nevada mountains; fine scenery & wildlife; site on steep hillside, poss diff lge o'fits; san facs at top of hill - own san facs saves climb; vg sh stay." 1 Mar-31 Oct. € 14.80   2003*

PLASENCIA *1D3* (4km NE Urban) **Camping La Chopera, 10600 Plasencia (Caceres)** [927-41 66 60; fax 927-41 33 53; www.plasenciaweb.com/ lachopera] In Plasencia on main N630 turn E on N110 sp Avila & foll sp indus est & sp to site. Med, shd; wc; serviced pitches; chem disp; baby facs; shwrs inc; el pts (6A) inc; gas; lndtte; ice; shop; rest; bar; BBQ; playgrnd; 2 pools in ssn; tennis; cycle hire; dogs; quiet but w/e disco; cc acc; CCI. "Conv Manfrague National Park (breeding of black/ Egyptian vultures, black storks, imperial eagles); excel pool & modern facs; helpful owners; gd long stay." ♦ Easter-20 Sep. € 15.10   2004*

†PLASENCIA *1D3* (10km S Rural) **Camping Parque Natural Monfrague, Ctra Plasencia-Trujillo, Km 10, 10680 Malpartida de Plasencia (Caceres)** [tel/fax 927-45 92 33; luzpilar@bbvnet. com] Fr N on N630 by-pass town, 5km S of town take EX108 dir Malpartida de Plasencia. In 6km take EX208 dir Trujilo, site on L in 5km. App fr S on EX208 not rec. Med, pt sl, terr, pt shd; wc; chem disp; mv service pnt; baby facs; shwrs inc; el pts (5A) €2.80; gas; lndtte; shop; tradsmn; hypmkt nr; rest; snacks; bar; BBQ; playgrnd; pool; tennis; games area; archery; cycle hire; rambling; 4x4 off-rd; horseriding; TV rm; 10% statics; dogs; phone; Eng spkn; no adv bkg; rlwy noise; cc acc; red long stay/CCI. "Friendly staff; ltd facs low ssn; dusty site but hoses avail; 10km to National Park (breeding vultures); excel base." ♦ € 13.50 (CChq acc)   2005*

PLAYA DE ARO *3B3* (1km N Coastal) **Camping Treumal, Aptdo Correos 348, Ctra Playa de Aro/Palamos, C253, Km 47.5, 17251 Calonge (Gerona) [972-65 10 95; fax 972-65 16 71; info@ campingtreumal.com; www.campingtreumal.com]** Exit m'way at junc 6, 7 or 9 dir St Feliu de Guixols to Playa de Aro; site is sp at km 47.5 fr C253 coast rd S of Palamos. Lge, hdg/mkd pitch, terr, shd; wc; baby facs; shwrs inc; chem disp; mv service pnt; el pts (6-10A) inc; gas; lndtte; ice; supmkt; rest; bar; snacks; playgrnd; sm pool; sand beach adj; fishing; games rm; sports facs; cycle hire 1km; golf 5km; entmnt; disco; 20% statics; no dogs; phone; car wash; Eng spkn; adv bkg; quiet; cc acc; red low ssn; CCI. "Set in pine trees; beautifully planted; peaceful; excel san facs; manhandling poss req onto terr pitches." ♦ 1 Apr-30 Sep. € 37.20   2005*

See advertisement opposite (top)

PLAYA DE ARO *3B3* (2km N Coastal) **Camping Cala Gogo, Ctra Sant Feliu-Palamos s/n, 17250 Platja d'Aro (Gerona) [972-65 15 64; fax 972-65 05 53; calagogo@calagogo.es; www. calagogo.es]** Exit AP7 junc 6 dir Palamos/Sant Feliu. Fr Palamos take C253 coast rd S twd Sant Antoni, site on R 2km fr Playa de Aro, sp. Lge, pt sl, pt terr, pt shd; wc; chem disp; mv service pnt; shwrs inc; el pts (5A) inc; gas; lndtte; ice; supmkt; rest; snacks; bar; 2 htd pools; paddling pool; sand beach adj; boat hire; diving school; games area; games rm; tennis; cycle hire; golf 4km; entmnt; child entmnt; internet; TV; no dogs 20/6-21/8 (€2); adv bkg; quiet. "Clean, airy facs; site terraced into pinewood on steep hillside; some manhandling may be req when siting; excel family site." 29 Apr-24 Sep. € 38.00
2005*

See advertisement opposite (middle)

†**PLAYA DE ARO** *3B3* (2km N Coastal) **Camping Internacional de Calonge, Ctra Sant Feliu-Palamos, Km 7.6, 17251 Calonge (Gerona) [972-65 12 33 or 972-65 14 64; fax 972-65 25 07; info@intercalonge.com; www.intercalonge.com]** A7 exit 6 onto C66 dir La Bisbal, Palamos & Playa d'Aro; 3km bef Palamos foll sp St Antoni de Calonge. At 2nd rndbt bear R onto C253 dir San Feliu, site on R in 3km. V lge, mkd pitch, terr, shd; htd wc; chem disp; mv service pnt; serviced pitch; baby facs; shwrs inc; el pts (5A) inc; gas; lndtte; ice; supmkt; rest; snacks; bar; BBQ; playgrnd; 2 pools; sand/shgl beach 300m; tennis; cycle hire; extensive sports facs; entmnt; internet; TV rm; car wash; 30% statics; phone; dogs €3.35; Eng spkn; adv bkg; quiet; red/low ssn/long stay; cc acc; CCI. "On side of steep hill - parking poss diff at times; conv Dali Museum; Roman ruins; excel." ♦ € 36.95   2005*

See advertisement opposite (bottom)

PLAYA DE ARO *3B3* (2km N Rural) **Camping Mas Sant Josep, Ctra Santa Cristina-Playa de Aro, Km 2, 17246 Santa Cristina de Aro (Gerona) [972-83 51 08; fax 972-83 70 18; info@camping massantjosep.com; www.campingmassantjosep. com]** Fr A7/E15 take exit 7 dir Sant Feliu de Guixols to Santa Christina town. Take old rd dir Playa de Aro, site in 2km. V lge, mkd pitch, shd; htd wc; chem disp; mv service pnt; baby facs; serviced pitches; sauna; shwrs inc; el pts (10A) inc; gas; lndtte; lndry rm; ice; shop; rest; snacks; bar; BBQ; playgrnd; lge pools; sand beach 3.5km; tennis; games rm; games area; mini-golf & assorted sports; cycle hire; entmnt; golf 4km; internet; TV rm; 60% statics; dogs; Eng spkn; adv bkg; quiet; cc acc; red low ssn; CCI. "Generous pitches; excel." ♦ 26 May-12 Sep. € 34.00   2005*

PLAYA DE ARO *3B3* (1km S Coastal) **Camping Valldaro, Avda Castell d'Aro 63, 17250 Playa de Aro (Gerona) [972-81 75 15; fax 972-81 66 62; valldaro@valldaro.com; www.valldaro.com]** Exit A7 junc 7 onto C65 dir Sant Feliu. Turn L onto C31 for Playa de Aro thro Castillo de Aro & site on R, 1km fr Playa at km 4.2. V lge, pt shd; wc; chem disp; mv service pnt; baby facs; shwrs inc; el pts (5A) inc; gas; lndtte; shop; rest; snacks; bar; playgrnd; 2 pools; waterslides; beach 1km; watersports; tennis; horseriding 2km; golf 3km; games area; cycle hire; internet; entmnt; 50% statics; dogs (no Pitbulls, Rottweilers or similar); phone; adv bkg; red long stay. "Gd family site; some lge pitches in new area; many facs." ♦ 31 Mar-1 Oct. € 36.10 (CChq acc)   2005*

PLAYA DE ARO *3B3* (1.5km S Coastal) **Camping Riembau, 17250 Playa de Aro (Gerona) [972-81 71 23; fax 972-82 52 10; camping@ riembau.com]** Fr Gerona take C250 thro Llagostera, turn for Playa de Aro. Fr Playa de Aro take C253 twd San Feliu. Site access rd 2km on R. V lge, pt shd; wc; chem disp; baby facs; shwrs inc; el pts (5A) inc; gas; lndtte; rest; snacks; bar; shop; beach 800m; 2 pools (1 indoor); playgrnd; tennis; fitness cent; entmnt; child entmnt; 30% statics; phone; adv bkg; some rd noise. ♦ Easter-30 Sep. € 32.10   2004*

†**PLAYA DE ARO** *3B3* (2km S Urban/Coastal) **Camping Vall d'Or, Avda Verona-Terual s/n, 17250 Playa de Aro (Gerona) [972-81 75 85; fax 972-67 44 95; valldor@betsa.es; www.betsa.es]** Exit A7 junc 7 onto C65 dir Sant Feliu de Guixols, then C31 to Playa d'Aro. V lge, pt shd; wc; chem disp; shwrs inc; el pts (5A) €3.50; gas; lndtte; shop; rest; bar; playgrnd; sand beach adj; TV; 50% statics; phone; site clsd 10 Dec-11 Jan; poss cr; adv bkg. "Gd family site." € 24.80   2004*

PLAYA DE OLIVA see Oliva *4E2*

PLAYA DE PALS see Pals *3B3*

PLAYA DE PINEDO see Valencia *4E2*

PLAYA DE VIDIAGO see Llanes *1A4*

PLAYA TAMARIT see Tarragona *3C3*

POBLA DE SEGUR, LA *3B2* (2km NE Rural) Camping Collegats, Ctra N260, Km 306, 25500 La Pobla de Segur (Lleida) [973-68 07 14; fax 973-68 14 02; collegats.cam@redestb.es] Fr Tremp N to La Pobla. Site sp in town at traff lts, turn R onto N260 dir Sort. Ent by hairpin bend. Med, mkd pitch, shd; wc; shwrs; el pts inc; gas; lndtte; shop & 4km; tradsmn; rest; snacks; bar; BBQ; playgrnd; pool; games area; dogs; Eng spkn; quiet; CCI. "Clean facs; site not suitable lge o'fits; gd sh stay." ♦ 1 Apr-31 Oct. € 20.00   2003*

Mustn't forget to post our site report forms to The Club, otherwise sites might be deleted.

PONT D'ARROS see Vielha *3B2*

PONT DE SUERT *3B2* (4km N Rural) Camping Can Roig, Ctra Caldes Boi, 25520 Pont de Suert (Lleida) [973-69 05 02; fax 973-69 12 06] 3km N of Pont de Suert on N230 turn NE onto L500 Caldes de Boi rd. Site in 1km. App narr for 100m. Med, mkd pitch, hdstg, pt sl, pt shd; wc; chem disp; shwrs inc; el pts (5A) €3.25; gas; lndtte; ice; shop & 3km; snacks; bar; playgrnd; paddling pool; 5% statics; dogs; adv bkg; quiet; cc acc; red low ssn. "NH en rte S; san facs in need of refurb; beautiful valley." 1 Mar-31 Oct. € 15.00   2003*

†**PONT DE SUERT** *3B2* (5km N Rural) Camping Del Remei, 25520 Pont de Suert (Lleida) [tel/fax 973-69 12 19] N of Pont de Suert on N230 turn NE onto L500 Caldes de Boi rd. Site on R in 2km. Med, pt sl, pt shd; wc; shwrs; el pts €3.85; lndtte; shop & 4km; snacks; bar; pool; playgrnd; no dogs; quiet; cc acc. "Gd walking & skiing cent." € 20.86   2002*

†**PONT DE SUERT** *3B2* (16km NE Rural) Camping Taull, 25528 Taull (Lleida) [973 69 61 74] Fr Pont de Suert 3km N on N230 then NE onto Caldes de Boi rd. In 13km turn R into Taull. Site sp on R. Med, terr, pt shd; wc; chem disp; shwrs inc; el pts €6.45; lndry rm; shop, rest, bar 300m; 30% statics; poss cr; quiet; CCI. "Excel facs; taxis into National Park avail; ltd touring pitches; gd long/sh stay." € 18.20 2003*

PONTEAREAS *1B2* (1.5km N Rural) Camping A Freixa, 36866 Ribadetea (Pontevedra) [986-64 02 99; fax 986-74 72 76] On N120 fr Vigo & Porrino, turn L at fountain bef bdge at ent to Ponteareas. In 1.5km at tall chimney on L, turn R & site in 200m adj Rv Tea. Med, sl, pt shd; wc; shwrs; el pts €3; lndtte; shop; rest; bar; playgrnd; sand beach & rv sw; tennis; phone; quiet. Holy Week & 1 Jul-9 Sep. € 15.30   2004*

PORT DE LA SELVA, EL see Cadaques *3B3*

POTES *1A4* (1.5km W Rural) Camping La Viorna, Ctra Santa Toribio, Km 1, 39570 Potes (Cantabria) [942-73 20 21; fax 942-73 20 19; campinglaviorna@hotmail.com] Fr Potes take rd to Fuente De sp Espinama; in 1km turn L sp Toribio. Site on R in 1km. (See Mountain Passes & Tunnels in the section Planning & Travelling at front of guide). Med, mkd pitch, terr, pt shd; wc; chem disp; shwrs inc; el pts (3-6A) €1.90-2.40; lndtte; shop & 2km; rest; snacks; bar; playgrnd; pool (caps ess) high ssn; cycle hire; Eng spkn; adv bkg; quiet; cc acc; CCI; "Lovely views; gd walks; friendly, family-run, v clean site; gd pool; ideal Picos de Europa area; conv cable car; 4x4 tours; trekking; mkt on Mon; festival mid-Sep v noisy; superb quality & clean facs; some pitches diff in wet & diff lge o'fits; excel." ♦ 1 Apr-31 Oct. € 17.60   2005*

POTES *1A4* (3km W Rural) Camping La Isla-Picos de Europa, Ctra Potes-Fuente De, 39586 Turieno Calameno (Cantabria) [tel/fax 942-73 08 96; campicoseuropa@terra.es] Take N521 W fr Potes twd Espinama, site on R in 3km thro vill of Turieno (app Potes fr N). (See Mountain Passes & Tunnels in the section Planning & Travelling at front of guide.) Med, hdg/mkd pitch, pt sl, shd; wc; chem disp; mv service pnt; shwrs inc; el pts (8A) €2.80 (rev pol); gas; lndtte; shop; tradsmn; rest; bar; BBQ; playgrnd; pool (caps ess); walking; horseriding; cycling; 4WD touring; hang-gliding; mountain treks in area; phone; poss cr; adv bkg; poss noisy high ssn; Eng spkn; cc acc; red long stay; CCI. "Delightful family-run site; friendly, helpful owners; superb san facs; conv Potes; conv cable car & mountain walks (map fr recep); magnificent Picos Europa mountains; many trees, poss not suitable for tall o'fits (low branches); highly rec." Holy Week-31 Oct. € 18.00   2005*

POTES *1A4* (5km W Rural) Camping San Pelayo, Ruta Potes, Fuente de, Km 5, 39587 San Pelayo (Cantabria) [tel/fax 942-73 30 87] Take CA185 W fr Potes twd Espinama, site on R in 5km, 2km past Camping La Isla. (See Mountain Passes & Tunnels in the section Planning & Travelling at front of guide.) Med, mkd pitch, pt sl, pt shd; wc; chem disp; shwrs inc; el pts (6A) inc; lndtte; shop; rest; snacks; bar; playgrnd; pool; cycle hire; games rm; adv bkg; quiet, but noise fr bar; poss cr; cc acc high ssn; 20% red 5+ days; CCI. "Friendly, helpful owner; some pitches poss sm; conv mountain walking; excel pool." Easter-15 Oct. € 15.53   2005*

POZO ALCON *2G4* (7km N Rural) Camping Hoyo de Los Pinos, Pantano de Bolera, 23485 Pozo Alcon (Jaen) [953-73 90 05] Fr Pozo Alcon take A326 N dir Castril. Site on L. Med, pt sl, pt shd; wc; chem disp; shwrs inc; el pts (5A) €2.60; gas; shop; rest; bar; BBQ; playgrnd; quiet; cc acc; CCI. "Excel scenery & wildlife; vg sh stay." 1 Feb-19 Dec. € 10.00   2002*

PRADES see Vilanova de Prades *3C2*

PUCOL see Sagunto *4E2*

PUEBLA DE CASTRO, LA see Graus *3B2*

PUEBLA DE SANABRIA *1B3* (500m S Rural) Camping Isla de Puebla, Pago de Barregas, 49300 Puebla de Sanabria (Zamora) [980-56 79 54; fax 980-56 79 55] Fr Portugal border on C622, at ent to Puebla de Sanabria foll sp down short track twd rv. Fr N525 ent vill & foll sp Isla de Puebla. Med, mkd pitch, pt shd; wc; chem disp; shwrs inc; el pts (10A) €2.40; gas; lndtte; ice; shop; rest; snacks; bar; playgrnd; pool (caps ess); trout-fishing; adv bkg; quiet; red long stay; cc acc; CCI. "V clean, spacious facs; interesting town; vg for nature lovers; friendly, helpful wardens; facs ltd low ssn; internet facs at stn (fr 1500)." Easter-15 Sep. € 19.75   2005*

PUEBLA DE SANABRIA *1B3* (10km NW Rural) Camping El Folgoso, Ctra Puebla de Sanabria-San Martin de Castaneda, Km 13, 49361 Vigo de Sanabria (Zamora) [980-62 67 74; fax 980-62 68 00; camping@elfolgoso.com] Exit A52 sp Puebla de Sanabria & foll sp for Lago/Vigo de Sanabria thro Puente de Sanabria & Galende; site 2km beyond vill of Galende; sp. Med, pt sl, terr, shd; wc; chem disp; shwrs €1; el pts (5A) €2.46; gas; lndtte; shop high ssn; rest high ssn; snacks; bar; playgrnd; cycle hire; statics; phone; cc acc. "Lovely setting beside lake; v cold in winter." ♦ ltd. 15 Mar-15 Nov. € 16.50   2005*

PUEBLA DE SANABRIA *1B3* (10km NW) **Camping Pena-Gullon**, Lago de Sanabria, 49360 Galende (Zamora) [980-62 67 72] Fr Puebla de Sanabria foll sp for Lago de Sanabria. Site 3km beyond vill of Galende clearly sp. Lge, pt shd; wc; shwrs inc; el pts (15A) €2.46; gas; lndtte; shop in ssn; rest; lake adj; poss cr; quiet; red long stay; CCI. "Site in nature park 35km fr Portugal's Montesinho Park; rec arr by 1200; beautiful area; excel site." 15 Jul-31 Aug. € 14.80   2003*

PUEBLA DO CARAMINAL see Ribeira *1B2*

†**PUERTO DE MAZARRON** *4G1* (3km NE Rural/Coastal) **Camping Las Torres**, Ctra N332, Km 29, 30860 Puerto de Mazarron (Murcia) [tel/fax 968-59 52 25; www.campinglastorres. com] At km stone 29 on N332 bet Cartegena & Mazarron, turn up rd foll sp. Site 100m on L. Lge, hdg/mkd pitch, terr, hdstg, pt shd; wc; chem disp; mv service pnt; 40% serviced pitch (€1.80 extra); baby facs; shwrs inc; el pts (6A) inc; gas; lndtte; rest (w/e only); snacks; bar; sm shop & 3km; playgrnd; htd, covrd pool; sand/shgl beach 2km; tennis; cycle hire; sat TV; 60% statics; dogs; phone; Eng spkn; adv bkg (dep req) rec in winter; poss noisy; cc acc; red low ssn/long stay 16+ days; CCI. "Unspoilt coastline; busy at w/e; poss full winter months; well-managed, family site; excel pool; sm pitches." ♦ € 19.25   2004*

†**PUERTO DE MAZARRON** *4G1* (5km NE Coastal) Camping Los Madriles, Ctra a la Azohia 60, Km 4.5, 30868 Isla Plana (Murcia) [968-15 21 51; fax 968-15 20 92; camplosmadriles@terra.es; www. campinglosmadriles.com] Fr Cartegena on N332 dir Puerto de Mazarron. Turn L at rd junc sp La Azohia (32km). Site in 4km sp. Fr Murcia on E15/N340 dir Lorca exit junc 627 onto MU603 to Mazarron, then foll sp. (Do not use rd fr Cartegena unless powerful tow vehicle/gd weight differential - use rte fr m'way thro Mazarron.) Lge, hdstg, pt sl, terr, pt shd; wc; chem disp; mv service pnt; serviced pitches; shwrs inc; el pts (10A) €3.20; gas; lndtte; ice; shop; rest high ssn; bar; playgrnd; 2 htd pools; jacuzzi; shgl beach 500m; no dogs; bus; poss cr; Eng spkn; adv bkg (fr Oct for min 2 months only); quiet; cc acc high ssn; red long stay/low ssn/CCI. "V clean, popular winter site; adv bkg ess fr Oct; some sm pitches; some pitches sea views; unspoilt coast; delightful countryside; care needed on wet tiles in pool changing rm; may not be suitable for disabled due to sl between terr; Easter high ssn rates; 3 days min Jul/Aug; excel." ♦ € 25.00
2005*

†**PUERTO DE MAZARRON** *4G1* (5km E Rural/Coastal) **Camping Los Delfines**, Ctra Isla Plana, 30860 Puerto de Mazarron (Murcia) [tel/fax 968-59 45 27] Fr N332 turn S sp La Azohia & Isla Plana. Site on L in 3km. Med, hdstg, mkd pitch, unshd; wc; chem disp; mv service pnt; serviced pitches; shwrs inc; el pts (5A) inc; gas; lndtte; tradsmn; snacks & bar high ssn; shgl beach adj; playgrnd; 5% statics; dogs; quiet; poss cr; Eng spkn; phone; red long stay; CCI. "Fair long/sh stay; gd sized pitches; popular low ssn." € 11.50   2002*

†**PUERTO DE MAZARRON** *4G1* (5km SW Coastal) **Camping Playa de Mazarron**, Ctra Mazarron-Bolnuevo, Bolnuevo, 30877 Mazarron (Murcia) [968-15 06 60; fax 968-15 08 37] Take Bolnuevo rd fr Mazarron, at rndabt go strt, site immed on L. Lge, pt shd, mkd pitch, hdstg; wc; 90% serviced pitches; chem disp; mv service pnt; shwrs inc; el pts (5A) €2.70; gas; lndtte; shop; snacks (in ssn only); rest; bar; tennis; games area; playgrnd; sand beach adj; TV; bus; phone; adv bkg; cc acc. "Rec winter - gd red long stays + activities; excel facs; well-kept; lge pitches; excel value; friendly staff; metal-framed sunshades in ssn on most pitches but low for m'vans; gd security; gd for wheelchair users, but steps to pool." ♦ € 17.00   2003*

†**PUERTO DE SANTA MARIA, EL** *2H3* (10km W Coastal) **Camping Punta Candor**, Aptdo de Correos 15, 11520 Rota (Cadiz) [956-813303; fax 956-813211] Fr El Puerto on A491; in Rota turn onto CA604 sp Punta Candor & camping. Lge, mkd pitch; wc; shwrs inc; el pts inc; gas; lndtte; rest; shop; playgrnd; beach nrby; phone; 40% statics; cc acc. "V helpful staff; all pitches covrd by 2.50m high sun blinds - m'vans beware!" € 25.50   2004*

†PUERTO DE SANTA MARIA, EL *2H3* (12km W Coastal) **Camping Playa Aguadulce, Ctra Chipiona/Rota, 11520 Rota (Cadiz) [956-84 70 78; fax 956-84 71 94]** W fr El Puerto on A491, twd Chipiona. Ignore sp Rota & turn L at sp Costa Ballena. Foll site sp & track. Med, hdg pitch, hdstg, shd; wc; chem disp; mv service pnt; shwrs inc; el pts (6A) inc; gas; lndtte; ice; shop & 7km; tradsmn; rest; snacks; bar; playgrnd; sand beach adj; dogs; 25% statics; noisy; adv bkg (dep req); Eng spkn; cc acc; CCI. "Well-kept, attractive site; adj to excel beach; noisy at w/e & school holidays; v helpful owners; sm pitches poss diff lge o'fits." € 24.60
2004*

†PUERTO DE SANTA MARIA, EL *2H3* (3km NW Coastal) **Camping Playa Las Dunas, Paseo Maritimo La Pontilla s/n, 11500 El Puerto de Santa Maria (Cadiz) [956-87 22 10; fax 956-86 01 17; info@lasdunascamping.com; www.lasdunas camping.com]** Fr N or S exit N1V m'way at El Puerto de Sta Maria. Foll site sp carefully to avoid narr streets of town cent. Site 2-3km S of marina & leisure complex of Puerto Sherry. Alternatively, fr N1V take Rota rd & look for sp to site & Hotel Playa Las Dunas. Site better sp fr this dir. Lge, pt sl, pt shd; wc; chem disp; shwrs inc; el pts (5-10A) €3.10-6.30; gas; lndtte; shop; tradsmn; snacks; bar; playgrnd; pool adj; sand beach 50m; sports facs; 30% statics; phone; guarded; poss cr; adv bkg rec; poss noisy; red facs low ssn; cc acc; red CCI. "Friendly staff; conv Cadiz & Jerez sherry region, birdwatching areas & beaches; conv ferry or catamaran to Cadiz; sm area for tourers; facs poss stretched high ssn; take care caterpillars in spring - poss dangerous to dogs." ♦ € 17.25   2005*

†PUERTO LUMBRERAS *4G1* (1km E Urban) **Camping Los Angeles, Ctra N340, Km 579-A, 30890 Puerto Lumbreras (Murcia) [968-40 27 82]** Exit 580 fr new dual c'way section of N340 at rndabt dir Lorca. Site 200m on R, ent beside rest, at rear. Steep driveway. Sm, hdstg, pt shd; wc; shwrs inc; el pts (6A) inc (poss no earth); gas; shop 1km; rest/bar adj high ssn; playgrnd; htd pool; phone; quiet; adv bkg; CCI. "Site run down low ssn, but fair NH; site yourself." ♦ € 12.50   2004*

PUIGCERDA *3B3* (2km NE Rural) **Camping Stel, Ctra Llivia s/n, 17520 Puigcerda (Gerona) [972-88 23 61; fax 972-14 04 19; puigcerda@stel. es]** Fr France head for Bourg-Madame on N20 or N116. Cross border dir Llivia on N154, site is 1km after rndabt. Lge, mkd pitch, terr, pt shd; htd wc; chem disp; mv service pnt; baby facs; shwrs; el pts (7A) €3.42; lndtte; shop; rest; snacks; bar; playgrnd; htd pool; canoeing; watersports; archery; cycle hire; golf 4km; internet; entmnt; TV rm; 10% statics; dogs; Eng spkn; adv bkg; some rd noise; cc acc. "Pitches on upper terr quieter; superb scenery." ♦
27 May-25 Sep. € 31.90 (CChq acc)   2005*

PUIGCERDA *3B3* (2km W Rural) **Camping Pirineus, 17528 Guils de Cerdanya (Gerona) [972-88 10 62; fax 972-88 24 71; guils@stel.es; www.stel.es]** Fr Puigcerda take N260 twd Seo de Urgel. In 1km take R twd Guils de Cerdanya. Site in 1km. Lge, mkd pitch, pt shd; wc; chem disp; baby facs; shwrs inc; el pts €3; gas; lndtte; shop; rest; bar; playgrnd; pool; tennis; canoe hire; no dogs; quiet; some Eng spkn; cc acc; CCI. "Excel long stay; beautiful scenery; well run site; conv Andorra, Barcelona 2 hrs by train; no depth markings in pool." ♦ Holy Week & 22 Jun-11 Sep. € 23.90   2002*

QUEVEDA see Santillana del Mar *1A4*

RIANO *1A3* (7km E Rural) **Camping Alto Esla, 24911 Boca de Huergano (Leon) [987-74 01 39]** SW on N621 fr Potes just past junc with LE241 at Boca de Huergano. Site on L. (See Picos de Europa in Mountain Passes & Tunnels in the section Planning & Travelling at front of guide.) Sm, pt sl, shd; wc; chem disp; el pts (10A) €2; lndtte; shops 500m; phone; quiet; cc acc; CCI. ♦ 18 Jun-8 Sep. € 12.50   2004*

RIBADEO *1A2* (4km E Coastal) **Camping Playa Penarronda, Playa de Peñarronda-Barres, 33794 Castropol (Asturias) [tel/fax 985-62 30 22]** Fr N634 turn S onto N640 dir Lugo. Immed take 1st R, then foll site sp for 2km. Med, mkd pitch, shd; wc; chem disp; 80% serviced pitches; shwrs inc; el pts (6A) €2.90; gas; lndtte; shop; rest; snacks; bar; BBQ; playgrnd; sand beach adj; games area; cycle hire; 50% statics; phone; Eng spkn; quiet; red long stay; CCI. "Beautifully-kept, friendly, family-run site on 'Blue Flag' beach; rec arr early to get pitch; gd cycling paths along coastal paths & to Ribadeo; ltd facs low ssn, poss no hot water for shwrs."
Easter-20 Sep. € 21.00   2005*

†RIBADEO *1A2* (4km E Coastal) **Camping Vegamar, 33794 Castropol (Asturias) [985-62 39 48]** Fr E on E70/N634 turn L at junc (rndabt) N640 & N634 dir Vegadeo. Immed take 1st R & immed R under main rd. Site sp 500m. Med, pt shd; wc; chem disp; mv service pnt; shwrs; el pts inc; gas; lndtte; shop; rest; snacks; bar; playgrnd; pool; sand beach 1km; 60% statics; dogs; adv bkg; quiet; CCI. "Excel facs; family-run site; excel NH." ♦ € 13.50   2003*

RIBADEO *1A2* (4km W Rural) **Camping Ribadeo, Ctra Ribadeo La Coruna, Km 2, 27700 Ribadeo (Lugo) [tel/fax 982-13 11 67]** W fr Ribadeo on N634/E70 twd La Coruna, in 2km pass sp Camping Ribadeo. Ignore 1st camping sp, take next L in 1.4km. Lge, mkd pitch, pt shd; wc; chem disp; shwrs inc; el pts (3A) €2.90 (rev pol); gas 4km; lndtte; shop; tradsmn; rest; bar; BBQ; playgrnd; pool; sand beach 3km; no dogs; quiet; red for 10+ days; CCI. "Gd NH; friendly, family owners; gd san facs, request hot water for shwrs; everything immac, highly rec; many interesting local features."
Holy Week & 1 Jun-30 Sep. € 15.00   2003*

RIBADESELLA *1A3* (3km W Coastal) **Camping Los Sauces, 33560 Ribadesella (Asturias)** [985-86 13 12] Cross narr bdge fr town twd W. Turn R to Playa, sp. Access via narr, single track bdge immed off main rd. Med, pt shd; wc; baby facs; shwrs; el pts €6.50; lndtte; shop; snacks; bar; sand beach 1km; phone; quiet; cc acc. "Cave paintings on edge of town; excel facs." ♦ 25 Jun-11 Sep.
€ 16.50   2005*

As we're travelling out of season, we'd better phone ahead to check that the site is actually open.

RIBADESELLA *1A3* (4km W) **Camping Ribadesella, Sebreno s/n, 33560 Ribadesella (Asturias)** [tel/fax 985-85 82 93; camping. reservas@fade.es; www.camping-ribadesella. com] W fr Ribadesella take N632. After 2km fork L up hill. Site on L after 2km. Poss diff for lge o'fits & alternative route fr Ribadesella vill to site to avoid steep uphill turn can be used. Lge, mkd pitch, pt sl, pt terr, pt shd; wc; chem disp; baby facs; shwrs inc; el pts (5A) €2.90; gas; lndtte; shop, rest, snacks; bar; BBQ; playgrnd; pool high ssn; sand beach 4km; tennis; sports facs; poss cr; adv bkg; quiet; cc acc; red low ssn/long stay; CCI. "Clean san facs; some sm pitches; attractive fishing vill; prehistoric cave paintings nrby." ♦ Easter-30 Sep. € 19.00   2005*

RIBADESELLA *1A3* (8km W Coastal/Rural) **Camping Playa de Vega, Vega, 33345 Ribadesella (Asturias)** [985-86 04 06] Fr A8 exit junc 333 sp Ribadesella W, thro Bones. At rndabt cont W dir Caravia, turn R opp quarry sp Playa de Vega. Fr cent of Ribadesella W on N632. After passing sp to Camping Les Sauces on R cont for 5km passing turning to autovia. Turn R at sp Vega & site. Med, hdg pitch, pt terr, pt shd; wc; serviced pitch; shwrs inc; el pts €2.70; lndtte; ice; shop; snacks; bar; BBQ; sand beach 1km; TV; dogs; phone; quiet; cc acc; CCI. "Attractive site; sh walk to beach thro orchards; not suitable lge o'fits."
1 Jul-15 Sep. € 19.00   2004*

†RIBEIRA *1B2* (8km NE Coastal) **Camping Ria de Arosa I, Playa de Cabio s/n, 15940 Puebla (Pobra) do Caraminal (La Coruna)** [981-83 13 05; fax 981-83 32 93; info@camping.riadearosa. com] Exit AP9/E1 junc 93 at Padron onto C550 along N side of Ria de Arosa into Puebla del Caraminal. Site is 1.5km S of Puebla, sp fr town. Lge, pt shd; wc; chem disp; mv service pnt; shwrs; el pts (5A) €3; gas; lndtte; shop; rest; bar; playgrnd; sand beach; cycle hire; TV; some statics; phone; poss cr; adv bkg; quiet; cc acc. € 17.70   2004*

RIBEIRA *1B2* (2km E Coastal) **Camping Coroso, Santa Eugeria (Uxía) de Ribeira, Playa de Coroso, 15950 Coroso (La Coruna)** [981-83 80 02; fax 981-83 85 77; info@campingcoroso.com; www. campingcoroso.com] Fr Padron on N550 6km S of Santiago de Compostela take VRG11 (fast rd) to Ribeira, then foll sp to site. Lge, some hdg/mkd pitches, hdstg, pt sl, terr, pt shd; wc; chem disp; baby facs; fam bthrm; shwrs inc; el pts (10A) inc; gas; lndtte; ice; shop in ssn; café in ssn; snacks; bar; BBQ; sandy beach; sailing; tennis; fairly quiet; Eng spkn; bus; poss cr; adv bkg; red 15+ days; cc acc; CCI. "Marvellous views; gd coastal walks + adj mkts; friendly staff; ltd pitches; gd rest."
1 Apr-30 Sep. € 20.20   2004*

RIBERA DE CARDOS see Llavorsi *3B2*

†RIPOLL *3B3* (2km N Rural) **Camping Ripolles, Ctra Barcelona/Puigcerda, 17500 Ripoll (Gerona)** [972-70 37 70; fax 972-70 35 54] At km 109.3 up hill N fr town; well sp. Steep access rd. Med, mkd pitch, pt sl, pt shd; htd wc; chem disp; baby facs; shwrs inc; el pts €3.60; lndtte; shop 2km; rest; snacks; bar; BBQ; playgrnd; pool; tennis; 20% statics; phone; adv bkg; quiet; cc acc; CCI. "V pleasant; gd bar/rest; not suitable med/lge o'fit." ♦
€ 18.20   2004*

RIPOLL *3B3* (2km S Urban) **Camping Solana del Ter, Ctra Barcelona-Puigcerda, C17, Km 92.5, 17500 Ripoll (Gerona)** [972-70 10 62; fax 972-71 43 43; hotel@solanadelter.com; www. solanadelter.com] Site sp S of Ripoll. Med, mkd pitch, hdstg, pt shd; htd wc; chem disp; baby facs; shwrs inc; el pts (4A) €5; lndtte; ice; shop; rest; snacks; bar; playgrnd; pool; tennis; TV; Eng spkn; phone; some rd & rlwy noise; cc acc. "Historic monastery in town; scenic drives nr." 1 Apr-30 Oct.
€ 22.10   2005*

†ROCIO, EL *2G3* (500m N Rural) **Camping La Aldea, Ctra Rocio, Km 25, 21750 El Rocio (Huelva)** [tel/fax 959-44 26 77; info@camping laaldea.com; www.campinglaaldea.com] Fr A49 turn S at junc 48 onto rd 483 to Almonte, site sp just bef El Rocio rndabt. Fr W (Portugal) turn off at junc 60 to A484 to Almonte, then A483. Lge, hdg/mkd pitch, hdstg, pt shd; htd wc; chem disp; mv service pnt; 15% serviced pitches; shwrs inc; el pts (10A) €3.75; gas; lndtte; ice; shop; tradsmn; rest; snacks; bar; BBQ; playgrnd; pool; sand beach 16km; horseriding nrby; van washing facs; 50% statics; dogs; phone; bus 500m; poss cr; Eng spkn; adv bkg (dep req); some rd noise; red long stay; cc acc; CCI. "Well-appointed & maintained site; friendly, helpful staff; tight turns on site; site rds & pitches soft after rain; gd birdwatching (lagoon 1km) & cycling; unusual Spanish town; parades with horses most Sundays; safari in National Park; annual pilgrimage at Pentecost & w/e visits by religious brotherhoods; poss exposed to winds until hdg grows; excel."
♦ ltd. € 19.20 (CChq acc)   2005*

RODA DE BARA, EL see Vendrell, El *3C3*

SPAIN

RONDA _2H3_ (4km NE Rural) **Camping El Cortijo,** Ctra Campillos, Km 5, 29400 Ronda (Malaga) [952-87 07 46 or 952-87 88 88; fax 952 87 86 75] Fr Ronda by-pass take A367 twd Campillos. Site on L after 4.5km opp new development 'Hacienda Los Pinos'. Med, mkd pitch, pt shd; wc; chem disp; serviced pitches; baby facs; shwrs inc; el pts €2.40; lndtte; shop; rest; bar; playgrnd; pool; tennis; games area; cycle hire; 5% statics; dogs; phone; Eng spkn; some rd noise; CCI. "New site; friendly, helpful owner; gd sh stay/NH." ♦ 1 Apr-15 Oct. € 14.30
2003*

†**RONDA** _2H3_ (6km NE) **Camping El Abogao,** Ctra Ronda-Campillos Km 5, 29400 Ronda (Malaga) [952-87 58 44] Fr Marbella take the A376 NW twds Ronda (NB: this rte is v mountainous); turn R onto the A367 twds Campillos; site on R in 6km. Sm, pt shd, mkd pitch; wc; chem disp; shwrs inc; el pts (6A) inc; gas; lndry rm; shop 6km; rest; bar; pool; cycle hire; phone; adv bkg; quiet; cc acc; CCI. "V narr ent, tight corners; poss diff access to pitches for long o'fits; take care low level obstructions when manoeuvring; v sandy & soft after rain; gd for touring mountains; san facs gd but site bit run down; vg when quiet but ltd facs." € 14.70 2005*

†**RONDA** _2H3_ (1.5km S Rural) **Camping El Sur,** Ctra Ronda-Algeciras Km 1.5, 29400 Ronda (Malaga) [952-87 59 39; fax 952-87 70 54; info@ campingelsur.com; www.campingelsur.com] Site on W side of A369 to Algeciras. Fr N or S leave A374 foll sp for San Pedro/Algeciras, then Algeciras & foll sp for site. Do not tow thro Ronda. Med, mkd pitch, hdstg, terr, pt shd; wc; chem disp; mv service pnt; shwrs inc; el pts (5-10A) €3.50-5 (poss rev pol &/or no earth); lndtte; shop; rest adj; snacks; bar; playgrnd; pool high ssn; dogs €1.60; phone; internet; poss cr; Eng spkn; adv bkg; quiet; red long stay/low ssn; CCI. "Gd rd fr coast with spectacular views; long haul for lge o'fits; busy family-run site in lovely setting; strict rules about noise; conv National Parks & Pileta Caves; poss diff access some pitches due trees; hard, rocky ground; poor lighting around facs block & heating not always working in winter; san facs poss stretched high ssn; unreliable elec supply & trip switches kept locked; easy walk to town; friendly staff; vg rest; excel." ♦ € 17.20 2005*

ROQUETAS DE MAR see Almeria _4G1_

†**ROSAS** _3B3_ (2km N Coastal) **Camping Salata,** Port Reig s/n, 17480 Rosas (Gerona) [972-25 60 86; fax 972-15 02 33; info@campingsalata.com; www. campingsalata.com] At Figueres take Rosas rd C260. On ent Rosas site on R, sp. Lge, mkd pitch, hdstg, pt shd; htd wc; chem disp; mv service pnt; shwrs inc; el pts (6-10A) inc; gas; lndtte; shop; tradsmn; rest; snacks; bar; playgrnd; htd pool high ssn; sand beach 500m; internet; 10% statics; dogs; phone; site clsd Jan; poss cr; Eng spkn; adv bkg (bkg fee); red long stay/low ssn; cc acc; CCI. "Vg area for sub-aqua sports; lge part of site new with trees yet to grow; vg clean facs; red facs low ssn; excel winter site." ♦ € 34.25 2005*

ROSAS _3B3_ (200m SW Coastal) **Camping Rodas,** 17480 Rosas (Gerona) [972-25 76 17; fax 972-15 24 66] Figueras-Rosas rd, at o'skts of Rosas sp on R after supmkt. Lge, hdg/mkd pitch, pt shd; wc; chem disp; serviced pitches; shwrs inc; el pts inc; gas; rest; snacks; bar; lndtte; ice; shop adj; tradsmn; sm playgrnd; htd pool; sand beach 600m; poss cr; Eng spkn; adv bkg; quiet; cc acc; CCI. "Gd pool & children's pool; site rds all tarmac; Rosas gd cent for region; well-run site; gates clsd at midnight." 1 Jun-30 Sep. € 25.00 2002*

†**ROSAS** _3B3_ (1km W Urban/Coastal) **Camping Joncar Mar,** Ctra Figueres s/n, 17480 Rosas (Gerona) [tel/fax 972-25 67 02; joncarmar@ hotmail.com; www.joncarmar.com] At Figueres take C260 W for Rosas. On ent Rosas turn sharp R at last rndabt at end of dual c'way. Lge, pt sl, pt shd; htd wc; chem disp; baby facs; shwrs; el pts (10A) €3.45 (poss no earth); gas; lndtte; shop; rest; bar; playgrnd; pool; sand beach adj; golf 15km; entmnt; games rm; 15% statics; phone; bus 500m; poss cr; Eng spkn; adv bkg; rd noise; cc acc; red low ssn/long stay. "Conv walk into Rosas; gd, but dusty, sm, poss cramped/tight pitches; narr rds; vg value low ssn." € 24.70 2005*

ROTA see Puerto de Santa Maria, El _2H3_

RUILOBA see Comillas _1A4_

†**SABINANIGO** _3B2_ (6km N Rural) **Camping Valle de Tena,** Ctra N260, Km 512.6, 22600 Senegue (Huesca). [974-48 09 77; fax 974-48 25 51; correo@campingvalledetena.com; www.camping valledetena.com] Fr Jaca take N330, in 12km turn L onto N260 dir Biescas. In 5km turn L sp Sorripas, foll sp to site in 1km. Lge, mkd pitch, unshd; wc; chem disp; serviced pitches; shwrs inc; el pts €3.60; shop; rest; snacks; bar; playgrnd; pool; TV rm; internet; sports facs; hiking & rv rafting nr; 5% statics; phone; adv bkg; rd noise during the day but quiet at night; Eng spkn. "Vg long/sh stay." € 16.72
2003*

†**SABINANIGO** _3B2_ (1km E Urban) **Camping Confortel (Aurin),** 22600 Sabinanigo (Huesca) [974-48 34 45; fax 974-48 32 80; confcom@once. es] On Sabinanigo by-pass (N330) 1km SE of junc with N260. Fr Jaca (S) site on L, go past to turning point in 800m. Sp Confortel. Site behind & beside Confortel. Lge, mkd pitch, pt shd; wc; mv service pnt; chem disp; baby facs; shwrs inc; el pts (5A) inc; gas; lndtte; shop 2km; supmkt opp; rest, bar in hotel; snacks; playgrnd; 2 pools; tennis; watersports; car wash; 90% statics; dogs; site clsd 1 Nov-19 Dec; Eng spkn; quiet excl w/e; cc acc; CCI. "V sm area for tourers; lge o'fits park adj pool low ssn; mountain walking; skiing; all hotel facs avail to campers; site in area of outstanding beauty; wide range of activities on offer; gd sh stay/NH." ♦ € 20.40 2004*

†SACEDON *3D1* (500m E Rural) **Camp Municipal Sacedon, 19120 Sacedon (Guadalajara)** [949-35 10 18] At km 115 on N320 E fr Sacedon on. Site on L. Med, mkd pitch, hdstg, pt sl, shd; wc (cont); shwrs; el pts €1.80; lndry rm; shop 500m; lake sw 1km; quiet. "NH only in area of few sites; sm pitches; low ssn phone to check open." ♦ € 10.80
2003*

> We're having a great holiday -
> must fill in some site report forms
> and send them to The Club as soon
> as possible.

†SAGUNTO *4E2* (7km NE Coastal) **Camping Malvarrosa de Corinto, Playa Malvarrosa de Corinto, 46500 Sagunto (Valencia)** [962-60 89 06; fax 962-60 89 43; camalva@ctv.es; www.malvacorinto.com] Exit 49 fr A7 onto N340, foll dir Almenara-Casa Blanca. Turn E twd Port de Sagunto & Canet d'en Berenguer on CV320. Foll site sp. Lge, pt shd; wc; chem disp; sauna; shwrs inc; el pts (10A) €3.50; gas; lndtte; ice; shop & 5km; rest; snacks; bar; BBQ; playgrnd; sand & shgl beach adj; tennis; horseriding; gym; 80% statics; dogs; phone; poss cr; Eng spkn; quiet; red long stay; CCI. "Site a bit untidy/run down but friendly & helpful owners; gd facs; lge nos feral cats on site; owners' dogs v noisy; excel pitches adj beach; plenty of touring pitches, but access to some poss diff; ltd facs & poss neglected low ssn; no local transport." € 14.90
2004*

SAGUNTO *4E2* (8km S Coastal) **Camping Puzol, Playa de Pucol, 46500 Pucol (Valencia)** [961-42 15 27; fax 963-20 93 63; info@camping puzol.com; www.campingpuzol.com] Exit AP7 sp Pucol, foll sp to Playa fr Pucol, site well sp. Med, hdg/mkd pitch, hdstg, shd; wc; chem disp; baby facs; shwrs inc; el pts (6A) €4; gas; lndtte; shop; bar; playgrnd; pool; paddling pool; waterslide; sand beach adj; games area; entmnt; child entmnt; TV; 10% statics; dogs €4; poss cr; Eng spkn; red long stay/low ssn/CCI. "Gd family atmosphere; excel touring base; vg." 15 Feb-15 Dec. € 19.00   2005*

See advertisement on page 794

SALAMANCA *1C3* (6.5km N) **Camping La Capea, Ctra N630, Km 384, Aldeaseca de Aruma (Salamanca)** [923-25 10 66] Close to km post 333 on N630. Site sp fr both dirs. Ent on brow of a hill on W side of rd. Med, hdg/mkd pitch, hdstg, shd; wc; chem disp; mv service pnt; shwrs inc; el pts (10A) inc; lndtte; lndry rm; ice; shop; snacks; bar; playgrnd; pool; TV; 10% statics; dogs; some Eng spkn; some rd noise; CCI. "Friendly; variety of pitch sizes; vg all stays." Easter-30 Sep. € 16.75   2004*

†SALAMANCA *1C3* (4km E Urban) **Camping Regio, Ctra Avila-Madrid, Km 4, 37900 Santa Marta de Tormes (Salamanca)** [923-13 88 88; fax 923-13 80 44; recepcion@campingregio.com; www.campingregio.com] Fr S, N or W, take N501 dual c'way dir Avila & L at rndabt sp Sta Marta de Tormes & Salamanca, site in 2km directly behind Hotel Regio. Rec foll sp to hotel as more clearly mkd. Lge, pt sl, pt shd; wc; chem disp; mv service pnt; baby facs; shwrs inc; el pts (10A) inc (poss no earth); gas; lndtte; shop & 1km; hypmkt 3km; rest; poss discount hotel meals for campers; bar; playgrnd; hotel pool; cycle hire; TV; 5% statics; dogs; phone; bus to Salamanca (every 30 mins); car wash; poss cr; Eng spkn; quiet; cc acc; CCI. "In winter stop at 24hr hotel recep; poss v cold in winter; poss no hdstg in wet conditions; conv en rte Portugal; refurbished facs to excel standard; site poss untidy low ssn; spacious pitches but some poss tight for lge o'fits; take care lge brick placement markers when reversing; excel pool; vg." ♦ € 21.50
2005*

†SALAMANCA *1C3* (2.5km NW Rural) **Camping Ruta de la Plata, Ctra de Villamayor, 37184 Villares de la Reina (Salamanca)** [tel/fax 923-28 95 74; recepcion@campingrutadelaplata. com; www.campingrutadelaplata.com] Fr N620, exit Zamora N630, twds Salamanca; 1st turn R, opp football stadium. Site on R in 800m. Or fr junc N620 with SA300 (Salamanca-Ledesma) turn N sp Ledesma for 1km. Turn R at 1st rndabt & turn R at next rndabt. Go thro vill of Villamayor. Site at end of vill. Well sp. Med, some hdg/mkd pitch, terr, pt sl, pt shd; htd wc; chem disp; mv service pnt; shwrs inc; el pts (6A) €2.90; gas; lndtte; ice; shop & 1km; tradsmn; snacks; bar; playgrnd; pool high ssn; golf 3km; TV rm; dogs; reg bus to city at gate; poss cr; quiet but some rd noise at night; CCI. "Clean, tidy, family-owned site; new & refurbed san facs 2004; red facs low ssn; conv NH." ♦ ltd. € 12.40
(CChq acc)   2005*

†SALDANA *1B4* (250m S Urban) **Camp Municipal El Soto, Avda del Instituto, 34100 Saldana (Palencia)** [979-89 20 10] Cross rv bdge S of Saldana twds Carrion de los Condes. Turn R immed & then immed R again, site not sp. Med, pt shd; wc; chem disp; shwrs; el pts (10A) €1.80; lndtte; shop in vill; tradsmn; snacks; bar; 20% statics; dogs; phone; quiet; cc acc; CCI. "Fair sh stay; gd base for Roman mosaics at Villa de la Olmeda, Pedrosa de la Vega."
€ 11.70   2003*

†SALDES *3B3* (Rural) **Camping Repos del Pedraforca**, Ctra B400, Km 13.5, 08697 Saldes (Barcelona) [938-25 80 44; fax 938-25 80 61; pedra@campingpedraforca.com; www.camping pedraforca.com] S fr Puigcerda on C1411 for 35km, turn R at B400, site on L in 13.5km. Med, mkd pitch, pt sl, shd; htd wc; chem disp; mv service pnt; baby facs; sauna; shwrs inc; el pts (5-10A) €3.30; lndtte; shop; tradsmn; rest, snacks high ssn; bar; playgrnd; 2 htd pools (1 covrd); cycle hire; gym; entmnt; TV rm; 50% statics; dogs €1.75; phone; Eng spkn; some rd noise; adv bkg; red 14+ days; cc acc; CCI. "Tow to pitches avail; vg walking; in heart of nature reserve; poss diff ent long o'fits; excel." € 22.30 (CChq acc) 2004*

SALOU *3C2* (Urban/Coastal) **Camping La Siesta**, Calle Norte 37, 43840 Salou (Tarragona) [977-38 08 52; fax 977-38 31 91] Site in cent of town, well sp. Lge, mkd pitch, pt sl, shd; wc; chem closet; chem disp; baby facs; shwrs; el pts €3.10; gas; lndtte; ice; shop; rest; bar; pool; sand beach 200m; cycle hire; sports area; 30% statics; poss cr; adv bkg ess; some rd noise & disco; adv bkg; cc acc; CCI. "Gd cycle path by beach to Cambrils; site guarded; conv for beach & Port Aventura; gd sh stay." 14 Mar-3 Nov. € 30.00 2004*

This site entry hasn't been updated for a while; we'd better fill in a site report form and send it to The Club.

†SALOU *3C2* (2km NE Coastal) **Camping La Pineda de Salou**, Ctra Tarragona-Salou, Km 5, 43481 La Pineda-Vilaseca (Tarragona) [977-37 30 80; fax 977-37 30 81; info@camping lapineda.com; www.campinglapineda.com] Exit A7 junc 35 dir Salou, Vilaseca & Port Aventura. Foll sp Port Aventura then La Pineda/Platjes on rd TV 3148. Med, mkd pitch, pt shd; wc; baby facs; chem disp; shwrs; el pts (5A) €3.60; gas; lndtte; ice; shop; rest; snacks; bar; playgrnd; pool & paddling pool; beach 400m; watersports; fishing; tennis; horseriding; cycle hire; mini club; tourist info; entmnt; TV; some statics; dogs €3; phone; cc acc; red low ssn. "Conv Port Aventura & Tarragona." € 26.80 2005*

See advertisement above

Cambrils • Costa Daurada • España

The only luxury Camping on the Costa Daurada

SALOU *3C2* (1km S Urban/Coastal) **Camping Sanguli-Salou, Paseo Miramar, 43840 Salou (Tarragona) [977-38 16 41; fax 977-38 46 16; mail@ sanguli.es; www.sanguli.es]** Exit AP7/E15 junc 35. At 1st rndbt take dir to Salou (Plaça Europa), at 2nd rndabt foll site sp. V lge, mkd pitch, pt sl, shd; htd wc; chem disp; mv service pnt; some serviced pitches; baby facs; shwrs inc; el pts (10A) inc; gas; lndtte; ice; shop; 2 supmkts; rest; snacks; bar; BBQ; playgrnd; 3 pools & 3 paddling pools; waterslide; jacuzzi; sand beach 50m; games area; tennis; games rm; mini-golf; fitness rm; entmnt; excursions; cinema; youth club; mini-club; amphitheatre; internet; TV; dogs; phone; bus; car wash; Eng spkn; adv bkg rec Jul-Aug; some rlwy noise; 25-45% red low ssn + 7 days/snr citizens; cc acc; CCI. "Quiet end of Salou nr Cambrils & 3km Port Aventura; lge o'fits take care manoeuvring on some pitches; take care overhanging trees; excel, well-maintained site." ♦ 24 Mar-29 Oct. € 49.00 ABS - E18   2005*

See advertisement on page 781

SALOU *3C2* (2km W Coastal) **Camping Cambrils Park, Avda Mas Clariana s/n, 43850 Cambrils (Tarragona) [977-35 10 31; fax 977-35 22 10; mail@ cambrilspark.es; www.cambrilspark.es]** Fr A7 exit junc 35 Salou. At 1st rndabt foll sp Cambrils; after 2km turn R 200m past petrol stn & cont over rlwy bdge, site 400m on R. V lge, mkd pitch, pt sl, shd; htd wc; chem disp; mv service pnt; baby facs; 50% serviced pitches; shwrs inc; el pts (10A) inc; gas; lndtte; shop; rest; snacks; bar; BBQ; playgrnd; pools; sand beach 400m; tennis; child mini-club; entmnt; excursions; mini-golf; games rm; internet; TV rm; car wash; 15% statics; phone; no dogs; Eng spkn; adv bkg; quiet; cc acc; red low ssn/long stay/snr citizens; children free low ssn; CCI. "Excel facs; conv Port Aventura; helpful staff; access to pitches poss diff long o'fits." ♦ 7 Apr-8 Oct. € 49.00 (CChq acc)   2005*

See advertisement opposite

†**SAN JAVIER** *4F2* (500m W) **Camping La Encina, Ctra Balsicas 30, 30730 San Javier (Murcia) [tel/fax 968-19 10 80]** N332 to Javier town cent, take Murcia-Balsicas rd, site on R in 500m. Lge, pt shd; wc; chem disp; shwrs inc; el pts (5A) €3.54; gas; lndtte; ice; shop; bar; snacks; sand beach 3km; pool; playgrnd; TV; tennis; poss cr; quiet; dogs; mainly statics; red low ssn/long stay; cc acc. "Site in indus area; miles of beaches nr; 2 golf courses in 20km." ♦ € 18.22   2002*

SAN JOSE see Nijar *4G1*

SAN MIGUEL DE SALINAS see Torrevieja *4F2*

†**SAN ROQUE** *2H3* (4km E) **Camping La Casita, Ctra N340, Km 126, 11360 San Roque (Cadiz) [tel/fax 956-78 00 31]** Site sp 'Via de Servicio' parallel to N340/E15. Access at km 119 fr S, km 127 fr N. Site visible fr rd. Med, pt sl, pt terr, pt shd, wc; chem disp; mv service pnt; shwrs; el pts (10A) €3.20; ice; shop; rest; bar; playgrnd; pool; sand beach 3km; mini-golf; horseriding; disco; 90% statics; phone; poss cr; Eng spkn; adv bkg ess; noisy; 10% red 30+ days; cc acc; CCI. "Ltd touring pitches; shwrs solar htd - water temp depends on weather (poss cold); conv Gibraltar & Morocco; daily buses to La Linea & Algeciras; ferries to N Africa (secure parking at port); cattle on site at times." ♦ € 17.75   2004*

Some of these sites have changed their opening dates - we'd better fill in some site report forms and let the editor of the guide know.

†**SAN SEBASTIAN/DONOSTIA** *3A1* (5km NW Rural) **Camping Igueldo, Barrio de Igueldo, 20008 San Sebastian (Gipuzkoa) [943-21 45 02; fax 943-28 04 11; info@campingigueldo.com; www. campingigueldo.com]** Fr W on A8, leave m'way at junc 9 twd city cent, take 1st R & R at rndabt onto Avda de Tolosa. At sea front turn hard L at rndabt sp to site (Avda Sarrustegui) & foll sp up steep hill 4km to site. Fr E foll N1 thro city nr end of sea front, just after tunnel, fork R onto Avda Sarrustegui, then as above. Lge, hdg/mkd pitches, terr, pt shd, 40% serviced pitches; wc; mv service pnt; baby facs; shwrs inc; el pts (5A) €2.90; gas; lndtte; shop; rest; bar high ssn; playgrnd; pool 5km; sand beach 5km; TV; phone; bus; poss cr/noisy; Eng spkn; red long stay/low ssn; cc acc; CCI. "Gd facs; spectacular views; steep app poss diff for lge o'fits; site poss unkempt low ssn." ♦ € 24.90   2005*

SAN VICENTE DE LA BARQUERA *1A4* (1km E Coastal) **Camping El Rosal, Ctra de la Playa s/n, 39540 San Vicente de la Barquera (Cantabria) [942-71 01 65; fax 942-71 00 11; cogeote@ campingelrosal.jazztel.es; www.campingelrosal. jazztel.es]** Fr A8 km 264, foll sp San Vicente. Turn R over bdge then 1st L (site sp) immed at end of bdge; keep L & foll sp to site. Med, mkd pitch, pt sl, pt shd; wc; chem disp; shwrs; el pts (6A) €2.50; gas; lndtte; shop; rest; snacks; bar; sand beach adj; phone; poss cr; Eng spkn; adv bkg; quiet; cc acc; CCI. "Excel site in pine wood o/looking bay; excel, modern, v clean facs; helpful staff; few petrol stns on autovias app San Vicente." ♦ 1 May-30 Sep. € 23.00   2005*

SANGONERA LA SECA see Murcia *4F1*

SPAIN

Last year of report

SANGUESA *3B1* (500m S Urban) **Camping Cantolagua,** Paseo de Cantolagua, 31400 Sanguesa (Navarra) [948-43 03 52; fax 948-87 13 13] Turn off N240 fr Pamplona onto N127 to Sanguesa. Turn into town over bdge, foll sp, 2nd R up thro town, R at Bull Ring then L, then 1st R. Site well sp in town. Med, hdg pitch, pt shd; wc; chem disp (wc); mv service pnt; some serviced pitches; shwrs inc (solar htd); el pts (8A) inc; lndtte; shops 1km; tradsmn; rest; snacks; bar; BBQ; htd pool adj; playgrnd; horseriding; tennis; cycle hire; TV rm; phone; poss cr; Eng spkn; 10% statics; quiet; cc acc; CCI. "Serviced pitches not suitable for m'vans; hot water avail all day, cold water only avail fr wc block; lovely historic unspoilt town." ♦ ltd.
15 Feb-30 Oct. € 10.80   2003*

SANT ANTONI DE CALONGE see Palamos *3B3*

SANT FELIU DE GUIXOLS *3B3* (500m E Urban/Coastal) **Camping Sant Pol,** Ctra Dr Fleming 1, 17220 Sant Feliu de Guixols (Gerona) [972-32 72 69 or 972-20 86 67; fax 972-32 72 11 or 972-22 24 09; info@campingsantpol.com; www. campingsantpol.com] Exit A7 junc 7 onto C31 dir Sant Feliu. At km 312 take dir S'Agaro; at rndabt foll sp to site. Med, mkd pitch, pt sl, terr, shd; htd wc; chem disp; mv service pnt; baby facs; some serviced pitches; shwrs inc; el pts (10A) inc; lndtte; ice; shop; tradsmn; rest; snacks; bar; BBQ; playgrnd; htd 3 pools; sand beach 350m; games rm; cycle hire; child entmnt; internet; 30% statics; dogs; sep car park; Eng spkn; adv bkg; some rd noise; cc acc; red long stay/snr citizens/CCI. "Vg, well-run site; sm area for c'vans; excel facs; lovely pool." ♦
31 Mar-12 Nov. € 44.94   2005*

See advertisement above

SANT JOAN DE LES ABADESSES see Sant Pau de Seguries *3B3*

SANT LLORENC DE LA MUGA see Figueres *3B3*

†**SANT LLORENC DE MORUNYS** *3B3* (2km N Rural) **Camping Morunys,** Ctra de la Coma, Km.1,5, 25282 Sant Llorenc de Morunys (Lleida) [973-49 22 13; fax 973-49 21 03] Fr Solsona take rd N sp Sant Llorenc for approx 24km, site well sp. Lge, mkd pitch, hdstg, terr, pt shd; wc; chem disp; baby facs; shwrs; el pts (6A) €3.30; gas; lndtte; shop; rest; bar; playgrnd; pool; phone; 80% statics; noisy; adv bkg; cc acc; red CCI. "Vg long stay."
€ 16.40   2004*

†**SANT PAU DE SEGURIES** *3B3* (6km NE Rural) **Camping Abadesses,** Ctra Camprodon, Km 14.6, 17860 Sant Joan de les Abadesses (Gerona) [tel/fax 972-72 22 72] Fr Ripoll take C26 in dir Sant Joan, site approx 4km on R after vill. Steep access. Sm, terr, unshd; wc; shwrs; el pts (6A) €2.88; gas; lndtte; shop; snacks; bar; playgrnd; pool; 70% statics; quiet; cc acc. "Vg facs; gd views fr most pitches; steep access to recep; poss diff access around terraces; gd sh stay." ♦ € 16.20   2004*

†**SANT PAU DE SEGURIES** *3B3* (500m S) **Camping Els Roures,** Avda del Mariner 34, 17864 Sant Pau de Seguries (Gerona) [972-74 70 00; fax 972-74 71 09; elsroures@mx3.redestb.es; www. elsroures.com] On C151 Camprodon to Ripoll. In Sant Pau take L 50m after traff lts. Site on R after 400m. Lge, mkd pitch, terr, shd; wc; baby facs; shwrs inc; el pts (6A) €3.10; gas; lndtte; shop; rest; bar; playgrnd; 2 pools; tennis; cinema; games rm; gym; internet; 80% statics; phone; poss cr; some noise; CCI. "Gd sh stay." ♦ € 23.20   2004*

SANT PERE PESCADOR *3B3* (Coastal) **Camping La Gaviota,** 17470 Sant Pere Pescador (Gerona) [972-52 05 69; fax 972-55 03 48; www.lagaviota. com] Exit 5 fr A7 dir San Marti d'Empurias, site at end of beach rd. Med, pt shd; wc; chem disp; baby facs; shwrs inc; el pts €2.64; gas; lndtte; ice; shop; rest; bar; playgrnd; sand beach 100m; games rm; internet; 20% statics; phone; dogs; poss cr; Eng spkn; adv bkg; quiet; cc acc; CCI. "V friendly owners; clean site; excel facs & constant hot water; some sm pitches & narr site rds; poss ltd access for lge o'fit; take care overhanging trees; poss mosquito problem." ♦ 1 Mar-31 Oct. € 30.75   2004*

SANT PERE PESCADOR *3B3* (Coastal) **Camping L'Amfora, Avda Josep Tarradellas 2, 17470 Sant Pere Pescador (Gerona) [972-52 05 40 or 972-52 05 42; fax 972-52 05 39; info@camping amfora.com; www.campingamfora.com]** Fr AP7 exit 3 dir Rosas. In 9km turn R dir Sant Pere Pescador. In town turn L over bdge, L & foll sp. V lge, hdg/mkd pitch, pt shd; htd wc; chem disp; mv service pnt; serviced pitches; baby facs; shwrs inc; el pts (10A) inc; gas; lndtte; shop; supmkt; rest; snacks; bar; BBQ; playgrnd; 4 pools; waterslide; sand beach adj; windsurf school; tennis; horseriding; cycle hire; mini-golf; games rm; entmnt; children's club; TV; internet; 10% statics; dogs €4.28; phone; adv bkg; Eng spkn; quiet; red long stay/low ssn/snr citizens/CCI. "Choice of 3 pitch sizes; larger pitches have own san facs & may be shared with another family to reduce cost; immac san facs; excel, v well-run, clean site; helpful staff; Parque Acuatico 18km." ♦ 8 Apr-30 Sep. € 43.20 (CChq acc)
2005*

See advertisement above

Will you fill in the site report forms at the back of the guide, or shall I?

SANT PERE PESCADOR *3B3* (200m E Rural) **Camping Riu, Ctra de la Playa s/n, 17470 Sant Pere Pescador (Gerona) [972-52 02 16; fax 972-55 04 69; info@campingriu.com; www. campingriu.com]** Fr N exit AP7 junc 4 dir L'Escala & foll sp Sant Pere Pescador, then turn L twds coast, site on L. Fr S exit AP7 junc 5 dir L'Escala, then as above & turn R to beaches & site. Lge, mkd pitch, shd; wc; chem disp; baby facs; shwrs inc; el pts (3A) €3.30; gas; lndtte; shop & 300m; rest; snacks; bar; BBQ; playgrnd; pool; sand beach 2km; boat-launching on rv adj; fishing; kayak hire; games area; entmnt; child entmnt; internet; 5% statics; dogs €2.60; Eng spkn; adv bkg; quiet; cc acc; red long stay; CCI. "Excel boating facs & fishing on site; gd situation; rec site." ♦ 1 Apr-17 Sep. € 287.00
2005*

SPAIN

LAS Dunas
CAMPING CARAVANING

**SANT PERE PESCADOR
COSTA BRAVA ~ SPAIN**

**The Holiday-Park
for all the family**

**Special
off-season
offers**

• 40km from the French border situated on the coast with its own golden sandy beach, shopping centre, restaurant, swimming pools and tennis courts. • Clean and modern amenities with special facilities for disabled visitors. • Suitable for caravan rallies.
• This is an ideal site for all the family with organised entertainment during the high season, and is in easy distance to visit Barcelona and Gerona.

Information and reservation:
Camping Las Dunas . Apdo. Correos 23 . E-17130 L'Escala (Girona)
Tel.: +34 972 52 17 17 . Fax: +34 972 55 00 46
Your contact person: Family Callaway. Tel. 01205366856

*How to find us: A-7 exit (sortida) nr. 5.
to L'Escala. 2 km vbefore L'Escala turn direction Sant Martí d'Empúries.
Then another 4,5 km.*

www.campinglasdunas.com ~ info@campinglasdunas.com

SANT PERE PESCADOR *3B3* (2km E Coastal) Camping Las Dunas, 17470 Sant Pere Pescador (Gerona) (Postal Address: Aptdo Correos 23, 17130 L'Escala) [972-52 17 17; fax 972-52 00 46; info@campinglasdunas.com; www.campinglas dunas.com] Fr Figueras take main Barcelona rd, in 2km turn L for Costa Brava. Foll rd Vilademat-La Escala, 2km bef L'Escala turn L for San Marti de Ampurias, turn L bef ent vill for 2km, camp sp. Fr A7 take exit 5 dir L'Escala. V lge, mkd pitch, pt sl, pt shd; wc; chem disp; mv service pnt; baby facs; serviced pitches; shwrs inc; el pts (6-10A) inc; gas; lndtte; ice; kiosk; supmkt; souvenir shop; rest; snacks; bar; BBQ; 2 pools; sand beach adj; playgrnd; tennis & sports; entmnt; disco; TV; money exchange; cash machines; doctor; 5% statics; dogs €4; phone; quiet; adv bkg (ess high ssn); Eng spkn; red low ssn; CCI. "Greco-Roman ruins Ampurias; gd sized pitches - extra for serviced; excel facs." ♦ 19 May-22 Sep. € 47.00   2004*

See advertisement opposite

SANT PERE PESCADOR *3B3* (3km SE Coastal) Camping Aquarius, Playa s/n Can Cristia, 17470 Sant Pere Pescador (Gerona) [972-52 00 03; fax 972-55 02 16; camping@aquarius.es; www. aquarius.es] Fr AP7 m'way exit 3, foll sp to Roses. Join C260, after 7km bear R to Sant Pere Pescador. Cross rv bdge in vill, take 1st L & foll camp sp. Turn R at next rndabt, site on L in 1.5km. Lge, pt shd; wc; chem disp; mv service pnt; baby facs; fam bthrm; serviced pitches; shwrs; el pts (6A) €2.80; gas; lndtte; ice; supmkt; rest; snacks; bar; 2 playgrnds; sand beach adj; nursery in ssn; games rm; games area; car wash; some statics; dogs €3; phone; cash point in recep; poss cr; Eng spkn; adv bkg (ess Jul/Aug); quiet; red low ssn/long stay/snr citizens (except Jul/Aug); red CCI low ssn. "Immac site; vg rest; windsurfing; vast beach; 2% pitches reserved for dog owners; recycling facs." ♦ ltd. 15 Mar-31 Oct. € 38.00   2005*

See advertisement above

SPAIN

*Last year of report

SANT PERE PESCADOR *3B3* (1.3km S Coastal) Camping Las Palmeras, Ctra de la Platja s/n, 17470 Sant Pere Pescador (Gerona) [972-52 05 06; fax 972-55 02 85; info@campinglaspalmeras. com; www.campinglaspalmeras.com] Exit AP7 junc 3 or 4 at Figueras onto C260 dir Rosas/ Cadaques rd. After 8km at Castello de Ampurias turn S for Sant Pere Pescador & cont twd beach. Site on R of rd. Med, shd; wc; chem disp; mv service pnt; some serviced pitches; baby facs; shwrs inc; el pts (5-16A) €2.70; gas; lndtte; ice; shop; tradsmn; rest; snacks; bar; playgrnd; htd pools; paddling pool; sand beach 200m; tennis; cycle hire; games area; internet; entmnt; TV; cash point; 10% statics; dogs €3.50; phone; poss cr; Eng spkn; adv bkg; quiet; red CCI. "Helpful, friendly staff; superb, clean san facs; excel site." ♦ 3 Apr-28 Oct. € 38.00   2005*

See advertisement on previous page

Mustn't forget to post our site report forms to The Club, otherwise sites might be deleted.

SANT PERE PESCADOR *3B3* (4km S Coastal) Camping La Ballena Alegre 2, Ctra San Marti-Empuries, 17470 Sant Pere Pescador (Gerona) [902-51 05 20; fax 902 51 05 21; infb2@ ballena-alegre.com; www.ballena-alegre.com] Fr A7 exit 5, dir L'Escala to rd Gl 623, km 18.5. At 1st rndabt turn L dir Sant Marti d'Empuries, site on R in 1km. V lge, hdstg, terr, pt shd; htd wc; chem disp; mv service pnt; serviced pitches; baby facs; shwrs inc; el pts (5A) inc; gas; lndtte; supmkt; rest; snacks; bar; BBQ; playgrnd; 3 pools; sand beach adj; watersports; tennis; games area; games rm; fitness rm; cycle hire; money exchange; surf shop; doctor; entmnt; internet; TV; 10% statics; dogs €4; poss cr; Eng spkn; quiet; red low ssn/snr citizens/long stay; CCI. "Excel site; superb facs." ♦ 13 May-24 Sep. € 49.75   2005*

See advertisement opposite

†**SANT QUIRZE SAFAJA** *3C3* (2km E Rural) Camping L'Illa, Ctra Sant Feliu de Codines a Centelles, Km 3.9, 08189 Sant Quirze Safaja (Barcelona) [938-66 25 26; fax 935-72 96 21] N fr Sabadell on C1413 to Caldes de Montbui; then twds Moia on C59. Turn R at golf club, site 2km on R. Lge, mkd pitch, hdstg, terr, pt shd; wc; shwrs inc; el pts (6A) €3.60; gas; lndtte; rest; sm shop; playgrnd; pool; 50% statics; dogs €3.50; site clsd mid-Dec to mid-Jan; adv bkg; CCI. "Easy drive to Barcelona; poss open w/e only low ssn." € 18.00   2004*

†**SANTA CILIA DE JACA** *3B2* (3km W Rural) Camping Los Pirineos, Ctra Pamplona N240, KM 300, 22791 Santa Cilia de Jaca (Huesca) [tel/fax 974-37 73 51; pirineos@pirinet.com] Fr Jaca on N240 twd Pamplona. Site on R after Santa Cilia de Jaca, clearly sp. Lge, mkd pitch, terr, pt shd; wc; chem disp; mv service pnt; baby facs; shwrs inc; el pts (5A) €4 (check for earth); gas; lndtte; shop; rest; snacks; bar; playgrnd; pool in ssn; tennis; 90% statics; dogs; Eng spkn;adv bkg (dep req); some rd noise; cc acc; CCI. "Excel site in lovely area; on Caminho de Santiago pilgrim rte; ltd access for tourers; conv NH." ♦ € 21.70   2005*

SANTA CRISTINA DE ARO see Playa de Aro *3B3*

SANTA CRUZ see Coruna, La *1A2*

SANTA ELENA see Carolina, La *2F4*

SANTA MARINA DE VALDEON *1A3* (500m N Rural) Camping El Cares, 24915 Santa Marina de Valdeon (Leon) [tel/fax 987-74 26 76; cares@ elcares.com] Fr S take N621 to Portilla de la Reina. Turn L onto LE243 to Santa Marina. Turn L thro vill, just beyond vill turn L at camping sp. Vill street is narr & narr bdge 2.55m on app to site. Do not attempt to app fr N if towing - 4km of single track rd fr Posada. Med, terr, pt shd; wc; chem disp; shwrs; el pts (5A) €2.50; lndtte; shop; tradsmn; rest; bar; 10% statics; dogs €2; phone; quiet; cc acc; CCI. "Site high in mountains; gd base for Cares Gorge; friendly, helpful staff; gd views; tight access; gd sh stay." ♦ 1 Jun-30 Sep. € 14.50   2004*

SANTA MARTA DE TORMES see Salamanca *1C3*

†**SANTA POLA** *4F2* (Urban) Camping Bahia de Santa Pola, N332, Km 38, 03130 Santa Pola (Alicante) [965-41 10 12; fax 965-41 67 90] Exit A7 junc 72. Site at junc bet N332 & C3317 or fr Elche take C3317 to Santa Pola. Lge, mkd pitch, hdstg, pt shd; wc; chem disp; baby facs; shwrs inc; el pts (6A) €2.50 or metered; gas; lndtte; shop; supmkt; rest; playgrnd; pool; sand beach 2km; 50% statics; phone; Eng spkn; adv bkg; rd noise; cc acc; red long stay/CCI. "Helpful, friendly manager; well-organised site; excel san facs; site rds steep; attractive coastal cycle path; vg long/sh stay/NH." ♦ € 17.10   2004*

†**SANTAELLA** *2G3* (5km N Rural) Camping La Campina, Ctra Aldea Quintania, KM 11.500, 14547 Santaella (Cordoba) [957-31 53 03; fax 957-31 51 58; info@campinglacampina.com; www.campinglacampina.com] Fr NIV/E5 leave at km 441 onto A386 rd dir La Rambla to Santaella for 11km, turn L for 5km & foll sp. Sm, mkd pitch, hdstg, pt sl, pt shd; wc; chem disp; baby facs; shwrs inc; el pts (5A) inc; gas; lndtte; ice; shop & 6km; rest; snacks; bar; BBQ; playgrnd; pool; TV; Eng spkn; bus at gate to Cordoba; adv bkg; quiet; cc acc; red long stay/low ssn; CCI. "Fine views; friendly, warm welcome; family-run site; many pitches sm for lge o'fits; guided walks; poss clsd winter - phone to check." ♦ € 31.90   2005*

SANTANDER *1A4* (4km E Coastal) **Camping Latas, Pinar de Ama, 39140 Somo (Cantabria) [tel/fax 942-51 06 31]** Exit A8 junc 11 dir Pedrena/ Heres, thro Somo up hill; L at 2nd rndabt (sp Loredo NOT Laredo); turn L after camp sp; call at bar for access on R. Med, hdg pitch, pt sl, pt shd; wc; chem disp; baby facs; shwrs inc; el pts (2-6A) €2.80; gas; lndtte; shop; rest; snacks; bar; pool; sand beach nr; watersports; tennis; 50% statics; phone; poss cr; adv bkg; poss noisy; no cc acc; CCI. "Noisy until midnight then strict silence." ♦ 15 Jun-15 Sep.
€ 17.50   2004*

SANTANDER *1A4* (8km E Coastal) **Camping Derby, Bajada a la Playa 6, 39140 Loredo (Cantabria) [942-50 91 85; fax 942-50 92 52; campingderby@ campingderby.com; www.campingderby.com]** Fr Santander exit A8 junc 7 onto CA141 twd Loredo. At 2nd rndabt after Somo take CA440 to Loredo, turn L at top of hill, site sp. Fr Bilbao exit A8 junc 11 onto CA145 sp Pedrena. At 1st rndabt turn R onto CA141, then as above. Lge, mkd pitch, pt sl, pt shd; wc; chem disp; shwrs inc; el pts (3A) €2.25; gas; lndtte; ice; shop; tradsmn; rest; snacks; bar; BBQ; playgrnd; sm pool; sand beach adj; windsurfing school; child entmnt; 50% statics; dogs; phone; bus 2km; poss cr; Eng spkn; adv bkg; quiet; cc acc; CCI. "Vg." Easter-31 Oct. € 15.60   2004*

†SANTANDER *1A4* (12km E) **Camping Somo Parque, Ctra Somo-Suesa, 39150 Suesa (Cantabria) [tel/fax 942-51 03 09; somoparque@ somoparque.com; www.somoparque.com]** Fr car ferry foll sp Bilbao. After approx 8km turn L over bdge sp Pontejos & Somo. After Pedrena climb hill at Somo Playa & take 1st R sp Suesa. Foll site sp. Med, pt shd; wc; chem disp; shwrs & bath; el pts €2.90; gas; ice; shop; snacks; bar; playgrnd; beach 1.5km; 75% statics; site clsd 16 Dec-14 Jan; some Eng spkn; quiet; CCI. "Fair NH; peaceful rural setting; poor facs low ssn but refurb in 2004; sm ferry bet Somo & Santander." € 15.50   2004*

†SANTANDER *1A4* (6km W Coastal) **Camping Virgen del Mar, Ctra Santander-Liencres, San Roman-Corban s/n, 39000 Santander (Cantabria) [942-34 24 25; fax 942-32 24 90; cvirdman@ ceoecant.es; www.ceoecant.es/aehc/virgenmar]** Fr ferry turn R, then L up to football stadium, L again leads strt into San Roman. If app fr W, take A67 (El Sardinero) then S20, leave at junc 2 dir Liencres, strt on. Site well sp. Lge, mkd pitch, pt shd; wc; chem disp; mv service pnt; shwrs; el pts (6A) inc; lndtte; shop; supmkt 2km; rest; snacks; bar; playgrnd; pool; sand beach 300m; no dogs; adv bkg; quiet; cc acc; red long stay; CCI. "Some basic facs but gd hot water; some sm pitches not suitable lge vans; site adj cemetary; phone in low ssn to check site open; excel site but expensive low ssn." ♦ ltd.
€ 27.00   2004*

SANTANDER *1A4* (6km NW Coastal) **Camping Cabo Mayor, Avda. del Faro s/n, 39012 Santander (Cantabria) [tel/fax 942-39 15 42; info@cabomayor.com; www.cabomayor.com]** Sp thro town but not v clearly. On waterfront (turn R if arr by ferry). At lge junc do not foll quayside, take uphill rd (resort type prom) & foll sp for Faro de Cabo Mayor. Site 200m bef lighthouse on L. Lge, mkd pitch, terr, pt shd; wc; chem disp (wc); serviced pitches; baby facs; shwrs inc; el pts (5A) inc; gas; lndtte; shop; rest; snacks; bar; playgrnd; pool high ssn; many beaches adj; tennis; TV; some statics; no dogs; phone; poss cr; Eng spkn; CCI. "Gd san facs; v sm pitches; site pop with lge youth groups high ssn; shwrs clsd 2200-0800 & stretched in high ssn." ♦ 1 Apr-15 Oct. € 25.70   2005*

†SANTIAGO DE COMPOSTELA *1A2* (2km E Urban) **Camping As Cancelas, Rua 25 de Julio 35, 15704 Santiago de Compostela (La Coruna) [981-58 02 66 or 981-58 04 76; fax 981-57 55 53; info@campingascancelas.com; www.campingas cancelas.com]** Fr E on N634 or N547 cont across AP9 m'way to next rndabt. Turn L sp Santiago N. In 1km filter R to turn L sp Ourense & Lugo. Take immed L & foll site sp. Or app fr city & foll sp for Lugo until sp to site. Fr N or S leave A9 junc 67, at 1st rndabt take 2nd (sm) exit sp Santiago Historic City (not 3rd exit sp Ourense.) At next rndabt take 1st exit & site sp within 500m. Lge, mkd pitch, hdstg, terr, shd; htd wc; chem disp; baby facs; shwrs inc; el pts (5-10A) €3.20; gas; lndtte; shop, rest, snacks & bar in ssn; BBQ; playgrnd; pool & paddling pool high ssn; entmnt; TV; phone; poss cr; Eng spkn; adv bkg ess high ssn; quiet; red low ssn; CCI. "Well-kept, busy site but quiet low ssn; rec arr early high ssn; some sm pitches poss diff c'vans; excel san facs, spotless but poss stretched when site busy; hot water avail all day low ssn; bus 300m fr gate avoids steep walk back fr town (low ssn adequate car parks in town); conv for pilgrims; poss interference with car/c'van electrics fr local transmitter - if probs report to site recep; excel rest; in winter recep in bar." ♦
€ 21.00   2005*

SANTIAGO DE COMPOSTELA *1A2* (4km E Urban) **Camping Monte do Gozo, Ctra Aeropuerto, Km 2, 15820 Santiago de Compostela (La Coruna) [981-55 89 42; fax 981-56 28 92; comercial.mdg@ terra.es or gozo@galice.net]** Site sp on 'old' rd N634 (not new autovia) into town fr E, nr San Marcos. Do not confuse with pilgrim site nr to city. Lge, pt sl, shd; wc; chem disp; shwrs; el pts inc; gas; lndtte; shop; rest; bar; playgrnd; 2 pools; tennis; cycle hire; 20% statics; no dogs; phone; bus 1km; cc acc. 20 Jun-25 Sep. € 18.75   2004*

Galicia
www.turgalicia.es

TURGALICIA.
Estrada Santiago-Noia, km 3.
E-15896 Santiago de Compostela
(Spain)
Tel.+34 981 542 500
Fax: +34 981 542 659
e-mail: cir.turgalicia@xunta.es

Culture

Trekking

Gastronomy

Nature

Galicia
(Spain)

XUNTA DE GALICIA
CONSELLERÍA DE INNOVACIÓN
E INDUSTRIA

†SANTIAGO DE COMPOSTELA *1A2* (6km E Rural) **Camping San Marcos, 15704 Santiago de Compostela (La Coruna)** [981-58 79 17; fax 981-58 74 30] Exit AP9 junc 67 sp Aeropuerto. Exit sp San Marcos, turn L in vill. After 800m turn R at sp Bando/TV Galicia, site sp in 500m. Med, pt shd; wc; chem disp; shwrs inc; el pts (6A) €3.75; lndtte; bar; playgrnd; pool; TV rm; no dogs; phone; bus 800m; quiet. "Lovely, grassy site; excel san facs; gd touring base." € 16.60   2005*

SANTILLANA DEL MAR *1A4* (2km E Rural) **Camping Altamira, Las Quintas, 39314 Queveda (Cantabria)** [942-84 01 81; fax 942-26 01 55; altamiracamping@yahoo.es; www.altamira camping.com] Clear sp to Santillana fr Santander-Torrelavega m'way; site on R 2km bef vill. Med, mkd pitch, pt sl, terr, unshd; wc; shwrs; el pts (3A) €3.20 (poss rev pol); gas; lndtte; sm shop; rest; bar; pool; sand beach 8km; horseriding; TV rm; 30% statics; poss cr; Eng spkn; adv bkg ess high ssn; quiet but barking dogs; cc acc in ssn; CCI. "Nr Altimira cave paintings; easy access Santander ferry on m'way; excel." Easter-10 Nov. € 18.20   2005*

†SANTILLANA DEL MAR *1A4* (500m W Rural) **Camping Santillana del Mar, Ctra de Comillas s/n, 39330 Santillana del Mar (Cantabria)** [942-81 82 50; fax 942-84 01 83; complejo santillana@cantabria.com; www.cantabria.com/ complejosantillana] Exit A8 junc 16 Santillana-Comillas, then foll sp Santillana & site on rd CA131. Lge, sl, pt shd; wc; chem disp (wc); mv service pnt; baby facs; shwrs inc; el pts (5A) inc; gas; lndtte; shop high ssn; rest; snacks; bar; playgrnd; pool & paddling pool; beach 5km; tennis; cycle hire; horseriding; golf 15km; entmnt; car wash; cash machine; 20% statics; dogs; phone; poss cr; Eng spkn; rd noise; CCI. "Gd facs but ltd low ssn; poss itinerants; care needed to some pitches due narr, winding access rds & ent restricted by hdgs & low trees v close to rd; not rec after dark as movement restricted for turning & diff lge o'fits; take care poss v hot shwrs; poss muddy/v wet grass low ssn; gd views; conv ferry & Altimira caves; vg." ♦ ltd. € 24.50 (CChq acc)   2005*

SANXENXO *1B2* (2km E Coastal) **Camping Airinos do Mar, Playa de Areas, El Grove, 36960 Sanxenxo (Pontevedra)** [986-72 31 54] Fr Pontevedra take C550 W twd Sanxenxo & El Grove. Turn L at km post 65; site sp on S side of rd. Access rd needs care in negotiation. Sm, mkd pitch, pt shd; wc; shwrs inc; el pts (16A) €2.70; gas; lndtte; shop; rest; bar; beach adj; poss cr; Eng spkn; adv bkg; quiet. "Not suitable for mv's over 2.50m high; vans over 6m may need help of staff at ent; bar & rest overlook beach; lovely views; indiv pitches approx 6m wide." 1 Jun-30 Sep. € 18.20   2004*

---

†SANXENXO *1B2* (3km W Coastal) **Camping Paxarinas, Ctra C550, Km 2.3 Lanzada-Portonovo, 36960 Sanxenxo (Pontevedra)** [986-72 30 55 or 986-69 07 49; fax 986-72 30 66] Fr Pontevedra W on C550; 3km after Sanxenxo on coast rd. Site thro hotel on L at bend. Site poorly sp. Fr AP9 fr N exit junc 119 onto VRG41 & exit for Sanxenxo. Turn R at 3rd rndabt for Portonovo to site - do not ent Portonovo. Lge, mkd pitch, pt sl, terr, shd; wc (some cont); chem disp; mv service pnt; serviced pitches; baby facs; shwrs inc; el pts (5A) €2.95; gas; lndry rm; ice; shop & 2km; tradsmn; rest; snacks; bar; playgrnd; sand beach adj; TV; 10% statics; dogs; phone; Eng spkn; adv bkg; quiet; red long stay/CCI. "Beautiful location; excel san facs; secluded beaches in area; walks on hills & in woods; views over estuary; v ltd facs low ssn." ♦ € 20.00   2005*

See advertisement

SANXENXO *1B2* (4km W Rural/Coastal) **Camping Suavila, Playa de Montalvo, 36970 Portonovo (Pontevedra)** [tel/fax 986-72 37 60] Fr Sanxenxo take C550 W; at km 57.5 site sp on L. Med, mkd pitch, shd; wc; serviced pitches; baby facs; shwrs inc; el pts (6A) €3.20; gas; lndtte; shop; tradsmn; rest; snacks; bar; BBQ; playgrnd; sand beach; TV rm; phone; adv bkg (tel 986-690203); cc acc; red long stay; quiet; CCI. "Warm welcome; v friendly owner; sm pitches in 1 part of site; excel long/sh stay." ♦ ltd. Holy Week-30 Sep. € 16.05   2004*

SAVINAN see Calatayud *3C1*

SEGOVIA *1C4* (3km SE Urban) **Camping El Acueducto, Avda Don Juan de Bourbon y Battenberg 49, 40004 Segovia [tel/fax 921-42 50 00 or 921-42 95 17; campingsg@ navegalia.com]** Turn off Segovia by-pass at La Granja exit, but head twd Segovia. Site in approx 500m off dual c'way just bef Restaurante Lago. If coming fr Madrid via N603 turn L twd Segovia onto N601 fr La Granja Lge, mkd pitch, pt sl, pt shd; wc; chem disp; mv service pnt; shwrs inc; el pts (10A) €3.90; gas; lndtte; sm shop; mkt 1km; rest adj; bar; BBQ; playgrnd; pool & paddling pool high ssn; cycle hire; dogs; phone; bus to city; poss cr; m'way noise (& donkeys!); CCI. "Excel; v helpful staff; lovely views; v clean facs; gates locled 0000-0800; city worth visit; gd bus service; pitches sm for lge o'fits." ♦ ltd. 1 Apr-30 Sep. € 25.50   2005*

SENEGUE see Sabinanigo *3B2*

†**SEO DE URGEL** *3B3* (8km N Rural) **Camping Frontera, Ctra de Andorra, Km 8, 25799 La Farga de Moles (Lleida) [973-35 14 27; fax 973-35 33 40; info@fronterapark.com; www.fronterapark.com]** Sp on N145 about 500m fr Spanish Customs sheds. Access poss diff. Lge, mkd pitch, hdstg, pt sl, pt shd; htd wc; chem disp; shwrs inc; el pts (3-6A) €4; gas; lndtte; hypmkt 2km; tradsmn; rest; snacks; bar; playgrnd; 2 pools; rv sw; TV rm; phone; car wash; poss cr; adv bkg; noisy; CCI. "Ideal for shopping in Andorra, winter skiing; beautiful situation but poss dusty; v helpful owners." ♦ € 18.00 (CChq acc)
                    2005*

†**SEO DE URGEL** *3B3* (3km SW Urban) **Camping Gran Sol, 25711 Montferrer (Lleida) [tel/fax 973-35 13 32; campgransol@jazzfree.com]** S fr Seo de Urgel on N260/C1313 twds Lerida/ Lleida. Site approx 3km on L fr town. Med, pt shd; wc; chem disp (wc); mv service pnt; shwrs inc; el pts (2-6A) inc; gas; lndtte; ice; shop; rest; playgrnd; pool; some Eng spkn; adv bkg; some rd noise; CCI. "Gd site & facs (poss stretched if full); conv for Andorra; beautiful vills & mountain scenery; in low ssn phone to check site open; gd NH." ♦ € 21.00
                    2003*

SEO DE URGEL *3B3* (9km W Rural) **Camping Buchaca, 25712 Castellbo (Lleida) [973-35 21 55]** Leave Seo de Urgel on N260/1313 twd Lerida. In approx 3km turn N (R) sp Castellbo. Site on L, well sp. Sm, mkd pitch, pt sl, pt shd; wc; chem disp (wc); shwrs inc; el pts (5A) €3.40; lndry rm; shop; snacks; playgrnd; pool; phone; poss cr; adv bkg; quiet. "CL-type site in beautiful surroundings; v friendly recep; poss diff access lge o'fits." 1 May-30 Sep. € 19.70   2003*

SEVILLA see also sites listed under Dos Hermanas and Alcala de Guadaira *2G3*

†**SEVILLA** *2G3* (2km E) **Camping Sevilla, Ctra Madrid-Cadiz, Km 534, 41008 Sevilla [tel/fax 954-51 43 79; campingsevilla@turinet.net]** Fr Seville take A4/E5 twds Cordoba; exit junc 535 sp Brenes (busy rndabt under m'way) onto slip/ service rd on S side of A4 & head away fr Seville; turn R off slip rd at camping sp. Fr Madrid after airport on L take next exit sp site, but keep L immed at fork at exit. To visit Seville fr site, ent E5 dir Madrid, exit into airport sp departure terminal. Cross over m'way & rejoin dir Seville. Med, pt shd; wc; chem disp; mv service pnt; shwrs inc; el pts (6A) €2.25 (poss no earth); gas; lndtte; shop; tradsmn; rest; bar; playgrnd; pool; tennis; games area; internet; phone; bus to Seville 1km; car wash; poss cr; Eng spkn; red CCI. "Clean facs; noise fr airport (site under flight path) & adj m'way, but quieter at night; gd NH/sh stay; closed New Year's Day."
€ 15.00   2005*

As we're travelling out of season, we'd better phone ahead to check that the site is actually open.

SIGUES *3B1* (4km S Rural) **Camp Municipal Mar del Pirineo, Ctra Pamplona-Jaca, Km 337, 50682 Sigues [948-39 80 74; fax 948-88 71 77]** On N240 approx 55km E of Pamplona by Yesa reservoir, site sp. Med, pt shd; wc; chem disp; shwrs €0.60; el ptsl gas; lndtte; shop; rest; snacks; bar; shop; beach/ lake adj; watersports; 50% statics; poss cr; some noise; cc not acc; CCI. "Rec inspect pitch on foot bef booking; NH only." Holy Week & 1 Jun-15 Sep.
€ 15.00   2004*

SITGES *3C3* (N Urban) **Camping El Roca, Avda de Ronda s/n, 08870 Sitges (Barcelona) [938-94 00 43; fax 938-94 01 50; elroca@camping elroca.com; www.campingelroca.com]** On Barcelona-Tarragona rd C246 turn N at camp sp (after rlwy x-ing fr Barcelona) or, heading west on C32 fr Barcelona dir Tarragona, exit sp Sitges Cent. Turn L after rndabt & foll sp to site. Lge, mkd pitch, hdstg, terr, shd; wc; chem disp; shwrs inc; el pts (6A) €3; gas; lndtte; ice; shop; supmkt 1km; rest; snacks; bar; playgrnd; sand beach 800m; watersports carwash facs; 20% statics; train 300m; Eng spkn; adv bkg (dep req); red long stay; cc acc; CCI. "Clean facs; poss tight acc to pitches; tourist info avail at site office." 14 Apr-15 Oct. € 21.80
                    2004*

SPAIN

†SITGES *3C3* (1.5km SW Urban/Coastal) **Camping El Garrofer, Ctra C246, Km 39, 08870 Sitges (Barcelona) [938-94 17 80; fax 938-11 06 23; info@garroferpark.com; www.garroferpark.com & www.sportnature.com]** Fr N fr AP7 take exit 28 or 29 dir Sitges. Thro Sitges twd Tarragona, site 1km on L, sp. Lge, mkd pitch, hdstg, pt shd; wc; chem disp; mv service pnt; baby facs; shwrs inc; serviced pitches; el pts (6A) inc; gas; lndtte; ice; shop; tradsmn; rest; snacks; bar; BBQ; pool; shgl beach 500m; tennis 500m; horseriding; cycle hire; windsurfing; sports ground; entmnt; TV; internet; car wash; 80% statics; dogs €3.95; phone; bus to Barcelona; recep open 0800-2100; site clsd early Dec-mid Jan to tourers; poss cr; Eng spkn; adv bkg; red low ssn; cc acc; red snr citizen/low ssn; site clsd 18 Dec-16 Jan; CCI. "Well-equipped site in good location; sep area for m'vans with water & drainage (open all yr); vg san facs; nice atmosphere; excel winter stay." ♦ € 27.00   2005*

We're having a great holiday - must fill in some site report forms and send them to The Club as soon as possible.

SITGES *3C3* (2km SW Urban/Coastal) **Camping Sitges, Ctra C31, Km 38, 08870 Sitges (Barcelona) [938-94 10 80; fax 938-94 98 52; info@campingsitges.com; www.campingsitges. com]** Fr A7/E15 exit junc 28 or 29 dir Sitges. Thro Sitges & under rlwy arch, then turn R twd Vilanova/Tarragona. Site on L immed after x-ing rlwy bdges. Lge, mkd pitch, hdstg, pt shd; wc; chem disp; mv service pnt; baby facs; shwrs inc; el pts (4A) €3.15; gas; lndry rm; ice; shop; rest; snacks; bar; BBQ; playgrnd; pool high ssn; sand beach 800m; 20% statics; dogs; phone; bus to Barcelona; train 2km; quiet but some rlwy noise; Eng spkn; cc acc; CCI. "Friendly staff; excel san facs; well-maintained site." ♦ 1 Mar-20 Oct. € 20.60   2005*

†SOLSONA *3B3* (2km N) **Camping El Sonsones, Ctra St Llorenc Km 2, 25280 Solsona (Lleida) [973-48 28 61; fax 973-48 13 00; camping solsones@cbscat.com]** Fr Solsona to St Llorenc site on R in 2km well sp. Ignore new rd sp St Llorenc, cont on thro rd. Lge, pt sl, pt shd; wc; chem disp; shwrs; el pts (6A) €3.40; lndtte; shops & 2km; snacks; pool; 25% statics; poss cr w/e; quiet off peak; cc acc; red CCI. "V helpful staff; v restful." € 19.60   2003*

†SOLSONA *3B3* (8km SE Rural) **Camping La Ribera, Pantano de Sant Ponc, 25290 Clariana de Cardener (Lleida) [tel/fax 973-48 25 52]**
Fr Solsona S on C55, turn L onto C26 at km 71. Go 2.7km, site sp immed bef Sant Ponc Dam. Lge, mkd pitch, hdstg, pt shd; wc; chem disp; shwrs; el pts (4-10A) €3.30; lndtte; shop; bar; playgrnd; pool; lake sw; tennis; 90% statics. "Excel facs; gd site." ♦
€ 20.80   2005*

SOMO see Santander *1A4*

SOPELANA see Bilbao *1A4*

SORIA *3C1* (2km S Rural) **Camping Fuente de la Teja, Carlos Morales Garijo, Km 223, 42004 Soria [tel/fax 975-22 29 67]** Fr N on N111 1km R after x-ing N122. Site 300m on L. Fr Soria on NIII dir Madrid sp just past km 223. V tight RH turn onto site app rd; poss diff lge o'fits. Fr S on N111 site sp fr 2 exits. Med, mkd pitch, pt sl, pt shd; wc; chem disp; baby facs; shwrs inc; el pts (6A) €2.45 (poss no earth); gas; lndtte; hypmkt 3km; tradsmn; rest; snacks; bar; playgrnd; pool high ssn; TV rm; 10% statics; dogs; bus 500m; phone; poss cr; adv bkg; some rd noise; cc acc; CCI. "Excel NH bet France & Spain; vg refurbed san facs; interesting town, superb historical churches; phone ahead to check site open if travelling bet 1 Oct & Easter." ♦ ltd.
Easter-30 Sep. € 17.60   2005*

†SORT *3B2* (1km N Rural) **Camping Noguera Palleresa, 25560 Sort (Lleida) [973-62 08 20; fax 973-62 12 04]** Leave C13 at km 110.9, site sp. Lge, pt sl, pt shd; wc; shwrs; el pts €4; gas; lndtte; shop; snacks; bar; playgrnd; white watersports; phone quiet. "Popular canoeing resort close to Aigue Tortes National Park; exit via steep rough rd, may be diff for low power ratio o'fits; gd NH/sh stay." ♦
€ 18.20   2002*

SOTO DEL REAL see Manzanares el Real *1D4*

†SUECA *4E2* (5km NE Coastal) **Camping Les Barraquetes, Playa de Sueca, 46410 Mareny de Barraquetes (Valencia) [961-76 07 23; fax 963-20 93 63; info@barraquetes.com; www. campingbarraquetes.com]** Exit AP7 junc 58 dir Sueca onto N332. In Sueca take CV500 to Mareny de Barraquetes. Or S fr Valencia on CV500 coast rd. Foll sp for Cullera & Sueca. Site on L. Lge, mkd pitch, shd; wc; chem disp; mv service pnt; shwrs inc; el pts (6A) €4.50; gas; lndtte; ice; shop; bar; BBQ; playgrnd; pool; paddling pool; waterslide; sand beach 500m; tennis; games area; entmnt; child entmnt; TV rm; 10% statics; dogs €3; phone; site clsd mid-Dec to mid-Jan; poss cr; cc acc; red low ssn/long stay/snr citizens; CCI. "Much improved site; conv touring base & Valencia; highly rec." ♦
€ 19.00   2005*

See advertisement

SUECA *4E2* (6km SE Coastal) **Camping Santa Marta, 46408 Cullera (Valencia) [961-72 14 40; fax 961-73 12 45]** On the N332 ent Cullera & foll sp. Turn up steep lane beside bullring (white building). Lge, terr, pt sl, shd; wc; chem disp; shwrs; el pts (10A) €3.10; lndtte; shop (high ssn); bar; playgrnd; pool; sand beach 200m; no dogs; phone; cc acc. "Beach across busy rd between high rise hotels; pitching diff on steep terrs." ♦ 1 Apr-30 Sep.
€ 18.00   2003*

†TABERNAS *4G1* (5km E Rural) **Camping Oro Verde, 04200 Tabernas (Almeria) [687-62 99 96 or 01434 320495 (UK); www.oroverde.co.uk]**
Fr N340 take Turillas turning bet Calatravas Hotel & Oro Verde filling stn & take 1st R. Site 200m on L. Sm, mkd pitch, hdstg, pt shd; wc; chem disp; shwrs inc; el pts (10A) inc; gas; lndtte; ice; rest, bar nrby in hotel; pool; sand beach 40km; adv bkg; quiet; red long stay; CCI. "In sm olive grove; beautiful views; friendly British owners." ♦ € 14.00   2005*

TALARN see Tremp *3B2*

TAMARIT see Tarragona *3C3*

TAMARIU see Palafrugell *3B3*

TAPIA DE CASARIEGO *1A3* (2km W) **Camping El Carbayin, Serantes, 33740 Tapia de Casariego (Asturias) [tel/fax 985-62 37 09]** Foll N634/E70 E fr Ribadeo for 2km to Serantes. Site on R 400m fr rd, well sp. Sm, mkd pitch, pt sl, pt shd; wc; chem disp; shwrs inc; el pts (3A) €3; lndtte; rest; bar; playgrnd; sand beach 1km; fishing; watersports; no statics; phone; adv bkg; quiet; cc acc; CCI. "Gd for coastal walks & trips to mountains; excel all stays." ♦ Holy Week & 1 Jun-15 Sep. € 12.60   2003*

TAPIA DE CASARIEGO *1A3* (3km W Coastal) **Camping Playa de Tapia, La Reburdia, 33740 Tapia de Casariego (Asturias) [985-47 27 21]**
N634 fr Navia twd W go past 2 exits sp Tapia de Casariego; then 500m on R foll sp over x-rd to site on L. Med, hdg/mkd pitch, pt sl, pt shd; wc; chem disp; shwrs inc; el pts (16A) inc; gas; lndtte; shop; rest; bar; sand beach 500m; phone; Eng spkn; adv bkg; quiet; CCI. "Gd access; well-maintained, friendly site; harbour & coastal views; walking dist to town." ♦ 1 Jun-15 Sep. € 18.30   2004*

TARAZONA *3B1* (8km SE Rural) **Camping Veruela Moncayo, 50580 Vera de Moncayo (Zaragoza) [976-64 91 54; fax 976-56 87 88; www.arrakis.es]** Fr Zaragoza, take the AP68 or the N232 twd Tudela/Logrono; after approx. 50km, turn L to join the N122 (km stone 75) twd Tarazona; cont 30km & turn L twd Vera de Moncayo; go thro town cent; site on R; well sp. Lge, hdg pitch, pt sl, unshd; wc; shwrs inc (2200-1000); el pts inc; gas; rest, snacks, bar & shop 300m; playgrnd adj; pool 500m; cycle hire; dogs; adv bkg; CCI. "Quiet site adj to monastery; gd birdwatching; poss problem with elect at peak times; neglected; inadequate facs; NH only." ♦ ltd.
Holy Week & 15 Jun-15 Oct. € 11.50   2003*

SPAIN

†TARIFA *2H3* (11km W Coastal) **Camping El Jardin de las Dunas, Ctra N340, Km 74, Punta Paloma, 11380 Tarifa (Cadiz)** [956-68 91 01; fax 956-69 91 06] W on N340 fr Tarifa, L at sp Punta Paloma. Turn L 300m after Camping Paloma, site in 500m. Lge, hdg pitch; pt shd; wc; chem disp; serviced pitches; baby facs; shwrs inc; el pts (10A); lndtte; shop; rest; snacks; bar; playgrnd; beach 50m; entmnt; TV rm; phone; noisy; cc acc; red low ssn. "Poss strong winds; unsuitable lge o'fits due tight turns & trees." ♦   2005*

†TARIFA *2H3* (3km NW Coastal) **Camping Rio Jara, 11380 Tarifa (Cadiz)** [tel/fax 956-68 05 70; campingriojara@terra.es] Site on S of N340 Cadiz-Algeciras rd at km post 81.2; 3km after Tarifa; clearly visible & sp. Med, mkd pitch, pt shd; wc (some cont); chem disp; mv service pnt; shwrs inc; el pts (10A) €3; gas; lndtte; ice; tradsmn; rest; snacks; bar; playgrnd; sand beach 200m; fishing; dogs; poss cr; adv bkg; rd noise; cc acc; CCI. "Clean, well-kept site; friendly recep; long, narr pitches diff for awnings; daily trips to N Africa; gd windsurfing nrby; poss strong winds; mosquitoes in summer." ♦ € 22.00   2005*

†TARIFA *2H3* (6km NW Coastal) **Camping Tarifa, N340, Km 78.87, 11380 Tarifa (Cadiz)** [tel/fax 956-68 47 78; info@camping-tarifa.com; www.camping-tarifa.com] Site on R of Cadiz-Malaga rd N340. Med, mkd pitch, hdstg, shd; wc; chem disp; mv service pnt; serviced pitch; baby facs; shwrs inc; el pts (3A) inc; gas; lndtte; shop; rest; snacks; bar; playgrnd; pool; sand beach adj; dogs; phone; car wash; Eng spkn. "Vg; ideal for windsurfing; immed access to beach; lovely site with beautiful pool; v secure - fenced & locked at night; some pitches sm & poss diff access due bends, trees & kerbs; conv ferry to Morocco; poss strong winds; many dogs!" ♦ € 28.00   2004*

†TARIFA *2H3* (7km NW Coastal) **Camping Torre de la Pena 1, Ctra Cadiz, 11380 Tarifa (Cadiz)** [956-68 49 03; fax 956-68 14 73; info@campingtp.com] Site at km 79 on both sides of N340, sp. Steep access fr fast main rd. Lge, terr, pt sl, pt shd; wc; shwrs; el pts (5A) inc; gas; lndtte; shop; rest; bar; pool; sand beach adj (via tunnel under rd); few statics; poss cr; adv bkg; quiet; red long stay & low ssn. "Excel; superb view to Africa; conv for Gibraltar & Tangiers; upper level poss diff lge o'fits; helpful staff; poss strong winds." € 17.00   2003*

†TARIFA *2H3* (9km NW Coastal) **Camping Torre de la Pena II, Ctra N340, Km 75.5, 11380 Tarifa (Cadiz)** [956-68 41 74; fax 956-68 18 98; info@campingtp.com] Site on N340 at km 75.5, sp. Med, pt shd; wc; shwrs; el pts (5A) €3; lndtte; shop; rest; bar; playgrnd; pool; sand beach 400m; tennis; adv bkg; quiet; cc acc. € 17.10   2004*

†TARIFA *2H3* (11km NW Coastal) **Camping Paloma, Ctra Cádiz-Málaga, Km 74, Punta Paloma, 11380 Tarifa (Cadiz)** [956-68 42 03; fax 956-68 18 80; info@campingpaloma.com; www.campingpaloma.com] Fr Tarifa on N340, site on L at 74km stone sp Punta Paloma, site on R. Lge, mkd pitch, hdstg, pt sl, terr, pt shd; wc (some cont); chem disp; mv service pnt; shwrs inc; el pts (6A) €2.75; gas; lndtte; shop; rest; snacks; bar; playgrnd; pool high ssn; sand beach 1km; waterspsports; windsurfing; horseriding; cycle hire; 20% statics; poss cr; Eng spkn; no adv bkg; quiet; cc acc; red long stay/low ssn; CCI. "Trips to N Africa & whale-watching arranged; gd mountain views; well-run site; vg facs; ideal for peace & quiet away fr busy rds; lge o'fits poss diff due low trees." ♦ ltd. € 22.80   2005*

> This site entry hasn't been updated for a while; we'd better fill in a site report form and send it to The Club.

TARRAGONA *3C3* (NE Coastal) **Camping Tarraco, Ctra. N340 Playa de L'Arrabassada, 43080 Tarragona** [977 23 99 89; fax 977 21 91 16] Fr N340 foll sp to Playa de L'Arrabassada; site on R bef beach. Med, mkd pitch, pt shd; wc; chem disp; shwrs inc; el pts (10A) inc; gas; lndtte; ice; supmkt adj; snacks; sand beach; cycle hire; playgrnd; 25% statics; bus; quiet but some rlwy noise; cc acc; CCI. "Sm, friendly site; conv bus to town; sandy beach sep fr site by rlwy embankment; poor san facs; poss ltd drinking water." Easter-30 Sep. € 20.00   2004*

TARRAGONA *3C3* (4km NE Coastal) **Camping Las Salinas, Playa Larga, 43007 Tarragona** [977-20 76 28] Access via N340 bet km 1167 & 1168. Med, shd; wc; shwrs; el pts €2.90; gas; lndtte; shop; snacks; bar; beach adj; poss cr; rlwy noise. Holy Week & 15 May-30 Sep. € 16.30   2003*

TARRAGONA *3C3* (5km NE Coastal) **Camping Las Palmeras, N340, Km 1169.5, 43007 Tarragona** [977-20 80 81; fax 977-20 78 17; laspalmeras@laspalmeras.com; www.laspalmeras.com] Exit m'way N of Tarragona at junc 32 (sp Altafulla). After about 5km on N340 twd Tarragona take sp L turn at crest of hill. Site sp. V lge, mkd pitch, pt shd; wc; chem disp; shwrs inc; el pts (3-5A) €2.70; gas; lndtte; ice; shop; rest; snacks; bar; playgrnd; pool; sand beach adj; naturist beach 1km; tennis; games area; phone; poss cr; rlwy noise; cc acc; red long stay/low ssn; CCI. "Gd beach, ideal for families; mosquito prob; sea warm." ♦ 1 Apr-10 Oct. € 34.00 (CChq acc)   2005*

TAMARIT PARK CAMPING, BUNGALOWS

Exceptionally beautiful situation, very quiet and isolated, by Tamarit Castle, 7 km north of Tarragona (world heritage). Ideal to enjoy nature and sun, at a 3 km long beach with swallow waters and 20 km from theme park 'Universal Port Aventura'. • Restuarant and snack-bar by the beach and swimmin pools, sports, tennis courts, illuminated paddle, football, volley, ping-pong, petanque, amphitheatre, organised leisure, disco. • Social club with television, film, internet, bar with terrace • Fee reductions up to 45% ouside main season • 07/04/2006 - 15/10/2006. Platja Tamarit - Ctra. N-340, Km. 1172 - 43008 Tarragona · Tel. (34) 977 65 01 28 - Fax (34) 977 65 04 51 www.tamarit.com tamaritpark@tamarit.com

TARRAGONA *3C3* (7km NE Coastal) **Camping Torre de la Mora**, Ctra N340, Km 1171, 43080 Tarragona-Tamarit [977-65 02 77; fax 977-65 28 58; camtmora@tinet.fut.es; www.torredelamora.com] Fr A7 exit junc 32 (sp Altafulla), at rndabt join N340 sp Tarragona, leave at Tamarit/Altafulla exit. At rndabt take La Mora rd. Then foll site sp to ent 1km on L. Avoid ent thro low bdge, go thro fence into unmade site rd. Lge, hdstg, terr, pt shd; wc; chem disp; mv service pnt; baby facs; shwrs inc; el pts (6A) €3.50; gas; Indtte; ice; shop & 1km; tradsmn; rest; snacks; bar; playgrnd; pool; sand beach adj; tennis; sports club adj; golf 2km; entmnt; internet; 50% statics; dogs €1; bus 200m; Eng spkn; adv bkg; quiet away fr rd & rlwy; cc acc; red long stay; CCI. "Improved, clean site set in attractive bay with fine beach; excel pool; conv Tarragona & Port Aventura; sports club adj; various pitch sizes; private bthrms avail." ♦ 18 Mar-31 Oct. € 24.60   2005*

TARRAGONA *3C3* (7km NE Coastal) **Camping-Caravaning Tamarit Park**, Playa Tamarit, Ctra N340, Km 1172, 43008 Playa Tamarit (Tarragona) [977-65 01 28; fax 977-65 04 51; tamaritpark@tamarit.com; www.tamarit.com] Fr A7/E15 exit junc 32 sp Altafulla/Torredembarra, at rndabt join N340 by-pass sp Tarragona. At rndabt foll sp Altafulla, turn sharp R to cross rlwy bdge to site in 1.2km, sp. V lge, hdg pitch, some hdstg, pt sl, shd; htd wc; chem disp; mv service pnt; serviced pitches; baby facs; fam bthrm; private bthrms avail; shwrs inc; el pts (10A) inc; gas; Indtte; ice; supmkt; rest; snacks; bar; BBQ; playgrnd; htd pool; paddling pool; sand/shgl beach adj; watersports; tennis; games area; entmnt; internet; TV; 30% statics; dogs €3; phone; cash machine; car wash; adv bkg (rec Jul/Aug); Eng spkn; red long stay/snr citizens/low ssn; cc acc; red long stay; CCI. "Superb pool; well-maintained site; gets better & better; best site in area due to excel facs but poss noisy at night & w/e; beachside pitches avail; take care overhanging trees; excel." ♦ ltd. 7 Apr-15 Oct. € 43.50   2005*

See advertisement

†**TOLEDO** *1D4* (2km W) **Camping El Greco**, Ctra CM 4000, Km.0.7, 45004 Toledo [tel/fax 925-22 00 90; campingelgreco@telefonica.net; www.campingelgreco.ya.st] Site on C4000 fr Toledo dir La Puebla de Montalban & Talavera. When app, avoid town cent, keep to N outside of old town & watch for camping sp. Or use outer ring rd. Med, hdg/mkd pitch, pt sl, shd; wc; chem disp; mv service pnt; shwrs inc; el pts (6A) €4 (poss rev pol); gas; Indtte; shop; tradsmn; bar; BBQ; playgrnd; pool; paddling pool; games area; dogs; bus; phone; Eng spkn; cc acc. "V clean & tidy; all pitches on gravel; gd rest; reg bus into town useful due to narr streets but easy parking on o'skts - adj Puerta de San Martin rec; some pitches poss tight; excel san facs but could be cleaner - stretched if site full; lovely situation, superb views; friendly, helpful owners; excel info on site; lge supermkt in town off Ave de Europa, 20 min walk into town." € 22.60
2005*

TORDESILLAS *1C3* (1km SW Urban) **Camping El Astral**, Camino de Pollos 8, 47100 Tordesillas (Valladolid) [tel/fax 983-77 09 53; info@camping elastral.com; www.campingelastral.com] Fr NE on A62/E80 thro town turn L at rndabt over rv & immed after bdge turn R dir Salamanca & R again past Hostel Lorenzo & foll rd for 500m to ent to site; foll camping sp & Parador Nacional. Poorly sp. Fr A6 exit sp Tordesillas & take N620. Cross bdge out of town & foll site sp. Med, hdg/mkd pitch, hdstg, pt shd; wc; chem disp; mv service pnt; baby facs; shwrs inc; el pts (5A) €3.30 (rev pol); gas; Indtte; shop; supmkt in town; tradsmn; rest; snacks; bar; playgrnd; pool in ssn; rv sand beach 200m; fishing; tennis; cycle hire; excursions; TV rm; 10% statics; dogs €2.35; phone; site open w/end Mar & Oct; Eng spkn; quiet, but some traff noise; cc acc; CCI. "Helpful owners; easy walk to interesting town; v nice site by rv; excel facs; narr access lane not suitable long o'fits." ♦ 1 Apr-30 Sep. € 20.00 (CChq acc)   2005*

TORLA see Broto *3B2*

SPAIN

†TORRE DEL MAR *2H4* (1km SW Coastal) Camping Torre del Mar, Paseo Maritimo s/n, 29740 Torre del Mar (Malaga) [952-54 02 24; fax 952-54 04 31] Clearly sp fr N340A at W end of town. Site on beach rd past lighthouse 200m E fr Mercadona supmkt. Lge, hdg/mkd pitch, hdstg, shd; wc; chem disp; mv service pnt; serviced pitches; shwrs inc; el pts (10A) €2.30; gas; lndtte; shop & 500m; rest; snacks; bar in ssn; playgrnd; pool & paddling pool; sandy/shgl beach 50m; sat TV; tennis; few statics; no dogs; phone; poss cr all year; quiet but noise fr adj football pitch; red low ssn/long stay; CCI. "Tidy, clean, friendly, well-run site; sm pitches; gd san facs; popular low ssn; building works in area." ♦ € 27.10   2005*

TORRE DEL MAR *2H4* (3km W Coastal) Camping Almayate Costa, Ctra N340, Km 267, 29749 Almayate (Malaga) [952-55 62 89; fax 952-55 63 10; almayatecosta@campings.net] E fr Malaga on N340/E15 coast rd. Exit junc 258 dir Almeria, site on R 3km bef Torre-del-Mar. Easy access. Lge, mkd pitch, hdstg, shd; wc; chem disp; mv service pnt; shwrs inc; el pts (10A) inc; gas; lndtte; ice; supmkt; bar; BBQ; playgrnd; pool & paddling pool; sand beach adj; games rm; golf 7km; no dogs Jul/Aug; car wash; phone; Eng spkn; adv bkg; quiet but some rd noise; red long stay; cc acc; CCI. "Helpful manager; vg resort; vg long/sh stay." ♦ 19 Mar-30 Sep. € 27.00   2004*

> Some of these sites have changed their opening dates - we'd better fill in some site report forms and let the editor of the guide know.

†TORRE DEL MAR *2H4* (1km W Coastal) Camping Laguna Playa, Prolongacion Paseo Maritimo s/n, 29740 Torre del Mar (Malaga) [952-54 06 31; fax 952-54 04 84; info@lagunaplaya.com; www.lagunaplaya.com] Clearly sp fr N340A nr W end of town. Sp to site 400m along (rubbish-strewn) track past ent Camping Torre del Mar. Med, pt shd; wc; chem disp; mv service pnt; shwrs inc; el pts (5-10A) €2.40; gas; lndtte; ice; shop; rest; snacks; bar; playgrnd; pool; sand beach 1km; 40% statics; dogs; poss cr; Eng spkn; adv bkg; quiet; red low ssn. "Popular low ssn; sm pitches; excel san facs, v clean; gd location, easy walk to town; pity about rd leading to site!" € 18.70   2005*

†TORRE DEL MAR *2H4* (2km W Coastal) Camping Naturista Almanat (Naturist), Ctra de la Torre Alta, 29749 Almayate (Malaga) [952-55 64 62; fax 952-55 62 71; almanat@arrakis.es; www.almanat.de] Exit E15/N340 junc 274 sp Velez Malaga for Torre del Mar. Exit Torre del Mar on coast rd sp Malaga. In 2km bef lge black bull on R on hill & bef water tower turn L at sp. If rd not clear cont to next turning point & return in dir Torre del Mar & turn R to site at km 269. Site well sp. Lge, hdg/mkd pitch, hdstg (gravel), pt shd; htd wc; chem disp; mv service pnt (on request); sauna; shwrs inc; el pts (10-16A) €2.40; gas; lndtte; ice; shop; rest; bar; BBQ; playgrnd; pool; jacuzzi; sand/shgl beach adj; tennis; entmnt; cinema; games area; gym; golf 10km; some statics; dogs €1.65; phone; bus 500m; poss cr; Eng spkn; adv bkg (dep req); quiet; cc acc; red long stay/low ssn/snr citizens up to 50%; INF card. "Superb facs; v popular; highly rec; reasonable dist Seville, Granada, Cordoba; excel." ♦ € 20.00   2004*

†TORREBLANCA *3D2* (3km SE Coastal) Camping Mon Rossi, 12596 Torreblanca (Castellon) [964-42 50 96; fax 964-42 11 47; camping monrossi@hotmail.com] Exit A7 junc 44 & turn R to cross N340 & foll narr rd over rlwy bdge to Torrenostra, site on R in approx 3km, 150m bef beach. N'bound on N340 turn R immed bef access rd to A7; s'bound turn onto A7 access rd & immed L to cross N340. Med, hdg pitch, hdstg, pt shd; wc; chem disp; shwrs inc; el pts €3; gas; lndtte; shop; tradsmn; snacks; bar; pool; shgl beach adj; cycle hire; TV; 10% statics; phone; poss cr; adv bkg; quiet; cc acc. "Friendly, family-run site; only 6 pitches suitable for lge o'fits; vg long stay." € 17.00   2004*

†TORREMOLINOS *2H4* (3km NE Coastal) Camping Torremolinos, Loma del Paraíso 2., 29620 Torremolinos (Malaga) [952-38 26 02] Fr Malaga by-pass heading W take exit sp 'aeropuerto' & foll sp Torremolinos & site. Med, hdstg; terr, pt sl, pt shd; wc (some cont); shwrs; el pts (5A) €2.90; gas; lndtte; shop; rest 200m; snacks; bar; sand beach 700m; golf 500m; no dogs; buses & trains nrby; no adv bkg; noise fr rd, rlwy & aircraft; red CCI. "V helpful staff; v clean site; new san facs 2004." € 25.60   2004*

TORREVIEJA *4F2* (4km S Urban) Camping La Campana, Ctra Torrevieja-Cartagena, Km 4, 03180 Torrevieja (Alicante) [965-71 21 52] Take N332 S fr Torrevieja. Site ent dir off rndabt for Rocio del Mar at S end of Torrevieja by-pass. Med, mkd pitch, hdstg, pt shd; wc; chem disp; shwrs; el pts (6A) inc; gas; 500m; lndtte; shop; rest; snacks; bar; playgrnd; pool; shngle beach 1km; 40% statics; dogs €2.50; phone adj; bus 500m; poss cr; Eng spkn; noisy; red up to 25% low ssn; 10% red CCI. ♦ 1 Apr-30 Sep. € 22.00   2004*

†TORREVIEJA *4F2* (7km SW Rural) **Camping Florantilles, Ctra San Miguel de Salinas-Torrevieja, 03193 San Miguel de Salinas (Alicante) [965-72 04 56; fax 966-72 32 50; florantilles@terra.es]** Take new AP7 Alicante-Cartegena m'way & exit junc 758 onto CV95, sp Orihuela, Torrevieja Sud. Turn R at rndabt & after 300m turn R again, site immed on L. Or if travelling on A7, foll N332 S past Alicante airport twd Torrevieja. Leave Torrevieja by-pass at its most S exit, sp Torrevieja, San Miguel. Turn R onto CV95 & foll for about 3km, passing over 3 rndabts thro the urbanisation 'Los Balcones'. After leaving Los Balcones, cont for another 500m, under new by-pass, round rndabt & up hill, site sp on R. Turn R & site on L. Lge, hdg/mkd, hdstg, terr, pt shd; wc; chem disp; mv service pnt; shwrs inc; el pts (10A) inc; gas; lndtte; ice; supmkt; tradsmn; rest; snacks; bar; BBQ; pool & paddling pool (high ssn); sand beach 5km; horseriding 10km; fitness studio; TV; 80% statics; no dogs; recep clsd 1330-1630; poss cr in winter; adv bkg; quiet; various red; cc acc; CCI. NB: Sm number of touring pitches ONLY avail if booked through The Caravan Club, remaining pitches avail for a 12-month rental period only; recep clsd 1330-1630. "Friendly staff; British-managed; popular site; many long stay visitors & all year vans; Spanish lessons, exercise sessions & walking clubs; own transport ess; shwrs poor; m'way noise." ♦ ltd. € 25.17 ABS - E11   2005*

> Will you fill in the site report forms at the back of the guide, or shall I?

TORROELLA DE MONTGRI *3B3* (8km SE Coastal) **Camping El Delfin Verde, 17257 Torroella de Montgri (Gerona) [972-75 84 54; fax 972-76 00 70; info@eldelfinverde.com; www.eldelfinverde.com]** Fr N leave A7 at junc 5 (N of Gerona) in dir L'Escala. At Vilademat turn R onto C-31 sp La Bisbal. After a few km turn L twd Torroella de Montgri. At rndabt foll sp for Pals (also sp El Delfin Verde), site on L in 5km just bef Pals. Lge, mkd pitch, pt sl, pt shd; wc; chem disp; mv service pnt; baby facs; shwrs inc; el pts (5A) inc; gas; lndtte; ice; supmkt; rests; snacks; 3 bars; BBQ; pool; sand beach adj; tennis; horseriding 4km; cycle hire; windsurfing; sportsgrnd; mini-golf; hairdresser; money exchange; entmnt; disco; winter storage; TV/video; 40% statics (sep area); no dogs 11/7-14/8, at low ssn €3; poss cr; quiet; red low ssn; cc acc; CCI. "Superb site, faultless; excel pool; gd value; all water de-salinated fr fresh water production plant; bottled water rec for drinking & cooking; mkt Mon; excel long stay." ♦ 8 Apr-15 Oct. € 49.20 ABS - E01   2005*

See advertisement on next page

TOSSA DE MAR *3B3* (500m N Coastal) **Camping Can Marti, Avda Paul Casals s/n, 17320 Tossa de Mar (Gerona) [972-34 08 51; fax 972-34 24 61; www.canmarti.org]** App fr Lloret, turn L at rndabt by Bahia de Tossa Hotel; strt at next rndabt, then L at Champion supmkt, site in 300m. Fr Llagostera turn L at rndabt, then L at Champion supmkt as above. Mountain rd fr San Feliu not rec. V lge, mkd pitch; pt shd; wc; chem disp; baby facs; shwrs inc; el pts (10A) inc; gas; lndtte; ice; shop; rest; snacks; bar; playgrnd; pool & paddling pool; shgl beach 500m; fishing; tennis; horseriding; 10% statics; phone; car wash; sep car park; Eng spkn; no adv bkg; quiet; red long stay/CCI. "Security guards; helpful, friendly staff; facs v clean; boat trips." ♦ 25 May-10 Sep. € 31.00   2005*

TOSSA DE MAR *3B3* (4km NE Coastal) **Camping Pola, Ctra Tossa-Sant Feliu, Km 4, 17320 Tossa de Mar (Gerona) [972-34 10 50; fax 972-34 10 83; campingpola@arrakis.es]** Fr Tossa on rd GE682 dir Sant Feliu. Narr, winding rd but gd. Site lge, pt sl, pt shd; wc; shwrs inc; el pts (15A) inc; gas; shop; rest; bar; gas; playgrnd; pool; paddling pool; sand beach adj; tennis; games area; entmnt; dogs €3.10; sep car park high ssn; adv bkg; cc acc. 28 May-1 Oct. € 34.00   2005*

TOSSA DE MAR *3B3* (3km SW Coastal) **Camping Cala Llevado, Ctra Tossa-Lloret Km 3, 17320 Tossa de Mar (Gerona) [972-34 03 14; fax 972-34 11 87; info@calallevado.com; www.calallevado.com]** Exit AP7 junc 9 dir Lloret. In Lloret take GI 682 dir Tossa de Mar. Site well sp. V lge, mkd pitch, terr, shd; wc; chem disp; mv service pnt; baby facs; shwrs inc; el pts (5-10A) €3.50; gas; lndtte; ice; supmkt; rest; snacks; bar; playgrnd; 3 pools inc paddling pool; sand/shgl beach adj; waterskiing; windsurfing; diving; fishing; boat trips; tennis; games/sports facs; child entmnt Jul/Aug; internet; TV; 10% statics; no dogs; phone; Eng spkn; adv bkg; quiet; CCI. ♦ Holy Week & 1 May-30 Sep. € 28.85   2005*

†TOTANA *4G1* (2km SW Rural) **Camping Totana, Ctra N340, Km 614, 30850 Totana (Murcia) [tel/fax 968-42 48 64]** Fr N340/E15 exit at km 612 fr N. Fr S exit km 609. Foll Totana rd, site 2km on R. Sl ent. Sm, mkd pitch, hdstg, terr, pt shd; wc; chem disp; shwrs inc; el pts (6A) €2.14; shop & 4km; rest; bar; BBQ; playgrnd; pool high ssn; games rm; entmnt; 80% statics; dogs; Eng spkn; 10% red 2+ days; CCI. "Conv mountains & National Park; access to sm pitches tight due trees; helpful owners; tidy site; communal drying in shwr area; vg NH." € 14.00   2005*

SPAIN

TREMP *3B2* (4km N Rural) **Camping Gaset, 25630 Talarn (Lleida)** [973-65 07 37; fax 973-65 01 02; campingaset@catalunya.com] Fr Tremp, take C147 N sp Talarn. Site clearly visible on R by lake. Lge, pt sl, terr, pt shd; wc; shwrs; el pts (4A) €3.40; lndtte; shop; rest 4km; snacks; bar; playgrnd; pool; paddling pool; sand beach for lake sw; tennis; 15% statics; dogs; phone; poss cr; quiet; cc acc. "Picturesque setting by San Antonio Lake; gd fishing & boating on lake; some sm pitches." 1 Apr-15 Oct. € 19.70   2003*

TURIENO CALAMENO see Potes *1A4*

UBRIQUE *2H3* (15km N Rural) **Camping Los Linares, Nacimiento s/n, 11679 Benamahoma (Cadiz)** [tel/fax 956-71 62 75] N fr Ubrique to El Bosque, turn E dir Benamahoma & Grazalema. Site well sp in vill. To avoid narr streets ent fr El Bosque end of vill. Med, mkd pitch, unshd; wc; chem disp; shwrs inc; el pts inc; shop 500m; rest; snacks; bar; pool; poss cr; CCI. "Gd walking/birdwatching area in National Park; narr vill streets poss diff lge o'fits; open w/e & public hols all year." ♦ ltd. 15 Jun-15 Sep. € 19.50   2003*

UNQUERA *1A4* (3km N Coastal) **Camping Las Arenas, Ctra Unquera Pechón, Km. 2, 39594 Pechon (Cantabria)** [tel/fax 942-71 71 88; lasarenas@ctv.es] On N634 10km W of San Vicente de Barquera turn sharp R (N) at sp Pechon, climb narr winding rd to site ent at top on L. Lge, mkd pitch, pt sl, terr, pt shd; wc; chem disp; shwrs el pts (8A) €2.30; gas; lndtte; rest; shop & 3km; bar; playgrnd; pool; shgl beach adj; fishing; cycle hire; no statics; poss cr; Eng spkn; quiet; cc acc; CCI. "Magnificent position on terr cliffs; peaceful; well kept & clean; vg all stays." 1 Jun-20 Sep. € 17.20
                                                          2004*

UNQUERA *1A4* (3km S Rural) **Camping El Mirador de Llavandres, Vegas Grandes, 33590 Colombres (Asturias)** [tel/fax 985-41 22 44; c. rural@teleline.es] Fr N634 12km W of San Vicente de la Barquera turn at km 283/284 dir Noriega, site in 1.3km. Med, mkd pitch, terr, unshd; wc; chem disp; shwrs inc; el pts (3A) €2.25; gas; lndtte; shop & 3km; playgrnd; sand beach 1km; TV; phone; quiet; cc acc; CCI. "Peaceful setting; excel for touring Picos." ♦ 15 Jun-15 Sep. € 17.30 2004*

VALDOVINO *1A2* (700m W Coastal) **Camping Valdovino, Ctra de la Playa 28, 15552 Valdovino (La Coruna)** [981-48 70 76; fax 981-48 61 31] Fr Ortigueira on C642; turn W onto C646 sp Cadeira then Ferrol; turn R at camping sp, down hill R again, site on R almost on beach. Med, terr, pt shd; wc; chem disp; baby facs; shwrs inc; el pts (15A) €3; gas; lndtte; ice; shop; rest; bar; snacks; playgrnd; sand beach adj; playgrnd; internet; TV; some statics; no dogs; bus; poss cr; quiet; Eng spkn; CCI. "Beautiful beach with lagoon & cliffs but poss windy; busy site; vg rest." ♦ Easter & 1 May-30 Sep. € 19.85   2005*

VALENCIA *4E2* (9km S Coastal) **Camping Coll Vert, Ctra Nazaret-Oliva, Km 7.5, 46024 Playa de Pinedo (Valencia)** [961-83 00 36; fax 961-83 00 40] Fr Valencia on coast rd, foll sp El Saler. Site on R 1km bef El Saler. Med, pt shd; wc; shwrs; el pts; gas; lndtte; shop; bar; sand beach 200m; pool; playgrnd; phone; car wash; bus; 75% statics; bus to city & marine park; no dogs; poss cr; Eng spkn; adv bkg; quiet; some rd noise; cc acc. "Hourly bus service fr outside site to cent of Valencia & marine park; helpful, friendly staff. ♦ Easter-15 Oct. € 17.80   2005*

VALENCIA *4E2* (10km S Urban/Coastal) **Camping Los Pinos, Ctra del Riu 548, 46012 El Saler (Valencia)** [961-83 02 44] Fr Valencia foll coast rd or V15 to El Saler. Site adj rndabt just N of El Saler. Med, hdg pitch, pt shd; wc; chem disp; shwrs inc; el pts (5A) inc; shop; rest; snacks; bar; pool; sand beach 500m; 75% statics; dogs; bus 50m; poss cr; rd noise; CCI. "V conv Valencia - 30 mins by bus; fair." € 37.00   2005*

†**VALENCIA** *4E2* (16km S Rural) **Camping Devesa Gardens, Ctra El Saler, Km 13, 46012 Valencia** [961-61 11 36; fax 961-61 11 05; www.devesa gardens.com] S fr Valencia on CV500, site well sp on R 4km S of El Saler. Med, mkd pitch, hdstg, pt shd; htd wc; chem disp; mv service pnt; baby facs; el pts (7-15A) €3.80; gas; lndtte; ice; supmkt & 4km; rest; bar; BBQ; playgrnd; pool; beach 700m; tennis; lake canoeing; horseriding; 70% statics; no dogs; phone; bus; quiet; adv bkg; Eng spkn; cc acc; CCI. "Friendly staff; warden needed to connect to el pt; site has own zoo; excel." ♦ € 27.50 2005*

VALENCIA DE DON JUAN see Villamanan *1B3*

VALL LLOBREGA see Palamos *3B3*

†**VALLE DE CABUERNIGA** *1A4* (Rural) **Camping El Molino de Cabuerniga, Sopena, 39510 Cabuerniga (Cantabria)** [942-70 62 59; fax 942-70 62 78; cmcabuerniga@campingcabue] SW on N634. At Cabezon de la Sal L onto C625. Site at km 42. Keep to R in vill, foll v sm green sp to site. Sp not v clear thro vill - v narr rds to site. Lge, pt shd; wc; shwrs inc; el pts (3A) €2.50; gas; lndtte; shop; snacks; bar; playgrnd; rv sw 200m; fishing; tennis; phone; bus 500m; adv bkg; CCI. "Excel site & facs on edge of vill; no shops in vicinity, but gd location." ♦ € 18.10   2005*

VEGUELLINA DE ORBIGO *1B3* (Rural) **Camping La Manga, Ctra LE421 Matalobos-Veguilla, Km 5, 24350 Veguellina de Orbigo (Leon)** [987-37 63 76; fax 987-37 61 35] Fr 1km S of Astorga fr A6, turn E onto N120 twds Leon; cont for 12km. At Hospital de Orbigo at LE421/420 turn S twds Veguellina de Orbigo; site sp fr vill. Med, pt shd; wc; chem disp; shwrs; el pts €1.55; gas; lndtte; shop; snacks; bar; watersports adj; some statics; dogs; phone; quiet. Holy Week & 15 Jun-15 Sep. € 9.35   2004*

SPAIN

†VEJER DE LA FRONTERA *2H3* (4km SE) Camping Vejer, 11150 Vejer de la Frontera (Cadiz) [tel/fax 956-45 00 98; info@campingvejer. com; www.campingvejer.com] App fr Malaga dir on N340, at km stone 39.5, exit to L, bet 2 rests, site in 100m. Do not take o'fit into Vejer. Sm, pt sl, terr, pt shd; wc; chem disp; shwrs; el pts (10A) €3; lndtte; shop; snacks; bar; playgrnd; pool; sand beach 9km; mini-golf; golf 2km; cycle hire; internet; 10% statics; dogs; phone; adv bkg; quiet; cc acc; CCI. "In wooded area away fr main rd." € 20.00
2004*

VEJER DE LA FRONTERA *2H3* (10km S Coastal) Camping Canos de Meca, Ctra de Vejer-Canos de Meca, Km 10, 11160 Barbate (Cadiz) [956-43 71 20; fax 956-43 71 37; info@camping-canos-de-meca.com; www.camping-canos-de-meca.com] Fr N340 foll sp to Barbate then foll dir Canos de Meca. Turn R at seashore rd. Site on L 2km beyond town. Med, mkd pitch, shd; wc; chem disp; shwrs inc; el pts (5A) €3.20; gas; lndtte; shop; rest; snacks; bar; playgrnd; pool; sand beach 600m; watersports; cycle hire; child entmnt; 20% statics; no dogs Jul/Aug; phone; poss cr; adv bkg; cc acc; CCI. "Vg." ♦ Easter-15 Oct. € 26.70
2005*

†VEJER DE LA FRONTERA *2H3* (10km SE Coastal) Camping Bahia de la Plata, Avda de las Palmeras, s/n, 11399 Zahara de los Atunes (Cadiz) [956-43 90 40; fax 956-43 90 87] Fr Vejer de la Frontera, take A393 twds Barbate; thro town & onto A2223 coastal rd twds Zahara de los Atunes; go thro Zahara, foll lorry rte to avoid narr streets & sharp corners of cent twds Atlanterra; site sp. Lge, mkd pitch, shd; wc; chem disp; shwrs inc; el pts (16A) inc; lndtte; ice; shop; rest; snacks; bar; playgrnd; beach adj; cycle hire; entmnt; TV; some statics; no dogs; phone; cc acc. "Site opens onto the beach; well-equipped & managed." ♦ ltd. € 13.25
2002*

†VELEZ BLANCO *4G1* (1km S Rural) Camping El Pinar del Rey, Paseo de los Sauces 5, 04830 Velez Blanco (Almeria) [950-52 71 02 or 639-18 71 16] Fr A92 turn off at Velez Rubio & foll sp Velez Blanco. Site on R bef vill. Sm, hdstg, pt shd; htd wc; chem disp (wc); shwrs inc; el pts (6A) €2.50; rest; snacks; bar; playgrnd; pool; TV rm; no statics; poss cr; some Eng spkn; adv bkg; CCI. "Beautiful area; clean mountain air; site still being developed; friendly staff." ♦ ltd. € 12.00
2004*

VENDRELL, EL *3C3* (5km SW Coastal) **Camping Park Playa Bara**, N340, Km 1.183, 43883 Roda de Bara (Tarragona) [977-80 27 01; fax 977-80 04 56; info@barapark.es; www.barapark.es] Exit A7 junc 31 onto N340, cont to Bara Roman Arch. Turn halfway bet Vendrell & Torredembarra at km 1183. V lge, hdg/mkd pitch, terr, shd; htd wc; 100% serviced pitches; chem disp; mv service pnt; baby facs; shwrs inc; el pts (5A) €3; gas; lndtte; supmkt; rest; snacks; bar; playgrnd; htd pool; sand beach adj; watersports; jacuzzi; solarium; tennis; games area; cycle hire; horseriding; entmnt; sat TV; doctor; car wash; 10% statics; dogs; bus; adv bkg; Eng spkn; quiet; red long stay/low ssn/snr citizens; CCI. "Vg bathing in beautiful surroundings; conv Port Aventura; excel site." ♦ 31 Mar-29 Sep. € 36.60   2005*

See advertisement

†VENDRELL, EL *3C3* (7km SW Coastal/Rural) **Camping Arc de Bara**, N340, Km 1182, 43883 Roda de Bara (Tarragona) [977-80 09 02; fax 977-80 15 52; camping@campingarcdebara.com; www.campingarcdebara.com] Exit A7 junc 31 or 32, foll sp Arc de Bara on N340 dir Tarragona. Site on L after 5km shortly after Camping Park Playa Bara. Lge, shd; htd wc; chem disp; baby facs; shwrs inc; el pts €2.90; gas; lndtte; supmkt 200m; rest; snacks; bar; BBQ; pool; sand beach adj; 75% statics in sep area; dogs €2; phone; site clsd Nov; poss cr; Eng spkn; rlwy noise; cc acc; CCI. "Sm pitches; gd NH en rte Alicante; phone ahead winter/low ssn to check open." ♦ € 26.00 (3 persons)   2005*

VENDRELL, EL *3C3* (7km SW Coastal) **Camping Stel**, Ctra N340, Km 1182, 43883 Roda de Bara (Tarragona) [977-80 20 02; fax 977-80 05 25; stel@stel.es; www.stel.es] Exit A7 junc 31, foll sps for Tarragona on N340. Site on L immed after Arco de Bara. Lge, mkd pitch, pt shd; wc; chem disp; baby facs; shwrs inc; el pts (5A) inc; gas; lndtte; ice; shop; rest; snacks; bar; playgrnd; htd pool; waterslides; sand beach adj; watersports; tennis; sports & entmnt; golf 20km; TV; 10% statics; no dogs; phone; poss cr; adv bkg; some rd/rlwy noise; red long stay/low ssn; CCI. "Some sm pitches, poss ltd access for parking." ♦ Easter-25 Sep. € 35.80 (CChq acc)   2005*

VENDRELL, EL *3C3* (10km SW Coastal) **Camping Gavina**, N340, Km 1181, Platja Creixell, 43839 Creixell (Tarragona) [977-80 15 03; fax 977-80 05 27; info@gavina.net; www.gavina.net] Exit A7 junc 31 (Coma-Ruga) onto N340 dir Tarragona. Site 1km S of Creixell, adj beach. Lge, mkd pitch, pt shd; wc; chem disp; baby facs; fam bthrm; shwrs inc; el pts (6A) €3.40; gas; lndtte; shop; rest; snacks; bar; playgrnd; sand beach adj; watersports; tennis; entmnt; car wash; 20% statics; dogs; poss cr; adv bkg rec Jul/Aug; some train noise; cc acc; red long stay; CCI. "Rest overlooks beach; Port Aventura 20km." ♦ 1 Apr-31 Oct. € 25.20 (CChq acc)   2003*

†VENDRELL, EL *3C3* (10km SW Coastal) **Camping La Sirena Dorada**, 43839 Creixell (Tarragona) [977-80 13 03; fax 977-80 12 15] Fr N exit A7 at junc 31, foll N340 sp Tarragona, site 200m past Roman arch on L. Fr S exit junc 32 onto N340 to Creixall. Lge, pt shd; wc; shwrs inc; el pts (5A) €3.80; gas; lndtte; ice; shop; rest; bar; playgrnd; pool; sand beach 200m; games area; mini-golf; 15% statics; poss cr; adv bkg; quiet; CCI. "Winter/low ssn phone to check site open; gd long stay." ♦ € 23.55   2002*

VENDRELL, EL *3C3* (10km SW Coastal) **Gavina Platja Creixell**, Km 1180, Ctra N340, 43839 Creixell (Tarragona) [977-80 15 03; fax 977-80 05 27; info@gavina.net; www.gavina.net] On N340 Barcelona-Tarragona rd, km 1180, site at Creixell, adj beach. V lge, hdg/mkd pitch, hdstg, pt shd; htd wc; chem disp; mv service pnt; baby facs; shwrs inc; el pts €3.40; gas; lndtte; shop; tradsmn; rest; snacks; bar; playgrnd; 2 pools; waterslide; sand beach adj; tennis; games area; entmnt; 20% statics; phone; adv bkg; red long stay. ♦ Holy Week-30 Oct. € 25.70 (CChq acc)   2005*

VENDRELL, EL *3C3* (1km W Coastal) **Camping Sant Salvador**, Coma-Ruga, 43880 Sant Salvador (Tarragona) [tel/fax 977-68 08 04; campingsant salvador@troc.es; www.campingsantsalvador. com] Exit A7 junc 31 onto N340, after 1km turn L. Site bet Calafell & Coma-Ruga, in vill of Sant Salvador. Lge, pt shd; wc; baby facs; shwrs inc; el pts €3.20; gas; lndtte; shop; rest; bar; playgrnd; beach; 75% statics; poss cr; cc acc; red 10+ days/low ssn; CCI. "Secure site; not suitable lge o'fits; conv Safari Park & Port Aventura." ♦ 2 Mar-30 Sep. € 22.00   2003*

VERA see Garrucha *4G1*

VIELHA *3B2* (6km N Rural) **Camping Verneda**, Ctra Francia N230, Km 171, 25537 Pont d'Arros (Lleida) [973-64 10 24; fax 973-64 32 18; info@ campingverneda.com; www.campingverneda. com] Fr Lerida N on N230 twd Spain/France border, turn at km post 171. Site is 2km W of Pont d'Arros on rvside. Med, pt shd; wc; chem disp; baby facs; shwrs inc; el pts (4A) €3.60; gas; ice; lndtte; rest; snacks; bar; playgrnd; pool; horseriding; games rm; cycle hire; entmnt; TV; 10% statics; dogs €2.50; adv bkg; Eng spkn; cc acc; CCI. "Gd area for walking; site open w/e rest of year; well-run site; gd facs." 1 May-15 Oct. € 20.00   2005*

SPAIN

VIELHA *3B2* (7km N) **Camping Artigane, Val d'Aran, 25537 Pont d'Arros (Lleida)** [973-64 01 89] Fr French border head S on N230 for 15km. Fr Vielha head N to France & turn L at Pont d'Arros. Site on main rd by rv. Lge, pt sl, pt shd; wc; own san rec; chem disp; baby facs; shwrs inc; el pts €2.50; gas; lndry rm; shop; rest, snacks, bar in high ssn; BBQ; playgrnd; htd pool; golf; 5% statics; phone; poss cr; quiet. "V scenic area; excel for wild flowers, butterflies; friendly warden; low ssn site yourself - warden calls; simple facs, poss stretched when site full; poss unkempt low ssn; fair NH only." ♦ Holy Week-15 Oct. € 16.80
2003*

†**VIELHA** *3B2* (6km SE Urban) **Camping Era Yerla D'Arties, Ctra C-142, de Vielha a Baquiera, 25599 Arties, Val d'Aran (Lleida)** [973-64 16 02; fax 973-64 29 53; yerla@coac.net; www.aranweb.com/yerla] Fr Vielha take C28 dir Baquiera, site sp. Turn R at rndabt into Arties, site in 30m on R. Med, shd; wc; chem disp; baby facs; shwrs inc; el pts €3.40; gas; lndtte; shop & rest nrby; snacks; bar; pool; skiing nr; phone; quiet; cc acc; CCI. "Ideal for ski resort; gd shops, tapas bars & rests in vill; gd walking cent in summer; ltd facs low ssn; vg long/sh stay." € 19.70
2003*

VILAFRANCA DEL CID see Morella *3D2*

VILANOVA DE LA BARCA see Lerida/Lleida *3C2*

†**VILANOVA DE PRADES** *3C2* (500m NE Rural) **Camping Serra de Prades, Calle Sant Antoni s/n, 43439 Vilanova de Prades (Tarragona)** [tel/fax 977-86 90 50; info@serradeprades.com; www.serradeprades.com] Fr AP2 take exit 8 (L'Albi) or 9 (Montblanc), foll C240 to Vimbodi. At km 47.5 take TV7004 for 10km to Vilanova de Prades. Site ent on R immed after rndabt at ent to vill. Lge, some hdg/mkd pitch, terr, pt shd; wc; chem disp; mv service pnt; baby facs; shwrs inc; el pts (6A) €4.70 gas; lndtte; ice; basic shop & 8km; tradsmn; rest; snacks; bar; playgrnd; htd pool; lake sw 20km; tennis; games area; games rm; child entmnt; TV rm; 10% statics; dogs; phone; Eng spkn; adv bkg high ssn; red long stay/CCI. "Well-maintained, well-run, friendly site; sm pitches; access some pitches diff due steep, gravel site rds & storm gullies; facs spotless; gd walks fr site; mountain setting; wine rte; monasteries & musuems to visit; conv Barcelona; vg touring base &/or NH." ♦ € 22.00 (CChq acc)
2005*

†**VILANOVA DE PRADES** *3C2* (4km S Rural) **Camping Prades, Ctra T-701, Km 6.850, 43364 Prades (Tarragona)** [977-86 82 70; fax 977-86 82 79; camping@campingprades.com; www.campingprades.com] Fr S take A240 W fr Reus, C242 N to Albarca, T701 E to Prades. Fr N take exit 9 off AP2/E90 at Montblanc. W on N240 to T700 S. Site sp. Narr rds & hairpins fr both dirs. Lge, mkd pitch, pt shd; wc; chem disp; baby facs; shwrs; el pts (3A) €3.57; gas; lndtte; shop; rest; snacks; bar; playgrnd; pool; cycle hire; 30% statics; phone; poss cr; adv bkg; CCI. "Excel." ♦ € 19.00
2002*

Mustn't forget to post our site report forms to The Club, otherwise sites might be deleted.

†**VILANOVA I LA GELTRU** *3C3* (3km Coastal) **Camping Vilanova Park, Ctra Arboc, Km 2.5, 08800 Villanova i la Geltru (Barcelona)** [938-93 34 02; fax 938-93 55 28; info@vilanovapark.es or reservas@vilanovapark.es; www.vilanovapark.es] Fr E on C32 (A16), take Vilanova i la Geltru/Sant Pere de Ribes onto C31 & at 153km exit take BV2115 dir L'Arboç to site. Fr E15/AP7 W leave at exit sp dir Vilanova i la Geltru/L'Arboc. At rndabt turn R onto BV2115, site on L in 1km. Entry via loop to R to cross BV2115. Parked cars may block loop & obscure sp. V lge, hdg/mkd pitch, hdstg, terr, pt shd; htd wc (some cont); chem disp; mv service pnt; serviced pitch; baby facs; fam bthrm; sauna; shwrs inc; el pts (10A) inc (poss rev pol); gas; lndry service; ice; supmkt; tradsmn; rest; snacks; bar; BBQ (charcoal); playgrnd; 2 pools (1 covrd); paddling pool; jacuzzi; sand beach 3km; lake sw 2km; watersports 4km; fishing; tennis; horseriding, golf 1km; entmnt; excursions; games rm; gym; TV; cash point; 40% statics; dogs €4.70; phone; bus/train; recep 0700-2300; poss cr; Eng spkn; adv bkg ess (dep req+bkg fee); poss noisy nights & w/e high ssn; cc acc; red snr citizens/long stay; CCI. "Lovely site & facs; gd for children; excel san facs; gd security; poss muddy in wet & some sm pitches with diff access due trees & high kerbs; poss diff pitch access on terr due ramps; v helpful staff; gd lndry rm, rest & bar; nature walk with goats & deer in enclosures; conv Barcelona, Tarragona & Port Aventura; gd bus (with guide) & train service; gd sat TV; mostly desalinated water - 2 drinking water points; mkt Sat; excel." ♦ ltd. € 35.70 (CChq acc)
ABS - E08
2005*

See advertisement opposite (bottom)   *See advertisement opposite (top)*

VILANOVA I LA GELTRU *3C3* (5km SW Coastal)
Camping La Rueda, Ctra C31, Km 146.2, 08880
Cubelles (Barcelona) [938-95 02 07; fax
938-95 03 47; larueda@la-rueda.com; www.
la-rueda.com] Exit A7 junc 29 then take C15 dir
Vilanova onto autopista C32 & take exit 13 dir Cunit.
Site is 2.5km S of Cubelles on C31 at km stone 146.2.
Lge, mkd pitch, shd; htd wc; chem disp; mv service pnt;
shwrs inc; el pts (4A) €5.86; gas; ice; lndtte; shop; rest;
snacks; bar; sand beach 100m; playgrnd; pool; tennis;
horseriding; watersports; fishing; entmnt; car wash;
12% statics; dogs €3.14; phone; bus; train; Eng spkn;
adv bkg; quiet; red long stay/low ssn; cc acc; red CCI.
"Conv Port Aventura & Barcelona; vg family site."
8 Apr-11 Sep. € 29.27   2005*

VILLADANGOS DEL PARAMO see Leon *1B3*

†**VILLAJOYOSA** *4F2* (3km NE Coastal) **Camping
Playa del Torres, Partida Torres Norte 11, 03570
Villajoyosa (Alicante)** [966-81 00 31; fax
966-81 01 73; capto@ctv.es] Exit A7/E15 at junc
65A onto N332. S fr Benidorm, exit L at km 140.5, site
sp on main rd. Use traff lts/rndabt to turn round. Med,
mkd pitch, hdstg, terr, pt shd; wc; chem disp; mv
service pnt; 15% serviced pitches; shwrs inc; el pts
(16A) metered + conn fee; gas; lndtte; sm shop;
supmkt 5km; rest; snacks; bar; htd pool; shgl beach adj;
5% statics; dogs; phone; Eng spkn; cc acc; red long
stay; CCI. "Diff access for disabled to shwrs/wc due
steep slope; excel long stay." ♦ ltd. € 25.60   2005*

†VILLAMANAN 1B3 (1km SE) Camping Palazuelo (formerly Covadonga), 24680 Villamanan (Leon) [987-76 80 64] Fr N630 Salamanca-Leon turn SE at Villamanan onto C621 dir Valencia de Don Juan. Site on R in 1km behind hotel. Med, pt shd; wc; shwrs inc; el pts (10A) €2.40; shop 1km; rest; snacks; pool; quiet but some rd noise; cc acc. "NH only; neglected & run down low ssn; new san facs 2004 but ltd privacy in shwrs." € 18.00   2005*

VILLAMANAN 1B3 (6km SE) Camping Pico Verde, 24200 Valencia de Don Juan (Leon) [tel/fax 987-75 05 25; campingpicoverd@terra. es] Fr N630 S, turn E at km 32.2 onto C621 sp Valencia de Don Juan. Site in 4km on R. Med, shd, mkd pitch; wc; shwrs inc; el pts (6A) €2.20; lndtte; shop; rest; snacks 1km; playgrnd; 2 covrd pools; tennis; 25% statics; quiet; red CCI. "Friendly, helpful staff; conv Leon; picturesque vill; phone ahead to check site open if travelling close to opening/closing dates." 23 Jun-10 Sep. € 14.50   2004*

VILLAMANIN 1A3 (500m NW Rural) Camping Ventosilla, Calle Camping s/n, 24680 Villamanin (Leon) [987-59 83 08] Fr N630 turn W over rv, site up thro vill of Villamanin, sp. Med, pt shd; wc (some cont); chem disp; baby facs; shwrs; el pts (5-10A) €1.50; gas; lndtte; shop in vill; snacks; bar; rv sw; playgrnd; cycle hire; TV; adv bkg; quiet; cc acc. "Superb caves; mountain walks; fishing." 1 Jul-31 Aug. € 10.00   2002*

†VILLARGORDO DEL CABRIEL 4E1 (3km NW Rural) Kiko Park Rural, Ctra Embalse Contreras, Km 3, 46317 Villargordo del Cabriel (Valencia) [tel/fax 962-13 90 82; kikoparkrural@kikopark.com; www. kikopark.com/rural] A3/E901 Valencia-Madrid, exit junc 255 Villargordo del Cabriel, foll sp to site. Med, mkd pitch, hdstg, terr, pt shd; wc; chem disp; mv service pnt; some serviced pitches; shwrs inc; el pts (6A) €2.80; gas; lndtte; ice; shop; tradsmn; rest; snacks; bar; pool; lake sw 1km; canoeing; watersports; fishing; horseriding; white water rafting; cycle hire; TV; some statics; dogs €0.50; Eng spkn; adv bkg rec high ssn; quiet; cc acc; red long stay/low ssn; red CCI. "Beautiful location; gd walking; many activities; pitches poss muddy after heavy rain; excel." ♦ € 26.25 (CChq acc)   2005*

See advertisement on page 762

VILLAVICIOSA 1A3 (8km NE Rural) Camping La Rasa, Ctra La Busta-Selorio, 33316 Villaviciosa (Asturias) [985-89 15 29; www.campinglarasa. com] Fr A8 exit km 353 sp Villaviciosa. In approx 500m foll site sp, cross bdge over m'way to site. Lge, hdg/mkd pitch, sl, unshd; wc; chem disp; serviced pitches; shwrs inc; el pts (6A) €2.80; lndtte; shop; snacks; bar; playgrnd; pool; sand beach 7km; 60% statics; phone; site open w/e low ssn/winter; Eng spkn; CCI. "Pleasant, friendly site; conv m'way & coast; tight access rds to pitches." ♦ 15 Jun-15 Sep. € 17.30   2005*

VILLAVICIOSA 1A3 (15km W) Camping Playa Espana, 33300 Villaviciosa (Asturias) [tel/fax 985-89 42 73] Sp on N632 approx 12km fr Villaviciosa & 10km fr Gijon. Last 3km of app rd narr & steep with sharp bends. Med, pt shd; wc; chem disp; shwrs; el pts inc (pos rev pol); gas; shop; snacks; bar; beach 200m; phone; quiet; cc acc. "Gd site; lovely coast & scenery with mountains behind; clean; vg san facs." 1 Mar-30 Sep. € 17.00   2004*

As we're travelling out of season, we'd better phone ahead to check that the site is actually open.

†VINAROS 3D2 (5km N Coastal) Camping Vinaros, Ctra N340, Km 1054, 12500 Vinaros (Castellon) [tel/fax 964-40 24 24; info@ campingvinaros.com; www.campingvinaros. com] Exit AP7 junc 42 onto N340 dir Valencia. Turn L at km 1054 to site. Fr S exit AP7 junc 43 Lge, hdg/mkd pitch, hdstg, pt shd; htd wc; chem disp; mv service pnt; 85% serviced pitches; baby facs; shwrs inc; el pts (6A) €2.85; gas; lndtte; ice; shop 500m; tradsmn; rest adj; snacks; bar; playgrnd; pool; sand/shgl beach 1km; 15% statics; phone; currency exchange; poss cr; Eng spkn; adv bkg; quiet but some rd noise; cc acc; red long stay/low ssn; CCI. "Excel busy, well-run site; many long-stay winter residents; gd value; spacious pitches; vg clean san facs; gd rest; friendly, helpful staff; Peniscola Castle & Morello worth a visit; site set amongst orange groves; easy cycle to town." ♦ ltd. € 19.80   2005*

VINUESA 3B1 (Rural) Cobijo Camping, Ctra Laguna Negra Km 2, 42150 Vinuesa (Soria) [tel/fax 975-37 83 31] Travelling W fr Soria to Burgos, at Abejar R on SO840. by-pass Abejar cont to Vinuesa. Well sp fr there. Lge, pt sl, pt shd; wc; chem disp; baby facs; shwrs inc; el pts (3A) inc (long lead poss req); gas; lndtte; shop; bar; rest; snacks; BBQ; playgrnd; pool; cycle hire; 10% statics; dogs; poss cr w/e; Eng spkn; phone; quiet; cc acc; CCI. "Friendly young management; v clean & attractive site; some pitches in wooded area poss diff lge o'fits; ltd bar & rest low ssn, excel rests in town 1.5km; gd walks." ♦ 8 Apr-30 Sep. € 19.00   2005*

†VITORIA/GASTEIZ 3B1 (3km W Urban) Camping Ibaya, Arbolado de Acacias en la N102, Km 346.5, 01195 Vitoria/Gasteiz (Alava) [945-14 76 20] Foll N102 W of Gasteiz/Vitoria 3km to Miranda; site ent via rest gate. If app fr S do not attempt to turn; cont to turning point 1.5km past site ent at rndabt next to Agip g'ge. Site sp fr N102. Sm, mkd pitch, pt sl, pt shd; wc; chem disp; shwrs inc; el pts (10A) inc; gas; lndry rm; sm shop; supmkt 2km; tradsmn; rest adj; bar; playgrnd; 5-10% statics; phone; poss cr; rd noise; CCI. "Poor NH only; unkempt early ssn; phone ahead to check opening low ssn." € 15.30   2003*

VIU DE LINAS see Broto *3B2*

We're having a great holiday - must fill in some site report forms and send them to The Club as soon as possible.

VIVEIRO *1A2* (500m NW Coastal) **Camping Viveiro, Cantarrana s/n, 27850 Viveiro (Lugo) [982-56 00 04; fax 982-56 00 84]** Fr Viveiro on El Ferrol rd C642, turn R in town over rv bdge & bear R. Site in 500m, sp. Med, shd; wc; chem disp; shwrs inc; el pts (10A) €3; lndtte; ice; shop & 1.5km; snacks; beach 500m; phone; cc acc. "Gd clean site; uninspiring town." 1 Jun-30 Sep. € 12.80   2003*

ZAHARA DE LOS ATUNES see Vejer de la Frontera *2H3*

ZAMORA *1C3* (2.5km SE Urban) **Camping Ciudad de Zamora, Ctra Zamora-Fuentesauco, Km 2.5, 49021 Zamora (Zamora) [980-53 72 95; fax 980-52 14 29; campingzamora@telefonica.net; www.campingzamora.com]** Fr N630 fr N or S, turn onto C605 dir Fuentesauco, site sp. Med, mkd pitch, pt shd; wc; chem disp; mv service pnt; baby facs; shwrs inc; el pts (6A) inc; gas; lndry service; ice; shop; tradsmn; rest; snacks; bar; BBQ; playgrnd; pool high ssn; rv sw, sand beach 3km; TV; dogs €1; phone; bus 2km; Eng spkn; adv bkg; quiet; cc acc; red long stay/low ssn; cc acc; CCI. "Clean, well-run, conv site for town cent; friendly, helpful owners; gd cycling; excel." ♦ 1 Apr-15 Sep. € 19.30   2005*

†ZARAUTZ *3A1* (3km E Coastal) **Gran Camping Zarautz, Monte Talai-Mendi s/n, 20800 Zarautz (Gipuzkoa) [943-83 12 38; fax 943-13 24 86]** Exit A8 junc 11 Zarautz, turn R at 2nd rndbt onto N634 to site sp on L in 200m. On N634 fr San Sebastian to Zarautz, thro Orio & turn R 300m bef m'way exit foll sps. Long, steep app (approx 1km). Lge, hdg/mkd pitch, hdstg, pt sl, terr, pt shd; wc; chem disp; mv service pnt; shwrs inc; el pts (6A) €3.30; gas; lndry rm; shop; tradsmn; rest; bar; BBQ; playgrnd; beach 1km (steep walk); games rm; golf 1km; 50% statics; phone; poss cr; Eng spkn; adv bkg; cc acc; CCI. "Excel, clean site on cliff overlooking beautiful bay; excel beach at Zarautz, gd base for coast & mountains; fiesta in Jun; helpful staff; some pitches sm & overlooked fr terr above; lge san facs in need of upgrade; excel disabled facs; NH for Bilbao ferry." ♦ € 25.40 (CChq acc)   2005*

ZARAUTZ *3A1* (4km E Coastal) **Camping Playa de Orio, 20810 Orio (Gipuzkoa) [943-83 48 01; fax 943-13 34 33; kanpina@terra.es; www.oriora.com]** Exit A8 m'way junc 11 at Zarautz & foll N634 to Orio, cross rv & turn L into town (v narr streets in town cent); sp fr town to site, about 1km. Or to avoid town cent cross bdge & foll N634 for 1km, turn L at sp Orio & camping, turn R at rndabt to site. Lge, mkd pitch, pt sl, pt shd; wc; chem disp; mv service pnt; baby facs; shwrs inc; el pts (5A) inc; gas; lndtte; shop; tradsmn; rest adj; snacks; bar; playgrnd; pool; paddling pool; sand beach adj; tennis; 50% statics (sep area); no dogs; phone; car wash; poss cr at w/e; Eng spkn; adv bkg; quiet; red low ssn; cc acc; CCI. "Excel site; much construction work 2005; flats now built bet site & beach & new marina adj - now no sea views; walks; gd facs; friendly staff; useful stop bef leaving Spain." ♦ 1 Mar-1 Nov. € 23.00   2005*

ZUBIA, LA see Granada *2G4*

SPAIN

SPAIN – WEST

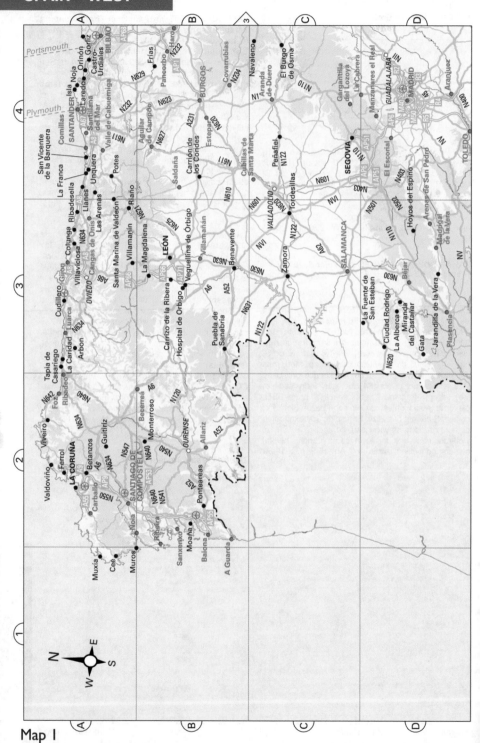

Map 1

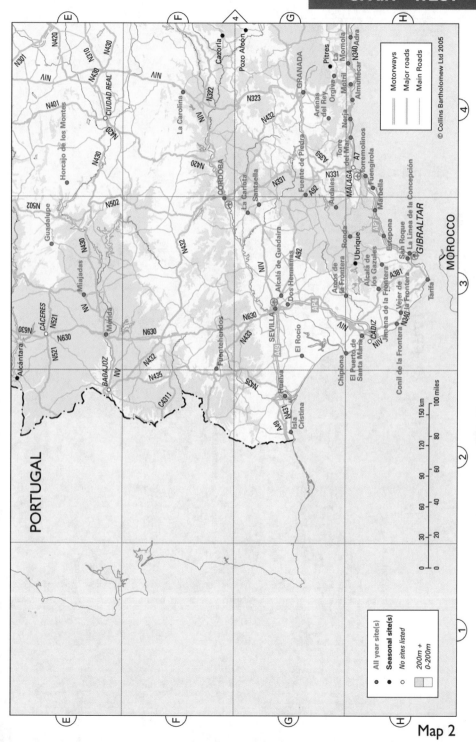

SPAIN – WEST

Map 2

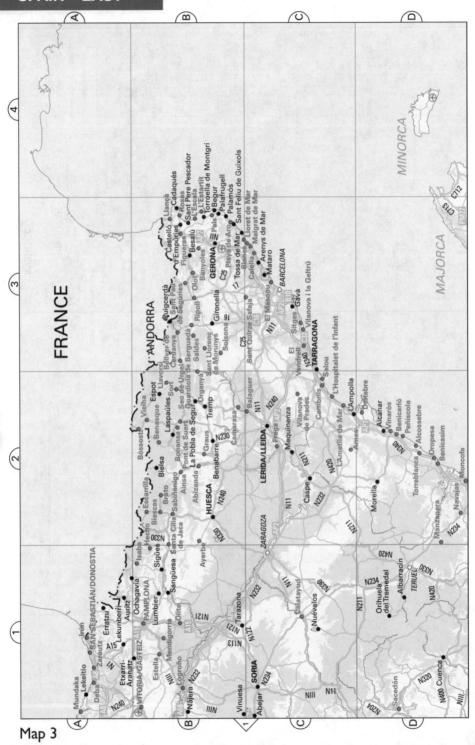

Map 3

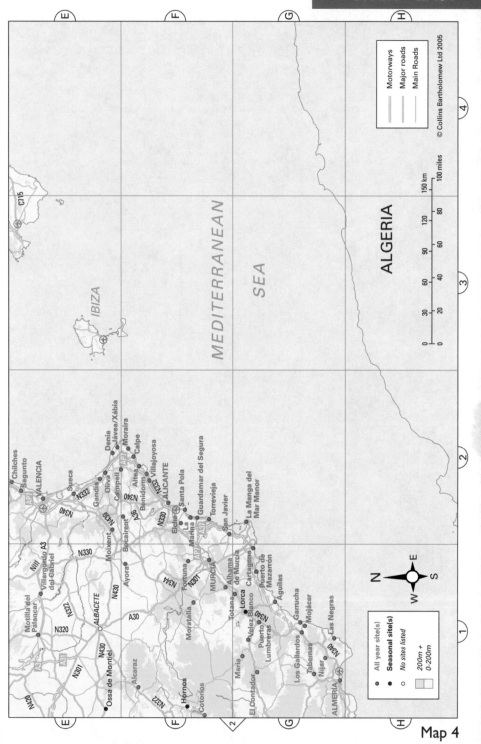

© Collins Bartholomew Ltd 2005

Motorways
Major roads
Main Roads

MEDITERRANEAN

SEA

IBIZA

ALGERIA

0   30   60   90   120   150 km
0   20   40   60   80   100 miles

Chilches
Sagunto
VALENCIA
Sueca
N332
Gandia
Oliva
Denia
Xàbia/Jávea
Moraira
Calpe
Altea
Benidorm
Villajoyosa
ALICANTE
Santa Pola
La Marina
Guardamar del Segura
Torrevieja
San Javier
La Manga del Mar Menor
Elche
Crevillente
Orihuela
MURCIA
Alhama de Murcia
Cartagena
Puerto de Mazarrón
Águilas
Garrucha
Mojácar
Las Negras
Lorca
Vélez Blanco
Puerto Lumbreras
Totana
Los Gallardos
Tabernas
Níjar
ALMERÍA
María
El Contador
Cotorios
Hornos
Alcaraz
Ossa de Montiel
Motilla del Palancar
Villargordo del Cabriel
ALBACETE
Ayora
Bocairent
Moixent
Alcoy
N330
N320
N301
N430
N340
N322
N344

C715

All year site(s)
Seasonal site(s)
No sites listed

200m +
0-200m

N
W   E
S

Map 4

CARAVAN EUROPE SITE REPORT

IF SITE ALREADY LISTED, COMPLETE ONLY THOSE SECTIONS OF THE FORM WHERE CHANGES APPLY.

Please print, type or tick in the white areas. (Sites not reported on for 4 years may be deleted from the guide.)

Year of guide used		Is site listed?	Listed on page no		Unlisted	Date of visit....../......./ ....

A — SITE NAME AND LOCATION

Country		Name of town/village site listed under (see Site Location Maps)			
Distance & direction from centre of town site is listed under **(in straight line)**	.......km	*eg. N, NE, S, SW*	Urban	Rural	Coastal
Opening dates	Open all Year?	**Y/N**	Period site is open (if not all year)	......./......... to ..../.........	
Site Name				Naturist site: Y/N	
Site Address					
Telephone		Fax			
Email		Internet			

B — SITE CHARGES

Charge for car, caravan + 2 adults per night *in local currency*	High Season	Low Season	El pts inc: in price quoted Y / N

C — DIRECTIONS

Brief, specific directions to site (in km) *To convert miles to kilometres multiply by 8 and divide by 5 or use Conversion Table in guide*	

D — SITE DESCRIPTION

Site size – number of pitches	Small Max 50	SM	Medium 51 - 150	MED	Large 150 - 500	LGE	Very large 500 +	VLGE	UNCHANGED FROM CURRENT EDITION
Pitch features if **not** open-plan/grassy	Hedged	HDG PITCH	Marked or numbered	MKD PITCH	Hardstanding or gravel	HDSTG			UNCHANGED FROM CURRENT EDITION
If site is **not** level – is it	Part Sloping	PT SL	Sloping	SL	Terraced	TERR			UNCHANGED FROM CURRENT EDITION
Site is shaded	SHD	Part shaded	PT SHD	Unshaded	UNSHD				UNCHANGED FROM CURRENT EDITION

E — SITE FACILITIES

FACILITIES	ABBREVIATION	FACS AVAILABLE ✓	ADDITIONAL DESCRIPTION Please tick or complete blanks		
Toilet block *(clean flush toilets assumed unless otherwise advised)*	WC		Heated	Continental	Own san recommended
Chemical disposal point	CHEM DISP		Dedicated point		WC only
Motorvan waste discharge point	MV SERVICE PNT		Twin-axle vans allowed?		Y / N
Child/baby facilities (bathroom)	CHILD/BABY FACS		Family Bathroom	FAM BTHRM	
Hot shower(s)	SHWR(S)		Included in site fee? Y / N	Price .... (if not included)	
Mains electric hook-up	EL PTS		Amp(s)............	Included in site fee? Y / N	Price .... (if not included)
Supplies of bottled gas	GAS		On site	And/or ....km	

FACILITIES	ABBREVIATION	FACS AVAILABLE ✓	ADDITIONAL DESCRIPTION Please tick or complete blanks					
Washing or drying machines	LNDTTE		Clothes wash room			LNDRY RM		
Ice / freezer facilities	ICE		Barbecues allowed			Y / N		
Shop(s)	SHOP(S)		On site			and/or................................km		
Bread / milk delivered	TRADSMN		Cooking facilities			COOKING FACS		
Restaurant / cafeteria	REST		On site			and/or................................km		
Snack bar / take-away	SNACKS		On site			and/or................................km		
Bar	BAR		On site			And/or ....km		
Children's playground	PLAYGRND		Entertainment in high season			ENTMNT		
Swimming pool	POOL(S)		On site	or ....km		Heated	Covered	
Beach – nearest	BEACH		Adj	or ....km		Sand	Shingle	
Alternative swimming	SW		Adj	or ....km		Lake	River	
Television room	TV RM		Cable / Satellite TV to pitches			TV CAB / SAT		
% of static caravans / mobile homes / chalets / fixed tents on site	STATICS		%	Dogs allowed on site?		Y / N		
				Charge?		..............................per day		
Bus / metro / tram ....distance	BUS / TRAM / METRO		Public payphone on site or adjacent			Y / N		
In high season site possibly crowded	POSS CR		Y / N		English spoken		Y / N	
Advance bookings accepted	ADV BKG		Deposit required?	Y / N		Booking fee charged?	Y / N	
Noise levels on site in season	NOISY / QUIET		Noisy, why?					
Reduction for long stay	RED .... DAYS		% red. for more than ....days					
Camping Card International accepted in lieu of passport	CCI		Reduction for CCI:	........% RED		Credit cards accepted?	Y / N	
Standard of site (in your opinion)			Excel	Vg	Gd	Fair	Poor	
Facilities for disabled	◆		Full wheelchair facs			Limited facs		

ADDITIONAL REMARKS OR INFORMATION (TOURIST ATTRACTIONS, UNUSUAL FEATURES OR FACILITIES e.g. tennis, cycle hire, watersports, internet available, etc, REC LENGTH OF STAY). PLEASE PRINT OR TYPE

Your comments and opinions may be used in future editions of the guide; if you do not wish them to be used, please tick ☐

ARE YOU A: Caravanner	Motor caravanner	Trailer-tenter?
NAME	CARAVAN CLUB MEMBERSHIP NO:	
Do you need more blank Site Report Forms ☐ Yes ☐ No	POSTCODE:	
ADDRESS: (NON-MEMBERS ONLY PLEASE COMPLETE THIS SECTION)		

Please use a separate form for each site and do not send receipts. It is hoped that you will appreciate that owing to the large number of site reports received, it is not possible to enter into correspondence. More forms are available on request from the address below. Please return completed form to:

The Caravan Club
Editor - Caravan Europe
FREEPOST WD3000
East Grinstead
West Sussex RH19 1BR

(FREEPOST to be used when mailing within the UK only.)

CARAVAN EUROPE SITE REPORT

IF SITE ALREADY LISTED, COMPLETE ONLY THOSE SECTIONS OF THE FORM WHERE CHANGES APPLY.

Please print, type or tick in the white areas. (Sites not reported on for 4 years may be deleted from the guide.)

Year of guide used		Is site listed?	Listed on page no		Unlisted	Date of visit ..../......./ ....

A – SITE NAME AND LOCATION

Country		Name of town/village site listed under (see Site Location Maps)		
Distance & direction from centre of town site is listed under **(in straight line)**	........km	*eg. N, NE, S, SW*	Urban	Rural	Coastal
Opening dates	Open all Year?	**Y/N**	Period site is open (if not all year)	......./......... **to** ..../.........
Site Name			Naturist site:	Y/N
Site Address				
Telephone		Fax		
Email		Internet		

B – SITE CHARGES

Charge for car, caravan + 2 adults per night *in local currency*	High Season	Low Season	El pts inc: in price quoted Y / N

C – DIRECTIONS

Brief, specific directions to site (in km) *To convert miles to kilometres multiply by 8 and divide by 5 or use Conversion Table in guide*	

D – SITE DESCRIPTION

Site size – number of pitches	Small Max 50	SM	Medium 51 - 150	MED	Large 150 - 500	LGE	Very large 500 +	VLGE	UNCHANGED FROM CURRENT EDITION
Pitch features if **not** open-plan/grassy	Hedged	HDG PITCH	Marked or numbered	MKD PITCH	Hardstanding or gravel	HDSTG			UNCHANGED FROM CURRENT EDITION
If site is **not** level – is it	Part Sloping	PT SL	Sloping	SL	Terraced	TERR			UNCHANGED FROM CURRENT EDITION
Site is shaded	SHD	Part shaded		PT SHD	Unshaded	UNSHD			UNCHANGED FROM CURRENT EDITION

E – SITE FACILITIES

FACILITIES	ABBREVIATION	FACS AVAILABLE ✓	ADDITIONAL DESCRIPTION Please tick or complete blanks		
Toilet block *(clean flush toilets assumed unless otherwise advised)*	WC		Heated	Continental	Own san recommended
Chemical disposal point	CHEM DISP		Dedicated point		WC only
Motorvan waste discharge point	MV SERVICE PNT		Twin-axle vans allowed?		Y / N
Child/baby facilities (bathroom)	CHILD/BABY FACS		Family Bathroom	FAM BTHRM	
Hot shower(s)	SHWR(S)		Included in site fee? Y / N	Price .... (if not included)	
Mains electric hook-up	EL PTS		Amp(s)............	Included in site fee? Y / N	Price .... (if not included)
Supplies of bottled gas	GAS		On site	And/or ....km	

FACILITIES	ABBREVIATION	FACS AVAILABLE ✓	ADDITIONAL DESCRIPTION Please tick or complete blanks				
Washing or drying machines	LNDTTE		Clothes wash room		LNDRY RM		
Ice / freezer facilities	ICE		Barbecues allowed		Y / N		
Shop(s)	SHOP(S)		On site		and/or.............................km		
Bread / milk delivered	TRADSMN		Cooking facilities		COOKING FACS		
Restaurant / cafeteria	REST		On site		and/or.............................km		
Snack bar / take-away	SNACKS		On site		and/or.............................km		
Bar	BAR		On site		And/or ....km		
Children's playground	PLAYGRND		Entertainment in high season		ENTMNT		
Swimming pool	POOL(S)		On site	or ....km	Heated		Covered
Beach – nearest	BEACH		Adj	or ....km	Sand		Shingle
Alternative swimming	SW		Adj	or ....km	Lake		River
Television room	TV RM		Cable / Satellite TV to pitches		TV CAB / SAT		
% of static caravans / mobile homes / chalets / fixed tents on site	STATICS		%	Dogs allowed on site?	Y / N		
				Charge?	..............................per day		
Bus / metro / tram ....distance	BUS / TRAM / METRO		Public payphone on site or adjacent		Y / N		
In high season site possibly crowded	POSS CR		Y / N		English spoken		Y / N
Advance bookings accepted	ADV BKG		Deposit required?	Y / N	Booking fee charged?		Y / N
Noise levels on site in season	NOISY / QUIET		Noisy, why?				
Reduction for long stay	RED .... DAYS		% red. for more than ....days				
Camping Card International accepted in lieu of passport	CCI		Reduction for CCI:	.......% RED	Credit cards accepted?		Y / N
Standard of site (in your opinion)			Excel	Vg	Gd	Fair	Poor
Facilities for disabled	◆		Full wheelchair facs		Limited facs		

ADDITIONAL REMARKS OR INFORMATION (TOURIST ATTRACTIONS, UNUSUAL FEATURES OR FACILITIES e.g. tennis, cycle hire, watersports, internet available, etc, REC LENGTH OF STAY). PLEASE PRINT OR TYPE

Your comments and opinions may be used in future editions of the guide; if you do not wish them to be used, please tick ☐

ARE YOU A: Caravanner	Motor caravanner	Trailer-tenter?
NAME	CARAVAN CLUB MEMBERSHIP NO:	
Do you need more blank Site Report Forms ☐ Yes ☐ No	POSTCODE:	
ADDRESS: (NON-MEMBERS ONLY PLEASE COMPLETE THIS SECTION)		

Please use a separate form for each site and do not send receipts. It is hoped that you will appreciate that owing to the large number of site reports received, it is not possible to enter into correspondence. More forms are available on request from the address below. Please return completed form to:

The Caravan Club
Editor - Caravan Europe
FREEPOST WD3000
East Grinstead
West Sussex RH19 1BR

(FREEPOST to be used when mailing within the UK only.)

CARAVAN EUROPE SITE REPORT

IF SITE ALREADY LISTED, COMPLETE ONLY THOSE SECTIONS OF THE FORM WHERE CHANGES APPLY.

Please print, type or tick in the white areas. (Sites not reported on for 4 years may be deleted from the guide.)

Year of guide used		Is site listed?	Listed on page no		Unlisted	Date of visit ..../......./ ....

A – SITE NAME AND LOCATION

Country			Name of town/village site listed under (see Site Location Maps)			
Distance & direction from centre of town site is listed under **(in straight line)**	........km	eg. N, NE, S, SW	Urban	Rural		Coastal
Opening dates	Open all Year?	**Y/N**	Period site is open (if not all year)	......./......... to ..../.........		
Site Name				Naturist site:	Y/N	
Site Address						
Telephone		Fax				
Email		Internet				

B – SITE CHARGES

Charge for car, caravan + 2 adults per night *in local currency*	High Season	Low Season	El pts inc: in price quoted Y / N

C – DIRECTIONS

Brief, specific directions to site (in km) *To convert miles to kilometres multiply by 8 and divide by 5 or use Conversion Table in guide*	

D – SITE DESCRIPTION

Site size – number of pitches	Small Max 50	SM	Medium 51 - 150	MED	Large 150 - 500	LGE	Very large 500 +	VLGE	UNCHANGED FROM CURRENT EDITION
Pitch features if **not** open-plan/grassy	Hedged	HDG PITCH	Marked or numbered	MKD PITCH	Hardstanding or gravel	HDSTG			UNCHANGED FROM CURRENT EDITION
If site is **not** level – is it	Part Sloping	PT SL	Sloping	SL	Terraced	TERR			UNCHANGED FROM CURRENT EDITION
Site is shaded	SHD	Part shaded		PT SHD	Unshaded	UNSHD			UNCHANGED FROM CURRENT EDITION

E – SITE FACILITIES

FACILITIES	ABBREVIATION	FACS AVAILABLE ✓	ADDITIONAL DESCRIPTION Please tick or complete blanks		
Toilet block *(clean flush toilets assumed unless otherwise advised)*	WC		Heated	Continental	Own san recommended
Chemical disposal point	CHEM DISP		Dedicated point		WC only
Motorvan waste discharge point	MV SERVICE PNT		Twin-axle vans allowed?		Y / N
Child/baby facilities (bathroom)	CHILD/BABY FACS		Family Bathroom	FAM BTHRM	
Hot shower(s)	SHWR(S)		Included in site fee? Y / N	Price .... (if not included)	
Mains electric hook-up	EL PTS		Amp(s)............	Included in site fee? Y / N	Price .... (if not included)
Supplies of bottled gas	GAS		On site	And/or ....km	

FACILITIES	ABBREVIATION	FACS AVAILABLE ✓	ADDITIONAL DESCRIPTION Please tick or complete blanks			
Washing or drying machines	LNDTTE		Clothes wash room		LNDRY RM	
Ice / freezer facilities	ICE		Barbecues allowed		Y / N	
Shop(s)	SHOP(S)		On site		and/or.............................km	
Bread / milk delivered	TRADSMN		Cooking facilities		COOKING FACS	
Restaurant / cafeteria	REST		On site		and/or.............................km	
Snack bar / take-away	SNACKS		On site		and/or.............................km	
Bar	BAR		On site		And/or ....km	
Children's playground	PLAYGRND		Entertainment in high season		ENTMNT	
Swimming pool	POOL(S)		On site	or ....km	Heated	Covered
Beach – nearest	BEACH		Adj	or ....km	Sand	Shingle
Alternative swimming	SW		Adj	or ....km	Lake	River
Television room	TV RM		Cable / Satellite TV to pitches		TV CAB / SAT	
% of static caravans / mobile homes / chalets / fixed tents on site	STATICS		%	Dogs allowed on site?	Y / N	
				Charge?	..............................per day	
Bus / metro / tram ....distance	BUS / TRAM / METRO		Public payphone on site or adjacent		Y / N	
In high season site possibly crowded	POSS CR		Y / N	English spoken		Y / N
Advance bookings accepted	ADV BKG		Deposit required?	Y / N	Booking fee charged?	Y / N
Noise levels on site in season	NOISY / QUIET		Noisy, why?			
Reduction for long stay	RED .... DAYS		% red. for more than ....days			
Camping Card International accepted in lieu of passport	CCI		Reduction for CCI:	.......% RED	Credit cards accepted?	Y / N
Standard of site (in your opinion)			Excel	Vg	Gd	Fair	Poor
Facilities for disabled	◆		Full wheelchair facs		Limited facs	

ADDITIONAL REMARKS OR INFORMATION (TOURIST ATTRACTIONS, UNUSUAL FEATURES OR FACILITIES e.g. tennis, cycle hire, watersports, internet available, etc, REC LENGTH OF STAY). PLEASE PRINT OR TYPE

Your comments and opinions may be used in future editions of the guide; if you do not wish them to be used, please tick ☐

ARE YOU A: Caravanner	Motor caravanner	Trailer-tenter?
NAME	CARAVAN CLUB MEMBERSHIP NO:	
Do you need more blank Site Report Forms ☐ Yes ☐ No	POSTCODE:	
ADDRESS: (NON-MEMBERS ONLY PLEASE COMPLETE THIS SECTION)		

Please use a separate form for each site and do not send receipts. It is hoped that you will appreciate that owing to the large number of site reports received, it is not possible to enter into correspondence. More forms are available on request from the address below. Please return completed form to:

The Caravan Club
Editor - Caravan Europe
FREEPOST WD3000
East Grinstead
West Sussex RH19 1BR

(FREEPOST to be used when mailing within the UK only.)

CARAVAN EUROPE
ABBREVIATED SITE REPORT FORM

Use this abbreviated Site Report Form if you have visited a number of sites and there are no changes (or only very insignificant changes) to their entries in the guide. If reporting on a new site, or reporting several changes, please use the full version of the report form. **If advising prices**, these should be for a car, caravan and 2 adults for one night's stay. Please indicate high or low season prices and whether electricity is included – if not included, please give price.

Remember, if you don't tell us about sites you have visited, they may eventually be deleted from the guide.

Year of guide used	200.....	Page No.	Site Name		
Name of town/village site listed under (see Site Location maps)				Date of Visit ..../......../........	
Circle country site is in: Andorra / Austria / Belgium / Croatia / Czech Republic / Denmark / Finland / France / Germany / Greece / Hungary / Italy / Luxembourg / Netherlands / Norway / Poland / Portugal / Slovakia / Slovenia / Spain / Sweden / Switzerland.					
Charge for car, caravan & 2 adults *in local currency*	High Season		Low Season		El pts included in price quoted? Y / N

Year of guide used	200.....	Page No.	Site Name		
Name of town/village site listed under (see Site Location maps)				Date of Visit ..../......../........	
Circle country site is in: Andorra / Austria / Belgium / Croatia / Czech Republic / Denmark / Finland / France / Germany / Greece / Hungary / Italy / Luxembourg / Netherlands / Norway / Poland / Portugal / Slovakia / Slovenia / Spain / Sweden / Switzerland.					
Charge for car, caravan & 2 adults *in local currency*	High Season		Low Season		El pts included in price quoted? Y / N

Year of guide used	200.....	Page No.	Site Name		
Name of town/village site listed under (see Site Location maps)				Date of Visit ..../......../........	
Circle country site is in: Andorra / Austria / Belgium / Croatia / Czech Republic / Denmark / Finland / France / Germany / Greece / Hungary / Italy / Luxembourg / Netherlands / Norway / Poland / Portugal / Slovakia / Slovenia / Spain / Sweden / Switzerland.					
Charge for car, caravan & 2 adults *in local currency*	High Season		Low Season		El pts included in price quoted? Y / N

Name ....

Membership No. (or post code) ....

Do you need more blank Site Report Forms?

☐ Yes ☐ No

Please return completed form to:
The Caravan Club
Editor - Caravan Europe
FREEPOST WD3000
East Grinstead
West Sussex RH19 1BR

(FREEPOST to be used when mailing within the UK only.)

PTO

Year of guide used	200.....	Page No.	Site Name	
Name of town/village site listed under (see Site Location maps)				Date of Visit ..../........./.........

Circle country site is in: Andorra / Austria / Belgium / Croatia / Czech Republic / Denmark / Finland / France / Germany / Greece / Hungary / Italy / Luxembourg / Netherlands / Norway / Poland / Portugal / Slovakia / Slovenia / Spain / Sweden / Switzerland.

Charge for car, caravan & 2 adults *in local currency*	High Season	Low Season	El pts included in price quoted? Y / N

Year of guide used	200.....	Page No.	Site Name	
Name of town/village site listed under (see Site Location maps)				Date of Visit ..../........./.........

Circle country site is in: Andorra / Austria / Belgium / Croatia / Czech Republic / Denmark / Finland / France / Germany / Greece / Hungary / Italy / Luxembourg / Netherlands / Norway / Poland / Portugal / Slovakia / Slovenia / Spain / Sweden / Switzerland.

Charge for car, caravan & 2 adults *in local currency*	High Season	Low Season	El pts included in price quoted? Y / N

Year of guide used	200.....	Page No.	Site Name	
Name of town/village site listed under (see Site Location maps)				Date of Visit ..../........./.........

Circle country site is in: Andorra / Austria / Belgium / Croatia / Czech Republic / Denmark / Finland / France / Germany / Greece / Hungary / Italy / Luxembourg / Netherlands / Norway / Poland / Portugal / Slovakia / Slovenia / Spain / Sweden / Switzerland.

Charge for car, caravan & 2 adults *in local currency*	High Season	Low Season	El pts included in price quoted? Y / N

Year of guide used	200.....	Page No.	Site Name	
Name of town/village site listed under (see Site Location maps)				Date of Visit ..../........./.........

Circle country site is in: Andorra / Austria / Belgium / Croatia / Czech Republic / Denmark / Finland / France / Germany / Greece / Hungary / Italy / Luxembourg / Netherlands / Norway / Poland / Portugal / Slovakia / Slovenia / Spain / Sweden / Switzerland.

Charge for car, caravan & 2 adults *in local currency*	High Season	Low Season	El pts included in price quoted? Y / N

ARE YOU A: Caravanner	Motor caravanner	Trailer-tenter?

Your comments and opinions may be used in future editions of the guide, if you do not wish them to be used, please tick ☐

CARAVAN EUROPE
ABBREVIATED SITE REPORT FORM

Use this abbreviated Site Report Form if you have visited a number of sites and there are no changes (or only very insignificant changes) to their entries in the guide. If reporting on a new site, or reporting several changes, please use the full version of the report form. If advising prices, these should be for a car, caravan and 2 adults for one night's stay. Please indicate high or low season prices and whether electricity is included – if not included, please give price.

Remember, if you don't tell us about sites you have visited, they may eventually be deleted from the guide.

Year of guide used	200.....	Page No.	Site Name	
Name of town/village site listed under (see Site Location maps)			Date of Visit ..../........./........	
Circle country site is in: Andorra / Austria / Belgium / Croatia / Czech Republic / Denmark / Finland / France / Germany / Greece / Hungary / Italy / Luxembourg / Netherlands / Norway / Poland / Portugal / Slovakia / Slovenia / Spain / Sweden / Switzerland.				
Charge for car, caravan & 2 adults *in local currency*	High Season	Low Season	El pts included in price quoted? Y / N	

Year of guide used	200.....	Page No.	Site Name	
Name of town/village site listed under (see Site Location maps)			Date of Visit ..../........./........	
Circle country site is in: Andorra / Austria / Belgium / Croatia / Czech Republic / Denmark / Finland / France / Germany / Greece / Hungary / Italy / Luxembourg / Netherlands / Norway / Poland / Portugal / Slovakia / Slovenia / Spain / Sweden / Switzerland.				
Charge for car, caravan & 2 adults *in local currency*	High Season	Low Season	El pts included in price quoted? Y / N	

Year of guide used	200.....	Page No.	Site Name	
Name of town/village site listed under (see Site Location maps)			Date of Visit ..../........./........	
Circle country site is in: Andorra / Austria / Belgium / Croatia / Czech Republic / Denmark / Finland / France / Germany / Greece / Hungary / Italy / Luxembourg / Netherlands / Norway / Poland / Portugal / Slovakia / Slovenia / Spain / Sweden / Switzerland.				
Charge for car, caravan & 2 adults *in local currency*	High Season	Low Season	El pts included in price quoted? Y / N	

Name ....   Do you need more blank Site Report Forms?

Membership No. (or post code) ....   ☐ Yes   ☐ No

Please return completed form to:
The Caravan Club
Editor - Caravan Europe
FREEPOST WD3000
East Grinstead
West Sussex RH19 1BR

(FREEPOST to be used when mailing within the UK only.)   PTO

Year of guide used	200.....	Page No.	Site Name	

Name of town/village site listed under (see Site Location maps)		Date of Visit ..../........./........

Circle country site is in: Andorra / Austria / Belgium / Croatia / Czech Republic / Denmark / Finland / France / Germany / Greece / Hungary / Italy / Luxembourg / Netherlands / Norway / Poland / Portugal / Slovakia / Slovenia / Spain / Sweden / Switzerland.

Charge for car, caravan & 2 adults *in local currency*	High Season	Low Season	El pts included in price quoted? Y / N

Year of guide used	200.....	Page No.	Site Name	

Name of town/village site listed under (see Site Location maps)		Date of Visit ..../........./........

Circle country site is in: Andorra / Austria / Belgium / Croatia / Czech Republic / Denmark / Finland / France / Germany / Greece / Hungary / Italy / Luxembourg / Netherlands / Norway / Poland / Portugal / Slovakia / Slovenia / Spain / Sweden / Switzerland.

Charge for car, caravan & 2 adults *in local currency*	High Season	Low Season	El pts included in price quoted? Y / N

Year of guide used	200.....	Page No.	Site Name	

Name of town/village site listed under (see Site Location maps)		Date of Visit ..../........./........

Circle country site is in: Andorra / Austria / Belgium / Croatia / Czech Republic / Denmark / Finland / France / Germany / Greece / Hungary / Italy / Luxembourg / Netherlands / Norway / Poland / Portugal / Slovakia / Slovenia / Spain / Sweden / Switzerland.

Charge for car, caravan & 2 adults *in local currency*	High Season	Low Season	El pts included in price quoted? Y / N

Year of guide used	200.....	Page No.	Site Name	

Name of town/village site listed under (see Site Location maps)		Date of Visit ..../........./........

Circle country site is in: Andorra / Austria / Belgium / Croatia / Czech Republic / Denmark / Finland / France / Germany / Greece / Hungary / Italy / Luxembourg / Netherlands / Norway / Poland / Portugal / Slovakia / Slovenia / Spain / Sweden / Switzerland.

Charge for car, caravan & 2 adults *in local currency*	High Season	Low Season	El pts included in price quoted? Y / N

ARE YOU A: Caravanner	Motor caravanner	Trailer-tenter?

Your comments and opinions may be used in future editions of the guide, if you do not wish them to be used, please tick ☐

INDEX – CARAVAN EUROPE 1